2020–2021
FORTY-THIRD EDITION

New York School Directory

A State Guide to K-12 Districts, Dioceses, and Schools...

Powered by MDR's ConnectED Cloud

Key Features In This Edition

- Charter Management Organization Index
- Facebook and Twitter Indicators
- Email Address Availability Highlighted
- Detailed School and District Listings
- Names and Job Titles of Key Personnel
- New Schools and Personnel Index

A Dun & Bradstreet Division

Copyright 2020 Market Data Retrieval | 6 Armstrong Road, Shelton, CT 06484

Copyright 2020 Market Data Retrieval, a D&B Company. All Rights Reserved. No information furnished hereby may be reproduced or transmitted in any form or by any means, electronic or mechanical, including photocopying and recording, or by any information storage or retrieval system, except as may be expressly permitted by MDR, 6 Armstrong Road, Shelton, CT 06484.

The information in this directory is licensed with the express understanding and agreement that the information will be solely for internal use and will not be used for the creation and/or updating of databases, electronic or otherwise, that are sold or provided to any third party without the express written permission of MDR.

51-Volume National Set   ISBN# 978-1-57953-640-4

Individual Bound State Editions

	ISSN#	ISBN#		ISSN#	ISBN#
Alabama	1077-7393	978-1-951295-52-3	Montana	1077-7652	978-1-57953-608-4
Alaska	1077-7407	978-1-57953-332-8	Nebraska	1077-7660	978-1-57953-609-1
Arizona	1077-7415	978-1-57953-343-4	Nevada	1077-7679	978-1-57953-610-7
Arkansas	1077-7423	978-1-57953-353-3	New Hampshire	1077-7687	978-1-57953-612-1
California	1077-7431	978-1-57953-355-7	New Jersey	1077-7695	978-1-57953-613-8
Colorado	1077-744X	978-1-57953-374-8	New Mexico	1077-7709	978-1-57953-614-5
Connecticut	1077-7458	978-1-57953-376-2	New York	1077-7717	978-1-57953-615-2
Delaware	1077-7466	978-1-57953-430-1	North Carolina	1077-7725	978-1-57953-616-9
District of Columbia	1077-7474	978-1-57953-484-4	North Dakota	1077-7733	978-1-57953-617-6
Florida	1077-7482	978-1-57953-538-4	Ohio	1077-7741	978-1-57953-618-3
Georgia	1077-7490	978-1-57953-592-6	Oklahoma	1077-775X	978-1-57953-619-0
Hawaii	1077-7504	978-1-57953-593-3	Oregon	1077-7768	978-1-57953-620-6
Idaho	1077-7512	978-1-57953-594-0	Pennsylvania	1077-7776	978-1-57953-621-3
Illinois	1077-7520	978-1-57953-595-7	Rhode Island	1077-7784	978-1-57953-622-0
Indiana	1077-7539	978-1-57953-596-4	South Carolina	1077-7792	978-1-57953-624-4
Iowa	1077-7547	978-1-57953-597-1	South Dakota	1077-7806	978-1-57953-626-8
Kansas	1077-7555	978-1-57953-598-8	Tennessee	1077-7814	978-1-57953-627-5
Kentucky	1077-7563	978-1-57953-599-5	Texas	1077-7822	978-1-57953-629-9
Louisiana	1077-7571	978-1-57953-600-8	Utah	1077-7830	978-1-57953-630-5
Maine	1077-758X	978-1-57953-601-5	Vermont	1077-7849	978-1-57953-632-9
Maryland	1077-7598	978-1-57953-602-2	Virginia	1077-7857	978-1-57953-633-6
Massachusetts	1077-7601	978-1-57953-603-9	Washington	1077-7865	978-1-57953-634-3
Michigan	1077-761X	978-1-57953-604-6	West Virginia	1077-7873	978-1-57953-635-0
Minnesota	1077-7628	978-1-57953-605-3	Wisconsin	1077-7881	978-1-57953-637-4
Mississippi	1077-7636	978-1-57953-606-0	Wyoming	1077-789X	978-1-57953-638-1
Missouri	1077-7644	978-1-57953-607-7	Sales Manager's Guide	2150-2021	978-1-57953-639-8

If you have any questions or comments concerning this directory, please write to MDR, 6 Armstrong Road, Shelton, CT 06484, or call us toll-free at 800-333-8802 or collect at 203-926-4800.

MDR's School Directory

TABLE OF CONTENTS

Sample Directory Listings iv
- A complete listing of codes, definitions and data elements used throughout this directory.

Directory Statistics (Yellow Section)

State Statistics A1
- An overview of state statistics showing the distribution of districts, schools and personnel by key indicators.

County Statistics B1
- A county-by-county census of districts and schools and their enrollments.

District Buying Power Index C1
- A complete listing of counties and districts ranked by the amount of money they spend on instructional materials.

New Public Schools and Key Personnel Index (Cream Section) NEW1
- A summary of new public schools that have opened for the current school year, plus Superintendents and Principals who are new to their institution.

District and School Listings (White Section) 1
- Complete information provided for each district and school in the state, organized alphabetically by county.
- Listings within each county are in the following order: County Centers and Schools, Public School Districts and Schools, Catholic Diocesan Offices and/or Schools, Other Private Schools and Regional Centers.

Directory Indices

District Index (Ivory Section) Q1
- A complete listing of districts in alphabetical order for each district type: Public School Districts, Catholic Dioceses, County Centers and Regional Centers.
- Includes number of schools, enrollment, county location and page number.

County Index (Tan Section) R1
- A complete alphabetical listing by county of Public School Districts, Catholic Dioceses, County Centers and Regional Centers.

Supervisory Union Index (Gold Section) S1
- Included for the states of Maine, Massachusetts, New Hampshire and Vermont, where several local school districts are administered by the same administrative personnel located at a Supervisory Union office. The index lists each Supervisory Union followed by their local school districts.

District Personnel Index (Gray Section) T1
- A complete listing, in last name sequence, of all district personnel.

Principal Index (Green Section) U1
- A complete listing, in last name sequence, of all school principals.

District and School Telephone Index (Blue Section) V1
- A complete listing of all districts and schools in the state with their telephone and PID numbers.

District URL Index (Salmon Section) W1
- A listing of districts that have URL addresses.

Charter Management Organization (CMO) Index (Orchid Section) CMO1
- An alphabetical listing, by state-CMO sequence, of Charter Management Organizations.
- Includes CMO number, PID, full address and phone number.

Directory Code Reference Guide located on the bottom of each page.

Sample Directory Listings

MDR's School Directories are your complete reference source, providing comprehensive data on public school districts and schools, Catholic and other independent schools, and regional and county centers in all 50 states and the District of Columbia. Every public school district and school entry in MDR's School Directories is updated each year through telephone interviews conducted with school district personnel. These interviews take place from July to September, capturing the most current school year data available. In addition, information obtained from state, district and school directories is used to verify information contained in MDR's School Directories.

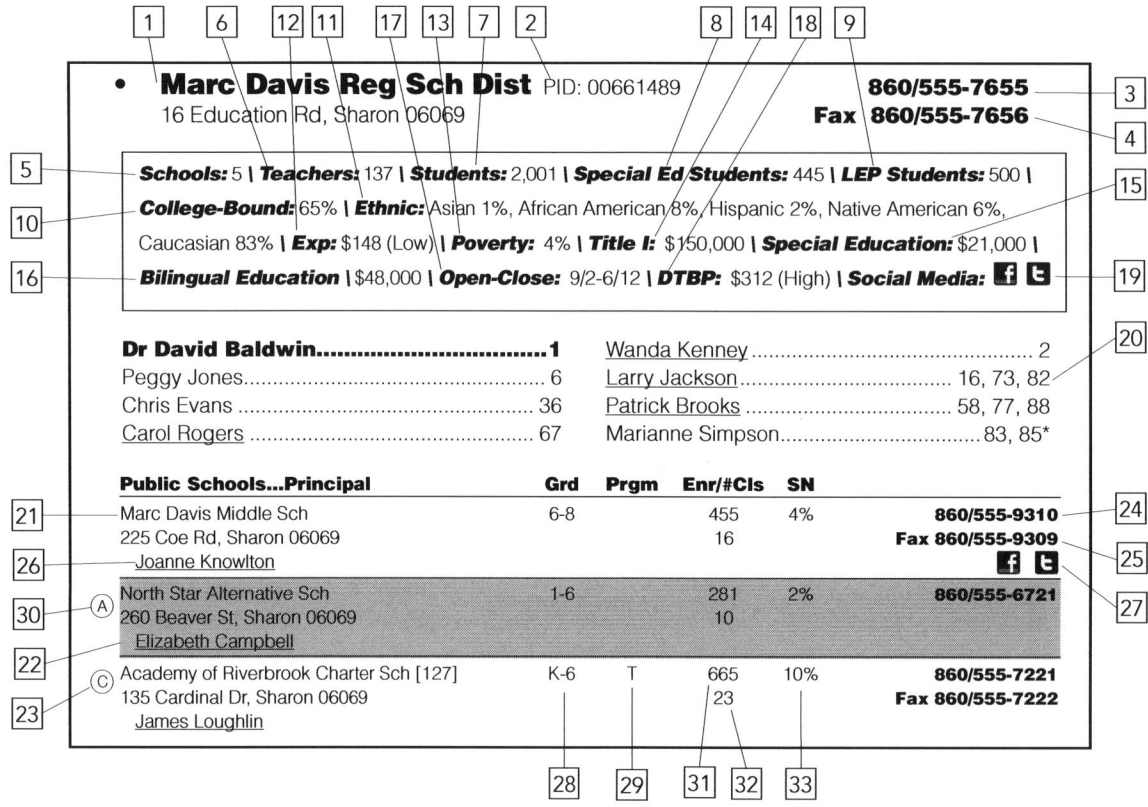

Each directory listing is uniformly organized to reflect the following data as applicable.

Definitions of Codes and Data:

DISTRICT DATA

1 District Name and Address
The physical location address for the superintendent's office is listed. MDR also maintains the mailing address, if different, for each district office. For this alternative mailing address, contact MDR directly at 800-333-8802.

2 District PID Number
Personal Identification Number of the district. Helps identify specific institutions when speaking to an MDR Representative or searching in Education MarketView.

3 Telephone Number
The telephone number of the district's central administration office.

4 Fax Number
The fax number of the district's central administration office. Please use the fax numbers in the directory appropriately.

The FCC prohibits the use of a telephone facsimile machine to send unsolicited advertisements. If you need further clarification of the laws that exist, you can contact the FCC directly at 888-225-5322, or you can visit their website at http://www.fcc.gov.

5 Number of Schools
The number of schools reporting directly to the district. In the case of decentralized large districts (such as Chicago Public Schools), the number of schools reflects those reporting directly to the central school district in addition to those administered directly by each of the subdistrict offices.

6 Number of Teachers
The number of full-time equivalent teachers throughout the district as reported by the U.S. Department of Education.

7 District Enrollment
The projected number of students enrolled in the district for fall 2020.

8 Special Ed Students
The number of students having a written Individualized Education Plan (IEP) indicating their participation in a Special Education Program.

9 LEP Students
The number of Limited-English Proficient students being served in appropriate programs of language assistance (i.e., English as a second language, high-intensity language training, bilingual education).

10 College-Bound Students
The percentage of the district's 12th grade enrollment planning to attend two- or four-year colleges.

11 Student Ethnic Percentages
The student enrollment percentage by ethnic group: Asian, African American, Hispanic, Native American and Caucasian. This information is reported annually by the U.S. Department of Education. Due to rounding, the percentages may not add up to 100%.

12 District Expenditure
The district's expenditure per student for instructional materials. In addition to the actual dollar amount, a level of expenditure is provided as follows:
- High = $300+
- Med = $200-299
- Low = Under $200

13 Poverty Level
This census data reflects the percentage of school-age children in the district from families below the poverty line. Poverty levels are as follows:
- Low = 0-5%
- Med-Low = 6-15%
- Med-High = 16-29%
- High = 30%+

14 Title I
The district's Title I dollar allocation is for the 2019 fiscal year. Funding levels are as follows:
- Highest = $2.5 Million+
- High = $500,000-2.49 Million
- Medium = $150,000-499,999
- Low = Under $150,000

15 Special Education
The sum of federal and state dollars earmarked for special education programs in the district.

16 Bilingual Education
The sum of federal and state dollars earmarked for English Language Acquisition programs in the district.

17 District Opening/Closing Dates
The month and day of the official opening and closing dates of the school district.

18 District Tech Budget Per Pupil
The district's total IT technology budget dollars per pupil. DTBP levels are as follows:
- High = $100+
- Med = $80-99
- Low = $1-79

19 Social Media
The use of Facebook and/or Twitter for information communication, messaging and other content.

20 District-Level Administrators and Job Title Codes
The names of administrative staff with district-wide responsibilities are listed, followed by numeric codes representing their specific areas of responsibility. A full list of job title codes and their descriptions can be found on the bottom of the directory pages.

The names are listed, from left to right, in numeric job title sequence to facilitate identification of individuals responsible for specific administrative areas. In cases where an individual has multiple responsibilities, the job title with the lowest code number is used for sequencing.

An asterisk (*) denotes district administrators who maintain offices at one of the schools in the district rather than at the district office.

Superintendents who are new to the district are printed in **bold** type. Also see our index of new personnel on page NEW1.

An underscore of a district-level administrator indicates an email address at that institution in our database and in Education MarketView.

SCHOOL DATA

21 School Name and Address
The physical location address of the school is listed. MDR also maintains the mailing address, if different, for every school. For this alternative address, contact MDR directly at 800-333-8802.

22 New Schools
The listings of public schools opening for the first time during this school year are shaded for easy identification. Also see our index of new public schools on page NEW1.

23 Charter Management Organization (CMO)
Indicates the CMO number from the CMO Index to which this school reports.

24 Telephone Number
The telephone number of the school's central administration office. Note that in some cases a school district may require that all calls to schools must first go through a central switchboard to be routed to individual schools. In these cases, the central switchboard number is given for all schools affected.

25 Fax Number
The fax number of the school's administration office. Please use the fax numbers in the directory appropriately.

> The FCC prohibits the use of a telephone facsimile machine to send unsolicited advertisements. If you need further clarification of the laws that exist, you can contact the FCC directly at 888-225-5322, or you can visit their website at http://www.fcc.gov.

v

26 Principal Name
The name of the school principal. When a school has both an elementary and secondary principal, both names are given. The elementary principal is listed first, with the secondary principal listed below.

Principals who are new to their public school are printed in **bold** type. Also see our index of new personnel on page NEW1.

All principals printed with an underscore have an email address at that institution in our database and in Education MarketView.

27 Social Media
The use of Facebook and/or Twitter for information communication, messaging and other content.

28 School Grade Span/Voc, Special, Adult Schools
The lowest and highest grades taught in the school. Schools with dedicated programs in the areas of vocational, special and adult education are designated as Voc, Spec and Adult, respectively.

29 School Program Codes
In addition to the grades taught within the school, schools that have special curriculum programs are indicated with these codes following the school grade span.

- A = Alternative Program: Identifies traditional schools that also provide a special setting/curriculum for students who do not function well in traditional classroom settings.
- G = Adult Classes: Identifies schools that offer adult education classes.
- M = Magnet Program: Identifies traditional schools that also offer an enriched curricula in a special subject area to qualified students.
- T = Title I Schoolwide: Identifies public schools that have a Title I Schoolwide program, allowing greater spending flexibility.
- V = Career & Technical Education Programs: Identifies schools that offer Career & Technical Education programs.

30 Other School Types
Schools that are unique in the curriculum they offer or in the way they operate are indicated to the left of the school name.

- (A) = Alternative School: Identifies schools that provide instruction exclusively for students who do not function well in traditional classroom settings.
- (C) = Charter School: Public schools that have certain freedoms from state and local regulations and policies, having more administrative independence.
- (M) = Magnet School: Identifies schools where all students are offered enriched curricula. Students qualify for admission by competitive exams.
- (Y) = Year-Round School: Schools that operate 12 months a year.

31 Student Enrollment
The projected number of students enrolled for fall 2020.

32 Number of Classrooms
The number of classrooms within a school. The number of classrooms prints below student enrollment when known.

33 Student Need
Percentage of students eligible for the free and reduced-price lunch program at the school.

New York

STATE STATISTICS

DISTRICT PERSONNEL BY JOB FUNCTION

Job Code	Job Description	Total	Under 2,500	Enrollment 2,500-9,000	10,000+
1	SUPERINTENDENT	764	482	191	10
2	BUS/FINANCE/PURCHASING	809	505	234	24
3	BUILDINGS AND GROUNDS	689	419	217	18
4	FOOD SERVICE	543	360	161	11
5	TRANSPORTATION	601	395	185	10
6	ATHLETIC	590	397	185	8
7	HEALTH SERVICES	281	162	101	7
8	CURRIC/INSTRUCT K-12	543	303	187	16
9	CURRIC/INSTRUCT ELEM	112	73	33	6
10	CURRIC/INSTRUCT SEC	73	42	26	4
11	FEDERAL PROGRAM	602	422	160	10
12	TITLE I	155	110	44	0
13	TITLE V	22	12	10	0
15	ASST SUPERINTENDENT	788	219	414	45
16	INSTRUCTIONAL MEDIA SERVICES	367	246	88	5
17	CHIEF OPERATIONS OFFICER	26	10	5	3
18	CHIEF ACADEMIC OFFICER	19	8	8	2
19	CHIEF FINANCIAL OFFICER	47	31	8	3
20	ART K-12	72	13	52	6
21	ART ELEM	1	1	0	0
22	ART SEC	3	0	3	0
23	MUSIC K-12	86	18	60	7
24	MUSIC ELEM	4	4	0	0
25	MUSIC SEC	6	0	6	0
26	BUSINESS EDUCATION	23	8	14	0
27	CAREER & TECH ED	129	56	26	10
28	TECHNOLOGY EDUCATION	26	13	11	1
29	FAMILY/CONSUMER SCIENCE	16	7	8	1
30	ADULT EDUCATION	117	30	56	4
31	CAREER/SCH-TO-WORK K-12	140	91	22	2
32	CAREER/SCH-TO-WORK ELEM	2	1	1	0
33	CAREER/SCH-TO-WORK SEC	9	9	0	0
34	EARLY CHILDHOOD ED	107	44	47	8
35	HEALTH/PHYS EDUCATION	292	147	135	9
36	GUIDANCE SERVICES K-12	255	170	76	7
37	GUIDANCE SERVICES ELEM	37	36	1	0
38	GUIDANCE SERVICES SEC	106	93	13	0
39	SOCIAL STUDIES K-12	43	4	33	5
40	SOCIAL STUDIES ELEM	3	0	3	0
41	SOCIAL STUDIES SEC	7	1	5	1
42	SCIENCE K-12	57	8	43	5
43	SCIENCE ELEM	4	0	2	1
44	SCIENCE SEC	8	4	3	1
45	MATH K-12	64	8	47	7
46	MATH ELEM	3	0	3	0
47	MATH SEC	8	2	5	1
48	ENGLISH/LANG ARTS K-12	61	10	44	5
49	ENGLISH/LANG ARTS ELEM	8	1	7	0
50	ENGLISH/LANG ARTS SEC	9	3	5	1
51	READING K-12	49	27	19	3
52	READING ELEM	12	6	6	0
53	READING SEC	3	1	2	0
54	REMEDIAL READING K-12	48	29	17	2
55	REMEDIAL READING ELEM	9	9	0	0
56	REMEDIAL READING SEC	2	2	0	0
57	BILINGUAL/ELL	309	173	115	15
58	SPECIAL EDUCATION K-12	691	404	215	29
59	SPECIAL EDUCATION ELEM	48	31	17	0
60	SPECIAL EDUCATION SEC	28	5	23	0
61	FOREIGN/WORLD LANG K-12	42	10	26	5
62	FOREIGN/WORLD LANG ELEM	1	0	1	0
63	FOREIGN/WORLD LANG SEC	7	3	3	1
64	RELIGIOUS EDUCATION K-12	0	0	0	0
65	RELIGIOUS EDUCATION ELEM	1	0	0	0
66	RELIGIOUS EDUCATION SEC	0	0	0	0
67	SCHOOL BOARD PRESIDENT	716	479	190	11
68	TEACHER PERSONNEL	292	68	165	19
69	ACADEMIC ASSESSMENT	298	188	86	8
70	RESEARCH/DEVELOPMENT	45	13	14	6
71	PUBLIC INFORMATION	201	76	99	8
72	SUMMER SCHOOL	30	15	11	1
73	INSTRUCTIONAL TECH	658	417	193	15
74	INSERVICE TRAINING	123	47	42	5
75	MARKETING/DISTRIBUTIVE	5	3	1	0
76	INFO SYSTEMS	273	125	119	11
77	PSYCHOLOGICAL ASSESSMENT	155	94	54	2
78	AFFIRMATIVE ACTION	45	15	28	1
79	STUDENT PERSONNEL	344	161	158	17
80	DRIVER ED/SAFETY	20	3	17	0
81	GIFTED/TALENTED	48	18	25	2
82	VIDEO SERVICES	101	73	26	2
83	SUBSTANCE ABUSE PREVENTION	326	231	90	2
84	ERATE	22	12	7	2
85	AIDS EDUCATION	165	116	44	4
88	ALTERNATIVE/AT RISK	266	171	73	3
89	MULTI-CULTURAL CURRICULUM	8	0	7	0
90	SOCIAL WORK	81	37	42	2
91	SAFETY/SECURITY	282	121	136	13
92	MAGNET SCHOOL	3	1	2	0
93	PARENTAL INVOLVEMENT	24	11	9	4
95	TECH PREP PROGRAM	27	9	17	1
97	CHIEF INFORMATION OFFICER	80	45	31	3
98	CHIEF TECHNOLOGY OFFICER	24	19	3	2
270	CHARACTER EDUCATION	85	65	20	0
271	MIGRANT EDUCATION	99	70	23	2
273	TEACHER MENTOR	149	105	40	4
274	BEFORE/AFTER SCH	69	48	19	2
275	RESPONSE TO INTERVENTION	100	57	36	4
277	REMEDIAL MATH K-12	18	5	13	0
280	LITERACY COACH	78	37	38	3
285	STEM	146	82	61	1
286	DIGITAL LEARNING	175	106	64	3
288	COMMON CORE STANDARDS	280	196	82	2
294	ACCOUNTABILITY	80	33	34	10
295	NETWORK SYSTEM	341	218	100	15
296	TITLE II PROGRAMS	197	145	51	1
297	WEBMASTER	39	19	18	1
298	GRANT WRITER/PTNRSHIPS	231	152	66	8
750	CHIEF INNOVATION OFFICER	7	6	1	0
751	CHIEF OF STAFF	8	2	0	3
752	SOCIAL EMOTIONAL LEARNING	51	39	10	1

DISTRICTS BY EXPENDITURE AND ENROLLMENT

Expenditure	Total	Under 2500	2500-9999	10,000+
Low (Under $200)	95	64	28	3
Medium ($200 - 299)	286	191	93	2
High ($300+)	306	229	70	7
TOTAL DISTRICTS	687	484	191	12

SCHOOLS BY LEVEL AND TYPE

School Level	Total	Public	Private	Catholic
Elementary	3,351	2,642	401	308
Middle/Junior	803	783	16	4
Senior	1,272	1,067	126	79
K-12 (Combined)	584	287	289	8
Adult/Special/Voc Ed	376	219	157	0
TOTAL SCHOOLS	6,386	4,998	989	399

School Year 2020-2021   800-333-8802

New York School Directory — COUNTY STATISTICS

COUNTY		DISTRICTS	SCHOOLS	ELEM ENROLL[1]	MIDDLE/JHS ENROLL[2]	SENIOR ENROLL[3]	TOTAL ENROLL[4]	% OF STATE	K-5[5]	K-6	K-8	5-8[6]	7-9[7]	7-12[8]	K-12[9]	OTHER[10]
ALBANY	PUBLIC	12	71	17,156	7,431	11,812	36,883		28	12	1	11	1	12	2	4
	NONPUBLIC	0	26	3,607	0	1,087	4,694		0	0	11	0	0	2	7	6
	TOTAL	12	97	20,763	7,431	12,899	41,577	1.3	28	12	12	11	1	14	9	10
ALLEGANY	PUBLIC	12	17	3,782	616	1,860	6,417		4	0	0	0	0	1	12	0
	NONPUBLIC	0	2	150	0	142	292		0	0	1	0	0	1	0	0
	TOTAL	12	19	3,932	616	2,002	6,709	0.2	4	0	1	0	0	2	12	0
BRONX	PUBLIC	0	0	0	0	0	0		0	0	0	0	0	0	0	0
	NONPUBLIC	0	72	17,514	0	11,207	28,721		5	2	38	1	0	14	7	5
	TOTAL	0	72	17,514	0	11,207	28,721	0.9	5	2	38	1	0	14	7	5
BROOME	PUBLIC	12	59	11,965	6,048	7,874	27,023		30	1	0	11	0	12	3	2
	NONPUBLIC	0	9	946	0	380	1,326		2	3	0	0	0	1	2	1
	TOTAL	12	68	12,911	6,048	8,254	28,349	0.9	32	4	0	11	0	13	5	3
CATTARAUGUS	PUBLIC	13	30	5,955	2,645	4,243	13,686		8	2	0	5	0	7	7	1
	NONPUBLIC	0	4	218	0	93	311		0	1	1	0	0	1	1	0
	TOTAL	13	34	6,173	2,645	4,336	13,997	0.5	8	3	1	5	0	8	8	1
CAYUGA	PUBLIC	7	23	4,606	1,277	3,072	9,220		3	8	0	2	1	7	1	1
	NONPUBLIC	0	6	133	0	151	284		0	0	3	0	0	2	1	0
	TOTAL	7	29	4,739	1,277	3,223	9,504	0.3	3	8	3	2	1	9	2	1
CHAUTAUQUA	PUBLIC	18	48	9,825	3,494	5,920	20,173		17	4	0	7	0	9	10	1
	NONPUBLIC	0	4	349	0	41	390		0	0	1	0	0	0	2	1
	TOTAL	18	52	10,174	3,494	5,961	20,563	0.7	17	4	1	7	0	9	12	2
CHEMUNG	PUBLIC	3	22	5,897	2,204	2,804	11,545		9	5	0	1	3	3	0	1
	NONPUBLIC	0	6	564	0	463	1,027		0	3	1	0	0	2	0	0
	TOTAL	3	28	6,461	2,204	3,267	12,572	0.4	9	8	1	1	3	5	0	1
CHENANGO	PUBLIC	8	22	3,691	1,328	2,216	7,493		8	1	0	4	0	5	3	1
	NONPUBLIC	0	2	172	0	19	191		0	1	0	0	0	0	1	0
	TOTAL	8	24	3,863	1,328	2,235	7,684	0.2	8	2	0	4	0	5	4	1
CLINTON	PUBLIC	8	26	5,448	2,064	3,373	11,020		11	2	0	4	0	5	3	1
	NONPUBLIC	0	2	197	0	79	276		0	0	0	0	0	0	2	0
	TOTAL	8	28	5,645	2,064	3,452	11,296	0.4	11	2	0	4	0	5	5	1
COLUMBIA	PUBLIC	7	18	2,994	1,301	2,382	6,694		3	2	0	3	0	8	3	1
	NONPUBLIC	0	5	246	0	248	494		0	0	1	0	0	1	3	0
	TOTAL	7	23	3,240	1,301	2,630	7,188	0.2	3	2	1	3	0	9	4	1

[1] **Elem Enroll** is the school by school total of enrollments in K-4, K-5, K-6, K-8 schools, elementary and middle/JHS students in K-12 schools and students in special ed schools. Public enrollments include public and county-operated schools.

[2] **Middle/JHS Enroll** is the school by school total of enrollments in 5-8 and 7-9 public schools. Public enrollments include public and county-operated schools. Private middle/JHS enrollments are included in Senior Enroll.

[3] **Senior Enroll** is the school by school total of enrollments in 7-12 and 9-12 schools, the secondary students in K-12 schools and students in vocational ed schools. Public enrollments include public and county-operated schools. For private schools, Senior Enroll includes middle/JHS enrollment plus senior enrollment.

[4] **Public Total Enroll** columns are not the sum of school building enrollments. They are projected district-wide Fall enrollments provided to MDR by each school district office, plus county-operated school enrollments.

[5] **K-5** includes pre-kindergarten, kindergarten, K-3, K-4, K-5 schools.

[6] **5-8** includes schools with low grades of 4, 5, 6 and high grades of 7, 8, 9 (e.g., 4-8, 5-8, 6-8, 6-9).

[7] **7-9** includes schools with low grades of 7, 8 and high grades of 7, 8, 9 (e.g., 7-7, 7-8, 7-9, 8-9).

[8] **7-12** includes 7-12, 8-12, 9-12, 10-12, etc.

[9] **K-12** includes schools with both elementary and secondary grades.

[10] **Other** includes special ed, vocational ed and adult schools.

*Public State Totals for all columns can exceed the sum of the counties because state totals include state-operated schools and their enrollments.

School Year 2020-2021 — 800-333-8802 — NY–B1

COUNTY STATISTICS — Market Data Retrieval

COUNTY		DISTRICTS	SCHOOLS	ELEM ENROLL[1]	MIDDLE/JHS ENROLL[2]	SENIOR ENROLL[3]	TOTAL ENROLL[4]	% OF STATE	K-5[5]	K-6	K-8	5-8[6]	7-9[7]	7-12[8]	K-12[9]	OTHER[10]
CORTLAND	PUBLIC	5	15	2,831	600	2,262	5,589		5	3	0	1	0	4	1	1
	NONPUBLIC	0	3	299	0	57	356		0	1	0	0	0	0	2	0
	TOTAL	5	18	3,130	600	2,319	5,945	0.2	5	4	0	1	0	4	3	1
DELAWARE	PUBLIC	12	20	3,008	660	1,505	5,928		3	1	0	1	1	2	10	2
	NONPUBLIC	0	0	0	0	0	0		0	0	0	0	0	0	0	0
	TOTAL	12	20	3,008	660	1,505	5,928	0.2	3	1	0	1	1	2	10	2
DUTCHESS	PUBLIC	13	76	17,066	8,395	12,765	38,087		35	9	0	12	2	15	1	2
	NONPUBLIC	0	27	2,917	0	1,673	4,590		2	1	8	0	2	3	6	7
	TOTAL	13	103	19,983	8,395	14,438	42,677	1.4	37	10	8	12	2	18	7	9
ERIE	PUBLIC	28	211	57,454	21,638	36,101	116,755		81	3	30	30	2	47	6	12
	NONPUBLIC	0	74	11,493	0	6,216	17,709		2	1	34	2	0	12	11	12
	TOTAL	28	285	68,947	21,638	42,317	134,464	4.3	83	4	64	32	2	59	17	24
ESSEX	PUBLIC	10	14	2,591	141	1,291	3,951		1	1	0	0	0	1	10	1
	NONPUBLIC	0	7	313	0	327	640		1	0	1	1	0	2	2	0
	TOTAL	10	21	2,904	141	1,618	4,591	0.2	2	1	1	1	0	3	12	1
FRANKLIN	PUBLIC	7	21	3,740	1,144	2,312	8,039		7	2	0	3	0	5	2	2
	NONPUBLIC	0	1	80	0	0	80		1	0	0	0	0	0	0	0
	TOTAL	7	22	3,820	1,144	2,312	8,119	0.3	8	2	0	3	0	5	2	2
FULTON	PUBLIC	7	21	4,687	859	2,900	8,521		6	4	0	1	1	7	1	0
	NONPUBLIC	0	0	0	0	0	0		0	0	0	0	0	0	0	0
	TOTAL	7	21	4,687	859	2,900	8,521	0.3	6	4	0	1	1	7	1	0
GENESEE	PUBLIC	8	20	4,000	1,035	2,931	8,359		5	4	0	1	0	6	3	1
	NONPUBLIC	0	4	369	0	145	514		1	0	1	0	0	1	1	0
	TOTAL	8	24	4,369	1,035	3,076	8,873	0.3	6	4	1	1	0	7	4	1
GREENE	PUBLIC	6	16	2,533	1,300	1,803	5,825		5	1	0	4	0	5	1	0
	NONPUBLIC	0	1	44	0	20	64		0	0	0	0	0	0	1	0
	TOTAL	6	17	2,577	1,300	1,823	5,889	0.2	5	1	0	4	0	5	2	0
HAMILTON	PUBLIC	4	4	279	0	113	392		0	0	0	0	0	0	4	0
	NONPUBLIC	0	0	0	0	0	0		0	0	0	0	0	0	0	0
	TOTAL	4	4	279	0	113	392		0	0	0	0	0	0	4	0
HERKIMER	PUBLIC	10	21	4,310	1,705	2,767	8,947		6	1	1	3	0	5	1	0
	NONPUBLIC	0	2	66	0	9	75		1	0	0	0	0	0	1	0
	TOTAL	10	23	4,376	1,705	2,776	9,022	0.3	7	1	1	3	0	5	6	0
JEFFERSON	PUBLIC	11	38	9,308	2,932	4,804	18,309		18	3	0	4	1	6	5	1
	NONPUBLIC	0	6	522	0	410	932		0	1	1	0	0	1	2	1
	TOTAL	11	44	9,830	2,932	5,214	19,241	0.6	18	4	1	4	1	7	7	2

[1] **Elem Enroll** is the school by school total of enrollments in K-4, K-5, K-6, K-8 schools, elementary and middle/JHS students in K-12 schools and students in special ed schools. Public enrollments include public and county-operated schools.
[2] **Middle/JHS Enroll** is the school by school total of enrollments in 5-8 and 7-9 public schools. Public enrollments include public and county-operated schools. Private middle/JHS enrollments are included in Senior Enroll.
[3] **Senior Enroll** is the school by school total of enrollments in 7-12 and 9-12 schools, the secondary students in K-12 schools and students in vocational ed schools. Public enrollments include public and county-operated schools. For private schools, Senior Enroll includes middle/JHS enrollment plus senior enrollment.
[4] **Public Total Enroll** columns are not the sum of school building enrollments. They are projected district-wide Fall enrollments provided to MDR by each school district office, plus county-operated school enrollments.
[5] **K-5** includes pre-kindergarten, kindergarten, K-3, K-4, K-5 schools.
[6] **5-8** includes schools with low grades of 4, 5, 6 and high grades of 7, 8, 9 (e.g., 4-8, 5-8, 6-8, 6-9).
[7] **7-9** includes schools with low grades of 7, 8 and high grades of 7, 8, 9 (e.g., 7-7, 7-8, 7-9, 8-9).
[8] **7-12** includes 7-12, 8-12, 9-12, 10-12, etc.
[9] **K-12** includes schools with both elementary and secondary grades.
[10] **Other** includes special ed, vocational ed and adult schools.

*****Public State Totals** for all columns can exceed the sum of the counties because state totals include state-operated schools and their enrollments

NY—B2 · 800-333-8802 · School Year 2020-2021

New York School Directory — COUNTY STATISTICS

COUNTY		DISTRICTS	SCHOOLS	ELEM ENROLL[1]	MIDDLE/JHS ENROLL[2]	SENIOR ENROLL[3]	TOTAL ENROLL[4]	% OF STATE	SCHOOLS BY GRADE SPAN							
									K-5[5]	K-6	K-8	5-8[6]	7-9[7]	7-12[8]	K-12[9]	OTHER[10]
KINGS	PUBLIC	0	0	0	0	0	0		0	0	0	0	0	0	0	0
	NONPUBLIC	0	256	67,247	0	25,066	92,313		15	7	109	2	0	44	62	17
	TOTAL	0	256	67,247	0	25,066	92,313	2.9	15	7	109	2	0	44	62	17
LEWIS	PUBLIC	5	9	2,599	298	1,177	4,072		2	0	0	1	0	1	4	1
	NONPUBLIC	0	1	36	0	9	45		0	0	0	0	0	0	1	0
	TOTAL	5	10	2,635	298	1,186	4,117	0.1	2	0	0	1	0	1	5	1
LIVINGSTON	PUBLIC	8	19	3,812	514	2,745	7,371		5	3	0	2	0	6	2	1
	NONPUBLIC	0	3	318	0	55	373		0	1	1	0	0	0	1	0
	TOTAL	8	22	4,130	514	2,800	7,744	0.3	5	4	1	2	0	6	3	1
MADISON	PUBLIC	10	25	4,434	1,567	3,187	9,258		11	1	0	3	0	4	6	0
	NONPUBLIC	0	3	171	0	118	289		0	1	0	0	0	1	1	0
	TOTAL	10	28	4,605	1,567	3,305	9,547	0.3	11	2	0	3	0	5	7	0
MONROE	PUBLIC	18	180	50,904	17,543	32,955	104,359		67	30	11	17	5	38	6	6
	NONPUBLIC	0	44	5,855	0	3,694	9,549		8	7	5	0	0	2	14	8
	TOTAL	18	224	56,759	17,543	36,649	113,908	3.6	75	37	16	17	5	40	20	14
MONTGOMERY	PUBLIC	4	13	3,521	1,002	2,172	6,735		5	1	0	2	0	4	1	0
	NONPUBLIC	0	4	316	0	31	347		0	0	1	0	0	0	3	0
	TOTAL	4	17	3,837	1,002	2,203	7,082	0.2	5	1	1	2	0	4	4	0
NASSAU	PUBLIC	56	327	93,420	38,531	68,850	203,557		149	54	0	41	8	60	0	15
	NONPUBLIC	0	97	20,259	0	11,483	31,742		10	4	35	4	1	16	16	11
	TOTAL	56	424	113,679	38,531	80,333	235,299	7.5	159	58	35	45	9	76	16	26
NEW YORK	PUBLIC	1	1,676	499,422	172,885	290,010	1,150,000		670	19	151	264	0	409	90	73
	NONPUBLIC	0	157	35,389	0	17,274	52,663		14	2	56	5	0	22	38	20
	TOTAL	1	1,833	534,811	172,885	307,284	1,202,663	38.2	684	21	207	269	0	431	128	93
NIAGARA	PUBLIC	10	54	13,556	5,241	8,815	29,150		19	12	0	5	4	10	1	3
	NONPUBLIC	0	12	1,693	0	71	1,764		2	0	7	0	0	0	2	1
	TOTAL	10	66	15,249	5,241	8,886	30,914	1.0	21	12	7	5	4	10	3	4
ONEIDA	PUBLIC	15	70	17,361	5,559	9,771	33,494		14	28	0	5	6	14	1	2
	NONPUBLIC	0	6	595	0	369	964		0	2	0	0	0	1	2	1
	TOTAL	15	76	17,956	5,559	10,140	34,458	1.1	14	30	0	5	6	15	3	3
ONONDAGA	PUBLIC	18	127	31,272	15,643	20,931	67,922		50	13	8	21	6	23	2	4
	NONPUBLIC	0	24	3,184	0	1,834	5,018		0	13	3	0	0	3	5	0
	TOTAL	18	151	34,456	15,643	22,765	72,940	2.3	50	26	11	21	6	26	7	4
ONTARIO	PUBLIC	9	29	7,580	2,797	4,832	15,480		10	3	0	3	2	6	3	2
	NONPUBLIC	0	5	935	0	0	935		1	1	2	0	0	0	0	1
	TOTAL	9	34	8,515	2,797	4,832	16,415	0.5	11	4	2	3	2	6	3	3

[1] **Elem Enroll** is the school by school total of enrollments in K-4, K-5, K-6, K-8 schools, elementary and middle/JHS students in K-12 schools and students in special ed schools. Public enrollments include public and county-operated schools.

[2] **Middle/JHS Enroll** is the school by school total of enrollments in 5-8 and 7-9 schools. Public enrollments include public and county-operated schools. Private middle/JHS enrollments are included in Senior Enroll.

[3] **Senior Enroll** is the school by school total of enrollments in 7-12 and 9-12 schools, the secondary students in K-12 schools and students in vocational ed schools. Public enrollments include public and county-operated schools. For private schools, Senior Enroll includes middle/JHS enrollment plus senior enrollment.

[4] **Public Total Enroll** columns are not the sum of school building enrollments. They are projected district-wide Fall enrollments provided to MDR by each school district office, plus county-operated school enrollments.

[5] **K-5** includes pre-kindergarten, kindergarten, K-3, K-4, K-5 schools.

[6] **5-8** includes schools with low grades of 4, 5, 6 and high grades of 7, 8, 9 (e.g., 4-8, 5-8, 6-8, 6-9).

[7] **7-9** includes schools with low grades of 7, 8 and high grades of 7, 8, 9 (e.g., 7-7, 7-8, 7-9, 8-9).

[8] **7-12** includes 7-12, 8-12, 9-12, 10-12, etc.

[9] **K-12** includes schools with both elementary and secondary grades.

[10] **Other** includes special ed, vocational ed and adult schools.

***Public State Totals** for all columns can exceed the sum of the counties because state totals include state-operated schools and their enrollments

COUNTY STATISTICS

Market Data Retrieval

COUNTY		DISTRICTS	SCHOOLS	ELEM ENROLL[1]	MIDDLE/JHS ENROLL[2]	SENIOR ENROLL[3]	TOTAL ENROLL[4]	% OF STATE	K-5[5]	K-6	K-8	5-8[6]	7-9[7]	7-12[8]	K-12[9]	OTHER[10]
ORANGE	PUBLIC	18	85	25,898	13,431	19,966	59,612		41	3	3	15	1	16	3	3
	NONPUBLIC	0	26	4,535	0	1,832	6,367		2	2	9	2	0	4	6	1
	TOTAL	**18**	**111**	**30,433**	**13,431**	**21,798**	**65,979**	**2.1**	**43**	**5**	**12**	**17**	**1**	**20**	**9**	**4**
ORLEANS	PUBLIC	5	13	2,611	872	2,173	5,945		2	3	0	2	0	5	0	1
	NONPUBLIC	0	1	15	0	6	21		0	0	0	0	0	0	1	0
	TOTAL	**5**	**14**	**2,626**	**872**	**2,179**	**5,966**	**0.2**	**2**	**3**	**0**	**2**	**0**	**5**	**1**	**1**
OSWEGO	PUBLIC	9	37	9,087	3,676	5,750	19,889		10	10	0	4	2	7	2	2
	NONPUBLIC	0	2	257	0	23	280		0	1	0	0	0	0	0	0
	TOTAL	**9**	**39**	**9,344**	**3,676**	**5,773**	**20,169**	**0.6**	**10**	**11**	**0**	**4**	**2**	**7**	**3**	**2**
OTSEGO	PUBLIC	12	20	3,953	578	2,061	6,592		4	1	0	2	0	3	9	1
	NONPUBLIC	0	4	157	0	41	198		1	0	0	0	0	0	2	1
	TOTAL	**12**	**24**	**4,110**	**578**	**2,102**	**6,790**	**0.2**	**5**	**1**	**0**	**2**	**0**	**3**	**11**	**2**
PUTNAM	PUBLIC	6	19	5,562	3,382	4,651	13,595		9	0	1	4	0	4	1	0
	NONPUBLIC	0	5	532	0	18	550		1	0	2	0	0	0	1	1
	TOTAL	**6**	**24**	**6,094**	**3,382**	**4,669**	**14,145**	**0.5**	**10**	**0**	**3**	**4**	**0**	**4**	**2**	**1**
QUEENS	PUBLIC	0	0	0	0	14,417	14,417		0	0	0	0	0	0	0	0
	NONPUBLIC	0	142	33,252	0	0	47,669		10	4	77	0	0	23	17	11
	TOTAL	**0**	**142**	**33,252**	**0**	**14,417**	**47,669**	**1.5**	**10**	**4**	**77**	**0**	**0**	**23**	**17**	**11**
RENSSELAER	PUBLIC	12	39	9,312	3,417	6,381	20,692		18	4	1	4	0	8	2	2
	NONPUBLIC	0	15	1,763	0	1,456	3,219		0	2	4	0	0	3	2	2
	TOTAL	**12**	**54**	**11,075**	**3,417**	**7,837**	**23,911**	**0.8**	**18**	**6**	**5**	**4**	**0**	**11**	**6**	**4**
RICHMOND	PUBLIC	0	0	0	0	0	0		0	0	0	0	0	0	0	0
	NONPUBLIC	0	33	8,234	0	4,888	13,122		1	0	22	0	0	7	2	1
	TOTAL	**0**	**33**	**8,234**	**0**	**4,888**	**13,122**	**0.4**	**1**	**0**	**22**	**0**	**0**	**7**	**2**	**1**
ROCKLAND	PUBLIC	8	64	17,907	8,298	13,278	39,974		32	8	0	6	4	11	1	2
	NONPUBLIC	0	59	15,228	0	5,597	20,825		5	1	19	0	0	15	15	4
	TOTAL	**8**	**123**	**33,135**	**8,298**	**18,875**	**60,799**	**1.9**	**37**	**9**	**19**	**6**	**4**	**26**	**16**	**6**
SARATOGA	PUBLIC	12	54	14,573	7,335	10,680	32,795		29	3	0	10	0	10	1	1
	NONPUBLIC	0	13	1,491	0	386	1,877		3	2	1	0	0	0	5	2
	TOTAL	**12**	**67**	**16,064**	**7,335**	**11,066**	**34,672**	**1.1**	**32**	**5**	**1**	**10**	**0**	**10**	**6**	**3**
SCHENECTADY	PUBLIC	6	40	9,792	4,961	6,911	22,128		23	1	0	8	0	6	0	2
	NONPUBLIC	0	10	1,529	0	429	1,958		2	0	1	0	0	0	3	4
	TOTAL	**6**	**50**	**11,321**	**4,961**	**7,340**	**24,086**	**0.8**	**25**	**1**	**1**	**8**	**0**	**6**	**3**	**6**
SCHOHARIE	PUBLIC	6	12	2,185	357	1,488	4,058		2	2	0	0	0	3	3	1
	NONPUBLIC	0	1	4	0	2	6		0	0	0	1	0	0	1	0
	TOTAL	**6**	**13**	**2,189**	**357**	**1,490**	**4,064**	**0.1**	**2**	**2**	**0**	**1**	**0**	**3**	**4**	**1**

[1] **Elem Enroll** is the school by school total of enrollments in K-4, K-5, K-6, K-8 schools, elementary and middle/JHS students in K-12 schools and students in special ed schools. Public enrollments include public and county-operated schools.

[2] **Middle/JHS Enroll** is the school by school total of enrollments in 5-8 and 7-9 public schools. Public enrollments include public and county-operated schools. Private middle/JHS enrollments are included in Senior Enroll.

[3] **Senior Enroll** is the school by school total of enrollments in 7-12 and 9-12 schools, the secondary students in K-12 schools and students in vocational ed schools. Public enrollments include public and county-operated schools. For private schools, Senior Enroll includes middle/JHS enrollment plus senior enrollment.

[4] **Public Total Enroll** columns are not the sum of school building enrollments. They are projected district-wide Fall enrollments provided to MDR by each school district office, plus county-operated school enrollments.

[5] **K-5** includes pre-kindergarten, kindergarten, K-3, K-4, K-5 schools.

[6] **5-8** includes schools with low grades of 4, 5, 6 and high grades of 7, 8, 9 (e.g., 4-8, 5-8, 6-8, 6-9).

[7] **7-9** includes schools with low grades of 7, 8 and high grades of 7, 8, 9 (e.g., 7-7, 7-8, 7-9, 8-9).

[8] **7-12** includes 7-12, 8-12, 9-12, 10-12, etc.

[9] **K-12** includes schools with both elementary and secondary grades.

[10] **Other** includes special ed, vocational ed and adult schools.

*****Public State Totals** for all columns can exceed the sum of the counties because state totals include state-operated schools and their enrollments.

New York School Directory — COUNTY STATISTICS

COUNTY		DISTRICTS	SCHOOLS	ELEM ENROLL[1]	MIDDLE/JHS ENROLL[2]	SENIOR ENROLL[3]	TOTAL ENROLL[4]	% OF STATE	K-5[5]	K-6	K-8	5-8[6]	7-9[7]	7-12[8]	K-12[9]	OTHER[10]
SCHUYLER	PUBLIC	3	6	1,204	0	876	2,038		1	2	0	0	0	2	1	0
	NONPUBLIC	0	0	0	0	0	0		0	0	0	0	0	0	0	0
	TOTAL	3	6	1,204	0	876	2,038	0.1	1	2	0	0	0	2	1	0
SENECA	PUBLIC	4	11	1,848	797	1,170	3,831		5	0	0	2	0	2	2	0
	NONPUBLIC	0	3	96	0	24	120		0	0	1	0	0	0	2	0
	TOTAL	4	14	1,944	797	1,194	3,951	0.1	5	0	1	2	0	2	4	0
ST LAWRENCE	PUBLIC	17	36	7,775	2,277	4,572	14,691		5	5	0	5	1	7	10	3
	NONPUBLIC	0	6	519	0	47	566		0	2	2	0	0	0	2	0
	TOTAL	17	42	8,294	2,277	4,619	15,257	0.5	5	7	2	5	1	7	12	3
STEUBEN	PUBLIC	12	36	6,857	2,169	4,966	14,078		13	5	0	3	0	9	4	2
	NONPUBLIC	0	5	413	0	190	603		0	1	2	1	0	0	1	0
	TOTAL	12	41	7,270	2,169	5,156	14,681	0.5	13	6	2	4	0	9	5	2
SUFFOLK	PUBLIC	69	359	102,145	49,832	78,253	237,086		180	31	3	54	8	59	5	19
	NONPUBLIC	0	64	9,789	0	5,541	15,330		6	8	23	0	0	5	10	12
	TOTAL	69	423	111,934	49,832	83,794	252,416	8.0	186	39	26	54	8	64	15	31
SULLIVAN	PUBLIC	8	21	4,534	1,247	3,438	9,482		4	5	0	2	0	7	1	2
	NONPUBLIC	0	6	1,207	0	0	1,207		0	0	5	0	0	0	0	1
	TOTAL	8	27	5,741	1,247	3,438	10,689	0.3	4	5	5	2	0	7	1	3
TIOGA	PUBLIC	6	20	3,014	1,791	2,384	7,450		7	1	0	5	0	7	0	0
	NONPUBLIC	0	1	57	0	23	80		0	0	0	0	0	0	1	0
	TOTAL	6	21	3,071	1,791	2,407	7,530	0.2	7	1	0	5	0	7	1	0
TOMPKINS	PUBLIC	7	32	4,912	2,561	3,278	10,956		15	0	0	6	0	6	3	2
	NONPUBLIC	0	5	414	0	50	464		0	0	3	0	0	1	0	1
	TOTAL	7	37	5,326	2,561	3,328	11,420	0.4	15	0	3	6	0	7	3	3
ULSTER	PUBLIC	9	46	9,740	4,914	7,353	22,942		16	9	0	6	3	10	0	2
	NONPUBLIC	0	13	1,167	0	495	1,662		0	0	4	0	0	2	3	4
	TOTAL	9	59	10,907	4,914	7,848	24,604	0.8	16	9	4	6	3	12	3	6
WARREN	PUBLIC	9	20	4,084	1,325	3,076	8,569		5	4	0	2	0	5	3	1
	NONPUBLIC	0	2	398	0	0	398		0	0	1	0	0	0	0	1
	TOTAL	9	22	4,482	1,325	3,076	8,967	0.3	5	4	1	2	0	5	3	2
WASHINGTON	PUBLIC	11	23	4,598	895	2,908	8,534		7	4	0	1	0	4	6	1
	NONPUBLIC	0	2	25	0	8	33		0	0	1	0	0	0	1	0
	TOTAL	11	25	4,623	895	2,916	8,567	0.3	7	4	1	1	0	4	7	1
WAYNE	PUBLIC	11	37	6,185	2,876	4,411	13,754		13	3	0	8	0	11	0	2
	NONPUBLIC	0	3	280	0	15	295		0	0	1	0	0	0	1	1
	TOTAL	11	40	6,465	2,876	4,426	14,049	0.5	13	3	1	8	0	11	1	3

[1] **Elem Enroll** is the school by school total of enrollments in K-4, K-5, K-6, K-8 schools, elementary and middle/JHS students in K-12 schools and students in special ed schools. Public enrollments include public and county-operated schools.

[2] **Middle/JHS Enroll** is the school by school total of enrollments in 5-8 and 7-9 public schools. Public enrollments include public and county-operated schools. Private middle/JHS enrollments are included in Senior Enroll.

[3] **Senior Enroll** is the school by school total of enrollments in 7-12 and 9-12 schools, the secondary students in K-12 schools and students in vocational ed schools. Public enrollments include public and county-operated schools. For private schools, Senior Enroll includes middle/JHS enrollment plus senior enrollment.

[4] **Public Total Enroll** columns are not the sum of school building enrollments. They are projected district-wide Fall enrollments provided to MDR by each school district office, plus county-operated school enrollments.

[5] **K-5** includes pre-kindergarten, kindergarten, K-3, K-4, K-5 schools.

[6] **5-8** includes schools with low grades of 4, 5, 6 and high grades of 7, 8, 9 (e.g., 4-8, 5-8, 6-8, 6-9).

[7] **7-9** includes schools with low grades of 7, 8 and high grades of 7, 8, 9 (e.g., 7-7, 7-8, 7-9, 8-9).

[8] **7-12** includes 7-12, 8-12, 9-12, 10-12, etc.

[9] **K-12** includes schools with both elementary and secondary grades.

[10] **Other** includes special ed, vocational ed and adult schools.

*****Public State Totals** for all columns can exceed the sum of the counties because state totals include state-operated schools and their enrollments

School Year 2020-2021   800-333-8802

COUNTY STATISTICS — Market Data Retrieval

COUNTY		DISTRICTS	SCHOOLS	ELEM ENROLL[1]	MIDDLE/JHS ENROLL[2]	SENIOR ENROLL[3]	TOTAL ENROLL[4]	% OF STATE[4]	K-5[5]	K-6	K-8	5-8[6]	7-9[7]	7-12[8]	K-12[9]	OTHER[10]
WESTCHESTER	PUBLIC	46	257	73,686	25,873	46,361	148,984		100	19	27	34	1	49	5	22
	NONPUBLIC	0	86	15,372	0	9,280	24,652		9	0	28	1	0	13	17	18
	TOTAL	46	343	89,058	25,873	55,641	173,636	5.5	109	19	55	35	1	62	22	40
WYOMING	PUBLIC	5	11	1,786	820	1,316	3,822		3	1	1	2	0	3	1	0
	NONPUBLIC	0	2	110	0	50	160		0	0	0	0	0	0	2	0
	TOTAL	5	13	1,896	820	1,366	3,982	0.1	3	1	1	2	0	3	3	0
YATES	PUBLIC	2	6	1,003	303	688	2,124		1	1	0	1	0	2	0	1
	NONPUBLIC	0	4	148	0	18	166		1	0	1	0	0	0	2	0
	TOTAL	2	10	1,151	303	706	2,290	0.1	2	1	1	1	0	2	2	1
STATE TOTAL	PUBLIC*	688	4,998	1,245,258	474,384	800,944	2,870,898		1,840	358	239	659	63	1,003	270	214
	NONPUBLIC	0	1,388	273,189	0	127,607	400,796		106	75	528	19	1	205	297	157
	TOTAL	688	6,386	1,518,447	474,384	928,551	3,271,694		1,946	433	767	678	64	1,208	567	371

[1] **Elem Enroll** is the school by school total of enrollments in K-4, K-5, K-6, K-8 schools, elementary and middle/JHS students in K-12 schools and students in special ed schools. Public enrollments include public and county-operated schools.
[2] **Middle/JHS Enroll** is the school by school total of enrollments in 5-8 and 7-9 public schools. Public enrollments include public and county-operated schools. Private middle/JHS enrollments are included in Senior Enroll.
[3] **Senior Enroll** is the school by school total of enrollments in 7-12 and 9-12 schools, the secondary students in K-12 schools and students in vocational ed schools. Public enrollments include public and county-operated schools. For private schools, Senior Enroll includes middle/JHS enrollment plus senior enrollment.
[4] **Public Total Enroll** columns are not the sum of school building enrollments. They are projected district-wide Fall enrollments provided to MDR by each school district office, plus county-operated school enrollments.
[5] **K-5** includes pre-kindergarten, kindergarten, K-3, K-4, K-5 schools.
[6] **5-8** includes schools with low grades of 4, 5, 6 and high grades of 7, 8, 9 (e.g., 4-8, 5-8, 6-8, 6-9).
[7] **7-9** includes schools with low grades of 7, 8 and high grades of 7, 8, 9 (e.g., 7-7, 7-8, 7-9, 8-9).
[8] **7-12** includes 7-12, 8-12, 9-12, 10-12, etc.
[9] **K-12** includes schools with both elementary and secondary grades.
[10] **Other** includes special ed, vocational ed and adult schools.

*__Public State Totals__ for all columns can exceed the sum of the counties because state totals include state-operated schools and their enrollments

New York School Directory

DISTRICT BUYING POWER INDEX

DISTRICT BUYING POWER INDEX
COUNTIES RANKED BY PERCENTAGE OF STATE SPENDING

COUNTY / DISTRICT	PID	COUNTY % OF STATE	DISTRICT % OF COUNTY	DISTRICT % OF STATE	NUMBER OF SCHOOLS	ENROLL	EXP	POV
NEW YORK		48.72						
New York City Dept of Ed	00740626		100.00	48.72	1,680	1,150,000	HIGH	MED-HIGH
SUFFOLK		8.23						
Brentwood Union Free Sch Dist	00772203		8.20	0.67	17	20,000	HIGH	MED-HIGH
Sachem Central School Dist	00775138		7.10	0.58	15	13,500	HIGH	LOW
Middle Country Ctl Sch Dist	00774201		5.22	0.43	14	9,860	HIGH	MED-LOW
Smithtown Central Sch Dist	00775504		4.20	0.35	12	8,946	HIGH	LOW
Half Hollow Hills Central SD	00773439		4.04	0.33	9	8,017	HIGH	LOW
Three Village Central Sch Dist	00775970		3.21	0.26	9	6,400	HIGH	LOW
Huntington Union Free Sch Dist	00773776		3.12	0.26	8	4,545	HIGH	MED-LOW
Longwood Central School Dist	00774378		3.12	0.26	7	9,150	MED	MED-LOW
Patchogue-Medford Unified SD	00774811		2.59	0.21	11	7,503	MED	MED-LOW
West Islip School Dist	00776209		2.39	0.20	7	3,720	HIGH	LOW
Connetquot Central School Dist	00772863		2.36	0.19	11	5,653	HIGH	LOW
William Floyd School Dist	00776376		2.36	0.19	8	8,700	MED	MED-LOW
Lindenhurst Union Free SD	00774043		2.28	0.19	8	5,694	MED	MED-LOW
Bay Shore Union Free Sch Dist	00771998		2.27	0.19	7	6,000	MED	MED-LOW
Sayville Union Free Sch Dist	00775360		2.27	0.19	5	2,823	HIGH	MED-LOW
Riverhead Central School Dist	00775011		2.26	0.19	7	5,600	HIGH	MED-LOW
Central Islip Union Free SD	00772435		2.16	0.18	8	7,400	MED	MED-HIGH
Northport-East Northport UFSD	00774653		2.06	0.17	9	5,141	HIGH	LOW
South Huntington Union Free SD	00775736		1.85	0.15	7	5,900	MED	MED-LOW
Hauppauge Union Free Sch Dist	00773697		1.82	0.15	5	3,200	HIGH	LOW
Amityville Union Free Sch Dist	00771895		1.69	0.14	5	3,100	HIGH	MED-LOW
Copiague Union Free Sch Dist	00772980		1.62	0.13	6	4,864	MED	MED-LOW
Commack Union Free School Dist	00772576		1.60	0.13	8	5,889	MED	LOW
Southampton Union Free SD	00775877		1.56	0.13	3	1,575	HIGH	MED-LOW
Rocky Point Union Free SD	00775102		1.50	0.12	4	2,947	HIGH	MED-LOW
South Country Central Sch Dist	00772136		1.41	0.12	7	4,400	MED	MED-LOW
North Babylon Union Free SD	00774548		1.39	0.11	7	4,491	MED	MED-LOW
Cold Spring Harbor Central SD	00772526		1.32	0.11	4	1,650	HIGH	LOW
Deer Park Union Free Sch Dist	00773051		1.29	0.11	5	4,015	MED	MED-LOW
East Islip Union Free SD	00773180		1.18	0.10	6	3,782	MED	LOW
West Babylon Union Free SD	00776118		1.16	0.10	7	4,000	MED	MED-LOW
Islip Union Free School Dist	00773881		1.11	0.09	5	2,726	HIGH	LOW
Wyandanch Union Free Sch Dist	00776429		1.10	0.09	4	2,811	HIGH	MED-HIGH
Kings Park Ctl School Dist	00773946		1.09	0.09	5	2,888	MED	LOW
East Hampton Union Free SD	00773142		1.05	0.09	3	1,781	HIGH	MED-LOW
Harborfields Ctl School Dist	00773623		0.97	0.08	4	2,965	MED	LOW
Brookhaven Comsewogue Unif SD	00772784		0.93	0.08	6	3,702	LOW	MED-LOW
Shoreham-Wading River Ctl SD	00775451		0.89	0.07	4	2,000	HIGH	LOW
Westhampton Beach School Dist	00776338		0.89	0.07	3	1,819	HIGH	MED-LOW
Hampton Bays Union Free SD	00773594		0.86	0.07	3	2,060	HIGH	MED-LOW
Eastport-South Manor Ctrl SD	00775853		0.86	0.07	6	3,294	LOW	MED-LOW
Miller Place Union Free SD	00774445		0.81	0.07	4	2,489	MED	LOW
Bayport- Blue Point USD	00772071		0.78	0.06	5	2,080	MED	LOW
Mt Sinai Union Free SD	00774500		0.73	0.06	3	2,100	MED	MED-LOW
Center Moriches Union Free SD	00772411		0.71	0.06	3	1,400	HIGH	MED-LOW
Elwood Union Free School Dist	00773336		0.69	0.06	4	2,049	MED	LOW
Port Jefferson Union Free SD 6	00774938		0.68	0.06	3	1,048	HIGH	LOW
Babylon Union Free Sch Dist	00771950		0.65	0.05	3	1,554	HIGH	LOW
Mattituck-Cutchogue UFSD	00774160		0.59	0.05	2	1,100	HIGH	LOW
Sag Harbor Union Free Sch Dist	00775310		0.49	0.04	2	953	HIGH	MED-LOW
Southold Union Free Sch Dist	00775918		0.46	0.04	2	750	HIGH	MED-LOW
Springs Union Free School Dist	00775956		0.44	0.04	1	750	HIGH	MED-LOW
Greenport Union Free Sch Dist	00773415		0.38	0.03	1	627	HIGH	MED-LOW
East Quogue Union Free SD	00773295		0.36	0.03	1	390	HIGH	MED-LOW
East Moriches Union Free SD	00773271		0.25	0.02	2	750	MED	LOW
Bridgehampton Union Free SD	00772394		0.25	0.02	1	227	HIGH	LOW
Tuckahoe Common School Dist	00776077		0.23	0.02	1	285	HIGH	MED-LOW
Quogue Union Free School Dist	00774976		0.18	0.01	1	130	HIGH	LOW
Montauk Union Free School Dist	00774483		0.18	0.01	1	320	HIGH	MED-LOW
Amagansett Union Free Sch Dist	00771871		0.18	0.01	1	79	HIGH	LOW
Shelter Island Union Free SD	00775437		0.17	0.01	1	202	HIGH	LOW
Remsenburg-Speonk UFSD	00774990		0.15	0.01	1	132	HIGH	LOW
Fishers Island Union Free SD	00773398		0.09	0.01	1	65	HIGH	MED-LOW
Little Flower Union Free Sch	01854713		0.08	0.01	1	96	HIGH	
Fire Island Union Free SD	00774770		0.04	0.00	1	32	HIGH	MED-LOW
Oysterponds Union Free SD	00774794		0.03	0.00	1	104	MED	LOW
Sagaponack Common School Dist	00775346		0.02	0.00	1	16	HIGH	
Wainscott Common School Dist	00776091		0.02	0.00	1	30	HIGH	HIGH
New Suffolk Common School Dist	00774524		0.01	0.00	1	13	HIGH	

School Year 2020-2021

DISTRICT BUYING POWER INDEX

Market Data Retrieval

DISTRICT BUYING POWER INDEX
COUNTIES RANKED BY PERCENTAGE OF STATE SPENDING

COUNTY / DISTRICT	PID	COUNTY % OF STATE	DISTRICT % OF COUNTY	DISTRICT % OF STATES	NUMBER OF SCHOOLS	ENROLL	EXP	POV
NASSAU		7.64						
Hempstead Union Free SD	00736089		4.18	0.32	10	7,355	HIGH	MED-HIGH
Levittown Union Free Sch Dist	00736730		3.74	0.29	11	7,215	HIGH	LOW
Farmingdale Union Free SD	00735437		3.54	0.27	6	5,900	HIGH	LOW
East Meadow Union Free SD	00735164		3.26	0.25	9	7,100	HIGH	LOW
Syosset Central School Dist	00738556		3.26	0.25	10	6,500	HIGH	LOW
Plainview-Old Bethpage Ctl SD	00738013		3.17	0.24	7	5,000	HIGH	LOW
Hewlett Woodmere Union Free SD	00736273		3.08	0.24	5	3,000	HIGH	LOW
Baldwin Union Free School Dist	00734873		3.03	0.23	7	5,450	HIGH	MED-LOW
Oceanside Union Free Sch Dist	00737760		2.86	0.22	10	5,400	HIGH	LOW
Massapequa Union Free SD 23	00737227		2.56	0.20	9	8,000	MED	LOW
Port Washington Union Free SD	00738130		2.46	0.19	7	5,000	HIGH	MED-LOW
Long Beach City School Dist	00736950		2.42	0.19	7	3,800	HIGH	MED-LOW
Great Neck Public Schools	00735920		2.41	0.18	12	6,700	MED	MED-LOW
Westbury Union Free Sch Dist	00739122		2.33	0.18	6	5,000	HIGH	MED-HIGH
Garden City School Dist	00735750		2.31	0.18	7	3,800	HIGH	LOW
Uniondale Union Free Sch Dist	00738697		2.25	0.17	9	6,970	MED	MED-LOW
Jericho Union Free School Dist	00736572		2.24	0.17	5	3,155	HIGH	LOW
Freeport Public School Dist	00735671		2.19	0.17	8	6,885	MED	MED-HIGH
Bellmore-Merrick Ctl High SD	00737344		2.00	0.15	5	5,273	MED	LOW
Locust Valley Ctl School Dist	00736900		1.99	0.15	6	2,000	HIGH	LOW
Mineola Union Free Sch Dist	00737461		1.97	0.15	5	2,927	HIGH	LOW
Lawrence Union Free Sch Dist	00736649		1.93	0.15	5	2,600	HIGH	MED-LOW
Sewanhaka Ctl High Sch Dist	00735554		1.84	0.14	5	8,145	LOW	MED-LOW
Hicksville Union Free Sch Dist	00736352		1.81	0.14	9	5,000	MED	MED-LOW
Bethpage Union Free Sch Dist	00735059		1.77	0.14	5	2,946	HIGH	LOW
Elmont Union Free School Dist	00735360		1.76	0.13	6	3,500	HIGH	MED-LOW
Plainedge Union Free Sch Dist	00737928		1.67	0.13	5	2,825	HIGH	LOW
Manhasset Union Free Sch Dist	00737186		1.65	0.13	4	3,250	HIGH	LOW
Glen Cove City School Dist	00735839		1.57	0.12	6	3,200	HIGH	MED-LOW
Herricks Union Free Sch Dist	00736194		1.55	0.12	5	3,950	MED	LOW
Valley Stream Ctl High SD	00738790		1.52	0.12	4	4,600	MED	MED-LOW
Valley Stream Union Free SD 30	00738946		1.48	0.11	3	1,450	HIGH	MED-LOW
Lynbrook Union Free Sch Dist	00737045		1.46	0.11	7	2,809	HIGH	LOW
North Shore Central SD	00737708		1.37	0.10	5	2,548	HIGH	LOW
Roosevelt Union Free Sch Dist	00738336		1.36	0.10	5	3,511	MED	MED-HIGH
Wantagh Union Free Sch Dist 23	00738996		1.34	0.10	5	2,770	HIGH	LOW
Roslyn School Dist	00738403		1.33	0.10	5	3,150	MED	LOW
West Hempstead School Dist	00739067		1.30	0.10	5	2,300	HIGH	MED-LOW
Malverne Union Free Sch Dist	00737124		1.30	0.10	4	1,725	HIGH	MED-LOW
Rockville Ctr Union Free SD	00738245		1.29	0.10	7	3,500	MED	LOW
Valley Stream Union Free SD 13	00738843		1.26	0.10	4	1,964	HIGH	MED-LOW
Island Trees Union Free SD	00736508		1.08	0.08	4	2,236	HIGH	LOW
Seaford Union Free SD	00738491		1.02	0.08	4	2,249	HIGH	LOW
Floral Park Bellerose Sch Dist	00735528		0.98	0.07	2	1,479	HIGH	LOW
Oyster Bay East Norwich Ctl SD	00737863		0.97	0.07	3	1,565	HIGH	LOW
Island Park Union Free SD	00736467		0.91	0.07	2	743	HIGH	MED-LOW
North Bellmore Union Free SD	00737590		0.89	0.07	5	2,031	HIGH	LOW
East Williston Union Free SD	00735322		0.88	0.07	3	1,722	HIGH	LOW
New Hyde-Garden City Park UFSD	00737540		0.86	0.07	4	1,785	HIGH	LOW
Merrick Union Free School Dist	00737423		0.76	0.06	3	1,490	HIGH	LOW
Carle Place Union Free SD	00735126		0.76	0.06	3	1,360	HIGH	LOW
East Rockaway Union Free SD	00735281		0.72	0.06	3	1,200	HIGH	MED-LOW
Bellmore Union Free Sch Dist	00735011		0.71	0.05	3	1,100	HIGH	LOW
Franklin Square Union Free SD	00735621		0.69	0.05	3	1,940	MED	LOW
North Merrick Union Free SD	00737667		0.61	0.05	3	1,177	HIGH	LOW
Valley Stream Union Free SD 24	00738893		0.36	0.03	3	1,093	MED	MED-LOW
WESTCHESTER		4.65						
Mount Vernon City School Dist	00780860		7.86	0.37	16	8,000	HIGH	MED-LOW
White Plains City School Dist	00782105		7.19	0.33	9	7,000	HIGH	MED-LOW
Yonkers Public School Dist	00782234		6.82	0.32	40	27,000	LOW	MED-HIGH
New Rochelle City School Dist	00781096		4.17	0.19	10	11,000	LOW	MED-HIGH
Rye City School Dist	00781682		4.04	0.19	6	3,510	HIGH	LOW
Scarsdale Union Free Sch Dist	00781802		4.00	0.19	7	4,771	HIGH	LOW
Mamaroneck Union Free Sch Dist	00780717		3.99	0.19	6	5,230	HIGH	LOW
Chappaqua Central School Dist	00779811		3.57	0.17	6	3,900	HIGH	LOW
Katonah-Lewisboro Sch Dist	00780535		3.24	0.15	5	2,917	HIGH	LOW
Lakeland Central School Dist	00780602		3.08	0.14	8	5,845	MED	LOW
Yorktown Central School Dist	00782703		2.63	0.12	5	3,400	HIGH	LOW
Bedford Central School Dist	00780781		2.61	0.12	8	4,100	MED	MED-LOW
Ossining Union Free Sch Dist	00781292		2.45	0.11	6	5,100	MED	MED-LOW
Peekskill City School Dist	00781369		2.42	0.11	6	3,400	MED	MED-LOW
Harrison Central School Dist	00780274		2.37	0.11	6	3,600	MED	LOW
Tarrytown Union Free Sch Dist	00781955		2.32	0.11	5	2,900	HIGH	MED-LOW

New York School Directory

DISTRICT BUYING POWER INDEX

COUNTIES RANKED BY PERCENTAGE OF STATE SPENDING

COUNTY / DISTRICT	PID	COUNTY % OF STATE	DISTRICT % OF COUNTY	DISTRICT % OF STATES	NUMBER OF SCHOOLS	ENROLL	EXP	POV
Port Chester Rye Union Free SD	00781577		2.30	0.11	6	5,000	MED	MED-LOW
Greenburgh Central School Dist	00780183		2.23	0.10	5	1,903	HIGH	MED-LOW
Byram Hills Central Sch Dist	00779756		2.01	0.09	4	2,300	HIGH	LOW
Ardsley Union Free School Dist	00779639		1.98	0.09	3	2,326	HIGH	LOW
Irvington Union Free Sch Dist	00780494		1.93	0.09	4	1,781	HIGH	LOW
Eastchester Union Free SD	00779976		1.89	0.09	5	3,140	MED	LOW
Edgemont Union Free Sch Dist	00780066		1.75	0.08	3	2,050	HIGH	LOW
Hendrick Hudson Ctl Sch Dist	00780420		1.72	0.08	5	2,122	HIGH	LOW
Somers Central School Dist	00781888		1.61	0.07	4	2,866	MED	LOW
Croton-Harmon Union Free SD	00779897		1.57	0.07	3	1,568	HIGH	LOW
Valhalla Union Free Sch Dist	00782052		1.55	0.07	3	1,420	HIGH	LOW
Pelham Union Free School Dist	00781436		1.50	0.07	6	2,800	MED	LOW
Dobbs Ferry Union Free SD	00779938		1.40	0.07	3	1,500	HIGH	LOW
Mt Pleasant Ctl School Dist	00781034		1.25	0.06	4	2,000	MED	LOW
Bronxville Union Free SD	00779720		1.18	0.06	3	1,640	HIGH	LOW
Pleasantville Union Free SD	00781503		1.12	0.05	3	1,700	MED	LOW
Hastings on Hudson Union FR SD	00780365		1.11	0.05	3	1,654	MED	LOW
Briarcliff Manor Union Free SD	00779689		1.08	0.05	3	1,347	HIGH	LOW
Blind Brook-Rye Union Free SD	00781656		1.03	0.05	3	1,364	HIGH	LOW
North Salem Central Sch Dist	00781242		0.93	0.04	2	1,046	HIGH	LOW
Tuckahoe Union Free SD	00782026		0.93	0.04	3	1,100	HIGH	LOW
Elmsford Union Free SD	00780107		0.89	0.04	3	1,002	HIGH	MED-LOW
Rye Neck Union Free Sch Dist	00781735		0.81	0.04	4	1,525	MED	LOW
Pocantico Hills Ctl Sch Dist	00781553		0.73	0.03	1	308	HIGH	MED-LOW
Greenburgh-Graham UFSD	00780169		0.67	0.03	2	286	HIGH	
Greenburgh-North Castle SD	00781931		0.58	0.03	4	309	HIGH	
Hawthorne Cedar Knolls UFSD	00780406		0.52	0.02	4	400	HIGH	
Greenburgh 11 Union Free SD	00780042		0.45	0.02	2	85	HIGH	
Mt Pleasant Cottage UFSD	01854737		0.44	0.02	2	215	HIGH	
Mt Pleasant-Blythedale UFSD	01854749		0.12	0.01	1	134	HIGH	
ERIE		3.51						
Buffalo Public Schools	00722557		41.42	1.45	68	33,428	HIGH	HIGH
Williamsville Ctl School Dist	00725535		7.42	0.26	13	9,900	MED	LOW
Kenmore-Tonawanda UF Sch Dist	00724373		5.83	0.20	9	7,000	MED	MED-LOW
Lancaster Central Sch Dist	00724828		4.50	0.16	7	5,630	MED	LOW
West Seneca Central Sch Dist	00725377		4.27	0.15	9	6,100	MED	MED-LOW
Orchard Park Central Sch Dist	00725016		3.35	0.12	6	5,010	MED	LOW
Clarence Central School Dist	00723599		2.62	0.09	6	4,600	LOW	MED-LOW
Sweet Home Central Sch Dist	00725171		2.31	0.08	6	3,300	MED	MED-LOW
East Aurora Union Free SD	00723771		2.07	0.07	3	1,760	HIGH	MED-LOW
Hamburg Central School Dist	00724177		2.00	0.07	6	3,550	LOW	LOW
Grand Island Central Sch Dist	00724048		1.88	0.07	5	2,905	MED	MED-LOW
Frontier Ctl School Dist	00723915		1.84	0.06	6	4,760	LOW	MED-LOW
Amherst Central School Dist	00722521		1.82	0.06	4	2,990	MED	MED-LOW
Cheektowaga Maryvale UFSD	00724919		1.56	0.05	4	2,183	MED	MED-LOW
Tonawanda City School Dist	00725262		1.56	0.05	4	2,000	MED	MED-LOW
Akron Central School Dist	00722430		1.53	0.05	3	1,500	HIGH	MED-LOW
Evans-Brant Central Sch Dist	00724737		1.50	0.05	5	2,260	MED	MED-LOW
Depew Union Free School Dist	00723719		1.49	0.05	3	1,785	MED	MED-LOW
Springville Griffith Inst CSD	00724103		1.46	0.05	4	1,700	MED	MED-LOW
Iroquois Central School Dist	00724309		1.42	0.05	5	2,127	MED	LOW
Alden Central School Dist	00722466		1.40	0.05	4	1,581	MED	MED-LOW
Cheektowaga Central SD	00723549		1.24	0.04	3	2,249	LOW	MED-HIGH
Cheektowaga-Sloan UFSD	00725092		1.13	0.04	4	1,279	MED	MED-LOW
Eden Central School Dist	00723836		1.13	0.04	3	1,538	MED	MED-LOW
Lackawanna City School Dist	00724622		0.96	0.03	4	1,946	LOW	HIGH
Cleveland Hill Union Free SD	00723678		0.90	0.03	3	1,284	MED	MED-LOW
Holland Central School Dist	00724268		0.72	0.03	3	800	MED	MED-LOW
North Collins Ctl Sch Dist	00724983		0.71	0.02	2	620	HIGH	MED-LOW
MONROE		2.85						
Rochester City School Dist	00732526		31.99	0.91	57	28,000	MED	HIGH
Greece Central School Dist	00731869		8.53	0.24	17	10,700	MED	MED-LOW
Webster Central School Dist	00733374		7.13	0.20	11	8,331	MED	LOW
Pittsford Central Sch Dist	00732423		5.30	0.15	9	6,000	MED	LOW
Gates Chili Central Sch Dist	00731766		5.29	0.15	6	4,000	HIGH	MED-LOW
Penfield Central School Dist	00732332		5.08	0.14	6	4,600	MED	LOW
Fairport Ctl School Dist	00731663		4.56	0.13	8	5,900	MED	MED-LOW
Rush Henrietta Central SD	00733166		4.42	0.13	9	5,300	MED	MED-LOW
Churchville Chili Ctl Sch Dist	00731479		4.26	0.12	6	3,900	MED	MED-LOW
East Irondequoit Ctl Sch Dist	00731534		3.67	0.10	6	3,000	HIGH	MED-HIGH
West Irondequoit Ctl SD	00732186		3.57	0.10	10	3,600	MED	MED-LOW
Hilton Central School Dist	00732069		3.26	0.09	5	4,482	LOW	MED-LOW
Brighton Central School Dist	00731352		3.11	0.09	4	3,518	MED	MED-LOW

School Year 2020-2021

DISTRICT BUYING POWER INDEX

Market Data Retrieval

DISTRICT BUYING POWER INDEX
COUNTIES RANKED BY PERCENTAGE OF STATE SPENDING

COUNTY / DISTRICT	PID	COUNTY % OF STATE	DISTRICT % OF COUNTY	DISTRICT % OF STATES	NUMBER OF SCHOOLS	ENROLL	EXP	POV
Brockport Ctl School Dist	00731429		2.76	0.08	5	3,562	MED	MED-LOW
Spencerport Central Sch Dist	00733295		2.57	0.07	6	3,700	LOW	MED-LOW
Honeoye Falls Lima Sch Dist	00732136		1.81	0.05	4	2,122	MED	MED-LOW
Wheatland Chili Ctl Sch Dist	00733506		1.53	0.04	2	637	HIGH	MED-LOW
East Rochester Union Free SD	00731625		1.16	0.03	2	1,007	HIGH	MED-LOW
ONONDAGA		2.59						
Syracuse City School Dist	00762193		52.03	1.35	37	21,116	HIGH	HIGH
North Syracuse Ctl Sch Dist	00761917		9.02	0.23	11	8,400	MED	MED-LOW
Liverpool Ctl School Dist	00761577		6.02	0.16	14	7,000	MED	MED-LOW
West Genesee Ctl School Dist	00761163		4.63	0.12	7	4,600	MED	MED-LOW
Baldwinsville Central Sch Dist	00761072		4.32	0.11	8	5,500	LOW	MED-LOW
Fayetteville-Manlius Ctl SD	00761773		4.00	0.10	6	4,259	MED	LOW
East Syracuse Minoa Ctl SD	00761278		3.92	0.10	7	3,600	MED	MED-LOW
Westhill Central School Dist	00762686		2.33	0.06	4	1,700	HIGH	MED-LOW
Jordan Elbridge Ctl Sch Dist	00761486		2.05	0.05	3	1,300	HIGH	MED-LOW
Skaneateles Central Sch Dist	00762090		1.99	0.05	4	1,200	HIGH	MED-LOW
Jamesville-DeWitt Central SD	00761412		1.90	0.05	5	2,694	LOW	MED-LOW
Solvay Union Free Sch Dist	00762143		1.50	0.04	3	1,500	MED	MED-HIGH
Onondaga Central School Dist	00762052		1.41	0.04	3	830	HIGH	MED-LOW
La Fayette Central School Dist	00761527		1.39	0.04	4	825	HIGH	MED-LOW
Marcellus Central School Dist	00761864		1.38	0.04	3	1,507	MED	MED-LOW
Tully Central School Dist	00762650		1.13	0.03	2	770	HIGH	MED-LOW
Fabius Pompey Central SD	00761371		0.72	0.02	2	611	MED	MED-LOW
Lyncourt Union Free Sch Dist	00761759		0.26	0.01	1	450	LOW	MED-HIGH
ORANGE		2.34						
Newburgh Enlarged City SD	00764579		37.84	0.89	13	11,562	HIGH	MED-HIGH
Warwick Valley Central SD	00764945		8.01	0.19	4	3,569	HIGH	LOW
Monroe Woodbury Central SD	00764426		7.99	0.19	7	6,900	MED	MED-LOW
Middletown Enlarged City SD	00764270		7.03	0.16	6	7,312	MED	MED-HIGH
Kiryas Joel Union Free SD	03423956		5.35	0.13	1	167	HIGH	HIGH
Pine Bush Central School Dist	00764799		5.10	0.12	8	5,000	MED	MED-LOW
Minisink Valley Central SD	00764373		4.84	0.11	5	3,493	MED	MED-LOW
Goshen Central School Dist	00764141		4.69	0.11	4	2,935	HIGH	MED-LOW
Valley Central School Dist	00764490		4.26	0.10	7	4,200	MED	MED-LOW
Port Jervis City School Dist	00764854		3.59	0.08	4	2,332	HIGH	MED-HIGH
Cornwall Central School Dist	00764098		3.32	0.08	5	3,122	MED	LOW
Washingtonville Central SD	00765004		2.59	0.06	5	3,793	LOW	MED-LOW
Chester Union Free School Dist	00764050		1.43	0.03	2	986	HIGH	MED-LOW
Highland Falls-Ft Montgmry SD	00764220		1.43	0.03	3	1,000	HIGH	MED-LOW
Greenwood Lake Union Free SD	00764191		1.17	0.03	2	500	HIGH	MED-LOW
Florida Union Free Sch Dist	00764907		0.72	0.02	2	807	LOW	MED-LOW
Tuxedo Union Free Sch Dist	00764921		0.65	0.02	2	225	HIGH	LOW
ROCKLAND		1.73						
East Ramapo Central Sch Dist	00767911		30.86	0.53	14	8,843	HIGH	HIGH
North Rockland Central SD	00767569		18.53	0.32	8	8,000	HIGH	MED-LOW
Clarkstown Central School Dist	00767301		18.17	0.31	13	7,907	HIGH	MED-LOW
Suffern Central School Dist	00768123		9.05	0.16	7	4,283	HIGH	MED-LOW
South Orangetown Central SD	00767820		8.32	0.14	4	2,911	HIGH	LOW
Nyack Union Free School Dist	00767686		8.18	0.14	5	3,000	HIGH	MED-LOW
Nanuet Union Free School Dist	00767519		4.07	0.07	5	2,220	MED	MED-LOW
Pearl River School Dist	00767753		2.81	0.05	5	2,360	LOW	MED-LOW
DUTCHESS		1.22						
Arlington Central School Dist	00721400		19.63	0.24	11	7,000	MED	MED-LOW
Wappingers Central Sch Dist	00722129		18.19	0.22	15	10,616	LOW	MED-LOW
Poughkeepsie City School Dist	00721890		12.86	0.16	8	4,420	HIGH	MED-HIGH
Beacon City School Dist	00721527		10.74	0.13	6	3,200	HIGH	MED-LOW
Pawling Ctl School Dist	00721826		7.39	0.09	3	1,100	HIGH	LOW
Hyde Park Central School Dist	00721670		7.36	0.09	6	3,500	MED	MED-LOW
Red Hook Central School Dist	00721981		5.53	0.07	4	1,750	HIGH	MED-LOW
Spackenkill Union Free SD	00722064		3.81	0.05	4	1,500	MED	LOW
Dover Union Free School Dist	00721618		3.27	0.04	4	1,352	MED	MED-LOW
Pine Plains Ctl School Dist	00721852		3.22	0.04	3	905	HIGH	MED-LOW
Rhinebeck Central School Dist	00722026		3.20	0.04	3	1,000	HIGH	MED-LOW
Millbrook Ctl School Dist	00721785		2.73	0.03	4	875	HIGH	MED-LOW
Webutuck Ctl School Dist	00722272		2.07	0.03	3	649	HIGH	MED-LOW
ALBANY		1.06						
Albany City School Dist	00714110		33.63	0.36	19	9,024	HIGH	MED-HIGH
North Colonie Central SD	00714665		15.75	0.17	8	5,800	MED	
South Colonie Central Sch Dist	00714835		10.97	0.12	8	4,700	MED	MED-LOW
Guilderland Central Sch Dist	00714550		10.54	0.11	7	5,000	MED	LOW
Bethlehem Central School Dist	00714366		10.33	0.11	7	4,400	MED	LOW

DISTRICT BUYING POWER INDEX

COUNTIES RANKED BY PERCENTAGE OF STATE SPENDING

COUNTY / DISTRICT	PID	COUNTY % OF STATE	DISTRICT % OF COUNTY	DISTRICT % OF STATES	NUMBER OF SCHOOLS	ENROLL	EXP	POV
Ravena Coeymans Selkirk Ctl SD	00714768		5.41	0.06	4	1,839	MED	MED-LOW
Cohoes City School Dist	00714457		3.35	0.04	5	2,000	LOW	MED-HIGH
Voorheesville Central Sch Dist	00714952		3.18	0.03	3	1,175	MED	LOW
Berne-Knox-Westerlo Central SD	00714328		2.73	0.03	2	751	HIGH	MED-LOW
Watervliet City School Dist	00714988		2.54	0.03	2	1,297	LOW	MED-HIGH
Green Island Union Free SD	00714536		0.85	0.01	1	262	HIGH	MED-HIGH
Menands Union Free Sch Dist	00714641		0.71	0.01	1	305	MED	MED-HIGH
ONEIDA		0.83						
Utica City School Dist	00760614		38.20	0.32	13	10,000	HIGH	HIGH
Rome City School Dist	00760327		13.04	0.11	10	5,300	LOW	MED-HIGH
Whitesboro Ctl School Dist	00760913		8.35	0.07	7	3,135	MED	MED-LOW
New Hartford Central Sch Dist	00760145		7.94	0.07	5	2,553	MED	LOW
Vernon-Verona-Sherrill CSD	00760547		6.24	0.05	5	1,900	MED	MED-LOW
Holland Patent Ctl School Dist	00760080		5.63	0.05	4	1,316	HIGH	MED-LOW
Camden Central School Dist	00759940		4.64	0.04	4	2,000	LOW	MED-LOW
Adirondack Central Sch Dist	00759885		3.09	0.03	4	1,200	LOW	MED-LOW
Clinton Central School Dist	00760030		2.83	0.02	3	1,258	LOW	MED-LOW
Sauquoit Valley Central SD	00760511		1.92	0.02	3	900	LOW	MED-LOW
New York Mills Union Free SD	00760212		1.82	0.02	1	550	MED	MED-LOW
Waterville Central Sch Dist	00760846		1.74	0.01	2	742	LOW	MED-LOW
Oriskany Ctl School Dist	00760248		1.72	0.01	2	587	MED	MED-LOW
Westmoreland Central Sch Dist	00760884		1.47	0.01	3	853	LOW	MED-LOW
Remsen Central School Dist	00760298		1.36	0.01	2	400	MED	MED-HIGH
SARATOGA		0.80						
Shenendehowa Central Sch Dist	00769828		26.89	0.22	12	9,499	MED	LOW
Ballston Spa Ctl School Dist	00769402		20.35	0.16	6	4,200	HIGH	MED-LOW
Saratoga Springs City Sch Dist	00769696		15.55	0.12	8	6,375	LOW	MED-LOW
Burnt Hills Ballston Lake SD	00769488		9.87	0.08	5	3,000	MED	LOW
South Glens Falls Ctl Sch Dist	00769933		6.39	0.05	6	3,000	LOW	MED-LOW
Schuylerville Central Sch Dist	00769787		4.81	0.04	3	1,500	MED	MED-LOW
Corinth Central School Dist	00769555		3.50	0.03	3	1,139	MED	MED-LOW
Galway Central School Dist	00769634		3.39	0.03	2	837	HIGH	LOW
Stillwater Central Sch Dist	00770009		3.32	0.03	3	1,035	MED	MED-LOW
Mechanicville City Sch Dist	00769660		2.97	0.02	2	1,345	LOW	MED-LOW
Waterford Halfmoon School Dist	00770035		2.43	0.02	2	800	MED	MED-LOW
Edinburg Common School Dist	00769610		0.55	0.00	1	65	HIGH	MED-LOW
BROOME		0.74						
Binghamton City School Dist	00716417		25.03	0.19	10	5,500	HIGH	HIGH
Union-Endicott Ctl Sch Dist	00716728		14.50	0.11	7	4,000	MED	MED-HIGH
Johnson City Central Sch Dist	00716871		10.41	0.08	5	2,443	MED	MED-HIGH
Vestal Ctl School Dist	00717095		10.24	0.08	7	3,397	MED	MED-LOW
Maine Endwell Ctl School Dist	00716950		7.60	0.06	4	2,492	LOW	MED-LOW
Chenango Valley Ctl Sch Dist	00716625		7.01	0.05	4	1,719	MED	MED-LOW
Windsor Central School Dist	00717253		6.77	0.05	5	1,700	MED	MED-HIGH
Susquehanna Valley Central SD	00717033		4.26	0.03	4	1,412	MED	MED-LOW
Chenango Forks Central SD	00716572		4.09	0.03	3	1,404	LOW	MED-HIGH
Deposit Central School Dist	00716699		3.72	0.03	2	482	HIGH	MED-HIGH
Whitney Point Central Sch Dist	00717203		3.72	0.03	3	1,359	LOW	MED-HIGH
Harpursville Central Sch Dist	00716845		2.65	0.02	2	677	MED	MED-HIGH
ULSTER		0.67						
Kingston City School Dist	00777837		19.89	0.13	10	6,800	LOW	MED-HIGH
Wallkill Central School Dist	00778362		15.21	0.10	5	2,831	HIGH	MED-LOW
Onteora Central School Dist	00778142		14.88	0.10	4	1,200	HIGH	MED-HIGH
Saugerties Central School Dist	00778295		11.54	0.08	6	2,500	MED	MED-LOW
Rondout Valley Ctl Sch Dist	00778207		8.40	0.06	5	1,975	MED	MED-LOW
Marlboro Central School Dist	00778037		7.97	0.05	3	1,893	MED	MED-LOW
Highland Ctl School Dist	00777796		7.62	0.05	3	1,667	MED	MED-LOW
New Paltz Ctl School Dist	00778099		7.43	0.05	4	2,035	MED	MED-LOW
Ellenville Central School Dist	00777760		7.07	0.05	3	1,500	MED	MED-HIGH
NIAGARA		0.60						
Niagara Falls City Sch Dist	00759249		20.11	0.12	12	7,100	LOW	HIGH
Lockport City School Dist	00759055		18.96	0.11	9	5,100	MED	MED-HIGH
North Tonawanda City Sch Dist	00759598		13.55	0.08	6	3,400	MED	MED-LOW
Niagara-Wheatfield Ctl SD	00759483		12.55	0.08	6	3,650	LOW	MED-LOW
Starpoint Central School Dist	00759768		10.11	0.06	4	2,931	LOW	LOW
Lewiston Porter Ctl Sch Dist	00758996		8.25	0.05	4	2,187	MED	MED-LOW
Newfane Central School Dist	00759172		6.06	0.04	4	1,511	MED	MED-LOW
Royalton Hartland Central SD	00759720		4.23	0.03	3	1,271	LOW	MED-LOW
Wilson Central School Dist	00759794		3.89	0.02	2	1,060	LOW	MED-LOW
Barker Central School Dist	00758960		2.28	0.01	2	750	LOW	MED-LOW

School Year 2020-2021

DISTRICT BUYING POWER INDEX

Market Data Retrieval

DISTRICT BUYING POWER INDEX
COUNTIES RANKED BY PERCENTAGE OF STATE SPENDING

COUNTY / DISTRICT	PID	COUNTY % OF STATE	DISTRICT % OF COUNTY	DISTRICT % OF STATES	NUMBER OF SCHOOLS	ENROLL	EXP	POV
CHAUTAUQUA		0.59						
Jamestown City School Dist	00718738		21.46	0.13	9	5,000	MED	HIGH
Dunkirk City School Dist	00718465		12.59	0.07	6	2,300	HIGH	HIGH
Southwestern Central Sch Dist	00719067		7.76	0.05	3	1,400	HIGH	MED-LOW
Silver Creek Central Sch Dist	00719029		6.24	0.04	3	1,212	MED	MED-LOW
Fredonia Central School Dist	00718647		6.11	0.04	4	1,500	MED	MED-LOW
Falconer Central School Dist	00718544		6.02	0.04	3	1,200	MED	MED-HIGH
Cassadaga Valley Ctl Sch Dist	00718336		5.16	0.03	2	851	HIGH	MED-HIGH
Chautauqua Lake Central SD	00718867		5.15	0.03	1	950	HIGH	MED-HIGH
Bemus Point Ctl School Dist	00718257		4.19	0.02	2	715	HIGH	MED-LOW
Frewsburg Central School Dist	00718702		3.77	0.02	2	805	MED	MED-LOW
Sherman Central School Dist	00718996		3.46	0.02	1	434	HIGH	MED-HIGH
Westfield Central School Dist	00719110		3.34	0.02	1	700	MED	MED-HIGH
Forestville Central Sch Dist	00718611		2.87	0.02	2	457	HIGH	MED-HIGH
Panama Central School Dist	00718893		2.80	0.02	1	450	HIGH	MED-HIGH
Brocton Central School Dist	00718300		2.73	0.02	1	540	LOW	HIGH
Clymer Central School Dist	00718427		2.50	0.01	1	444	MED	MED-HIGH
Pine Valley Central Sch Dist	00718934		2.13	0.01	2	550	MED	MED-HIGH
Ripley Central School Dist	00718960		1.70	0.01	1	165	HIGH	MED-HIGH
RENSSELAER		0.57						
Troy City School Dsitrict	00767090		28.05	0.16	7	4,090	HIGH	MED-HIGH
East Greenbush Central SD	00766773		17.98	0.10	7	5,042	LOW	MED-LOW
Averill Park Central Sch Dist	00766591		11.93	0.07	5	2,665	MED	LOW
Lansingburgh Central Sch Dist	00766931		9.08	0.05	4	2,335	MED	MED-HIGH
Brunswick Central School Dist	00766723		7.82	0.04	2	1,200	HIGH	MED-LOW
Hoosic Valley Central Sch Dist	00766876		6.37	0.04	2	931	HIGH	MED-LOW
Hoosick Falls Central Sch Dist	00766905		5.27	0.03	2	1,200	MED	MED-HIGH
Schodack Central School Dist	00767052		4.23	0.02	2	900	MED	LOW
Berlin Central School Dist	00766668		3.54	0.02	2	800	MED	MED-LOW
Rensselaer City School Dist	00767014		3.10	0.02	2	1,060	LOW	MED-HIGH
Wynantskill Union Free SD	00767234		2.30	0.01	1	400	MED	MED-LOW
North Greenbush Common SD	00767210		0.33	0.00	1	13	HIGH	MED-LOW
JEFFERSON		0.56						
Watertown City School Dist	00730334		37.44	0.21	8	3,800	HIGH	MED-HIGH
Indian River Ctl School Dist	00730140		21.10	0.12	8	3,900	MED	MED-LOW
Carthage Central School Dist	00729971		13.26	0.07	5	3,200	MED	MED-LOW
General Brown Ctl School Dist	00730061		6.87	0.04	3	1,600	MED	MED-LOW
South Jefferson Central SD	00730243		5.46	0.03	4	1,894	LOW	MED-LOW
Thousand Islands Central SD	00730293		4.31	0.02	4	867	MED	MED-LOW
Belleville Henderson Sch Dist	00729957		3.11	0.02	1	450	HIGH	MED-LOW
Alexandria Central School Dist	00729933		2.97	0.02	1	492	HIGH	MED-LOW
Sackets Harbor Ctl School Dist	00730126		2.10	0.01	1	418	MED	MED-LOW
La Fargeville Central Sch Dist	00730205		1.77	0.01	1	539	LOW	MED-LOW
Lyme Central School Dist	00730229		1.61	0.01	1	349	MED	MED-LOW
SCHENECTADY		0.56						
Schenectady City School Dist	00770396		52.00	0.29	17	9,921	MED	MED-HIGH
Niskayuna Central School Dist	00770217		14.36	0.08	8	4,240	LOW	LOW
Schalmont Central School Dist	00770308		10.56	0.06	3	1,798	MED	MED-LOW
Scotia Glenville Ctl Sch Dist	00770645		9.23	0.05	6	2,600	LOW	MED-LOW
Mohonasen Central Sch Dist	00770152		9.14	0.05	4	2,799	LOW	MED-LOW
Duanesburg Central Sch Dist	00770126		4.70	0.03	2	770	HIGH	LOW
OSWEGO		0.51						
Fulton City School Dist	00765482		22.03	0.11	6	3,500	HIGH	MED-HIGH
Mexico Central School Dist	00765640		15.02	0.08	5	2,055	HIGH	MED-HIGH
Central Square Central SD	00765406		14.80	0.08	6	3,800	LOW	MED-LOW
Oswego City School Dist	00765705		13.81	0.07	7	3,669	LOW	MED-HIGH
Phoenix Central School Dist	00765781		10.02	0.05	3	1,684	MED	MED-HIGH
Hannibal Central School Dist	00765602		7.68	0.04	3	1,310	MED	MED-HIGH
Sandy Creek Central Sch Dist	00765872		7.23	0.04	1	800	HIGH	MED-HIGH
Pulaski Central School Dist	00765846		5.03	0.03	2	971	MED	MED-HIGH
Altmar-Parish-Williamstown SD	00765353		4.37	0.02	2	1,500	LOW	MED-HIGH
STEUBEN		0.51						
Corning-Painted Post Area SD	00771376		28.86	0.15	9	4,500	MED	MED-LOW
Hornell City School Dist	00771651		21.68	0.11	4	1,700	HIGH	MED-HIGH
Wayland-Cohocton Central SD	00771821		9.99	0.05	4	1,246	HIGH	MED-LOW
Bath Central School Dist	00771613		7.48	0.04	3	1,500	MED	MED-HIGH
Canisteo-Greenwood Central SD	00771326		6.70	0.03	2	1,000	HIGH	MED-LOW
Addison Central School Dist	00771209		5.59	0.03	3	1,100	MED	MED-HIGH
Campbell-Savona Ctl Sch Dist	00771302		4.54	0.02	2	829	MED	MED-HIGH
Hammondsport Ctl School Dist	00771584		4.16	0.02	2	450	HIGH	MED-LOW
Avoca Central School Dist	00771261		3.79	0.02	1	440	HIGH	MED-LOW

New York School Directory

DISTRICT BUYING POWER INDEX

DISTRICT BUYING POWER INDEX
COUNTIES RANKED BY PERCENTAGE OF STATE SPENDING

COUNTY / DISTRICT	PID	COUNTY % OF STATE	DISTRICT % OF COUNTY	DISTRICT % OF STATES	NUMBER OF SCHOOLS	ENROLL	EXP	POV
Arkport Central School Dist	00771247		3.71	0.02	1	475	HIGH	MED-LOW
Jasper Troupsburg Central SD	00771742		1.94	0.01	2	450	MED	MED-HIGH
Prattsburgh Central Sch Dist	00771766		1.55	0.01	1	388	LOW	MED-HIGH
ONTARIO		0.50						
Canandaigua City School Dist	00763666		22.87	0.11	3	3,500	HIGH	MED-LOW
Geneva City School Dist	00763719		19.24	0.10	4	2,078	HIGH	MED-HIGH
Victor Central School Dist	00763977		17.55	0.09	5	4,450	LOW	LOW
Phelps-Clifton Springs Ctl SD	00763874		16.95	0.08	4	1,549	HIGH	MED-LOW
Manchester-Shortsville Ctl SD	00763939		7.14	0.04	3	800	HIGH	MED-LOW
Naples Central School Dist	00763848		5.61	0.03	2	600	HIGH	MED-HIGH
Marcus Whitman Central SD	00763800		5.28	0.03	3	1,227	MED	MED-LOW
Honeoye Central School Dist	00763783		3.80	0.02	1	251	HIGH	MED-LOW
Bloomfield Central SD	00763630		1.55	0.01	2	850	LOW	MED-LOW
CATTARAUGUS		0.45						
Salamanca City Central SD	00717784		21.31	0.09	3	1,400	HIGH	MED-HIGH
Olean City School Dist	00717588		16.91	0.08	4	2,075	HIGH	MED-HIGH
Yorkshire-Pioneer Ctl Sch Dist	00717679		15.21	0.07	4	2,700	MED	MED-HIGH
Gowanda Central School Dist	00717459		7.46	0.03	3	1,063	MED	MED-HIGH
Franklinville Ctl School Dist	00717423		6.45	0.03	2	700	HIGH	MED-HIGH
Cattaraugus-Little Vly Ctl SD	00717368		6.26	0.03	3	975	MED	
Allegany-Limestone Ctl SD	00717332		6.06	0.03	2	1,156	LOW	MED-LOW
Randolph Central School Dist	00717758		5.84	0.03	2	903	MED	MED-HIGH
Portville Central School Dist	00717722		4.47	0.02	1	1,030	LOW	MED-LOW
Ellicottville Central Sch Dist	00717394		4.22	0.02	1	600	MED	MED-LOW
Hinsdale Central School Dist	00717502		3.15	0.01	1	404	HIGH	MED-HIGH
West Valley Ctl Sch Dist	00717837		1.75	0.01	1	230	HIGH	MED-LOW
Randolph Acad Union Free SD	00717564		0.89	0.00	2	200	LOW	
WAYNE		0.43						
Newark Central School Dist	00779263		15.71	0.07	5	2,091	MED	MED-HIGH
Palmyra-Macedon Central SD	00779380		14.93	0.06	4	1,861	HIGH	MED-LOW
Wayne Central School Dist	00779524		12.17	0.05	4	2,180	MED	MED-LOW
Clyde-Savannah Central SD	00779160		10.49	0.05	3	784	HIGH	MED-HIGH
North Rose Wolcott Central SD	00779330		8.51	0.04	3	1,155	MED	MED-LOW
Lyons Central School Dist	00779201		8.05	0.03	2	920	HIGH	MED-HIGH
Sodus Central School Dist	00779483		7.54	0.03	3	1,050	MED	MED-HIGH
Red Creek Central School Dist	00779433		5.74	0.02	3	870	MED	MED-HIGH
Gananda Central School Dist	02205490		5.71	0.02	3	960	MED	LOW
Williamson Central School Dist	00779598		5.59	0.02	3	1,106	MED	MED-LOW
Marion Central School Dist	00779237		5.57	0.02	2	687	HIGH	MED-LOW
PUTNAM		0.41						
Carmel Central School Dist	00766369		31.89	0.13	5	3,973	MED	MED-LOW
Mahopac Ctl School Dist	00766474		21.70	0.09	5	3,968	MED	LOW
Brewster Central School Dist	00766319		19.66	0.08	4	3,066	MED	MED-LOW
Putnam Valley Ctl School Dist	00766541		16.37	0.07	3	1,587	HIGH	MED-LOW
Haldane Central School Dist	00766448		6.92	0.03	1	794	HIGH	LOW
Garrison Union Free Sch Dist	00766424		3.47	0.01	1	207	HIGH	LOW
ST LAWRENCE		0.41						
Gouverneur Ctl School Dist	00768460		17.52	0.07	3	1,515	HIGH	MED-HIGH
Massena Central School Dist	00768692		11.47	0.05	5	2,500	LOW	MED-HIGH
Canton Central School Dist	00768355		10.09	0.04	3	1,000	MED	MED-LOW
Ogdensburg City School Dist	00768848		9.85	0.04	3	1,535	MED	MED-HIGH
Norwood-Norfolk Ctl SD	00768800		8.14	0.03	3	987	HIGH	MED-HIGH
Potsdam Central School Dist	00768941		6.33	0.03	3	1,200	LOW	MED-LOW
Hermon-DeKalb Central Sch Dist	00768551		4.45	0.02	1	430	HIGH	MED-LOW
Brasher Falls School Dist	00768989		4.27	0.02	3	1,000	LOW	MED-HIGH
Heuvelton Central School Dist	00768587		4.13	0.02	1	580	MED	MED-HIGH
Madrid-Waddington Central SD	00768654		3.94	0.02	1	647	MED	MED-HIGH
Colton Pierrepont School Dist	00768422		3.88	0.02	1	368	HIGH	MED-LOW
Edwards-Knox Central Sch Dist	00768604		3.71	0.02	1	537	MED	MED-HIGH
Lisbon Central School Dist	00768628		2.97	0.01	1	587	LOW	MED-LOW
Parishville Hopkinton Sch Dist	00768915		2.72	0.01	1	420	MED	MED-LOW
Hammond Central School Distict	00768537		2.34	0.01	1	257	HIGH	MED-HIGH
Morristown Ctl School Dist	00768783		2.13	0.01	1	333	MED	MED-HIGH
Clifton-Fine Central Sch Dist	00768408		2.05	0.01	1	295	MED	MED-HIGH
CHEMUNG		0.37						
Elmira City School Dist	00719158		72.22	0.27	11	6,000	HIGH	MED-HIGH
Horseheads Ctl School Dist	00719421		22.47	0.08	7	4,245	LOW	MED-LOW
Elmira Heights Ctl Sch Dist	00719366		5.31	0.02	3	1,100	LOW	MED-HIGH
SULLIVAN		0.34						
Monticello Central School Dist	00776857		36.83	0.13	5	2,785	HIGH	MED-HIGH

DISTRICT BUYING POWER INDEX

Market Data Retrieval

DISTRICT BUYING POWER INDEX
COUNTIES RANKED BY PERCENTAGE OF STATE SPENDING

COUNTY / DISTRICT	PID	COUNTY % OF STATE	DISTRICT % OF COUNTY	DISTRICT % OF STATES	NUMBER OF SCHOOLS	ENROLL	EXP	POV
Fallsburg Central School Dist	00776754		17.87	0.06	2	1,440	HIGH	HIGH
Liberty Central School Dist	00776807		14.66	0.05	3	1,700	HIGH	MED-HIGH
Tri-Valley Central School Dist	00776962		9.99	0.03	2	975	HIGH	MED-HIGH
Sullivan West Central SD	00776780		9.10	0.03	2	1,068	MED	MED-HIGH
Livingston Manor Ctl Sch Dist	00776833		7.13	0.02	2	432	HIGH	MED-HIGH
Eldred Central School Dist	00776730		3.36	0.01	2	525	MED	MED-HIGH
Roscoe Central School Dist	00776948		1.07	0.00	1	257	LOW	MED-LOW
TOMPKINS		0.33						
Ithaca City School Dist	00777435		42.89	0.14	12	5,103	MED	MED-LOW
Dryden Central School Dist	00777332		13.28	0.04	5	1,500	MED	MED-LOW
Trumansburg Central SD	00777681		13.01	0.04	3	1,043	HIGH	MED-LOW
Groton Central School Dist	00777409		10.82	0.04	2	852	HIGH	MED-HIGH
Lansing Central School Dist	00777617		8.07	0.03	3	1,187	MED	MED-LOW
Newfield Central School Dist	00777655		6.62	0.02	3	780	MED	MED-LOW
George Junior Republic UFSD	00777382		5.31	0.02	1	186	HIGH	
CLINTON		0.31						
Beekmantown Ctl School Dist	00719964		27.77	0.09	4	2,000	HIGH	MED-HIGH
Peru Central School Dist	00720171		17.63	0.05	2	1,857	MED	MED-LOW
Plattsburgh City School Dist	00720236		16.69	0.05	5	1,852	MED	MED-HIGH
Saranac Central School Dist	00720303		14.75	0.05	4	1,400	MED	MED-HIGH
Ausable Valley Ctl Sch Dist	00719926		9.18	0.03	3	1,151	MED	MED-LOW
Northeastern Clinton Ctl SD	00720066		6.16	0.02	4	1,200	LOW	MED-HIGH
Northern Adirondack Ctl SD	00720121		5.07	0.02	2	805	LOW	MED-LOW
Chazy Central Rural Sch Dist	00720016		2.75	0.01	1	455	LOW	MED-LOW
CAYUGA		0.30						
Auburn Enlarged City Sch Dist	00717863		30.28	0.09	7	4,200	MED	MED-HIGH
Moravia Central School Dist	00718025		20.05	0.06	2	907	HIGH	MED-HIGH
Union Springs Ctl School Dist	00718154		14.84	0.05	3	823	HIGH	MED-LOW
Port Byron Ctl School Dist	00718051		11.46	0.03	2	800	HIGH	MED-LOW
Southern Cayuga Central SD	00718099		8.62	0.03	2	683	HIGH	MED-LOW
Weedsport Ctl School Dist	00718207		8.60	0.03	2	800	HIGH	MED-LOW
Cato Meridian Central Sch Dist	00717980		6.15	0.02	3	922	LOW	MED-LOW
GENESEE		0.29						
Batavia City School Dist	00728812		20.90	0.06	4	2,374	MED	MED-HIGH
Pembroke Ctl School Dist	00728927		15.89	0.05	3	1,000	HIGH	MED-LOW
Le Roy Central School Dist	00728991		15.27	0.04	2	1,350	HIGH	MED-LOW
Alexander Ctl School Dist	00728783		13.26	0.04	2	788	HIGH	MED-LOW
Byron-Bergen Ctl School Dist	00728886		9.91	0.03	2	864	MED	MED-LOW
Pavilion Ctl School Dist	00729062		9.59	0.03	2	680	HIGH	MED-LOW
Oakfield Alabama Ctl SD	00729024		8.51	0.02	2	800	MED	MED-LOW
Elba Central School Dist	00728965		6.68	0.02	1	403	HIGH	MED-LOW
WARREN		0.26						
Glens Falls City School Dist	00778520		28.05	0.07	5	2,058	HIGH	MED-LOW
Queensbury Union Free Sch Dist	00778714		25.69	0.07	4	3,200	LOW	MED-LOW
Lake George Central Sch Dist	00778685		12.05	0.03	2	721	HIGH	MED-LOW
Warrensburg Central Sch Dist	00778752		7.84	0.02	2	687	MED	MED-HIGH
Hadley-Luzerne Ctl Sch Dist	00778609		7.63	0.02	2	665	MED	MED-LOW
Bolton Central School Dist	00778465		7.48	0.02	1	200	HIGH	LOW
North Warren Cent Sch Dist	00778489		5.66	0.01	1	508	MED	MED-HIGH
Johnsburg Central School Dist	00778661		4.47	0.01	1	333	HIGH	MED-LOW
Glens Falls Common Sch Dist	00778441		1.12	0.00	1	155	LOW	MED-HIGH
WASHINGTON		0.25						
Hudson Falls Central Sch Dist	00778984		24.65	0.06	5	2,400	MED	MED-LOW
Granville Central School Dist	00778881		13.98	0.04	3	1,200	HIGH	MED-HIGH
Cambridge Central School Dist	00778805		11.64	0.03	1	844	HIGH	MED-LOW
Whitehall Central School Dist	00779108		10.91	0.03	2	719	HIGH	MED-HIGH
Greenwich Central School Dist	00778922		9.90	0.03	2	943	MED	MED-LOW
Argyle Central School Dist	00778788		7.23	0.02	2	480	HIGH	MED-LOW
Fort Ann Central School Dist	00778831		7.16	0.02	2	500	HIGH	MED-LOW
Salem Central School Dist	00779081		4.96	0.01	1	550	MED	MED-LOW
Ft Edward Union Free Sch Dist	00778855		4.87	0.01	2	450	LOW	MED-HIGH
Hartford Central School Dist	00778960		3.95	0.01	1	413	LOW	MED-HIGH
Putnam Central School Dist	00779067		0.75	0.00	1	35	HIGH	MED-HIGH
HERKIMER		0.24						
Central Valley School Dist	00729646		19.04	0.05	4	2,201	LOW	MED-HIGH
Herkimer Ctl School Dist	00729581		13.85	0.03	2	1,112	MED	MED-HIGH
Frankfort-Schuyler Ctl SD	00729531		12.10	0.03	2	893	MED	MED-HIGH
Little Falls City School Dist	00729696		10.91	0.03	3	1,116	MED	MED-HIGH
Mount Markham Central Sch Dist	00729763		10.41	0.03	3	1,100	MED	MED-HIGH
Dolgeville Central School Dist	00729505		9.87	0.02	2	900	MED	MED-HIGH

New York School Directory

DISTRICT BUYING POWER INDEX

DISTRICT BUYING POWER INDEX
COUNTIES RANKED BY PERCENTAGE OF STATE SPENDING

COUNTY / DISTRICT	PID	COUNTY % OF STATE	DISTRICT % OF COUNTY	DISTRICT % OF STATES	NUMBER OF SCHOOLS	ENROLL	EXP	POV
West Canada Valley Ctl SD	00729880		9.07	0.02	2	650	MED	MED-LOW
Poland Central School Dist	00729830		6.70	0.02	1	523	MED	MED-LOW
Town of Webb Union Free SD	00729866		5.04	0.01	1	270	HIGH	MED-LOW
Owen D Young Central Sch Dist	00729816		3.01	0.01	1	182	HIGH	MED-HIGH
LIVINGSTON		0.24						
Dansville Ctl School Dist	00730712		27.30	0.07	3	1,300	HIGH	MED-HIGH
Livonia Ctl School Dist	00730815		17.70	0.04	2	1,500	MED	MED-LOW
Geneseo Central Sch Dist	00730762		13.35	0.03	1	853	HIGH	MED-LOW
York Central School Dist	00730889		10.10	0.02	2	780	MED	MED-LOW
Keshequa Central School Dist	00730786		8.45	0.02	3	617	HIGH	MED-LOW
Avon Central School Dist	00730645		8.38	0.02	3	1,006	LOW	MED-LOW
Caledonia-Mumford Ctl Sch Dist	00730683		7.77	0.02	3	815	MED	MED-LOW
Mt Morris Central School Dist	00730853		6.94	0.02	1	500	MED	MED-HIGH
MADISON		0.24						
Oneida City School Dist	00731247		19.82	0.05	6	2,000	MED	MED-HIGH
Chittenango Central SD	00731065		18.42	0.04	4	1,904	MED	MED-LOW
Cazenovia Ctl School Dist	00731015		16.40	0.04	3	1,360	MED	MED-LOW
Canastota Central School Dist	00730968		15.58	0.04	4	1,275	MED	MED-LOW
Morrisville Eaton Central SD	00731211		10.01	0.02	2	621	HIGH	MED-LOW
Hamilton Central Sch Dist	00731156		6.47	0.02	1	588	MED	MED-LOW
Stockbridge Valley Central SD	00731338		4.65	0.01	1	460	MED	MED-LOW
De Ruyter Central School Dist	00731120		4.08	0.01	2	360	MED	MED-HIGH
Madison Central School Dist	00731170		2.67	0.01	1	450	LOW	MED-HIGH
Brookfield Central School Dist	00730944		1.91	0.00	1	240	LOW	MED-HIGH
COLUMBIA		0.22						
Hudson City School Dist	00720482		25.18	0.06	4	1,652	HIGH	MED-HIGH
Taconic Hills Central Sch Dist	00720652		22.46	0.05	2	1,241	HIGH	MED-LOW
Ichabod Crane Central Schools	00720561		20.90	0.05	3	1,683	MED	MED-LOW
Chatham Central School Dist	00720391		18.95	0.04	3	1,100	HIGH	MED-LOW
Germantown Central School Dist	00720468		6.68	0.01	1	550	MED	MED-LOW
New Lebanon Ctl School Dist	00720626		4.06	0.01	2	428	LOW	MED-LOW
Berkshire Union Free Sch Dist	00720377		1.77	0.00	2	40	HIGH	
FRANKLIN		0.22						
Saranac Lake Central Sch Dist	00728329		27.35	0.06	4	1,280	HIGH	MED-LOW
Malone Central School Dist	00728202		25.14	0.06	5	2,289	MED	MED-HIGH
Salmon River Central Sch Dist	00728288		21.50	0.05	4	1,800	MED	MED-HIGH
Tupper Lake Ctl School Dist	00728393		8.78	0.02	2	749	MED	MED-LOW
Brushton Moira Ctl Sch Dist	00728147		8.67	0.02	1	800	MED	MED-HIGH
Chateaugay Central School Dist	00728185		4.64	0.01	2	503	LOW	MED-LOW
St Regis Falls Ctl Sch Dist	00728367		3.92	0.01	1	268	MED	MED-HIGH
ALLEGANY		0.21						
Wellsville Central Sch Dist	00716326		13.02	0.03	2	1,118	MED	MED-HIGH
Cuba-Rushford Central Sch Dist	00716168		12.48	0.03	2	818	MED	MED-HIGH
Belfast Central School Dist	00716077		10.89	0.02	1	343	HIGH	MED-HIGH
Fillmore Central School Dist	00716194		10.52	0.02	1	680	MED	MED-HIGH
Genesee Valley Ctl School Dist	00716091		9.56	0.02	1	536	HIGH	MED-HIGH
Alfred Almond Ctl School Dist	00716003		9.30	0.02	1	600	MED	MED-HIGH
Bolivar-Richburg Ctrl Sch Dist	00716118		9.28	0.02	3	850	MED	MED-HIGH
Friendship Central Sch Dist	00716223		8.35	0.02	1	350	HIGH	MED-HIGH
Andover Central School Dist	00716039		6.50	0.01	1	300	HIGH	MED-LOW
Canaseraga Central Sch Dist	00716144		4.09	0.01	1	272	HIGH	MED-HIGH
Scio Central School Dist	00716297		3.55	0.01	1	300	MED	MED-HIGH
Whitesville Central Sch Dist	00716376		2.47	0.01	1	200	MED	MED-LOW
OTSEGO		0.21						
Oneonta City School Dist	00766125		24.58	0.05	5	1,736	MED	MED-LOW
Cooperstown Ctl School Dist	00765987		13.46	0.03	2	818	HIGH	MED-LOW
Milford Central School Dist	00766084		8.78	0.02	1	361	HIGH	MED-LOW
Richfield Springs Central SD	00766199		8.55	0.02	1	450	HIGH	MED-LOW
Morris Central School Dist	00766101		8.37	0.02	1	322	HIGH	MED-LOW
Edmeston Ctl School Dist	00766022		8.26	0.02	1	390	HIGH	MED-HIGH
Unatego Unadilla Central SD	00766254		5.83	0.01	3	716	LOW	MED-LOW
Cherry Valley-Springfield SD	00765963		4.88	0.01	1	449	LOW	MED-LOW
Gilbertsville-Mt Upton SD	00766046		4.78	0.01	1	350	MED	MED-HIGH
Worcester Ctl School Dist	00766292		4.52	0.01	1	350	MED	MED-HIGH
Schenevus Ctl School Dist	00765949		4.33	0.01	1	350	MED	MED-LOW
Laurens Central School Dist	00766060		3.66	0.01	1	300	MED	MED-LOW
FULTON		0.20						
Gloversville Enlarged Sch Dist	00728460		34.55	0.07	6	2,521	MED	MED-HIGH
Broadalbin-Perth Ctl Sch Dist	00728434		21.77	0.04	2	1,800	MED	MED-LOW
Greater Johnstown Sch Dist	00728549		19.98	0.04	5	1,700	MED	MED-LOW

DISTRICT BUYING POWER INDEX

Market Data Retrieval

DISTRICT BUYING POWER INDEX
COUNTIES RANKED BY PERCENTAGE OF STATE SPENDING

COUNTY / DISTRICT	PID	COUNTY % OF STATE	DISTRICT % OF COUNTY	DISTRICT % OF STATES	NUMBER OF SCHOOLS	ENROLL	EXP	POV
Northville Central School Dist	00728654		8.17	0.02	1	500	HIGH	MED-LOW
O E S J Central School Dist	00728678		6.37	0.01	2	719	LOW	MED-HIGH
Mayfield Ctl School Dist	00728628		6.26	0.01	2	876	LOW	MED-HIGH
Wheelerville Union Free SD	00728733		2.90	0.01	1	130	HIGH	MED-LOW
SENECA		0.19						
Waterloo Central School Dist	00771156		61.64	0.11	4	1,538	HIGH	MED-HIGH
Seneca Falls Central Sch Dist	00771053		16.53	0.03	4	1,173	MED	MED-LOW
South Seneca Ctl Sch Dist	00771118		14.13	0.03	2	700	HIGH	MED-HIGH
Romulus Ctl School Dist	00771027		7.69	0.01	1	420	MED	MED-HIGH
TIOGA		0.19						
Waverly Ctl School Dist	00777277		24.32	0.05	4	1,700	MED	MED-HIGH
Owego Apalachin Ctl Sch Dist	00777112		21.38	0.04	4	2,005	LOW	MED-LOW
Spencer Van Etten Central SD	00777186		15.56	0.03	3	985	MED	MED-LOW
Candor Central School Dist	00777021		12.95	0.02	2	750	HIGH	MED-LOW
Newark Valley Central Sch Dist	00777057		12.90	0.02	3	1,060	MED	MED-LOW
Tioga Central School Dist	00777227		12.89	0.02	3	950	MED	MED-HIGH
CHENANGO		0.18						
Norwich City School Dist	00719720		20.99	0.04	4	2,000	LOW	MED-HIGH
Sherburne Earlville Central SD	00719811		20.06	0.04	3	1,267	MED	MED-HIGH
Greene Ctl School Dist	00719627		12.53	0.02	4	954	MED	MED-HIGH
Oxford Academy Central SD	00719770		11.05	0.02	3	750	MED	MED-HIGH
Bainbridge Guilford CSD	00719586		10.77	0.02	2	850	MED	MED-HIGH
Afton Central School Dist	00719550		9.47	0.02	1	522	HIGH	MED-HIGH
Unadilla Valley Ctl Sch Dist	00719691		9.20	0.02	2	850	LOW	MED-HIGH
Otselic Valley Central SD	00719897		5.94	0.01	1	300	HIGH	MED-HIGH
GREENE		0.18						
Catskill Central School Dist	00729153		25.31	0.05	3	1,385	MED	MED-HIGH
Cairo-Durham Ctl School Dist	00729127		19.66	0.04	3	1,275	MED	MED-HIGH
Greenville Central School Dist	00729256		19.10	0.03	3	1,100	MED	MED-LOW
Coxsackie-Athens Central SD	00729218		17.82	0.03	4	1,400	MED	MED-LOW
Windham Ashland Jewett Ctl SD	00729323		12.88	0.02	1	310	HIGH	MED-LOW
Hunter Tannersville Ctl SD	00729294		5.22	0.01	2	355	MED	MED-HIGH
MONTGOMERY		0.18						
Greater Amsterdam School Dist	00734586		50.53	0.09	6	3,690	MED	MED-HIGH
Fonda Fultonville Central SD	00734770		20.42	0.04	1	1,340	MED	MED-LOW
Canajoharie Ctl School Dist	00734718		17.47	0.03	3	855	HIGH	MED-HIGH
Ft Plain Central School Dist	00734811		11.59	0.02	2	750	MED	MED-HIGH
ORLEANS		0.18						
Albion Central School Dist	00765133		47.71	0.09	3	1,860	HIGH	MED-LOW
Medina Central School Dist	00765274		16.59	0.03	3	1,475	LOW	MED-HIGH
Lyndonville Central Sch Dist	00765248		13.71	0.02	2	700	HIGH	MED-LOW
Kendall Central School Dist	00765212		12.88	0.02	2	710	MED	MED-LOW
Holley Central School Dist	00765183		9.11	0.02	2	1,200	LOW	MED-LOW
DELAWARE		0.17						
Sidney Central School Dist	00721216		18.98	0.03	3	1,090	MED	MED-HIGH
Delaware Academy Ctrl SD Delhi	00721034		16.19	0.03	2	797	HIGH	MED-HIGH
Walton Central School Dist	00721319		12.46	0.02	3	900	MED	MED-HIGH
Charlotte Valley Ctl Sch Dist	00721010		10.82	0.02	1	300	HIGH	MED-HIGH
Roxbury Central School Dist	00721199		7.29	0.01	1	260	HIGH	MED-LOW
Stamford Central School Dist	00721292		6.85	0.01	1	270	HIGH	MED-HIGH
South Kortright Ctl SD	00721278		6.53	0.01	1	350	MED	MED-HIGH
Downsville Central Sch Dist	00721072		5.81	0.01	1	240	HIGH	MED-HIGH
Margaretville Central Sch Dist	00721163		5.69	0.01	1	370	MED	MED-HIGH
Franklin Central School Dist	00721096		4.06	0.01	1	262	MED	MED-HIGH
Hancock Central School Dist	00721137		3.59	0.01	2	316	LOW	MED-HIGH
Andes Central School Dist	00720999		1.73	0.00	1	73	HIGH	MED-LOW
ESSEX		0.16						
Ticonderoga Central Sch Dist	00728020		30.75	0.05	2	735	HIGH	MED-HIGH
Boquet Valley Central Sch Dist	00728068		16.36	0.03	2	202	HIGH	MED-HIGH
Lake Placid Ctl School Dist	00727911		14.81	0.02	2	650	HIGH	MED-LOW
Moriah Central School Dist	00727959		9.16	0.01	1	780	LOW	MED-HIGH
Schroon Lake Ctl School Dist	00728006		8.95	0.01	1	230	HIGH	MED-HIGH
Crown Point Central Sch Dist	00727856		6.06	0.01	1	306	HIGH	MED-HIGH
Willsboro Central Sch Dist	00728082		5.50	0.01	1	243	HIGH	MED-LOW
Keene Central School Dist	00727894		3.92	0.01	1	170	HIGH	LOW
Newcomb Central School Dist	00727985		2.43	0.00	1	405	HIGH	MED-HIGH
Minerva Central School Dist	00727935		2.07	0.00	1	110	HIGH	MED-LOW
CORTLAND		0.15						
Homer Central School Dist	00720860		43.65	0.06	4	1,700	HIGH	MED-LOW

DISTRICT BUYING POWER INDEX

COUNTIES RANKED BY PERCENTAGE OF STATE SPENDING

COUNTY / DISTRICT	PID	COUNTY % OF STATE	DISTRICT % OF COUNTY	DISTRICT % OF STATES	NUMBER OF SCHOOLS	ENROLL	EXP	POV
Cortland Enlarged City SD	00720779		26.11	0.04	4	2,100	LOW	MED-HIGH
Marathon Ctl School Dist	00720925		12.63	0.02	2	689	MED	MED-HIGH
McGraw Central School Dist	00720951		9.89	0.01	2	570	MED	MED-LOW
Cincinnatus Ctl School Dist	00720743		7.72	0.01	2	530	LOW	MED-HIGH
WYOMING		0.13						
Letchworth Central School Dist	00783109		30.84	0.04	3	936	HIGH	MED-LOW
Attica Central School Dist	00783056		29.69	0.04	3	1,150	MED	MED-LOW
Perry Central School Dist	00783161		18.55	0.02	2	806	MED	MED-LOW
Warsaw Central School Dist	00783197		18.40	0.02	2	800	MED	MED-LOW
Wyoming Central School Dist	00783226		2.52	0.00	1	130	MED	MED-LOW
LEWIS		0.10						
Lowville Acad-Central Sch Dist	00730554		31.69	0.03	1	1,350	MED	MED-HIGH
South Lewis Central Sch Dist	00730580		26.62	0.03	4	1,028	MED	MED-LOW
Beaver River Central Sch Dist	00730487		17.46	0.02	1	875	LOW	MED-HIGH
Harrisville Central Sch Dist	00730528		16.67	0.02	1	359	HIGH	MED-LOW
Copenhagen Central SD	00730504		7.57	0.01	1	460	LOW	MED-HIGH
SCHOHARIE		0.10						
Cobleskill Richmondville SD	00770736		34.54	0.04	4	1,700	LOW	MED-LOW
Schoharie Central SD	00770865		22.17	0.02	2	875	MED	MED-LOW
Middleburgh Ctl School Dist	00770815		18.69	0.02	2	750	MED	MED-LOW
Sharon Springs Ctl SD	00770891		10.91	0.01	1	226	HIGH	MED-HIGH
Gilboa-Conesville Central SD	00770774		8.73	0.01	1	312	MED	MED-LOW
Jefferson Central Sch Dist	00770798		4.96	0.01	1	195	MED	MED-HIGH
SCHUYLER		0.08						
Watkins Glen Central Sch Dist	00770956		67.42	0.06	2	1,040	HIGH	MED-HIGH
Odessa Montour Ctl Sch Dist	00770918		21.56	0.02	3	733	MED	MED-HIGH
Bradford Central Sch Dist	00771285		11.01	0.01	1	265	HIGH	MED-HIGH
YATES		0.07						
Penn Yan Ctl School Dist	00783276		67.92	0.05	3	1,338	HIGH	MED-HIGH
Dundee Ctl School Dist	00783240		32.08	0.02	2	700	HIGH	MED-HIGH
HAMILTON		0.03						
Lake Pleasant Central Sch Dist	00729397		41.33	0.01	1	80	HIGH	MED-HIGH
Indian Lake Ctl School Dist	00729359		29.35	0.01	1	112	HIGH	MED-LOW
Wells Central School Dist	00729476		16.77	0.00	1	135	MED	MED-LOW
Long Lake Central School Dist	00729414		12.55	0.00	1	65	HIGH	MED-LOW

New York School Directory

NEW PUBLIC SCHOOLS AND KEY PERSONNEL

NEW SCHOOLS/NEW PRINCIPALS

SCHOOL	PRINCIPAL	GRADES	ENROLLMENT	COUNTY	PAGE
PS 939 Sunset ES Cultural Lrng	Mousouroulis, Georgia	K-K	401	Kings	90
Teach	Davis, Justin	9-12	176	Kings	89
PS 390Q Civic ES Bayside Hills	Leib, Melody	PK-K	61	Queens	180

NEW PRINCIPALS

SCHOOL	PRINCIPAL	GRADES	ENROLLMENT	COUNTY	PAGE
IS 219 New Venture	Roberts, Kizhaya	6-8	331	Bronx	19
Pharos Acad Charter Sch	Duggins, Elix	9-12	401	Bronx	24
Walkabout Bronx High Sch	Gordon, Kameca	9-9	401	Bronx	17
Milton J Fletcher Elem Sch	Sischo, Amanda	PK-4	513	Chautauqua	38
Bard HS Early Clg Hudson	Sadowski, Michael	9-12	100	Columbia	46
Marathon Jr Sr High Sch	Marcolina, Holly	7-12	295	Cortland	48
O'Neill High Sch	Loomis, Arthur	9-12	267	Delaware	50
Arlington High Sch	Fanuele, Paul	9-12	2,835	Dutchess	51
Buffalo Sch Culinary-Hospitly	Schuta, Katie	9-12	386	Erie	57
Woodrow Wilson Elem Sch	Weir, Hillary	3-5	268	Erie	59
Lake View Campus	Meyer, Joshua	K-12	202	Essex	67
Jackson Primary Sch	Notaro, Maureen	PK-1	440	Genesee	73
Hunter Tannersville Mid & HS	Funck, Ryan	7-12	150	Greene	76
Academy for Health Careers	Grevenberg, L	9-12	276	Kings	86
MS 907 Legacy Sch of the Arts	Guidarelli, Christopher	6-6	40	Kings	89
MS 936 Arts Off 3rd	Nastasi, Donna	6-6	150	Kings	90
PS 938	Benn, Teneika	K-K	19	Kings	89
Athena High Sch	Flagler, Kelly	9-12	1,104	Monroe	108
Brockport High Sch	Davis, Melody	9-12	1,021	Monroe	107
John James Audubon School 33	Ellison, Larry, Dr	PK-6	1,140	Monroe	111
Canajoharie High Sch	Bottino, Nicholas	9-12	263	Montgomery	115
Canajoharie Middle Sch	DePaolo, Christopher	6-8	192	Montgomery	115
East Hill Elem Sch	D'Ambrosio, Alicia	PK-5	400	Montgomery	115
School 6 Kindergarten Center	McAssey, Lucille	K-K	395	Nassau	127
Harlem C Z Promise Academy II	James, Shondell	K-5	600	New York	140
MS 371 Seed Harlem	Hill, Meredith	6-6	140	New York	140
Tep Equity Project Charter ECC	Vanderhoek, Zeke	PK-PK	60	New York	142
Niagara Falls High Sch	Jones, Cynthia	9-12	1,971	Niagara	148
Gansevoort Elem Sch	Bragan, Kathy	K-6	342	Oneida	151
N A Walbran Elem Sch	Ranieri, Mark	PK-6	313	Oneida	151
Walberta Park Primary Sch	Kramer, Beth	K-1	268	Onondaga	160
Millard Hawk Elem Sch	Viel, Amanda	PK-5	483	Oswego	170
Carmel High Sch	Fink, John	9-12	1,422	Putnam	175
PS 35 Nathaniel Woodhull	Peebles-Davis, Mia	PK-5	686	Queens	183
Pomona Middle Sch	Alexander, Angela	7-8	573	Rockland	196
Gouverneur Elem Sch	Zawatski, Charity	PK-4	620	St Lawrence	210
Wayland-Cohocton Middle Sch	Manne, Scott	5-8	405	Steuben	215
Livingston Manor Elem Sch	Hubert, Christopher	PK-6	238	Sullivan	236
Livingston Mid High Sch	Davis, Shirlee	7-12	194	Sullivan	236
Tioga Elem Sch	Bombard, Michelle	PK-4	368	Tioga	239
Hamilton Elem Sch	Wesolowski, Jennifer	K-6	413	Westchester	258

NEW SUPERINTENDENTS

DISTRICT	SUPERINTENDENT	GRADES	ENROLLMENT	COUNTY	PAGE
South Colonie Central Sch Dist	Perry, David, Dr	PK-12	4,700	Albany	12
Voorheesville Central Sch Dist	Macri, Frank	K-12	1,175	Albany	12
Alfred Almond Ctl School Dist	Bliven, Tracie	PK-12	600	Allegany	13
Bemus Point Ctl School Dist	Spasiano, Michelle	K-12	715	Chautauqua	36
Chautauqua Lake Central SD	Curtin, Rachel	PK-12	950	Chautauqua	36
Clymer Central School Dist	Olson, Beth	PK-12	444	Chautauqua	37
Dunkirk City School Dist	Mansfield, Michael	PK-12	2,300	Chautauqua	37
Jamestown City School Dist	Whitaker, Kevin, Dr	PK-12	5,000	Chautauqua	38
Pine Valley Central Sch Dist	Mortiz Booth, Bryna	PK-12	550	Chautauqua	38
Westfield Central School Dist	Cipolla, Michael	PK-12	700	Chautauqua	39
Elmira Heights Ctl Sch Dist	Gill, Michael	PK-12	1,100	Chemung	40
Otselic Valley Central SD	Drahos, Michael	PK-12	300	Chenango	42
Sherburne Earlville Central SD	Berson, Robert	PK-12	1,267	Chenango	42
Ichabod Crane Central Schools	Guntlow, Suzanne	K-12	1,683	Columbia	46
Cortland Enlarged City SD	Edwards, Robert	K-12	2,100	Cortland	47
Delaware Academy Ctrl SD Delhi	Zimmerman, Kelly	K-12	797	Delaware	49
Roxbury Central School Dist	Bennett, Jefffrey	PK-12	260	Delaware	50
Walton Central School Dist	McDonald, Michael	PK-12	900	Delaware	50

School Year 2020-2021   800-333-8802

NEW PUBLIC SCHOOLS AND KEY PERSONNEL

Market Data Retrieval

District	Contact	Grades	Enrollment	County	Page
Arlington Central School Dist	Licopoli, Lorenzo	K-12	7,000	Dutchess	51
Millbrook Ctl School Dist	Mitchell, Laura	K-12	875	Dutchess	52
Red Hook Central School Dist	Warden, Janet	PK-12	1,750	Dutchess	53
Rhinebeck Central School Dist	Couisins, Albert	K-12	1,000	Dutchess	53
Kenmore-Tonawanda UF Sch Dist	Cimato, Sabatino	K-12	7,000	Erie	62
Newcomb Central School Dist	Fischer, Chris	PK-12	405	Essex	68
Ticonderoga Central Sch Dist	Ford-Johnston, Cynthia	PK-12	735	Essex	68
St Regis Falls Ctl Sch Dist	Seymour, Timothy	PK-12	268	Franklin	70
Tupper Lake Ctl School Dist	Bartlett, Russ	PK-12	749	Franklin	70
Greater Johnstown Sch Dist	Geelan, Karen, Dr	PK-12	1,700	Fulton	71
O E S J Central School Dist	Heroth, Adam	PK-12	719	Fulton	72
Wheelerville Union Free SD	Dettenrider, Nicole	PK-8	130	Fulton	72
Batavia City School Dist	Soler, Anabell	PK-12	2,374	Genesee	73
Hunter Tannersville Ctl SD	Jones, Nathan	PK-12	355	Greene	76
Mount Markham Central Sch Dist	Dapice, Joseph	PK-12	1,100	Herkimer	78
Carthage Central School Dist	Premo, Jennifer	PK-12	3,200	Jefferson	80
South Jefferson Central SD	Slater, Scott	PK-12	1,894	Jefferson	81
Community School District 16	Amon-Harris, Rahesha	PK-12		Kings	85
Community School District 20	O'Brien, Jpseph	PK-12		Kings	89
Avon Central School Dist	Pacatte, Ryan	K-12	1,006	Livingston	102
Canastota Central School Dist	Bissetta, Shawn	PK-12	1,275	Madison	104
Hamilton Central Sch Dist	Dowsland, William	PK-12	588	Madison	105
Madison Central School Dist	Mitchell, Jason	PK-12	450	Madison	105
Brockport Ctl School Dist	Bruno, Sean	PK-12	3,562	Monroe	106
East Rochester Union Free SD	Haugh, James	PK-12	1,007	Monroe	107
Rochester City School Dist	Myers-Small, Lesli	PK-12	28,000	Monroe	110
Wheatland Chili Ctl Sch Dist	Quick, Lynda	K-12	637	Monroe	113
Ft Plain Central School Dist	Bishop, John	PK-12	750	Montgomery	115
Greater Amsterdam School Dist	Ruberti, Richard	PK-12	3,690	Montgomery	115
Locust Valley Ctl School Dist	Graham, Kenneth, Dr	K-12	2,000	Nassau	123
Malverne Union Free Sch Dist	Lewis, Loran, Dr	K-12	1,725	Nassau	124
Plainview-Old Bethpage Ctl SD	O'Meara, Mary, Dr	K-12	5,000	Nassau	127
Rockville Ctr Union Free SD	Chang, June	K-12	3,500	Nassau	128
Roosevelt Union Free Sch Dist	Wortham, Deborah, Dr	PK-12	3,511	Nassau	128
Community School District 3	Altschul, Ilene	PK-12		New York	138
Community School District 4	De La Cruz, Kristy, Dr	PK-12		New York	139
Skaneateles Central Sch Dist	Knuth, Eric	K-12	1,200	Onondaga	157
Geneva City School Dist	Garcia, Patricia, Dr	PK-12	2,078	Ontario	161
Honeoye Central School Dist	Ashton, Elizabeth	K-12	251	Ontario	161
Cornwall Central School Dist	Dade, Terry	K-12	3,122	Orange	163
Washingtonville Central SD	Washington, Larry, Dr	PK-12	3,793	Orange	167
Mexico Central School Dist	Schiedo, Michael	PK-12	2,055	Oswego	171
Oswego City School Dist	Calvin, Mathis, Dr	PK-12	3,669	Oswego	171
Laurens Central School Dist	Dorritie, William	K-12	300	Otsego	173
Community School District 28	Pate, Tammy, Dr	PK-12		Queens	181
Hoosic Valley Central Sch Dist	Apostol, G Michael	K-12	931	Rensselaer	190
Lansingburgh Central Sch Dist	Abitabile, Antonio, Dr	PK-12	2,335	Rensselaer	190
North Rockland Central SD	Felicello, Kris, Dr	K-12	8,000	Rockland	197
Ballston Spa Ctl School Dist	Slentz, Kenneth	K-12	4,200	Saratoga	200
Duanesburg Central Sch Dist	Niedermeier, James, Dr	K-12	770	Schenectady	203
Schalmont Central School Dist	Reardon, Thomas	K-12	1,798	Schenectady	204
Gilboa-Conesville Central SD	Etter, John	PK-12	312	Schoharie	206
Clifton-Fine Central Sch Dist	Southwick, Matthew	PK-12	295	St Lawrence	209
Morristown Ctl School Dist	Vaughn, Staci	PK-12	333	St Lawrence	211
Arkport Central School Dist	Harper, Jesse	PK-12	475	Steuben	213
Corning-Painted Post Area SD	Caulfield, Michelle	K-12	4,500	Steuben	214
Prattsburgh Central Sch Dist	Bay, Kory	PK-12	388	Steuben	215
Brookhaven Comsewogue Unif SD	Quinn, Jennifer	PK-12	3,702	Suffolk	218
Central Islip Union Free SD	Dungee, Sharon	PK-12	7,400	Suffolk	218
East Moriches Union Free SD	McKeon, Daniel	K-8	750	Suffolk	221
Greenport Union Free Sch Dist	Small, Marlon	PK-12	627	Suffolk	222
New Suffolk Common School Dist	Kent, Phill	PK-6	13	Suffolk	226
Port Jefferson Union Free SD 6	Schmettan, Jessica	PK-12	1,048	Suffolk	228
Riverhead Central School Dist	Tona, Christine	K-12	5,600	Suffolk	228
Rocky Point Union Free SD	O'Brien, Scott, Dr	PK-12	2,947	Suffolk	228
Sag Harbor Union Free Sch Dist	Nichols, Jeff	PK-12	953	Suffolk	229
Shelter Island Union Free SD	Doelger, Brian	PK-12	202	Suffolk	230
Southold Union Free Sch Dist	Mauro, Anthony	K-12	750	Suffolk	231
Wyandanch Union Free Sch Dist	Talbert, Gina	PK-12	2,811	Suffolk	234
Monticello Central School Dist	Evans, Matthew, Dr	K-12	2,785	Sullivan	237
New Paltz Ctl School Dist	Urbina Medina, Angela	K-12	2,035	Ulster	242
Hadley-Luzerne Ctl Sch Dist	Baker, Beecher	K-12	665	Warren	245
Queensbury Union Free Sch Dist	Gannon, Kyle	K-12	3,200	Warren	246
Hudson Falls Central Sch Dist	Hunter, John, Dr	PK-12	2,400	Washington	248
North Rose Wolcott Central SD	Pullins, Michael	K-12	1,155	Wayne	250
Wayne Central School Dist	Siracuse, Joseph, Dr	K-12	2,180	Wayne	251

New York School Directory

NEW PUBLIC SCHOOLS AND KEY PERSONNEL

District	Contact	Grades	Enrollment	County	Page
Williamson Central School Dist	Mazzullo, Mary Grace	PK-12	1,106	Wayne	251
Bedford Central School Dist	Adelberg, Joel, Dr	K-12	4,100	Westchester	252
Blind Brook-Rye Union Free SD	Brimstein, Patrick	K-12	1,364	Westchester	252
Lakeland Central School Dist	Lyons, Brendan	PK-12	5,845	Westchester	257
Pocantico Hills Ctl Sch Dist	Calkins, Richard	PK-8	308	Westchester	260
Warsaw Central School Dist	Wilkens, Matthew	PK-12	800	Wyoming	267

New York School Directory

NEW YORK

• **New York State Dept Education** PID: 00714108   518/474-3852
89 Washington Ave, Albany 12234   Fax 518/473-2977

Schools: 352

Shannon Tahoe 1	Phyllis Morris 2,19
Rosanne Groff 3	Paula Tyner-Doyle 4
Paul Overbaugh 5	Karen Hollowood 7
Martha Morrissey 7,85	Dr Kim Wilkins 8,15
Marybeth Casey 8	Melissa Montague 8
Ira Schwartz 12,15,70,271,294	Christopher Suriano 15,58
Douglas Lentivech 15,31	Kevin Smith 15,30,88
Mark Schaming 15,89	Sharon Cates-Williams 15,69,70
Dr Joanne Shawhan 16	John Brock 16
Jennifer Childress 20,23	Eric Suhr 26,27,31,75
Deborah Reiter 27	Phillip Dettelis 28
Winona Hao 34	Darryl Daily 35
Dan King 39	Ann Crotty 42
John Svendsen 45	Susan Brockley 45
David Coffey 48	Erik Sweet 48
Lisette Colon-Collins 57,61	Joanne LaCrosse 58
Patti Rosa-Farleigh 58	Betty Rosa 67
Keturah Colbert 69,88	Steven Katz 69
Zachary Warner 69	Emily DeSantis 71
Linda Seaman 72,83,91	Dawn Graham 81

STATE-OPERATED SCHOOLS

State Schs..Principal	Grd	Prgm	Enr/#Cls	SN	
Ⓒ Academic Leadership Chtr Sch 677 E 141st St, Bronx 10454 Leena Varghese	K-8	T	603	93%	718/585-4215 Fax 718/585-4837
Ⓒ Academy Charter Elem Sch [247] 117 N Franklin St, Hempstead 11550 C Morris	K-6	T	795	85%	516/408-2200 Fax 516/292-2329
Ⓒ Academy Charter ES-Uniondale 100 Charles Lindbergh Blvd, Uniondale 11553 C Avin	K-2	T	179	79%	516/591-3030
Ⓒ Academy Charter High Sch 159 N Franklin St, Hempstead 11550 Mr Holloway	9-9		401		516/408-2200
Ⓒ Academy Charter Middle Sch 159 N Franklin St, Hempstead 11550 Mr Mattison	5-8		206		516/408-2200
Academy of Health Sciences CS 1001 Lake Ave, Rochester 14613 Wanda Perez-Brundage	5-5		102		585/254-1003
Ⓒ Academy of the City Chtr Sch 3129 60th St, Woodside 11377 Katie-Lyn Santacruz	K-3	T	406	70%	718/487-9857 Fax 718/785-9592
Ⓒ Achievement First Apollo ES [128] 350 Linwood St, Brooklyn 11208 Noah Hellman	K-4	T	469	89%	347/471-2620 Fax 718/235-1649
Ⓒ Achievement First Aspire ES [128] 982 Hegeman Ave, Brooklyn 11208 Georgia Bambrick	K-4	T	449	84%	347/471-2055 Fax 718/228-8839
Ⓒ Achievement First Brooklyn HS [128] 1485 Pacific St, Brooklyn 11216 Claire Shin	9-12		430		718/363-2260 Fax 718/363-2262
Ⓒ Achievement First Brownsville [128] 2021 Bergen St, Brooklyn 11233 Zonya Hicks	K-4	T	432	75%	347/471-2600 Fax 347/402-2900
Ⓒ Achievement First Bushwick ES [128] 125 Covert St 3rd Fl, Brooklyn 11207 Courtney Saretzky	K-4		470		718/443-1213 Fax 718/228-9540
Ⓒ Achievement First Bushwick MS [128] 1300 Greene Ave Fl 4, Brooklyn 11237 Bobby Bridges	5-8	T	403	85%	347/471-2560 Fax 718/453-0428
Ⓒ Achievement First E Brooklyn [128] 301 Vermont St, Brooklyn 11207 Sabrina Silver	9-11		275		347/471-2650 Fax 347/402-8015
Ⓒ Achievement First East NY ES [128] Ⓨ 557 Pennsylvania Ave, Brooklyn 11207 Lucy Volkmar	K-4	MT	480		718/485-4924 Fax 718/228-6028
Ⓒ Achievement First Endeavor Sch [128] Ⓨ 510 Waverly Ave, Brooklyn 11238 Justin Tesser	K-8	MT	828 24	67%	718/622-5994 Fax 718/789-1649
Ⓒ Achievement First Linden ES [128] 800 Van Siclen Ave, Brooklyn 11207 Amanda Hageman	K-4	T	470	80%	347/471-2700 Fax 718/228-3778
Ⓒ Achievement First N Brooklyn [128] 200 Woodbine St, Brooklyn 11221 Peter Weiss	K-4	T	433	88%	347/471-2690 Fax 347/402-1818
Ⓒ Achievement First Univ Prep HS [128] 35 Starr St, Brooklyn 11221 Claire Shin	9-12		386		718/363-2270 Fax 347/402-1166
Ⓒ Achievement First Voyager MS [128] 601 Parkside Ave, Brooklyn 11226 Priam Dutta	5-7	T	188	78%	347/471-2640 Fax 347/402-6221
Ⓒ Aeci II-Sch for Computer Engr 423 E 138th St, Bronx 10454 Dr Charles Gallo	9-9		113		646/741-7470 Fax 718/741-8280
Ⓒ Albany Cmty Charter Sch 65 Krank St, Albany 12202 Sherrmain Moore-Boakye	K-8	T	645 15	87%	518/433-1500 Fax 518/433-1501
Ⓒ Albany Leadrshp CHS for Girls 19 Hackett Blvd, Albany 12208 Carina Cook	9-12	T	310	88%	518/694-5300 Fax 518/694-5307
Ⓒ Amani Public Charter Sch 60 S 3rd Ave Ste 1, Mount Vernon 10550 Jamell Scott	5-8	T	351	54%	914/668-6450 Fax 914/699-0839
Ⓒ Amber Charter Sch East Harlem 220 E 106th St Frnt 1, New York 10029 Matthew Bull	K-5	T	467 21	77%	212/534-9667 Fax 212/534-5474
Ⓒ Amber Charter Sch Kingsbridge 3120 Corlear Ave Frnt, Bronx 10463 Veronica Almedina	K-2	T	401	75%	646/802-1140 Fax 212/298-8360
Ⓒ American Dream Charter Sch 510 E 141st St 4th Fl, Bronx 10454 Melissa Melkonian	6-10	T	392	97%	718/585-3071 Fax 917/388-8271
Ⓒ Atmosphere Acad PCS 22 Marble Hill Ave Frnt A, Bronx 10463 Colin Greene	6-8	T	408	94%	718/757-5852
Baker Academy 120 Alexander Ave, Buffalo 14211 Yvonne Ibarra	Spec		90		716/828-7955 Fax 716/893-0435
Ⓒ Bedford Stuy Collegiate CS [246] 800 Gates Ave, Brooklyn 11221 Justin Pigeon	5-8	T	346	86%	718/669-7460 Fax 718/669-7771
Ⓒ Beginning with Children CS 2 [233] 215 Heyward St, Brooklyn 11206 Mike Ferrara	K-5		412	92%	718/302-7700
Ⓒ Bold Charter Sch 1090 Close Ave, Bronx 10472 Andrew Foglia	K-1		120		
Ⓒ Boys Prep Bronx School of NY [244] 192 E 151st St, Bronx 10451 Dr Khalek Kirkland	K-6	T	633	89%	718/742-4321 Fax 718/744-2497
Brentwood Residential Center 1230 Commack Rd, Dix Hills 11746 Susan Ginter	7-12	AV	25 3	80%	631/667-1188 Fax 631/667-0591
Ⓒ Bridge Prep Charter Sch 715 Ocean Ter Bldg E, Staten Island 10301 Tim Castanza	1-2		87		718/274-3437
Ⓒ Brighter Choice CS for Boys [234] Ⓨ 116 N Lake Ave, Albany 12206 Karen McLean	K-5	MT	305	91%	518/694-8200 Fax 518/694-8201
Ⓒ Brighter Choice CS for Girls [234] 250 Central Ave, Albany 12206 Kristina Ford	K-5	T	328 12	80%	518/694-4100 Fax 518/694-4123

Market Data Retrieval

School	Grades		Enroll	%	Phone
© Brilla Caritas Elem Sch 2336 Andrews Ave, Bronx 10468 Zoranlly Burgos	K-K		401		347/523-5832
© Brilla Charter School Pax 2336 Andrews Ave, Bronx 10468 Shingi Mutasa	K-K		140		
© Brilla College Prep CS-Veritas 600 E 156th St, Bronx 10455 Zoranlly Castillo	K-K	T	115	93%	917/924-0258 Fax 718/585-5800
© Brilla College Prep Elem CS 413 E 144th St, Bronx 10454 Alexandra Apfel	K-4	T	430	87%	347/273-8439 Fax 917/591-6594
© Brilla College Prep Mid Sch CS 500 Courtlandt Ave, Bronx 10451 Matthew Larsen	5-8		155		347/273-8439
© Bronx Arts & Science CS [231] 915 Hutchinson River Pkwy, Bronx 10465 Sandra Beauvoir-Soto	K-2		156		718/230-0851
© Bronx Charter Sch Better Lrng 3740 Baychester Ave, Bronx 10466 Anne Clarke-Raysor	K-5	T	553 9	81%	718/655-6660 Fax 718/655-5555
© Bronx Charter Sch for the Arts 950 Longfellow Ave, Bronx 10474 Jonea Thomas	K-8	T	314 12	76%	718/893-1042 Fax 718/893-7910
© Bronx CS Better Learning II 2545 Gunther Ave, Bronx 10469 Ann Clarke-Raysor	K-3	T	150	74%	718/655-6660 Fax 718/794-9816
© Bronx Excellence 1 [236] 1960 Benedict Ave, Bronx 10462 Maria Saryan \ Florence Bolton	K-8	T	810	79%	718/828-7301 Fax 718/828-7302
© Bronx Excellence 2 Elementary [236] 1804 Holland Ave, Bronx 10462 Adije Okpo	K-4	T	298	78%	718/892-1276 Fax 718/239-2439
© Bronx Excellence 3 Elementary [236] 3956 Carpenter Ave, Bronx 10466 Charleton Clarke	K-3	T	314	61%	718/882-0231
© Bronx Excellence 4 Elementary [236] 3956 Carpenter Ave, Bronx 10466 Tanya White	K-2	T	173	68%	347/420-4321
© Bronx Excellence 5 Elementary [236] 1946 Bathgate Ave, Bronx 10457 Charlene Reid	K-1		79		718/882-1058 Fax 718/828-7302
© Bronx Prep Charter Sch [235] 3872 3rd Ave, Bronx 10457 Ryan Silver \ Lourdes Flores	6-12	T	767 11	86%	718/294-0841 Fax 718/294-2381
ⓐ Bronx Residential Center 170 E 210th St, Bronx 10467 Joe Dennison	9-12		22 6		718/798-6660 Fax 718/882-2430
© Brooklyn Ascend Chtr Sch 205 Rockaway Pkwy, Brooklyn 11212 Elena Strauss	K-12	T	732	84%	718/907-9150 Fax 718/240-9140
© Brooklyn Ascend High Sch 1501 Pitkin Ave, Brooklyn 11212 Erica Smith	9-12		344		347/750-1200
© Brooklyn Ascend Mid Chtr Sch 123 E 98th St, Brooklyn 11212 Crystal Lane	5-8		400		347/289-9000 Fax 718/773-7681
© Brooklyn Dreams Charter Sch [210] 259 Parkville Ave, Brooklyn 11230 Omar Thomas	K-8	T	606	74%	718/859-8400 Fax 347/586-0347
© Brooklyn East Collegiate CS [246] 832 Marcy Ave, Brooklyn 11216 Adwoa Bediako	5-8		255	76%	718/250-5760
© Brooklyn Emerging Leaders Acad 125 Stuyvesant Ave Rm 213, Brooklyn 11221 Nicia Fullwood	9-10	T	120	51%	347/473-8830
© Brooklyn Excelsior Charter Sch [210] 856 Quincy St, Brooklyn 11221 Sally Girouard	K-8	T	656	90%	718/246-5681 Fax 718/504-5864
© Brooklyn Lab CS Chapel St 40 Flatbush Avenue Ext 10th Fl, Brooklyn 11201 Eric Tucker	6-10		210		347/473-8333 Fax 914/612-9127
© Brooklyn Lab CS Jay St Campus 240 Jay St, Brooklyn 11201 Eric Tucker	6-8	T	770	98%	347/281-6892 Fax 914/612-9127
© Brooklyn Prospect Charter HS 3002 Fort Hamilton Pkwy, Brooklyn 11218 Kim Raccio	9-12		700	39%	347/889-7041 Fax 347/889-7083
© Brooklyn Prospect Charter MS 3002 Fort Hamilton Pkwy, Brooklyn 11218 Carolyn Michael	6-8		260		347/889-7041
© Brooklyn Prospect Clinton Hill 1100 Fulton St, Brooklyn 11238 Jaclyn DeLuca	6-8		230		718/783-1570 Fax 347/514-6000
© Brooklyn Prospect CS Downtown 80 Willoughby St, Brooklyn 11201 Jumaane Saunders	K-5		359		718/722-7634 Fax 347/514-6000
© Brooklyn Rise Charter Sch 475 53rd St 2nd Fl, Brooklyn 11220 Cary Finnegan	K-1		52		347/470-9833
© Brooklyn Urban Garden CS 500 19th St, Brooklyn 11215 Wynette Caesar	6-8	T	299	64%	718/280-9556
ⓐ Brookwood Secure Center 419-8 Spookrock Rd, Claverack 12513 Joe Robinson	7-12	V	60 14	91%	518/851-3211 Fax 518/851-2685
© Broome Street Academy CHS 555 Broome St Fl 4, New York 10013 Melissa Silberman	9-12	T	336	97%	212/453-0295 Fax 212/966-7253
© Brownsville Ascend Lower CS 1501 Pitkin Ave, Brooklyn 11212 Billie Quigley	K-4	T	600	84%	347/294-2600 Fax 718/240-9140
© Brownsville Ascend Middle CS 1501 Pitkin Ave, Brooklyn 11212 Emily Fernandez	6-8		305		347/294-2600
© Brownsville Collegiate Charter [246] 364 Sackman St, Brooklyn 11212 Joel Tracy	5-8	T	300	81%	718/636-0370 Fax 347/296-8321
© Buffalo Academy of Science CS 190 Franklin St, Buffalo 14202 Mucahit Polat	7-12	TV	391	83%	716/854-2490 Fax 716/854-5039
© Buffalo Collegiate Charter Sch 45 Jewett Ave, Buffalo 14214 Brian Pawloski	4-5	T	117	81%	716/713-2162 Fax 716/271-4592
© Buffalo United Charter Sch [210] 325 Manhattan Ave, Buffalo 14214 Teresa Gerchman	K-8	T	633	93%	716/835-9862 Fax 716/408-9575
© Bushwick Ascend Lower CS 751 Knickerbocker Ave, Brooklyn 11221 Zelda Washington	K-4	T	554	89%	347/294-2500 Fax 718/417-1317
© Bushwick Ascend Middle Sch 2 Aberdeen St, Brooklyn 11207 Malik Russell	5-8		345		718/744-6100
© Campa Charter Sch 1962 Linden Blvd 84, Brooklyn 11207 George Leonard	5-6	T	125	94%	347/619-6800
© Canarsie Ascend Lower CS 9719 Flatlands Ave, Brooklyn 11236 Anastasia Michals	K-4	T	606	75%	347/713-0101 Fax 718/272-2305
© Canarsie Ascend Mid CS 744 E 87th St, Brooklyn 11236 Tracy Lewis	5-7		325		347/578-8400 Fax 718/251-1094

1	Superintendent	8	Curric/Instruct K-12	19	Chief Financial Officer	29	Family/Consumer Science	39	Social Studies K-12	49	English/Lang Arts Elem	59	Special Education Elem	69	Academic Assessment
2	Bus/Finance/Purchasing	9	Curric/Instruct Elem	20	Art K-12	30	Adult Education	40	Social Studies Elem	50	English/Lang Arts Sec	60	Special Education Sec	70	Research/Development
3	Buildings And Grounds	10	Curric/Instruct Sec	21	Art Elem	31	Career/Sch-to-Work K-12	41	Social Studies Sec	51	Reading K-12	61	Foreign/World Lang K-12	71	Public Information
4	Food Service	11	Federal Program	22	Art Sec	32	Career/Sch-to-Work Elem	42	Science K-12	52	Reading Elem	62	Foreign/World Lang Elem	72	Summer School
5	Transportation	12	Title I	23	Music K-12	33	Career/Sch-to-Work Sec	43	Science Elem	53	Reading Sec	63	Foreign/World Lang Sec	73	Instructional Tech
6	Athletic	13	Title V	24	Music Elem	34	Early Childhood Ed	44	Science Sec	54	Remedial Reading K-12	64	Religious Education K-12	74	Inservice Training
7	Health Services	15	Asst Superintendent	25	Music Sec	35	Health/Phys Education	45	Math K-12	55	Remedial Reading Elem	65	Religious Education Elem	75	Marketing/Distributive
		16	Instructional Media Svcs	26	Business Education	36	Guidance Services K-12	46	Math Elem	56	Remedial Reading Sec	66	Religious Education Sec	76	Info Systems
		17	Chief Operations Officer	27	Career & Tech Ed	37	Guidance Services Elem	47	Math Sec	57	Bilingual/ELL	67	School Board President	77	Psychological Assess
		18	Chief Academic Officer	28	Technology Education	38	Guidance Services Sec	48	English/Lang Arts K-12	58	Special Education K-12	68	Teacher Personnel	78	Affirmative Action

New York School Directory

School	Grades	Prog	Enroll	%	Phone
ⓒ Capital Prep Bronx CS 755 Co-Op City Blvd, Bronx 10475 Isaiah Brown	6-7		140		929/436-2728 Fax 718/504-5444
ⓒ Capital Prep Harlem CS 1 E 104th St, New York 10029 Danita Jones	6-9	T	238	61%	212/328-9370 Fax 315/400-0930
ⓒ Cardinal McCloskey Cmty CS 685 E 182nd St, Bronx 10457 Jennifer Fedele	K-1		138		646/660-2491
ⓒ Central Brooklyn Ascend Lwr CS 465 E 29th St, Brooklyn 11226 Shani Foster	K-4	T	423	79%	917/246-4800
ⓒ Central Queens Academy CS 5530 Junction Blvd, Elmhurst 11373 Glenn Leibeck	5-8	T	407	85%	718/271-6200 Fax 718/271-6900
ⓒ Charter HS Law-Social Justice 1960 Dr Martin L King Jr Blvd, Bronx 10453 Courtney Crawford	9-10	T	248	68%	646/450-2240 Fax 718/744-2007
ⓒ Charter Sch for Applied Tech 2303 Kenmore Ave, Buffalo 14207 Susan Jurewicz \ Gregory Mott \ Ann Morgante	K-12	T	2,344	77%	716/871-7400 Fax 716/876-9758
ⓒ Charter School of Educ Excell [247] 260 Warburton Ave, Yonkers 10701 Jennifer Spina \ Jessica Jacaruso	K-8	T	758	86%	914/476-5070 Fax 914/476-2858
ⓒ Charter School of Inquiry 404 Edison Ave, Buffalo 14215 John Sheffield	K-5	T	241	93%	716/833-3250 Fax 716/831-7947
ⓒ Children's AID College Prep CS 1919 Prospect Ave, Bronx 10457 Casey Vier	K-8	T	644	76%	347/871-9002 Fax 718/853-6233
ⓒ Community Partnership Lwr Sch [233] 241 Emerson Pl Fl Ps270, Brooklyn 11205 Derrick Dunlap	PK-5	T	271	88%	718/399-3824 Fax 718/399-2149
ⓒ Compass Charter Sch 300 Adelphi St 4th Fl, Brooklyn 11205 Brooke Peters	K-5		305	25%	718/310-3588 Fax 718/852-4682
ⓒ Coney Island Prep Public CS 501 West Ave, Brooklyn 11224 Juliana Bryansmith \ Amanda Stroud \ Kate Baxter	K-12	T	1,015	82%	718/513-6951 Fax 718/513-6955
ⓒ Creo College Prep Charter Sch 524 Courtlandt Ave, Bronx 10451 Ben Samuels-Kalow	5-5		92		347/216-9246
Ⓐ Cuny Preparatory High Sch 2122 White Plains Rd, Bronx 10462 Jenny Ristenbatt	9-12		212		718/839-8862 Fax 718/239-5236
ⓒ Cypress Hills Ascend CS 396 Grant Ave, Brooklyn 11208 Lissette Roman	K-1	T	125	92%	347/227-6070
ⓒ Democracy Prep Charter HS [235] 222 W 134th St 3rd Fl, New York 10030 Elisa DiMauro	9-12		365		212/281-3061 Fax 212/281-3064
ⓒ Democracy Prep Charter Mid Sch [235] 2230 5th Ave, New York 10037 Tanya Nunez	6-8	T	330	75%	212/281-8247 Fax 212/283-4202
ⓒ Democracy Prep Endurance HS [235] 240 E 123rd St Fl 2, New York 10035 Emmanuel George	9-12		319		646/490-3693
ⓒ Democracy Prep Endurance MS [235] 250 W 127th St, New York 10027 Katherine Perez	6-8	T	332	76%	212/316-7602
ⓒ Democracy Prep Harlem ES [235] 2005 Madison Ave, New York 10035 Mia Backon	K-5		398		212/876-9953 Fax 212/876-9926
ⓒ Democracy Prep Harlem High Sch [235] 212 W 120th St, New York 10027 Mark Forman	9-12		305		212/932-7791 Fax 212/666-3706
ⓒ Democracy Prep Harlem MS [235] 207 W 133rd St, New York 10030 Josef Robinson	6-8	T	294	87%	212/281-3061 Fax 212/281-3064
ⓒ Discovery Charter Sch 133 Hoover Dr, Rochester 14615 Joseph Saia	K-6	T	289	97%	585/342-4032 Fax 585/342-4003
ⓒ Dream Charter Sch-Mott Haven 411 Wales Ave, Bronx 10454 Eve Colavito	K-K		58		212/722-1608
ⓒ Dream Charter Sch 1991 2nd Ave, New York 10029 Kara Brockett \ Marjorie Gardner	K-11	T	805	87%	212/722-0232 Fax 212/348-5979
ⓒ East Brooklyn Ascend CS 396 Grant Ave, Brooklyn 11208 Meghan Daly	K-K		27		347/464-7600
ⓒ East Flatbush Ascend CS 870 Albany Ave, Brooklyn 11203 Shannon-Re Ismael	K-1		75		347/464-7600
ⓒ East Harlem Scholars Acad CS 2050 2nd Ave, New York 10029 Desree Cabrall-Njenga	PK-7	T	533	100%	212/348-2518 Fax 212/831-7967
ⓒ East Harlem Scholars Acad CS 2 1573 Madison Ave Rm 320A, New York 10029 Desiree Cabrall-Njenga	PK-4	T	350	88%	212/348-2518
ⓒ Elm Cmty Charter Sch 69-26 Cooper Ave, Glendale 11385 Priscilla Walton	K-2	T	152	78%	646/886-0234
ⓒ Elmwood Village CS-Days Park 40 Days Park, Buffalo 14201 Danielle Bruno	K-8	T	449 7	53%	716/886-4581 Fax 716/348-3707
ⓒ Elmwood Village CS-Hertel 655 Hertel Ave, Buffalo 14207 Kathy Jamil	K-5	T	401	64%	716/424-0555
ⓒ Emblaze Academy Charter Sch 1164 Garrison Ave, Bronx 10474 Kristen Shroff	5-6	T	164	100%	917/415-6547
ⓒ Eugenio Maria De Hostos CS HS 343 State St Bldg 10, Rochester 14650 Wellington Munoz	9-12		200 15		585/697-7115 Fax 585/544-3848
ⓒ Eugenio Maria De Hostos K-8 CS 27 Zimbrich St, Rochester 14621 Shirley Flores	K-8	T	210	78%	585/544-6170 Fax 585/697-0222
ⓒ Evergreen Charter Sch 605 Peninsula Blvd, Hempstead 11550 Christine Weigand	K-4	T	325	41%	516/292-2060 Fax 516/292-0575
ⓒ Excellence Boys Charter Sch [246] 225 Patchen Ave, Brooklyn 11233 Mr Bell	K-4	T	420 13	66%	718/638-1830 Fax 718/638-2548
ⓒ Excellence Girls CS Elem Acad [246] 794 Monroe St 3rd Fl, Brooklyn 11221 Nikki Bowen	K-4	T	450	68%	718/638-1875 Fax 718/301-2349
ⓒ Exploration Elem CS Sci & Tech 1001 Lake Ave, Rochester 14613 Rachelle Simmons	K-1	T	166	79%	585/694-5234
ⓒ Explore Charter Sch [237] 655 Parkside Ave, Brooklyn 11226 Rod Bowen	K-8	T	546 17	82%	718/703-4484 Fax 718/703-8550
ⓒ Explore Empower Chtr Sch 742 [237] 188 Rochester Ave, Brooklyn 11213 Brian Ferreira	K-8	T	492	83%	718/771-2090 Fax 718/771-2128
ⓒ Explore Exceed Charter Sch [237] 443 Saint Marks Ave, Brooklyn 11238 Loretta Hickman	K-8	T	503	80%	718/989-6702 Fax 718/701-8328
ⓒ Explore Excel Charter Sch [237] 1077 Remsen Ave, Brooklyn 11236 Anna Dallis	K-4	T	288	80%	718/303-3245 Fax 718/272-1827

79 Student Personnel	91 Safety/Security	275 Response To Intervention	298 Grant Writer/Ptnrships	**School Programs**	**Social Media**
80 Driver Ed/Safety	92 Magnet School	277 Remedial Math K-12	750 Chief Innovation Officer	A = Alternative Program	
81 Gifted/Talented	93 Parental Involvement	280 Literacy Coach	751 Chief of Staff	G = Adult Classes	▮ = Facebook
82 Video Services	95 Tech Prep Program	285 STEM	752 Social Emotional Learning	M = Magnet Program	
83 Substance Abuse Prev	97 Chief Information Officer	286 Digital Learning		T = Title I Schoolwide	▮ = Twitter
84 Erate	98 Chief Technology Officer	288 Common Core Standards	**Other School Types**	V = Career & Tech Ed Programs	
85 AIDS Education	270 Character Education	294 Accountability	Ⓐ = Alternative School		
88 Alternative/At Risk	271 Migrant Education	295 Network System	ⓒ = **Charter School**	New Schools are shaded	
89 Multi-Cultural Curriculum	273 Teacher Mentor	296 Title II Programs	Ⓜ = **Magnet School**	New Superintendents and Principals are bold	
90 Social Work	274 Before/After Sch	297 Webmaster	Ⓨ = **Year-Round School**	Personnel with email addresses are underscored	

Market Data Retrieval

School	Grades		Enroll	%	Phone
© Family Life Acad Charter Sch I 14 W 170th St, Bronx 10452 Evelyn Centeno	K-8	T	470 11	100%	718/410-8100 Fax 718/410-8800
© Family Life Academy CS II 296 E 140th St, Bronx 10454 Kathy Ortiz	K-2	T	151	91%	718/665-2805 Fax 718/665-2811
© Family Life Academy CS III 370 Gerard Ave, Bronx 10451 Andrea Hernandez	K-4	T	254	89%	718/585-6580 Fax 718/585-6581
© Finn Academy-Elmira Chtr Sch 610 Lake St, Elmira 14901 Aimee Ciarlo	K-6	T	362	47%	607/737-8040
© Forte Prep Academy 3220 108th St, East Elmhurst 11369 Graham Browne	5-6	T	180	89%	347/709-1197
© Genesee Cmty Charter Sch 657 East Ave, Rochester 14607 Shannon Hillman	K-6		218 7	32%	585/697-1960 Fax 585/271-5904
© Girls Prep Bronx Charter ES [244] 681 Kelly St Rm 205, Bronx 10455 Tomasz Krzyzostaniak	PK-5	T	575	97%	718/901-3855 Fax 718/292-5586
© Girls Prep Bronx Middle Sch [244] 890 Cauldwell Ave Rm 120, Bronx 10456 Michael Farkosh	6-8		200		718/665-6090 Fax 718/665-6095
© Girls Prep Elem Sch-Bronx II 192 E 151st St, Bronx 10451 Dezchell Rodriguez	PK-K		401		917/435-6599
© Girls Prep Lower East Side ES [244] 442 E Houston St Rm 312, New York 10002 Rebekah Adamek	PK-4	T	266	71%	212/388-0241 Fax 212/208-4421
© Girls Prep Lower East Side MS [244] 420 E 12th St Rm 103, New York 10009 Jessica Strong	5-8		300		212/358-8216 Fax 212/358-8219
© Global Cmty Charter Sch 2350 5th Ave, New York 10037 Phyllis Siwiec	K-5	T	426	86%	646/360-2363
© Global Concepts Charter ES 1001 Ridge Rd, Lackawanna 14218 John Turner	K-8	T	600	80%	716/821-1903 Fax 716/821-9563
© Global Concepts Charter HS 30 Johnson St, Lackawanna 14218 Liz Mastramatteo	9-12		380		716/939-2554
© Gordon Brooklyn Lab CS Sands 77 Sands St 4th Fl, Brooklyn 11201 Dr Eric Tucker	6-10	T	401	98%	347/429-8439
© Grand Concourse Academy CS 625 Bolton Ave, Bronx 10473 Ira Victor	K-8	T	587	80%	718/684-6505 Fax 718/684-6513
© Great Oaks CS-New York City [238] 38 Delancey St Fl 3, New York 10002 Timberly Wilson	6-8	T	293	71%	212/233-5152 Fax 212/267-4357
© Green Tech High Charter Sch 99 Slingerland St, Albany 12202 Dr Paul Miller	9-12	T	353	62%	518/694-3400 Fax 518/694-3401
© Growing Up Green CS II 8435 152nd St, Jamaica 11432 Dr Nancy Wong	PK-4	T	255	77%	347/642-4306 Fax 718/291-1121
© Harbor Science & Arts Chtr Sch 132 E 111th St, New York 10029 Mark Johnson	K-8	T	248 13	70%	212/427-2244 Fax 212/360-7429
© Harlem Hebrew Language Acad CS [240] 147 Saint Nicholas Ave, New York 10026 Emily Carson	K-6		289	68%	212/866-4608 Fax 212/866-1099
© Harlem Link Charter Sch 21 W 111th St, New York 10026 Steven Evangelista	K-5	T	421	97%	212/289-3249 Fax 212/289-3686
© Harlem Prep Campus CS [235] 240 E 123rd St, New York 10035 Kevin Shrum \ Greg Daniel	K-12	T	1,071	85%	212/831-5394 Fax 212/876-9926
© Harlem Prep Middle Sch [235] 232 E 103rd St, New York 10029 Andre Geddes	6-8		324		212/860-7128 Fax 212/860-1783
© Harlem Village Acad East Elem [239] 2351 1st Ave 3rd Fl, New York 10035 Brandi Womack	K-5		347		646/812-9600 Fax 212/996-1626
© Harlem Village Acad East MS HS [239] 2351 1st Ave 4th Fl, New York 10035 Todd Richardson	5-12		230		646/812-9600 Fax 212/996-1626
© Harlem Village Acad High Sch [239] 35 W 124th St, New York 10027 Abe Correa	9-12	T	350	73%	646/812-9200 Fax 212/881-9023
© Harlem Village Acad W Lower ES [239] 74 W 124th St, New York 10027 Meg Limbo	K-2		250		646/812-9700 Fax 212/881-9588
© Harlem Village Acad W Upper ES [239] 132 W 124th St, New York 10027 Deborah Kenny	3-5		401		646/812-9800
© Harlem Village Acad West MS [239] 244 W 144th St 4th Fl, New York 10030 Nordia Hewitt	6-8		180		646/812-9300 Fax 646/548-9576
© Harriet Tubman Charter Sch [143] 3565 3rd Ave, Bronx 10456 Cleveland Person	K-8		664 14	99%	718/537-9912 Fax 718/537-9858
© Health Sciences Charter Sch 1140 Ellicott St, Buffalo 14209 Robert Baxter	9-12	T	380	92%	716/888-4080 Fax 716/464-7623
© Hebrew Language Academy CS 2 [240] 1870 Stillwell Ave, Brooklyn 11223 Ashley Furan	K-2	T	141	78%	718/682-5610 Fax 718/777-7220
© Heketi Community Charter Sch 403 Concord Ave, Bronx 10454 David Rosas	K-5	T	279	96%	718/260-6002 Fax 718/292-7154
© Hellenic Classical CS-Statn IS 1641 Richmond Ave, Staten Island 10314 Cathy Kakleas	K-1		71		212/557-7200 Fax 718/499-0958
© Henry Johnson Charter Sch 30 Watervliet Ave, Albany 12206 George Borum	K-4	T	363	91%	518/432-4300 Fax 518/432-4311
Hilltop Sch 20 George St, Haverstraw 10927 Dr Christine Ditrano	K-8	A	150		845/942-7550 Fax 845/942-7555
Hunter College Elem Sch 71 E 94th St, New York 10128 Dawn Roy	K-6		350 14		212/860-1292 Fax 212/722-6693
Hunter College High Sch 71 E 94th St, New York 10128 Dr Tony Fisher	7-12		1,210		212/860-1267 Fax 212/289-2209
© Hyde Leadership CS 730 Bryant Ave, Bronx 10474 Celia Sosa	K-12	T	964	90%	718/991-5500 Fax 718/842-8617
© Icahn Charter School 1 1525 Brook Ave, Bronx 10457 Lawford Cunningham	K-8	T	311	99%	718/716-8105 Fax 718/294-6596
© Icahn Charter School 2 1640 Bronxdale Ave, Bronx 10462 Brenda Carrasquillo	K-8	T	323	65%	718/828-6107 Fax 718/828-7308
© Icahn Charter School 3 1500 Pelham Pkwy S Frnt 1, Bronx 10461 Marcia Glattstein	K-8	T	319	80%	718/828-0034 Fax 718/794-2357
© Icahn Charter School 4 1500 Pelham Pkwy S Frnt 1, Bronx 10461 Michelle Allen	K-7		320	74%	718/828-0034 Fax 718/828-0664

1 Superintendent	8 Curric/Instruct K-12	19 Chief Financial Officer	29 Family/Consumer Science	39 Social Studies K-12	49 English/Lang Arts Elem	59 Special Education Elem	69 Academic Assessment
2 Bus/Finance/Purchasing	9 Curric/Instruct Elem	20 Art K-12	30 Adult Education	40 Social Studies Elem	50 English/Lang Arts Sec	60 Special Education Sec	70 Research/Development
3 Buildings And Grounds	10 Curric/Instruct Sec	21 Art Elem	31 Career/Sch-to-Work K-12	41 Social Studies Sec	51 Reading K-12	61 Foreign/World Lang K-12	71 Public Information
4 Food Service	11 Federal Program	22 Art Sec	32 Career/Sch-to-Work Elem	42 Science K-12	52 Reading Elem	62 Foreign/World Lang Elem	72 Summer School
5 Transportation	12 Title I	23 Music K-12	33 Career/Sch-to-Work Sec	43 Science Elem	53 Reading Sec	63 Foreign/World Lang Sec	73 Instructional Tech
6 Athletic	13 Title V	24 Music Elem	34 Early Childhood Ed	44 Science Sec	54 Remedial Reading K-12	64 Religious Education K-12	74 Inservice Training
7 Health Services	15 Asst Superintendent	25 Music Sec	35 Health/Phys Education	45 Math K-12	55 Remedial Reading Elem	65 Religious Education Elem	75 Marketing/Distributive
	16 Instructional Media Svcs	26 Business Education	36 Guidance Services K-12	46 Math Elem	56 Remedial Reading Sec	66 Religious Education Sec	76 Info Systems
	17 Chief Operations Officer	27 Career & Tech Ed	37 Guidance Services Elem	47 Math Sec	57 Bilingual/ELL	67 School Board President	77 Psychological Assess
	18 Chief Academic Officer	28 Technology Education	38 Guidance Services Sec	48 English/Lang Arts K-12	58 Special Education K-12	68 Teacher Personnel	78 Affirmative Action

New York School Directory

School	Grades	Prog	Enroll	%	Phone
ⓒ Icahn Charter School 5 1500 Pelham Pkwy S Frnt 1, Bronx 10461 Danielle Masi	K-8	T	322	70%	718/828-0034 Fax 718/828-0664
ⓒ Icahn Charter School 6 1701 Fulton Ave, Bronx 10457 Jason Cartagena	K-8	T	324	96%	718/294-1706 Fax 718/583-6194
ⓒ Icahn Charter School 7 1535 Story Ave, Bronx 10473 Naudia Bethany	K-8	T	316	73%	718/328-5480
Industry Residential Center 375 Rush Scottsville Rd, Rush 14543 Ms Poll	6-12	AV	50 8	90%	585/533-2600 Fax 585/533-2664
ⓒ International CS of New York 55 Willoughby St, Brooklyn 11201 Ellen Borenstein	K-5		439	34%	718/305-4199
ⓒ International Leadership CS 3030 Riverdale Ave, Bronx 10463 Elaine Lopez	9-12	T	377	98%	718/562-2300 Fax 347/245-6466
ⓒ Ivy Hill Prep Charter Sch 475 E 57th St, Brooklyn 11203 Ambrosia Johnson	K-1		111		917/789-8959
ⓒ John W LaVelle Prep Chtr Sch 1 Teleport Dr Ste 300, Staten Island 10311 Christopher Zilinski	3-12	T	738	58%	347/855-2238 Fax 347/466-5746
ⓒ Key Collegiate Charter Sch 257 Chester St, Brooklyn 11212 Katie Mazer	4-5	T	113	99%	646/604-4428 Fax 646/604-4427
ⓒ King Center Charter Sch 156 Newburgh Ave, Buffalo 14211 Antoinette Rhodes	K-8	GT	422 8	97%	716/891-7912 Fax 716/895-2058
ⓒ Kings Collegiate Charter Sch [246] 1084 Lenox Rd, Brooklyn 11212 Scott Schuster	5-8		352		718/342-6047 Fax 718/342-6727
ⓒ Kings Elem Sch [246] 905 Winthrop St, Brooklyn 11203 Rob Sgobbo	K-3	T	261	87%	347/390-0460 Fax 347/750-1528
ⓒ KIPP AIM Middle Sch [242] 2502 Lorillard Pl, Bronx 10458 Kate Baughman	5-7		401		929/288-4730
ⓒ KIPP Amp Elem Middle Sch [242] ⓨ 1224 Park Pl 2nd Fl, Brooklyn 11213 Antoine Lewis	K-8	M	788 6		718/943-3740 Fax 718/774-3673
ⓒ KIPP Elements Primary Sch 338 E 146th St, Bronx 10451 Diamond Graham	K-2		401		929/288-4740
ⓒ KIPP Freedom Elem Sch [242] 2246 Jerome Ave, Bronx 10453 Sarah English	K-6	T	235	92%	718/841-6160
ⓒ KIPP Freedom Middle Sch [242] 1825 Prospect Ave, Bronx 10457 Lariely Sanchez	5-5		401		718/841-6165
ⓒ KIPP Infinity Elem Mid Sch [242] ⓨ 625 W 133rd St Rm 261, New York 10027 Daisy Salazar \ Glenn Davis	K-8	MT	1,100 12	87%	212/991-2622 Fax 212/234-8396
ⓒ KIPP NYC College Prep High Sch [242] 201 E 144th St, Bronx 10451 Carlos Capellan	9-12		914		212/991-2626 Fax 347/862-9679
ⓒ KIPP Star Harlem Clg Prep ES [242] 625 W 133rd St, New York 10027 Brandi Vardiman	K-4		370		212/991-2655
ⓒ KIPP Star Middle Sch [242] 433 W 123rd St, New York 10027 Chrystal Griffin	5-8	T	304 17	84%	212/991-2650 Fax 212/666-4723
ⓒ KIPP Tech Valley Charter Sch [241] 321 Northern Blvd, Albany 12210 Scott Thompson	5-8	T	301	80%	518/694-9494 Fax 518/694-9411
ⓒ KIPP Tech Valley Primary CS [241] 1 Dudley Hts, Albany 12210 Maya Tucci	K-4		400		518/242-7725 Fax 518/694-9406
ⓒ KIPP Washington Heights ES [242] 586 W 177th St 4th Fl, New York 10033 Rebecca McMurdie	K-3		375		212/991-2630
ⓒ KIPP Washington Hts MS [242] 21 Jumel Pl, New York 10032 Danny Swersky	4-8	T	456	89%	212/991-2620 Fax 212/342-2521
ⓒ La Cima Elem Charter Sch 800 Gates Ave, Brooklyn 11221 Letta Belle	K-5	T	333	77%	718/443-2136 Fax 718/443-7291
ⓒ Lamad Academy Charter Sch 1060 Clarkson Ave, Brooklyn 11212 Alfred Cockfield	6-6		401		833/465-2623
ⓒ Launch Expeditionary Lrng CS 1580 Dean St, Brooklyn 11213 Efrat Kussell	6-8	T	303	85%	718/221-1064 Fax 347/402-3013
ⓒ Leadership Prep Bed Stuy CS [246] 141 Macon St, Brooklyn 11216 Ishani Mehta \ Aidan Thomas	K-8	T	410	82%	718/636-0360 Fax 718/301-2311
ⓒ Leadership Prep Brwnsvlle Acad [246] 985 Rockaway Ave, Brooklyn 11212 Jacobi Clifton	K-4		440	87%	718/669-7461 Fax 718/534-4072
ⓒ Leadership Prep Canarsie ES [246] 1001 E 100th St, Brooklyn 11236 Jen Rugani	K-4		450		347/390-0570 Fax 718/534-3881
ⓒ Leadership Prep Canarsie MS [246] 1070 E 104th St, Brooklyn 11236 Michael Scott	5-8	T	355	79%	347/390-0560 Fax 718/535-5492
ⓒ Leadership Prep Ocean Hill El [246] 51 Christopher Ave 3rd Fl, Brooklyn 11212 Caroline Kerns	K-4		450	73%	718/250-5767 Fax 212/881-9666
ⓒ Leadership Prep Ocean Hill Mid 51 Christopher Ave, Brooklyn 11212 Nikki Bowen	5-8		401		347/390-0550
ⓒ Leep Dual Language Acad CS 5323 5th Ave 2nd Fl, Brooklyn 11220 Delines Rodriguez	K-1		127		917/819-5337
ⓒ Lefferts Gardens Ascend ES 870 Albany Ave 1, Brooklyn 11203 Nadine Rubinstein	K-1		45		347/464-7600
ⓒ Legacy College Prep CS 400 E 145th St, Bronx 10454 Summer Schneider	6-8		390		347/746-1558
ⓒ Lyceum Charter Sch 421 W 145th St, New York 10031 Susan DeJesus	K-8		401		917/653-6885
MacCormick Secure Center 300 South Rd, Brooktondale 14817 Troy Hopson	8-12	GV	20 6	77%	607/539-7121 Fax 607/539-6588
ⓒ Manhattan Charter Sch 100 Attorney St, New York 10002 Genie Depolo	K-5	T	251	82%	212/533-2743 Fax 212/533-2820
ⓒ Manhattan Charter School II 220 Henry St, New York 10002 Amy Salazar	K-5	T	157	83%	212/964-3792 Fax 212/964-3795
ⓒ Math Engineering & Sci Academy 231 Palmetto St, Brooklyn 11221 Pagee Cheung	9-12	T	493	77%	718/282-7426 Fax 718/919-1479
ⓒ Merrick Academy-Queens PCS 13625 218th St, Laurelton 11413 Samantha Pugh	K-6	T	520 14	59%	718/479-3753 Fax 718/479-8108
ⓒ Middle Village Prep Mid CS 6802 Metropolitan Ave, Middle Vlg 11379 Nancy Velez	6-8	T	398	52%	718/869-2933 Fax 718/821-2498

79 Student Personnel	91 Safety/Security	275 Response To Intervention	298 Grant Writer/Ptnrships
80 Driver Ed/Safety	92 Magnet School	277 Remedial Math K-12	750 Chief Innovation Officer
81 Gifted/Talented	93 Parental Involvement	280 Literacy Coach	751 Chief of Staff
82 Video Services	95 Tech Prep Program	285 STEM	752 Social Emotional Learning
83 Substance Abuse Prev	97 Chief Infomation Officer	286 Digital Learning	
84 Erate	98 Chief Technology Officer	288 Common Core Standards	
85 AIDS Education	270 Character Education	294 Accountability	
88 Alternative/At Risk	271 Migrant Education	295 Network System	
89 Multi-Cultural Curriculum	273 Teacher Mentor	296 Title II Programs	
90 Social Work	274 Before/After Sch	297 Webmaster	

School Programs
A = Alternative Program
G = Adult Classes
M = Magnet Program
T = Title I Schoolwide
V = Career & Tech Ed Programs

Other School Types
Ⓐ = Alternative School
ⓒ = Charter School
Ⓜ = Magnet School
ⓨ = Year-Round School

Social Media
[f] = Facebook
[t] = Twitter

New Schools are shaded
New Superintendents and Principals are bold
Personnel with email addresses are underscored

Market Data Retrieval

School	Grades	Type	Enroll	%	Phone
© Mott Hall Charter Sch 1260 Franklin Ave, Bronx 10456 Conney Lobdell	6-8	T	263	98%	718/991-9139 Fax 718/991-9150
© Neighborhood Charter Sch Bronx 411 Wales Ave, Bronx 10454 Nick Carton	K-1		111		646/701-7117
© Neighborhood Chtr Sch Harlem 691 St Nicholas Ave, New York 10030 Michael Renda	K-8		705		646/701-7117
© Neighborhood CS-Harlem 691 St Nicholas Ave, New York 10030 Michael Renda	K-8		700		646/701-7117 Fax 646/484-6652
© Neighborhood CS-NW 421 W 145th St, New York 10031 Michael Renda	K-2		188		646/701-7117 Fax 646/484-6652
© New American Academy Chtr Sch 9301 Avenue B, Brooklyn 11236 Lisa Silva	K-5	T	331	70%	718/385-1709 Fax 718/385-1856
© New Dawn Charter High Sch II 8917 161st St, Jamaica 11432 Dr Lisa Digaudio	9-9		96		212/209-6036
© New Dawn Charter High Sch 242 Hoyt St, Brooklyn 11217 Lisa Digudio	9-12		273		347/505-9101
© New Hope Academy Charter Sch 475 E 57th St 3rd Fl, Brooklyn 11203 Temica Francis	K-5		388		718/337-8303
© New Roots Charter Sch 116 N Cayuga St Ste 2, Ithaca 14850 Tina Nilsen-Hodges	9-12	T	108	88%	607/697-0446
© New Ventures Charter Sch 1 Teleport Dr Ste 300, Staten Island 10311 Ronald Gorsky			122	54%	347/855-2238 Fax 718/709-7680
© New Visions Aim CS I [243] 1150 E New York Ave, Brooklyn 11212 Kristin Greer	9-12	T	172	93%	718/269-7090 Fax 718/498-0604
ⓐ New Visions Aim CS II [243] © 1010 Rev James A Polite Ave, Bronx 10459 Tameka Jackson	9-12	T	220	90%	718/861-7515 Fax 718/861-7518
© New Visions CHS Humanities [243] 99 Terrace View Ave, Bronx 10463 Magaly Hicks	9-9	T	530	71%	718/817-7686 Fax 718/817-7688
© New Visions CHS Humanities II [243] 455 Southern Blvd, Bronx 10455 David Neagley	9-12	T	490	71%	212/645-5110 Fax 718/665-5583
© New Visions CHS Humanities III [243] 3000 Avenue X, Brooklyn 11235 Janique Cambridge	9-12		200		718/368-4145 Fax 718/368-4148
© New Visions CHS Humanities IV [243] 10000 Beach Channel Dr, Rockaway Park 11694 Hannah Kehn	9-10	T	187	75%	718/734-3350 Fax 718/734-3351
© New Visions CHS Math & Sci [243] 99 Terrace View Ave, Bronx 10463 Robert Hiller	9-12	T	509	64%	718/817-7683 Fax 718/817-7638
© New Visions CHS Math & Sci II [243] 900 Tinton Ave, Bronx 10456 Mrs Clacken	9-12	T	535	82%	718/665-3671 Fax 718/742-7896
© New Visions CHS Math & Sci III [243] 3000 Avenue X, Brooklyn 11235 Nissi Jonathan	9-12	T	363	93%	718/934-9240 Fax 718/934-9171
© New Visions CHS Math & Sci IV [243] 15610 Baisley Blvd, Jamaica 11434 William Romney	9-10		490		718/525-2041 Fax 718/525-2636
© New World Preparatory CS 26 Sharpe Ave, Staten Island 10302 Amanda Ainley	6-8	T	379	90%	718/705-8990 Fax 718/442-1583
© New York City Montessori CS 423 E 138th St, Bronx 10454 Abeku Hayes	K-5	T	279	98%	347/226-9094 Fax 347/226-9097
New York St Sch for the Blind 2A Richmond Ave, Batavia 14020 Barara Lemon	Spec	V	55 9	94%	585/343-5384 Fax 585/344-5557
New York St Sch for the Deaf 401 Turin St, Rome 13440 Daniel Roberts	Spec	AV	52 17	42%	315/337-8400 Fax 315/336-8859
© Niagara Charter Sch 2077 Lockport Rd, Niagara Falls 14304 D Novak	K-6	T	347 17	86%	716/297-4520 Fax 716/297-4617
© Nicotra Early College CS 300 Genesee Ave, Staten Island 10312 Joseph Zaza	8-10		140		929/419-9001 Fax 347/466-5746
© Northside Charter High Sch 424 Leonard St 4th Fl, Brooklyn 11222 Danielle Bero	9-12	T	395	72%	347/390-1273 Fax 347/390-1274
© NYC Charter School of the Arts 26 Broadway, New York 10004 Elisa Murphy	6-8	T	287	41%	646/793-6320 Fax 646/786-9427
© Nycacs CS East Harlem 433 E 100th St, New York 10029 Jessica Seeman	1-12	T	40	90%	212/860-2580 Fax 212/860-2960
© Nycacs-Bronx 1180 Tinton Ave 4th Fl, Bronx 10456 Jennifer Connelly	Spec		20	80%	718/991-5910 Fax 718/991-1343
© Ocean Hill Collegiate Chtr Sch [246] 1137 Herkimer St, Brooklyn 11233 Meghann Fallon	5-8	T	352	80%	718/250-5765 Fax 718/766-2031
© Ontech Charter High Sch 810 Willis Ave, Syracuse 13204 Jana Rogers	9-12	T	401	84%	315/396-0558
© Our World Neighborhood ES CS 1 3612 35th Ave, Astoria 11106 Douglas Ricketts	K-8	T	700 29	73%	718/392-3405 Fax 718/392-2840
© Our World Neighborhood ES CS 2 13525 79th St, Howard Beach 11414 Rodney Wilkins	K-2		95	76%	347/390-3290
© Our World Neighborhood MS CS 1 3120 37th St, Astoria 11103 Lisa Edmiston	6-8		380		718/274-2902 Fax 718/274-7146
© Persistence Prep Acad CS 833 Michigan Ave, Buffalo 14203 Joelle Formato	K-2		170		716/235-1520 Fax 716/768-1187
© Reach Academy Charter Sch 115 Ash St, Buffalo 14204 Linda Marszalek	K-2	T	160	90%	716/248-1485 Fax 716/248-2833
© Renaissance Acad of the Arts 299 Kirk Rd, Rochester 14612 Ben Koch	K-6	T	483	92%	585/225-4200 Fax 585/225-4201
© Renaissance Charter Sch 2 6002 Maspeth Ave, Maspeth 11378 Everett Boyd	K-1		145		917/242-3505
© Riverhead Charter Sch 3685 Middle Country Rd, Calverton 11933 Laura Arcuri \ Patrick McKinney	K-8	T	588 15	100%	631/369-5800 Fax 631/369-6687
© Rochester Academy Charter Sch 1757 Latta Rd, Rochester 14612 Deanna Wilkinson \ Jennifer Doyle \ Tyler Manchester	K-12	T	533	99%	585/467-9201 Fax 585/232-1357
© Rochester Prep Elem Sch [246] 899 Jay St, Rochester 14611 Danielle Hinman	K-4		464		585/235-0008 Fax 585/235-0014
© Rochester Prep ES-West 85 Saint Jacob St, Rochester 14621 Emily Volpe	K-4	T	750	79%	585/368-5100 Fax 585/467-4155

1	Superintendent	8	Curric/Instruct K-12	19	Chief Financial Officer	29	Family/Consumer Science	39 Social Studies K-12
2	Bus/Finance/Purchasing	9	Curric/Instruct Elem	20	Art K-12	30	Adult Education	40 Social Studies Elem
3	Buildings And Grounds	10	Curric/Instruct Sec	21	Art Elem	31	Career/Sch-to-Work K-12	41 Social Studies Sec
4	Food Service	11	Federal Program	22	Art Sec	32	Career/Sch-to-Work Elem	42 Science K-12
5	Transportation	12	Title I	23	Music K-12	33	Career/Sch-to-Work Sec	43 Science Elem
6	Athletic	13	Title V	24	Music Elem	34	Early Childhood Ed	44 Science Sec
7	Health Services	14	Instructional Media Svcs	25	Music Sec	35	Health/Phys Education	45 Math K-12
		15	Asst Superintendent	26	Business Education	36	Guidance Services K-12	46 Math Elem
		16		27	Career & Tech Ed	37	Guidance Services Elem	47 Math Sec
		17	Chief Operations Officer	28	Technology Education	38	Guidance Services Sec	48 English/Lang Arts K-12
		18	Chief Academic Officer					

49 English/Lang Arts Elem	59 Special Education Elem	69 Academic Assessment
50 English/Lang Arts Sec	60 Special Education Sec	70 Research/Development
51 Reading K-12	61 Foreign/World Lang K-12	71 Public Information
52 Reading Elem	62 Foreign/World Lang Elem	72 Summer School
53 Reading Sec	63 Foreign/World Lang Sec	73 Instructional Tech
54 Remedial Reading K-12	64 Religious Education K-12	74 Inservice Training
55 Remedial Reading Elem	65 Religious Education Elem	75 Marketing/Distributive
56 Remedial Reading Sec	66 Religious Education Sec	76 Info Systems
57 Bilingual/ELL	67 School Board President	77 Psychological Assess
58 Special Education K-12	68 Teacher Personnel	78 Affirmative Action

New York School Directory

School	Grades	Title I	Enroll	%	Phone
© Rochester Prep High Sch [246] 305 Andrews St, Rochester 14604 Edward Eckert	9-12		364		585/368-5111 Fax 585/423-9625
© Rochester Prep MS-Brooks [246] 630 Brooks Ave, Rochester 14619 Patrick Pastore	5-8	T	355 20	78%	585/436-8629 Fax 585/436-5985 ⓕ
© Rochester Prep MS-West [246] 432 Chili Ave, Rochester 14611 Kris Hirsch	5-8		342		585/368-5090 Fax 585/368-5091 ⓕ ⓣ
Rockland Children Psy Center 2 1st Ave, Orangeburg 10962 Gus Augustin	Spec		20 8		845/680-4080 Fax 845/680-8904
© Roosevelt Children's Acad CS 105 Pleasant Ave, Roosevelt 11575 Desiree Galashaw \ Darryl Wilson	K-8	T	635 8	87%	516/867-6202 Fax 516/867-6206
© Rosalyn Yalow Charter Sch 116 E 169th St, Bronx 10452 Darlene Morris	K-4	T	426	98%	347/735-5480
© School In the Square PCS 120 Wadsworth Ave, New York 10033 Carrie Amon	6-8	T	304	80%	718/916-7683 Fax 929/274-2877
© Sisulu-Walker CS of Harlem [247] 125 W 115th St, New York 10026 Michelle Haynes	K-5	T	210 10	85%	212/663-8216 Fax 212/866-5793
© South Bronx Classical CS 977 Fox St, Bronx 10459 Lester Long	K-8	T	486	74%	718/860-4340 Fax 718/744-2030 ⓕ ⓣ
© South Bronx Classical CS II 333 E 135th St, Bronx 10454 Leena Konda	K-6	T	350	90%	718/292-9526 Fax 718/732-2945
© South Bronx Classical CS III 3458 3rd Ave, New York 10156 Rebecca Scognamiglio	K-5		322		929/285-3025
© South Bronx Classical CS IV 3458 3rd Ave, Bronx 10456 Rebecca Geary	K-1	T	128	90%	929/285-3025 Fax 929/285-2025
© South Bronx Cmty Charter HS 730 Concourse Vlg W, Bronx 10451 Harvey Chism	9-12	T	331	74%	718/292-4115
© South Bronx Early Clg Acad CS 801 E 156th St, Bronx 10455 Brian Blough	6-8	T	326	86%	929/291-7700 Fax 929/291-7721
© South Buffalo Charter Sch 154 S Ogden St, Buffalo 14210 David Ehrle	K-8	T	902	80%	716/826-7213 Fax 716/826-7168
© Southside Academy Charter Sch [210] 2200 Onondaga Creek Blvd, Syracuse 13207	K-8	T	681 24	90%	315/476-3019 Fax 315/410-5540
© Storefront Acad Harlem CS 70 E 129th St, New York 10035 Taleema Chesney	K-1		44		646/221-3450
© Storefront Acad South Bronx CS 609 Jackson Ave, Bronx 10455 Nicole Garcia	K-4	T	180	96%	646/758-7201 Fax 646/476-1409
© Success Acad CS Bed Stuy 1 [245] 70 Tompkins Ave Fl 2, Brooklyn 11206 Rishabh Agarwal	K-4	T	245	73%	718/635-3294 Fax 646/964-6598
© Success Acad CS Bed Stuy 2 [245] 211 Throop Ave Fl 3, Brooklyn 11206 Alisha Nettune	K-4	T	320	81%	718/704-1439 Fax 646/349-3972
© Success Acad CS Bed Sty MS [245] 70 Tompkins Ave Fl 3, Brooklyn 11206 Marnl Aronson	5-8		102		718/635-3296 Fax 718/683-9033
© Success Acad CS Bensonhurst [245] 99 Avenue P Fl 4, Brooklyn 11204 Terri Lynch	K-4	T	562	55%	347/514-7082 Fax 646/219-1663
© Success Acad CS Bergen Bch [245] 1420 E 68th St, Brooklyn 11234 Catherine Fabian	K-4	T	430	66%	347/817-2017 Fax 347/521-7879
© Success Acad CS Bronx 1 [245] 339 Morris Ave Fl 2, Bronx 10451 Jackie Gridelli	K-4	T	620	87%	347/286-7950 Fax 347/479-1192
© Success Acad CS Bronx 1 MS [245] 339 Morris Ave Fl 2, Bronx 10451 Jackie Gridelli	K-4		240		347/286-7950
© Success Acad CS Bronx 2 [245] 450 Saint Pauls Pl Fl 5, Bronx 10456 Angela Inslee	K-4	T	497	87%	347/286-7965 Fax 347/479-1194
© Success Acad CS Bronx 2 MS [245] 270 E 167th St Fl 2, Bronx 10456 Todd Tentitore	5-8		315		646/558-0038 Fax 646/808-3538
© Success Acad CS Bronx 3 Lwr [245] 1000 Teller Ave, Bronx 10456 Kimberly Vincent	K-4	T	480	81%	646/790-2145 Fax 646/619-4260
© Success Acad CS Bronx 4 [245] 885 Bolton Ave Fl 3, Bronx 10473 Samantha Cheslow	K-4	T	470	70%	646/558-0043 Fax 646/219-2838
© Success Acad CS Bushwick [245] 139 Menahan St, Brooklyn 11221 Katherine Haves	K-3	T	244	83%	646/790-2173
© Success Acad CS Cobble Hill [245] 284 Baltic St, Brooklyn 11201 Alissa Bishop	K-4	T	412	53%	718/704-1460 Fax 646/478-9383 ⓕ ⓣ
© Success Acad CS Crown Heights [245] 330 Crown St Fl 5, Brooklyn 11225 Libby Ashton	K-4	T	92	77%	646/790-2129 Fax 914/462-3286
© Success Acad CS Ditmas Park [245] 72 Veronica Pl, Brooklyn 11226 Asha Woldemarian	5-6		401		646/597-4641 Fax 646/961-4739
© Success Acad CS E Flatbush MS [245] 3109 Newkirk Ave, Brooklyn 11226 Mary Magruder	5-8		100		718/395-6346
© Success Acad CS Far Rockaway [245] 1045 Nameoke St Fl 3, Far Rockaway 11691 Ty Redmond	K-3	T	272	79%	718/704-1421
© Success Acad CS Flatbush ES [245] 15 Snyder Ave, Brooklyn 11226 Wintanna Abai	K-3	T	228	72%	646/790-2150
© Success Acad CS Fort Greene [245] 101 Park Ave Fl 3, Brooklyn 11205 Victoria Brienza	K-4	T	260	76%	646/790-2137 Fax 914/462-3407
© Success Acad CS Harlem 1 [245] 34 W 118th St Frnt 2, New York 10026 Danique Day-Loving	K-4	T	570	73%	646/277-7170 Fax 212/457-5659
© Success Acad CS Harlem 2 [245] 144 E 128th St Fl 3, New York 10035 Raymie Fernandez	K-4	T	585	80%	646/442-6600 Fax 646/478-9491
© Success Acad CS Harlem 3 [245] 410 E 100th St Fl 4, New York 10029 Tara Stant	K-4	T	400	75%	646/790-2177 Fax 646/478-9492
© Success Acad CS Harlem 4 [245] 240 W 113th St Fl 3, New York 10026 Francesca Vanin	K-4	T	390	68%	646/442-6500 Fax 646/478-9493
© Success Acad CS Harlem 5 [245] 301 W 140th St Fl 3, New York 10030 Molly Cohen	K-4	T	410	79%	646/380-2580 Fax 646/961-4731
© Success Acad CS Harlem 6 [245] 461 W 131st St, New York 10027 Emily Rezin	K-2		227	88%	646/569-5900
© Success Acad CS Harlem Central [245] 461 W 131st St, New York 10027 Kristen Damo	7-8		140		646/569-5900

79 Student Personnel	91 Safety/Security	275 Response To Intervention	298 Grant Writer/Ptnrships	**School Programs**	**Social Media**
80 Driver Ed/Safety	92 Magnet School	277 Remedial Math K-12	750 Chief Innovation Officer	A = Alternative Program	ⓕ = Facebook
81 Gifted/Talented	93 Parental Involvement	280 Literacy Coach	751 Chief of Staff	G = Adult Classes	
82 Video Services	95 Tech Prep Program	285 STEM	752 Social Emotional Learning	M = Magnet Program	ⓣ = Twitter
83 Substance Abuse Prev	97 Chief Information Officer	286 Digital Learning		T = Title I Schoolwide	
84 Erate	98 Chief Technology Officer	288 Common Core Standards	**Other School Types**	V = Career & Tech Ed Programs	
85 AIDS Education	270 Accountability	294 Assessment	Ⓐ = Alternative School		
88 Alternative/At Risk	271 Migrant Education	295 Network System	Ⓒ = Charter School	New Schools are shaded	
89 Multi-Cultural Curriculum	273 Teacher Mentor	296 Title II Programs	Ⓜ = Magnet School	New Superintendents and Principals are bold	
90 Social Work	274 Before/After Sch	297 Webmaster	Ⓨ = Year-Round School	Personnel with email addresses are underscored	

Market Data Retrieval

© Success Acad CS Harlem East [245] 6-8 396 646/747-6700
141 E 111th St Fl 3, New York 10029
Brooke Rosenkrantz

© Success Acad CS Harlem N Cen [245] 5-8 340 646/790-2169
175 W 134th St Fl 3, New York 10030 Fax 914/462-3237
Rachel Keene

© Success Acad CS Harlem NW [245] 5-8 201 646/558-0093
509 W 129th St Fl 3, New York 10027 Fax 646/619-4124
Megan Maines

© Success Acad CS Harlem West [245] 5-8 400 646/569-5920
215 W 114th St Fl 5, New York 10026
Khari Shabazz

© Success Acad CS Hell's Kitchen [245] K-4 T 434 61% 646/790-2153
439 W 49th St Fl 2, New York 10019 Fax 646/304-5660
Michael Lafrancis

© Success Acad CS Hudson Yards [245] K-2 T 200 63% 212/845-9683
500 W 41st St, New York 10036 Fax 212/504-0813
William Loskoch

© Success Acad CS Lafayette MS [245] 5-5 96 646/790-2126
787 Lafayette Ave, Brooklyn 11221
Kristin Damo

© Success Acad CS Midtown West [245] 5-8 388 646/558-0050
439 W 49th St Fl 3, New York 10019 Fax 212/409-8694
Jennifer Haynes

© Success Acad CS Prospect Hgts [245] K-4 T 350 68% 646/790-2121
801 Park Pl Fl 4, Brooklyn 11216 Fax 646/514-2070
Darielle Petrucci

© Success Acad CS Rosedale [245] K-4 T 571 64% 347/514-7060
14765 249th St, Rosedale 11422 Fax 646/219-4826
Elizabeth Miller

© Success Acad CS S Jamaica [245] K-3 T 230 69% 718/704-1441
12027 141st St, Jamaica 11436
Meghan Daly

© Success Acad CS Union Square [245] K-4 T 425 44% 646/790-2161
40 Irving Pl Fl 2, New York 10003 Fax 646/514-5551
Ms Sulisa

© Success Acad CS Upper West [245] K-4 T 490 46% 646/274-1580
145 W 84th St Fl 2, New York 10024 Fax 646/478-9383
Regina Lostus

© Success Acad CS Washington Hts [245] K-4 T 531 68% 646/558-0027
701 Fort Washington Ave, New York 10040 Fax 646/219-4756
Kelsey Depalo

© Success Acad CS Williamsburg [245] K-4 T 400 59% 718/704-1419
183 S 3rd St Fl 4, Brooklyn 11211 Fax 646/349-5421
Chelsey Palmer \ Alison Levy

© Success Acad CS-Lafayette MS [245] 5-5 401 646/790-2125
700 Park Ave, Brooklyn 11206
Kristin Damo

© Success Acad CS-Myrtle MS [245] 5-7 401 646/569-5914
700 Park Ave Fl 3, Brooklyn 11206
Lauren Jonas

© Success Acad CS-Queens 1 MS [245] 5-5 401 347/602-4335
13255 Ridgedale St, Sprngfld GDNS 11413
Kristin Jones

© Success Acad CS-Sprngfld Grdn [245] K-4 T 479 67% 347/602-4335
13255 Ridgedale St Fl 3, Sprngfld GDNS 11413 Fax 718/228-3515
Michelle Cooper

© Success Acad HS Lib Arts-Bronx [245] 9-10 401 646/558-0056
878 Brooks Ave, Bronx 10451

© Success Acad HS Lib Arts-Mnhtn [245] 9-12 500 646/558-0056
111 E 33rd St Fl 4, New York 10016
Michael Lafrancis

© Syracuse Acad Sci & Citiznshp K-3 T 240 82% 315/671-0270
301 Valley Dr, Syracuse 13207 Fax 315/671-0275
Dominic Firsina

© Syracuse Academy of Science CS 8-12 TV 350 76% 315/428-8997
1001 Park Ave, Syracuse 13204 27 Fax 315/428-9109
Jeannine Brand

© Tapestry Charter Sch K-12 T 987 66% 716/332-0754
65 Great Arrow Ave, Buffalo 14216 Fax 716/332-0758
Jennifer Pangborn \ Lindsay Lee \ Sara Hilligas

© The Uft Charter Sch 9-12 T 260 76% 718/927-5540
800 Van Siclen Ave, Brooklyn 11207 16 Fax 718/228-9828
Justin Davis

© Troy Prep Charter Sch [246] K-10 T 600 85% 518/445-3100
2 Polk St, Troy 12180 Fax 518/445-3101
Samantha Deluke \ Lauren Catlett

© Truxton Academy Charter Sch K-2 44 607/842-6252
6337 Academy St, Truxton 13158
Sarah Petit-McClure

© Uncommon Charter High Sch [246] 9-12 530 718/638-1868
1485 Pacific St, Brooklyn 11216 Fax 347/296-8322
Thomas O'Brien

© Uncommon Collegiate Charter HS [246] 9-12 350 347/390-0300
832 Marcy Ave, Brooklyn 11216 Fax 212/881-9611
Aneka Roberts

© Uncommon Prep Charter HS [246] 9-11 456 718/307-5077
6565 Flatlands Ave, Brooklyn 11236 Fax 718/766-2021
Sean Healy

© Unity Prep CS Brooklyn HS 9-11 246 718/682-3725
584 Driggs Ave, Brooklyn 11211
C Fuller

© Unity Preparatory CS- Brooklyn 6-8 T 265 62% 718/455-5046
432 Monroe St, Brooklyn 11221 Fax 718/455-5049
Casey Burns

© University Prep Charter HS 9-12 T 450 86% 718/585-0560
600 Saint Anns Ave, Bronx 10455 Fax 718/585-0563
Andrew Ayers

© University Prep Charter MS 5-6 155 917/985-8300
470 Jackson Ave 3rd Fl, Bronx 10455 Fax 929/220-8110
David Patterson

© University Prep CS Young Men 7-12 T 330 28% 585/672-1280
1290 Lake Ave, Rochester 14613 Fax 585/458-2732
Tracy Delgrego

© Urban Assembly CS Computer Sci 9-11 T 112 85% 646/421-4523
1300 Boynton Ave, Bronx 10472
David Noah

© Urban Choice Charter Sch K-8 T 392 96% 585/288-5702
545 Humboldt St, Rochester 14610 Fax 585/654-9882
Michael Samuel

© Urban Dove Team Charter Sch 9-12 T 249 86% 718/783-8232
600 Lafayette Ave, Brooklyn 11216 Fax 718/783-8239
Amit Bahl

Ⓐ Urban Dove Team CS II 9-10 T 110 97% 718/682-3975
860 Forest Ave, Bronx 10456 Fax 718/292-9212
Sharon Aiuvalasit

© Utica Academy of Science CS 6-8 T 413 83% 315/266-1072
1214 Lincoln Ave, Utica 13502 Fax 315/266-1073
Mustafa Ersoy

© Valence College Prep CS 5-5 115 646/854-8414
7501 31st Ave, East Elmhurst 11370
Mitch Flax

© Vertus Charter Sch 9-12 T 283 78% 585/747-8911
21 Humboldt St Ste 3, Rochester 14609 Fax 585/254-1251
Julie Lacey

© West Buffalo Charter Sch K-8 T 511 88% 716/923-1534
113 Lafayette Ave, Buffalo 14213 Fax 716/768-0980
Rachel Banas \ Shawn Siddall

© Western New York Maritime CS 9-12 T 350 79% 716/842-6289
266 Genesee St, Buffalo 14204 Fax 716/842-4241
Catherine Oldenburg

1	Superintendent	8	Curric/Instruct K-12	19	Chief Financial Officer	29	Family/Consumer Science	39	Social Studies K-12	49	English/Lang Arts Elem	59	Special Education Elem	69	Academic Assessment
2	Bus/Finance/Purchasing	9	Curric/Instruct Elem	20	Art K-12	30	Adult Education	40	Social Studies Elem	50	English/Lang Arts Sec	60	Special Education Sec	70	Research/Development
3	Buildings And Grounds	10	Curric/Instruct Sec	21	Art Elem	31	Career/Sch-to-Work K-12	41	Social Studies Sec	51	Reading K-12	61	Foreign/World Lang K-12	71	Public Information
4	Food Service	11	Federal Program	22	Art Sec	32	Career/Sch-to-Work Elem	42	Science K-12	52	Reading Elem	62	Foreign/World Lang Elem	72	Summer School
5	Transportation	12	Title I	23	Music K-12	33	Career/Sch-to-Work Sec	43	Science Elem	53	Reading Sec	63	Foreign/World Lang Sec	73	Instructional Tech
6	Athletic	13	Title V	24	Music Elem	34	Early Childhood Ed	44	Science Sec	54	Remedial Reading K-12	64	Religious Education K-12	74	Inservice Training
7	Health Services	15	Asst Superintendent	25	Music Sec	35	Health/Phys Education	45	Math K-12	55	Remedial Reading Elem	65	Religious Education Elem	75	Marketing/Distributive
		16	Instructional Media Svcs	26	Business Education	36	Guidance Services K-12	46	Math Elem	56	Remedial Reading Sec	66	Religious Education Sec	76	Info Systems
		17	Chief Operations Officer	27	Career & Tech Ed	37	Guidance Services Elem	47	Math Sec	57	Bilingual/ELL	67	School Board President	77	Psychological Assess
		18	Chief Academic Officer	28	Technology Education	38	Guidance Services Sec	48	English/Lang Arts K-12	58	Special Education K-12	68	Teacher Personnel	78	Affirmative Action

New York School Directory

Albany County

© Whin Music Cmty Charter Sch 401 W 164th St 4th Fl, New York 10032 Annie Nuynh	K-3	T	184	75%	844/489-0817 Fax 212/227-2763
© Wildflower Rose and Alston CS 1332 Fulton Ave, Bronx 10456	PK-1		60		718/635-0474
© Williamsburg Charter High Sch 198 Varet St, Brooklyn 11206 Tanishia Williams	9-12	T	944 40	79%	718/782-9830 Fax 347/464-7604
© Williamsburg Collegiate CS [246] 157 Wilson St, Brooklyn 11211 J Leaird	5-8	T	288	84%	718/302-4018 Fax 718/302-4641
© Young Women's College Prep CS 133 Hoover Dr, Rochester 14615 Barbara Zelazny	7-9	T	252	85%	585/254-0320
© Zeta Bronx 1 Elem Sch 222 Alexander Ave, Bronx 10454 Emily Kim	K-1	T	182	90%	929/458-3000
© Zeta Inwood 1 Elem Sch 652 W 187th St, New York 10033 Emily Kim	K-1	T	170	77%	929/447-5281

ALBANY COUNTY

ALBANY COUNTY SCHOOLS

County Schs..Principal	Grd	Prgm	Enr/#Cls	SN	
Airline Drive Academy 10C Airline Dr, Albany 12205 Barb Lounello	Spec		100		518/464-6303
Capitol Reg Career & Tech Sch 1015 Watervliet Shaker Rd, Albany 12205 Charles Paravella	Voc	AG	800 40		518/862-4800 Fax 518/862-4808
Maywood Sch 1979 Central Ave, Albany 12205 Sarah Horaczek	Spec		95 14		518/464-6363 Fax 518/464-6366
Tech Valley High Sch 246 Tri Centennial Dr, Albany 12203 James Niedermeier	9-12	V	135 12		518/862-4960 Fax 518/437-8677

ALBANY PUBLIC SCHOOLS

• **Albany City School Dist** PID: 00714110   518/475-6000
1 Academy Park, Albany 12207   Fax 518/475-6009

Schools: 19 \ **Teachers:** 748 \ **Students:** 9,024 \ **Special Ed Students:** 1,613 \ **LEP Students:** 1,026 \ **College-Bound:** 73% \ **Ethnic:** Asian 10%, African American 49%, Hispanic 20%, Caucasian 21% \ **Exp:** $325 (High) \ **Poverty:** 29% \ **Title I:** $6,490,025 \ **Special Education:** $31,536,000 \ **Open-Close:** 09/08 - 06/25 \ **DTBP:** $195 (High)

Kaweeda Adams 1		Brian Dengler 3	
Lisa Finkenbinder 4*		Denise Towne 5	
Kathy Ryan 6*		Suzanne McCarthy 7*	
Karen Bechdol 8*		Cecily Wilson-Turner 9,15*	
Lori McKenna 10,15		Kent Baker 15,69,76,294	
Nicole Lindeman 16,73*		Kathryn Wright 20,23	
Brigid Dodson 34		Lisa Momberger 34	
Melissa Hasty 34*		Ashley Chapple 35,83,85*	
Tom Giglio 57,89,271*		Anne Savage 67	
Matthew Petrin 68		Cathy Edmondson 71	
Ron Lesko 71		Patricia Wolfe 76	
Dr Kerri Canzone-Ball 79		Jack Grogan 91*	
Frank Delsignore 285*		Sarah McGraw 285*	
Eileen Leffler 298			

Public Schs..Principal	Grd	Prgm	Enr/#Cls	SN	
Abrookin Career & Tech Ctr 99 Kent St, Albany 12206 Andrea Marques	Voc	G	129 20		518/475-6400 Fax 518/475-6202
Albany High Sch 700 Washington Ave, Albany 12203 Julie Barber	9-12	T	2,579 113	65%	518/475-6200 Fax 518/475-6202
Albany International Center 570 N Pearl St, Albany 12204 Rachel Stead	6-12		175		518/475-6900 Fax 518/475-6902
Ⓜ Albany School of Humanities 108 Whitehall Rd, Albany 12209 Marie Culihan	K-6	T	484 20	64%	518/475-6575 Fax 518/475-6577
Arbor Hill Elem Sch 1 Arbor Dr, Albany 12207 Rosalind Gaines-Harrell	K-5	T	314 36	88%	518/475-6625 Fax 518/462-7344
Delaware Cmty Sch 43 Bertha St, Albany 12209 Kenneth Lein	PK-5	T	412 22	76%	518/475-6750 Fax 518/475-6754
Eagle Point Elem Sch 1044 Western Ave, Albany 12203 Gabriel Barbato	K-6	T	318 15	45%	518/475-6825 Fax 518/475-6827
Edmund O'Neal MS of Excellence 50 Lark St, Albany 12210 Kandie Antonetti	6-8	T	454	90%	518/475-6600 Fax 518/475-6602
Giffen Memorial Elem Sch 274 S Pearl St, Albany 12202 Mrs Brown	K-6	T	485 50	90%	518/475-6650 Fax 518/475-6652
Ⓜ Montessori Magnet Sch 45 Tremont St, Albany 12205 John Powell	PK-5	T	336 14	33%	518/475-6675 Fax 518/475-6677
New Scotland Elem Sch 369 New Scotland Ave, Albany 12208 David Amodeo	K-5	T	483	43%	518/475-6775 Fax 518/475-6777
North Albany Middle Sch 570 N Pearl St, Albany 12204 Julie Barber	6-7	T	90	88%	518/475-6800 Fax 518/475-6802
Pine Hills Elem Sch 41 N Allen St, Albany 12203 Tia Corniel	K-5	T	384 50	73%	518/475-6725 Fax 518/475-6729
Schuyler Achievement Academy 676 Clinton Ave, Albany 12206 Kendra Francis	K-5	T	286 15	91%	518/475-6700 Fax 518/475-6704
Sheridan Preparatory Academy 400 Sheridan Ave, Albany 12206 Zuleika Sanchez-Gayle	K-5	T	333 21	93%	518/475-6850 Fax 518/475-6852
Stephen & Harriet Myers MS 100 Elbel Ct, Albany 12209 Jennifer Chatain	6-8	T	620 100	66%	518/475-6425 Fax 518/475-6427
Ⓜ Thomas O'Brien Acad-Sci & Tech 94 Delaware Ave, Albany 12202 Teresa Brown	K-6	T	444 25	73%	518/475-6875 Fax 518/475-6877
Ⓐ Tony Clement Ctr for Education 395 Elk St, Albany 12206 Sophia Newell	7-12	G	250 10		518/475-6525 Fax 518/475-6527
William S Hackett Middle Sch 45 Delaware Ave, Albany 12202 Michael Paolino	6-8	T	655 100	66%	518/475-6475 Fax 518/475-6477

---

79 Student Personnel	91 Safety/Security	275 Response To Intervention	298 Grant Writer/Ptnrships	**School Programs**
80 Driver Ed/Safety	92 Magnet School	277 Remedial Math K-12	750 Chief Innovation Officer	A = Alternative Program
81 Gifted/Talented	93 Parental Involvement	280 Literacy Coach	751 Chief of Staff	G = Adult Classes
82 Video Services	95 Tech Prep Program	285 STEM	752 Social Emotional Learning	M = Magnet Program
83 Substance Abuse Prev	97 Chief Infomation Officer	286 Digital Learning		T = Title I Schoolwide
84 Erate	98 Chief Technology Officer	288 Common Core Standards	**Other School Types**	V = Career & Tech Ed Programs
85 AIDS Education	270 Character Education	294 Accountability	Ⓐ = Alternative School	
88 Alternative/At Risk	271 Migrant Education	295 Network System	© = Charter School	**Social Media**
89 Multi-Cultural Curriculum	273 Teacher Mentor	296 Title II Programs	Ⓜ = Magnet School	🅕 = Facebook
90 Social Work	274 Before/After Sch	297 Webmaster	Ⓨ = Year-Round School	🅣 = Twitter

New Schools are shaded
New Superintendents and Principals are bold
Personnel with email addresses are underscored

Albany County

Market Data Retrieval

- **Berne-Knox-Westerlo Central SD** PID: 00714328   518/872-0909
  1738 Helderberg Trl, Berne 12023   Fax 518/872-0341

  Schools: 2 \ **Teachers:** 77 \ **Students:** 751 \ **Special Ed Students:** 122 \ **College-Bound:** 70% \ **Ethnic:** African American 1%, Hispanic 2%, Caucasian 96% \ **Exp:** $351 (High) \ **Poverty:** 9% \ **Title I:** $139,065 \ **Special Education:** $2,025,000 \ **Open-Close:** 09/04 - 06/25 \ **DTBP:** $379 (High) \

Timothy Mundell	1	Terrence Blanchfield	2
Keith Domermuth	3*	Claire Groduina	4
Amy Santandrea	5	Annette Landry	8
Michele Diamond	11,88,273*	Beth Davis	16,82*
Karen Corso	36*	Susan Casper	58*
Nathan Elble	67	Bill DeVoe	71
Jesse Blommer	73,295,297	Kelly Smith	85*
Mark Peterson	296		

Public Schs..Principal	Grd	Prgm	Enr/#Cls	SN	
Berne-Knox-Westerlo Elem Sch 1738 Helderberg Trl, Berne 12023 Annette Landry	PK-6	T	407 18	38%	518/872-2030 Fax 518/872-2031
Berne-Knox-Westerlo Jr/Sr HS 1738 Helderberg Trl, Berne 12023 Mark Pitterson	7-12	T	344 45	37%	518/872-1482 Fax 518/872-2083

- **Bethlehem Central School Dist** PID: 00714366   518/439-7481
  700 Delaware Ave, Delmar 12054   Fax 518/475-0352

  Schools: 7 \ **Teachers:** 324 \ **Students:** 4,400 \ **Special Ed Students:** 633 \ **LEP Students:** 62 \ **College-Bound:** 94% \ **Ethnic:** Asian 7%, African American 3%, Hispanic 3%, Caucasian 87% \ **Exp:** $233 (Med) \ **Poverty:** 4% \ **Title I:** $205,413 \ **Special Education:** $6,336,000 \ **Open-Close:** 09/08 - 06/24 \ **DTBP:** $320 (High) \

Jody Monroe	1,11	Judith Kehoe	2,19
Phyllis Albano	2	Bob Court	3,15
Gregg Nolte	3	Nick Insognia	3,15
Allissa Eiser	4	Cindy Jurewicz	5
Leonard Kies	6*	David Hurst	8,15,280,288,296,298
Melanie Painter	20	Frederick Powers	35,85*
Kristen Connor	36	Jennifer Gonyea	42
William Clairmont	45	Andrew Baker	48
Luis Aviles	57	Kathleen Johnston	58
Holly Dellenbaugh	67	Bruce Turek	71,97
Raymond Nardelli	73,76,295		

Public Schs..Principal	Grd	Prgm	Enr/#Cls	SN	
Bethlehem Central High Sch 700 Delaware Ave, Delmar 12054 David Doemel	9-12		1,501 60	12%	518/439-4921 Fax 518/439-2837
Bethlehem Central Middle Sch 332 Kenwood Ave, Delmar 12054 Michael Klugman	6-8	T	1,026	13%	518/439-7460 Fax 518/475-0092
Eagle Elem Sch 27 Van Dyke Rd, Delmar 12054 Dianna Reagan	K-5	T	426	13%	518/694-8825 Fax 518/439-7517
Elsmere Elem Sch 247 Delaware Ave, Delmar 12054 Kate Kloss	K-5	T	261 13	14%	518/439-4996 Fax 518/439-7546
Glenmont Elem Sch 328 Route 9W, Glenmont 12077 Laura Heffernan	K-5	T	342 19	13%	518/463-1154 Fax 518/432-5209
Hamagrael Elem Sch 1 McGuffey Ln, Delmar 12054 David Ksanznak	K-5	T	326 21	11%	518/439-4905 Fax 518/439-8732

Slingerlands Elem Sch 25 Union Ave, Delmar 12054 Heidi Bonacquist	K-5	T	455 19	11%	518/439-7681 Fax 518/475-1931

- **Cohoes City School Dist** PID: 00714457   518/237-0100
  21 Page Ave, Cohoes 12047   Fax 518/233-1878

  Schools: 5 \ **Teachers:** 176 \ **Students:** 2,000 \ **Special Ed Students:** 400 \ **LEP Students:** 24 \ **Ethnic:** Asian 2%, African American 11%, Hispanic 9%, Caucasian 78% \ **Exp:** $173 (Low) \ **Poverty:** 22% \ **Title I:** $781,250 \ **Special Education:** $4,126,000 \ **Open-Close:** 09/09 - 06/25 \ **DTBP:** $157 (High) \

Dr Jennifer Spring	1	Stacey Mackey	2
James Stapleton	3	Brian Nolan	4
Jeff Huneau	6*	Peggy O'Shea	8,11,57,83,88,273,288,298
Erin Hill	58	Matthew Nolin	67
Jennifer Sangiacomo	73*	Sylvi Joseph	73,98
Tom Ross	91		

Public Schs..Principal	Grd	Prgm	Enr/#Cls	SN	
Abram Lansing Elem Sch 26 James St, Cohoes 12047 Clifford Bird	K-5	T	373 22	59%	518/237-5044 Fax 518/237-1879
Cohoes High Sch 1 Tiger Cir, Cohoes 12047 Bryan Wood	9-12	AV	545 30	66%	518/237-9100 Fax 518/238-0169
Cohoes Middle Sch 7 Bevan St, Cohoes 12047 Daniel Martinelli	6-8	T	426	77%	518/237-4131 Fax 518/237-2253
Harmony Hill Sch Madelon K Hickey Way, Cohoes 12047 Mark Perry	K-5	T	360 23	57%	518/233-1900 Fax 518/237-1964
Van Schaick Grade Sch 150 Continental Ave, Cohoes 12047 Jacqueline Dechiaro	K-5	T	169 9	61%	518/237-2828 Fax 518/237-3597

- **Green Island Union Free SD** PID: 00714536   518/273-1422
  171 Hudson Ave, Green Island 12183   Fax 518/270-0818

  Schools: 1 \ **Teachers:** 35 \ **Students:** 262 \ **Special Ed Students:** 56 \ **Ethnic:** Asian 1%, African American 7%, Hispanic 3%, Caucasian 90% \ **Exp:** $309 (High) \ **Poverty:** 20% \ **Title I:** $109,879 \ **Special Education:** $629,000 \ **Open-Close:** 09/04 - 06/18 \ **DTBP:** $163 (High) \

Kimberly Ross	1,11,288	Christopher Karwiel	2
Dave Filieau	3,91*	Brian Ford	6*
Tiffany Dzembo	12*	Andrea Ryan	67

Public Schs..Principal	Grd	Prgm	Enr/#Cls	SN	
Heatly Sch 171 Hudson Ave, Green Island 12183 Jodi Mazzeo \ Erin Peteani	K-12	T	262 20	56%	518/273-1422

- **Guilderland Central Sch Dist** PID: 00714550   518/456-6200
  8 School Rd, Guildrlnd CTR 12085   Fax 518/456-1152

  Schools: 7 \ **Teachers:** 425 \ **Students:** 5,000 \ **Special Ed Students:** 710 \ **LEP Students:** 204 \ **College-Bound:** 93% \ **Ethnic:** Asian 14%, African American 4%, Hispanic 4%, Caucasian 78% \ **Exp:** $205 (Med) \ **Poverty:** 5% \ **Title I:** $368,112 \ **Special Education:** $6,620,000 \ **Open-Close:** 09/08 - 06/25 \ **DTBP:** $494 (High) \

Dr Marie Wiles	1	Neil Sanders	2,15

---

1 Superintendent	8 Curric/Instruct K-12	19 Chief Financial Officer	29 Family/Consumer Science	39 Social Studies K-12	49 English/Lang Arts Elem	59 Special Education Elem	69 Academic Assessment
2 Bus/Finance/Purchasing	9 Curric/Instruct Elem	20 Art K-12	30 Adult Education	40 Social Studies Elem	50 English/Lang Arts Sec	60 Special Education Sec	70 Research/Development
3 Buildings And Grounds	10 Curric/Instruct Sec	21 Art Elem	31 Career/Sch-to-Work K-12	41 Social Studies Sec	51 Reading K-12	61 Foreign/World Lang K-12	71 Public Information
4 Food Service	11 Federal Program	22 Art Sec	32 Career/Sch-to-Work Elem	42 Science K-12	52 Reading Elem	62 Foreign/World Lang Elem	72 Summer School
5 Transportation	12 Title I	23 Music K-12	33 Career/Sch-to-Work Sec	43 Science Elem	53 Reading Sec	63 Foreign/World Lang Sec	73 Instructional Tech
6 Athletic	13 Title V	24 Music Elem	34 Early Childhood Ed	44 Science Sec	54 Remedial Reading K-12	64 Religious Education K-12	74 Inservice Training
7 Health Services	15 Asst Superintendent	25 Music Sec	35 Health/Phys Education	45 Math K-12	55 Remedial Reading Elem	65 Religious Education Elem	75 Marketing/Distributive
	16 Instructional Media Svcs	26 Business Education	36 Guidance Services K-12	46 Math Elem	56 Remedial Reading Sec	66 Religious Education Sec	76 Info Systems
	17 Chief Operations Officer	27 Career & Tech Ed	37 Guidance Services Elem	47 Math Sec	57 Bilingual/ELL	67 School Board President	77 Psychological Assess
	18 Chief Academic Officer	28 Technology Education	38 Guidance Services Sec	48 English/Lang Arts K-12	58 Special Education K-12	68 Teacher Personnel	78 Affirmative Action

New York School Directory — Albany County

Clifford Nooney 3,91
Danielle Poirier 5
Dr Demian Singleton 8,11,57,69,275,285,286,288
9,273*
Lisa Knowles 11,58,77,88,90*
Jeff Gregory 30
Aubree Kammler 71
Pierre Val 73,295*
Megan Beck 4
Reagan Johnston 6
Suzanne LaMendola
Dr Lin Severance 15,68,78
Seema Rivera 67
Steven Wolf 72

Robert Pollaro 41*
Linda Harrison 67
Taryn Kane 71
Keith Bogert 44,285*
Jenna Bongermino 68
Julie Scriven 73*

Public Schs..Principal	Grd	Prgm	Enr/#Cls	SN		
Altamont Elem Sch 117 Grand St, Altamont 12009 Peter Brabant	K-5	T	305 17	29%	518/861-8528 Fax 518/861-5189	
Farnsworth Middle Sch 6072 State Farm Rd, Guilderland 12084 Michael Laster	6-8	V	1,072 87	20%	518/456-6010 Fax 518/456-3747	
Guilderland Elem Sch 2225 Western Ave, Guilderland 12084 Allan Lockwood	K-5		517 26	16%	518/869-0293 Fax 518/464-6458	
Guilderland High Sch 8 School Rd, Guildrlnd CTR 12085 Michael Piscitelli	9-12	AGV	1,532 60	17%	518/861-8591 Fax 518/861-5874	
Lynnwood Elem Sch 8 Regina Dr, Schenectady 12303 Alicia Rizzo	K-5	T	415 24	15%	518/355-7930 Fax 518/356-3087	f t
Pine Bush Elem Sch 3437 Carman Rd, Schenectady 12303 Christopher Sanita	K-5		475 24	12%	518/357-2770 Fax 518/356-3172	
Westmere Elem Sch 6270 Johnston Rd, Albany 12203 Dr Beth Bini	K-5		525 33	21%	518/456-3771 Fax 518/464-6443	

Public Schs..Principal	Grd	Prgm	Enr/#Cls	SN		
Blue Creek Elem Sch 18 Clinton Rd, Latham 12110 Annette Trapini	K-6		527 21	28%	518/785-7451 Fax 518/785-3273	
Boght Hills Elem Sch 38 Dunsbach Ferry Rd, Cohoes 12047 Marcus Puccioni	K-6		591 19	15%	518/785-0222 Fax 518/785-8801	f t
Forts Ferry Elem Sch 95 Forts Ferry Rd, Latham 12110 Candace Lobdell	K-6		519 21	27%	518/785-9203 Fax 518/783-8874	
Latham Ridge Elem Sch 6 Mercer Ave, Latham 12110 Aaron Thiell	K-6		529 20	26%	518/785-3211 Fax 518/783-8875	
Loudonville Elem Sch 349 Osborne Rd, Loudonville 12211 Abby North	K-6		322 13	12%	518/434-1960 Fax 518/434-0739	
Shaker High Sch 445 Watervliet Shaker Rd, Latham 12110 Richard Murphy	9-12		2,038	24%	518/785-5511 Fax 518/783-5905	
Shaker Junior High Sch 475 Watervliet Shaker Rd, Latham 12110 Davis Chamberlain	7-8		886 45	24%	518/785-1341 Fax 518/786-0640	t
Southgate Elem Sch 30 Southgate Rd, Loudonville 12211 Jerri Dedrick	K-6		502 34	24%	518/785-6607 Fax 518/783-8878	t

- **Menands Union Free Sch Dist** PID: 00714641   518/465-4561
  19 Wards Ln, Menands 12204   Fax 518/434-2840

Schools: 1 \ **Teachers:** 27 \ **Students:** 305 \ **Special Ed Students:** 54 \ **LEP Students:** 45 \ **Ethnic:** Asian 34%, African American 33%, Hispanic 5%, Native American: 1%, Caucasian 27% \ **Exp:** $234 (Med) \ **Poverty:** 22% \ **Title I:** $148,822 \ **Special Education:** $236,000 \ **Open-Close:** 09/08 - 06/24 \ **DTBP:** $152 (High)

Dr Maureen Long 1
Scott Losee 3*
Shirah Fudin 7*
Jeff Masline 67
Kathy Cietek 2
Ryan Ahl 7*
Antonietta Schroeder 9,59,88,270,273*

Public Schs..Principal	Grd	Prgm	Enr/#Cls	SN	
Menands Elem Sch 19 Wards Ln, Menands 12204 Antonietta Schroeder	K-8		305 14	31%	518/465-4561

- **North Colonie Central SD** PID: 00714665   518/785-8591
  91 Fiddlers Ln, Latham 12110   Fax 518/785-8502

Schools: 8 \ **Teachers:** 453 \ **Students:** 5,800 \ **Special Ed Students:** 899 \ **LEP Students:** 336 \ **College-Bound:** 95% \ **Ethnic:** Asian 19%, African American 6%, Hispanic 6%, Caucasian 68% \ **Exp:** $269 (Med) \ **Title I:** $1,098,884 \ **Special Education:** $4,428,000 \ **Open-Close:** 09/10 - 06/25 \ **DTBP:** $316 (High) \ f t

D Joseph Corr 1
Brian Craft 3,91
Lisa Ostrowski 4
Matt Stein 6
Casey Bardin 11,36,57,58,85,270,294*
Anne Manzella 20*
Eric Phillips 27,95*
Steven Zautner 2
Mark Wiegert 3
John Myers 5
Kathleen Skeals 10,69,288
Scott Hoot 15
Deborah Keough 23*
Edward Dopp 30*

- **Ravena Coeymans Selkirk Ctl SD** PID: 00714768   518/756-5200
  15 Mountain Rd, Ravena 12143   Fax 518/756-4561

Schools: 4 \ **Teachers:** 191 \ **Students:** 1,839 \ **Special Ed Students:** 372 \ **LEP Students:** 8 \ **College-Bound:** 68% \ **Ethnic:** Asian 1%, African American 5%, Hispanic 8%, Caucasian 86% \ **Exp:** $281 (Med) \ **Poverty:** 11% \ **Title I:** $335,391 \ **Special Education:** $4,988,000 \ **Open-Close:** 09/04 - 06/25 \ **DTBP:** $169 (High) \ f

Brian Bailey 1,11
Bill Schrom 3,73,91,295
Robert Dorrance 6,35,85*
Ann Jackson 58*
Fred Englehardt 83
Joann Moran 2
Douglas Porter 4
Charles Englehardt 8,12,15,285,288
Edward Reville 67

Public Schs..Principal	Grd	Prgm	Enr/#Cls	SN	
Albertus W Becker Elem Sch 1146 US Route 9W, Selkirk 12158 Debra Neubart	PK-5		428 28	34%	518/756-5200 Fax 518/767-2512
Pieter B Coeymans Elem Sch 66 Church St, Coeymans 12045 Hakim Jones	PK-5	T	459 26	46%	518/756-5200 Fax 518/756-9162
Ravena Coeymans Selkirk HS 2025 US Route 9W, Ravena 12143 Lisa Patierne	9-12	AGV	524	41%	518/756-5200 Fax 518/756-3534
Ravena Coeymans Selkirk MS 2025 US Route 9W, Ravena 12143 Laura Buzas	6-8	AGV	428 36	44%	518/756-5200 Fax 518/756-1988

---

79 Student Personnel
80 Driver Ed/Safety
81 Gifted/Talented
82 Video Services
83 Substance Abuse Prev
84 Erate
85 AIDS Education
88 Alternative/At Risk
89 Multi-Cultural Curriculum
90 Social Work

91 Safety/Security
92 Magnet School
93 Parental Involvement
95 Tech Prep Program
97 Chief Information Officer
98 Chief Technology Officer
270 Character Education
271 Migrant Education
273 Teacher Mentor
274 Before/After Sch

275 Response To Intervention
277 Remedial Math K-12
280 Literacy Coach
285 STEM
286 Digital Learning
288 Common Core Standards
294 Accountability
295 Network System
296 Title II Programs
297 Webmaster

298 Grant Writer/Ptnrships
750 Chief Innovation Officer
751 Chief of Staff
752 Social Emotional Learning

Other School Types
Ⓐ = Alternative School
Ⓒ = Charter School
Ⓜ = Magnet School
Ⓨ = Year-Round School

School Programs
A = Alternative Program
G = Adult Classes
M = Magnet Program
T = Title I Schoolwide
V = Career & Tech Ed Programs

New Schools are shaded
New Superintendents and Principals are bold
Personnel with email addresses are underscored

Social Media
f = Facebook
t = Twitter

Albany County

Market Data Retrieval

- **South Colonie Central Sch Dist** PID: 00714835 518/869-3576
  102 Loralee Dr, Albany 12205 Fax 518/869-6517

Schools: 8 \ **Teachers:** 407 \ **Students:** 4,700 \ **Special Ed Students:** 793 \ **LEP Students:** 126 \ **College-Bound:** 83% \ **Ethnic:** Asian 11%, African American 9%, Hispanic 9%, Caucasian 72% \ **Exp:** $227 (Med) \ **Poverty:** 9% \ **Title I:** $708,957 \ **Special Education:** $5,783,000 \ **Open-Close:** 09/08 - 06/25 \ **DTBP:** $331 (High) \

Dr David Perry	1	Anjelieeque Martinez	2
Gordon Webster	3	James Maloney	3
James Gooshaw	3	Sherri Fisher	3,30
Annette Chamberlain	4	Peter Tunny	5
Joseph Guardino	6,35	Timothy Fowler	7,34
Tim Backus	8,11,16,57,270,288,296,298	Jennifer Wells	40,49,52,280*
Greg Bearup	43,46,277	William Boardman	58
Ed Simms	67	John Noetzel	71
James Lovett	73,286	David Wetzel	88*

Public Schs..Principal	Grd	Prgm	Enr/#Cls	SN	
Colonie Central High Sch 1 Raider Blvd, Albany 12205 Chris Robilotti	9-12	V	1,526 100	35%	518/459-1220 Fax 518/459-8524
Forest Park Elem Sch 100 Forest Dr, Albany 12205 Jill Penn	K-4		269 40	34%	518/869-3006 Fax 518/869-5891
Lisha Kill Middle Sch 68 Waterman Ave, Albany 12205 David Wetzel	5-8		632 32	28%	518/456-2306 Fax 518/452-8165
Roessleville Elem Sch 100 California Ave, Albany 12205 Marybeth Tedisco	PK-4	T	385 22	34%	518/459-2157 Fax 518/459-0268
Saddlewood Elem Sch 100 Loralee Dr, Albany 12205 Stacey Roberts	PK-4		420 40	22%	518/456-2608 Fax 518/862-0271
Sand Creek Middle Sch 329 Sand Creek Rd, Albany 12205 Thomas Nicholson	5-8	T	815	40%	518/459-1333 Fax 518/459-1404
Shaker Road Elem Sch 512 Albany Shaker Rd, Albany 12211 William Dollard	K-4		359 14	37%	518/458-1440 Fax 518/459-1283
Veeder Elem Sch 25 Veeder Dr, Albany 12205 Sullivan Nora	K-4		413 23	26%	518/869-4661 Fax 518/869-4495

- **Voorheesville Central Sch Dist** PID: 00714952 518/765-3313
  432 New Salem Rd, Voorheesville 12186 Fax 518/765-2751

Schools: 3 \ **Teachers:** 95 \ **Students:** 1,175 \ **Special Ed Students:** 149 \ **LEP Students:** 6 \ **College-Bound:** 87% \ **Ethnic:** Asian 2%, Hispanic 3%, Caucasian 94% \ **Exp:** $266 (Med) \ **Poverty:** 4% \ **Title I:** $49,029 \ **Special Education:** $1,480,000 \ **Open-Close:** 09/10 - 06/25 \ **DTBP:** $358 (High) \

Frank Macri	1	Joseph Natale	2,3,15
Robin Burch	2	Paul Franchini	4*
Anne Potts	5	Karen Conroy	8,11,69,288,296*
Karen Conroy	11,83,286	Chris Jantson	20,23
Karen Jones	34,58,79,752*	Joseph Sapienza	35
Cindy Monaghan	67	Rob Carte	73*

Public Schs..Principal	Grd	Prgm	Enr/#Cls	SN	
C A Bouton High Sch 432 New Salem Rd, Voorheesville 12186 Laura Schmitz	9-12		359 40	7%	518/765-3314 Fax 518/765-5547

Voorheesville Elem Sch 129 Maple Ave, Voorheesville 12186 Jeffrey Vivienzio	K-5		569 40	7%	518/765-2382 Fax 518/765-3842
Voorheesville Middle Sch 432 New Salem Rd, Voorheesville 12186 Jennifer Drautz	6-8		252	11%	518/765-3314 Fax 518/765-5547

- **Watervliet City School Dist** PID: 00714988 518/629-3200
  1245 Hillside Dr, Watervliet 12189 Fax 518/629-3265

Schools: 2 \ **Teachers:** 108 \ **Students:** 1,297 \ **Special Ed Students:** 249 \ **LEP Students:** 80 \ **College-Bound:** 79% \ **Ethnic:** Asian 9%, African American 20%, Hispanic 19%, Caucasian 52% \ **Exp:** $192 (Low) \ **Poverty:** 21% \ **Title I:** $552,980 \ **Special Education:** $4,075,000 \ **Open-Close:** 09/08 - 06/25 \ **DTBP:** $165 (High) \

Dr Lori Caplan	1	Keith Heid	2
Darryl Whited	4*	Roni O'Brien	5
Kirsten Demento	8,69,76,273,286,288,298*	Janelle Yanni	12,58,79
Donald Stevens	15	Amanda Cavanaugh	67
Judy Frost	71	Dan Lindeman	73*
Kelly Webster	88,270*		

Public Schs..Principal	Grd	Prgm	Enr/#Cls	SN	
Watervliet Elem Sch 2557 10th Ave, Watervliet 12189 Kelly Webster	K-6	T	743 35	65%	518/629-3400 Fax 518/629-3250
Watervliet Jr Sr High Sch 1245 Hillside Dr, Watervliet 12189 Ryan Groat	7-12	AV	554	65%	518/629-3300 Fax 518/273-1207

ALBANY CATHOLIC SCHOOLS

- **Diocese of Albany Ed Office** PID: 00715059 518/453-6602
  40 N Main Ave, Albany 12203 Fax 518/453-6667

Schools: 21 \ **Students:** 5,553

Listing includes only schools located in this county. See District Index for location of Diocesan Offices.

Giovanni Virgiglio	1	Joann Gamello	2
Christopher Bott	15	Michael Buckley	67
Bridget Frament	68	Nathan Vandeusen	73
Jacquelyn Chiera	83	Sal Carbone	91

Catholic Schs..Principal	Grd	Prgm	Enr/#Cls		
All Saints Catholic Academy 10 Rosemont St, Albany 12203 Traci Johnson	PK-8		200 15		518/438-0066 Fax 518/438-4066
Bishop Maginn High Sch 75 Park Ave, Albany 12202 Michael Tolan	9-12		130		518/463-2247 Fax 518/463-9880
Blessed Sacrament Sch 605 Central Ave, Albany 12206 Maureen Daurio	PK-8		205 11		518/438-5854 Fax 518/438-1532
Mater Christi Sch 35 Hurst Ave, Albany 12208 Sr Deborah Timmis	PK-8		230 13		518/489-3111 Fax 518/489-5865
St Ambrose Sch 347 Old Loudon Rd, Latham 12110 Lily Spera	PK-8		180 16		518/785-6453 Fax 518/785-8370

1	Superintendent	8	Curric/Instruct K-12	19	Chief Financial Officer	29	Family/Consumer Science	39	Social Studies K-12	49	English/Lang Arts Elem	59	Special Education Elem	69	Academic Assessment
2	Bus/Finance/Purchasing	9	Curric/Instruct Elem	20	Art K-12	30	Adult Education	40	Social Studies Elem	50	English/Lang Arts Sec	60	Special Education Sec	70	Research/Development
3	Buildings And Grounds	10	Curric/Instruct Sec	21	Art Elem	31	Career/Sch-to-Work K-12	41	Social Studies Sec	51	Reading K-12	61	Foreign/World Lang K-12	71	Public Information
4	Food Service	11	Federal Program	22	Art Sec	32	Career/Sch-to-Work Elem	42	Science K-12	52	Reading Elem	62	Foreign/World Lang Elem	72	Summer School
5	Transportation	12	Title I	23	Music K-12	33	Career/Sch-to-Work Sec	43	Science Elem	53	Reading Sec	63	Foreign/World Lang Sec	73	Instructional Tech
6	Athletic	13	Title V	24	Music Elem	34	Early Childhood Ed	44	Science Sec	54	Remedial Reading K-12	64	Religious Education K-12	74	Inservice Training
7	Health Services	15	Asst Superintendent	25	Music Sec	35	Health/Phys Education	45	Math K-12	55	Remedial Reading Elem	65	Religious Education Elem	75	Marketing/Distributive
		16	Instructional Media Svcs	26	Business Education	36	Guidance Services K-12	46	Math Elem	56	Remedial Reading Sec	66	Religious Education Sec	76	Info Systems
		17	Chief Operations Officer	27	Career & Tech Ed	37	Guidance Services Elem	47	Math Sec	57	Bilingual/ELL	67	School Board President	77	Psychological Assess
		18	Chief Academic Officer	28	Technology Education	38	Guidance Services Sec	48	English/Lang Arts K-12	58	Special Education K-12	68	Teacher Personnel	78	Affirmative Action

New York School Directory

Allegany County

St Pius X Sch 75 Upper Loudon Rd, Loudonville 12211 Dennis Mullahy	PK-8		590 30	518/465-4539 Fax 518/465-4895
St Thomas the Apostle Sch 42 Adams Pl, Delmar 12054 Thomas Kane	PK-8		224 9	518/439-5573 Fax 518/478-9773

ALBANY PRIVATE SCHOOLS

Private Schs..Principal	Grd	Prgm	Enr/#Cls	SN	
Academy of the Holy Names-Uppr 1075 New Scotland Rd, Albany 12208 Mary Vigliante	9-12		218 20		518/489-7895 Fax 518/438-7368
Albany Academy 140 Academy Rd, Albany 12208 Christopher Lauricella	PK-12		300 33		518/429-2300 Fax 518/463-5096
Albany Academy-West 135 Academy Rd, Albany 12208 Dr Douglas North	PK-12		350 35		518/429-2300 Fax 518/427-7016
Albany Free Sch 8 Elm St, Albany 12202 Bhawin Suchak	PK-8	G	56 12		518/434-3072
Bet Shraga Hebrew Academy 100 Academy Rd Ste 100, Albany 12208 Julie Pollack	K-8		106 22		518/482-0464 Fax 518/482-0129 f
Bethlehem Children's Sch 12 Fisher Blvd, Slingerlands 12159 Christine Vaughan	PK-8		50 3		518/478-0224 Fax 518/478-9113
Christian Brothers Academy 12 Airline Dr, Albany 12205 James Schlegel	6-12		385 16		518/452-9809 Fax 518/452-9804
Ctr for Dis Serv-Langan Sch 314 S Manning Blvd, Albany 12208 Karen Macri	Spec		160 16		518/437-5700
LaSalle Sch 391 Western Ave, Albany 12203 Jim Meyer	Spec		91 30		518/242-4731 Fax 518/242-4747
Latham Christian Academy 495 Watervliet Shaker Rd, Latham 12110 Bryan Fry	PK-12		157 7		518/785-5916 Fax 518/785-5922 f t
Loudonville Christian Sch 374 Loudon Rd, Loudonville 12211 Amanda Bigham	PK-12		300 18		518/434-6051 Fax 518/935-2258 f
Maimonides Hebrew Day Sch 404 Partridge St, Albany 12208 Leah Rubin	PK-12		90 10		518/453-9363 Fax 518/453-9362
Mt Moriah Academy 262 Route 9W, Glenmont 12077 Anna Young	PK-12		37 6		518/426-4510 Fax 518/426-3405
Neil Hellman Sch 60 Academy Rd, Albany 12208 Michael Norely \ Jodie Ebel	Spec	G	160 22		518/426-2600
Our Savior's Lutheran Sch 63 Mountain View Ave, Albany 12205 John Richardson	PK-8		141 12		518/459-2273 Fax 518/459-1330 f
St Anne Institute 160 N Main Ave, Albany 12206 Ralph Rothacker	Spec		84 48		518/437-6500 Fax 518/437-6532
St Catherines Ctr for Children 30 N Main Ave, Albany 12203 Jennifer Elliott	Spec		50 10		518/453-6710 Fax 518/453-6733
St Coleman's Home 11 Haswell Rd, Watervliet 12189 Heather Worthington	Spec		50 3		518/273-7559 Fax 518/273-3312

St Gregory's School for Boys 121 Old Niskayuna Rd, Loudonville 12211 Katie Helm	PK-8		150 20	518/785-6621 Fax 518/782-1364

ALBANY REGIONAL CENTERS

● **Capital Region BOCES** PID: 00715035   518/862-4900
900 Watervliet Shaker Rd, Albany 12205   Fax 518/862-4903

Anita Murphy 1   Mark Jones 2,3,15,17,68
Dr Lynne Wells 8,15   Dr Joseph Dragone 15
Valerie Kelsey 27,31   Maria Huntington 30
Kevin Kutzscher 67

ALLEGANY COUNTY

ALLEGANY COUNTY SCHOOLS

County Schs..Principal	Grd	Prgm	Enr/#Cls	SN	
ⓐ Elm Street Academy 20 Elm St, Cuba 14727 Christopher McNell	9-12		50		585/968-1923

ALLEGANY PUBLIC SCHOOLS

● **Alfred Almond Ctl School Dist** PID: 00716003   607/276-6555
6795 State Route 21, Almond 14804   Fax 607/276-6556

Schools: 1 \ **Teachers:** 64 \ **Students:** 600 \ **Special Ed Students:** 81 \
College-Bound: 89% \ **Ethnic:** Asian 4%, African American 1%, Hispanic 2%, Caucasian 93% \ **Exp:** $289 (Med) \ **Poverty:** 16% \ **Title I:** $178,478 \
Special Education: $809,000 \ **Open-Close:** 09/03 - 06/25 \ **DTBP:** $494 (High) \ f

Tracie Bliven 1   Tracy Condie 2
Gene Snyder .... 3,91*   Michelle Miller 4*
Bryan Burdick .... 5*   Brett Dusinberre 6*
Melissa Rivers .... 11,273*   Amy Perry 16,82*
Barrie Clark .... 55*   Kate Palmer 58*
Earl Pierce 67   Amy Decker 69,83*
Terry Caleb 295

Public Schs..Principal	Grd	Prgm	Enr/#Cls	SN	
Alfred Almond Sch 6795 State Route 21, Almond 14804 Brett Dusinberre \ Susan Bain-Lucey	K-12		600 25	31%	607/276-6555 f

● **Andover Central School Dist** PID: 00716039   607/478-8491
31 Elm St 35, Andover 14806   Fax 607/478-8833

Schools: 1 \ **Teachers:** 37 \ **Students:** 300 \ **Special Ed Students:** 55
\ **College-Bound:** 62% \ **Ethnic:** African American 1%, Hispanic 1%, Caucasian 98% \ **Exp:** $418 (High) \ **Poverty:** 15% \ **Title I:** $96,733 \
Special Education: $572,000 \ **Open-Close:** 09/03 - 06/24 \ **DTBP:** $127 (High)

79	Student Personnel	91	Safety/Security	275	Response To Intervention	298 Grant Writer/Ptnrships
80	Driver Ed/Safety	92	Magnet School	277	Remedial Math K-12	750 Chief Innovation Officer
81	Gifted/Talented	93	Parental Involvement	280	Literacy Coach	751 Chief of Staff
82	Video Services	95	Tech Prep Program	285	STEM	752 Social Emotional Learning
83	Substance Abuse Prev	97	Chief Information Officer	286	Digital Learning	
84	Erate	98	Chief Technology Officer	288	Common Core Standards	**Other School Types**
85	AIDS Education	270	Character Education	294	Accountability	ⓐ = Alternative School
88	Alternative/At Risk	271	Migrant Education	295	Network System	ⓒ = Charter School
89	Multi-Cultural Curriculum	273	Teacher Mentor	296	Title II Programs	ⓜ = Magnet School
90	Social Work	274	Before/After Sch	297	Webmaster	ⓨ = Year-Round School

School Programs
A = Alternative Program
G = Adult Classes
M = Magnet Program
T = Title I Schoolwide
V = Career & Tech Ed Programs

Social Media
f = Facebook
t = Twitter

New Schools are shaded
New Superintendents and Principals are bold
Personnel with email addresses are underscored

NY—13

Allegany County

Market Data Retrieval

Lawrence Spangenburg 1
Michael Hulse 3,5
Jacob Bannerman 6,31,271
Jon Morris 8,68,74,79,90,273,288*
Alyssa Potter 11,27,36,69,88,271,294
Erica Jacobs 20*
Linda Shaner 26
Will Brown 39
Sean Reilly 45
Megan Duke 58,77,78,93*
Lynne Roeske 76*
Teresa O Connor 90,752
Doreen Taylor 277
Bruce Blank 295*

Jennifer Joyce 2,11,71,275,296,298
Carol Richmond 4*
Beth Klein 7*
Kathryn Slavinski 10,30,34,48,51
Michael Chaffee 16,28,73,286,297*
Melissa Harrison 23*
Brigette Bannerman 29,35,85
Timothy Demster 42
Denise Burrows 54
Michelle Calladine 67
Jennifer Smith 81*
Kim Fanton 274
Stephanie Harrington 280,285*

Public Schs..Principal	Grd	Prgm	Enr/#Cls	SN	
Andover Central Sch 31 Elm St 35, Andover 14806 Jon Morris	PK-12	AT	300 30	53%	607/478-8491

● **Belfast Central School Dist** PID: 00716077   585/365-9940
1 King St, Belfast 14711   Fax 585/365-2648

Schools: 1 \ **Teachers:** 39 \ **Students:** 343 \ **Special Ed Students:** 74 \
Ethnic: African American 1%, Hispanic 1%, Caucasian 98% \ **Exp:** $626
(High) \ **Poverty:** 25% \ **Title I:** $185,009 \ **Special Education:** $780,000 \
Open-Close: 09/08 - 06/25 \ **DTBP:** $418 (High)

Dr Wendy Butler 1
James Schneider 3*
Dr Wendy Butler 8*
Amy Giboo 35
Jessica Heff 58
Robert Mangan 73,76,286

Robert Lingenfelter 2,11
James Schneider 5
Michael Roche 12
Teresa Heaney 36*
Josie Preston 67
Michael Roche 288*

Public Schs..Principal	Grd	Prgm	Enr/#Cls	SN	
Belfast Central Sch 1 King St, Belfast 14711 Michael Roche \ Jessica Hess	PK-12	T	343 30	53%	585/365-2646

● **Bolivar-Richburg Ctrl Sch Dist** PID: 00716118   585/928-2561
100 School St, Bolivar 14715   Fax 585/928-1368

Schools: 3 \ **Teachers:** 79 \ **Students:** 850 \ **Special Ed Students:** 125
\ **College-Bound:** 74% \ **Ethnic:** African American 1%, Hispanic 1%,
Caucasian 98% \ **Exp:** $237 (Med) \ **Poverty:** 21% \ **Title I:** $265,555 \
Special Education: $1,460,000 \ **Open-Close:** 09/01 - 06/24 \ **DTBP:** $352
(High)

Michael Retzlaff 1,11
Megan Saunders 2
Ann Feuchter 5
Jessica Rose 8
Susan Bokman 58*
Dan Davidson 73

Kristen Woodhead 2
Randy Harmon 3*
Dustin Allen 6
Margaret Werner 16,82
Erin Baldwin 67
Amy Jones 77*

Public Schs..Principal	Grd	Prgm	Enr/#Cls	SN	
Bolivar-Richburg Central Sch 100 School St, Bolivar 14715 Daniel Quartley	6-12	TV	386 50	49%	585/928-2561
Bolivar-Richburg Early CDC 422 Main St, Bolivar 14715 Andrea McLaughlin	PK-PK	T	11 2		585/928-2851 Fax 585/928-2159
Bolivar-Richburg Elem Sch 211 Main St, Richburg 14774 Brett Dusinberre	PK-5	T	344 22	56%	585/928-2561 Fax 585/928-2362

● **Canaseraga Central Sch Dist** PID: 00716144   607/545-6421
4 8 Main St, Canaseraga 14822   Fax 607/545-6265

Schools: 1 \ **Teachers:** 30 \ **Students:** 272 \ **Special Ed Students:** 36 \
College-Bound: 60% \ **Ethnic:** Hispanic 4%, Caucasian 95% \ **Exp:** $331
(High) \ **Poverty:** 19% \ **Title I:** $81,781 \ **Special Education:** $525,000 \
Open-Close: 09/08 - 06/18 \ **DTBP:** $365 (High)

Chad Groff 1
Greg Elliott 4*
Shannon Gilbert 7,8,11,69,74,288,294*
Dan Bishop 36*
Richard Kinney 67

Brad Giglio 3
Tammy Marble 5
Brianne Payne 16
Lori Rung 58

Public Schs..Principal	Grd	Prgm	Enr/#Cls	SN	
Canaseraga Sch 4-8 Main St, Canaseraga 14822 Shannon Gilbert	PK-12	TV	272 20	48%	607/545-6421

● **Cuba-Rushford Central Sch Dist** PID: 00716168   585/968-2650
5476 Route 305, Cuba 14727   Fax 585/968-2651

Schools: 2 \ **Teachers:** 71 \ **Students:** 818 \ **Special Ed Students:** 188 \
College-Bound: 70% \ **Ethnic:** Asian 1%, African American 2%, Hispanic
1%, Caucasian 95% \ **Exp:** $295 (Med) \ **Poverty:** 23% \ **Title I:** $378,627 \
Special Education: $2,162,000 \ **Open-Close:** 09/09 - 06/24 \ **DTBP:** $359
(High)

Carlos Gildemeister 1
Dave Hardman 3*
Michael Sears 5*
Cindy Bichler 7,83
Jay Morris 16,73,295*
Kelly Volz 38*
Kim Fisher 58*

Diane Weatherell 2
Alex Leyva 4
Chris Cappelletti 6,35,85
Kevin Erickson 8,11,51,57,69,270*
Paul Austin 16*
Mike Ackerman 38*
Mark Neu 67

Public Schs..Principal	Grd	Prgm	Enr/#Cls	SN	
Cuba-Rushford Elem Sch 15 Elm St, Cuba 14727 Kevin Erickson	PK-5	T	390 21	45%	585/968-1760 Fax 585/968-3181
Cuba-Rushford Middle High Sch 5476 Route 305, Cuba 14727 Katie Ralston \ Carrie Bold	6-12		428 45	40%	585/968-2650 Fax 585/968-1091

● **Fillmore Central School Dist** PID: 00716194   585/567-2251
104 W Main St, Fillmore 14735   Fax 585/567-2541

Schools: 1 \ **Teachers:** 59 \ **Students:** 680 \ **Special Ed Students:** 106 \
LEP Students: 3 \ **College-Bound:** 83% \ **Ethnic:** Asian 1%, Hispanic 2%,
Caucasian 97% \ **Exp:** $297 (Med) \ **Poverty:** 20% \ **Title I:** $286,537 \
Special Education: $1,304,000 \ **Open-Close:** 09/02 - 06/24 \ **DTBP:** $359
(High) \ ▪

Michael Dodge 1,83
Ken Redman 3*
Chad Potter 5
Chelsey Aylor 8,11,273,288,296,752*
Anne West 58
Betsy Hardy 73,98,295*

Joe Butler 2
Priscilla Beardsley 4*
Stacy Parmenter 7*
William Kelley 36*
Dr Marcus Dean 67
Deborah Cutting 275*

Public Schs..Principal	Grd	Prgm	Enr/#Cls	SN	
Fillmore Central Sch 104 W Main St, Fillmore 14735 Chelsey Aylor	PK-12	T	680 60	52%	585/567-2251

1	Superintendent	8	Curric/Instruct K-12	19	Chief Financial Officer	29	Family/Consumer Science	39	Social Studies K-12	49	English/Lang Arts Elem	59	Special Education Elem	69	Academic Assessment
2	Bus/Finance/Purchasing	9	Curric/Instruct Elem	20	Art K-12	30	Adult Education	40	Social Studies Elem	50	English/Lang Arts Sec	60	Special Education Sec	70	Research/Development
3	Buildings And Grounds	10	Curric/Instruct Sec	21	Art Elem	31	Career/Sch-to-Work K-12	41	Social Studies Sec	51	Reading K-12	61	Foreign/World Lang K-12	71	Public Information
4	Food Service	11	Federal Program	22	Art Sec	32	Career/Sch-to-Work Elem	42	Science K-12	52	Reading Elem	62	Foreign/World Lang Elem	72	Summer School
5	Transportation	12	Title I	23	Music K-12	33	Career/Sch-to-Work Sec	43	Science Elem	53	Reading Sec	63	Foreign/World Lang Sec	73	Instructional Tech
6	Athletic	13	Title V	24	Music Elem	34	Early Childhood Ed	44	Science Sec	54	Remedial Reading K-12	64	Religious Education K-12	74	Inservice Training
7	Health Services	15	Asst Superintendent	25	Music Sec	35	Health/Phys Education	45	Math K-12	55	Remedial Reading Elem	65	Religious Education Elem	75	Marketing/Distributive
		16	Instructional Media Svcs	26	Business Education	36	Guidance Services K-12	46	Math Elem	56	Remedial Reading Sec	66	Religious Education Sec	76	Info Systems
		17	Chief Operations Officer	27	Career & Tech Ed	37	Guidance Services Elem	47	Math Sec	57	Bilingual/ELL	67	School Board President	77	Psychological Assess
		18	Chief Academic Officer	28	Technology Education	38	Guidance Services Sec	48	English/Lang Arts K-12	58	Special Education K-12	68	Teacher Personnel	78	Affirmative Action

New York School Directory — Allegany County

- **Friendship Central Sch Dist** PID: 00716223   585/973-3311
  46 W Main St, Friendship 14739   Fax 585/973-2023

Schools: 1 \ **Teachers:** 39 \ **Students:** 350 \ **Special Ed Students:** 88 \ **College-Bound:** 60% \ **Ethnic:** African American 1%, Hispanic 1%, Caucasian 98% \ **Exp:** $512 (High) \ **Poverty:** 26% \ **Title I:** $171,743 \ **Special Education:** $1,060,000 \ **Open-Close:** 09/01 - 06/25 \ **DTBP:** $363 (High)

Judy May 1	Constance Spring 2,11
Chad Fries 3,5	Megan Solomon 4*
Bradley Gertis 6*	Kathy Morris 7,83*
Thomas Fadale 8,12,79,88,296,298*	Christian Cornwell 11,273*
Wade Pearsall 36,69,83,88*	Kim Riordan 58
William Ritchie 67	

Public Schs..Principal	Grd	Prgm	Enr/#Cls	SN	
Friendship Central Sch 46 W Main St, Friendship 14739 Christian Cornwell	PK-12	T	350 60	70%	585/973-3311

- **Genesee Valley Ctl School Dist** PID: 00716091   585/268-7900
  1 Jaguar Dr, Belmont 14813   Fax 585/268-5810

Schools: 1 \ **Teachers:** 60 \ **Students:** 536 \ **Special Ed Students:** 80 \ **College-Bound:** 75% \ **Ethnic:** Asian 1%, African American 1%, Hispanic 1%, Native American: 2%, Caucasian 94% \ **Exp:** $364 (High) \ **Poverty:** 19% \ **Title I:** $207,924 \ **Special Education:** $1,252,000 \ **Open-Close:** 09/01 - 06/24 \ **DTBP:** $374 (High)

Brian Schmitt 1,11	Erin Ostrander 2
Kelli Zenoski-Bartle 4*	William Weaver 5
Brian Brockway 6*	Carol McCarville 8,12,58,69,288*
Paula Mighells 8,12,58,83,288*	Jeff Labenne 16,73,295*
Nicole Norasethaporn 16*	Josie Preston 31,38,88*
Timothy Hand 67	Chris Gyr 285
Terry Delahunt 298	

Public Schs..Principal	Grd	Prgm	Enr/#Cls	SN	
Genesee Valley Ctrl Sch 1 Jaguar Dr, Belmont 14813 Brian Edmister \ Sara Donlon	PK-12	T	536 96	53%	585/268-7900

- **Scio Central School Dist** PID: 00716297   585/593-5510
  3968 Washington St, Scio 14880   Fax 585/593-0653

Schools: 1 \ **Teachers:** 39 \ **Students:** 300 \ **Special Ed Students:** 63 \ **College-Bound:** 69% \ **Ethnic:** African American 1%, Hispanic 1%, Caucasian 98% \ **Exp:** $204 (Med) \ **Poverty:** 20% \ **Title I:** $130,871 \ **Special Education:** $859,000 \ **Open-Close:** 09/08 - 06/22 \ **DTBP:** $377 (High)

Jennifer Cappelletti 1,11	Nichelle Linderman 2
Doreen Martin 3,6,35,83*	Cindy Winchell 4*
Jayson Chandler 5	Deborah Fuller 7*
Cristy McKinley 8,69,285*	Amber Hardy 31,36
Ann Guilford 54*	Kelly Morehouse 58,752*
Lauren Knapp 67	Cathy Law 71
Mike Pavlock 73*	

Public Schs..Principal	Grd	Prgm	Enr/#Cls	SN	
Scio Central Sch 3968 Washington St, Scio 14880 Cristy McKinley	PK-12	T	300 30	56%	585/593-5510

- **Wellsville Central Sch Dist** PID: 00716326   585/596-2170
  126 W State St, Wellsville 14895   Fax 585/596-2177

Schools: 2 \ **Teachers:** 106 \ **Students:** 1,118 \ **Special Ed Students:** 231 \ **LEP Students:** 3 \ **Ethnic:** Asian 1%, African American 2%, Hispanic 2%, Caucasian 96% \ **Exp:** $212 (Med) \ **Poverty:** 17% \ **Title I:** $398,272 \ **Special Education:** $725,000 \ **Open-Close:** 09/04 - 06/23 \ **DTBP:** $351 (High) \ [f] [t]

David Foster 1	Michelle Dunbar 2
Bob Meyers 4*	Dave Saunders 5
Dean Giopulos 6,35	Elizabeth Sinski 9*
Emily Peavey 11,91	Tony Fountain 16,297*
Mary Van Etten 58,79	Allan Mosher 67

Public Schs..Principal	Grd	Prgm	Enr/#Cls	SN	
Wellsville Elem Sch 50 School St 98, Wellsville 14895 Dean Giopulos	PK-5	T	493 35	55%	585/596-2122 Fax 585/596-2120
Wellsville Secondary Sch 126 W State St, Wellsville 14895 Mary Ellen O'Connell	6-12	T	625 18	44%	585/596-2188 Fax 585/596-2180

- **Whitesville Central Sch Dist** PID: 00716376   607/356-3301
  692 Main St, Whitesville 14897   Fax 607/356-3598

Schools: 1 \ **Teachers:** 20 \ **Students:** 200 \ **Special Ed Students:** 30 \ **College-Bound:** 66% \ **Ethnic:** African American 1%, Hispanic 2%, Caucasian 98% \ **Exp:** $243 (Med) \ **Poverty:** 15% \ **Title I:** $59,272 \ **Special Education:** $620,000 \ **Open-Close:** 09/08 - 06/24

Tammy Emery 1	Douglas Moot 2,73,76,295*
Mike McIntyre 3*	Joan Coleman 4*
Joseph Chapman 5	Erin Rawady 6*
Joan Cobb 7	Tessa Levitt 8,288*
Renee McNeely 11,58,69,294,298	Sally Severtson 16*
Elizabeth Potter 36,79,83,88,275*	Linda Tronetti 54,57,280*
Jeffery Erdmann 67	Judy Gear 77
Melissa Flowers 97	Jacob Wood 285

Public Schs..Principal	Grd	Prgm	Enr/#Cls	SN	
Whitesville Central Sch 692 Main St, Whitesville 14897 Renee McNeely	PK-12	T	200 29	57%	607/356-3301

ALLEGANY CATHOLIC SCHOOLS

- **Diocese of Buffalo Ed Office** PID: 00725846
  Listing includes only schools located in this county. See District Index for location of Diocesan Offices.

Catholic Schs..Principal	Grd	Prgm	Enr/#Cls	SN	
Immaculate Conception Sch 24 Maple Ave, Wellsville 14895 Nora Burdick	PK-8		150 11		585/593-5840 Fax 585/593-5846

---

79 Student Personnel	91 Safety/Security	275 Response To Intervention	298 Grant Writer/Ptnrships	**School Programs**
80 Driver Ed/Safety	92 Magnet School	277 Remedial Math K-12	750 Chief Innovation Officer	A = Alternative Program
81 Gifted/Talented	93 Parental Involvement	280 Literacy Coach	751 Chief of Staff	G = Adult Classes
82 Video Services	95 Tech Prep Program	285 STEM	752 Social Emotional Learning	M = Magnet Program
83 Substance Abuse Prev	97 Chief Information Officer	286 Digital Learning		T = Title I Schoolwide
84 Erate	98 Chief Technology Officer	288 Common Core Standards	**Other School Types**	V = Career & Tech Ed Programs
85 AIDS Education	270 Character Education	294 Accountability	A = Alternative School	
88 Alternative/At Risk	271 Migrant Education	295 Network System	C = Charter School	New Schools are shaded
89 Multi-Cultural Curriculum	273 Teacher Mentor	296 Title II Programs	M = Magnet School	New Superintendents and Principals are bold
90 Social Work	274 Before/After Sch	297 Webmaster	Y = Year-Round School	Personnel with email addresses are underscored

Social Media
[f] = Facebook
[t] = Twitter

Bronx County

Market Data Retrieval

ALLEGANY PRIVATE SCHOOLS

Private Schs..Principal	Grd	Prgm	Enr/#Cls	SN
Houghton Academy 9790 Thayer St, Houghton 14744 John Nelson	7-12		142 11	585/567-8115 Fax 585/567-8048 f

BRONX COUNTY

BRONX PUBLIC SCHOOLS

● **Community School District 7** PID: 10909620   718/742-6500
501 Courtlandt Ave, Bronx 10451

(Part of New York City Dept of Ed in New York County)
Rafael Alvarez 1

Public Schs..Principal	Grd	Prgm	Enr/#Cls	SN
Academy Applied Math & Tech 345 Brook Ave, Bronx 10454 Vincent Gassetto	6-8	T	299 38	93% 718/292-3883 Fax 718/292-4473
Academy of Public Relations 778 Forest Ave, Bronx 10456 Amy Andino-Flohr	6-8	T	253 10	90% 718/665-8866 Fax 718/401-0051
ⓐ Alfred E Smith Campus YABC 333 E 151st St, Bronx 10451 Arleen Milton	10-12		250	718/993-1706
Alfred E Smith Career-Tech HS 333 E 151st St, Bronx 10451 Evan Schwartz	Voc	GT	439 95	92% 718/993-5000 Fax 718/292-1944
ⓒ Bronx Charter Sch for Children 388 Willis Ave, Bronx 10454 Denise Alexander	K-5	T	404 12	90% 718/402-3300 Fax 718/402-3258
Bronx Design & Const Academy 333 E 151st St, Bronx 10451 A Lovett	9-12	T	395	90% 718/402-7690 Fax 718/402-4216
ⓒ Bronx Global Lrng Inst-Girls 750 Concourse Vlg W, Bronx 10451 Courtne Thomas \ Carmen Umpierre	K-8	T	441	81% 718/993-1740 Fax 718/993-1965
Bronx Haven High Sch 333 E 151st St, Bronx 10451 Jazmin Rivera-Polanco	9-12	T	128	81% 718/292-3638 Fax 718/292-6065
Bronx Leadership Academy II HS 730 Concourse Vlg W, Bronx 10451 Rose Lobianco	9-12	T	494 25	94% 718/292-7171 Fax 718/292-2355
Careers In Sports High Sch 730 Concourse Vlg W, Bronx 10451 Johanny Garcia	9-12	T	500 13	84% 718/292-7110 Fax 718/292-5565
Community HS-Social Justice 350 Gerard Ave, Bronx 10451 Jamie Guzman	9-12	T	313 15	90% 718/402-8481 Fax 718/402-8650
Concourse Village Elem Sch 750 Concourse Vlg W, Bronx 10451 Alexa Sorden	PK-5	T	336	86% 718/402-7503 Fax 718/402-7509
ⓜ Health Opportunities High Sch 350 Gerard Ave, Bronx 10451 Andrew Clayman	9-12	TV	471 50	87% 718/401-1826 Fax 718/401-1632
Hero High Sch 455 Southern Blvd, Bronx 10455 Kristin Garcia	9-12	T	540	81% 718/585-8013 Fax 718/585-8019
Hostos-Lincoln Academy of Sci 600 Saint Anns Ave, Bronx 10455 Nicholas Paarlberg	6-12	GT	535 19	79% 718/402-5640 Fax 718/402-5645
International Cmty High Sch 345 Brook Ave, Bronx 10454 Berena Cabarcas	9-12	T	384 15	98% 718/665-4128 Fax 718/665-4547
IS 584 600 Saint Anns Ave, Bronx 10455 Tannis Sertima	6-8	T	241	96% 718/742-2900 Fax 718/292-5735
JHS 151 Lou Gehrig 250 E 156th St, Bronx 10451 Diedra Thomas	6-8	T	185 15	96% 718/292-0260 Fax 718/292-5704
Jill Chaifetz Transfer HS 778 Forest Ave, Bronx 10456 Carlos Benitez	9-12	T	168	82% 718/402-2429 Fax 718/402-3120
ⓒ KIPP Academy Elem Sch [242] 730 Concourse Vlg W, Bronx 10451 Tyritia Groves	K-4		525	718/943-3737 Fax 718/292-7199
ⓒ KIPP Academy Middle Sch [242] ⓨ 250 E 156th St 4th Fl, Bronx 10451 Frank Corcoran	5-8	MT	480 10	87% 718/665-3555 Fax 718/585-7982
Learning Through Play PK Ctr 535 Union Ave, Bronx 10455 Carlyn Rahynes	PK-PK		401	718/292-4120 Fax 718/293-7103
ⓒ Mott Haven Academy Charter Sch 170 Brown Pl, Bronx 10454 Ashlyn Field	K-7	T	414	97% 718/292-7015 Fax 718/292-7823
ⓐ Mott Haven Community High Sch 455 Southern Blvd, Bronx 10455 Helene Spadaccini	10-12	T	248	84% 718/665-8512 Fax 718/665-8518
Mott Haven Village Prep HS 701 Saint Anns Ave, Bronx 10455 Melanie Williams	9-12	T	306 13	97% 718/402-0571 Fax 718/665-2363
MS 223 Lab Sch of Fin & Tech 360 E 145th St, Bronx 10454 Ramon Gonzalez	6-12	T	688	95% 718/585-8202 Fax 718/292-7435
ⓒ NYC Charter HS Arch-Engr-Const 838 Brook Ave, Bronx 10451 Colin Healy	9-12	T	448	92% 646/400-5566 Fax 718/585-4780
PS 1 Courtlandt Sch 335 E 152nd St, Bronx 10451 Jorge Perdomo	PK-5	T	619	96% 718/299-3700 Fax 718/292-2227
PS 5 Port Morris Sch 564 Jackson Ave, Bronx 10455 Danielle Keane	PK-8	T	658 34	96% 718/292-2683
PS 18 John Peter Zenger 502 Morris Ave, Bronx 10451 Lauren Walker	PK-5	GT	553 30	100% 718/292-2868 Fax 718/292-2862
PS 25 Bilingual Sch 811 E 149th St, Bronx 10455 Carmen Toledo	PK-5	T	525 40	94% 718/292-2995 Fax 718/292-2997
PS 30 Wilton 510 E 141st St, Bronx 10454 Debra Michaux	PK-5	T	532 45	92% 718/292-8817 Fax 718/292-3962
PS 43 Jonas Bronck 165 Brown Pl, Bronx 10454 Giovanna Delucchi	PK-5	T	416	96% 718/292-4502 Fax 718/292-4504
PS 49 Willis Avenue 383 E 139th St, Bronx 10454 Frank Hernandez	PK-5	T	646 40	96% 718/292-4623 Fax 718/292-4568
PS 65 Mother Hale Academy 677 E 141st St, Bronx 10454 Jasmine Gonzalez	PK-5	T	348 21	97% 718/292-4628 Fax 718/292-4695
PS 154 Jonathan D Hyatt 333 E 135th St, Bronx 10454 Alison Coviello	PK-5	T	304 32	97% 718/292-4742 Fax 718/292-4721

1 Superintendent	8 Curric/Instruct K-12	19 Chief Financial Officer	29 Family/Consumer Science	39 Social Studies K-12	49 English/Lang Arts Elem	59 Special Education Elem	69 Academic Assessment
2 Bus/Finance/Purchasing	9 Curric/Instruct Elem	20 Art K-12	30 Adult Education	40 Social Studies Elem	50 English/Lang Arts Sec	60 Special Education Sec	70 Research/Development
3 Buildings And Grounds	10 Curric/Instruct Sec	21 Art Elem	31 Career/Sch-to-Work K-12	41 Social Studies Sec	51 Reading K-12	61 Foreign/World Lang K-12	71 Public Information
4 Food Service	11 Federal Program	22 Art Sec	32 Career/Sch-to-Work Elem	42 Science K-12	52 Reading Elem	62 Foreign/World Lang Elem	72 Summer School
5 Transportation	12 Title I	23 Music K-12	33 Career/Sch-to-Work Sec	43 Science Elem	53 Reading Sec	63 Foreign/World Lang Sec	73 Instructional Tech
6 Athletic	13 Title V	24 Music Elem	34 Early Childhood Ed	44 Science Sec	54 Remedial Reading K-12	64 Religious Education K-12	74 Inservice Training
7 Health Services	15 Asst Superintendent	25 Music Sec	35 Health/Phys Education	45 Math K-12	55 Remedial Reading Elem	65 Religious Education Elem	75 Marketing/Distributive
	16 Instructional Media Svcs	26 Business Education	36 Guidance Services K-12	46 Math Elem	56 Remedial Reading Sec	66 Religious Education Sec	76 Info Systems
	17 Chief Operations Officer	27 Career & Tech Ed	37 Guidance Services Elem	47 Math Sec	57 Bilingual/ELL	67 School Board President	77 Psychological Assess
	18 Chief Academic Officer	28 Technology Education	38 Guidance Services Sec	48 English/Lang Arts K-12	58 Special Education K-12	68 Teacher Personnel	78 Affirmative Action

New York School Directory

Bronx County

PS 157 Grove Hill 757 Cauldwell Ave, Bronx 10456 Ramona Duran	PK-5	T	595 50	95%	718/292-5255 Fax 718/292-5258
PS 161 Juan Ponce De Leon 628 Tinton Ave, Bronx 10455 Eliamarie Soto	PK-5	T	449 50	98%	718/292-5478 Fax 718/292-5476
PS 179 468 E 140th St, Bronx 10454 Sherry Williams	PK-5	T	311 20	94%	718/292-2237 Fax 718/292-3623
PS 277 519 Saint Anns Ave, Bronx 10455 Natasha Bracey	PK-5	T	437 38	91%	718/292-3594 Fax 718/292-3630
PS-IS 224 345 Brook Ave, Bronx 10454 Patricia Catania	6-8	T	281 15	97%	718/665-9804 Fax 718/665-0078
PS/MS 29 Melrose Sch 758 Courtlandt Ave, Bronx 10451 Deborah Sanabria	PK-8	T	796 37	92%	718/292-3785 Fax 718/292-3784
PS/MS 31 William Garrison 250 Thurman Munson Way, Bronx 10451 William Hewlett	PK-8	T	684	89%	718/292-4397
ⓒ S Bronx CS-Int'l Culture & Art 164 Bruckner Blvd, Bronx 10454 Evelyn Hey	K-6	T	454	92%	718/401-9216 Fax 718/401-9219
South Bronx Academy Appl Media 778 Forest Ave, Bronx 10456 Ault Roshone	6-8	T	212	89%	718/401-0059 Fax 718/401-0577
South Bronx Preparatory Sch 360 E 145th St, Bronx 10454 Ellen Flanagan	6-12	T	650 12	94%	718/292-2211 Fax 718/292-2172
ⓐ University Heights Sec Sch 701 Saint Anns Ave, Bronx 10455 Hazel Roseboro	9-12	TV	568 20	82%	718/292-0578 Fax 718/292-4276
Urban Assembly Bronx Letters 339 Morris Ave, Bronx 10451 Erin Garry	6-12	T	589	90%	718/401-4891 Fax 718/401-6626
Walkabout Bronx High Sch 730 Concourse Village W, Bronx 10451 **Kameca Gordon**	9-9		401		718/292-8225
Young Leaders Elem Sch 468 E 140th St, Bronx 10454 Jaleelah Cooke	PK-5	T	245	98%	718/292-7391 Fax 718/292-8535

• **Community School District 8** PID: 10909632   718/239-5890
  650 White Plains Rd, Bronx 10473   Fax 718/828-6239
     (Part of New York City Dept of Ed in New York County)
Erika Tobia 1

Public Schs..Principal	Grd	Prgm	Enr/#Cls	SN	
ⓐ Adlai Stevenson Campus YABC 1980 Lafayette Ave, Bronx 10473 Gladys Delacruz	10-12		250		718/792-8264
Antonia Pantoja Prep Academy 1980 Lafayette Ave, Bronx 10473 Nalini Singh	6-12	T	396	83%	718/824-3152 Fax 718/824-3543
Archimedes Acad Math Sci Tech 456 White Plains Rd, Bronx 10473 Miriam Lazar	6-12	T	592	77%	718/617-5046 Fax 718/617-7395
Blueprint Middle Sch 1111 Pugsley Ave, Bronx 10472 Tyneka Harrington	6-8	T	629	89%	718/822-2780 Fax 718/822-2279
Bronx Arena High Sch 1440 Story Ave, Bronx 10473 Ty Cesene	9-12	AGT	171	89%	718/860-5056 Fax 718/860-5058
Bronx Bridges High Sch 1980 Lafayette Ave, Bronx 10473 Nelsie Castillo	9-12	T	332	82%	718/829-2984 Fax 718/829-2987
Bronx Cmty High Sch 1980 Lafayette Ave, Bronx 10473 Flora Greenaway	9-12	T	112	84%	718/892-1026 Fax 718/892-6941
Bronx Compass High Sch 1980 Lafayette Ave, Bronx 10473 Brett Roer	9-12	T	387	83%	718/828-1206 Fax 718/828-3732
Bronx Mathematics Prep Sch 456 White Plains Rd, Bronx 10473 Dyon Rozier	6-8	T	207	97%	718/542-5063 Fax 718/542-5236
Bronx River High Sch 3000 E Tremont Ave, Bronx 10461 Gregory Fucheck	9-12	T	465	80%	718/904-4210
Bronx Studio Sch for Writers 928 Simpson St, Bronx 10459 Dawn Verhille	6-12	T	606 11	84%	718/893-5158 Fax 718/893-5982
Gotham Collaborative High Sch 1980 Lafayette Ave, Bronx 10473 David Liu	9-12	T	492	85%	718/597-1587 Fax 718/824-1663
Herbert H Lehman High Sch 3000 E Tremont Ave, Bronx 10461 John Powers	9-12	GTV	916	77%	718/904-4200 Fax 718/904-4235
ⓐ Herbert Lehman YABC 3000 E Tremont Ave, Bronx 10461 Martin Smallhorne	10-12		250		718/904-4280
JHS 123 James M Kieran 1025 Morrison Ave, Bronx 10472 Richard Hallenbeck	6-8	T	487	86%	718/328-2105 Fax 718/328-8561
JHS 131 Albert Einstein 885 Bolton Ave, Bronx 10473 Monique Mason	6-8	TV	443 35	83%	718/991-7490 Fax 718/328-6705
Longwood Preparatory Academy 965 Longwood Ave Frnt 1, Bronx 10459 Asya Johnson	9-12	T	332 24	88%	718/860-1241 Fax 718/860-1934
Millennium Art Academy 1980 Lafayette Ave, Bronx 10473 Herman Guy	9-12	T	413 16	75%	718/824-0978 Fax 718/824-0963
Mott Hall Community Sch 650 Hollywood Ave, Bronx 10465 Benjamin Basile	6-8	T	339	86%	718/829-3254 Fax 718/829-3859
MS 101 Ed R Byrne Sch 2750 Lafayette Ave, Bronx 10465 Jared Rosoff	6-8	T	541 23	73%	718/829-6372 Fax 718/829-6594
MS 301 Paul L Dunbar 890 Cauldwell Ave, Bronx 10456 Hesham Farid	6-8	TV	200 20	93%	718/585-2950 Fax 718/401-2567
MS 302 Luisa Dessus Cruz 681 Kelly St, Bronx 10455 Liza Ortiz	6-8	T	480	97%	718/901-3520 Fax 718/901-3529
MS 424 Hunts Point Middle Sch 730 Bryant Ave, Bronx 10474 David Vazquez	6-8	T	284	90%	718/328-1972 Fax 718/328-7330
Pelham Lab High Sch 3000 E Tremont Ave, Bronx 10461 Jason Wagner	9-12	T	450	73%	718/904-5090 Fax 718/904-5099
PS 36 Unionport Sch 1070 Castle Hill Ave, Bronx 10472 Elvira Maresca	PK-5	T	749 31	72%	718/822-5345 Fax 718/239-6390
PS 48 Joseph R Drake 1290 Spofford Ave, Bronx 10474 Joseph Dicrescento	PK-5	T	624 58	94%	718/589-4312 Fax 718/842-6993
PS 62 Inocensio Casanova 660 Fox St, Bronx 10455 Lisa Manfredonia	PK-5	T	610 40	97%	718/585-1617 Fax 718/292-6327

79	Student Personnel	91	Safety/Security	275	Response To Intervention	298	Grant Writer/Ptnrships	School Programs	Social Media
80	Driver Ed/Safety	92	Magnet School	277	Remedial Math K-12	750	Chief Innovation Officer	A = Alternative Program	
81	Gifted/Talented	93	Parental Involvement	280	Literacy Coach	751	Chief of Staff	G = Adult Classes	📘 = Facebook
82	Video Services	95	Tech Prep Program	285	STEM	752	Social Emotional Learning	M = Magnet Program	
83	Substance Abuse Prev	97	Chief Information Officer	286	Digital Learning			T = Title I Schoolwide	🇹 = Twitter
84	Erate	98	Chief Technology Officer	288	Common Core Standards		Other School Types	V = Career & Tech Ed Programs	
85	AIDS Education	270	Character Education	294	Accountability		ⓐ = Alternative School		
88	Alternative/At Risk	271	Migrant Education	295	Network System		ⓒ = Charter School	New Schools are shaded	
89	Multi-Cultural Curriculum	273	Teacher Mentor	296	Title II Programs		ⓜ = Magnet School	New Superintendents and Principals are bold	
90	Social Work	274	Before/After Sch	297	Webmaster		ⓨ = Year-Round School	Personnel with email addresses are underscored	

NY–17

Bronx County

Market Data Retrieval

School	Grd	Prgm	Enr/#Cls	SN	Phone
PS 69 Journey Prep 560 Thieriot Ave, Bronx 10473 Sheila Durant	PK-5	T	604 28	84%	718/378-4736 Fax 718/328-0925
PS 71 Rose E Scala 3040 Roberts Ave, Bronx 10461 Margaret Donofrio	K-8	T	1,453	73%	718/822-5351 Fax 718/239-3111
PS 72 Dr William Dorney 2951 Dewey Ave, Bronx 10465 Margarita Colon	PK-5	T	721 45	86%	718/822-5311 Fax 718/828-4459
PS 75 Research & Discovery 984 Faile St, Bronx 10459 Marines Cruz	PK-5	T	604	83%	718/860-1630 Fax 718/860-4480
PS 93 Albert G Oliver 1535 Story Ave, Bronx 10473 Jonathan Kaplan	PK-5	T	394 28	70%	718/430-1700 Fax 718/430-1705
PS 100 Isaac Clason 800 Taylor Ave, Bronx 10473 Ariana Arbolino	PK-5	T	543 40	83%	718/842-1461 Fax 718/328-5520
PS 107 1695 Seward Ave, Bronx 10473 Katherine Hamm	PK-5	T	582 39	98%	718/860-8760 Fax 718/328-5799
PS 119 Dr Emmett W Bassett Sch 1075 Pugsley Ave, Bronx 10472 Michelle Montana	PK-5	T	742 24	83%	718/822-5198 Fax 718/239-3112
PS 130 A S Hewitt Elem Sch 750 Prospect Ave, Bronx 10455 Lourdes Velazquez	PK-5	T	396 24	88%	718/665-0962 Fax 718/292-0417
PS 138 Samuel Randall 2060 Lafayette Ave, Bronx 10473 Jeanna Dickerson	PK-5	T	635	86%	718/822-5325 Fax 718/239-3114
PS 140 Eagle Sch 916 Eagle Ave, Bronx 10456 Paul Cannon	PK-5	T	548 34	95%	718/585-1205 Fax 718/292-1349
PS 146 Edward J Collins 968 Cauldwell Ave, Bronx 10456 Janette Rodriguez	PK-5	T	387 24	97%	718/378-9664
PS 152 Evergreen 1007 Evergreen Ave, Bronx 10472 Frances Lynch	K-5	AT	761	90%	718/589-4560
PS 182 601 Stickball Blvd, Bronx 10473 Anne O'Grady	PK-5	T	686 45	87%	718/828-6607 Fax 718/409-8152
PS 304 Early Childhood Lab Sch 2750 Lafayette Ave, Bronx 10465 Joseph Nobile	PK-5	T	515	66%	718/822-5307 Fax 718/904-0956
PS 333 Longwood Acad Discovery 888 Rev James A Polite Ave, Bronx 10459 Victoria Najera	PK-5	T	581	96%	718/860-3313 Fax 718/842-8734
PS 392 Bronx Delta Sch 650 Hollywood Ave, Bronx 10465 Maria Rogalle	PK-4	T	340	71%	718/319-7147 Fax 718/319-2450
PS 583 1028 White Plains Rd, Bronx 10472 Glorimer Lopez	PK-1	T	190	82%	929/348-4960 Fax 929/348-4964
PS X14 Sen John Calandra 3041 Bruckner Blvd, Bronx 10461 Ira Schulman	K-5	T	568 26	67%	718/822-5341 Fax 718/239-6386
Renaissance HS Music Theatre 3000 E Tremont Ave, Bronx 10461 Maria Herrera	9-12	T	434	71%	718/430-6390 Fax 718/430-6308
Sch for Inquiry Social Justice 1025 Morrison Ave, Bronx 10472 Andrea Cyprys	6-8	T	493 25	78%	718/860-4181 Fax 718/860-4163
School for Tourism-Hospitality 900 Tinton Ave, Bronx 10456 Avis Terrell	9-12	T	261	93%	718/401-4214 Fax 718/401-4219
Schuylerville Prep HS 3000 E Tremont Ave, Bronx 10461 Melissa Ramos	9-12	T	387	68%	718/904-5080 Fax 718/935-5089
Soundview Acad-Cult & Schlrshp 885 Bolton Ave, Bronx 10473 William Frackelton	6-8	T	378	81%	718/991-4027 Fax 718/991-4807
Urban Institute of Math 650 Hollywood Ave, Bronx 10465 Joshua Partridge	6-8	T	365	73%	718/823-6042 Fax 718/823-6347
Westchester Square Academy 3000 E Tremont Ave, Bronx 10461 Yira Salcedo	9-12	T	520	79%	718/904-5050 Fax 718/904-5055
Women's Academy of Excellence 456 White Plains Rd, Bronx 10473 Arnette Crocker	9-12	T	244 8	89%	718/542-0740 Fax 718/542-0841

● **Community School District 9** PID: 10909644   718/579-7143
1245 Washington Ave, Bronx 10456

(Part of New York City Dept of Ed in New York County)
Leticia Rosario 1

Public Schs..Principal	Grd	Prgm	Enr/#Cls	SN	Phone
Academy for Language & Tech 1700 Macombs Rd, Bronx 10453 Jose Vinales	9-12	T	321	100%	718/731-0219 Fax 718/731-2031
© Bronx Academy of Promise CS 1349 Inwood Ave, Bronx 10452 Denise Schiraldi	K-8	T	599	93%	718/293-6950 Fax 718/293-6958
Bronx Center Sci & Math 1363 Fulton Ave, Bronx 10456 Edward Tom	9-12	T	441	88%	718/992-7089 Fax 718/590-1052
Bronx Collegiate Academy 240 E 172nd St, Bronx 10457 Darryl White	9-12	T	360 26	88%	718/410-4077 Fax 718/340-3659
Bronx Early Clg Teach & Lrng 250 E 164th St, Bronx 10456 Yvette Rivera	6-12	T	468	88%	718/681-8287 Fax 718/681-8650
Bronx High School of Business 240 E 172nd St, Bronx 10457 Alice Bajana	9-12	T	278	93%	718/410-4060 Fax 718/992-5760
Bronx HS for Medical Science 240 E 172nd St, Bronx 10457 William Quintana	6-12	TV	432 20	81%	718/410-4040 Fax 718/992-4129
Bronx International High Sch 1110 Boston Rd, Bronx 10456 Joaquin Vega	9-12	T	360 15	89%	718/620-1053 Fax 718/620-1056
ⓜ Bronx Leadership Academy 1710 Webster Ave, Bronx 10457 Geralda Valcin	9-12	T	463 20	87%	718/299-4274 Fax 718/299-4707
ⓜ Bronx Sch for Law-Gov-Justice 244 E 163rd St, Bronx 10451 Johanie Hernandez	6-12	T	735 7	87%	718/410-3430 Fax 718/410-3950
Bronx Writing Academy 270 E 167th St, Bronx 10456 Lauren Hasson	6-8	T	375	92%	718/293-9048 Fax 718/293-9748
Claremont International HS 240 E 172nd St, Bronx 10457 Elizabeth Demchak	9-12	T	364	98%	718/410-4001 Fax 718/410-4038
Dreamyard Prep Sch 240 E 172nd St Rm 477, Bronx 10457 Alicia Wargo	9-12	T	283	88%	718/410-4242
Eagle Acad for Young Men-Bronx 4143 3rd Ave, Bronx 10457 Hector Velazquez	6-12	T	496	78%	718/466-8000 Fax 718/466-8090

1 Superintendent	8 Curric/Instruct K-12	19 Chief Financial Officer	29 Family/Consumer Science	39 Social Studies K-12	49 English/Lang Arts Elem	59 Special Education Elem	69 Academic Assessment
2 Bus/Finance/Purchasing	9 Curric/Instruct Elem	20 Art K-12	30 Adult Education	40 Social Studies Elem	50 English/Lang Arts Sec	60 Special Education Sec	70 Research/Development
3 Buildings And Grounds	10 Curric/Instruct Sec	21 Art Elem	31 Career/Sch-to-Work K-12	41 Social Studies Sec	51 Reading K-12	61 Foreign/World Lang K-12	71 Public Information
4 Food Service	11 Federal Program	22 Art Sec	32 Career/Sch-to-Work Elem	42 Science K-12	52 Reading Elem	62 Foreign/World Lang Elem	72 Summer School
5 Transportation	12 Title I	23 Music K-12	33 Career/Sch-to-Work Sec	43 Science Elem	53 Reading Sec	63 Foreign/World Lang Sec	73 Instructional Tech
6 Athletic	13 Title V	24 Music Elem	34 Early Childhood Ed	44 Science Sec	54 Remedial Reading K-12	64 Religious Education K-12	74 Inservice Training
7 Health Services	15 Asst Superintendent	25 Music Sec	35 Health/Phys Education	45 Math K-12	55 Remedial Reading Elem	65 Religious Education Elem	75 Marketing/Distributive
	16 Instructional Media Svcs	26 Business Education	36 Guidance Services K-12	46 Math Elem	56 Remedial Reading Sec	66 Religious Education Sec	76 Info Systems
	17 Chief Operations Officer	27 Career & Tech Ed	37 Guidance Services Elem	47 Math Sec	57 Bilingual/ELL	67 School Board President	77 Psychological Assess
	18 Chief Academic Officer	28 Technology Education	38 Guidance Services Sec	48 English/Lang Arts K-12	58 Special Education K-12	68 Teacher Personnel	78 Affirmative Action

New York School Directory — Bronx County

School	Grades	Prog	Enroll	Attend	Phone
Eximius Clg Prep Academy 1363 Fulton Ave, Bronx 10456 Jonathan Daly	9-12	T	392	81%	718/992-7154 Fax 718/590-1081
Family Sch 1116 Sheridan Ave, Bronx 10456 Rowena Penn	PK-5	TV	540	92%	718/538-3266
Frederick Douglass Academy III 3630 3rd Ave, Bronx 10456 Jumel Carlos	9-12	T	338	87%	718/538-9726 Fax 718/538-9796
Garden of Lrng & Discovery PK 1434 Ogden Ave, Bronx 10452 Roxanne Batista	PK-PK		401		718/583-8975 Fax 718/583-8987
Grant Avenue Elem Sch 250 E 164th St, Bronx 10456 Kristin Erat	PK-5	T	428	93%	718/681-6288 Fax 718/681-6687
High School for Violin & Dance 1110 Boston Rd, Bronx 10456 Franklin Sim	9-12	T	230 11	92%	718/842-0687 Fax 718/589-9849
Highbridge Green Sch 200 W 167th St, Bronx 10452 Kyle Brillante	6-8	T	381	97%	718/410-5770 Fax 718/410-5779
IS 117 Joseph H Wade 1865 Morris Ave, Bronx 10453 DeLise Jones	6-8	T	437 60	95%	718/583-7750 Fax 718/583-7658
IS 219 New Venture 3630 3rd Ave, Bronx 10456 **Kizhaya Roberts**	6-8	T	331 21	94%	718/681-7093 Fax 718/681-7324
IS 229 Dr Roland Patterson 275 Roberto Clemente State Brg, Bronx 10453 Dr Ezra Matthias	6-8	T	245 32	94%	718/583-6266 Fax 718/583-6325
IS 232X Alexander Macomb Sch 1700 Macombs Rd, Bronx 10453 Desiree Martinez	6-8	T	456	97%	718/583-7007 Fax 718/583-4864
IS 303 Ldrshp & Cmty Svc Acad 1700 Macombs Rd 5th Fl, Bronx 10453 Monica Brady	6-8	T	312 13	98%	718/583-5466 Fax 718/583-2463
IS 313 Sch of Leadership Dev 1600 Webster Ave 4th Fl, Bronx 10457 Earl Brathwaite	6-8	T	270	91%	718/583-1736 Fax 718/299-5559
IS 339 1600 Webster Ave Frnt 3, Bronx 10457 Kim Outerbridge	6-8	T	423 60	92%	718/583-6767 Fax 718/583-0281
JHS 22 Jordan L Mott 270 E 167th St, Bronx 10456 Edgar Lin	6-8	T	403	97%	718/681-6850
Kappa MS 215 3630 3rd Ave, Bronx 10456 Sheri Warren	6-8	T	341 17	87%	718/590-5455 Fax 718/681-4266
Lucero Elem Sch 1425 Walton Ave, Bronx 10452 Kattia Cuba	K-5	T	371	97%	718/681-8701 Fax 718/681-8707
ⓒ Metropolitan Lighthouse CS [149] 180 W 165th St, Bronx 10452 Kurt Davison \ Tyra Williams	K-11	T	634	88%	718/893-0640 Fax 718/893-0675
Morris Academy/Collab Studies 1110 Boston Rd, Bronx 10456 Matthew Mazzaroppi	9-12	T	432 20	94%	718/617-5312 Fax 718/893-7368
Mott Hall Bronx High Sch 1595 Bathgate Ave, Bronx 10457 Kathryn Malloy	9-12	T	359	91%	718/466-6800 Fax 718/466-6801
Mott Hall III MS 128 580 Crotona Park S, Bronx 10456 Jorisis Stupart	6-8	T	343	93%	718/842-6138 Fax 718/842-6348
Mount Eden Children's Academy 1501 Jerome Ave, Bronx 10452 Jacqueline Radoslovich	PK-5	T	432	93%	718/294-8155 Fax 718/294-8154
MS 327 Comp Model Sch 1501 Jerome Ave, Bronx 10452 Alixandre Ricci	6-12	T	712	88%	718/294-8111
MS 593 South Bronx Int'l MS 1000 Teller Ave, Bronx 10456 Alison Angrisani	6-6	T	43	88%	718/588-0341
MS 594 New Pathways Academy 1000 Teller Ave, Bronx 10456 Lyne James	6-8	T	246	94%	718/588-8349
New Directions Secondary Sch 240 E 172nd St, Bronx 10457 James Waslawski	6-12	T	188	94%	718/410-4343 Fax 718/410-4101
New Millennium Bus Academy 1000 Teller Ave, Bronx 10456 Dorald Bastian	6-8	T	321 19	87%	718/588-8308 Fax 718/588-8767
PS 11 Highbridge Sch 1257 Ogden Ave, Bronx 10452 Joan Kong	PK-5	T	557 33	92%	718/681-7553 Fax 718/681-7711
PS 28 Mt Hope Sch 1861 Anthony Ave, Bronx 10457 Stephen Beckles	PK-5	T	698 40	94%	718/583-6444 Fax 718/583-6537
PS 35 Franz Sigel Sch 261 E 163rd St, Bronx 10451 Graciela Fuentes	K-5	T	529 28	95%	718/681-7214 Fax 718/681-7264
PS 42 Claremont 1537 Washington Ave, Bronx 10457 Lucia Castillo	PK-5	T	369 30	98%	718/583-7366 Fax 718/583-7345
PS 53 Basheer Quisim 360 E 168th St, Bronx 10456 Dr Collin Wolfe	PK-5	T	894	91%	718/681-7276 Fax 718/681-7298
PS 55 Benjamin Franklin Sch 450 Saint Pauls Pl, Bronx 10456 Luis Torres	PK-5	T	613 60	98%	718/681-6227 Fax 718/681-6247
PS 58 459 E 176th St, Bronx 10457 Velma Gunn	PK-5	T	395 31	93%	718/583-6866 Fax 718/583-6895
PS 63 Author's Academy 1260 Franklin Ave, Bronx 10456 Reinaldo Lens	PK-5	T	532 24	95%	718/589-3058 Fax 718/589-4917
PS 70 Max Schoenfeld Sch 1691 Weeks Ave, Bronx 10457 Kerry Castellano	PK-5	T	1,038 70	96%	718/583-6000 Fax 718/586-6006
PS 73X Bronx 1020 Anderson Ave, Bronx 10452 Vivian Bueno	PK-5	T	537 44	94%	718/681-6776 Fax 718/681-6749
PS 88 Silverstein Ltl Sparrow 1340 Sheridan Ave, Bronx 10456 Melinda Hyer	K-3	T	121 15	95%	718/716-7369 Fax 718/681-6224
PS 109 Sedgwick 1771 Popham Ave, Bronx 10453 Josette Claudio	PK-5	T	564 40	90%	718/583-8878 Fax 718/583-7618
PS 110 Theodore Schoenfeld 580 Crotona Park S, Bronx 10456 Daisy Perez	PK-5	T	407 24	98%	718/861-0759 Fax 718/861-2750
PS 114 Luis Llorens Torres 1155 Cromwell Ave, Bronx 10452 Olivia Webber	PK-5	T	670 38	95%	718/681-7507 Fax 718/681-7519
PS 126 Dr Marjorie Dunbar Sch 175 W 166th St, Bronx 10452 Princess Kent	PK-5	T	571 43	94%	718/681-6120 Fax 718/681-6131
PS 132 Garrett A Morgan 1245 Washington Ave, Bronx 10456 Anissa Reilly	PK-5	T	376 40	91%	718/681-6455 Fax 718/681-6466
PS 163 Arthur Schomberg 2075 Webster Ave, Bronx 10457 Barbara Headley	PK-5	T	432 36	98%	718/584-3045 Fax 718/584-3276

---

79 Student Personnel
80 Driver Ed/Safety
81 Gifted/Talented
82 Video Services
83 Substance Abuse Prev
84 Erate
85 AIDS Education
88 Alternative/At Risk
89 Multi-Cultural Curriculum
90 Social Work
91 Safety/Security
92 Magnet School
93 Parental Involvement
95 Tech Prep Program
97 Chief Information Officer
98 Chief Technology Officer
270 Character Education
271 Migrant Education
273 Teacher Mentor
274 Before/After Sch
275 Response To Intervention
277 Remedial Math K-12
280 Literacy Coach
285 STEM
286 Digital Learning
288 Common Core Standards
294 Accountability
295 Network System
296 Title II Programs
297 Webmaster
298 Grant Writer/Ptnrships
750 Chief Innovation Officer
751 Chief of Staff
752 Social Emotional Learning

School Programs
A = Alternative Program
G = Adult Classes
M = Magnet Program
T = Title I Schoolwide
V = Career & Tech Ed Programs

Other School Types
Ⓐ = Alternative School
Ⓒ = Charter School
Ⓜ = Magnet School
Ⓨ = Year-Round School

Social Media
= Facebook
= Twitter

New Schools are shaded
New Superintendents and Principals are bold
Personnel with email addresses are underscored

Bronx County

Market Data Retrieval

School	Grd	Prgm	Enr/#Cls	SN	Phone
PS 170 1598 Townsend Ave, Bronx 10452 Sonia Acevedo Suarez	PK-2	T	218 12	85%	718/583-0662 Fax 718/583-0685
PS 199 Shakespeare 1449 Shakespeare Ave, Bronx 10452 Yasmin Quezada	PK-5	T	657	98%	718/681-7172 Fax 718/681-7176
PS 204 Morris Heights Sch 1780 Dr Mlk Jr Blvd, Bronx 10453 Amanda Blatter	PK-5	T	626 20	84%	718/960-9520 Fax 718/960-9529
PS 236 Langston Hughes 1871 Walton Ave, Bronx 10453 Afrina Talukdar	PK-5	T	313 19	95%	718/299-6128 Fax 718/299-6503
PS 274X New American Acad 275 Roberto Clemente State Brg, Bronx 10453 Pepe Gutierrez	PK-5	T	615	97%	718/901-9703 Fax 718/901-9709
PS/IS 218 Hernandez Dual Lang 1220 Gerard Ave, Bronx 10452 Sergio Caceres	K-8	T	1,017 70	86%	718/410-7230
PS/MS 4 Crotona Park West 1701 Fulton Ave, Bronx 10457 Vincent Resto	PK-8	T	452 56	94%	718/583-6655
School for Excellence 1110 Boston Rd, Bronx 10456 Leslie Aquino	9-12	T	256	87%	718/860-1385 Fax 718/860-4882
Sci & Tech Acad-A Mott Hall 250 E 164th St, Bronx 10456 Dr Patrick Awosogba	6-8	T	426	94%	718/293-4017 Fax 718/293-7396
Sheridan Academy Young Leaders 1116 Sheridan Ave, Bronx 10456 Lisette Febus	PK-5	T	521	97%	718/538-3411 Fax 718/538-3499
Urban Assembly Math & Science 1595 Bathgate Ave, Bronx 10457 Ingrid Chung	6-12	T	601 8	94%	718/466-7800 Fax 718/466-7801
Validus Prep Academy 1595 Bathgate Ave, Bronx 10457 Christophe Hibbert	9-12	T	358	89%	718/466-4000 Fax 718/466-4001
Walton Avenue Sch 1425 Walton Ave, Bronx 10452 Daniel Russo	K-5	T	457	93%	718/293-5970 Fax 718/293-2091
Young Women's Leadership Sch 1865 Morris Ave, Bronx 10453 Lemarie Laureano	6-12	T	551	84%	718/731-2590 Fax 718/731-2595

- **Community School District 10** PID: 10909656   718/741-5852
  1 Fordham Plz, Bronx 10458   Fax 718/741-7098

  (Part of New York City Dept of Ed in New York County)
  Maribel Hulla 1

Public Schs..Principal	Grd	Prgm	Enr/#Cls	SN	Phone
Acad-Personal Ldrshp & Excell 120 E 184th St, Bronx 10468 Angelo Ledda	6-8	T	881	91%	718/220-3139 Fax 718/220-6018
Ampark Neighborhood Sch 3981 Hillman Ave, Bronx 10463 Kelly Lennon	PK-5		383	51%	718/548-3451 Fax 718/581-2411
Angelo Patri Middle Sch 2225 Webster Ave, Bronx 10457 Giselle Fortiche	6-8	T	462 65	91%	718/584-1295 Fax 718/584-1358
Bedford Park Elem Sch 3177 Webster Ave, Bronx 10467 Carolyn Heredia	PK-4	T	421	86%	718/696-6400 Fax 718/696-6405
Belmont Preparatory High Sch 500 E Fordham Rd, Bronx 10458 Stephen Gumbs	9-12	T	396 20	84%	718/733-4559 Fax 718/295-3655
Bronx Acad-Software Engineer 2474 Crotona Ave, Bronx 10458 Benjamin Grossman	9-12	T	404	76%	718/733-6024 Fax 718/733-6429
© Bronx Cmty Charter Sch 3170 Webster Ave, Bronx 10467 Martha Andrews	K-8	T	518	87%	718/584-1400 Fax 718/584-2800
Bronx Collaborative High Sch 100 W Mosholu Pkwy S, Bronx 10468 Brett Schneider	9-12	T	575	81%	718/543-1023 Fax 718/543-1029
Bronx Dance Academy Sch 3617 Bainbridge Ave, Bronx 10467 Sandra Sanchez	6-8	T	263 16	92%	718/515-0410 Fax 718/515-0345
Bronx Engr & Tech Academy 99 Terrace View Ave Rm 544, Bronx 10463 Vijayal Montgomery	9-12	T	406	92%	718/563-6678 Fax 718/817-7698
Bronx High School of Science 75 Bronx Science Blvd, Bronx 10468 Jean Donahue	9-12	GV	2,982 35	43%	718/817-7700 Fax 718/733-7951
Bronx HS Law-Community Service 500 E Fordham Rd, Bronx 10458 Michael Barakat	9-12	T	402 2	90%	718/733-5274 Fax 718/295-3631
Bronx Sch of Young Leaders 40 W Tremont Ave, Bronx 10453 Serapha Cruz	6-8	T	440 20	85%	718/583-4146 Fax 718/583-4292
Bronx School of Law & Finance 99 Terrace View Ave Rm 804, Bronx 10463 Jessica Goring	9-12	T	398 22	88%	718/561-0113 Fax 718/561-0595
Bronx Theatre High Sch 99 Terrace View Ave, Bronx 10463 Daniel Albetta	9-12	T	322 10	85%	718/329-2902 Fax 718/329-0433
Celia Cruz Bronx HS of Music 2780 Reservoir Ave, Bronx 10468 Jerrod Mabry	9-12	T	443	87%	718/329-8550 Fax 718/329-8559
Creston Academy 125 E 181st St, Bronx 10453 Mellissa Miller	6-8	T	459	95%	718/367-5035 Fax 718/367-5176
Crotona Int'l High Sch 2474 Crotona Ave, Bronx 10458 Shweta Ratra	9-12	T	339	85%	718/561-8701 Fax 718/561-8707
DeWitt Clinton High Sch 100 W Mosholu Pkwy S, Bronx 10468 Pierre Orbe	9-12	AGTV	997	79%	718/543-1000 Fax 718/548-0036
Ⓐ DeWitt Clinton YABC 2474 Crotona Ave, Bronx 10458 Veronica Jackson	10-12		250		718/584-2700
Discovery High Sch 2780 Reservoir Ave, Bronx 10468 Rolando Rivera	8-12	T	492 13	86%	718/733-3872 Fax 718/733-3621
Ellis Preparatory Academy 99 Terrace View Ave, Bronx 10463 Norma Vega	9-12	T	291	86%	718/220-1889 Fax 718/220-8758
Fordham High School of Arts 500 E Fordham Rd, Bronx 10458 Iris Blige	9-12	T	371 3	89%	718/733-4656 Fax 718/295-3605
Fordham Leadership Academy 500 E Fordham Rd, Bronx 10458 Fiorella Cabrejos	9-12	T	386	83%	718/733-5024
Fuentes Sch of Sci & Discovery 124 Eames Pl, Bronx 10468 Yolanda Valez	K-5		298	83%	718/601-2632 Fax 718/796-7490
HS for Energy & Technology 2474 Crotona Ave, Bronx 10458 Marie Guillaume	9-12	T	386	81%	718/733-3080 Fax 718/733-3085
HS of American Studies-Lehman 2925 Goulden Ave, Bronx 10468 Alessandro Weiss	9-12		382 13	24%	718/329-2144 Fax 718/329-0792

1	Superintendent	8	Curric/Instruct K-12	19	Chief Financial Officer	29	Family/Consumer Science
2	Bus/Finance/Purchasing	9	Curric/Instruct Elem	20	Art K-12	30	Adult Education
3	Buildings And Grounds	10	Curric/Instruct Sec	21	Art Elem	31	Career/Sch-to-Work Elem
4	Food Service	11	Federal Program	22	Art Sec	32	Career/Sch-to-Work Elem
5	Transportation	12	Title I	23	Music K-12	33	Career/Sch-to-Work Sec
6	Athletic	13	Title V	24	Music Elem	34	Early Childhood Ed
7	Health Services	15	Asst Superintendent	25	Music Sec	35	Health/Phys Education
		16	Instructional Media Svcs	26	Business Education	36	Guidance Services K-12
		17	Chief Operations Officer	27	Career & Tech Ed	37	Guidance Services Elem
		18	Chief Academic Officer	28	Technology Education	38	Guidance Services Sec

39	Social Studies K-12	49	English/Lang Arts Elem	59	Special Education Elem	69	Academic Assessment
40	Social Studies Elem	50	English/Lang Arts Sec	60	Special Education Sec	70	Research/Development
41	Social Studies Sec	51	Reading K-12	61	Foreign/World Lang K-12	71	Public Information
42	Science K-12	52	Reading Elem	62	Foreign/World Lang Elem	72	Summer School
43	Science Elem	53	Reading Sec	63	Foreign/World Lang Sec	73	Instructional Tech
44	Science Sec	54	Remedial Reading K-12	64	Religious Education K-12	74	Inservice Training
45	Math K-12	55	Remedial Reading Elem	65	Religious Education Elem	75	Marketing/Distributive
46	Math Elem	56	Remedial Reading Sec	66	Religious Education Sec	76	Info Systems
47	Math Sec	57	Bilingual/ELL	67	School Board President	77	Psychological Assess
48	English/Lang Arts K-12	58	Special Education K-12	68	Teacher Personnel	78	Affirmative Action

New York School Directory
Bronx County

School	Grades	Type	Enroll	%	Phone
HS Teaching & the Professions 2780 Reservoir Ave, Bronx 10468 Kamele McLaren	9-12	T	410 15	87%	718/329-7380 Fax 718/329-7381
In-Tech Academy Middle HS 368 2975 Tibbett Ave, Bronx 10463 Stephen Seltzer	6-12	T	1,017 42	86%	718/432-4300 Fax 718/432-4310
International Sch for Lib Arts 2780 Reservoir Ave, Bronx 10468 Francine Cruz	6-12	T	503	98%	718/329-8570 Fax 718/329-8572
IS 206 Ann Mersereau 2280 Aqueduct Ave, Bronx 10468 Rafael Cabral	6-8	TV	269 24	93%	718/584-1570 Fax 718/584-7928
Ⓜ IS 254 2452 Washington Ave, Bronx 10458 Javier Ocampo	6-8	T	455 23	89%	718/220-8700 Fax 718/220-4881
Ⓜ JHS 80 the Mosholu Pkwy Sch 149 E Mosholu Pkwy N, Bronx 10467 Emmanuel Polanco	6-8	TV	644 52	88%	718/405-6300 Fax 718/405-6324
JHS 118 William W Niles 577 E 179th St, Bronx 10457 Giulia Cox	6-8	TV	1,059 60	90%	718/584-2330 Fax 718/584-7763
Ⓐ John F Kennedy YABC 99 Terrace View Ave, Bronx 10463 James Barron	10-12		250		718/817-7470
Jonas Bronck Academy 400 E Fordham Rd Frnt H, Bronx 10458 Brenda Gonzalez	6-8	T	267 8	86%	718/365-2502 Fax 718/365-3892
Kappa Int'l High Sch 500 E Fordham Rd, Bronx 10458 Panorea Panagiosoulis	9-12	T	423	87%	718/933-1247 Fax 718/933-1568
Kingsbridge Int'l High Sch 2780 Reservoir Ave Rm 215, Bronx 10468 William Gagstetter	9-12	T	424	96%	718/329-8580 Fax 718/329-8582
Marble Hill HS-Int'l Studies 99 Terrace View Ave, Bronx 10463 Kirsten Larson	9-12	T	443 8	89%	718/561-0973 Fax 718/561-5612
Marie Curie High Sch 120 W 231st St, Bronx 10463 Peta Williams	9-12	T	392	75%	718/432-6491 Fax 718/796-7051
MS 390 1930 Andrews Ave, Bronx 10453 Robert Mercedes	6-8	GT	551 28	95%	718/583-5501 Fax 718/583-5556
New Sch Leadership Journalism 120 W 231st St, Bronx 10463 Eduardo Mora	6-8	T	725	98%	718/601-2869 Fax 718/601-2867
PS 3 Raul Julia Micro Society 2100 Lafontaine Ave, Bronx 10457 Denise Gould	PK-8	T	325 30	98%	718/584-1899 Fax 718/584-3590
PS 7 Milton Fein Sch 3201 Kingsbridge Ave, Bronx 10463 Miosoitis Ramos	K-5	T	603 35	79%	718/796-8695 Fax 718/796-7204
PS 8 Issac Varian 3010 Briggs Ave, Bronx 10458 Claudia Tahiri	PK-5	T	895 45	87%	718/584-3043 Fax 718/584-7376
PS 9 Ryer Ave Elem Sch 230 E 183rd St, Bronx 10458 Jacqueline Bailey	PK-5	T	814 62	92%	718/584-3291 Fax 718/584-7579
PS 23 New Childrens Sch 2151 Washington Ave, Bronx 10457 Shirley Torres	PK-5	T	444 35	97%	718/584-3992 Fax 718/584-7252
PS 24 Spuyten Duyvil 660 W 236th St, Bronx 10463 Steven Schwartz	K-5		837 37	27%	718/796-8845 Fax 718/796-7243
PS 32 Belmont 690 E 183rd St, Bronx 10458 Rebecca Lew	PK-5	T	725 38	97%	718/584-3645 Fax 718/584-7927
PS 33 Timothy Dwight 2424 Jerome Ave, Bronx 10468 Lynette Santos	PK-5	GT	844 50	91%	718/584-3926 Fax 718/584-7004
PS 46 Edgar Allan Poe 2760 Briggs Ave, Bronx 10458 Jennifer Ade	K-5	GT	817 51	88%	718/584-4450 Fax 718/584-7402
PS 51 Bronx STEM & Arts Acad 695 E 182nd St, Bronx 10457 Min Hong	PK-5	T	203 10	85%	718/733-0347 Fax 718/733-5142
PS 54 2703 Webster Ave, Bronx 10458 Marybelle Ferreira	PK-5	T	452 26	96%	718/584-4203 Fax 718/584-4326
PS 56 Norwood Heights 341 E 207th St, Bronx 10467 Maureen O'Neill	K-5	T	673 27	83%	718/920-1100 Fax 718/920-1105
PS 59 Community Sch of Tech 2185 Bathgate Ave, Bronx 10457 Sita Basu	PK-5	T	522 30	98%	718/584-4730 Fax 718/584-7518
PS 81 Robert J Christen 5550 Riverdale Ave, Bronx 10471 Anna Kirrane	K-5		762 30	44%	718/796-8965 Fax 718/796-7242
PS 85 Great Expectations 2400 Marion Ave, Bronx 10458 Sara Medina	PK-5	T	836 51	95%	718/584-5275 Fax 718/584-7765
PS 86 Kingbridge Heights 2756 Reservoir Ave, Bronx 10468 Fiona Gleeson	PK-6	GT	1,634 77	86%	718/584-5585 Fax 718/584-7027
PS 91 Bronx 2200 Aqueduct Ave E, Bronx 10453 Meridith Nasjlett	K-5	GT	588	96%	718/584-5805 Fax 718/584-7495
PS 94 Kings College Sch 3530 Kings College Pl, Bronx 10467 Diane Sesin	K-5	GT	1,149 49	93%	718/405-6345 Fax 718/405-6358
PS 95 Sheila Mencher 3961 Hillman Ave, Bronx 10463 Serge Davis	K-8	T	1,135	81%	718/796-9200 Fax 718/796-7330
PS 159 Luis Munoz Marin Biling 2315 Washington Ave, Bronx 10458 Luis Liz	K-5	GT	186 13	87%	718/584-6140 Fax 718/584-7794
PS 205 Fiorello Laguardia 2475 Southern Blvd, Bronx 10458 Jenneth Santiago	K-5	T	899 27	89%	718/584-6390 Fax 718/584-7941
PS 207 3030 Godwin Ter, Bronx 10463 Tara O'Brien	PK-3	GT	337 30	90%	718/796-9645 Fax 718/796-7206
PS 209 313 E 183rd St, Bronx 10458 Anne Keegan	PK-2	T	277 12	94%	718/364-0085 Fax 718/364-9548
PS 226 1950 Sedgwick Ave, Bronx 10453 Gloria Darden	PK-5	GT	409 25	96%	929/452-3090 Fax 929/452-3095
PS 246 Poe Center 2641 Grand Concourse, Bronx 10468 Andrea Johnson	K-5	T	625 36	92%	718/584-6764 Fax 718/584-7005
PS 279 Capt Manuel Rivera Jr 2100 Walton Ave, Bronx 10453 Jean Dalton	K-8	AT	947	95%	718/584-6004 Fax 718/584-7220
PS 291 2195 Andrews Ave, Bronx 10453 Carlos Velez	K-5	GT	573 26	100%	718/563-0776 Fax 718/563-1499
PS 306 40 W Tremont Ave, Bronx 10453 Darryl Harrington	K-5	T	610	88%	718/583-5355 Fax 718/583-5885
PS 310 Marble Hill 260 W Kingsbridge Rd, Bronx 10463 Elizabeth Cardona	PK-5	GT	648 42	93%	718/796-9434 Fax 718/796-9528

79 Student Personnel
80 Driver Ed/Safety
81 Gifted/Talented
82 Video Services
83 Substance Abuse Prev
84 Erate
85 AIDS Education
88 Alternative/At Risk
89 Multi-Cultural Curriculum
90 Social Work
91 Safety/Security
92 Magnet School
93 Parental Involvement
95 Tech Prep Program
97 Chief Information Officer
98 Chief Technology Officer
270 Character Education
271 Migrant Education
273 Teacher Mentor
274 Before/After Sch
275 Response To Intervention
277 Remedial Math K-12
280 Literacy Coach
285 STEM
286 Digital Learning
288 Common Core Standards
294 Accountability
295 Network System
296 Title II Programs
297 Webmaster
298 Grant Writer/Ptnrships
750 Chief Innovation Officer
751 Chief of Staff
752 Social Emotional Learning

Other School Types
Ⓐ = Alternative School
Ⓒ = Charter School
Ⓜ = Magnet School
Ⓨ = Year-Round School

School Programs
A = Alternative Program
G = Adult Classes
M = Magnet Program
T = Title I Schoolwide
V = Career & Tech Ed Programs

Social Media
 = Facebook
 = Twitter

New Schools are shaded
New Superintendents and Principals are bold
Personnel with email addresses are underscored

NY—21

Bronx County

Market Data Retrieval

School	Grd	Prgm	Enr/#Cls	SN	Phone
PS 315 Lab Sch 2865 Claflin Ave, Bronx 10468 Gaby Flores	K-8	T	230 11	94%	929/237-7750 Fax 929/237-7752
PS 340 25 W 195th St, Bronx 10468 Alexei Nichols	PK-5	T	567 25	84%	718/220-1830 Fax 718/220-1866
PS 360 2880 Kingsbridge Ter, Bronx 10463 Iris Aldea-Pollack	PK-5	T	392 25	94%	718/548-1511 Fax 718/548-1536
PS 382- ES Math Sci & Tech Sch 125 E 181st St, Bronx 10453 Avon Cowell	K-5	T	276	96%	718/933-8061 Fax 718/933-8157
PS 386-Envir Citizenship Sch 125 E 181st St, Bronx 10453 Lynnann Fox	PK-5	T	574	98%	718/563-3292 Fax 718/563-3453
PS 396 1930 Andrews Ave, Bronx 10453 Nicole Tine	PK-5	T	289 22	93%	718/294-0862 Fax 718/583-5556
PS X15 Inst for Enviro Lrng 2195 Andrews Ave, Bronx 10453 Tara Edmonds	K-8	T	487 25	78%	718/563-0473 Fax 718/563-1568
PS/MS 20 P O George Werdan III 3050 Webster Ave, Bronx 10467 Carla Ling	PK-8	T	895 59	96%	718/515-9370 Fax 718/515-9378
PS/MS 37 Multiple Intelligence 360 W 230th St, Bronx 10463 Eftyhia Karanikolas	K-8	T	614 29	86%	718/796-0360
PS/MS 280 Mosholu Parkway 3202 Steuben Ave, Bronx 10467 James Weeks	K-8	T	798 23	93%	718/405-6360 Fax 718/405-6329
ⓐ Pulse High Sch 560 E 179th St, Bronx 10457 Carol Wiggins	9-12	T	202 14	91%	718/294-0230
Riverdale-Kingsbridge Academy 660 W 237th St, Bronx 10463 Lori Omara	6-12	GV	1,541 45	51%	718/796-8516 Fax 718/796-8657
Theatre Arts Production Co Sch 2225 Webster Ave, Bronx 10457 Ron Link	6-12	T	539 6	79%	718/584-0832 Fax 718/584-5102
Thomas C Giordano MS 45 2502 Lorillard Pl, Bronx 10458 Annamaria Giordano	6-8	GTV	704 56	96%	718/584-1660 Fax 718/584-7968
ⓐ Walton Campus YABC 2780 Reservoir Ave, Bronx 10468 Thomas Lopez	10-12		250		718/329-7380
West Bronx Acad for the Future 500 E Fordham Rd, Bronx 10458 Wilper Morales	6-12	T	613 50	94%	718/563-7139 Fax 718/563-7362
World View High Sch 100 W Mosholu Pkwy S, Bronx 10468 Martin Hernandez	9-12	T	585	76%	718/601-0391 Fax 718/601-0821

- **Community School District 11** PID: 10909668 718/519-2620
  1250 Arnow Ave, Bronx 10469 Fax 718/519-2626
  (Part of New York City Dept of Ed in New York County)
  Cristine Vaughan 1

Public Schs..Principal	Grd	Prgm	Enr/#Cls	SN	Phone
Academy Scholarship & Entrepnr 921 E 228th St, Bronx 10466 Zenobia White	9-12	T	361	74%	718/696-3840 Fax 718/696-3841
Astor Collegiate Academy 925 Astor Ave, Bronx 10469 Sandra Burgos	9-12	T	489 15	73%	718/944-3418 Fax 718/944-3638
Baychester Academy 3500 Edson Ave, Bronx 10466 Cristine Vaughan	PK-5	T	415	81%	718/325-1138 Fax 718/325-1558
Baychester Middle Sch 3750 Baychester Ave, Bronx 10466 Shawn Mangar	6-8	T	291 4	85%	718/547-1890 Fax 718/547-1895
Bronx Academy Health Careers 800 E Gun Hill Rd, Bronx 10467 Dawn Santiago	9-12	T	369	79%	718/696-3340 Fax 718/696-3380
Bronx Aerospace High Sch 800 E Gun Hill Rd, Bronx 10467 Erika Hurtado	9-12	T	271	78%	718/696-6010 Fax 718/696-6030
Bronx Green Middle Sch 2441 Wallace Ave, Bronx 10467 Charles Johnson	6-8	T	402	92%	718/325-6593 Fax 718/653-3625
Bronx Health Sciences High Sch 750 Baychester Ave, Bronx 10475 Miriam Rivas	9-12	T	291 10	70%	718/904-5450 Fax 718/904-5451
Bronx HS for the Visual Arts 2040 Antin Pl, Bronx 10462 Iris Witherspoon	9-12	T	443 8	78%	718/319-5160 Fax 718/319-5165
Bronx HS Writing/Comm Arts 800 E Gun Hill Rd, Bronx 10467 Terri Grey	9-12	T	298 16	71%	718/944-5660
Bronx Lab Sch 800 E Gun Hill Rd, Bronx 10467 Sarah Marcy	9-12	T	352	83%	718/696-3700 Fax 718/696-3730
Bronx Park Middle Sch 2441 Wallace Ave, Bronx 10467 Renee Rinaldi	6-8	T	402	93%	718/652-6090 Fax 718/652-6096
Bronxdale High Sch 925 Astor Ave, Bronx 10469 Grace White	9-12	T	452	79%	718/944-3655 Fax 718/944-3662
Bronxwood Preparatory Academy 921 E 228th St, Bronx 10466 Janet Gallardo	9-12	T	356	70%	718/696-3820 Fax 718/696-3821
ⓐ Christopher Columbus YABC 925 Astor Ave, Bronx 10469 Ruth Colton	10-12		250		718/944-3700
Collegiate Inst-Math & Science 925 Astor Ave, Bronx 10469 Fredrick Nelson	9-12	T	575 16	72%	718/944-3635 Fax 718/652-3525
Cornerstone Acad-Soc Action ES 3441 Steenwick Ave, Bronx 10475 James Bellon	PK-5	T	366	88%	718/794-6160 Fax 718/794-6170
Cornerstone Acad-Soc Action MS 3441 Steenwick Ave, Bronx 10475 Jamaal Bowman	6-8	T	251	74%	718/794-7970 Fax 718/794-7981
© Equality Charter High Sch 2141 Seward Ave, Bronx 10473 Favrol Philemy	9-12	T	311		718/159-9597 Fax 718/824-6046
© Equality Charter Middle Sch 4140 Hutchinson River Pkwy E, Bronx 10475 Amanda Huza	6-8	T	311	77%	718/517-3169 Fax 718/320-3721
Harry S Truman High Sch 750 Baychester Ave, Bronx 10475 Keri Alfano	9-12	GTV	2,185	72%	718/904-5400 Fax 718/904-5502
ⓜ HS for Contemporary Arts 800 E Gun Hill Rd, Bronx 10467 Pedro Cubero	9-12	T	372	79%	718/944-5610 Fax 718/944-5650
HS for Language & Innovation 925 Astor Ave, Bronx 10469 Julie Nariman	9-12	T	362	99%	718/944-3625 Fax 718/944-3641
HS of Computers & Technology 800 E Gun Hill Rd, Bronx 10467 David Wills	9-12	T	539	76%	718/696-3930 Fax 718/696-3950

1 Superintendent	8 Curric/Instruct K-12	19 Chief Financial Officer	29 Family/Consumer Science	39 Social Studies K-12	49 English/Lang Arts Elem	59 Special Education Elem	69 Academic Assessment
2 Bus/Finance/Purchasing	9 Curric/Instruct Elem	20 Art K-12	30 Adult Education	40 Social Studies Elem	50 English/Lang Arts Sec	60 Special Education Sec	70 Research/Development
3 Buildings And Grounds	10 Curric/Instruct Sec	21 Art Elem	31 Career/Sch-to-Work K-12	41 Social Studies Sec	51 Reading K-12	61 Foreign/World Lang K-12	71 Public Information
4 Food Service	11 Federal Program	22 Art Sec	32 Career/Sch-to-Work Elem	42 Science K-12	52 Reading Elem	62 Foreign/World Lang Elem	72 Summer School
5 Transportation	12 Title I	23 Music K-12	33 Career/Sch-to-Work Sec	43 Science Elem	53 Reading Sec	63 Foreign/World Lang Sec	73 Instructional Tech
6 Athletic	13 Title V	24 Music Elem	34 Early Childhood Ed	44 Science Sec	54 Remedial Reading K-12	64 Religious Education K-12	74 Inservice Training
7 Health Services	15 Asst Superintendent	25 Music Sec	35 Health/Phys Education	45 Math K-12	55 Remedial Reading Elem	65 Religious Education Elem	75 Marketing/Distributive
	16 Instructional Media Svcs	26 Business Education	36 Guidance Services K-12	46 Math Elem	56 Remedial Reading Sec	66 Religious Education Sec	76 Info Systems
	17 Chief Operations Officer	27 Career & Tech Ed	37 Guidance Services Elem	47 Math Sec	57 Bilingual/ELL	67 School Board President	77 Psychological Assess
	18 Chief Academic Officer	28 Technology Education	38 Guidance Services Sec	48 English/Lang Arts K-12	58 Special Education K-12	68 Teacher Personnel	78 Affirmative Action

New York School Directory — Bronx County

School	Grades	Prog	Enroll	%	Phone
IS 181 Pablo Casals 800 Baychester Ave, Bronx 10475 Christopher Warnock	6-8	T	878 31	79%	718/904-5600 Fax 718/904-5620
JHS 127 Castle Hill 1560 Purdy St, Bronx 10462 Harry Sherman	6-8	T	812 50	74%	718/892-8600 Fax 718/892-8300
JHS 144 Michelangelo Sch 2545 Gunther Ave, Bronx 10469 Ellen Barrett	6-8	T	446	76%	718/794-9749 Fax 718/794-9755
Leaders of Tomorrow 3710 Barnes Ave, Bronx 10467 Joseph Biernat	6-8	T	461	92%	718/994-1028 Fax 718/345-3327
Linden Tree Elem Sch 1560 Purdy St, Bronx 10462 Lisa DeBonis	PK-5	T	387	76%	718/239-7401 Fax 718/239-7406
Matilida Avenue School PS 483 4520 Matilda Ave, Bronx 10470 Maria Cioffi	K-3	T	165	76%	718/325-4360 Fax 718/325-4365
MS 180 Dr Daniel Hale Williams 700 Baychester Ave, Bronx 10475 Marlon Williams	6-8	T	1,041 75	68%	718/904-5650 Fax 718/904-5655
MS 355 Bronx Alliance Mid Sch 3750 Baychester Ave, Bronx 10466 Steven Cobb	6-8	T	317	86%	718/652-2060 Fax 718/652-3682
New World High Sch 921 E 228th St, Bronx 10466 Mithat Gashi	9-12	T	390	96%	718/696-3800 Fax 718/696-3801
North Bronx Sch of Empowerment 3710 Barnes Ave, Bronx 10467 Magdalen Neyra	6-8	T	514	88%	718/652-0519 Fax 718/652-0428
One World Middle Sch-Edenwald 3750 Baychester Ave, Bronx 10466 Patricia Wynne	6-8	T	328	88%	718/515-6780 Fax 718/515-6785
Pelham Academy 2441 Wallace Ave, Bronx 10467 Anthony Rivera	6-8	T	356	87%	718/881-3136 Fax 718/881-3413
Pelham Gardens Middle Sch 2545 Gunther Ave, Bronx 10469 Denise Williams	6-8	T	439	76%	718/794-9750 Fax 718/794-9756
Pelham Preparatory Academy 925 Astor Ave, Bronx 10469 Benvenuto Ferron	9-12	T	490	73%	718/944-3601 Fax 718/944-3479
PS 16 Wakefield Sch 4550 Carpenter Ave, Bronx 10470 Eduardo Calderon	PK-5	T	321 35	93%	718/324-1262 Fax 718/324-8370
PS 19 Judith K Weiss Woodlawn 4318 Katonah Ave, Bronx 10470 Ellen O'Brien	K-8		527 18	52%	718/324-1924 Fax 718/994-9132
PS 21 Philip H Sheridan 715 E 225th St, Bronx 10466 Joyce Coleman	K-5	T	602 40	91%	718/652-3903 Fax 718/231-2556
PS 41 Gun Hill Road 3352 Olinville Ave, Bronx 10467 Michelle Moore	K-5	T	817 41	97%	718/652-3461 Fax 718/231-2668
PS 68 Bronx 4011 Monticello Ave, Bronx 10466 Aidimaris Soler	PK-5		578 45	66%	718/324-2854 Fax 718/324-3852
PS 76 Bennington 900 Adee Ave, Bronx 10469 Louise Sedotto	K-5	T	830 30	77%	718/882-8865 Fax 718/882-8870
PS 78 Anne Hutchinson 1400 Needham Ave, Bronx 10469 Dr Claudina Skerritt	PK-5	T	749 51	81%	718/652-1244 Fax 718/231-2756
PS 83 Donald Hertz 950 Rhinelander Ave, Bronx 10462 Brandon Muccino	K-8		1,631 40	65%	718/863-1993 Fax 718/863-5525
PS 87 Bronx 1935 Bussing Ave, Bronx 10466 Donna Anaman	K-5	T	514 27	74%	718/324-5188 Fax 718/325-1148
PS 89 Bronx 980 Mace Ave, Bronx 10469 Ralph Martinez	PK-8		1,504	77%	718/653-0835 Fax 718/231-2863
PS 96 Richard Rodgers 2385 Olinville Avenue, Bronx 10467 Marta Garcia	K-5	T	850 41	77%	718/652-4959 Fax 718/231-2889
PS 97 Bronx 1375 Mace Ave, Bronx 10469 Kathleen Bornkamp	PK-5	T	598 70	77%	718/655-4446 Fax 718/655-6063
PS 103 Hector Fontanez 4125 Carpenter Ave, Bronx 10466 Farid Reyes	PK-5	T	955 57	88%	718/655-0261 Fax 718/654-7930
PS 105 Sen Abraham Bernstein 725 Brady Ave, Bronx 10462 Christopher Eustace	PK-5	T	952 70	91%	718/824-7350 Fax 718/828-4531
PS 106 Parkchester 1514 Olmstead Ave, Bronx 10462 Eugenia Montalvo	PK-5	T	1,073 58	75%	718/892-1006 Fax 718/823-8008
PS 108 Philip J Abinanti 1166 Neill Ave, Bronx 10461 Charles Sperrazza	PK-5	T	581 27	77%	718/863-9829 Fax 718/828-1712
PS 111 Seton Falls 3740 Baychester Ave, Bronx 10466 Celina Gutierrez	PK-5	T	603 44	89%	718/881-2418 Fax 718/405-5927
PS 112 Bronxwood 1925 Schieffelin Ave, Bronx 10466 Andrea Tucci	PK-5	T	392 35	88%	718/654-6377 Fax 718/654-7931
PS 121 Throop 2750 Throop Ave, Bronx 10469 Gloria Martinez	PK-5	T	785 38	69%	718/654-2055 Fax 718/519-2613
PS 153 Helen Keller 650 Baychester Ave, Bronx 10475 Meghan Kelley	PK-5		608 40	61%	718/904-5550 Fax 718/904-5564
PS 160 Walt Disney 4140 Hutchinson River Pkwy E, Bronx 10475 L Baker	PK-5	T	390 40	70%	718/822-8402 Fax 718/822-8146
PS 175 City Island 200 City Island Ave, Bronx 10464 Amy Lipson	K-8		297 18	50%	718/885-1093 Fax 718/885-2315
PS 178 Dr Selman Waksman 850 Baychester Ave, Bronx 10475 Deborah Levine	K-5	T	359 27	77%	718/904-5570 Fax 718/904-5575
PS MS 11X498 Van Nest Academy 1640 Bronxdale Ave, Bronx 10462 Carol Gilligan	K-8		659	78%	718/409-3001 Fax 718/409-3002
PS/MS 194 2365 Waterbury Ave, Bronx 10462 Rosa Sifuentes	K-8	T	1,273 30	79%	718/892-5270 Fax 718/892-2495
Steam Bridge School PS 481 1684 White Plains Rd, Bronx 10462 Katiria Rojas	PK-3	T	216	89%	718/239-5660 Fax 718/239-5665
Young Voices Academy of Bronx 800 Lydig Ave, Bronx 10462 Nadia Cruz-Perez	PK-5	T	431	82%	718/794-4080 Fax 718/798-4089

- **Community School District 12** PID: 10909670 718/328-2310
  1970 W Farms Rd Rm 154, Bronx 10460

  (Part of New York City Dept of Ed in New York County)
  Jacqueline Rosado 1

---

79 Student Personnel
80 Driver Ed/Safety
81 Gifted/Talented
82 Video Services
83 Substance Abuse Prev
84 Erate
85 AIDS Education
88 Alternative/At Risk
89 Multi-Cultural Curriculum
90 Social Work

91 Safety/Security
92 Magnet School
93 Parental Involvement
95 Tech Prep Program
97 Chief Information Officer
98 Chief Technology Officer
270 Character Education
271 Migrant Education
273 Teacher Mentor
274 Before/After Sch

275 Response To Intervention
277 Remedial Math K-12
280 Literacy Coach
285 STEM
286 Digital Learning
288 Common Core Standards
294 Accountability
295 Network System
296 Title II Programs
297 Webmaster

298 Grant Writer/Ptnrships
750 Chief Innovation Officer
751 Chief of Staff
752 Social Emotional Learning

Other School Types
Ⓐ = Alternative School
Ⓒ = Charter School
Ⓜ = Magnet School
Ⓨ = Year-Round School

School Programs
A = Alternative Program
G = Adult Classes
M = Magnet Program
T = Title I Schoolwide
V = Career & Tech Ed Programs

New Schools are shaded
New Superintendents and Principals are bold
Personnel with email addresses are underscored

Social Media
 = Facebook
 = Twitter

Bronx County

Market Data Retrieval

Public Schs..Principal	Grd	Prgm	Enr/#Cls	SN		
Accion Academy 977 Fox St, Bronx 10459 Victor Frias	6-8	T	382 15	96%	718/378-1649 Fax 718/378-4707	
Archer Elem Sch 1827 Archer St, Bronx 10460 M Finerty	PK-5	T	433	95%	718/828-3791 Fax 718/828-3989	
Ⓐ Arturo Schomburg Satelite Acad 1010 Rev James A Polite Ave, Bronx 10459 Flora Padro	10-12	T	132	86%	718/518-3050 Fax 718/589-3710	
Bronx Career & College Prep HS 800 Home St, Bronx 10456 Julia Baly	9-12	T	279	86%	718/542-4011 Fax 718/542-4377	
Bronx Envision Academy 1619 Boston Rd, Bronx 10460 Emily Shu	9-12	T	396	87%	718/589-1590 Fax 718/589-1595	
Bronx Latin Sch 800 Home St, Bronx 10456 Annette Fiorentino	6-12	T	537	95%	718/991-6349 Fax 718/991-6627	
Bronx Little Sch 1827 Archer St, Bronx 10460 Beverly Urquiza	PK-5	T	318 7	88%	718/792-2650 Fax 718/792-4149	
Ⓐ Bronx Regional High Sch 1010 Rev James A Polite Ave, Bronx 10459 Colin Thomas	10-12	T	176 20	90%	718/991-2020 Fax 718/617-0257	
Cinema Sch 1551 E 172nd St, Bronx 10472 Keisha Warner	9-12	T	359	78%	718/620-2560 Fax 718/620-2561	
© Dr R Izquierdo Health & Sci CS 800 Home St, Bronx 10456 Richard Burke	6-12	T	773	98%	718/378-0490 Fax 718/378-0492	
East Bronx Academy for Future 1716 Southern Blvd, Bronx 10460 Sarah Scrogin	6-12	T	648 21	94%	718/861-8641 Fax 718/861-8634	
Emolior Academy 1970 W Farms Rd, Bronx 10460 Michael Abbey	6-8	T	347	90%	718/842-2670 Fax 718/842-2857	
Esmt IS 190 1550 Crotona Park E, Bronx 10460 Castella McKenzie	6-8	T	269 12	94%	718/620-9423 Fax 718/620-9927	
Explorations Academy 1619 Boston Rd, Bronx 10460 Susana Hernandez	9-12	T	321	87%	718/893-6173 Fax 718/893-6439	
Fairmont Neighborhood Sch 1550 Vyse Ave, Bronx 10460 Dr Scott Wolfson	PK-5	T	278	94%	718/860-5210 Fax 718/860-5215	
Ⓐ Fannie Lou Hamer Freedom HS 1021 Jennings St, Bronx 10460 Jeffrey Palladino	9-12	T	472 50	82%	718/861-0521 Fax 718/861-0619	
Fannie Lou Hamer Middle Sch 1001 Jennings St, Bronx 10460 Abbey Wilson	6-8	T	281 11	83%	718/319-7270 Fax 718/319-7275	
Frederick Douglass Academy V 2111 Crotona Ave, Bronx 10457 Sayi Neufeld	6-8	T	184 7	89%	718/561-1617 Fax 718/561-2184	
High School of World Cultures 1300 Boynton Ave, Bronx 10472 Ramon Namnun	9-12	T	382 15	98%	718/860-8120 Fax 718/893-7152	
IS 217 Sch of Performing Arts 977 Fox St, Bronx 10459 Dionne Williams	6-8	T	340	89%	718/589-4844 Fax 718/589-7998	
IS 318 Sch Math Sci & Tech 1919 Prospect Ave, Bronx 10457 Suleika Dotel	6-8	T	224 25	95%	718/294-8504 Fax 718/901-0778	
Ⓐ James Monroe Ed Campus YABC 1300 Boynton Ave, Bronx 10472 Carmel Belizaire	10-12		250		718/860-8287	
JHS 98 Herman Ridder 1619 Boston Rd, Bronx 10460 Mark Turcotte	6-8	T	245 50	92%	718/589-8200 Fax 718/589-8179	
Kappa III 2055 Mapes Ave, Bronx 10460 Jean Colon	6-8	T	362 11	91%	718/561-3580 Fax 718/561-3719	
Metropolitan High Sch 1180 Rev James A Polite Ave, Bronx 10459 Leslie Chislett	9-12	T	274	94%	718/991-4634 Fax 718/542-7294	
Metropolitan Soundview HS 1300 Boynton Ave, Bronx 10472 Emarilix Lopez-Tua	9-12	T	420	91%	718/860-8240 Fax 718/860-8232	
Mott Hall V Sch 1551 E 172nd St, Bronx 10472 Peter Oroszlany	6-12	T	664	88%	718/620-8160 Fax 718/620-8161	
MS 129 Acad Indep Lrng & Ldrsp 2055 Mapes Ave, Bronx 10460 Jason Reyes	6-8	T	513 22	90%	718/933-5976 Fax 718/933-8132	
Pan American Int'l HS-Monroe 1300 Boynton Ave, Bronx 10472 Bridgit Clair Bye	9-12	T	421	99%	718/991-7238	
© Pharos Acad Charter Sch 1005 Intervale Ave, Bronx 10459 **Elix Duggins**	9-12		401		646/915-0025 Fax 646/915-0037	
PS 6 West Farms 1000 E Tremont Ave, Bronx 10460 Tiawana Perez	PK-5	T	523 45	98%	718/542-7676 Fax 718/589-7278	
PS 44 David C Farragut 1825 Prospect Ave, Bronx 10457 Melissa Klein	PK-5	T	263 28	97%	718/583-2360 Fax 718/901-4068	
PS 47 John Randolph 1794 E 172nd St, Bronx 10472 Thomas Guarnieri	K-5	T	1,018	95%	718/824-0950 Fax 718/904-1166	
PS 57 Crescent 2111 Crotona Ave, Bronx 10457 Mary Sanchez	PK-5	T	538 28	91%	718/367-9446 Fax 718/561-7972	
PS 61 Francisco Oller 1550 Crotona Park E, Bronx 10460 Marjorie Sanchez	PK-5	T	261 22	95%	718/542-7230 Fax 718/589-7361	
PS 66 Sch Higher Expectations 1001 Jennings St, Bronx 10460 Kevin Goodman	PK-5	T	531	89%	718/319-2820 Fax 718/589-7375	
PS 67 Mohegan Sch 2024 Mohegan Ave, Bronx 10460 Jeffrey Santiago	PK-5	T	424	99%	718/823-4101 Fax 718/823-4105	
PS 134 George F Bristow 1330 Bristow St, Bronx 10459 Martin Alvara	PK-5	T	567 44	97%	718/328-3351 Fax 718/589-7581	
PS 150 Charles James Fox 920 E 167th St, Bronx 10459 Norma Sanchez	PK-5	T	704 36	93%	718/328-7729 Fax 718/589-7590	
PS 195 1250 Ward Ave, Bronx 10472 Unal Karakas	PK-5	T	871 22	91%	718/861-4461 Fax 718/861-7935	
PS 196 1250 Ward Ave, Bronx 10472 Lizzette Rivera	PK-5	T	811 35	87%	718/328-7187 Fax 718/861-8401	
PS 211 1919 Prospect Ave, Bronx 10457 Tanya Drummond	PK-8	T	520 37	91%	718/901-0436 Fax 718/901-4681	
PS 214 1970 W Farms Rd, Bronx 10460 David Cintron	PK-8	T	1,080 70	85%	718/589-6728 Fax 718/328-7762	
PS 536 1827 Archer St, Bronx 10460 Jesse Yarbrough	PK-5	T	402	94%	718/931-4270 Fax 718/931-4275	

1	Superintendent	8	Curric/Instruct K-12	19	Chief Financial Officer	29	Family/Consumer Science	39	Social Studies K-12
2	Bus/Finance/Purchasing	9	Curric/Instruct Elem	20	Art K-12	30	Adult Education	40	Social Studies Elem
3	Buildings And Grounds	10	Curric/Instruct Sec	21	Art Elem	31	Career/Sch-to-Work K-12	41	Social Studies Sec
4	Food Service	11	Federal Program	22	Art Sec	32	Career/Sch-to-Work Elem	42	Science K-12
5	Transportation	12	Title I	23	Music K-12	33	Career/Sch-to-Work Sec	43	Science Elem
6	Athletic	13	Title V	24	Music Elem	34	Early Childhood Ed	44	Science Sec
7	Health Services	14	Asst Superintendent	25	Music Sec	35	Health/Phys Education	45	Math K-12
		16	Instructional Media Svcs	26	Business Education	36	Guidance Services K-12	46	Math Elem
		17	Chief Operations Officer	27	Career & Tech Ed	37	Guidance Services Elem	47	Math Sec
		18	Chief Academic Officer	28	Technology Education	38	Guidance Services Sec	48	English/Lang Arts K-12
49	English/Lang Arts Elem	59	Special Education Elem	69	Academic Assessment				
50	English/Lang Arts Sec	60	Special Education Sec	70	Research/Development				
51	Reading K-12	61	Foreign/World Lang K-12	71	Public Information				
52	Reading Elem	62	Foreign/World Lang Elem	72	Summer School				
53	Reading Sec	63	Foreign/World Lang Sec	73	Instructional Tech				
54	Remedial Reading K-12	64	Religious Education K-12	74	Inservice Training				
55	Remedial Reading Elem	65	Religious Education Elem	75	Marketing/Distributive				
56	Remedial Reading Sec	66	Religious Education Sec	76	Info Systems				
57	Bilingual/ELL	67	School Board President	77	Psychological Assess				
58	Special Education K-12	68	Teacher Personnel	78	Affirmative Action				

NY—24

New York School Directory | Bronx County

PS 595 700 E 179th St, Bronx 10457 Suheil Soto	K-2	T	152	92%	
Samara Cmty Sch 1550 Vyse Ave, Bronx 10460 Danielle Derrig	PK-4	T	253	95%	718/935-3448 Fax 718/860-5333
Sch of Science & Applied Lrng 2050 Prospect Ave, Bronx 10457 Venessa Singleton	PK-5	T	551 30	91%	718/584-6310 Fax 718/220-1370
Urban Scholars Cmty Sch 1180 Tinton Ave, Bronx 10456 Debra Clarke	PK-5	T	287	96%	718/842-8133 Fax 718/842-8442
Ⓐ Wings Academy 1122 E 180th St, Bronx 10460 Tuwanna Gray	9-12	T	402 20	88%	718/597-1751 Fax 718/931-8366

- **District 75 City Wide Programs** PID: 00740626
  (Part of New York City Dept of Ed in New York County)

Public Schs..Principal	Grd	Prgm	Enr/#Cls	SN	
Ⓨ Hospital Schools M401 3450 E Tremont Ave, Bronx 10465 Mary Maher	Spec	M	49		718/794-7260 Fax 718/794-7263
Ⓨ J M Rapport School Career Dev 470 Jackson Ave, Bronx 10455 Daniel Hoehn	Spec	MV	455 32	92%	718/993-5581 Fax 718/585-4624
Ⓨ P469X Bronx Sch Continuous Lrn 3177 Webster Ave, Bronx 10467 Janine Tubiolo	Spec		125	92%	718/696-6440 Fax 718/696-6441
Ⓨ PS 12X Lewis & Clark Sch 2555 Tratman Ave, Bronx 10461 Kuvana Jones	Spec	M	310 29	94%	718/409-9040 Fax 718/931-8121
Ⓨ PS 168X 339 Morris Ave, Bronx 10451 Maureen Fullerton	Spec	M	510 56	90%	718/585-2100 Fax 718/585-8316
Ⓨ PS 176X 750 Baychester Ave, Bronx 10475 Alexandra Guerriero	Spec	M	921 70	84%	718/904-5750 Fax 718/904-5689
Ⓨ PS 186X Walter J Damrosch 750 Jennings St, Bronx 10459 Ava Cara Kaplan	Spec	M	768 46	93%	718/378-0006 Fax 718/589-9544
Ⓨ PS 188X 770 Grote St, Bronx 10460 Shanie Smith-Baugh	Spec	M	504	90%	718/561-2052 Fax 718/561-2683
PS 596X 850 Baychester Ave, Bronx 10475 John Siracuse	PK-8		406		718/904-5750
Ⓨ PS 721X Stephen McSweeney Sch 2697 Westchester Ave, Bronx 10461 Frank DeGennaro	Spec	M	571 45	92%	718/597-6404 Fax 718/829-5752
Ⓨ PS 723X 3540 Bivona St, Bronx 10475 Shante Chunn	Spec	GM	473 6	95%	718/320-1222 Fax 718/320-2213
Ⓨ PS X010 2750 Lafayette Ave, Bronx 10465 Christoph Reda	Spec	M	150 60		718/828-4022 Fax 718/823-1573
Ⓨ PS X017 778 Forest Ave, Bronx 10456 Marlin Hoggard	Spec	M	484	89%	718/665-5617 Fax 718/665-6372
Ⓨ PS X811 1434 Longfellow Ave Rm 22, Bronx 10459 Rosa Greene	Spec	M	642 20	93%	718/589-3060 Fax 718/589-9551
Vida Bogart Sch All Chldrn 1000 E Tremont Ave, Bronx 10460 Lourdes Mendez	Spec		494		718/328-3913 Fax 347/868-8400

- **New York Alt High Sch SD 79** PID: 00740626
  (Part of New York City Dept of Ed in New York County)

Public Schs..Principal	Grd	Prgm	Enr/#Cls	SN	
Ⓐ Passages Acad-Horizon 560 Brook Ave, Bronx 10455 Carolyn Rudder	5-12		600 12		718/401-3053 Fax 718/401-8814
Ⓐ Passages Acad-Ryer 2250 Ryer Ave, Bronx 10457 Brendan Daly	9-12		401		
Ⓐ Passages Academy-Bronx Hope 108 W 174th St, Bronx 10453 Brendan Daly	9-12		401		718/294-4832

BRONX CATHOLIC SCHOOLS

- **Archdiocese of New York Ed Off** PID: 00754976
  Listing includes only schools located in this county. See District Index for location of Diocesan Offices.

Catholic Schs..Principal	Grd	Prgm	Enr/#Cls	SN	
Academy of Mt St Ursula 330 Bedford Park Blvd, Bronx 10458 Sr Jean Humphries	9-12		342 18		718/364-5353 Fax 718/364-2354
All Hallows High School-Boys 111 E 164th St, Bronx 10452 Susan Natale	9-12		625 25		718/293-4545 Fax 718/410-8298
Cardinal Hayes High Sch 650 Grand Concourse, Bronx 10451 William Lessa	9-12		1,031 70		718/292-6100 Fax 718/292-9178
Cardinal Spellman High Sch 1 Cardinal Spellman Pl, Bronx 10466 Daniel O'Keefe	9-12		1,450 76		718/881-8000 Fax 718/515-6615
Christ the King Sch 1345 Grand Concourse, Bronx 10452 Steven Iuso	K-8		256 15		718/538-5959 Fax 718/538-6369
Fordham Preparatory Sch 441 E Fordham Rd, Bronx 10458 Dr Joseph Petriello	9-12		1,000 45		718/367-7500 Fax 718/367-7598
Holy Family Sch 2169 Blackrock Ave, Bronx 10472 Danielle Gonzalez	PK-8		703 26		718/863-7280 Fax 718/931-8690
Holy Rosary Sch 1500 Arnow Ave, Bronx 10469 Maryann Fusco	PK-8		589 25		718/652-1838 Fax 718/515-9872
Immaculate Conception Sch 760 E Gun Hill Rd, Bronx 10467 Amy Rodriguez	PK-8		400 30		718/547-3346 Fax 718/547-5505
Immaculate Conception Sch 378 E 151st St, Bronx 10455 Alexandra Benjamin	PK-8		515 24		718/585-4843 Fax 718/585-6846
Monsignor Scanlan High Sch 915 Hutchinson River Pkwy, Bronx 10465 Kris Keelin	9-12		550 51		718/430-0100 Fax 718/892-8845
Mt St Michael Academy 4300 Murdock Ave, Bronx 10466 Steve Schlitte	6-12		900		718/515-6400 Fax 718/994-7729
Our Lady Mt Carmel-Bronx Sch 2465 Bathgate Ave, Bronx 10458 John Musto	PK-8		290 10		718/295-6080 Fax 718/561-5205
Our Lady of Grace Sch 3981 Bronxwood Ave, Bronx 10466 Richard Helmrich	PK-8		240 16		718/547-9918 Fax 718/547-7602

79	Student Personnel	91	Safety/Security	275	Response To Intervention	298	Grant Writer/Ptnrships
80	Driver Ed/Safety	92	Magnet School	277	Remedial Math K-12	750	Chief Innovation Officer
81	Gifted/Talented	93	Parental Involvement	280	Literacy Coach	751	Chief of Staff
82	Video Services	95	Tech Prep Program	285	STEM	752	Social Emotional Learning
83	Substance Abuse Prev	97	Chief Infomation Officer	286	Digital Learning		
84	Erate	98	Chief Technology Officer	288	Common Core Standards		
85	AIDS Education	270	Character Education	294	Accountability		
88	Alternative/At Risk	271	Migrant Education	295	Network System		
89	Multi-Cultural Curriculum	273	Teacher Mentor	296	Title II Programs		
90	Social Work	274	Before/After Sch	297	Webmaster		

School Programs
A = Alternative Program
G = Adult Classes
M = Magnet Program
T = Title I Schoolwide
V = Career & Tech Ed Programs

Other School Types
Ⓐ = Alternative School
Ⓒ = Charter School
Ⓜ = Magnet School
Ⓨ = Year-Round School

Social Media
f = Facebook
t = Twitter

New Schools are shaded
New Superintendents and Principals are bold
Personnel with email addresses are underscored

Bronx County

School	Grades	Enr/#Cls	Phone
Our Lady of Refuge Sch 2708 Briggs Ave, Bronx 10458 Robert Billings	PK-8	275 10	718/367-3081 Fax 718/367-0741
Preston High Sch 2780 Schurz Ave, Bronx 10465 Jane Grendell	9-12	500 30	718/863-9134 Fax 718/863-6125
Sacred Heart Sch 1248 Nelson Ave, Bronx 10452 Abigail Akano	PK-8	438 27	718/293-4288
Santa Maria Sch 1510 Zerega Ave, Bronx 10462 Sr Maureen Flynn	PK-8	245 1	718/823-3636 Fax 718/823-7008
St Angela Merici Sch 266 E 163rd St, Bronx 10451 Yessenia Teron	PK-8	520	718/293-3365 Fax 718/293-6617
St Anselm Sch 685 Tinton Ave, Bronx 10455 Teresa Lopes	PK-8	468	718/993-9464 Fax 718/292-3496
St Athanasius Sch 830 Southern Blvd, Bronx 10459 Jessica Aybar	PK-8	310 16	718/542-5161 Fax 718/542-7584
St Barnabas Elem Sch 413 E 241st St, Bronx 10470 Jonathan Morano	PK-8	400 12	718/324-1088 Fax 718/324-2397
St Barnabas High Sch 425 E 240th St, Bronx 10470 Theresa Napoli	9-12	210 23	718/325-8800 Fax 718/325-8820
St Benedict Sch 1016 Edison Ave, Bronx 10465 Raymond Vitiello	PK-8	350 13	718/829-9557 Fax 718/319-1989
St Brendan Sch 268 E 207th St, Bronx 10467 Michele Pasquale	PK-8	304 20	718/653-2292 Fax 718/653-3234
St Catharine Academy 2250 Williamsbridge Rd, Bronx 10469 Sr Ann Welch	9-12	480 40	718/882-2882 Fax 718/231-9099
St Clare of Assisi Sch 1911 Hone Ave, Bronx 10461 Theresa Bivona	PK-8	500 19	718/892-4080 Fax 718/239-1007
St Frances De Chantal Sch 2962 Harding Ave, Bronx 10465 Sr Patricia Brito	PK-8	319 32	718/892-5359 Fax 718/892-6937
St Francis Assisi Sch 4300 Baychester Ave, Bronx 10466 Marc Silva	PK-8	400 11	718/994-4650 Fax 718/994-6990
St Francis Xavier Sch 1711 Haight Ave, Bronx 10461 Marie O'Shea	PK-8	294 10	718/863-0531 Fax 718/319-1152
St Gabriel Sch 590 W 235th St, Bronx 10463 Anthony Naccari	PK-8	275 12	718/548-0444 Fax 718/796-2638
St Helena Sch 2050 Benedict Ave, Bronx 10462 Richard Meller	PK-8	365 22	718/892-3234 Fax 718/892-3924
St John Chrysostom Sch 1144 Hoe Ave, Bronx 10459 Sr Mary Mooney	PK-8	350 20	718/328-7226 Fax 718/378-5368
St Lucy Sch 830 Mace Ave, Bronx 10467 Jane Stefanini	PK-8	540 22	718/882-2203 Fax 929/222-5886
St Margaret Mary Sch 121 E 177th St, Bronx 10453 Sr Ann Veronica RSM	PK-8	300 13	718/731-5905 Fax 718/731-8924
St Margaret of Cortona Sch 452 W 260th St, Bronx 10471 Hugh Keenan	PK-8	244 20	718/549-8580 Fax 718/884-3298
St Philip Neri Sch 3031 Grand Concourse, Bronx 10468 Ajeia Beebe	PK-8	339 11	718/365-8806 Fax 718/365-1482
St Raymond Academy for Girls 1725 Castle Hill Ave, Bronx 10462 Sr Maryann D'Antonio	9-12	320 18	718/824-4220 Fax 718/829-3571
St Raymond Elem Sch 2380 E Tremont Ave, Bronx 10462 Eugene Scanlon	PK-8	900 19	718/597-3232 Fax 718/892-4449
St Raymond High Sch for Boys 2151 Saint Raymond Ave, Bronx 10462 Judith Carew	9-12	720	718/824-5050 Fax 718/863-8808
St Simon Stock Sch 2195 Valentine Ave, Bronx 10457 Tara Braswell	PK-8 G	261 20	718/367-0453 Fax 718/733-1441
St Theresa Sch 2872 Saint Theresa Ave, Bronx 10461 Josephine Fanelli	PK-8	480 13	718/792-3688 Fax 718/892-9441
Villa Maria Academy 3335 Country Club Rd, Bronx 10465 Sr Teresa Barton	PK-8	410 19	718/824-3260 Fax 718/824-7315

BRONX PRIVATE SCHOOLS

Private Schs..Principal	Grd	Prgm	Enr/#Cls SN
Argus Community High Sch 760 E 160th St, Bronx 10456 Joan Inzarde	9-12		30 718/401-5700 Fax 718/993-5308
Biondi Elem Education Center 1529 Williamsbridge Rd, Bronx 10461 Roland Lewis	K-6		150 718/794-8514 Fax 718/794-8583
Bronx Manhattan SDA Sch 1440 Plimpton Ave, Bronx 10452 Evelyn Chavez	PK-8		150 718/588-7598 10
Faith Christian Academy 1137 E 223rd St, Bronx 10466 Donna Taylor	K-8		100 718/881-1085 9
Fieldston Lower Sch 3901 Fieldston Rd, Bronx 10471 Joseph McCauley	PK-5		276 718/329-7310 13 Fax 718/329-7304
Fieldston Middle Upper Sch 3901 Fieldston Rd, Bronx 10471 Chia-Chee Chiu \ Nigel Furlonge	6-12		585 718/329-7300 50 Fax 718/329-7305
Garvey Sch 950 Baychester Ave 1, Bronx 10475 June O'Connor	PK-6		165 718/320-3902 Fax 718/320-5159
Greek American Institute 3573 Bruckner Blvd, Bronx 10461 John Attanas	PK-8		170 718/823-2393 10 Fax 718/823-0790
Horace Mann Lower Sch 4440 Tibbett Ave, Bronx 10471 Deena Neuwirth	K-5		465 718/432-3300 30 Fax 718/601-0949
Horace Mann Mid Upper Sch 231 W 246th St, Bronx 10471 Javaid Khan \ Dr Jessica Levenstein	6-12		1,183 718/432-4000 Fax 718/432-3610
Islamic Leadership Sch 2008 Westchester Ave, Bronx 10462 Shireena Drammeh	1-12		85 718/892-5555 5
Joy Fellowship Christian Acad 66 E Mount Eden Ave, Bronx 10452 Keith Bender	K-5		51 718/583-9300 5 Fax 718/299-6465
Kinneret Day Sch 2600 Netherland Ave, Bronx 10463 Asher Abramovitz	PK-8		250 718/548-0900 12 Fax 718/548-0901

#		#		#		#		#		#		#	
1	Superintendent	8	Curric/Instruct K-12	19	Chief Financial Officer	29	Family/Consumer Science	39	Social Studies K-12	49	English/Lang Arts Elem	59	Special Education Elem	69	Academic Assessment
2	Bus/Finance/Purchasing	9	Curric/Instruct Elem	20	Art K-12	30	Adult Education	40	Social Studies Elem	50	English/Lang Arts Sec	60	Special Education Sec	70	Research/Development
3	Buildings And Grounds	10	Curric/Instruct Sec	21	Art Elem	31	Career/Sch-to-Work K-12	41	Social Studies Sec	51	Reading K-12	61	Foreign/World Lang K-12	71	Public Information
4	Food Service	11	Federal Program	22	Art Sec	32	Career/Sch-to-Work Elem	42	Science K-12	52	Reading Elem	62	Foreign/World Lang Elem	72	Summer School
5	Transportation	12	Title I	23	Music K-12	33	Career/Sch-to-Work Sec	43	Science Elem	53	Reading Sec	63	Foreign/World Lang Sec	73	Instructional Tech
6	Athletic	13	Title V	24	Music Elem	34	Early Childhood Ed	44	Science Sec	54	Remedial Reading K-12	64	Religious Education K-12	74	Inservice Training
7	Health Services	15	Asst Superintendent	25	Music Sec	35	Health/Phys Education	45	Math K-12	55	Remedial Reading Elem	65	Religious Education Elem	75	Marketing/Distributive
		16	Instructional Media Svcs	26	Business Education	36	Guidance Services K-12	46	Math Elem	56	Remedial Reading Sec	66	Religious Education Sec	76	Info Systems
		17	Chief Operations Officer	27	Career & Tech Ed	37	Guidance Services Elem	47	Math Sec	57	Bilingual/ELL	67	School Board President	77	Psychological Assess
		18	Chief Academic Officer	28	Technology Education	38	Guidance Services Sec	48	English/Lang Arts K-12	58	Special Education K-12	68	Teacher Personnel	78	Affirmative Action

New York School Directory

Broome County

LaVelle School for the Blind 3830 Paulding Ave, Bronx 10469 Diane Tucker	Spec	179		718/882-1212 Fax 718/882-0005
Learning Tree Prep 801 Bartholdi St Ste 2, Bronx 10467 Lois Gregory	PK-8	300		718/944-0958 Fax 718/944-8909
New Covenant Christian Sch 1497 Needham Ave, Bronx 10469 Verna Blake	PK-5	150 11		718/519-8884
New Covenant Chrn High Sch 1179 Boston Rd, Bronx 10456 Margo Manbode	6-12	120 10		718/328-6072 Fax 718/620-2040
New Life Sch 831 Eagle Ave, Bronx 10456 Dr Matthew Tucker	Spec	180		718/665-2760 Fax 718/665-2761
New York Inst for Special Ed 999 Pelham Pkwy N, Bronx 10469 Joe Catavero	Spec	300 40		718/519-7000 Fax 718/231-9314
Our Saviour Lutheran Sch 1734 Williamsbridge Rd, Bronx 10461 Kenneth Samulare	K-12	250 15		718/792-5665 Fax 718/409-3877
R T Hudson SDA Sch 1122 Forest Ave, Bronx 10456 Ann Guy	PK-8	44 7		718/328-3322 Fax 718/328-5922
Regent Sch 719 E 216th St, Bronx 10467 Howard Sterling	PK-5	170 8		718/653-2900 Fax 718/653-1166
Riverdale Country Sch 5250 Fieldston Rd, Bronx 10471 James Duval \ Milton Sipp \ Kelley Flynn	PK-12	1,000 70		718/549-8810 Fax 718/519-2795
Sar Academy 655 W 254th St, Bronx 10471 Binyamin Krauss	PK-8	900 10		718/548-1717 Fax 718/601-0082
Sar High Sch 503 W 259th St, Bronx 10471 Tully Harcsztark	9-12	500		718/548-2727 Fax 718/548-4400
Shield Institute/Bronx ELC 1800 Andrews Ave, Bronx 10453 Kimberly Moro	Spec	180 16		718/299-7600 Fax 718/299-8995
St Ignatius Sch 740 Manida St, Bronx 10474 Richard Darrell	6-8	90 6		718/861-9084 Fax 718/861-9096
St Joseph School for the Deaf 1000 Hutchinson River Pkwy, Bronx 10465 Debra Arles	Spec	110 21		718/828-9000 Fax 718/792-6631
Yeshiva of the Telshe Alumni 4904 Independence Ave, Bronx 10471	9-12	180 5		718/601-3523 Fax 718/601-2141

BROOME COUNTY

BROOME COUNTY SCHOOLS

County Schs..Principal	Grd	Prgm	Enr/#Cls	SN	
Broome Tioga BOCES 435 Glenwood Rd, Binghamton 13905 Rebecca Flank	Spec	AGV	238 40	68%	607/763-3348 Fax 607/763-3464
Broome-Tioga BOCES Voc Ed Ctr 435 Glenwood Rd, Binghamton 13905 Matt Sheehan	Voc	G	1,000 30		607/763-3451 Fax 607/763-3213

Ⓐ East Learning Center 164 Hawley St, Binghamton 13901 Chuck Wheeler	5-12	200		607/762-6400 Fax 607/762-6402

BROOME PUBLIC SCHOOLS

- **Binghamton City School Dist** PID: 00716417   607/762-8100
  164 Hawley St, Binghamton 13901   Fax 607/762-8112

Schools: 10 \ **Teachers:** 524 \ **Students:** 5,500 \ **Special Ed Students:** 1,110 \ **LEP Students:** 238 \ **College-Bound:** 78% \ **Ethnic:** Asian 3%, African American 31%, Hispanic 17%, Caucasian 48% \ **Exp:** $310 (High) \ **Poverty:** 38% \ **Title I:** $4,931,492 \ **Special Education:** $13,450,000 \ **Open-Close:** 09/04 - 06/25 \ **DTBP:** $226 (High)

Tonya Thompson 1	Karry Mullins 2,5,11,15
Mario Lisi 3,91	Mark Bordeau 4
David Garbarino 6,7,35,85	Jennifer Dove 8,48
Margaret McGarry 20,23,61	Brenda Lidestri 27,42,45
Scout Orr 42	Deb Card 57,79*
Tia Rodriguez 58	Vevlet Tanner 58,77,90
Brian Whalen 67	David Thon 68,273
Erin Thompsonmiller 70,73	

Public Schs..Principal	Grd	Prgm	Enr/#Cls	SN	
Benjamin Franklin Elem Sch 262 Conklin Ave, Binghamton 13903 Kyle Skinner	PK-5	T	458 30	70%	607/762-8340 Fax 607/762-8393
Binghamton High Sch 31 Main St, Binghamton 13905 Kevin Richman	9-12	ATV	1,450	64%	607/762-8200 Fax 607/762-6072
Calvin Coolidge Elem Sch 261 Robinson St, Binghamton 13904 Mary Ryan	PK-5	T	310 24	69%	607/762-8290 Fax 607/762-8396
East Middle Sch 167 E Frederick St, Binghamton 13904 Michael Holly	6-8	T	563 100	79%	607/762-8300 Fax 607/762-8398
Horace Mann Elem Sch 30 College St, Binghamton 13905 Peter Stewart	K-5	T	258 17	68%	607/762-8270 Fax 607/762-8394
MacArthur Elem Sch 1123 Vestal Ave, Binghamton 13903 Lori Asquith	PK-5	T	458 29	58%	607/762-8119
Theodore Roosevelt Elem Sch 9 Ogden St, Binghamton 13901 David Chilson	PK-5	T	384 24	76%	607/762-8280 Fax 607/762-8395
Thomas Jefferson Elem Sch 151 Helen St, Binghamton 13905 Sarah Wiggins	K-5	T	300 17	53%	607/763-8430 Fax 607/763-8436
West Middle Sch W Middle Ave, Binghamton 13905 Kristine Battaglino	6-8	T	625 60	66%	607/763-8400 Fax 607/763-8429
Woodrow Wilson Elem Sch 287 Prospect St, Binghamton 13905 Daniel Miller	K-5	T	365 32	78%	607/763-8440 Fax 607/763-8448

---

79 Student Personnel	91 Safety/Security	275 Response To Intervention	298 Grant Writer/Ptnrships	**School Programs**
80 Driver Ed/Safety	92 Magnet School	277 Remedial Math K-12	750 Chief Innovation Officer	A = Alternative Program
81 Gifted/Talented	93 Parental Involvement	280 Literacy Coach	751 Chief of Staff	G = Adult Classes
82 Video Services	95 Tech Prep Program	285 STEM	752 Social Emotional Learning	M = Magnet Program
83 Substance Abuse Prev	97 Chief Information Officer	286 Digital Learning		T = Title I Schoolwide
84 Erate	98 Chief Technology Officer	288 Common Core Standards	**Other School Types**	V = Career & Tech Ed Programs
85 AIDS Education	270 Character Education	294 Accountability	Ⓐ = Alternative School	
88 Alternative/At Risk	271 Migrant Education	295 Network System	Ⓒ = Charter School	New Schools are shaded
89 Multi-Cultural Curriculum	273 Teacher Mentor	296 Title II Programs	Ⓜ = Magnet School	New Superintendents and Principals are bold
90 Social Work	274 Before/After Sch	297 Webmaster	Ⓨ = Year-Round School	Personnel with email addresses are underscored

Social Media
 = Facebook
 = Twitter

NY—27

Broome County — Market Data Retrieval

Chenango Forks Central SD
PID: 00716572
1 Gordon Dr, Binghamton 13901
607/648-7543
Fax 607/648-7560

Schools: 3 \ Teachers: 124 \ Students: 1,404 \ Special Ed Students: 224 \ LEP Students: 4 \ College-Bound: 80% \ Ethnic: Asian 1%, African American 2%, Hispanic 2%, Caucasian 95% \ Exp: $192 (Low) \ Poverty: 16% \ Title I: $420,182 \ Special Education: $3,683,000 \ Open-Close: 09/04 - 06/25 \ DTBP: $161 (High) \

Dr Lloyd Peck	1	Bernard McDermott	2,3,5
Mark Putrino	2	John Silvanic	3
Mark Bordeau	4	David Hogan	6,35*
Melissa Slater	16*	Patricia Kuhl	58,77
Amy O'Brien	67	Linda Snyder	71
Joe Wasecka	73	Rick Borchardt	91

Public Schs..Principal	Grd	Prgm	Enr/#Cls	SN	
Chenango Forks Elem Sch 6 Patch Rd, Binghamton 13901 Catherine Kacyvenski	PK-5	T	599 17	44%	607/648-7580 Fax 607/648-7596
Chenango Forks High Sch 1 Gordon Dr, Binghamton 13901 Tim Simonds	9-12	V	470 45	37%	607/648-7544
Chenango Forks Middle Sch 1 Gordon Dr, Binghamton 13901 Andrew Rullo	6-8	TV	335 35	40%	607/648-7576 Fax 607/648-2767

Chenango Valley Ctl Sch Dist
PID: 00716625
221 Chenango Bridge Rd, Binghamton 13901
607/762-6800
Fax 607/762-6946

Schools: 4 \ Teachers: 129 \ Students: 1,719 \ Special Ed Students: 288 \ LEP Students: 18 \ College-Bound: 87% \ Ethnic: Asian 1%, African American 2%, Hispanic 2%, Caucasian 94% \ Exp: $271 (Med) \ Poverty: 14% \ Title I: $513,093 \ Special Education: $3,555,000 \ Open-Close: 09/09 - 06/24 \ DTBP: $166 (High)

Dave Gill	1	Elizabeth Donahue	2,11
George Zlock	3	John Marino	4
Mark Bordeau	4	Sue Ticknor	5
Tamara Ivan	8,69	Elizabeth Dicosimo	15,288*
Michelle Feyerabend	15	Christopher Ruf	16*
Tara Whittaker	34,58	Tara Williams	58
Kelly Warwick	67	Brad Tomm	69,79*
Molly Darrow	71	Sarah Latimer	73,286*
Diane Vidulich	77,88*		

Public Schs..Principal	Grd	Prgm	Enr/#Cls	SN	
Chenango Bridge Elem Sch 741 River Rd, Binghamton 13901 James Pritchard	3-5	T	378 20	44%	607/762-6950 Fax 607/648-8959
Chenango Valley High Sch 221 Chenango Bridge Rd, Binghamton 13901 Jennifer Ostrander	9-12	AV	471	37%	607/762-6900
Chenango Valley Middle Sch 221 Chenango Bridge Rd, Binghamton 13901 Eric Attleson	6-8	ATV	398	46%	607/762-6902 Fax 607/762-6945
Port Dickinson Elem Sch 770 Chenango St, Binghamton 13901 Mary Hammond	PK-2	T	472 23	46%	607/762-6970 Fax 607/762-6979

Deposit Central School Dist
PID: 00716699
171 2nd St, Deposit 13754
607/467-2197
Fax 607/467-5504

Schools: 2 \ Teachers: 54 \ Students: 482 \ Special Ed Students: 117 \ College-Bound: 72% \ Ethnic: African American 2%, Hispanic 2%, Caucasian 96% \ Exp: $434 (High) \ Poverty: 20% \ Title I: $202,336 \ Special Education: $1,185,000 \ Open-Close: 09/14 - 06/29 \ DTBP: $450 (High)

Denise Cook	1	Ethan Berry	2
Tom Williams	3	Jodi Newman	5
Matt Mastropieto	6*	Lauriel Thomas-McCoy	58
Dean Price	67		

Public Schs..Principal	Grd	Prgm	Enr/#Cls	SN	
Deposit Elem Sch 171 2nd St, Deposit 13754 Kelli Vosbury	PK-5	T	223 23	55%	607/467-2198 Fax 607/467-4495
Deposit Middle High Sch 171 2nd St, Deposit 13754 Hal Pettersen \ Karen Armbrust	6-12	TV	259 35	51%	607/467-2197

Harpursville Central Sch Dist
PID: 00716845
54 Main St, Harpursville 13787
607/693-8101
Fax 607/693-1480

Schools: 2 \ Teachers: 60 \ Students: 677 \ Special Ed Students: 157 \ College-Bound: 67% \ Ethnic: African American 1%, Caucasian 98% \ Exp: $254 (Med) \ Poverty: 19% \ Title I: $397,668 \ Special Education: $1,926,000 \ Open-Close: 09/07 - 06/22 \ DTBP: $286 (High)

Michael Rullo	1	Joseph McLaughlin	2
David Johnson	3	Norene Tasber	4*
Danielle Maxim	5	Josh Quick	6,58
Shana Hinman	7	Pamela Horton	9,12*
Karen Slesinsky	27,35,36,69,88*	Michael Rhodes	67

Public Schs..Principal	Grd	Prgm	Enr/#Cls	SN	
Harpursville Jr Sr HS 54 Main St, Harpursville 13787 Kristine Conrow	7-12	TV	323 24	68%	607/693-8105
W A Olmsted Elem Sch 54 Main St, Harpursville 13787 Jim DiMaria	PK-6	T	354 37	57%	607/693-8115

Johnson City Central Sch Dist
PID: 00716871
666 Reynolds Rd, Johnson City 13790
607/930-1005
Fax 607/930-1143

Schools: 5 \ Teachers: 210 \ Students: 2,443 \ Special Ed Students: 395 \ LEP Students: 122 \ Ethnic: Asian 8%, African American 15%, Hispanic 12%, Caucasian 65% \ Exp: $276 (Med) \ Poverty: 28% \ Title I: $1,343,135 \ Special Education: $5,921,000 \ Open-Close: 09/14 - 06/25 \ DTBP: $309 (High)

Marykay Roland	1	Eric Race	2,7,15,71,91*
Scott Fisher	3	Paul Cerasaro	4
Louis Castellucci	5	Jeffrey Paske	6,7*
Joseph Guccia	8,15,294	Jeff Smith	39
Mark Buza	42*	Kristina Kline	57
Elisa Eaton	58,271	Karen Larnerd	61*
Shannon Edmondson	67	Cliff Butler	73,295

Public Schs..Principal	Grd	Prgm	Enr/#Cls	SN	
Johnson City High Sch 666 Reynolds Rd, Johnson City 13790 Paula Grassi	9-12	TV	719 85	64%	607/930-1009 Fax 607/930-1655

1	Superintendent	8	Curric/Instruct K-12	19	Chief Financial Officer	29	Family/Consumer Science	39	Social Studies K-12	49	English/Lang Arts Elem
2	Bus/Finance/Purchasing	9	Curric/Instruct Elem	20	Art K-12	30	Adult Education	40	Social Studies Elem	50	English/Lang Arts Sec
3	Buildings And Grounds	10	Curric/Instruct Sec	21	Art Elem	31	Career/Sch-to-Work K-12	41	Social Studies Sec	51	Reading K-12
4	Food Service	11	Federal Program	22	Art Sec	32	Career/Sch-to-Work Elem	42	Science K-12	52	Reading Elem
5	Transportation	12	Title I	23	Music K-12	33	Career/Sch-to-Work Sec	43	Science Elem	53	Reading Sec
6	Athletic	13	Title V	24	Music Elem	34	Early Childhood Ed	44	Science Sec	54	Remedial Reading K-12
7	Health Services	14	Instructional Media Svcs	25	Music Sec	35	Health/Phys Education	45	Math K-12	55	Remedial Reading Elem
		15	Asst Superintendent	26	Business Education	36	Guidance Services K-12	46	Math Elem	56	Remedial Reading Sec
		16	Chief Operations Officer	27	Career & Tech Ed	37	Guidance Services Elem	47	Math Sec	57	Bilingual/ELL
		18	Chief Academic Officer	28	Technology Education	38	Guidance Services Sec	48	English/Lang Arts K-12	58	Special Education K-12

59	Special Education Elem	69	Academic Assessment		
60	Special Education Sec	70	Research/Development		
61	Foreign/World Lang K-12	71	Public Information		
62	Foreign/World Lang Elem	72	Summer School		
63	Foreign/World Lang Sec	73	Instructional Tech		
64	Religious Education K-12	74	Inservice Training		
65	Religious Education Elem	75	Marketing/Distributive		
66	Religious Education Sec	76	Info Systems		
67	School Board President	77	Psychological Assess		
68	Teacher Personnel	78	Affirmative Action		

New York School Directory — Broome County

School	Grd	Prgm	Enr/#Cls	SN	Phone
Johnson City Intermediate Sch 601 Columbia Dr, Johnson City 13790 Margaret Kucko	3-5	T	573	67%	607/930-1015
Johnson City Middle Sch 601 Columbia Dr, Johnson City 13790 Daniel Erickson	6-8	TV	571	69%	607/930-1012 Fax 607/930-1432
Johnson City Primary Sch 601 Columbia Dr, Johnson City 13790 Daniel Erickson	PK-2	T	537	63%	607/930-1015 Fax 607/930-1430
Ⓐ Pathways 666 Reynolds Rd, Johnson City 13790 David McGinnis	9-12		45 5		607/930-1009

• **Maine Endwell Ctl School Dist** PID: 00716950   607/754-1400
712 Farm to Market Rd, Endwell 13760   Fax 607/754-1650

Schools: 4 \ **Teachers:** 183 \ **Students:** 2,492 \ **Special Ed Students:** 400 \ **LEP Students:** 34 \ **College-Bound:** 89% \ **Ethnic:** Asian 2%, African American 3%, Hispanic 4%, Caucasian 92% \ **Exp:** $195 (Low) \ **Poverty:** 12% \ **Title I:** $400,833 \ **Special Education:** $5,363,000 \ **Open-Close:** 09/04 - 06/25 \ **DTBP:** $320 (High) \ 📘

Jason Van Fossen 1
Bryan McCoy 4
David Cook 6*
Vanessa Dubrava 12,34,58,79,275*
Gregg Armezzani 67

Jeffery Lamoreaux 2,11,15,68
Michael Aubel 5
Julie Gallagher 8,15,294
Tom Guillon 18,73,76,288,295

Public Schs..Principal	Grd	Prgm	Enr/#Cls	SN	Phone
Homer Brink Elem Sch 3618 Briar Ln, Endwell 13760 William Dundon	K-5		758 36	36%	607/786-8244 Fax 607/786-8213
Maine Endwell Senior High Sch 750 Farm to Market Rd, Endwell 13760 Thomas Burkhardt	9-12		745 35	36%	607/748-8070 Fax 607/786-8209
Maine Memorial Elem Sch 2693 Main St, Maine 13802 Linda Kelly	PK-5	T	444 50	49%	607/862-3263 Fax 607/862-3323
Maine-Endwell Middle Sch 1119 Farm to Market Rd, Endwell 13760 Rick Otis	6-8		545 34	42%	607/786-8271 Fax 607/786-5137

• **Susquehanna Valley Central SD** PID: 00717033   607/775-0170
1040 Conklin Rd, Conklin 13748   Fax 607/775-4575

Schools: 4 \ **Teachers:** 137 \ **Students:** 1,412 \ **Special Ed Students:** 223 \ **LEP Students:** 4 \ **College-Bound:** 77% \ **Ethnic:** Asian 1%, African American 3%, Hispanic 2%, Caucasian 94% \ **Exp:** $206 (Med) \ **Poverty:** 14% \ **Title I:** $380,355 \ **Special Education:** $2,801,000 \ **Open-Close:** 09/08 - 06/25 \ **DTBP:** $163 (High)

Roland Doig 1
Mark Bordeau 4
Ed Swartwout 6
Jeff Renner 20*
David Daniel 31,88*
Robert Strick 67
Scott Snyder 83*

Ethan Berry 2
Sue Hull 5
Natalie Brubaker 8,11,15,34,69,273,274,288*
James Apicella 23*
Maureen Kline 58*
Jason Luke 71,73,76,95,97

Public Schs..Principal	Grd	Prgm	Enr/#Cls	SN	Phone
Brookside Elem Sch 3849 Saddlemire Rd, Binghamton 13903 Erin Eckert	PK-5	T	369 19	51%	607/669-4105 Fax 607/669-4811
Donnelly Elem Sch 1168 Conklin Rd, Conklin 13748 Jill Rich	PK-5	T	289 15	54%	607/775-0176 Fax 607/775-9313
Richard T Stank Middle Sch 1040 Conklin Rd, Conklin 13748 Donald Gerlach	6-8	T	324 51	51%	607/775-9129 Fax 607/775-9142
Susquehanna Valley Sr High Sch 1040 Conklin Rd, Conklin 13748 Charles Hutchinson	9-12	T	413 50	41%	607/775-0304

• **Union-Endicott Ctl Sch Dist** PID: 00716728   607/757-2811
1100 E Main St, Endicott 13760   Fax 607/757-2809

Schools: 7 \ **Teachers:** 324 \ **Students:** 4,000 \ **Special Ed Students:** 617 \ **LEP Students:** 32 \ **College-Bound:** 85% \ **Ethnic:** Asian 2%, African American 11%, Hispanic 11%, Native American: 1%, Caucasian 76% \ **Exp:** $235 (Med) \ **Poverty:** 19% \ **Title I:** $1,422,033 \ **Special Education:** $8,171,000 \ **Open-Close:** 09/14 - 06/25 \ **DTBP:** $322 (High)

Nicole Wolfe 1
Toby Riddleberger 3,91*
Ryan Hallenbeck 6,35,85*
Jennifer Kazmark 15,68
Linda Myers 71

Pamela Riddleberger 2,12,15
Lisa Bennett 5
Sarah Miller 10
Dick Testa 67
Shannon Gillette 73,76,98,286*

Public Schs..Principal	Grd	Prgm	Enr/#Cls	SN	Phone
Ann G McGuinness Elem Sch 1301 Union Center Maine Hwy, Endicott 13760 Elaine Taylor	K-5	T	353 14	53%	607/757-2131 Fax 607/757-2127
Charles F Johnson Elem Sch 715 Paden St, Endicott 13760 Alicia Boyce	K-5	T	403 20	75%	607/757-2137 Fax 607/757-2878
George F Johnson Elem Sch 999 Taft Ave, Endicott 13760 Johanna Hickey	K-5	T	595 22	49%	607/757-2143 Fax 607/658-7119
Jennie F Snapp Middle Sch 101 S Loder Ave, Endicott 13760 Tim Lowie	6-8	AT	784 60	56%	607/757-2156 Fax 607/658-7117
Ⓐ Linnaeus W West Sch 1201 Union Center Maine Hwy, Endicott 13760 Mary Mullock	3-11	TV	84	88%	607/757-2149
Thomas J Watson Elem Sch 263 Ridgefield Rd, Endicott 13760 Emily Regan	K-5	T	276 17	54%	607/757-2152 Fax 607/757-2864
Union-Endicott High Sch 1200 E Main St, Endicott 13760 Steven DiStefano	9-12	AV	1,086 60	47%	607/757-2181 Fax 607/757-2592

• **Vestal Ctl School Dist** PID: 00717095   607/757-2241
201 Main St, Vestal 13850   Fax 607/757-2227

Schools: 7 \ **Teachers:** 282 \ **Students:** 3,397 \ **Special Ed Students:** 507 \ **LEP Students:** 73 \ **College-Bound:** 87% \ **Ethnic:** Asian 11%, African American 3%, Hispanic 4%, Caucasian 81% \ **Exp:** $208 (Med) \ **Poverty:** 9% \ **Title I:** $489,453 \ **Special Education:** $5,471,000 \ **Open-Close:** 09/14 - 06/22 \ **DTBP:** $343 (High)

Jeffrey Ahearn 1
Joseph Loretz 3
Ken Starr 5
Dr Laura Lamash 8,15
Patrick Clark 57
Michon Stuart 67
Merryl Wallach 83,88*

Matt Bechtel 2
Mark Bordeau 4
Josh Gannon 6,35*
Cliff Kasson 15,19
Rosalee Sullivan 58
Regina Felice 71

---

79 Student Personnel	91 Safety/Security	275 Response To Intervention	298 Grant Writer/Ptnrships	**School Programs**	**Social Media**
80 Driver Ed/Safety	92 Magnet School	277 Remedial Math K-12	750 Chief Innovation Officer	A = Alternative Program	📘 = Facebook
81 Gifted/Talented	93 Parental Involvement	280 Literacy Coach	751 Chief of Staff	G = Adult Classes	🐦 = Twitter
82 Video Services	95 Tech Prep Program	285 STEM	752 Social Emotional Learning	M = Magnet Program	
83 Substance Abuse Prev	97 Chief Information Officer	286 Digital Learning		T = Title I Schoolwide	
84 Erate	98 Chief Technology Officer	288 Common Core Standards	**Other School Types**	V = Career & Tech Ed Programs	
85 AIDS Education	270 Character Education	294 Accountability	Ⓐ = Alternative School		
88 Alternative/At Risk	271 Migrant Education	295 Network System	Ⓒ = Charter School	New Schools are shaded	
89 Multi-Cultural Curriculum	273 Teacher Mentor	296 Title II Programs	Ⓜ = Magnet School	New Superintendents and Principals are bold	
90 Social Work	274 Before/After Sch	297 Webmaster	Ⓨ = Year-Round School	Personnel with email addresses are underscored	

NY—29

Broome County — Market Data Retrieval

Public Schs..Principal	Grd	Prgm	Enr/#Cls	SN	
African Road Elem Sch 600 S Benita Blvd, Vestal 13850 Meghan Stenta	K-5		295 25	30%	607/757-2311 Fax 607/757-2705
Clayton Ave Elem Sch 209 Clayton Ave, Vestal 13850 Bradley Bruce	K-5		291 22	37%	607/757-2271 Fax 607/757-2372
Glenwood Elem Sch 337 Jones Rd, Vestal 13850 Doreen McSain	K-5		305 26	27%	607/757-2391 Fax 607/757-2233
Tioga Hills Elem Sch 40 W Glann Rd 48, Apalachin 13732 Hayley Crimmins	K-5		266 22	27%	607/757-2366 Fax 607/757-2344
Vestal Hills Elem Sch 709 Country Club Rd, Vestal 13850 Therese Mastro	K-5		367 16	28%	607/757-2357 Fax 607/757-2347
Vestal Middle Sch 600 S Benita Blvd, Vestal 13850 Ann Loose	6-8	A	756 100	29%	607/757-2333 Fax 607/757-2305
Vestal Senior High Sch 205 Woodlawn Dr, Vestal 13850 Dawn Young	9-12	A	1,011 75	23%	607/757-2281 Fax 607/757-2301

- **Whitney Point Central Sch Dist** PID: 00717203
  10 Keibel Rd, Whitney Point 13862
  607/692-8202 Fax 607/692-4434

> **Schools:** 3 \ **Teachers:** 128 \ **Students:** 1,359 \ **Special Ed Students:** 256 \ **LEP Students:** 3 \ **College-Bound:** 50% \ **Ethnic:** African American 1%, Hispanic 1%, Caucasian 98% \ **Exp:** $182 (Low) \ **Poverty:** 17% \ **Title I:** $396,868 \ **Special Education:** $3,082,000 \ **Open-Close:** 09/07 - 06/25 \ **DTBP:** $358 (High)

Patricia Follette 1
Jeff Dumhan 3,91
Robert Wolf 5
Joann Sexton 8,57,270,285,288,296,298
Stephanie Champney 67
Kristie Miner 280*
Zachary Woodard 2
Mark Bordeau 4
Murphee Hayes 6,7,83,88*
Aaron Kaminski 11,58
Jamie Pane 73,98

Public Schs..Principal	Grd	Prgm	Enr/#Cls	SN	
Caryl E Adams Primary Sch 24 Keibel Rd, Whitney Point 13862 Jo-Anne Knapp	PK-3	T	447 25	55%	607/692-8241 Fax 607/692-8297
Tioughnioga Riverside Academy 2887 New York Rte 11, Whitney Point 13862 John Whalen	4-8	T	536 12	61%	607/692-8232 Fax 607/692-8283
Whitney Point High Sch 10 Keibel Rd, Whitney Point 13862 Daniel Sweeney	9-12	V	376 50	54%	607/692-8201 Fax 607/692-8256

- **Windsor Central School Dist** PID: 00717253
  1191 State Route 79, Windsor 13865
  607/655-8216 Fax 607/655-3553

> **Schools:** 5 \ **Teachers:** 154 \ **Students:** 1,700 \ **Special Ed Students:** 233 \ **LEP Students:** 8 \ **College-Bound:** 74% \ **Ethnic:** Asian 1%, African American 2%, Hispanic 3%, Caucasian 94% \ **Exp:** $271 (Med) \ **Poverty:** 16% \ **Title I:** $466,378 \ **Special Education:** $3,504,000 \ **Open-Close:** 09/08 - 06/25 \ **DTBP:** $373 (High) \

Dr Jason Andrews 1
Christopher Durdon 3,5,6,35*
Scott Beattie 8,11,16,73,83,275,288,296
Heather Noyd 31
Christine Taylor 36,69,79
Peter Nowacki 67
Barbara Phillips 76,294
Andrew Fiorentino 2,15
Jessica Faris 4
Jeff Salasny 27,72,88*
Mary Jo Wardell 31*
Dr Jason Hans 54,57,58
Jason Weinstein 71

Public Schs..Principal	Grd	Prgm	Enr/#Cls	SN	
A F Palmer Elem Sch 213 Main St, Windsor 13865 Toby Youngs	PK-5		220		607/655-8225 Fax 607/655-8309
C R Weeks Elem Sch 440 Foley Rd, Windsor 13865 Kristin Beriman	PK-5	T	299 35	54%	607/775-3226 Fax 607/775-4835
Floyd L Bell Elem Sch 15 Golden St, Kirkwood 13795 Lorraine Hulbert	PK-5	T	263 18	49%	607/775-2730 Fax 607/775-4834
Windsor Central High Sch 1191 State Route 79, Windsor 13865 Jeff Salasny	9-12	V	489 50	44%	607/655-8250 Fax 607/655-3622
Windsor Central Middle Sch 213 Main St, Windsor 13865 Kevin Strahley	6-8	T	400	55%	607/655-8247 Fax 607/655-3760

BROOME CATHOLIC SCHOOLS

- **Diocese of Syracuse Ed Office** PID: 00762765
  Listing includes only schools located in this county. See District Index for location of Diocesan Offices.

Catholic Schs..Principal	Grd	Prgm	Enr/#Cls	SN	
Seton Catholic Ctl High Sch 70 Seminary Ave, Binghamton 13905 Matthew Martinkovic	7-12		315		607/723-5307 Fax 607/723-4811
Seton Catholic-All Saints Sch 1112 Broad St, Endicott 13760 Bill Pipher	PK-6		200 20		607/748-7423 Fax 607/484-9576
St James Elem Sch 143 Main St, Johnson City 13790 Suzy Kitchen	PK-6		190 15		607/797-5444 Fax 607/797-6794
St John the Evangelist Sch 9 Livingston St, Binghamton 13903 James Fountaine	PK-6		200 10		607/723-0703 Fax 607/772-6210

BROOME PRIVATE SCHOOLS

Private Schs..Principal	Grd	Prgm	Enr/#Cls	SN	
Central Baptist Christian Acad 1606 State Route 12, Binghamton 13901 Darren Krewson	PK-12		143 20		607/648-6210 Fax 607/648-7652
Children's Home of Wyoming 1182 Chenango St, Binghamton 13901 Maria Cali	Spec	V	120 15		607/772-6904 Fax 607/723-2617
Crescent Academy 1 Endicott Ave, Johnson City 13790 Sr Amber Smith	PK-5		49		607/729-3431
Hillel Academy of Broome Co 4737 Deerfield Pl, Vestal 13850 Dr Caleb Conklin	K-5	G	26 8		607/722-9274 Fax 607/723-0632
Ross Corners Christian Academy 2101 Owego Rd, Vestal 13850 Toby Wyse	PK-12		83 24		607/748-3301

---

1 Superintendent
2 Bus/Finance/Purchasing
3 Buildings And Grounds
4 Food Service
5 Transportation
6 Athletic
7 Health Services
8 Curric/Instruct K-12
9 Curric/Instruct Elem
10 Curric/Instruct Sec
11 Federal Program
12 Title I
13 Title V
14 Instructional Media Svcs
15 Asst Superintendent
16 Chief Operations Officer
17 Chief Operations Officer
18 Chief Academic Officer
19 Chief Financial Officer
20 Art K-12
21 Art Elem
22 Art Sec
23 Music K-12
24 Music Elem
25 Music Sec
26 Business Education
27 Career & Tech Ed
28 Technology Education
29 Family/Consumer Science
30 Adult Education
31 Career/Sch-to-Work K-12
32 Career/Sch-to-Work Elem
33 Career/Sch-to-Work Sec
34 Early Childhood Ed
35 Health/Phys Education
36 Guidance Services K-12
37 Guidance Services Elem
38 Guidance Services Sec
39 Social Studies K-12
40 Social Studies Elem
41 Social Studies Sec
42 Science K-12
43 Science Elem
44 Science Sec
45 Math K-12
46 Math Elem
47 Math Sec
48 English/Lang Arts K-12
49 English/Lang Arts Elem
50 English/Lang Arts Sec
51 Reading K-12
52 Reading Elem
53 Reading Sec
54 Remedial Reading K-12
55 Remedial Reading Elem
56 Remedial Reading Sec
57 Bilingual/ELL
58 Special Education K-12
59 Special Education Elem
60 Special Education Sec
61 Foreign/World Lang K-12
62 Foreign/World Lang Elem
63 Foreign/World Lang Sec
64 Religious Education K-12
65 Religious Education Elem
66 Religious Education Sec
67 School Board President
68 Teacher Personnel
69 Academic Assessment
70 Research/Development
71 Public Information
72 Summer School
73 Instructional Tech
74 Inservice Training
75 Marketing/Distributive
76 Info Systems
77 Psychological Assess
78 Affirmative Action

New York School Directory — Cattaraugus County

BROOME REGIONAL CENTERS

• **Broome-Tioga BOCES** PID: 00717306   607/763-3300
435 Glenwood Rd, Binghamton 13905   Fax 607/763-3215

Allen Buyck	1,11	John Harvey	2,3,17
Kathryn Blackman	2	Mark Bordeau	4
Mike Lynch	7,91	James Mullins	8,15
Nicole Waskie-Laura	16	Tom McNair	27
Melinda Russell	31	Maggie Collins	58
Sandra Ruffo	67	Robin Eccleston	68
Michelle Savory	70,74	Don Silvera	71
Kerri Bullock	74	Charles Wheeler	88

CATTARAUGUS COUNTY

CATTARAUGUS COUNTY SCHOOLS

County Schs..Principal	Grd	Prgm	Enr/#Cls	SN	
Career Tech Ctr-Olean 1825 Windfall Rd, Olean 14760 Stephen Dieteman	Voc		250 20		716/376-8200 Fax 716/376-8450

CATTARAUGUS PUBLIC SCHOOLS

• **Allegany-Limestone Ctl SD** PID: 00717332   716/375-6600
3131 Five Mile Rd, Allegany 14706   Fax 716/375-6629

Schools: 2 \ **Teachers:** 97 \ **Students:** 1,156 \ **Special Ed Students:** 160 \ **LEP Students:** 3 \ **College-Bound:** 78% \ **Ethnic:** Asian 1%, African American 2%, Hispanic 1%, Caucasian 95% \ **Exp:** $199 (Low) \ **Poverty:** 15% \ **Title I:** $294,027 \ **Special Education:** $1,691,000 \ **Open-Close:** 09/04 - 06/15 \ **DTBP:** $352 (High) \ t

Tony Giannicchi	1	Mike Watson	2,5,11,68
Allen Backer	3*	Rhonda Herbert	4*
Shawn Phinney	5	Jon Luce	6
Paige Kinnard	8,12,57,69,296	Greta Gregory	10,37*
Amber Cheladyn	16*	Jill Bogart	38,270*
Alicia Bockmier	58	Sue Schifley	67
Kevin Straub	73,295*		

Public Schs..Principal	Grd	Prgm	Enr/#Cls	SN	
Allegany-Limestone Elem Sch 120 Maple Ave, Allegany 14706 Meghan Janora	PK-5	T	502 29	44%	716/375-6600 Fax 716/375-6628
Allegany-Limestone High Sch 3131 Five Mile Rd, Allegany 14706 Cory Pecorella	6-12		654 37	35%	716/375-6600

• **Cattaraugus-Little Vly Ctl SD** PID: 00717368   716/257-5293
25 N Franklin St, Cattaraugus 14719   Fax 716/257-5298

Schools: 3 \ **Teachers:** 93 \ **Students:** 975 \ **Special Ed Students:** 165 \ **LEP Students:** 3 \ **College-Bound:** 70% \ **Ethnic:** African American 1%, Hispanic 2%, Native American: 1%, Caucasian 96% \ **Exp:** $279 (Med) \ **Title I:** $664,068 \ **Special Education:** $2,084,000 \ **Open-Close:** 09/03 - 06/24 \ **DTBP:** $358 (High)

Dr Sharon Huff	1	Sally Hadley	2
Wayne McGuire	3	Maria Stang	5
Matt Minnekine	6,35*	Amy Lincoln	12,298
Lisa Laquay	16,82	Casey Barber	36,57*
Shauna McMahon	58	Ben Stoll	67
Richard Weinberd	73,295		

Public Schs..Principal	Grd	Prgm	Enr/#Cls	SN	
Cattaraugus Elem Sch 25 N Franklin St, Cattaraugus 14719 Jennifer Conklin-Frank	PK-4	T	370 16	56%	716/257-3436 Fax 716/257-5237
Cattaraugus Middle Sch 25 N Franklin St, Cattaraugus 14719 April Preston	5-8		268 27	55%	716/257-3483 Fax 716/257-5108
Cattaraugus-Lttle Vly High Sch 25 N Franklin St, Cattaraugus 14719 Tina Maines	9-12	V	280 30	51%	716/257-3483 Fax 716/257-5108

• **Ellicottville Central Sch Dist** PID: 00717394   716/699-2316
5873 Route 219 S, Ellicottville 14731   Fax 716/699-6017

Schools: 1 \ **Teachers:** 51 \ **Students:** 600 \ **Special Ed Students:** 81 \ **College-Bound:** 70% \ **Ethnic:** Asian 1%, African American 1%, Hispanic 2%, Native American: 4%, Caucasian 92% \ **Exp:** $274 (Med) \ **Poverty:** 13% \ **Title I:** $106,593 \ **Special Education:** $110,000 \ **Open-Close:** 09/02 - 06/24 \ **DTBP:** $345 (High)

Robert Miller	1	Aimee Kilby	2*
Mark Waters	3	Vicky Williams	4*
Todd Lovell	5	Dave McCann	6
Karin Hager	7,85*	Maren Bush	8,11,58,69,296,298
Pamela Illig	16*	Kate Boutet	35,83
Tammy Eddy	38*	Robert Van Wicklin	67
Shawne Hunt	73,76,274,295*	Erich Ploetz	270*

Public Schs..Principal	Grd	Prgm	Enr/#Cls	SN	
Ellicottville Sch 5873 Route 219 S, Ellicottville 14731 Erich Ploetz \ Maren Bush	PK-12	V	600 60	35%	716/699-2316 Fax 716/699-5423

• **Franklinville Ctl School Dist** PID: 00717423   716/676-8000
31 N Main St, Franklinville 14737   Fax 716/676-8041

Schools: 2 \ **Teachers:** 73 \ **Students:** 700 \ **Special Ed Students:** 99 \ **College-Bound:** 90% \ **Ethnic:** Asian 1%, Hispanic 3%, Native American: 1%, Caucasian 94% \ **Exp:** $416 (High) \ **Poverty:** 23% \ **Title I:** $286,262 \ **Special Education:** $1,683,000 \ **Open-Close:** 09/08 - 06/24 \ f

Christopher Swiatek	1	Donna Howard	2,12,17,19,298
Ted Wing	5	Mark Blecha	6*
Tori Rosetti	7	Warren Scott	8,11
Thomas Riddock	9,81	Megan Russell	13,77,83,88,270
Andrew Potter	16,73,76,286,295,752*	Elizabeth Brisky	16
Scott Rudnicki	18,58,76,98,288,296,750,751	Cindi Rhoades	27,36,69*
Sue Ciesla	67	Derek Schunke	273*

---

79 Student Personnel	91 Safety/Security	275 Response To Intervention	298 Grant Writer/Ptnrships	**School Programs**	**Social Media**	
80 Driver Ed/Safety	92 Magnet School	277 Remedial Math K-12	750 Chief Innovation Officer	A = Alternative Program	f = Facebook	
81 Gifted/Talented	93 Parental Involvement	280 Literacy Coach	751 Chief of Staff	G = Adult Classes		
82 Video Services	95 Tech Prep Program	285 STEM	752 Social Emotional Learning	M = Magnet Program	t = Twitter	
83 Substance Abuse Prev	97 Chief Infomation Officer	286 Digital Learning		T = Title I Schoolwide		
84 Erate	98 Chief Technology Officer	288 Common Core Standards	**Other School Types**	V = Career & Tech Ed Programs		
85 AIDS Education	270 Character Education	294 Accountability	Ⓐ = Alternative School			
88 Alternative/At Risk	271 Migrant Education	295 Network System	Ⓒ = Charter School	New Schools are shaded		
89 Multi-Cultural Curriculum	273 Teacher Mentor	296 Title II Programs	Ⓜ = Magnet School	New Superintendents and Principals are bold		
90 Social Work	274 Before/Aft Sch	297 Webmaster	Ⓨ = Year-Round School	Personnel with email addresses are underscored		

Cattaraugus County

Market Data Retrieval

Public Schs..Principal	Grd	Prgm	Enr/#Cls	SN		
Franklinville Elem Sch 32 N Main St, Franklinville 14737 Thomas Riddoch	PK-6	T	355 35	45%	716/676-8020 Fax 716/676-2797	
Franklinville Jr Sr High Sch 31 N Main St, Franklinville 14737 Jennifer Fisk	7-12	TV	280 40	54%	716/676-8060 Fax 716/676-8042	

- **Gowanda Central School Dist** PID: 00717459   716/532-3325
  10674 Prospect St, Gowanda 14070   Fax 716/995-2154

Schools: 3 \ **Teachers:** 127 \ **Students:** 1,063 \ **Special Ed Students:** 230 \ **College-Bound:** 65% \ **Ethnic:** Hispanic 5%, Native American: 25%, Caucasian 70% \ **Exp:** $274 (Med) \ **Poverty:** 22% \ **Title I:** $568,953 \ **Special Education:** $2,799,000 \ **Open-Close:** 09/04 - 06/25 \ **DTBP:** $463 (High)

Bob Anderson 1		Barb Smith 2	
James Nunweiler 3		Patrick Nixon 3	
Rich Smith 3		Amy Lineberger 4*	
Annette Nelson 5		Joseph Bruening 6,35*	
Sandra Cimbricz 8		Janine Jalal 11,58,298	
Paula Ondus 26*		Carol Denny 30	
Stefanena Kysor 30		Beth Gerarde 36,83,90*	
Patricia Krajewski 38*		Carrie Dziebra 57*	
Mark Nephew 67		Doug Pine 73,76,95,286*	
Caroline Young 88		Lottie Gill 88	
Mary Mohawk-Jensen 88*		James Klubek 288	
Paula Troutman 296			

Public Schs..Principal	Grd	Prgm	Enr/#Cls	SN	
Gowanda Elem Sch 10674 Prospect St, Gowanda 14070 Carrie Dzierba	K-4	T	425 29	65%	716/532-3328 Fax 716/241-3116
Gowanda High Sch 10674 Prospect St, Gowanda 14070 Dr Robert Anderson	9-12	GTV	328 40	58%	716/532-3325 Fax 716/995-2108
Gowanda Middle Sch 10674 Prospect St, Gowanda 14070 Todd Miklas	5-8	T	310 40	65%	716/532-3325 Fax 716/995-2127

- **Hinsdale Central School Dist** PID: 00717502   716/557-2227
  3701 Main St, Hinsdale 14743   Fax 716/557-2259

Schools: 1 \ **Teachers:** 45 \ **Students:** 404 \ **Special Ed Students:** 76 \ **Ethnic:** Asian 1%, African American 1%, Hispanic 1%, Caucasian 97% \ **Exp:** $315 (High) \ **Poverty:** 23% \ **Title I:** $190,749 \ **Special Education:** $775,000 \ **Open-Close:** 09/08 - 06/24 \ **DTBP:** $784 (High)

Larry Ljungberg 1	Jennifer Jaquith 2
Matt Parmalee 3*	Lisa Parker 4
Mark Crino 6*	Laurie Cuddy 8,69,88,270,273,274*
Chris Dzierzanowski 11	Nancy Clayson 16,73,82*
Andrea Fidurko 58	Jennifer Howell 67

Public Schs..Principal	Grd	Prgm	Enr/#Cls	SN	
Hinsdale Central Sch 3701 Main St, Hinsdale 14743 Laurie Cuddy	PK-12	AT	404 50	56%	716/557-2227

- **Olean City School Dist** PID: 00717588   716/375-8001
  410 W Sullivan St, Olean 14760   Fax 716/375-8048

Schools: 4 \ **Teachers:** 175 \ **Students:** 2,075 \ **Special Ed Students:** 386 \ **LEP Students:** 4 \ **College-Bound:** 87% \ **Ethnic:** Asian 3%, African American 4%, Hispanic 3%, Native American: 1%, Caucasian 89% \ **Exp:** $334 (High) \ **Poverty:** 26% \ **Title I:** $1,124,171 \ **Special Education:** $4,229,000 \ **Open-Close:** 09/04 - 06/25 \ **DTBP:** $330 (High) \

Rick Moore 1	Kathy Elser 2,5
Mark Huselstein 3,91	Kevin Fisher 4
Steven Anastasia 6*	Jen Mahar 11,51
Matt Threehouse 27,38	Csobanka Woodworth 28,73,295*
Mary Lee Wenke 38*	Marcella Richmond 58,88
Mary Hirsch-Schena 67	Aaron Wolfe 68,74
Marc Friends 295	Nick Patrone 298

Public Schs..Principal	Grd	Prgm	Enr/#Cls	SN	
East View Elem Sch 690 E Spring St, Olean 14760 Brian Crawford	PK-3	T	351 25	52%	716/375-8920 Fax 716/375-8929
Olean Interm Middle Sch 401 Wayne St, Olean 14760 Joel Whitcher	4-7	TV	650 35	58%	716/375-8061 Fax 716/375-8070
Olean Senior High Sch 410 W Sullivan St, Olean 14760 Jeffrey Andreano	8-12	AGV	738 52	46%	716/375-8010
Washington West Elem Sch 1626 Washington St, Olean 14760 Lauren Stuff	PK-3	T	346 26	66%	716/375-8960 Fax 716/375-8970

- **Portville Central School Dist** PID: 00717722   716/933-6000
  500 Elm St, Portville 14770   Fax 716/933-7124

Schools: 1 \ **Teachers:** 73 \ **Students:** 1,030 \ **Special Ed Students:** 100 \ **College-Bound:** 68% \ **Ethnic:** Hispanic 1%, Caucasian 98% \ **Exp:** $178 (Low) \ **Poverty:** 15% \ **Title I:** $196,542 \ **Special Education:** $965,000 \ **Open-Close:** 09/04 - 06/25 \ **DTBP:** $319 (High)

Thomas Simon 1,11	Robin Owens 2
Platt Jeff 3	Laura Watson 4
David Young 5	Elizabeth Colligan 6,35*
Anne Mitchell 8,273	Tanya Burke 11,58,296
Lynn Corder 12*	Elizabeth Griffith 37*
Amanda Luther 38*	Dan Wenke 67
Monica Pascucci 69,83,85,88*	Mike Torrey 73,295*

Public Schs..Principal	Grd	Prgm	Enr/#Cls	SN	
Portville Central Sch 500 Elm St, Portville 14770 Lynn Corder · Lawrence Welty	K-12	AT	1,030 90	41%	716/933-6000

- **Randolph Acad Union Free SD** PID: 00717564   716/358-6866
  336 Main Street Er, Randolph 14772   Fax 716/358-9076

Schools: 2 \ **Teachers:** 36 \ **Students:** 200 \ **Special Ed Students:** 11 \ **College-Bound:** 67% \ **Ethnic:** Asian 1%, African American 14%, Hispanic 16%, Native American: 6%, Caucasian 63% \ **Exp:** $181 (Low) \ **Open-Close:** 09/04 - 06/25 \ **DTBP:** $194 (High)

Lori DeCarlo 1,11,288	Dave Ditanna 2
Cynthia Johnson 7,8,12,85,298*	Sue Vanderzyden 58*
Mary Myers 67	Tina Rogers 68
Brian Fleischmann 73,76,295*	

---

1 Superintendent	8 Curric/Instruct K-12	19 Chief Financial Officer	29 Family/Consumer Science	39 Social Studies K-12	49 English/Lang Arts Elem	59 Special Education Elem	69 Academic Assessment
2 Bus/Finance/Purchasing	9 Curric/Instruct Elem	20 Art K-12	30 Adult Education	40 Social Studies Elem	50 English/Lang Arts Sec	60 Special Education Sec	70 Research/Development
3 Buildings And Grounds	10 Curric/Instruct Sec	21 Art Elem	31 Career/Sch-to-Work K-12	41 Social Studies Sec	51 Reading K-12	61 Foreign/World Lang K-12	71 Public Information
4 Food Service	11 Federal Program	22 Art Sec	32 Career/Sch-to-Work Elem	42 Science K-12	52 Reading Elem	62 Foreign/World Lang Elem	72 Summer School
5 Transportation	12 Title I	23 Music K-12	33 Career/Sch-to-Work Sec	43 Science Elem	53 Reading Sec	63 Foreign/World Lang Sec	73 Instructional Tech
6 Athletic	13 Title V	24 Music Elem	34 Early Childhood Ed	44 Science Sec	54 Remedial Reading K-12	64 Religious Education K-12	74 Inservice Training
7 Health Services	15 Asst Superintendent	25 Music Sec	35 Health/Phys Education	45 Math K-12	55 Remedial Reading Elem	65 Religious Education Elem	75 Marketing/Distributive
	16 Instructional Media Svcs	26 Business Education	36 Guidance Services K-12	46 Math Elem	56 Remedial Reading Sec	66 Religious Education Sec	76 Info Systems
	17 Chief Operations Officer	27 Career & Tech Ed	37 Guidance Services Elem	47 Math Sec	57 Bilingual/ELL	67 School Board President	77 Psychological Assess
	18 Chief Academic Officer	28 Technology Education	38 Guidance Services Sec	48 English/Lang Arts K-12	58 Special Education K-12	68 Teacher Personnel	78 Affirmative Action

New York School Directory — Cattaraugus County

Public Schs..Principal	Grd	Prgm	Enr/#Cls	SN	
Randolph Academy 336 Main Street Er, Randolph 14772 Mary Pauly	K-12	V	81 30	40%	716/358-6866
Randolph Academy-Hamburg 4655 Logans Ln, Hamburg 14075 John Kwietniewski	K-12	V	78 30	22%	716/648-1930 Fax 716/648-2371

● **Randolph Central School Dist** PID: 00717758   716/358-6161   Fax 716/358-7072
18 Main St, Randolph 14772

Schools: 2 \ **Teachers:** 83 \ **Students:** 903 \ **Special Ed Students:** 151 \ **College-Bound:** 71% \ **Ethnic:** African American 1%, Hispanic 2%, Native American: 5%, Caucasian 92% \ **Exp:** $265 (Med) \ **Poverty:** 22% \ **Title I:** $544,534 \ **Special Education:** $1,617,000 \ **Open-Close:** 09/02 - 06/25 \ **DTBP:** $318 (High) \ 📘

Kaine Kelly 1
Dave Flaherty 3*
Kourtney Almeida 11,58
Carly Wright 16*
Mike Frame 73*
Charles Shevlin 2,5
Robin Maycock 6*
Toni Indriolo 11,31,83,88*
Daniel Jackson 67

Public Schs..Principal	Grd	Prgm	Enr/#Cls	SN	
Gail N Chapman Elem Sch 22 Main St, Randolph 14772 Kristy Carlson	PK-6	T	506 25	51%	716/358-7030 Fax 716/358-7060 📘
Randolph Jr Sr High Sch 18 Main St, Randolph 14772 Jason Halpainy	7-12	T	397 60	45%	716/358-7007 Fax 716/358-7070

● **Salamanca City Central SD** PID: 00717784   716/945-2400   Fax 716/945-3964
50 Iroquois Dr, Salamanca 14779

Schools: 3 \ **Teachers:** 123 \ **Students:** 1,400 \ **Special Ed Students:** 184 \ **LEP Students:** 5 \ **Ethnic:** African American 1%, Hispanic 6%, Native American: 38%, Caucasian 55% \ **Exp:** $624 (High) \ **Poverty:** 26% \ **Title I:** $566,457 \ **Special Education:** $2,508,000 \ **Open-Close:** 09/01 - 06/24 \ **DTBP:** $363 (High)

Robert Breidenstein 1
Richard Pincoski 3
Robert Finch 5
Dr Mark Beehler 7,8,11,15,91,285,288
Mark Reid 38*
Teresa Ray 67
Vincent Pezzementi 71
Raymond Haley 91
Karen Magara 2,4,5,15
Drew Venezia 4
Richard Morton 6*
Aaron Straus 30*
Kristen Dudek 58,77,79,298
Penny Beattie 68,74
Robert Miller 73,76,286,295

Public Schs..Principal	Grd	Prgm	Enr/#Cls	SN	
Prospect Elem Sch 300 Prospect Ave, Salamanca 14779 Gayle Pavone	PK-3	T	435 24	62%	716/945-5170 Fax 716/945-2374
Salamanca High Sch 50 Iroquois Dr, Salamanca 14779 Christopher Siebert	8-12	T	408 51	60%	716/945-2404 Fax 716/945-5983
Seneca Intermediate Sch 50 Iroquois Dr, Salamanca 14779 Peter Morgante	4-7	T	408 17	64%	716/945-5140 Fax 716/945-3567

● **West Valley Ctl Sch Dist** PID: 00717837   716/942-3100   Fax 716/942-3440
5359 School St, West Valley 14171

Schools: 1 \ **Teachers:** 32 \ **Students:** 230 \ **Special Ed Students:** 44 \ **College-Bound:** 77% \ **Ethnic:** African American 2%, Hispanic 1%, Caucasian 96% \ **Exp:** $313 (High) \ **Poverty:** 12% \ **Title I:** $78,200 \ **Special Education:** $545,000 \ **Open-Close:** 09/08 - 06/24 \ **DTBP:** $392 (High)

Eric Lawton 1
Bill Sloand 3*
Chris Schiumo 6
Bryan Hansen 16,73,82*
Shawna Gugino 58*
Matthew Labrake 69*
Diane Westfall 298
Ann O'Brien 2
Bob Harrington 5*
Daniel Amodeo 8*
Gerald Stead 27*
Tim Plotze 67
Kyle Woodin 83,85,88*

Public Schs..Principal	Grd	Prgm	Enr/#Cls	SN	
West Valley Central Sch 5359 School St, West Valley 14171 Daniel Amodeo	PK-12	T	230 43	11%	716/942-3293

● **Yorkshire-Pioneer Ctl Sch Dist** PID: 00717679   716/492-9300   Fax 716/492-9360
12145 County Line Rd, Yorkshire 14173

Schools: 4 \ **Teachers:** 211 \ **Students:** 2,700 \ **Special Ed Students:** 551 \ **LEP Students:** 7 \ **College-Bound:** 64% \ **Ethnic:** Asian 1%, African American 1%, Hispanic 2%, Caucasian 96% \ **Exp:** $253 (Med) \ **Poverty:** 17% \ **Title I:** $679,357 \ **Special Education:** $5,886,000 \ **Open-Close:** 09/03 - 06/25 \ **DTBP:** $296 (High) \ 📘 🐦

Benjamin Halsey 1
Nick Titus 3*
William Weidner 6,7
Janine Wagner 11,68
Deb Zuppo 49
Melissa Nocera-Collins 67
Michael Irizary 73*
Jane Antkowiak 97,295
Nicholas Silvaroli 2,5,15
Catherine Pritchard 4*
Michael Irizarry 8,11,48,57,69,72,73,288
Louise Herrick 47
Jean Vallance 58
Skip Tillinghast 71,297*
Kay Kilburn 83*

Public Schs..Principal	Grd	Prgm	Enr/#Cls	SN	
Arcade Elem Sch 315 Main St, Arcade 14009 Mellisa Devitt	PK-4		550 30	46%	716/492-9421 Fax 716/492-9433
Delevan Elem Sch 30 School St, Delevan 14042 Tiffany Giannicchi	PK-4	T	410 31	59%	716/492-9461 Fax 716/492-9477
Pioneer High Sch 12125 County Line Rd, Yorkshire 14173 Mark Schultz	9-12	AV	720 50	46%	716/492-9300 Fax 716/492-9350
Pioneer Middle Sch 12132 Old Olean Rd, Yorkshire 14173 Melissa Prorok	5-8	ATV	729 40	54%	716/492-9300 Fax 716/492-9417

CATTARAUGUS CATHOLIC SCHOOLS

● **Diocese of Buffalo Ed Office** PID: 00725846
Listing includes only schools located in this county. See District Index for location of Diocesan Offices.

Catholic Schs..Principal	Grd	Prgm	Enr/#Cls	SN	
Archbishop Walsh Academy 208 N 24th St, Olean 14760 Thomas Manko	9-12	V	62 21		716/372-8122 Fax 716/372-6707

---

79 Student Personnel
80 Driver Ed/Safety
81 Gifted/Talented
82 Video Services
83 Substance Abuse Prev
84 Erate
85 AIDS Education
88 Alternative/At Risk
89 Multi-Cultural Curriculum
90 Social Work
91 Safety/Security
92 Magnet School
93 Parental Involvement
95 Tech Prep Program
97 Chief Information Officer
98 Chief Technology Officer
270 Character Education
271 Migrant Education
273 Teacher Mentor
274 Before/After Sch
275 Response To Intervention
277 Remedial Math K-12
280 Literacy Coach
285 STEM
286 Digital Learning
288 Common Core Standards
294 Accountability
295 Network System
296 Title II Programs
297 Webmaster
298 Grant Writer/Ptnrships
750 Chief Innovation Officer
751 Chief of Staff
752 Social Emotional Learning

School Programs
A = Alternative Program
G = Adult Classes
M = Magnet Program
T = Title I Schoolwide
V = Career & Tech Ed Programs

Other School Types
Ⓐ = Alternative School
Ⓒ = Charter School
Ⓜ = Magnet School
Ⓨ = Year-Round School

Social Media
📘 = Facebook
🐦 = Twitter

New Schools are shaded
New Superintendents and Principals are bold
Personnel with email addresses are underscored

NY—33

Cayuga County

Market Data Retrieval

Southern Tier Catholic Sch 208 N 24th St, Olean 14760 Thomas Manko	K-8	139 19	716/372-8122 Fax 716/372-6707

CATTARAUGUS PRIVATE SCHOOLS

Private Schs..Principal	Grd	Prgm	Enr/#Cls	SN	
Central Baptist Christian Sch 12045 Old Olean Rd, Yorkshire 14173 Greg Reger	K-12		100 6		716/492-2203 Fax 716/492-2627
Portville Baptist Chrn Sch 24 Temple St, Portville 14770	K-6		10 3		716/933-8164

CATTARAUGUS REGIONAL CENTERS

• **Cattaraugus-Allegany BOCES** PID: 00717851　　716/376-8200
1825 Windfall Rd, Olean 14760　　　　　　　　　　Fax 716/376-8450

Lynn Fusco 1	Thomas Potter 2
Tim Cox 8,15,16,74	Carol Fial 15,58
Tracie Preston 15,27,30	Amy Windus 16
Michelle Spasiano 17	Candace Clemens 67
Pam Kirkwood 68	Michael Graf 73

CAYUGA COUNTY

CAYUGA COUNTY SCHOOLS

County Schs..Principal	Grd	Prgm	Enr/#Cls	SN	
Regional Education Center 1879 W Genesee Street Rd, Auburn 13021 Steve Woodard	Voc	AG	300 30	56%	315/253-0361 Fax 315/252-6493
Ⓐ Summit Sch 29 William St, Auburn 13021 Elaine Hobart	7-12		85		315/253-2019

CAYUGA PUBLIC SCHOOLS

• **Auburn Enlarged City Sch Dist** PID: 00717863　　315/255-8822
78 Thornton Ave, Auburn 13021　　　　　　　　　　Fax 315/252-5248

Schools: 7 \ **Teachers:** 310 \ **Students:** 4,200 \ **Special Ed Students:** 668 \ **LEP Students:** 7 \ **College-Bound:** 88% \ **Ethnic:** Asian 1%, African American 7%, Hispanic 5%, Caucasian 87% \ **Exp:** $201 (Med) \ **Poverty:** 19% \ **Title I:** $1,443,774 \ **Special Education:** $6,037,000 \ **Open-Close:** 09/03 - 06/25 \ **DTBP:** $229 (High)

Jeffrey Pirozzolo 1	Lisa Green 2
Sandy Vangiesen 2	Larry Garuccio 3,91
Carolann DiFabio 5	Tam Ray 6,35,83
Caren Radell 7	Deborah Radcliff 8
Michelle Kolceski 8	Camille Johnson 15,69,77,79,271
Jeffrey Evener 15,68	Babette Valentine 59
Brandi Wicks 60	Joseph Sheppard 67

Thomas Bunn 73,95,295	David Oliver 270*
Jeremy Vevone 295	Jesse Chehovich 295

Public Schs..Principal	Grd	Prgm	Enr/#Cls	SN	
Auburn High Sch 250 Lake Ave, Auburn 13021 Brian Morgan	9-12	AT	1,198 80	43%	315/255-8300 Fax 315/255-8357
Auburn Junior High Sch 191 Franklin St, Auburn 13021 David Oliver	7-8	T	621 45	50%	315/255-8480 Fax 315/255-8495
Casey Park Elem Sch 101 Pulaski St, Auburn 13021 Kelly Garback	K-6	T	496 23	72%	315/255-8760 Fax 315/255-8790
Genesee Elem Sch 244 Genesee St, Auburn 13021 Heather Costello	K-6	T	374 18	79%	315/255-8640 Fax 315/255-8675
Herman Avenue Elem Sch 2 N Herman Ave, Auburn 13021 Ronald Gorney	K-6	T	471 30	44%	315/255-8680 Fax 315/255-8693
Owasco Elem Sch 66 Letchworth St, Auburn 13021 Jeremy Moore	K-6	T	436 23	44%	315/255-8720
W H Seward Elem Sch 52 Metcalf Dr, Auburn 13021 Amy Mahunik	K-6	T	509 24	49%	315/255-8600 Fax 315/255-8611

• **Cato Meridian Central Sch Dist** PID: 00717980　　315/626-3439
2851 State Route 370, Cato 13033　　　　　　　　　　Fax 315/626-2888

Schools: 3 \ **Teachers:** 87 \ **Students:** 922 \ **Special Ed Students:** 117 \ **LEP Students:** 3 \ **College-Bound:** 70% \ **Ethnic:** African American 1%, Hispanic 2%, Caucasian 97% \ **Exp:** $187 (Low) \ **Poverty:** 10% \ **Title I:** $156,074 \ **Special Education:** $1,470,000 \ **Open-Close:** 09/03 - 06/25 \ **DTBP:** $623 (High)

Dr Terry Ward 1	Brenda Semeraro 2,11,83,88,91
Joseph Phillips 3	Melissa Sherwood 4*
Tammy Cady 5	David Scholl 6,7
Robert Wren 9*	Elizabeth Kupiec 11,58,79,296,298*
Aaron Berube 16,73,295*	Paul Byrne 67
Erica Butchko 68	Sarah Mavretish 69*
Susan Hawker 73*	Karen Bertram 285

Public Schs..Principal	Grd	Prgm	Enr/#Cls	SN	
Cato Meridian Elem Sch 2851 State Route 370, Cato 13033 Robert Wren	PK-4	T	375 21	44%	315/626-3320 Fax 315/626-2293
Cato Meridian High Sch 2851 State Route 370, Cato 13033 Danielle Mahoney	9-12		287 50	37%	315/626-3317 Fax 315/626-2551
Cato Meridian Middle Sch 2851 State Route 370, Cato 13033 Sean Gleason	5-8	T	260 40	43%	315/626-3319 Fax 315/626-2327

• **Moravia Central School Dist** PID: 00718025　　315/497-2670
68 S Main St, Moravia 13118　　　　　　　　　　Fax 315/497-2260

Schools: 2 \ **Teachers:** 77 \ **Students:** 907 \ **Special Ed Students:** 186 \ **LEP Students:** 3 \ **College-Bound:** 86% \ **Ethnic:** Hispanic 2%, Caucasian 98% \ **Exp:** $591 (High) \ **Poverty:** 17% \ **Title I:** $268,504 \ **Special Education:** $2,301,000 \ **Open-Close:** 09/08 - 06/24 \ **DTBP:** $359 (High)

John Birmingham 1	Jeffery Lawrence 2,91
Dale Sharpsteen 3	Jennifer Parker-Smith 4*
Danielle Winters 5	Todd Mulvaney 6

1	Superintendent	8	Curric/Instruct K-12	19	Chief Financial Officer	29	Family/Consumer Science
2	Bus/Finance/Purchasing	9	Curric/Instruct Elem	20	Art K-12	30	Adult Education
3	Buildings And Grounds	10	Curric/Instruct Sec	21	Art Elem	31	Career/Sch-to-Work K-12
4	Food Service	11	Federal Program	22	Art Sec	32	Career/Sch-to-Work Elem
5	Transportation	12	Title I	23	Music K-12	33	Career/Sch-to-Work Sec
6	Athletic	13	Title V	24	Music Elem	34	Early Childhood Ed
7	Health Services	15	Asst Superintendent	25	Music Sec	35	Health/Phys Education
		16	Instructional Media Svcs	26	Business Education	36	Guidance Services K-12
		17	Chief Operations Officer	27	Career & Tech Ed	37	Guidance Services Elem
		18	Chief Academic Officer	28	Technology Education	38	Guidance Services Sec

39	Social Studies K-12	49	English/Lang Arts Elem	59	Special Education Elem	69	Academic Assessment
40	Social Studies Elem	50	English/Lang Arts Sec	60	Special Education Sec	70	Research/Development
41	Social Studies Sec	51	Reading K-12	61	Foreign/World Lang K-12	71	Public Information
42	Science K-12	52	Reading Elem	62	Foreign/World Lang Elem	72	Summer School
43	Science Elem	53	Reading Sec	63	Foreign/World Lang Sec	73	Instructional Tech
44	Science Sec	54	Remedial Reading K-12	64	Religious Education K-12	74	Inservice Training
45	Math K-12	55	Remedial Reading Elem	65	Religious Education Elem	75	Marketing/Distributive
46	Math Elem	56	Remedial Reading Sec	66	Religious Education Sec	76	Info Systems
47	Math Sec	57	Bilingual/ELL	67	School Board President	77	Psychological Assess
48	English/Lang Arts K-12	58	Special Education K-12	68	Teacher Personnel	78	Affirmative Action

New York School Directory — Cayuga County

Howard Seamans	9,34,51,54,273*	Bruce MacBain	10,69*
Tracy Muffo	10	Chris Fisher	11,57,58,83,88,271,298*
Jenifer Westover	16*	Michelle Lyon	67
John Owen	73,76	Karen Schaub	285
Lorraine McNair	295		

Public Schs..Principal	Grd	Prgm	Enr/#Cls	SN	
Millard Fillmore Elem Sch 24 S Main St, Moravia 13118 Howard Seamans	PK-5	T	414 30	45%	315/497-2670 Fax 315/497-3961
Moravia Jr Sr High Sch 68 S Main St, Moravia 13118 Bruce MacBain \ Karl O'Leary	6-12	T	493 42	49%	315/497-2670 Fax 315/497-3852

● Port Byron Ctl School Dist PID: 00718051   315/776-5728
30 Maple Ave, Port Byron 13140   Fax 315/776-4050

Schools: 2 \ **Teachers:** 69 \ **Students:** 800 \ **Special Ed Students:** 150 \ **Ethnic:** African American 1%, Hispanic 3%, Caucasian 96% \ **Exp:** $383 (High) \ **Poverty:** 14% \ **Title I:** $243,713 \ **Special Education:** $1,760,000 \ **Open-Close:** 09/08 - 06/25 \ **DTBP:** $359 (High)

Neil O'Brien	1	Anthony Scro	2
Mitchell Toleson	2,15	Corey Rooker	3,5*
Gina Kilmer	4	Kim Brown	6
Michael Jorgensen	8*	Jacqueline Skelton	35,83
Tracey Pirozzolo	36*	Kevin Barber	38*
Erica Sinicropi	58,77*	Dr Paul Ryan	67
Wenwei Hsu	73,76,295*		

Public Schs..Principal	Grd	Prgm	Enr/#Cls	SN	
A A Gates Elem Sch 30 Maple Ave, Port Byron 13140 Julie Podolak	PK-6	T	384 34	41%	315/776-5728 Fax 315/776-8613
Dana L West Jr Sr High Sch 30 Maple Ave, Port Byron 13140 Michael Jorgensen	7-12		377 50	47%	315/776-5728 t

● Southern Cayuga Central SD PID: 00718099   315/364-7211
2384 State Route 34B, Aurora 13026   Fax 315/364-7863

Schools: 2 \ **Teachers:** 64 \ **Students:** 683 \ **Special Ed Students:** 113 \ **LEP Students:** 36 \ **College-Bound:** 73% \ **Ethnic:** Hispanic 11%, Native American: 1%, Caucasian 87% \ **Exp:** $374 (High) \ **Poverty:** 13% \ **Title I:** $204,178 \ **Special Education:** $1,138,000 \ **Open-Close:** 09/04 - 06/25 \ **DTBP:** $359 (High)

Patrick Jensen	1	Kimberly Vile	2
Kevin Baylor	3	Ronald Leonard	5
Lindsay Herrling	58	Kelsey Rossbach	67
Heather Snyder	285		

Public Schs..Principal	Grd	Prgm	Enr/#Cls	SN	
Emily Howland Elem Sch 2384 State Route 34B, Aurora 13026 Jean Amodeo	PK-6	T	369 16	47%	315/364-7098 Fax 315/364-7050
Southern Cayuga Jr Sr HS 2384 State Route 34B, Aurora 13026 Luke Carnicelli	7-12	ATV	314	47%	315/364-7111 Fax 315/364-8207

● Union Springs Ctl School Dist PID: 00718154   315/889-4101
239 Cayuga St, Union Springs 13160   Fax 315/889-4108

Schools: 3 \ **Teachers:** 76 \ **Students:** 823 \ **Special Ed Students:** 116 \ **LEP Students:** 6 \ **College-Bound:** 78% \ **Ethnic:** African American 2%, Hispanic 5%, Caucasian 93% \ **Exp:** $460 (High) \ **Poverty:** 10% \ **Title I:** $133,611 \ **Special Education:** $1,810,000 \ **Open-Close:** 09/03 - 06/30 \ **DTBP:** $373 (High)

Jarrett Powers	1	Marge Robbins	2,15
Todd Rafferty	3	Kathleen Smith	4
Andrea Lang	5	Todd Salls	6*
Stephanie Berry	16,82*	Lisa Winters	30
Sheila Ladouce	59*	Ann Daum	67
David Lima	73*		

Public Schs..Principal	Grd	Prgm	Enr/#Cls	SN	
A J Smith Elem Sch 26 Homer St, Union Springs 13160 Sheila Ladouce	PK-5	T	393 20	39%	315/889-4170 Fax 315/889-4175
Union Springs Central High Sch 239 Cayuga St, Union Springs 13160 Charles Walker	9-12		245 25	36%	315/889-4110 Fax 315/889-4133
Union Springs Middle Sch 239 Cayuga St, Union Springs 13160 Mike Wurster	6-8		185 15	37%	315/889-4112 Fax 315/889-4133

● Weedsport Ctl School Dist PID: 00718207   315/834-6637
2821 E Brutus Street Rd, Weedsport 13166   Fax 315/834-8693

Schools: 2 \ **Teachers:** 75 \ **Students:** 800 \ **Special Ed Students:** 138 \ **LEP Students:** 3 \ **College-Bound:** 76% \ **Ethnic:** Asian 1%, Hispanic 4%, Caucasian 95% \ **Exp:** $305 (High) \ **Poverty:** 9% \ **Title I:** $110,434 \ **Special Education:** $5,000 \ **Open-Close:** 09/08 - 06/25 \ **DTBP:** $359 (High)

Shaun O'Connor	1	Peter Colucci	2,15
Chuck Roach	3,5,73*	Donna O'Brien	4
Nancy Hares	5	Annmarie Brown	7
Melinda Ervay	8,69	Ann DeFazio	11,58,76,296,298*
Jessica Bradtke	38*	Colleen Borza	67
Kenneth Rakowski	77*	John Sgarlata	83
Lisa Mabbett	285*		

Public Schs..Principal	Grd	Prgm	Enr/#Cls	SN	
Weedsport Elem Sch 8954 Jackson St, Weedsport 13166 Timothy Cowin	PK-6		385 23	29%	315/834-6685 Fax 315/834-6712
Weedsport Jr Sr High Sch 2821 E Brutus Street Rd, Weedsport 13166 Brett Fingland	7-12		369 50	27%	315/834-6652

CAYUGA PRIVATE SCHOOLS

Private Schs..Principal	Grd	Prgm	Enr/#Cls	SN	
Frontenac SDA Elem Sch 963 Spring Street Rd, Union Springs 13160 Rebecca Runnals	K-8		19 3		315/889-5094
Hillside Childrens Center 7432 County House Rd, Auburn 13021 Elaine Quintaina	K-12		52 9		315/258-2151 Fax 315/258-2130
Montessori Sch of Finger Lakes 6734 Pine Ridge Rd, Auburn 13021 Jilda Brower	PK-8		52 3		315/252-2225

---

79 Student Personnel	91 Safety/Security	275 Response To Intervention	298 Grant Writer/Ptnrships	**School Programs**	**Social Media**
80 Driver Ed/Safety	92 Magnet School	277 Remedial Math K-12	750 Chief Innovation Officer	A = Alternative Program	
81 Gifted/Talented	93 Parental Involvement	280 Literacy Coach	751 Chief of Staff	G = Adult Classes	= Facebook
82 Video Services	95 Tech Prep Program	285 STEM	752 Social Emotional Learning	M = Magnet Program	
83 Substance Abuse Prev	97 Chief Infomation Officer	286 Digital Learning		T = Title I Schoolwide	= Twitter
84 Erate	98 Chief Technology Officer	288 Common Core Standards	**Other School Types**	V = Career & Tech Ed Programs	
85 AIDS Education	270 Accountability	294 Accountability	Ⓐ = Alternative School		
88 Alternative/At Risk	271 Migrant Education	295 Network System	Ⓒ = Charter School	New Schools are shaded	
89 Multi-Cultural Curriculum	273 Teacher Mentor	296 Title II Programs	Ⓜ = Magnet School	New Superintendents and Principals are bold	
90 Social Work	274 Before/After Sch	297 Webmaster	Ⓨ = Year-Round School	Personnel with email addresses are underscored	

Chautauqua County

Market Data Retrieval

Peachtown Elem Sch 170 Main St, Aurora 13026 Barbara Post	PK-8	26 3	315/364-8721
Tyburn Academy 17 Clymer St, Auburn 13021 Maura Delfavero	7-12	81 15	315/252-2937 Fax 315/252-4173
Union Springs Academy 40 Spring St, Union Springs 13160 Hilde Barrera	9-12	54 8	315/889-7314 Fax 315/889-7188

CAYUGA REGIONAL CENTERS

• **Cayuga-Onondaga BOCES** PID: 00718233   315/253-0361
1879 W Genesee Street Rd, Auburn 13021   Fax 315/252-6361

Dr Brian Hartwell 1
Jessica Docteur 15,74
Steve Woodard 27,30,31,88
Melinda Quanbeck 67
Tony Abbatiello 73,286

Doug Tomandi 2
Andrew Dutcher 16
Susan Lynch 58
Patrick Shanahan 68

CHAUTAUQUA COUNTY

CHAUTAUQUA COUNTY SCHOOLS

County Schs..Principal	Grd	Prgm	Enr/#Cls	SN	
ⓐ Academy at Maple Avenue 175 Maple Ave, Cassadaga 14718 Kevin Bourgoine	7-12		25		716/672-3222 Fax 716/595-2170
Hewes Career & Tech Ed Center 2615 N Maple Ave, Ashville 14710 Paul Mihalko	Voc	AG	500 14		716/763-1801 Fax 716/763-7726 [f]
Loguidice Educational Center 9520 Fredonia Stockton Rd, Fredonia 14063 Jose Pagan	K-12	AGV	500		716/672-4371 Fax 716/679-3363

CHAUTAUQUA PUBLIC SCHOOLS

• **Bemus Point Ctl School Dist** PID: 00718257   716/386-2375
3980 Dutch Hollow Rd, Bemus Point 14712   Fax 716/386-2376

Schools: 2 \ Teachers: 68 \ Students: 715 \ Special Ed Students: 80 \ Ethnic: Asian 1%, African American 1%, Hispanic 2%, Caucasian 96% \ Exp: $339 (High) \ Poverty: 11% \ Title I: $117,251 \ Special Education: $708,000 \ Open-Close: 09/08 - 06/25 \ DTBP: $361 (High)

Michelle Spasiano 1
Tim Rowan 3
Kathy Burnett 6*
Carrie Yohe 11,58,298*
Barry Swanson 67

Holly Griffith 2
Joseph Dustin 5
Carrie Yohe 8,57,74
William Arthurs 16,73,76,286,295*
Mary Osgood 88

Public Schs..Principal	Grd	Prgm	Enr/#Cls	SN	
Bemus Point Elem Sch 41 Liberty St, Bemus Point 14712 Sonja DuBois	PK-5		284 21	32%	716/386-3795 Fax 716/386-4293
Maple Grove Jr Sr High Sch 3980 Dutch Hollow Rd, Bemus Point 14712 Julie Verdonik	6-12	V	367 50	26%	716/386-2855

• **Brocton Central School Dist** PID: 00718300   716/792-2171
138 W Main St, Brocton 14716   Fax 716/792-9965

Schools: 1 \ Teachers: 56 \ Students: 540 \ Special Ed Students: 133 \ LEP Students: 10 \ College-Bound: 90% \ Ethnic: Hispanic 10%, Caucasian 89% \ Exp: $184 (Low) \ Poverty: 30% \ Title I: $392,918 \ Special Education: $1,916,000 \ Open-Close: 09/08 - 06/25 \ DTBP: $367 (High)

Jason Delcamp 1
Larry Dolce 3,91*
Jennifer Rammelt 7*
Elizabeth Parra 12*
Maria Sigeti 35*
Michael Ridegiato 67
Laura Neratto 83

Kaitlyn Barkley 2,11,76,286,296
Kenneth Roberts 5
Melanie Ulinger 8,58,275,288,294*
Ashley Means 17
Katherine Putcher 36*
Michael Schultz 73,98,295*
Jodi Huber 285*

Public Schs..Principal	Grd	Prgm	Enr/#Cls	SN	
Brocton Central Sch 138 W Main St, Brocton 14716 Elizabeth Antolina \ Sandra Kopiczak	K-12	GT	540 80	58%	716/792-9121 Fax 716/792-2246

• **Cassadaga Valley Ctl Sch Dist** PID: 00718336   716/962-5155
5935 Route 60, Sinclairville 14782   Fax 716/962-5976

Schools: 2 \ Teachers: 83 \ Students: 851 \ Special Ed Students: 151 \ LEP Students: 3 \ College-Bound: 65% \ Ethnic: African American 1%, Hispanic 2%, Caucasian 97% \ Exp: $325 (High) \ Poverty: 19% \ Title I: $403,006 \ Special Education: $2,138,000 \ Open-Close: 09/03 - 06/25 \ DTBP: $420 (High)

Charles Leichner 1
Laura Watt 2
Heidi Ottaway 4
Marcy Sweetman 8,12,285,288*
Joyce Beichner 16*
Rebecca Donnelly 58
Phillip Bens 73,286*

Joelle Woodward 2,298
Thomas Zanghi 3,5*
Mark Petersen 6,35*
Joshua Gilevski 11,31,34*
Heather Nocero 38,69,83,88*
Jeanne Oag 67

Public Schs..Principal	Grd	Prgm	Enr/#Cls	SN	
Cassadaga Valley Middle HS 5935 Route 60, Sinclairville 14782 Scot Stutzman	6-12	TV	438 55	53%	716/962-8581 Fax 716/962-5788
Sinclairville Elem Sch 43 Sinclair Dr, Sinclairville 14782 Joshua Gilevski	PK-5	T	413 20	56%	716/962-5195 Fax 716/962-5468

• **Chautauqua Lake Central SD** PID: 00718867   716/753-5808
100 N Erie St, Mayville 14757   Fax 716/753-5813

Schools: 1 \ Teachers: 86 \ Students: 950 \ Special Ed Students: 108 \ Ethnic: Hispanic 2%, Native American: 1%, Caucasian 97% \ Exp: $376 (High) \ Poverty: 17% \ Title I: $297,245 \ Special Education: $166,000 \ Open-Close: 09/08 - 06/24 \ DTBP: $351 (High)

Rachel Curtin 1
Patrick Quinn 3
Jim Morrison 5
Megan Lundgren 12,58,296*
Amy Webb 67

Jackson Graham 2,71
Jennifer Shearer 4*
Josh Liddell 6*
Jason Richardson 38,88*
Derek Svenson 73*

1	Superintendent	8	Curric/Instruct K-12	19	Chief Financial Officer	29	Family/Consumer Science	39	Social Studies K-12	49	English/Lang Arts Elem	59	Special Education Elem	69	Academic Assessment
2	Bus/Finance/Purchasing	9	Curric/Instruct Elem	20	Art K-12	30	Adult Education	40	Social Studies Elem	50	English/Lang Arts Sec	60	Special Education Sec	70	Research/Development
3	Buildings And Grounds	10	Curric/Instruct Sec	21	Art Elem	31	Career/Sch-to-Work K-12	41	Social Studies Sec	51	Reading K-12	61	Foreign/World Lang K-12	71	Public Information
4	Food Service	11	Federal Program	22	Art Sec	32	Career/Sch-to-Work Elem	42	Science K-12	52	Reading Elem	62	Foreign/World Lang Elem	72	Summer School
5	Transportation	12	Title I	23	Music K-12	33	Career/Sch-to-Work Sec	43	Science Elem	53	Reading Sec	63	Foreign/World Lang Sec	73	Instructional Tech
6	Athletic	13	Title V	24	Music Elem	34	Early Childhood Ed	44	Science Sec	54	Remedial Reading K-12	64	Religious Education K-12	74	Inservice Training
7	Health Services	14	Asst Superintendent	25	Music Sec	35	Health/Phys Education	45	Math K-12	55	Remedial Reading Elem	65	Religious Education Elem	75	Marketing/Distributive
		15	Instructional Media Svcs	26	Business Education	36	Guidance Services K-12	46	Math Elem	56	Remedial Reading Sec	66	Religious Education Sec	76	Info Systems
		16	Chief Operations Officer	27	Career & Tech Ed	37	Guidance Services Elem	47	Math Sec	57	Bilingual/ELL	67	School Board President	77	Psychological Assess
		18	Chief Academic Officer	28	Technology Education	38	Guidance Services Sec	48	English/Lang Arts K-12	58	Special Education K-12	68	Teacher Personnel	78	Affirmative Action

New York School Directory — Chautauqua County

Public Schs..Principal	Grd	Prgm	Enr/#Cls	SN	
Chautauqua Lake Sch 100 N Erie St, Mayville 14757 Megan Lundgren \ Josh Liddell	PK-12	T	950 70	41%	716/753-5801

• Clymer Central School Dist PID: 00718427
8672 E Main St, Clymer 14724
716/355-4444
Fax 716/355-4467

Schools: 1 \ **Teachers:** 46 \ **Students:** 444 \ **Special Ed Students:** 77 \ **College-Bound:** 75% \ **Ethnic:** Asian 1%, African American 1%, Hispanic 3%, Caucasian 95% \ **Exp:** $292 (Med) \ **Poverty:** 19% \ **Title I:** $219,654 \ **Special Education:** $639,000 \ **Open-Close:** 09/08 - 06/25 \ **DTBP:** $351 (High)

Beth Olson 1
Richard Luke 3
Tracy Tewinkle 5
Lynne Bemis 11,298*
Corey Rhodes 27,31,36
Brianne Fadale 58
Stuart Strother 73,286,295
Velvette Persons 280
Louann Bahgat 2,11
Susan Watrous 4*
Scott Neckers 6*
Paul Smardz 16*
Carrie Shampoe 57,63*
Ed Mulkearn 67
Irvin King 83,85,88*
Julia Heiser 285*

Public Schs..Principal	Grd	Prgm	Enr/#Cls	SN	
Clymer Central Sch 8672 E Main St, Clymer 14724 Kirby Oldham	PK-12	T	444 30	49%	716/355-4444

• Dunkirk City School Dist PID: 00718465
620 Marauder Dr, Dunkirk 14048
716/366-9300
Fax 716/366-9399

Schools: 6 \ **Teachers:** 208 \ **Students:** 2,300 \ **Special Ed Students:** 302 \ **LEP Students:** 388 \ **College-Bound:** 71% \ **Ethnic:** African American 5%, Hispanic 57%, Caucasian 37% \ **Exp:** $306 (High) \ **Poverty:** 32% \ **Title I:** $1,240,851 \ **Special Education:** $4,702,000 \ **Open-Close:** 09/08 - 06/25 \ **DTBP:** $175 (High)

Michael Mansfield 1
Cynthia Mackowiak 2
Kisun Peters 34,752
David Damico 67
Corinna Kester 2,11,70,274
Timothy Abbey 3,5
Michele Heenan 58
Jeremy Dobek 73

Public Schs..Principal	Grd	Prgm	Enr/#Cls	SN	
Dunkirk Elem School 3 742 Lamphere St, Dunkirk 14048 Daniel Genovese	K-5	T	252 12	82%	716/366-9330 Fax 716/366-0565
Dunkirk Elem School 4 752 Central Ave, Dunkirk 14048 Kimberlee Texter	K-5	T	241 13	63%	716/366-9340 Fax 716/366-0548
Dunkirk Elem School 5 117 Birghum Rd, Dunkirk 14048 David Boyda	K-5	T	192 17	66%	716/366-4500 Fax 716/366-9355
Dunkirk Elem School 7 348 Lake Shore Dr E, Dunkirk 14048 Connie Meginnis	PK-5	T	321 14	60%	716/366-9300 Fax 716/366-9426
Dunkirk High Sch 75 W 6th St, Dunkirk 14048 Alan Gens	9-12	AGTV	572 75	58%	716/366-9300 Fax 716/366-0321
Dunkirk Middle Sch 525 Eagle St, Dunkirk 14048 Rebecca Farwell	6-8	T	439 30	63%	716/366-9300 Fax 716/366-9357

• Falconer Central School Dist PID: 00718544
2 East Ave N, Falconer 14733
716/665-6624
Fax 716/665-9265

Schools: 3 \ **Students:** 1,200 \ **Special Ed Students:** 140 \ **LEP Students:** 3 \ **Ethnic:** African American 2%, Hispanic 3%, Caucasian 94% \ **Exp:** $268 (Med) \ **Poverty:** 19% \ **Title I:** $369,499 \ **Special Education:** $1,248,000 \ **Open-Close:** 09/03 - 06/25 \ **DTBP:** $367 (High)

Stephen Penhollow 1,11,73
David Micek 3
Scott Peterson 5
Michelle Brunco 7,85
April Binkley 16*
Tara Swan 38,83*
Ashly Warner 69,77
Brent Agett 2
Mary Lynch 4
David Nelson 6*
Judith Roach 8,12,273*
Julie Widen 34,58
Todd Beckerink 67
Terry English 91*

Public Schs..Principal	Grd	Prgm	Enr/#Cls	SN	
Falconer Middle Sr High Sch 2 East Ave N, Falconer 14733 Terry English \ Jeffrey Jordan	6-12	V	614	45%	716/665-6624
Harvey C Fenner Elem Sch 2 East Ave N, Falconer 14733 Gary Gilbert	3-5	T	278 14	52%	716/665-6627 Fax 716/665-6668
Paul B D Temple Elem Sch 3470 Cemetery St, Kennedy 14747 Holly Hannon	PK-2	T	287 15	48%	716/267-3255 Fax 716/267-9420

• Forestville Central Sch Dist PID: 00718611
12 Water St, Forestville 14062
716/965-2742
Fax 716/965-2117

Schools: 2 \ **Teachers:** 50 \ **Students:** 457 \ **Special Ed Students:** 80 \ **College-Bound:** 68% \ **Ethnic:** African American 1%, Hispanic 6%, Native American: 1%, Caucasian 91% \ **Exp:** $343 (High) \ **Poverty:** 16% \ **Title I:** $135,686 \ **Special Education:** $839,000 \ **Open-Close:** 09/08 - 06/25 \ **DTBP:** $365 (High)

Renee Garrett 1
Mike Gajewski 5
Carla Wineks 58*
Mike Murphy 73*
Jennifer Fitzgerald 2
Lindsay Marcinelli 9*
Carol Woodward 67

Public Schs..Principal	Grd	Prgm	Enr/#Cls	SN	
Forestville Elem Sch 12 Water St, Forestville 14062 Lindsay Marcinelli	PK-6	T	228 15	52%	716/965-2742 Fax 716/965-2265
Forestville Middle High Sch 4 Academy St, Forestville 14062 Dan Grande	7-12		219 35	49%	716/965-2711 Fax 716/965-2102

• Fredonia Central School Dist PID: 00718647
425 E Main St, Fredonia 14063
716/679-1581
Fax 716/679-1555

Schools: 4 \ **Teachers:** 141 \ **Students:** 1,500 \ **Special Ed Students:** 194 \ **LEP Students:** 33 \ **Ethnic:** Asian 1%, African American 1%, Hispanic 14%, Caucasian 84% \ **Exp:** $219 (Med) \ **Poverty:** 15% \ **Title I:** $344,342 \ **Special Education:** $1,992,000 \ **Open-Close:** 09/08 - 06/25 \ **DTBP:** $391 (High)

Jeff Sortisio 1
Dave Winchell 3*
Kim Leid 4
Gloria Hayes 7,83,85*
Liz Gruber 16,28*
Linda Smith 29*
Joanne Lotter 35
Kristen Ferro 54,58*
John Forbes 2,19
Colleen Kubera 4*
Greg Lauer 6*
Joseph Reyda 8,11,69,74,271,296,298
Bernard Garassi 27
Laura DePue 31*
Steven Romans 36,79*
Bonnie Burnett 57*

---

79 Student Personnel	91 Safety/Security	275 Response To Intervention	298 Grant Writer/Ptnrships	**School Programs**	**Social Media**
80 Driver Ed/Safety	92 Magnet School	277 Remedial Math K-12	750 Chief Innovation Officer	A = Alternative Program	= Facebook
81 Gifted/Talented	93 Parental Involvement	280 Literacy Coach	751 Chief of Staff	G = Adult Classes	
82 Video Services	95 Tech Prep Program	285 STEM	752 Social Emotional Learning	M = Magnet Program	= Twitter
83 Substance Abuse Prev	97 Chief Information Officer	286 Digital Learning		T = Title I Schoolwide	
84 Erate	98 Chief Technology Officer	288 Common Core Standards	**Other School Types**	V = Career & Tech Ed Programs	
85 AIDS Education	270 Character Education	294 Accountability	Ⓐ = Alternative School		
88 Alternative/At Risk	271 Migrant Education	295 Network System	Ⓒ = Charter School	New Schools are shaded	
89 Multi-Cultural Curriculum	273 Teacher Mentor	296 Title II Programs	Ⓜ = Magnet School	New Superintendents and Principals are bold	
90 Social Work	274 Before/After Sch	297 Webmaster	Ⓨ = Year-Round School	Personnel with email addresses are underscored	

Chautauqua County

Market Data Retrieval

Michael Bobseine 67
Amy Piper 275*

Doug Prince 71,73,76,82,97,98,295

Public Schs..Principal	Grd	Prgm	Enr/#Cls	SN		
Fredonia Elem Sch 425 E Main St, Fredonia 14063 Mark Drollenger	1-4	T	400 33		41%	716/679-1581 Fax 716/679-9043
Fredonia Middle Sch 425 E Main St, Fredonia 14063 Paula Troutman	5-8	V	457 46		39%	716/679-1581 Fax 716/672-2686
Fredonia Senior High Sch 425 E Main St, Fredonia 14063 Darrin Paschke	9-12	A	463 60		31%	716/679-1581 Fax 716/672-8687
Wheelock Primary Sch 75 Chestnut St, Fredonia 14063 Amy Piper	PK-K		183			716/679-0007

- **Frewsburg Central School Dist** PID: 00718702 716/569-7000
  26 Institute St, Frewsburg 14738   Fax 716/569-7050

Schools: 2 \ **Teachers:** 68 \ **Students:** 805 \ **Special Ed Students:** 116 \ **LEP Students:** 3 \ **College-Bound:** 90% \ **Ethnic:** Asian 1%, African American 1%, Hispanic 2%, Native American: 1%, Caucasian 96% \ **Exp:** $258 (Med) \ **Poverty:** 13% \ **Title I:** $140,428 \ **Special Education:** $1,124,000 \ **Open-Close:** 09/08 - 06/24 \ **DTBP:** $359 (High)

Shelly O'Boyle 1
Dan Hallberg 3*
Ryan Sluga 5
Danielle Patti 8,11,15,288
Tami McKotch 37,58,79,83,90
Erica Lobb 51,54,273,280*
Chad Chitester 67
Michelle Dziubinski 77*

Jerome Leeyaw 2,19*
Janet Bennett 4*
Terry Gray 6*
Jennifer Sears 23*
Lindsay Marzec 48*
Jan Parsons 57,61*
Heidi Reale 73,297*

Public Schs..Principal	Grd	Prgm	Enr/#Cls	SN		
Frewsburg Jr Sr High Sch 26 Institute St, Frewsburg 14738 Tiffany Frederes	7-12	G	411 43		38%	716/569-7055
Robert H Jackson Elem Sch 135 Ivory St, Frewsburg 14738 Ann Morrison	PK-6	T	397 26		43%	716/569-7031 Fax 716/569-7006

- **Jamestown City School Dist** PID: 00718738 716/483-4350
  197 Martin Rd, Jamestown 14701   Fax 716/483-4421

Schools: 9 \ **Teachers:** 409 \ **Students:** 5,000 \ **Special Ed Students:** 787 \ **LEP Students:** 209 \ **Ethnic:** African American 4%, Hispanic 25%, Caucasian 70% \ **Exp:** $232 (Med) \ **Poverty:** 34% \ **Title I:** $3,390,569 \ **Special Education:** $10,306,000 \ **Open-Close:** 09/03 - 06/25 \ **DTBP:** $330 (High) 📘

Dr Kevin Whitaker 1
Carl Pillittieri 3,5,91
Daniel Lemk 5
Jill Muntz 7,83
Tina Sandstrom 11,34,271
Traci Thompson 42
Brett Muscarella 58
John Panebianco 68
Cathy Panebianco 71
Amanda Gesing 298

Karen Christopherson 2
Jeffery Smith 4*
Benjamin Drake 6,35*
Michelle McDowell 8,12,18
Lisa Almasi 17
Denise Pusateri 45
Paul Abbott 67
Jessie Joy 69,71,97,294
Charles Marzec 73,76,286,295*

Public Schs..Principal	Grd	Prgm	Enr/#Cls	SN		
Carlyle C Ring Elem Sch 333 Buffalo St, Jamestown 14701 Annette Miller	PK-4	T	405 24		58%	716/483-4407 Fax 716/483-4232
Clinton V Bush Elem Sch 150 Pardee Ave, Jamestown 14701 Daniel Bracey	PK-4	T	323 15		59%	716/483-4401 Fax 716/483-7100
Jamestown High Sch 350 E 2nd St, Jamestown 14701 Dr Rosemary Bradley	9-12		1,312		59%	716/483-3470 Fax 716/483-4399
Jefferson Middle Sch 195 Martin Rd, Jamestown 14701 Leslie Melquist	5-8	T	390 39		72%	716/483-4411 Fax 716/483-4273
Lincoln Elem Sch 301 Front St, Jamestown 14701 Katie Russo	PK-4	T	397 21		48%	716/483-4412 Fax 716/483-4435
Milton J Fletcher Elem Sch 301 Cole Ave, Jamestown 14701 Amanda Sischo	PK-4	T	513 26		60%	716/483-4404 Fax 716/483-4210
Persell Middle Sch 375 Baker St, Jamestown 14701 Philip Cammarata	5-8	T	502 30		66%	716/483-4406 Fax 716/483-4417 📘
Samuel G Love Elem Sch 50 E 8th St, Jamestown 14701 Renee Hartling	PK-4	T	343 20		75%	716/483-4405 Fax 716/483-4291
Washington Middle Sch 159 Buffalo St, Jamestown 14701 Melissa Emerson	5-8	T	507 35		75%	716/483-4413 Fax 716/483-4268

- **Panama Central School Dist** PID: 00718893 716/782-2455
  41 North St, Panama 14767   Fax 716/782-4674

Schools: 1 \ **Teachers:** 50 \ **Students:** 450 \ **Special Ed Students:** 73 \ **LEP Students:** 4 \ **College-Bound:** 70% \ **Ethnic:** Hispanic 3%, Caucasian 97% \ **Exp:** $313 (High) \ **Poverty:** 19% \ **Title I:** $178,915 \ **Special Education:** $1,185,000 \ **Open-Close:** 09/08 - 06/25 \ **DTBP:** $370 (High)

Bert Lictus 1
Kevin Miktuk 3
Emily Harvey 8,11,58,69,74,273,275*
Donald Butler 67
Danielle Cook 83,85,90*

Amanda Kolstee 2,4,5,7
Christopher Payne 6*
Dane Simmons 31,36,78,90,270
Brynne Hinsdale 73,76,295*
Laura Myers 83,85,90

Public Schs..Principal	Grd	Prgm	Enr/#Cls	SN		
Panama Central Sch 41 North St, Panama 14767 Lauren Harper \ Danielle Cook	PK-12		450 27		38%	716/782-2455

- **Pine Valley Central Sch Dist** PID: 00718934 716/988-3293
  7755 Route 83, South Dayton 14138   Fax 716/988-3142

Schools: 2 \ **Teachers:** 52 \ **Students:** 550 \ **Special Ed Students:** 107 \ **LEP Students:** 3 \ **Ethnic:** Hispanic 5%, Native American: 1%, Caucasian 93% \ **Exp:** $217 (Med) \ **Poverty:** 27% \ **Title I:** $453,666 \ **Special Education:** $1,333,000 \ **Open-Close:** 09/08 - 06/24

Bryna Mortiz Booth 1
David Vanzile 3
Joe Goodway 5
Jordan Campese 8,30,73,295
Carrie Davenport 58

Jamie Rodgers 2
Terry Brown 4*
Chris Buczek 6*
Brandi Meacham 11,58
Jeff Chase 67

Public Schs..Principal	Grd	Prgm	Enr/#Cls	SN		
Pine Valley Ctl Jr Sr High Sch 7827 Route 83, South Dayton 14138 Joshua Tedone	7-12	T	230 35		57%	716/988-3276 Fax 716/988-3139
Pine Valley Elem Sch 7755 Route 83, South Dayton 14138 Kelly Zimmerman	PK-6	T	283 25		66%	716/988-3291 Fax 716/988-3864

1	Superintendent	8	Curric/Instruct K-12	19	Chief Financial Officer	29	Family/Consumer Science	39	Social Studies K-12	49	English/Lang Arts Elem	59	Special Education Elem	69	Academic Assessment
2	Bus/Finance/Purchasing	9	Curric/Instruct Elem	20	Art K-12	30	Adult Education	40	Social Studies Elem	50	English/Lang Arts Sec	60	Special Education Sec	70	Research/Development
3	Buildings And Grounds	10	Curric/Instruct Sec	21	Art Elem	31	Career/Sch-to-Work K-12	41	Social Studies Sec	51	Reading K-12	61	Foreign/World Lang K-12	71	Public Information
4	Food Service	11	Federal Program	22	Art Sec	32	Career/Sch-to-Work Elem	42	Science K-12	52	Reading Elem	62	Foreign/World Lang Elem	72	Summer School
5	Transportation	12	Title I	23	Music K-12	33	Career/Sch-to-Work Sec	43	Science Elem	53	Reading Sec	63	Foreign/World Lang Sec	73	Instructional Tech
6	Athletic	13	Title V	24	Music Elem	34	Early Childhood Ed	44	Science Sec	54	Remedial Reading K-12	64	Religious Education K-12	74	Inservice Training
7	Health Services	14	Instructional Media Svcs	25	Music Sec	35	Health/Phys Education	45	Math K-12	55	Remedial Reading Elem	65	Religious Education Elem	75	Marketing/Distributive
		15	Asst Superintendent	26	Business Education	36	Guidance Services K-12	46	Math Elem	56	Remedial Reading Sec	66	Religious Education Sec	76	Info Systems
		16	Instructional Media Svcs	27	Career & Tech Ed	37	Guidance Services Elem	47	Math Sec	57	Bilingual/ELL	67	School Board President	77	Psychological Assess
		17	Chief Operations Officer	28	Technology Education	38	Guidance Services Sec	48	English/Lang Arts K-12	58	Special Education K-12	68	Teacher Personnel	78	Affirmative Action
		18	Chief Academic Officer												

New York School Directory — Chautauqua County

- **Ripley Central School Dist** PID: 00718960   716/736-2631
  12 N State St, Ripley 14775   Fax 716/736-6210

  Schools: 1 \ **Teachers:** 19 \ **Students:** 165 \ **Special Ed Students:** 41 \ **LEP Students:** 3 \ **Ethnic:** African American 3%, Hispanic 2%, Caucasian 96% \ **Exp:** $582 (High) \ **Poverty:** 17% \ **Title I:** $133,589 \ **Special Education:** $648,000 \ **Open-Close:** 09/03 - 06/24 \ **DTBP:** $343 (High)

  William Caldwell 1
  Sara Fisher 7,83*
  Micah Oldham 12,59,69,73,286*
  Paul McCutcheon 67
  Luann Lauritobahgat 2,11
  William Caldwell 11,288*
  Karen Kondrick 16,82*

Public Schs..Principal	Grd	Prgm	Enr/#Cls	SN	
Ripley Central Sch 12 N State St, Ripley 14775 Micah Oldham	PK-6	ATV	165 38	66%	716/736-2631

- **Sherman Central School Dist** PID: 00718996   716/761-6121
  127 Park St, Sherman 14781   Fax 716/761-6119

  Schools: 1 \ **Teachers:** 49 \ **Students:** 434 \ **Special Ed Students:** 64 \ **LEP Students:** 5 \ **College-Bound:** 17% \ **Ethnic:** African American 1%, Hispanic 3%, Native American: 1%, Caucasian 95% \ **Exp:** $462 (High) \ **Poverty:** 24% \ **Title I:** $243,225 \ **Special Education:** $683,000 \ **Open-Close:** 09/08 - 06/24 \ **DTBP:** $317 (High)

  Michael Ginestre 1
  Jared Oehlbeck 3*
  David Maleski 5
  Joann Uopta 7*
  Lisa Carlson 16,82*
  Emily Eckwahl 35,83*
  Courtney Taylor 58,298*
  Michael Shimmel 73,295*
  Shawn McKane 270,275*
  Kimberly Oehlbeck 2,296
  Susan Bates 4*
  Cory Emory 6*
  Erika Stormer 12,51,54,280*
  Alan Tanski 28,95*
  Lori Svenson 36,88*
  Brian Bates 67
  Uris Soderberg 77*
  Molly Martin 286*

Public Schs..Principal	Grd	Prgm	Enr/#Cls	SN	
Sherman Central Sch 127 Park St, Sherman 14781 Ann Morrison	PK-12	T	434 48	55%	716/761-6121

- **Silver Creek Central Sch Dist** PID: 00719029   716/934-2603
  1 Dickinson St, Silver Creek 14136   Fax 716/934-7983

  Schools: 3 \ **Teachers:** 113 \ **Students:** 1,212 \ **Special Ed Students:** 218 \ **LEP Students:** 10 \ **College-Bound:** 65% \ **Ethnic:** African American 1%, Hispanic 8%, Native American: 14%, Caucasian 77% \ **Exp:** $290 (Med) \ **Poverty:** 19% \ **Title I:** $304,724 \ **Special Education:** $1,880,000 \ **Open-Close:** 09/08 - 06/29 \ **DTBP:** $380 (High)

  Todd Crandall 1
  Scott Pound 3
  Kari Turner 5
  Michele Helmer 8,12,74,288
  Allison Gondek 27,36*
  Michael Kempster 73,295
  Paula Michalak 286
  Lisa Rohloff 2,11,68
  Jen Polowy 4
  Sean Helmer 6*
  Lisa Brennan 16,76
  Stephen Boothe 67
  Amy Seiders 83,85,88

Public Schs..Principal	Grd	Prgm	Enr/#Cls	SN	
Silver Creek Elem Sch 1 Dickinson St, Silver Creek 14136 Merrie Maxon	PK-5	T	490 37	58%	716/934-2603 Fax 716/934-2173
Silver Creek High Sch 1 Dickinson St, Silver Creek 14136 Thomas Buczkowski	9-12	TV	314 54	51%	716/934-2103
Silver Creek Middle Sch 1 Dickinson St, Silver Creek 14136 Eleanor Payne	6-8	T	261 20	54%	716/934-2603 Fax 716/934-3760

- **Southwestern Central Sch Dist** PID: 00719067   716/484-1136
  600 Hunt Rd, Jamestown 14701   Fax 716/488-2442

  Schools: 3 \ **Teachers:** 107 \ **Students:** 1,400 \ **Special Ed Students:** 202 \ **LEP Students:** 14 \ **College-Bound:** 83% \ **Ethnic:** Asian 2%, African American 1%, Hispanic 5%, Caucasian 92% \ **Exp:** $316 (High) \ **Poverty:** 14% \ **Title I:** $282,616 \ **Special Education:** $1,486,000 \ **Open-Close:** 09/08 - 06/25 \ **DTBP:** $370 (High)

  Maureen Donahue 1
  Steve Olson 3
  Kevin Salisbury 6*
  Amy McCloskey 58,79*
  Annette Rhebergen 2
  John Spacht 5
  Molly Moore 8,11,69,73,77,79,288,295
  James Butler 67

Public Schs..Principal	Grd	Prgm	Enr/#Cls	SN	
Southwestern Elem Sch 600 Hunt Rd, Jamestown 14701 Matt Langworthy	PK-5		583 40	39%	716/664-1881 Fax 716/487-3170
Southwestern High Sch 600 Hunt Rd, Jamestown 14701 Scott Cooper	9-12	AV	417 60	33%	716/664-6273 Fax 716/484-1167
Southwestern Middle Sch 600 Hunt Rd, Jamestown 14701 Rich Rybicki	6-8		330 35	39%	716/664-6270 Fax 716/487-0855

- **Westfield Central School Dist** PID: 00719110   716/326-2151
  203 E Main St, Westfield 14787   Fax 716/326-2195

  Schools: 1 \ **Teachers:** 70 \ **Students:** 700 \ **Special Ed Students:** 126 \ **LEP Students:** 3 \ **College-Bound:** 80% \ **Ethnic:** Asian 1%, African American 1%, Hispanic 4%, Native American: 1%, Caucasian 93% \ **Exp:** $259 (Med) \ **Poverty:** 19% \ **Title I:** $228,914 \ **Special Education:** $1,335,000 \ **Open-Close:** 09/01 - 06/25 \ **DTBP:** $368 (High)

  Michael Cipolla 1,11,288
  Jake Hitchcock 6,35,38,88*
  Dr Mary Rockey 9,12,58,271,752*
  Melissa Zastrow 16,82*
  Wendy Dyment 67
  Ashley Raynor 275*
  Julia Murphy 2,3,4,5
  Molly Anderson 8,13*
  Corey Markhum 10,57,270
  Scott Cooper 27,31,36,69,83*
  Can Tannamore 73*

Public Schs..Principal	Grd	Prgm	Enr/#Cls	SN	
Westfield Central Sch 203 E Main St, Westfield 14787 Corey Markham \ Dr Mary Rockey	PK-12	T	700 200	44%	716/326-2151

CHAUTAUQUA CATHOLIC SCHOOLS

- **Diocese of Buffalo Ed Office** PID: 00725846
  Listing includes only schools located in this county. See District Index for location of Diocesan Offices.

Catholic Schs..Principal	Grd	Prgm	Enr/#Cls	SN	
Northern Chautauqua Cath Sch 336 Washington Ave, Dunkirk 14048 Andrew Ludwig	PK-8		163 16		716/366-0630 Fax 716/366-5101

---

79 Student Personnel	91 Safety/Security	275 Response To Intervention	298 Grant Writer/Ptnrships	**School Programs**	**Social Media**		
80 Driver Ed/Safety	92 Magnet School	277 Remedial Math K-12	750 Chief Innovation Officer	A = Alternative Program			
81 Gifted/Talented	93 Parental Involvement	280 Literacy Coach	751 Chief of Staff	G = Adult Classes	= Facebook		
82 Video Services	95 Tech Prep Program	285 STEM	752 Social Emotional Learning	M = Magnet Program			
83 Substance Abuse Prev	97 Chief Infomation Officer	286 Digital Learning		T = Title I Schoolwide	= Twitter		
84 Erate	98 Chief Technology Officer	288 Common Core Standards	**Other School Types**	V = Career & Tech Ed Programs			
85 AIDS Education	270 Character Education	294 Accountability	Ⓐ = Alternative School				
88 Alternative/At Risk	271 Migrant Education	295 Network System	Ⓒ = Charter School	New Schools are shaded			
89 Multi-Cultural Curriculum	273 Teacher Mentor	296 Title II Programs	Ⓜ = Magnet School	New Superintendents and Principals are bold			
90 Social Work	274 Before/After Sch	297 Webmaster	Ⓨ = Year-Round School	Personnel with email addresses are underscored			

Chemung County

Market Data Retrieval

CHAUTAUQUA PRIVATE SCHOOLS

Private Schs..Principal	Grd	Prgm	Enr/#Cls	SN	
Bethel Baptist Christian Acad 200 Hunt Rd, Jamestown 14701 Andy Frudd	K-12		72 11		716/484-7420 Fax 716/484-0087
Central Christian Academy 876 Central Ave, Dunkirk 14048 Stephanie Pollok	PK-12		65 7 ⒻⓉ		716/366-6634 Fax 716/366-6638
Gustavus Adolphus Lrng Center 200 Gustavus Ave, Jamestown 14701	Spec	V	90 12		716/665-2772

CHEMUNG COUNTY

CHEMUNG COUNTY SCHOOLS

County Schs..Principal	Grd	Prgm	Enr/#Cls	SN	
Phoenix Academy 459 Philo Rd, Elmira 14903 Jesse Ferris	Spec		200 12		607/739-3581 Fax 607/795-2242

CHEMUNG PUBLIC SCHOOLS

• **Elmira City School Dist** PID: 00719158 607/735-3000
951 Hoffman St, Elmira 14905 Fax 607/735-3009

Schools: 11 \ **Teachers:** 414 \ **Students:** 6,000 \ **Special Ed Students:** 1,057 \ **LEP Students:** 17 \ **College-Bound:** 78% \ **Ethnic:** African American 15%, Hispanic 3%, Caucasian 81% \ **Exp:** $411 (High) \ **Poverty:** 23% \ **Title I:** $3,038,287 \ **Special Education:** $12,701,000 \ **Open-Close:** 09/04 - 06/25 \ **DTBP:** $221 (High) \ Ⓣ

Hilary Austin 1	Melissa Mendolera 2		
Michael Dunn 3	Kari Crouse 4*		
Mark Yusko 5	Thomas Morrell 6,35		
John Hillman 8	Meachele Manchester 11		
Derek Almy 34,36,57,79,88,90,274	Joyce Carr 58,77		
Rebecca Trank 58	Sara Lattin 67		
Brian Sheehan 68	Beth Manwaring 71		
Kathy McDarby 71	Joshua Miller 73,76,295		
Betsy Fisk 294	Thomas Allen 297		

Public Schs..Principal	Grd	Prgm	Enr/#Cls	SN	
Beecher Elem Sch 310 Sullivan St, Elmira 14901 Kelley Bacalles	3-6	T	366 22	81%	607/735-3500 Fax 607/735-3509
Broadway Academy 1000 Broadway St, Elmira 14904 Robert Bailey	7-7	T	459 42	62%	607/735-3300 Fax 607/735-3309
Broadway Elem Sch 1000 Broadway St, Elmira 14904 Rebecca Kiley	3-6	T	414 24	48%	607/735-3600 Fax 607/735-3609
Coburn Elem Sch 216 Mount Zoar St, Elmira 14904 Chris Sancomb	3-6	T	458 46	74%	607/735-3650 Fax 607/735-3659
Elmira High Sch 777 S Main St, Elmira 14904 Christopher Krantz	10-12	TV	1,248 48	51%	607/735-3200 Fax 607/735-3209
Ernie Davis Academy 933 Hoffman St, Elmira 14905 Carrie Rollins	8-9	TV	884 80	61%	607/735-3100 Fax 607/735-3109
Fassett Elem Sch 309 W Thurston St, Elmira 14901 Mary Cox	PK-2	T	390	69%	607/735-3900 Fax 607/735-3909
George M Diven Elem Sch 1115 Hall St, Elmira 14901 Colin Werfelman	PK-2	T	417 20	54%	607/735-3700 Fax 607/735-3709
Hendy Elem Sch 110 Hendy Ave, Elmira 14905 Marc Vesci	3-6	T	432 20	69%	607/735-3750 Fax 607/735-3759
Pine City Elem Sch 1551 Pennsylvania Ave, Pine City 14871 Rhonda Baran	PK-2	T	343 24	40%	607/735-3800 Fax 607/735-3809
Riverside Elem Sch 409 Riverside Ave, Elmira 14904 Heather Donovan	PK-2	T	432 30	62%	607/735-3850 Fax 607/735-3859

• **Elmira Heights Ctl Sch Dist** PID: 00719366 607/734-7114
2083 College Ave, Elmira Hgts 14903 Fax 607/734-7134

Schools: 3 \ **Teachers:** 89 \ **Students:** 1,100 \ **Special Ed Students:** 162 \ **College-Bound:** 85% \ **Ethnic:** African American 2%, Hispanic 3%, Caucasian 94% \ **Exp:** $164 (Low) \ **Poverty:** 17% \ **Title I:** $313,489 \ **Special Education:** $2,374,000 \ **Open-Close:** 09/08 - 06/23 \ **DTBP:** $176 (High)

Michael Gill 1	Martha Clark 2
Richard VanHouten 5	Dawn Hanrahan 8,12,57,58*
Harry Blish 67	

Public Schs..Principal	Grd	Prgm	Enr/#Cls	SN	
Cohen Elem Sch 100 Robinwood Ave, Elmira Hgts 14903 Andy Lutz	PK-5	T	518 24	55%	607/734-7132 Fax 607/734-9574
Cohen Middle Sch 100 Robinwood Ave, Elmira Hgts 14903 Dawn Hanrahan	6-8	T	255 30	48%	607/734-5078 Fax 607/734-9382
Thomas Edison High Sch 2083 College Ave, Elmira Hgts 14903 Ronald Boyanowski	9-12	T	285 31	45%	607/733-5604 Fax 607/737-7976

• **Horseheads Ctl School Dist** PID: 00719421 607/739-5601
1 Raider Ln, Horseheads 14845 Fax 607/795-2405

Schools: 7 \ **Teachers:** 298 \ **Students:** 4,245 \ **Special Ed Students:** 559 \ **LEP Students:** 27 \ **College-Bound:** 76% \ **Ethnic:** Asian 4%, African American 2%, Hispanic 4%, Caucasian 91% \ **Exp:** $181 (Low) \ **Poverty:** 8% \ **Title I:** $489,165 \ **Special Education:** $5,481,000 \ **Open-Close:** 09/04 - 06/25 \ **DTBP:** $321 (High)

Dr Thomas Douglas 1	Katie Buzzetti 2
Linda Klievoneit 2	Mike Coghlin 3
Joseph Kilmer 4	Peter Wilcox 5
Bert Conklin 6,35	Kelly Squires 7,11,34,57,58,88,90,296
Anthony Gill 15	Kristine Dale 67
Kaitlyn DeFilippo 68	Shawn McDonough 71,97
Susan Pirozzolo 71	William Giancoli 73,295
Tony Stager 91	Ryan Wissiak 285
Tiffany Owens 285	

New York School Directory — Chenango County

Public Schs..Principal	Grd	Prgm	Enr/#Cls	SN	
Big Flats Elem Sch 543 Maple St, Big Flats 14814 Elizabeth Scaptura	PK-4		362 21	29%	607/739-6373 Fax 607/795-2555
Center Street Elem Sch 812 Center St, Horseheads 14845 Patricia Sotero	PK-4	T	366 24	50%	607/795-2580 Fax 607/795-2585
Gardner Road Elem Sch 541 Gardner Rd, Horseheads 14845 Patrick Patterson	PK-4		426 24	34%	607/739-6347 Fax 607/795-2545
Horseheads High Sch 401 Fletcher St, Horseheads 14845 Kristina Earl	9-12		1,271	27%	607/795-2500 Fax 607/795-2505
Horseheads Intermediate Sch 952 Sing Sing Rd, Horseheads 14845 Michael Bostwick	5-6		573 45	32%	607/739-6366 Fax 607/795-2495
Horseheads Middle Sch 950 Sing Sing Rd, Horseheads 14845 Ron Holloway	7-8		606 60	32%	607/739-6357 Fax 607/795-2525
Ridge Road Elem Sch 112 Ridge Rd, Horseheads 14845 Anne-Marie Bailey	PK-4		400 21	36%	607/739-6351 Fax 607/795-2485

CHEMUNG CATHOLIC SCHOOLS

• **Diocese of Rochester Ed Office** PID: 00733623
Listing includes only schools located in this county. See District Index for location of Diocesan Offices.

Catholic Schs..Principal	Grd	Prgm	Enr/#Cls	SN	
Holy Family Elem Sch 421 Fulton St, Elmira 14904 Paula Smith	PK-6		232 11		607/732-3588 Fax 607/732-1850
St Mary Our Mother Sch 811 Westlake St, Horseheads 14845 Jean Yorio	PK-6		140 12		607/739-9157 Fax 607/739-2532 [f]

CHEMUNG PRIVATE SCHOOLS

Private Schs..Principal	Grd	Prgm	Enr/#Cls	SN	
Chemung Valley Montessori Sch 23 Winters Rd, Elmira 14903 Marcy Cathey	K-8		117		607/562-8754
Horseheads Christian Sch 2293 Grand Central Ave, Horseheads 14845 Jim Kane	K-6		75 8		607/739-9811 Fax 866/802-2705 [f]
Notre Dame High Sch 1400 Maple Ave, Elmira 14904 Deborah Franklin	7-12		365 25		607/734-2267 Fax 607/737-8903
Twin Tiers Christian Academy 1811 N Chemung Rd, Breesport 14816 Dr Cary Shaw	7-12	V	98 9		607/739-3619 [f]

CHENANGO COUNTY

CHENANGO COUNTY SCHOOLS

County Schs..Principal	Grd	Prgm	Enr/#Cls	SN	
Dcmo BOCES Tech Center 6678 County Road 32, Norwich 13815 Randy Smith	Voc	AG	300 16	47%	607/335-1200 Fax 607/334-9848

CHENANGO PUBLIC SCHOOLS

• **Afton Central School Dist** PID: 00719550 607/639-8229
29 Academy St, Afton 13730 Fax 607/639-8257

Schools: 1 \ **Teachers:** 61 \ **Students:** 522 \ **Special Ed Students:** 95 \ **College-Bound:** 40% \ **Ethnic:** Asian 2%, African American 3%, Hispanic 3%, Caucasian 92% \ **Exp:** $641 (High) \ **Poverty:** 18% \ **Title I:** $198,250 \ **Special Education:** $1,268,000 \ **Open-Close:** 09/04 - 06/25 \ **DTBP:** $382 (High)

Timothy McNamara	1,11		Ken Howard	2
Connie Babino	4		Lynn Bradley	5
Cindy Bostelman	6*		Tracey Caezza	11,58,275,288*
Jillian Norberg	36*		Maryann Palmetier	67
Stacey Gridley	73*		Laura Zanrucha	285,298*
Matt Bostelman	295*			

Public Schs..Principal	Grd	Prgm	Enr/#Cls	SN	
Afton Central Sch 29 Academy St, Afton 13730 Laura Zanrucha \ Tracey Caezza	PK-12	AGT	522 40	48%	607/639-8200

• **Bainbridge Guilford CSD** PID: 00719586 607/967-6300
18 Juliand St, Bainbridge 13733 Fax 607/967-4231

Schools: 3 \ **Teachers:** 73 \ **Students:** 850 \ **Special Ed Students:** 107 \ **College-Bound:** 95% \ **Ethnic:** Asian 1%, African American 1%, Hispanic 3%, Caucasian 95% \ **Exp:** $210 (Med) \ **Poverty:** 16% \ **Title I:** $205,408 \ **Special Education:** $1,334,000 \ **Open-Close:** 09/08 - 06/25 \ **DTBP:** $344 (High)

Tim Ryan	1		Janice Rideout	2
James Rideout	3		Billie Reigles	4
Kyle Fuller	5		Kevin Horese	6,35,296
Ed Monico	11,73,76		Keren Seiler	37*
Nanci Miller	38,288*		Joanne Moxley	57,83,88*
Coleen Head	58		Heather Pratt	61
Emily Hall	67		Linda Maynard	70,71,97,294,750
Brian Foster	285		Scott Graham	286

Public Schs..Principal	Grd	Prgm	Enr/#Cls	SN	
Bainbridge Guilford Jr Sr HS 18 Juliand St, Bainbridge 13733 William Zakrajsek	7-12		367 30	47%	607/967-6300
Greenlawn Elem Sch 43 Greenlawn Ave, Bainbridge 13733 Jennifer Henderson	2-6	T	284 14	57%	607/967-6301 Fax 607/967-3080

---

79 Student Personnel	91 Safety/Security	275 Response To Intervention	298 Grant Writer/Ptnrships	**School Programs**	**Social Media**		
80 Driver Ed/Safety	92 Magnet School	277 Remedial Math K-12	750 Chief Innovation Officer	A = Alternative Program	[f] = Facebook		
81 Gifted/Talented	93 Parental Involvement	280 Literacy Coach	751 Chief of Staff	G = Adult Classes			
82 Video Services	95 Tech Prep Program	285 STEM	752 Social Emotional Learning	M = Magnet Program	[t] = Twitter		
83 Substance Abuse Prev	97 Chief Information Officer	286 Digital Learning		T = Title I Schoolwide			
84 Erate	98 Chief Technology Officer	288 Common Core Standards	**Other School Types**	V = Career & Tech Ed Programs			
85 AIDS Education	270 Character Education	294 Accountability	Ⓐ = Alternative School				
88 Alternative/At Risk	271 Migrant Education	295 Network System	Ⓒ = Charter School	**New Schools are shaded**			
89 Multi-Cultural Curriculum	273 Teacher Mentor	296 Title II Programs	Ⓜ = Magnet School	**New Superintendents and Principals are bold**			
90 Social Work	274 Before/After Sch	297 Webmaster	Ⓨ = Year-Round School	Personnel with email addresses are underscored			

Chenango County

Market Data Retrieval

Guilford Elem Sch — PK-1 — T — 152 — 41% — 607/895-6700
138 School St, Guilford 13780 — 8 — Fax 607/895-6713
Linda Maynard

- **Greene Ctl School Dist** PID: 00719627 — 607/656-4161
  40 S Canal St, Greene 13778 — Fax 607/656-9362

Schools: 4 \ Teachers: 91 \ Students: 954 \ Special Ed Students: 161 \ LEP Students: 3 \ Ethnic: Asian 1%, African American 1%, Hispanic 2%, Native American: 1%, Caucasian 95% \ Exp: $218 (Med) \ Poverty: 22% \ Title I: $429,466 \ Special Education: $2,354,000 \ Open-Close: 09/04 - 06/22 \ DTBP: $359 (High)

Timothy Calice	1	Mark Rubitski	2,13
Kim Corcoran	4	Rosemary Badger	4
Brian Ayres	6,11,57,270,271*	Rick Smith	6
Pam Gerst	7,85*	January Pratt	8,273*
James Walters	10,72*	John Fish	67
Kim Kalem	73,76	Tim Calice	285*
John McGraw	295		

Public Schs..Principal	Grd	Prgm	Enr/#Cls	SN	
Greene Central Interm Sch 40 S Canal St, Greene 13778 Brian Ayres	3-5	T	205 14	44%	607/656-9891 Fax 607/656-8092
Greene High Sch 40 S Canal St, Greene 13778 Penny Connolly	9-12		269 40	43%	607/656-4161 Fax 607/656-8872
Greene Middle Sch 40 S Canal St, Greene 13778 Mark Wilson	6-8	T	230 47	49%	607/656-4161 Fax 607/656-4520
Greene Primary Sch 405 Canal St, Greene 13778 January Pratt	PK-2	T	250 16	46%	607/656-5174 Fax 607/656-4044

- **Norwich City School Dist** PID: 00719720 — 607/334-1600
  89 Midland Dr, Norwich 13815 — Fax 607/336-8652

Schools: 4 \ Teachers: 170 \ Students: 2,000 \ Special Ed Students: 327 \ LEP Students: 13 \ Ethnic: Asian 1%, African American 3%, Hispanic 3%, Caucasian 92% \ Exp: $198 (Low) \ Poverty: 20% \ Title I: $660,153 \ Special Education: $4,141,000 \ Open-Close: 09/04 - 06/25 \ DTBP: $367 (High)

Diana Bowers	1,11	Bryan Burton	2,15,67
Stanley Foulds	3,91	Delores Shalna	4
William Loomis	5	Rich Turnbull	6
Katherine Goolden	57,58,270,298	Steve Andrews	73,295

Public Schs..Principal	Grd	Prgm	Enr/#Cls	SN	
Norwich High Sch 89 Midland Dr, Norwich 13815 Kisten Giglio	9-12	ATV	518 62	51%	607/334-1600 Fax 607/334-6680
Norwich Middle Sch 89 Midland Dr, Norwich 13815 Scott Ryan	6-8	T	417 50	59%	607/334-1600 Fax 607/334-6210
Perry Browne Intermediate Sch 89 Midland Dr, Norwich 13815 Michelle Osterhoudt	3-5	T	363 23	61%	607/334-1600 Fax 607/334-6201
Stanford J Gibson Primary Sch 2 Ridgeland Rd, Norwich 13815 Jennifer Oliver	PK-2	T	457 28	48%	607/334-1600 Fax 607/334-4193

- **Otselic Valley Central SD** PID: 00719897 — 315/653-7218
  125 County Rd 13A, South Otselic 13155 — Fax 315/653-7500

Schools: 1 \ Teachers: 32 \ Students: 300 \ Special Ed Students: 55 \ LEP Students: 3 \ College-Bound: 60% \ Ethnic: African American 1%, Hispanic 2%, Caucasian 97% \ Exp: $314 (High) \ Poverty: 21% \ Title I: $166,889 \ Special Education: $683,000 \ Open-Close: 09/09 - 06/25 \ DTBP: $359 (High) \ **C**

Michael Drahos	1,11	Daniel Silky	2,298
Barbara Hillman	4*	Lacey Eaves	8,13,58*
Paul O'Connor	67	Kimberly Kalem	73,286
James Dunne	295	James Dunne	295*

Public Schs..Principal	Grd	Prgm	Enr/#Cls	SN	
Otselic Valley Central Sch 125 County Road 13A, South Otselic 13155 Debra Kurtz	PK-12	TV	300 23	50%	315/653-7218

- **Oxford Academy Central SD** PID: 00719770 — 607/843-2025
  12 Fort Hill Park, Oxford 13830 — Fax 607/843-3241

Schools: 3 \ Teachers: 78 \ Students: 750 \ Special Ed Students: 117 \ LEP Students: 3 \ College-Bound: 64% \ Ethnic: African American 2%, Hispanic 3%, Native American: 1%, Caucasian 94% \ Exp: $243 (Med) \ Poverty: 18% \ Title I: $250,750 \ Special Education: $290,000 \ Open-Close: 09/10 - 06/25 \ DTBP: $349 (High)

John Hillis	1	Joseph Gugino	2,7,11,71
Mark Hodge	3*	Debra Morris	4
Denise Carey	5	Timothy Davis	6*
Jodi Carey	38	Timothy O'Brien	67
Jennifer Davis	73,97,295*	Greg Lehr	83,88

Public Schs..Principal	Grd	Prgm	Enr/#Cls	SN	
Oxford Academy High Sch 50 S Washington Ave, Oxford 13830 Gordie Daniels	9-12	V	220 30	57%	607/843-2025 Fax 607/843-3231
Oxford Academy Middle Sch 12 Fort Hill Park, Oxford 13830 Gregory Lehr	5-8	T	210 40	55%	607/843-2025
Oxford Academy Primary Sch 50 S Washington Ave, Oxford 13830 Brian Collier	PK-4	T	312 21	60%	607/843-2025 Fax 607/843-7030

- **Sherburne Earlville Central SD** PID: 00719811 — 607/674-7300
  15 School St, Sherburne 13460 — Fax 607/674-9742

Schools: 3 \ Teachers: 138 \ Students: 1,267 \ Special Ed Students: 320 \ LEP Students: 5 \ College-Bound: 63% \ Ethnic: African American 1%, Hispanic 1%, Caucasian 97% \ Exp: $243 (Med) \ Poverty: 18% \ Title I: $378,896 \ Special Education: $4,668,000 \ Open-Close: 09/08 - 06/25 \ DTBP: $359 (High)

Robert Berson	1,11	Todd Griffin	2,15,16,73,286
Jeff Genter	3	Kim Corcoran	4*
Julio Morbidi	5	Brad Perry	6*
Peggy Jessup	7*	Ginger Rinaldo	8,58*
Rebecca Hagmann	37*	Debra Kurst	67
Candice Poyer	83*	Lynda Stoddard	85*
Michelle Villante	91	Antoinette Halliday	271,274,275*

Public Schs..Principal	Grd	Prgm	Enr/#Cls	SN	
Sherburne Earlville Elem Sch 15 School St, Sherburne 13460 Antoinette Halliday	PK-5	T	696 45	26%	607/674-7336 Fax 607/674-8478

1 Superintendent	8 Curric/Instruct K-12	19 Chief Financial Officer	29 Family/Consumer Science	39 Social Studies K-12	49 English/Lang Arts Elem	59 Special Education Elem	69 Academic Assessment
2 Bus/Finance/Purchasing	9 Curric/Instruct Elem	20 Art K-12	30 Adult Education	40 Social Studies Elem	50 English/Lang Arts Sec	60 Special Education Sec	70 Research/Development
3 Buildings And Grounds	10 Curric/Instruct Sec	21 Art Elem	31 Career/Sch-to-Work Elem	41 Social Studies Sec	51 Reading K-12	61 Foreign/World Lang K-12	71 Public Information
4 Food Service	11 Federal Program	22 Art Sec	32 Career/Sch-to-Work Elem	42 Science K-12	52 Reading Elem	62 Foreign/World Lang Elem	72 Summer School
5 Transportation	12 Title I	23 Music K-12	33 Career/Sch-to-Work Sec	43 Science Elem	53 Reading Sec	63 Foreign/World Lang Sec	73 Instructional Tech
6 Athletic	13 Title V	24 Music Elem	34 Early Childhood Ed	44 Science Sec	54 Remedial Reading K-12	64 Religious Education K-12	74 Inservice Training
7 Health Services	15 Asst Superintendent	25 Music Sec	35 Health/Phys Education	45 Math K-12	55 Remedial Reading Elem	65 Religious Education Elem	75 Marketing/Distributive
	16 Instructional Media Svcs	26 Business Education	36 Guidance Services K-12	46 Math Elem	56 Remedial Reading Sec	66 Religious Education Sec	76 Info Systems
	17 Chief Operations Officer	27 Career & Tech Ed	37 Guidance Services Elem	47 Math Sec	57 Bilingual/ELL	67 School Board President	77 Psychological Assess
	18 Chief Academic Officer	28 Technology Education	38 Guidance Services Sec	48 English/Lang Arts K-12	58 Special Education K-12	68 Teacher Personnel	78 Affirmative Action

New York School Directory

Clinton County

	Grd	Prgm	Enr/#Cls	SN	
Sherburne Earlville Middle Sch 13 School St, Sherburne 13460 Jolene Emhof	6-8	T	289 30	42%	607/674-7350 Fax 607/674-7392
Sherburne Earlville Sr HS 13 School St, Sherburne 13460 Nick Colosi	9-12		364 45	48%	607/674-7380 Fax 607/674-7368

- **Unadilla Valley Ctl Sch Dist** PID: 00719691   607/847-7500
  4238 State Highway 8, New Berlin 13411   Fax 607/847-6924

Schools: 2 \ **Teachers:** 77 \ **Students:** 850 \ **Special Ed Students:** 161 \ **College-Bound:** 66% \ **Ethnic:** African American 1%, Hispanic 1%, Native American: 1%, Caucasian 97% \ **Exp:** $190 (Low) \ **Poverty:** 20% \ **Title I:** $274,171 \ **Special Education:** $1,881,000 \ **Open-Close:** 09/08 - 06/21 \ **DTBP:** $359 (High)

Robert Mackey 1	Wayne Tilley 2,5,7,91
Bill Beadle 3	Bonnie Schowe 4,295*
Matt Osborne 6	Diane Meredith 8,271*
Kim Murray 8,296	Rob Converse 11
Steven Bliss 12,73	Freida Lyons 58
Kristin Rumovicz 67	Katie Hansen 68
Megan Tumilowicz 273	Bruce McGowan 288*

Public Schs..Principal	Grd	Prgm	Enr/#Cls	SN	
Unadilla Valley Elem Sch 4238 State Highway 8, New Berlin 13411 Christopher Harper	PK-5	T	385 27	56%	607/847-7500 Fax 607/847-9194
Unadilla Valley Secondary Sch 4238 State Highway 8, New Berlin 13411 Katie Hansen \ Kimberly Murray	6-12	V	425 30	63%	607/847-7500 Fax 607/847-9194

CHENANGO CATHOLIC SCHOOLS

- **Diocese of Syracuse Ed Office** PID: 00762765
  Listing includes only schools located in this county. See District Index for location of Diocesan Offices.

Catholic Schs..Principal	Grd	Prgm	Enr/#Cls	SN	
Holy Family Sch 17 Prospect St, Norwich 13815 Tom Sorci	PK-6		123 10		607/337-2207 Fax 607/337-2210

CHENANGO PRIVATE SCHOOLS

Private Schs..Principal	Grd	Prgm	Enr/#Cls	SN	
Valley Heights Christian Acad 75 Calvary Dr, Norwich 13815 Rebeca Summers	PK-12		68 9		607/336-8422 Fax 607/334-2212

CHENANGO REGIONAL CENTERS

- **Dcmo BOCES Chenango** PID: 00721345   607/335-1200
  6678 County Road 32, Norwich 13815   Fax 607/334-9848

Perry Dewey 1	Doreen Rowe 2,15
Janet Laytham 8,16,74	Michael MacDonald 15,58,79
Jennifer Waite-Ambra 27,30,31,88	Patricia Gallaher 58,275
Linda Zaczek 67	Liz Bunce 68
Rebecca Roberts 73	Dave Potter 285

CLINTON COUNTY

CLINTON COUNTY SCHOOLS

County Schs..Principal	Grd	Prgm	Enr/#Cls	SN	
Champlain Valley Ed Svcs 1585 Military Tpke, Plattsburgh 12901 Adam Facteau	Voc	AG	300 25		518/561-0100 Fax 518/561-0494

CLINTON PUBLIC SCHOOLS

- **Ausable Valley Ctl Sch Dist** PID: 00719926   518/834-2845
  1273 Route 9N, Clintonville 12924   Fax 518/834-2843

Schools: 3 \ **Teachers:** 108 \ **Students:** 1,151 \ **Special Ed Students:** 181 \ **College-Bound:** 83% \ **Ethnic:** African American 2%, Caucasian 98% \ **Exp:** $225 (Med) \ **Poverty:** 15% \ **Title I:** $291,908 \ **Special Education:** $2,691,000 \ **Open-Close:** 09/03 - 06/25 \ **DTBP:** $360 (High)

Paul Savage 1	Josh Hotaling 2
Randy Pray 3*	Michelle Martineau 4*
Kevin Holbert 6,35	Garth Houde 16,82*
Aime Defayette 27,58,77*	Matt Rogers 36,69*
Robyn Pray 67	

Public Schs..Principal	Grd	Prgm	Enr/#Cls	SN	
Ausable Forks Elem Sch 28 Church Ln, Au Sable FRKS 12912 Abby Seymour	PK-6	T	245 16	50%	518/647-5503 Fax 518/647-8471
Ausable Valley Middle High Sch 1490 Route 9N, Clintonville 12924 Brittany Trybendis \ Chris Fey	7-12	AT	508 50	53%	518/834-2800 Fax 518/834-6016
Keeseville Elem Sch 1825 Main St, Keeseville 12944 Michael Francia	PK-6	T	398 23	59%	518/834-2839 Fax 518/834-2857

- **Beekmantown Ctl School Dist** PID: 00719964   518/563-8250
  37 Eagle Way, West Chazy 12992   Fax 518/563-8132

Schools: 4 \ **Teachers:** 182 \ **Students:** 2,000 \ **Special Ed Students:** 360 \ **LEP Students:** 3 \ **Ethnic:** Asian 1%, African American 2%, Hispanic 2%, Caucasian 95% \ **Exp:** $392 (High) \ **Poverty:** 16% \ **Title I:** $503,631 \ **Special Education:** $3,996,000 \ **Open-Close:** 09/11 - 06/25 \ **DTBP:** $378 (High) \

Daniel Mannix 1	Jennifer Parliament 2
Daniel Noonan 3	Roxann Barnes 4
James Chauvin 5	Polly Tavernia 11,58,72
Gary Lambert 16,73,286	Cathy Buckley 67

Public Schs..Principal	Grd	Prgm	Enr/#Cls	SN	
Beekmantown Elem Sch 37 Eagle Way, West Chazy 12992 Sarah Paquette	PK-5	T	493 27	43%	518/563-8035 Fax 518/563-8087
Beekmantown High Sch 37 Eagle Way, West Chazy 12992 Matthew Bezio	9-12	ATV	556 40	43%	518/563-8787 Fax 518/563-8789

---

79 Student Personnel	91 Safety/Security	275 Response To Intervention	298 Grant Writer/Ptnrships	School Programs	Social Media
80 Driver Ed/Safety	92 Magnet School	277 Remedial Math K-12	750 Chief Innovation Officer	A = Alternative Program	
81 Gifted/Talented	93 Parental Involvement	280 Literacy Coach	751 Chief of Staff	G = Adult Classes	▯ = Facebook
82 Video Services	95 Tech Prep Program	285 STEM	752 Social Emotional Learning	M = Magnet Program	
83 Substance Abuse Prev	97 Chief Infomation Officer	286 Digital Learning		T = Title I Schoolwide	▯ = Twitter
84 Erate	98 Chief Technology Officer	288 Common Core Standards	Other School Types	V = Career & Tech Ed Programs	
85 AIDS Education	270 Accountability	294 Character Education	Ⓐ = Alternative School		
88 Alternative/At Risk	271 Migrant Education	295 Network System	Ⓒ = Charter School	New Schools are shaded	
89 Multi-Cultural Curriculum	273 Teacher Mentor	296 Title II Programs	Ⓜ = Magnet School	New Superintendents and Principals are bold	
90 Social Work	274 Before/After Sch	297 Webmaster	Ⓨ = Year-Round School	Personnel with email addresses are underscored	

NY—43

Clinton County

Market Data Retrieval

Beekmantown Middle Sch	6-8	T	439	48%	518/563-8690
37 Eagle Way, West Chazy 12992			52		Fax 518/563-8691
Duffy Nelson					
Cumberland Head Elem Sch	PK-5	T	535	48%	518/563-8321
37 Eagle Way, West Chazy 12992			30		Fax 518/563-8343
Darcy Stoutenger					

• Chazy Central Rural Sch Dist PID: 00720016
609 Miner Farm Rd, Chazy 12921
518/846-7135
Fax 518/846-8322

Schools: 1 \ **Teachers:** 42 \ **Students:** 455 \ **Special Ed Students:** 81 \ **LEP Students:** 3 \ **College-Bound:** 80% \ **Ethnic:** Asian 1%, African American 2%, Hispanic 1%, Caucasian 96% \ **Exp:** $170 (Low) \ **Poverty:** 10% \ **Title I:** $66,806 \ **Special Education:** $492,000 \ **Open-Close:** 09/04 - 06/25 \ **DTBP:** $346 (High)

Scott Osborne	1	Emelin Koss	2*	
Barry West	3,5	Brian Norcross	6*	
Kim Gosselin	7,69*	Amy Racine	8,31,36*	
Robert McAulisse	9,12,13,270,275,296*	Theda Wilfore	11,58,88*	
Steven Patnode	16,82*	Susan Duffy	51*	
Kathleen Wilson	54*	Kim Brandell	57*	
Joey Trombley	67	Matthew Palkovic	73*	
Sonya Lambert	273*			

Public Schs..Principal	Grd	Prgm	Enr/#Cls	SN	
Chazy Central Rural Sch	K-12	T	455	29%	518/846-7135
609 Miner Farm Rd, Chazy 12921			25		
Rob McAuliffe					

• Northeastern Clinton Ctl SD PID: 00720066
103 State Route 276, Champlain 12919
518/298-8242
Fax 518/298-4293

Schools: 4 \ **Teachers:** 112 \ **Students:** 1,200 \ **Special Ed Students:** 282 \ **LEP Students:** 3 \ **College-Bound:** 69% \ **Ethnic:** Asian 1%, African American 1%, Hispanic 2%, Caucasian 97% \ **Exp:** $128 (Low) \ **Poverty:** 19% \ **Title I:** $442,210 \ **Special Education:** $3,186,000 \ **Open-Close:** 09/08 - 06/25 \ **DTBP:** $350 (High)

Rob Garrand	1	Jennifer Brown	2
Matthew Arno	3	Nadine LaBelle-Matott	4
Steven Stone	5	Nicholas Trombley	6*
Thomas Brandell	8*	Heidi Sample	9,12*
Daniel Marangiello	11,58	Amber Beggs	30*
Heather DuPrey	34,37	Stephen Southwick	67
Todd Stone	73,295	Heidi Pellerin	83*

Public Schs..Principal	Grd	Prgm	Enr/#Cls	SN	
Mooers Elem Sch	PK-5	T	349	48%	518/236-7373
16 School St, Mooers 12958			20		Fax 518/236-5027
Dennis Rasco					
Northeastern Clinton Mid Sch	6-8	T	266	53%	518/298-8681
103 State Route 276, Champlain 12919			25		Fax 518/298-7987
Thomas Brandell					
Northeastern Clinton Sr HS	9-12	T	396	40%	518/298-8638
103 State Route 276, Champlain 12919			35		Fax 518/298-3329
Joshua Harrica					
Rouses Point Elem Sch	PK-5	T	276	55%	518/297-7211
80 Maple St, Rouses Point 12979			12		Fax 518/297-2970
Heidi Sample					

• Northern Adirondack Ctl SD PID: 00720121
5572 Route 11, Ellenburg Dep 12935
518/594-7060
Fax 518/594-7255

Schools: 2 \ **Teachers:** 81 \ **Students:** 805 \ **Special Ed Students:** 146 \ **College-Bound:** 60% \ **Ethnic:** Caucasian 99% \ **Exp:** $175 (Low) \ **Poverty:** 13% \ **Title I:** $216,490 \ **Special Education:** $2,254,000 \ **Open-Close:** 09/04 - 06/25 \ **DTBP:** $409 (High)

James Knight	1	Brian Tousignant	2
Jay Bouchard	3	Lisa Carter	4*
Julie LeClair	5	Rebecca Trombley	11,273,296,298
Shawn Strack	16,48*	Amy Hayes	27,36,69,83*
Christine Brudvig	37	Timothy McAfee	38*
Cindy Hoff	58,69,77*	Paul Gilmore	67
Alex Inflesey	73,295		

Public Schs..Principal	Grd	Prgm	Enr/#Cls	SN	
Northern Adirondack Elem Sch	PK-5	T	382	46%	518/594-3962
5572 Route 11, Ellenburg Dep 12935			23		Fax 518/594-7330
Lisa Silver					
Northern Adirondack Jr Sr HS	6-12	AGV	423	50%	518/594-3962
Route 11, Ellenburg Dep 12935			50		Fax 518/594-7330
Robert Witkiewicz \ Michael Loughman					

• Peru Central School Dist PID: 00720171
17 School St, Peru 12972
518/643-6000
Fax 518/643-2043

Schools: 2 \ **Teachers:** 163 \ **Students:** 1,857 \ **Special Ed Students:** 370 \ **LEP Students:** 6 \ **College-Bound:** 77% \ **Ethnic:** Asian 1%, African American 1%, Hispanic 1%, Caucasian 96% \ **Exp:** $264 (Med) \ **Poverty:** 10% \ **Title I:** $351,393 \ **Special Education:** $4,760,000 \ **Open-Close:** 09/08 - 06/25 \ **DTBP:** $378 (High)

Dr Thomas Palmer	1	Randolph Sapp	2,11
Sue Wagner	2	Matt LeFevre	3
Jeannine Kerr	4*	David Wagner	5
Matt Berry	6,7,35,83*	Amy Campbell	8
Irene Stephney	12,58,79,298*	Ian Patterson	16,82*
Kim Loughan	36	Bonnie Berry	67
Nicholas Damiani	73	Scott Storms	74*
Jared Duquette	295		

Public Schs..Principal	Grd	Prgm	Enr/#Cls	SN	
Peru Elem Sch	PK-5	T	847	48%	518/643-6100
116 Pleasant St, Peru 12972			23		Fax 518/643-6126
Michelle Rawson \ Matthew Slattery					
Peru Jr/Sr High Sch	6-12	TV	1,010	43%	518/643-6400
17 School St, Peru 12972					Fax 518/643-8357
Scott Storms \ Matt Berry					

• Plattsburgh City School Dist PID: 00720236
49 Broad St, Plattsburgh 12901
518/957-6000
Fax 518/561-6605

Schools: 5 \ **Teachers:** 183 \ **Students:** 1,852 \ **Special Ed Students:** 422 \ **LEP Students:** 13 \ **College-Bound:** 77% \ **Ethnic:** Asian 2%, African American 8%, Hispanic 2%, Caucasian 88% \ **Exp:** $258 (Med) \ **Poverty:** 18% \ **Title I:** $539,006 \ **Special Education:** $4,419,000 \ **Open-Close:** 09/02 - 06/25 \ **DTBP:** $386 (High) \ 🛇

Jay LeBrun	1	David Baroody	2,15
Norbert Neiderer	3,5	Charlene O'Connor	4
Christopher Hartmann	6,7*	Carrie Zales	8,15
Fortune Ellison	58	Leisa Boise	67
Kimberly Quinn	83,85*	Rick Durham	285*

---

1 Superintendent	8 Curric/Instruct K-12	19 Chief Financial Officer	29 Family/Consumer Science	39 Social Studies K-12	49 English/Lang Arts Elem	59 Special Education Elem	69 Academic Assessment
2 Bus/Finance/Purchasing	9 Curric/Instruct Elem	20 Art K-12	30 Adult Education	40 Social Studies Elem	50 English/Lang Arts Sec	60 Special Education Sec	70 Research/Development
3 Buildings And Grounds	10 Curric/Instruct Sec	21 Art Elem	31 Career/Sch-to-Work K-12	41 Social Studies Sec	51 Reading K-12	61 Foreign/World Lang K-12	71 Public Information
4 Food Service	11 Federal Program	22 Art Sec	32 Career/Sch-to-Work Elem	42 Science K-12	52 Reading Elem	62 Foreign/World Lang Elem	72 Summer School
5 Transportation	12 Title I	23 Music K-12	33 Career/Sch-to-Work Sec	43 Science Elem	53 Reading Sec	63 Foreign/World Lang Sec	73 Instructional Tech
6 Athletic	13 Title V	24 Music Elem	34 Early Childhood Ed	44 Science Sec	54 Remedial Reading K-12	64 Religious Education K-12	74 Inservice Training
7 Health Services	15 Asst Superintendent	25 Music Sec	35 Health/Phys Education	45 Math K-12	55 Remedial Reading Elem	65 Religious Education Elem	75 Marketing/Distributive
	16 Instructional Media Svcs	26 Business Education	36 Guidance Services K-12	46 Math Elem	56 Remedial Reading Sec	66 Religious Education Sec	76 Info Systems
	17 Chief Operations Officer	27 Career & Tech Ed	37 Guidance Services Elem	47 Math Sec	57 Bilingual/ELL	67 School Board President	77 Psychological Assess
	18 Chief Academic Officer	28 Technology Education	38 Guidance Services Sec	48 English/Lang Arts K-12	58 Special Education K-12	68 Teacher Personnel	78 Affirmative Action

New York School Directory — Columbia County

Public Schs..Principal	Grd	Prgm	Enr/#Cls	SN	
Arthur P Momot Elem Sch 60 Monty St, Plattsburgh 12901 Susan Wilson	PK-5	T	383 28	57%	518/563-1140 Fax 518/566-7739
Bailey Avenue Elem Sch 50 Bailey Ave, Plattsburgh 12901 Claudine Clark	PK-2		247 17	42%	518/563-2410 Fax 518/566-7663
Oak Street Elem Sch 108 Oak St, Plattsburgh 12901 Jayson Barnhart	3-5		238 15	46%	518/563-4950 Fax 518/561-5828
Plattsburgh Senior High Sch 1 Clifford Dr, Plattsburgh 12901 Glenn Hurlock	9-12	A	570 50	40%	518/561-7500 Fax 518/561-1895
Ronald B Stafford Middle Sch 15 Broad St, Plattsburgh 12901 Jamie LaBarge	6-8		414	49%	518/563-6800 Fax 518/563-8520

- **Saranac Central School Dist** PID: 00720303   518/565-5600
  32 Emmons St, Dannemora 12929   Fax 518/565-5617

Schools: 4 \ **Teachers:** 132 \ **Students:** 1,400 \ **Special Ed Students:** 254 \ **Ethnic:** Hispanic 1%, Caucasian 98% \ **Exp:** $279 (Med) \ **Poverty:** 16% \ **Title I:** $400,636 \ **Special Education:** $4,298,000 \ **Open-Close:** 09/03 - 06/25

Javier Perez 1   Danielle McAffee 2
James Giroux 3   Issac Dirolf 4*
Benjamin Perry 5   Connie Garman 8,58
Connie Garman .... 8,58*   Shannon Vagres 8,58*
Michael White .... 11,271,273*   Alison Rosenbaum 38*
Tracy Allen Waite 67   Jamie Steenberge 76
Lisa Dew 84

Public Schs..Principal	Grd	Prgm	Enr/#Cls	SN	
Morrisonville Elem Sch 47 Sand Rd, Morrisonville 12962 Kathleen Moore	PK-5		368 18	37%	518/565-5980 Fax 518/565-5972
Saranac Elem Sch 18 Picketts Corners Rd, Saranac 12981 Tracey Manor	PK-5	T	372 22	41%	518/565-5900 Fax 518/565-5890
Saranac Middle Sch 70 Picketts Corners Rd, Saranac 12981 Katie Francisco	6-8	A	331 50	40%	518/565-5700 Fax 518/565-5706
Saranac Senior High Sch 60 Picketts Corners Rd, Saranac 12981 Steven Grenville	9-12	V	384 38	40%	518/565-5800 Fax 518/565-5809

CLINTON CATHOLIC SCHOOLS

- **Diocese of Ogdensburg Ed Off** PID: 00769050
  Listing includes only schools located in this county. See District Index for location of Diocesan Offices.

Catholic Schs..Principal	Grd	Prgm	Enr/#Cls	SN	
Seton Catholic Sch 206 New York Rd, Plattsburgh 12903 Mary Forbes	PK-12		255 20		518/561-4031 Fax 518/563-1193

CLINTON PRIVATE SCHOOLS

Private Schs..Principal	Grd	Prgm	Enr/#Cls	SN	
Lake Shore Christian Sch 4635 State Route 9, Plattsburgh 12901 Robert Fry	K-12		21 2		518/563-4098 Fax 518/563-3594

CLINTON REGIONAL CENTERS

- **Champlain Valley Ed Services** PID: 00720365   518/561-0100
  1585 Military Tpke, Plattsburgh 12901   Fax 518/562-1471

Dr Mark Davey 1   Eric Bell 2,15,68
Teri Calabese-Gray 8,15   Michele Friedman 27,31
Cathy Snow 30   Bonnie Berry 58

COLUMBIA COUNTY

COLUMBIA COUNTY SCHOOLS

County Schs..Principal	Grd	Prgm	Enr/#Cls	SN	
Columbia Greene Ed Center 131 Union Tpke, Hudson 12534 Jake Stomieroski	Voc	AG	400 20		518/828-4157 Fax 518/828-0084

COLUMBIA PUBLIC SCHOOLS

- **Berkshire Union Free Sch Dist** PID: 00720377   518/781-3500
  13640 State Route 22, Canaan 12029   Fax 518/781-4890

Schools: 2 \ **Teachers:** 16 \ **Students:** 40 \ **Special Ed Students:** 14 \ **College-Bound:** 80% \ **Ethnic:** African American 26%, Hispanic 25%, Caucasian 49% \ **Exp:** $955 (High) \ **Open-Close:** 09/04 - 06/25 \ **DTBP:** $323 (High) \ 🅵 🆃

Michael Vanyo 1,11   Christine Burke 2,3,15
Neil Hanlon .... 35,85*   Andrew Hyde 38*
Brian Parchesky 67   Gary Doughty 83
Bailey Naples 88   Hope Willsky 298

Public Schs..Principal	Grd	Prgm	Enr/#Cls	SN	
Ⓨ Berkshire Jr Sr High Sch 13640 State Route 22, Canaan 12029 Brett Fortran	7-12	AMTV	40 24	61%	518/781-3500
Ⓐ Warren Street Academy 11 Warren St, Hudson 12534 Dotan Schips	7-12		150	66%	518/781-3500

---

79 Student Personnel
80 Driver Ed/Safety
81 Gifted/Talented
82 Video Services
83 Substance Abuse Prev
84 Erate
85 AIDS Education
88 Alternative/At Risk
89 Multi-Cultural Curriculum
90 Social Work
91 Safety/Security
92 Magnet School
93 Parental Involvement
95 Tech Prep Program
97 Chief Infomation Officer
98 Chief Technology Officer
270 Character Education
271 Migrant Education
273 Teacher Mentor
274 Before/After Sch
275 Response To Intervention
277 Remedial Math K-12
280 Literacy Coach
285 STEM
286 Digital Learning
288 Common Core Standards
294 Accountability
295 Network System
296 Title II Programs
297 Webmaster
298 Grant Writer/Ptnrships
750 Chief Innovation Officer
751 Chief of Staff
752 Social Emotional Learning

Other School Types
Ⓐ = Alternative School
Ⓒ = Charter School
Ⓜ = Magnet School
Ⓨ = Year-Round School

School Programs
A = Alternative Program
G = Adult Classes
M = Magnet Program
T = Title I Schoolwide
V = Career & Tech Ed Programs

Social Media
🅵 = Facebook
🆃 = Twitter

New Schools are shaded
New Superintendents and Principals are bold
Personnel with email addresses are underscored

Columbia County — Market Data Retrieval

- **Chatham Central School Dist** PID: 00720391   518/392-2400
  50 Woodbridge Ave, Chatham 12037   Fax 518/392-2413

Schools: 3 \ **Teachers:** 103 \ **Students:** 1,100 \ **Special Ed Students:** 201 \ **LEP Students:** 19 \ **Ethnic:** Asian 1%, African American 1%, Hispanic 6%, Caucasian 92% \ **Exp:** $382 (High) \ **Poverty:** 11% \ **Title I:** $185,419 \ **Special Education:** $1,302,000 \ **Open-Close:** 09/14 - 06/25 \ **DTBP:** $359 (High) \ 🅕

Dr Sal De Angelo 1	Michael Chudy 2
Andrew Davey 3	Barbara Murray 4*
Steve Oleynek 5,8	John Brantley 6*
Brian Simon 11,58,88,275*	Chelsea Phillips 16*
Teri Howard 30	Michael Loomis 31*
Debra Oligny 57*	Craig Simmons 67
Giles Felton 73,295	Tracy Kelly 90*
Jackie Hoffman 270*	Lucas Christensen 298

Public Schs..Principal	Grd	Prgm	Enr/#Cls	SN	
Chatham High Sch 50 Woodbridge Ave, Chatham 12037 John Thorsen	9-12	V	321 40	34%	518/392-2400 Fax 518/392-0908
Chatham Middle Sch 50 Woodbridge Ave, Chatham 12037 Michael Burns	6-8		243 43	39%	518/392-2400 Fax 518/392-1559
Mary E Dardess Elem Sch 50 Woodbridge Ave, Chatham 12037 Kristen Reno	PK-5	T	419	47%	518/392-2400 Fax 518/392-2795

- **Germantown Central School Dist** PID: 00720468   518/537-6281
  123 Main St, Germantown 12526   Fax 518/537-6283

Schools: 1 \ **Teachers:** 55 \ **Students:** 550 \ **Special Ed Students:** 96 \ **LEP Students:** 9 \ **College-Bound:** 80% \ **Ethnic:** Asian 1%, Hispanic 8%, Caucasian 91% \ **Exp:** $261 (Med) \ **Poverty:** 9% \ **Title I:** $73,018 \ **Special Education:** $1,274,000 \ **Open-Close:** 09/09 - 06/24 \ **DTBP:** $381 (High) \ 🅕 🅣

Susan Brown 1,73,288	Deana Bizzarro 2
Jim Palmieri 3	Beth Kelly 4
Linda Anderson 5	Christina Pudney 6*
Devin Jackowski 36,69	Karen Moore 52*
Yvonne Waters 58,79	Tammi Kellenbenz 67
Jane Didonna 270*	

Public Schs..Principal	Grd	Prgm	Enr/#Cls	SN	
Germantown Central Sch 123 Main St, Germantown 12526 Beverly Meagher \ James Didonna	PK-12	T	550 46	41%	518/537-6281

- **Hudson City School Dist** PID: 00720482   518/828-4360
  215 Harry Howard Ave, Hudson 12534   Fax 518/697-8315

Schools: 4 \ **Teachers:** 157 \ **Students:** 1,652 \ **Special Ed Students:** 363 \ **LEP Students:** 172 \ **Ethnic:** Asian 14%, African American 22%, Hispanic 18%, Caucasian 46% \ **Exp:** $302 (High) \ **Poverty:** 19% \ **Title I:** $561,413 \ **Special Education:** $5,523,000 \ **Open-Close:** 09/04 - 06/25 \ **DTBP:** $355 (High)

Maria Suttmeier 1	Deborah Long 2
Sharifa Carbon 2	George Keeler 3*
Christopher Bateman 4	Nikki DeDominicis 5
Derek Reardon 6*	Kim Lybolt 7,58,77,90
April Prestipino 8,11,288,296	Judith Roehr 16*
Julia Coryell 57*	Carrie Otty 67
Rachel Rissetto 68	William Hallenbeck 91*
Kathleen Clark 274*	Laurie Campbell 280*

Public Schs..Principal	Grd	Prgm	Enr/#Cls	SN	
Bard HS Early Clg Hudson 364 Warren St, Hudson 12534 **Michael Sadowski**	9-12		100		518/249-4779
Hudson High Sch 215 Harry Howard Ave, Hudson 12534 Robert LaCasse	9-12	T	452 50	67%	518/828-4360 Fax 518/697-8418
Hudson Junior High Sch 215 Harry Howard Ave, Hudson 12534 Derek Reardon	6-8	T	399	75%	518/828-4360 Fax 518/697-8522
Montgomery C Smith Elem Sch 102 Harry Howard Ave, Hudson 12534 Mark Brenneman	PK-5	T	801 25	72%	518/828-4650 Fax 518/697-8434

- **Ichabod Crane Central Schools** PID: 00720561   518/758-7575
  2910 Route 9, Valatie 12184   Fax 518/758-7579

Schools: 3 \ **Teachers:** 158 \ **Students:** 1,683 \ **Special Ed Students:** 281 \ **LEP Students:** 96 \ **College-Bound:** 85% \ **Ethnic:** Asian 2%, African American 2%, Hispanic 8%, Caucasian 88% \ **Exp:** $248 (Med) \ **Poverty:** 8% \ **Title I:** $238,591 \ **Special Education:** $3,028,000 \ **Open-Close:** 09/08 - 06/25 \ **DTBP:** $359 (High)

Suzanne Guntlow 1	Michael Brennan 2,11
Steven Marotta 3,91	Todd DiGrigoli 4
Dan Doyle 5	Tim Stewart 6*
Michelle Warner 7*	Vikki Skarzynski 12,298
Jennifer Two-Axe 16,82*	Amy Boothby 30
David Manarel 57	Peg Warner 58,88
Matthew Nelson 67	Paul Caputo 73
Crory Drumnond 285	

Public Schs..Principal	Grd	Prgm	Enr/#Cls	SN	
Ichabod Crane High Sch 2910 Route 9, Valatie 12184 Craig Shull	9-12	V	512	26%	518/758-7575 Fax 518/758-2181
Ichabod Crane Middle Sch 2910 Route 9, Valatie 12184 Tim Farley	4-8		659 40	32%	518/758-7575 Fax 518/758-1405
Ichabod Crane Primary Sch 2910 Route 9, Valatie 12184 Andrea Williams	K-3		512 23	38%	518/758-7575 Fax 518/758-2199

- **New Lebanon Ctl School Dist** PID: 00720626   518/794-9016
  14665 State Route 22, New Lebanon 12125   Fax 518/766-5574

Schools: 2 \ **Teachers:** 49 \ **Students:** 428 \ **Special Ed Students:** 63 \ **College-Bound:** 68% \ **Ethnic:** African American 1%, Hispanic 3%, Caucasian 96% \ **Exp:** $193 (Low) \ **Poverty:** 11% \ **Title I:** $84,921 \ **Special Education:** $554,000 \ **Open-Close:** 09/04 - 06/25 \ **DTBP:** $386 (High)

Leslie Whitcomb 1,288	Kevin Fottrell 2
Matthew Klafehn 10*	Jennifer Morris 12*
Timothy Lambert 67	David Hawkins 73*
Ethan Race 295*	

Public Schs..Principal	Grd	Prgm	Enr/#Cls	SN	
New Lebanon Jr Sr High Sch 14665 State Route 22, New Lebanon 12125 Matthew Klafehn	7-12		192 35	39%	518/794-7600 Fax 518/766-6265
Walter B Howard Elem Sch 1478 Route 20, New Lebanon 12125 Andrew Kourt	PK-6	T	236 15	45%	518/794-8554 Fax 518/766-2220

1	Superintendent	8	Curric/Instruct K-12	19	Chief Financial Officer	29	Family/Consumer Science	39	Social Studies K-12	49	English/Lang Arts Elem	59	Special Education Elem	69	Academic Assessment
2	Bus/Finance/Purchasing	9	Curric/Instruct Elem	20	Art K-12	30	Adult Education	40	Social Studies Sec	50	English/Lang Arts Sec	60	Special Education Sec	70	Research/Development
3	Buildings And Grounds	10	Curric/Instruct Sec	21	Art Elem	31	Career/Sch-to-Work K-12	41	Social Studies Sec	51	Reading K-12	61	Foreign/World Lang K-12	71	Public Information
4	Food Service	11	Federal Program	22	Art Sec	32	Career/Sch-to-Work Elem	42	Science K-12	52	Reading Elem	62	Foreign/World Lang Elem	72	Summer School
5	Transportation	12	Title I	23	Music K-12	33	Career/Sch-to-Work Sec	43	Science Elem	53	Reading Sec	63	Foreign/World Lang Sec	73	Instructional Tech
6	Athletic	13	Title V	24	Music Elem	34	Early Childhood Ed	44	Science Sec	54	Remedial Reading K-12	64	Religious Education K-12	74	Inservice Training
7	Health Services	15	Asst Superintendent	25	Music Sec	35	Health/Phys Education	45	Math K-12	55	Remedial Reading Elem	65	Religious Education Elem	75	Marketing/Distributive
		16	Instructional Media Svcs	26	Business Education	36	Guidance Services K-12	46	Math Elem	56	Remedial Reading Sec	66	Religious Education Sec	76	Info Systems
		17	Chief Operations Officer	27	Career & Tech Ed	37	Guidance Services Elem	47	Math Sec	57	Bilingual/ELL	67	School Board President	77	Psychological Assess
		18	Chief Academic Officer	28	Technology Education	38	Guidance Services Sec	48	English/Lang Arts K-12	58	Special Education K-12	68	Teacher Personnel	78	Affirmative Action

New York School Directory — Cortland County

- **Taconic Hills Central Sch Dist** PID: 00720652 518/325-2800
  73 County Route 11A, Craryville 12521 Fax 518/325-2817

Schools: 2 \ **Teachers:** 127 \ **Students:** 1,241 \ **Special Ed Students:** 190 \ **LEP Students:** 32 \ **College-Bound:** 71% \ **Ethnic:** African American 2%, Hispanic 13%, Caucasian 85% \ **Exp:** $361 (High) \ **Poverty:** 15% \ **Title I:** $431,231 \ **Special Education:** $1,966,000 \ **Open-Close:** 09/08 - 06/25 \ **DTBP:** $359 (High)

Dr Neil Howard 1	Cybil Howard 2,11
Nicholas Smith 3	Pam Strompf 4
Richard Viebrock 5	Angela Webster 6*
Sandra Gardner .. 8,12,69,74,286,288,296,298	Denise Dellarocco 52,55*
Stella Ridder 58,79	Bonnie Torchia 67
Terri Hoffman 70	John Dodds 73
James Buhrmaster 88*	John Gulisane 274*
Karen Regina 295	

Public Schs..Principal	Grd	Prgm	Enr/#Cls	SN	
Taconic Hills Central High Sch 73 County Route 11A, Craryville 12521 James Buhrmaster	7-12	ATV	608 55	56%	518/325-2840 Fax 518/325-2845
Taconic Hills Elem Sch 73 County Route 11A, Craryville 12521 John Gulisane	PK-6	T	633 29	65%	518/325-2820 Fax 518/325-2825

COLUMBIA PRIVATE SCHOOLS

Private Schs..Principal	Grd	Prgm	Enr/#Cls	SN	
Academy of Chrn Leadership 3429 US Highway 9, Valatie 12184 Larry Cavagnaro	6-12		50		Fax 518/784-2224
Columbia Christian Academy 1323 County Route 21, Ghent 12075 Jeff Brown	K-12		24 3		518/392-2361
Darrow Sch 110 Darrow Rd, New Lebanon 12125 Andrew Vadnais	9-12		120 20		518/794-6000 Fax 518/794-7065
Hawthorne Valley Sch 330 County Route 21C, Ghent 12075 Marla Tolz	PK-12		250 20		518/672-7092 Fax 518/672-0181
Mountain Road Sch 4565 County Route 9, New Lebanon 12125 Cynthia Gray	PK-8		50 4		518/794-8520

CORTLAND COUNTY

CORTLAND COUNTY SCHOOLS

County Schs..Principal	Grd	Prgm	Enr/#Cls	SN	
McEvoy BOCES Voc Center 1710 State Route 13, Cortland 13045 Debra Wood	Voc	G	350 10		607/758-5100 Fax 607/753-9546

CORTLAND PUBLIC SCHOOLS

- **Cincinnatus Ctl School Dist** PID: 00720743 607/863-3200
  2809 Cincinnatus Rd, Cincinnatus 13040 Fax 607/863-4109

Schools: 2 \ **Teachers:** 67 \ **Students:** 530 \ **Special Ed Students:** 125 \ **College-Bound:** 61% \ **Ethnic:** African American 1%, Hispanic 1%, Caucasian 98% \ **Exp:** $193 (Low) \ **Poverty:** 19% \ **Title I:** $211,639 \ **Special Education:** $1,191,000 \ **Open-Close:** 09/04 - 06/25 \ **DTBP:** $374 (High)

Todd Freeman 1	Troy Bilodeau 2,12
Eric Benedict 3	Greg Bilodeau 4*
Michele Reakes 16*	Teresa Merihew 35*
Ramona Luettger 58	Debra Kressler 67
Carolyn Nowalk 68	Nicole Rice 73*

Public Schs..Principal	Grd	Prgm	Enr/#Cls	SN	
Cincinnatus Elem Sch 2809 Cincinnatus Rd, Cincinnatus 13040 Thomas Durkot	PK-6	T	240 14	62%	607/863-3200 Fax 607/863-4148
Cinncinnatus Secondary Sch 2809 Cincinnatus Rd, Cincinnatus 13040 David Phetteplace	7-12	TV	190	46%	607/863-3200 Fax 607/863-4148

- **Cortland Enlarged City SD** PID: 00720779 607/758-4100
  1 Valley View Dr, Cortland 13045 Fax 607/758-4109

Schools: 4 \ **Teachers:** 217 \ **Students:** 2,100 \ **Special Ed Students:** 406 \ **LEP Students:** 12 \ **College-Bound:** 71% \ **Ethnic:** Asian 1%, African American 4%, Hispanic 5%, Caucasian 90% \ **Exp:** $159 (Low) \ **Poverty:** 16% \ **Title I:** $810,019 \ **Special Education:** $5,865,000 \ **Open-Close:** 09/10 - 06/24 \ **DTBP:** $211 (High)

Robert Edwards 1	Kimberly Vile 2
Robert Martin 3	Francis Zaryski 4*
Jordon Lilley 5	Jeffery Craig 8,12
Judy Riley 11,31,34,75,77,79,83,298	Karen Jordan 57*
Janet Griffin 67	Sandra Swierczek 68
Denise Fox 73,76*	Paul Smith 91

Public Schs..Principal	Grd	Prgm	Enr/#Cls	SN	
Cortland Jr Sr High Sch 8 Valley View Dr, Cortland 13045 Kevin Cafararo \ Joseph Mack	7-12	T	1,020 110	49%	607/758-4110 Fax 607/758-4119
F E Smith Interm Sch 33 Wheeler Ave, Cortland 13045 Angela Wanish	3-4	T	309 14	50%	607/758-4180 Fax 607/758-4189
Franklyn S Barry Primary Sch 20 Raymond Ave, Cortland 13045 Lisa Kaup	K-2	T	453 29	57%	607/758-4150 Fax 607/758-4159
Randall Middle Sch 31 Randall St, Cortland 13045 Jordan Ashley	5-6	T	350 16	69%	607/758-4170 Fax 607/758-4179

- **Homer Central School Dist** PID: 00720860 607/749-7241
  80 S West St, Homer 13077 Fax 607/749-2312

Schools: 4 \ **Teachers:** 175 \ **Students:** 1,700 \ **Special Ed Students:** 253 \ **LEP Students:** 22 \ **Ethnic:** Asian 1%, African American 1%, Hispanic 2%, Caucasian 96% \ **Exp:** $309 (High) \ **Poverty:** 13% \ **Title I:** $422,775 \ **Special Education:** $2,884,000 \ **Open-Close:** 09/08 - 06/25 \ **DTBP:** $338 (High)

---

79 Student Personnel	91 Safety/Security	275 Response To Intervention	298 Grant Writer/Ptnrships	**School Programs**
80 Driver Ed/Safety	92 Magnet School	277 Remedial Math K-12	750 Chief Innovation Officer	A = Alternative Program
81 Gifted/Talented	93 Parental Involvement	280 Literacy Coach	751 Chief of Staff	G = Adult Classes
82 Video Services	95 Tech Prep Program	285 STEM	752 Social Emotional Learning	M = Magnet Program
83 Substance Abuse Prev	97 Chief Information Officer	286 Digital Learning		T = Title I Schoolwide
84 Erate	98 Chief Technology Officer	288 Common Core Standards	**Other School Types**	V = Career & Tech Ed Programs
85 AIDS Education	270 Character Education	294 Accountability	Ⓐ = Alternative School	
88 Alternative/At Risk	271 Migrant Education	295 Network System	Ⓒ = Charter School	**Social Media**
89 Multi-Cultural Curriculum	273 Teacher Mentor	296 Title II Programs	Ⓜ = Magnet School	f = Facebook
90 Social Work	274 Before/After Sch	297 Webmaster	Ⓨ = Year-Round School	t = Twitter

New Schools are shaded
New Superintendents and Principals are bold
Personnel with email addresses are underscored

Delaware County

Market Data Retrieval

Thomas Turck 1	Mike Falls 2,11,15,296
Scott Cavellier 3	Wendi Swift 4
Jeff Delia 5	Todd Liisi 6,35
Theodore Love 8,27,31,285,288*	Betsy Davison 16,82
Darlene Latten 38*	Chris Moore 51,54,58,69,77*
Sonia Apker 67	Josh Finn 73,98,295
Lynne Renner 80*	

Public Schs..Principal	Grd	Prgm	Enr/#Cls	SN
Homer Elem Sch 9 Central Park Pl, Homer 13077 Jim McGory	PK-2	T	434 24	42% 607/749-1250 Fax 607/749-1261
Homer High Sch 80 S West St, Homer 13077 Doug Van Etten	9-12	AG	590 50	38% 607/749-7246 Fax 607/749-1217
Homer Intermediate Sch 58 Clinton St, Homer 13077 Stephanie Falls	3-5	T	399 30	47% 607/749-1240 Fax 607/749-1238
Homer Junior High Sch 58 Clinton St, Homer 13077 Kara Schneider	6-8	AT	474 60	43% 607/749-1230 Fax 607/749-1238

- **Marathon Ctl School Dist** PID: 00720925   607/849-3117
1 Park St, Marathon 13803   Fax 607/849-3305

Schools: 2 \ **Teachers:** 77 \ **Students:** 689 \ **Special Ed Students:** 152 \ **LEP Students:** 5 \ **Ethnic:** African American 2%, Hispanic 1%, Caucasian 97% \ **Exp:** $242 (Med) \ **Poverty:** 21% \ **Title I:** $265,037 \ **Special Education:** $1,307,000 \ **Open-Close:** 09/08 - 06/24 \ **DTBP:** $379 (High)

Rebecca Stone 1,11	Tom Goskoski 2
Rich Young 3,91	Lisa Leber 5
Todd James 6,31*	Kathleen Hoyt 8,298
Jerry Hence 16,73,286,295*	Deb James 36,69,288*
Christopher Leins 58*	Rebecca Edsall 67

Public Schs..Principal	Grd	Prgm	Enr/#Cls	SN
Marathon Jr Sr High Sch 1 Park St, Marathon 13803 Holly Marcolina	7-12	AGTV	295 35	51% 607/849-3251
William Appleby Elem Sch 24 Albro Rd, Marathon 13803 Jonathan Hillis	PK-6	T	394 23	51% 607/849-3281 Fax 607/849-4702

- **McGraw Central School Dist** PID: 00720951   607/836-3600
10 W Academy St, Mc Graw 13101   Fax 607/836-3635

Schools: 2 \ **Teachers:** 58 \ **Students:** 570 \ **Special Ed Students:** 115 \ **Ethnic:** Hispanic 2%, Caucasian 98% \ **Exp:** $239 (Med) \ **Poverty:** 13% \ **Title I:** $118,084 \ **Special Education:** $1,093,000 \ **Open-Close:** 09/08 - 06/24 \ **DTBP:** $362 (High)

Melinda McCool 1,11	Troy Bilodeau 2*
Tom McCall 3,5,91	Wendy Swift 4*
Karen Genzel 9,12,58,69*	Danie'L Fish 16,82*
Nancy Harriger 35,85*	Patricia Walter 38*
Anthony Opera 67	Kevin Solan 73*

Public Schs..Principal	Grd	Prgm	Enr/#Cls	SN
McGraw Elem Sch 50 W Academy St, Mc Graw 13101 Susan Prince	PK-5	T	252 21	64% 607/836-3650 Fax 607/836-3609
McGraw Jr Sr High Sch 10 W Academy St, Mc Graw 13101 Mark Dimorier	6-12	T	293 35	51% 607/836-3601

CORTLAND CATHOLIC SCHOOLS

- **Diocese of Syracuse Ed Office** PID: 00762765
Listing includes only schools located in this county. See District Index for location of Diocesan Offices.

Catholic Schs..Principal	Grd	Prgm	Enr/#Cls	SN
St Mary's Sch 61 N Main St, Cortland 13045 Denise Hall	PK-6		156 17	607/756-5614 Fax 607/756-5626

CORTLAND PRIVATE SCHOOLS

Private Schs..Principal	Grd	Prgm	Enr/#Cls	SN
Cortland Christian Academy 15 West Rd, Cortland 13045 Nathanael Cobb	PK-12		150 9	607/756-7716
Marathon Christian Academy 5 Park St, Marathon 13803 Tom Boice	PK-12		50 4	607/849-3824

DELAWARE COUNTY

DELAWARE COUNTY SCHOOLS

County Schs..Principal	Grd	Prgm	Enr/#Cls	SN
Northern Catskills Occup Ctr 2020 Jump Brook Rd, Grand Gorge 12434 Monica Towne	Voc	AG	300 30	607/588-6291 Fax 607/588-6808
Robert W Harrold Ed Campus 270 Boces Dr, Sidney Center 13839 Jennifer Waite	Voc	AG	400 35	607/865-2500 Fax 607/865-8685

DELAWARE PUBLIC SCHOOLS

- **Andes Central School Dist** PID: 00720999   845/676-3167
85 Delaware Ave, Andes 13731   Fax 845/676-3181

Schools: 1 \ **Teachers:** 16 \ **Students:** 73 \ **Special Ed Students:** 22 \ **College-Bound:** 75% \ **Ethnic:** African American 1%, Hispanic 8%, Caucasian 91% \ **Exp:** $363 (High) \ **Poverty:** 12% \ **Title I:** $36,015 \ **Special Education:** $163,000 \ **Open-Close:** 09/04 - 06/18 \ **DTBP:** $359 (High)

Dr Robert Chakar 1,288	Greg Beall 2
Wayne Snyder 3,91	Fredrick Reed 5*
Katie Pardee 6	Susan Little 8*
Jennifer Finkle 11,274,296,298*	Bob Uaplou 16,58,73
Adam Vanbalkeburg 35*	Nicole Bishop 36,69,286*
Kelly Kilpatrick 67	Cindy Bramley 83*

---

1 Superintendent	8 Curric/Instruct K-12	19 Chief Financial Officer	29 Family/Consumer Science	39 Social Studies K-12	49 English/Lang Arts Elem	59 Special Education Elem	69 Academic Assessment
2 Bus/Finance/Purchasing	9 Curric/Instruct Elem	20 Art K-12	30 Adult Education	40 Social Studies Elem	50 English/Lang Arts Sec	60 Special Education Sec	70 Research/Development
3 Buildings And Grounds	10 Curric/Instruct Sec	21 Art Elem	31 Career/Sch-to-Work K-12	41 Social Studies Sec	51 Reading K-12	61 Foreign/World Lang K-12	71 Public Information
4 Food Service	11 Federal Program	22 Art Sec	32 Career/Sch-to-Work Elem	42 Science K-12	52 Reading Elem	62 Foreign/World Lang Elem	72 Summer School
5 Transportation	12 Title I	23 Music K-12	33 Career/Sch-to-Work Sec	43 Science Elem	53 Reading Sec	63 Foreign/World Lang Sec	73 Instructional Tech
6 Athletic	13 Title V	24 Music Elem	34 Early Childhood Ed	44 Science Sec	54 Remedial Reading K-12	64 Religious Education K-12	74 Inservice Training
7 Health Services	15 Asst Superintendent	25 Music Sec	35 Health/Phys Education	45 Math K-12	55 Remedial Reading Elem	65 Religious Education Elem	75 Marketing/Distributive
	16 Instructional Media Svcs	26 Business Education	36 Guidance Services K-12	46 Math Elem	56 Remedial Reading Sec	66 Religious Education Sec	76 Info Systems
	17 Chief Operations Officer	27 Career & Tech Ed	37 Guidance Services Elem	47 Math Sec	57 Bilingual/ELL	67 School Board President	77 Psychological Assess
	18 Chief Academic Officer	28 Technology Education	38 Guidance Services Sec	48 English/Lang Arts K-12	58 Special Education K-12	68 Teacher Personnel	78 Affirmative Action

New York School Directory — Delaware County

Public Schs..Principal	Grd	Prgm	Enr/#Cls	SN	
Andes Central Sch 85 Delaware Ave, Andes 13731 Robert Chakar	PK-12	T	73 18	53%	845/676-3166

• **Charlotte Valley Ctl Sch Dist** PID: 00721010   607/278-5511
15611 State Highway 23, Davenport 13750   Fax 607/278-5900

Schools: 1 \ **Teachers:** 40 \ **Students:** 300 \ **Special Ed Students:** 62 \ **College-Bound:** 53% \ **Ethnic:** Hispanic 4%, Caucasian 95% \ **Exp:** $431 (High) \ **Poverty:** 23% \ **Title I:** $165,907 \ **Special Education:** $1,059,000 \ **Open-Close:** 09/08 - 06/25 \ **DTBP:** $385 (High)

James Harter 1,11,73		David Carrington 2,3,5	
Mica Thornsland 4*		Cheryl Butler 6*	
Mitchell Rapp 11,296		Jim Wolf 35*	
Robert Hildebrandt 36,69*		Kelly Coon 58*	
Matt Moyse 67		Christine Losie 83*	
Jen Jester 274*			

Public Schs..Principal	Grd	Prgm	Enr/#Cls	SN	
ⓨ Charlotte Valley Central Sch 15611 State Highway 23, Davenport 13750 Mitchell Rapp	PK-12	MT	300 39	52%	607/278-5511

• **Delaware Academy Ctrl SD Delhi** PID: 00721034   607/746-1300
2 Sheldon Dr, Delhi 13753   Fax 607/746-6028

Schools: 2 \ **Teachers:** 75 \ **Students:** 797 \ **Special Ed Students:** 133 \ **LEP Students:** 6 \ **College-Bound:** 89% \ **Ethnic:** Asian 1%, Hispanic 1%, Caucasian 98% \ **Exp:** $335 (High) \ **Poverty:** 20% \ **Title I:** $258,218 \ **Special Education:** $1,273,000 \ **Open-Close:** 09/08 - 06/24 \ **DTBP:** $360 (High) \

Kelly Zimmerman 1	Carey Schultz 2,11,296
Bill Bartlett 3*	Christine Miller 4*
Gregg Verspoor 5	Mary Schmitt 7*
Julie Mable 9*	Megan Oliver 16
Michelle Cleveland 38*	Willaim Petrell 58
Elizabeth Huneke 67	Luke Potrzeba 73,76,286,295
Allison Yando 83*	

Public Schs..Principal	Grd	Prgm	Enr/#Cls	SN	
Delaware Academy 2 Sheldon Dr, Delhi 13753 Robin Robbins	6-12	TV	390 40	36%	607/746-1300 Fax 607/746-1324
Delhi Central Elem Sch 2 Sheldon Dr, Delhi 13753 Julie Mable	K-5	T	356 18	44%	607/746-2105 Fax 607/746-6223

• **Downsville Central Sch Dist** PID: 00721072   607/363-2100
14784 State Highway 30, Downsville 13755   Fax 607/363-2105

Schools: 1 \ **Teachers:** 34 \ **Students:** 240 \ **Special Ed Students:** 58 \ **College-Bound:** 38% \ **Ethnic:** African American 3%, Hispanic 5%, Caucasian 92% \ **Exp:** $396 (High) \ **Poverty:** 26% \ **Title I:** $182,016 \ **Special Education:** $316,000 \ **Open-Close:** 09/08 - 06/25 \ **DTBP:** $462 (High) \

John Evans 1	Timothy MaGuire 2,11
Ryan Bogler 3	Gerard Ormandy 5*
Jeff Baier 6*	Georgia Odell 7
Robert Rhinehart 8,11,88,90,270*	Ben Rhoades 16,82
Corin Bonsick 58,77*	Richard Bell 67
Melissa Frisbee 83	

Public Schs..Principal	Grd	Prgm	Enr/#Cls	SN	
Downsville Central Sch 14784 State Hwy 30, Downsville 13755 Robert Rhinehart	PK-12	T	240 30	51%	607/363-2100

• **Franklin Central School Dist** PID: 00721096   607/829-3551
26 Institute Street, Franklin 13775   Fax 607/829-2101

Schools: 1 \ **Teachers:** 27 \ **Students:** 262 \ **Special Ed Students:** 50 \ **College-Bound:** 74% \ **Ethnic:** Asian 1%, African American 2%, Hispanic 3%, Native American: 1%, Caucasian 92% \ **Exp:** $242 (Med) \ **Poverty:** 21% \ **Title I:** $106,585 \ **Special Education:** $620,000 \ **Open-Close:** 09/04 - 06/29

Brad Zilliox 1	Kelly Renwick 2,11,296,298
Brett Wood 3	Karen Terry 4*
John Nolan 5	Darryl Beers 6*
Nicole Seymour 7	Bonnie Johnson 11,58,69,74,273*
Barbara Lennon 16,82*	Eric Haight 35,83,85*
Brendon Coyle 36,57,271,752*	Stanley Surears 67
Jennifer Potrzeba 69,77*	John Gorton 73,76,752
John Girton 76,286,294,295*	

Public Schs..Principal	Grd	Prgm	Enr/#Cls	SN	
Franklin Central Sch 26 Institute St, Franklin 13775 Bonnie Johnson	PK-12	T	262 17	47%	607/829-3551

• **Hancock Central School Dist** PID: 00721137   607/637-2511
67 Education Ln, Hancock 13783   Fax 607/637-2512

Schools: 2 \ **Teachers:** 42 \ **Students:** 316 \ **Special Ed Students:** 38 \ **LEP Students:** 3 \ **Ethnic:** Asian 1%, African American 1%, Hispanic 6%, Native American: 1%, Caucasian 91% \ **Exp:** $174 (Low) \ **Poverty:** 19% \ **Title I:** $138,790 \ **Special Education:** $837,000 \ **Open-Close:** 09/07 - 06/29 \ **DTBP:** $445 (High)

Terrance Dougherty 1	Paul Bartholomew 3*
Joanne Smith 4*	Jodi Newman 5
Ann Messenger 6*	Jennifer Hunt 7*
Deb Darling 8,288	Sandra Barnes 16*
Joan Rice 36*	Terry Whitt 67
Jackie Beamer 79	Gail Schoonmaker 82*

Public Schs..Principal	Grd	Prgm	Enr/#Cls	SN	
Hancock Elem Sch 67 Education Ln, Hancock 13783 Julie Bergman	PK-4	T	103 11	56%	607/637-1328 Fax 607/637-1229
Hancock Jr Sr High Sch 67 Education Ln, Hancock 13783 Julie Bergman	5-12	TV	213 50	54%	607/637-1305 Fax 607/637-1380

• **Margaretville Central Sch Dist** PID: 00721163   845/586-2647
415 Main St, Margaretville 12455   Fax 845/586-2949

Schools: 1 \ **Teachers:** 39 \ **Students:** 370 \ **Special Ed Students:** 66 \ **LEP Students:** 23 \ **College-Bound:** 70% \ **Ethnic:** Asian 2%, Hispanic 23%, Native American: 2%, Caucasian 74% \ **Exp:** $260 (Med) \ **Poverty:** 24% \ **Title I:** $185,932 \ **Special Education:** $496,000 \ **Open-Close:** 09/08 - 06/25 \ **DTBP:** $485 (High)

Dr Robert Chakar 1	Beth Tuber 2
John O'Reilly 3	Constance Mathieson 4
Beth Smith 5	Tracy Reither 6,35
Laura Norris 8,11,69*	Tina Kelder 16,27
Nancy Millen 37*	Britney Triebe 38*

79	Student Personnel	91	Safety/Security	275	Response To Intervention	298	Grant Writer/Ptnrships
80	Driver Ed/Safety	92	Magnet School	277	Remedial Math K-12	750	Chief Innovation Officer
81	Gifted/Talented	93	Parental Involvement	280	Literacy Coach	751	Chief of Staff
82	Video Services	95	Tech Prep Program	285	STEM	752	Social Emotional Learning
83	Substance Abuse Prev	97	Chief Infomation Officer	286	Digital Learning		
84	Erate	98	Chief Technology Officer	288	Common Core Standards		
85	AIDS Education	270	Character Education	294	Accountability		
88	Alternative/At Risk	271	Migrant Education	295	Network System		
89	Multi-Cultural Curriculum	273	Teacher Mentor	296	Title II Programs		
90	Social Work	274	Before/After Sch	297	Webmaster		

School Programs
A = Alternative Program
G = Adult Classes
M = Magnet Program
T = Title I Schoolwide
V = Career & Tech Ed Programs

Other School Types
Ⓐ = Alternative School
Ⓒ = Charter School
Ⓜ = Magnet School
Ⓨ = Year-Round School

Social Media
f = Facebook
t = Twitter

New Schools are shaded
New Superintendents and Principals are bold
Personnel with email addresses are underscored

Delaware County

Market Data Retrieval

Frank Hayes 57
Doris Warner 67
Diane Castillo 90
Joy Holden 58,77*
Beth Johnson 73*

Public Schs..Principal	Grd	Prgm	Enr/#Cls	SN	
Margaretville Central Sch 415 Main St, Margaretville 12455 Laura Norris	PK-12	TV	370 50	65%	845/586-2647

- **Roxbury Central School Dist** PID: 00721199   607/326-4151
  53729 State Highway 30, Roxbury 12474   Fax 607/326-4154

Schools: 1 \ **Teachers:** 37 \ **Students:** 260 \ **Special Ed Students:** 56 \ **College-Bound:** 76% \ **Ethnic:** African American 2%, Hispanic 3%, Caucasian 96% \ **Exp:** $431 (High) \ **Poverty:** 14% \ **Title I:** $137,913 \ **Special Education:** $690,000 \ **Open-Close:** 09/08 - 06/25 \ **DTBP:** $364 (High)

Jefffrey Bennett 1
Alan Davis 3*
Thomas Faraci 6*
Maria Johnson 16*
Ed Fersch 67
Karen Hinkley 83,85,88*
Kristi Hadden 274*
Wendy Sprague 2,298
Lori Davie 4*
Jill Ten Eyck 8,273*
Mary Hinkley 58*
Brenda Hill 73,295*
Jo Hinkley 270

Public Schs..Principal	Grd	Prgm	Enr/#Cls	SN	
Roxbury Central Sch 53729 State Highway 30, Roxbury 12474 Jill Ten Eyck	PK-12	ATV	260 51	52%	607/326-4151

- **Sidney Central School Dist** PID: 00721216   607/563-2135
  95 W Main St, Sidney 13838   Fax 607/563-2386

Schools: 3 \ **Teachers:** 91 \ **Students:** 1,090 \ **Special Ed Students:** 151 \ **LEP Students:** 10 \ **College-Bound:** 73% \ **Ethnic:** Asian 1%, African American 1%, Hispanic 6%, Caucasian 91% \ **Exp:** $265 (Med) \ **Poverty:** 26% \ **Title I:** $499,562 \ **Special Education:** $2,718,000 \ **Open-Close:** 09/10 - 06/25 \ **DTBP:** $400 (High)

Dr Willaim Christensen 1
Christopher Stillman 3,91
Douglas Russell 5
Kerrie Johnston 8,15
Katherin Bailey 11,280,285,286,288,298*
Christine Race 27
Scott Hertzog 57*
Kerri Green 67
Michael Pavlovich 2
Kim Corcoran 4
Jim Karl 6
Tony Stenta 8
Karen Clark 16*
Jody Gravelin 36*
Gary Williams 58

Public Schs..Principal	Grd	Prgm	Enr/#Cls	SN	
Sidney Elem Sch 15 Pearl St E, Sidney 13838 Robert Hansen	PK-6	T	621 24	49%	607/561-7701 Fax 607/563-9257
Sidney High Sch 95 W Main St, Sidney 13838 Lori Pourby	9-12	T	301 52	42%	607/561-7703 Fax 607/563-1800
Sidney Junior High Sch 95 W Main St, Sidney 13838 Lori Pourby	7-8	T	168 30	50%	607/561-7703 Fax 607/563-1800

- **South Kortright Ctl SD** PID: 00721278   607/538-9111
  58200 State Highway 10, S Kortright 13842   Fax 607/538-9205

Schools: 1 \ **Teachers:** 37 \ **Students:** 350 \ **Special Ed Students:** 43 \ **College-Bound:** 90% \ **Ethnic:** Asian 1%, African American 2%, Hispanic 4%, Caucasian 93% \ **Exp:** $284 (Med) \ **Poverty:** 24% \ **Title I:** $155,929 \ **Special Education:** $700,000 \ **Open-Close:** 09/02 - 06/24 \ **DTBP:** $336 (High)

Dr Krislynn Dengler 1,11
Mike Dengler 3*
Randy Porter 5*
Jessica Morton 27,38*
Terri Chichester 67
Nathan Kanarek 2,19*
Christy Pietrantoni 4*
Robert Vanvalkenberg 6
Kira Licalzi 29,83,85*
Debra White 274*

Public Schs..Principal	Grd	Prgm	Enr/#Cls	SN	
South Kortright Central Sch 58200 State Highway 10, S Kortright 13842 Rachel Wright	PK-12	T	350 39	47%	607/538-9111

- **Stamford Central School Dist** PID: 00721292   607/652-7301
  1 River St, Stamford 12167   Fax 607/652-3446

Schools: 1 \ **Teachers:** 29 \ **Students:** 270 \ **Special Ed Students:** 51 \ **College-Bound:** 70% \ **Ethnic:** Asian 1%, African American 4%, Hispanic 3%, Caucasian 92% \ **Exp:** $384 (High) \ **Poverty:** 22% \ **Title I:** $120,655 \ **Special Education:** $801,000 \ **Open-Close:** 09/09 - 06/25 \ **DTBP:** $390 (High)

Glenn Huot 1
Brian Stoutenburg 3
Spence Clareen 5
Shawna Davis 8,11,15,57,69,273,288
Kim Stahl 58
Donna Bright 2
Dawn Townsend 4*
Greg O'Connell 6,35,85*
Bruce Voorhees 16,73,82
Ellen Hagert 67

Public Schs..Principal	Grd	Prgm	Enr/#Cls	SN	
Stamford Central Sch 1 River St, Stamford 12167 Shawn Davis	PK-12	T	270 56	59%	607/652-7301

- **Walton Central School Dist** PID: 00721319   607/865-4116
  47-49 Stockton Ave, Walton 13856   Fax 607/865-8568

Schools: 3 \ **Teachers:** 88 \ **Students:** 900 \ **Special Ed Students:** 169 \ **LEP Students:** 3 \ **College-Bound:** 68% \ **Ethnic:** Asian 1%, African American 1%, Hispanic 3%, Caucasian 95% \ **Exp:** $210 (Med) \ **Poverty:** 24% \ **Title I:** $517,616 \ **Special Education:** $2,524,000 \ **Open-Close:** 09/09 - 06/24 \ **DTBP:** $281 (High)

Michael McDonald 1
Meg Hungerford 2,298
Kim Corcoran 4*
Justin Preston 6,69*
Amanda Hoover 11,57,296*
Elizabeth Howland 37
Tara Sackett 58
David Potter 73
Leah Campbell 2
John Jackson 3
Tracy Williams 5
Jane Oshea 8,286,288
Barbara Geidel 16*
Karen Gilbertson 38*
Ronda Williams 67
Richard Robinson 76,295

Public Schs..Principal	Grd	Prgm	Enr/#Cls	SN	
Dr George F Mack Middle Sch 47 Stockton Ave 49, Walton 13856 Robert Knuschke	6-8		218 25	40%	607/865-4116 Fax 607/865-8658
O'Neill High Sch 47 Stockton Ave 49, Walton 13856 Arthur Loomis	9-12	AV	267 25		607/865-4116 Fax 607/865-8658

1	Superintendent	8	Curric/Instruct K-12	19	Chief Financial Officer	29	Family/Consumer Science	39	Social Studies K-12	49	English/Lang Arts Elem	59	Special Education Elem	69	Academic Assessment
2	Bus/Finance/Purchasing	9	Curric/Instruct Elem	20	Art K-12	30	Adult Education	40	Social Studies Elem	50	English/Lang Arts Sec	60	Special Education Sec	70	Research/Development
3	Buildings And Grounds	10	Curric/Instruct Sec	21	Art Elem	31	Career/Sch-to-Work K-12	41	Social Studies Sec	51	Reading K-12	61	Foreign/World Lang K-12	71	Public Information
4	Food Service	11	Federal Program	22	Art Sec	32	Career/Sch-to-Work Elem	42	Science K-12	52	Reading Elem	62	Foreign/World Lang Elem	72	Summer School
5	Transportation	12	Title I	23	Music K-12	33	Career/Sch-to-Work Sec	43	Science Elem	53	Reading Sec	63	Foreign/World Lang Sec	73	Instructional Tech
6	Athletic	13	Title V	24	Music Elem	34	Early Childhood Ed	44	Science Sec	54	Remedial Reading K-12	64	Religious Education K-12	74	Inservice Training
7	Health Services	15	Asst Superintendent	25	Music Sec	35	Health/Phys Education	45	Math K-12	55	Remedial Reading Elem	65	Religious Education Elem	75	Marketing/Distributive
		16	Instructional Media Svcs	26	Business Education	36	Guidance Services K-12	46	Math Elem	56	Remedial Reading Sec	66	Religious Education Sec	76	Info Systems
		17	Chief Operations Officer	27	Career & Tech Ed	37	Guidance Services Elem	47	Math Sec	57	Bilingual/ELL	67	School Board President	77	Psychological Assess
		18	Chief Academic Officer	28	Technology Education	38	Guidance Services Sec	48	English/Lang Arts K-12	58	Special Education K-12	68	Teacher Personnel	78	Affirmative Action

New York School Directory — Dutchess County

Townsend Elem Sch 42-66 North St, Walton 13856 Amanda Hoover	PK-5	T	411 28	41%	607/865-5220 Fax 607/865-9211

DELAWARE REGIONAL CENTERS

- **Onc BOCES** PID: 00721371   607/588-6291
  2020 Jump Brook Rd, Grand Gorge 12434   Fax 607/588-6808

Nicholas Savin 1,11		Lynn Chase 2,3,4	
Mica Thorsland 4		Joe Booan 8,15,27,30,58	
Dr Jennifer Avery 15		Eileen Coryat 16	
Jason Sanchez 58		Paul Beisler 67	
Diane Matteson 68		Anne Pallischeck 73	
Bonnie Johnson 74		Genevieve Ballard 76	

DUTCHESS COUNTY

DUTCHESS COUNTY SCHOOLS

County Schs..Principal	Grd	Prgm	Enr/#Cls	SN	
Career & Technical Institute 5 Boces Rd, Poughkeepsie 12601 Mitchell Shron	Voc	AG	1,000 45		845/486-8001 Fax 845/486-8171
Salt Point Center 5 Boces Rd, Poughkeepsie 12601 Melissa Murphy	Spec		220		845/486-8004 Fax 845/486-8044

DUTCHESS PUBLIC SCHOOLS

- **Arlington Central School Dist** PID: 00721400   845/486-4460
  144 Todd Hill Rd, Lagrangeville 12540   Fax 845/486-4457

> **Schools:** 11 \ **Teachers:** 615 \ **Students:** 7,000 \ **Special Ed Students:** 1,556 \ **LEP Students:** 191 \ **College-Bound:** 92% \ **Ethnic:** Asian 4%, African American 8%, Hispanic 17%, Caucasian 71% \ **Exp:** $271 (Med) \ **Poverty:** 6% \ **Title I:** $921,644 \ **Special Education:** $13,499,000 \ **Open-Close:** 09/09 - 06/24 \ **DTBP:** $249 (High) \ 📘

Lorenzo Licopoli 1	Kevin Sheldon 2,15
John Willson 3,91	Joseph Mascarenhas 3
Mark Hicks 4*	Daniel McNamara 5
Michael Cring 6,35*	Dana Brown 8,39,48,57,280
Dr Tina Desa 11,15,79,83	Dr Alfred Brown 15,288,296
Paul Finch 15,68	Ellen McDonell 16,73,295
Richard Guillen 23*	Karen Turcio 30
Karen Turcio 30*	Dawn Galente 42,45,285
Alysha Hershey 58	Carole Davies 58
Margaret Fitzgerald 58	Maria Wrobel 58
Michelle Bahn 58	Vanessa Weeks 58
Peter Bodnar 67	Danielle Pitcher 73
Robert Carroll 76	

Public Schs..Principal	Grd	Prgm	Enr/#Cls	SN	
Arlington High Sch 1157 Route 55, Lagrangeville 12540 Paul Fanuele	9-12	GV	2,835	25%	845/486-4860 Fax 845/350-4204
Arthur S May Elem Sch 601 Dutchess Tpke, Poughkeepsie 12603 Sheri Primeaux	K-5	T	502 35	43%	845/486-4960 Fax 845/350-4122
Beekman Elem Sch 201 Lime Ridge Rd, Poughquag 12570 Matthew Latvis	K-5		445 26	22%	845/227-1834 Fax 845/350-4151
Joseph D'Aquanni West Road IS 181 West Rd, Pleasant Vly 12569 Heather Ogborn 📘	3-5		384	32%	845/635-4310 Fax 845/350-4126
LaGrange Middle Sch 110 Stringham Rd, Lagrangeville 12540 Eric Schetter	6-8	V	916	38%	845/486-4880 Fax 845/486-8863
Noxon Road Elem Sch 4 Old Noxon Rd, Poughkeepsie 12603 Kelly Murray	K-5		309 17	17%	845/486-4950 Fax 845/350-4133
Overlook Primary Sch 11 Mapleview Road Ext, Poughkeepsie 12603 Jessica Wheeler	K-2		391 18	33%	845/486-4970 Fax 845/350-4134
Titusville Intermediate Sch 128 Meadow Ln, Poughkeepsie 12603 Richard Sutton	3-5		367 21	39%	845/486-4470 Fax 845/350-4143
Traver Road Primary Sch 801 Traver Rd, Pleasant Vly 12569 Cara Conrad	K-2		310 17	32%	845/635-4300 Fax 845/350-4125
Union Vale Middle Sch 1657 E Noxon Rd, Lagrangeville 12540 Scott Wood	6-8		901	18%	845/223-8600 Fax 845/223-8610
Vail Farm Elem Sch 1659 E Noxon Rd, Lagrangeville 12540 Claudine Khare	K-5		603	18%	845/223-8030 Fax 845/350-4150

- **Beacon City School Dist** PID: 00721527   845/838-6900
  10 Education Dr, Beacon 12508   Fax 845/838-6905

> **Schools:** 6 \ **Teachers:** 243 \ **Students:** 3,200 \ **Special Ed Students:** 621 \ **LEP Students:** 60 \ **College-Bound:** 85% \ **Ethnic:** Asian 3%, African American 17%, Hispanic 33%, Caucasian 47% \ **Exp:** $376 (High) \ **Poverty:** 10% \ **Title I:** $579,313 \ **Special Education:** $6,780,000 \ **Open-Close:** 09/04 - 06/25 \ **DTBP:** $313 (High)

Dr Matthew Landahl 1	Anthony Damato 3
Karen Pagano 4	Ron Mackey 5
John Giametta 6,7,35*	Erik Wright 8,15,69
Dawn Condello 11,58,79,81,85,88,90	Cassandra Orser 34*
Meredith Heuer 67	Michael Keley 73
Julisa Tomizawa 79	

Public Schs..Principal	Grd	Prgm	Enr/#Cls	SN	
Beacon High Sch 101 Matteawan Rd, Beacon 12508 Elisa Soto	9-12		900 60	41%	845/838-6900 Fax 845/838-0796
Glenham Elem Sch 20 Chase Dr, Fishkill 12524 Cassandra Orser	PK-5		390 23	36%	845/838-6900 Fax 845/838-6976
J V Forrestal Elem Sch 125 Liberty St, Beacon 12508 Crystal Sessoms	PK-5	T	269 16	46%	845/838-6900 Fax 845/838-0792
Rombout Middle Sch 84 Matteawan Rd, Beacon 12508 Brian Soltish	6-8	T	625 42	41%	845/838-6900 Fax 845/231-0474
Sargent Elem Sch 29 Education Dr, Beacon 12508 Brian Archer	PK-5	T	287 19	43%	845/838-6900 Fax 845/838-6978
South Avenue Elem Sch 60 South Ave, Beacon 12508 Laura Cahill	K-5	T	343 20	50%	845/838-6900 Fax 845/838-6922

---

79 Student Personnel	91 Safety/Security	275 Response To Intervention	298 Grant Writer/Ptnrships
80 Driver Ed/Safety	92 Magnet School	277 Remedial Math K-12	750 Chief Innovation Officer
81 Gifted/Talented	93 Parental Involvement	280 Literacy Coach	751 Chief of Staff
82 Video Services	95 Tech Prep Program	285 STEM	752 Social Emotional Learning
83 Substance Abuse Prev	97 Chief Infomation Officer	286 Digital Learning	
84 Erate	98 Chief Technology Officer	288 Common Core Standards	
85 AIDS Education	270 Character Education	294 Accountability	
88 Alternative/At Risk	271 Migrant Education	295 Network System	
89 Multi-Cultural Curriculum	273 Teacher Mentor	296 Title II Programs	
90 Social Work	274 Before/After Sch	297 Webmaster	

School Programs
A = Alternative Program
G = Adult Classes
M = Magnet Program
T = Title I Schoolwide
V = Career & Tech Ed Programs

Other School Types
Ⓐ = Alternative School
Ⓒ = Charter School
Ⓜ = Magnet School
Ⓨ = Year-Round School

Social Media
📘 = Facebook
🐦 = Twitter

New Schools are shaded
New Superintendents and Principals are bold
Personnel with email addresses are underscored

NY—51

Dutchess County

Market Data Retrieval

• **Dover Union Free School Dist** PID: 00721618 845/877-5700
2368 Route 22, Dover Plains 12522 Fax 845/877-5762

Schools: 4 \ **Teachers:** 116 \ **Students:** 1,352 \ **Special Ed Students:** 229 \ **LEP Students:** 84 \ **College-Bound:** 81% \ **Ethnic:** Asian 2%, African American 4%, Hispanic 27%, Caucasian 67% \ **Exp:** $274 (Med) \ **Poverty:** 13% \ **Title I:** $362,348 \ **Special Education:** $2,881,000 \ **Open-Close:** 09/02 - 06/25 \ **DTBP:** $357 (High)

Michael Tierney 1,11	Christopher Prill 2,5
Rudy Abrams 3	Carol Jankowski 4
Paul Kenny 6*	Donna Basting 8,15,68,69
Patrica Rizzo 11,58,271,273	Russel Infantino 67
Stephen Haneman 73,295*	

Public Schs..Principal	Grd	Prgm	Enr/#Cls	SN	
Dover Elem Sch 9 School St, Dover Plains 12522 Herman Harmelink	3-5	T	286 18	62%	845/877-5730 Fax 845/877-5739
Dover High Sch 2368 Route 22, Dover Plains 12522 Genie Angelis	9-12	V	435 70	52%	845/877-5750 Fax 845/877-5759
Dover Middle Sch 2368 Route 22, Dover Plains 12522 Christopher O'Connor	6-8	T	352 30	55%	845/877-5740 Fax 845/877-5749
Wingdale Elem Sch 6413 Route 55, Wingdale 12594 Dr Mary Beth Kenny	K-2	T	279 17	55%	845/877-5720 Fax 845/877-5729

• **Hyde Park Central School Dist** PID: 00721670 845/229-4000
11 Boice Rd, Hyde Park 12538 Fax 845/229-4056

Schools: 6 \ **Teachers:** 284 \ **Students:** 3,500 \ **Special Ed Students:** 661 \ **LEP Students:** 108 \ **College-Bound:** 78% \ **Ethnic:** Asian 2%, African American 13%, Hispanic 19%, Caucasian 66% \ **Exp:** $235 (Med) \ **Poverty:** 13% \ **Title I:** $895,205 \ **Special Education:** $7,189,000 \ **Open-Close:** 09/10 - 06/25 \ **DTBP:** $317 (High)

Dr Greer Rychcik 1	Linda Steinberg 2,15
Elliot Sheldon 3	George Treadwell 5
Thomas Cunningham 6,7,35*	Aviva Kafka 8,11,57,74,83,88,91,285
Melinda Dimaio 20,23	Kim Knisell 42,45*
Jennifer Criser-Eighmy 50,280	Heather Dennis 58
Andrew Dease 59	Joanna Murphy 60
Denise Biery 67	Rick Wert 73,76,95,286,295*

Public Schs..Principal	Grd	Prgm	Enr/#Cls	SN	
F D Roosevelt High Sch 156 S Cross Road, Hyde Park 12538 Rick Pardy	9-12	AV	1,163 74	44%	845/229-4020 Fax 845/229-4029
Haviland Middle Sch 23 Haviland Rd, Hyde Park 12538 Eric Shaw	6-8	AV	832 50	53%	845/229-4030 Fax 845/229-2475
Netherwood Elem Sch 648 Netherwood Rd, Hyde Park 12538 James Daley	K-5	T	278 23	44%	845/229-4055 Fax 845/229-2797
North Park Elem Sch 1593 Route 9G, Hyde Park 12538 Lynnette Williams	K-5	T	466 19	50%	845/229-4040 Fax 845/229-5655
Ralph R Smith Elem Sch 16 Smith Ct, Hyde Park 12538 Melissa Lawson	K-5	T	378 16	51%	845/229-4060 Fax 845/229-2828
Violet Avenue Elem Sch 191 Violet Ave, Poughkeepsie 12601 Deanna Gonzalez	K-5	T	289 21	64%	845/486-4499 Fax 845/486-7796

• **Millbrook Ctl School Dist** PID: 00721785 845/677-4200
43 Alden Pl, Millbrook 12545 Fax 845/677-4206

Schools: 4 \ **Teachers:** 91 \ **Students:** 875 \ **Special Ed Students:** 204 \ **LEP Students:** 19 \ **College-Bound:** 87% \ **Ethnic:** Asian 1%, African American 2%, Hispanic 14%, Caucasian 83% \ **Exp:** $343 (High) \ **Poverty:** 8% \ **Title I:** $147,245 \ **Special Education:** $1,314,000 \ **Open-Close:** 09/08 - 06/25 \ **DTBP:** $369 (High)

Laura Mitchell 1	Ashley Burhans 2
Brian Fried 2,15,298	Michael Ragusa 3
Holly Heady 4	Caroline Pidala 8,11,38,58,79,288,296
Tom Libka 9,57*	Kelly Mahoney 31,271*
Tom Chanowski 33*	Lauren Prince 38*
Perry Hartswick 67	Elliot Garcia 73
Jessica Gilmour 83,85*	

Public Schs..Principal	Grd	Prgm	Enr/#Cls	SN	
Alden Place Elem Sch 41 Alden Pl, Millbrook 12545 Tom Libka	3-5		197 11	29%	845/677-4220 Fax 845/677-4213
Elm Drive Elem Sch 12 Elm Dr, Millbrook 12545 Karen Ferguson	K-2		176 11	26%	845/677-4225 Fax 845/677-4224
Millbrook High Sch 70 Church St, Millbrook 12545 Eric Seipp	9-12	V	295	28%	845/677-2510 Fax 845/677-2525
Millbrook Middle Sch 43 Alden Pl, Millbrook 12545 Steven Cabello	6-8	V	212 40	28%	845/677-4210 Fax 845/677-6913

• **Pawling Ctl School Dist** PID: 00721826 845/855-4600
515 Route 22, Pawling 12564 Fax 845/855-4612

Schools: 3 \ **Teachers:** 95 \ **Students:** 1,100 \ **Special Ed Students:** 151 \ **LEP Students:** 64 \ **College-Bound:** 93% \ **Ethnic:** Asian 2%, African American 2%, Hispanic 21%, Caucasian 75% \ **Exp:** $743 (High) \ **Poverty:** 5% \ **Title I:** $123,952 \ **Special Education:** $1,812,000 \ **Open-Close:** 09/08 - 06/25 \ **DTBP:** $385 (High)

Kim Fontana 1	Janet Heubel 2
Mimi Henslin 2,15	Gary Green 3
Lauren Collica 4	Delos Luther 5
Tamara Anne Barbour 6	Debra Kirkhus ... 11,69,273,288,294,295,296,298
Joan Roberts 28,76*	Michelle Rivas 57
Scott Rice 58,79	Karen Burka 67
Christopher Quinones 73	

Public Schs..Principal	Grd	Prgm	Enr/#Cls	SN	
Pawling Central Middle Sch 80 Wagner Dr, Pawling 12564 Megan Gleason	5-8		356	28%	845/855-4653 Fax 845/855-4134
Pawling Elem Sch 7 Haight St, Pawling 12564 Jennifer Jacobs	K-4		381 27	36%	845/855-4607 Fax 845/855-4636
Pawling High Sch 30 Wagner Dr, Pawling 12564 Helen Callan	9-12		378 35	24%	845/855-4620 Fax 845/855-2029

1	Superintendent	8	Curric/Instruct K-12	19	Chief Financial Officer	29	Family/Consumer Science	39	Social Studies K-12	49	English/Lang Arts Elem	59	Special Education Elem	69	Academic Assessment
2	Bus/Finance/Purchasing	9	Curric/Instruct Elem	20	Art K-12	30	Adult Education	40	Social Studies Elem	50	English/Lang Arts Sec	60	Special Education Sec	70	Research/Development
3	Buildings And Grounds	10	Curric/Instruct Sec	21	Art Elem	31	Career/Sch-to-Work K-12	41	Social Studies Sec	51	Reading K-12	61	Foreign/World Lang K-12	71	Public Information
4	Food Service	11	Federal Program	22	Art Sec	32	Career/Sch-to-Work Elem	42	Science K-12	52	Reading Elem	62	Foreign/World Lang Elem	72	Summer School
5	Transportation	12	Title I	23	Music K-12	33	Career/Sch-to-Work Sec	43	Science Elem	53	Reading Sec	63	Foreign/World Lang Sec	73	Instructional Tech
6	Athletic	13	Title V	24	Music Elem	34	Early Childhood Ed	44	Science Sec	54	Remedial Reading K-12	64	Religious Education K-12	74	Inservice Training
7	Health Services	15	Asst Superintendent	25	Music Sec	35	Health/Phys Education	45	Math K-12	55	Remedial Reading Elem	65	Religious Education Elem	75	Marketing/Distributive
		16	Instructional Media Svcs	26	Business Education	36	Guidance Services K-12	46	Math Elem	56	Remedial Reading Sec	66	Religious Education Sec	76	Info Systems
		17	Chief Operations Officer	27	Career & Tech Ed	37	Guidance Services Elem	47	Math Sec	57	Bilingual/ELL	67	School Board President	77	Psychological Assess
		18	Chief Academic Officer	28	Technology Education	38	Guidance Services Sec	48	English/Lang Arts K-12	58	Special Education K-12	68	Teacher Personnel	78	Affirmative Action

New York School Directory — Dutchess County

- **Pine Plains Ctl School Dist** PID: 00721852 518/398-7181
  2829 Church St, Pine Plains 12567 Fax 518/398-6592

  Schools: 3 \ **Teachers:** 90 \ **Students:** 905 \ **Special Ed Students:** 177 \ **LEP Students:** 21 \ **College-Bound:** 82% \ **Ethnic:** Asian 1%, Hispanic 14%, Caucasian 85% \ **Exp:** $402 (High) \ **Poverty:** 10% \ **Title I:** $163,605 \ **Special Education:** $1,916,000 \ **Open-Close:** 09/09 - 06/25

Dr Martin Handler 1	Margaret Bonneville 2
Michael Goldbeck 2,15	Michael Remsburger 3
Richard McKibben 3	Lawrence Anthony 4
Drew Weaver 5	Robert Scott 6
Brian Timm 8	Maryann Stoorvogel 12,58,83,88,298*
Jack Edwards 31,88*	Jeremy Weber 35*
Fred Couse 67	Richard Harlin 73,286*
Patricia DeCato 78	Rebecca Green 79

Public Schs..Principal	Grd	Prgm	Enr/#Cls	SN	
Cold Spring Early Lrng Ctr 358 Homan Rd, Stanfordville 12581 Gian Starr	PK-1	T	156 13	42%	845/868-7451 Fax 845/868-1105
Seymour Smith Inter Lrng Ctr 41 Academy St, Pine Plains 12567 Julie Roberts	2-5		241 20	46%	518/398-3000 Fax 518/398-1141
Stissing Mountain Jr Sr HS 2829 Church St, Pine Plains 12567 Tara Grieb	6-12	AG	508 30	36%	518/398-7181 Fax 518/398-5804

- **Poughkeepsie City School Dist** PID: 00721890 845/867-6194
  18 S Perry St, Poughkeepsie 12601 Fax 845/451-4973

  Schools: 8 \ **Teachers:** 326 \ **Students:** 4,420 \ **Special Ed Students:** 959 \ **LEP Students:** 471 \ **College-Bound:** 70% \ **Ethnic:** Asian 1%, African American 53%, Hispanic 39%, Caucasian 7% \ **Exp:** $326 (High) \ **Poverty:** 27% \ **Title I:** $2,147,202 \ **Special Education:** $16,024,000 \ **Open-Close:** 09/04 - 06/25 \ **DTBP:** $313 (High)

Dr Eric Rosser 1	Steve Schloicka 2,3,15
John Willabay 3	David Dunn 4*
Dawn Rodger 5	Christian Hodge 6,35
Dr Elizabeth Ten Dyke 8,11,15,294	Sean Daneshvar 16,73
Dr Felisha Watson 67	Dr Elizabeth Dyke 76
Yvonne Palmer 79	

Public Schs..Principal	Grd	Prgm	Enr/#Cls	SN	
Ⓨ Early Learning Center 372 Church St, Poughkeepsie 12601 Margaret Pineiro	PK-K	MT	447	33%	845/451-4721 Fax 845/437-3425
G W Krieger Elem Sch 265 Hooker Ave, Poughkeepsie 12603 Jeffrey Noto	1-5	T	510 23	71%	845/451-4661 Fax 845/451-4672
Gov George Clinton Elem Sch 100 Montgomery St, Poughkeepsie 12601 David Scott	1-5	T	312 18	74%	845/451-4600 Fax 845/451-4614
Ⓜ Morse Elem Sch 101 Mansion St, Poughkeepsie 12601 Nadine Dargan	1-5	T	555 16	82%	845/451-4690 Fax 845/451-4701
Ⓐ Pace Academy 18 S Perry St, Poughkeepsie 12601 Joseph Mazzetti	7-12		125		845/275-4102 Fax 845/451-4639
Poughkeepsie High Sch 70 Forbus St, Poughkeepsie 12603 Phee Simpson	9-12	GTV	1,153 100	71%	845/451-4850 Fax 845/451-4807
Poughkeepsie Middle Sch 55 College Ave, Poughkeepsie 12603 Dwayne D'Avilar	6-8	TV	962	78%	845/451-4800 Fax 845/451-4836
Ⓨ Warring Elem Sch 283 Mansion St, Poughkeepsie 12601 Julliet Coxum	1-5	T	375 16	81%	845/451-4750 Fax 845/451-4769

- **Red Hook Central School Dist** PID: 00721981 845/758-2241
  9 Mill Rd, Red Hook 12571 Fax 845/758-3366

  Schools: 4 \ **Teachers:** 162 \ **Students:** 1,750 \ **Special Ed Students:** 294 \ **LEP Students:** 42 \ **College-Bound:** 84% \ **Ethnic:** Asian 3%, African American 2%, Hispanic 10%, Caucasian 86% \ **Exp:** $333 (High) \ **Poverty:** 6% \ **Title I:** $264,495 \ **Special Education:** $3,443,000 \ **Open-Close:** 09/09 - 06/25 \ **DTBP:** $161 (High) \ 🇹

Janet Warden 1	Bruce Martin 2,298
Perry Sheldon 3,91	Lawrence Anthony 4*
Jeffrey Popp 5	Tom Cassata 6,7,35*
Dr Kitty Summers 8,15,57,68,74,288	Jack Costello 11,58,79,271
Donna Seelbach 16,73,82,295	Gail Jaffe-Bennek 30
Nicole Schmidt 31,36,69,83*	Kate Kortbus 67

Public Schs..Principal	Grd	Prgm	Enr/#Cls	SN	
Linden Avenue Middle Sch 65 W Market St, Red Hook 12571 Dr Katie Zahedi	6-8		405 40	29%	845/758-2241 Fax 845/758-0688
Mill Road Intermediate Sch 9 Mill Rd, Red Hook 12571 Brian Boyd	3-5		392 28	27%	845/758-2241 Fax 845/758-0385
Mill Road Primary Sch 9 Mill Rd, Red Hook 12571 Erin Hayes	PK-2		338	24%	845/758-2241 Fax 845/758-0385
Red Hook Senior High Sch 103 W Market St, Red Hook 12571 Robert McKiernan	9-12	V	653 40	22%	845/758-2241 Fax 845/758-0482

- **Rhinebeck Central School Dist** PID: 00722026 845/871-5520
  45 N Park Rd, Rhinebeck 12572 Fax 845/876-4276

  Schools: 3 \ **Teachers:** 96 \ **Students:** 1,000 \ **Special Ed Students:** 128 \ **LEP Students:** 22 \ **College-Bound:** 95% \ **Ethnic:** Asian 3%, African American 1%, Hispanic 9%, Caucasian 87% \ **Exp:** $361 (High) \ **Poverty:** 8% \ **Title I:** $219,973 \ **Special Education:** $870,000 \ **Open-Close:** 09/09 - 06/25 \ **DTBP:** $371 (High)

Albert Cousins 1	Natoli Christine 2
Sheldon Tieder 3*	Larry Anthony 4
Steve Boucher 6	Dave Aierstok 7
Marvin Kreps 8,11*	Thomas Burnell 15,79
Emily Davison 58	Diane Lyons 67
Stephen Jensen 71,73,98,295*	

Public Schs..Principal	Grd	Prgm	Enr/#Cls	SN	
Buckeley Middle Sch 45 N Park Rd, Rhinebeck 12572 John Kemnitzer	6-8		242 14	21%	845/871-5500 Fax 845/871-5553
Chancellor Livingston Elem Sch 48 Knollwood Rd, Rhinebeck 12572 Brett King	K-5		377 26	22%	845/871-5570 Fax 845/876-4174
Rhinebeck High Sch 45 N Park Rd, Rhinebeck 12572 Dr Edwin Davenport	9-12		328 30	20%	845/871-5500 Fax 845/876-8755

79 Student Personnel	91 Safety/Security	275 Response To Intervention	298 Grant Writer/Ptnrships	**School Programs**
80 Driver Ed/Safety	92 Magnet School	277 Remedial Math K-12	750 Chief Innovation Officer	A = Alternative Program
81 Gifted/Talented	93 Parental Involvement	280 Literacy Coach	751 Chief of Staff	G = Adult Classes
82 Video Services	95 Tech Prep Program	285 STEM	752 Social Emotional Learning	M = Magnet Program
83 Substance Abuse Prev	97 Chief Infomation Officer	286 Digital Learning		T = Title I Schoolwide
84 Erate	98 Chief Technology Officer	288 Common Core Standards	**Other School Types**	V = Career & Tech Ed Programs
85 AIDS Education	270 Character Education	294 Accountability	Ⓐ = Alternative School	
88 Alternative/At Risk	271 Migrant Education	295 Network System	Ⓒ = Charter School	**Social Media**
89 Multi-Cultural Curriculum	273 Teacher Mentor	296 Title II Programs	Ⓜ = Magnet School	🇫 = Facebook
90 Social Work	274 Before/After Sch	297 Webmaster	Ⓨ = Year-Round School	🇹 = Twitter

New Schools are shaded
New Superintendents and Principals are bold
Personnel with email addresses are underscored

NY—53

Dutchess County

Market Data Retrieval

- **Spackenkill Union Free SD** PID: 00722064 845/463-7800
  15 Croft Rd, Poughkeepsie 12603 Fax 845/463-7804

Schools: 4 \ **Teachers:** 143 \ **Students:** 1,500 \ **Special Ed Students:** 238 \ **LEP Students:** 32 \ **College-Bound:** 95% \ **Ethnic:** Asian 12%, African American 13%, Hispanic 14%, Caucasian 60% \ **Exp:** $284 (Med) \ **Poverty:** 5% \ **Title I:** $115,058 \ **Special Education:** $2,111,000 \ **Open-Close:** 09/09 - 06/24 \ **DTBP:** $169 (High) \

Michele Moloney 2	David Downes 3,91
Lisa French 4*	Doreen Wright 5
Marco Lanzoni 6,7,35,83*	Dr Lori Mulford 8,11,58,73,273,288,294,295
Kathleen Defreest 31*	Adam Hammond 36*
Thomas Keith 67	Brett Hasbrouck 295*

Public Schs..Principal	Grd	Prgm	Enr/#Cls	SN	
Hagan Elem Sch 42 Hagan Dr, Poughkeepsie 12603 John Farrell	3-5		303 24	21%	845/463-7840 Fax 845/463-7881
Nassau Elem Sch 7 Nassau Rd, Poughkeepsie 12601 Deborah Weisel	K-2		308 12	17%	845/463-7843 Fax 845/463-7842
Orville A Todd Middle Sch 11 Croft Rd, Poughkeepsie 12603 Daniel Doherty	6-8		370 30	26%	845/463-7830 Fax 845/463-7832
Spackenkill High Sch 112 Spackenkill Rd, Poughkeepsie 12603 Steven Malkisher	9-12	AV	467 30	25%	845/463-7810 Fax 845/463-7826

- **Wappingers Central Sch Dist** PID: 00722129 845/298-5000
  25 Corporate Park Rd, Hopewell Jct 12533 Fax 845/298-5041

Schools: 15 \ **Teachers:** 772 \ **Students:** 10,616 \ **Special Ed Students:** 1,917 \ **LEP Students:** 166 \ **College-Bound:** 85% \ **Ethnic:** Asian 4%, African American 7%, Hispanic 17%, Caucasian 71% \ **Exp:** $194 (Low) \ **Poverty:** 6% \ **Title I:** $1,015,103 \ **Special Education:** $16,681,000 \ **Open-Close:** 09/08 - 06/24 \ **DTBP:** $240 (High)

Jose Carrion 1	Kristen Crandall 2,15
Jeff Estremera 3	Ron Broas 3
Matthew Flusser 4	Kim Catalano 5,91
Kurt Jesman 6,35*	Dr Michelle Cardwell 8,15,274
Jessica Turner 9	Daren Lolkema 15,76
Dwight Bonk 15,68,273	Richard Zipp 15,58,79
Art Schouten 16,73	Bonnie King 20,23,61
Adam Panzer 27,44,47	Jeff Behnke 30
Lizzette Giovinazzi 41,50	Kerri Bohringer 57*
John Lumia 67	Amy Watkins 71

Public Schs..Principal	Grd	Prgm	Enr/#Cls	SN	
Brinckerhoff Elem Sch 16 Wedgewood Rd, Fishkill 12524 Kristin Rimmer	K-6		572 26	12%	845/897-6800 Fax 845/897-6802
Fishkill Elem Sch 20 Church St, Fishkill 12524 Dr Andrew McNally	K-6		385	28%	845/897-6780 Fax 845/897-6788
Fishkill Plains Elem Sch 17 Lake Walton Rd, Wappingers Fl 12590 Amy Fazio	K-6		537 26	17%	845/227-1770 Fax 845/227-1747
Gayhead Elem Sch 15 Entry Rd, Hopewell Jct 12533 Adam Gerson	K-6		929	13%	845/227-1756 Fax 845/227-1764
James S Evans Elem Sch 747 Sergeant Palmateer Way, Wappingers Fl 12590 Lauren Hernandez	K-6	T	326 18	38%	845/298-5240 Fax 845/298-5232

Public Schs..Principal	Grd	Prgm	Enr/#Cls	SN	
John Jay High Sch 2012 Route 52, Hopewell Jct 12533 David Kedzielawa	9-12	GV	1,960	16%	845/897-6700 Fax 845/897-6720
Kinry Road Elem Sch 58 Kinry Rd, Poughkeepsie 12603 Mary Bish	3-6		382 19	28%	845/463-7322 Fax 845/463-7327
Myers Corners Elem Sch 156 Myers Corners Rd, Wappingers Fl 12590 Sydnie Goldstein	K-6		786 40	22%	845/298-5260 Fax 845/298-5258
Oak Grove Elem Sch 40 Kerr Rd, Poughkeepsie 12601 Angelina Alvarez-Rooney	K-6		441 17	23%	845/298-5280 Fax 845/298-5270
Ⓐ Orchard View Alternative Sch 25 Corporate Park Rd, Hopewell Jct 12533 Laura DiStefano	9-12		56 6	54%	845/298-5000 Fax 845/297-6805
Roy C Ketcham Senior High Sch 99 Myers Corners Rd, Wappingers Fl 12590 David Seipp	9-12	GV	1,653 76	29%	845/298-5100 Fax 845/298-5099
Sheafe Road Elem Sch 287 Sheafe Rd, Wappingers Fl 12590 Michael Corsano	K-6	T	612 32	42%	845/298-5290 Fax 845/298-5199
Van Wyck Junior High Sch 10 Hillside Lake Rd, Wappingers Fl 12590 Steven Shuchat	7-8	V	910	18%	845/227-1700 Fax 845/227-1748
Vassar Road Elem Sch 174 Vassar Rd, Poughkeepsie 12603 Richard Dominick	K-2		264 19	18%	845/463-7860 Fax 845/463-7859
Wappingers Junior High Sch 30 Major MacDonald Way, Wappingers Fl 12590 Terrence Thompson	7-8	V	832 62	33%	845/298-5200 Fax 845/298-5156

- **Webutuck Ctl School Dist** PID: 00722272 845/373-4100
  194 Haight Rd, Amenia 12501 Fax 845/373-4102

Schools: 3 \ **Teachers:** 67 \ **Students:** 649 \ **Special Ed Students:** 149 \ **LEP Students:** 77 \ **Ethnic:** Asian 1%, African American 2%, Hispanic 22%, Caucasian 75% \ **Exp:** $346 (High) \ **Poverty:** 13% \ **Title I:** $200,417 \ **Special Education:** $1,041,000 \ **Open-Close:** 09/08 - 06/24 \ **DTBP:** $381 (High)

Raymond Castellani 1	Gazella LeJeune 2
Walt Kilmer 3	Sheila Moran 4
Jerry Heiser 5	Kathleen Pascale 6
Kathleen Howard 6	Matt Pascuale 6,35*
Katy McEnroe 8,11,79,273*	James Orr 57,271*
Jennifer Hengen 59*	Judy Moran 67
Paul Caputo 73	Cara Tomasetti 88

Public Schs..Principal	Grd	Prgm	Enr/#Cls	SN	
Eugene Brooks Intermediate Sch 194 Haight Rd, Amenia 12501 Erik Lynch	4-8	T	262 15	52%	845/373-4114 Fax 845/373-4425
Webutuck Elem Sch 175 Haight Rd, Amenia 12501 Jennifer Hengen	PK-3	T	188 12	46%	845/373-4122 Fax 845/373-4125
Webutuck High Sch 194 Haight Rd, Amenia 12501 Kathleen McEnroe	9-12		199 25	38%	845/373-4106 Fax 845/373-8529

1	Superintendent	8	Curric/Instruct K-12	19	Chief Financial Officer	29	Family/Consumer Science	
2	Bus/Finance/Purchasing	9	Curric/Instruct Elem	20	Art K-12	30	Adult Education	
3	Buildings And Grounds	10	Curric/Instruct Sec	21	Art Elem	31	Career/Sch-to-Work K-12	
4	Food Service	11	Federal Program	22	Art Sec	32	Career/Sch-to-Work Elem	
5	Transportation	12	Title I	23	Music K-12	33	Career/Sch-to-Work Sec	
6	Athletic	13	Title V	24	Music Elem	34	Early Childhood Ed	
7	Health Services	15	Asst Superintendent	25	Music Sec	35	Health/Phys Education	
		16	Instructional Media Svcs	26	Business Education	36	Guidance Services K-12	
		17	Chief Operations Officer	27	Career & Tech Ed	37	Guidance Services Elem	
		18	Chief Academic Officer	28	Technology Education	38	Guidance Services Sec	

39	Social Studies K-12	49	English/Lang Arts Elem	59	Special Education Elem	69	Academic Assessment
40	Social Studies Elem	50	English/Lang Arts Sec	60	Special Education Sec	70	Research/Development
41	Social Studies Sec	51	Reading K-12	61	Foreign/World Lang K-12	71	Public Information
42	Science K-12	52	Reading Elem	62	Foreign/World Lang Elem	72	Summer School
43	Science Elem	53	Reading Sec	63	Foreign/World Lang Sec	73	Instructional Tech
44	Science Sec	54	Remedial Reading K-12	64	Religious Education K-12	74	Inservice Training
45	Math K-12	55	Remedial Reading Elem	65	Religious Education Elem	75	Marketing/Distributive
46	Math Elem	56	Remedial Reading Sec	66	Religious Education Sec	76	Info Systems
47	Math Sec	57	Bilingual/ELL	67	School Board President	77	Psychological Assess
48	English/Lang Arts K-12	58	Special Education K-12	68	Teacher Personnel	78	Affirmative Action

New York School Directory

DUTCHESS CATHOLIC SCHOOLS

- **Archdiocese of New York Ed Off** PID: 00754976
  Listing includes only schools located in this county. See District Index for location of Diocesan Offices.

Catholic Schs..Principal	Grd	Prgm	Enr/#Cls SN	
Holy Trinity Sch 20 Springside Ave, Poughkeepsie 12603 Kathleen Spina	PK-8		300 11	845/471-0520 Fax 845/471-0309
Our Lady of Lourdes HS 131 Boardman Rd, Poughkeepsie 12603 Catherine Merryman	9-12	G	734 38	845/463-0400 Fax 845/463-0174
St Denis & St Columba Sch 849 Route 82, Hopewell Jct 12533 Sr Kathleen Marie	K-8		410 20	845/227-7777 Fax 845/226-8470
St Martin De Porres Sch 122 Cedar Valley Rd, Poughkeepsie 12603 Greg Viceroy	PK-8		265 18	845/452-4428 Fax 845/452-9013
St Mary Sch 106 Jackson St, Fishkill 12524 Thomas Hamilton	K-8		185 9	845/896-9561 Fax 845/896-8477

DUTCHESS PRIVATE SCHOOLS

Private Schs..Principal	Grd	Prgm	Enr/#Cls SN	
Abilities First Sch 24 Firemens Way, Poughkeepsie 12603 Karyn Lange	Spec		95 6	845/452-0774 Fax 845/452-7358
Anderson Center for Autism 4885 Route 9, Staatsburg 12580 Andrew Dease	Spec		130 23	845/889-4034 Fax 845/889-3104
Astor Learning Center 6339 Mill St, Rhinebeck 12572 John Kegan	Spec		70 12	845/876-4081 Fax 845/876-2020
Bethel Christian Academy 514 Shenandoah Rd, Hopewell Jct 12533 Ralph Verdu	K-12		4 1	845/226-7973
Cardinal Hayes Day Sch 3374 Franklin Ave, Millbrook 12545 Dara Russell	Spec		57	845/677-3251 Fax 845/677-0356
Devereux School In New York 40 Devereux Way, Red Hook 12571 Colleen Lynch	Spec	V	150 23	845/758-1899 Fax 845/758-1817
Dutchess Day Sch 415 Route 343, Millbrook 12545 Matthew Heard	PK-8		163 15	845/677-5014 Fax 845/677-6722
Faith Christian Academy 25 Golf Club Ln, Poughkeepsie 12601 Alex Averin	PK-12		250 15	845/462-0266 Fax 845/462-1561
Hawk Meadow Montessori Sch 110 Overlook Rd, Poughkeepsie 12603 Barbara Katavolos	PK-9		50 4	845/223-3783 Fax 845/214-0261
Kildonan Sch 425 Morse Hill Rd, Amenia 12501 Kevin Pendergast	Spec		85	845/373-8111 Fax 845/373-9793
Maplebrook Sch 5142 Route 22, Amenia 12501 Dominick Ferrusi	Spec	GV	135 12	845/373-9511 Fax 845/373-8368
Millbrook Sch 131 Millbrook School Rd, Millbrook 12545 Drew Casertano	9-12		300 30	845/677-8261 Fax 845/677-8598
Mizzentop Day Sch 64 E Main St, Pawling 12564 Karin Shultz	PK-8		120 18	845/855-7338
New Covenant Learning Center 95 Catherine St, Beacon 12508 John Kelly	PK-5		50	845/765-1292
Oakwood Friends Sch 22 Spackenkill Rd, Poughkeepsie 12603 Chad Cianfrani	6-12		150 23	845/462-4200 Fax 845/462-4251
Poughkeepsie Day Sch 260 Boardman Rd, Poughkeepsie 12603 Benedict Chant	PK-12		200 30	845/462-7600 Fax 845/462-7602
Poughkeepsie SDA Elem Sch 71 Mitchell Ave, Poughkeepsie 12603 Carol Ashe	PK-8		47 4	845/454-1781 Fax 845/790-5223
Primrose Hill Sch 23 Spring Brook Park, Rhinebeck 12572 Jennifer Nelson	PK-6		92	845/876-1226
Randolph Sch 2467 Route 9D, Wappingers Fl 12590 Joshua Kaplan	PK-5		54 10	845/297-5600 Fax 845/297-5617
Tabernacle Christian Academy 155 Academy St, Poughkeepsie 12601 Timothy Hostetter	K-12		120 12	845/454-2792 Fax 845/483-0926
Trinity-Pawling Sch 700 Route 22, Pawling 12564 Will Taylor	7-12		300 35	845/855-3100 Fax 845/855-3816
Upton Lake Christian Sch 37 Shepherds Way, Clinton Cors 12514 Barbara Marrine	K-12	G	74 11	845/266-3497 Fax 845/266-3828

DUTCHESS REGIONAL CENTERS

- **Dutchess Co BOCES** PID: 00722325   845/486-4800
  5 Boces Rd, Poughkeepsie 12601   Fax 845/486-4981

Dr Richard Hooley 1	Dr Sherre Wesley 2,15
Cole Bender 3,5	Chris Fiorentino 8,69,74,81
Cora Stempel 15	Elizabeth Hayter 27,30,31
Denise Dzikowski 58	Norah Merritt 68
Genevieve Kellam 71,298	Duane Sharrock 88
Mark Stein 286	

ERIE COUNTY

ERIE COUNTY SCHOOLS

County Schs..Principal	Grd	Prgm	Enr/#Cls SN	
Carrier Educational Center 8685 Erie Rd, Angola 14006 Brandon Wojcik	Adult	AV	200	24% 716/549-4454 Fax 716/549-1758
Ⓐ Edge Academy 1635 E Delavan Ave, Cheektowaga 14215 Robert Boccaccio	9-12		50	716/558-5050
Harkness Career & Tech Center 99 Aero Dr, Cheektowaga 14225 John Wodjeski	Voc		1,300 40	716/961-4070 Fax 716/632-1076
Kenton Career & Tech Center 151 Two Mile Creek Rd, Tonawanda 14150 Jeffrey Sikora	Voc		500	716/961-4010 Fax 716/877-6140

---

79 Student Personnel	91 Safety/Security	275 Response To Intervention	298 Grant Writer/Ptnrships	**School Programs**	**Social Media**
80 Driver Ed/Safety	92 Magnet School	277 Remedial Math K-12	750 Chief Innovation Officer	A = Alternative Program	▸ = Facebook
81 Gifted/Talented	93 Parental Involvement	280 Literacy Coach	751 Chief of Staff	G = Adult Classes	
82 Video Services	95 Tech Prep Program	285 STEM	752 Social Emotional Learning	M = Magnet Program	▸ = Twitter
83 Substance Abuse Prev	97 Chief Information Officer	286 Digital Learning		T = Title I Schoolwide	
84 Erate	98 Chief Technology Officer	288 Common Core Standards	**Other School Types**	V = Career & Tech Ed Programs	
85 AIDS Education	270 Character Education	294 Accountability	Ⓐ = Alternative School		
88 Alternative/At Risk	271 Migrant Education	295 Network System	Ⓒ = Charter School	New Schools are shaded	
89 Multi-Cultural Curriculum	273 Teacher Mentor	296 Title II Programs	Ⓜ = Magnet School	New Superintendents and Principals are bold	
90 Social Work	274 Before/After Sch	297 Webmaster	Ⓨ = Year-Round School	Personnel with email addresses are underscored	

NY–55

Erie County

Market Data Retrieval

Lake Shore Career & Tech Acad 8685 Erie Rd, Angola 14006 Robert Merkle	Voc	G	200 4	716/549-4454 Fax 716/549-1248	
ⓐ Northtowns Academy 333 Dexter Ter, Tonawanda 14150 Robert Boccaccio	7-12		150	716/961-4040 Fax 716/694-5576	
Potter Career & Tech Center 705 Potters Rd, West Seneca 14224 Donna Mann	Voc		600	716/821-7331 Fax 716/821-7342	
ⓐ Southtown Academy 4540 Southwestern Blvd, Hamburg 14075 Gary Braun	9-12		150	716/961-4060 Fax 716/312-0947	
Wallace D Ormsby Center 1010 Center St, East Aurora 14052 Thomas Huebert	Voc	AG	470 20	716/652-8250	

ERIE PUBLIC SCHOOLS

● **Akron Central School Dist** PID: 00722430   716/542-5010
47 Bloomingdale Ave, Akron 14001   Fax 716/542-5018

Schools: 3 \ **Teachers:** 111 \ **Students:** 1,500 \ **Special Ed Students:** 203 \ **LEP Students:** 3 \ **College-Bound:** 75% \ **Ethnic:** Asian 1%, African American 1%, Hispanic 1%, Native American: 12%, Caucasian 85% \ **Exp:** $363 (High) \ **Poverty:** 10% \ **Title I:** $239,955 \ **Special Education:** $2,879,000 \ **Open-Close:** 09/08 - 06/24 \ **DTBP:** $163 (High)

Patrick McCabe	1	Cynthia Tretter	2	
Michael Coram	3	Barbara Goodman	4	
Mark Alexander	5	Dr Taweeton Farrar	8,11,71,97	
Timothy Dunham	58,77*	James Grant	67	
Douglas Dailey	73			

Public Schs..Principal	Grd	Prgm	Enr/#Cls	SN	
Akron Elem Sch 47 Bloomingdale Ave, Akron 14001 Todd Esposito	PK-5	T	588 43	46%	716/542-5050
Akron High Sch 47 Bloomingdale Ave, Akron 14001 Brandon Ricci	9-12	AV	462 70	32%	716/542-5030
Akron Middle Sch 47 Bloomingdale Ave, Akron 14001 Joseph Caprio	6-8	AT	311 20	45%	716/542-5040

● **Alden Central School Dist** PID: 00722466   716/937-9116
13190 Park St, Alden 14004   Fax 716/937-7132

Schools: 4 \ **Teachers:** 128 \ **Students:** 1,581 \ **Special Ed Students:** 215 \ **LEP Students:** 5 \ **College-Bound:** 72% \ **Ethnic:** African American 1%, Hispanic 1%, Caucasian 97% \ **Exp:** $289 (Med) \ **Poverty:** 7% \ **Title I:** $243,971 \ **Special Education:** $3,348,000 \ **Open-Close:** 09/03 - 06/25 \ **DTBP:** $161 (High)

Adam Stoltman	1	Pam Millar	2	
Paul Karpik	2,3	Anita Trautwein	4	
Debbie Hoffman	5	Nancy Rusinski	8,11,88	
Sharon Hance	8,34,58,74,79,273,288*	Frank Rizzo	16,71,73,97*	
Lynn Koelbl	30	Jill Hopcia	67	
Judy Baumgartner	83,90*			

Public Schs..Principal	Grd	Prgm	Enr/#Cls	SN	
Alden High Sch 13190 Park St, Alden 14004 Kevin Ryan	9-12	GV	511 65	29%	716/937-9116 Fax 716/937-1740
Alden Intermediate Sch 1648 Crittenden Rd, Alden 14004 John Mikulski	3-5		326	28%	716/937-9116 Fax 716/937-3376
Alden Middle Sch 13250 Park St, Alden 14004 Steven Smith	6-8	V	364	28%	716/937-9116 Fax 716/937-3563
Alden Primary Sch 11197 Broadway St, Alden 14004 Michael Stepnick	K-2		380 20	29%	716/937-9116 Fax 716/937-9839

● **Amherst Central School Dist** PID: 00722521   716/362-3000
55 Kings Hwy, Amherst 14226   Fax 716/836-2537

Schools: 4 \ **Teachers:** 257 \ **Students:** 2,990 \ **Special Ed Students:** 465 \ **LEP Students:** 178 \ **College-Bound:** 81% \ **Ethnic:** Asian 8%, African American 16%, Hispanic 6%, Caucasian 71% \ **Exp:** $200 (Med) \ **Poverty:** 9% \ **Title I:** $444,461 \ **Special Education:** $3,860,000 \ **Open-Close:** 09/08 - 06/23 \ **DTBP:** $74 (Low) \

Anthony Panella	1	Barbara Williams	2	
Laura Bosinski	2,13	Mark Rampado	3	
Tracey Ogilvie	4	Darcy Daigler	5,30	
Jeffrey Wheaton	6,35	Dr Lynn Shanahan	8,15,73	
Michael Belle-Isle	15,58,68,71,79	Amy Steger	34	
Maria Oddo	57	Paul Steimle	67	
Daniel Farley	71,97	Donna Frymire	73	
Brandon Watson	295,297			

Public Schs..Principal	Grd	Prgm	Enr/#Cls	SN	
Amherst Central High Sch 4301 Main St, Amherst 14226 Gregory Pigeon	9-12	V	874 70	24%	716/362-8100 Fax 716/836-4972
Amherst Middle Sch 55 Kings Hwy, Amherst 14226 John Griesmer	6-8	GV	705 79	31%	716/362-7100 Fax 716/836-0193
Smallwood Drive Elem Sch 300 Smallwood Dr, Amherst 14226 Daniel Lewis	K-5		654 30	17%	716/362-2100 Fax 716/839-3578
Windermere Blvd Elem Sch 291 Windermere Blvd, Amherst 14226 Julie Flanagan	PK-5		757 35	40%	716/362-4100 Fax 716/838-3764

● **Buffalo Public Schools** PID: 00722557   716/816-3500
65 Niagara Sq Rm 2201, Buffalo 14202   Fax 716/851-3033

Schools: 68 \ **Teachers:** 2,810 \ **Students:** 33,428 \ **Special Ed Students:** 9,397 \ **LEP Students:** 5,605 \ **College-Bound:** 80% \ **Ethnic:** Asian 10%, African American 47%, Hispanic 21%, Native American: 1%, Caucasian 20% \ **Exp:** $428 (High) \ **Poverty:** 36% \ **Title I:** $34,136,104 \ **Special Education:** $115,082,000 \ **Open-Close:** 09/08 - 06/24 \ **DTBP:** $203 (High) \

Dr Kriner Cash	1	Geoffrey Pritchard	2,19	
Keith Robertson	2,15,298	Teresa Turpin	2	
Dr Kevin Eberle	3	Bridget Wood	4	
Ruth Conner	4	Albert Diamico	5	
Robin Craddock	5	Cecelie Owens	6,15,35	
Holly Dickerson	7	Anne Botticelli	8,18,74,273	
Dr Fatima Morrell	8,15,69,271,288	Kelly Baudo	8,15,16,69	
Tatiana Merrick	8	Jaime Cohen	11	
Maria Fasolino	11	Richard Dombkowski	11	
Casandra Wright	15,27	Darren Brown	15,751	
Dr Eric Rosser	15,79,83,85	James Weimer	15,17	

---

1 Superintendent	8 Curric/Instruct K-12	19 Chief Financial Officer	29 Family/Consumer Science	39 Social Studies K-12	49 English/Lang Arts Elem	59 Special Education Elem	69 Academic Assessment
2 Bus/Finance/Purchasing	9 Curric/Instruct Elem	20 Art K-12	30 Adult Education	40 Social Studies Elem	50 English/Lang Arts Sec	60 Special Education Sec	70 Research/Development
3 Buildings And Grounds	10 Curric/Instruct Sec	21 Art Elem	31 Career/Sch-to-Work K-12	41 Social Studies Sec	51 Reading K-12	61 Foreign/World Lang K-12	71 Public Information
4 Food Service	11 Federal Program	22 Art Sec	32 Career/Sch-to-Work Elem	42 Science K-12	52 Reading Elem	62 Foreign/World Lang Elem	72 Summer School
5 Transportation	12 Title I	23 Music K-12	33 Career/Sch-to-Work Sec	43 Science Elem	53 Reading Sec	63 Foreign/World Lang Sec	73 Instructional Tech
6 Athletic	13 Title V	24 Music Elem	34 Early Childhood Ed	44 Science Sec	54 Remedial Reading K-12	64 Religious Education K-12	74 Inservice Training
7 Health Services	15 Asst Superintendent	25 Music Sec	35 Health/Phys Education	45 Math K-12	55 Remedial Reading Elem	65 Religious Education Elem	75 Marketing/Distributive
	16 Instructional Media Svcs	26 Business Education	36 Guidance Services K-12	46 Math Elem	56 Remedial Reading Sec	66 Religious Education Sec	76 Info Systems
	17 Chief Operations Officer	27 Career & Tech Ed	37 Guidance Services Elem	47 Math Sec	57 Bilingual/ELL	67 School Board President	77 Psychological Assess
	18 Chief Academic Officer	28 Technology Education	38 Guidance Services Sec	48 English/Lang Arts K-12	58 Special Education K-12	68 Teacher Personnel	78 Affirmative Action

New York School Directory — Erie County

Name	Page
Jamie Warren	15,68
Nadia Nashir	15,57
Michele Agosto	20*
Robert Harris	27
Susan Tunis	34
Ann Collesano	36
Woody Brandy	39
Robyn Tate	45,58
Barbara Shea	51,280
Jenna Colerick	57
Rosemarie Colon	57
Kyle Morrison	58
Herbert Cadle	68
Edward Kuzan	70,294
Elena Cala	71
Eric Stockmeyer	73
Sarah Edwards	73
Ann Zsebehazy	76,294
Crista Scheiten	79
Joseph Argo	79
Maria Conrad	88*
Ramona Reynolds	93
Danielle Schwanekamp	298
Kim Hoelscher	15,58
Sabatino Cimato	15
James Schwanz	23*
Jessica Sipes	34
Dr Sue Baldwin	35
Martha Younger	36
Jadawn Wagstaff	45
Julie Romain	48,54
Jane Byrnes	51
Pietro Mendola	57,61
Wilfredo Garcia	57
Sharon Belton-Cottman	67
Anne Henry-Montante	69
Marianne Dixon	70
Dr Genelle Morris	71,97,294
Michael Hume	73,76
William Russo	73
Carmen Milioto	79
Eileen Bohen	79
Kelli Daniels	79
Lori Conroy	91
Angela Ryan	297

Public Schs..Principal	Grd	Prgm	Enr/#Cls	SN		
Adult Education Center 389 Virginia St, Buffalo 14201 Amanda Vellake	Adult	V	300 10		716/888-7088 Fax 716/888-7097	
Buffalo Sch Culinary-Hospitly 75 W Huron St, Buffalo 14202 Katie Schuta	9-12	V	386		716/816-4778 Fax 716/847-8490	
Career Collegiate Institute 756 Saint Lawrence Ave, Buffalo 14216 Lisa Baines	Adult		100		716/838-7404 Fax 716/888-7097	
ⒸEnterprise Charter Sch 275 Oak St Ste 100, Buffalo 14203 Andrew Prinzing	K-8	T	405 28	100%	716/855-2114 Fax 716/855-2967	
Lewis J Bennett Sch Innov Tech 2885 Main St, Buffalo 14214 Carlos Alvarez	9-10	GTV	80 50	78%	716/816-4250 Fax 716/838-7507	
Ⓜ PS 3 D'Youville Porter Campus 255 Porter Ave, Buffalo 14201 Freddy Barrera	PK-8	T	625 29	82%	716/816-3120 Fax 716/888-7004	
Ⓜ PS 6 Buffalo ES of Tech 414 S Division St, Buffalo 14204 Karen Piotrowski	PK-8	TV	592 50	81%	716/816-3767 Fax 716/816-3770 ❑❑	
PS 17 Early Childhood Center 1045 W Delavan Ave, Buffalo 14209 Marianna Cecchini	PK-4	T	387 32	71%	716/816-3150 Fax 716/888-7023	
PS 18 Pantoja Sch Excellance 750 West Ave, Buffalo 14213 Aakta Patel	PK-8	T	481 50	84%	716/816-3160 Fax 716/888-7036	
Ⓜ PS 19 Native American Mag Sch 97 W Delavan Ave, Buffalo 14213 Michael Suwala	PK-8	T	402 24	83%	716/816-3180 Fax 716/888-7042 ❑❑	
PS 27 Hillery Park Elem Sch 73 Pawnee Pkwy, Buffalo 14210 Vincent Vanderlip	PK-8	T	671 24	69%	716/816-4770 Fax 716/828-4771	
Ⓜ PS 30 Frank A Sedita Academy 21 Lowell Pl, Buffalo 14213 Rafael Perez	PK-8	T	803	86%	716/816-3220 Fax 716/888-2032	
PS 31 Harriet Ross Tubman Sch 212 Stanton St, Buffalo 14212 Heather Short-English	PK-8	T	499 16	80%	716/816-3780 Fax 716/851-3787	
Ⓜ PS 32 Bennett Park Mont Sch 342 Clinton St, Buffalo 14204 Jennifer Stockmeyer	PK-8	T	705 20	66%	716/816-4603 Fax 716/851-3895	
Ⓜ PS 33 Bilingual Center 157 Elk St, Buffalo 14210 Hadassa Bachellor	PK-8	T	445 25	84%	716/816-4783 Fax 716/828-4786	
Ⓜ PS 37 Futures Academy 295 Carlton St, Buffalo 14204 Serena Restivo	PK-8	T	528 35	70%	716/816-3800 Fax 716/851-3796	
PS 42 Occ Training Center 2495 Main St Ste 100, Buffalo 14214 Thomas Vitale	Spec	TV	75 9	92%	716/816-3250 Fax 716/838-2226	
PS 43 Lovejoy Discovery Sch 161 Benzinger St, Buffalo 14206 Orniece Hill	PK-8	T	630 23	76%	716/816-3260 Fax 716/897-8012	
PS 45 International Sch 141 Hoyt St, Buffalo 14213 Lynn Piccirillo	PK-6	T	836 78	85%	716/816-3300 Fax 718/888-7074	
Ⓜ PS 48 at 39 MLK Multcltrl Inst 487 High St, Buffalo 14211 Miguel Medina	PK-8	V	610 44		716/816-3240 Fax 716/888-7014	
PS 50 North Park Cmty Sch 780 Parkside Ave, Buffalo 14216 Carla Graves	PK-K	T	66	18%	716/816-3440 Fax 716/838-7448	
PS 53 Community Sch 329 Roehrer Ave, Buffalo 14208 Denisca Thompson	PK-8	T	493 30	81%	716/816-3330 Fax 716/888-7099	
PS 54 Dr George Blackman ECC 2358 Main St, Buffalo 14214 Gregory Johnson	PK-4	T	454 25	70%	716/816-3340 Fax 716/838-7403	
PS 59 Annex 50 A St, Buffalo 14211 Mirlene Dere	PK-2		356 25		716/816-4120 Fax 716/897-8105	
Ⓜ PS 59 Dr Drew Science Mag Sch 1 Martin Luther King Park, Buffalo 14211 Mirlene Dere	3-8	T	450 19	81%	716/816-3370 Fax 716/897-8049	
PS 61 Arthur Eve-Distinction 453 Leroy Ave, Buffalo 14215 Parette Walker	PK-4	T	290 30	76%	716/816-3400 Fax 716/838-7436 ❑❑	
PS 64 Frederick Law Olmsted 874 Amherst St, Buffalo 14216 Marquita Bryant	PK-4	T	550 21	24%	716/816-3420 Fax 716/871-6021 ❑❑	
PS 65 Roosevelt ECC 249 Skillen St, Buffalo 14207 Michelle Hope-Barnes	PK-4	T	333 23	64%	716/816-3430 Fax 716/871-6031	
PS 66 North Park Mid Academy 780 Parkside Ave, Buffalo 14216 Rose Schneider	5-8	TV	234 7	86%	716/816-3440 Fax 716/838-7448	
PS 67 Discovery Sch 911 Abbott Rd, Buffalo 14220 Karen Murray	PK-8	T	564 25	36%	716/816-4922 Fax 716/828-4925	
PS 69 Houghton Academy 1725 Clinton St, Buffalo 14206 Elaine Vandi-Kirkland	PK-8	TV	511 23	76%	716/816-4794 Fax 716/828-4797	
PS 72 Lorraine Elem Sch 71 Lorraine Ave, Buffalo 14220 Jeffrey Banks	PK-8	T	761 36	67%	716/816-4809 Fax 716/828-4811	
PS 74 Hamlin Park Sch 126 Donaldson Rd, Buffalo 14208 Patrick Cook	PK-8	T	474 30	84%	716/816-3490 Fax 716/888-7109	
Ⓜ PS 76 Herman Badillo Bil Acad 315 Carolina St, Buffalo 14201 Kathryn Foy	PK-8	GT	656 25	84%	716/816-3848 Fax 716/851-3853	
PS 79 Pfc William Grabiarz Sch 225 Lawn Ave, Buffalo 14207 Marlon Lee	PK-8	TV	658 32	77%	716/816-4040 Fax 716/871-6115	
PS 80 Highgate Heights ES 600 Highgate Ave, Buffalo 14215 Gayle Irving-White	PK-8	T	412 30	78%	716/816-4050 Fax 716/838-7475 ❑	

79	Student Personnel
80	Driver Ed/Safety
81	Gifted/Talented
82	Video Services
83	Substance Abuse Prev
84	Erate
85	AIDS Education
88	Alternative/At Risk
89	Multi-Cultural Curriculum
90	Social Work
91	Safety/Security
92	Magnet School
93	Parental Involvement
95	Tech Prep Program
97	Chief Information Officer
98	Chief Technology Officer
270	Character Education
271	Migrant Education
273	Teacher Mentor
274	Before/After Sch
275	Response To Intervention
277	Remedial Math K-12
280	Literacy Coach
285	STEM
286	Digital Learning
288	Common Core Standards
294	Accountability
295	Network System
296	Title II Programs
297	Webmaster
298	Grant Writer/Ptnrships
750	Chief Innovation Officer
751	Chief of Staff
752	Social Emotional Learning

School Programs
A = Alternative Program
G = Adult Classes
M = Magnet Program
T = Title I Schoolwide
V = Career & Tech Ed Programs

Other School Types
Ⓐ = Alternative School
Ⓒ = Charter School
Ⓜ = Magnet School
Ⓨ = Year-Round School

Social Media
❑ = Facebook
❑ = Twitter

New Schools are shaded
New Superintendents and Principals are bold
Personnel with email addresses are underscored

Erie County — Market Data Retrieval

School	Grd	Prgm	Enr/#Cls	SN	Phone/Fax	Principal
PS 81 Sch, 140 Tacoma Ave, Buffalo 14216	PK-8	T	787 / 30	64%	716/816-4060 Fax 716/871-6041	Nicholas Klaich
PS 82 Early Childhood Center, 230 Easton Ave, Buffalo 14215	PK-4	T	337 / 29	76%	716/816-4070 Fax 716/897-8073	Tracie Lewis
PS 84 Erie Co Health Center, 462 Grider St, Buffalo 14215	Spec	T	201	76%	716/816-4080 Fax 716/897-8081	Jennifer Kapsiak
Ⓜ PS 89 Dr L T Wright Sch, 106 Appenheimer Ave, Buffalo 14214	PK-8	TV	643 / 50	77%	716/816-4110 Fax 716/897-8093	Natasha Hendricks
Ⓜ PS 92 Build Cmty Sch, 340 Fougeron St, Buffalo 14211	PK-8	TV	414 / 35	91%	716/816-4140 Fax 716/897-8107	Tanika Shedrick
PS 93 Southside Elem Sch, 430 Southside Pkwy, Buffalo 14210	PK-8	T	1,002 / 58	75%	716/816-4818 Fax 716/828-4820	Patricia Dixon
PS 94 W Hertel Academy, 489 Hertel Ave, Buffalo 14207	PK-8	V	795 / 45	82%	716/816-4150 Fax 716/871-6111	Cecelie Owens
Ⓜ PS 95 Waterfront Elem Sch, 95 4th St, Buffalo 14202	PK-8	T	837 / 34	83%	716/816-3900 Fax 716/851-3861	Terrance Jenkins
PS 97 Harvey Austin Sch, 1405 Sycamore St, Buffalo 14211	PK-8	T	544	81%	716/816-4460 Fax 716/897-8162	DeMario Strickland
PS 99 Stanley Makowski ECC, 1095 Jefferson Ave, Buffalo 14208	PK-4	T	715 / 52	77%	716/816-4180 Fax 716/888-2012	Dawn DiNatale
PS 131 Academy School at 4, 425 S Park Ave, Buffalo 14204	7-8		99		716/816-7180 Fax 716/839-3943	Adriann Cofield
Ⓜ PS 156 Frederick Law Olmsted, 319 Suffolk St, Buffalo 14215	5-12	T	858 / 34	46%	716/816-4330 Fax 716/838-7530	Dr Michael Gruber
Ⓜ PS 192 Buffalo Visual Perf Art, 450 Masten Ave, Buffalo 14209	5-12	TV	689 / 60	60%	716/816-4220 Fax 716/888-7136	Jody Covington
Ⓜ PS 195 City Honors Sch, 186 E North St, Buffalo 14204	5-12	GTV	1,073 / 50	25%	716/816-4230 Fax 716/888-7145	Alexis Williams
PS 196 Math Sci Tech Prep Sch, 487 High St, Buffalo 14211	5-8		200		716/816-3501 Fax 716/888-7014	Michael Mogavero
Ⓐ PS 197 Math Sci Tech Prep Sch, 646 E Delavan Ave, Buffalo 14215	9-12		697		716/816-4500 Fax 716/897-8058	Kevin Eberle
PS 198 Int'l Prep Sch-Clevelnd, 110 14th St, Buffalo 14213	5-12	T	769	85%	716/816-4300 Fax 716/888-7158	Ella Dunne
PS 206 South Park High Sch, 150 Southside Pkwy, Buffalo 14220	9-12	GTV	889	73%	716/816-4828 Fax 716/828-4905	Theresa Schuta
PS 207 Lafayette Int'l HS, 370 Lafayette Ave, Buffalo 14213	9-10	GT	840 / 50	91%	716/816-4358 Fax 716/888-7096	John Starkey
PS 208 Riverside Academy, 51 Ontario St, Buffalo 14207	9-10	T	175	86%	716/816-4530 Fax 716/871-6097	David Hills
PS 212 Leonardo DaVinci HS, 320 Porter Ave, Buffalo 14201	9-12	GT	383 / 25	63%	716/816-4380 Fax 716/888-7181	Gregory Lodinsky
PS 301 Burgard High Sch, 400 Kensington Ave, Buffalo 14214	9-12	GTV	459 / 50	80%	716/816-4450 Fax 716/838-7546	Charlene Watson
PS 302 Emerson-Hospitality, 70 W Chippewa St, Buffalo 14202	Voc	T	443	83%	716/816-3018 Fax 716/851-3017	Debbie Stokes
PS 304 Hutchinson Tech HS, 256 S Elmwood Ave, Buffalo 14201	Voc	T	1,174	63%	716/816-3888 Fax 716/851-3890	Dr Gabrielle Morquecho
PS 305 McKinley High Sch, 1500 Elmwood Ave, Buffalo 14207	9-12	GT	990 / 75	80%	716/816-4480 Fax 716/871-6086	Marck Abraham
PS 309 East Cmty High Sch, 820 Northampton St, Buffalo 14211	8-11	T	256	83%	716/816-3997 Fax 716/897-8130	Adriann Cofield
PS 335 Middle Early College HS, 2885 Main St, Buffalo 14214	9-12	T	320 / 20	70%	716/816-4010 Fax 716/838-7507	Susan Doyle
PS 353 Newcomer Academy, 370 Lafayette Ave, Buffalo 14213	9-10	T	150	89%	716/816-4345 Fax 716/888-7096	Teena Jones
PS 357 Pathways Academy East, 820 Northampton St, Buffalo 14211	9-12	T	249	71%	716/816-4526 Fax 716/897-8128	Darryl King
PS 366 Research Lab Bioinfo, 2885 Main St, Buffalo 14214	9-11		401		716/816-4250 Fax 716/838-7490	Angela Cullen
PS131 Academy Sch at 44 & Ltep, 425 S Park Ave, Buffalo 14204	9-12	AT	296	82%	716/816-3270 Fax 716/851-3761	Adriann Cofield
© Westminster Cmty Charter Sch, 24 Westminster Ave, Buffalo 14215	K-8	TV	545 / 27	83%	716/816-3450 Fax 716/838-7458	Robert Ross

• **Cheektowaga Central SD** PID: 00723549
3600 Union Rd, Cheektowaga 14225
716/686-3612   Fax 716/681-5232

Schools: 3 \ **Students:** 2,249 \ **Special Ed Students:** 397 \
LEP Students: 90 \ **Ethnic:** Asian 7%, African American 39%, Hispanic 9%, Caucasian 45% \ **Exp:** $186 (Low) \ **Poverty:** 18% \ **Title I:** $809,774 \
Special Education: $2,939,000 \ **Open-Close:** 09/04 - 06/25 \ **DTBP:** $225 (High)

Mary Morris 1
Bruce Vona 3,5*
Brian Hickson 6*
Steven Wright 15,16
Renee Wilson 67
Kaitlyn Tokarczyk 2,7
Wendy Doster 4
Maureen George 8,57,288
Gretchen Sukdollak 58
Ron Lavere 73,76*

Public Schs..Principal	Grd	Prgm	Enr/#Cls	SN	Phone/Fax
Cheektowaga High Sch, 3600 Union Rd, Cheektowaga 14225, Scott Zipp	9-12	T	702 / 80	59%	716/686-3600 Fax 716/686-3619
Cheektowaga Middle Sch, 3600 Union Rd, Cheektowaga 14225, Micah Hanford	5-8	T	623 / 39	63%	716/686-3600 Fax 716/686-3669
Union East Elem Sch, 3550 Union Rd, Cheektowaga 14225, Melissa Mitchell	PK-4	T	924 / 38	63%	716/686-3620 Fax 716/686-3666

• **Cheektowaga Maryvale UFSD** PID: 00724919
1050 Maryvale Dr, Cheektowaga 14225
716/631-0300   Fax 716/631-7408

Schools: 4 \ **Teachers:** 167 \ **Students:** 2,183 \ **Special Ed Students:** 373 \ **LEP Students:** 166 \ **College-Bound:** 83% \ **Ethnic:** Asian 5%, African American 11%, Hispanic 6%, Caucasian 78% \ **Exp:** $224 (Med) \ **Poverty:** 15% \ **Title I:** $561,970 \ **Special Education:** $3,360,000 \ **Open-Close:** 09/04 - 06/25 \ **DTBP:** $251 (High)

#	Title	#	Title	#	Title	#	Title	#	Title	#	Title	#	Title
1	Superintendent	8	Curric/Instruct K-12	19	Chief Financial Officer	29	Family/Consumer Science	39	Social Studies K-12	49	English/Lang Arts Elem	59	Special Education Elem	69	Academic Assessment
2	Bus/Finance/Purchasing	9	Curric/Instruct Elem	20	Art K-12	30	Adult Education	40	Social Studies Elem	50	English/Lang Arts Sec	60	Special Education Sec	70	Research/Development
3	Buildings And Grounds	10	Curric/Instruct Sec	21	Art Elem	31	Career/Sch-to-Work K-12	41	Social Studies Sec	51	Reading K-12	61	Foreign/World Lang K-12	71	Public Information
4	Food Service	11	Federal Program	22	Art Sec	32	Career/Sch-to-Work Elem	42	Science K-12	52	Reading Elem	62	Foreign/World Lang Elem	72	Summer School
5	Transportation	12	Title I	23	Music K-12	33	Career/Sch-to-Work Sec	43	Science Elem	53	Reading Sec	63	Foreign/World Lang Sec	73	Instructional Tech
6	Athletic	13	Title V	24	Music Elem	34	Early Childhood Ed	44	Science Sec	54	Remedial Reading K-12	64	Religious Education K-12	74	Inservice Training
7	Health Services	15	Asst Superintendent	25	Music Sec	35	Health/Phys Education	45	Math K-12	55	Remedial Reading Elem	65	Religious Education Elem	75	Marketing/Distributive
		16	Instructional Media Svcs	26	Business Education	36	Guidance Services K-12	46	Math Elem	56	Remedial Reading Sec	66	Religious Education Sec	76	Info Systems
		17	Chief Operations Officer	27	Career & Tech Ed	37	Guidance Services Elem	47	Math Sec	57	Bilingual/ELL	67	School Board President	77	Psychological Assess
		18	Chief Academic Officer	28	Technology Education	38	Guidance Services Sec	48	English/Lang Arts K-12	58	Special Education K-12	68	Teacher Personnel	78	Affirmative Action

New York School Directory — Erie County

Joseph D'Angelo 1
Terry Pluta 4
Timothy Climtzak 6,35,85
James Maloney 15
Michael Swords 30
Nancy Sledziewski 60*
Shelly Phillips 72*

Dr Stephen Lunden 2,15,68,71,78,97
Nadine Rattle 4
Elizabeth Giangreco 8,11,57,88,288,296,298,750
Kelly Squires 27,31,36,83,88*
Joelle Burke 58,79
Melissa Marguccio 61*
Ernie Bussick 73,98,295,297

Public Schs..Principal	Grd	Prgm	Enr/#Cls	SN		
Maryvale High Sch 1050 Maryvale Dr, Cheektowaga 14225 Thomas Stack	9-12	AGTV	653 70	45%	716/631-7481 Fax 716/631-7404	
Maryvale Intermediate Sch 1050 Maryvale Dr, Cheektowaga 14225 Eileen Crumb	3-5	T	473 23	51%	716/631-7423 Fax 716/631-4858	
Maryvale Middle Sch 1050 Maryvale Dr, Cheektowaga 14225 Peter Frank	6-8	T	464	51%	716/631-7425 Fax 716/631-7499	
Maryvale Primary Sch 1 Nagel Dr, Cheektowaga 14225 Elizabeth Giangreco	PK-2		593 30	37%	716/631-7471 Fax 716/651-0031	

● **Cheektowaga-Sloan UFSD** PID: 00725092 716/891-6402
166 Halstead Ave, Sloan 14212 Fax 716/891-6435

Schools: 4 \ **Teachers:** 115 \ **Students:** 1,279 \ **Special Ed Students:** 251 \ **LEP Students:** 27 \ **College-Bound:** 81% \ **Ethnic:** Asian 2%, African American 8%, Hispanic 7%, Caucasian 83% \ **Exp:** $274 (Med) \ **Poverty:** 15% \ **Title I:** $384,540 \ **Special Education:** $3,806,000 \ **Open-Close:** 09/04 - 06/25 \ **DTBP:** $219 (High)

Andrea Galenski 1
Joseph Goodrow 3
Norine Godzich 5
Janelle Finn 8,12,74,285,294
Richard Keller 16,23*
Jacquie Fowler 57,58
Carolyn Segal 69,91,295*
Jessica Stiglmeier 88,90,275*

Linda Hybicki 2
Mary Brucz 4*
Mark Ostempowski 6*
Wayne Dresher 8,18
Jerome Wysocki 36*
Denise McCowan 61
Jason Zuba 73,74
Jeffrey Mochrie 93,273,274*

Public Schs..Principal	Grd	Prgm	Enr/#Cls	SN		
John F Kennedy High Sch 305 Cayuga Creek Rd, Cheektowaga 14227 Robert Julian	9-12	AG	399 33	38%	716/891-6407 Fax 716/270-0160	
John F Kennedy Middle Sch 305 Cayuga Creek Rd, Cheektowaga 14227 Gretchen Cercone	6-8	AT	280 40	45%	716/897-7300 Fax 716/892-2624	
Theodore Roosevelt Primary Sch 2495 William St, Cheektowaga 14206 Jeffrey Mochrie	PK-2	T	332 30	45%	716/891-6424 Fax 716/892-2537	
Woodrow Wilson Elem Sch 166 Halstead Ave, Sloan 14212 Hillary Weir	3-5	T	268 17	45%	716/891-6419 Fax 716/892-6956	

● **Clarence Central School Dist** PID: 00723599 716/407-9100
9625 Main St, Clarence 14031 Fax 716/407-9126

Schools: 6 \ **Teachers:** 340 \ **Students:** 4,600 \ **Special Ed Students:** 665 \ **LEP Students:** 29 \ **Ethnic:** Asian 4%, African American 1%, Hispanic 3%, Caucasian 91% \ **Exp:** $192 (Low) \ **Poverty:** 6% \ **Title I:** $500,360 \ **Special Education:** $5,576,000 \ **Open-Close:** 09/08 - 06/23 \ **DTBP:** $278 (High)

Geoffrey Hicks 1
Richard Mancuso 2,4,91
Joan DiBartolomeo 4
Finune Shaibi 8,97

Nichole Kuss 2
Brian Logel 3
Linda Forster 5
Kate Celej 8

Kristin Overholt 8,11,15,27,31,273,296,298
Nicholas Rizzo 36*
Michael Fuchs 67

Andrew Johnston 16
Maryellen Colling 57,58,271
Robert Michel 68,78,79

Public Schs..Principal	Grd	Prgm	Enr/#Cls	SN		
Clarence Center Elem Sch 9600 Clarence Center Rd, Clarence CTR 14032 Colleen Coggins	K-5		379 25	7%	716/407-9150 Fax 716/407-9157	
Clarence Middle Sch 10150 Greiner Rd, Clarence 14031 Robert Moore	6-8	AV	984	9%	716/407-9206 Fax 716/407-9200	
Clarence Senior High Sch 9625 Main St, Clarence 14031 Kenneth Smith	9-12	AGV	1,452 85	7%	716/407-9020 Fax 716/407-9061	
Harris Hill Elem Sch 4260 Harris Hill Rd, Williamsville 14221 Margaret Aldrich	K-5		475 25	13%	716/407-9175 Fax 716/407-9182	
Ledgeview Elem Sch 5150 Old Goodrich Rd, Clarence 14031 Keith Kuwik	K-5		473 28	9%	716/407-9275 Fax 716/407-9279	
Sheridan Hill Elem Sch 4560 Boncrest Dr E, Williamsville 14221 Jenna Arroyo	K-5		464 34	7%	716/407-9250 Fax 716/407-9258	

● **Cleveland Hill Union Free SD** PID: 00723678 716/836-7200
105 Mapleview Rd, Cheektowaga 14225 Fax 716/836-0675

Schools: 3 \ **Teachers:** 128 \ **Students:** 1,284 \ **Special Ed Students:** 258 \ **LEP Students:** 49 \ **College-Bound:** 82% \ **Ethnic:** Asian 3%, African American 35%, Hispanic 7%, Native American: 1%, Caucasian 54% \ **Exp:** $225 (Med) \ **Poverty:** 15% \ **Title I:** $430,095 \ **Special Education:** $3,011,000 \ **Open-Close:** 09/08 - 06/25 \ **DTBP:** $211 (High)

John Macswan 1
David Hehr 3*
Daryl Janus 8,69
Ann Marshall 16*
Robert Polino 67

Dennis Corsaro 2
Jason Perez 6
David Evans 15
Janice Kowalski-Kelly 16*
Larry King 73

Public Schs..Principal	Grd	Prgm	Enr/#Cls	SN		
Cleveland Hill Elem Sch 105 Mapleview Rd, Cheektowaga 14225 Marcie Pascual	PK-5	T	640 40	59%	716/836-7200 Fax 716/836-3700	
Cleveland Hill High Sch 105 Mapleview Rd, Cheektowaga 14225 Timothy Wiles	9-12	V	385	55%	716/836-7200 Fax 716/836-7741	
Cleveland Hill Middle Sch 105 Mapleview Rd, Cheektowaga 14225 Andrea Kersten	6-8	TV	259 36	61%	716/836-7200 Fax 716/836-7741	

● **Depew Union Free School Dist** PID: 00723719 716/686-5104
5201 Transit Rd, Depew 14043 Fax 716/686-5101

Schools: 3 \ **Teachers:** 156 \ **Students:** 1,785 \ **Special Ed Students:** 352 \ **LEP Students:** 21 \ **College-Bound:** 76% \ **Ethnic:** Asian 2%, African American 3%, Hispanic 4%, Caucasian 90% \ **Exp:** $266 (Med) \ **Poverty:** 15% \ **Title I:** $536,395 \ **Special Education:** $4,450,000 \ **Open-Close:** 09/09 - 06/25 \ **DTBP:** $164 (High)

Dr Jeffrey Rabey 1
David Hess 3,91
Doug Baumgarden 5
Gale Kandefer 7*
Lisa Zielinski 16,82
Janet Gajewski 58*

Susan Arena 2
Barbara Albi 4*
Robert Koczyals 6
Susan Frey 8,11,15,68,69,288,296,298
Joseph D'Maato 36,73,79,83,88*
David Chef 67

---

79 Student Personnel	91 Safety/Security	275 Response To Intervention	298 Grant Writer/Ptnrships	**School Programs**	**Social Media**	
80 Driver Ed/Safety	92 Magnet School	277 Remedial Math K-12	750 Chief Innovation Officer	A = Alternative Program	▮ = Facebook	
81 Gifted/Talented	93 Parental Involvement	280 Literacy Coach	751 Chief of Staff	G = Adult Classes		
82 Video Services	95 Tech Prep Program	285 STEM	752 Social Emotional Learning	M = Magnet Program	▮ = Twitter	
83 Substance Abuse Prev	97 Chief Information Officer	286 Digital Learning		T = Title I Schoolwide		
84 Erate	98 Chief Technology Officer	288 Common Core Standards	**Other School Types**	V = Career & Tech Ed Programs		
85 AIDS Education	270 Character Education	294 Accountability	Ⓐ = Alternative School			
88 Alternative/At Risk	271 Migrant Education	295 Network System	Ⓒ = Charter School	New Schools are shaded		
89 Multi-Cultural Curriculum	273 Teacher Mentor	296 Title II Programs	Ⓜ = Magnet School	New Superintendents and Principals are bold		
90 Social Work	274 Before/After Sch	297 Webmaster	Ⓨ = Year-Round School	Personnel with email addresses are underscored		

NY—59

Erie County

Market Data Retrieval

Lee Hoffman 71,97
Nicole Gugino 71
Sheri Barsottelli 280*
Lori Sosenko 71
Brian Richards 73,295

Public Schs..Principal	Grd	Prgm	Enr/#Cls	SN		
Cayuga Heights Elem Sch 1780 Como Park Blvd, Depew 14043 Michelle Kudla	K-5	T	841 51	49%	716/686-5005 Fax 716/686-5016	
Depew High Sch 5201 Transit Rd, Depew 14043 Carol Townsend	9-12		544 60	41%	716/686-5065 Fax 716/686-5094	
Depew Middle Sch 5201 Transit Rd, Depew 14043 James Lupini	6-8		400 45	48%	716/686-5045 Fax 716/686-5057	

● **East Aurora Union Free SD** PID: 00723771
430 Main St, East Aurora 14052
716/687-2302
Fax 716/687-2441

Schools: 3 \ **Teachers:** 126 \ **Students:** 1,760 \ **Special Ed Students:** 324 \ **LEP Students:** 3 \ **College-Bound:** 85% \ **Ethnic:** Asian 1%, African American 1%, Hispanic 3%, Caucasian 96% \ **Exp:** $377 (High) \ **Poverty:** 7% \ **Title I:** $233,138 \ **Special Education:** $1,759,000 \ **Open-Close:** 09/03 - 06/25 \ **DTBP:** $161 (High)

Brian Russ 1
Douglas Wicks 3,91
Matthew Librock 6,35
Jerome Polakiewicz .. 11,27,57,58,79,83,88,275
Mary Ann Huber 38*
Richard Clements 73,295
Joanne George 2,5
Iris Reed 4
Mark Mambretti 8,11,68,69,97,285,298,750
Carrie Cole 37,270*
Marybeth Covert 67

Public Schs..Principal	Grd	Prgm	Enr/#Cls	SN		
East Aurora High Sch 1003 Center St, East Aurora 14052 William Roberts	9-12		636 60	15%	716/687-2505 Fax 716/687-2552	
East Aurora Middle Sch 430 Main St, East Aurora 14052 Matthew Brown	5-8		519 25	13%	716/687-2453 Fax 716/687-2443	
Parkdale Elem Sch 141 Girard Ave, East Aurora 14052 Jessica Lyons	K-4		605 16	15%	716/687-2352 Fax 716/687-2350	

● **Eden Central School Dist** PID: 00723836
8289 N Main St, Eden 14057
716/992-3630
Fax 716/992-3656

Schools: 3 \ **Teachers:** 114 \ **Students:** 1,538 \ **Special Ed Students:** 249 \ **LEP Students:** 3 \ **Ethnic:** Hispanic 2%, Native American: 1%, Caucasian 97% \ **Exp:** $238 (Med) \ **Poverty:** 7% \ **Title I:** $163,605 \ **Special Education:** $1,529,000 \ **Open-Close:** 09/08 - 06/23 \ **DTBP:** $376 (High)

Sandra Anzalone 1,11
David Martin 3
Kelly LaRosa 8,288*
Shawn Johnson 58,79*
Lucinda Karstedt 71,73,97
Laura Feldman 2,5
Marisa Fallacaro 6*
David Hassett 38*
Jennifer Horschel 67

Public Schs..Principal	Grd	Prgm	Enr/#Cls	SN		
Eden Elem Sch 8289 N Main St, Eden 14057 Kelly LaRosa	3-5		285 45	28%	716/992-3610 Fax 716/992-3658	
Eden Middle High Sch 3150 Schoolview Rd, Eden 14057 Jeffrey Cervoni \ Jason Lyons	6-12	V	739 80	24%	716/992-3600 Fax 716/992-3652	
G L Priess Primary Sch 3000 Schoolview Rd, Eden 14057 Loran Carter	PK-2		329 40	21%	716/992-3638 Fax 716/992-3631	

● **Evans-Brant Central Sch Dist** PID: 00724737
959 Beach Rd, Angola 14006
716/926-2201
Fax 716/549-6407

Schools: 5 \ **Teachers:** 203 \ **Students:** 2,260 \ **Special Ed Students:** 498 \ **LEP Students:** 3 \ **College-Bound:** 82% \ **Ethnic:** African American 1%, Hispanic 3%, Native American: 15%, Caucasian 81% \ **Exp:** $217 (Med) \ **Poverty:** 14% \ **Title I:** $572,075 \ **Special Education:** $6,183,000 \ **Open-Close:** 09/02 - 06/25 \ **DTBP:** $253 (High)

Dr Charles Galluzzo 1
John Wilson 3
Perry Oddi 5
Patti Binaxas 7,83*
Jill Benedict 11,57,58
Jennifer Michalec 67
Jill Clarke 280
Daniel Pacos 2,12,15,91
Debbie Becker 4*
Daryl Besant 6*
Melissa Bergler ..8,15,17,285,288,296,298,751
Katie Zittel 20,286
Jeff Barnes 73,76,98

Public Schs..Principal	Grd	Prgm	Enr/#Cls	SN		
A J Schmidt Elem Sch 9455 Lake Shore Rd, Angola 14006 Jill Clark	K-5	T	288 12	22%	716/926-2350 Fax 716/549-4428	
Highland Elem Sch 6745 Erie Rd, Derby 14047 Colleen Politowski	K-5		329 22	21%	716/926-2460 Fax 716/947-2337	
John T Waugh Elem Sch 100 High St, Angola 14006 Paula Eastman	K-5	T	337 28	31%	716/926-2370 Fax 716/549-2380	
Lake Shore Middle Sch 8855 Erie Rd, Angola 14006 Erich Reidell	6-8	T	527 75	16%	716/926-2400 Fax 716/549-4374	
Lake Shore Senior High Sch 959 Beach Rd, Angola 14006 Christine Koch	9-12	AV	698	19%	716/926-2307 Fax 716/549-4033	

● **Frontier Ctl School Dist** PID: 00723915
5120 Orchard Ave, Hamburg 14075
716/926-1700
Fax 716/926-1776

Schools: 6 \ **Teachers:** 372 \ **Students:** 4,760 \ **Special Ed Students:** 924 \ **LEP Students:** 43 \ **College-Bound:** 81% \ **Ethnic:** Asian 1%, African American 1%, Hispanic 5%, Caucasian 92% \ **Exp:** $124 (Low) \ **Poverty:** 7% \ **Title I:** $565,802 \ **Special Education:** $7,361,000 \ **Open-Close:** 09/09 - 06/15 \ **DTBP:** $313 (High)

Dr Richard Hughes 1
William Thiel 2
Martin Lipczynski 3,91
Tim Blevins 5
Colleen Duggan 8,11,15,69,77,285,288,298
Andrew Tamol 28
Davis Podkulski 67
Gail Lewis 79
Danae Parent 274
Mary Clouden 2
David Boffey 3
Jason Whipple 4
Richard Gray 6,7,35*
Myra Pinker 15,68
Patricia Cannan 36*
Deniz Cetinkaya 76
Minser Bernys 79

Public Schs..Principal	Grd	Prgm	Enr/#Cls	SN		
Big Tree Elem Sch 4460 Bay View Rd, Hamburg 14075 Julia Bermingham	K-5	T	527 35	35%	716/926-1740 Fax 716/646-2111	
Blasdell Elem Sch 3780 S Park Ave, Blasdell 14219 Deanne Lester	PK-5	T	454 30	53%	716/926-1750 Fax 716/823-6153	
Cloverbank Elem Sch 2761 Cloverbank Rd, Hamburg 14075 Renee Kumiega	PK-5	T	563 30	26%	716/926-1760 Fax 716/627-7959	

1 Superintendent	8 Curric/Instruct K-12	19 Chief Financial Officer	29 Family/Consumer Science	39 Social Studies K-12	49 English/Lang Arts Elem	59 Special Education Elem	69 Academic Assessment
2 Bus/Finance/Purchasing	9 Curric/Instruct Elem	20 Art K-12	30 Adult Education	40 Social Studies Elem	50 English/Lang Arts Sec	60 Special Education Sec	70 Research/Development
3 Buildings And Grounds	10 Curric/Instruct Sec	21 Art Elem	31 Career/Sch-to-Work K-12	41 Social Studies Sec	51 Reading K-12	61 Foreign/World Lang K-12	71 Public Information
4 Food Service	11 Federal Program	22 Art Sec	32 Career/Sch-to-Work Elem	42 Science K-12	52 Reading Elem	62 Foreign/World Lang Elem	72 Summer School
5 Transportation	12 Title I	23 Music K-12	33 Career/Sch-to-Work Sec	43 Science Elem	53 Reading Sec	63 Foreign/World Lang Sec	73 Instructional Tech
6 Athletic	13 Title V	24 Music Elem	34 Early Childhood Ed	44 Science Sec	54 Remedial Reading K-12	64 Religious Education K-12	74 Inservice Training
7 Health Services	15 Asst Superintendent	25 Music Sec	35 Health/Phys Education	45 Math K-12	55 Remedial Reading Elem	65 Religious Education Elem	75 Marketing/Distributive
	16 Instructional Media Svcs	26 Business Education	36 Guidance Services K-12	46 Math Elem	56 Remedial Reading Sec	66 Religious Education Sec	76 Info Systems
	17 Chief Operations Officer	27 Career & Tech Ed	37 Guidance Services Elem	47 Math Sec	57 Bilingual/ELL	67 School Board President	77 Psychological Assess
	18 Chief Academic Officer	28 Technology Education	38 Guidance Services Sec	48 English/Lang Arts K-12	58 Special Education K-12	68 Teacher Personnel	78 Affirmative Action

New York School Directory

Erie County

Frontier Central High Sch	9-12	AV	1,363	31%	716/926-1720
4432 Bay View Rd, Hamburg 14075			150		Fax 716/646-2195
Daniel Charland					

Frontier Middle Sch	6-8	TV	1,141	32%	716/926-1730
2751 Amsdell Rd, Hamburg 14075			83		Fax 716/646-2207
Ryan Sikorski					

Pinehurst Elem Sch	K-5		635	15%	716/926-1770
6050 Fairway Ct, Lake View 14085			27		Fax 716/627-3132
Jennifer Makowski					

• Grand Island Central Sch Dist PID: 00724048   716/773-8800
1100 Ransom Rd, Grand Island 14072   Fax 716/773-8843

Schools: 5 \ **Teachers:** 208 \ **Students:** 2,905 \ **Special Ed Students:** 425 \ **LEP Students:** 47 \ **College-Bound:** 88% \ **Ethnic:** Asian 3%, African American 2%, Hispanic 5%, Caucasian 90% \ **Exp:** $212 (Med) \ **Poverty:** 7% \ **Title I:** $373,938 \ **Special Education:** $4,348,000 \ **Open-Close:** 09/08 - 06/24 \ **DTBP:** $313 (High)

Dr Brian Graham 1	Dr Ruby Harris 2,15	
James Rozler 3,91	Patrick Smith 4	
Theresa Alizadeh 5	Jon Roth 6,85	
Cheryl Cardone 7,13,57,58,79,90	Karen Cuddy-Miller 8,12,15,296	
Mary Ells 23	Christopher DeMarco 35	
Aliscia Krecisz 51	Ashli Dreher 67	
Robin Kwiatek 73,76		

Public Schs..Principal	Grd	Prgm	Enr/#Cls	SN
Grand Island Sr High Sch	9-12	AGV	956	25% 716/773-8820
1100 Ransom Rd, Grand Island 14072			75	Fax 716/773-8951
Michael Lauria				
Huth Road Elem Sch	2-5		448	25% 716/773-8850
1773 Huth Rd, Grand Island 14072			20	Fax 716/773-8984
Max Pikula				
Kaegebein Elem Sch	2-5		406	29% 716/773-8840
1690 Love Rd, Grand Island 14072			21	Fax 716/773-8991
Mary Haggerty				
Sidway Elem Sch	PK-1		437	18% 716/773-8870
2451 Baseline Rd, Grand Island 14072			21	Fax 716/773-8985
Denise Dunbar				
Veronica E Connor Middle Sch	6-8	V	658	25% 716/773-8830
1100 Ransom Rd, Grand Island 14072			52	Fax 716/773-8983
John Fitzpatrick				

• Hamburg Central School Dist PID: 00724177   716/646-3200
5305 Abbott Rd, Hamburg 14075   Fax 716/646-3209

Schools: 6 \ **Teachers:** 301 \ **Students:** 3,550 \ **Special Ed Students:** 603 \ **LEP Students:** 5 \ **College-Bound:** 87% \ **Ethnic:** Asian 1%, African American 1%, Hispanic 3%, Caucasian 96% \ **Exp:** $180 (Low) \ **Poverty:** 5% \ **Title I:** $279,493 \ **Special Education:** $5,381,000 \ **Open-Close:** 09/08 - 06/23 \ **DTBP:** $323 (High) \ [facebook]

Michael Cornell 1,11	Kathleen Selby 2
Stephen Bykowicz 3	Anne Rich 4
Patrick Cauley 6,35*	Colleen Kaney 8,15,36,58,79,83,275,288
Kaitlin Sylvester 8	Barbara Sporyz 15,91
Danielle Lango 34*	Thomas Flynn 67
Brent Jordan 71,73,76,97	Michele Darstein 71
Jennifer Barker 79,90	

Public Schs..Principal	Grd	Prgm	Enr/#Cls	SN
Armor Elem Sch	K-5		328	28% 716/646-3350
5301 Abbott Rd, Hamburg 14075			36	Fax 716/646-3368
Leslie Bennett				

Boston Valley Elem Sch	K-5		233	23%	716/646-3240
7476 Back Creek Rd, Hamburg 14075			28		Fax 716/646-3244
Nicole Lauer					
Charlotte Avenue Elem Sch	PK-5		419	19%	716/646-3370
301 Charlotte Ave, Hamburg 14075			18		Fax 716/646-6396
Danielle Lango					
Hamburg High Sch	9-12	AGV	1,082	21%	716/646-3300
4111 Legion Dr, Hamburg 14075			60		Fax 716/646-3028
Michael Gallagher					
Hamburg Middle Sch	6-8		772	22%	716/646-3250
360 Division St, Hamburg 14075			52		Fax 716/646-6380
Thomas Adams					
Union Pleasant Elem Sch	K-5		641	23%	716/646-3280
150 Pleasant Ave, Hamburg 14075					Fax 716/646-3237
Jackie Peffer					

• Holland Central School Dist PID: 00724268   716/537-8200
103 Canada St, Holland 14080   Fax 716/537-8203

Schools: 3 \ **Teachers:** 76 \ **Students:** 800 \ **Special Ed Students:** 159 \ **Ethnic:** Hispanic 2%, Caucasian 97% \ **Exp:** $259 (Med) \ **Poverty:** 9% \ **Title I:** $133,611 \ **Special Education:** $1,755,000 \ **Open-Close:** 09/03 - 06/24 \ **DTBP:** $366 (High)

Cathy Fabiatos 1	Christine Ljungberg 2
Scott Christ 3	Elizabeth Flitton 4
Susan Ehelers 5	Matthew Adams 6
Laurie Gregory 8,76,288	Kelly Westler 9
Carl Guidotti 10,11,83,85,88*	Debra Kozlowski 16*
Scott Hunt 27*	Allan Bett 35*
Kathleen Bell 36,69	Lisa Hanlon 38*
Brian Jones 67	Dave Fox 73*
Erik Smith 79*	Kevin Burd 91

Public Schs..Principal	Grd	Prgm	Enr/#Cls	SN
Harold O Brumsted Elem Sch	PK-4		331	32% 716/537-8250
103 Canada St, Holland 14080			22	Fax 716/537-8252
Kelly Wetzler				
Holland High Sch	9-12	AV	261	25% 716/537-8221
103 Canada St, Holland 14080			24	Fax 716/537-8233
Carl Guidotti				
Holland Middle Sch	5-8		288	31% 716/537-8275
11720 Partridge Rd, Holland 14080				
Jason Smith				

• Iroquois Central School Dist PID: 00724309   716/652-3000
2111 Girdle Rd, Elma 14059   Fax 716/652-9305

Schools: 5 \ **Teachers:** 205 \ **Students:** 2,127 \ **Special Ed Students:** 413 \ **LEP Students:** 3 \ **Ethnic:** Asian 1%, Hispanic 1%, Caucasian 97% \ **Exp:** $208 (Med) \ **Poverty:** 5% \ **Title I:** $201,780 \ **Special Education:** $3,355,000 \ **Open-Close:** 09/08 - 06/23 \ **DTBP:** $255 (High)

Douglas Scofield 1	John Wolski 2
David Carlin 3	Lynn Dombrowski 4
Eric Nagel 5	Carrie Vetter 6
Dr Robert Erickson 7	Dr Mary Jo Dudek 8,11,15
Ken Piacente 16,73,82,295	Debbie Metz 30
Patrick O'Brien 30,83,88,270*	Jane Sullivan 67
Kristin Kendall-Jakus 69,77,79	

Public Schs..Principal	Grd	Prgm	Enr/#Cls	SN
Elma Primary Sch	K-4	T	295	14% 716/652-3000
711 Rice Rd, Elma 14059			17	Fax 716/995-2321
Darcy Walker				

---

79 Student Personnel	91 Safety/Security	275 Response To Intervention	298 Grant Writer/Ptnrships	**School Programs**
80 Driver Ed/Safety	92 Magnet School	277 Remedial Math K-12	750 Chief Innovation Officer	A = Alternative Program
81 Gifted/Talented	93 Parental Involvement	280 Literacy Coach	751 Chief of Staff	G = Adult Classes
82 Video Services	95 Tech Prep Program	285 STEM	752 Social Emotional Learning	M = Magnet Program
83 Substance Abuse Prev	97 Chief Information Officer	286 Digital Learning		T = Title I Schoolwide
84 Erate	98 Chief Technology Officer	288 Common Core Standards	**Other School Types**	V = Career & Tech Ed Programs
85 AIDS Education	270 Accountability	294 Accountability	Ⓐ = Alternative School	
88 Alternative/At Risk	271 Migrant Education	295 Network System	Ⓒ = Charter School	**Social Media**
89 Multi-Cultural Curriculum	273 Teacher Mentor	296 Title II Programs	Ⓜ = Magnet School	[f] = Facebook
90 Social Work	274 Before/After Sch	297 Webmaster	Ⓨ = Year-Round School	[t] = Twitter

New Schools are shaded
New Superintendents and Principals are bold
Personnel with email addresses are underscored

NY-61

Erie County Market Data Retrieval

Iroquois High Sch 2111 Girdle Rd, Elma 14059 Dean Ramirez	9-12	GT	722 60	18%	716/995-2440 Fax 716/995-2441
Iroquois Middle Sch 2111 Girdle Rd, Elma 14059 Ross Esslinger	5-8	GTV	657 49	20%	716/652-3000 Fax 716/995-2337
Marilla Primary Sch 11683 Bullis Rd, Marilla 14102 Amy Cavaretta	K-4		227 12	19%	716/652-3000 Fax 716/995-2331
Wales Primary Sch 4650 Woodchuck Rd, East Aurora 14052 Kimberly Morrison	K-4		226 14	23%	716/652-3000 Fax 716/995-2341

● **Kenmore-Tonawanda UF Sch Dist** PID: 00724373 716/874-8400
1500 Colvin Blvd, Buffalo 14223 Fax 716/874-8621

> **Schools:** 9 \ **Teachers:** 639 \ **Students:** 7,000 \ **Special Ed Students:** 1,628 \ **LEP Students:** 221 \ **College-Bound:** 70% \ **Ethnic:** Asian 3%, African American 8%, Hispanic 9%, Native American: 1%, Caucasian 80% \ **Exp:** $268 (Med) \ **Poverty:** 11% \ **Title I:** $1,675,217 \ **Special Education:** $16,848,000 \ **Open-Close:** 09/08 - 06/25 \ **DTBP:** $229 (High)

Sabatino Cimato	1	John Brucato	2,15
Margaret Weglarski	2	Timothy Ames	3,91
Kim Roll	4	James Nestico	5
James Ciulis	5	Brett Banker	6,35
Debra Carey	7	Kelly White	8,15,69,79,288
Michael Muscarella	9	Lisa Cross	10
Patrick Moses	11,68	Jeff Richards	15,68
Liza Acanfora	30	Jennifer Conway	57
Dr Michael Lewis	58,79	Matthew Chimera	67
Patrick Fanelli	71	Deb Eppolito	73,286,295
Frank Spagnolo	76,294		

Public Schs..Principal	Grd	Prgm	Enr/#Cls	SN	
Benjamin Franklin Elem Sch 500 Parkhurst Blvd, Buffalo 14223 Patricia Kosis	K-4	T	517 25	62%	716/874-8415 Fax 716/874-8520
Benjamin Franklin Middle Sch 540 Parkhurst Blvd, Buffalo 14223 Christopher Ginestre	5-7		658 69	56%	716/874-8404 Fax 716/874-8480
C A Lindbergh Elem Sch 184 Irving Ter, Buffalo 14223 Ann MacCagnano	K-4		510 30	40%	716/874-8410 Fax 716/874-8570
Herbert Hoover Elem Sch 199 Thorncliff Rd, Buffalo 14223 Michael Huff	K-4	T	613	47%	716/874-8414 Fax 716/874-8460
Herbert Hoover Middle Sch 249 Thorncliff Rd, Buffalo 14223 Elaine Thomas	5-7		841	53%	716/874-8405 Fax 716/874-8470
Holmes Elem Sch 365 Dupont Ave, Tonawanda 14150 Matt Raines	K-4	T	309 21	84%	716/874-8423 Fax 716/874-8560
Kenmore East High Sch 350 Fries Rd, Tonawanda 14150 Patrick Heyden	8-12	A	1,219 20	45%	716/874-8402 Fax 716/874-8443
Kenmore West High Sch 33 Highland Pkwy, Buffalo 14223 Dean Johnson	8-12	A	1,398	48%	716/874-8401 Fax 716/874-8527
Thomas A Edison Elem Sch 236 Grayton Rd, Tonawanda 14150 David King	K-4		576 34	40%	716/874-8416 Fax 716/874-8526

● **Lackawanna City School Dist** PID: 00724622 716/821-5610
245 S Shore Blvd, Lackawanna 14218 Fax 716/827-6710

> **Schools:** 4 \ **Teachers:** 150 \ **Students:** 1,946 \ **Special Ed Students:** 512 \ **LEP Students:** 343 \ **College-Bound:** 67% \ **Ethnic:** Asian 3%, African American 15%, Hispanic 16%, Caucasian 66% \ **Exp:** $160 (Low) \ **Poverty:** 35% \ **Title I:** $2,055,497 \ **Special Education:** $8,622,000 \ **Open-Close:** 09/02 - 06/25 \ **DTBP:** $161 (High)

Keith Lewis	1	Lisa Almasi	2
Kiel Illg	6,15,68	Angela McCaffrey	8,11
Daniel Grant	15	Sue Galvin	58
Leonard Kowalski	67	Bruce Axelson	98*
Sandra Falsioni	273		

Public Schs..Principal	Grd	Prgm	Enr/#Cls	SN	
Lackawanna High Sch 500 Martin Rd, Lackawanna 14218 Bruce Axelson	9-12	T	512	74%	716/821-5610 Fax 716/821-5621
Lackawanna Middle Sch 550 Martin Rd, Lackawanna 14218 Bethany Schill	6-8	T	414 25	81%	716/821-5610 Fax 716/821-5622
Martin Road Elem Sch 135 Martin Rd, Lackawanna 14218 Frederick Hahn	2-5	T	568 25	85%	716/821-5610 Fax 716/821-5623
Truman Elem Sch 15 Inner Dr, Lackawanna 14218 Ashley Wakelee	PK-1	T	398 26	64%	716/821-5610 Fax 716/821-5624

● **Lancaster Central Sch Dist** PID: 00724828 716/686-3200
177 Central Ave, Lancaster 14086 Fax 716/686-3350

> **Schools:** 7 \ **Teachers:** 435 \ **Students:** 5,630 \ **Special Ed Students:** 1,090 \ **LEP Students:** 38 \ **College-Bound:** 84% \ **Ethnic:** Asian 2%, African American 1%, Hispanic 3%, Caucasian 94% \ **Exp:** $259 (Med) \ **Poverty:** 5% \ **Title I:** $482,636 \ **Special Education:** $5,900,000 \ **Open-Close:** 09/08 - 06/23

Dr Michael Valley	1	Jamie Phillips	2,15
Michael Bryniarski	3,91	Tami Auyugliaro	4
Judy Feldmeyer	5	Brian Wild	6*
Karen Marchioli	9	Krazmien Andrew	10
Christine Stockslader	16,82*	Nancy Mariani	20*
Dr Ami Alderman	30	Chris Dixon	35*
Don Marchese	38*	John Armstrong	58
Sandra Cammarata	58	Michael Sage	67
Cheryl Reukauf	68	Patricia Burgio	71
Michelle Zigler	73,294	Margaret Barrett	90*
Patricia Bruce	295*		

Public Schs..Principal	Grd	Prgm	Enr/#Cls	SN	
Como Park Elem Sch 1985 Como Park Blvd, Lancaster 14086 Mary Marcinelli	K-3	T	372 23	26%	716/686-3235 Fax 716/686-3303
Court Street Elem Sch 91 Court St, Lancaster 14086 Jacqueline Clinard	K-3		379 21	18%	716/686-3240 Fax 716/686-3284
Hillview Elem Sch 11 Pleasant View Dr, Lancaster 14086 Amy Moeller	K-3		538 30	13%	716/686-3280 Fax 716/686-3307
John A Sciole Elem Sch 86 Alys Dr E, Depew 14043 Carrie Greene	K-3		402 22	27%	716/686-3285 Fax 716/686-3309
Lancaster High Sch 1 Forton Dr, Lancaster 14086 Cesar Marchioli	9-12	V	1,820	20%	716/686-3255 Fax 716/686-3347

1	Superintendent	8	Curric/Instruct K-12	19	Chief Financial Officer	29	Family/Consumer Science	39	Social Studies K-12	49	English/Lang Arts Elem	59	Special Education Elem	69	Academic Assessment
2	Bus/Finance/Purchasing	9	Curric/Instruct Elem	20	Art K-12	30	Adult Education	40	Social Studies Sec	50	English/Lang Arts Sec	60	Special Education Sec	70	Research/Development
3	Buildings And Grounds	10	Curric/Instruct Sec	21	Art Elem	31	Career/Sch-to-Work K-12	41	Reading K-12	51	Reading K-12	61	Foreign/World Lang K-12	71	Public Information
4	Food Service	11	Federal Program	22	Art Sec	32	Career/Sch-to-Work Elem	42	Science K-12	52	Reading Elem	62	Foreign/World Lang Elem	72	Summer School
5	Transportation	12	Title I	23	Music K-12	33	Career/Sch-to-Work Sec	43	Science Elem	53	Reading Sec	63	Foreign/World Lang Sec	73	Instructional Tech
6	Athletic	13	Title V	24	Music Elem	34	Early Childhood Ed	44	Science Sec	54	Remedial Reading K-12	64	Religious Education K-12	74	Inservice Training
7	Health Services	15	Asst Superintendent	25	Music Sec	35	Health/Phys Education	45	Math K-12	55	Remedial Reading Elem	65	Religious Education Elem	75	Marketing/Distributive
		16	Instructional Media Svcs	26	Business Education	36	Guidance Services K-12	46	Math Elem	56	Remedial Reading Sec	66	Religious Education Sec	76	Info Systems
		17	Chief Operations Officer	27	Career & Tech Ed	37	Guidance Services Elem	47	Math Sec	57	Bilingual/ELL	67	School Board President	77	Psychological Assess
		18	Chief Academic Officer	28	Technology Education	38	Guidance Services Sec	48	English/Lang Arts K-12	58	Special Education K-12	68	Teacher Personnel	78	Affirmative Action

New York School Directory — Erie County

Lancaster Middle Sch 148 Aurora St, Lancaster 14086 Peter Kruszynski	7-8		850 45	19%	716/686-3220 Fax 716/686-3223
William Street Sch 5201 William St, Lancaster 14086 Jacqueline Bull	4-6		1,268 45	23%	716/686-3800 Fax 716/686-3822

• **North Collins Ctl Sch Dist** PID: 00724983   716/337-0101
2045 School St, North Collins 14111   Fax 716/337-3457

Schools: 2 \ **Teachers:** 56 \ **Students:** 620 \ **Special Ed Students:** 121 \ **LEP Students:** 5 \ **College-Bound:** 56% \ **Ethnic:** Asian 1%, African American 1%, Hispanic 5%, Native American: 1%, Caucasian 92% \ **Exp:** $368 (High) \ **Poverty:** 12% \ **Title I:** $138,681 \ **Special Education:** $1,129,000 \ **Open-Close:** 09/04 - 06/25 \ **DTBP:** $459 (High)

Scott Taylor	1,11	Mathew Sanders	3
Albert Durrett	5*	Paul Kellner	6
Barbara Senus	7*	John Cataldo	9,12,97*
Brandon Wojcik	10*	Scott Kaplan	16,273*
Robert English	31,36,88,95,270*	Madison Turnbull	67
Brian Zolnowski	71,73,295	Jinelle Burger	79

Public Schs..Principal	Grd	Prgm	Enr/#Cls	SN	
North Collins Elem Sch 10469 Bantle Rd, North Collins 14111 John Cataldo	PK-6	T	250 50	36%	716/337-0166 Fax 716/337-0598
North Collins Jr Sr High Sch 2045 School St, North Collins 14111 Brandon Wojcik	7-12	T	269 30	39%	716/337-0101 Fax 716/337-3630

• **Orchard Park Central Sch Dist** PID: 00725016   716/620-6222
2240 Southwestern Blvd, West Seneca 14224   Fax 716/209-8191

Schools: 6 \ **Teachers:** 383 \ **Students:** 5,010 \ **Special Ed Students:** 821 \ **LEP Students:** 34 \ **College-Bound:** 84% \ **Ethnic:** Asian 2%, African American 1%, Hispanic 2%, Caucasian 95% \ **Exp:** $216 (Med) \ **Poverty:** 3% \ **Title I:** $192,733 \ **Special Education:** $6,875,000 \ **Open-Close:** 09/08 - 06/23 \ **DTBP:** $259 (High)

Matthew McGarrity	1	Jeff Petrus	2,15
Bill Bosinski	3,91	Peggy Petrell	4
Joe Haier	5	David Hack	6
Lynn Czemerynski	7,79	Dr Lisa Krueger	8,15
David Lilleck	15,68,78,79	Deby Eppolito	16,73,82,270
Robert Farwell	30	Wendy Gloss	58
Dr Christine Gray-Tinnesz	67	Julianne Becker	71
Debra Eppolito	76		

Public Schs..Principal	Grd	Prgm	Enr/#Cls	SN	
Eggert Road Elem Sch 3580 Eggert Rd, Orchard Park 14127 Terrence Tryon	PK-5		532 30	16%	716/209-6215 Fax 716/209-6371
Ellicott Road Elem Sch 5180 Ellicott Rd, Orchard Park 14127 Paul Pietrantone	K-5		640	8%	716/209-6278 Fax 716/209-6203
Orchard Park High Sch 4040 Baker Rd, Orchard Park 14127 Jonathan Wolf	9-12	AGV	1,434 40	12%	716/209-6242 Fax 716/209-6281
Orchard Park Middle Sch 60 S Lincoln Ave, Orchard Park 14127 Aaron Grupka	6-8		1,129 100	15%	716/209-6220 Fax 716/209-6338
South Davis Elem Sch 51 S Davis St, Orchard Park 14127 Julie Mampe	K-5		345 20	8%	716/209-6246 Fax 716/209-8195

Windom Elem Sch 3870 Sheldon Rd, Orchard Park 14127 Philip Johnson	K-5		606 32	25%	716/209-6279 Fax 716/209-6490

• **Springville Griffith Inst CSD** PID: 00724103   716/592-3200
267 Newman St, Springville 14141   Fax 716/592-3209

Schools: 4 \ **Teachers:** 147 \ **Students:** 1,700 \ **Special Ed Students:** 245 \ **LEP Students:** 8 \ **College-Bound:** 58% \ **Ethnic:** African American 1%, Hispanic 2%, Native American: 1%, Caucasian 96% \ **Exp:** $276 (Med) \ **Poverty:** 10% \ **Title I:** $314,940 \ **Special Education:** $3,211,000 \ **Open-Close:** 09/10 - 06/25 \ **DTBP:** $166 (High) \ 🇹

Kimberly Moritz	1	Jennifer Carlton	2
Maureen Lee	2	Dave Seiflein	3
Laura Watson	4*	Ann Rugg	5
Joe DeMartino	6,35*	Joann DePue	11,69,73,76*
Katherine Townsend	58,79*	Allison Duwe	67
Norm Johnson	82*	Deb Skokrwatson	83
Benjamin Higgins	297*	Cindy Gow	298,752

Public Schs..Principal	Grd	Prgm	Enr/#Cls	SN	
Colden Elem Sch 8263 Boston Colden Rd, Colden 14033 Brooke Adams	K-5		140 18	34%	716/592-3217 Fax 716/592-3254
Griffith Institute Middle Sch 267 Newman St, Springville 14141 Shanda Duclon	6-8		399 36	35%	716/592-3203 Fax 716/592-3268
Springville Elem Sch 283 North St, Springville 14141 Christopher Scarpine	K-5		554 37	39%	716/592-3204 Fax 716/592-3264
Springville Griffith Inst HS 290 N Buffalo St, Springville 14141 James Bialasik	9-12		552 57	28%	716/592-3202 Fax 716/592-3297

• **Sweet Home Central Sch Dist** PID: 00725171   716/250-1400
1901 Sweet Home Rd, Amherst 14228   Fax 716/250-1361

Schools: 6 \ **Teachers:** 277 \ **Students:** 3,300 \ **Special Ed Students:** 394 \ **LEP Students:** 167 \ **Ethnic:** Asian 7%, African American 22%, Hispanic 5%, Caucasian 66% \ **Exp:** $226 (Med) \ **Poverty:** 14% \ **Title I:** $830,609 \ **Special Education:** $4,950,000 \ **Open-Close:** 09/04 - 06/24 \ **DTBP:** $327 (High) \ 🇫

Anthony Day	1	Deborah Sarkees	2
Gerald Stuitje	2,3	Sandra Cocca	4
Robert Weselak	5	Marissa Dauria	6*
Donald Feldmann	7,71	Scott Wolf	8,285
Thomas Roberts	12,298*	Debbi Coniglio	23
Anne Nowak	36,83,90,93	John Cole	58,79
Scott Johnson	67	Robert Ehlenfield	73,76,82
Paul Szymendera	273*		

Public Schs..Principal	Grd	Prgm	Enr/#Cls	SN	
Glendale Elem Sch 101 Glendale Dr, Tonawanda 14150 Joleen Dimitroff	K-5	T	370 24	45%	716/250-1500 Fax 716/250-1510 🇫
Heritage Heights Elem Sch 2545 Sweet Home Rd, Amherst 14228 Gregory Smorol	K-5	T	314 20	55%	716/250-1525 Fax 716/250-1531
Maplemere Elem Sch 236 E Maplemere Rd, Amherst 14221 James Ryan	K-5		414 24	46%	716/250-1550 Fax 716/250-1555
Sweet Home High Sch 1901 Sweet Home Rd, Amherst 14228 Scott Martin	9-12	AGV	1,042 70	52%	716/250-1200 Fax 716/250-1382

---

79 Student Personnel	91 Safety/Security	275 Response To Intervention	298 Grant Writer/Ptnrships	**School Programs**	**Social Media**
80 Driver Ed/Safety	92 Magnet School	277 Remedial Math K-12	750 Chief Innovation Officer	A = Alternative Program	🇫 = Facebook
81 Gifted/Talented	93 Parental Involvement	280 Literacy Coach	751 Chief of Staff	G = Adult Classes	
82 Video Services	95 Tech Prep Program	285 STEM	752 Social Emotional Learning	M = Magnet Program	🇹 = Twitter
83 Substance Abuse Prev	97 Chief Information Officer	286 Digital Learning		T = Title I Schoolwide	
84 Erate	98 Chief Technology Officer	288 Common Core Standards	**Other School Types**	V = Career & Tech Ed Programs	
85 AIDS Education	270 Character Education	294 Accountability	Ⓐ = Alternative School		
88 Alternative/At Risk	271 Migrant Education	295 Network System	Ⓒ = Charter School	New Schools are shaded	
89 Multi-Cultural Curriculum	273 Teacher Mentor	296 Title II Programs	Ⓜ = Magnet School	New Superintendents and Principals are bold	
90 Social Work	274 Before/After Sch	297 Webmaster	Ⓨ = Year-Round School	Personnel with email addresses are underscored	

NY-63

Erie County

Market Data Retrieval

Sweet Home Middle Sch 4150 Maple Rd, Amherst 14226 Derek Baker	6-8	TV	764 54	53%	716/250-1450 Fax 716/250-1490
Willow Ridge Elem Sch 480 Willow Ridge Dr, Amherst 14228 Robert Polino	K-5		358 40	40%	716/250-1575 Fax 716/250-1585

- **Tonawanda City School Dist** PID: 00725262   716/694-7690
  100 Hinds St, Tonawanda 14150   Fax 716/694-9467

> Schools: 4 \ Teachers: 156 \ Students: 2,000 \ Special Ed Students: 301 \ LEP Students: 34 \ College-Bound: 70% \ Ethnic: Asian 1%, African American 1%, Hispanic 6%, Native American: 1%, Caucasian 91% \ Exp: $252 (Med) \ Poverty: 14% \ Title I: $446,090 \ Special Education: $3,396,000 \ Open-Close: 09/02 - 06/24 \ DTBP: $161 (High)

Dr Timothy Oldenburg 1	Donna Hill 2,5	
Jeffery Hatten 3,91	Evie Riordan 4*	
Ben Morton 6	Mary Scullion 8,11,69,74,275,280,285,288	
Heather Sternin 19,67	Amy Edgerton 36,58,79,88,752	
Jessi Donner 73	Andrea Tamarazio 76	

Public Schs..Principal	Grd	Prgm	Enr/#Cls	SN	
Fletcher Elem Sch 555 Fletcher St, Tonawanda 14150 Michelle Siebert	4-5	T	274 15	57%	716/694-7694 Fax 716/692-3449
Mullen Elem Sch 130 Syracuse St, Tonawanda 14150 Diana Nigro	K-3	T	250 22	45%	716/694-6805 Fax 716/694-5897
Riverview Elem Sch 55 Taylor Dr, Tonawanda 14150 Cladia Panaro	PK-3	T	325 14	48%	716/694-7697 Fax 716/694-7172
Tonawanda Middle-High Sch 600 Fletcher St, Tonawanda 14150 David Sellan \ Michael Brown	6-12	T	925 30	47%	716/694-7670 Fax 716/743-8839

- **West Seneca Central Sch Dist** PID: 00725377   716/677-3100
  675 Potters Rd, West Seneca 14224   Fax 716/677-3104

> Schools: 9 \ Teachers: 447 \ Students: 6,100 \ Special Ed Students: 1,130 \ LEP Students: 47 \ College-Bound: 79% \ Ethnic: Asian 2%, African American 4%, Hispanic 5%, Caucasian 89% \ Exp: $226 (Med) \ Poverty: 8% \ Title I: $906,647 \ Special Education: $13,775,000 \ Open-Close: 09/04 - 06/24 \ DTBP: $313 (High)

Matthew Bystrak 1	Brian Schultz 2,70
Janice Lewandowski 2,295	Joseph Farr 3
Ann Ralph 4*	Linda Ogrady 5
Vinnie Delloso 6	Carmelina Persico 8,15
Franco Di Pasqua 11,42,45,89	Jonathan Cervoni 15
Jeff Pacer 16,82	Robert Merkal 26,27,31,75
Stephanie Wright 30,274	Jonathon Dalbo 39,71,73,76,97
Dana McManus 57*	Kristin Collins 58
Diane Beres 67	Beth Johnson 68
Jennifer Falore 71	Scott Firkins 76
Jonthan Cervoli 78,93	Tracy Spagnolo 79
David Urbanek 91	

Public Schs..Principal	Grd	Prgm	Enr/#Cls	SN	
Allendale Elem Sch 1399 Orchard Park Rd, West Seneca 14224 Holly Quinn	PK-5		562 30	32%	716/677-3660 Fax 716/675-3104
Clinton Street Elem Sch 4100 Clinton St, West Seneca 14224 Kimberly McCartan	K-4		565	31%	716/677-3620 Fax 716/674-7821
East Middle Sch 1445 Center Rd, West Seneca 14224 Sharon Loughran	5-8		812 26	38%	716/677-3530 Fax 716/674-1046
Northwood Elem Sch 250 Northwood Ave, West Seneca 14224 Angela Ferri-Cordaro	PK-4		489 28	38%	716/677-3641 Fax 716/674-3505
West Elem Sch 1397 Orchard Park Rd, West Seneca 14224 Kristen Frawley	K-5		676 65	25%	716/677-3250 Fax 716/677-3123
West Middle Sch 395 Center Rd, West Seneca 14224 Dave Kean	6-8	V	828	40%	716/677-3500 Fax 716/675-6134
West Seneca East Sr High Sch 4760 Seneca St, West Seneca 14224 Jason Winnicki	9-12	GV	792 66	39%	716/677-3300 Fax 716/677-2933
West Seneca West Sr High Sch 3330 Seneca St, West Seneca 14224 Jay Brinker	9-12	GV	1,195 89	36%	716/677-3350 Fax 716/674-3551
Winchester Elem Sch 650 Harlem Rd, West Seneca 14224 Robyn Brady	1-5	T	360 31	58%	716/677-3580 Fax 716/822-2670

- **Williamsville Ctl School Dist** PID: 00725535   716/626-8000
  105 Casey Rd, East Amherst 14051   Fax 716/626-8089

> Schools: 13 \ Teachers: 805 \ Students: 9,900 \ Special Ed Students: 1,311 \ LEP Students: 363 \ College-Bound: 89% \ Ethnic: Asian 14%, African American 4%, Hispanic 4%, Caucasian 77% \ Exp: $242 (Med) \ Poverty: 4% \ Title I: $475,915 \ Special Education: $8,703,000 \ Open-Close: 09/08 - 06/24 \ DTBP: $233 (High)

Dr Scott Martzloff 1,11	Thomas Maturski 2,15,76,298
Tracy Sullivan 2	Keith Langlotz 3,91
Robert Farleo 3	Kathryn Christopher 4
Graham Violino 5	Chris Mucica 6,35
Christine Harding 7*	Dr Marie Balen 8,15,31,34,69,288
Anthony Scanzuso 15,58,77,275	Dr John McKenna 15,68
Thomas Bird 28,29,42,285*	Karen Greco 39,57,61*
Dr Christopher McGinley 45*	Gail Militello 48,51,54,280*
Cheryl Lazzaro 58	John D'Angelo 58
Teresa Leatherbarrow 67	Rita Wolff 71
Deborah Radice 73,295	Dr Rosa D'Abate 79

Public Schs..Principal	Grd	Prgm	Enr/#Cls	SN	
Casey Middle Sch 105 Casey Rd, East Amherst 14051 Peter Dobmeier	5-8		629 30	19%	716/626-8567 Fax 716/626-8562
Country Parkway Elem Sch 35 Hollybrook Dr, Williamsville 14221 Andrew Bowen	K-4		559 40	13%	716/626-9860 Fax 716/626-9879
Dodge Elem Sch 1900 Dodge Rd, East Amherst 14051 Charles Smilinich	K-4		549 30	17%	716/626-9821 Fax 716/626-9849
East High Sch 151 Paradise Rd, East Amherst 14051 Brian Swatland	9-12	GV	1,013	13%	716/626-8404 Fax 716/626-8408
Forest Elem Sch 250 N Forest Rd, Williamsville 14221 Keith Wing	K-4		520 28	25%	716/626-9800 Fax 716/626-9819
Heim Elem Sch 155 Heim Rd, Williamsville 14221 Bonnie Stafford	K-4		619 31	16%	716/626-8697 Fax 716/626-8679
Heim Middle Sch 175 Heim Rd, Williamsville 14221 Jeff Jachlewski	5-8		662 70	16%	716/626-8600 Fax 716/626-8626

1	Superintendent	8	Curric/Instruct K-12	19	Chief Financial Officer	29	Family/Consumer Science	
2	Bus/Finance/Purchasing	9	Curric/Instruct Elem	20	Art K-12	30	Adult Education	
3	Buildings And Grounds	10	Curric/Instruct Sec	21	Art Elem	31	Career/Sch-to-Work K-12	
4	Food Service	11	Federal Program	22	Art Sec	32	Career/Sch-to-Work Elem	
5	Transportation	12	Title I	23	Music K-12	33	Career/Sch-to-Work Sec	
6	Athletic	13	Title V	24	Music Elem	34	Early Childhood Ed	
7	Health Services	14	Instructional Media Svcs	25	Music Sec	35	Health/Phys Education	
		15	Asst Superintendent	26	Business Education	36	Guidance Services K-12	
		16	Chief Operations Officer	27	Career & Tech Ed	37	Guidance Services Elem	
		17	Chief Academic Officer	28	Technology Education	38	Guidance Services Sec	
39	Social Studies K-12	49	English/Lang Arts Elem	59	Special Education Elem	69	Academic Assessment	
40	Social Studies Elem	50	English/Lang Arts Sec	60	Special Education Sec	70	Research/Development	
41	Social Studies Sec	51	Reading K-12	61	Foreign/World Lang K-12	71	Public Information	
42	Science K-12	52	Reading Elem	62	Foreign/World Lang Elem	72	Summer School	
43	Science Elem	53	Reading Sec	63	Foreign/World Lang Sec	73	Instructional Tech	
44	Science Sec	54	Remedial Reading K-12	64	Religious Education K-12	74	Inservice Training	
45	Math K-12	55	Remedial Reading Elem	65	Religious Education Elem	75	Marketing/Distributive	
46	Math Elem	56	Remedial Reading Sec	66	Religious Education Sec	76	Info Systems	
47	Math Sec	57	Bilingual/ELL	67	School Board President	77	Psychological Assess	
48	English/Lang Arts K-12	58	Special Education K-12	68	Teacher Personnel	78	Affirmative Action	

New York School Directory — Erie County

School	Grd	Prgm	Enr/#Cls	SN	Phone
Maple East Elem Sch 1500 Maple Rd, Williamsville 14221 Dr William Bohen	K-4		633 28	11%	716/626-8801 Fax 716/626-8808
Maple West Elem Sch 851 Maple Rd, Williamsville 14221 Jason Smith	K-4		648 40	22%	716/626-8840 Fax 716/626-8859
Mill Middle Sch 505 Mill St, Williamsville 14221 Michael Calandra	5-8		823 65	23%	716/626-8300 Fax 716/626-8326 t
North High Sch 1595 Hopkins Rd, Williamsville 14221 Andre Thomas	9-12	AGV	1,412 70	19%	716/626-8505 Fax 716/626-8597 t
South High Sch 5950 Main St, Williamsville 14221 Keith Boardman	9-12	GV	911	19%	716/626-8281 Fax 716/626-8207 t
Transit Middle Sch 8730 Transit Rd, East Amherst 14051 Daniel Walh	5-8		935 75	14%	716/626-8701 Fax 716/626-8796

ERIE CATHOLIC SCHOOLS

- **Diocese of Buffalo Ed Office** PID: 00725846 716/847-5520
  795 Main St, Buffalo 14203 Fax 716/847-5593

Schools: 49 \ **Students:** 15,000

Listing includes only schools located in this county. See District Index for location of Diocesan Offices.

Dr Michael Lafever 1

Catholic Schs..Principal	Grd	Prgm	Enr/#Cls	SN	Phone
Bishop Timon-St Jude High Sch 601 McKinley Pkwy, Buffalo 14220 Dr Jim Newton	9-12		178 25		716/826-3610 Fax 716/824-5833 f
Buffalo Acad of Sacred Heart 3860 Main St, Buffalo 14226 Jennifer Demert	9-12		492		716/834-2101 Fax 716/834-2944 f
Canisius High Sch 1180 Delaware Ave, Buffalo 14209 Andrea Tyrpak-Endres	9-12		815 49		716/882-0466 Fax 716/883-1870
Cardinal O'Hara High Sch 39 Ohara Rd, Tonawanda 14150 Mary Holzerland	9-12		250 40		716/695-2600 Fax 716/692-8697
Catholic Academy of W Buffalo 1069 Delaware Ave, Buffalo 14209 Sr Gail Glenn	PK-8		200 8		716/885-6111 Fax 716/885-6452
Christ the King Sch 2 Lamarck Dr, Snyder 14226 Samuel Zalacca	PK-8		245 16		716/839-0473 Fax 716/568-8198
Immaculate Conception Sch 510 Oakwood Ave, East Aurora 14052 Joseph Duttweiler	K-8		205 9		716/652-5855 Fax 716/805-0912
Mt Mercy Academy 88 Red Jacket Pkwy, Buffalo 14220 Margaret Staszak	9-12		300 50		716/825-8796 Fax 716/825-0976
Mt St Mary Academy 3756 Delaware Ave, Kenmore 14217 Katherine Spillman	9-12		376 48		716/877-1358 Fax 716/877-0548
Nardin Academy Middle Sch 135 Cleveland Ave, Buffalo 14222 Christopher Pitek	5-8		220		716/881-6262
Nativity Miguel MS of Buffalo 21 Davidson Ave, Buffalo 14215 Edward Durkin	5-8		109 14		716/836-5188 Fax 716/836-5189
Nativity of Blessed Mary Sch 8550 Main St, Williamsville 14221 Dr Robert Cluckey	PK-8		218 10		716/633-7441 Fax 716/626-1637
Nativity of Our Lord Sch 4414 S Buffalo St, Orchard Park 14127 Christopher Gardon	PK-8		220 27		716/662-7572 Fax 716/662-3483
Our Lady Blessed Sacrament Sch 20 French Rd, Depew 14043 Debbie Szczepanski	PK-8		142 13		716/685-2544 Fax 716/685-9103
Our Lady of Black Rock Sch 16 Peter St, Buffalo 14207 Martha Eadie	PK-8		170 9		716/873-7497 Fax 716/447-9926
Our Lady of Victory Sch 2760 S Park Ave, Lackawanna 14218 Carolyn Kraus	PK-8	G	180 10		716/828-9434 Fax 716/828-7728
Queen of Heaven Sch 839 Mill Rd, West Seneca 14224 Mary Damico	PK-8		364 14		716/674-5206 Fax 716/674-2793 f t
Sbcs Notre Dame Academy 1125 Abbott Rd, Buffalo 14220 Tristan D'Angelo	PK-8		490 24		716/824-0726 Fax 716/825-7685 f t
Southtowns Catholic Sch 2052 Lakeview Rd, Lake View 14085 Marc Bandelian	PK-8		191 13		716/627-5011 Fax 716/627-5335 f t
SS Peter & Paul Sch 68 E Main St, Hamburg 14075 Sr Marilyn Dudek	PK-8		351 30		716/649-7030 Fax 716/649-5218 f
SS Peter & Paul Sch 5480 Main St, Williamsville 14221 Melissa Lindner	PK-8		350 30		716/632-6146 Fax 716/626-0971 f t
St Aloysius Regional Sch 186 Franklin St, Springville 14141 Mary Beth Webster	PK-8		100 14		716/592-7002 Fax 716/592-4032
St Amelia Sch 2999 Eggert Rd, Tonawanda 14150 Scott Kapperman	PK-8		558 30		716/836-2230 Fax 716/832-9700
St Andrew's Country Day Sch 1545 Sheridan Dr, Kenmore 14217 Pamela Giannantonio	PK-8		210 15		716/877-0422 Fax 716/877-3973
St Benedict Sch 3980 Main St, Amherst 14226 Maryalice Bagwell	PK-8		290 17		716/835-2518 Fax 716/834-4932 f
St Christopher Sch 2660 Niagara Falls Blvd, Tonawanda 14150 Dr Camille Pontrello	PK-8		467 24		716/693-5604 Fax 716/693-5127
St Francis High Sch 4129 Lake Shore Rd, Hamburg 14075 Sean Obrochta	9-12		469 36		716/627-1200 Fax 716/627-4610 f
St Gregory the Great Sch 250 Saint Gregory Ct, Williamsville 14221 Julie Gajewski	PK-8		645 27		716/688-5323 Fax 716/688-6629
St John the Baptist Sch-Alden 2028 Sandridge Rd, Alden 14004 Jonna Johnson	PK-8		130 9		716/937-9483 Fax 716/937-9794
St John the Baptist Sch-Knmore 1085 Englewood Ave, Kenmore 14223 Jenny Bainbridge	PK-8		387 18		716/877-6401 Fax 716/877-9139 f
St John Vianney Sch 2950 Southwestern Blvd, Orchard Park 14127 Kristine Hider	PK-8		220 15		716/674-9232 Fax 716/674-9248 f t
St Joseph Collegiate Institute 845 Kenmore Ave, Buffalo 14223 James Spillman	9-12		850 30		716/874-4024 Fax 716/874-4956

---

79 Student Personnel
80 Driver Ed/Safety
81 Gifted/Talented
82 Video Services
83 Substance Abuse Prev
84 Erate
85 AIDS Education
88 Alternative/At Risk
89 Multi-Cultural Curriculum
90 Social Work
91 Safety/Security
92 Magnet School
93 Parental Involvement
95 Tech Prep Program
97 Chief Information Officer
98 Chief Technology Officer
270 Character Education
271 Migrant Education
273 Teacher Mentor
274 Before/After Sch
275 Response To Intervention
277 Remedial Math K-12
280 Literacy Coach
285 STEM
286 Digital Learning
288 Common Core Standards
294 Accountability
295 Network System
296 Title II Programs
297 Webmaster
298 Grant Writer/Ptnrships
750 Chief Innovation Officer
751 Chief of Staff
752 Social Emotional Learning

School Programs
A = Alternative Program
G = Adult Classes
M = Magnet Program
T = Title I Schoolwide
V = Career & Tech Ed Programs

Other School Types
Ⓐ = Alternative School
Ⓒ = Charter School
Ⓜ = Magnet School
Ⓨ = Year-Round School

Social Media
f = Facebook
t = Twitter

New Schools are shaded
New Superintendents and Principals are bold
Personnel with email addresses are underscored

Erie County

School	Grd	Prgm	Enr/#Cls	SN	Phone
St Joseph University Sch 3275 Main St, Buffalo 14214 Mark Mattle	PK-8		170 11		716/835-7395 Fax 716/833-6550
St Mark Sch 399 Woodward Ave, Buffalo 14214 Robert Clemens	K-8		395 14		716/836-1191 Fax 716/836-0391
St Mary Sch-Swormville 6919 Transit Rd, Swormville 14051 Mary Jo Aiken	K-8		195 16		716/689-8424
St Mary's Elem Sch-Lancaster 2 Saint Marys Hl, Lancaster 14086 Kim Kwitowski	PK-8		200 17		716/683-2112 Fax 716/683-2134
St Mary's High Sch 142 Laverack Ave, Lancaster 14086 Keith Junik	9-12		425 50		716/683-4824 Fax 716/683-4996
St Stephen Sch 2080 Baseline Rd, Grand Island 14072 Scott Gruenauer	PK-8		210 20		716/773-4347 Fax 716/773-1438

ERIE PRIVATE SCHOOLS

Private Schs..Principal	Grd	Prgm	Enr/#Cls	SN	Phone
Amherst Christian Academy 2625 Tonawanda Creek Rd, Amherst 14228 Michael Caban	PK-12		77 3		716/689-9944
Aspire Centr for Learning 4635 Union Rd, Cheektowaga 14225 Cathy Voyer	Spec		225 25		716/505-5700 Fax 716/633-9351
Aurora Waldorf Sch 525 W Falls Rd, West Falls 14170 Anna Harp	PK-8		125 15		716/655-2029 Fax 716/655-3265
Baker Hall Sch 777 Ridge Rd, Buffalo 14218 Lyndsey Todard	Spec	V	111 16		716/828-9737
Baptist Sch 72 E Niagara St, Tonawanda 14150 Scott Tracey	K-12		50 17		716/695-5334 Fax 716/695-8806
Blossom Garden Friends Sch 13961 Sisson Hwy, Collins 14034 Janice Ninan	K-12		13 4		716/532-1004
Buffalo Seminary Sch 205 Bidwell Pkwy, Buffalo 14222 Helen Marlette	9-12	G	171 22		716/885-6780 Fax 716/885-6785
Cantalician Center for Lrng 2049 George Urban Blvd, Depew 14043 Mark Blesy	Spec		190 17		716/901-8700 Fax 716/901-8800
Center Road Christian Academy 412 Center Rd, Buffalo 14224 Michael Rader	K-12		25 1		716/675-6545 Fax 716/408-5517
Chc Learning Center 1085 Eggert Rd, Buffalo 14226 Nancy Godson	Spec		37 6		716/831-8422 Fax 716/831-8428
Children's League 393 North St, Springville 14141	Spec		120		716/592-9331 Fax 716/592-4683
Christian Central Academy 39 Academy St, Williamsville 14221 Thad Gaebelein	K-12		456 25		716/634-4821 Fax 716/634-5851
Darul Ullom AL Madania Sch 182 Sobieski St, Buffalo 14212 Faifal Ansari	K-10		312		716/895-3318 Fax 716/892-6621
Elmwood Franklin Sch 104 New Amsterdam Ave, Buffalo 14216 Sarah Duddy \ Annie Lotempio	PK-8		350 14		716/877-5035 Fax 716/877-9680
Gateway-Longview-Lynde Sch 6350 Main St, Williamsville 14221 Wendy Emerling	Spec	V	105 20		716/783-3100 Fax 716/634-3925
Gow Sch 2491 Emery Rd, South Wales 14139 Luke Salerno \ Robin Marshman	7-12		150 20		716/652-3450 Fax 716/652-3457
Jewish Heritage Day Sch 411 John James Audubon Pkwy, Amherst 14228 S Shanowitz	PK-8		89		716/568-0226 Fax 716/276-8668
Kadimah School-Buffalo 1085 Eggert Rd, Buffalo 14226 Fran Paskowitz	PK-8		78 10		716/836-6903 Fax 716/837-7322
Nardin Academy Elem Sch 135 Cleveland Ave, Buffalo 14222 Callie Georger	1-8		298 35		716/881-6262 Fax 716/881-4681
Nardin Academy High Sch 135 Cleveland Ave, Buffalo 14222 Adrienne Forgette	9-12		470 40		716/881-6262 Fax 716/881-0086
Nardin Montessori Academy 700 W Ferry St, Buffalo 14222 Kristin Whitlock	PK-3		127		716/881-6565 Fax 716/886-5931
New Creation Fellowship Acad 3325 Genesee St, Buffalo 14225 Michael Ward	PK-12		30		716/632-6084 Fax 716/631-8596
New Life Christian Sch 80 Luksin Dr, Tonawanda 14150 Patricia Robinson	K-12		58 5		716/694-0071
Nichols Sch 1250 Amherst St, Buffalo 14216 Paul Errickson \ Aranya Maritime	5-12		560 41		716/332-6300 Fax 716/875-2169
Park School-Buffalo 4625 Harlem Rd, Snyder 14226 Jeremy Besch	PK-12		260		716/839-1242 Fax 716/839-2014
Renaissance Campus Sch 920 Harlem Rd, West Seneca 14224 Phillip Muluso	Spec		62		716/821-0391 Fax 716/828-1009
St Mary's School for the Deaf 2253 Main St, Buffalo 14214 Aimee Bell	Spec		115		716/834-7200 Fax 716/834-2720
Stanley G Falk Sch 31 Rossler Ave, Cheektowaga 14206 Rebecca Armstrong	Spec		200 30		716/894-3892 Fax 716/894-3961
Stanley G Falk Sch 848 Delaware Ave, Buffalo 14209	K-6		140		716/882-0090 Fax 716/882-2986
Strong Academy 301 14th St, Buffalo 14213	PK-K		50		716/474-8455
Summit Center-Brighton 150 Stahl Rd, Getzville 14068 Susan Whittaker	Spec		270 16		716/629-3400 Fax 716/629-3499
Summit Educational Resources 165 Creekside Dr # 108, Amherst 14228 Susan Whittaker	Spec		57		716/810-7700 Fax 716/810-7799
Trinity Lutheran Sch 146 Reserve Rd, West Seneca 14224 Kathy Fretthold	PK-8		75 6		716/674-5353 Fax 716/674-4910
Universal Sch 1957 Genesee St, Buffalo 14211 Asiyah Teruel	PK-8		111		716/597-0102 Fax 716/597-0280
West Seneca Christian Sch 511 Union Rd, West Seneca 14224 Joshua Sexton	PK-12		120 20		716/674-1820 Fax 716/674-4894
Western NY Childrens Psyc Ctr 1010 East and West Rd, West Seneca 14224 Joshua Twarozek	Spec		35		716/674-9730 Fax 716/677-7075

---

1 Superintendent	8 Curric/Instruct K-12	19 Chief Financial Officer	29 Family/Consumer Science	39 Social Studies K-12	49 English/Lang Arts Elem	59 Special Education Elem	69 Academic Assessment
2 Bus/Finance/Purchasing	9 Curric/Instruct Elem	20 Art K-12	30 Adult Education	40 Social Studies Elem	50 English/Lang Arts Sec	60 Special Education Sec	70 Research/Development
3 Buildings And Grounds	10 Curric/Instruct Sec	21 Art Elem	31 Career/Sch-to-Work K-12	41 Social Studies Sec	51 Reading K-12	61 Foreign/World Lang K-12	71 Public Information
4 Food Service	11 Federal Program	22 Art Sec	32 Career/Sch-to-Work Elem	42 Science K-12	52 Reading Elem	62 Foreign/World Lang Elem	72 Summer School
5 Transportation	12 Title I	23 Music K-12	33 Career/Sch-to-Work Sec	43 Science Elem	53 Reading Sec	63 Foreign/World Lang Sec	73 Instructional Tech
6 Athletic	13 Title V	24 Music Elem	34 Early Childhood Ed	44 Science Sec	54 Remedial Reading K-12	64 Religious Education K-12	74 Inservice Training
7 Health Services	15 Asst Superintendent	25 Music Sec	35 Health/Phys Education	45 Math K-12	55 Remedial Reading Elem	65 Religious Education Elem	75 Marketing/Distributive
	16 Instructional Media Svcs	26 Business Education	36 Guidance Services K-12	46 Math Elem	56 Remedial Reading Sec	66 Religious Education Sec	76 Info Systems
	17 Chief Operations Officer	27 Career & Tech Ed	37 Guidance Services Elem	47 Math Sec	57 Bilingual/ELL	67 School Board President	77 Psychological Assess
	18 Chief Academic Officer	28 Technology Education	38 Guidance Services Sec	48 English/Lang Arts K-12	58 Special Education K-12	68 Teacher Personnel	78 Affirmative Action

New York School Directory — Essex County

ERIE REGIONAL CENTERS

- **Erie 1 BOCES** PID: 00725688 — 716/821-7000
  355 Harlem Rd, West Seneca 14224 — Fax 716/821-7452

Dr Lynn Fusco 1	James Freglette 2,76
Michael Capuana 27	Kristen MacChiole 58
John Sherman 67	Barbara Mocarski 73

- **Erie 2 Chautauqua-Catta BOCES** PID: 00719134 — 716/549-4454
  8685 Erie Rd, Angola 14006 — Fax 716/549-1758

Dr David O'Rourke 1	Dr John O'Connor 2,15
Kevin Deering 3	Danielle O'Connor 8,15
Robin Brown 16	Leo Fial 27
Janiel Rey 30	Jennifer Saboda 58,77,275
Ronald Catalano 67	Laurie Burger 68
Jennifer Osborne-Coy 71	

- **Southtown Teachers Center** PID: 04498514 — 716/649-6775
  4460 Bay View Rd, Hamburg 14075

Annette Baldwin 1	Kathy Northway 15

ESSEX COUNTY

ESSEX COUNTY SCHOOLS

County Schs..Principal	Grd	Prgm	Enr/#Cls	SN	
Champlain Valley Education Ctr 3092 Plank Road, Mineville 12956 Dr Grace Stay	Voc	AG	120 9		518/942-6691 Fax 518/942-3368

ESSEX PUBLIC SCHOOLS

- **Boquet Valley Central Sch Dist** PID: 00728068 — 518/962-8244
  25 Sisco St, Westport 12993 — Fax 518/962-4571

  Schools: 2 \ **Teachers:** 23 \ **Students:** 202 \ **Special Ed Students:** 29 \ **College-Bound:** 65% \ **Ethnic:** Caucasian 99% \ **Exp:** $1,185 (High) \ **Poverty:** 28% \ **Title I:** $103,003 \ **Special Education:** $276,000 \ **Open-Close:** 09/03 - 06/25 \ **DTBP:** $389 (High)

Joshua Meyer 1	Charlene Petro-Durgen 2
Michael Mitchell 3*	Julie Holbrook 4*
Debrah Spaulding 5*	Tyler Atwell 5*
Paul Bueller 6*	Tom Smith 6*
Rob Witkiewicz 8,11,58,69,88,273,294*	Tracey Cross-Baker 31,69*
Laura Napper 57*	Philip Mero 67
Connie Blaine 73*	Shane Porter 73*
Tonya Lackey 285*	

Public Schs..Principal	Grd	Prgm	Enr/#Cls	SN	
Lake View Campus 25 Sisco St, Westport 12993 Joshua Meyer	K-12	T	202 30	43%	518/962-8244
Mountain View Campus 7530 Court St, Elizabethtown 12932 Rob Witkiewicz	PK-12	T	273 40	49%	518/873-6371

- **Crown Point Central Sch Dist** PID: 00727856 — 518/597-3285
  2758 Main Street, Crown Point 12928 — Fax 518/597-4121

  Schools: 1 \ **Teachers:** 27 \ **Students:** 306 \ **Special Ed Students:** 55 \ **College-Bound:** 59% \ **Ethnic:** Caucasian 100% \ **Exp:** $304 (High) \ **Poverty:** 16% \ **Title I:** $62,341 \ **Special Education:** $989,000 \ **Open-Close:** 09/04 - 06/25 \ **DTBP:** $329 (High)

Shari Brannock 1,11	Vicki Russell 2
John Swinton 6*	Joanne Mazzotte 8,36,57,69,73,270*
Tia Gunnison 58	Mitch St Pierre 67
Rudy Brouwer 76	Tara Celotti 83*

Public Schs..Principal	Grd	Prgm	Enr/#Cls	SN	
Crown Point Central Sch 2758 Main St, Crown Point 12928 Tara Celotti	PK-12	T	306 30	59%	518/597-3285

- **Keene Central School Dist** PID: 00727894 — 518/576-4555
  33 Market St, Keene Valley 12943 — Fax 518/576-4599

  Schools: 1 \ **Teachers:** 24 \ **Students:** 170 \ **Special Ed Students:** 19 \ **Ethnic:** African American 1%, Hispanic 4%, Native American: 1%, Caucasian 94% \ **Exp:** $361 (High) \ **Poverty:** 5% \ **Title I:** $2,119 \ **Special Education:** $125,000 \ **Open-Close:** 09/08 - 06/25 \ **DTBP:** $380 (High)

Daniel Mayberry 1,288	Melissa Durham 2
Jacob Riggins 3,5	Julie Holbrook 4*
Matthew Mills 6*	Melissa Lavallee 11,51,54
Mark Sturges 13,73,91,295*	Margaret Sheldon 16
Jatha Johnson 31,69,81,83,85,88*	Sarah Tremblay 57*
Robert Woughter 58*	Sheryl Quinn 67

Public Schs..Principal	Grd	Prgm	Enr/#Cls	SN	
Keene Central Sch 33 Market St, Keene Valley 12943 Robert Woughter	K-12		170 25	36%	518/576-4555

- **Lake Placid Ctl School Dist** PID: 00727911 — 518/523-2475
  50 Cummings Rd, Lake Placid 12946 — Fax 518/523-4971

  Schools: 2 \ **Teachers:** 76 \ **Students:** 650 \ **Special Ed Students:** 109 \ **LEP Students:** 4 \ **Ethnic:** Asian 1%, African American 2%, Hispanic 1%, Caucasian 96% \ **Exp:** $350 (High) \ **Poverty:** 9% \ **Title I:** $109,070 \ **Special Education:** $743,000 \ **Open-Close:** 09/03 - 06/25 \ **DTBP:** $356 (High)

Dr Roger Catania 1	Dana Wood 2,3*
Joshua Favro 5	Cora Clark 7*
Tammy Casey 10,88	Laura Coffin 11,69*
Caitlyn Patenaude 16,82	Sarah Allen 58
Dr Richard Preston 67	Jason Leon 73*
Tina Clark 83*	Joseph Bellew 295

Public Schs..Principal	Grd	Prgm	Enr/#Cls	SN	
Lake Placid Elem Sch 318 Old Military Rd, Lake Placid 12946 Sonja Franklin	K-5	T	240 30	42%	518/523-3640 Fax 518/523-4314
Lake Placid Middle High Sch 34 School St, Lake Placid 12946 Teresa Lindsay	6-12	AV	329 50	39%	518/523-2474 Fax 518/523-2896

---

79 Student Personnel	91 Safety/Security	275 Response To Intervention	298 Grant Writer/Ptnrships	**School Programs**	**Social Media**
80 Driver Ed/Safety	92 Magnet School	277 Remedial Math K-12	750 Chief Innovation Officer	A = Alternative Program	
81 Gifted/Talented	93 Parental Involvement	280 Literacy Coach	751 Chief of Staff	G = Adult Classes	= Facebook
82 Video Services	95 Tech Prep Program	285 STEM	752 Social Emotional Learning	M = Magnet Program	
83 Substance Abuse Prev	97 Chief Infomation Officer	286 Digital Learning		T = Title I Schoolwide	= Twitter
84 Erate	98 Chief Technology Officer	288 Common Core Standards	**Other School Types**	V = Career & Tech Ed Programs	
85 AIDS Education	270 Character Education	294 Accountability	Ⓐ = Alternative Program		
88 Alternative/At Risk	271 Migrant Education	295 Network System	Ⓒ = Charter School	New Schools are shaded	
89 Multi-Cultural Curriculum	273 Teacher Mentor	296 Title II Programs	Ⓜ = Magnet School	New Superintendents and Principals are bold	
90 Social Work	274 Before/After Sch	297 Webmaster	Ⓨ = Year-Round School	Personnel with email addresses are underscored	

Essex County — Market Data Retrieval

• Minerva Central School Dist PID: 00727935
1466 County Route 29, Olmstedville 12857
518/251-2000
Fax 518/251-2395

Schools: 1 \ **Teachers:** 19 \ **Students:** 110 \
Special Ed Students: 24 \ **College-Bound:** 33% \ **Ethnic:** Asian 1%, Hispanic 4%, Caucasian 95% \ **Exp:** $306 (High) \ **Poverty:** 13% \
Title I: $38,400 \ **Special Education:** $145,000 \ **Open-Close:** 09/10 - 06/25 \ **DTBP:** $356 (High) \

Timothy Farrell	1	Nancy O'Brien	2
Martin Turcotte	3*	Joseph Gonyo	5
Candice Husson	6	Sue Frazer	7,85*
James Dorsey	8,27,36,58*	Sharon Stone Martin	16*
Tamerlane Feiden	35,83,88,270*	Eric Knierim	51,54*
Kevin Stockman	57*	Danae Tucker	67
Steve Wilk	77*	Amy Lupinski	91

Public Schs..Principal	Grd	Prgm	Enr/#Cls	SN	
Minerva Central Sch 1466 County Route 29, Olmstedville 12857 Timothy Farrell	PK-12	GT	110 23	54%	518/251-2000

• Moriah Central School Dist PID: 00727959
39 Viking Ln, Port Henry 12974
518/546-3301
Fax 518/546-7895

Schools: 1 \ **Teachers:** 72 \ **Students:** 780 \ **Special Ed Students:** 175 \ **College-Bound:** 66% \ **Ethnic:** Hispanic 1%, Caucasian 98% \ **Exp:** $190 (Low) \ **Poverty:** 24% \ **Title I:** $278,205 \ **Special Education:** $1,662,000 \ **Open-Close:** 09/08 - 06/25 \ **DTBP:** $23 (Low)

William Larrow	1,288	Valrie Mildon	2
Joseph Kazlo	3,5*	Alicia Flattery	4*
Brian Cross	6*	Rosemary Toomey	7*
Carrie Langey	11,58,83,296,298*	Stacey Stahl	12
Jessica Bosarge	36*	Emily Labombard	57*
Michael Flaherty	67	Cindy Grinnell	273*
Erin Gilbo	295		

Public Schs..Principal	Grd	Prgm	Enr/#Cls	SN	
Moriah Central Sch 39 Viking Ln, Port Henry 12974 Valerie Stahl \ Alison Burch	PK-12	T	780 65	41%	518/546-3301

• Newcomb Central School Dist PID: 00727985
5535 State Route 28 N, Newcomb 12852
518/582-3341
Fax 518/582-2163

Schools: 1 \ **Teachers:** 18 \ **Students:** 405 \ **Special Ed Students:** 8 \ **College-Bound:** 66% \ **Ethnic:** Asian 2%, African American 1%, Hispanic 1%, Caucasian 95% \ **Exp:** $439 (High) \ **Poverty:** 24% \ **Title I:** $22,510 \ **Special Education:** $51,000 \ **Open-Close:** 09/01 - 06/25 \ **DTBP:** $319 (High)

Chris Fischer	1	Coleen Sage	2
Ray Bush	3,91*	Robert Bessey	5
Milly Winslow	6	Kathryn Markwica	8,31,36,69*
Jared Doyle	26*	Nicole Belden	34*
Martha Swan	57*	Steven Wilk	58*
Peter Armstrong	67		

Public Schs..Principal	Grd	Prgm	Enr/#Cls	SN	
Newcomb Central Sch 5535 State Route 28N, Newcomb 12852 Clark Hults	PK-12	GT	405 15	41%	518/582-3341

• Schroon Lake Ctl School Dist PID: 00728006
1125 US Route 9, Schroon Lake 12870
518/532-7164
Fax 518/532-0284

Schools: 1 \ **Teachers:** 27 \ **Students:** 230 \ **Special Ed Students:** 31 \ **LEP Students:** 3 \ **College-Bound:** 60% \ **Ethnic:** Hispanic 1%, Caucasian 98% \ **Exp:** $507 (High) \ **Poverty:** 22% \ **Title I:** $84,468 \ **Special Education:** $183,000 \ **Open-Close:** 09/08 - 06/25 \ **DTBP:** $373 (High)

Stephen Gratto	1	Danielle Fosella	2*
Dan Grey	3,91	Julie Holbrook	4*
Brent Dezali	5*	Lee Silvernail	6*
Sharon Kelly	7*	Michelle Crandall	11,58,271,275,294,296,298*
Mike Sharp	35,85*	Natalie Royer-Loiselle	57*
Bruce Murdock	67	Mike Pockett	73*
Matt Riddle	273	Barbara Taylor	274
Christine Gonyeau	280*		

Public Schs..Principal	Grd	Prgm	Enr/#Cls	SN	
Schroon Lake Central Sch 1125 US R9, Schroon Lake 12870 Stephen Grotto	PK-12	T	230 20	54%	518/532-7164

• Ticonderoga Central Sch Dist PID: 00728020
5 Calkins Pl, Ticonderoga 12883
518/585-7400
Fax 518/585-2682

Schools: 2 \ **Teachers:** 80 \ **Students:** 735 \ **Special Ed Students:** 171 \ **LEP Students:** 3 \ **College-Bound:** 71% \ **Ethnic:** African American 2%, Caucasian 98% \ **Exp:** $593 (High) \ **Poverty:** 17% \ **Title I:** $199,367 \ **Special Education:** $1,018,000 \ **Open-Close:** 09/03 - 06/25 \ **DTBP:** $359 (High)

Cynthia Ford-Johnston	1	Laurie Cossey	2,5,12
John Garcia	3	Bobbie Jean	4
Bob Sutphen	6*	Wendy Bush	7
Tracy Price	11,58,271,275	Mark Russell	67
Michael Pockett	73		

Public Schs..Principal	Grd	Prgm	Enr/#Cls	SN	
Ticonderoga Elem Sch 116 Alexandria Ave, Ticonderoga 12883 Elizabeth Hayes	PK-6	T	416 23	38%	518/585-7400 Fax 518/585-9065
Ticonderoga Jr Sr High Sch 5 Calkins Pl, Ticonderoga 12883 John Donohue	7-12	A	319 27	27%	518/585-7400 Fax 518/585-4076

• Willsboro Central Sch Dist PID: 00728082
29 School Ln, Willsboro 12996
518/963-4456
Fax 518/963-7577

Schools: 1 \ **Teachers:** 32 \ **Students:** 243 \ **Special Ed Students:** 55 \ **College-Bound:** 79% \ **Ethnic:** Hispanic 2%, Caucasian 98% \ **Exp:** $314 (High) \ **Poverty:** 14% \ **Title I:** $57,689 \ **Special Education:** $502,000 \ **Open-Close:** 09/04 - 06/25 \ **DTBP:** $348 (High) \

Justin Gardner	1,11,83	Allison Sucharzewski	2
John Sucharzewski	3,5	Jane Casamento	4*
Michael Douglas	6*	Christian Ford	8,27,36*
Dawn Bronson	35,85*	Sheree Ford	51,54*
Francesca Duso	57*	Jennifer Leibeck	58*
Phyllis Klein	67	Brian White	73*
Rudy Brower	76,295*	Sue Boces	298

Public Schs..Principal	Grd	Prgm	Enr/#Cls	SN	
Willsboro Central Sch 29 School Ln, Willsboro 12996 Stephen Broadwell	PK-12	T	243 45	52%	518/963-4456

---

1 Superintendent	8 Curric/Instruct K-12	19 Chief Financial Officer	29 Family/Consumer Science	39 Social Studies K-12	49 English/Lang Arts Elem	59 Special Education Elem	69 Academic Assessment
2 Bus/Finance/Purchasing	9 Curric/Instruct Elem	20 Art K-12	30 Adult Education	40 Social Studies Elem	50 English/Lang Arts Sec	60 Special Education Sec	70 Research/Development
3 Buildings And Grounds	10 Curric/Instruct Sec	21 Art Elem	31 Career/Sch-to-Work K-12	41 Social Studies Sec	51 Reading K-12	61 Foreign/World Lang K-12	71 Public Information
4 Food Service	11 Federal Program	22 Art Sec	32 Career/Sch-to-Work Elem	42 Science K-12	52 Reading Elem	62 Foreign/World Lang Elem	72 Summer School
5 Transportation	12 Title I	23 Music K-12	33 Career/Sch-to-Work Sec	43 Science Elem	53 Reading Sec	63 Foreign/World Lang Sec	73 Instructional Tech
6 Athletic	13 Title V	24 Music Elem	34 Early Childhood Ed	44 Science Sec	54 Remedial Reading K-12	64 Religious Education K-12	74 Inservice Training
7 Health Services	15 Asst Superintendent	25 Music Sec	35 Health/Phys Education	45 Math K-12	55 Remedial Reading Elem	65 Religious Education Elem	75 Marketing/Distributive
	16 Instructional Media Svcs	26 Business Education	36 Guidance Services K-12	46 Math Elem	56 Remedial Reading Sec	66 Religious Education Sec	76 Info Systems
	17 Chief Operations Officer	27 Career & Tech Ed	37 Guidance Services Elem	47 Math Sec	57 Bilingual/ELL	67 School Board President	77 Psychological Assess
	18 Chief Academic Officer	28 Technology Education	38 Guidance Services Sec	48 English/Lang Arts K-12	58 Special Education K-12	68 Teacher Personnel	78 Affirmative Action

New York School Directory — Franklin County

ESSEX CATHOLIC SCHOOLS

• **Diocese of Ogdensburg Ed Off** PID: 00769050
Listing includes only schools located in this county. See District Index for location of Diocesan Offices.

Catholic Schs..Principal	Grd	Prgm	Enr/#Cls	SN
St Agnes Elem Sch 2322 Saranac Ave, Lake Placid 12946 Catherine Bemis	PK-3		160 10	518/523-3771 Fax 518/523-2203
St Mary's Grade Sch 64 Amherst Ave, Ticonderoga 12883 Sr Sharon Dalton	PK-8		105 9	518/585-7433 Fax 518/585-1433

ESSEX PRIVATE SCHOOLS

Private Schs..Principal	Grd	Prgm	Enr/#Cls	SN
Adirondack Christian Sch 6065 Route 86, Wilmington 12997 Harold Akey	PK-12		27 3	518/946-2487
Mountain Lake Academy 386 River Rd, Lake Placid 12946 Chris Mariano	7-12		44 7	518/523-4300 Fax 518/523-5322
Mountainside Christian Academy 165 US Route 9, Schroon Lake 12870 Karl Storman	PK-12		40 10	518/532-7129 Fax 518/532-0174
North Country Sch 4382 Cascade Rd, Lake Placid 12946 David Hochschartner	4-9		84 10	518/523-9329 Fax 518/523-4858
Northwood Sch 92 Northwood Rd, Lake Placid 12946 Michael Mayher	9-12		180 25	518/523-3357 Fax 518/523-3405

FRANKLIN COUNTY

FRANKLIN COUNTY SCHOOLS

County Schs..Principal	Grd	Prgm	Enr/#Cls	SN
Adirondack Educational Center 711 State Route 3, Saranac Lake 12983 Rick Swanston	Voc	AG	200 6	518/891-1330 Fax 518/891-6043
North Franklin Education Ctr 23 Husky Ln, Malone 12953 Shawn McMahon	Voc	AG	350 20	54% 518/483-5230 Fax 518/483-1399

FRANKLIN PUBLIC SCHOOLS

• **Brushton Moira Ctl Sch Dist** PID: 00728147 518/529-7342
758 County Route 7, Brushton 12916 Fax 518/529-6062

Schools: 1 \ **Teachers:** 73 \ **Students:** 800 \ **Special Ed Students:** 162 \ **College-Bound:** 72% \ **Ethnic:** African American 1%, Native American: 1%, Caucasian 98% \ **Exp:** $218 (Med) \ **Poverty:** 21% \ **Title I:** $441,676 \ **Special Education:** $1,803,000 \ **Open-Close:** 09/03 - 06/25 \ **DTBP:** $223 (High)

Todd LaPage	1	Michael Malette	3*
Michelle Riches	4*	Darrin Jock	5
Missie Lavigne	6*	Donna Steenberg	12*
Beth Kemp	16,82*	Amanda Bruce	31,69
Kari Flynn	36*	Todd LaPage	58,88*
Marice Bright	67	Robert Ludlam	73*
Brenda Collette	83		

Public Schs..Principal	Grd	Prgm	Enr/#Cls	SN
Brushton Moira Sch 758 County Route 7, Brushton 12916 Jennifer Lynch / Donna Steenberg	PK-12	TV	800 70	61% 518/529-7342

• **Chateaugay Central School Dist** PID: 00728185 518/497-6611
42 River St, Chateaugay 12920 Fax 518/497-3170

Schools: 2 \ **Teachers:** 52 \ **Students:** 503 \ **Special Ed Students:** 92 \ **College-Bound:** 86% \ **Ethnic:** Caucasian 99% \ **Exp:** $184 (Low) \ **Poverty:** 15% \ **Title I:** $162,954 \ **Special Education:** $2,249,000 \ **Open-Close:** 09/03 - 06/25 \ **DTBP:** $349 (High) \

Loretta Fowler	1	Brian Beach	3
Rex Woodward	5	Michelle Reynolds	6*
Nicole Kalman	9,11,58	Kate Dwyer	11,288,296
Cindy Pickering	16,82*	Bruce Gugliotta	33,38,69
Josh Gidding	35,85	Tony Martin	67
Vicki Gardiner	73*	Mary Vondel	271
John Staib	295		

Public Schs..Principal	Grd	Prgm	Enr/#Cls	SN
Chateaugay Elem Sch 42 River St, Chateaugay 12920 Nicole Calnon	PK-6	T	288 14	51% 518/497-6611
Chateaugay High Sch 42 River St, Chateaugay 12920 Lori Tourville	7-12	T	215 30	43% 518/497-6611

• **Malone Central School Dist** PID: 00728202 518/483-7800
42 Husky Ln, Malone 12953 Fax 518/483-3071

Schools: 5 \ **Teachers:** 202 \ **Students:** 2,289 \ **Special Ed Students:** 368 \ **College-Bound:** 70% \ **Ethnic:** African American 1%, Hispanic 1%, Native American: 1%, Caucasian 97% \ **Exp:** $225 (Med) \ **Poverty:** 17% \ **Title I:** $752,566 \ **Special Education:** $4,972,000 \ **Open-Close:** 09/03 - 06/25 \ **DTBP:** $352 (High) \

Jerry Griffin	1	Rhonda Poirier	2
Chad Lawrence	3,91	Troy Reynolds	4
Dominic Barse	5	Eileen Kilcullen	6,35,85*
Sheila Glinski	7,83*	Reginald McDonald	11,58,79,88,271,275,280,298
Roberta Stillin-Dowman	12	Mark Dalton	16,73
Edith Thompson	20*	Jenifer Vanier	23
Rosalyn Poirier	36	John Miletich	44*

---

79 Student Personnel	91 Safety/Security	275 Response To Intervention	298 Grant Writer/Ptnrships	**School Programs**	**Social Media**
80 Driver Ed/Safety	92 Magnet School	277 Remedial Math K-12	750 Chief Innovation Officer	A = Alternative Program	= Facebook
81 Gifted/Talented	93 Parental Involvement	280 Literacy Coach	751 Chief of Staff	G = Adult Classes	= Twitter
82 Video Services	95 Tech Prep Program	285 STEM	752 Social Emotional Learning	M = Magnet Program	
83 Substance Abuse Prev	97 Chief Information Officer	286 Digital Learning		T = Title I Schoolwide	
84 Erate	98 Chief Technology Officer	288 Common Core Standards	**Other School Types**	V = Career & Tech Ed Programs	
85 AIDS Education	270 Character Education	294 Accountability	Ⓐ = Alternative School		
88 Alternative/At Risk	271 Migrant Education	295 Network System	Ⓒ = Charter School	New Schools are shaded	
89 Multi-Cultural Curriculum	273 Teacher Mentor	296 Title II Programs	Ⓜ = Magnet School	New Superintendents and Principals are bold	
90 Social Work	274 Before/After Sch	297 Webmaster	Ⓨ = Year-Round School	Personnel with email addresses are underscored	

Franklin County

Market Data Retrieval

Danielle Keating .... 48* Philip Hans 67

Public Schs..Principal	Grd	Prgm	Enr/#Cls	SN
Davis Elem Sch 183 Webster St, Malone 12953 Michelle Bailey	PK-5	T	587 35	59% 518/483-7802 Fax 518/483-6390
Flanders Elem Sch 524 E Main St, Malone 12953 Joe Coakley	PK-5	T	243 12	53% 518/483-7803 Fax 518/483-9491
Franklin Academy High Sch 42 Husky Ln, Malone 12953 Brandon Pelkey	9-12	TV	680 90	51% 518/483-7807 Fax 518/483-7813
Malone Middle Sch 15 Francis St, Malone 12953 Dustin Relation	6-8	T	553 80	53% 518/483-7801 Fax 518/483-9497
St Joseph's Elem Sch 99 Elm St, Malone 12953 Lisa DuPree	PK-5		226 12	53% 518/483-7806 Fax 518/483-9567

- **Salmon River Central Sch Dist** PID: 00728288   518/358-6600
  637 County Route 1, Ft Covington 12937   Fax 518/358-2145

Schools: 4 \ Teachers: 148 \ Students: 1,800 \ Special Ed Students: 208 \ Ethnic: Hispanic 2%, Native American: 66%, Caucasian 33% \ Exp: $283 (Med) \ Poverty: 26% \ Title I: $717,121 \ Special Education: $4,326,000 \ Open-Close: 09/03 - 06/25 \ DTBP: $365 (High)

Dr Stanley Harper 1   Natascha Jock 2
Ryan Adams 3   Nicole Foster 4
Norman Treptow 5   Shawn Miller 6*
Angela Robert 8,11,15,285,286,298   Allen Gravell 58*
Emily Lauzon 67   Jeff Boulais 73,295

Public Schs..Principal	Grd	Prgm	Enr/#Cls	SN
Salmon River Elem Sch 637 County Route 1, Ft Covington 12937 Ben Barkley	PK-5	T	349 30	70% 518/358-6670 Fax 518/358-6325
Salmon River High Sch 637 County Route 1, Ft Covington 12937 Monica Baron-Meyer	9-12	ATV	432	72% 518/358-6620
Salmon River Middle Sch 637 County Route 1, Ft Covington 12937 Tammy Russell	6-8	T	310	75% 518/358-6650 Fax 518/358-6510
St Regis Mohawk Sch 385 Church St, Hogansburg 13655 Kevin Walbridge	PK-5	T	364 27	75% 518/358-2763 Fax 518/358-9275

- **Saranac Lake Central Sch Dist** PID: 00728329   518/891-5460
  79 Canaras Ave, Saranac Lake 12983   Fax 518/891-6773

Schools: 4 \ Teachers: 110 \ Students: 1,280 \ Special Ed Students: 176 \ LEP Students: 5 \ College-Bound: 65% \ Ethnic: African American 1%, Hispanic 1%, Caucasian 98% \ Exp: $498 (High) \ Poverty: 15% \ Title I: $471,882 \ Special Education: $1,971,000 \ Open-Close: 09/03 - 06/25 \ DTBP: $358 (High)

Diane Fox 1   Cynthia Moody 2
Vernon James .... 3*   Ruth Pino 4
Leonard Barker 5   Eric Bennett 6*
Suzanne Nicholas 11,57,58,79,83,88,275   Christine Bell 38*
Aurora White 67   Caroleigh Meserole 73,295
Kathy McHugh 76   Cecily Dramm 85*
Scott Prue 91*

Public Schs..Principal	Grd	Prgm	Enr/#Cls	SN
Bloomingdale Elem Sch W Main St, Bloomingdale 12913 Mr Vanweelden	K-5		108 11	39% 518/891-3198 Fax 518/891-4675
Petrova Elem Sch 141 Petrova Ave, Saranac Lake 12983 Bryan Munn	K-5	T	378 20	47% 518/891-4221 Fax 518/891-6548
Saranac Lake High Sch 79 Canaras Ave, Saranac Lake 12983 Joshua Dann	9-12		365 28	36% 518/891-4450 Fax 518/891-6813
Saranac Lake Middle Sch 141 Petrova Ave, Saranac Lake 12983 Trisha Wickwire	6-8	T	281 40	43% 518/891-4221 Fax 518/891-6615

- **St Regis Falls Ctl Sch Dist** PID: 00728367   518/856-9421
  92 N Main St, St Regis FLS 12980   Fax 518/856-0142

Schools: 1 \ Teachers: 35 \ Students: 268 \ Special Ed Students: 57 \ LEP Students: 3 \ College-Bound: 47% \ Ethnic: Hispanic 2%, Native American: 1%, Caucasian 96% \ Exp: $299 (Med) \ Poverty: 20% \ Title I: $131,921 \ Special Education: $745,000 \ Open-Close: 08/31 - 06/22 \ DTBP: $341 (High)

Timothy Seymour 1   Susan Perkins 2
Lyndon Farmer 67

Public Schs..Principal	Grd	Prgm	Enr/#Cls	SN
St Regis Falls Central Sch 92 N Main St, St Regis FLS 12980 Corey Flynn \ Kathryn Dwyer	PK-12	MT	268 50	60% 518/856-9421

- **Tupper Lake Ctl School Dist** PID: 00728393   518/359-3371
  294 Hosley Ave, Tupper Lake 12986   Fax 518/359-7862

Schools: 2 \ Teachers: 74 \ Students: 749 \ Special Ed Students: 121 \ College-Bound: 89% \ Ethnic: Asian 1%, Hispanic 2%, Caucasian 96% \ Exp: $234 (Med) \ Poverty: 12% \ Title I: $144,518 \ Special Education: $1,630,000 \ Open-Close: 09/04 - 06/25 \ DTBP: $417 (High) \

Russ Bartlett 1   Daniel Bower 2
Pierre St Pierre 3,91   Bob Lamare 4*
Sean Auclair 5   Dan Brown 6
Matt Southwick ...... 10,11,58,79,88,273,296*   Maureen Harriman 45*
Jane Whitmore 67   Bret Fancher 286*

Public Schs..Principal	Grd	Prgm	Enr/#Cls	SN
L P Quinn Elem Sch 294 Hosley Ave, Tupper Lake 12986 Dr Michele Pinard	PK-6	T	435 28	45% 518/359-2981 Fax 518/359-3415
Tupper Lake Middle High Sch 25 Chaney Ave, Tupper Lake 12986 Russell Bartlett	7-12	V	314 53	52% 518/359-3322 Fax 518/359-9636

FRANKLIN CATHOLIC SCHOOLS

- **Diocese of Ogdensburg Ed Off** PID: 00769050
  Listing includes only schools located in this county. See District Index for location of Diocesan Offices.

New York School Directory — Fulton County

Catholic Schs..Principal	Grd	Prgm	Enr/#Cls	SN	
St Bernard's Grade Sch	K-5		80		518/891-2830
63 River St, Saranac Lake 12983			5		Fax 518/891-4619
Raymond Dora					

FRANKLIN REGIONAL CENTERS

- **Franklin-Essex-Hamilton BOCES** PID: 00728422   518/483-6420
  23 Huskie Ln, Malone 12953   Fax 518/483-2178

Stephen Shafer 1,11	Stacy Vincent 2
Cheryl Felt 8,15	Denise Luka 58
Dennis Egan 67	Michele Frazier 297

FULTON COUNTY

FULTON COUNTY SCHOOLS

County Schs..Principal	Grd	Prgm	Enr/#Cls	SN	
Ⓐ Adirondack Academy	7-12	V	75		518/736-4321
2755 State Highway 67, Johnstown 12095			12		Fax 518/736-4322
Rick Potter					
Ptech	9-12		200		718/221-1593
305 Jansen Ave, Johnstown 12095					
Matthew Davis					

FULTON PUBLIC SCHOOLS

- **Broadalbin-Perth Ctl Sch Dist** PID: 00728434   518/954-2500
  20 Pine St, Broadalbin 12025   Fax 518/954-2509

Schools: 2 \ **Teachers:** 145 \ **Students:** 1,800 \ **Special Ed Students:** 207 \ **LEP Students:** 3 \ **Ethnic:** African American 2%, Hispanic 1%, Caucasian 97% \ **Exp:** $226 (Med) \ **Poverty:** 10% \ **Title I:** $313,195 \ **Special Education:** $2,577,000 \ **Open-Close:** 09/10 - 06/25 \ **DTBP:** $365 (High) \

Stephen Tomlinson 1	Marco Zumbolo 2
Michael Carney 3,5,91	James Garner 4
Tucker Gifford 6,35	Terry LaFountain 8,11,285,288,296
Sarah Cordts 16	Bradley Strait 58,275
Steve Syzdek 67	Charla Simonson 69,79*
Michelle Kelley 71,298	Stephen Gennett 73,286,295*
Erin Compani 77	Mark Brooks 83,85,88*
Margaret Marsden 273	

Public Schs..Principal	Grd	Prgm	Enr/#Cls	SN	
Broadalbin-Perth Elem Sch	PK-6	T	943	40%	518/954-2500
1870 County Highway 107, Amsterdam 12010			18		
Dan Casey					
Broadalbin-Perth Jr Sr HS	7-12	T	857	37%	518/954-2600
100 Bridge St, Broadalbin 12025			43		Fax 518/954-2609
Mark Brooks					

- **Gloversville Enlarged Sch Dist** PID: 00728460   518/775-5791
  234 Lincoln St, Gloversville 12078   Fax 518/773-7280

Schools: 6 \ **Teachers:** 225 \ **Students:** 2,521 \ **Special Ed Students:** 582 \ **LEP Students:** 15 \ **College-Bound:** 62% \ **Ethnic:** African American 5%, Hispanic 8%, Caucasian 87% \ **Exp:** $225 (Med) \ **Poverty:** 25% \ **Title I:** $1,470,379 \ **Special Education:** $7,721,000 \ **Open-Close:** 09/08 - 06/25 \ **DTBP:** $212 (High) \

David Holloran 1	Cathy Meher 2
Vincenza Ecker 4	Michael Demagistris 6,35,80*
James Wagner 8,11,15,298	Ryan Collins 58,77,79,93
Robert Curtis 67	Osama Mustafa 71
William Cooper 73,76,295,297	Helen Stuetzel 280

Public Schs..Principal	Grd	Prgm	Enr/#Cls	SN	
Boulevard Elem Sch	3-5	T	583	63%	518/775-5700
56 East Blvd, Gloversville 12078			28		Fax 518/725-9216
Thomas Komp					
Gloversville High Sch	9-12	AGTV	742	55%	518/775-5700
199 Lincoln St, Gloversville 12078			70		Fax 518/773-3674
Richard Demallie					
Gloversville Middle Sch	6-8	TV	595	61%	518/775-5700
234 Lincoln St, Gloversville 12078					Fax 518/773-0628
Mark Batty					
Kingsborough Elem Sch	PK-2	T	340	51%	518/775-5700
24 W 11th Ave, Gloversville 12078			16		Fax 518/773-7357
Trisha Bobowski					
McNab Elem Sch	PK-5		235		518/775-5760
230 W Fulton St, Gloversville 12078			11		Fax 518/725-6754
James Crawford					
Park Terrace Elem Sch	PK-2	T	324	49%	518/775-5750
50 Bloomingdale Ave, Gloversville 12078			14		Fax 518/725-7156
Brian Di Pasquale					

- **Greater Johnstown Sch Dist** PID: 00728549   518/762-4611
  1 Sirbill Cir Ste 101, Johnstown 12095   Fax 518/762-6379

Schools: 5 \ **Teachers:** 129 \ **Students:** 1,700 \ **Special Ed Students:** 234 \ **LEP Students:** 17 \ **College-Bound:** 66% \ **Ethnic:** Asian 1%, African American 1%, Hispanic 4%, Caucasian 94% \ **Exp:** $214 (Med) \ **Poverty:** 13% \ **Title I:** $363,004 \ **Special Education:** $3,653,000 \ **Open-Close:** 09/08 - 06/25 \ **DTBP:** $51 (Low)

Dr Karen Geelan 1	Melissa Baker 2
David Wood 3	Terry Kersting 5
Mike Saterlee 6,35,85	Nicole Panton 8,71,74
Ruthie Cook 15	Terry Dewey 58,79
Christopher Tallon 67	Rachel Heroth 73
Rachel Harris 76	Todd Walker 286*
Donald Groff 295	

Public Schs..Principal	Grd	Prgm	Enr/#Cls	SN	
Glebe Street Elem Sch	2-3	T	226	53%	518/762-3714
502 Glebe St, Johnstown 12095			14		Fax 518/762-3756
Christina Lais					
Johnstown High Sch	9-12	T	466	45%	518/762-4661
1 Sirbill Cir, Johnstown 12095			47		Fax 518/736-1489
Scott Hale					
Knox Junior High Sch	7-8	T	264	41%	518/762-3711
400 S Perry St, Johnstown 12095			35		Fax 518/762-2775
Robert Kraemer					
Pleasant Avenue Elem Sch	PK-1	T	300	46%	518/762-8610
235 Pleasant Ave, Johnstown 12095			16		Fax 518/762-1217
Corinne Cotter					

---

79 Student Personnel	91 Safety/Security	275 Response To Intervention	298 Grant Writer/Ptnrships	**School Programs**	**Social Media**
80 Driver Ed/Safety	92 Magnet School	277 Remedial Math K-12	750 Chief Innovation Officer	A = Alternative Program	= Facebook
81 Gifted/Talented	93 Parental Involvement	280 Literacy Coach	751 Chief of Staff	G = Adult Classes	
82 Video Services	95 Tech Prep Program	285 STEM	752 Social Emotional Learning	M = Magnet Program	= Twitter
83 Substance Abuse Prev	97 Chief Information Officer	286 Digital Learning		T = Title I Schoolwide	
84 Erate	98 Chief Technology Officer	288 Common Core Standards	**Other School Types**	V = Career & Tech Ed Programs	
85 AIDS Education	270 Character Education	294 Accountability	Ⓐ = Alternative School		
88 Alternative/At Risk	271 Migrant Education	295 Network System	Ⓒ = Charter School	New Schools are shaded	
89 Multi-Cultural Curriculum	273 Teacher Mentor	296 Title II Programs	Ⓜ = Magnet School	New Superintendents and Principals are bold	
90 Social Work	274 Before/After Sch	297 Webmaster	Ⓨ = Year-Round School	Personnel with email addresses are underscored	

Genesee County

Market Data Retrieval

Warren Street Elem Sch — 4-6 T 346 52% 518/762-3715
110 Warren St, Johnstown 12095 — 15 — Fax 518/762-8805
Nicole Lent

- **Mayfield Ctl School Dist** PID: 00728628 — 518/661-8207
  27 School St, Mayfield 12117 — Fax 518/661-7666

Schools: 2 \ **Teachers:** 72 \ **Students:** 876 \ **Special Ed Students:** 136 \ **College-Bound:** 60% \ **Ethnic:** Asian 1%, African American 1%, Hispanic 3%, Caucasian 96% \ **Exp:** $125 (Low) \ **Poverty:** 21% \ **Title I:** $346,272 \ **Special Education:** $1,428,000 \ **Open-Close:** 09/08 - 06/25 \ **DTBP:** $332 (High) \ f t

Name	#	Name	#
Christopher Harper	1	Samantha Schweizer	2
Richard Hoose	3	Darla Sandford	4
Leta Aldous	5	Brian Dunn	6*
Nicholas Criscone	11*	Michael Valovic	27*
Eileen Rovito	35*	Robin Lair	36*
Veronica Swart	57*	Colleen Ulrich	58*
Aaron Flynn	67	Robert Hanlon	71
Matthew Toomer	73,295*		

Public Schs..Principal	Grd	Prgm	Enr/#Cls	SN	
Mayfield Elem Sch 80 N Main St, Mayfield 12117 Katria Hitrick	PK-6	T	473 32	48%	518/661-8222 Fax 518/661-6590
Mayfield Jr Sr High Sch 27 School St, Mayfield 12117 Dr Christopher Wojeski	7-12		403 40	49%	518/661-8222

- **Northville Central School Dist** PID: 00728654 — 518/863-7000
  131 S 3rd St, Northville 12134 — Fax 518/863-7011

Schools: 1 \ **Teachers:** 42 \ **Students:** 500 \ **Special Ed Students:** 67 \ **LEP Students:** 3 \ **College-Bound:** 89% \ **Ethnic:** Asian 1%, Hispanic 3%, Caucasian 95% \ **Exp:** $335 (High) \ **Poverty:** 14% \ **Title I:** $92,648 \ **Special Education:** $674,000 \ **Open-Close:** 09/04 - 06/25 \ **DTBP:** $359 (High)

Name	#	Name	#
Dr Leslie Ford	1,11	Bruce Ellsworth	2
John Karbowski	6*	Annette Fordyce	7*
Kyle McFarland	10,57,69*	Christine Brown	12*
Theresa Brown	16	Karen Izzo	31,36*
Erin Gardineer	58*	John Sira	67
Lauren Luckert	73,98,295	Shannon Fitzgerald	97

Public Schs..Principal	Grd	Prgm	Enr/#Cls	SN	
Northville Central Sch 131 S 3rd St, Northville 12134 Tammy Reidell \ Kyle McFarland	PK-12	AGTV	500 50	47%	518/863-7000

- **O E S J Central School Dist** PID: 00728678 — 518/568-2011
  61 Monroe St, St Johnsville 13452 — Fax 518/568-5407

Schools: 2 \ **Teachers:** 69 \ **Students:** 719 \ **Special Ed Students:** 152 \ **College-Bound:** 47% \ **Ethnic:** African American 1%, Hispanic 2%, Caucasian 97% \ **Exp:** $162 (Low) \ **Poverty:** 21% \ **Title I:** $349,412 \ **Special Education:** $2,071,000 \ **Open-Close:** 09/04 - 06/25 \ **DTBP:** $364 (High)

Name	#	Name	#
Adam Heroth	1	Karen Mettler	2*
Jeffrey Swartz	3*	Myra Trumbull	4*
Bruce Laquay	5	Travis Heiser	6
Karyn Bergen	7	Christina Van Wie	8*
Dr Joseph Natale	11	April Stalteri	36,88*
Kyle O'Brien	58	Neil Clark	67

Name	#	Name	#
John Libritz	73	Gregg Roth	76,286,295
Stephanie Bonk	79		

Public Schs..Principal	Grd	Prgm	Enr/#Cls	SN	
O E S J Elem Sch 6486 State Highway 29, St Johnsville 13452 Jeanine Kawryga	PK-6	T	430 41	46%	518/568-2014
O E S J Jr Sr High Sch 44 Center St, St Johnsville 13452 Adam Heroth	7-12	T	289 30	56%	518/568-2011 Fax 518/568-2797

- **Wheelerville Union Free SD** PID: 00728733 — 518/835-2171
  2417 State Highway 10, Caroga Lake 12032 — Fax 518/835-3551

Schools: 1 \ **Teachers:** 14 \ **Students:** 130 \ **Special Ed Students:** 10 \ **Ethnic:** Asian 2%, Hispanic 1%, Caucasian 98% \ **Exp:** $420 (High) \ **Poverty:** 12% \ **Title I:** $31,195 \ **Special Education:** $34,000 \ **Open-Close:** 09/08 - 06/25 \ **DTBP:** $364 (High)

Name	#	Name	#
Nicole Dettenrider	1,11,73,288	Bonnie Turnbull	2
Dave Richards	3*	Dannell Bartlett	4*
Paul Pavlus	5	Ryan Gander	6*
Sue Schneider	7*	Dave Richards	17
Michael Bruce	67	Jen Kryzak	76,97,98

Public Schs..Principal	Grd	Prgm	Enr/#Cls	SN	
Wheelerville Union Free Sch 2417 State Highway 10, Caroga Lake 12032 Nicole Dettenrieder	PK-8	T	130 9	52%	518/835-2171

FULTON REGIONAL CENTERS

- **Hamilton-Fulton-Montgmry BOCES** PID: 00728757 518/736-4681
  2755 State Highway 67, Johnstown 12095 — Fax 518/736-4311

Name	#	Name	#
Dr David Ziskin	1	Kathie Lewis	2,19
Dr Lorraine Hohenforst	15	Kristi Beedon	16
Jay Detraglia	27	Laurie Bargstedt	30
Michael Jacob	58	Craig Clark	71
Rick Potter	88		

GENESEE COUNTY

GENESEE COUNTY SCHOOLS

County Schs..Principal	Grd	Prgm	Enr/#Cls	SN	
Genesee Valley Career & Tech 8250 State Street Rd, Batavia 14020 Jon Sanfratello	Voc	G	200		585-344-7711 Fax 585-344-7760
Western New York Tech Academy 6917 W Bergen Rd, Bergen 14416	9-12		100		585-494-1220 Fax 585-494-2613

1 Superintendent	8 Curric/Instruct K-12	19 Chief Financial Officer	29 Family/Consumer Science	39 Social Studies K-12	49 English/Lang Arts Elem	59 Special Education Elem	69 Academic Assessment
2 Bus/Finance/Purchasing	9 Curric/Instruct Elem	20 Art K-12	30 Adult Education	40 Social Studies Elem	50 English/Lang Arts Sec	60 Special Education Sec	70 Research/Development
3 Buildings And Grounds	10 Curric/Instruct Sec	21 Art Elem	31 Career/Sch-to-Work K-12	41 Social Studies Sec	51 Reading K-12	61 Foreign/World Lang K-12	71 Public Information
4 Food Service	11 Federal Program	22 Art Sec	32 Career/Sch-to-Work Elem	42 Science K-12	52 Reading Elem	62 Foreign/World Lang Elem	72 Summer School
5 Transportation	12 Title I	23 Music K-12	33 Career/Sch-to-Work Sec	43 Science Elem	53 Reading Sec	63 Foreign/World Lang Sec	73 Instructional Tech
6 Athletic	13 Title V	24 Music Elem	34 Early Childhood Ed	44 Science Sec	54 Remedial Reading K-12	64 Religious Education K-12	74 Inservice Training
7 Health Services	15 Asst Superintendent	25 Music Sec	35 Health/Phys Education	45 Math K-12	55 Remedial Reading Elem	65 Religious Education Elem	75 Marketing/Distributive
	16 Instructional Media Svcs	26 Business Education	36 Guidance Services K-12	46 Math Elem	56 Remedial Reading Sec	66 Religious Education Sec	76 Info Systems
	17 Chief Operations Officer	27 Career & Tech Ed	37 Guidance Services Elem	47 Math Sec	57 Bilingual/ELL	67 School Board President	77 Psychological Assess
	18 Chief Academic Officer	28 Technology Education	38 Guidance Services Sec	48 English/Lang Arts K-12	58 Special Education K-12	68 Teacher Personnel	78 Affirmative Action

New York School Directory — Genesee County

GENESEE PUBLIC SCHOOLS

• Alexander Ctl School Dist PID: 00728783
3314 Buffalo St, Alexander 14005
585/591-1551
Fax 585/591-1098

Schools: 2 \ **Teachers:** 78 \ **Students:** 788 \ **Special Ed Students:** 102 \ **LEP Students:** 6 \ **College-Bound:** 75% \ **Ethnic:** Asian 1%, African American 1%, Hispanic 3%, Caucasian 95% \ **Exp:** $422 (High) \ **Poverty:** 7% \ **Title I:** $88,508 \ **Special Education:** $1,878,000 \ **Open-Close:** 09/04 - 06/24 \ **DTBP:** $354 (High)

Dr Katherine Huber	1,11	Tim Batzel	2,3
Jim Tyx	4	Shea Schreiber	5
Robert Adams	6*	Ryan Keating	8,285,288
Matthew Stroud	9,12,34*	Kristy Miller	16*
Hathy Bush	58	Brian Paris	67
Matthew Perry	73,286,295*	Kathy Busch	79

Public Schs..Principal	Grd	Prgm	Enr/#Cls	SN	
Alexander Elem Sch 3314 Buffalo St, Alexander 14005 J Taft	K-5	T	328 25	37%	585/591-1551 Fax 585/591-4713
Alexander Middle High Sch 3314 Buffalo St, Alexander 14005 Shannon Whitcombe	6-12		460	32%	585/591-1551

• Batavia City School Dist PID: 00728812
260 State St, Batavia 14020
585/343-2480
Fax 585/344-8204

Schools: 4 \ **Teachers:** 221 \ **Students:** 2,374 \ **Special Ed Students:** 297 \ **LEP Students:** 43 \ **Ethnic:** Asian 1%, African American 14%, Hispanic 8%, Native American: 1%, Caucasian 75% \ **Exp:** $232 (Med) \ **Poverty:** 17% \ **Title I:** $699,705 \ **Special Education:** $4,301,000 \ **Open-Close:** 09/08 - 06/25 \ **DTBP:** $359 (High)

Anabell Soler	1	Scott Rozanski	2,5
Jason DeGraff	3,91	Susan Presher	4
Michael Bromley	6,7,35*	Nancy Haitz	7,85*
Dr Molly Corey	8,11,57,280,285,288,296,298	Amanda Cook	9*
Tom Redband	31	Trisha Finnigan	36,58,77,79,88,90
Alice Ann Benedict	67	David Yoder	73
Janice Smith	79	Kelly Radley	273*

Public Schs..Principal	Grd	Prgm	Enr/#Cls	SN	
Batavia High Sch 260 State St, Batavia 14020 Paul Kesler	9-12	T	648 100	49%	585/343-2480 Fax 585/344-8609
Batavia Middle Sch 96 Ross St, Batavia 14020 Ashley Grillo	5-8	T	693 80	59%	585/343-2480 Fax 585/344-8626
Jackson Primary Sch 411 S Jackson St, Batavia 14020 Maureen Notaro	PK-1	T	440 21	56%	585/343-2480 Fax 585/344-8621
John Kennedy Intermediate Sch 166 Vine St, Batavia 14020 Amanda Cook	2-4	T	515 20	64%	585/343-2480 Fax 585/344-8617

• Byron-Bergen Ctl School Dist PID: 00728886
6917 W Bergen Rd, Bergen 14416
585/494-1220
Fax 585/494-2613

Schools: 2 \ **Teachers:** 85 \ **Students:** 864 \ **Special Ed Students:** 120 \ **LEP Students:** 8 \ **College-Bound:** 69% \ **Ethnic:** Asian 1%, African American 2%, Hispanic 5%, Caucasian 92% \ **Exp:** $286 (Med) \ **Poverty:** 10% \ **Title I:** $177,406 \ **Special Education:** $1,828,000 \ **Open-Close:** 09/08 - 06/25 \ **DTBP:** $254 (High)

Mickey Edwards	1	Lori Prinz	2,11,296
Roger Caldwell	3,91	Mary Della Penna	4
Jamie Bindigni	5	Richard Hannan	6*
Rebecca Manfreda	8	Debi List	67
Thomas Moore	73	Dr Christina Pascarella	77*
Nichole Whiteford	77*	Maureen Calmes	83,88

Public Schs..Principal	Grd	Prgm	Enr/#Cls	SN	
Byron-Bergen Elem Sch 6971 W Bergen Rd, Bergen 14416 Brian Meister	PK-6	T	483 25	46%	585/494-1220 Fax 585/494-2433
Byron-Bergen Jr Sr High Sch 6917 W Bergen Rd, Bergen 14416 Pat McGee	7-12	V	381 25	37%	585/494-1220

• Elba Central School Dist PID: 00728965
57 S Main St, Elba 14058
585/757-9967
Fax 585/757-2713

Schools: 1 \ **Teachers:** 47 \ **Students:** 403 \ **Special Ed Students:** 43 \ **LEP Students:** 39 \ **College-Bound:** 80% \ **Ethnic:** African American 1%, Hispanic 20%, Native American: 1%, Caucasian 78% \ **Exp:** $449 (High) \ **Poverty:** 8% \ **Title I:** $54,535 \ **Special Education:** $735,000 \ **Open-Close:** 09/08 - 06/24 \ **DTBP:** $364 (High)

Ned Dale	1	Lisa Penna	2
Lisa Crnkovich	4	Andrew Reeb	5
Karen Cusmano	6*	Mark Beehler	6
Jennifer Manley	7	Carol Bush	8,11,69,83,88,273,296,298
Gretchen Rosales	12	Gina Klips	31
Kelly Carlie	37	Julie Maderer	54
Katlyn Richert	57*	Nicole Kohlstaedt	58
Michael Augello	67	Bethany Anderson	285

Public Schs..Principal	Grd	Prgm	Enr/#Cls	SN	
Elba Central Sch 57 S Main St, Elba 14058 Carol Bush \ Gretchen Rosales	PK-12	T	403 50	45%	585/757-9967

• Le Roy Central School Dist PID: 00728991
2-6 Trigon Park, Le Roy 14482
585/768-8133
Fax 585/768-5505

Schools: 2 \ **Teachers:** 100 \ **Students:** 1,350 \ **Special Ed Students:** 133 \ **LEP Students:** 5 \ **College-Bound:** 75% \ **Ethnic:** Asian 1%, African American 2%, Hispanic 3%, Caucasian 94% \ **Exp:** $335 (High) \ **Poverty:** 10% \ **Title I:** $177,239 \ **Special Education:** $2,535,000 \ **Open-Close:** 09/08 - 06/23 \ **DTBP:** $365 (High)

Merritt Holly	1	Brian Foeller	2,78,298
Teresa McMullen	2	Pj Fannon	3,91
Laurie Locke	4	Andy Hart	5
Jamie Clark	6	Allison Luxon	7
Patricia Dansen	7	Robert Blake	8,11,16,73,74,285,286*
Carol Messura	9,34,69,72,88,270*	Tim McArdle	10,33,69,88*
Chelsea Eaton	11,55,57,58,79,271*	Jenna Johnson	16*
Helene Beswick	49,52*	Jackie Whiting	67
Sue Riggi	76	Sonja Armbrewster	77*
Kelly Ronan	83*	John Cacioppo	295

---

79 Student Personnel	91 Safety/Security	275 Response To Intervention	298 Grant Writer/Ptnrships	**School Programs**	**Social Media**	
80 Driver Ed/Safety	92 Magnet School	277 Remedial Math K-12	750 Chief Innovation Officer	A = Alternative Program	= Facebook	
81 Gifted/Talented	93 Parental Involvement	280 Literacy Coach	751 Chief of Staff	G = Adult Classes		
82 Video Services	95 Tech Prep Program	285 STEM	752 Social Emotional Learning	M = Magnet Program	= Twitter	
83 Substance Abuse Prev	97 Chief Information Officer	286 Digital Learning		T = Title I Schoolwide		
84 Erate	98 Chief Technology Officer	288 Common Core Standards	**Other School Types**	V = Career & Tech Ed Programs		
85 AIDS Education	270 Character Education	294 Accountability	Ⓐ = Alternative School			
88 Alternative/At Risk	271 Migrant Education	295 Network System	Ⓒ = Charter School	New Schools are shaded		
89 Multi-Cultural Curriculum	273 Teacher Mentor	296 Title II Programs	Ⓜ = Magnet School	New Superintendents and Principals are bold		
90 Social Work	274 Before/After Sch	297 Webmaster	Ⓨ = Year-Round School	Personnel with email addresses are underscored		

NY—73

Genesee County

Market Data Retrieval

Public Schs..Principal	Grd	Prgm	Enr/#Cls	SN	
Le Roy Jr Sr High Sch 9300 S Street Rd, Le Roy 14482 Tim McArdle	7-12		559 55	34%	585/768-8131 Fax 585/768-5515
Wolcott Street Sch 2 Trigon Park 6, Le Roy 14482 Carol Messura	PK-6		652 35	36%	585/768-7115 Fax 585/768-5510

- **Oakfield Alabama Ctl SD** PID: 00729024   585/948-5211
  7001 Lewiston Rd, Oakfield 14125   Fax 585/948-9362

Schools: 2 \ **Teachers:** 86 \ **Students:** 800 \ **Special Ed Students:** 85 \ **LEP Students:** 8 \ **College-Bound:** 50% \ **Ethnic:** African American 1%, Hispanic 4%, Caucasian 94% \ **Exp:** $275 (Med) \ **Poverty:** 8% \ **Title I:** $106,344 \ **Special Education:** $1,814,000 \ **Open-Close:** 09/09 - 06/24 \ **DTBP:** $372 (High)

John Fisgus 1		Lee Tyler 2	
Nicole Morasco 2,17		Jordan Yager 3	
Mary DellaPenna 4		Joshua Luxon 5	
Connie Rockew 8,12		Hayley Lown 16	
Denelle Backe 58		Matthew Lamb 67	
Robert Zdrogewski 73		Karin Gelz 77	
Carol Nicometo 83		Kathy Starkweather 85	

Public Schs..Principal	Grd	Prgm	Enr/#Cls	SN	
Oakfield Alabama Elem Sch 7001 Lewiston Rd, Oakfield 14125 Lynn Phillips	PK-6	T	453 24	52%	585/948-5211 Fax 585/948-8913
Oakfield Alabama Jr Sr HS 7001 Lewiston Rd, Oakfield 14125 Matthew Peterson	7-12		364 50	49%	585/948-5211

- **Pavilion Ctl School Dist** PID: 00729062   585/584-3115
  7014 Big Tree Rd, Pavilion 14525   Fax 585/584-3421

Schools: 2 \ **Teachers:** 83 \ **Students:** 680 \ **Special Ed Students:** 96 \ **LEP Students:** 4 \ **College-Bound:** 70% \ **Ethnic:** African American 1%, Hispanic 2%, Caucasian 97% \ **Exp:** $366 (High) \ **Poverty:** 10% \ **Title I:** $118,364 \ **Special Education:** $2,007,000 \ **Open-Close:** 09/08 - 06/25 \ **DTBP:** $374 (High)

Ken Ellison 1	Donald Childs 2,11,296,298
Rex Eighmey 3	Susan Slate 4
Tom Hart 5	James Sattora 6*
Lisa Sauer 7*	Kathy Wommack 8
Stacey Tallon 11,51,57,58,275*	Melissa Wawrzynski 38,69*
Marirose Ethington 67	Cindy Pilc 73,286*
Kim Daniel 83,85,90*	Ann Pursel 285*

Public Schs..Principal	Grd	Prgm	Enr/#Cls	SN	
Dorothy B Bunce Elem Sch 7071 York Rd, Pavilion 14525 Jon Wilson	PK-5	T	342 17	45%	585/584-3011 Fax 585/584-1050
Pavilion Ctl Jr Sr High Sch 7014 Big Tree Rd, Pavilion 14525 Dr Sheila Eigenbrod	6-12	TV	338 56	44%	585/584-3115

- **Pembroke Ctl School Dist** PID: 00728927   585/599-4525
  Route 5 & 77, Corfu 14036   Fax 585/599-4213

Schools: 3 \ **Teachers:** 98 \ **Students:** 1,000 \ **Special Ed Students:** 139 \ **LEP Students:** 3 \ **College-Bound:** 75% \ **Ethnic:** African American 1%, Hispanic 2%, Caucasian 97% \ **Exp:** $441 (High) \ **Poverty:** 12% \ **Title I:** $174,492 \ **Special Education:** $1,824,000 \ **Open-Close:** 09/08 - 06/25 \ **DTBP:** $420 (High)

Matt Calderon 1	Linda Greig 2
Mike Nuwer 3,91*	Jim Tyx 4
Donna Hackett 5*	Ryan Winchip 6
Cindy Marinaccil 11,34,58,77,79,93	Christie Maisano 16,73,82,295*
Cortney Chase 23	John Cima 67
Peg Haney 273*	

Public Schs..Principal	Grd	Prgm	Enr/#Cls	SN	
Pembroke Intermediate Sch 58 Alleghany Rd, Corfu 14036 Norman Foster	3-6	T	310 18	43%	585/599-4531
Pembroke Jr Sr High Sch Route 5 & 77, Corfu 14036 Nathan Work	7-12		408	35%	585/599-4525
Pembroke Primary Sch 2486 Main Rd, East Pembroke 14056 Lisa Blake	K-2		189 23	41%	585/762-8713

GENESEE CATHOLIC SCHOOLS

- **Diocese of Buffalo Ed Office** PID: 00725846
  Listing includes only schools located in this county. See District Index for location of Diocesan Offices.

Catholic Schs..Principal	Grd	Prgm	Enr/#Cls	SN	
Notre Dame High Sch 73 Union St, Batavia 14020 Wade Bianco	9-12		143 20		585/343-2783 Fax 585/343-7323
St Joseph Sch-Batavia 2 Summit St, Batavia 14020 Karen Green	PK-8		296 15		585/343-6154 Fax 585/343-8911

GENESEE PRIVATE SCHOOLS

Private Schs..Principal	Grd	Prgm	Enr/#Cls	SN	
Calvary Baptist Church 3515 Galloway Rd, Batavia 14020 Philip Floyd	PK-12		8 3		585/297-8605
St Paul's Lutheran Sch 31 Washington Ave, Batavia 14020 Jason Clark	PK-5		67 4		585/343-0488 Fax 585/344-0470

GENESEE REGIONAL CENTERS

- **Genesee Valley BOCES** PID: 00730918   585/344-7900
  80 Munson St, Le Roy 14482   Fax 585/344-7510

Kevin MacDonald 1	Daniel Groth 2,19
Matt Della Penna 3,91	Dr Julie Donlon-Yates 8,15,70
Dr Christopher Harris 16	Charles DiPasquale 30
Kathryn Zuroski 58	Norbert Fuest 67

1 Superintendent	8 Curric/Instruct K-12	19 Chief Financial Officer	29 Family/Consumer Science	39 Social Studies K-12	49 English/Lang Arts Elem	59 Special Education Elem	69 Academic Assessment
2 Bus/Finance/Purchasing	9 Curric/Instruct Elem	20 Art K-12	30 Adult Education	40 Social Studies Elem	50 English/Lang Arts Sec	60 Special Education Sec	70 Research/Development
3 Buildings And Grounds	10 Curric/Instruct Sec	21 Art Elem	31 Career/Sch-to-Work K-12	41 Social Studies Sec	51 Reading K-12	61 Foreign/World Lang K-12	71 Public Information
4 Food Service	11 Federal Program	22 Art Sec	32 Career/Sch-to-Work Elem	42 Science K-12	52 Reading Elem	62 Foreign/World Lang Elem	72 Summer School
5 Transportation	12 Title I	23 Music K-12	33 Career/Sch-to-Work Sec	43 Science Elem	53 Reading Sec	63 Foreign/World Lang Sec	73 Instructional Tech
6 Athletic	13 Title V	24 Music Elem	34 Early Childhood Ed	44 Science Sec	54 Remedial Reading K-12	64 Religious Education K-12	74 Inservice Training
7 Health Services	14 Asst Superintendent	25 Music Sec	35 Health/Phys Education	45 Math K-12	55 Remedial Reading Elem	65 Religious Education Elem	75 Marketing/Distributive
	15 Instructional Media Svcs	26 Business Education	36 Guidance Services K-12	46 Math Elem	56 Remedial Reading Sec	66 Religious Education Sec	76 Info Systems
	17 Chief Operations Officer	27 Career & Tech Ed	37 Guidance Services Elem	47 Math Sec	57 Bilingual/ELL	67 School Board President	77 Psychological Assess
	18 Chief Academic Officer	28 Technology Education	38 Guidance Services Sec	48 English/Lang Arts K-12	58 Special Education K-12	68 Teacher Personnel	78 Affirmative Action

New York School Directory — Greene County

Stepehen Mahoney .... 68 Maggie Fitzgibbon 71
Crystal Nelson .... 73,76 Dr Patrick Whipple 74

GREENE COUNTY

GREENE PUBLIC SCHOOLS

• **Cairo-Durham Ctl School Dist** PID: 00729127   518/622-8534
424 Main St, Cairo 12413   Fax 518/622-9566

Schools: 3 \ **Teachers:** 118 \ **Students:** 1,275 \ **Special Ed Students:** 254 \ **LEP Students:** 10 \ **College-Bound:** 75% \ **Ethnic:** Asian 1%, African American 2%, Hispanic 10%, Caucasian 88% \ **Exp:** $271 (Med) \ **Poverty:** 19% \ **Title I:** $415,933 \ **Special Education:** $541,000 \ **Open-Close:** 09/04 - 06/25 \ **DTBP:** $369 (High)

Michael Wetherbee 1   Jeff Miriello 2
Kevin Lawton 3,91   Herb Schwanse 5
Greg Hagan .... 6*   Sarah Brown 7
Dr Michelle Reed 8   Douglas Morrissey 11,34,58,79,88,270,296
Justin Karker .... 27,31,36*   Elizabeth Daly 67
Jamie Kikpole 73,295   Karen Drossel 83
Thrisha Whitbeck 294

Public Schs..Principal	Grd	Prgm	Enr/#Cls	SN	
Cairo-Durham Elem Sch 424 Main St, Cairo 12413 C Stein	K-5	T	534 38	53%	518/622-3231 Fax 518/622-9060
Cairo-Durham High Sch 1301 Route 145, Cairo 12413 Dr P McKeown	9-12	ATV	348 20	49%	518/622-8543 Fax 518/622-8857 🅵🅣
Cairo-Durham Middle Sch 1301 Route 145, Cairo 12413 S Krum	6-8	AT	298 30	56%	518/622-0490 Fax 518/622-0493

• **Catskill Central School Dist** PID: 00729153   518/943-4696
343 W Main St, Catskill 12414   Fax 518/943-7116

Schools: 3 \ **Teachers:** 132 \ **Students:** 1,385 \ **Special Ed Students:** 266 \ **LEP Students:** 47 \ **College-Bound:** 65% \ **Ethnic:** Asian 2%, African American 9%, Hispanic 13%, Caucasian 77% \ **Exp:** $299 (Med) \ **Poverty:** 16% \ **Title I:** $397,832 \ **Special Education:** $3,396,000 \ **Open-Close:** 09/04 - 06/25 \ **DTBP:** $397 (High)

Dr Ronel Cook 1   Holly Sanford 2
Bill Muirhead .... 4,5*   Eric Joyce 6
Dr Kari Brown 8,11,58   Nancy Kunz 16,82*
Deborah Johnson 67   Cheryl Rabinowitz 73*
Don Marino 76,295   Nicole Field 273*

Public Schs..Principal	Grd	Prgm	Enr/#Cls	SN	
Catskill Elem Sch 770 Embought Rd, Catskill 12414 John Rivers	PK-5	T	632 27	41%	518/943-0574 Fax 518/943-5396
Catskill High Sch 341 W Main St, Catskill 12414 Benjamin Bragg	9-12	ATV	435 25	51%	518/943-2300 Fax 518/943-7700
Catskill Middle Sch 345 W Main St, Catskill 12414 Kerry Overbaugh	6-8	T	318 42	60%	518/943-5665 Fax 518/943-3001

• **Coxsackie-Athens Central SD** PID: 00729218   518/731-1700
24 Sunset Blvd, Coxsackie 12051   Fax 518/731-1729

Schools: 4 \ **Teachers:** 113 \ **Students:** 1,400 \ **LEP Students:** 6 \ **Ethnic:** Asian 1%, African American 3%, Hispanic 8%, Caucasian 88% \ **Exp:** $231 (Med) \ **Poverty:** 10% \ **Title I:** $238,322 \ **Special Education:** $1,616,000 \ **Open-Close:** 09/08 - 06/25 \ **DTBP:** $352 (High)

Randall Squier 1   Leslie Copleston 2,15
Eric Besenfelder 3   Mary DiStefano 4
Theodore Nugent 5   Ryan Naccarato 6
Kerry Houlihan 8,11,15,69,74,296,298   Carolyn Brook 16*
Kim Taylor 16   Katie Castle 27,34,58,77
Michael Donahue 67   Paul Cardettino 73,295

Public Schs..Principal	Grd	Prgm	Enr/#Cls	SN	
Coxsackie Athens High Sch 24 Sunset Blvd, Coxsackie 12051 Freya Mercer	9-12	AGV	411	24%	518/731-1800 Fax 518/731-1809
Coxsackie Athens Middle Sch 24 Sunset Blvd, Coxsackie 12051 David Proper	5-8	T	405 25	37%	518/731-1850 Fax 518/731-1859
Coxsackie Elem Sch 24 Sunset Blvd, Coxsackie 12051 Karen Miller	K-4	T	281 18	38%	518/731-1770 Fax 518/731-1785
Edward J Arthur Elem Sch 51 3rd St, Athens 12015 Jim Martino	K-4		186 16	37%	518/731-1750 Fax 518/731-1765

• **Greenville Central School Dist** PID: 00729256   518/966-5070
4982 Route 81, Greenville 12083   Fax 518/966-8346

Schools: 3 \ **Teachers:** 111 \ **Students:** 1,100 \ **Special Ed Students:** 182 \ **LEP Students:** 3 \ **College-Bound:** 75% \ **Ethnic:** Asian 1%, African American 1%, Hispanic 2%, Caucasian 96% \ **Exp:** $284 (Med) \ **Poverty:** 12% \ **Title I:** $243,141 \ **Special Education:** $2,394,000 \ **Open-Close:** 09/11 - 06/25 \ **DTBP:** $297 (High)

Tammy Sutherland 1   Janet Maassmann 2,26
Richard Outtrim 3   Tracey Churchill 4
Mary Judeikis 5   Denise Wickham 6,35
Todd Hilgendorff 8,69,288   Peter Mahan 9,11,34*
Brook Van Fleet .... 12,57,58,77,79*   Erin DuBois 15,68,296,298
Nancy Lockwood .... 16*   Johnathan Kurner 27,28
Kenneth Landversicht .... 36*   Patricia Macko 67
Scott Gardiner .... 73*   Sheila Brady 273*
Daniel Hash 275   Kyle Grennan 295

Public Schs..Principal	Grd	Prgm	Enr/#Cls	SN	
Greenville High Sch 4976 State Route 81, Greenville 12083 Matthew Ward	9-12	AV	370 45	35%	518/966-5070 Fax 518/966-4054
Greenville Middle Sch 4976 State Route 81, Greenville 12083 Brian Reeve	6-8		279 40	33%	518/966-5070 Fax 518/966-5408
Scott M Ellis Elem Sch 11219 Route 32, Greenville 12083 Peter Mahan	K-5		476 34	36%	518/966-5070 Fax 518/966-5785

---

79 Student Personnel	91 Safety/Security	275 Response To Intervention	298 Grant Writer/Ptnrships	**School Programs**	**Social Media**		
80 Driver Ed/Safety	92 Magnet School	277 Remedial Math K-12	750 Chief Innovation Officer	A = Alternative Program	🅵 = Facebook		
81 Gifted/Talented	93 Parental Involvement	280 Literacy Coach	751 Chief of Staff	G = Adult Classes			
82 Video Services	95 Tech Prep Program	285 STEM	752 Social Emotional Learning	M = Magnet Program	🅣 = Twitter		
83 Substance Abuse Prev	97 Chief Information Officer	286 Digital Learning		T = Title I Schoolwide			
84 Erate	98 Chief Technology Officer	288 Common Core Standards	**Other School Types**	V = Career & Tech Ed Programs			
85 AIDS Education	270 Character Education	294 Accountability	Ⓐ = Alternative School				
88 Alternative/At Risk	271 Migrant Education	295 Network System	Ⓒ = Charter School	New Schools are shaded			
89 Multi-Cultural Curriculum	273 Teacher Mentor	296 Title II Programs	Ⓜ = Magnet School	New Superintendents and Principals are bold			
90 Social Work	274 Before/After Sch	297 Webmaster	Ⓨ = Year-Round School	Personnel with email addresses are underscored			

Hamilton County

Market Data Retrieval

- **Hunter Tannersville Ctl SD** PID: 00729294   518/589-5400
  6094 Main St, Tannersville 12485   Fax 518/589-5403

Schools: 2 \ **Teachers:** 45 \ **Students:** 355 \ **Special Ed Students:** 78 \ **LEP Students:** 5 \ **College-Bound:** 68% \ **Ethnic:** Asian 3%, African American 1%, Hispanic 11%, Caucasian 85% \ **Exp:** $239 (Med) \ **Poverty:** 28% \ **Title I:** $228,932 \ **Special Education:** $518,000 \ **Open-Close:** 09/08 - 06/25 \ **DTBP:** $359 (High)

Nathan Jones	1,11,288	Kayla France	2
James Partridge	3	Donna Brower	4
Amy Sylak	5	Brent Dearing	6*
Ryan Funck	10,83*	Jen Gardner	58
Andrea Benjamin-Legg	67	Steven Beauregard	73*
Donna Bonnville	77*		

Public Schs..Principal	Grd	Prgm	Enr/#Cls	SN	
Hunter Elem Sch 7794 Main Street, Hunter 12442 Nathan Jones	PK-6	T	203 16	57%	518/263-4256 Fax 518/263-4086
Hunter Tannersville Mid & HS 6094 Main St, Tannersville 12485 **Ryan Funck**	7-12	AGTV	150 20	49%	518/589-5880 Fax 518/589-7071

- **Windham Ashland Jewett Ctl SD** PID: 00729323   518/734-3400
  5411 State Route 23, Windham 12496   Fax 518/734-6050

Schools: 1 \ **Teachers:** 35 \ **Students:** 310 \ **Special Ed Students:** 53 \ **LEP Students:** 5 \ **College-Bound:** 96% \ **Ethnic:** Asian 3%, African American 1%, Hispanic 8%, Caucasian 88% \ **Exp:** $691 (High) \ **Poverty:** 13% \ **Title I:** $73,220 \ **Special Education:** $337,000 \ **Open-Close:** 09/10 - 06/30 \ **DTBP:** $359 (High)

John Wiktorko	1	Michelle Mattice	2,12
John Mattice	3*	Lara McAney	8,11,69,288*
Sandy Miller	58	Dr Terri Martin	67
Anthony Savasta	73,295*	Gabrielle Gonzalez	85*

Public Schs..Principal	Grd	Prgm	Enr/#Cls	SN	
Windham Ashland Jewett Ctl Sch 5411 State Route 23, Windham 12496 David Donner	PK-12	ATV	310 50	40%	518/734-3400

GREENE PRIVATE SCHOOLS

Private Schs..Principal	Grd	Prgm	Enr/#Cls	SN	
Grapeville Christian Sch 2416 County Route 26, Climax 12042 Rebecca Chmielewski	K-12		64 8		518/966-5037 Fax 518/966-5498

HAMILTON COUNTY

HAMILTON PUBLIC SCHOOLS

- **Indian Lake Ctl School Dist** PID: 00729359   518/648-5024
  6345 Nys Route 30, Indian Lake 12842   Fax 518/648-6346

Schools: 1 \ **Teachers:** 24 \ **Students:** 112 \ **Special Ed Students:** 21 \ **College-Bound:** 100% \ **Ethnic:** Asian 3%, African American 1%, Caucasian 96% \ **Exp:** $610 (High) \ **Poverty:** 6% \ **Special Education:** $111,000 \ **Open-Close:** 09/09 - 06/25 \ **DTBP:** $397 (High)

David Snide	1,11,288	Elizabeth Fedorspiel	2
Jay Griffin	3,5	Kathy Bennett	4*
Genine Longacker	8,13,36,69,88*	David Snide	11,288,296*
George DeChant	16*	Megan Nevinsm	58
David Harrington	67	Michael Miller	73,76,295*

Public Schs..Principal	Grd	Prgm	Enr/#Cls	SN	
Indian Lake Central Sch 6345 Nys Route 30, Indian Lake 12842 David Snide	PK-12	T	112 25	41%	518/648-5024

- **Lake Pleasant Central Sch Dist** PID: 00729397   518/548-7571
  120 Elm Lake Rd, Speculator 12164   Fax 518/548-3230

Schools: 1 \ **Teachers:** 19 \ **Students:** 80 \ **Special Ed Students:** 11 \ **Ethnic:** African American 1%, Hispanic 1%, Caucasian 97% \ **Exp:** $1,352 (High) \ **Poverty:** 19% \ **Title I:** $29,281 \ **Special Education:** $112,000 \ **Open-Close:** 09/07 - 06/25 \ **DTBP:** $340 (High)

Heather Philo	1,11,288	Elisha Christman	2,84
Ryan Jermaine	3*	Melanie O'Connell	4*
William Ralph	5	John Swift	6,73,76
Joseph Parslow	35*	Jen Branius	58,88,273*
Andrew Weaver	67	Amy Peters	280*

Public Schs..Principal	Grd	Prgm	Enr/#Cls	SN	
Lake Pleasant Central Sch 120 Elm Lake Rd, Speculator 12164 Heather Philo	PK-12	T	80 12	41%	518/548-7571

- **Long Lake Central School Dist** PID: 00729414   518/624-2221
  20 School Ln, Long Lake 12847   Fax 518/624-3896

Schools: 1 \ **Teachers:** 17 \ **Students:** 65 \ **Special Ed Students:** 8 \ **College-Bound:** 100% \ **Ethnic:** Caucasian 100% \ **Exp:** $489 (High) \ **Poverty:** 11% \ **Special Education:** $54,000 \ **Open-Close:** 09/09 - 06/25 \ **DTBP:** $353 (High)

Noelle Short	1,288	Lisa Walker	2
Victoria Snide	2,5	Tony Clark	3*
Karl Geiger	4*	Dana Goetze	6,35*
Elisha Pylman	8,11,36,69*	Megan Nebins	31,58*
Joseph Koehring	57*	Brian Penrose	67
Dennis Rust	73		

1 Superintendent	8 Curric/Instruct K-12	19 Chief Financial Officer	29 Family/Consumer Science	39 Social Studies K-12	49 English/Lang Arts Elem	59 Special Education Elem	69 Academic Assessment
2 Bus/Finance/Purchasing	9 Curric/Instruct Elem	20 Art K-12	30 Adult Education	40 Social Studies Elem	50 English/Lang Arts Sec	60 Special Education Sec	70 Research/Development
3 Buildings And Grounds	10 Curric/Instruct Sec	21 Art Elem	31 Career/Sch-to-Work K-12	41 Social Studies Sec	51 Reading K-12	61 Foreign/World Lang K-12	71 Public Information
4 Food Service	11 Federal Program	22 Art Sec	32 Career/Sch-to-Work Elem	42 Science K-12	52 Reading Elem	62 Foreign/World Lang Elem	72 Summer School
5 Transportation	12 Title I	23 Music K-12	33 Career/Sch-to-Work Sec	43 Science Elem	53 Reading Sec	63 Foreign/World Lang Sec	73 Instructional Tech
6 Athletic	13 Title V	24 Music Elem	34 Early Childhood Ed	44 Science Sec	54 Remedial Reading K-12	64 Religious Education K-12	74 Inservice Training
7 Health Services	15 Asst Superintendent	25 Music Sec	35 Health/Phys Education	45 Math K-12	55 Remedial Reading Elem	65 Religious Education Elem	75 Marketing/Distributive
	16 Instructional Media Svcs	26 Business Education	36 Guidance Services K-12	46 Math Elem	56 Remedial Reading Sec	66 Religious Education Sec	76 Info Systems
	17 Chief Operations Officer	27 Career & Tech Ed	37 Guidance Services Elem	47 Math Sec	57 Bilingual/ELL	67 School Board President	77 Psychological Assess
	18 Chief Academic Officer	28 Technology Education	38 Guidance Services Sec	48 English/Lang Arts K-12	58 Special Education K-12	68 Teacher Personnel	78 Affirmative Action

New York School Directory

Herkimer County

Public Schs..Principal	Grd	Prgm	Enr/#Cls	SN	
Long Lake Central Sch 20 School Ln, Long Lake 12847 Noelle Short	PK-12	G	65 20	52%	518/624-2221

● **Wells Central School Dist** PID: 00729476   518/924-6000
1571 State Route 30, Wells 12190   Fax 518/924-9246

Schools: 1 \ **Teachers:** 24 \ **Students:** 135 \ **Special Ed Students:** 25 \ **College-Bound:** 83% \ **Ethnic:** African American 3%, Hispanic 1%, Caucasian 97% \ **Exp:** $285 (Med) \ **Poverty:** 14% \ **Title I:** $35,968 \ **Special Education:** $155,000 \ **Open-Close:** 09/08 - 06/25 \ **DTBP:** $353 (High)

Thomas Sincavage 1   Martha Brown 2*
Marguirte Welch 4   Mindy Morrison 5
Jeremy Siddon 6,288   Kristy Wright 7*
Sharon Parslow ....8,31,69,88,270,285*   Michelle Barros 11,58,296*
Kristine Suhr ....16,82*   Edward Pruden 42*
Jeanette Brown ....45*   Susan Chittenden 48,273
Cathie Rust 67   Don Gifford 73,295
Stephen Stolfelano 286

Public Schs..Principal	Grd	Prgm	Enr/#Cls	SN	
Wells Central Sch 1571 Route State 30, Wells 12190 Jeremy Siddon	PK-12	ATV	135 20	49%	518/924-6000

HERKIMER COUNTY

HERKIMER PUBLIC SCHOOLS

● **Central Valley School Dist** PID: 00729646   315/894-9934
111 Frederick St, Ilion 13357   Fax 315/894-2716

Schools: 4 \ **Teachers:** 181 \ **Students:** 2,201 \ **Special Ed Students:** 403 \ **LEP Students:** 9 \ **College-Bound:** 77% \ **Ethnic:** Asian 1%, African American 2%, Hispanic 2%, Caucasian 95% \ **Exp:** $186 (Low) \ **Poverty:** 19% \ **Title I:** $727,193 \ **Special Education:** $4,772,000 \ **Open-Close:** 09/04 - 06/25 \ **DTBP:** $162 (High) \ 🇫 🇹

Jeremy Rich 1   James Humphrey 2,5
Brady Boyd 3   Barbara Cristman 4
Chad Francisco 5   Garrett Olds 6,10*
Kathy Carney 8,288   Fran LaPaglia 9,11,68
Jason Sanchez 67   Cuyle Rockwell 71
Steven Smith 73   Lisa Hoffman 79,271*

Public Schs..Principal	Grd	Prgm	Enr/#Cls	SN	
Barringer Road Elem Sch 326 Barringer Rd, Ilion 13357 Aaron Carey	2-4	T	497 24	60%	315/894-8420 Fax 315/894-0153
Central Valley Academy 111 Frederick St, Ilion 13357 Richard Keeler	9-12		616 68	62%	315/895-7471 Fax 315/895-5255
Gregory Jarvis Middle Sch 111 Frederick St, Ilion 13357 Charles Pratt	5-8		649 45		315/866-2620 Fax 315/867-2909
Harry Fisher Elem Sch 10 Fisher Ave, Mohawk 13407 Michele Pilla	PK-1		439 25	37%	315/866-4851 Fax 315/866-0055

● **Dolgeville Central School Dist** PID: 00729505   315/429-3155
38 Slawson St, Dolgeville 13329   Fax 315/429-8473

Schools: 2 \ **Teachers:** 90 \ **Students:** 900 \ **Special Ed Students:** 123 \ **LEP Students:** 6 \ **College-Bound:** 61% \ **Ethnic:** African American 1%, Caucasian 99% \ **Exp:** $289 (Med) \ **Poverty:** 17% \ **Title I:** $271,199 \ **Special Education:** $1,985,000 \ **Open-Close:** 09/04 - 06/25 \ **DTBP:** $348 (High) \ 🇫

Lynn Rhone 1   Jessica Radley 2,19
David Redmond 3   Anthony DuPuis 4
Joseph Stack 5   Daniel Zilkowski 6
Bethany Straney ....7*   Michelle Primeau 11,58,88
Daniel Guenthner ....27,36,69*   Bruce Risley 35,83,85*
Mirella Pazzaglia ....38,79*   Scott Hongo 67
Ruth Leavitt 288

Public Schs..Principal	Grd	Prgm	Enr/#Cls	SN	
Dolgeville Elem Middle Sch 38 Slawson St, Dolgeville 13329 Crystal Chrisman \ Ruth Leavitt	PK-8	T	500 28	57%	315/429-3155 Fax 315/429-9328
James A Green High Sch 38 Slawson St, Dolgeville 13329 Timothy Jenny	9-12	T	261 40	53%	315/429-3155

● **Frankfort-Schuyler Ctl SD** PID: 00729531   315/894-5083
605 Palmer St, Frankfort 13340   Fax 315/895-7011

Schools: 2 \ **Teachers:** 73 \ **Students:** 893 \ **Special Ed Students:** 157 \ **LEP Students:** 21 \ **College-Bound:** 74% \ **Ethnic:** African American 1%, Hispanic 2%, Caucasian 96% \ **Exp:** $298 (Med) \ **Poverty:** 16% \ **Title I:** $330,777 \ **Special Education:** $1,377,000 \ **Open-Close:** 09/04 - 06/25 \ **DTBP:** $173 (High)

Robert Reina 1,11   Kacey Sheppard 2,11,73
John Stever 3,91   Tom Pfister 4
Karen Wasielewski 5   Jeff Lagase 6*
Melanie Welch ....9,11,51,54*   Michael Stalteri 10,69,88,273*
Sue Shue 16   Brenna Kosicki 27,57,58,271*
Andrea Cordero ....36*   Kelly Hawse 39*
Robert Trotta ....42*   Audrey Cucci 45*
Lisa Lore 48   Lisa Morgan 67
Andrea Mazza ....85*   Patrick Bliss 295

Public Schs..Principal	Grd	Prgm	Enr/#Cls	SN	
Ⓨ Frankfort-Schuyler Elem Sch 610 Reese Rd, Frankfort 13340 Melanie Welch	K-5	MT	383 35	48%	315/895-7491 Fax 315/895-4102
Ⓨ Frankfort-Schuyler Jr Sr HS 605 Palmer St, Frankfort 13340 Molly Libritz \ Michael Stalteri	6-12	MT	510 50	41%	315/895-7461 Fax 315/895-4032

● **Herkimer Ctl School Dist** PID: 00729581   315/866-2230
801 W German St, Herkimer 13350   Fax 315/866-2234

Schools: 2 \ **Teachers:** 87 \ **Students:** 1,112 \ **Special Ed Students:** 204 \ **LEP Students:** 7 \ **College-Bound:** 74% \ **Ethnic:** Asian 1%, African American 3%, Hispanic 2%, Caucasian 93% \ **Exp:** $286 (Med) \ **Poverty:** 21% \ **Title I:** $444,751 \ **Special Education:** $2,273,000 \ **Open-Close:** 09/08 - 06/24 \ **DTBP:** $44 (Low)

Robert Miller 1   Robert Walker 3
Thomas Pfister 4   Cristi Paragi 6
Carolyn LaSalle 38   Brian Crandall 67

---

79 Student Personnel	91 Safety/Security	275 Response To Intervention	298 Grant Writer/Ptnrships	**School Programs**	**Social Media**
80 Driver Ed/Safety	92 Magnet School	277 Remedial Math K-12	750 Chief Innovation Officer	A = Alternative Program	🇫 = Facebook
81 Gifted/Talented	93 Parental Involvement	280 Literacy Coach	751 Chief of Staff	G = Adult Classes	
82 Video Services	95 Tech Prep Program	285 STEM	752 Social Emotional Learning	M = Magnet Program	🇹 = Twitter
83 Substance Abuse Prev	97 Chief Information Officer	286 Digital Learning		T = Title I Schoolwide	
84 Erate	98 Chief Technology Officer	288 Common Core Standards	**Other School Types**	V = Career & Tech Ed Programs	
85 AIDS Education	270 Character Education	294 Accountability	Ⓐ = Alternative School		
88 Alternative/At Risk	271 Migrant Education	295 Network System	Ⓒ = Charter School	New Schools are shaded	
89 Multi-Cultural Curriculum	273 Teacher Mentor	296 Title II Programs	Ⓜ = Magnet School	New Superintendents and Principals are bold	
90 Social Work	274 Before/After Sch	297 Webmaster	Ⓨ = Year-Round School	Personnel with email addresses are underscored	

NY–77

Herkimer County — Market Data Retrieval

James Lavere .... 73 Ryan Orilio 73

Public Schs..Principal	Grd	Prgm	Enr/#Cls	SN	
Herkimer Elem Sch 255 Gros Blvd, Herkimer 13350 Renee Vogt	PK-5	T	556 40	68%	315/866-8562 Fax 315/866-8568
Herkimer Jr Sr High Sch 801 W German St, Herkimer 13350 Zachary Abbe \ Mary Tomaso	6-12		556 50	62%	315/866-2230 Fax 315/866-8595

● **Little Falls City School Dist** PID: 00729696   315/823-1470
15 Petrie St, Little Falls 13365   Fax 315/823-0321

Schools: 3 \ Teachers: 100 \ Students: 1,116 \ Special Ed Students: 189 \ LEP Students: 4 \ College-Bound: 73% \ Ethnic: African American 1%, Caucasian 98% \ Exp: $220 (Med) \ Poverty: 19% \ Title I: $392,583 \ Special Education: $1,732,000 \ Open-Close: 09/04 - 06/25 \ DTBP: $162 (High) \

Dr Keith Levatino 1   Ashraf Allam 2,73
Cletus McLaughlin 2,5   Melissa Reff 2
Michael Kelly 3   Donna Todd 4
Bart Tooley 6,12,15,58   Joe Long 11
Elizabeth Mosher .... 29*   Kristina Hameister 67
Joseph Morotti 81

Public Schs..Principal	Grd	Prgm	Enr/#Cls	SN	
Benton Hall Academy 1 Ward Sq, Little Falls 13365 John Long	K-5	T	487 25	57%	315/823-1400 Fax 315/823-4407
Little Falls High Sch 1 High School Rd, Little Falls 13365 Leeann Dooley	9-12	GT	332 30	51%	315/823-1167 Fax 315/823-1209
Little Falls Middle Sch 1 High School Rd, Little Falls 13365 Maria Lindsay	6-8	T	280 25	61%	315/823-4300 Fax 315/823-3920

● **Mount Markham Central Sch Dist** PID: 00729763   315/822-2824
500 Fairground Rd, West Winfield 13491   Fax 315/822-6162

Schools: 3 \ Teachers: 100 \ Students: 1,100 \ Special Ed Students: 237 \ LEP Students: 15 \ College-Bound: 85% \ Ethnic: Hispanic 2%, Caucasian 97% \ Exp: $212 (Med) \ Poverty: 16% \ Title I: $311,074 \ Special Education: $2,010,000 \ Open-Close: 09/08 - 06/25 \ DTBP: $380 (High)

Joseph Dapice 1   Joanna Johnson 2
Louis Dambro 2,71,91   Keith Williams 3
Stephen Fitch 5   Laura Nelson 11,34,51,58,271,296,298*
Robin Tabor .... 16,82* Heather Lewis-Hoover 37*
Jeffrey Parow .... 38*   Cynthia Miller 67
John-Henry Lane 73,295   Christopher Martin 77*
Dawn Yerkie .... 83*   Alan Bard 273*

Public Schs..Principal	Grd	Prgm	Enr/#Cls	SN	
Mt Markham Elem Sch 500 Fairground Rd, West Winfield 13491 Jennifer McDonald	PK-4	T	420 27	51%	315/822-2840 Fax 315/822-3436
Mt Markham High Sch 500 Fairground Rd, West Winfield 13491 Victor Zampetti	9-12		352 30	45%	315/822-2900 Fax 315/822-3486
Mt Markham Middle Sch 500 Fairground Rd, West Winfield 13491 Dawn Yerkie	5-8	T	319 39	56%	315/822-2870 Fax 315/822-6125

● **Owen D Young Central Sch Dist** PID: 00729816   315/858-0729
2316 State Route 80, Van Hornesvle 13475   Fax 315/858-2019

Schools: 1 \ Teachers: 22 \ Students: 182 \ Special Ed Students: 9 \ College-Bound: 80% \ Ethnic: Hispanic 2%, Caucasian 98% \ Exp: $361 (High) \ Poverty: 18% \ Title I: $83,059 \ Special Education: $312,000 \ Open-Close: 09/08 - 06/24 \ DTBP: $444 (High)

Brennan Fahey 1   Fred Seifried 2,11,296
Cory Pike 6,69   Christine Tucker 8*
Brennen Fahey .... 12,288*   Lisa Wilber 16*
Alicia Soper .... 31,58,752* Linda Tharp 67
Steve Smithson 73   Scott Walker 295*

Public Schs..Principal	Grd	Prgm	Enr/#Cls	SN	
Owen D Young Central Sch 2316 State Route 80, Van Hornesvle 13475 Brennen Fahey	K-12	T	182 14	57%	315/858-0729

● **Poland Central School Dist** PID: 00729830   315/826-7900
PO Box 8, Poland 13431   Fax 315/826-7516

Schools: 1 \ Teachers: 50 \ Students: 523 \ Special Ed Students: 70 \ LEP Students: 3 \ College-Bound: 70% \ Ethnic: Hispanic 2%, Caucasian 97% \ Exp: $271 (Med) \ Poverty: 15% \ Title I: $189,283 \ Special Education: $1,016,000 \ Open-Close: 09/04 - 06/25 \ DTBP: $385 (High) \

Laura Dutton 1,11,57   Chad Hess 2,3,11,78,294*
Tanya Steves 4   Jeffrey DeLucia 5
Greg Haver 6,35   Rosanne Ozog 7,83*
Greg Cuthbertson .... 8,58,275,296*   Janice Watrous 31,36,270,271*
Jan Kochan .... 37*   Robert Batson 67
Karen Livingston 273*

Public Schs..Principal	Grd	Prgm	Enr/#Cls	SN	
Poland Central Sch 74 Cold Brook St, Poland 13431 Greg Cuthbertson	PK-12	T	523 70	37%	315/826-7900

● **Town of Webb Union Free SD** PID: 00729866   315/369-3222
3002 State Rt 28, Old Forge 13420   Fax 315/369-6216

Schools: 1 \ Teachers: 30 \ Students: 270 \ Special Ed Students: 36 \ College-Bound: 85% \ Ethnic: African American 2%, Hispanic 1%, Caucasian 97% \ Exp: $450 (High) \ Poverty: 7% \ Title I: $24,814 \ Special Education: $166,000 \ Open-Close: 09/08 - 06/25 \ DTBP: $347 (High)

Rex Germer 1,11,73   Jennifer Dunn 2
Michael Gardner .... 3,5*   Katherine Rouse 4
Tanner Ruffell 6,35,83,85   Mary Dieffenbacher 8,12,57,58,69,77,271*
Tracey Down .... 16*   Dana Dornburg 36,79,273*
Judy Ehrensbeck .... 51*   Joseph Phaneuf 67
Robert Schafer .... 73,295*   John Swick 288*

Public Schs..Principal	Grd	Prgm	Enr/#Cls	SN	
Town of Webb Sch 3002 State Rt 28, Old Forge 13420 John Swick	PK-12	T	270 20	37%	315/369-3222

---

1 Superintendent	8 Curric/Instruct K-12	19 Chief Financial Officer	29 Family/Consumer Science	39 Social Studies K-12	49 English/Lang Arts Elem	59 Special Education Elem	69 Academic Assessment
2 Bus/Finance/Purchasing	9 Curric/Instruct Elem	20 Art K-12	30 Adult Education	40 Social Studies Elem	50 English/Lang Arts Sec	60 Special Education Sec	70 Research/Development
3 Buildings And Grounds	10 Curric/Instruct Sec	21 Art Elem	31 Career/Sch-to-Work K-12	41 Social Studies Sec	51 Reading K-12	61 Foreign/World Lang K-12	71 Public Information
4 Food Service	11 Federal Program	22 Art Sec	32 Career/Sch-to-Work Elem	42 Science K-12	52 Reading Elem	62 Foreign/World Lang Elem	72 Summer School
5 Transportation	12 Title I	23 Music K-12	33 Career/Sch-to-Work Sec	43 Science Elem	53 Reading Sec	63 Foreign/World Lang Sec	73 Instructional Tech
6 Athletic	13 Title V	24 Music Elem	34 Early Childhood Ed	44 Science Sec	54 Remedial Reading K-12	64 Religious Education K-12	74 Inservice Training
7 Health Services	15 Asst Superintendent	25 Music Sec	35 Health/Phys Education	45 Math K-12	55 Remedial Reading Elem	65 Religious Education Elem	75 Marketing/Distributive
	16 Instructional Media Svcs	26 Business Education	36 Guidance Services K-12	46 Math Elem	56 Remedial Reading Sec	66 Religious Education Sec	76 Info Systems
	17 Chief Operations Officer	27 Career & Tech Ed	37 Guidance Services Elem	47 Math Sec	57 Bilingual/ELL	67 School Board President	77 Psychological Assess
	18 Chief Academic Officer	28 Technology Education	38 Guidance Services Sec	48 English/Lang Arts K-12	58 Special Education K-12	68 Teacher Personnel	78 Affirmative Action

New York School Directory

Jefferson County

- **West Canada Valley Ctl SD** PID: 00729880   315/845-6800
  5447 State Route 28, Newport 13416   Fax 315/845-8652

Schools: 2 \ **Teachers:** 63 \ **Students:** 650 \ **Special Ed Students:** 109 \ **LEP Students:** 6 \ **College-Bound:** 76% \ **Ethnic:** Hispanic 2%, Caucasian 98% \ **Exp:** $299 (Med) \ **Poverty:** 15% \ **Title I:** $199,896 \ **Special Education:** $150,000 \ **Open-Close:** 09/08 - 06/24 \ **DTBP:** $359 (High)

Donald Shepardson 1   Kelley Crossett 2
Joanna Vanaerman 4   Felix Ray 5
Edmund Dougherty ....6,58,83,286,296*   Jeremy Kozak 8,74,85,92,288*
Donald Shepardson ....11*   Danielle Novak 16,82
Kady Conklin 31,36,270   Julie Purinton 52,54,280*
Alana Boylan 73,76,295   Joe Frank 273*
Julie Purinton 275   Vanessa Boyer 752

Public Schs..Principal	Grd	Prgm	Enr/#Cls	SN	
West Canada Valley Elem Sch 5447 State Route 28, Newport 13416 Correne Holmes	K-6	T	335 30	49%	315/845-6801 Fax 315/845-1640
West Canada Valley Jr Sr HS 5447 State Route 28, Newport 13416 Jeremy Kozak	7-12	T	315 40	41%	315/845-6802

HERKIMER CATHOLIC SCHOOLS

- **Diocese of Albany Ed Office** PID: 00715059
  Listing includes only schools located in this county. See District Index for location of Diocesan Offices.

Catholic Schs..Principal	Grd	Prgm	Enr/#Cls	SN	
St Francis DeSales ECLC 220 Henry St, Herkimer 13350 Rebecca Marzeski	PK-1		45 9		315/866-4831 Fax 315/866-9043

HERKIMER PRIVATE SCHOOLS

Private Schs..Principal	Grd	Prgm	Enr/#Cls	SN	
Mohawk Valley Christian Acad 156 W Monroe St, Little Falls 13365 Chris Wintermutt	K-12		30 8		315/823-3696 Fax 315/679-5217

HERKIMER REGIONAL CENTERS

- **Herkimer BOCES** PID: 00729921   315/867-2023
  352 Gros Blvd, Herkimer 13350   Fax 315/867-2002

Sandra Sherwood 1   Jodie Rodriquez 2,15
James Picolla 3,15,91   Sarah Nicolette 7
Kathy Fox 8,27,31   Mary Kline 30,34,57,271
Roberta Matthews 58,88   Dan LaLonde 67
Johnathan Griffith 74   John Gillette 295

JEFFERSON COUNTY

JEFFERSON COUNTY SCHOOLS

County Schs..Principal	Grd	Prgm	Enr/#Cls	SN	
Bohlen Technical Center 20104 Nys Route 3, Watertown 13601 Joanne Witt	Voc	AG	800 27		315/779-7200 Fax 315/779-7209

JEFFERSON PUBLIC SCHOOLS

- **Alexandria Central School Dist** PID: 00729933   315/482-9971
  34 Bolton Ave, Alex Bay 13607   Fax 315/482-9973

Schools: 1 \ **Teachers:** 49 \ **Students:** 492 \ **Special Ed Students:** 99 \ **LEP Students:** 3 \ **College-Bound:** 80% \ **Ethnic:** Hispanic 3%, Native American: 1%, Caucasian 96% \ **Exp:** $307 (High) \ **Poverty:** 9% \ **Title I:** $123,277 \ **Special Education:** $723,000 \ **Open-Close:** 09/04 - 06/25 \ **DTBP:** $370 (High)

Christopher Clapper 1   Brianne Kirchoff 2
Anne Remington ....4*   Rod Tidd 5,82*
Teri Lowe 6   Amy St Croix 8,11,296,298
Amy St Croix ....12*   Patty Wagoner 37*
Kevin Durr ....38,57*   Pam Monica 58
Jane Aikins 67   Teri Lowe 81*
Barbara Bresnahan ....85*   Kendra Moshier 90
Kylie Morgia 273,288

Public Schs..Principal	Grd	Prgm	Enr/#Cls	SN	
Alexandria Central Sch 34 Bolton Ave, Alex Bay 13607 Kylie Morgia	PK-12	AGT	492 23	46%	315/482-9971

- **Belleville Henderson Sch Dist** PID: 00729957   315/846-5826
  8372 County Route 75, Adams 13605   Fax 315/846-5617

Schools: 1 \ **Teachers:** 42 \ **Students:** 450 \ **Special Ed Students:** 78 \ **LEP Students:** 3 \ **Ethnic:** Asian 1%, African American 1%, Hispanic 4%, Caucasian 95% \ **Exp:** $333 (High) \ **Poverty:** 13% \ **Title I:** $175,398 \ **Special Education:** $517,000 \ **Open-Close:** 09/03 - 06/25 \ **DTBP:** $371 (High)

Jane Collins 1   Stephen Magouney 2*
Mindy Grandjean ....4*   Phil Gleason 5
Scott Storey ....8,11,288*   Shaun Gagan 36*
Erica Pettit 58   John Allen 67

Public Schs..Principal	Grd	Prgm	Enr/#Cls	SN	
Belleville Henderson Ctl Sch 8372 County Route 75, Adams 13605 Scott Storey	PK-12	T	450 50	54%	315/846-5411

---

79 Student Personnel	91 Safety/Security	275 Response To Intervention	298 Grant Writer/Ptnrships	**School Programs**	**Social Media**
80 Driver Ed/Safety	92 Magnet School	277 Remedial Math K-12	750 Chief Innovation Officer	Ⓐ = Alternative Program	📘 = Facebook
81 Gifted/Talented	93 Parental Involvement	280 Literacy Coach	751 Chief of Staff	Ⓖ = Adult Classes	
82 Video Services	95 Tech Prep Program	285 STEM	752 Social Emotional Learning	Ⓜ = Magnet Program	🐦 = Twitter
83 Substance Abuse Prev	97 Chief Information Officer	286 Digital Learning		Ⓣ = Title I Schoolwide	
84 Erate	98 Chief Technology Officer	288 Common Core Standards	**Other School Types**	Ⓥ = Career & Tech Ed Programs	
85 AIDS Education	270 Accountability	294 Accountability	Ⓐ = Alternative School		
88 Alternative/At Risk	271 Migrant Education	295 Network System	Ⓒ = Charter School	New Schools are shaded	
89 Multi-Cultural Curriculum	273 Teacher Mentor	296 Title II Programs	Ⓜ = Magnet School	New Superintendents and Principals are bold	
90 Social Work	274 Before/After Sch	297 Webmaster	Ⓨ = Year-Round School	Personnel with email addresses are underscored	

Jefferson County

Carthage Central School Dist PID: 00729971   315/493-5000
25059 Woolworth St, Carthage 13619   Fax 315/493-7036

Schools: 5 \ **Teachers:** 264 \ **Students:** 3,200 \ **Special Ed Students:** 580 \ **LEP Students:** 47 \ **Ethnic:** Asian 1%, African American 6%, Hispanic 11%, Native American: 1%, Caucasian 81% \ **Exp:** $208 (Med) \ **Poverty:** 10% \ **Title I:** $908,724 \ **Special Education:** $5,164,000 \ **Open-Close:** 09/08 - 06/25 \ **DTBP:** $211 (High)

Jennifer Premo 1
Jeremy Thesier 3*
John Gibbons 5
Barbara Zehr 8,57,69,88,275,280,288,296
Michele Capone 58,79*
Cathryn Haug 68
Tasha Thompson 82
Stan VanZandt 91
Tracy Strock 2,11
Kelly Filus 4
Jason Brown 6,30*
Heather Randall-Nevel 42
Gary Schwartz 67
Ramona Dent 73,76,295*
Angela Robbins 83,85*

Public Schs..Principal	Grd	Prgm	Enr/#Cls	SN		
Black River Elem Sch 160 Leray St, Black River 13612 Jared Plantz	K-4	T	481 29	46%	315/773-5911 Fax 315/773-3747	
Carthage Elem Sch 900 Beaver Ln, Carthage 13619 Hope Foy	K-4	T	390 23	62%	315/493-1570 Fax 315/493-6028	
Carthage High Sch 36500 State Route 26, Carthage 13619 Kathaleen Beattie	9-12	AV	863 100	48%	315/493-5030 Fax 315/493-6402	
Carthage Middle Sch 21986 Cole Rd, Carthage 13619 Emily Remington	5-8	TV	943 60	51%	315/493-5020 Fax 315/493-6031	
West Carthage Elem Sch 21568 Cole Rd, Carthage 13619 Jamie Sweeney	K-4	T	388 23	41%	315/493-2400 Fax 315/493-6536	

General Brown Ctl School Dist PID: 00730061   315/779-2300
17643 Cemetery Rd, Dexter 13634   Fax 315/639-6916

Schools: 3 \ **Teachers:** 102 \ **Students:** 1,600 \ **Special Ed Students:** 280 \ **LEP Students:** 9 \ **College-Bound:** 73% \ **Ethnic:** Asian 1%, African American 2%, Hispanic 2%, Caucasian 96% \ **Exp:** $246 (Med) \ **Poverty:** 10% \ **Title I:** $292,631 \ **Special Education:** $1,854,000 \ **Open-Close:** 09/08 - 06/24 \ **DTBP:** $359 (High)

Barbara Case 1
Garrett Grimm 3,5,17,91
Laurie Nohle 6
Kelly Milkowich 67
Lisa Smith 2,8,11,15,19,285,296
Jim Nevers 4*
Melissa Nabinger 57,58,77,88,271
Michael Parobeck 71,73,76,97,295,297

Public Schs..Principal	Grd	Prgm	Enr/#Cls	SN	
Brownville-Glen Park Elem Sch 771 Main St, Brownville 13615 Joseph O'Donnell	PK-6		526 24	27%	315/779-2300 Fax 315/788-6976
Dexter Elem Sch 415 E Grove St, Dexter 13634 David Ramie	PK-6		301 15	28%	315/639-2300 Fax 315/639-6845
General Brown Jr Sr High Sch 17643 Cemetery Rd, Dexter 13634 Nicole Donaldson	7-12		629 70	34%	315/779-2300 Fax 315/639-3444

Indian River Ctl School Dist PID: 00730140   315/642-3441
32735 County Route 29 Ste B, Philadelphia 13673   Fax 315/642-3738

Schools: 8 \ **Teachers:** 299 \ **Students:** 3,900 \ **Special Ed Students:** 649 \ **LEP Students:** 94 \ **Ethnic:** Asian 2%, African American 10%, Hispanic 17%, Native American: 1%, Caucasian 71% \ **Exp:** $280 (Med) \ **Poverty:** 12% \ **Title I:** $918,894 \ **Special Education:** $7,095,000 \ **Open-Close:** 09/08 - 06/25 \ **DTBP:** $201 (High)

Maryann Dobrmeier 1
Noah Prior 3*
Rick Burr 5*
O Jeanne Dolly 7*
Troy Decker 8,15
Tina Frank 16,82*
Thomas Lapp 67
Dr Donna Kennedy 78
Audrey Stevenson 2
Ann Easter 4*
Jay Brown 6,35,83,85*
Christina Chamberlain 8
Tamara Metz 11,36,58,69,271,294
Barbara Zehr 57*
Tom Turgeon 73
Shelly Siebels 295*

Public Schs..Principal	Grd	Prgm	Enr/#Cls	SN	
Antwerp Primary Sch 6 Academy St, Antwerp 13608 Elizabeth Culbertson	K-3	T	183 11	50%	315/659-8386 Fax 315/659-8944
Calcium Primary Sch 25440 Indian River Dr, Calcium 13616 Kristen Freeman	K-3	T	569 33	48%	315/629-1100 Fax 315/629-5254
Evans Mills Primary Sch 8442 S Main St, Evans Mills 13637 Pamela Knight	K-3	T	343 23	57%	315/629-4331 Fax 315/629-5257
Indian River High Sch 32925 US Route 11, Philadelphia 13673 Brian Moore	9-12	G	817 80	50%	315/642-3427 Fax 315/642-5658
Indian River Intermediate Sch 32430 US Route 11, Philadelphia 13673 Sarah Matteson	4-5	T	544 25	56%	315/642-0405 Fax 315/642-3180
Indian River Middle Sch 32735 County Route 29 Ste A, Philadelphia 13673 Angela Green	6-8	T	759 53	52%	315/642-0125 Fax 315/642-0128
Philadelphia Primary Sch 3 Sand St, Philadelphia 13673 Barbara Zehr	K-3	T	128 8	47%	315/642-3432 Fax 315/642-5650
Theresa Primary Sch 125 Bridge St, Theresa 13691 Brenda Leddy	K-3	T	200 12	44%	315/628-4432 Fax 315/628-5890

La Fargeville Central Sch Dist PID: 00730205   315/658-2241
20414 Sunrise Ave, La Fargeville 13656   Fax 315/658-4223

Schools: 1 \ **Teachers:** 45 \ **Students:** 539 \ **Special Ed Students:** 85 \ **College-Bound:** 65% \ **Ethnic:** Asian 1%, Hispanic 1%, Caucasian 97% \ **Exp:** $171 (Low) \ **Poverty:** 12% \ **Title I:** $124,169 \ **Special Education:** $672,000 \ **Open-Close:** 09/08 - 06/25 \ **DTBP:** $379 (High)

Travis Hoover 1
Dennis Kriwox 3
Deanna Henry 16*
Sheryl Wilson 67
Nicole Parliament 2*
Jaycee Welsh 11,58,270,288*
Hanna Zimbrich 38
William Trender 73,76,286

Public Schs..Principal	Grd	Prgm	Enr/#Cls	SN	
La Fargeville Central Sch 20414 Sunrise Ave, La Fargeville 13656 Jaycee Welsh \ Steven Newcombe	PK-12	T	539 47	53%	315/658-2241

1	Superintendent	8	Curric/Instruct K-12	19	Chief Financial Officer	29	Family/Consumer Science	39	Social Studies K-12	49	English/Lang Arts Elem	59	Special Education Elem	69	Academic Assessment
2	Bus/Finance/Purchasing	9	Curric/Instruct Elem	20	Adult Education	30	Career/Sch-to-Work K-12	40	Social Studies Elem	50	English/Lang Arts Sec	60	Special Education Sec	70	Research/Development
3	Buildings And Grounds	10	Curric/Instruct Sec	21	Art Elem	31	Career/Sch-to-Work Elem	41	Social Studies Sec	51	Reading K-12	61	Foreign/World Lang K-12	71	Public Information
4	Food Service	11	Federal Program	22	Art Sec	32	Career/Sch-to-Work Sec	42	Science K-12	52	Reading Elem	62	Foreign/World Lang Elem	72	Summer School
5	Transportation	12	Title I	23	Music K-12	33	Career/Sch-to-Work Sec	43	Science Elem	53	Reading Sec	63	Foreign/World Lang Sec	73	Instructional Tech
6	Athletic	13	Title V	24	Music Elem	34	Early Childhood Ed	44	Science Sec	54	Remedial Reading K-12	64	Religious Education K-12	74	Inservice Training
7	Health Services	15	Asst Superintendent	25	Music Sec	35	Health/Phys Education	45	Math K-12	55	Remedial Reading Elem	65	Religious Education Elem	75	Marketing/Distributive
		16	Instructional Media Svcs	26	Business Education	36	Guidance Services K-12	46	Math Elem	56	Remedial Reading Sec	66	Religious Education Sec	76	Info Systems
		17	Chief Operations Officer	27	Career & Tech Ed	37	Guidance Services Elem	47	Math Sec	57	Bilingual/ELL	67	School Board President	77	Psychological Assess
		18	Chief Academic Officer	28	Technology Education	38	Guidance Services Sec	48	English/Lang Arts K-12	58	Special Education K-12	68	Teacher Personnel	78	Affirmative Action

New York School Directory — Jefferson County

Lyme Central School Dist PID: 00730229
11868 Academy St, Chaumont 13622
315/649-2417
Fax 315/649-2663

Schools: 1 \ **Teachers:** 30 \ **Students:** 349 \ **Special Ed Students:** 62 \ **College-Bound:** 80% \ **Ethnic:** Asian 1%, African American 3%, Hispanic 2%, Caucasian 94% \ **Exp:** $239 (Med) \ **Poverty:** 15% \ **Title I:** $98,679 \ **Special Education:** $96,000 \ **Open-Close:** 09/04 - 06/25 \ **DTBP:** $357 (High)

Cammy Morrison 1
Todd Lafage 3*
Dina Jareo 5
Patricia Gibbons 8,11,58,69,273,288,298*
Deanna Lathrop 67
Sandra Rooney 2*
Greg Orvis 4
Barry Davis 6*
Christopher Rowland 36,88*
Mike Gebo 73,295*

Public Schs..Principal	Grd	Prgm	Enr/#Cls	SN	
Ⓨ Lyme Central Sch 11868 Academy St, Chaumont 13622 Barry Davis	PK-12	MT	349	52%	315/649-2417

Sackets Harbor Ctl School Dist PID: 00730126
215 S Broad St, Sackets HBR 13685
315/646-3575
Fax 315/646-1038

Schools: 1 \ **Teachers:** 40 \ **Students:** 418 \ **Special Ed Students:** 73 \ **LEP Students:** 5 \ **College-Bound:** 82% \ **Ethnic:** African American 1%, Hispanic 5%, Caucasian 93% \ **Exp:** $253 (Med) \ **Poverty:** 11% \ **Title I:** $168,387 \ **Special Education:** $630,000 \ **Open-Close:** 09/08 - 06/24 \ **DTBP:** $39 (Low)

Jennifer Gaffney 1,11,288
Randy Kellar 3*
Larry Carpenter 5*
Jennifer Johannessen 7
Ryan Tastor 31,36,83,270*
Christopher Forte 73*
Julie Gayne 2*
Joanne Patrick 4
Dan Green 6
Alynda Haycock 11,88,280,296*
Dale Phillips 67

Public Schs..Principal	Grd	Prgm	Enr/#Cls	SN	
Sackets Harbor Central Sch 215 S Broad St, Sackets HBR 13685 Amy Fiedler-Horack	K-12	V	418 44	37%	315/646-3575

South Jefferson Central SD PID: 00730243
13180 US Route 11, Adams Center 13606
315/583-6104
Fax 315/583-6381

Schools: 4 \ **Teachers:** 137 \ **Students:** 1,894 \ **Special Ed Students:** 327 \ **LEP Students:** 4 \ **Ethnic:** Hispanic 2%, Caucasian 97% \ **Exp:** $149 (Low) \ **Poverty:** 12% \ **Title I:** $400,866 \ **Special Education:** $3,091,000 \ **Open-Close:** 09/03 - 06/25 \ **DTBP:** $42 (Low)

Scott Slater 1,11,57
David Hatchell 3*
Rebecca Dalrymple 5
Lisa Parsons 8,15
Sarah Oyoung 58,79
Rae Ann Thomas 73*
Andrew Zuber 295
Cora Harvey 2
Cassandra Morse 4
Jay Wiley 6*
Heidi Edgar 31,83*
Todd Dack 67
Jim Pelton 88,273*

Public Schs..Principal	Grd	Prgm	Enr/#Cls	SN	
Mannsville Manor Elem Sch 423 N Main St, Mannsville 13661 Jeffrey Ginger	PK-5	T	351 19	53%	315/465-4281 Fax 315/465-4088
Maynard P Wilson Elem Sch 13180 US Route 11, Adams Center 13606 Rebecca Dalrymple	PK-5	T	542 33	43%	315/583-5418 Fax 315/583-5451

South Jefferson High Sch 11060 US Route 11, Adams 13605 Jeffrey Ginger	9-12	GTV	543 67	47%	315/232-4531 Fax 315/232-3728
South Jefferson Middle Sch 11060 US Route 11, Adams 13605 Jon Christopher	6-8	T	458 32	50%	315/232-4531 Fax 315/232-4620

Thousand Islands Central SD PID: 00730293
8481 County Route 9, Clayton 13624
315/686-5521
Fax 315/686-5511

Schools: 4 \ **Teachers:** 82 \ **Students:** 867 \ **Special Ed Students:** 123 \ **College-Bound:** 64% \ **Ethnic:** African American 1%, Hispanic 3%, Native American: 1%, Caucasian 95% \ **Exp:** $239 (Med) \ **Poverty:** 10% \ **Title I:** $176,682 \ **Special Education:** $1,531,000 \ **Open-Close:** 09/04 - 06/25 \ **DTBP:** $440 (High)

Michael Bashaw 1
Kenny Garnsey 3
Dina Jareo 5
Jonathan Benner ... 16,73,74,76,275,285,295*
Lisa Freitag 37,58,69,83,288*
Angela Picunas 2,11,271
Lynette Chapman 4*
Shayne Robbins 6*
Joseph Gilfus 27,30,88*
Erik Swenson 67

Public Schs..Principal	Grd	Prgm	Enr/#Cls	SN	
Cape Vincent Elem Sch 410 S Esselstyne St, Cape Vincent 13618 Lisa Freitag	K-5	T	108 6	56%	315/654-2142 Fax 315/654-4599
Guardino Elem Sch 600 High St, Clayton 13624 Lisa Freitag	K-5	T	288 22	45%	315/686-5578 Fax 315/686-2874
Thousand Islands High Sch 8481 County Route 9, Cape Vincent 13618 Joseph Gilfus	9-12	GV	272 80	44%	315/686-5594 Fax 315/654-5039
Thousand Islands Middle Sch 8481 County Route 9, Cape Vincent 13618 Andrea Lomber	6-8	T	199 24	52%	315/686-5199 Fax 315/654-5038

Watertown City School Dist PID: 00730334
1351 Washington St, Watertown 13601
315/785-3700
Fax 315/785-6855

Schools: 8 \ **Teachers:** 297 \ **Students:** 3,800 \ **Special Ed Students:** 855 \ **LEP Students:** 72 \ **College-Bound:** 57% \ **Ethnic:** Asian 2%, African American 8%, Hispanic 12%, Native American: 1%, Caucasian 77% \ **Exp:** $511 (High) \ **Poverty:** 24% \ **Title I:** $2,266,165 \ **Special Education:** $6,330,000 \ **Open-Close:** 09/08 - 06/24 \ **DTBP:** $217 (High)

Patricia LaBarr 1,11,57
Jason Compo 3,91
George Emrich 6*
Tina Lane 15,68,79
Shannon Whitney 58,77
Lisa Blank 285
Joshua Harstone 2,298
Mary Hughes 4
Stacey Eger 8,286,288,296
David Campbell 16,73,76,295*
Maria Mesires 67

Public Schs..Principal	Grd	Prgm	Enr/#Cls	SN	
Case Middle Sch 1237 Washington St, Watertown 13601 Mark Taylor	7-8	T	573 50	77%	315/785-3870 Fax 315/785-3731
Harold T Wiley Interm Sch 1351 Washington St, Watertown 13601 Elizabeth Maurer	5-6	T	662 31	76%	315/785-3780 Fax 315/785-3769
Knickerbocker Elem Sch 739 Knickerbocker Dr, Watertown 13601 Janelle Dupee	K-4	T	378 21	54%	315/785-3740 Fax 315/779-5654
North Elem Sch 171 E Hoard St, Watertown 13601 Sandra Cain	K-4	T	471 26	62%	315/785-3750 Fax 315/779-5405

---

79 Student Personnel
80 Driver Ed/Safety
81 Gifted/Talented
82 Video Services
83 Substance Abuse Prev
84 Erate
85 AIDS Education
88 Alternative/At Risk
89 Multi-Cultural Curriculum
90 Social Work

91 Safety/Security
92 Magnet School
93 Parental Involvement
95 Tech Prep Program
97 Chief Information Officer
98 Chief Technology Officer
270 Character Education
271 Migrant Education
273 Teacher Mentor
274 Before/After Sch

275 Response To Intervention
277 Remedial Math K-12
280 Literacy Coach
285 STEM
286 Digital Learning
288 Common Core Standards
294 Accountability
295 Network System
296 Title II Programs
297 Webmaster

298 Grant Writer/Ptnrships
750 Chief Innovation Officer
751 Chief of Staff
752 Social Emotional Learning

School Programs
A = Alternative Program
G = Adult Classes
M = Magnet Program
T = Title I Schoolwide
V = Career & Tech Ed Programs

Other School Types
Ⓐ = Alternative School
Ⓒ = Charter School
Ⓜ = Magnet School
Ⓨ = Year-Round School

Social Media
 = Facebook
 = Twitter

New Schools are shaded
New Superintendents and Principals are bold
Personnel with email addresses are underscored

NY-81

Kings County Market Data Retrieval

Ohio Elem Sch 1537 Ohio St, Watertown 13601 Thomas Dunckel	K-4	T	369 18	65%	315/785-3755 Fax 315/779-5502
Sherman Elem Sch 836 Sherman St, Watertown 13601 Terry Gonseth	K-4	T	301 16	45%	315/785-3760 Fax 315/779-5575
Starbuck Elem Sch 430 E Hoard St, Watertown 13601 Michael Lennox	K-4	T	190	64%	315/785-3765 Fax 315/779-5472
Watertown High Sch 1335 Washington St, Watertown 13601 Chad Fairchild	9-12	AT	1,027 90	63%	315/785-3800 Fax 315/785-3733

JEFFERSON CATHOLIC SCHOOLS

- **Diocese of Ogdensburg Ed Off** PID: 00769050
  Listing includes only schools located in this county. See District Index for location of Diocesan Offices.

Catholic Schs..Principal	Grd	Prgm	Enr/#Cls	SN	
Augustinian Academy 317 West St, Carthage 13619 Mary Margrey	PK-8		133 10		315/493-1301 Fax 315/493-0632
Immaculate Heart Ctl ES 122 Winthrop St, Watertown 13601 Daniel Charlebois	PK-6		180 11		315/788-7011
Immaculate Heart Ctl Jr/Sr HS 1316 Ives St, Watertown 13601 Daniel Charlebois	7-12	V	350 30		315/788-4670 Fax 315/788-4672

JEFFERSON PRIVATE SCHOOLS

Private Schs..Principal	Grd	Prgm	Enr/#Cls	SN	
Faith Fellowship Christian Sch 131 Moore Ave, Watertown 13601 Ted Curinga	PK-12		185 11		315/782-9342 Fax 315/786-0309
Genesis Sch 12749 State Route 12E, Chaumont 13622 James Hayes	PK-12		24 3		315/649-3050
Jefferson Rehabilitation Ctr 420 Gassney Drive, Watertown 13601 Paula Roukous	Spec		60 3		315/788-2730 Fax 315/788-8557

JEFFERSON REGIONAL CENTERS

- **Jefferson Lewis BOCES** PID: 00730463 315/779-7000
  20104 State Route 3, Watertown 13601 Fax 315/779-7009

Stephen Todd	1,11	Michele Traynor	2,15
Fred Hauck	7,91	Leslie LaRose	8,15
Meghan Davison	16	Tracy Gyoerkoe	30,31
Michael Lively	58	Grace Rice	67
Pamela Hebert	68	Eli Stawicki	73,76
Tim Dauey	73	Lynn Gaffney	74

KINGS COUNTY

KINGS PUBLIC SCHOOLS

- **Community School District 13** PID: 10909682 718/636-3284
  355 Park Pl, Brooklyn 11238
  (Part of New York City Dept of Ed in New York County)
  Kamar Samuels 1

Public Schs..Principal	Grd	Prgm	Enr/#Cls	SN	
Arts & Letters 305 United 344 Monroe St, Brooklyn 11216 Pilar Ramos	PK-8	T	102 36	94%	718/789-3962 Fax 718/622-3474
Bedford Academy High Sch 1119 Bedford Ave, Brooklyn 11216 Adofo Muhammed	9-12	T	392	90%	718/398-3061 Fax 718/636-3819
Benjamin Banneker Academy 71 Clinton Ave 77, Brooklyn 11205 Kinsley Kwateng	9-12	T	834 30	73%	718/797-3702 Fax 718/797-3862
Bklyn HS Ldrshp & Cmty Serv 300 Willoughby Ave, Brooklyn 11205 Georgia Serves	9-12	T	154	81%	718/638-3062 Fax 718/638-3404
Brooklyn Academy High Sch 832 Marcy Ave, Brooklyn 11216 Charon Hall	10-12	GT	124 17	84%	718/857-4237 Fax 718/399-1909
Brooklyn Cmty Arts & Media HS 300 Willoughby Ave, Brooklyn 11205 James Obrien	9-12	T	461 15	88%	718/230-5748 Fax 718/230-3050
Brooklyn International HS 49 Flatbush Avenue Ext, Brooklyn 11201 Kathleen Rucker	9-12	T	330 20	79%	718/643-9315 Fax 718/643-9516
Brooklyn Technical High Sch 29 Fort Greene Pl, Brooklyn 11217 David Newman	9-12	V	6,040	59%	718/804-6400 Fax 718/260-9245
City Polytechnic High Sch 105 Tech Place, Brooklyn 11201 April McKoy	Voc	T	433	76%	718/875-1473 Fax 718/875-1947
Community Roots Charter Sch 51 Saint Edwards St Ste 3, Brooklyn 11205 Allison Keil	K-8	T	473	26%	718/858-1629 Fax 718/858-1754
Dock Street Sch 19 Dock St, Brooklyn 11201 Dr Melissa Vaughan	6-8	T	288	64%	718/780-7660 Fax 718/780-7675
Downtown Brooklyn YABC 105 Johnson St, Brooklyn 11201 Joe Arzuaga	10-12		250		718/222-0918
Dr Susan McKinney Sch of Arts 101 Park Ave, Brooklyn 11205 Edgar Lin	6-12	TV	303	89%	718/834-6760 Fax 718/243-0815
Ft Greene Prep Academy 100 Clermont Ave, Brooklyn 11205 Paula Lettiere	6-8	T	211	91%	718/254-9401 Fax 718/254-9407
George Westinghouse Cte HS 105 Tech Pl, Brooklyn 11201 Joey Arzuaga	Voc	GT	790 50	77%	718/625-6130 Fax 718/596-9434
MS 113 Ronald Edmonds Lrng Ctr 300 Adelphi St, Brooklyn 11205 Dawnique Daughtry	6-8	ATV	335 40	88%	718/834-6734 Fax 718/596-2802
MS 266 Park Place Cmty Mid Sch 62 Park Pl, Brooklyn 11217 Mr Torres	6-8	T	168 8	81%	718/230-1216 Fax 718/857-2347

1	Superintendent	8	Curric/Instruct K-12	19	Chief Financial Officer	29	Family/Consumer Science	
2	Bus/Finance/Purchasing	9	Curric/Instruct Elem	20	Art K-12	30	Adult Education	
3	Buildings And Grounds	10	Curric/Instruct Sec	21	Art Elem	31	Career/Sch-to-Work K-12	
4	Food Service	11	Federal Program	22	Art Sec	32	Career/Sch-to-Work Elem	
5	Transportation	12	Title I	23	Music K-12	33	Career/Sch-to-Work Sec	
6	Athletic	13	Title V	24	Music Elem	34	Early Childhood Ed	
7	Health Services	15	Asst Superintendent	25	Music Sec	35	Health/Phys Education	
		16	Instructional Media Svcs	26	Business Education	36	Guidance Services K-12	
		17	Chief Operations Officer	27	Career & Tech Ed	37	Guidance Services Elem	
		18	Chief Academic Officer	28	Technology Education	38	Guidance Services Sec	
39	Social Studies K-12	49	English/Lang Arts Elem	59	Special Education Elem	69	Academic Assessment	
40	Social Studies Elem	50	English/Lang Arts Sec	60	Special Education Sec	70	Research/Development	
41	Social Studies Sec	51	Reading K-12	61	Foreign/World Lang K-12	71	Public Information	
42	Science K-12	52	Reading Elem	62	Foreign/World Lang Elem	72	Summer School	
43	Science Elem	53	Reading Sec	63	Foreign/World Lang Sec	73	Instructional Tech	
44	Science Sec	54	Remedial Reading K-12	64	Religious Education K-12	74	Inservice Training	
45	Math K-12	55	Remedial Reading Elem	65	Religious Education Elem	75	Marketing/Distributive	
46	Math Elem	56	Remedial Reading Sec	66	Religious Education Sec	76	Info Systems	
47	Math Sec	57	Bilingual/ELL	67	School Board President	77	Psychological Assess	
48	English/Lang Arts K-12	58	Special Education K-12	68	Teacher Personnel	78	Affirmative Action	

New York School Directory | Kings County

School	Grd	Prgm	Enr/#Cls	SN	
MS 915 105 Johnson St, Brooklyn 11201 Danielle Scott	6-8		273		718/875-1021
PS 3 Bedford Village 50 Jefferson Ave, Brooklyn 11216 Kristina Beecher	PK-5	T	302 30	92%	718/622-2960 Fax 718/623-3193
PS 8 Robert Fulton 37 Hicks St, Brooklyn 11201 Patricia Peterson	K-8		901 20	20%	718/834-6740 Fax 718/834-7690
PS 9 Sarah Smith Garnet 80 Underhill Ave, Brooklyn 11238 Emma Velazquez	PK-5		930 27	36%	718/638-3260 Fax 718/622-2961
PS 11 Purvis J Behan 419 Waverly Ave, Brooklyn 11238 Abidemi Hope	PK-5		950	40%	718/638-2661 Fax 718/622-3028
PS 20 Clinton Hill 225 Adelphi St, Brooklyn 11205 Lena Barbera	PK-5	T	527 22	58%	718/834-6744 Fax 718/243-0712
PS 44 Marcus Garvey 432 Monroe St, Brooklyn 11221 Roxanne James	PK-5	T	124 26	95%	718/834-6939 Fax 718/574-8501
PS 46 Edward C Blum 100 Clermont Ave, Brooklyn 11205 Maria Guzman	PK-5	T	249	89%	718/834-7694 Fax 718/243-0726
PS 54 Samuel C Barnes 195 Sandford St, Brooklyn 11205 Anthony Pirro	PK-5	T	199 25	88%	718/834-6752 Fax 718/852-8129
PS 56 Lewis H Latimer 170 Gates Ave, Brooklyn 11238 Eric Grande	PK-5	T	278 30	65%	718/857-3149 Fax 718/783-7379
PS 67 Charles A Dorsey 51 Saint Edwards St Ste 1, Brooklyn 11205 Kyesha Jackson	PK-5	T	223 36	98%	718/834-6756 Fax 718/834-6719
PS 93 William H Prescott 31 New York Ave, Brooklyn 11216 Janeice Bailey	PK-5	AT	179 30	95%	718/604-7363 Fax 718/771-1369
PS 133 William A Butler 610 Baltic St, Brooklyn 11217 Heather Mann	PK-5		723 20	34%	718/398-5320 Fax 718/385-5325
PS 256 Benjamin Banneker 114 Kosciuszko St, Brooklyn 11216 Sharyn Hemphill	PK-5		213 36	97%	718/857-9820 Fax 718/783-7384
PS 270 Johann DeKalb 241 Emerson Pl, Brooklyn 11205 Alyssa Roye	PK-5		95	86%	718/623-5280 Fax 718/622-3370
PS 282 Park Slope 180 6th Ave, Brooklyn 11217 Rashan Hoke	PK-8		579 33	44%	718/622-1626 Fax 718/622-3471
PS 287 Bailey K Ashford 50 Navy St, Brooklyn 11201 Michele Rawlins	PK-5	T	117 13	91%	718/834-4745 Fax 718/834-6766
PS 307 Daniel Hale Williams 209 York St, Brooklyn 11201 Stephanie Carroll	PK-5		363 23	77%	718/834-4748 Fax 718/855-4181
Satellite East Middle Sch 31 New York Ave, Brooklyn 11216 Santosha Troutman	6-8	T	87	95%	718/245-8766 Fax 718/245-8769
ⓂScience Skills Center 49 Flatbush Avenue Ext, Brooklyn 11201 Dahlia McGregor	9-12	T	596 30	82%	718/243-9413 Fax 718/243-1016
Urban Assem MA-Sci Young Women 283 Adams St, Brooklyn 11201 Kiri Soares	6-12	T	482 24	82%	718/260-2300 Fax 718/260-2301
Urban Assembly Law & Justice 283 Adams St, Brooklyn 11201 Merilee Valentino	9-12	T	449	69%	718/858-1160 Fax 718/858-4733
Urban Assembly Sch Music & Art 49 Flatbush Avenue Ext Fl 8, Brooklyn 11201 Paul Thompson	9-12	T	191	86%	718/858-0249 Fax 718/858-0492
Urban Assembly Unison Sch 170 Gates Ave, Brooklyn 11238 Emily Paige	6-8	T	167	81%	718/399-1061 Fax 718/857-0548

● **Community School District 14** PID: 10909694   718/302-7600
215 Heyward St, Brooklyn 11206

(Part of New York City Dept of Ed in New York County)

Alicja Winnicki 1

Public Schs..Principal	Grd	Prgm	Enr/#Cls	SN	
A-Tech High Sch 50 Bedford Ave, Brooklyn 11222 Kevin Bryant	Voc	GT	314	83%	718/218-9301 Fax 718/599-4351
ⒶAutomotive YABC 50 Bedford Ave, Brooklyn 11222 Michael Pollicino	10-12		250		718/218-9301
Brooklyn Arbor Elem Sch 414 325 S 3rd St, Brooklyn 11211 Eva Irivarry	PK-5		611	57%	718/963-0393 Fax 718/963-2083
ⒸBrooklyn Charter Sch 545 Willoughby Ave, Brooklyn 11206 Joanne Hunt	K-5	T	222 12	81%	718/302-2085 Fax 718/302-2426
Brooklyn Latin High Sch 223 Graham Ave, Brooklyn 11206 Gina Mitchell	9-12		785	60%	718/366-0154 Fax 718/381-3012
Brooklyn Preparatory HS 257 N 6th St, Brooklyn 11211 Noah Lansner	9-12	T	536 25	83%	718/486-2550 Fax 718/486-2505
ⒶConselyea Prep Sch 208 N 5th St, Brooklyn 11211 Maria Masullo	6-8	T	473	49%	718/486-6211 Fax 718/486-6771
ⒶEast Williamsburg Scholars 850 Grand St, Brooklyn 11211 Rosemary Vega	9-12	T	294 35	90%	718/387-2800 Fax 718/387-3281
El Puente Acad Peace Soc Just 250 Hooper St, Brooklyn 11211 Wanda Vazquez	9-12	T	226 9	83%	718/387-1125 Fax 718/387-4229
ⒶEnterprise Bus & Tech HS 850 Grand St, Brooklyn 11211 Holger Carrillo	9-12	T	782 37	86%	718/387-2800 Fax 718/387-2748
IS 318 Eugenio Maria Dehostos 101 Walton St, Brooklyn 11206 Leander Windley	6-8	T	1,266 75	62%	718/782-0589 Fax 718/384-7715
JHS 50 John D Wells 183 S 3rd St, Brooklyn 11211 Benjamin Honoroff	6-8	TV	323 20	89%	718/387-4184 Fax 718/302-2320
John Ericsson MS 126 Env Engr 424 Leonard St, Brooklyn 11222 Rosemary Ochoa	6-8	T	325	86%	718/782-2527 Fax 718/302-2319
Juan Morel Campos Sec Sch 215 Heyward St, Brooklyn 11206 Esther Shali-Ogli	6-12	TV	481 45	85%	718/302-7900 Fax 718/302-7979
Lyons Cmty Sch 223 Graham Ave, Brooklyn 11206 Taeko Onishi	6-12	T	432	90%	718/782-0918 Fax 718/782-5283
MS 582 207 Bushwick Ave, Brooklyn 11206 Jeffrey Merced	6-8		330 12	83%	718/456-8218 Fax 718/456-8220
ⒶProgress HS-Prof Careers 850 Grand St, Brooklyn 11211 William Jusino	9-12	T	638 45	84%	718/387-0228 Fax 718/218-1650

Student Personnel (79), Driver Ed/Safety (80), Gifted/Talented (81), Video Services (82), Substance Abuse Prev (83), Erate (84), AIDS Education (85), Alternative/At Risk (88), Multi-Cultural Curriculum (89), Social Work (90)

Safety/Security (91), Magnet School (92), Parental Involvement (93), Tech Prep Program (95), Chief Information Officer (97), Chief Technology Officer (98), Character Education (270), Migrant Education (271), Teacher Mentor (273), Before/After Sch (274)

Response To Intervention (275), Remedial Math K-12 (277), Literacy Coach (280), STEM (285), Digital Learning (286), Common Core Standards (288), Accountability (294), Network System (295), Title II Programs (296), Webmaster (297)

Grant Writer/Ptnrships (298), Chief Innovation Officer (750), Chief of Staff (751), Social Emotional Learning (752)

School Programs
A = Alternative Program
G = Adult Classes
M = Magnet Program
T = Title I Schoolwide
V = Career & Tech Ed Programs

Other School Types
Ⓐ = Alternative School
Ⓒ = Charter School
Ⓜ = Magnet School
Ⓨ = Year-Round School

Social Media
 = Facebook
 = Twitter

New Schools are shaded
New Superintendents and Principals are bold
Personnel with email addresses are underscored

Kings County — Market Data Retrieval

School	Grd	Prgm	Enr/#Cls	SN	Phone
PS 16 Leonard Dunkly 157 Wilson St, Brooklyn 11211 Mary Renny	PK-5	T	193 25	89%	718/782-5352
PS 17 Henry Woodworth 208 N 5th St, Brooklyn 11211 Dr Robert Marchi	PK-5	GT	296 21	68%	718/387-2929 Fax 718/302-2311
PS 18 Edward Bush 101 Maujer St, Brooklyn 11206 Alison Alexander	PK-5	T	176 13	83%	718/387-3241 Fax 718/599-7744
PS 23 Carter G Woodson 545 Willoughby Ave, Brooklyn 11206 Joseph Mattina	PK-5	T	268	89%	718/387-0375
PS 31 Samuel F DuPont 75 Meserole Ave, Brooklyn 11222 Mary Scarlato	PK-5	T	620	72%	718/383-8998 Fax 718/383-5652
PS 34 Oliver H Perry 131 Norman Ave, Brooklyn 11222 Carmen Asselta	PK-5	T	480 24	27%	718/389-5842 Fax 718/389-0356
PS 59 William Floyd 211 Throop Ave, Brooklyn 11206 Cherry-Ann Joseph-Hislop	PK-5	T	328 28	94%	718/443-3600
PS 84 Jose De Diego 250 Berry St, Brooklyn 11249 Sereida Rodriguez	PK-8	T	730 27	48%	718/384-8063 Fax 718/302-2313
PS 110 the Monitor 124 Monitor St, Brooklyn 11222 Anna Amato	PK-5	T	591 29	23%	718/383-7600 Fax 718/383-5053
PS 120 Carlos Tapia 18 Beaver St, Brooklyn 11206 Liza Caraballo	PK-5	T	372 22	87%	718/455-1000 Fax 718/574-6637
PS 132 Conselyea 320 Manhattan Ave, Brooklyn 11211 Beth Ceffalia	PK-5	T	709	38%	718/599-7301 Fax 718/599-7417
PS 147 Isaac Remsen 325 Bushwick Ave, Brooklyn 11206 Sandra Noyola	PK-5	T	358 21	70%	718/497-0326
PS 157 Benjamin Franklin Acad 850 Kent Ave, Brooklyn 11205 Kourtney Boyd	PK-8	T	398 23	83%	718/622-9285 Fax 718/398-4155
PS 196 Ten Eyck 207 Bushwick Ave, Brooklyn 11206 Janine Santaromita	PK-5	T	309	86%	718/497-0139 Fax 718/628-5134
PS 250 George Lindsay 108 Montrose Ave, Brooklyn 11206 Jill Amott	PK-5	T	462 42	78%	718/384-0889 Fax 718/302-2314
PS 257 John F Hylan 60 Cook St, Brooklyn 11206 Brian De Vale	PK-5	T	542 34	83%	718/384-7128 Fax 718/387-8115
PS 297 Abraham Stockton 700 Park Ave, Brooklyn 11206 James Brown	PK-5	T	205 19	87%	718/388-4581
PS 319 360 Keap St, Brooklyn 11211 Aleyda Martinez	PK-1	T	123 9	66%	718/388-1588 Fax 718/302-2316
PS 380 John Wayne Elem Sch 370 Marcy Ave, Brooklyn 11206 Victoria Prisinzano	PK-5	T	533	77%	718/388-0607 Fax 718/599-3231
Williamsburg HS Art & Tech 223 Graham Ave, Brooklyn 11206 Cara Tait	9-12	T	314 20	78%	718/599-1207 Fax 718/387-7945
Williamsburg HS-Arch Design 257 N 6th St, Brooklyn 11211 Gill Cornell	9-12	T	594	79%	718/388-1260 Fax 718/486-2580
Williamsburg Preparatory Sch 257 N 6th St, Brooklyn 11211 Michael Shadrick	9-12	T	695 20	80%	718/302-2306 Fax 718/302-3726
Young Women's Ldrshp Sch-Bklyn 325 Bushwick Ave, Brooklyn 11206 Catherine Mitchell	6-12	T	387	79%	718/387-5641 Fax 718/387-6153

● **Community School District 15** PID: 10909709   718/935-3424
131 Livingston St, Brooklyn 11201

(Part of New York City Dept of Ed in New York County)
Anita Skop 1

Public Schs..Principal	Grd	Prgm	Enr/#Cls	SN	Phone
Boerum Hill Sch Int'l Studies 284 Baltic St, Brooklyn 11201 Nicole Lanzillotto	6-12		813 50	45%	718/330-9390 Fax 718/875-7522
ⓐ Brooklyn Frontiers HS 112 Schermerhorn St, Brooklyn 11201 Alona Cohen	9-12	T	166	88%	718/722-4727 Fax 718/722-7919
Brooklyn HS of the Arts 345 Dean St, Brooklyn 11217 Daniel Vecchiano	9-12	T	938 30	71%	718/855-2412 Fax 718/596-5027
Brooklyn New Sch at PS 146 610 Henry St, Brooklyn 11231 Anna Allanbrook	PK-5		723 25	33%	718/923-4750 Fax 718/923-4780
Brooklyn Sch-Collab Studies 610 Henry St, Brooklyn 11231 Priscilla Chan	6-12		639 24	65%	718/923-4700 Fax 718/923-4730
Cobble Hill Sch of Amer Study 347 Baltic St, Brooklyn 11201 Annamaria Mule	9-12	T	522 15	89%	718/403-9544 Fax 718/403-9553
Cyberarts Studio Academy 237 7th Ave, Brooklyn 11215 Sharon Evans	9-12	T	260	83%	718/832-4201 Fax 718/832-0273
Digital Arts & Cinema Tech HS 284 Baltic St, Brooklyn 11201 Dawn Meconi	9-12	T	285 35	80%	718/694-9741 Fax 718/694-9745
© Hellenic Classical Charter Sch 646 5th Ave, Brooklyn 11215 Christina Tettonis	K-8	T	480 10	54%	718/499-0957 Fax 718/499-0959
IS 136 Charles O Dewey 4004 4th Ave, Brooklyn 11232 Eric Sackler	6-8	TV	511 22	93%	718/840-1950 Fax 718/840-1955
JHS 88 Peter Rouget 544 7th Ave, Brooklyn 11215 Ailene Altman	6-8	T	1,442	79%	718/788-4482
John Jay School for Law 237 7th Ave, Brooklyn 11215 Deborah Glauner	9-12	T	451 40	78%	718/832-4250 Fax 718/499-3947
Khalil Gibran Int'l Academy 362 Schermerhorn St, Brooklyn 11217 Winston Hamann	9-12	T	187	83%	718/237-2502 Fax 718/488-1724
Math & Sci Exploratory Sch 345 Dean St, Brooklyn 11217 Arin Rusch	6-8		547 52	27%	718/330-9284 Fax 718/330-0944
Maurice Sendak Community Sch 211 8th St, Brooklyn 11215 Elizabeth Garraway	PK-5		340	17%	718/840-5660 Fax 718/840-5666
Millennium Brooklyn High Sch 237 7th Ave, Brooklyn 11215 Kevin Conway	9-12		684	35%	718/832-4333 Fax 718/499-2126
MS 51 William Alexander 350 5th Ave, Brooklyn 11215 Lenore Berner	6-8	V	1,149 40	32%	718/369-7603 Fax 718/499-4948
MS 442-Carroll Gardens Innovat 500 19th St, Brooklyn 11215 Noreen Mills	6-8		339 10	33%	718/369-4480 Fax 718/369-4481

1 Superintendent	8 Curric/Instruct K-12	19 Chief Financial Officer	29 Family/Consumer Science	39 Social Studies K-12	49 English/Lang Arts Elem	59 Special Education Elem	69 Academic Assessment
2 Bus/Finance/Purchasing	9 Curric/Instruct Elem	20 Art K-12	30 Adult Education	40 Social Studies Elem	50 English/Lang Arts Sec	60 Special Education Sec	70 Research/Development
3 Buildings And Grounds	10 Curric/Instruct Sec	21 Art Elem	31 Career/Sch-to-Work K-12	41 Social Studies Sec	51 Reading K-12	61 Foreign/World Lang K-12	71 Public Information
4 Food Service	11 Federal Program	22 Art Sec	32 Career/Sch-to-Work Elem	42 Science K-12	52 Reading Elem	62 Foreign/World Lang Elem	72 Summer School
5 Transportation	12 Title I	23 Music K-12	33 Career/Sch-to-Work Sec	43 Science Elem	53 Reading Sec	63 Foreign/World Lang Sec	73 Instructional Tech
6 Athletic	13 Title V	24 Music Elem	34 Early Childhood Ed	44 Science Sec	54 Remedial Reading K-12	64 Religious Education K-12	74 Inservice Training
7 Health Services	15 Asst Superintendent	25 Music Sec	35 Health/Phys Education	45 Math K-12	55 Remedial Reading Elem	65 Religious Education Elem	75 Marketing/Distributive
	16 Instructional Media Svcs	26 Business Education	36 Guidance Services K-12	46 Math Elem	56 Remedial Reading Sec	66 Religious Education Sec	76 Info Systems
	17 Chief Operations Officer	27 Career & Tech Ed	37 Guidance Services Elem	47 Math Sec	57 Bilingual/ELL	67 School Board President	77 Psychological Assess
	18 Chief Academic Officer	28 Technology Education	38 Guidance Services Sec	48 English/Lang Arts K-12	58 Special Education K-12	68 Teacher Personnel	78 Affirmative Action

New York School Directory

Kings County

School	Grd	Prgm	Enr/#Cls	SN	Phone
MS 839 713 Caton Ave, Brooklyn 11218 Michael Perlberg	6-8		365	41%	718/686-2730 Fax 718/686-2735
New Voices Sch 330 18th St, Brooklyn 11215 Frank Giordano	6-8		571 30	28%	718/965-0390 Fax 718/965-0603
Park Slope Collegiate Sch 237 7th Ave, Brooklyn 11215 Jill Bloomberg	6-12	T	691	66%	718/832-4300 Fax 718/788-8127
©Pave Academy Charter Sch 732 Henry St, Brooklyn 11231 Spencer Robertson	K-8	T	517	84%	718/858-7813 Fax 718/858-7814
PS 1 the Bergen 309 47th St, Brooklyn 11220 Arlene Ramos	PK-5	T	1,086 50	81%	718/567-7661 Fax 718/567-9771
Ⓜ PS 10 Magnet Sch Math-Sci-Tech 511 7th Ave, Brooklyn 11215 Laura Scott	K-6	T	948 35	21%	718/965-1190 Fax 718/369-1736
PS 15 Patrick F Daly 71 Sullivan St, Brooklyn 11231 Peggy Madison	PK-5	T	471 26	71%	718/330-9280 Fax 718/596-2576
PS 24 427 38th St, Brooklyn 11232 Jacqueline Nikovic	PK-5	T	585 40	94%	718/832-9366 Fax 718/832-9360
PS 29 John M Harrigan 425 Henry St, Brooklyn 11201 Rebecca Fagin	PK-5		926 31	14%	718/330-9277 Fax 718/596-1887
PS 32 Samuel Mills Sprole 317 Hoyt St, Brooklyn 11231 Denise Watson	PK-5		446 19	42%	718/222-6400 Fax 718/222-6405
PS 38 the Pacific 450 Pacific St, Brooklyn 11217 Pascale Pradel	PK-5		592 30	48%	718/330-9305 Fax 718/802-9542
PS 39 Henry Bristow Sch 417 6th Ave, Brooklyn 11215 Sara Panag	K-5		417 18	14%	718/330-9310 Fax 718/832-2010
PS 58 the Carroll 330 Smith St, Brooklyn 11231 Katie Dello Stritto	PK-5		1,002 28	12%	718/330-9322 Fax 718/596-2969
PS 94 Henry Longfellow 5010 6th Ave, Brooklyn 11220 Janette Caban	K-5	T	1,208	99%	718/435-6034 Fax 718/871-6251
PS 107 John W Kimball 1301 8th Ave, Brooklyn 11215 Eve Litwack	PK-5		566 22	9%	718/499-2054 Fax 718/499-4019
PS 124 Silas B Dutcher 515 4th Ave, Brooklyn 11215 Maria Interlandi	PK-5	T	283 19	63%	718/788-0246
PS 130 the Parkside 70 Ocean Pkwy, Brooklyn 11218 Maria Nunziata	PK-5	T	873 22	37%	718/686-1940 Fax 718/854-9756
Ⓜ PS 131 Brooklyn 4305 Fort Hamilton Pkwy, Brooklyn 11219 Stamatina Hatzimichalis	PK-5		846 53	85%	718/431-1960 Fax 718/431-1970
PS 154 Windsor Terrace Sch 1625 11th Ave, Brooklyn 11215 Jason Foreman	K-5		536	16%	718/768-0057 Fax 718/832-2573
PS 169 Sunset Park 4305 7th Ave, Brooklyn 11232 Tang Eujin	K-5		1,268 47	91%	718/853-3224 Fax 718/633-9621
PS 172 Beacon Sch Excellence 825 4th Ave, Brooklyn 11232 Erika Gundersen	PK-6	T	583 10	84%	718/965-4200 Fax 718/965-2468
PS 230 Doris Cohen 1 Albemarle Rd, Brooklyn 11218 Maria Ragione	PK-5		1,083 42	72%	718/437-6135 Fax 718/871-2624
PS 261 Philip Livingston 314 Pacific St, Brooklyn 11201 Erica Davis	PK-5		777 38	35%	718/330-9275 Fax 718/875-9503
PS 295 330 18th St, Brooklyn 11215 Linda Mazza	PK-5	T	434 22	39%	718/965-0390 Fax 718/965-0603
PS 321 William Penn 180 7th Ave, Brooklyn 11215 Elizabeth Phillips	K-5		1,381 50	9%	718/499-2412 Fax 718/965-9605 facebook
PS 516 Sunset Park Avenues 4222 4th Ave, Brooklyn 11232 Jessica Knudson	PK-5	T	469	85%	718/369-8330 Fax 718/965-7685
PS 767 Little Brooklyn Pre-K 173-177 25th St, Brooklyn 11232 Cynthia Lascano	PK-PK		66		718/840-2840 Fax 718/840-2845
Red Hook Neighborhood Sch 27 Huntington St, Brooklyn 11231 Priscilla Figueroa	PK-5	T	109	96%	718/330-2238 Fax 718/596-6446
School of Creativity-Innovatn 736 48th St, Brooklyn 11220 Ruth Rivera	PK-K	T	42	90%	929/419-6049
Ⓐ South Brooklyn Cmty High Sch 173 Conover St, Brooklyn 11231 Latoya Kittrell	9-12	T	149	88%	718/237-8902 Fax 718/422-1927
©Summit Academy Charter Sch 27 Huntington St, Brooklyn 11231 Cheryl Swift	6-12	T	303	68%	718/875-1403 Fax 718/875-1891
Sunset Park High Sch 153 35th St, Brooklyn 11232 Victoria Antonini	9-12	T	1,240	85%	718/840-1900 Fax 718/840-1925
Sunset Park Prep Sch 4004 4th Ave, Brooklyn 11232 Jennifer Spalding	6-8		538 6	93%	718/840-1951 Fax 718/840-1962
West Brooklyn Cmty High Sch 1053 41st St, Brooklyn 11219 Malik Lewis	10-12	T	253	75%	718/686-1444 Fax 718/686-1189

● **Community School District 16** PID: 10909711   718/574-2834
1010 Lafayette Ave, Brooklyn 11221   Fax 718/453-1048

(Part of New York City Dept of Ed in New York County)
Rahesha Amon-Harris 1

Public Schs..Principal	Grd	Prgm	Enr/#Cls	SN	Phone
©Bedford-Stuy New Beginnings CS 82 Lewis Ave, Brooklyn 11206 Nicholas Tishuk	K-8	T	717	90%	718/453-1001 Fax 718/452-2090
Boys & Girls High Sch 1700 Fulton St, Brooklyn 11213 Grecian Walker	9-12	TV	468	81%	718/467-1700 Fax 718/221-0645
Ⓐ Boys & Girls High School YABC 1700 Fulton St, Brooklyn 11213 Bernard Gossaway	10-12		250		718/467-1700
Brighter Choice Community Sch 280 Hart St, Brooklyn 11206 Jeremy Daniel	PK-5	T	307	79%	718/574-2378 Fax 718/443-0639
Brooklyn Acad Global Finance 125 Stuyvesant Ave, Brooklyn 11221 Dannielle Darbee	9-12		119	96%	718/574-3126 Fax 718/574-3681
Brooklyn Brownstone Sch 272 MacDonough St, Brooklyn 11233 Alexander Brunner	PK-5	T	295	73%	718/573-2307 Fax 718/573-2434
Brooklyn HS for Law & Tech 1396 Broadway, Brooklyn 11221 Vernon Johnson	9-12	T	579 30	82%	718/919-1256 Fax 718/852-4593

79 Student Personnel	91 Safety/Security	275 Response To Intervention	298 Grant Writer/Ptnrships	**School Programs**
80 Driver Ed/Safety	92 Magnet School	277 Remedial Math K-12	750 Chief Innovation Officer	A = Alternative Program
81 Gifted/Talented	93 Parental Involvement	280 Literacy Coach	751 Chief of Staff	G = Adult Classes
82 Video Services	95 Tech Prep Program	285 STEM	752 Social Emotional Learning	M = Magnet Program
83 Substance Abuse Prev	97 Chief Information Officer	286 Digital Learning		T = Title I Schoolwide
84 Erate	98 Chief Technology Officer	288 Common Core Standards	**Other School Types**	V = Career & Tech Ed Programs
85 AIDS Education	270 Character Education	294 Accountability	Ⓐ = Alternative School	
88 Alternative/At Risk	271 Migrant Education	295 Network System	© = Charter School	
89 Multi-Cultural Curriculum	273 Teacher Mentor	296 Title II Programs	Ⓜ = Magnet School	
90 Social Work	274 Before/After Sch	297 Webmaster	Ⓨ = Year-Round School	

Social Media
 = Facebook
 = Twitter

New Schools are shaded
New Superintendents and Principals are bold
Personnel with email addresses are underscored

Kings County — Market Data Retrieval

School	Grd	Prgm	Enr/#Cls	SN	Phone
© Ember Sch for Mindful Educ CS 616 Quincy St, Brooklyn 11221 Rafiq Id-Din	K-6	T	527	79%	718/285-3787
Gotham Professional Arts Acad 561 Grand Ave, Brooklyn 11238 Robert Michelin	9-12	T	153	79%	718/230-7270 Fax 718/574-3971
Madiba Prep Middle Sch 1014 Lafayette Ave, Brooklyn 11221 Anne-Marie Malcolm	6-8	T	224	91%	718/574-2804 Fax 718/574-2805
MS 35 Stephen Decatur 272 MacDonough St, Brooklyn 11233 Jacqueline Charles	6-8	T	198 17	88%	718/574-2345
MS 57 Whitelaw Reid Acad 125 Stuyvesant Ave, Brooklyn 11221 Anthony Lett	6-8	TV	119 30	94%	718/574-2357 Fax 718/453-0577
MS 267 Math Science & Tech 800 Gates Ave, Brooklyn 11221 Patricia King	6-8	T	199 37	86%	718/574-2318
MS 898 Brooklyn Green Sch 130 Rochester Ave, Brooklyn 11213 Marcella Carr-Gay	6-7	T	83	91%	929/397-3340
Nelson Mandela High Sch 1700 Fulton St, Brooklyn 11213 Tabari Bomani	9-12	TV	238	79%	718/804-6805 Fax 718/804-6808
PS 5 Dr Ronald E McNair 820 Hancock St, Brooklyn 11233 Lena Gates	PK-5	T	245 35	83%	718/218-2444 Fax 718/218-2445
PS 21 Crispus Attucks 180 Chauncey St, Brooklyn 11233 Leslie Frazier	PK-5	T	557 33	72%	718/493-9681 Fax 718/953-3980
PS 25 Eubie Blake Sch 787 Lafayette Ave, Brooklyn 11221 Anita Coley	PK-5	T	72	95%	718/574-2336 Fax 718/455-5838
PS 26 Jesse Owens 1014 Lafayette Ave, Brooklyn 11221 Dr Cynthia Celestine	PK-5	T	239 30	72%	718/919-5707 Fax 718/574-2803
PS 40 George W Carver 265 Ralph Ave, Brooklyn 11233 Louise Antoine	PK-5	T	387 40	84%	718/574-2353 Fax 718/453-0686
PS 81 Thaddeus Stevens 990 DeKalb Ave, Brooklyn 11221 Cheryl Ault-Baker	PK-5	T	288 40	92%	718/574-2365 Fax 718/919-9872
PS 243 Weeksville 1580 Dean St, Brooklyn 11213 Karen Hambright	PK-5	T	217	93%	718/604-6909 Fax 718/604-6914
PS 262 El Hajj Malik El Shabaz 500 Macon St, Brooklyn 11233 Joeletha Ferguson	PK-5	T	161 35	90%	718/453-0780 Fax 718/453-0679
Ⓜ PS 308 Clara Cardwell 616 Quincy St, Brooklyn 11221 Sharon Odwin	PK-8	T	238 4	92%	718/571-6960 Fax 718/453-0663
PS 309 George E Wibecan Prep 794 Monroe St, Brooklyn 11221 Tanya Bryant	PK-5	T	211 36	84%	718/574-2381 Fax 718/453-0643
PS 335 Granville T Woods 130 Rochester Ave, Brooklyn 11213 Karena Thompson	PK-5	AT	213 25	89%	718/493-7736 Fax 718/953-4697
Research & Service High Sch 1700 Fulton St, Brooklyn 11213 Allison Farrington	9-12	T	288	90%	718/804-6800 Fax 718/804-6801

● **Community School District 17** PID: 10909723   718/221-4372
1224 Park Pl, Brooklyn 11213

(Part of New York City Dept of Ed in New York County)
Clarence Ellis 1

Public Schs..Principal	Grd	Prgm	Enr/#Cls	SN	Phone
Acad Clg Prep Career Explore 911 Flatbush Ave, Brooklyn 11226 Joan Mosely	6-12	T	350	83%	718/564-2566 Fax 718/564-2567
Acad of Hospitality & Tourism 911 Flatbush Ave, Brooklyn 11226 Dr Shirley Miller	9-12	T	239 20	94%	718/564-2580 Fax 718/564-2581
Academy for Health Careers 150 Albany Ave, Brooklyn 11213 L Grevenberg	9-12	T	276	84%	718/773-0128 Fax 718/773-0648
© Achievement First Crown Hghts [128] ⊙ 790 E New York Ave, Brooklyn 11203 Roseann Basile	K-8	MT	1,290	76%	347/471-2580 Fax 718/504-4742
Brooklyn Acad for Sci & Enviro 883 Classon Ave, Brooklyn 11225 Gail Lambert	9-12	T	340	75%	718/230-6363 Fax 718/230-6370
Brooklyn Arts & Science ES 443 Saint Marks Ave, Brooklyn 11238 Sandra Soto	PK-5	T	322	66%	718/230-0851
Brooklyn Institute-Lib Arts 600 Kingston Ave, Brooklyn 11203 Ann Marie Stephens	9-12	T	468	85%	718/221-1097 Fax 718/221-1794
Brooklyn Sch Music & Theatre 883 Classon Ave, Brooklyn 11225 Pamela Randazzo	9-12	T	283 23	79%	718/230-6250 Fax 718/230-6262
Ⓐ Brownsville Academy High Sch 1150 E New York Ave, Brooklyn 11212 Carol Ying	10-12	T	115	83%	718/778-7305 Fax 718/778-7385
Clara Barton High Sch 901 Classon Ave, Brooklyn 11225 Dr Richard Forman	9-12	ATV	1,261	75%	718/636-4900 Fax 718/857-3688
Dr Jacqueline Peek-Davis Sch 430 Howard Ave, Brooklyn 11233 Shamika Gamble	PK-5	T	239	94%	718/953-4569 Fax 718/953-4428
Ebbets Field Middle Sch 46 McKeever Pl, Brooklyn 11225 Jeanne Rowe	6-8	T	123	93%	718/941-5097
Elijah Stroud Middle Sch 750 Classon Ave, Brooklyn 11238 Tricia Delauney	6-8	T	162 11	87%	718/638-3067 Fax 718/638-3515
Ⓐ Erasmus Campus YABC 911 Flatbush Ave, Brooklyn 11226 Angela Pugh-Roberson	10-12		250		718/564-2590
HS for Global Citizenship 883 Classon Ave 3rd Fl, Brooklyn 11225 Michelle Rochon	9-12	T	225	90%	718/230-6300 Fax 718/230-6301
HS for Public Service 600 Kingston Ave, Brooklyn 11203 Sean Rice	9-12	T	477 25	76%	718/756-5325 Fax 718/363-3206
HS for Service & Learning 911 Flatbush Ave, Brooklyn 11226 Josephine Van-Ess	9-12	T	302	76%	718/564-2551 Fax 718/564-2552
HS for Youth & Cmty Dev 911 Flatbush Ave, Brooklyn 11226 Mary Prendergast	9-12	T	459 8	79%	718/564-2470 Fax 718/564-2471
International HS-Prospect Hgts 883 Classon Ave, Brooklyn 11225 Nedda De Castro	9-12	T	354	79%	718/230-6333 Fax 718/230-6322
Ⓜ Medgar Evers College Prep Sch 1186 Carroll St, Brooklyn 11225 Dr Michael Wiltshire	6-12	T	1,422 50	67%	718/703-5400
MS 61 Dr Gladstone H Atwell 400 Empire Blvd, Brooklyn 11225 Dewana Daids	6-8	AGTV	563	72%	718/774-1002 Fax 718/467-4335
MS 246 Walt Whitman 72 Veronica Pl, Brooklyn 11226 Bently Warrington	6-8	TV	407 70	85%	718/282-5230 Fax 718/284-6429

1	Superintendent	8	Curric/Instruct K-12	19	Chief Financial Officer	29	Family/Consumer Science
2	Bus/Finance/Purchasing	9	Curric/Instruct Elem	20	Art K-12	30	Adult Education
3	Buildings And Grounds	10	Curric/Instruct Sec	21	Art Elem	31	Career/Sch-to-Work K-12
4	Food Service	11	Federal Program	22	Art Sec	32	Career/Sch-to-Work Elem
5	Transportation	12	Title I	23	Music K-12	33	Career/Sch-to-Work Sec
6	Athletic	13	Title V	24	Music Elem	34	Early Childhood Ed
7	Health Services	15	Asst Superintendent	25	Music Sec	35	Health/Phys Education
		16	Instructional Media Svcs	26	Business Education	36	Guidance Services K-12
		17	Chief Operations Officer	27	Career & Tech Ed	37	Guidance Services Elem
		18	Chief Academic Officer	28	Technology Education	38	Guidance Services Sec

39	Social Studies K-12	49	English/Lang Arts Elem	59	Special Education Elem	69	Academic Assessment
40	Social Studies Elem	50	English/Lang Arts Sec	60	Special Education Sec	70	Research/Development
41	Social Studies Sec	51	Reading K-12	61	Foreign/World Lang K-12	71	Public Information
42	Science K-12	52	Reading Elem	62	Foreign/World Lang Elem	72	Summer School
43	Science Elem	53	Reading Sec	63	Foreign/World Lang Sec	73	Instructional Tech
44	Science Sec	54	Remedial Reading K-12	64	Religious Education K-12	74	Inservice Training
45	Math K-12	55	Remedial Reading Elem	65	Religious Education Elem	75	Marketing/Distributive
46	Math Elem	56	Remedial Reading Sec	66	Religious Education Sec	76	Info Systems
47	Math Sec	57	Bilingual/ELL	67	School Board President	77	Psychological Assess
48	English/Lang Arts K-12	58	Special Education K-12	68	Teacher Personnel	78	Affirmative Action

NY—86

New York School Directory

Kings County

School	Grd	Prgm	Enr/#Cls	SN	Phone
MS 340 North Star Academy 227 Sterling Pl, Brooklyn 11238 Tamara Johnson	6-8	T	198	82%	718/857-5516
New Heights Middle Sch 722 790 E New York Ave, Brooklyn 11203 Ativia Sandusky	6-8	T	244	78%	718/467-4501 Fax 718/467-4506
Parkside Preparatory Academy 655 Parkside Ave, Brooklyn 11226 Adrienne Spencer	6-8	T	437	89%	718/462-6992 Fax 718/284-7717
Pathways In Tech Early Clg HS 150 Albany Ave, Brooklyn 11213 Rashid Davis	9-12	T	579	72%	718/221-1593 Fax 718/221-1781
PS 6 Norma Adams Clemons Acad 43 Snyder Ave, Brooklyn 11226 Sharon Porter	PK-5	T	645 31	81%	718/856-6560 Fax 718/856-7493
PS 91 the Albany Ave Sch 532 Albany Ave, Brooklyn 11203 Tessa Alleyne	PK-5	T	218 65	88%	718/756-0243 Fax 718/221-1316
PS 92 Adrian Hegeman 601 Parkside Ave, Brooklyn 11226 John Samerson	PK-5	T	346 35	87%	718/462-2087 Fax 718/284-8289
PS 138 Brooklyn 760 Prospect Pl, Brooklyn 11216 Marie Monchik	PK-8	T	523	85%	718/467-0800 Fax 718/953-3422
PS 161 the Crown 330 Crown St, Brooklyn 11225 Michael Johnson	PK-5	T	338 45	92%	718/756-3100 Fax 718/953-3605
PS 181 Brooklyn 1023 New York Ave, Brooklyn 11203 Victor Esannason	PK-8	T	602 54	76%	718/462-5298 Fax 718/284-5053
PS 189 the Bilingual Center 1100 E New York Ave, Brooklyn 11212 Berthe Faustin	K-8	T	1,006 45	90%	718/756-0210 Fax 718/604-1865
PS 191 Paul Robeson Elem Sch 1600 Park Pl, Brooklyn 11233 Hadar Gahfi	PK-5	AT	172 40	96%	718/756-1206 Fax 718/756-5417
PS 221 Toussaint L'Ouverture 791 Empire Blvd, Brooklyn 11213 Florentine Ulysse	PK-5	T	226 38	81%	718/756-0122 Fax 718/953-2657
PS 241 Emma L Johnston 976 President St, Brooklyn 11225 Frantz Lucius	PK-5	T	450 38	86%	718/636-4725 Fax 718/230-5468
PS 249 the Caton 18 Marlborough Rd, Brooklyn 11226 Elisa Brown	PK-5	T	848 40	72%	718/282-8828 Fax 718/284-5146
PS 289 George V Brower 900 Saint Marks Ave, Brooklyn 11213 Marc Mardy	PK-6	T	365	80%	718/493-3824 Fax 718/467-3735
PS 316 Elijah G Stroud 750 Classon Ave, Brooklyn 11238 Olga Maluf	PK-5	T	596 40	65%	718/638-4043 Fax 718/230-5366
PS 375 Jackie Robinson 46 McKeever Pl, Brooklyn 11225 Schwanna Fllman	PK-5	T	289 50	94%	718/693-6655 Fax 718/284-6433
PS 397 Foster-Laurie 490 Fenimore St, Brooklyn 11203 Marie Monteau	PK-5	T	173 17	86%	718/774-5200 Fax 718/953-4856
PS 398 Walter Weaver 60 E 94th St, Brooklyn 11212 Tammy Brown	PK-5	T	257 43	96%	718/774-4466 Fax 718/467-4018
PS 399 Stanley Eugene Clark 2707 Albemarle Rd, Brooklyn 11226 Lakeasha Williams	K-5	T	284 18	95%	718/693-3023 Fax 718/940-0702
PS 532 New Bridges 1025 Eastern Pkwy, Brooklyn 11213 Kevin Bowles	PK-5	T	442	85%	718/363-8200 Fax 718/363-8202
PS 770 New American Academy 60 E 94th St, Brooklyn 11212 Jessica Saratovsky	PK-5		290	52%	718/221-5837 Fax 718/221-5947
PS/MS 394K 188 Rochester Ave, Brooklyn 11213 Sojourner Welch	PK-8	AT	335 45	85%	718/756-3164 Fax 718/756-3177
Ronald Edmonds Lrng Center II 430 Howard Ave, Brooklyn 11233 Michele Luard	6-8	T	172 9	86%	718/467-0306 Fax 718/953-0682
School for Human Rights 600 Kingston Ave, Brooklyn 11203 Michael Alexander	8-12	T	350 24	82%	718/771-4793 Fax 718/771-4815
School of Integrated Learning 1224 Park Pl, Brooklyn 11213 Monique Campbell	6-8	T	371	84%	718/774-0362 Fax 718/774-0521
Science Tech & Research HS 911 Flatbush Ave, Brooklyn 11226 Dr Eric Blake	6-12	T	624	78%	718/564-2540 Fax 718/564-2541

• **Community School District 18** PID: 10909735   718/566-6008
1106 E 95th St, Brooklyn 11236

(Part of New York City Dept of Ed in New York County)
Beverly Wilkins 1

Public Schs..Principal	Grd	Prgm	Enr/#Cls	SN	Phone
Acad-Conservation-Environ 6565 Flatlands Ave, Brooklyn 11236 Eugene Mazzola	9-12	T	303	80%	718/968-4101 Fax 718/968-4296
Brooklyn Bridge Academy 6565 Flatlands Ave, Brooklyn 11236 Max Paul	9-12	T	174	76%	718/968-1689 Fax 718/968-1678
Brooklyn Cmty HS Excel Equity 6565 Flatlands Ave, Brooklyn 11236 Louis Garcia	9-12	T	203	77%	718/968-4200 Fax 718/444-5419
Brooklyn Sci Engineering Acad 5404 Tilden Ave, Brooklyn 11203 Angela DeFilippis	6-8	T	355	78%	718/240-3790 Fax 718/240-3791
Brooklyn Theatre Arts High Sch 6565 Flatlands Ave, Brooklyn 11236 David Ward	9-12	T	350	83%	718/968-1072 Fax 718/968-1065
Cultural Acad Arts & Sciences 5800 Tilden Ave, Brooklyn 11203 Sanatha Alexis	9-12	T	249	74%	718/968-6630 Fax 718/968-6635
Ⓒ Cultural Arts Acad-Sprg Crk 1400 Linden Blvd, Brooklyn 11212 Laurie Midgette	K-5	T	274	65%	718/683-3300 Fax 718/272-1330
East Brooklyn Cmty High Sch 9517 Kings Hwy, Brooklyn 11212 Patrick McGillicuddy	9-12	T	185	80%	718/927-6880 Fax 718/927-6885
HS for Medical Professions 1600 Rockaway Pkwy, Brooklyn 11236 Pauline Obrien	9-12	T	461	97%	718/290-8700 Fax 718/290-8705
HS Innovation Adver-Media 1600 Rockaway Pkwy, Brooklyn 11236 Adaleza Michelena	9-12	T	202	69%	718/290-8760
IS 68 Isaac Bildersee 956 E 82nd St, Brooklyn 11236 Merve Williams	6-8	T	233 56	81%	718/241-4800 Fax 718/241-5582
IS 211 John Wilson 1001 E 100th St, Brooklyn 11236 Carolyn James	6-8	T	343 67	81%	718/251-4411 Fax 718/241-2503
IS 285 Meyer Levin 5909 Beverley Rd, Brooklyn 11203 George Patterson	6-8	T	728 54	76%	718/451-2200 Fax 718/228-4118

---

79 Student Personnel	91 Safety/Security	275 Response To Intervention	298 Grant Writer/Ptnrships	**School Programs**
80 Driver Ed/Safety	92 Magnet School	277 Remedial Math K-12	750 Chief Innovation Officer	A = Alternative Program
81 Gifted/Talented	93 Parental Involvement	280 Literacy Coach	751 Chief of Staff	G = Adult Classes
82 Video Services	95 Tech Prep Program	285 STEM	752 Social Emotional Learning	M = Magnet Program
83 Substance Abuse Prev	97 Chief Information Officer	286 Digital Learning		T = Title I Schoolwide
84 Erate	98 Chief Technology Officer	288 Common Core Standards	**Other School Types**	V = Career & Tech Ed Programs
85 AIDS Education	270 Character Education	294 Accountability	Ⓐ = Alternative School	
88 Alternative/At Risk	271 Migrant Education	295 Network System	Ⓒ = Charter School	New Schools are shaded
89 Multi-Cultural Curriculum	273 Teacher Mentor	296 Title II Programs	Ⓜ = Magnet School	New Superintendents and Principals are bold
90 Social Work	274 Before/After Sch	297 Webmaster	Ⓨ = Year-Round School	Personnel with email addresses are underscored

Social Media
= Facebook
= Twitter

NY−87

Kings County — Market Data Retrieval

School	Grd	Prgm	Enr/#Cls	SN	Phone
It Takes A Village Academy 5800 Tilden Ave, Brooklyn 11203 Angelo Marra	9-12	T	619	69%	718/629-2307 Fax 718/629-6162
Kurt Hahn Expeditionary Sch 5800 Tilden Ave, Brooklyn 11203 Veronica Coleman	9-12	T	264	81%	718/629-1204 Fax 718/629-1076
MS for Art & Philosophy 1084 Lenox Rd, Brooklyn 11212 Christopher Padmore	6-8	T	161	90%	718/342-7563 Fax 718/342-8131
MS of Media Law & Fine Arts 905 Winthrop St 3rd Fl, Brooklyn 11203 Jameela Horton	6-8	T	232		718/773-3059 Fax 718/773-3827
Olympus Academy 755 E 100th St, Brooklyn 11236 Bruce Gonzales	9-12	T	180	84%	718/272-1926 Fax 718/272-5713
PS 66 845 E 96th St, Brooklyn 11236 Lucille Jackson	PK-8	T	760 30	68%	718/922-3505 Fax 718/922-3105
PS 114 Ryder Elem Sch 1077 Remsen Ave, Brooklyn 11236 Darwin Smith	PK-5	T	496 50	76%	718/257-4428 Fax 718/649-5216
PS 115 Daniel Mucatel Sch 1500 E 92nd St, Brooklyn 11236 Jonathan Lee	PK-5	T	860 55	61%	718/241-1000 Fax 718/209-1714
PS 135 Sheldon Brookner 684 Linden Blvd, Brooklyn 11203 Trevlyn McRae	PK-5	T	462	85%	718/693-4363 Fax 718/941-0847
PS 208 Elsa Ebeling 4801 Avenue D, Brooklyn 11203 Nakoley Renville	PK-5	T	339	87%	718/629-1670 Fax 718/451-0185
PS 219 Kennedy-King 1060 Clarkson Ave, Brooklyn 11212 Winsome Smith	PK-5	T	362 66	79%	929/397-9566
PS 233 Langston Hughes 9301 Avenue B, Brooklyn 11236 Denean Spellman	PK-5	T	329 38	81%	718/346-8103 Fax 718/345-3078
PS 235 Janice Knight Sch 525 Lenox Rd, Brooklyn 11203 Laurence Lord	PK-8	T	1,168	65%	718/773-4869 Fax 718/773-0048
PS 244 Richard R Green Sch 5404 Tilden Ave, Brooklyn 11203 Deon Edwards	PK-5	T	421	81%	718/346-6240 Fax 718/345-3083
PS 268 Emma Lazarus 133 E 53rd St, Brooklyn 11203 Sylvia Leslie	PK-5	T	321 26	80%	718/773-5332 Fax 718/493-7448
PS 272 Curtis Estabrook 10124 Seaview Ave, Brooklyn 11236 Dakota Reyes	PK-5	T	429 42	88%	929/437-5000 Fax 929/437-5009
PS 276 Louis Marshall 1070 E 83rd St, Brooklyn 11236 Yasmine Albertini	PK-5	T	542 57	85%	718/241-5757 Fax 718/241-5560
Ⓜ PS 279 Herman Schreiber 1070 E 104th St, Brooklyn 11236 Lorenzo Chambers	PK-5	T	346 45	80%	718/444-4316 Fax 718/241-5581
Science & Medicine Middle Sch 965 E 107th St, Brooklyn 11236 Dennis Herring	6-8	T	408	80%	718/688-6400 Fax 718/688-6401
Ⓐ South Shore Ed Campus YABC 6565 Flatlands Ave, Brooklyn 11236 Dawn Harris	10-12		250		718/968-1689
Urban Action Academy 1600 Rockaway Pkwy, Brooklyn 11236 Fareeda Garcia	9-12	T	208 15	77%	718/290-8720 Fax 718/290-8721
Victory Collegiate High Sch 6565 Flatlands Ave, Brooklyn 11236 Claubentz Dieujuste	9-12	T	304	75%	718/968-1530 Fax 718/968-1526

● **Community School District 19** PID: 10909747 929/397-2938
590 Sheffield Ave, Brooklyn 11207 Fax 718/240-2747
(Part of New York City Dept of Ed in New York County)
Thomas McBryde 1

Public Schs..Principal	Grd	Prgm	Enr/#Cls	SN	Phone
Academy for Young Writers 1065 Elton St, Brooklyn 11239 Aaden Stern	6-12	T	545	85%	718/688-7230 Fax 718/688-7236
Academy of Innovative Tech 999 Jamaica Ave, Brooklyn 11208 Meghan Lynch	9-12	T	449	83%	718/827-2469 Fax 718/827-4013
Brooklyn Gardens Elem Sch 574 Dumont Ave, Brooklyn 11207 Ciani Espada	PK-5	T	297	95%	718/495-7012 Fax 718/495-7018
Brooklyn Lab Sch 999 Jamaica Ave, Brooklyn 11208 Gerard Henry	9-12	T	445	87%	718/235-3592 Fax 718/235-4028
ⓒ Brooklyn Scholars Charter Sch [210] 2635 Linden Blvd, Brooklyn 11208 Desiree Kirton	K-8	T	695	85%	718/348-9360 Fax 718/348-9362
Cypress Hills Collegiate Prep 999 Jamaica Ave, Brooklyn 11208 Amy Yager	9-12	T	358	90%	718/647-1672 Fax 718/647-6719
East New York ES of Excellence 605 Shepherd Ave, Brooklyn 11208 Janet Huger	PK-5	T	489	93%	718/272-6075 Fax 718/272-6257
Ⓐ East New York Family Academy 145 Pennsylvania Ave, Brooklyn 11207 Anthony Yard	6-12	T	518 20	82%	718/498-5240 Fax 718/927-0411
East New York MS of Excellence 605 Shepherd Ave, Brooklyn 11208 Malik Small	6-8	T	260	91%	718/257-4061 Fax 718/257-4738
Fdny High School Fire & Safety 400 Pennsylvania Ave, Brooklyn 11207 James Anderson	9-12	T	278 8	82%	718/922-0389 Fax 718/922-0593
Ⓐ Franklin K Lane Campus YABC 999 Jamaica Ave, Brooklyn 11208 Rosalie Marks	10-12		250		646/784-6841
Frederick Douglass Acad VIII 1400 Pennsylvania Ave, Brooklyn 11239 Chantal Grandchamps	6-8	T	309	90%	718/348-2465 Fax 718/642-4537
High School for Civil Rights 400 Pennsylvania Ave, Brooklyn 11207 Michael Steele	9-12	T	233 22	80%	718/688-7960 Fax 718/922-7253
Highland Park Cmty Sch 528 Ridgewood Ave, Brooklyn 11208 Jamilah Seifullah	6-8	T	365	90%	718/235-1785 Fax 718/235-4190
ⓒ Hyde Leadership CS Brooklyn 330 Alabama Ave, Brooklyn 11207 Sandra DuPree	K-6	T	456	82%	718/495-5620 Fax 718/495-5827
ⓒ Imagine ME Leadership Chtr Sch 818 Schenck Ave, Brooklyn 11207 Bevon Thompson	K-5	T	225	80%	347/985-2140 Fax 347/985-2145
IS 171 Abraham Lincoln 528 Ridgewood Ave, Brooklyn 11208 Indira Mota	6-8	TV	380 60	94%	718/647-0111 Fax 718/827-5834
IS 364 Gateway 1426 Freeport Loop, Brooklyn 11239 Nicole Fraser	6-8	TV	267 20	82%	718/642-3007 Fax 718/642-8516
Ⓜ JHS 218 James Peter Sinnott 370 Fountain Ave, Brooklyn 11208 Lisa Hermann	6-8	AT	371	96%	718/647-9050 Fax 718/827-5839
JHS 292 Margaret S Douglas 301 Vermont St, Brooklyn 11207 Ahmed Edwards	6-8	TV	513 80	94%	718/498-6562 Fax 718/345-3327

---

1 Superintendent	8 Curric/Instruct K-12	19 Chief Financial Officer	29 Family/Consumer Science	39 Social Studies K-12	49 English/Lang Arts Elem	59 Special Education Elem	69 Academic Assessment
2 Bus/Finance/Purchasing	9 Curric/Instruct Elem	20 Art K-12	30 Adult Education	40 Social Studies Elem	50 English/Lang Arts Sec	60 Special Education Sec	70 Research/Development
3 Buildings And Grounds	10 Curric/Instruct Sec	21 Art Elem	31 Career/Sch-to-Work K-12	41 Social Studies Sec	51 Reading K-12	61 Foreign/World Lang K-12	71 Public Information
4 Food Service	11 Federal Program	22 Art Sec	32 Career/Sch-to-Work Elem	42 Science K-12	52 Reading Elem	62 Foreign/World Lang Elem	72 Summer School
5 Transportation	12 Title I	23 Music K-12	33 Career/Sch-to-Work Sec	43 Science Elem	53 Reading Sec	63 Foreign/World Lang Sec	73 Instructional Tech
6 Athletic	13 Title V	24 Music Elem	34 Early Childhood Ed	44 Science Sec	54 Remedial Reading K-12	64 Religious Education K-12	74 Inservice Training
7 Health Services	15 Asst Superintendent	25 Music Sec	35 Health/Phys Education	45 Math K-12	55 Remedial Reading Elem	65 Religious Education Elem	75 Marketing/Distributive
	16 Instructional Media Svcs	26 Business Education	36 Guidance Services K-12	46 Math Elem	56 Remedial Reading Sec	66 Religious Education Sec	76 Info Systems
	17 Chief Operations Officer	27 Career & Tech Ed	37 Guidance Services Elem	47 Math Sec	57 Bilingual/ELL	67 School Board President	77 Psychological Assess
	18 Chief Academic Officer	28 Technology Education	38 Guidance Services Sec	48 English/Lang Arts K-12	58 Special Education K-12	68 Teacher Personnel	78 Affirmative Action

New York School Directory

Kings County

School	Grd	Prgm	Enr/#Cls	SN	Phone
MS 654 Van Siclen Cmty Mid Sch 800 Van Siclen Ave, Brooklyn 11207 Adonna McFarland	6-8	T	292	93%	718/927-4701 Fax 718/927-4707
MS 661 Vista Academy 350 Linwood St, Brooklyn 11208 Bernard Addo	6-8	T	472	96%	718/647-0913 Fax 718/647-0919
MS 662 Liberty Avenue Mid Sch 350 Linwood St, Brooklyn 11208 Kaia Nordtvedt	6-8	T	512	95%	718/647-1301 Fax 718/647-1307
MS 663 Sch of the Future-Bklyn 574 Dumont Ave, Brooklyn 11207 Robert Burnside	6-8	T	171	96%	718/345-5190 Fax 718/345-5196
MS 907 Legacy Sch of the Arts 590 Sheffield Ave, Brooklyn 11207 **Christopher Guidarelli**	6-6	T	40	88%	929/397-2967
Multicultural High Sch 999 Jamaica Ave, Brooklyn 11208 Alexandra Hernandez	9-12	T	292 5	92%	718/827-2796 Fax 718/827-3970
Performing Arts & Tech HS 400 Pennsylvania Ave, Brooklyn 11207 Franklin Encarnacion	9-12	T	384 20	89%	718/688-7900 Fax 718/922-0953
PS 7 Abraham Lincoln 858 Jamaica Ave, Brooklyn 11208 Carolyn Noel	PK-5	T	790 47	91%	718/647-3600
PS 13 Roberto Clemente 557 Pennsylvania Ave, Brooklyn 11207 Maxine Cameron	PK-5	T	429 40	94%	718/498-3717
PS 65 696 Jamaica Ave, Brooklyn 11208 Daysi Garcia	PK-5	T	549 16	82%	718/235-2223 Fax 718/235-2033
Ⓜ PS 89 Cypress Hills 265 Warwick St, Brooklyn 11207 Irene Leon	PK-8	T	484 12	95%	718/964-1180 Fax 718/964-1185
PS 108 Sal Abbracciamento 200 Linwood St, Brooklyn 11208 Constance Hahn	PK-5	T	900	79%	718/277-7010 Fax 718/827-4137
PS 149 Danny Kaye 700 Sutter Ave, Brooklyn 11207 Yvette Donald	PK-5	T	591 41	94%	718/688-7620 Fax 718/345-8118
PS 158 Warwick 400 Ashford St, Brooklyn 11207 Latishia Towles	PK-5	T	513 36	89%	718/277-6116 Fax 718/827-4300
PS 159 Isaac Pitkin 2781 Pitkin Ave, Brooklyn 11208 Monica Duncan	PK-5	T	745	84%	718/277-4828 Fax 718/827-4531
PS 190 Sheffield 590 Sheffield Ave, Brooklyn 11207 Stephaun Hill	PK-5	AT	186 30	94%	718/346-8780 Fax 718/345-8765
PS 202 Ernest Jenkyns 982 Hegeman Ave, Brooklyn 11208 Ronald James	PK-5	T	345 60	96%	718/649-7880 Fax 718/927-2173
PS 213 New Lots 580 Hegeman Ave, Brooklyn 11207 Stanley Moise	PK-5	T	260 30	91%	718/257-4034 Fax 718/272-3446
PS 214 Michael Friedsam 2944 Pitkin Ave, Brooklyn 11208 Sharon Mahabir	PK-5	T	872 90	79%	718/647-1740 Fax 718/827-5838
PS 224 Hale A Woodruff 757 Wortman Ave, Brooklyn 11208 Rochelle Hinds	PK-5	AT	339	94%	718/235-3600 Fax 718/827-5840
PS 273 Wortman 923 Jerome St, Brooklyn 11207 Melessa Avery	PK-5	T	329 34	85%	718/649-5739 Fax 718/927-2230
PS 290 Juan Morel Campos 135 Schenck Ave, Brooklyn 11207 Bridget Newell	PK-5	T	435	95%	718/647-1113 Fax 718/827-5842
PS 306 Ethan Allen 970 Vermont St, Brooklyn 11207 Lenika Vane	PK-5	T	314 38	92%	718/649-3155 Fax 718/927-2243
PS 325 Fresh Creek Sch 875 Williams Ave, Brooklyn 11207 Lisa Goodson	PK-5	T	189	93%	718/272-1843 Fax 718/272-2813
PS 328 Phyllis Wheatley 330 Alabama Ave, Brooklyn 11207 Marie Desforges	PK-5	AT	310 30	99%	718/345-9393 Fax 718/345-6566
PS 345 Patrolman Robert Bolden 111 Berriman St, Brooklyn 11208 Wanda Holt	PK-5	T	574 45	83%	718/647-8387 Fax 718/827-5884
PS 346 Abe Stark 1400 Pennsylvania Ave, Brooklyn 11239 Kevin Caifa	PK-5	T	554 55	89%	718/642-3000 Fax 718/642-8498
PS 938 76 Dinsmore Pl, Brooklyn 11208 **Teneika Benn**	K-K		19		
School for Classics Academy 370 Fountain Ave, Brooklyn 11208 Nicole Tancredi	9-12	T	267	92%	718/277-1069 Fax 718/277-1873
Spring Creek Cmty Sch 1065 Elton St, Brooklyn 11239 Christina Koza	6-12	T	534	82%	718/688-7200 Fax 718/688-7206
Teach 800 Van Siclen Ave, Brooklyn 11207 **Justin Davis**	9-12		176		718/927-5540
Ⓐ Thomas Jefferson Campus YABC 400 Pennsylvania Ave, Brooklyn 11207 Franklin Encarnacion	10-12		250		718/922-0762
Transit Tech Career High Sch 1 Wells St, Brooklyn 11208 Marlon Bynum	Voc	T	720 59	76%	718/647-5204 Fax 718/647-4458
Urban Assem Collab Healthcare 999 Jamaica Ave, Brooklyn 11208 Candace Hugee	9-12	T	337	77%	718/277-1572 Fax 718/277-6041
William Maxwell Career Tech HS 145 Pennsylvania Ave, Brooklyn 11207 Jocelyn Badette	9-12	AT	395	89%	718/345-9100 Fax 718/345-5470
World Acad Total Cmty Hlth HS 400 Pennsylvania Ave, Brooklyn 11207 Claudette Christie	9-12	T	202 15	92%	718/688-7980 Fax 718/922-0709

• **Community School District 20** PID: 10909797   718/759-4908
  415 89th St, Brooklyn 11209   Fax 718/759-4842

(Part of New York City Dept of Ed in New York County)
Jpseph O'Brien 1

Public Schs..Principal	Grd	Prgm	Enr/#Cls	SN	Phone
Academy of Talented Scholars 50 Avenue P, Brooklyn 11204 Josephine Giusto	K-5		421	42%	718/621-2730 Fax 718/621-2735
Brooklyn School of Inquiry 50 Avenue P, Brooklyn 11204 Eric Havlik	K-8		531	27%	718/621-5730 Fax 718/621-5735
District 20 Pre-K Center 1355 84th St, Brooklyn 11228 Dianne Gourades	PK-PK		162		718/621-8510
Franklin D Roosevelt High Sch 5800 20th Ave, Brooklyn 11204 Melanie Katz	9-12	ATV	3,301	78%	718/621-8800 Fax 718/232-9513
Ⓐ Franklin D Roosevelt YABC 5800 20th Ave, Brooklyn 11204 Michael Ragucci	10-12		250		718/256-1346

79 Student Personnel	91 Safety/Security	275 Response To Intervention	298 Grant Writer/Ptnrships
80 Driver Ed/Safety	92 Magnet School	277 Remedial Math K-12	750 Chief Innovation Officer
81 Gifted/Talented	93 Parental Involvement	280 Literacy Coach	751 Chief of Staff
82 Video Services	95 Tech Prep Program	285 STEM	752 Social Emotional Learning
83 Substance Abuse Prev	97 Chief Information Officer	286 Digital Learning	
84 Erate	98 Chief Technology Officer	288 Common Core Standards	**Other School Types**
85 AIDS Education	270 Character Education	294 Accountability	Ⓐ = Alternative School
88 Alternative/At Risk	271 Migrant Education	295 Network System	Ⓒ = Charter School
89 Multi-Cultural Curriculum	273 Teacher Mentor	296 Title II Programs	Ⓜ = Magnet School
90 Social Work	274 Before/After Sch	297 Webmaster	Ⓨ = Year-Round School

School Programs
A = Alternative Program
G = Adult Classes
M = Magnet Program
T = Title I Schoolwide
V = Career & Tech Ed Programs

Social Media
◼ = Facebook
◼ = Twitter

New Schools are shaded
New Superintendents and Principals are bold
Personnel with email addresses are underscored

NY—89

Kings County — Market Data Retrieval

School	Grades	Media	Enroll	%	Phone
Ft Hamilton High Sch 8301 Shore Rd, Brooklyn 11209 Kaye Houlihan	9-12	TV	4,682	71%	718/748-1537 Fax 718/836-3955
HS of Telecom Arts & Tech 350 67th St, Brooklyn 11220 Xhenete Shepard	9-12	TV	1,227	77%	718/759-3400 Fax 718/759-3490
IS 187 Christa McAuliffe Sch 1171 65th St, Brooklyn 11219 Justin Berman	6-8		982 60	61%	718/236-3394 Fax 718/236-3638
JHS 62 Ditmas Sch 700 Cortelyou Rd, Brooklyn 11218 Marielena Santiago	6-8	T	1,169 2	85%	718/941-5450 Fax 718/693-7433
JHS 201 Dyker Heights 8010 12th Ave, Brooklyn 11228 Robert Ciulla	6-8	AT	1,748 61	73%	718/833-9363 Fax 718/836-1786
JHS 220 John Pershing 4812 9th Ave, Brooklyn 11220 Sheldon Dempster	6-8	ATV	1,483 60	85%	718/633-8200 Fax 718/871-7466
JHS 223 the Montauk 4200 16th Ave, Brooklyn 11204 Andrew Frank	6-8	TV	886 60	97%	718/438-0155 Fax 718/871-7477
JHS 227 Edward Shallow 6500 16th Ave, Brooklyn 11204 Edwin Hernandez	6-8	T	1,631 100	90%	718/256-8218 Fax 718/234-6204
JHS 259 William McKinley 7305 Fort Hamilton Pkwy, Brooklyn 11228 Janice Geary	6-8	T	1,862 54	79%	718/833-1000 Fax 718/833-3419
MS 936 Arts Off 3rd 270 59th St, Brooklyn 11220 Donna Nastasi	6-6		150		
New Utrecht High Sch 1601 80th St, Brooklyn 11214 Maureen Goldfarb	9-12	AT	3,508	79%	718/232-2500 Fax 718/259-5526
PS 48 Mapleton 6015 18th Ave, Brooklyn 11204 Diane Picucci	PK-5	T	565 28	70%	718/232-3873 Fax 718/232-3451
PS 69 Vincent D Grippo Sch 6302 9th Ave, Brooklyn 11220 Jaynemarie Capetanakis	K-5	T	772	97%	718/630-3899 Fax 718/630-3894
PS 102 the Bayview 211 72nd St, Brooklyn 11209 Cornelia Sichenze	K-5	T	1,395 50	62%	718/748-7404 Fax 718/836-9265
PS 105 the Blythebourne 1031 59th St, Brooklyn 11219 Johanna Castronovo	K-5	T	1,385	85%	718/438-3230 Fax 718/853-9633
PS 112 Lefferts Park 7115 15th Ave, Brooklyn 11228 Louise Verdemare	PK-5	T	728 21	68%	718/232-0685 Fax 718/232-3609
PS 127 McKinley Park 7805 7th Ave, Brooklyn 11228 Agatha Alicandro	K-5	T	518 19	81%	718/833-2323 Fax 718/836-9427
PS 160 William Sampson 5105 Fort Hamilton Pkwy, Brooklyn 11219 Margaret Russo	K-5	T	1,234	83%	718/438-0337 Fax 718/871-7920
PS 163 Bath Beach 109 Bay 14th St, Brooklyn 11214 Jessica Riccio	K-8	T	632 30	83%	718/236-9003 Fax 718/259-3042
PS 164 Caesar Rodney 4211 14th Ave, Brooklyn 11219 Erica Steinberg	PK-5	T	667 40	81%	718/854-4100 Fax 718/853-9306
PS 170 Ralph A Fabrizio Sch 619 72nd St, Brooklyn 11209 Tony Wu	K-5	T	1,015	90%	718/491-8400 Fax 718/491-8405
PS 176 Ovington Sch 1225 Bay Ridge Ave, Brooklyn 11219 Elizabeth Culkin	K-5	T	1,216 46	85%	718/236-7755 Fax 718/331-9188
PS 179 Kensington 202 Avenue C, Brooklyn 11218 Bernel Connelly	PK-5	T	797 45	82%	718/438-4010 Fax 718/871-7484
PS 185 Walter Kassenbrock 8601 Ridge Blvd, Brooklyn 11209 Rena Goudelias	K-5		635 40	43%	718/745-6610 Fax 718/836-9631
PS 186 Dr Irving Gladstone 7601 19th Ave, Brooklyn 11214 Bayan Cadotte	K-5	T	1,120 30	74%	718/236-7071 Fax 718/331-9181
ⓦ PS 192 Magnet Sch-Math & Sci 4715 18th Ave, Brooklyn 11204 Liset Isaac	PK-8	T	637 32	80%	718/633-3061 Fax 718/871-8721
PS 200 Benson Sch 1940 Benson Ave, Brooklyn 11214 Javier Muniz	PK-5	T	1,332 45	81%	718/236-5466 Fax 718/232-3428
PS 204 Vince Lombardi 8101 15th Ave, Brooklyn 11228 Nancy Tomasuolo	PK-5	T	1,105 41	72%	718/236-2906 Fax 718/232-9265
PS 205 Clarion 6701 20th Ave, Brooklyn 11204 Feiga Mandel	PK-5	T	1,307 55	64%	718/236-2380 Fax 718/331-7299
PS 229 Dyker 1400 Benson Ave, Brooklyn 11228 William Kirk	PK-8		1,251 21	57%	718/236-5447 Fax 718/331-8173
PS 247 Brooklyn 7000 21st Ave, Brooklyn 11204 Christopher Ogno	K-5		852 29	63%	718/236-4205 Fax 718/331-8563
PS 264 Bay Ridge ES-the Arts 371 89th St, Brooklyn 11209 Marisa Bolognino	K-5	T	450	66%	718/630-1650 Fax 718/630-1655
PS 310 Sch for Future Leaders 942 62nd St, Brooklyn 11219 Yuqing Hong	K-5	T	430	96%	718/491-7670 Fax 718/765-4635
PS 503 the School of Discovery 330 59th St, Brooklyn 11220 Nina Demos	K-5		945 86	94%	718/439-5962 Fax 718/439-0948
PS 506 School Journalism/Tech 330 59th St, Brooklyn 11220 Dana Parentini	K-5	T	737	93%	718/492-0087 Fax 718/492-9431
PS 748 Sch Global Scholars 1664 Benson Ave, Brooklyn 11214 Ursula Annio	K-5	T	495	74%	718/382-3130 Fax 718/382-3140
PS 939 Sunset ES Cultural Lrng 270 59th St, Brooklyn 11220 Georgia Mousouroulis	K-K		401		212/346-5274
PS/IS 30 Mary White Ovington 7002 4th Ave, Brooklyn 11209 Carol Heeraman	K-8	T	976 12	79%	718/491-8440 Fax 718/491-8445
ⓦ PS/IS 104 the Ft Hamilton Sch 9115 5th Ave, Brooklyn 11209 Marie DiBella	K-8	A	1,221	62%	718/836-4630 Fax 718/836-9412
Sch Math Sci & Healthy Living 6214 4th Ave, Brooklyn 11220 Ruth Stanislaus	K-5	T	307	92%	718/765-2200
Seeall Academy 5601 16th Ave, Brooklyn 11204 Gary Williams	PK-8	T	1,068 26	86%	718/851-8070 Fax 718/853-9308
Urban Assmbly Ldrshp & Emprmnt 4200 16th Ave, Brooklyn 11204 Natalie Jufer	6-12	T	573	91%	718/438-3893 Fax 929/506-3914

• **Community School District 21** PID: 10909802 718/648-0209
1401 Emmons Ave, Brooklyn 11235

(Part of New York City Dept of Ed in New York County)
Isabel Dimola 1

1	Superintendent	8	Curric/Instruct K-12	19	Chief Financial Officer	29	Family/Consumer Science	39	Social Studies K-12	49	English/Lang Arts Elem	59	Special Education K-12	69	Academic Assessment
2	Bus/Finance/Purchasing	9	Curric/Instruct Elem	20	Art K-12	30	Adult Education	40	Social Studies Elem	50	English/Lang Arts Sec	60	Special Education Sec	70	Research/Development
3	Buildings And Grounds	10	Curric/Instruct Sec	21	Art Elem	31	Career/Sch-to-Work K-12	41	Social Studies Sec	51	Reading K-12	61	Foreign/World Lang K-12	71	Public Information
4	Food Service	11	Federal Program	22	Art Sec	32	Career/Sch-to-Work Elem	42	Science K-12	52	Reading Elem	62	Foreign/World Lang Elem	72	Summer School
5	Transportation	12	Title I	23	Music K-12	33	Career/Sch-to-Work Sec	43	Science Elem	53	Reading Sec	63	Foreign/World Lang Sec	73	Instructional Tech
6	Athletic	13	Title V	24	Music Elem	34	Early Childhood Ed	44	Science Sec	54	Remedial Reading K-12	64	Religious Education K-12	74	Inservice Training
7	Health Services	15	Asst Superintendent	25	Music Sec	35	Health/Phys Education	45	Math K-12	55	Remedial Reading Elem	65	Religious Education Elem	75	Marketing/Distributive
		16	Instructional Media Svcs	26	Business Education	36	Guidance Services K-12	46	Math Elem	56	Remedial Reading Sec	66	Religious Education Sec	76	Info Systems
		17	Chief Operations Officer	27	Career & Tech Ed	37	Guidance Services Elem	47	Math Sec	57	Bilingual/ELL	67	School Board President	77	Psychological Assess
		18	Chief Academic Officer	28	Technology Education	38	Guidance Services Sec	48	English/Lang Arts K-12	58	Special Education K-12	68	Teacher Personnel	78	Affirmative Action

New York School Directory — Kings County

Public Schs..Principal	Grd	Prgm	Enr/#Cls	SN	
Abraham Lincoln High Sch 2800 Ocean Pkwy, Brooklyn 11235 Ari Hoogenboom	9-12	TV	1,878	76%	718/333-7400 Fax 718/946-5035
Ⓐ Abraham Lincoln YABC 2800 Ocean Pkwy, Brooklyn 11235 Neal Reich	10-12		250		718/333-7455
Brooklyn Studio Secondary Sch 8310 21st Ave, Brooklyn 11214 Andrea Ciliotta	6-12	TV	925 30	76%	718/266-5032 Fax 718/266-5093
Edward R Murrow High Sch 1600 Avenue L, Brooklyn 11230 Allen Barge	9-12	AT	3,577	66%	718/258-9283 Fax 718/252-2611
Expeditionary Sch Cmty Leaders 2630 Benson Ave, Brooklyn 11214 Thomas Mullen	9-12	T	386	76%	718/333-7700 Fax 718/333-7725
HS of Sports Management 2630 Benson Ave, Brooklyn 11214 Derek Cradle	9-12	T	251	76%	718/333-7650 Fax 718/333-7675
International HS at Lafayette 2630 Benson Ave, Brooklyn 11214 Jon Harriman	9-12	T	360	87%	718/333-7860 Fax 718/333-7861
IS 96 Seth Low 99 Avenue P, Brooklyn 11204 Erin Lynch	6-8	TV	831 60	75%	718/236-1344 Fax 718/236-2397
IS 98 Bay Academy 1401 Emmons Ave, Brooklyn 11235 Maria Timo	6-8		1,602	51%	718/891-9005 Fax 718/646-7250
Ⓜ IS 228 David A Boody 228 Avenue S, Brooklyn 11223 Dominick DAngelo	6-8	T	1,493 40	75%	718/375-7635 Fax 718/376-1209
Ⓜ IS 239 Mark Twain Gifted Sch 2401 Neptune Ave, Brooklyn 11224 Karen Ditolla	6-8	V	1,347	35%	718/266-0814 Fax 718/266-1693
IS 281 Joseph B Cavallaro 8787 24th Ave, Brooklyn 11214 Maria Bender	6-8	T	1,259 43	83%	718/996-6706 Fax 718/996-4186
IS 303 Herbert Eisenberg Sch 501 West Ave, Brooklyn 11224 Carmen Amador	6-8	T	569 45	74%	718/996-0100 Fax 718/996-3785
John Dewey High Sch 50 Avenue X, Brooklyn 11223 Connie Hamilton	9-12	ATV	2,207	82%	718/373-6400 Fax 718/266-4385
Kingsborough Early College Sch 2630 Benson Ave, Brooklyn 11214 Tracee Murren	6-12	T	706	69%	718/333-7850 Fax 718/333-7875
Liberation Diploma Plus HS 2865 W 19th St, Brooklyn 11224 April Leong	9-12	T	188 8	81%	718/946-6812 Fax 718/946-6825
Life Academy HS Film & Music 2630 Benson Ave, Brooklyn 11214 Eugenia Kelch	9-12	T	279	76%	718/333-7750 Fax 718/333-7775
PS 90 Edna Cohen Sch 2840 W 12th St, Brooklyn 11224 Greta Hawkins	PK-5	T	594	82%	718/787-3333 Fax 718/787-3335
PS 95 the Gravesend 345 Van Sicklen St, Brooklyn 11223 Janet Ndzibah	PK-8	T	986 50	70%	718/449-5050 Fax 718/449-3047
PS 97 the Highlawn Sch 1855 Stillwell Ave, Brooklyn 11223 Irina Cabello	K-5	T	741 50	64%	718/627-7550 Fax 718/627-7555
PS 99 Isaac Asimov 1120 E 10th St, Brooklyn 11230 Gregory Pirraglia	PK-8	T	880 40	71%	718/338-9201 Fax 718/951-0418
PS 100 Coney Island Sch 2951 W 3rd St, Brooklyn 11224 Chiara Spagnolo	PK-5		828 32	49%	718/382-2760 Fax 718/382-2765
PS 101 the Verrazano 8696 24th Ave, Brooklyn 11214 Gregg Korrol	K-5	T	921 40	61%	718/372-0221 Fax 718/372-1873
PS 121 Nelson A Rockefeller 5301 20th Ave, Brooklyn 11204 Anthony Mungioli	K-8	T	334 17	65%	718/377-8845 Fax 718/252-4075
PS 128 Bensonhurst 2075 84th St, Brooklyn 11214 Jessica Drzewucki	K-5	T	451 15	85%	718/373-5900 Fax 718/266-6254
PS 153 Homecrest 1970 Homecrest Ave, Brooklyn 11229 Carl Santa Maria	PK-5	T	577 27	77%	718/375-4484 Fax 718/375-4439
PS 177 the Marlboro Sch 346 Avenue P, Brooklyn 11204 Ann Marie Baker	PK-5	T	981 38	73%	718/375-9506 Fax 718/375-4450
PS 188 Michael E Berdy 3314 Neptune Ave, Brooklyn 11224 Antoinette Tucci	PK-5	T	348	88%	718/265-7580 Fax 718/265-7589
PS 199 Frederick Wachtel 1100 Elm Ave, Brooklyn 11230 Rosalia Bacarella	PK-5	T	566 20	83%	718/339-1422 Fax 718/336-5562
PS 209 Margaret Mead 2609 E 7th St, Brooklyn 11235 Francesca Novella	PK-8	T	731 50	73%	718/743-1954 Fax 718/743-6361
PS 212 Lady Deborah Moody 87 Bay 49th St, Brooklyn 11214 Rina Horne	PK-5	T	692 31	84%	718/266-4841 Fax 718/266-7080
PS 215 Morris H Weiss 415 Avenue S, Brooklyn 11223 Antonella Bove	PK-5	T	819 25	69%	718/339-2464 Fax 718/998-7235
PS 216 Arturo Toscanini 350 Avenue X, Brooklyn 11223 Donna Neglia	PK-5	T	759	74%	718/645-2862 Fax 718/645-2610
PS 225 the Eileen Zaglin 1075 Ocean View Ave, Brooklyn 11235 Michael Cosmai	PK-8	T	1,007	81%	718/743-9793 Fax 718/743-7096
PS 226 Alfred De B Mason 6006 23rd Ave, Brooklyn 11204 Evan Klein	PK-8	T	1,021	81%	718/234-4940 Fax 718/234-4945
PS 238 Anne Sullivan 1633 E 8th St, Brooklyn 11223 Harla Weiss	PK-8	T	594 30	86%	718/339-4355 Fax 718/998-4351
PS 253 601 Ocean View Ave, Brooklyn 11235 Lisa Speroni	PK-5	T	940 40	79%	718/332-3331 Fax 718/743-7194
PS 288 Shirley Tanyhill 2950 W 25th St, Brooklyn 11224 Qadir Dixon	PK-8	T	583 40	94%	718/382-2100 Fax 718/382-2111
PS 329 Surfside 2929 W 30th St, Brooklyn 11224 Salema Marbury	PK-5	T	381 48	95%	718/787-3460 Fax 718/787-3471
Rachel Carson HS-Coastal Study 521 West Ave, Brooklyn 11224 Edward Wilensky	9-12	T	621	67%	718/265-0329 Fax 718/372-2514
William Grady Career & Tech HS 25 Brighton 4th Rd, Brooklyn 11235 Tarah Montalbano	Voc	GT	459	88%	718/332-5000 Fax 718/332-2544

● **Community School District 22** PID: 10909814   718/968-6117
5619 Flatlands Ave, Brooklyn 11234

(Part of New York City Dept of Ed in New York County)
Julianna Bove 1

---

79 Student Personnel	91 Safety/Security	275 Response To Intervention
80 Driver Ed/Safety	92 Magnet School	277 Remedial Math K-12
81 Gifted/Talented	93 Parental Involvement	280 Literacy Coach
82 Video Services	95 Tech Prep Program	285 STEM
83 Substance Abuse Prev	97 Chief Information Officer	286 Digital Learning
84 Erate	98 Chief Technology Officer	288 Common Core Standards
85 AIDS Education	270 Character Education	294 Accountability
88 Alternative/At Risk	271 Migrant Education	295 Network System
89 Multi-Cultural Curriculum	273 Teacher Mentor	296 Title II Programs
90 Social Work	274 Before/After Sch	297 Webmaster
		298 Grant Writer/Ptnrships
		750 Chief Innovation Officer
		751 Chief of Staff
		752 Social Emotional Learning

School Programs
A = Alternative Program
G = Adult Classes
M = Magnet Program
T = Title I Schoolwide
V = Career & Tech Ed Programs

Other School Types
Ⓐ = Alternative School
Ⓒ = Charter School
Ⓜ = Magnet School
Ⓨ = Year-Round School

Social Media
 = Facebook
 = Twitter

New Schools are shaded
New Superintendents and Principals are bold
Personnel with email addresses are underscored

Kings County — Market Data Retrieval

Public Schs..Principal	Grd	Prgm	Enr/#Cls	SN	Phone/Fax
Andries Hudde Sch, 2500 Nostrand Ave, Brooklyn 11210, Michelle Esposito	6-8	TV	683	82%	718/253-3700, Fax 718/253-0356
Ⓐ Brooklyn College Acad, 350 Coney Island Ave, Brooklyn 11218, Shernell Thomas	9-12	V	656 / 30	71%	718/853-6184, Fax 718/853-6356
Ⓒ Hebrew Language Academy CS [240], 2186 Mill Ave, Brooklyn 11234, Hadar Dohn	K-8	T	671	66%	718/377-7200, Fax 718/377-7220
Ⓜ IS 381, 2500 Nostrand Ave, Brooklyn 11210, Victoria Agard	6-8	T	285 / 18	76%	718/338-1534, Fax 718/338-2794
James Madison High Sch, 3787 Bedford Ave, Brooklyn 11229, Jodie Cohen	9-12	AGT	3,896 / 165	74%	718/758-7200, Fax 718/758-7341
JHS 14 Shell Bank, 2424 Batchelder St, Brooklyn 11235, Teri Ahearn	6-8	TV	532 / 35	85%	718/743-0220, Fax 718/769-8632
JHS 78 Roy H Mann, 1420 E 68th St, Brooklyn 11234, Anthony Cusumano	6-8	TV	543 / 50	75%	718/763-4701, Fax 718/251-3439
JHS 234 Arthur W Cunningham, 1875 E 17th St, Brooklyn 11229, Tami Flynn	6-8	TV	1,550	71%	718/645-1334, Fax 718/645-7759
JHS 278 Marine Park, 1925 Stuart St, Brooklyn 11229, Ms Moser	6-8	TV	1,211 / 40	70%	718/375-3523, Fax 718/998-7324
Leon M Goldstein HS Sciences, 1830 Shore Blvd, Brooklyn 11235, Scott Hughes	9-12	V	980	46%	718/368-8500, Fax 718/368-8555
Midwood High Sch, 2839 Bedford Ave, Brooklyn 11210, Michael McDonnell	9-12	AGT	4,069	73%	718/724-8500, Fax 718/724-8515
MS 890, 21 Hinckley Pl, Brooklyn 11218, Nicholas Frangella	6-7	T	213	77%	929/397-9200, Fax 929/397-9205
Origins High Sch, 3000 Avenue X, Brooklyn 11235, John Banks	9-12	T	402	79%	718/891-0037, Fax 718/891-0047
Ⓐ Professional Pathways HS, 3000 Avenue X, Brooklyn 11235, David Decamp	9-12	T	192	77%	718/332-6290, Fax 718/332-6296
PS 52 Sheepshead Bay, 2675 E 29th St, Brooklyn 11235, Kristin Hurley	PK-5	T	792 / 40	76%	718/648-0882, Fax 718/648-4636
PS 119 Amersfort, 3829 Avenue K, Brooklyn 11210, Lisa Fernandez	PK-5	T	426 / 23	71%	718/377-7696, Fax 718/338-0694
PS 139 Alexine A Fenty, 330 Rugby Rd, Brooklyn 11226, Mary McDonald	PK-5	T	888 / 44	79%	718/282-5254, Fax 718/940-1205
PS 193 Gil Hodges, 2515 Avenue L, Brooklyn 11210, Sheila Phillip	PK-5	T	653 / 40	71%	718/338-9011, Fax 718/338-9074
PS 194 Raoul Wallenberg, 3117 Avenue W, Brooklyn 11229, Joy Mendelsohn	PK-5	T	548 / 23	88%	718/648-8804, Fax 718/934-0244
PS 195 Manhattan Beach, 131 Irwin St, Brooklyn 11235, Bernadette Toomey	PK-5		484 / 16	30%	718/648-9102, Fax 718/934-0625
PS 197 Kings Hwy Academy, 1599 E 22nd St, Brooklyn 11210, Rosemarie Nicoletti	PK-5	T	842 / 33	61%	718/377-7890, Fax 718/377-7505
PS 198 Brooklyn, 4105 Farragut Rd, Brooklyn 11210, Joy Ann Morgan	PK-5	T	388	81%	718/282-4920, Fax 718/940-0821
PS 203 Floyd Bennett Sch, 5101 Avenue M, Brooklyn 11234, Yocasta Dominguezmill	PK-5	T	608 / 42	65%	718/241-8488, Fax 718/209-9641
PS 206 Joseph F Lamb, 2200 Gravesend Neck Rd, Brooklyn 11229, Ellen Quigley	K-8	T	1,515 / 52	70%	718/743-5598, Fax 718/332-4986
PS 207 Elizabeth Leary, 4011 Fillmore Ave, Brooklyn 11234, Neil McNeill	PK-8	T	1,082 / 40	48%	718/645-8667, Fax 718/645-8139
PS 217 Col David Marcus Sch, 1100 Newkirk Ave, Brooklyn 11230, Robert Bonilla	PK-5	T	1,117 / 62	76%	718/434-6960, Fax 718/434-8170
PS 222 Katherine R Snyder, 3301 Quentin Rd, Brooklyn 11234, Theresa Olivieri	K-5		861	52%	718/998-4298, Fax 718/339-2107
PS 236 Mill Basin, 6302 Avenue U, Brooklyn 11234, Salil Paingankar	PK-5		605	45%	718/444-6969, Fax 718/241-6630
PS 245, 249 E 17th St, Brooklyn 11226, Erica Williams	PK-5	T	269 / 10	95%	718/284-2330, Fax 718/284-2333
PS 251 Paerdegat, 1037 E 54th St, Brooklyn 11234, Sheldon Noel	PK-5	T	433 / 28	76%	718/251-4110
PS 254 Dag Hammarskjold, 1801 Avenue Y, Brooklyn 11235, John Norton	K-5	T	751 / 30	56%	718/743-0890
PS 255 Barbara Reing Sch, 1866 E 17th St, Brooklyn 11229, Kelly McCann	K-5	T	858 / 36	77%	718/376-8494, Fax 718/627-0626
PS 277 Gerritsen Beach, 2529 Gerritsen Ave, Brooklyn 11229, Theresa Vlantis	PK-5		416 / 20	49%	718/743-6689, Fax 718/368-0920
PS 312 Bergen Beach, 7103 Avenue T, Brooklyn 11234, Sungmin Yoo	PK-5		737 / 50	55%	718/763-4015, Fax 718/531-2796
PS 326, 1800 Utica Ave, Brooklyn 11234, Colleen Duccy	PK-2	T	145	72%	718/241-4828, Fax 718/763-5567
PS 361 E Flatbush EC Sch, 1957 Nostrand Ave, Brooklyn 11210, Tiffany Frazier	PK-5	T	554 / 28	80%	718/941-2800, Fax 718/940-3098
PS 889, 21 Hinckley Pl, Brooklyn 11218, Kathryn Anderson	PK-1		137	61%	929/397-9171
PS IS 109 Glenwood Academy, 1001 E 45th St, Brooklyn 11203, Kerdy Bertrand	PK-8	T	510 / 35	84%	718/693-3426, Fax 718/693-3072
PS K134, 4001 18th Ave, Brooklyn 11218, Debra Ramsaran	K-5	T	609	88%	718/436-7200, Fax 718/686-2205
PS K315, 2310 Glenwood Rd, Brooklyn 11210, Judith Quartano	PK-5		639	87%	718/421-9560
School of Science & Tech, 725 E 23rd St, Brooklyn 11210, Gina Smalley	PK-5	T	593 / 32	76%	718/434-5222, Fax 718/859-5965

● **Community School District 23**   PID: 10909838   718/346-0816
1665 Saint Marks Ave, Brooklyn 11233   Fax 718/385-3768

(Part of New York City Dept of Ed in New York County)
Miatheresa Pate 1

---

1 Superintendent	20 Art K-12	40 Social Studies Elem	60 Special Education Sec
2 Bus/Finance/Purchasing	21 Art Elem	41 Social Studies Sec	61 Foreign/World Lang K-12
3 Buildings And Grounds	22 Art Sec	42 Science K-12	62 Foreign/World Lang Elem
4 Food Service	23 Music K-12	43 Science Elem	63 Foreign/World Lang Sec
5 Transportation	24 Music Elem	44 Science Sec	64 Religious Education K-12
6 Athletic	25 Music Sec	45 Math K-12	65 Religious Education Elem
7 Health Services	26 Business Education	46 Math Elem	66 Religious Education Sec
8 Curric/Instruct K-12	27 Career & Tech Ed	47 Math Sec	67 School Board President
9 Curric/Instruct Elem	28 Technology Education	48 English/Lang Arts K-12	68 Teacher Personnel
10 Curric/Instruct Sec	29 Family/Consumer Science	49 English/Lang Arts Elem	69 Academic Assessment
11 Federal Program	30 Adult Education	50 English/Lang Arts Sec	70 Research/Development
12 Title I	31 Career/Sch-to-Work K-12	51 Reading K-12	71 Public Information
13 Title V	32 Career/Sch-to-Work Elem	52 Reading Elem	72 Summer School
14 Instructional Media Svcs	33 Career/Sch-to-Work Sec	53 Reading Sec	73 Instructional Tech
15 Asst Superintendent	34 Early Childhood Ed	54 Remedial Reading K-12	74 Inservice Training
16 Instructional Media Svcs	35 Health/Phys Education	55 Remedial Reading Elem	75 Marketing/Distributive
17 Chief Operations Officer	36 Guidance Services K-12	56 Remedial Reading Sec	76 Info Systems
18 Chief Academic Officer	37 Guidance Services Elem	57 Bilingual/ELL	77 Psychological Assess
19 Chief Financial Officer	38 Guidance Services Sec	58 Special Education K-12	78 Affirmative Action
	39 Social Studies K-12	59 Special Education Elem	

New York School Directory — Kings County

Public Schs..Principal	Grd	Prgm	Enr/#Cls	SN	
Ⓐ Aspirations Diploma Plus HS 402 Eastern Pkwy, Brooklyn 11225 Sherma Fleming	9-12		187	80%	718/773-7765 Fax 718/498-5264
Brooklyn Collegiate High Sch 2021 Bergen St, Brooklyn 11233 Heather Newman	9-12	T	305	88%	718/922-1145 Fax 718/922-2347
Brooklyn Democracy Academy 985 Rockaway Ave, Brooklyn 11212	9-12	T	182	78%	718/342-6348 Fax 718/342-6708
Brooklyn Envir Exploration Sch 251 MacDougal St, Brooklyn 11233 Craig Garber	6-8	T	179	92%	718/453-3039 Fax 718/453-3508
Brooklyn Landmark Elem Sch 251 MacDougal St, Brooklyn 11233 Joyce Knights	PK-5	T	409	76%	718/443-2747 Fax 718/443-4365
Brownsville Collaborative MS 85 Watkins St, Brooklyn 11212 Gregory Jackson	6-8	T	270	95%	718/495-1202 Fax 718/495-1208
Christopher Ave Cmty Sch 51 Christopher Ave, Brooklyn 11212 Deon Mitchell	PK-5	T	327	96%	718/495-5761 Fax 718/495-5764
Eagle Acad Young Men II 1137 Herkimer St, Brooklyn 11233 Rashad Meade	6-12	T	637	80%	718/495-0863 Fax 718/732-2129
Frederick Douglass Acad VII HS 226 Bristol St 5th Fl, Brooklyn 11212 Tamika Matheson	9-12	T	143 16	89%	718/485-3789 Fax 718/922-2761
Ⓜ IS 392 104 Sutter Ave, Brooklyn 11212 Ingrid Joseph	6-8	T	325 13	76%	718/498-2491 Fax 718/346-2804
Kappa V 985 Rockaway Ave, Brooklyn 11212 Ronda Phillips	6-8	T	179 12	90%	718/922-4690 Fax 718/922-5053
Metropolitan Diploma Plus HS 985 Rockaway Ave, Brooklyn 11212 Meri Yallowitz	9-12	T	171 12	92%	718/342-6249 Fax 718/342-6329
Mott Hall Bridges Academy 210 Chester St, Brooklyn 11212 Nadia Anderson	6-8	T	205	93%	718/345-6912 Fax 718/345-6918
Mott Hall IV 1137 Herkimer St, Brooklyn 11233 Marica Myrie	6-8	T	148 12	82%	718/485-5240 Fax 718/485-5948
PS 41 Francis White 411 Thatford Ave, Brooklyn 11212 Shonelle Hall	K-8	T	335 50	97%	718/495-7732 Fax 718/346-2141
PS 150 Christopher Sch 364 Sackman St, Brooklyn 11212 Tracey Quarles	PK-5	T	189 31	96%	718/495-7746 Fax 718/922-3785
PS 156 Waverly 104 Sutter Ave, Brooklyn 11212 Naiyma Moore	PK-5	T	578 40	90%	718/498-2811 Fax 718/346-2804
PS 165 Ida Posner 76 Lott Ave, Brooklyn 11212 Jason Rivers	PK-5	T	288 30	82%	718/495-7759 Fax 718/345-8255
PS 178 St Clair McKelway 2163 Dean St, Brooklyn 11233 Joseph Henry	PK-8	T	323 37	85%	718/495-7768 Fax 718/495-2304
PS 184 Newport 273 Newport St, Brooklyn 11212 Lisa Linder	PK-8	T	522 60	98%	718/495-7775 Fax 718/385-4655
PS 284 Jackson Sports Art Tech 213 Osborn St, Brooklyn 11212 Keva Pitts	PK-5	T	283 37	95%	718/495-7791 Fax 718/495-7839
PS 298 Dr Betty Shabazz 85 Watkins St, Brooklyn 11212 Dr Betty Shabbaz	PK-5	AT	298 30	98%	718/495-7793
PS 327 Dr Rose B English 111 Bristol St, Brooklyn 11212 Georgette Malcolm	PK-5	T	291 40	96%	718/495-7801 Fax 718/495-7828
PS IS 155 Nicholas Herkimer 1355 Herkimer St, Brooklyn 11233 Michelle Manns	PK-8	T	381 42	97%	718/240-4340 Fax 718/345-9064
PS/IS 137 Rachel Jean Mitchell 121 Saratoga Ave, Brooklyn 11233 Suzette Rose	PK-8	T	286 26	89%	718/453-2926
PS/IS 323 210 Chester St, Brooklyn 11212 Linda Harris	PK-8	T	569	94%	718/495-7781 Fax 718/346-4614
Riverdale Ave Cmty Sch 76 Riverdale Ave, Brooklyn 11212 Meghan Dunn	PK-5	T	361	93%	718/485-1679 Fax 718/485-1768 ⓕ
Riverdale Avenue Middle Sch 76 Riverdale Ave, Brooklyn 11212 Yolanda Lawrence	6-8	T	143	98%	718/346-0764 Fax 718/346-1783
Teacher's Preparatory Sch 226 Bristol St, Brooklyn 11212 Carmen Simon	8-12	T	208	91%	718/498-2605 Fax 718/345-8069

• **Community School District 32** PID: 10909929 718/574-1100
  797 Bushwick Ave, Brooklyn 11221
  (Part of New York City Dept of Ed in New York County)
  Sheila Gorski 1

Public Schs..Principal	Grd	Prgm	Enr/#Cls	SN	
Acad Environmental Leadership 400 Irving Ave, Brooklyn 11237 Chantandre Blissett	9-12	T	290	90%	718/381-7100 Fax 718/381-0223
Academy of Urban Planning 400 Irving Ave, Brooklyn 11237 Jorge Sandoval	9-12	T	287	99%	718/381-7100 Fax 718/418-0314
All City Leadership Sec Sch 321 Palmetto St, Brooklyn 11237 Elvis Estevez	6-12	T	436	81%	718/246-6500 Fax 718/246-6509
Brooklyn Sch Social Justice 400 Irving Ave, Brooklyn 11237 Ana Marsh	9-12	T	327	83%	718/381-7100 Fax 718/418-0192
Brooklyn Sch-Math & Research 400 Irving Ave, Brooklyn 11237 Dr Perry Rainey	9-12	T	307	89%	718/381-7100 Fax 718/381-9897
Ⓐ Bushwick Community High Sch 231 Palmetto St, Brooklyn 11221 Llermi Gonzalez	9-12	GT	187 20	82%	718/443-3083 Fax 718/919-0781
Bushwick Leaders HS for Excel 797 Bushwick Ave, Brooklyn 11221 Catherine Reilly	9-12	GT	340	95%	718/919-4212 Fax 718/574-1103
Ⓐ EBC HS Pub Service Bushwick 1155 DeKalb Ave, Brooklyn 11221 Shawn Brown	9-12	TV	461 50	86%	718/452-3440 Fax 718/452-3603
Evergreen MS-Urban Exploration 125 Covert St, Brooklyn 11207 Lauren Reiss	6-8	T	376	94%	718/455-0180 Fax 718/455-4381
IS 347 School of Humanities 35 Starr St, Brooklyn 11221 John Barbella	6-8	GT	284 50	94%	718/821-4248 Fax 718/821-1332
IS 349 Math Science & Tech 35 Starr St, Brooklyn 11221 Tiffany D'Alessio	6-8	TV	298 35	97%	718/418-6389 Fax 718/418-6146
JHS 162 Willoughby 1390 Willoughby Ave, Brooklyn 11237 Amanda Lazerson	6-8	TV	317 36	87%	718/821-4860 Fax 718/821-1728

---

79 Student Personnel	91 Safety/Security	275 Response To Intervention	298 Grant Writer/Ptnrships	**School Programs**
80 Driver Ed/Safety	92 Magnet School	277 Remedial Math K-12	750 Chief Innovation Officer	A = Alternative Program
81 Gifted/Talented	93 Parental Involvement	280 Literacy Coach	751 Chief of Staff	G = Adult Classes
82 Video Services	95 Tech Prep Program	285 STEM	752 Social Emotional Learning	M = Magnet Program
83 Substance Abuse Prev	97 Chief Infomation Officer	286 Digital Learning		T = Title I Schoolwide
84 Erate	98 Chief Technology Officer	288 Common Core Standards	**Other School Types**	V = Career & Tech Ed Programs
85 AIDS Education	270 Character Education	294 Accountability	Ⓐ = Alternative School	
88 Alternative/At Risk	271 Migrant Education	295 Network System	Ⓒ = Charter School	
89 Multi-Cultural Curriculum	273 Teacher Mentor	296 Title II Programs	Ⓜ = Magnet School	
90 Social Work	274 Before/After Sch	297 Webmaster	Ⓨ = Year-Round School	

Social Media
ⓕ = Facebook
ⓣ = Twitter

New Schools are shaded
New Superintendents and Principals are bold
Personnel with email addresses are underscored

Kings County — Market Data Retrieval

School	Grd	Prgm	Enr/#Cls	SN	Phone
JHS 291 Roland Hayes 231 Palmetto St, Brooklyn 11221 Janice Bruce	6-8	TV	334 150	95%	718/574-0361 Fax 718/574-1360
JHS 383 Philippa Schuyler 1300 Greene Ave, Brooklyn 11237 Jeanette Smith	5-8	TV	891 70	82%	718/574-0390 Fax 718/574-1366
PS 75 Mayda Cortiella 95 Grove St, Brooklyn 11221 Yolanda Williams	PK-5	T	282 60	91%	718/574-0244 Fax 718/574-1051
PS 86 Irvington 220 Irving Ave, Brooklyn 11237 Tina Moschella	K-5	T	415 28	96%	718/574-0252 Fax 718/919-1839
PS 106 Edward Everett Hale 1328 Putnam Ave, Brooklyn 11221 Magaly Moncayo	PK-5	T	394 32	95%	718/574-0261 Fax 718/574-1054
PS 116 Elizabeth L Farrell 515 Knickerbocker Ave, Brooklyn 11237 Catherina Garzon	PK-5	T	339 25	90%	718/821-4623 Fax 718/821-0363
PS 123 Suydam 100 Irving Ave, Brooklyn 11237 Arelis Parache	PK-5	T	597 42	93%	718/821-4810 Fax 718/821-0858
PS 145 Andrew Jackson 100 Noll St, Brooklyn 11206 Linda Malloy	PK-5	T	500 55	87%	718/821-4823 Fax 718/417-3453
PS 151 Lyndon B Johnson 763 Knickerbocker Ave, Brooklyn 11207 Jayne Hunt	PK-5	T	315 30	92%	718/326-6360 Fax 718/226-2624
PS 274 Kosciusko 800 Bushwick Ave, Brooklyn 11221 Maritza Ollivierra	PK-5	T	357 45	98%	718/642-5300 Fax 718/574-1059
PS 299 Thomas Warren Field 88 Woodbine St, Brooklyn 11221 Wilma Kirk	PK-5	T	182 30	95%	718/473-8230
PS 376 194 Harman St, Brooklyn 11237 Maria Vera-Drucker	K-5	T	520 30	82%	718/573-0781 Fax 718/573-0769
PS 377 Alejandrina Degautier 200 Woodbine St, Brooklyn 11221 Dominic Zagami	PK-8	T	314 50	90%	718/574-0325 Fax 718/574-1082
PS IS 45 Horace E Greene 84 Schaefer St, Brooklyn 11207 Nadine Marshall	PK-8	T	593 61	81%	718/642-5360
PS/IS 384 Frances E Carter 242 Cooper St, Brooklyn 11207 Claudia Harris	PK-8	T	441 60	85%	718/642-4890 Fax 718/642-5029

- **District 75 City Wide Programs** PID: 00740626
  (Part of New York City Dept of Ed in New York County)

Public Schs..Principal	Grd	Prgm	Enr/#Cls	SN	Phone
ⓨ PS 36K 2045 Linden Blvd, Brooklyn 11207 Kevin Lenahan	Spec	M	303 16	89%	718/272-6483 Fax 718/272-6287
ⓨ PS 77K 62 Park Pl, Brooklyn 11217 Ebony Russell	Spec	M	305 40	83%	718/769-1039 Fax 718/769-1031
ⓨ PS 140K 141 Macon St, Brooklyn 11216 Roderick Palton	Spec	M	359 17	88%	718/783-4842 Fax 718/783-4869
ⓨ PS 141K 655 Parkside Ave, Brooklyn 11226 Michele Mannix	Spec	M	383 8	91%	718/941-0320 Fax 718/941-3152
ⓨ PS 231K 5601 16th Ave, Brooklyn 11204 Elizabeth Rueda	Spec	M	318 12	81%	718/853-1884 Fax 718/853-5388
ⓨ PS 368K 70 Tompkins Ave, Brooklyn 11206 Laverne Peter	Spec	M	274	91%	718/388-9494
PS 370K 3000 W 1st St, Brooklyn 11224 Susan Goldberg	Spec	M	251 15	79%	718/372-3777 Fax 718/449-4082
ⓨ PS 371K Lillian L Rashkis 355 37th St, Brooklyn 11232 Diane Zinn	Spec	M	253 25	90%	718/788-7608 Fax 718/832-2213
PS 372 the Children's Sch 512 Carroll St, Brooklyn 11215 Rosa Amato	Spec		498 22	17%	718/624-5271 Fax 718/522-1879
ⓨ PS 373K Bklyn Transition Ctr 185 Ellery St, Brooklyn 11206 Regina Tottenham	Spec	M	477	89%	718/782-6800 Fax 718/782-7098
ⓨ PS 721K Brooklyn Occu Trng Ctr 64 Avenue X, Brooklyn 11223 Barbara Tremblay	Spec	M	467 40	90%	718/996-8199 Fax 718/449-2176
ⓨ PS 771K 1075 Ocean View Ave, Brooklyn 11235 Denise Danna	Spec	M	456	80%	718/891-3600 Fax 718/769-0017
ⓨ PS 811K Connie Lekas Sch 2525 Haring St, Brooklyn 11235 Antoinette Rose	Spec	M	333 43	92%	718/769-6984 Fax 718/648-7816
ⓨ PS K004 923 Jerome St, Brooklyn 11207 Rebecca Schropfer	Spec	M	306 34	82%	718/272-7555 Fax 718/927-7554
ⓨ PS K053 544 7th Ave, Brooklyn 11215 Heather Leykam	Spec	M	450 30	88%	718/832-3563 Fax 718/965-1734
ⓨ PS K369 Coy L Cox Sch 383 State St, Brooklyn 11217 Marjorie Dalrymple	Spec	M	644	85%	718/852-1701 Fax 718/624-6746
ⓨ PS K396 110 Chester St, Brooklyn 11212 Dr Keisha McCoy-Dailey	Spec	M	227 27	90%	718/385-6200 Fax 718/345-3021
ⓨ PS K753 School for Career Dev 510 Clermont Ave, Brooklyn 11238 Yvrose Pierre	Spec	M	230 45	92%	718/857-4646 Fax 718/857-0565

- **New York Alt High Sch SD 79** PID: 00740626
  (Part of New York City Dept of Ed in New York County)

Public Schs..Principal	Grd	Prgm	Enr/#Cls	SN	Phone
Passages Acad-Belmont 619 Belmont Ave, Brooklyn 11207 Norma Delara	9-11		401		718/647-1800 Fax 718/348-9823
ⓐ Passages Acad-Crossroads 17 Bristol St, Brooklyn 11212 Shareef Rashid	9-12		401		718/240-3824

KINGS CATHOLIC SCHOOLS

- **Diocese of Brooklyn Ed Office** PID: 00752801 718/965-7300
  310 Prospect Park W, Brooklyn 11215 Fax 718/965-7353

Schools: 91 \ **Students:** 44,500 \ **Open-Close:** 09/08 - 06/27

Listing includes only schools located in this county. See District Index for location of Diocesan Offices.

Dr Thomas Chadzutko ....1 Dr Elizabeth Frangella 8,15
Diane Phelan ....15,69,77,79 Janet Heed 15
Joan McMaster ....15,68 Joanne Dreiss 15,34

New York School Directory

Kings County

Maria Viesta 15
Br Ralph Darmento 15
Michael Greiner 73,76
Michael LaForgia 15
Roxana De Pena-Elder 15

Catholic Schs..Principal	Grd	Prgm	Enr/#Cls	SN	
Bay Ridge Catholic Academy 365 83rd St, Brooklyn 11209 Kevin Flanagan	PK-8		477 20		718/745-7643 Fax 718/745-0086
Bishop Loughlin Memorial HS 357 Clermont Ave, Brooklyn 11238 Edward Bolan	9-12		700 35		718/857-2700 Fax 718/398-4227
Blessed Sacrament Sch 187 Euclid Ave, Brooklyn 11208 Marylou Celmer	PK-8		265 34		718/235-4863 Fax 718/235-1132
Brooklyn Jesuit Prep Sch 560 Sterling Pl, Brooklyn 11238 Gregory Arte	5-8		94		718/638-5884 Fax 718/638-5284
Fontbonne Hall Academy 9901 Shore Rd, Brooklyn 11209 Mary Ann Spicijaric	9-12		450 40		718/748-2244 Fax 718/745-3841
Good Shepherd Sch 1943 Brown St, Brooklyn 11229 John O'Brien	PK-8		307 17		718/339-2745 Fax 718/645-4513
Mary Queen of Heaven Sch 1326 E 57th St, Brooklyn 11234 Mary Bellone	PK-8		275		718/763-2360 Fax 718/763-7540
Midwood Catholic Academy 1501 Hendrickson St, Brooklyn 11234 Elena Heimbach	PK-8		240 22		718/377-1800 Fax 718/377-6374
Nazareth Regional High Sch 475 E 57th St, Brooklyn 11203 Providencia Quiles	9-12		370 40		718/763-1100 Fax 347/527-9154
Our Lady of Grace Sch 385 Avenue W, Brooklyn 11223 Kelly Wolf	K-8		177 18		718/375-2081 Fax 718/376-7685
Our Lady of Guadalupe Sch 1514 72nd St, Brooklyn 11228 Muriel Wilkinson	PK-8		200 22		718/331-2070 Fax 347/587-3714
Our Lady of Trust Sch-SJC 1696 Canarsie Rd, Brooklyn 11236 Muriel Wilkinson	PK-8		257 10		718/241-6633 Fax 718/531-8012
Our Lady Perpetual Help Sch 5902 6th Ave, Brooklyn 11220 Margaret Tyndall	PK-8		230 15		718/439-8067 Fax 718/439-8081
Queen of All Saints Cath Acad 300 Vanderbilt Ave, Brooklyn 11205 Manuela Adsuar-Pizzi	K-8		156 14		718/857-3114 Fax 718/857-0632
Salve Regina Catholic Academy 237 Jerome St, Brooklyn 11207 Michelle Donato	PK-8		650 12		718/277-6766 Fax 718/348-0513
SS Catherine & Therese Acad 4410 Avenue D, Brooklyn 11203 Jeanette Charles	PK-8		383 10		718/629-9330 Fax 718/629-6854
St Athanasius Sch 6120 Bay Pkwy, Brooklyn 11204 Diane Competello	PK-8		327 14		718/236-4791 Fax 718/621-1423
St Bernadette Sch 1313 83rd St, Brooklyn 11228 Sr Joan DiRienzo	PK-8		397 16		718/236-1560 Fax 718/236-3364
St Bernard Sch 2030 E 69th St, Brooklyn 11234 Tracy Flanagan	PK-8		335 20		718/241-6040 Fax 718/241-7258
St Brigid Catholic Academy 438 Grove St, Brooklyn 11237 Marcia Soria	PK-8		210 24		718/821-1477 Fax 718/821-1079
St Edmund Preparatory High Sch 2474 Ocean Ave, Brooklyn 11229 Allison McGinnis	9-12	G	750 30		718/743-6100 Fax 718/743-5243
St Edmund Sch 1902 Avenue T, Brooklyn 11229 Andrea D'Emic	PK-8		215 16		718/648-9229 Fax 718/743-6402
St Ephrem Sch 924 74th St, Brooklyn 11228 Craig Mercado	PK-8		408		718/833-1440 Fax 718/745-5301
St Frances Cabrini Cath Acad 181 Suydam St, Brooklyn 11221 Marcia Soria	PK-8		211 24		718/386-9277 Fax 718/386-9064
St Francis of Assisi Cath Acad 400 Lincoln Rd, Brooklyn 11225 Lorraine Pierre	PK-8		250 15		718/778-3700 Fax 718/778-7877
St Joseph High Sch 80 Willoughby St, Brooklyn 11201 Maysa Antonio	9-12		300 28		718/624-3618 Fax 718/624-2792
St Joseph the Worker Cath Acad 241 Prospect Park W, Brooklyn 11215 S Germann	3-8		250 11		718/768-7629 Fax 718/768-3007
St Mark Sch 2602 E 19th St, Brooklyn 11235 Mark Wilson	PK-8		327 13		718/332-9304
St Patrick Sch 401 97th St, Brooklyn 11209 Kathleen Curatolo	PK-8		267 10		718/833-0124 Fax 718/238-6480
St Peter Catholic Academy 8401 23rd Ave, Brooklyn 11214 Danielle Alfeo	PK-8		358 26		718/372-0025 Fax 718/265-6498
St Saviour Catholic Academy 701 8th Ave, Brooklyn 11215 Susan Walsh	PK-8		416 25		718/768-8000 Fax 718/768-0373
St Saviour High Sch 588 6th St, Brooklyn 11215 Carolann Timpone	9-12		235 12		718/768-4406 Fax 718/369-2688
St Stanislaus Kostka Cath Acad 12 Newell St, Brooklyn 11222 Christina Cieloszczyk	PK-8		210 15		718/383-1970 Fax 718/383-1711
Visitation Academy 8902 Ridge Blvd, Brooklyn 11209 Jean Bernieri	PK-8		190		718/680-9452 Fax 718/680-4441
Xaverian High Sch 7100 Shore Rd, Brooklyn 11209 Kevin McCormack	9-12	G	1,100		718/836-7100 Fax 718/836-7114

KINGS PRIVATE SCHOOLS

Private Schs..Principal	Grd	Prgm	Enr/#Cls	SN	
A Fantis Parochial Sch 195 State St, Brooklyn 11201 Theodore Tasoulas	PK-8		160		718/624-0501 Fax 718/246-5711
Adelphi Academy of Brooklyn 8515 Ridge Blvd, Brooklyn 11209 Iphizenia Romanos	PK-12		100 30		718/238-3308 Fax 718/238-2894
Ahi Ezer Yeshiva Sch 2433 Ocean Pkwy, Brooklyn 11235 B Segal	PK-8		310		718/648-6100 Fax 718/648-5521
AL Madinah Sch 383 3rd Ave, Brooklyn 11215 Sr Zenab Elkady \ Dr Farhana Masood \ Ahmed Jammoudy	K-12		601		718/222-4986 Fax 718/222-4985
AL Madrasa Alislamiya Sch 5224 3rd Ave, Brooklyn 11220 Abdul Basir Muhammad	PK-8		150 10		718/567-3334 Fax 718/567-7383

79 Student Personnel
80 Driver Ed/Safety
81 Gifted/Talented
82 Video Services
83 Substance Abuse Prev
84 Erate
85 AIDS Education
88 Alternative/At Risk
89 Multi-Cultural Curriculum
90 Social Work
91 Safety/Security
92 Magnet School
93 Parental Involvement
95 Tech Prep Program
97 Chief Information Officer
98 Chief Technology Officer
270 Character Education
271 Migrant Education
273 Teacher Mentor
274 Before/After Sch
275 Response To Intervention
277 Remedial Math K-12
280 Literacy Coach
285 STEM
286 Digital Learning
288 Common Core Standards
294 Accountability
295 Network System
296 Title II Programs
297 Webmaster
296 Grant Writer/Ptnrships
750 Chief Innovation Officer
751 Chief of Staff
752 Social Emotional Learning

Other School Types
Ⓐ = Alternative School
Ⓒ = Charter School
Ⓜ = Magnet School
Ⓨ = Year-Round School

School Programs
A = Alternative Program
G = Adult Classes
M = Magnet Program
T = Title I Schoolwide
V = Career & Tech Ed Programs

Social Media
= Facebook
= Twitter

New Schools are shaded
New Superintendents and Principals are bold
Personnel with email addresses are underscored

NY—95

Kings County — Market Data Retrieval

School	Grades		Enroll	Phone
AL Noor Sch 675 4th Ave, Brooklyn 11232 Abdelhakeem Alhasel	PK-12		603 27	718/768-7181 Fax 718/768-7088
Alpha Sch 2400 Linden Blvd, Brooklyn 11208 Barry Addison	Spec		40	718/257-5800 Fax 718/649-7040
Altschool Brooklyn Heights 212 Hicks St, Brooklyn 11201 Marla Pauker	PK-4		60	718/852-6069
Bais Brocho D'Stolin Karlin 4314 10th Ave, Brooklyn 11219 Ephram Scherman	PK-12		400	718/853-1222 Fax 718/851-0112
Bais Esther School for Girls 1353 50th St, Brooklyn 11219 Mindy Klein	PK-8		1,000	718/436-1234 Fax 718/436-1320
Bais Frima 1377 42nd St, Brooklyn 11219	PK-12		300 14	718/972-7666 Fax 718/972-0975
Bais Rachel D Satmar 84 Sandford St 88, Brooklyn 11205 Ruchy Paskesz	K-12		800	718/624-2819
Bais Rochel School-Boro Park 5301 14th Ave, Brooklyn 11219 Mindi Margulies	K-12	V	3,500	718/438-7822 Fax 718/438-3153
Bais Sarah 6101 16th Ave, Brooklyn 11204 Nachum Klien	PK-7		850	718/871-7571 Fax 718/256-3664
Bais Tziporah-Girls 1449 39th St, Brooklyn 11218 Esther Horowitz \ Sandle Rosengarten	PK-12		500 18	718/436-8336 Fax 718/436-1201
Bais Yaakov Academy 1213 Elm Ave, Brooklyn 11230 Lisa Wadler \ Avrohom Greenberg	PK-12		800 24	718/339-4747 Fax 718/998-5766
Bais Yaakov Adas Yereim 1169 43rd St, Brooklyn 11219 Felenda Feldman	PK-12		530	718/435-5111 Fax 718/435-5446
Bais Yaakov D'Khal Adas Yereim 563 Bedford Ave, Brooklyn 11211 Miriam Berger	PK-12		500	718/782-2486 Fax 718/384-5885
Bais Yaakov Dchassidei Gur Sch 1975 51st St, Brooklyn 11204 Chana Wosner \ Mrs Lederman	PK-12	V	750 18	718/338-5600 Fax 718/338-5974
Bais Yaakov-18th Ave Sch 4419 18th Ave, Brooklyn 11204 Rebbetzin Ziemba	PK-8		300 10	718/633-6050 Fax 718/633-6052
Bais Yaakov-Bensonhurst 2025 67th St, Brooklyn 11204 Rabbi Shain	PK-8		161	718/236-4100
Bais Yitzchak Yeshiva 1413 45th St, Brooklyn 11219 Shlomo Kolodny	PK-12	G	1,300 10	718/633-4802 Fax 718/633-3450
Barkai Yeshiva 5302 21st Ave, Brooklyn 11204 Vicky Kairy \ Sharon Esses	K-8		400	718/758-3525 Fax 718/758-3551
Bas Melech School for Girls 116 Avenue I, Brooklyn 11230 Berish Welz	K-1		36	718/677-7999 Fax 718/677-7994
Basis Independent Brooklyn 556 Columbia St, Brooklyn 11231 Hadley Ruggles	PK-12		815	917/473-1615
Battalion Christian Academy 661 Linden Blvd, Brooklyn 11203 Marcia DeSouza	PK-5		134 14	718/774-5447 Fax 718/774-4295
Bay Ridge Christian Academy 6324 7th Ave, Brooklyn 11220 Judith Vega	PK-8		145 10	718/238-4000 Fax 718/921-4005
Bay Ridge Preparatory High Sch 7420 4th Ave, Brooklyn 11209 Dr Michael Dealy	9-12		120	718/833-5839 Fax 718/833-1043
Bay Ridge Preparatory Sch 8101 Ridge Blvd, Brooklyn 11209 Michael Dealy	K-8		243 20	718/833-9090 Fax 718/833-6680
Be'ER Hagolah Institute 671 Louisiana Ave, Brooklyn 11239 Sheila Taub	PK-12		350	718/642-6800 Fax 718/642-4740
Be'Ikvei Hatzion 31 Division Ave, Brooklyn 11249 Shaindy Gross	PK-8		200 15	718/486-6363 Fax 718/486-6639
Beachbrook Sch 2953 Avenue X, Brooklyn 11235 Dr Joan Prideaux	Spec		50 4	718/648-7162 Fax 718/646-6329
Beitcher Yeshirva Sch 4414 12th Ave, Brooklyn 11219 Chaskel Horowitz	K-8		250	718/436-0954
Berkeley Carroll Sch 181 Lincoln Pl, Brooklyn 11217 Amanda Pike \ Yabome Kabia \ Jane Moore	PK-12		1,700 60	718/789-6060 Fax 718/398-3640
Bet Yaakov Ateret Torah 2166 Coney Island Ave, Brooklyn 11223 Rebecca Weiss	K-8		410	718/732-7770 Fax 718/732-7760
Bet Yaakov Orot Sarah 1123 Avenue N, Brooklyn 11230 David Maslaton	PK-12		300 10	718/627-8758 Fax 718/336-0149
Bet Yakov Ateret Torah HS 2166 Coney Island Ave, Brooklyn 11223 Naomi Sutton	9-12		200 8	718/382-7002 Fax 718/732-7767
Beth Chana School for Girls 620 Bedford Ave, Brooklyn 11249 Mordechai Scheiner	K-12	V	400	718/935-1845 Fax 718/852-4364
Beth Hamedrash Shaarei Yosher 4102 16th Ave, Brooklyn 11204 Rabbi Reichman	10-12		91 3	718/854-2290 Fax 718/436-9045
Beth Jacob Day Sch for Girls 85 Parkville Ave, Brooklyn 11230 Michael Levi	K-12		735 28	718/633-6555 Fax 718/633-2930
Beth Jacob High Sch 4420 15th Ave, Brooklyn 11219 Batya Nekritz	9-12		700 31	718/851-2255 Fax 718/851-4316
Beth Jacob of Boro Park Sch 1371 46th St, Brooklyn 11219 Oscar Ehrenreich	K-8		1,800 76	718/436-7300 Fax 718/436-7358
Beth Rivkah Elem School-Girls 470 Lefferts Ave, Brooklyn 11225 Gitty Rosenvelt	K-8		1,000	718/735-0770 Fax 718/735-4712
Beth Rivkah High School-Girls 310 Crown St, Brooklyn 11225 Bentzion Stock	9-12	GV	500	718/735-0400 Fax 718/735-0422
Bethel Elem Sch 457 Grand Ave, Brooklyn 11238 Kelestine Creighton	PK-8		40 6	718/783-3630
Big Apple Academy 2937 86th St, Brooklyn 11223 Vlad Gorney	K-8		1,000	718/333-0300 Fax 718/333-1311
Block Institute 376 Bay 44th St, Brooklyn 11214 Danielle Elkins	Spec	G	252 20	718/906-5400 Fax 718/714-0197
Bnos Esther Malka Sch 1784 E 17th St, Brooklyn 11229 Shoshanah Leibowitz	1-5		8	347/374-1298
Bnos Menachem 739 E New York Ave, Brooklyn 11203 Zahava Slae \ Rivka Karnowsky	PK-12		575 13	718/493-1100 Fax 718/943-4836

---

1 Superintendent	8 Curric/Instruct K-12	19 Chief Financial Officer	29 Family/Consumer Science	39 Social Studies K-12	49 English/Lang Arts Elem	59 Special Education Elem	69 Academic Assessment
2 Bus/Finance/Purchasing	9 Curric/Instruct Elem	20 Art K-12	30 Adult Education	40 Social Studies Elem	50 English/Lang Arts Sec	60 Special Education Sec	70 Research/Development
3 Buildings And Grounds	10 Curric/Instruct Sec	21 Art Elem	31 Career/Sch-to-Work K-12	41 Social Studies Sec	51 Reading K-12	61 Foreign/World Lang K-12	71 Public Information
4 Food Service	11 Federal Program	22 Art Sec	32 Career/Sch-to-Work Elem	42 Science K-12	52 Reading Elem	62 Foreign/World Lang Elem	72 Summer School
5 Transportation	12 Title I	23 Music K-12	33 Career/Sch-to-Work Sec	43 Science Elem	53 Reading Sec	63 Foreign/World Lang Sec	73 Instructional Tech
6 Athletic	13 Title V	24 Music Elem	34 Early Childhood Ed	44 Science Sec	54 Remedial Reading K-12	64 Religious Education K-12	74 Inservice Training
7 Health Services	15 Asst Superintendent	25 Music Sec	35 Health/Phys Education	45 Math K-12	55 Remedial Reading Elem	65 Religious Education Elem	75 Marketing/Distributive
	16 Instructional Media Svcs	26 Business Education	36 Guidance Services K-12	46 Math Elem	56 Remedial Reading Sec	66 Religious Education Sec	76 Info Systems
	17 Chief Operations Officer	27 Career & Tech Ed	37 Guidance Services Elem	47 Math Sec	57 Bilingual/ELL	67 School Board President	77 Psychological Assess
	18 Chief Academic Officer	28 Technology Education	38 Guidance Services Sec	48 English/Lang Arts K-12	58 Special Education K-12	68 Teacher Personnel	78 Affirmative Action

New York School Directory Kings County

School	Grades		Enrollment	Phone
Bnos Square of Williamsburg 165 Spencer St, Brooklyn 11205 Shulem Greenbaum	1-2		36	718/797-9844
Bnos Yaakov Education Center 1402 40th St, Brooklyn 11218 Judy Weiser	PK-12	V	673	718/851-0316 Fax 718/436-7280
Bnos Yaakov Girls Center 62 Harrison Ave, Brooklyn 11211 M Brull	K-12		758 24	718/387-7905 Fax 718/387-7124
Bnos Yisroel School for Girls 12 Franklin Ave, Brooklyn 11249 Eva Rozman	PK-12		639	718/330-0222 Fax 718/855-2852
Bnos Yisroel School-Girls 1629 E 15th St, Brooklyn 11229 Boruch Barnetsky	K-8		300	718/339-4229 Fax 718/645-3175
Bnos Zion of Bobov Sch 5000 14th Ave, Brooklyn 11219 Devorah Goldberger	PK-12	V	1,500	718/438-3080 Fax 718/438-3144
Bnos-Belz Girls Sch 600 McDonald Ave, Brooklyn 11218 Berl Hecht	PK-12	V	1,100	718/871-0500 Fax 718/435-4456
Bobover Yeshiva Bnei Zion 4206 15th Ave, Brooklyn 11219 Heshie Dembitzer	1-8	G	1,300	718/851-4000
Brooklyn Amity Sch 3867 Shore Pkwy, Brooklyn 11235 Eljasa Jashar	PK-12		300	718/891-6100 Fax 718/891-6841
Brooklyn Blue Feather Elem Sch 2335 Gerritsen Ave, Brooklyn 11229 Zoeann Deeds	Spec		130 16	718/834-0597 Fax 718/834-0768
Brooklyn Free Sch 372 Clinton Ave, Brooklyn 11238 Lily Mercogliano	PK-12		72	718/499-2707
Brooklyn Friends Sch 375 Pearl St, Brooklyn 11201 Jackie Condie \ Glen Pinder \ Lisa Arrastia	PK-12	V	980 70	718/852-1029 Fax 718/643-4868 f
Brooklyn Heights Mont Sch 185 Court St, Brooklyn 11201 Martha Haakmat	PK-8		250 16	718/858-5100 Fax 718/858-0500
Brooklyn Preparatory Sch 12020 Flatlands Ave, Brooklyn 11207 Sabrina Grier	PK-PK		48 5	718/306-1000 Fax 718/484-0560
Brooklyn SDA Sch 1260 Ocean Ave, Brooklyn 11230 Laura Mayne	PK-8		105 5	718/859-1313 Fax 718/859-8105
Brooklyn Waldorf Sch 11 Jefferson Ave, Brooklyn 11238 Denese Giordano	PK-8		216	718/783-3270 Fax 718/783-7209
Charles Churn Christian Acad 113 Osborn St Ste 1, Brooklyn 11212 Dr Linda Hunt	PK-12		101 12	718/919-6887 Fax 347/221-0773
Clara Muhammad Sch 1174 Bedford Ave, Brooklyn 11216 Darlene Bashir	K-8		111	718/783-1279 Fax 718/783-3308
Cong Yeshuos Moshe Williamsbrg 7787 Wallabout St, Brooklyn 11249 Pinchas Duitel	K-8		50	718/782-7383
Congregation Ohr Menachem 1729 President St, Brooklyn 11213 Chaya Itzhakov \ Menachem Hendel	K-12		110	718/778-8770
Cortelyou Academy 2739 Bedford Ave, Brooklyn 11210 Sophia Francis	PK-5		121 8	718/421-9581
Cristo Rey Brooklyn High Sch 710 E 37th St, Brooklyn 11203 Joseph Dugan	9-12		300	718/455-3555 Fax 718/455-3556
D & G Kaloidis Parochial Sch 8502 Ridge Blvd, Brooklyn 11209 Francesca Mannino	PK-8		205 15	718/836-8096 Fax 718/836-4772
Darkei Chaim 1470 56th St, Brooklyn 11219 Ben Kinhom	K-8		300	718/435-0894
East Midwood Hebrew Day Sch 1256 E 21st St, Brooklyn 11210 Shirley Weichselbaum	PK-8		200	718/253-1555 Fax 718/338-3934
Ebenezer Preparatory Sch 5464 Kings Hwy, Brooklyn 11203 Joy Jones	PK-8		160 11	718/629-4231 Fax 718/629-4238
Epiphany Lutheran Sch 721 Lincoln Pl, Brooklyn 11216 Judy Evans-Gill	PK-8		200 13	718/773-7200 Fax 718/773-1244
Flatbush SDA Sch 5810 Snyder Ave, Brooklyn 11203 Veronica Walker	PK-5		84 10	718/922-6390 Fax 718/922-6393
Followers of Jesus Sch 3065 Atlantic Ave, Brooklyn 11208 James Gochnauer	1-12		55	718/235-5493 Fax 718/484-1477
Fusion Academy-Brooklyn 1 Metrotech Ctr N Ste 2004, Brooklyn 11201 Sarah Hagens	6-12		60	718/522-3286 f t
Gan Yisroel Sch 13 Church Ave, Brooklyn 11218 Aaron Ginsberg	K-8		600	718/853-9853
Gateway City Academy 257 Bay Ridge Ave, Brooklyn 11220 Susan Nocera	PK-8		200 10	718/921-3737 Fax 718/921-0368
George H Murray Prepatory Acad 760 DeKalb Ave, Brooklyn 11216 Marc Titus	PK-8		82 9	718/384-1577 Fax 718/384-3379
Gerer Mesivta Bais Yisroel 5407 16th Ave, Brooklyn 11204 Dov Garfinkel	9-12	V	89	718/854-8777 Fax 718/851-1265
Gesher Yehuda Yeshiva 49 Avenue T, Brooklyn 11223 Deborah Katz	K-8		70 7	718/714-7400 Fax 718/714-9103
Gesher Yeshivah Prep High Sch 1412 Avenue J, Brooklyn 11230 Sion Setton	Spec		24	347/462-1807 Fax 347/462-1808
Great Oaks Elem Sch 4718 Farragut Rd, Brooklyn 11203 Jasmin Hoyt	K-8		120 6	718/346-4934 Fax 718/282-5615
Greene Hill Sch 39 Adelphi St, Brooklyn 11205 Diana Schlesinger	PK-8		150	718/230-3608
Guild for Excptnl Chldrn Sch 1273 57th St, Brooklyn 11219 Jolene Gunther	Spec		180 15	718/435-2554 Fax 718/435-2753
Hannah Senesh Cmty Day Sch 342 Smith St, Brooklyn 11231 Nicole Nash	K-8		180	718/858-8663 Fax 718/858-7190
Hanson Place SDA Sch 38 Lafayette Ave, Brooklyn 11217 Pauline Evans	PK-8		150 14	718/625-3030 Fax 718/625-1727
Hebrew Acad for Spec Children 1311 55th St, Brooklyn 11219 Julie Ben-Zvi	Spec	GV	50 6	718/851-6100 Fax 718/437-6654
Hebrew Institute-Deaf Excptnl 1401 Avenue I, Brooklyn 11230 Nancy Fleishman	Spec		150 14	718/377-7507 Fax 718/253-3259
Hebron SDA Bilingual Sch 920 Park Pl, Brooklyn 11213 Gladly Grant	PK-8		350 12	347/533-4923 Fax 347/533-4926

79 Student Personnel
80 Driver Ed/Safety
81 Gifted/Talented
82 Video Services
83 Substance Abuse Prev
84 Erate
85 AIDS Education
88 Alternative/At Risk
89 Multi-Cultural Curriculum
90 Social Work

91 Safety/Security
92 Magnet School
93 Parental Involvement
95 Tech Prep Program
97 Chief Infomation Officer
98 Chief Technology Officer
270 Character Education
271 Migrant Education
273 Teacher Mentor
274 Before/After Sch

275 Response To Intervention
277 Remedial Math K-12
280 Literacy Coach
285 STEM
286 Digital Learning
288 Common Core Standards
294 Accountability
295 Network System
296 Title II Programs
297 Webmaster

298 Grant Writer/Ptnrships
750 Chief Innovation Officer
751 Chief of Staff
752 Social Emotional Learning

Other School Types
Ⓐ = Alternative School
Ⓒ = Charter School
Ⓜ = Magnet School
Ⓨ = Year-Round School

School Programs
A = Alternative Program
G = Adult Classes
M = Magnet Program
T = Title I Schoolwide
V = Career & Tech Ed Programs

Social Media
f = Facebook
t = Twitter

New Schools are shaded
New Superintendents and Principals are bold
Personnel with email addresses are underscored

NY—97

Kings County

School	Grades		Enrollment / Teachers	Phone / Fax
Imagine Academy 1458 E 14th St, Brooklyn 11230 Elisa Chrem	Spec		32 4	718/376-8882 Fax 718/998-1018
Int'l School of Brooklyn 477 Court St, Brooklyn 11231 Joe Santos	K-5		190 7	718/369-3023 Fax 718/795-1998
International Christian Sch 312 Coney Island Ave, Brooklyn 11218 Charis Roberts	PK-12	V	100 18	718/436-8924 Fax 718/438-2789
Jewish Center for Special Ed 8109 Bay Pkwy, Brooklyn 11214 Shlome Roth	Spec	G	100 8	718/782-0064 Fax 718/782-5764
Joel Braverman High Sch 1609 Avenue J, Brooklyn 11230 Joseph Beyda	9-12		650	718/377-1100 Fax 718/258-0933
Joseph S Gruss Yeshiva 1904 Avenue N, Brooklyn 11230 Ephraim Bernstein	PK-12		400 9	718/375-0900 Fax 718/375-0272
Kerem Shlomo Yeshiva 1149 38th St, Brooklyn 11218 Rabbi Meisell	10-11		200	718/437-7665
Kesser Malka Girls Yeshiva 1019 46th St, Brooklyn 11219 S Rutnitzky	PK-1		40 4	718/854-7777 Fax 718/854-6642
League Sch 567 Kingston Ave, Brooklyn 11203 Stephanie Golub	Spec	V	120 18	718/498-2500 Fax 718/778-4018
Leif Ericson Day Sch 1037 72nd St, Brooklyn 11228 Christine Hauge	PK-8		170 12	718/748-9023 Fax 718/748-0473
Lev Bais Yaakov Sch 3574 Nostrand Ave, Brooklyn 11229 Miriam Fishman	PK-12		550 24	718/332-6000 Fax 718/332-8868
Lubavitcher School Chabad 841 Ocean Pkwy, Brooklyn 11230 Samuel Dechter	PK-8	V	200 16	718/434-0795 Fax 718/434-1519
Lubavitcher Yeshiva High Sch 885 Eastern Pkwy, Brooklyn 11213 Dov Baron	9-12		120	718/735-6601 Fax 718/778-7161
Lubavitcher Yeshiva Sch 570 Crown St, Brooklyn 11213 Joseph Simpson	K-8		501	718/774-4131 Fax 718/756-5324
Luria Academy of Brooklyn 238 Saint Marks Ave, Brooklyn 11238 Laura Weisblatt	PK-8		250	718/398-3290
Lutheran Elem Sch of Bay Ridge 440 Ovington Ave, Brooklyn 11209 Corinne King	PK-8		200 11	718/748-9502 Fax 718/748-0818
Machon Bais Yaakov High Sch 1681 42nd St 83, Brooklyn 11204 Faigie Gringras	10-12		58 18	718/972-7900 Fax 347/557-1300
Magen David Yeshiva High Sch 7801 Bay Pkwy, Brooklyn 11214 Richard Tobias	9-12		421 30	718/331-4002
Magen David Yeshivah 2130 McDonald Ave, Brooklyn 11223 Alan Berkowitz	PK-8		1,600 60	718/236-5905 Fax 718/954-3315
Mary McDowell Friends Sch 20 Bergen St, Brooklyn 11201 Debbie Zlotowitz	Spec		347 21	718/625-3939 Fax 718/625-1456
Masores Bais Yaakov 1395 Ocean Ave, Brooklyn 11230 Joseph Gelman	K-12		700	718/692-2424 Fax 718/692-3162
Merkaz Bnos High Sch 1400 W 6th St, Brooklyn 11204 Esther Miller	9-12		60 8	718/259-5600 Fax 718/259-8024
Mesivta Beth Sherim 5306 16th Ave, Brooklyn 11204 Josh Weinstein	9-12	GV	40 5	718/851-0806
Mesivta Imrei Yosef Spinka 1466 56th St, Brooklyn 11219 Leibush Rubin	9-12		75 8	718/851-1600 Fax 718/851-0148
Mesivta Rabbi Chaim Berlin 1585 Coney Island Ave, Brooklyn 11230 Yosef Landsberg	9-12	V	273 10	718/377-8400 Fax 718/338-5578
Mesivta Tifres Elimelech 4407 12th Ave, Brooklyn 11219 Mendel Rappaport	9-12		120 10	718/854-3062
Mevakshai Hashem Elem Sch 550 Ocean Pkwy, Brooklyn 11218 Isaac Gluck	PK-7		400	718/435-8900
Mill Basin Yeshiva Academy 6363 Avenue U, Brooklyn 11234 Rafael Farhi	PK-8		300 25	718/444-5800 Fax 718/444-5851
Mosdos Chasidei Square Sch 105 Heyward St, Brooklyn 11206 Mordechai Nosson Friesel \ Jacob Spira	K-12		260	718/852-0502 Fax 718/852-0512
Mt Moriah Christian Academy 1149 Eastern Pkwy, Brooklyn 11213 Jerry West	PK-8		60 5	718/953-4364
Nefesh Academy 2005 E 17th St, Brooklyn 11229 Susan Newhouse	8-12	G	40 7	718/627-4463 Fax 718/645-8755
Nesivos Bais Yaakov Sch 622 Foster Ave, Brooklyn 11230 Matti Katz	PK-8		300 14	718/972-0804 Fax 718/972-6633
New Grace Center Christian Sch 650 Livonia Ave, Brooklyn 11207 DeNaro Liverpool	PK-8		210 16	718/498-7175 Fax 718/498-1656
New Vistas Academy 3321 Glenwood Rd, Brooklyn 11210 Helen Hamilton	1-12		88	718/421-1786 Fax 718/483-9351
Oholei Torah Elem Sch 667 Eastern Pkwy, Brooklyn 11213 Hershel Lustig	PK-8		1,000	718/483-9000 Fax 718/771-0909
Packer Collegiate Institute 170 Joralemon St, Brooklyn 11201 Bill McCarthy \ Noah Reinhardt \ Maria Nunes	PK-12		1,000	718/250-0200 Fax 718/875-1363
Parkway Sch 5566 Kings Hwy, Brooklyn 11203 Linton Grant	PK-8		150	718/346-0369 Fax 718/346-0371
Poly Prep Country Day Sch-Lowr 50 Prospect Park W, Brooklyn 11215 Larry Donovan	PK-4		161 15	718/768-1103 Fax 718/768-1687
Poly Prep Country Day Sch-Uppr 9216 7th Ave, Brooklyn 11228 Andre Del Valle \ Sarah Bates	5-12	GV	775	718/836-9800 Fax 718/238-3190
Prospect Park Bnos Leah Girls 1601 Avenue R, Brooklyn 11229 Suzanne Press	9-12	V	250 12	718/376-3337 Fax 718/376-4497
Prospect Park Girls Yeshiva 1784 E 17th St, Brooklyn 11229 Arlene Klestvick	1-8		500 22	718/376-4446 Fax 718/382-9185
Rabbinical Clg Bobover Yeshyva 1577 48th St, Brooklyn 11219 David Mandelbaum	9-12		225 7	718/438-2018 Fax 718/871-9031
Raven's Sch 1102 E 92nd St, Brooklyn 11236 Maria Callender	PK-1		100	718/927-2316
Shaare Torah Sch 1680 Coney Island Ave, Brooklyn 11230 Armo Kuessous	1-8		241 15	718/339-9752

1 Superintendent	8 Curric/Instruct K-12	19 Chief Financial Officer	29 Family/Consumer Science	39 Social Studies K-12	49 English/Lang Arts Elem	59 Special Education Elem	69 Academic Assessment
2 Bus/Finance/Purchasing	9 Curric/Instruct Elem	20 Art K-12	30 Adult Education	40 Social Studies Elem	50 English/Lang Arts Sec	60 Special Education Sec	70 Research/Development
3 Buildings And Grounds	10 Curric/Instruct Sec	21 Art Elem	31 Career/Sch-to-Work K-12	41 Social Studies Sec	51 Reading K-12	61 Foreign/World Lang K-12	71 Public Information
4 Food Service	11 Federal Program	22 Art Sec	32 Career/Sch-to-Work Elem	42 Science K-12	52 Reading Elem	62 Foreign/World Lang Elem	72 Summer School
5 Transportation	12 Title I	23 Music K-12	33 Career/Sch-to-Work Sec	43 Science Elem	53 Reading Sec	63 Foreign/World Lang Sec	73 Instructional Tech
6 Athletic	13 Title V	24 Music Elem	34 Early Childhood Ed	44 Science Sec	54 Remedial Reading K-12	64 Religious Education K-12	74 Inservice Training
7 Health Services	15 Asst Superintendent	25 Music Sec	35 Health/Phys Education	45 Math K-12	55 Remedial Reading Elem	65 Religious Education Elem	75 Marketing/Distributive
	16 Instructional Media Svcs	26 Business Education	36 Guidance Services K-12	46 Math Elem	56 Remedial Reading Sec	66 Religious Education Sec	76 Info Systems
	17 Chief Operations Officer	27 Career & Tech Ed	37 Guidance Services Elem	47 Math Sec	57 Bilingual/ELL	67 School Board President	77 Psychological Assess
	18 Chief Academic Officer	28 Technology Education	38 Guidance Services Sec	48 English/Lang Arts K-12	58 Special Education K-12	68 Teacher Personnel	78 Affirmative Action

New York School Directory

Kings County

School	Grades		Enrollment	Phone
Shalsheles Bais Yaakov Sch 1681 42nd St, Brooklyn 11204 Esther Goodstein	PK-8		170 8	718/436-1122
Shema Kolainu Sch 4302 New Utrecht Ave, Brooklyn 11219 Suri Gruen	Spec		20 8	718/686-9600 Fax 718/686-6161
Shulamith School for Girls 60 W End Ave, Brooklyn 11235 Dr Judy Stoner \ Penina Karp	PK-12		370 8	718/338-4000 Fax 718/258-9626
Sinai Academy 2025 79th St, Brooklyn 11214 Moshe Silber	7-12		55 8	718/256-7400 Fax 718/256-7786
Soterios Ellenas Parochial Sch 224 18th St, Brooklyn 11215 Maria Manolis	PK-PK		25 1	718/499-5900 Fax 718/832-3712
South Brooklyn Academy 418 E 45th St, Brooklyn 11203 Ivanhoe Douglas	6-12	G	130 11	718/693-5502 Fax 718/940-4168
St Ann's Sch 129 Pierrepont St, Brooklyn 11201 Vincent Tompkins	PK-12	GV	1,000	718/522-1660
St Francis DeSales School-Deaf 260 Eastern Pkwy, Brooklyn 11225 Marie Bartolillo	Spec		82 17	718/636-4573 Fax 718/636-4577
St John Evangelist Luthern Sch 195 Maujer St, Brooklyn 11206 Gail Powell	PK-6		15 3	718/963-3074
St Mark's Day Sch 1346 President St, Brooklyn 11213 Derek Smith	PK-8		209 18	718/756-6602 Fax 718/467-4655
Sterling Sch 299 Pacific St Ste A, Brooklyn 11201 Ruth Arberman	2-6		25 3	718/625-3502 Fax 718/625-7393
Talmud Torad Ohr Moshe 1774 58th St, Brooklyn 11204 Moshe Lederer	K-8		300	718/234-6100
Talmud Torah D'Chasidei Gur 1371 42nd St, Brooklyn 11219 Abraham Schmidt	K-6		50	718/923-3113
Talmud Torah Imrei Chaim Sch 1824 53rd St, Brooklyn 11204 Nachman Mermelstein	K-9		697	718/234-2000 Fax 718/236-0970
Talmud Torah Ohel Yochanan 1325 38th St, Brooklyn 11218 Solomon Kernkruat	PK-6		106	718/431-2991
Talmud Torah Tiferes Bunim 5202 13th Ave, Brooklyn 11219 Efraim Probart	K-8		150	718/436-6868 Fax 718/633-9711
Talmud Torah Toldos Yakov Ysf 1373 43rd St, Brooklyn 11219 Eugene Greenwald	K-12		330	718/436-2550 Fax 718/436-2658
The Cheder Sch 129 Elmwood Ave, Brooklyn 11230 Meir Gutfreund	PK-12		700	718/252-6333
Tiferes Miriam Sch for Girls 6510 17th Ave, Brooklyn 11204 Chaim Stamm	Spec		40	718/837-3100 Fax 718/837-4225
Tomer Dvora Girls Sch 4500 9th Ave, Brooklyn 11220 Fraidy Friedman	1-8		500 16	718/228-4150 Fax 718/853-3042
Tomer Dvora High Sch 5801 16th Ave, Brooklyn 11204 Rivkah Taub	9-12	V	252 8	
Torah V'Yirah 110 Throop Ave, Brooklyn 11206 Rabbi Steinmetz	4-9		1,500	718/963-9570 Fax 347/689-1768
Trey Whitfield Sch 17 Hinsdale St, Brooklyn 11207 Janie Whitney	PK-8		449 23	718/342-7722 Fax 718/342-7775
Viznitzer Chadr Tifers Yisroel 1424 43rd St, Brooklyn 11219 Jacob Glick	PK-8		245	718/633-5543
Williamsburg Northside Sch 299 N 7th St, Brooklyn 11211 Elie Deu	PK-6		155	718/599-9600 Fax 718/384-3525
Windmill Montessori Sch 1317 Avenue T, Brooklyn 11229 Liza Herzberg	PK-8		90 7	718/375-7973
Yaldeinu Sch 1600 63rd St, Brooklyn 11204 Bluma Bar-Horin	Spec		39	718/851-0123 Fax 718/851-0455
Yde Elem Sch 325 Avenue Y, Brooklyn 11223 Rivka Dahan	PK-8		400	718/232-0100
Yde High Sch 2533 Coney Island Ave, Brooklyn 11223 Harvey Feldman	9-12		200	718/232-0100
Yeshiva & Msvta Karlin Stolin 1818 54th St, Brooklyn 11204 David Stein	K-12		560	718/232-7800 Fax 718/331-4833
Yeshiva Ahavas Yisroel Sch 2 Lee Ave, Brooklyn 11211 Rabbi Fuchs	K-11		490	718/388-0848 Fax 718/628-2545
Yeshiva Arugath Habosem 40 Lynch St, Brooklyn 11206 B Cohen	PK-9		529	718/237-4500 Fax 718/237-6064
Yeshiva Ateret Torah Boys 901 Quentin Rd, Brooklyn 11223 Rabbi Hooulu	PK-12	G	800	718/375-7100 Fax 718/375-2724
Yeshiva Ateret Torah Girls 2166 Coney Island Ave, Brooklyn 11223 Tziporah Weichbrodt	PK-12		600 20	718/732-7770 Fax 718/732-7766
Yeshiva Bais Meir 1327 38th St, Brooklyn 11218 Shimshan Baratz	8-12		120	718/437-5844 Fax 718/437-4883
Yeshiva Beis Chaya Mushkah 1505 Carroll St, Brooklyn 11213 Levi Plotkin	PK-12		250	718/756-0770 Fax 718/493-9336
Yeshiva Beth Hillel D'Krasna 1371 42nd St, Brooklyn 11219 David Vogel	1-8		325 24	718/438-3535 Fax 718/438-9434
Yeshiva Beth Hillel Williamsbg 35 Hewes St, Brooklyn 11249 Moshe Meisels	K-8		200	718/802-9567
Yeshiva Bicahon 1649 E 13th St, Brooklyn 11229 Arielle Jolovitz	K-8		100 9	718/474-0045
Yeshiva Bnos Spinka Girls 127 Wallabout St, Brooklyn 11206 Gitty Horowitz	K-1		130	718/254-8006 Fax 718/254-8009
Yeshiva Bonim Lamokom 425 E 9th St, Brooklyn 11218 Zev Horowitz	Spec		60	718/693-9032 Fax 718/693-9144
Yeshiva Boyan 1205 44th St, Brooklyn 11219 Yakov Fishman	PK-8		250 12	718/435-6060 Fax 718/435-4060
Yeshiva Chanoch Lenaar 876 Eastern Pkwy, Brooklyn 11213 Mr Tastp	8-12		80	718/774-8456 Fax 718/493-2424
Yeshiva Chsan Sofer 1876 50th St, Brooklyn 11204 Mordechai Stohl	K-12		575	718/236-1171 Fax 718/236-1119

79 Student Personnel
80 Driver Ed/Safety
81 Gifted/Talented
82 Video Services
83 Substance Abuse Prev
84 Erate
85 AIDS Education
88 Alternative/At Risk
89 Multi-Cultural Curriculum
90 Social Work
91 Safety/Security
92 Magnet School
93 Parental Involvement
95 Tech Prep Program
97 Chief Information Officer
98 Chief Technology Officer
270 Character Education
271 Migrant Education
273 Teacher Mentor
274 Before/After Sch
275 Response To Intervention
277 Remedial Math K-12
280 Literacy Coach
285 STEM
286 Digital Learning
288 Common Core Standards
294 Accountability
295 Network System
296 Title II Programs
297 Webmaster
298 Grant Writer/Ptnrships
750 Chief Innovation Officer
751 Chief of Staff
752 Social Emotional Learning

Other School Types
Ⓐ = Alternative School
Ⓒ = Charter School
Ⓜ = Magnet School
Ⓨ = Year-Round School

School Programs
A = Alternative Program
G = Adult Classes
M = Magnet Program
T = Title I Schoolwide
V = Career & Tech Ed Programs

Social Media
 = Facebook
 = Twitter

New Schools are shaded
New Superintendents and Principals are bold
Personnel with email addresses are underscored

NY—99

Kings County

Market Data Retrieval

School	Grades		Enrollment	Phone
Yeshiva Congreg Toras Yufa 1056 54th St, Brooklyn 11219 Chaya Lieberman	K-9		70 6	718/436-5683
Yeshiva Derech Hatorah ES 2810 Nostrand Ave, Brooklyn 11229 E Chanales	PK-8		260 13	718/258-4441 Fax 718/677-8230
Yeshiva Derech Hatorah HS 2810 Nostrand Ave, Brooklyn 11229 Ben Zion Ungar	9-12		140	347/492-6611
Yeshiva Farm Settlement Sch 194 Division Ave, Brooklyn 11211 Ernest Schwartz	K-12		285	718/387-0422 Fax 718/387-9400
Yeshiva Imrei Yosef Spinka 5801 15th Ave, Brooklyn 11219 Liavish Ruben	1-8		250	718/851-1600 Fax 718/851-0148
Yeshiva Kehilath Yaakov Boys 206 Wilson St, Brooklyn 11211 David Oberlander	K-8		629	718/963-3940 Fax 718/387-8586
Yeshiva Ktana Toldos Yakov 87 Heyward St, Brooklyn 11206 Yakov Shapiro	9-12		70	718/852-0502 Fax 718/852-0512
Yeshiva MacHzikei Hadas Belz 1601 42nd St, Brooklyn 11204 Aron Langsam	PK-12		1,039	718/436-4445 Fax 718/435-9046
Yeshiva MacHzikel Hadas 1601 42nd St, Brooklyn 11204 Aaron Langsam	PK-12		900 30	718/436-4445 Fax 718/435-9046
Yeshiva Meor Hatalmud 1368 39th St, Brooklyn 11218	9-12		127	718/927-3772
Yeshiva Mesivta Arugath Habosm 40 Lynch St, Brooklyn 11206 Shulem Taub	9-12		480	718/237-4500 Fax 718/237-6064
Yeshiva of Brooklyn-Boys 1200 Ocean Pkwy, Brooklyn 11230 Johnathan Rosenbaum	K-8		200 17	718/252-9500
Yeshiva of Brooklyn-Girls 1470 Ocean Pkwy 74, Brooklyn 11230 Mindy Salsburg \ Shainy Gornish	PK-12	V	800 34	718/376-3775 Fax 718/376-4280
Yeshiva of Flatbush Elem Sch 919 E 10th St, Brooklyn 11230 Yahel Tsaidi \ David Hertzberg	PK-8		1,007	718/377-4466 Fax 718/258-0824
Yeshiva Ohel Moshe 7914 Bay Pkwy, Brooklyn 11214 Shifra Stone	PK-8		210 12	718/236-4003 Fax 718/236-4923
Yeshiva Ohel Torah 1760 53rd St, Brooklyn 11204 Celia Abtan	PK-6		180 11	718/431-0915
Yeshiva Ohr Shraga D'Veretzky 1102 Avenue L, Brooklyn 11230 Sholom Landau	PK-12		300 14	718/252-7777 Fax 718/252-7797
Yeshiva Rabbi Chaim Berlin 1310 Avenue I, Brooklyn 11230 Moshe Monczyk	K-8		700 30	718/377-5800 Fax 718/576-2532
Yeshiva Ruach Chaim 2611 Avenue Z, Brooklyn 11235 Buruch Klein	PK-8		264	718/646-8500
Yeshiva Shaarei Hatzlucha 1535 63rd St, Brooklyn 11219 Rabbi Rosenbaum	PK-6		200	718/234-3476 Fax 718/532-0194
Yeshiva Shaarei Torah-Boys 1202 Avenue P, Brooklyn 11229 Joseph Abboud	9-12		110	718/645-6676 Fax 718/645-6685
Yeshiva Shaarei Torah-Girls HS 1768 Ocean Ave, Brooklyn 11230 Carol Haber	9-12	V	153 4	718/382-4000 Fax 718/382-7999
Yeshiva Shaari Torah Sch 1202 Avenue P, Brooklyn 11229 Gabriel Bigio	9-12		120 8	718/645-6676 Fax 718/645-6685
Yeshiva Tiferes D'Aleksander 1010 45th St, Brooklyn 11219 Boruch Singer	9-12		200	718/438-1818 Fax 718/438-7826
Yeshiva Tiferes Elimelech Boys 1650 56th St, Brooklyn 11204 Malka David	PK-12		500	718/438-1177 Fax 718/438-1779
Yeshiva Tiferes Yisroel 1271 E 35th St, Brooklyn 11210 Yehuzah Jacobson \ Kinzel Berg \ David Schonbrun	K-12		850 35	718/258-9006 Fax 718/258-9055
Yeshiva Torah Temimah 555 Ocean Pkwy, Brooklyn 11218 Abi Pearl	PK-12		631 40	718/853-8500 Fax 718/438-5779
Yeshiva Torah V'Yirah Academy 212 Williamsburg St E, Brooklyn 11211 Venzion Jacobowitz	1-3		200	718/963-9288 Fax 718/963-9260
Yeshiva Torah Vodaath 425 E 9th St, Brooklyn 11218 Isaac Fink \ Chaim Shilit	PK-12		401	718/941-8000 Fax 718/941-8032
Yeshiva Toras Emes Kamenitz 1904 Avenue N, Brooklyn 11230 Chaim Block	PK-12		400 20	718/375-0900 Fax 718/376-4661
Yeshiva Tzemach Tzadik Viznitz 186 Ross St Ste 1, Brooklyn 11211 Rabbi Kahan	PK-8		180	718/782-6383 Fax 718/782-2099
Yeshiva Yagdil Torah 5110 18th Ave, Brooklyn 11204 Aaron Grinblat	PK-8		580	718/871-9100 Fax 718/436-0549
Yeshiva Yesode Hatorah Adas 1350 50th St, Brooklyn 11219 Mordechai Landau	PK-8	G	279 12	718/851-6462 Fax 718/851-7298
Yeshiva-Mesivta V'Yoel Moshe 5301 14th Ave, Brooklyn 11219 Joseph Stern	9-12		750 29	718/438-7109 Fax 718/438-3153
Yeshivas Novominsk 1690 60th St, Brooklyn 11204 Yisroel Schwebel	9-12		300 4	718/438-2727 Fax 718/438-2472
Yeshivat Magen Abraham 723 Avenue Z, Brooklyn 11223 Yosef Churba	9-12		50	718/627-6200
Yeshivat OR Hatorah 2119 Homecrest Ave, Brooklyn 11229 Yaakov Marcus	9-12		48 5	718/645-4645 Fax 718/645-4693
Yeshivat OR Hatorah ES 2959 Avenue Y, Brooklyn 11235 Rabbi Zeytouneh	K-8		85	718/252-8308 Fax 718/252-8309
Yeshivat Shaare Torah Girls ES 222 Ocean Pkwy, Brooklyn 11218 Yael Bussu	K-8		300	718/437-6120 Fax 718/437-6119
Zdr Acad Yeshiva Rambam Sch 3300 Kings Hwy, Brooklyn 11234 Dennis Hodne	6-12		100 12	718/677-5100 Fax 718/677-7703

1	Superintendent	8	Curric/Instruct K-12	19	Chief Financial Officer	29	Family/Consumer Science	39	Social Studies K-12
2	Bus/Finance/Purchasing	9	Curric/Instruct Elem	20	Art K-12	30	Adult Education	40	Social Studies Elem
3	Buildings And Grounds	10	Curric/Instruct Sec	21	Art Elem	31	Career/Sch-to-Work K-12	41	Social Studies Sec
4	Food Service	11	Federal Program	22	Art Sec	32	Career/Sch-to-Work Elem	42	Science K-12
5	Transportation	12	Title I	23	Music K-12	33	Career/Sch-to-Work Sec	43	Science Elem
6	Athletic	13	Title V	24	Music Elem	34	Early Childhood Ed	44	Science Sec
7	Health Services	15	Asst Superintendent	25	Music Sec	35	Health/Phys Education	45	Math K-12
		16	Instructional Media Svcs	26	Business Education	36	Guidance Services K-12	46	Math Elem
		17	Chief Operations Officer	27	Career & Tech Ed	37	Guidance Services Elem	47	Math Sec
		18	Chief Academic Officer	28	Technology Education	38	Guidance Services Sec	48	English/Lang Arts K-12

49	English/Lang Arts Elem	59	Special Education Elem	69	Academic Assessment		
50	English/Lang Arts Sec	60	Special Education Sec	70	Research/Development		
51	Reading K-12	61	Foreign/World Lang K-12	71	Public Information		
52	Reading Elem	62	Foreign/World Lang Elem	72	Summer School		
53	Reading Sec	63	Foreign/World Lang Sec	73	Instructional Tech		
54	Remedial Reading K-12	64	Religious Education K-12	74	Inservice Training		
55	Remedial Reading Elem	65	Religious Education Elem	75	Marketing/Distributive		
56	Remedial Reading Sec	66	Religious Education Sec	76	Info Systems		
57	Bilingual/ELL	67	School Board President	77	Psychological Assess		
58	Special Education K-12	68	Teacher Personnel	78	Affirmative Action		

New York School Directory — Lewis County

LEWIS COUNTY

LEWIS COUNTY SCHOOLS

County Schs..Principal	Grd	Prgm	Enr/#Cls	SN	
Howard G Sackett Technical Ctr 5836 State Route 12, Glenfield 13343 Paul Mooney	Voc	AG	350 16		315/377-7300 Fax 315/377-7309

LEWIS PUBLIC SCHOOLS

• **Beaver River Central Sch Dist** PID: 00730487   315/346-1211
9508 Artz Rd, Beaver Falls 13305   Fax 315/346-6775

Schools: 1 \ **Teachers:** 69 \ **Students:** 875 \ **Special Ed Students:** 170 \ **College-Bound:** 80% \ **Ethnic:** African American 1%, Hispanic 2%, Caucasian 97% \ **Exp:** $184 (Low) \ **Poverty:** 19% \ **Title I:** $299,808 \ **Special Education:** $800,000 \ **Open-Close:** 09/01 - 06/30 \ **DTBP:** $359 (High)

Todd Green 1,11		Randolph Myers 2*	
Heather Pellam 4*		Franklyn Monnat 5	
Wanda Joslin 6,35*		Jennifer Wright 16*	
Nicky Kuhl 30		Alex Barrett 36*	
Eliza Boliver 58,77,88*		Carolyn Marolf 61*	
Samuel Chamberlin 67		Joseph Virkler 73*	

Public Schs..Principal	Grd	Prgm	Enr/#Cls	SN	
Beaver River Central Sch 9508 Artz Rd, Beaver Falls 13305 Kimberly Lyman-Wright \ Christine Labare \ Daniel Rains	PK-12	GT	875 94	45%	315/346-1211

• **Copenhagen Central SD** PID: 00730504   315/688-4411
3020 Mechanic St, Copenhagen 13626   Fax 315/688-2001

Schools: 1 \ **Teachers:** 44 \ **Students:** 460 \ **Special Ed Students:** 77 \ **College-Bound:** 80% \ **Ethnic:** Asian 1%, African American 1%, Hispanic 5%, Caucasian 94% \ **Exp:** $150 (Low) \ **Poverty:** 17% \ **Title I:** $158,721 \ **Special Education:** $641,000 \ **Open-Close:** 09/08 - 06/30 \ **DTBP:** $401 (High) \ 📘

Scott Connell 1,11		Scott Luther 2,12,58*	
Dale Clarke 3*		Nicole Grandjean 4*	
Russell Groff 5		Jenny Hovenden 20	
Cynthia Graves 23		Brigitte Gillette 31,36,69,83,85,88,270*	
Lynn Murraw 67		Adam Zehr 73,295	

Public Schs..Principal	Grd	Prgm	Enr/#Cls	SN	
Copenhagen Central Sch 3020 Mechanic St, Copenhagen 13626 Nadine O'Shaughnessy	PK-12	T	460 25	39%	315/688-4411

• **Harrisville Central Sch Dist** PID: 00730528   315/543-2707
14371 Pirate Ln, Harrisville 13648   Fax 315/543-2360

Schools: 1 \ **Teachers:** 41 \ **Students:** 359 \ **Special Ed Students:** 58 \ **College-Bound:** 59% \ **Ethnic:** Hispanic 3%, Caucasian 97% \ **Exp:** $412 (High) \ **Poverty:** 15% \ **Title I:** $119,821 \ **Special Education:** $579,000 \ **Open-Close:** 09/04 - 06/25 \ **DTBP:** $296 (High)

Robert Finster 1		Rebecca Phillips 2	
Rick Chartrand 3		Christine Bristol 4*	
Eric Luther 6*		Shelly Carr 36*	
Kathleen Cruikshank 58*		Jan Mosher 67	

Public Schs..Principal	Grd	Prgm	Enr/#Cls	SN	
Harrisville Central Sch 14371 Pirate Ln, Harrisville 13648 Eric Luther \ Kathleen Cruikshank	PK-12	T	359 43	52%	315/543-2707

• **Lowville Acad-Central Sch Dist** PID: 00730554   315/376-9000
7668 N State St, Lowville 13367   Fax 315/376-1933

Schools: 1 \ **Teachers:** 117 \ **Students:** 1,350 \ **Special Ed Students:** 216 \ **LEP Students:** 3 \ **College-Bound:** 80% \ **Ethnic:** Asian 1%, African American 3%, Hispanic 1%, Caucasian 96% \ **Exp:** $225 (Med) \ **Poverty:** 17% \ **Title I:** $432,368 \ **Special Education:** $1,766,000 \ **Open-Close:** 09/04 - 06/25 \ **DTBP:** $276 (High)

Rebecca Dunkle-King 1,11		Sandra Rivers 2	
Mike Hlad 3		Racheal Hoffman 4	
Amy Green 5		Rob Goss 6*	
Marie Western 8,288,296,298		Philomena Goss 9*	
Jackson Hyde 16*		Gil Monnat 27,36,69*	
Carol Kozin 31*		Jeffery Lasche 35	
Mary Compo 58*		Thomas Schneeberger 67	
Steve Bingle 73*		Amy Bingle 81*	
Sue Bush 83,85*		Jon Bassette 295	

Public Schs..Principal	Grd	Prgm	Enr/#Cls	SN	
Lowville Acad Central Sch 7668 N State St, Lowville 13367 Philomena Goss \ Scott Exford \ Brian Finn	PK-12	GT	1,350 60	45%	315/376-9001

• **South Lewis Central Sch Dist** PID: 00730580   315/348-2500
4264 East Rd, Turin 13473   Fax 315/348-2510

Schools: 4 \ **Teachers:** 94 \ **Students:** 1,028 \ **Special Ed Students:** 265 \ **LEP Students:** 3 \ **College-Bound:** 59% \ **Ethnic:** African American 1%, Hispanic 2%, Caucasian 97% \ **Exp:** $251 (Med) \ **Poverty:** 14% \ **Title I:** $269,262 \ **Special Education:** $1,819,000 \ **Open-Close:** 09/08 - 06/25 \ **DTBP:** $349 (High)

Douglas Premo 1		Barry Yette 2,11,296	
Richard Ponitkera 3		Lisa Strait 4	
Andrew Krokowski 5		C Brian Oaks 6,7,35,83	
Deborah Domagala 8,88,288,298		Julie Burmingham 38*	
Mariann Green 38*		Catherine Littlefield 58,88	
Andrew Liendecker 67		Scott Carpenter 73,76,286	
Rebecca Garner 77		Reid Covey 295	

Public Schs..Principal	Grd	Prgm	Enr/#Cls	SN	
Glenfield Elem Sch 5960 Main St, Glenfield 13343 Christine Sobel	PK-4	T	206 11	57%	315/348-2620
Port Leyden Elem Sch 3336 Lincoln St, Port Leyden 13433 Christoph Villiere	PK-4	T	219 14	55%	315/348-2660

---

79 Student Personnel	91 Safety/Security	275 Response To Intervention	298 Grant Writer/Ptnrships	**School Programs**
80 Driver Ed/Safety	92 Magnet School	277 Remedial Math K-12	750 Chief Innovation Officer	A = Alternative Program
81 Gifted/Talented	93 Parental Involvement	280 Literacy Coach	751 Chief of Staff	G = Adult Classes
82 Video Services	95 Tech Prep Program	285 STEM	752 Social Emotional Learning	M = Magnet Program
83 Substance Abuse Prev	97 Chief Information Officer	286 Digital Learning		T = Title I Schoolwide
84 Erate	98 Chief Technology Officer	288 Common Core Standards	**Other School Types**	V = Career & Tech Ed Programs
85 AIDS Education	270 Character Education	294 Accountability	Ⓐ = Alternative School	
88 Alternative/At Risk	271 Migrant Education	295 Network System	Ⓒ = Charter School	**Social Media**
89 Multi-Cultural Curriculum	273 Teacher Mentor	296 Title II Programs	Ⓜ = Magnet School	📘 = Facebook
90 Social Work	274 Before/After Sch	297 Webmaster	Ⓨ = Year-Round School	🐦 = Twitter

New Schools are shaded
New Superintendents and Principals are bold
Personnel with email addresses are underscored

Livingston County

Market Data Retrieval

South Lewis High Sch 4264 East Rd, Turin 13473 Chad Luther	9-12		307 45	58% 315/348-2520
South Lewis Middle Sch 4264 East Rd, Turin 13473 Judy Duppert	5-8		298 15	66% 315/348-2570

LEWIS PRIVATE SCHOOLS

Private Schs..Principal	Grd	Prgm	Enr/#Cls SN	
Crystal Light Mennonite Sch 9607 Highland Avenue, Castorland 13620 Mervin Nolt	1-10		45 4	315/376-8556

LIVINGSTON COUNTY

LIVINGSTON COUNTY SCHOOLS

County Schs..Principal	Grd	Prgm	Enr/#Cls SN	
Charles G May Career & Tech Ed 27 Lackawanna Ave, Mount Morris 14510 Matthew Flowers	Voc	AG	500 46	585/658-7811 Fax 585/658-7860

LIVINGSTON PUBLIC SCHOOLS

● Avon Central School Dist PID: 00730645
191 Clinton St, Avon 14414

585/226-2455
Fax 585/226-8202

Schools: 3 \ Teachers: 95 \ Students: 1,006 \ Special Ed Students: 89 \ LEP Students: 17 \ College-Bound: 79% \ Ethnic: Asian 1%, African American 3%, Hispanic 6%, Native American: 1%, Caucasian 90% \ Exp: $186 (Low) \ Poverty: 8% \ Title I: $111,797 \ Special Education: $1,503,000 \ Open-Close: 09/08 - 06/25 \ DTBP: $359 (High) \ [f]

Ryan Pacatte	1	Kristen Murphy	2,294
Susan Eadie	2	Tom LaGrou	3
Barbara Popp	4	Rebecca Gross	5
Andy Englert	6	Christina Ecklund	8,74*
Jacquiline Simpson	8,11,57,58,296	Robert Lupisella	9*
Suzanne Freeman	16*	Amanda Giansante	36*
Rodney George	67	Kyle Adamczak	71
Jim Ellis	73	Jackie Simpson	79,298

Public Schs..Principal	Grd	Prgm	Enr/#Cls SN	
Avon Central High Sch 245 Clinton St, Avon 14414 Ryan Wagner	9-12	TV	350 25	24% 585/226-2455
Avon Central Primary Sch 161 Clinton St, Avon 14414 Robert Lupisella	K-4	T	334 21	37% 585/226-2455
Avon Middle Sch 191 Clinton St, Avon 14414 Jennifer Miller	5-8	T	322 16	35% 585/226-2455 Fax 585/226-1736

● Caledonia-Mumford Ctl Sch Dist PID: 00730683
99 North St, Caledonia 14423

585/538-3400
Fax 585/538-3450

Schools: 3 \ Teachers: 80 \ Students: 815 \ Special Ed Students: 121 \ LEP Students: 7 \ College-Bound: 84% \ Ethnic: Asian 1%, African American 3%, Hispanic 3%, Caucasian 94% \ Exp: $214 (Med) \ Poverty: 11% \ Title I: $132,248 \ Special Education: $1,514,000 \ Open-Close: 09/08 - 06/25 \ DTBP: $308 (High)

Robert Molisani	1	Terrence Hasseler	2
Ernest Whaley	3*	Ron Otto	5
Michael Reed	6,7,85*	Michele Meyer	8
Tammy Nothnagoe	9,69	Paul Estabrooks	11,57,58,88,271*
Nichole Docteur	16*	Carolyn Richardson	26,31*
Sarah Santora	30*	Sarah Curran	38
John Bickford	67	Jaime Filli	73,295

Public Schs..Principal	Grd	Prgm	Enr/#Cls SN	
Caledonia-Mumford Elem Sch 99 North St, Caledonia 14423 David Bulter	PK-5	T	395 23	33% 585/538-3481 Fax 585/538-3460
Caledonia-Mumford Middle Sch 99 North St, Caledonia 14423 Paul Estabrooks	6-8	T	192 15	37% 585/538-3482 Fax 585/538-3430
Caledonia-Mumford Senior HS 99 North St, Caledonia 14423 Dr Rebekah Chenaille	9-12	T	221 30	32% 585/538-3483 Fax 585/538-3470

● Dansville Ctl School Dist PID: 00730712
337 Main St, Dansville 14437

585/335-4000
Fax 585/335-5047

Schools: 3 \ Teachers: 127 \ Students: 1,300 \ Special Ed Students: 234 \ LEP Students: 10 \ Ethnic: African American 1%, Hispanic 3%, Caucasian 96% \ Exp: $410 (High) \ Poverty: 16% \ Title I: $438,643 \ Special Education: $2,353,000 \ Open-Close: 09/08 - 06/25 \ DTBP: $154 (High) \ [t]

Dr Paul Alioto	1	Roger Parulski	2
Mike Mistretta	3,5,91	Rita Morrow	4
David Moody	6	Barb Pamper	10,73,286*
Lynne Blum	16*	Zach Matzek	27,38
Denise Dunham	58*	Maryann Holden	67
Margeret Mistretta	68	Jim Blum	73,295*
Michael Birmingham	295		

Public Schs..Principal	Grd	Prgm	Enr/#Cls SN	
Dansville High Sch 282 Main St, Dansville 14437 Tom Frazier	7-12	T	656 75	50% 585/335-4010 Fax 585/335-4080
Dansville Primary Sch 284 Main St, Dansville 14437 Daniel Dixon	PK-2	T	373 26	54% 585/335-4040 Fax 585/335-8181
Ellis B Hyde Elem Sch 280 Main St, Dansville 14437 Lisa Allen	3-6	T	392 22	55% 585/335-4030 Fax 585/335-4056

● Geneseo Central Sch Dist PID: 00730762
4050 Avon Rd, Geneseo 14454

585/243-3450
Fax 585/243-9481

Schools: 1 \ Teachers: 95 \ Students: 853 \ Special Ed Students: 149 \ LEP Students: 37 \ College-Bound: 83% \ Ethnic: Asian 1%, African American 2%, Hispanic 8%, Caucasian 89% \ Exp: $352 (High) \ Poverty: 12% \ Title I: $177,766 \ Special Education: $2,145,000 \ Open-Close: 09/08 - 06/25 \ DTBP: $169 (High) \ [f]

Cindy Flowers	1	Ken Forrester	2,11

---

1 Superintendent	8 Curric/Instruct K-12	19 Chief Financial Officer	29 Family/Consumer Science	39 Social Studies K-12	49 English/Lang Arts Elem	59 Special Education Elem	69 Academic Assessment
2 Bus/Finance/Purchasing	9 Curric/Instruct Elem	20 Art K-12	30 Adult Education	40 Social Studies Elem	50 English/Lang Arts Sec	60 Special Education Sec	70 Research/Development
3 Buildings And Grounds	10 Curric/Instruct Sec	21 Art Elem	31 Career/Sch-to-Work K-12	41 Social Studies Sec	51 Reading K-12	61 Foreign/World Lang K-12	71 Public Information
4 Food Service	11 Federal Program	22 Art Sec	32 Career/Sch-to-Work Elem	42 Science K-12	52 Reading Elem	62 Foreign/World Lang Elem	72 Summer School
5 Transportation	12 Title I	23 Music K-12	33 Career/Sch-to-Work Sec	43 Science Elem	53 Reading Sec	63 Foreign/World Lang Sec	73 Instructional Tech
6 Athletic	13 Title V	24 Music Elem	34 Early Childhood Ed	44 Science Sec	54 Remedial Reading K-12	64 Religious Education K-12	74 Inservice Training
7 Health Services	15 Asst Superintendent	25 Music Sec	35 Health/Phys Education	45 Math K-12	55 Remedial Reading Elem	65 Religious Education Elem	75 Marketing/Distributive
	16 Instructional Media Svcs	26 Business Education	36 Guidance Services K-12	46 Math Elem	56 Remedial Reading Sec	66 Religious Education Sec	76 Info Systems
	17 Chief Operations Officer	27 Career & Tech Ed	37 Guidance Services Elem	47 Math Sec	57 Bilingual/ELL	67 School Board President	77 Psychological Assess
	18 Chief Academic Officer	28 Technology Education	38 Guidance Services Sec	48 English/Lang Arts K-12	58 Special Education K-12	68 Teacher Personnel	78 Affirmative Action

New York School Directory — Livingston County

Stephanie Hilt	2	Tom Curtain	3
Jay Ballard	5	Craig Veley	6*
Dana MacIntyre	7,83,85*	Kelly Sattora	12*
Heather Greene	16,82*	Stephine Miller	18,58
Sara Kelly	57*	Jennifer Mehlenbacher	67
John Holt	73,76,295	Bettina Debell	81*

Public Schs..Principal	Grd	Prgm	Enr/#Cls	SN	
Geneseo Central Sch 4050 Avon Rd, Geneseo 14454 Michael Salatel \ Kelly Sattora	K-12	V	853 75	36%	585/243-3450

● **Keshequa Central School Dist** PID: 00730786   585/468-2900
13 Mill St, Nunda 14517   Fax 585/468-3814

Schools: 3 \ **Teachers:** 69 \ **Students:** 617 \ **Special Ed Students:** 97 \ **LEP Students:** 3 \ **College-Bound:** 79% \ **Ethnic:** Hispanic 2%, Caucasian 98% \ **Exp:** $302 (High) \ **Poverty:** 13% \ **Title I:** $161,203 \ **Special Education:** $1,939,000 \ **Open-Close:** 09/08 - 06/25 \ **DTBP:** $359 (High)

Thomas Kopp	1	Joanne Greene	2
James VanSickle	3	Sue Slate	4
Leon Babcock	5	Bradley Lehman	6*
Ami Hunt	9,69,273,280,288*	Tina Button	11,73,76,286,295
Sarah Bull	36*	Todd Galton	67
Tricia Bressler	76	Ross Gerace	275*

Public Schs..Principal	Grd	Prgm	Enr/#Cls	SN	
Keshequa Interm Sch 13 Mill St, Nunda 14517 Brad Lehman	4-6		140		585/468-2900
Keshequa Middle High Sch 13 Mill St, Nunda 14517 Karen Bennett	7-12	T	285 25	43%	585/468-2541 Fax 585/468-5493
Keshequa Primary Sch 1716 Church St, Dalton 14836 Casey Vanepps	PK-3	T	192 40	51%	585/468-2900 Fax 585/476-5606

● **Livonia Ctl School Dist** PID: 00730815   585/346-4000
40 Spring St, Livonia 14487   Fax 585/346-6145

Schools: 2 \ **Teachers:** 136 \ **Students:** 1,500 \ **Special Ed Students:** 177 \ **LEP Students:** 8 \ **College-Bound:** 83% \ **Ethnic:** African American 1%, Hispanic 2%, Caucasian 97% \ **Exp:** $265 (Med) \ **Poverty:** 9% \ **Title I:** $235,864 \ **Special Education:** $2,685,000 \ **Open-Close:** 09/09 - 06/23 \ **DTBP:** $395 (High) \ f t

Matthew Cole	1,11	Jeremy Lonneville	2,68
Robbin Carll	3,16,73,76	Rebecca Schorr	4
Bob Orman	5	Charles Whittel	9*
Jennifer McMahon	9,296*	Margaret Hooker	31,36*
Nicole McGarry	58	Dr David Woodruff	67
Ryan Hill	295*		

Public Schs..Principal	Grd	Prgm	Enr/#Cls	SN	
Livonia Elem Sch 6 Puppy Lane, Livonia 14487 Charles Whittel	PK-5		644 53	38%	585/346-4000 Fax 585/346-4082
Livonia High Sch 2 Bulldog Blvd, Livonia 14487 Audra Schmitt	9-12	AGV	478	32%	585/346-4000 Fax 585/346-9605

● **Mt Morris Central School Dist** PID: 00730853   585/658-3331
30 Bonadonna Ave, Mount Morris 14510   Fax 585/658-4814

Schools: 1 \ **Teachers:** 59 \ **Students:** 500 \ **Special Ed Students:** 144 \ **LEP Students:** 67 \ **College-Bound:** 71% \ **Ethnic:** Asian 1%, African American 3%, Hispanic 27%, Caucasian 69% \ **Exp:** $256 (Med) \ **Poverty:** 24% \ **Title I:** $205,876 \ **Special Education:** $1,538,000 \ **Open-Close:** 09/08 - 06/24 \ **DTBP:** $155 (High) \ f t

Gregory Bump	1	Michael Cox	2,11
Brandon Zingaro	3,295	Barbara Popp	4
Wayne Sweed	6,16,60,73,271	Allison Atwell	31,36,69
Krystal Van Valkenberg	58*	Danielle Dean	59,288*
Peter Priuitera	67		

Public Schs..Principal	Grd	Prgm	Enr/#Cls	SN	
Mt Morris Central Sch 30 Bonadonna Ave, Mount Morris 14510 Jesse Hamilton \ Danielle Dean	PK-12	AT	500 125	55%	585/658-3331

● **York Central School Dist** PID: 00730889   585/243-1730
2578 Genesee St, Retsof 14539   Fax 585/243-5269

Schools: 2 \ **Teachers:** 77 \ **Students:** 780 \ **Special Ed Students:** 117 \ **LEP Students:** 10 \ **Ethnic:** Asian 1%, Hispanic 2%, Caucasian 97% \ **Exp:** $281 (Med) \ **Poverty:** 9% \ **Title I:** $102,253 \ **Special Education:** $1,527,000 \ **Open-Close:** 09/14 - 06/24 \ **DTBP:** $359 (High) \ t

David Furletti	1,11	Paul Liess	2,12,36
Tony Gullo	3	Laurie Cutcliffe	4
Dwayne Dougal	5	Ed Orman	6,35
Aubrey Krenzer	8	Nicole Miller	16
William MacKenzie	31*	Na'Lisa Hussar	38,83,88*
Steven Beardsley	67	Ryan Fraser	73
Ameigh Coates	79	Rebecca Kane	91

Public Schs..Principal	Grd	Prgm	Enr/#Cls	SN	
York Central Elem Sch 2578 Genesee St, Retsof 14539 Kate Hoffman	PK-6	T	394	46%	585/243-3400
York Central Middle High Sch 2578 Genesee St, Retsof 14539 Lindsey Peet	7-12	T	350 40	39%	585/243-2990

LIVINGSTON CATHOLIC SCHOOLS

● **Diocese of Rochester Ed Office** PID: 00733623
Listing includes only schools located in this county. See District Index for location of Diocesan Offices.

Catholic Schs..Principal	Grd	Prgm	Enr/#Cls	SN	
St Agnes Sch 60 Park Pl, Avon 14414 Elizabeth Jensen	PK-6		118 9		585/226-8500 f

79	Student Personnel	91	Safety/Security	275	Response To Intervention	298	Grant Writer/Ptnrships
80	Driver Ed/Safety	92	Magnet School	277	Remedial Math K-12	750	Chief Innovation Officer
81	Gifted/Talented	93	Parental Involvement	280	Literacy Coach	751	Chief of Staff
82	Video Services	95	Tech Prep Program	285	STEM	752	Social Emotional Learning
83	Substance Abuse Prev	97	Chief Information Officer	286	Digital Learning		
84	Erate	98	Chief Technology Officer	288	Common Core Standards		
85	AIDS Education	270	Character Education	294	Accountability		
88	Alternative/At Risk	271	Migrant Education	295	Network System		
89	Multi-Cultural Curriculum	273	Teacher Mentor	296	Title II Programs		
90	Social Work	274	Before/After Sch	297	Webmaster		

School Programs
A = Alternative Program
G = Adult Classes
M = Magnet Program
T = Title I Schoolwide
V = Career & Tech Ed Programs

Other School Types
Ⓐ = Alternative School
Ⓒ = Charter School
Ⓜ = Magnet School
Ⓨ = Year-Round School

Social Media
f = Facebook
t = Twitter

New Schools are shaded
New Superintendents and Principals are bold
Personnel with email addresses are underscored

Madison County

LIVINGSTON PRIVATE SCHOOLS

Private Schs..Principal	Grd	Prgm	Enr/#Cls	SN	
Genesee Country Christian Sch 4120 Long Point Rd, Geneseo 14454 Betsy Flickner	PK-8		75 5		585/243-9580 Fax 585/243-5604
Lima Christian Sch 1574 Rochester St, Lima 14485 John Reese	K-12		180 20		585/624-3841 Fax 585/624-8293

MADISON COUNTY

MADISON PUBLIC SCHOOLS

● **Brookfield Central School Dist** PID: 00730944 315/899-3324
1910 Fairground Rd, Brookfield 13314 Fax 315/899-8902

Schools: 1 \ Teachers: 21 \ Students: 240 \ Special Ed Students: 45 \ College-Bound: 88% \ Ethnic: Hispanic 1%, Caucasian 99% \ Exp: $183 (Low) \ Poverty: 21% \ Title I: $81,348 \ Special Education: $471,000 \ Open-Close: 09/04 - 06/25 \ DTBP: $354 (High)

James Plows 1,83   Paul Kupris 3,91*
Wayne Walker 5   Sarah Abrams 6*
Julie Jones ....7*   Carrie Smith 8,11,68,74,271,288,294*
Colleen Peavey ....16,73,76,295*   Bernie Whitacre 67

Public Schs..Principal	Grd	Prgm	Enr/#Cls	SN	
Brookfield Central Sch 1910 Fairground Rd, Brookfield 13314 Carrie Smith	PK-12	T	240 30	51%	315/899-3323

● **Canastota Central School Dist** PID: 00730968 315/697-2025
120 Roberts St, Canastota 13032 Fax 315/697-6368

Schools: 4 \ Teachers: 117 \ Students: 1,275 \ Special Ed Students: 239 \ LEP Students: 8 \ Ethnic: Asian 1%, African American 1%, Hispanic 3%, Native American: 1%, Caucasian 94% \ Exp: $264 (Med) \ Poverty: 14% \ Title I: $332,571 \ Special Education: $2,736,000 \ Open-Close: 09/07 - 06/29 \ DTBP: $161 (High)

Shawn Bissetta 1   Cara Stevens 2
Christina Omans 4   Cindy Clark 5
Stanley Congden ....6* Jason Mitchell 8,11,15,271,296
Christopher Clancy ....15,59,73*   Bill Haddad 67

Public Schs..Principal	Grd	Prgm	Enr/#Cls	SN	
Canastota Jr Sr High Sch 101 Roberts St, Canastota 13032 Jay Altobello	7-12	AT	579 56	47%	315/697-2003 Fax 315/697-6314
Peterboro St Elem Sch 220 N Peterboro St, Canastota 13032 Jennifer Carnhan	K-1	T	208 12	54%	315/697-2027
Roberts Street Elem Sch 120 Roberts St, Canastota 13032 Michael Faustino	4-6		289 16		315/697-2029 Fax 315/697-6343
South Side Elem Sch 200 High St, Canastota 13032 Robert Taube	2-3	T	199 10	59%	315/697-6372 Fax 315/697-6364

● **Cazenovia Ctl School Dist** PID: 00731015 315/655-1317
31 Emory Ave, Cazenovia 13035 Fax 315/655-1375

Schools: 3 \ Teachers: 121 \ Students: 1,360 \ Special Ed Students: 170 \ LEP Students: 10 \ Ethnic: Asian 1%, African American 1%, Hispanic 3%, Caucasian 95% \ Exp: $253 (Med) \ Poverty: 6% \ Title I: $136,338 \ Special Education: $2,007,000 \ Open-Close: 09/08 - 06/24 \ DTBP: $166 (High)

Matthew Reilly 1,11   Thomas Finnerty 2,15
Matthew Erwin ....3,91*   Karen Cowherd 5
Michael Byrnes ....6*   Benjamin New 8,58,275,296,298
Chris Hennigan ....16,73,76,295*   Molly Hagan 27,57,83,88
Maureen Carroll ....35*   Dr Jan Woodworth 67
Patrick Ruddy ....79*   Trish Moesch 85*

Public Schs..Principal	Grd	Prgm	Enr/#Cls	SN	
Burton Street Elem Sch 37 Burton St, Cazenovia 13035 Mary-Ann MacIntosh	K-4	T	490 27	24%	315/655-1325 Fax 315/655-1353
Cazenovia Jr Sr High Sch 31 Emory Ave, Cazenovia 13035 Molly Hagan	8-12	V	563 40	20%	315/655-1370 Fax 315/655-1371
Cazenovia Middle Sch 31 Emory Ave, Cazenovia 13035 Dr Jean Regan	5-7		307 30	21%	315/655-1324 Fax 315/655-5305

● **Chittenango Central SD** PID: 00731065 315/687-2840
1732 Fyler Rd, Chittenango 13037 Fax 315/687-2841

Schools: 4 \ Teachers: 168 \ Students: 1,904 \ Special Ed Students: 320 \ LEP Students: 5 \ Ethnic: Asian 1%, African American 1%, Hispanic 3%, Caucasian 95% \ Exp: $207 (Med) \ Poverty: 8% \ Title I: $248,135 \ Special Education: $2,853,000 \ Open-Close: 09/04 - 06/25 \ DTBP: $176 (High)

Michael Eisse 1   Scott Mahardy 2,15
Jeff Martin 3   Wendy Swift 4*
Connie Thorp 5   David Gryczka 6*
David Gryczka 6   Jason Clark 8,11,15,74
Nancy Starke ....30*   Mary Farber 58,79
Geoffery Zimmer 67   Paul Leonardi 73,295*
Lisa Murray 88*

Public Schs..Principal	Grd	Prgm	Enr/#Cls	SN	
Bolivar Road Elem Sch 6983 Bolivar Rd, Chittenango 13037 Lee Carulli	K-4		455 18	39%	315/687-2880 Fax 315/687-2881
Bridgeport Elem Sch 9076 North Rd, Bridgeport 13030 Melissa Stanek	K-4	T	209 14	46%	315/687-2280 Fax 315/687-2281
Chittenango High Sch 150 Genesee St, Chittenango 13037 Nicholas Fersch	9-12		642 65	38%	315/687-2900 Fax 315/687-2924
Chittenango Middle Sch 1732 Fyler Rd, Chittenango 13037 Arnold Merola	5-8	G	598	38%	315/687-2800 Fax 315/687-2801

1	Superintendent	8	Curric/Instruct K-12	19	Chief Financial Officer	29	Family/Consumer Science	39	Social Studies K-12	49	English/Lang Arts Elem	59	Special Education Elem	69	Academic Assessment
2	Bus/Finance/Purchasing	9	Curric/Instruct Elem	20	Art K-12	30	Adult Education	40	Social Studies Elem	50	English/Lang Arts Sec	60	Special Education Sec	70	Research/Development
3	Buildings And Grounds	10	Curric/Instruct Sec	21	Art Elem	31	Career/Sch-to-Work K-12	41	Social Studies Sec	51	Reading K-12	61	Foreign/World Lang K-12	71	Public Information
4	Food Service	11	Federal Program	22	Art Sec	32	Career/Sch-to-Work Elem	42	Science K-12	52	Reading Elem	62	Foreign/World Lang Elem	72	Summer School
5	Transportation	12	Title I	23	Music K-12	33	Career/Sch-to-Work Sec	43	Science Elem	53	Reading Sec	63	Foreign/World Lang Sec	73	Instructional Tech
6	Athletic	13	Title V	24	Music Elem	34	Early Childhood Ed	44	Science Sec	54	Remedial Reading K-12	64	Religious Education K-12	74	Inservice Training
7	Health Services	15	Asst Superintendent	25	Music Sec	35	Health/Phys Education	45	Math K-12	55	Remedial Reading Elem	65	Religious Education Elem	75	Marketing/Distributive
		16	Instructional Media Svcs	26	Business Education	36	Guidance Services K-12	46	Math Elem	56	Remedial Reading Sec	66	Religious Education Sec	76	Info Systems
		17	Chief Operations Officer	27	Career & Tech Ed	37	Guidance Services Elem	47	Math Sec	57	Bilingual/ELL	67	School Board President	77	Psychological Assess
		18	Chief Academic Officer	28	Technology Education	38	Guidance Services Sec	48	English/Lang Arts K-12	58	Special Education K-12	68	Teacher Personnel	78	Affirmative Action

New York School Directory

Madison County

- **De Ruyter Central School Dist** PID: 00731120   315/852-3400
  711 Railroad St, De Ruyter 13052   Fax 315/852-9600

Schools: 2 \ **Teachers:** 46 \ **Students:** 360 \ **Special Ed Students:** 66 \ **LEP Students:** 5 \ **Ethnic:** African American 3%, Hispanic 3%, Native American: 1%, Caucasian 93% \ **Exp:** $268 (Med) \ **Poverty:** 21% \ **Title I:** $155,464 \ **Special Education:** $721,000 \ **Open-Close:** 09/08 - 06/24 \ **DTBP:** $353 (High)

Dr David Brown 1	James Southard 2,11
Kevin Springer 3,5*	Brenda Scutt 4*
Sheri Smith 6*	Jessica Vadala 7*
Kimberly O'Brien 8*	Jenny Valente 9,59*
Jennifer Jones 16,82*	Melanie Lynch 37,83,88*
Maureen Alger 38,69,79*	Stephen Rafferty 60*
Dr Dean Hathaway 67	Zachary Miller 73*
Nancy Haws 295*	

Public Schs..Principal	Grd	Prgm	Enr/#Cls	SN	
De Ruyter Elem Sch 711 Railroad St, De Ruyter 13052 Jenny Valente	PK-5	T	164	53%	315/852-3400
De Ruyter Middle High Sch 711 Railroad St, De Ruyter 13052 Stephen Rafferty	6-12	T	190 35	55%	315/852-3400

- **Hamilton Central Sch Dist** PID: 00731156   315/824-6300
  47 W Kendrick Ave, Hamilton 13346   Fax 315/824-6314

Schools: 1 \ **Teachers:** 52 \ **Students:** 588 \ **Special Ed Students:** 100 \ **LEP Students:** 9 \ **College-Bound:** 78% \ **Ethnic:** Asian 3%, African American 1%, Hispanic 2%, Caucasian 94% \ **Exp:** $247 (Med) \ **Poverty:** 9% \ **Title I:** $68,169 \ **Special Education:** $737,000 \ **Open-Close:** 09/07 - 06/22 \ **DTBP:** $167 (High)

William Dowsland 1	Matthew Crumb 2,11
Craig Schick 3*	Andrea Cass 4*
Lorna Simchik 5	Lauren Reynolds 6
Kevin Ellis 8,79*	Mary Walker 11,58,77
Amy Jerome 16*	Jessica Barnum 36*
Michelle Jacobsen 67	Christopher Rogers 73

Public Schs..Principal	Grd	Prgm	Enr/#Cls	SN	
Hamilton Central Sch 47 W Kendrick Ave, Hamilton 13346 Mark Arquiett \ Kevin Ellis	PK-12	T	588 100	27%	315/824-6300

- **Madison Central School Dist** PID: 00731170   315/893-1878
  7303 State Route 20, Madison 13402   Fax 315/893-7111

Schools: 1 \ **Teachers:** 43 \ **Students:** 450 \ **Special Ed Students:** 69 \ **LEP Students:** 3 \ **College-Bound:** 71% \ **Ethnic:** Caucasian 99% \ **Exp:** $128 (Low) \ **Poverty:** 16% \ **Title I:** $157,497 \ **Special Education:** $812,000 \ **Open-Close:** 09/08 - 06/25 \ **DTBP:** $387 (High)

Jason Mitchell 1,11,83	Melanie Brouillette 2,19,97
Chris Post 3	William Cotter 4
Jeff Peters Haduke 5	Michael Lee 6,27,31,36,77,79,88
Lindsey Gallagher 7*	Jennifer LaVoie 67

Public Schs..Principal	Grd	Prgm	Enr/#Cls	SN	
Madison Central Sch 7303 State Route 20, Madison 13402 Brian Latella \ Larry Nichols	PK-12	T	450 40	53%	315/893-1878

- **Morrisville Eaton Central SD** PID: 00731211   315/684-9300
  5061 Fearon Road, Morrisville 13408   Fax 315/684-9399

Schools: 2 \ **Teachers:** 59 \ **Students:** 621 \ **Special Ed Students:** 123 \ **LEP Students:** 3 \ **College-Bound:** 66% \ **Ethnic:** Asian 1%, African American 1%, Hispanic 1%, Caucasian 97% \ **Exp:** $344 (High) \ **Poverty:** 13% \ **Title I:** $148,903 \ **Special Education:** $1,093,000 \ **Open-Close:** 09/08 - 06/25 \ **DTBP:** $328 (High)

Gregory Molloy 1	Elizabeth Wise 16*
Janine Anderalli 38*	Michelle Cesta 38*
Bryan Fairbrother 58,76,275	Nichole Doroshenko 67
Joseph Willis 73,295*	

Public Schs..Principal	Grd	Prgm	Enr/#Cls	SN	
Edward R Andrews Elem Sch 55 Eaton St, Morrisville 13408 Edward Waskiewicz	PK-5	T	281 33	58%	315/684-9288 Fax 315/684-7252
Morrisville-Eaton Middle HS 5061 Fearon Road, Morrisville 13408 Tracy Durkee	6-12	TV	340 35	49%	315/684-9121 Fax 315/684-7033

- **Oneida City School Dist** PID: 00731247   315/363-2550
  565 Sayles St, Oneida 13421   Fax 315/363-6728

Schools: 6 \ **Teachers:** 162 \ **Students:** 2,000 \ **Special Ed Students:** 400 \ **LEP Students:** 18 \ **College-Bound:** 71% \ **Ethnic:** Asian 1%, African American 1%, Hispanic 2%, Native American: 3%, Caucasian 92% \ **Exp:** $217 (Med) \ **Poverty:** 19% \ **Title I:** $802,711 \ **Special Education:** $3,644,000 \ **Open-Close:** 09/04 - 06/25 \ **DTBP:** $435 (High)

Mary-Margaret Zehr 1	James Rowley 2,15,79
Tanya Moore 2	Bernie Sharlette 3
Hollie Ackerman 4	Mike Klenotiz 5
Stacey Tice 6*	Eric Coriale 7*
Jessica Poyer 8,11,57,69,83,275,298	Marjorie Hawthorne 23*
Erica Hagerty 31,36	Peter Gleason 58,77
Robert Group 67	Genevieve Brauner 73,91
Matt Majewski 295	

Public Schs..Principal	Grd	Prgm	Enr/#Cls	SN	
Durhamville Elem Sch 5462 Main St, Durhamville 13054 Danielle Mullen	K-5	T	248 20	55%	315/363-8065 Fax 315/366-0615
North Broad Street Elem Sch 230 N Broad St, Oneida 13421 Eric Coriale	K-5	T	229 14	70%	315/363-3650 Fax 315/366-0617
Oneida High Sch 560 Seneca St, Oneida 13421 Kathy Davis	9-12	T	592 46	41%	315/363-6901 Fax 315/366-0619
Otto L Shortell Middle Sch 200 Markell Dr, Wampsville 13163 Todd Widrick	6-8	T	435 30	53%	315/363-1050 Fax 315/366-0622
Seneca Street Elem Sch 436 Seneca St, Oneida 13421 Penny Houser	K-5	T	201 14	39%	315/363-3930 Fax 315/366-0618
Willard Prior Elem Sch 205 East Ave, Oneida 13421 Moira Yardley	PK-5	T	231 17	58%	315/363-2190 Fax 315/366-0616

---

79 Student Personnel	91 Safety/Security	275 Response To Intervention	298 Grant Writer/Ptnrships	**School Programs**
80 Driver Ed/Safety	92 Magnet School	277 Remedial Math K-12	750 Chief Innovation Officer	A = Alternative Program
81 Gifted/Talented	93 Parental Involvement	280 Literacy Coach	751 Chief of Staff	G = Adult Classes
82 Video Services	95 Tech Prep Program	285 STEM	752 Social Emotional Learning	M = Magnet Program
83 Substance Abuse Prev	97 Chief Information Officer	286 Digital Learning		T = Title I Schoolwide
84 Erate	98 Chief Technology Officer	288 Common Core Standards	**Other School Types**	V = Career & Tech Ed Programs
85 AIDS Education	270 Character Education	294 Accountability	Ⓐ = Alternative School	
88 Alternative/At Risk	271 Migrant Education	295 Network System	Ⓒ = Charter School	**New Schools are shaded**
89 Multi-Cultural Curriculum	273 Teacher Mentor	296 Title II Programs	Ⓜ = Magnet School	**New Superintendents and Principals are bold**
90 Social Work	274 Before/After Sch	297 Webmaster	Ⓨ = Year-Round School	Personnel with email addresses are underscored

Social Media
- Facebook
- Twitter

NY—105

Monroe County

Market Data Retrieval

- **Stockbridge Valley Central SD** PID: 00731338   315/495-4400
  6011 Williams Rd, Munnsville 13409   Fax 315/495-1901

> **Schools:** 1 \ **Teachers:** 41 \ **Students:** 460 \ **Special Ed Students:** 58 \
> **LEP Students:** 3 \ **College-Bound:** 73% \ **Ethnic:** Hispanic 2%, Native American: 2%, Caucasian 95% \ **Exp:** $249 (Med) \ **Poverty:** 12% \
> **Title I:** $89,738 \ **Special Education:** $958,000 \ **Open-Close:** 09/04 - 06/25 \ **DTBP:** $377 (High)

Cynthia Stocker 1
Melissa Grogan 3,16,72
Brian Leach 5
Cassandra Gleason 36,69,88*
Julie Suber 57,72,270,274,288*
Robert Healy 273*
Beth Lamb 2,11,91,271,296
Kathy Carney 4*
Jay Lehmann 6,35,83,85
Barbara Holmes 51,54*
Barbary Reaves 67
Andrea Panoni 295,752

Public Schs..Principal	Grd	Prgm	Enr/#Cls	SN	
Stockbridge Valley Ctl Sch 6011 Williams Rd, Munnsville 13409 Jon Kilian \ Julie Suber	K-12	TV	460 32	51%	315/495-4400

MADISON CATHOLIC SCHOOLS

- **Diocese of Syracuse Ed Office** PID: 00762765
  Listing includes only schools located in this county. See District Index for location of Diocesan Offices.

Catholic Schs..Principal	Grd	Prgm	Enr/#Cls	SN	
St Patrick Sch 354 Elizabeth St, Oneida 13421 Kristin Healt	PK-6		110 7		315/363-3620 Fax 315/363-5075

MADISON PRIVATE SCHOOLS

Private Schs..Principal	Grd	Prgm	Enr/#Cls	SN	
Holy Cross Academy 4020 Barrington Rd, Oneida 13421 Therese Maciag	7-12		94 8		315/363-1669 Fax 315/280-6715
New Life Christian Sch 1528 River Rd, Hamilton 13346 Todd Slabaugh	PK-12		85 13		315/824-2625 Fax 315/824-5102

MONROE COUNTY

MONROE COUNTY SCHOOLS

County Schs..Principal	Grd	Prgm	Enr/#Cls	SN	
BOCES 2 Pre-School 3599 Big Ridge Rd, Spencerport 14559 Heather Malone	Spec		130 3	20%	585/352-2400 Fax 585/352-2756
Eastern Monroe Career Center 41 Oconnor Rd, Fairport 14450 Michael Ehret	Voc	AG	555 47		585/377-4660 Fax 585/387-3800
Lois E Bird Elem Sch 108 East Ave, E Rochester 14445 Ellen Howe	Spec		160 30		585/586-1850 Fax 585/385-5805
Monroe 1 Special Education Ctr 41 Oconnor Rd, Fairport 14450 Cheri Becker	Spec	AG	1,500	19%	585/383-2234 Fax 585/383-6446
Morgan Sch 120 East Ave, E Rochester 14445 Ellen Howe	Spec		110 33		585/586-1850 Fax 585/385-5805
Oconnor Academy-Monroe 1 BOCES 25 Oconnor Rd, Fairport 14450 Bonnie Masiuk	9-12		100		585/383-6670 Fax 585/387-3836
Wemoco BOCES-Career Tech Ctr 3589 Big Ridge Rd, Spencerport 14559 Jill Slaveny	Voc	AG	1,100 28		585/352-2471 Fax 585/352-0756

MONROE PUBLIC SCHOOLS

- **Brighton Central School Dist** PID: 00731352   585/242-5200
  2035 Monroe Ave, Rochester 14618   Fax 585/242-5212

> **Schools:** 4 \ **Teachers:** 321 \ **Students:** 3,518 \ **Special Ed Students:** 620 \ **LEP Students:** 159 \ **College-Bound:** 84% \ **Ethnic:** Asian 12%, African American 8%, Hispanic 7%, Caucasian 74% \ **Exp:** $225 (Med) \ **Poverty:** 6% \ **Title I:** $336,099 \ **Special Education:** $3,976,000 \ **Open-Close:** 09/09 - 06/24 \ **DTBP:** $316 (High)

Dr Kevin McGowan 1
Robert Luce 3*
Tom Hyman 5*
Carolyn Rabidoux 7,58,79,83,85
Mona Zamiarski 30
Lisa Hartman 68
Nadine Dykes 82
John McCabe 91*
Louis Alaimo 2,15,68
Nicole Vandermeid 4
Nate Merritt 6,35,85*
Dr Deborah Baker 8,11,57,81,286,288
Mark Kokanovich 67
Eric Jordan 73
Debbie Appleton 88

Public Schs..Principal	Grd	Prgm	Enr/#Cls	SN	
Brighton High Sch 1150 Winton Rd S, Rochester 14618 Thomas Hall	9-12	GV	1,199 130	20%	585/242-5000 Fax 585/242-7364
Council Rock Primary Sch 600 Grosvenor Rd, Rochester 14610 Matthew Tappon	K-2		632 32	17%	585/242-5170 Fax 585/242-5186
French Road Elem Sch 488 French Rd, Rochester 14618 Allison Rioux	3-5	T	786 36	21%	585/242-5140 Fax 585/242-5156
Twelve Corners Middle Sch 2643 Elmwood Ave, Rochester 14618 Rob Thomas	6-8	GV	901 100	19%	585/242-5100 Fax 585/242-2540

- **Brockport Ctl School Dist** PID: 00731429   585/637-5303
  40 Allen St, Brockport 14420   Fax 585/637-0165

> **Schools:** 5 \ **Teachers:** 296 \ **Students:** 3,562 \ **Special Ed Students:** 569 \ **LEP Students:** 54 \ **College-Bound:** 72% \ **Ethnic:** Asian 1%, African American 4%, Hispanic 10%, Caucasian 84% \ **Exp:** $202 (Med) \
> **Poverty:** 11% \ **Title I:** $599,936 \ **Special Education:** $8,326,000 \
> **Open-Close:** 09/03 - 06/23 \ **DTBP:** $326 (High) \

Sean Bruno 1
Jill Reichhart 2
Milton Waye 5
Lynn Carragher 8,36
Dr Rachael Kluth 10
Paulette Reddick 58
Diane Heed 68
Anthony Smith 73
Brian Lippold 295
Darrin Winkley 2,15
Christian Hansen 3
Todd Hagreen 6,35*
Susan Curtis 9
Jerilee DiLalla 15,68
Terry Ann Carbone 67
Erika Wood 68
Jeffery Phillips 91
Wayne Rickman 295

1	Superintendent	8	Curric/Instruct K-12	19	Chief Financial Officer	29	Family/Consumer Science
2	Bus/Finance/Purchasing	9	Curric/Instruct Elem	20	Art K-12	30	Adult Education
3	Buildings And Grounds	10	Curric/Instruct Sec	21	Art Elem	31	Career/Sch-to-Work K-12
4	Food Service	11	Federal Program	22	Art Sec	32	Career/Sch-to-Work Elem
5	Transportation	12	Title I	23	Music K-12	33	Career/Sch-to-Work Sec
6	Athletic	13	Title V	24	Music Elem	34	Early Childhood Ed
7	Health Services	14	Instructional Media Svcs	25	Music Sec	35	Health/Phys Education
		15	Asst Superintendent	26	Business Education	36	Guidance Services K-12
		16	Instructional Media Svcs	27	Career & Tech Ed	37	Guidance Services Elem
		17	Chief Operations Officer	28	Technology Education	38	Guidance Services Sec
		18	Chief Academic Officer				

39	Social Studies K-12	49	English/Lang Arts Elem	59	Special Education Elem	69	Academic Assessment
40	Social Studies Elem	50	English/Lang Arts Sec	60	Special Education Sec	70	Research/Development
41	Social Studies Sec	51	Reading K-12	61	Foreign/World Lang K-12	71	Public Information
42	Science K-12	52	Reading Elem	62	Foreign/World Lang Elem	72	Summer School
43	Science Elem	53	Reading Sec	63	Foreign/World Lang Sec	73	Instructional Tech
44	Science Sec	54	Remedial Reading K-12	64	Religious Education K-12	74	Inservice Training
45	Math K-12	55	Remedial Reading Elem	65	Religious Education Elem	75	Marketing/Distributive
46	Math Elem	56	Remedial Reading Sec	66	Religious Education Sec	76	Info Systems
47	Math Sec	57	Bilingual/ELL	67	School Board President	77	Psychological Assess
48	English/Lang Arts K-12	58	Special Education K-12	68	Teacher Personnel	78	Affirmative Action

New York School Directory — Monroe County

Public Schs..Principal	Grd	Prgm	Enr/#Cls	SN	
A D Oliver Middle Sch 40 Allen St, Brockport 14420 Jerrod Roberts	6-8	T	739	46%	585/637-1860 Fax 585/637-1869
Barclay Elem Sch 40 Allen St, Brockport 14420 Scott Morrison	2-3	T	462 24	46%	585/637-1840 Fax 585/637-1845 t
Brockport High Sch 40 Allen St, Brockport 14420 Melody Davis	9-12	V	1,021 80	38%	585/637-1870 Fax 585/637-1867
Fred W Hill Elem Sch 40 Allen St, Brockport 14420 Brandon Broughton	4-5	T	491 31	43%	585/637-1850 Fax 585/637-1855
Ginther Elem Sch 40 Allen St, Brockport 14420 Debra Waye	PK-1	T	576 27	34%	585/637-1830 Fax 585/637-1835

- **Churchville Chili Ctl Sch Dist** PID: 00731479 585/293-1800
  139 Fairbanks Rd, Churchville 14428 Fax 585/293-1013

Schools: 6 \ **Teachers:** 306 \ **Students:** 3,900 \ **Special Ed Students:** 520 \ **LEP Students:** 54 \ **College-Bound:** 80% \ **Ethnic:** Asian 2%, African American 8%, Hispanic 7%, Caucasian 83% \ **Exp:** $286 (Med) \ **Poverty:** 8% \ **Title I:** $493,543 \ **Special Education:** $8,284,000 \ **Open-Close:** 09/10 - 06/24 \ **DTBP:** $230 (High)

Lori Orologio 1	Frank Nardone 2,15
Nancy Sucy 2	Joseph Valenti 3
Roberta D'Agostino 4	Renee Hensel 5,16,88,273,274
Michael Murray 6,35,85	Larry Vito 7,11,15,68,294
Giulio Bosco 8,11,15,16,74,88,273,274*	Susan Witter 8,57,69,74,275,280,285,288
Jeffrey Smith 20,23	Kelley Fahy 27,31,95*
Derek Vandenhandel 28,73,76	Wendy Reese 30
Nicole Neal 34,36,77,79,81,270	Karen Coykendall 58
Dr Cheryl Repass 67	Amanda Puleo 71,82
Tracie Swalbach 83*	William Sanborn 91
Megan Hugg 286	Joseph Harmon 295

Public Schs..Principal	Grd	Prgm	Enr/#Cls	SN	
Chestnut Ridge Elem Sch 3560 Chili Ave, Rochester 14624 Kimberly Hale	K-4		516 30	34%	585/889-2188 Fax 585/293-4512
Churchville Chili High Sch 5786 Buffalo Rd, Churchville 14428 Scott Wilson	10-12	GV	953 115	30%	585/293-4540 Fax 585/293-4556
Churchville Chili Middle Sch 139 Fairbanks Rd, Churchville 14428 Carl Christensen	5-8		1,173 51	31%	585/293-4542 Fax 585/293-4516
Churchville Elem Sch 36 W Buffalo St, Churchville 14428 David Johnson	K-4	T	381 27	41%	585/293-2022 Fax 585/293-4504
Fairbanks Road Elem Sch 175 Fairbanks Rd, Churchville 14428 Todd Yunker	K-4		485 26	22%	585/293-4543 Fax 585/293-4510
Ninth Grade Academy 137 Fairbanks Rd, Churchville 14428 Mary Leach	9-9		315		585/293-4546 Fax 585/293-4521

- **East Irondequoit Ctl Sch Dist** PID: 00731534 585/339-1200
  600 Pardee Rd, Rochester 14609 Fax 585/288-0713

Schools: 6 \ **Teachers:** 270 \ **Students:** 3,000 \ **Special Ed Students:** 435 \ **LEP Students:** 142 \ **College-Bound:** 78% \ **Ethnic:** Asian 2%, African American 23%, Hispanic 25%, Caucasian 50% \ **Exp:** $326 (High) \ **Poverty:** 17% \ **Title I:** $991,121 \ **Special Education:** $5,630,000 \ **Open-Close:** 09/08 - 06/23 \ **DTBP:** $895 (High) \ f t

Mary Grow 1,11,57	John Abbott 2,15
Michael Mamo 3,91	Laurel Presher 4
Kathy Callon 5	Robert Crocetti 6*
Mark Anson 8,15	Terri Robson 9,46,49,52,280
Cheryl Dobbertin 10	Philip Oberst 15,68,74,78
Brian Smith 16,82*	Doreen Goossen 36,88*
Kim Lasher 67	David Yates 71
Christine Osadciw 73,97,286	Mark Christman 76,294
Jim Vallone 79	Lesley Powers 79

Public Schs..Principal	Grd	Prgm	Enr/#Cls	SN	
Durand Eastman Interm Sch 95 Point Pleasant Rd, Rochester 14622 Tim Roach	3-5	T	359 28	66%	585/339-1350 Fax 585/339-1359
East Irondequoit Middle Sch 155 Densmore Rd, Rochester 14609 Lori Garsin	6-8	T	663 25	64%	585/339-1400 Fax 585/339-1409
Eastridge High Sch 2350 E Ridge Rd, Rochester 14622 Timothy Heaphy	9-12	AG	940 60	58%	585/339-1450 Fax 585/339-1459
Helendale Road Primary Sch 220 Helendale Rd, Rochester 14609 Eric Daniels	PK-2		315 19	56%	585/339-1330 Fax 585/339-1339
Ivan Green Primary Sch 800 Brown Rd, Rochester 14622 Teralyn Strauss	PK-2	T	434 23	62%	585/339-1310 Fax 585/339-1319
Laurelton Pardee Interm Sch 600 Pardee Rd, Rochester 14609 Lucas Hiley	3-5	T	328 16	61%	585/339-1370 Fax 585/339-1379

- **East Rochester Union Free SD** PID: 00731625 585/248-6302
  222 Woodbine Ave, E Rochester 14445 Fax 585/586-3254

Schools: 2 \ **Teachers:** 103 \ **Students:** 1,007 \ **Special Ed Students:** 217 \ **LEP Students:** 13 \ **Ethnic:** African American 8%, Hispanic 13%, Native American: 1%, Caucasian 78% \ **Exp:** $309 (High) \ **Poverty:** 15% \ **Title I:** $356,898 \ **Special Education:** $2,621,000 \ **Open-Close:** 09/10 - 06/18 \ **DTBP:** $180 (High)

James Haugh 1	Sarah Calahan 2,8,11,57
Stacy Sansoucie 2	Dave Green 3,5
Nicole Van Dermeid 4	Jeffrey Onze 6,7
Julie Colvin 7	Monica Stadler 13,58,79,752
Dan O'Leary 31,77*	Bill Kelleher 36,83,85*
Jennifer Lesinski 67	David Rovitolli 73,88,286*

Public Schs..Principal	Grd	Prgm	Enr/#Cls	SN	
East Rochester Elem Sch 400 Woodbine Ave, E Rochester 14445 Marisa Capuano	PK-5	T	495 40	37%	585/248-6342 Fax 585/248-6318
East Rochester High Sch 200 Woodbine Ave, E Rochester 14445 Casey Van Harssel	6-12	V	512	47%	585/248-6350 Fax 585/248-6383

---

79 Student Personnel	91 Safety/Security	275 Response To Intervention	298 Grant Writer/Ptnrships	**School Programs**	**Social Media**
80 Driver Ed/Safety	92 Magnet School	277 Remedial Math K-12	750 Chief Innovation Officer	A = Alternative Program	f = Facebook
81 Gifted/Talented	93 Parental Involvement	280 Literacy Coach	751 Chief of Staff	G = Adult Classes	t = Twitter
82 Video Services	95 Tech Prep Program	285 STEM	752 Social Emotional Learning	M = Magnet Program	
83 Substance Abuse Prev	97 Chief Information Officer	286 Digital Learning		T = Title I Schoolwide	
84 Erate	98 Chief Technology Officer	288 Common Core Standards	**Other School Types**	V = Career & Tech Ed Programs	
85 AIDS Education	270 Character Education	294 Accountability	Ⓐ = Alternative School		
88 Alternative/At Risk	271 Migrant Education	295 Network System	Ⓒ = Charter School	New Schools are shaded	
89 Multi-Cultural Curriculum	273 Teacher Mentor	296 Title II Programs	Ⓜ = Magnet School	New Superintendents and Principals are bold	
90 Social Work	274 Before/After Sch	297 Webmaster	Ⓨ = Year-Round School	Personnel with email addresses are underscored	

Monroe County
Market Data Retrieval

- **Fairport Ctl School Dist** PID: 00731663   585/421-2000
  38 W Church St, Fairport 14450   Fax 585/421-3421

Schools: 8 \ **Teachers:** 439 \ **Students:** 5,900 \ **Special Ed Students:** 807 \ **LEP Students:** 134 \ **College-Bound:** 85% \ **Ethnic:** Asian 3%, African American 4%, Hispanic 4%, Caucasian 89% \ **Exp:** $202 (Med) \ **Poverty:** 6% \ **Title I:** $599,887 \ **Special Education:** $10,814,000 \ **Open-Close:** 09/08 - 06/25 \ **DTBP:** $310 (High)

Brett Provenzano 1	Matthew Stevens 2,15,91
Monica Shannon 2	Debra Tandoi 3
Ross Ciulla 3	Michele Resavage 4*
Peter Lawrence 5	Fritz Kilian 6,35
Deborah Miles 7,11,36,77,79,85,270*	Kerstin Wheeler 8,15*
Douglas Lauf 15,68,78	Tom Devitt 16,73,82,295*
Kristin Larsen 27,42,45	Ellen Reed 48
Dennis Des Rosiers 58*	Susan Walz 58
Peter Forsgren 67	Christina Lewis Gursslin 71
Kevin Henchen 74	

Public Schs..Principal	Grd	Prgm	Enr/#Cls	SN	
Brooks Hill Elem Sch 181 Hulburt Rd, Fairport 14450 Meredith Klus	K-5		635 38	24%	585/421-2170 Fax 585/421-2173
Dudley Elem Sch 211 Hamilton Rd, Fairport 14450 Karen Fingar	K-2		620 35	21%	585/421-2155 Fax 585/421-2328
Fairport High Sch 1 Dave Paddock Way, Fairport 14450 Robert Clark	10-12	AV	1,363	20%	585/421-2100 Fax 585/421-4645
Jefferson Avenue Elem Sch 303 Jefferson Ave, Fairport 14450 Richard Greene	K-5		632 34	17%	585/421-2185 Fax 585/377-3320
Johanna Perrin Middle Sch 85 Potter Pl, Fairport 14450 Patrick Grow	6-8	V	618 50	21%	585/421-2080 Fax 585/421-2097
Martha Brown Middle Sch 665 Ayrault Rd, Fairport 14450 David Dunn	6-8	V	726	21%	585/421-2065 Fax 585/421-2136
Minerva Deland Sch 140 Hulburt Rd, Fairport 14450 Pam Ciranni	9-9	A	438 37	24%	585/421-2030 Fax 585/421-1985
Northside Elem Sch 181 Hamilton Rd, Fairport 14450 Erin Moretter	3-5		654 38	25%	585/421-2140 Fax 585/421-2162

- **Gates Chili Central Sch Dist** PID: 00731766   585/247-5050
  3 Spartan Way, Rochester 14624   Fax 585/340-5569

Schools: 6 \ **Teachers:** 357 \ **Students:** 4,000 \ **Special Ed Students:** 702 \ **LEP Students:** 176 \ **College-Bound:** 76% \ **Ethnic:** Asian 6%, African American 18%, Hispanic 14%, Caucasian 61% \ **Exp:** $337 (High) \ **Poverty:** 13% \ **Title I:** $842,568 \ **Special Education:** $10,717,000 \ **Open-Close:** 09/09 - 06/25 \ **DTBP:** $330 (High)

Christopher Dailey 1	Mitchell Ball 2,15
Sally Sanford 2	George English 3
Janice Phillips 4	Matthew Helmbold 5
Patrick Irving 6,35	Jacqueline Dennison 7
Katie Coon 8,23	Carol Stern 11
Michaela Perrotto 12,15,68	Phillip Jay 16,295
Marla Chefalo 30	Erin Ugine 34
Danielle Latore 59	Julie Stark 60
Jeffrey Pettenski 67	Chantal Zambito 69,76
Troy Olin 73	Suzanne Goff 74
Angelina Pound 79,93	Jason De Jong 79,83
John Sodeman 91	

Public Schs..Principal	Grd	Prgm	Enr/#Cls	SN	
Florence Brasser Elem Sch 1000 Chili Center Coldwater Rd, Rochester 14624 Timothy Young	PK-5		402 15	44%	585/247-1880 Fax 585/340-5577
Gates Chili High Sch 1 Spartan Way, Rochester 14624 Kenneth Hammel	9-12	G	1,306 100	47%	585/247-5050 Fax 585/340-5518
Gates Chili Middle Sch 2 Spartan Way, Rochester 14624 Lisa Buckshaw	6-8		829 60	53%	585/247-5050 Fax 585/340-5532
Neil Armstrong Elem Sch 3273 Lyell Rd, Rochester 14606 Lisa McGary	PK-5	T	450 30	63%	585/247-3190 Fax 585/340-5550
Paul Road Elem Sch 571 Paul Rd, Rochester 14624 Peter Hens	PK-5		421 29	43%	585/247-2144 Fax 585/340-5571
Walt Disney Elem Sch 175 Coldwater Rd, Rochester 14624 Elaine Damelio	PK-5	T	451 27	54%	585/247-3151 Fax 585/340-5567

- **Greece Central School Dist** PID: 00731869   585/621-1000
  750 Maiden Ln, Rochester 14615   Fax 585/581-8145

Schools: 17 \ **Teachers:** 925 \ **Students:** 10,700 \ **Special Ed Students:** 1,681 \ **LEP Students:** 449 \ **College-Bound:** 71% \ **Ethnic:** Asian 4%, African American 16%, Hispanic 16%, Caucasian 64% \ **Exp:** $208 (Med) \ **Poverty:** 14% \ **Title I:** $3,116,788 \ **Special Education:** $19,134,000 \ **Open-Close:** 09/09 - 06/25 \ **DTBP:** $226 (High)

Kathleen Graupman 1	Jeanine Cushman 2
Paul Palmer 2	Chris Luther 3
Robert Linton 3	Philip Levey 4
Craig Banner 5	Mary Perrello 7
Norma Vetter 8	Dr Valerie Paine 9,11,15
Katryn Colicchio 10,15,79,294	Elizabeth Bentley 15,68
Michael Zaffuts 15	John Klein 23*
Kathleen Richardson 27	Nicole Viggiano 30,274
Edel Maeder 42	Todd Smith 45,275
Suzanne Pettifer 51,275	Annamaria Falzarano 57,61
Christine Baker 58	Emily Lathers 58
Lori Ruggeri 58	Melanie Stevenson 58
Sean McCabe 67	Elizabeth Camp 68
Julie Zink 68	Jeremy Smalline 70,79
Laurel Heiden 71	Thomas Mariano 71,73,286
Marguerite Dimgba 74	Keena Smith 76
Stacey Brindisi 79	Stephanie Rago 83
John Henderson 91	Steven Chatterton 91
Todd Prince 91	Andrew Thibault 295
Brian Palmer 295	Frank Porcella 295
Raymond Molyneux 295	Thomas Jenkins 295

Public Schs..Principal	Grd	Prgm	Enr/#Cls	SN	
Arcadia High Sch 120 Island Cottage Rd, Rochester 14612 Gina Larsen	9-12	GV	1,086	54%	585/966-3000 Fax 585/966-3039
Arcadia Middle Sch 130 Island Cottage Rd, Rochester 14612 Brian Lumb	6-8	T	756 40	59%	585/966-3300 Fax 585/966-3339
Athena High Sch 800 Long Pond Rd, Rochester 14612 Kelly Flagler	9-12	GV	1,104 75	48%	585/966-4000 Fax 585/966-4039
Athena Middle Sch 800 Long Pond Rd, Rochester 14612 Jason Fulkerson	6-8	V	789	48%	585/966-8800 Fax 585/966-4239
Autumn Lane Elem Sch 2089 Maiden Ln, Rochester 14626 Michael Ferris	PK-2		380 23	47%	585/966-4700 Fax 585/966-4739

1 Superintendent	8 Curric/Instruct K-12	19 Chief Financial Officer	29 Family/Consumer Science	39 Social Studies K-12	49 English/Lang Arts Elem	59 Special Education Elem	69 Academic Assessment
2 Bus/Finance/Purchasing	9 Curric/Instruct Elem	20 Art K-12	30 Adult Education	40 Social Studies Elem	50 English/Lang Arts Sec	60 Special Education Sec	70 Research/Development
3 Buildings And Grounds	10 Curric/Instruct Sec	21 Art Elem	31 Career/Sch-to-Work K-12	41 Social Studies Sec	51 Reading K-12	61 Foreign/World Lang K-12	71 Public Information
4 Food Service	11 Federal Program	22 Art Sec	32 Career/Sch-to-Work Elem	42 Science K-12	52 Reading Elem	62 Foreign/World Lang Elem	72 Summer School
5 Transportation	12 Title I	23 Music K-12	33 Career/Sch-to-Work Sec	43 Science Elem	53 Reading Sec	63 Foreign/World Lang Sec	73 Instructional Tech
6 Athletic	13 Title V	24 Music Elem	34 Early Childhood Ed	44 Science Sec	54 Remedial Reading K-12	64 Religious Education K-12	74 Inservice Training
7 Health Services	14 Asst Superintendent	25 Music Sec	35 Health/Phys Education	45 Math K-12	55 Remedial Reading Elem	65 Religious Education Elem	75 Marketing/Distributive
	15 Instructional Media Svcs	26 Business Education	36 Guidance Services K-12	46 Math Elem	56 Remedial Reading Sec	66 Religious Education Sec	76 Info Systems
	16 Chief Operations Officer	27 Career & Tech Ed	37 Guidance Services Elem	47 Math Sec	57 Bilingual/ELL	67 School Board President	77 Psychological Assess
	18 Chief Academic Officer	28 Technology Education	38 Guidance Services Sec	48 English/Lang Arts K-12	58 Special Education K-12	68 Teacher Personnel	78 Affirmative Action

New York School Directory

Monroe County

School	Grd	Prgm	Enr/#Cls	SN	Phone
Brookside Elem Sch 1144 Long Pond Rd, Rochester 14626 Anthony Reale	K-5		371 16	48%	585/966-4800 Fax 585/966-4839
Buckman Heights Elem Sch 550 Buckman Rd, Rochester 14615 Anitra Huchzermeier	3-5	T	373 20	63%	585/966-5900 Fax 585/966-5939
Craig Hill Elem Sch 320 W Craig Hill Dr, Rochester 14626 Melissa Pacelli	3-5	T	318 23	54%	585/966-4500 Fax 585/966-4539 FT
English Village Elem Sch 800 Tait Ave, Rochester 14616 Jason Lewis	PK-2	T	469 21	61%	585/966-3800 Fax 585/966-3839
Holmes Road Elem Sch 300 Holmes Rd, Rochester 14626 Kristin Tsang	PK-2	T	407 15	56%	585/966-4900 Fax 585/966-4939 FT
Lakeshore Elem Sch 1200 Latta Rd, Rochester 14612 James Palermo	3-5	T	450 17	65%	585/966-3900 Fax 585/966-3939 F
Longridge Elem Sch 190 Longridge Ave, Rochester 14616 Jason Juszczak	K-5	T	792 50	64%	585/966-5800 Fax 585/966-5839 F
Odyssey Academy 750 Maiden Ln, Rochester 14615 Jeff Henley	6-12	TV	1,001	61%	585/966-5200 Fax 585/966-5239 FT
Olympia High Sch 1139 Maiden Ln, Rochester 14615 Marc Fleming	6-12	GTV	1,092 80	67%	585/966-5000 Fax 585/966-5039
Paddy Hill Elem Sch 1801 Latta Rd, Rochester 14612 Michelle Barton	K-5		558 21	37%	585/966-3700 Fax 585/966-3739
Pine Brook Elem Sch 2300 English Rd, Rochester 14616 Elizabeth Boily	K-5		545 25	33%	585/966-4600 Fax 585/966-4639
West Ridge Elem Sch 1010 English Rd, Rochester 14616 Shannon Heller	PK-5	T	288 18	75%	585/966-3600 Fax 585/966-3639

● **Hilton Central School Dist** PID: 00732069 585/392-1000
225 West Ave, Hilton 14468

Schools: 5 \ **Teachers:** 354 \ **Students:** 4,482 \ **Special Ed Students:** 541 \ **LEP Students:** 34 \ **Ethnic:** Asian 1%, African American 3%, Hispanic 6%, Caucasian 91% \ **Exp:** $190 (Low) \ **Poverty:** 6% \ **Title I:** $444,844 \ **Special Education:** $6,479,000 \ **Open-Close:** 09/09 - 06/24 \ **DTBP:** $324 (High) \ F T

Dr Casey Kosiorek	1	Jeremy Nardone	2
Adam Norton	3	Mark Edwards	3
Scott Ziobrowski	4*	Joe LaMarca	5
Kim Phillips	5	Lori Palermo	5
Michael Giruzzi	6,35*	Dr Barbara Surash	8,11,15,69,286,288
Adam Geist	15	Scott Massie	15,68,78
Laura Whitcomb	58,79	Mark Hilburger	67
Karon Spillman	70*	Grace Scism	71,297
John Miller	73,286	David Inzana	91
Josh Ennis	295		

Public Schs..Principal	Grd	Prgm	Enr/#Cls	SN	Phone
Hilton High Sch 400 East Ave, Hilton 14468 Dr Jeffrey Green	9-12	AGV	1,450 90	26%	585/392-1000 Fax 585/392-1052
Merton Williams Middle Sch 200 School Ln, Hilton 14468 Tracie Czebatol	7-8	G	692 60	29%	585/392-1000 Fax 585/392-1054
Northwood Elem Sch 433 N Greece Rd, Hilton 14468 Kirk Ashton	K-6	G	824 40	20%	585/392-1000 Fax 585/392-1026
Quest Elem Sch 225 West Ave, Hilton 14468 Derek Warren	PK-6	GT	450 34	24%	585/392-1000 Fax 585/392-1026
Village Elem Sch 100 School Ln, Hilton 14468 Benjamin Rudd	PK-6	G	992 46	37%	585/392-1000 Fax 585/392-1012

● **Honeoye Falls Lima Sch Dist** PID: 00732136 585/624-7000
20 Church St, Honeoye Falls 14472 Fax 585/624-7003

Schools: 4 \ **Teachers:** 176 \ **Students:** 2,122 \ **Special Ed Students:** 306 \ **LEP Students:** 6 \ **College-Bound:** 92% \ **Ethnic:** Asian 2%, African American 1%, Hispanic 3%, Caucasian 94% \ **Exp:** $222 (Med) \ **Poverty:** 9% \ **Title I:** $364,526 \ **Special Education:** $2,847,000 \ **Open-Close:** 09/02 - 06/23 \ **DTBP:** $335 (High) \ T

Gene Mancuso	1	Dr Bruce Capron	2,3,12,15
Cindy Pfeifer	2	Aaron Smith	3
Dana Boldt	4	Bill Harvey	5
Brian Donohue	6,35*	Lindsay Ali	7,34,36,58,79,83,271,275*
Renee Williams	8,11,15,16,74,288,296,298*	Allison Cimmerer	9*
Holly Sidebottom	10,31*	Ari Freedman	30
Carol Bellavia	67	David Leahy	68
Leah Shepard	71	Cindy Gorley	73,76,95,286,295,297*

Public Schs..Principal	Grd	Prgm	Enr/#Cls	SN	Phone
Honeoye Falls Lima High Sch 83 East St, Honeoye Falls 14472 David Roth	9-12	AGTV	713 70	14%	585/624-7050 Fax 585/624-7118
Honeoye Falls Lima Middle Sch 619 Quaker Meeting House Rd, Honeoye Falls 14472 Shawn Williams	6-8	AT	510 42	18%	585/624-7100 Fax 585/624-7121
Lima Primary Sch 7342 College St, Lima 14485 Allison Cimmerer	K-1	T	290 16	15%	585/624-7140 Fax 585/624-7155
Manor Intermediate Sch 147 East St, Honeoye Falls 14472 Jeanine Lupisella	2-5	T	609 31	20%	585/624-7160 Fax 585/351-6070

● **Penfield Central School Dist** PID: 00732332 585/249-5700
2590 Atlantic Ave, Rochester 14625 Fax 585/248-8412

Schools: 6 \ **Teachers:** 388 \ **Students:** 4,600 \ **Special Ed Students:** 529 \ **LEP Students:** 70 \ **Ethnic:** Asian 3%, African American 4%, Hispanic 5%, Caucasian 87% \ **Exp:** $294 (Med) \ **Poverty:** 4% \ **Title I:** $189,347 \ **Special Education:** $6,168,000 \ **Open-Close:** 09/10 - 06/23 \ **DTBP:** $307 (High)

Tom Putnam	1	Dan Driffill	2
Scott Drechsler	2,15,34,58	Alan McNiff	3,91
Joseph Argento	4*	Peter Shambo	6*
James Peiffer	8,15	Bryan Bricco	23*
Stephanie Dana	38*	Catharine Deen	67
Nancy Bradstreet	71	Jason Delornze	73,295
Barbara Gregory	78		

Public Schs..Principal	Grd	Prgm	Enr/#Cls	SN	Phone
Bay Trail Middle Sch 1760 Scribner Rd, Penfield 14526 Winton Buddington	6-8		1,057 75	22%	585/249-6450 Fax 585/248-0735
Cobbles Elem Sch 140 Gebhardt Rd, Penfield 14526 Stephen Kenny	K-5		558 25	20%	585/249-6500 Fax 585/248-2108
Harris Hill Elem Sch 2126 Penfield Rd, Penfield 14526 Marc Nelson	K-5		436 27	15%	585/249-6600 Fax 585/249-6616

79 Student Personnel	91 Safety/Security	275 Response To Intervention	298 Grant Writer/Ptnrships
80 Driver Ed/Safety	92 Magnet School	277 Remedial Math K-12	750 Chief Innovation Officer
81 Gifted/Talented	93 Parental Involvement	280 Literacy Coach	751 Chief of Staff
82 Video Services	95 Tech Prep Program	285 STEM	752 Social Emotional Learning
83 Substance Abuse Prev	97 Chief Infomation Officer	286 Digital Learning	
84 Erate	98 Chief Technology Officer	288 Common Core Standards	
85 AIDS Education	270 Character Education	294 Accountability	
88 Alternative/At Risk	271 Migrant Education	295 Network System	
89 Multi-Cultural Curriculum	273 Teacher Mentor	296 Title II Programs	
90 Social Work	274 Before/After Sch	297 Webmaster	

School Programs
A = Alternative Program
G = Adult Classes
M = Magnet Program
T = Title I Schoolwide
V = Career & Tech Ed Programs

Other School Types
Ⓐ = Alternative School
Ⓒ = Charter School
Ⓜ = Magnet School
Ⓨ = Year-Round School

Social Media
F = Facebook
T = Twitter

New Schools are shaded
New Superintendents and Principals are bold
Personnel with email addresses are underscored

NY-109

Monroe County

Market Data Retrieval

Indian Landing Elem Sch — K-5 — 565 — 19% — 585/249-6900
702 Landing Rd N, Rochester 14625 — 30 — Fax 585/387-9276
Marcie Ware

Penfield Senior High Sch — 9-12 AV — 1,391 — 20% — 585/249-6700
25 High School Dr, Penfield 14526 — 50 — Fax 585/248-2810
Leslie Maloney

Scribner Road Elem Sch — K-5 — 580 — 16% — 585/249-6400
1750 Scribner Rd, Penfield 14526 — 24 — Fax 585/249-6411
Scott Hirschler

• Pittsford Central Sch Dist PID: 00732423
75 Barker Rd, Pittsford 14534 — 585/267-1000 — Fax 585/267-1088

Schools: 9 \ **Teachers:** 479 \ **Students:** 6,000 \ **Special Ed Students:** 728 \ **LEP Students:** 52 \ **College-Bound:** 95% \ **Ethnic:** Asian 13%, African American 3%, Hispanic 6%, Caucasian 78% \ **Exp:** $231 (Med) \ **Poverty:** 3% \ **Title I:** $177,517 \ **Special Education:** $3,913,000 \ **Open-Close:** 09/08 - 06/25 \ **DTBP:** $315 (High) \ f t

Michael Pero	1,11	Darrin Kenney	2,15	
Holly Evans	2	Leeanne Reister	2	
Daniel Fursman	3	Jeff Beardsley	3,91	
Paulette Vangellow	4*	Kathleen Herrick	5	
Scott Barker	6	Melanie Ward	8,15,288	
Michael Leone	12,15,68	Elizabeth Woods	58*	
Gail Lacek	58	Maria Hill	58	
Amy Thomas	67	Elizabeth Carpenter	68	
Jeff Cimmerer	71,97	Nancy Wayman	71	
Matthew Kwiatkowski	73	Patricia Vaughn Brogan	79	

Public Schs..Principal	Grd	Prgm	Enr/#Cls	SN	
Allen Creek Elem Sch 3188 East Ave, Rochester 14618 Michael Biondi	K-5		318 17	6%	585/267-1200 Fax 585/381-9217 f t
Barker Road Middle Sch 75 Barker Rd, Pittsford 14534 Shana Cutaia	6-8		706 96	2%	585/267-1800 Fax 585/385-5960
Calkins Road Middle Sch 1899 Calkins Rd, Pittsford 14534 Josh Walker	6-8		656	2%	585/267-1900 Fax 585/264-0053 f t
Jefferson Road Elem Sch 15 School Ln, Pittsford 14534 Shawn Clark	K-5		355 22	2%	585/267-1300 Fax 585/385-6426 f t
Mendon Center Elem Sch 110 Mendon Center Rd, Pittsford 14534 Heather Clayton	K-5		784 30	2%	585/267-1400 Fax 585/267-1430 f t
Park Road Elem Sch 50 Park Rd, Pittsford 14534 Mark Balsamo	K-5		419 24	3%	585/267-1500 Fax 585/385-6356 f t
Pittsford Mendon High Sch 472 Mendon Rd, Pittsford 14534 Melissa Julian	9-12		1,019 80	3%	585/267-1600 Fax 585/267-1609
Pittsford Sutherland High Sch 55 Sutherland St, Pittsford 14534 Mark Puma	9-12		927 40	4%	585/267-1100 Fax 585/267-1182 f t
Thornell Road Elem Sch 431 Thornell Rd, Pittsford 14534 Roger Debell	K-5		406 26	1%	585/267-1700 Fax 585/385-2099

• Rochester City School Dist PID: 00732526
131 W Broad St, Rochester 14614 — 585/262-8100 — Fax 585/263-3209

Schools: 57 \ **Teachers:** 2,472 \ **Students:** 28,000 \ **Special Ed Students:** 6,954 \ **LEP Students:** 4,038 \ **College-Bound:** 69% \ **Ethnic:** Asian 3%, African American 54%, Hispanic 32%, Caucasian 10% \ **Exp:** $279 (Med) \ **Poverty:** 39% \ **Title I:** $33,507,976 \ **Special Education:** $103,468,000 \ **Open-Close:** 09/09 - 06/24 \ **DTBP:** $195 (High) \ f

Lesli Myers-Small	1	Cerri Cupples	2	
David Adams	2	Derrek Blair	2	
Everton Sewell	2,19	Judy Schuster	2,298	
Suzanne Menz	2	Tim Schmandt	2	
Michael Schmitt	3,17	Wayne Kittelberger	5	
Carlos Cotto	6,35,85	Dr Michael Chan	8,42	
Elizabeth Miller	15	Fatimat Reid	15,751	
Colleen Sadowski	16,82	D Pickard	20,23*	
Rhonda Neal	27	Andrew MacGowan	34	
Davina McLean-Randall	34,58	Karen Spawton	34,58	
Robin Hooper	34	Audrey Korokeyi	35	
Steven Lamorte	39	Jeff Mikols	45,286	
Karen Fahy	48,280	Scott Robinson	48	
Abel Perez-Pherett	57,61	Mayra Ortiz	57*	
Sherley Flores	57	Amy Tata	58	
Catherine Accordo	58	Daniel Fontanez	58	
Eugene McNamara	58	Kisha Morgan	58	
Kristina Mileham	58,73	Marcia Pease	58	
Maria Petrella	58	Van Henri White	67	
Aneli Nothnagle	68	Anne Brady	68	
Madhavi Devarakonda	68	Meghan Abate	68	
Nancy Eichner	69	Carrie Pecor	70	
Michele Alberti	70	Carlos Garcia	71	
Glen Vanderwater	73,98	Tim Johnsen	73	
Stefan Cohen	74	Joseph Capezzuto	79	
Shannon Karcher	88	Lori Baldwin	91	
Tyra Lewis	275	Jen Coon	286	
Nicole Klimek	295	Tom Moughan	295	
Ruth Turner	752			

Public Schs..Principal	Grd	Prgm	Enr/#Cls	SN	
Abelard Reynolds School 42 3330 Lake Ave, Rochester 14612 Lisa Whitlow	PK-6	T	457	85%	585/663-4330 Fax 585/621-0276
Adlai E Stevenson School 29 88 Kirkland Rd, Rochester 14611 Joseph Baldino	PK-6	T	309 27	97%	585/328-8228 Fax 585/935-7429
All City High Sch 2 Austin St, Rochester 14606 Armando Ramirez	9-12	AV	260 100		585/458-2110 Fax 585/263-3207
Andrew J Townson School 39 145 Midland Ave, Rochester 14621 Jacquelyn Cox	PK-6	T	538 30	94%	585/467-8816 Fax 585/336-5575
Anna Murray-Douglas School 12 999 South Ave, Rochester 14620 Vicki Gouveia	K-8	T	815 40	85%	585/461-3280 Fax 585/935-7412
Charles Carroll School 46 250 Newcastle Rd, Rochester 14610 Dr DiTullio	PK-6	T	321 17	76%	585/288-8008 Fax 585/654-1078
Ⓜ Children's Sch of Rochester 15 85 Hillside Ave, Rochester 14610 Jay Piper	PK-6	AT	343 6	82%	585/262-8830 Fax 585/262-8834
Clara Barton School 2 180 Ridgeway Ave, Rochester 14615 Sharon Dilbert	PK-6		319 28		585/235-2820 Fax 585/464-6174
Dr Charles T Lunsford Sch 19 465 Seward St, Rochester 14608 Moniek Silas-Lee	PK-8	T	398 25	93%	585/328-7454 Fax 585/464-6195

1	Superintendent	8	Curric/Instruct K-12	19	Chief Financial Officer	29	Family/Consumer Science	39	Social Studies K-12	49	English/Lang Arts Elem	59	Special Education Elem	69	Academic Assessment
2	Bus/Finance/Purchasing	9	Curric/Instruct Elem	20	Art K-12	30	Adult Education	40	Social Studies Elem	50	English/Lang Arts Sec	60	Special Education Sec	70	Research/Development
3	Buildings And Grounds	10	Curric/Instruct Sec	21	Art Elem	31	Career/Sch-to-Work K-12	41	Social Studies Sec	51	Reading K-12	61	Foreign/World Lang K-12	71	Public Information
4	Food Service	11	Federal Program	22	Art Sec	32	Career/Sch-to-Work Elem	42	Science K-12	52	Reading Elem	62	Foreign/World Lang Elem	72	Summer School
5	Transportation	12	Title I	23	Music K-12	33	Career/Sch-to-Work Sec	43	Science Elem	53	Reading Sec	63	Foreign/World Lang Sec	73	Instructional Tech
6	Athletic	13	Title V	24	Music Elem	34	Early Childhood Ed	44	Science Sec	54	Remedial Reading K-12	64	Religious Education K-12	74	Inservice Training
7	Health Services	15	Asst Superintendent	25	Music Sec	35	Health/Phys Education	45	Math K-12	55	Remedial Reading Elem	65	Religious Education Elem	75	Marketing/Distributive
		16	Instructional Media Svcs	26	Business Education	36	Guidance Services K-12	46	Math Elem	56	Remedial Reading Sec	66	Religious Education Sec	76	Info Systems
		17	Chief Operations Officer	27	Career & Tech Ed	37	Guidance Services Elem	47	Math Sec	57	Bilingual/ELL	67	School Board President	77	Psychological Assess
		18	Chief Academic Officer	28	Technology Education	38	Guidance Services Sec	48	English/Lang Arts K-12	58	Special Education K-12	68	Teacher Personnel	78	Affirmative Action

New York School Directory — Monroe County

School	Grades	Prog	Enroll	%	Phone
Dr Louis A Cerulli School 34 530 Lexington Ave, Rochester 14613 David Passero	PK-6	T	476 27	92%	585/458-3210 Fax 585/277-0106
Dr Martin Luther King Jr Sch 9 485 N Clinton Ave, Rochester 14605 Sharon Jackson	PK-6	T	667 41	97%	585/325-7828 Fax 585/262-8962
Dr Walter Cooper Acad Sch 10 180 Ridgeway Ave, Rochester 14615 Camaron Clyburn	PK-6	T	329	89%	585/324-2010 Fax 585/464-6101
Ⓜ Early CH Sch of Rochester 57 15 Costar St, Rochester 14608 Eva Thomas	PK-2	T	186 11	91%	585/277-0190 Fax 585/277-0192
East Lower Sch 1801 E Main St, Rochester 14609 Dr Tanya Wilson	6-8	T	346	86%	585/288-3130
East Upper Sch 1801 E Main St, Rochester 14609 Marlene Blocker	9-12	T	670	85%	585/288-3130 Fax 585/654-1066 Ⓕ Ⓣ
Edison Career & Tech High Sch 655 Colfax St, Rochester 14606 Jacob Scott	9-12	T	1,746	90%	585/324-9700
Enrico Fermi School 17 158 Orchard St Ste 2, Rochester 14611 Caterina Mannino	PK-8	T	667 33	96%	585/436-2560 Fax 585/324-6705
Florence S Brown Pre-K Center 500 Webster Ave, Rochester 14609 Rose Marie Urzetta	PK-PK		150 6		585/288-2410 Fax 585/654-1089
Ⓜ Flower City School 54 950 Norton St, Rochester 14621 Lashara Evans	K-6		321 12		585/254-2080 Fax 585/254-1077
Ⓜ Francis Parker School 23 170 Barrington St, Rochester 14607 Kathryn Yarlett-Fenti	PK-6	T	313 18	63%	585/473-5099 Fax 585/256-8994
Frank Fowler Dow School 52 100 Farmington Rd, Rochester 14609 Dr Mary Ferguson	PK-6	T	325 15	81%	585/482-9614 Fax 585/654-1079
George Mather Forbes School 4 625 Scio St, Rochester 14605 Karon Jackson	K-8		360 30		585/235-7848 Fax 585/464-6194
Helen B Montgomery School 50 301 Seneca Ave, Rochester 14621 Connie Wehner	PK-8		665 27	92%	585/266-0331
Henry Hudson School 28 450 Humboldt St, Rochester 14610 Susan Ladd	K-8	T	652 31	92%	585/482-4836 Fax 585/935-7428
Ⓜ Henry Lomb School 20 54 Oakman St, Rochester 14605 D'Onnarae Johnson	PK-6	T	316 17	96%	585/325-2920 Fax 585/262-8885 Ⓕ
Integrated Arts & Tech HS 950 Norton St, Rochester 14621 Kevin Klein	7-12	T	898	92%	585/324-3750 Fax 585/324-3751
James Monroe High Sch 164 Alexander St, Rochester 14607 Sandra Blackman	7-12	TV	889 150	94%	585/232-1530 Fax 585/262-8965
John James Audubon School 33 500 Webster Ave, Rochester 14609 **Dr Larry Ellison**	PK-6	T	1,140 59	91%	585/482-9290 Fax 585/935-7433
John Walton Spencer School 16 625 Scio St, Rochester 14605 Lisa Garrow	PK-6		425 26		585/235-1272 Fax 585/464-6188
John Williams School 5 555 Plymouth Ave N, Rochester 14608 Terrilyn Hammond	PK-8	T	664 40	95%	585/325-2255 Fax 585/935-7405
Leadership Acad for Young Men 4115 Lake Ave, Rochester 14612 Djinga St Louis	7-12	T	559	92%	585/324-7760 Fax 585/935-7438
Lincoln Park School 44 820 Chili Ave, Rochester 14611 Shalonda Garfield	PK-6	T	242 25	92%	585/328-5272 Fax 585/464-6197
Lincoln School 22 595 Upper Falls Blvd, Rochester 14605 Clinton Bell	PK-6	T	556 38	97%	585/467-7160 Fax 585/324-6818
Ⓐ Lyncx Academy 30 Hart St, Rochester 14605 Christopher Smith	7-12		140		585/254-1240
Mary McLeod Bethune School 45 1445 Clifford Ave, Rochester 14621 Robert Snyder	PK-8	T	599	96%	585/325-6945 Fax 585/262-8037
Ⓜ Montessori Academy Sch 53 625 Scio St, Rochester 14605 Dr Kim Harris-Pappin	PK-6	T	292 9	73%	585/325-0935 Fax 585/324-3709
Nathaniel Hawthorne School 25 965 N Goodman St, Rochester 14609 Deb Lazio	PK-6	T	330 19	91%	585/288-3654 Fax 585/654-1074
Nathaniel Rochester Cmty Sch 3 85 Adams St, Rochester 14608 Deborah Washington	PK-8	T	503 65	91%	585/454-3525 Fax 585/262-8938
Ⓐ New Beginnings Sch 546 Oxford St, Rochester 14607 Michael Allen	7-12		50		585/683-7402
Northeast College Prep HS 940 Fernwood Park, Rochester 14609 N Abdulmateen	9-12	T	568	92%	585/324-9273 Fax 585/654-1039
Ⓐ Northstar 30 Hart St, Rochester 14605 Dr Shannon Karcher	7-12		100		585/324-9945
Northwest JHS at Douglass 940 Fernwood Park, Rochester 14609 Steve Soprano	7-8		295 26		585/324-9289 Fax 585/654-1039 Ⓕ
P-Tech 655 Colfax St, Rochester 14606 Anthony Smith	9-12	V	300		585/324-9722 Fax 585/935-7470
Pinnacle School 35 194 Field St, Rochester 14620 Brenda Torres-Santana	K-6		453 25	91%	585/271-4583 Fax 585/935-7435
Rise Community School 106 279 W Ridge Rd, Rochester 14615 Christine Poles	PK-6		348	94%	585/254-4472
Roberto Clemente School 8 1180 Saint Paul St, Rochester 14621 Stephanie Thompson	PK-8	T	551 34	97%	585/262-8888 Fax 585/262-8990
Rochester Early Clg Intl HS 200 Genesee St, Rochester 14611 Uma Mehta	9-12	T	350	90%	585/324-9010
Ⓐ Rochester International Acad 1 Edgerton Park, Rochester 14608 Mary Diaz	4-12		265		585/324-5250
Ⓐ Sch Without Walls Commenc Acad Ⓜ 480 Broadway, Rochester 14607 Coretta Bridges	9-12	T	257 13	86%	585/546-6732 Fax 585/262-8947
Ⓜ School of the Arts 45 Prince St, Rochester 14607 Kelly Nicastro	7-12	T	1,105 55	67%	585/242-7682 Fax 585/256-6580
Ⓜ Theodore Roosevelt School 43 1305 Lyell Ave, Rochester 14606 Wakili Moore	PK-6	T	475 29	95%	585/458-4200 Fax 585/277-0102
Vanguard Collegiate High Sch 950 Norton St, Rochester 14621 Edward Mascadri	9-12	T	568	94%	585/324-3760
Virgil I Grissom School 7 31 Bryan St, Rochester 14613 David Lincoln	PK-6	T	534 43	94%	585/254-3110 Fax 585/324-3910

---

79 Student Personnel
80 Driver Ed/Safety
81 Gifted/Talented
82 Video Services
83 Substance Abuse Prev
84 Erate
85 AIDS Education
88 Alternative/At Risk
89 Multi-Cultural Curriculum
90 Social Work

91 Safety/Security
92 Magnet School
93 Parental Involvement
95 Tech Prep Program
97 Chief Information Officer
98 Chief Technology Officer
270 Character Education
271 Migrant Education
273 Teacher Mentor
274 Before/After Sch

275 Response To Intervention
277 Remedial Math K-12
280 Literacy Coach
285 STEM
286 Digital Learning
288 Common Core Standards
294 Accountability
295 Network System
296 Title II Programs
297 Webmaster

298 Grant Writer/Ptnrships
750 Chief Innovation Officer
751 Chief of Staff
752 Social Emotional Learning

Other School Types
Ⓐ = Alternative School
Ⓒ = Charter School
Ⓜ = Magnet School
Ⓨ = Year-Round School

School Programs
A = Alternative Program
G = Adult Classes
M = Magnet Program
T = Title I Schoolwide
V = Career & Tech Ed Programs

New Schools are shaded
New Superintendents and Principals are bold
Personnel with email addresses are underscored

Social Media
Ⓕ = Facebook
Ⓣ = Twitter

Monroe County

Market Data Retrieval

Virtual Academy of Rochester	9-12		401		585/262-8109
131 W Brd St, Rochester 14614					
Christine Volkmar					
ⓜ Wilson Foundation Academy	K-8	TV	552	92%	585/463-4100
200 Genesee St, Rochester 14611			57		Fax 585/993-7464
Dr Deasure Matthew					
ⓜ Wilson Magnet High Sch	9-12	T	738	85%	585/328-3440
501 Genesee St, Rochester 14611			100		Fax 585/464-6153
Julie Vanderwater					
ⓜ World of Inquiry School 58	PK-12	T	1,088	75%	585/325-6170
200 University Ave, Rochester 14605			14		Fax 585/262-8964
T'Hani Pantoja					

● Rush Henrietta Central SD PID: 00733166   585/359-5000
2034 Lehigh Station Rd, Henrietta 14467   Fax 585/359-5045

Schools: 9 \ **Teachers:** 487 \ **Students:** 5,300 \ **Special Ed Students:** 725 \ **LEP Students:** 342 \ **College-Bound:** 83% \ **Ethnic:** Asian 14%, African American 15%, Hispanic 7%, Caucasian 63% \ **Exp:** $218 (Med) \ **Poverty:** 11% \ **Title I:** $922,677 \ **Special Education:** $10,479,000 \ **Open-Close:** 09/02 - 06/23 \ **DTBP:** $325 (High)

Laurence Bo Wright	1	Andrew Witmore	2,3,15
Mark MacMillan	2,39	David Flood	3,5
Kenneth Nelson	3	Geraldo Torres	4
Shirley Smith-Gravanda	5	Tom Stewart	6,35
Daniel Zdanowski	7,27,42,73,285	Dina Wilson	8,15,69,80,288
Paula Sharlow	11,296	Nerlande Anselme	13,15,77,79,90,294
Patrick McCue	15,68	Brad Malone	16,76,295
Donna Watts	20,23*	Lisa Clar	45,277
Jeanette Cannioto	48,54,57,280	David Patt	58
Jennifer Campbell	58	Jessica Bailey	58
Diane McBride	67	Kristin Dioguardi	68
Travis Anderson	71	Dominic Piacentini	74
Karen Milburn	76	Paul Swiatek	83*
Michael Paladino	91*		

Public Schs..Principal	Grd	Prgm	Enr/#Cls	SN	
Charles H Roth Jr High Sch	7-9	V	594	49%	585/359-5100
4000 E Henrietta Rd, Henrietta 14467					Fax 585/359-5141
Kerry Macko					
David B Crane Elem Sch	K-3	T	366	52%	585/359-5400
85 Shell Edge Dr, Rochester 14623			26		Fax 585/359-5403
Brian Hill					
Emma E Sherman Elem Sch	4-6	T	572	48%	585/359-5490
50 Authors Ave, Henrietta 14467			35		Fax 585/359-5493
Rhonda Morien					
Ethel K Fyle Elem Sch	K-3	T	396	43%	585/359-5430
133 Vollmer Pkwy, Rochester 14623			32		Fax 585/359-5433
Marcy Mooney					
Floyd S Winslow Elem Sch	PK-3	T	521	47%	585/359-5090
755 Pinnacle Rd, Henrietta 14467			30		Fax 585/359-5073
Jeffrey Pollard					
Henry Burger Jr High Sch	7-9	V	666	42%	585/359-5300
639 Erie Station Rd, W Henrietta 14586			70		Fax 585/359-5333
Greg Lane					
Monica B Leary Elem Sch	K-3		478	26%	585/359-5460
5509 E Henrietta Rd, Rush 14543			31		Fax 585/359-5463
Jennifer Tomalty					
Rush Henrietta Senior High Sch	10-12	AV	1,251	42%	585/359-5200
1799 Lehigh Station Rd, Henrietta 14467			70		Fax 585/359-5277
Timothy Shafer					
Vollmer Elem Sch	4-6		640		585/359-5550
2000 Lehigh Station Rd, Henrietta 14467					
Lisa Farina					

● Spencerport Central Sch Dist PID: 00733295   585/349-5000
71 Lyell Ave, Spencerport 14559   Fax 585/349-5011

Schools: 6 \ **Teachers:** 343 \ **Students:** 3,700 \ **Special Ed Students:** 506 \ **LEP Students:** 116 \ **Ethnic:** Asian 2%, African American 6%, Hispanic 8%, Caucasian 84% \ **Exp:** $181 (Low) \ **Poverty:** 9% \ **Title I:** $555,376 \ **Special Education:** $6,427,000 \ **Open-Close:** 09/09 - 06/24 \ **DTBP:** $289 (High)

Daniel Milgate	1	Richard Wood	2,15
Jonathan Saltzberg	3	Nelson Drake	3
Gary Miner	4	Julie Churnetski	5
Jen Placito	6,7,35	Kristen Paolini	8
Ty Zinkiewich	8,11,57,83,285,286,288,296	Lisa McCarthy	9,74,273*
Andrea Pascuzzi	12,58,77	Jamie Lissow	15,68
Christina Bowerman	30	Maria Dougherty	58
Michael Sorbera	58	Kevin Hutton	67
Cory Allen	71,73,97	Tim O'Connor	76,79,298
Toby Toscano	91	Erin Hassall	93
Paul Van Horn	295		

Public Schs..Principal	Grd	Prgm	Enr/#Cls	SN	
Canal View Elem Sch	K-5		466	34%	585/349-5700
1 Ranger Rd, Spencerport 14559			25		Fax 585/349-5766
Carol Robinson					
Cosgrove Middle Sch	6-8		879	34%	585/349-5300
2749 Spencerport Rd, Spencerport 14559			50		Fax 585/349-5346
James Centola					
Leo Bernabi Elem Sch	K-5		432	29%	585/349-5400
1 Bernabi Rd, Spencerport 14559			21		Fax 585/349-5466
David Caiazza					
Spencerport High Sch	9-12	AV	1,120	29%	585/349-5200
2707 Spencerport Rd, Spencerport 14559			100		Fax 585/349-5266
Sean McCabe					
Terry Taylor Elem Sch	K-5		383	31%	585/349-5600
399 Ogden Parma Town Line Rd, Spencerport 14559			27		Fax 585/349-5666
Telcie Pincelli					
William C Munn Elem Sch	K-5	T	338	47%	585/349-5500
2333 Manitou Rd, Spencerport 14559			19		Fax 585/349-5566
Michael Canny					

● Webster Central School Dist PID: 00733374   585/216-0000
119 South Ave, Webster 14580   Fax 585/265-6561

Schools: 11 \ **Teachers:** 639 \ **Students:** 8,331 \ **Special Ed Students:** 941 \ **LEP Students:** 180 \ **College-Bound:** 89% \ **Ethnic:** Asian 3%, African American 4%, Hispanic 7%, Caucasian 86% \ **Exp:** $222 (Med) \ **Poverty:** 5% \ **Title I:** $729,849 \ **Special Education:** $11,007,000 \ **Open-Close:** 09/04 - 06/23 \ **DTBP:** $316 (High) \ ⓕ

Carmen Gumina	1	Brian Freeman	2,15
Blaine Cunningham	3	Joseph Pustulka	3,5*
Neil Flood	3,91	Mark Balfour	4*
Salvatore Amoroso	5	Shawn Strege	6,35
Steve LaMonica	6,35	Michelle Brincka	7*
Brian Neenan	8,15	Colleen Armstrong	11,36,58,77,79
David Swinson	15,68	Laurence Wahl	16,48
Joseph Pustullca	17	Michael Roller	20,23
Eric Blask	26,45	Susan Clark	26,45
William Ottman	27,42,73,285	Jane Laskey	30
Terrance McCarthy	48	Catherine Lesio	58
Krista Quick	58	Marjorie Marble	58
Erin Land	59	Tammy Gurowski	67
Mary Sprague	68	Thomas Nicchitta	68
Brian Zimmer	69,73*	Krista Grose	71
Joe Montemaro	73	Brenda Roof	76
Paul Conley	82	Ricky Bennett	295
Jodi Roberts	752		

---

1 Superintendent	8 Curric/Instruct K-12	19 Chief Financial Officer	29 Family/Consumer Science	39 Social Studies K-12	49 English/Lang Arts Elem	59 Special Education Elem	69 Academic Assessment
2 Bus/Finance/Purchasing	9 Curric/Instruct Elem	20 Art K-12	30 Adult Education	40 Social Studies Elem	50 English/Lang Arts Sec	60 Special Education Sec	70 Research/Development
3 Buildings And Grounds	10 Curric/Instruct Sec	21 Art Elem	31 Career/Sch-to-Work K-12	41 Social Studies Sec	51 Reading K-12	61 Foreign/World Lang K-12	71 Public Information
4 Food Service	11 Federal Program	22 Art Sec	32 Career/Sch-to-Work Elem	42 Science K-12	52 Reading Elem	62 Foreign/World Lang Elem	72 Summer School
5 Transportation	12 Title I	23 Music K-12	33 Career/Sch-to-Work Sec	43 Science Elem	53 Reading Sec	63 Foreign/World Lang Sec	73 Instructional Tech
6 Athletic	13 Title V	24 Music Elem	34 Early Childhood Ed	44 Science Sec	54 Remedial Reading K-12	64 Religious Education K-12	74 Inservice Training
7 Health Services	15 Asst Superintendent	25 Music Sec	35 Health/Phys Education	45 Math K-12	55 Remedial Reading Elem	65 Religious Education Elem	75 Marketing/Distributive
	16 Instructional Media Svcs	26 Business Education	36 Guidance Services K-12	46 Math Elem	56 Remedial Reading Sec	66 Religious Education Sec	76 Info Systems
	17 Chief Operations Officer	27 Career & Tech Ed	37 Guidance Services Elem	47 Math Sec	57 Bilingual/ELL	67 School Board President	77 Psychological Assess
	18 Chief Academic Officer	28 Technology Education	38 Guidance Services Sec	48 English/Lang Arts K-12	58 Special Education K-12	68 Teacher Personnel	78 Affirmative Action

New York School Directory — Monroe County

Public Schs..Principal	Grd	Prgm	Enr/#Cls	SN	
DeWitt Road Elem Sch 722 DeWitt Rd, Webster 14580 Mark Schichtel	K-5		521 30	20%	585/671-0710 Fax 585/670-1004
Klem Road North Elem Sch 1015 Klem Rd, Webster 14580 Laura Ballou	PK-5		530 26	18%	585/872-1770 Fax 585/217-4108
Klem Road South Elem Sch 1025 Klem Rd, Webster 14580 Martha End	K-5		534 22	28%	585/872-1320 Fax 585/217-4137
Plank Road North Elem Sch 705 Plank Rd, Webster 14580 Craig Bodensteiner	PK-5		543 25	25%	585/671-8858 Fax 585/670-4012
Plank Road South Elem Sch 715 Plank Rd, Webster 14580 Jennifer Sullivan	K-5		601 27	12%	585/671-3190 Fax 585/670-4062
Schlegel Road Elem Sch 1548 Schlegel Rd, Webster 14580 Debra Reed	PK-5		454 24	25%	585/265-2500 Fax 585/265-2513
Schroeder High Sch 875 Ridge Rd, Webster 14580 Paul Benz	9-12	AG	1,349 106	23%	585/670-5000
Spry Middle Sch 119 South Ave, Webster 14580 James Baehr	6-8		980	25%	585/265-6500 Fax 585/265-6512
State Road Elem Sch 1401 State Rd, Webster 14580 Christine Noeth-Abele	PK 5		534 25	30%	585/872-4200 Fax 585/217-5306
Webster Thomas High Sch 800 Five Mile Line Rd, Webster 14580 Glenn Widor	9-12		1,298 100	17%	585/670-8000 Fax 585/671-1884
Willink Middle Sch 900 Publishers Pkwy, Webster 14580 Brian Powers	6-8		962 45	20%	585/670-1030 Fax 585/671-1785

- **West Irondequoit Ctl SD** PID: 00732186 585/342-5500
  321 List Ave, Rochester 14617 Fax 585/266-1556

Schools: 10 \ **Teachers:** 277 \ **Students:** 3,600 \ **Special Ed Students:** 465 \ **LEP Students:** 95 \ **Ethnic:** Asian 3%, African American 10%, Hispanic 12%, Caucasian 74% \ **Exp:** $275 (Med) \ **Poverty:** 8% \ **Title I:** $409,444 \ **Special Education:** $5,166,000 \ **Open-Close:** 09/08 - 06/23 \ **DTBP:** $313 (High)

Dr Aaron Johnson 1
John Conti 3,91
Kim Schon 6,35
Christina Miga 9,12,51,54,69,296
Michelle Cramer 15
Jakob Honan 16,82
Steve Zugelder 23*
Lavon Bucciarelli 31
Kimberly Cristil 39*
Barbara Hartford 45,277
David Long 67
Susan Slugg 77
James Brennan 2,5,15,19,294
Betsy Logiudice 4
Susan Flood 7,11,34,58,79,81,88,298*
Karen Finter 10,11,73,88*
Dan Fullerton 16,27,76,97,286,295,297
Sue Jacobs 20
Barbara Reardon 30,274
Gretchen Bush 36*
Jennifer Brooker 42,74,273,285
Brenna Farrell 48
Jeffery Diveronica 71
Lindsey Snyder 83

Public Schs..Principal	Grd	Prgm	Enr/#Cls	SN	
Briarwood Sch 215 Briarwood Dr, Rochester 14617 Kathleen Bush	K-3		157 8	24%	585/336-1610 Fax 585/336-1611
Brookview Elem Sch 300 Brookview Dr, Rochester 14617 Alicia Spitz	K-3		165 7	32%	585/336-1630 Fax 585/336-1631
Colebrook Sch 210 Colebrook Dr, Rochester 14617 Kathleen Bush	K-3		168 9	29%	585/336-1600 Fax 585/336-1601
Dake Junior High Sch 350 Cooper Rd, Rochester 14617 Michelle Cramer	7-8	V	595	34%	585/342-2140 Fax 585/336-3034
Irondequoit High Sch 260 Cooper Rd, Rochester 14617 Alecia McLaughlin	9-12	GV	1,148 45	33%	585/266-7351 Fax 585/336-2929
Iroquois Middle Sch 150 Colebrook Dr, Rochester 14617 Christian Zwahlen	4-6		423 30	30%	585/342-3450 Fax 585/336-3042
Listwood Sch 325 List Ave, Rochester 14617 Kelly Santora	K-3		160 9	13%	585/336-1640 Fax 585/336-1666
Rogers Middle Sch 219 Northfield Rd, Rochester 14617 Michelle Flood	4-6	T	427 20	40%	585/342-1330 Fax 585/336-3097
Seneca Elem Sch 4143 Saint Paul Blvd, Rochester 14617 Alicia Spitz	K-3	T	167 10	41%	585/336-1620 Fax 585/336-1621
Southlawn Sch 455 Rawlinson Rd, Rochester 14617 Kelly Santora	K-3		206 13	32%	585/266-5070 Fax 585/336-3097

- **Wheatland Chili Ctl Sch Dist** PID: 00733506 585/889-4500
  13 Beckwith Ave, Scottsville 14546 Fax 585/889-6284

Schools: 2 \ **Teachers:** 72 \ **Students:** 637 \ **Special Ed Students:** 115 \ **LEP Students:** 10 \ **College-Bound:** 90% \ **Ethnic:** Asian 1%, African American 14%, Hispanic 9%, Native American: 1%, Caucasian 75% \ **Exp:** $624 (High) \ **Poverty:** 14% \ **Title I:** $271,750 \ **Special Education:** $1,430,000 \ **Open-Close:** 09/09 - 06/24 \ **DTBP:** $359 (High)

Lynda Quick 1
Cynthia Kwiatkowski 3
Jennifer Sinsebox 8,288*
Mary Vito 57,58*
Jessica Jackson 2
Todd Grimes 6*
Dr Deborah Leh 11
James Musshafen 67

Public Schs..Principal	Grd	Prgm	Enr/#Cls	SN	
T J Connor Elem Sch 13 Beckwith Ave, Scottsville 14546 Daniel Murray	K-5		292 17	40%	585/889-6236 Fax 585/889-8227
Wheatland Chili Mid High Sch 940 North Rd, Scottsville 14546 Eric Windover	6-12	T	345 34	48%	585/889-6227 Fax 585/889-6217

MONROE CATHOLIC SCHOOLS

- **Diocese of Rochester Ed Office** PID: 00733623 585/328-3228
  1150 Buffalo Rd, Rochester 14624 Fax 585/328-3149

Schools: 16 \ **Students:** 2,800

Listing includes only schools located in this county. See District Index for location of Diocesan Offices.

James Tauzel 1
Ann Frank 11,69,74
Tammy Sylvester 68
Rebecca Williams 2
Linda Mehlenbacher 65
Doug Mandelaro 71

Catholic Schs..Principal	Grd	Prgm	Enr/#Cls	SN	
Holy Cross Sch 4488 Lake Ave, Rochester 14612 Mary Martell	PK-6		283 14		585/663-6533 Fax 585/434-3972

79 Student Personnel
80 Driver Ed/Safety
81 Gifted/Talented
82 Video Services
83 Substance Abuse Prev
84 Erate
85 AIDS Education
88 Alternative/At Risk
89 Multi-Cultural Curriculum
90 Social Work
91 Safety/Security
92 Magnet School
93 Parental Involvement
95 Tech Prep Program
97 Chief Information Officer
98 Chief Technology Officer
270 Character Education
271 Migrant Education
273 Teacher Mentor
274 Before/After Sch
275 Response To Intervention
277 Remedial Math K-12
280 Literacy Coach
285 STEM
286 Digital Learning
288 Common Core Standards
294 Accountability
295 Network System
296 Title II Programs
297 Webmaster
298 Grant Writer/Ptnrships
750 Chief Innovation Officer
751 Chief of Staff
752 Social Emotional Learning

Other School Types
Ⓐ = Alternative School
Ⓒ = Charter School
Ⓜ = Magnet School
Ⓨ = Year-Round School

School Programs
A = Alternative Program
G = Adult Classes
M = Magnet Program
T = Title I Schoolwide
V = Career & Tech Ed Programs

Social Media
= Facebook
= Twitter

New Schools are shaded
New Superintendents and Principals are bold
Personnel with email addresses are underscored

Monroe County

Private Schs..Principal	Grd	Prgm	Enr/#Cls	SN	Phone	Fax
Seton Catholic Sch 165 Rhinecliff Dr, Rochester 14618 Patricia Selig	PK-6		369 19		585/473-6604	Fax 585/473-3347
St Ambrose Academy 31 Empire Blvd, Rochester 14609 Christine Deutsch	K-5		120 7		585/288-0580	Fax 585/288-2612
St Joseph Sch 39 Gebhardt Rd, Penfield 14526 Amy Johnson	PK-6		175 16		585/586-6968	Fax 585/586-4619
St Kateri Sch 445 Kings Hwy S, Rochester 14617 Terri Morgan	PK-5		200 10		585/467-8730	Fax 585/467-5392
St Lawrence Sch 1000 N Greece Rd, Rochester 14626 Frank Arvizzigno	PK-5		214 10		585/225-3870	Fax 585/225-1336
St Louis Sch 11 Rand Pl, Pittsford 14534 Fran Barr	PK-5		277 21		585/586-5200	Fax 585/586-4561
St Pius Tenth Sch 3000 Chili Ave, Rochester 14624 Maria Cahill	PK-5		149 16		585/247-5650	Fax 585/247-7409
St Rita Sch 1008 Maple Dr, Webster 14580 Mary Ellen Wagner	PK-5		157 18		585/671-3132	Fax 585/671-4562

MONROE PRIVATE SCHOOLS

Private Schs..Principal	Grd	Prgm	Enr/#Cls	SN	Phone	Fax
Allendale Columbia Sch 519 Allens Creek Rd, Rochester 14618 Michelle Feiss \ Tina Duver \ Philip Schwartz	PK-12		404 30		585/381-4560	Fax 585/383-1191
Andrews Trahey Sch 1183 Monroe Ave, Rochester 14620 Lori Skelton	Spec		96 16		585/256-7626	Fax 585/256-7870
Aquinas Institute 1127 Dewey Ave, Rochester 14613 Theodore Mancini	6-12		782 42		585/254-2020	Fax 585/254-7403
Archangel Sch 2400 Chili Ave, Rochester 14624 Eric Graham	K-12		65		585/426-5990	
ⓨ Avalon Sch at Villa of Hope 3300 Dewey Ave, Rochester 14616 Kimberli Ward	Spec	M	112 16		585/227-6920	Fax 585/865-9334
Bay Knoll SDA Sch 2639 E Ridge Rd, Rochester 14622 Susan Kingman	PK-8		27 2		585/467-2722	
Bishop Kearney High Sch 125 Kings Hwy S, Rochester 14617 William Geraci	6-12	V	460 40		585/342-4000	Fax 585/342-4694
Charles Finney Sch 2070 Five Mile Line Rd, Penfield 14526 Yvonne Paganelli \ Bret Miller	PK-12		390		585/387-3770	
Cornerstone Christian Academy 60 Holley St, Brockport 14420 Christopher Johnson	K-12		47 5		585/637-4540	Fax 585/637-4518
CP Rochester Augustin Chld Ctr 3399 Winton Rd S, Rochester 14623 Diane Kozar	Spec		120 9		585/334-6000	Fax 585/334-1646
Crestwood Children's Center 2075 Scottsville Rd, Rochester 14623 Stephanie Ciccone	Spec		80		585/429-2700	Fax 585/429-2800
Greece Christian Sch 750 Long Pond Rd, Rochester 14612 Dr Herbert Parker	PK-8		202 14		585/723-1165	Fax 585/723-8241
Helpern Education Center 695 Bay Rd, Webster 14580 Dr Lillie Stone	Spec		70 15		585/671-7890	Fax 585/671-6704
Hillel Community Day Sch 191 Fairfield Dr, Rochester 14620 Tracie Glazer	K-8		80		585/271-6877	Fax 585/473-8039
Ⓐ Hope Hall Sch 1612 Buffalo Rd, Rochester 14624 Jacelyn Droegmoeller	2-12		158 10		585/426-0210	Fax 585/426-0212
Mary Cariola Children's Center 1000 Elmwood Ave Ste 100, Rochester 14620 Karen Zandi	Spec		380		585/271-0761	Fax 585/442-3143
McQuaid Jesuit High Sch 1800 Clinton Ave S, Rochester 14618 Adam Baber	6-12		900 57		585/473-1130	Fax 585/256-6171
Montessori School of Rochester 220 Idlewood Rd Ste 9, Rochester 14618	PK-3		102 5		585/256-2520	
Nazareth Elem Sch 311 Flower City Park, Rochester 14615 Sr Margaret Mancuso	PK-6		200 10		585/458-3786	Fax 585/647-8717
Norman Howard Sch 275 Pinnacle Rd, Rochester 14623 Paul Keller	5-12		140 30		585/334-8010	Fax 585/334-8073
Northside Christian Academy 634 Hudson Ave, Rochester 14621 Michael Mitchell	PK-6		21 3		585/266-3140	Fax 585/266-3114
Northstar Christian Academy 332 Spencerport Rd, Rochester 14606 Kiersten Roberts \ J Garwood	K-12	V	357 30		585/429-5530	Fax 585/429-7913
Ora Academy 139 Winton Rd S, Rochester 14610 Eliezer Lehrer	9-12		13 4		585/271-8711	
Our Lady of Mercy Sch 1437 Blossom Rd, Rochester 14610 Dr Sherylanne Diodato \ Dr Martin Kilbridge	6-12		730 30		585/288-7120	Fax 585/288-7966
Rochester Christian Sch 260 Embury Rd, Rochester 14625 Michelle Selvaggio	PK-8		113 15		585/671-4910	Fax 585/671-3676
Rochester Classical Academy 1775 East Ave, Rochester 14610	K-1		41			
Rochester School for the Deaf 1545 Saint Paul St, Rochester 14621 Susan Ogden	Spec	G	136 26		585/544-1240	Fax 585/544-0383
School of Holy Childhood 100 Groton Pkwy, Rochester 14623 David Halpern	Spec	G	122 11		585/359-3710	Fax 585/359-3722
Southeast Christian Academy 1850 Fairprt 9 Mile Pt Rd, Penfield 14526 Curtis Baker	PK-12		65 8		585/388-0850	
St John Bosco Sch 501 Garfield St, E Rochester 14445 Colleen Richards	PK-12		126		585/348-9401	
St Paul Lutheran Sch 158 East Ave, Hilton 14468 David Spiehler	PK-8		107 8		585/392-4361	Fax 585/392-4001
Talmudical Inst of Upstate NY 769 Park Ave, Rochester 14607 Chaim Goldstein	9-12		40		585/473-2810	
The Harley Sch 1981 Clover St, Rochester 14618 Terry Smith \ Hassan Jones \ Kim McDowell	PK-12		515 50		585/442-1770	
Trinity Montessori Sch 100 Golden Flyer Dr, Rochester 14618 Lorraine Scarafile	PK-6		260 10		585/586-1044	Fax 585/586-1821

---

1 Superintendent	8 Curric/Instruct K-12	19 Chief Financial Officer	29 Family/Consumer Science	39 Social Studies K-12	49 English/Lang Arts Elem	59 Special Education Elem	69 Academic Assessment
2 Bus/Finance/Purchasing	9 Curric/Instruct Elem	20 Art K-12	30 Adult Education	40 Social Studies Elem	50 English/Lang Arts Sec	60 Special Education Sec	70 Research/Development
3 Buildings And Grounds	10 Curric/Instruct Sec	21 Art Elem	31 Career/Sch-to-Work K-12	41 Social Studies Sec	51 Reading K-12	61 Foreign/World Lang K-12	71 Public Information
4 Food Service	11 Federal Program	22 Art Sec	32 Career/Sch-to-Work Elem	42 Science K-12	52 Reading Elem	62 Foreign/World Lang Elem	72 Summer School
5 Transportation	12 Title I	23 Music K-12	33 Career/Sch-to-Work Sec	43 Science Elem	53 Reading Sec	63 Foreign/World Lang Sec	73 Instructional Tech
6 Athletic	13 Title V	24 Music Elem	34 Early Childhood Ed	44 Science Sec	54 Remedial Reading K-12	64 Religious Education K-12	74 Inservice Training
7 Health Services	15 Asst Superintendent	25 Music Sec	35 Health/Phys Education	45 Math K-12	55 Remedial Reading Elem	65 Religious Education Elem	75 Marketing/Distributive
	16 Instructional Media Svcs	26 Business Education	36 Guidance Services K-12	46 Math Elem	56 Remedial Reading Sec	66 Religious Education Sec	76 Info Systems
	17 Chief Operations Officer	27 Career & Tech Ed	37 Guidance Services Elem	47 Math Sec	57 Bilingual/ELL	67 School Board President	77 Psychological Assess
	18 Chief Academic Officer	28 Technology Education	38 Guidance Services Sec	48 English/Lang Arts K-12	58 Special Education K-12	68 Teacher Personnel	78 Affirmative Action

New York School Directory — Montgomery County

Webster Montessori Sch	PK-6	144	585/347-0055
1310 Five Mile Line Rd, Webster 14580		5	Fax 585/347-0057
Jaclyn Griebel			

MONROE REGIONAL CENTERS

• Monroe 1 BOCES PID: 00733544   585/377-4660
41 Oconnor Rd, Fairport 14450   Fax 585/383-6404

Daniel White	1	Lisa Ryan	2,3,15
Scott Covell	2,3,15	Samantha Jensen	3
Cherie Becker	7,57,58,79	Dr Cathy Hauber	8,15
Dr Michelle Ryan	15,69,294	Katie Bertrand	16
Robert Dickson	67	Lawrence Mancuso	68
David Dennison	73,76		

• Monroe 2 Orleans BOCES PID: 00733532   585/352-2400
3599 Big Ridge Rd, Spencerport 14559   Fax 585/352-2442

Joanne Antonacci	1	Steve Roland	2
Dr Marijo Pearson	8,15,74	Timothy Dobbertin	8,15,34
Dr Michelle Ryan	15,69,294	Ray Miller	16,73
Dr Karen Poland	27,31	Kathy Arminio	43
Lourdos Roa	57	Barbara Martorana	58,77
Dennis Laba	67	Karen Brown	68
Shannon Alvorado	81	Laurie Streb	298

MONTGOMERY COUNTY

MONTGOMERY COUNTY SCHOOLS

County Schs..Principal	Grd	Prgm	Enr/#Cls	SN
AG-Ptech	9-10		100	518/568-7023
61 Monroe St, St Johnsville 13452				
Kevin Warren				

MONTGOMERY PUBLIC SCHOOLS

• Canajoharie Ctl School Dist PID: 00734718   518/673-6302
136 Scholastic Way, Canajoharie 13317   Fax 518/673-3177

Schools: 3 \ **Teachers:** 79 \ **Students:** 855 \ **Special Ed Students:** 100 \ **LEP Students:** 5 \ **College-Bound:** 79% \ **Ethnic:** African American 1%, Hispanic 2%, Caucasian 96% \ **Exp:** $317 (High) \ **Poverty:** 21% \ **Title I:** $386,595 \ **Special Education:** $1,851,000 \ **Open-Close:** 09/03 - 06/25 \ **DTBP:** $356 (High) \ f

Nick Fitzgerald	1	Leah Schaffer	2
Gary May	3*	Wayne Conbeer	5
Brian Dunn	6	Jennifer Schwabrow	8,58*
Stacy Ward	11*	Dr Mark Brody	67

Public Schs..Principal	Grd	Prgm	Enr/#Cls	SN
Canajoharie High Sch	9-12		263	35% 518/673-6330
136 Scholastic Way, Canajoharie 13317			38	Fax 518/673-8116
Nicholas Bottino				
Canajoharie Middle Sch	6-8	T	192	59% 518/673-6320
25 School District Rd, Canajoharie 13317			30	Fax 518/673-5557
Christopher DePaolo				
East Hill Elem Sch	PK-5	T	400	49% 518/673-6310
25 School District Rd, Canajoharie 13317			17	Fax 518/673-3887
Alicia D'Ambrosio				

• Fonda Fultonville Central SD PID: 00734770   518/853-4415
112 Old Johnstown Rd, Fonda 12068   Fax 518/853-4461

Schools: 1 \ **Teachers:** 105 \ **Students:** 1,340 \ **Special Ed Students:** 195 \ **LEP Students:** 14 \ **College-Bound:** 66% \ **Ethnic:** Asian 2%, African American 1%, Hispanic 4%, Caucasian 94% \ **Exp:** $261 (Med) \ **Poverty:** 13% \ **Title I:** $293,505 \ **Special Education:** $335,000 \ **Open-Close:** 09/08 - 06/24 \ **DTBP:** $350 (High)

Thomas Ciaccio	1	Tabatha Biggane	2,12
Vicki Palmer	4	Donna Hayes	5*
Eric Wilson	6*	Nancy Ballerstein	7*
Kristine Dickson	11,58,271,296,298*	Amber Smith	16
Barbara Barker	28*	Nicole Duell	34*
Ashley Stockbridge	35,74*	Matt Sullivan	67
Jarrod Baker	73*	Aaron Grady	83*
Briana Harden	274		

Public Schs..Principal	Grd	Prgm	Enr/#Cls	SN
Fonda Fultonville Central Sch	PK-12		1,340	37% 518/853-4415
112 Old Johnstown Rd, Fonda 12068			93	
Nellie Bush \ David Zadoorian \ Aaron Grady				

• Ft Plain Central School Dist PID: 00734811   518/993-4000
25 High St, Fort Plain 13339   Fax 518/993-3393

Schools: 2 \ **Teachers:** 80 \ **Students:** 750 \ **Special Ed Students:** 177 \ **LEP Students:** 3 \ **College-Bound:** 57% \ **Ethnic:** Asian 1%, African American 2%, Hispanic 6%, Caucasian 91% \ **Exp:** $236 (Med) \ **Poverty:** 24% \ **Title I:** $580,499 \ **Special Education:** $2,532,000 \ **Open-Close:** 09/08 - 06/25 \ **DTBP:** $355 (High)

John Bishop	1,11	Philene Hudson	2
Paul Van Avery	3	Charlie Karker	6
Katrina Canallatos	58*	Joseph Bartholomew	67
Jessica Sonders	68		

Public Schs..Principal	Grd	Prgm	Enr/#Cls	SN
Ft Plain High Sch	7-12	T	360	54% 518/993-4433
1 West St, Fort Plain 13339			35	Fax 518/993-2897
Deborah Larrabee				
Harry Hoag Elem Sch	PK-6	T	444	58% 518/993-4433
25 High St, Fort Plain 13339			44	Fax 518/993-4501
Lauren Crisman				

• Greater Amsterdam School Dist PID: 00734586   518/843-3180
140 Saratoga Ave, Amsterdam 12010   Fax 518/842-0012

Schools: 6 \ **Teachers:** 290 \ **Students:** 3,690 \ **Special Ed Students:** 649 \ **LEP Students:** 273 \ **College-Bound:** 81% \ **Ethnic:** Asian 1%, African American 5%, Hispanic 50%, Caucasian 43% \ **Exp:** $224 (Med) \ **Poverty:** 24% \ **Title I:** $1,888,995 \ **Special Education:** $7,550,000 \ **Open-Close:** 09/08 - 06/25 \ **DTBP:** $228 (High) \ t

Richard Ruberti	1	Colleen Dicaprio	2
Stanley Posluszny	3,5,91	Robert Bardin	4
Stephen Nolan	6,35	Christian Smith	13,58,78,79,275
Effie McBride	48	Sandra Polikowski	57,69,73,277,280,286,294,295
Dr Nellie Bush	67		

---

79 Student Personnel	91 Safety/Security	275 Response To Intervention	298 Grant Writer/Ptnrships	**School Programs**	**Social Media**
80 Driver Ed/Safety	92 Magnet School	277 Remedial Math K-12	750 Chief Innovation Officer	A = Alternative Program	f = Facebook
81 Gifted/Talented	93 Parental Involvement	280 Literacy Coach	751 Chief of Staff	G = Adult Classes	t = Twitter
82 Video Services	95 Tech Prep Program	285 STEM	752 Social Emotional Learning	M = Magnet Program	
83 Substance Abuse Prev	97 Chief Infomation Officer	286 Digital Learning		T = Title I Schoolwide	
84 Erate	98 Chief Technology Officer	288 Common Core Standards	**Other School Types**	V = Career & Tech Ed Programs	
85 AIDS Education	270 Character Education	294 Accountability	A = Alternative School		
88 Alternative/At Risk	271 Migrant Education	295 Network System	C = Charter School	New Schools are shaded	
89 Multi-Cultural Curriculum	273 Teacher Mentor	296 Title II Programs	M = Magnet School	New Superintendents and Principals are bold	
90 Social Work	274 Before/After Sch	297 Webmaster	Y = Year-Round School	Personnel with email addresses are underscored	

Nassau County
Market Data Retrieval

Public Schs..Principal	Grd	Prgm	Enr/#Cls	SN	
Amsterdam High Sch 140 Saratoga Ave, Amsterdam 12010 Tyrone O'Meally	9-12	AT	1,166	61%	518/843-4932 Fax 518/843-5432
Marie Curie Institute 9 Brice St, Amsterdam 12010 John Penman	PK-5	T	451 20	72%	518/843-2871 Fax 518/843-6290
Raphael J McNulty Academy 60 Brandt Pl, Amsterdam 12010 Todd Giagni	PK-5	T	485 21	72%	518/843-4773 Fax 518/843-5475
Wilbur H Lynch Literacy Acad 55 Brandt Pl, Amsterdam 12010 Elizabeth Hanan	6-8	AT	810 100	72%	518/843-3716 Fax 518/843-6287
Ⓜ William B Tecler Magnet Sch 210 Northern Blvd, Amsterdam 12010 John Miller	PK-5	T	487 24	75%	518/843-4805 Fax 518/843-6184
William Barkley Elem Sch 66 Destefano Pl, Amsterdam 12010 Donna Decker	PK-5	T	297 16	56%	518/843-1850 Fax 518/843-6183

MONTGOMERY CATHOLIC SCHOOLS

- **Diocese of Albany Ed Office** PID: 00715059
  Listing includes only schools located in this county. See District Index for location of Diocesan Offices.

Catholic Schs..Principal	Grd	Prgm	Enr/#Cls	SN	
St Mary's Institute 10 Kopernick Rd, Amsterdam 12010 Nicole Luft	PK-8		246 26		518/842-4100 Fax 518/842-0217

MONTGOMERY PRIVATE SCHOOLS

Private Schs..Principal	Grd	Prgm	Enr/#Cls	SN	
Faith Bible Academy 106 Crosby Rd, Sprakers 12166 David White	K-12		44 4		518/234-3497
Perth Bible Christian Academy 1863 County Highway 107, Amsterdam 12010 Craig Jones	PK-12		42 3		518/843-3290 Fax 518/843-3304
Victory Christian Academy 131 Clark Rd, Fort Plain 13339 Jessica Paliling	K-12		15 11		518/568-7606 Fax 518/568-3154

NASSAU COUNTY

NASSAU COUNTY SCHOOLS

County Schs..Principal	Grd	Prgm	Enr/#Cls	SN	
Barry Tech Ctr-Westbury 1196 Prospect Ave, Westbury 11590 Peter Dalton	Voc	AG	1,300 60		516/622-6800 Fax 516/333-9384
BOCES Hearing & Vision Imprd Rosemary Kennedy Ctr, Wantagh 11793 Monica Savino	Spec		500 4		516/931-8507 Fax 516/931-8566
BOCES Seamans Neck Middle Sch 1100 Crestline Pl, Seaford 11783 Christine Nardi	Spec		130 16		516/719-6000 Fax 516/783-9155
Career Preparatory High Sch 111 Cantiague Rock Rd, Westbury 11590 Jervey Edwards	Spec		110 20		516/546-7800 Fax 516/546-6357
Carman Rd Sch Phys Handicapped 1 Carmans Rd, Massapequa Pk 11762 Susan McNulty	Spec	A	185 20		516/608-6200 Fax 516/541-7368
Center for Community Adjustmnt 2850 N Jerusalem Rd, Wantagh 11793 Christopher Korolczuk	Spec	A	260 38		516/396-2900 Fax 516/396-2990
Children's Readiness Center 2351 Jerusalem Ave, N Bellmore 11710 Amy Goldstein	Spec		262		516/719-6070 Fax 516/719-6086
Nassau BOCES-Jerusalem ES 2351 Jerusalem Ave, N Bellmore 11710 Patricia Carman	Spec		187		516/608-6300 Fax 516/608-6314
Rosemary Kennedy Sch 2850 N Jerusalem Rd, Wantagh 11793 Matthew Zegers	Spec		420		516/396-2600 Fax 516/396-2626
Rosemary Kennedy Sch at Willet 57 Willet Ave, Hicksville 11801 Matthew Zegers	Spec		110		516/483-4650 Fax 516/483-7496
Ⓐ Teenage Parenting Program 1196 Prospect Ave, Westbury 11590 James Clark	9-12	V	50 10		516/608-6400 Fax 516/333-9384

NASSAU PUBLIC SCHOOLS

- **Baldwin Union Free School Dist** PID: 00734873　　516/434-6000
  960 Hastings St, Baldwin 11510　　Fax 516/434-6803

> **Schools:** 7 \ **Teachers:** 392 \ **Students:** 5,450 \ **Special Ed Students:** 903 \ **LEP Students:** 268 \ **College-Bound:** 91% \ **Ethnic:** Asian 5%, African American 49%, Hispanic 33%, Caucasian 14% \ **Exp:** $456 (High) \ **Poverty:** 7% \ **Title I:** $556,258 \ **Special Education:** $5,662,000 \ **Open-Close:** 09/03 - 06/25 \ **DTBP:** $313 (High) \ f

Dr Shari Camhi	1	Mr Robinson	2,15
Russ Randazzo	3	Kristina Orlando	5
Ed Ramirez	6,7,35,83,270*	Andrew DiNapoli	8
Anthony Mignella	8,12,15	Asheena Baez	9
Sherrisee Young	13,58,79,88,90	Michelle Gallo	15,68
Andre Poprilo	20,23	Melanie Kaplan	30
Mary Jo O'Hagan	67	Mary Furcht	71
Darren Faccilonga	73	Nomi Rosen	74

Public Schs..Principal	Grd	Prgm	Enr/#Cls	SN	
Baldwin Middle Sch 3211 Schreiber Pl, Baldwin 11510 Tim Maher	6-8		1,092 63	34%	516/434-6200 Fax 516/377-9432
Baldwin Senior High Sch 841 Ethel T Kloberg Dr, Baldwin 11510 Dr Neil Testa	9-12		1,540 100	31%	516/434-6100 Fax 516/377-9208
Brookside Elem Sch 940 Stanton Ave, Baldwin 11510 Unal Karakas	K-5		240 12	36%	516/434-6300 Fax 516/337-9425
Lenox Elem Sch 551 Lenox Rd, Baldwin 11510 Asheena Baez	K-5	T	279 18	40%	516/434-6400 Fax 516/434-6825
Meadow Elem Sch 880 Jackson St, Baldwin 11510 Echele May	K-5		582 28	35%	516/434-6500 Fax 516/434-6812

1	Superintendent	8	Curric/Instruct K-12	19	Chief Financial Officer	29	Family/Consumer Science	39	Social Studies K-12	49	English/Lang Arts Elem	59	Special Education Elem	69	Academic Assessment
2	Bus/Finance/Purchasing	9	Curric/Instruct Elem	20	Art K-12	30	Adult Education	40	Social Studies Elem	50	English/Lang Arts Sec	60	Special Education Sec	70	Research/Development
3	Buildings And Grounds	10	Curric/Instruct Sec	21	Art Elem	31	Career/Sch-to-Work K-12	41	Social Studies Sec	51	Reading K-12	61	Foreign/World Lang K-12	71	Public Information
4	Food Service	11	Federal Program	22	Art Sec	32	Career/Sch-to-Work Elem	42	Science K-12	52	Reading Elem	62	Foreign/World Lang Elem	72	Summer School
5	Transportation	12	Title I	23	Music K-12	33	Career/Sch-to-Work Sec	43	Science Elem	53	Reading Sec	63	Foreign/World Lang Sec	73	Instructional Tech
6	Athletic	13	Title V	24	Music Elem	34	Early Childhood Ed	44	Science Sec	54	Remedial Reading K-12	64	Religious Education K-12	74	Inservice Training
7	Health Services	15	Asst Superintendent	25	Music Sec	35	Health/Phys Education	45	Math K-12	55	Remedial Reading Elem	65	Religious Education Elem	75	Marketing/Distributive
		16	Instructional Media Svcs	26	Business Education	36	Guidance Services K-12	46	Math Elem	56	Remedial Reading Sec	66	Religious Education Sec	76	Info Systems
		17	Chief Operations Officer	27	Career & Tech Ed	37	Guidance Services Elem	47	Math Sec	57	Bilingual/ELL	67	School Board President	77	Psychological Assess
		18	Chief Academic Officer	28	Technology Education	38	Guidance Services Sec	48	English/Lang Arts K-12	58	Special Education K-12	68	Teacher Personnel	78	Affirmative Action

New York School Directory — Nassau County

Plaza Elem Sch	K-5		443	36%	516/434-6600
501 Seaman Ave, Baldwin 11510			30		Fax 516/377-9429
Mark Gray					
Steele Elem Sch	K-5	T	302	40%	516/434-6700
860 Church St, Baldwin 11510			13		Fax 516/377-9431
Nicole Hunn					

● **Bellmore Union Free Sch Dist** PID: 00735011 516/679-2900
  580 Winthrop Ave, Bellmore 11710 Fax 516/679-3027

Schools: 3 \ **Teachers:** 95 \ **Students:** 1,100 \ **Special Ed Students:** 179 \ **LEP Students:** 29 \ **Ethnic:** Asian 8%, African American 2%, Hispanic 11%, Caucasian 79% \ **Exp:** $462 (High) \ **Poverty:** 2% \ **Title I:** $27,457 \ **Special Education:** $876,000 \ **Open-Close:** 09/08 - 06/24

Dr Joseph Famularo 1	Robin Lufrano 2,15,73,76,295	
Joseph Fiorino 3,5	Dr Joanne Dacek 11,19,83,98,286,288,296,298	
Jay Breakstone 67	Randy Yee 71	

Public Schs..Principal	Grd	Prgm	Enr/#Cls	SN	
Reinhard Early Childhood Ctr	PK-2		475	7%	516/679-2930
2750 S Saint Marks Ave, Bellmore 11710			30		Fax 516/679-2936
Patricia Castine					
Shore Road Sch	5-6		293	13%	516/679-2950
2801 Shore Rd, Bellmore 11710			27		Fax 516/679-5637
Patrice Matthews					
Winthrop Avenue Sch	3-4		275	8%	516/679-2920
580 Winthrop Ave, Bellmore 11710			15		Fax 516/679-5643
Sally Curto					

● **Bellmore-Merrick Ctl High SD** PID: 00737344 516/992-1000
  1260 Meadowbrook Rd, North Merrick 11566 Fax 516/623-8911

Schools: 5 \ **Teachers:** 446 \ **Students:** 5,273 \ **Special Ed Students:** 809 \ **LEP Students:** 31 \ **College-Bound:** 94% \ **Ethnic:** Asian 6%, African American 2%, Hispanic 11%, Caucasian 80% \ **Exp:** $266 (Med) \ **Poverty:** 2% \ **Title I:** $131,025 \ **Special Education:** $5,594,000 \ **Open-Close:** 09/08 - 06/24 \ **DTBP:** $323 (High)

John Detommaso 1	Kate Freeman 2,15,294
Jon Simpkins 3	Joanne Finelli 4
Thomas Volpe 5,91	Michael Harrington ... 10,11,15,57,71,296,298
Dr Mara Bollettieri 15,68,273	Joseph Innaco 16,69,73,95,295
Cheryl Fontana 22,25,30	Eric Caballero 35,80
Emily Paluseo 60,79	Eric Arlin 60,77,79,275,280
Gina Piskin 67	Sharon Valente 76
Susan Ellinghaus 88	

Public Schs..Principal	Grd	Prgm	Enr/#Cls	SN	
Calhoun High Sch	9-12	G	1,199	13%	516/992-1300
1786 State St, Merrick 11566					Fax 516/827-7390
Nicole Hollings					t
Grand Ave Middle Sch	7-8		958	11%	516/992-1100
2301 Grand Ave, Bellmore 11710			50		Fax 516/679-5068
Carlos Conte					
John F Kennedy High Sch	9-12		1,078	10%	516/992-1400
3000 Bellmore Ave, Bellmore 11710			40		Fax 516/785-7198
Gerard Owenburg					
Merrick Ave Middle Sch	7-8		771	7%	516/992-1200
1870 Merrick Ave, Merrick 11566					Fax 516/867-6391
Katelyn Dunn					
W C Mepham High Sch	9-12	G	1,267	14%	516/992-1500
2401 Camp Ave, Bellmore 11710			42		Fax 516/785-7590
Eric Gomez					

● **Bethpage Union Free Sch Dist** PID: 00735059 516/644-4000
  10 Cherry Ave, Bethpage 11714 Fax 516/931-8783

Schools: 5 \ **Teachers:** 261 \ **Students:** 2,946 \ **Special Ed Students:** 405 \ **LEP Students:** 86 \ **College-Bound:** 94% \ **Ethnic:** Asian 17%, Hispanic 16%, Caucasian 67% \ **Exp:** $420 (High) \ **Poverty:** 4% \ **Title I:** $101,438 \ **Special Education:** $2,697,000 \ **Open-Close:** 09/04 - 06/25 \ **DTBP:** $287 (High) \ f t

David Schneider 1	Scott Harrington 2,3,4,15
Peter Cavassa 3	Stacey Popkin 5
John Franchi 6,35*	Michael Spence 8,15
Caroline LaVelle 12,15,68	Dr Patricia Hantzidiamants 15,79
Kerri Pillittier 30*	Thomas Kenny 38,88
Janice Yale 44*	John Titolo 47*
Mary Hannon 49,280*	Lisa Lucchesi 58*
Michael Kelly 67	Angelo Lisa 91
William Santoro 295*	

Public Schs..Principal	Grd	Prgm	Enr/#Cls	SN	
Bethpage High Sch	9-12	AGTV	942	19%	516/644-4100
10 Cherry Ave, Bethpage 11714			60		Fax 516/644-4110
Nicholas Jantz					
Central Blvd Elem Sch	K-5		513	11%	516/644-4300
60 Central Blvd, Bethpage 11714			30		Fax 516/644-4309
Steven Furrey					
Charles Campagne Elem Sch	K-5		450	7%	516/644-4400
601 Plainview Rd, Bethpage 11714			20		Fax 516/644-4409
Erin Difiglia					
John F Kennedy Middle Sch	6-8		676	19%	516/644-4200
500 Broadway, Bethpage 11714			90		Fax 516/644-4205
Kevin Fullerton					
Kramer Lane Elem Sch	K-5		365	6%	516/644-4500
1 Kramer Ln, Plainview 11803			20		Fax 516/644-4509
Kerri McCarthy					

● **Carle Place Union Free SD** PID: 00735126 516/622-6400
  168 Cherry Ln, Carle Place 11514 Fax 516/622-6489

Schools: 3 \ **Teachers:** 149 \ **Students:** 1,360 \ **Special Ed Students:** 233 \ **LEP Students:** 67 \ **College-Bound:** 91% \ **Ethnic:** Asian 8%, African American 2%, Hispanic 22%, Caucasian 69% \ **Exp:** $400 (High) \ **Poverty:** 5% \ **Title I:** $100,890 \ **Special Education:** $1,596,000 \ **Open-Close:** 09/09 - 06/25 \ **DTBP:** $169 (High)

Dr Christine Finn 1	Kevin Coffey 2,11,15,296
John Hendricken 3	Nancy Waskowitz 4
Mike Margulis 5	Christine Ceruti 6
Eileen Fredericks 8,69,288,298	Dr Anastasia Tvorttnaos 16,73,286,297
James Fisher 16,57*	Lorayne Feit 16*
Michael Limone 20,23,27,75*	Dr Philip Molnar 58,79,83,88
Leslie Runbincin 61	John Difrisco 67
Lindsay Waskowitz 83*	Joseph Mazzilia 275,285

Public Schs..Principal	Grd	Prgm	Enr/#Cls	SN	
Carle Place Middle Sr High Sch	7-12		595	23%	516/622-6400
168 Cherry Ln, Carle Place 11514					Fax 516/622-6515
Thomas DePaola					
Cherry Lane Elem Sch	K-2		314	18%	516/622-6402
475 Roslyn Ave, Carle Place 11514			20		Fax 516/622-6586
Susan Folkson					
Rushmore Avenue Elem Sch	3-6		450	17%	516/622-6421
251 Rushmore Ave, Carle Place 11514			22		Fax 516/622-6588
Catherine Silletti					

---

79 Student Personnel	91 Safety/Security	275 Response To Intervention	298 Grant Writer/Ptnrships	**School Programs**
80 Driver Ed/Safety	92 Magnet School	277 Remedial Math K-12	750 Chief Innovation Officer	A = Alternative Program
81 Gifted/Talented	93 Parental Involvement	280 Literacy Coach	751 Chief of Staff	G = Adult Classes
82 Video Services	95 Tech Prep Program	285 STEM	752 Social Emotional Learning	M = Magnet Program
83 Substance Abuse Prev	97 Chief Infomation Officer	286 Digital Learning		T = Title I Schoolwide
84 Erate	98 Chief Technology Officer	288 Common Core Standards	**Other School Types**	V = Career & Tech Ed Programs
85 AIDS Education	270 Character Education	294 Accountability	Ⓐ = Alternative School	
88 Alternative/At Risk	271 Migrant Education	295 Network System	Ⓒ = Charter School	New Schools are shaded
89 Multi-Cultural Curriculum	273 Teacher Mentor	296 Title II Programs	Ⓜ = Magnet School	New Superintendents and Principals are bold
90 Social Work	274 Before/After Sch	297 Webmaster	Ⓨ = Year-Round School	Personnel with email addresses are underscored

Social Media
f = Facebook
t = Twitter

Nassau County

Market Data Retrieval

- **East Meadow Union Free SD** PID: 00735164 516/478-5730
  718 the Plain Rd Ste 1, Westbury 11590 Fax 516/478-5779

Schools: 9 \ **Teachers:** 623 \ **Students:** 7,100 \ **Special Ed Students:** 1,067 \ **LEP Students:** 272 \ **College-Bound:** 90% \ **Ethnic:** Asian 23%, African American 5%, Hispanic 21%, Caucasian 51% \ **Exp:** $323 (High) \ **Poverty:** 5% \ **Title I:** $527,628 \ **Special Education:** $9,351,000 \ **Open-Close:** 09/08 - 06/25 \ **DTBP:** $325 (High)

Name	Ref
Dr Kenneth Card	1
Craig Cammarata	3,91
Kristi Detor	6,7,30,35,83,85
Frank Lukasik	11,48,51,280
Kelly Gelfer	20,23
Demetrios Mendonis	39
Jenice Morgani	57*
Dr Effie Kyvelos	60
Joanne Naccarato	69,73
Danielle Betz	77,79
Patrick Pizzo	2,5,15
Josh Friedman	6*
David Casamento	8,15,34,74,89,271,273
Anthony Russo	15,68
Dr Gerilyn Smith	36
Debra Harley	42,45
Patrice Dobies	58,77,79
Matthew Melnick	67
William Brennan	72*

Public Schs..Principal	Grd	Prgm	Enr/#Cls	SN
Barnum Woods Elem Sch 500 May Ln, East Meadow 11554 Gregory Bottari	K-5		759	20% 516/564-6500 Fax 516/564-6507
Bowling Green Elem Sch 2340 Stewart Ave, Westbury 11590 Maria Ciarametaro	K-5		833 40	21% 516/876-7480 Fax 516/876-8458
East Meadow High Sch 101 Carman Ave, East Meadow 11554 Richard Howard	9-12	AGV	1,447	23% 516/228-5331 Fax 516/228-5339
McVey Elem Sch 2201 Devon St, East Meadow 11554 Kerry Dunne	K-5		752 55	26% 516/228-5300 Fax 516/228-5317
Meadowbrook Elem Sch 241 Old Westbury Rd, East Meadow 11554 Kelly Di Scalfani	K-5		442 23	24% 516/520-4400 Fax 516/520-4403
Parkway Elem Sch 465 Bellmore Rd, East Meadow 11554 Jamie Glicker-Mack	K-5		515 22	21% 516/679-3500 Fax 516/679-3507
W T Clarke Middle Sch 740 Edgewood Dr, Westbury 11590 Stacy Breslin	6-8	V	636	27% 516/876-7401 Fax 516/876-7407
W T Clarke Senior High Sch 740 Edgewood Dr, Westbury 11590 Timothy Voels	9-12	AV	788	24% 516/876-7450 Fax 516/876-7416
Woodland Middle Sch 690 Wenwood Dr, East Meadow 11554 James Lethbridge	6-8	V	1,068 80	24% 516/564-6523 Fax 516/564-6519

- **East Rockaway Union Free SD** PID: 00735281 516/887-8300
  443 Ocean Ave, East Rockaway 11518 Fax 516/887-8308

Schools: 3 \ **Teachers:** 113 \ **Students:** 1,200 \ **Special Ed Students:** 172 \ **LEP Students:** 35 \ **College-Bound:** 87% \ **Ethnic:** Asian 5%, African American 3%, Hispanic 28%, Caucasian 64% \ **Exp:** $440 (High) \ **Poverty:** 6% \ **Title I:** $114,524 \ **Special Education:** $1,538,000 \ **Open-Close:** 09/04 - 06/25 \ **DTBP:** $161 (High)

Name	Ref
Lisa Ruiz	1
James Daly	3
Mona Hecht	8,15,288*
Janna Bonacorsi	36
T J Dicietro	69,270*
Kristen Mednick	83,90*
Jacqueline Scrio	2,3,15
David Barth	6*
Vincent Healy	11,57,58,79,85,88,271
Dominick Vulpis	67
Lee Araoz	73
Jim Zervas	285*

Public Schs..Principal	Grd	Prgm	Enr/#Cls	SN
Centre Avenue Elem Sch 55 Centre Ave, East Rockaway 11518 Sherry Ma	K-6		301 14	29% 516/887-8300 Fax 516/599-5727
East Rockaway Jr Sr High Sch 443 Ocean Ave, East Rockaway 11518 Richard Schaffer	7-12	A	566 25	34% 516/887-8300
Rhame Avenue Elem Sch 100 Rhame Ave, East Rockaway 11518 Dr Ayesha McArthur	K-6		305 21	25% 516/887-8300 Fax 516/887-8332

- **East Williston Union Free SD** PID: 00735322 516/333-1630
  11 Bacon Rd, Old Westbury 11568 Fax 516/333-1937

Schools: 3 \ **Teachers:** 171 \ **Students:** 1,722 \ **Special Ed Students:** 223 \ **LEP Students:** 45 \ **College-Bound:** 100% \ **Ethnic:** Asian 31%, African American 1%, Hispanic 6%, Caucasian 62% \ **Exp:** $364 (High) \ **Poverty:** 4% \ **Title I:** $75,331 \ **Special Education:** $1,375,000 \ **Open-Close:** 09/08 - 06/25 \ **DTBP:** $159 (High) \ 📧

Name	Ref
Dr Elaine Kanas	1
Nicholas Fusco	3*
Danielle Gately	8,288*
Robert Teseo	45*
Mark Kamberg	67
Diane Cansenary	2,15
Micheal Scatorro	6,35,85
Lynn Mazza	11,58,79
Stephen Collier	50*
Ed Curningnenser	73*

Public Schs..Principal	Grd	Prgm	Enr/#Cls	SN
North Side Sch 110 E Williston Ave, E Williston 11596 James Bloomgarden	K-4	T	586 30	4% 516/333-6860 Fax 516/333-6537
Wheatley Sch 11 Bacon Rd, Old Westbury 11568 Dr Sean Feeney	8-12		720 52	5% 516/333-7804 Fax 516/333-7458
Willets Road Sch 455 I U Willets Rd, Roslyn HTS 11577 Dr Robert Hanna	5-7		416 30	7% 516/333-8797 Fax 516/333-8915

- **Elmont Union Free School Dist** PID: 00735360 516/326-5500
  135 Elmont Rd, Elmont 11003 Fax 516/326-5574

Schools: 6 \ **Teachers:** 325 \ **Students:** 3,500 \ **Special Ed Students:** 469 \ **LEP Students:** 299 \ **Ethnic:** Asian 21%, African American 42%, Hispanic 31%, Caucasian 6% \ **Exp:** $334 (High) \ **Poverty:** 10% \ **Title I:** $616,247 \ **Special Education:** $5,417,000 \ **Open-Close:** 09/04 - 06/29 \ **DTBP:** $343 (High)

Name	Ref
Al Harper	1
Dave Polizzi	3
Monae Vick	5
Kenneth Rosner	9,11,69,72,74,273*
Hellse Palmore	34,59,79
Michael Jaime	67
Thomas Galante	2
Celestine Lloyd	4
Stephanie Muller	7,59,77,79,88
Pat Vultaggio	16,82*
Debra Bennet	35*
Fernando Debartolo	73,76,91

Public Schs..Principal	Grd	Prgm	Enr/#Cls	SN
Alden Terrace Elem Sch 1835 N Central Ave, Valley Stream 11580 Shawnee Warfield	PK-6	T	426 25	57% 516/285-8310 Fax 516/285-8610
Clara H Carlson Elem Sch 235 Belmont Blvd, Elmont 11003 Stacia Walfall	PK-6	T	790 40	60% 516/326-5570 Fax 516/326-0349
Covert Avenue Elem Sch 144 Covert Ave, Elmont 11003 Mary Natoli	PK-6	T	686 37	58% 516/326-5560 Fax 516/326-0547
Dutch Broadway Elem Sch 1880 Dutch Broadway, Elmont 11003 Amy Buchanan	PK-6		702 45	55% 516/326-5550 Fax 516/326-0519

#		#		#		#		#		#		#	
1	Superintendent	8	Curric/Instruct K-12	19	Chief Financial Officer	29	Family/Consumer Science	39	Social Studies K-12	49	English/Lang Arts Elem	59	Special Education Elem	69	Academic Assessment
2	Bus/Finance/Purchasing	9	Curric/Instruct Elem	20	Art K-12	30	Adult Education	40	Social Studies Elem	50	English/Lang Arts Sec	60	Special Education Sec	70	Research/Development
3	Buildings And Grounds	10	Curric/Instruct Sec	21	Art Elem	31	Career/Sch-to-Work K-12	41	Social Studies Sec	51	Reading K-12	61	Foreign/World Lang K-12	71	Public Information
4	Food Service	11	Federal Program	22	Art Sec	32	Career/Sch-to-Work Elem	42	Science K-12	52	Reading Elem	62	Foreign/World Lang Elem	72	Summer School
5	Transportation	12	Title I	23	Music K-12	33	Career/Sch-to-Work Sec	43	Science Elem	53	Reading Sec	63	Foreign/World Lang Sec	73	Instructional Tech
6	Athletic	13	Title V	24	Music Elem	34	Early Childhood Ed	44	Science Sec	54	Remedial Reading K-12	64	Religious Education K-12	74	Inservice Training
7	Health Services	15	Asst Superintendent	25	Music Sec	35	Health/Phys Education	45	Math K-12	55	Remedial Reading Elem	65	Religious Education Elem	75	Marketing/Distributive
		16	Instructional Media Svcs	26	Business Education	36	Guidance Services K-12	46	Math Elem	56	Remedial Reading Sec	66	Religious Education Sec	76	Info Systems
		17	Chief Operations Officer	27	Career & Tech Ed	37	Guidance Services Elem	47	Math Sec	57	Bilingual/ELL	67	School Board President	77	Psychological Assess
		18	Chief Academic Officer	28	Technology Education	38	Guidance Services Sec	48	English/Lang Arts K-12	58	Special Education K-12	68	Teacher Personnel	78	Affirmative Action

New York School Directory — Nassau County

Public Schs..Principal	Grd	Prgm	Enr/#Cls	SN	
Gotham Avenue Elem Sch 181 Gotham Ave, Elmont 11003 Marshall Zucker	PK-6	T	589 33	63%	516/326-5540 Fax 516/326-0563
Stewart Manor Elem Sch 38 Stewart Ave, Stewart Manor 11530 Hope Kranidis	PK-6		335 18	36%	516/326-5530 Fax 516/326-0548

- **Farmingdale Union Free SD** PID: 00735437 — 516/434-5000
  50 Van Cott Ave, Farmingdale 11735 — Fax 516/847-0363

Schools: 6 \ **Teachers:** 459 \ **Students:** 5,900 \ **Special Ed Students:** 994 \ **LEP Students:** 262 \ **College-Bound:** 88% \ **Ethnic:** Asian 6%, African American 7%, Hispanic 24%, Caucasian 63% \ **Exp:** $421 (High) \ **Poverty:** 5% \ **Title I:** $481,273 \ **Special Education:** $7,108,000 \ **Open-Close:** 08/06 - 06/25 \ **DTBP:** $312 (High) \ f

Paul Defendini 1
Nelson Dominguez 3,91
Joseph Williams 5
Yuvelin Baltar 9
Barbara Horsley 11,92,93,271,273,274,296
William Brennan 15,70,73,76,295,297*
Rose Marvel 20
Stanley Pelech 27
Jane Gruner 34
Garner Bass 39,89*
Josh Anisansel 48,51,54*
Susan Dorfman 60*
Mary Rogers 68
Kathy Hart 76
Brian Ernst 2
Maureen McCorkell 4*
Joan Ripley 8,12,15,16,69,74
Brian Norton 10
Glen Zakian 15,68
Jennifer Olsen 16,81*
Rita Padden 23,61*
Ellen Krammer 34
Maureen Moloughney 36*
Kristen Cummings 42*
Donald Cassidy 58*
Michael Goldberg 67
David Spielberg 72*
Dr Steve Kearney 77

Public Schs..Principal	Grd	Prgm	Enr/#Cls	SN	
Albany Ave Elem Sch 101 N Albany Ave, N Massapequa 11758 Joseph Valentine	K-5		524 40	10%	516/434-5510 Fax 516/434-5955
Farmingdale Senior High Sch 150 Lincoln St, Farmingdale 11735 Samuel Thompson	9-12		1,902 53	20%	516/434-5210 Fax 516/454-6196
Howitt Middle Sch 50 Van Cott Ave, Farmingdale 11735 Luis Pena	6-8	T	1,265	22%	516/434-5410 Fax 516/752-2004
Northside Elem Sch 55 Powell Pl, Farmingdale 11735 Michael Febbraro	K-5		443	16%	516/434-5610 Fax 516/434-5956 f
Saltzman East Memorial ES 25 Mill Ln, Farmingdale 11735 Patricia Oregan	K-5		596 31	38%	516/434-5710 Fax 516/434-5957
Woodward Parkway Elem Sch 95 Woodward Pkwy, Farmingdale 11735 Patrick Klocek	K-5		792	20%	516/434-5810 Fax 516/434-5958

- **Floral Park Bellerose Sch Dist** PID: 00735528 — 516/434-2725
  1 Poppy Pl, Floral Park 11001 — Fax 516/327-9304

Schools: 2 \ **Teachers:** 117 \ **Students:** 1,479 \ **Special Ed Students:** 241 \ **LEP Students:** 28 \ **Ethnic:** Asian 17%, African American 3%, Hispanic 17%, Caucasian 62% \ **Exp:** $440 (High) \ **Poverty:** 4% \ **Title I:** $59,172 \ **Special Education:** $2,335,000 \ **Open-Close:** 09/08 - 06/25 \ **DTBP:** $144 (High)

Kathleen Sottile 1
Paul Gustafsson 3
Tyrone Kelsie 5
Nora Epstien 7,83,85*
Laura Ferone 67
Daniel Cunneely 73,76,295
Michael Fabiano 2,15
Karen Crenshaw 4
Dr Juli Mulcahy 7,9,15,59,74
Sharon Meyer 9
Rose Morris 68

Public Schs..Principal	Grd	Prgm	Enr/#Cls	SN	
Floral Park Bellerose Elem Sch 2 Larch Ave, Floral Park 11001 Jaime Adams	PK-6		852	9%	516/434-2750
John Lewis Childs Elem Sch 10 Elizabeth St, Floral Park 11001 Susan Fazio	PK-6	T	627 45	19%	516/434-2780

- **Franklin Square Union Free SD** PID: 00735621 — 516/481-4100
  760 Washington St, Franklin Sq 11010 — Fax 516/505-6972

Schools: 3 \ **Teachers:** 144 \ **Students:** 1,940 \ **Special Ed Students:** 313 \ **LEP Students:** 59 \ **Ethnic:** Asian 12%, African American 2%, Hispanic 24%, Caucasian 61% \ **Exp:** $236 (Med) \ **Poverty:** 5% \ **Title I:** $143,155 \ **Special Education:** $2,396,000 \ **Open-Close:** 09/02 - 06/23 \ **DTBP:** $175 (High)

Dr Jared Bloom 1
Maura Gallagher . 9,15,69,74,273,285,288,294
Dr Pamela Taylor 59
Jane Centrella 68
Theresa Hennessy 2,3,15
Jung Lee 11,73,296,298*
Stephen Toto 67

Public Schs..Principal	Grd	Prgm	Enr/#Cls	SN	
John Street Elem Sch 560 Nassau Blvd, Franklin Sq 11010 Thomas Riccobono	PK-6		489 28	16%	516/481-5780 Fax 516/505-6988
Polk Street Elem Sch 960 Polk Ave, Franklin Sq 11010 Gilbert Torossian	PK-6	T	679 32	15%	516/352-6300 Fax 516/326-3794
Washington Street Elem Sch 760 Washington St, Franklin Sq 11010 John Stella	PK-6		813 41	18%	516/481-4100 Fax 516/505-6991

- **Freeport Public School Dist** PID: 00735671 — 516/867-5200
  235 N Ocean Ave, Freeport 11520 — Fax 516/623-4759

Schools: 8 \ **Teachers:** 524 \ **Students:** 6,885 \ **Special Ed Students:** 1,151 \ **LEP Students:** 1,365 \ **Ethnic:** Asian 1%, African American 23%, Hispanic 69%, Caucasian 7% \ **Exp:** $223 (Med) \ **Poverty:** 16% \ **Title I:** $1,760,430 \ **Special Education:** $15,982,000 \ **Open-Close:** 09/01 - 06/25 \ **DTBP:** $305 (High)

Dr Kishore Kuncham 1
Kevin Randazzo 3
Dr Catalina Castillo 11,76,92,298
Salvatore Carambia 15
Dr Anthony Murray 45
Suzanne Chaves 57
Ernest Kight 67
Jason Eckstein 73
Dr Beth Rella 2
Dr Marianne DeVivo 8,15,288
Ben Roberts 15,68
Emma Perdomo 36
Glori Engel 48
Dr Helen Kanellopoulos 58,79
Ruth Breidenbach 71
Glen Stewart 79

Public Schs..Principal	Grd	Prgm	Enr/#Cls	SN	
Ⓜ Archer Street Elem Sch 255 Archer St, Freeport 11520 Paula Lein	K-4	T	564 27	74%	516/867-5250 Fax 516/379-6577
Ⓜ Bayview Avenue Sch 325 W Merrick Rd, Freeport 11520 Mary Garguilo	K-4	T	559 26	65%	516/867-5255 Fax 516/379-6906
Caroline G Atkinson Interm Sch 58 W Seaman Ave, Freeport 11520 Tiffany Pendola	5-6	T	1,082 75	59%	516/867-5265 Fax 516/379-7678
Columbus Ave Early Chldhd Ctr 150 N Columbus Ave, Freeport 11520 Alma Rocha	PK-K		217 24	46%	516/867-5240 Fax 516/379-6793

---

79 Student Personnel
80 Driver Ed/Safety
81 Gifted/Talented
82 Video Services
83 Substance Abuse Prev
84 Erate
85 AIDS Education
88 Alternative/At Risk
89 Multi-Cultural Curriculum
90 Social Work
91 Safety/Security
92 Magnet School
93 Parental Involvement
95 Tech Prep Program
97 Chief Information Officer
98 Chief Technology Officer
270 Character Education
271 Migrant Education
273 Teacher Mentor
274 Before/After Sch
275 Response To Intervention
277 Remedial Math K-12
280 Literacy Coach
285 STEM
286 Digital Learning
288 Common Core Standards
294 Accountability
295 Network System
296 Title II Programs
297 Webmaster
298 Grant Writer/Ptnrships
750 Chief Innovation Officer
751 Chief of Staff
752 Social Emotional Learning

School Programs
A = Alternative Program
G = Adult Classes
M = Magnet Program
T = Title I Schoolwide
V = Career & Tech Ed Programs

Other School Types
Ⓐ = Alternative School
Ⓒ = Charter School
Ⓜ = Magnet School
Ⓨ = Year-Round School

Social Media
f = Facebook
t = Twitter

New Schools are shaded
New Superintendents and Principals are bold
Personnel with email addresses are underscored

Nassau County

Market Data Retrieval

	Grd	Prgm	Enr/#Cls	SN		
Freeport High Sch 50 S Brookside Ave, Freeport 11520 Joseph Mille	9-12		2,225 80	56%	516/867-5300 Fax 516/379-7592	
John W Dodd Middle Sch 25 Pine St, Freeport 11520 Johane Ligonde	7-8	T	1,062	63%	516/867-5280 Fax 516/379-6794	
ⓜ Leo F Giblyn Elem Sch 480 S Ocean Ave, Freeport 11520 Amanda Muldowney	K-4	T	585 12	57%	516/867-5260 Fax 516/379-6887	
ⓜ New Visions Elem Sch 80 Raynor St, Freeport 11520 Constance Malcolm-Grant	K-4	T	486 23	65%	516/867-5390 Fax 516/867-0392	

● **Garden City School Dist** PID: 00735750   516/478-1000
56 Cathedral Ave, Garden City 11530   Fax 516/294-1045

> **Schools:** 7 \ **Teachers:** 306 \ **Students:** 3,800 \ **Special Ed Students:** 608 \ **LEP Students:** 39 \ **College-Bound:** 97% \ **Ethnic:** Asian 6%, African American 1%, Hispanic 6%, Caucasian 87% \ **Exp:** $427 (High) \ **Poverty:** 2% \ **Title I:** $92,140 \ **Special Education:** $3,527,000 \ **Open-Close:** 09/02 - 06/25 \ **DTBP:** $320 (High) \ 🅣

Dr Kusum Sinha 1	Dana DiCapua 2,15,16,91
Patrick Mehr 3	Deanna Intintoli 4
David Murphy 5	Dawn Cerrone 6,35*
Lynette Abruzzo 7,57,58,69,77,79,81,85	Dr Edward Cannone 8,11,34,74,270,285,288,296
Dr Maureen Appiarias 11,15,68,298	Dina Bombardiere 16,82,83,88,90*
Judith Conforti 16*	Diane Johnson 36
William Holub 67	Joe Papa 72
Pat Galano 73	Dr Rita Melikian 73,286
Jacquelin Guerra 273*	

Public Schs..Principal	Grd	Prgm	Enr/#Cls	SN		
Garden City Middle Sch 98 Cherry Valley Ave, Garden City 11530 Dr Eric Nezowitz	6-8		881 60	3%	516/478-3000 Fax 516/294-0732	
Garden City Senior High Sch 170 Rockaway Ave, Garden City 11530 Kevin Steingruebner	9-12		1,209 55	4%	516/478-2000 Fax 516/294-2639	🅕🅣
Hemlock Sch 78 Bayberry Ave, Garden City 11530 Audrey Bellovin	K-1		227 17	2%	516/478-1600 Fax 516/747-4767	
Homestead Primary Sch 2 Homestead Ave, Garden City 11530 Dr Suzanne Viscovich	K-1		213 13	1%	516/478-1700 Fax 516/616-0906	
Locust Primary Sch 220 Boylston St, Garden City 11530 Jean Ricotta	K-1		164 10	2%	516/478-1800 Fax 516/747-4586	
Stewart Elem Sch 501 Stewart Ave, Garden City 11530 Linda Norton	2-5		642 30	3%	516/478-1400 Fax 516/294-5781	🅣
Stratford Avenue Elem Sch 97 Stratford Ave, Garden City 11530 Eileen Vota	2-5		602 35	2%	516/478-1500 Fax 516/294-9061	

● **Glen Cove City School Dist** PID: 00735839   516/759-7202
154 Dosoris Ln, Glen Cove 11542   Fax 516/801-7019

> **Schools:** 6 \ **Teachers:** 262 \ **Students:** 3,200 \ **Special Ed Students:** 687 \ **LEP Students:** 538 \ **College-Bound:** 91% \ **Ethnic:** Asian 3%, African American 8%, Hispanic 63%, Caucasian 26% \ **Exp:** $343 (High) \ **Poverty:** 13% \ **Title I:** $736,478 \ **Special Education:** $2,666,000 \ **Open-Close:** 09/08 - 06/25 \ **DTBP:** $313 (High)

Dr Maria Rianna 1	Victoria Galante 2,15
Viktor Tymchynyuk 3,91	Peter Cardone 6,35,83,85*
Dr Michael Israel 8,15,73,288	Sheena Jacob 39
Cassie Shannon 45	Monica Chavez 57*
Allison Hernandez 58	Monica Miller 67
Justin Lander 73	Michael Tweed 79*
Gayle Tullo 295	

Public Schs..Principal	Grd	Prgm	Enr/#Cls	SN	
Connolly Elem Sch 100 Ridge Dr, Glen Cove 11542 Julie Mullan	3-5	T	385 17	62%	516/801-7310 Fax 516/801-7319
Deasy Elem Sch 2 Dosoris Ln, Glen Cove 11542 Melanie Arfman	PK-2	T	369 22	46%	516/801-7110 Fax 516/801-7119
Glen Cove High Sch 150 Dosoris Ln, Glen Cove 11542 Antonio Santana	9-12	AV	1,059	61%	516/801-7600 Fax 516/801-7619
Gribbin Elem Sch 100 Seaman Rd, Glen Cove 11542 Francine Santoro	K-2	T	297 18	48%	516/801-7210 Fax 516/801-7001
Landing Elem Sch 60 McLoughlin St, Glen Cove 11542 Alexa Doeschner	3-5	T	369 16	66%	516/801-7410 Fax 516/801-7419
Robert M Finley Middle Sch 1 Forest Ave, Glen Cove 11542 Nelson Iocolano	6-8	V	715 65	63%	516/801-7510 Fax 516/801-7519

● **Great Neck Public Schools** PID: 00735920   516/441-4001
345 Lakeville Rd, Great Neck 11020   Fax 516/441-4994

> **Schools:** 12 \ **Teachers:** 637 \ **Students:** 6,700 \ **Special Ed Students:** 1,232 \ **LEP Students:** 366 \ **College-Bound:** 97% \ **Ethnic:** Asian 42%, African American 1%, Hispanic 9%, Caucasian 47% \ **Exp:** $256 (Med) \ **Poverty:** 6% \ **Title I:** $653,058 \ **Special Education:** $4,924,000 \ **Open-Close:** 09/02 - 06/25 \ **DTBP:** $297 (High)

Dr Teresa Prendergast 1	John Powell 2,11,15
Alfredo Cavallero 3	James Gounaris 4
James Popkin 5	David Zawatson 6
Dr Stephen Lando 10,15	Kelly Newman 12,15,32
Justin Lander 16,73,76,286	Dr Joseph Hickey 58,79
Barbara Berkowitz 67	Jennifer Kirby 68
Maria Giannopollous 72	Rich Castro 91

Public Schs..Principal	Grd	Prgm	Enr/#Cls	SN	
Adult Education Center 30 Cumberland Ave, Great Neck 11020 Dr Errin Hatwood	Adult		300 10		516/441-4949 Fax 516/441-4937
Clover Drive Adult Lrng Center 105 Clover Dr, Great Neck 11021 Dr Errin Hatwood	Adult		1,000 10		516/441-4950 Fax 516/441-4260
E M Baker Sch 69 Baker Hill Rd, Great Neck 11023 Dr Michael Grimaldi	K-5		677 30	15%	516/441-4100 Fax 516/441-4190
Great Neck North Middle Sch 77 Polo Rd, Great Neck 11023 Gerald Cozine	6-8		821 55	18%	516/441-4500 Fax 516/441-4594
Great Neck South High Sch 341 Lakeville Rd, Great Neck 11020 Dr Christopher Gitz	9-12	V	1,250 75	20%	516/441-4800 Fax 516/441-4893
Great Neck South Middle Sch 349 Lakeville Rd, Great Neck 11020 Dr Gina Cartolano	6-8		791	16%	516/441-4600 Fax 516/441-4690
JL Miller-Great Neck North HS 35 Polo Rd, Great Neck 11023 Dan Holtzman	9-12		1,193	19%	516/441-4700 Fax 516/441-4795

1	Superintendent	8	Curric/Instruct K-12	19	Chief Financial Officer	29	Family/Consumer Science
2	Bus/Finance/Purchasing	9	Curric/Instruct Elem	20	Art K-12	30	Adult Education
3	Buildings And Grounds	10	Curric/Instruct Sec	21	Art Elem	31	Career/Sch-to-Work K-12
4	Food Service	11	Federal Program	22	Art Sec	32	Career/Sch-to-Work Elem
5	Transportation	12	Title I	23	Music K-12	33	Career/Sch-to-Work Sec
6	Athletic	13	Title V	24	Music Elem	34	Early Childhood Ed
7	Health Services	15	Asst Superintendent	25	Music Sec	35	Health/Phys Education
		16	Instructional Media Svcs	26	Business Education	36	Guidance Services K-12
		17	Chief Operations Officer	27	Career & Tech Ed	37	Guidance Services Elem
		18	Chief Academic Officer	28	Technology Education	38	Guidance Services Sec

39	Social Studies K-12	49	English/Lang Arts Elem	59	Special Education Elem	69	Academic Assessment
40	Social Studies Elem	50	English/Lang Arts Sec	60	Special Education Sec	70	Research/Development
41	Social Studies Sec	51	Reading K-12	61	Foreign/World Lang K-12	71	Public Information
42	Science K-12	52	Reading Elem	62	Foreign/World Lang Elem	72	Summer School
43	Science Elem	53	Reading Sec	63	Foreign/World Lang Sec	73	Instructional Tech
44	Science Sec	54	Remedial Reading K-12	64	Religious Education K-12	74	Inservice Training
45	Math K-12	55	Remedial Reading Elem	65	Religious Education Elem	75	Marketing/Distributive
46	Math Elem	56	Remedial Reading Sec	66	Religious Education Sec	76	Info Systems
47	Math Sec	57	Bilingual/ELL	67	School Board President	77	Psychological Assess
48	English/Lang Arts K-12	58	Special Education K-12	68	Teacher Personnel	78	Affirmative Action

New York School Directory — Nassau County

John F Kennedy Sch 1A Grassfield Rd, Great Neck 11024 Ron Gimondo	PK-5		455 34	27%	516/441-4200 Fax 516/441-4290
Lakeville Elem Sch 4727 Jayson Ave, Great Neck 11020 Emily Zucal	1-5		746 30	16%	516/441-4300 Fax 516/441-4316
Parkville Sch 10 Campbell St, New Hyde Park 11040 Kathleen Murray	PK-K		317	13%	516/441-4350 Fax 516/441-4367
Saddle Rock Elem Sch 10 Hawthorne Ln, Great Neck 11023 Luci Bradley	K-5		542 31	17%	516/441-4400 Fax 516/441-4993
ⓐ Village Sch 614 Middle Neck Rd, Great Neck 11023 Stephen Goldberg	9-12	V	37 10	11%	516/441-4900 Fax 516/441-4909

● **Hempstead Union Free SD** PID: 00736089   516/434-4000
185 Peninsula Blvd, Hempstead 11550   Fax 516/292-0933

Schools: 10 \ **Teachers:** 458 \ **Students:** 7,355 \ **Special Ed Students:** 1,194 \ **LEP Students:** 2,764 \ **College-Bound:** 35% \ **Ethnic:** Asian 1%, African American 24%, Hispanic 74%, Caucasian 2% \ **Exp:** $387 (High) \ **Poverty:** 23% \ **Title I:** $2,833,626 \ **Special Education:** $22,638,000 \ **Open-Close:** 09/03 - 06/25 \ **DTBP:** $327 (High)

Regina Armstrong 1
Timothy Gregg 3
Dr Johnetta Hill 6
Robert Cincotta 6,58*
Dr Ahunna Akoma 15,73
Dr Rodney Gilmore 15,68
Susan Thompson 27,30,88
Janett Lovett 57
Andrew Hardwick 91
Larry Dobroff 2,15
Sharon Gardner 4*
Dr Johnetta Hill 6,58*
James Clark 10,15,288
Djuana Wilson 15,58
Angel Perez 16,20,23*
Robert Kurtz 39,74
Lamont Johnson 67

Public Schs..Principal	Grd	Prgm	Enr/#Cls		SN
Alverta B Gray Schultz Mid Sch 70 Greenwich St, Hempstead 11550 Adrian Manuel	6-8	GT	1,367 55	71%	516/434-4300 Fax 516/483-2549
Barack Obama Elem Sch 176 William St, Hempstead 11550 Kelly Fairclough	1-5	T	430 21	76%	516/434-4400 Fax 516/489-1107
David Paterson Sch 40 Fulton Ave, Hempstead 11550 Gary Rush	1-5	T	544 26	77%	516/434-4450 Fax 516/489-6492
Front Street Sch 436 Front St, Hempstead 11550 Arlise Carson	1-5	T	350	79%	516/434-4550 Fax 516/489-5701
Hempstead High Sch 201 President Ave, Hempstead 11550 Kenneth Klein	9-12	AGTV	2,248 90	72%	516/434-4202 Fax 516/292-7775
Jackson Annex Sch 380 Jackson St, Hempstead 11550 Sheena Burke	1-5	T	495 16	72%	516/434-4600 Fax 516/564-0340
Jackson Main Elem Sch 451 Jackson St, Hempstead 11550 Richard Brown	1-5	T	441 19	75%	516/434-4650 Fax 516/489-6396
Joseph A McNeil Elem Sch 335 S Franklin St, Hempstead 11550 Sandra Powell	1-5	T	619 37	72%	516/434-4500 Fax 516/434-4500
Marshall Sch 15 E Marshall St, Hempstead 11550 Juanita Diaz	PK-PK		252	7%	516/434-4750 Fax 516/292-1433
Prospect Sch 265 Peninsula Blvd, Hempstead 11550 Carol Eason	PK-K	T	491 10	32%	516/434-4700

● **Herricks Union Free Sch Dist** PID: 00736194   516/305-8900
999 Herricks Rd Ste B, New Hyde Park 11040   Fax 516/248-3281

Schools: 5 \ **Teachers:** 345 \ **Students:** 3,950 \ **Special Ed Students:** 544 \ **LEP Students:** 226 \ **Ethnic:** Asian 67%, African American 1%, Hispanic 6%, Caucasian 26% \ **Exp:** $271 (Med) \ **Poverty:** 3% \ **Title I:** $125,107 \ **Special Education:** $4,154,000 \ **Open-Close:** 09/01 - 06/25 \ **DTBP:** $313 (High)

Dr Fino Celano 1
Marty Abrams 3
Elizabeth Guercin 8,15,78,285,288
Dina Maggiacomo 15,68
Anissa Arnold 23*
Francisco Fratto 57,63*
Chris Connors 73*
Rosemarie LaMarca 273
Lisa Rutkoske 2,15
Shakia Hall 4*
Karen Hughes 11,42*
Mary Passero 20*
Natasha Khan 38
Henry Zanetti 67
Lois Jankeloff 79,88,298

Public Schs..Principal	Grd	Prgm	Enr/#Cls		SN
Center Street Elem Sch 240 Center St, Williston Pk 11596 Brennen Bierwiler	K-5		481 25	10%	516/305-8300 Fax 516/739-4739
Denton Avenue Elem Sch 1050 Denton Ave, New Hyde Park 11040 Loren Borgese	K-5		620 51	10%	516/305-8400 Fax 516/739-4754
Herricks High Sch 100 Shelter Rock Rd, New Hyde Park 11040 Joan Keegan	9-12	AV	1,300 85	18%	516/305-8700 Fax 516/248-3282
Herricks Middle Sch 7 Hilldale Dr, Albertson 11507 Brian McConaghy	6-8	V	1,016	14%	516/305-8600 Fax 516/739-4738
Searingtown Elem Sch 106 Beverly Dr, Albertson 11507 Diana Degiorgio	K-5		570 26	12%	516/305-8500 Fax 516/248-3277

● **Hewlett Woodmere Union Free SD** PID: 00736273   516/792-4800
1 Johnson Pl, Woodmere 11598   Fax 516/374-8101

Schools: 5 \ **Teachers:** 286 \ **Students:** 3,000 \ **Special Ed Students:** 623 \ **LEP Students:** 84 \ **Ethnic:** Asian 10%, African American 9%, Hispanic 15%, Caucasian 66% \ **Exp:** $722 (High) \ **Poverty:** 5% \ **Title I:** $268,586 \ **Special Education:** $2,626,000 \ **Open-Close:** 09/03 - 06/25 \ **DTBP:** $820 (High)

Dr Ralph Marino 1,11
Kim Parahus 3
Joseph DiBartolo 5
Barbara Giese 12,71,296,298
Walter Lastowski 20,23
Laura Peterson 58
Edward Fale 68
Frank DeLeo 91
Marie Donnelly 2,15
Michelle Rosenthal 4*
David Viegas 6,35,85*
David Flatley 15
Alba Gallegos 57
Debra Sheinin 67
Amanda Kavanagh 73,286

Public Schs..Principal	Grd	Prgm	Enr/#Cls		SN
Franklin Early Childhood Ctr 1180 Henrietta Pl, Hewlett 11557 Lorraine Smyth	PK-1		450 25	19%	516/792-4600 Fax 516/374-4690
George W Hewlett High Sch 60 Everit Ave, Hewlett 11557 William Galati	9-12	AGV	1,064	24%	516/792-4100 Fax 516/374-8173
Hewlett Elem Sch 1570 Broadway, Hewlett 11557 Colleen O'Hara	2-5		446 30	20%	516/792-4500 Fax 516/374-8182
Ogden Elem Sch 875 Longview Ave, Valley Stream 11581 Dina Anzalone	2-5		358 26	24%	516/792-4700 Fax 516/374-4643

---

79 Student Personnel	91 Safety/Security	275 Response To Intervention	298 Grant Writer/Ptnrships	**School Programs**
80 Driver Ed/Safety	92 Magnet School	277 Remedial Math K-12	750 Chief Innovation Officer	A = Alternative Program
81 Gifted/Talented	93 Parental Involvement	280 Literacy Coach	751 Chief of Staff	G = Adult Classes
82 Video Services	95 Tech Prep Program	285 STEM	752 Social Emotional Learning	M = Magnet Program
83 Substance Abuse Prev	97 Chief Information Officer	286 Digital Learning		T = Title I Schoolwide
84 Erate	98 Chief Technology Officer	288 Common Core Standards	**Other School Types**	V = Career & Tech Ed Programs
85 AIDS Education	270 Character Education	294 Accountability	Ⓐ = Alternative School	
88 Alternative/At Risk	271 Migrant Education	295 Network System	Ⓒ = Charter School	New Schools are shaded
89 Multi-Cultural Curriculum	273 Teacher Mentor	296 Title II Programs	Ⓜ = Magnet School	New Superintendents and Principals are bold
90 Social Work	274 Before/After Sch	297 Webmaster	Ⓨ = Year-Round School	Personnel with email addresses are underscored

Social Media
 = Facebook
 = Twitter

Nassau County

Market Data Retrieval

Woodmere Middle Sch — 6-8 — 655 — 25% — 516/792-4300
1170 Peninsula Blvd, Hewlett 11557 — Fax 516/374-4571
Al Bauer

• Hicksville Union Free Sch Dist PID: 00736352
200 Division Ave, Hicksville 11801
516/733-2100
Fax 516/733-6584

Schools: 9 \ **Teachers:** 428 \ **Students:** 5,000 \ **Special Ed Students:** 858 \ **LEP Students:** 539 \ **College-Bound:** 90% \ **Ethnic:** Asian 36%, African American 2%, Hispanic 33%, Caucasian 29% \ **Exp:** $253 (Med) \ **Poverty:** 8% \ **Title I:** $655,785 \ **Special Education:** $5,681,000 \ **Open-Close:** 09/09 - 06/25 \ **DTBP:** $301 (High)

Marianne Litzman	1	Ellen Reilly	2
Marcy Tannenbaum	2,15	David Bell	3
Virginia Polit	4	Joseph Delutri	5
Matt Calarco	6,35,80,83*	Susan Guiliano	8,69
Daniel Friedman	11,73	Anthony Lubrano	15*
Rosemarie Coletti	15,68	Dr Thomas Moss	16,48,51*
Philip Grusenmeyer	20	Linda Pfaffe	26,45*
Dr Rose Borda	31,39*	Michael O'Connell	42*
Lisa Estrada	57	Christine Snow	58,79
Claire Hochheiser	58,79	Phil Heckler	67

Public Schs..Principal	Grd	Prgm	Enr/#Cls	SN
Burns Avenue Elem Sch 40 Burns Ave, Hicksville 11801 Dr John Comer	PK-5	T	298 27	43% 516/733-2311 Fax 516/733-6694
Dutch Lane Elem Sch 50 Stewart Ave, Hicksville 11801 Janine Rossi	PK-5		281 22	25% 516/733-2361 Fax 516/733-3520
East Street Elem Sch 50 East St, Hicksville 11801 Jean-Marie Serra	K-5	T	383	43% 516/733-2321 Fax 516/733-3533
Fork Lane Elem Sch 4 Fork Ln, Hicksville 11801 Chris Scardino	K-5		283 13	33% 516/733-2341 Fax 516/733-3521
Hicksville High Sch 180 Division Ave, Hicksville 11801 Raymond Williams	9-12	GV	1,691	41% 516/733-2200 Fax 516/733-6626
Hicksville Middle Sch 215 Jerusalem Ave, Hicksville 11801 Mara Jorisch	6-8	T	1,316	45% 516/733-2261 Fax 516/733-6528
Lee Avenue Elem Sch 1 7th St, Hicksville 11801 Stephanie Stam	K-5		476	41% 516/733-2351 Fax 516/733-3522
Old Country Road Elem Sch 49 Rhodes Ln, Hicksville 11801 Laura McConnell	K-5	T	338 25	51% 516/733-2301 Fax 516/733-3523
Woodland Elem Sch 85 Ketcham Rd, Hicksville 11801 Beth Swanson	PK-5		326 17	28% 516/733-2331 Fax 516/733-3524

• Island Park Union Free SD PID: 00736467
99 Radcliffe Rd, Island Park 11558
516/434-2600
Fax 516/431-7550

Schools: 2 \ **Teachers:** 81 \ **Students:** 743 \ **Special Ed Students:** 114 \ **LEP Students:** 60 \ **Ethnic:** Asian 3%, African American 2%, Hispanic 38%, Caucasian 56% \ **Exp:** $873 (High) \ **Poverty:** 8% \ **Title I:** $118,614 \ **Special Education:** $574,000 \ **Open-Close:** 09/09 - 06/25 \ **DTBP:** $157 (High)

Dr Rosmarie Bovino	1	Idowu Ogundipe	2
Frank Santillo	3	Dena Debari	4
Kelly Angelo	5	Vincent Randazo	15
Jacob Russem	59,69	Jack Vobis	67

Public Schs..Principal	Grd	Prgm	Enr/#Cls	SN
Francis X Hegarty Elem Sch 100 Radcliffe Rd, Island Park 11558 Jacob Russum	PK-4		419 30	34% 516/434-2670 Fax 516/431-2372
Lincoln Orens Middle Sch 150 Trafalgar Blvd, Island Park 11558 Vincent Randazzo	5-8	GT	324 25	40% 516/434-2630 Fax 516/432-7732

• Island Trees Union Free SD PID: 00736508
74 Farmedge Rd, Levittown 11756
516/520-2100
Fax 516/520-2113

Schools: 4 \ **Teachers:** 185 \ **Students:** 2,236 \ **Special Ed Students:** 297 \ **LEP Students:** 62 \ **College-Bound:** 90% \ **Ethnic:** Asian 11%, African American 2%, Hispanic 20%, Caucasian 67% \ **Exp:** $345 (High) \ **Poverty:** 5% \ **Title I:** $175,876 \ **Special Education:** $3,723,000 \ **Open-Close:** 09/08 - 06/25 \ **DTBP:** $274 (High)

Dr Charles Murphy	1	Susan Hlavenka	2,15
Kenneth McLean	3,91	Carolynn Grodski	4*
Sean Burns	6,35	Elizabeth Roemer	8,15,74,280,296*
Dr Arlene Genden-Sage	15,58,69*	Christina Pesiri	16
Michael Rich	67	Leslie Tolan	68
John Rezek	73*	James Cranmer	85*

Public Schs..Principal	Grd	Prgm	Enr/#Cls	SN
Island Trees High Sch 59 Straight Ln, Levittown 11756 Nick Grande	9-12	A	752	23% 516/520-2136 Fax 516/520-2188
Island Trees Memorial Mid Sch 45 Wantagh Ave, Levittown 11756 Daniel Keegan	5-8	G	671 70	25% 516/520-2157 Fax 516/520-2168
J Fred Sparke Elem Sch 100 Robin Pl, Levittown 11756 Dr Penny Fisher	K-1		328 36	19% 516/520-2126 Fax 516/520-0987
Michael F Stokes Elem Sch 101 Owl Pl, Levittown 11756 Allison Ackerman	2-4		485 28	23% 516/520-2103 Fax 516/520-0984

• Jericho Union Free School Dist PID: 00736572
99 Old Cedar Swamp Rd, Jericho 11753
516/203-3600
Fax 516/203-3601

Schools: 5 \ **Teachers:** 324 \ **Students:** 3,155 \ **Special Ed Students:** 384 \ **LEP Students:** 173 \ **College-Bound:** 99% \ **Ethnic:** Asian 61%, African American 2%, Hispanic 3%, Caucasian 34% \ **Exp:** $514 (High) \ **Poverty:** 5% \ **Title I:** $220,867 \ **Special Education:** $2,546,000 \ **Open-Close:** 09/02 - 06/25 \ **DTBP:** $297 (High) \

Henry Grishman	1,11	Victor Manuel	2,15
Michael Hahn	3	Tracey Gilet	4
Lori-Ann Savino	5	John Mankowich	6,35*
Barbara Bauer	8,15,69,74,81,83,85,273	Ben Ciuffo	15,68
Denise Ryder	16,82*	Katie Behr	20,23
Dr Lionel Chen	27,61	Gregory Sloan	31,36
Brian Cummings	42*	Helene Kriegstein	45,277*
Daniel Salzman	48,51*	Kim Conger	58,79,298
William Ferro	67	Denise Nash	71
Patrick Fogerty	73,295		

Public Schs..Principal	Grd	Prgm	Enr/#Cls	SN
Cantiague Elem Sch 678 Cantiague Rock Rd, Jericho 11753 Gina Faust	K-5		386 17	7% 516/203-3650 Fax 516/203-3803
George A Jackson Elem Sch 58 Maytime Dr, Jericho 11753 Kim Conger	K-5		505	8% 516/203-3640 Fax 516/681-2891

---

1 Superintendent	8 Curric/Instruct K-12	19 Chief Financial Officer	29 Family/Consumer Science	39 Social Studies K-12	49 English/Lang Arts Elem	59 Special Education Elem	69 Academic Assessment
2 Bus/Finance/Purchasing	9 Curric/Instruct Elem	20 Art K-12	30 Adult Education	40 Social Studies Elem	50 English/Lang Arts Sec	60 Special Education Sec	70 Research/Development
3 Buildings And Grounds	10 Curric/Instruct Sec	21 Art Elem	31 Career/Sch-to-Work K-12	41 Social Studies Sec	51 Reading K-12	61 Foreign/World Lang K-12	71 Public Information
4 Food Service	11 Federal Program	22 Art Sec	32 Career/Sch-to-Work Elem	42 Science K-12	52 Reading Elem	62 Foreign/World Lang Elem	72 Summer School
5 Transportation	12 Title I	23 Music K-12	33 Career/Sch-to-Work Sec	43 Science Elem	53 Reading Sec	63 Foreign/World Lang Sec	73 Instructional Tech
6 Athletic	13 Title V	24 Music Elem	34 Early Childhood Ed	44 Science Sec	54 Remedial Reading K-12	64 Religious Education K-12	74 Inservice Training
7 Health Services	15 Asst Superintendent	25 Music Sec	35 Health/Phys Education	45 Math K-12	55 Remedial Reading Elem	65 Religious Education Elem	75 Marketing/Distributive
	16 Instructional Media Svcs	26 Business Education	36 Guidance Services K-12	46 Math Elem	56 Remedial Reading Sec	66 Religious Education Sec	76 Info Systems
	17 Chief Operations Officer	27 Career & Tech Ed	37 Guidance Services Elem	47 Math Sec	57 Bilingual/ELL	67 School Board President	77 Psychological Assess
	18 Chief Academic Officer	28 Technology Education	38 Guidance Services Sec	48 English/Lang Arts K-12	58 Special Education K-12	68 Teacher Personnel	78 Affirmative Action

New York School Directory — Nassau County

Public Schs..Principal	Grd	Prgm	Enr/#Cls	SN		
Jericho Middle Sch 99 Old Cedar Swamp Rd, Jericho 11753 Donald Gately	6-8		809 60	8%	516/203-3620 Fax 516/681-2984	
Jericho Senior High Sch 99 Old Cedar Swamp Rd, Jericho 11753 Joan Rosenberg	9-12		1,163 60	10%	516/203-3610 Fax 516/681-2895	
Robert Seaman Elem Sch 137 Leahy St, Jericho 11753 Ivy Sherman	K-5		292 30	2%	516/203-3630 Fax 516/681-9493	

- **Lawrence Union Free Sch Dist** PID: 00736649   516/295-8000
195 Broadway, Lawrence 11559

Schools: 5 \ **Teachers:** 243 \ **Students:** 2,600 \
Special Ed Students: 1,216 \ **LEP Students:** 520 \ **College-Bound:** 82%
\ **Ethnic:** Asian 5%, African American 19%, Hispanic 61%, Native American: 1%, Caucasian 14% \ **Exp:** $477 (High) \ **Poverty:** 9% \ **Title I:** $867,109 \
Special Education: $3,995,000 \ **Open-Close:** 09/04 - 06/25 \ **DTBP:** $448 (High)

Dr Ann Pedersen 1	Jeremy Feder 2,3,5,15	
Michael Gordon 6,35,85	Elise Danzger 7,36,58,77,79	
Murray Forman 67		

Public Schs..Principal	Grd	Prgm	Enr/#Cls	SN		
Lawrence Elem Sch 195 Broadway, Lawrence 11559 Rina Beach	3-5	T	530 18	72%	516/812-6121 Fax 516/812-6123	
Lawrence High Sch 2 Reilly Rd, Cedarhurst 11516 Jennifer Lagnado	9-12	AV	851 95	57%	516/295-8000 Fax 516/295-2754	
Lawrence Middle Sch 195 Broadway, Lawrence 11559 Willis Perry	6-8	T	569	68%	516/295-7000 Fax 516/295-7196	
Lawrence Primary Sch 1 Donahue Ave, Inwood 11096 Christine Moore	K-2	T	498 20	69%	516/295-6200 Fax 516/295-6213	
Lawrence Universal Pre-K 87 Wanser Ave, Inwood 11096 Patricia Almonaitis	PK-PK		175 23		516/295-6400 Fax 516/295-6416	

- **Levittown Union Free Sch Dist** PID: 00736730   516/434-7000
150 Abbey Ln, Levittown 11756   Fax 516/861-4414

Schools: 11 \ **Teachers:** 618 \ **Students:** 7,215 \ **Special Ed Students:** 1,017
\ **LEP Students:** 170 \ **College-Bound:** 86% \ **Ethnic:** Asian 10%,
African American 1%, Hispanic 21%, Caucasian 67% \ **Exp:** $373 (High)
\ **Poverty:** 3% \ **Title I:** $239,226 \ **Special Education:** $13,862,000 \
Open-Close: 09/08 - 06/25 \ **DTBP:** $318 (High)

Dr Toni McDonald 1	Christopher Dillon 2,15
Christopher Milano 3,91	Dajuana Reeves 5
Keith Snyder 6,7,35,83	Michele Ortiz 8,69
Todd Winch 8,15	Debbie Rifkin 15,68
Todd Connell 16,73	Vincent D Ulise 23*
Frank Creter 27,286*	Kenneth Walden 30*
Steve Costello 39	John Towers 45
Dr Susan Farber 58,79	Peggy Merenghi 67
Marylynn Eisele 76	Michael Gattus 274*
Michael Gibbone 295	Anthony Anzalone 297

Public Schs..Principal	Grd	Prgm	Enr/#Cls	SN		
Abbey Lane Elem Sch 239 Gardiners Ave, Levittown 11756 Dr George Maurer	K-5		625 50	16%	516/434-7400 Fax 516/520-8494	
Division Ave High Sch 120 Division Ave, Levittown 11756 John Coscia	9-12	AV	987	17%	516/434-7150 Fax 516/520-8364	
East Broadway Elem Sch 751 Seamans Neck Rd, Seaford 11783 Jeanmarie Wink	K-5		675 37	6%	516/434-7425 Fax 516/783-5186	
G R Claps Career & Tech Ctr 150 Abbey Ln, Levittown 11756 Joan Lorelli	Voc		210 15		516/520-8330 Fax 516/861-4408	
Gardiners Avenue Elem Sch 610 Gardiners Ave, Levittown 11756 John Vanderbeck	K-5		581 40	11%	516/434-7450 Fax 516/520-8490	
General Douglas MacArthur HS 3369 N Jerusalem Rd, Levittown 11756 Joseph Sheehan	9-12	V	1,301 60	9%	516/434-7225 Fax 516/520-8466	
Jonas E Salk Middle Sch 3359 Old Jerusalem Rd, Levittown 11756 John Zampaglione	6-8		933 53	11%	516/434-7350 Fax 516/520-8479	
Lee Road Elem Sch 901 Lee Rd, Wantagh 11793 Jami Anspach	K-5		291 26	4%	516/434-7475 Fax 516/783-5194	
Northside Elem Sch 35 Pelican Rd, Levittown 11756 Frank Mortillaro	K-5		529 32	13%	516/434-7500 Fax 516/520-8394	
Summit Lane Elem Sch 4 Summit Ln, Levittown 11756 Keith Squillacioti	K-5		408 26	18%	516/434-7525 Fax 516/520-8390	
Wisdom Lane Middle Sch 120 Center Ln, Levittown 11756 John Avena	6-8		777 30	19%	516/434-7300 Fax 516/520-8380	

- **Locust Valley Ctl School Dist** PID: 00736900   516/277-5000
22 Horse Hollow Rd, Locust Valley 11560   Fax 516/277-5098

Schools: 6 \ **Teachers:** 188 \ **Students:** 2,000 \ **Special Ed Students:** 401
\ **LEP Students:** 108 \ **College-Bound:** 94% \ **Ethnic:** Asian 4%,
African American 1%, Hispanic 18%, Caucasian 76% \ **Exp:** $674 (High) \
Poverty: 5% \ **Title I:** $192,236 \ **Special Education:** $1,935,000 \
Open-Close: 09/08 - 06/25 \ **DTBP:** $161 (High)

Dr Kenneth Graham 1	Toni Meliambro 2,15,68
Erik Nakutavicus 3	Elizabeth McLoughlin 4
Katherine Russo 5	Danielle Turner 6,7,35*
Anthony Davidson 8,15	Barbara Mierlak 16*
Tom Hogan 20*	Marc Yavoski 23
Michael Saidens 58,79	Brian Nolan 67
Pam Kaplan 71	

Public Schs..Principal	Grd	Prgm	Enr/#Cls	SN		
Ann M MacArthur Primary Sch 100 Ryefield Rd, Locust Valley 11560 Sophia Gary	K-2		215 13		516/277-5350 Fax 516/277-5358	
Bayville Intermediate Sch 50 Mountain Ave, Bayville 11709 Scott McElhiney	3-5		226 14	14%	516/277-5400 Fax 516/277-5408	
Bayville Primary Sch 50 Godfrey Ave, Bayville 11709 Scott McElhiney	K-2		192 15		516/277-5450 Fax 516/277-5458	
Locust Valley High Sch 99 Horse Hollow Rd, Locust Valley 11560 Patrick Diclemente	9-12		660 150	20%	516/277-5100 Fax 516/277-5108	
Locust Valley Intermediate Sch 119 Ryefield Rd, Locust Valley 11560 Sophia Gary	3-5	T	256 18	15%	516/277-5300 Fax 516/277-5308	
Locust Valley Middle Sch 99 Horse Hollow Rd, Locust Valley 11560 H Thomas Hogan	6-8		494	19%	516/277-5200 Fax 516/277-5208	

79 Student Personnel	91 Safety/Security	275 Response To Intervention	298 Grant Writer/Ptnrships	**School Programs**
80 Driver Ed/Safety	92 Magnet School	277 Remedial Math K-12	750 Chief Innovation Officer	A = Alternative Program
81 Gifted/Talented	93 Parental Involvement	280 Literacy Coach	751 Chief of Staff	G = Adult Classes
82 Video Services	95 Tech Prep Program	285 STEM	752 Social Emotional Learning	M = Magnet Program
83 Substance Abuse Prev	97 Chief Infomation Officer	286 Digital Learning		T = Title I Schoolwide
84 Erate	98 Chief Technology Officer	288 Common Core Standards	**Other School Types**	V = Career & Tech Ed Programs
85 AIDS Education	270 Character Education	294 Accountability	Ⓐ = Alternative School	
88 Alternative/At Risk	271 Migrant Education	295 Network System	Ⓒ = Charter School	**Social Media**
89 Multi-Cultural Curriculum	273 Teacher Mentor	296 Title II Programs	Ⓜ = Magnet School	📘 = Facebook
90 Social Work	274 Before/After Sch	297 Webmaster	Ⓨ = Year-Round School	🐦 = Twitter

New Schools are shaded
New Superintendents and Principals are bold
Personnel with email addresses are underscored

Nassau County

Market Data Retrieval

• Long Beach City School Dist   PID: 00736950   516/897-2000
235 Lido Blvd, Lido Beach 11561

Schools: 7 \ **Teachers:** 351 \ **Students:** 3,800 \ **Special Ed Students:** 672 \ **LEP Students:** 183 \ **College-Bound:** 85% \ **Ethnic:** Asian 4%, African American 10%, Hispanic 26%, Caucasian 61% \ **Exp:** $448 (High) \ **Poverty:** 7% \ **Title I:** $466,275 \ **Special Education:** $4,393,000 \ **Open-Close:** 09/08 - 06/25 \ **DTBP:** $315 (High)

Name	Code(s)
Dr Jennifer Gallagher	1
Michael DeVito	2,3,15,17
Steven Kamlet	4*
Arnold Epstein	6,7,35,83*
Lorane Radice	9
Dr Michele Natali	15,68,74
Gina Reddock	30
Serena Whitfield	58
Peter Russo	60
Patrick Kiley-Rendon	73
Joan Ramirez	2
Steve Lahey	3
Nancy Nunziata	5
Dr Paul Romanelli	8,15
Theresa Scudiero	10,16,41,50,53,57
Julia Lang-Shapiro	22,25*
Kerry Fallon	36
Kim Liguori	59
Tina Posterli	67
Dr Deborah Lovrich	285*

Public Schs..Principal	Grd	Prgm	Enr/#Cls	SN	Phone
East Elem Sch 456 Neptune Blvd, Long Beach 11561 Kathleen Connolly	K-5		355 16	28%	516/897-2184 Fax 516/897-2291
Lido Elem Sch 237 Lido Blvd, Long Beach 11561 Ivelisse Hernandez	PK-5		560 24	20%	516/897-2140 Fax 516/771-3783
Lindell Elem Sch 601 Lindell Blvd, Long Beach 11561 Karen Sauter	K-5		403 27	30%	516/897-2209 Fax 516/771-3782
Long Beach High Sch 322 Lagoon Dr W, Long Beach 11561 Jeffrey Myers	9-12	AV	1,298 84	33%	516/897-2012 Fax 516/897-2052
Long Beach Middle Sch 239 Lido Blvd, Long Beach 11561 Lorie Beard	6-8		820 80	33%	516/897-2166 Fax 516/897-2162
Ⓐ Nike Alternative High Sch 839 861 Lido Blvd, Lido Beach 11561 Christopher Webel	9-12		60		516/897-2131
West Elem Sch 91 Maryland Ave, Long Beach 11561 Amy Dirolf	K-5		358	27%	516/897-2215 Fax 516/431-7827

• Lynbrook Union Free Sch Dist   PID: 00737045   516/887-0253
111 Atlantic Ave, Lynbrook 11563   Fax 516/887-3263

Schools: 7 \ **Teachers:** 248 \ **Students:** 2,809 \ **Special Ed Students:** 470 \ **LEP Students:** 62 \ **College-Bound:** 94% \ **Ethnic:** Asian 6%, African American 5%, Hispanic 18%, Caucasian 70% \ **Exp:** $366 (High) \ **Poverty:** 4% \ **Title I:** $113,273 \ **Special Education:** $551,000 \ **Open-Close:** 09/04 - 06/25 \ **DTBP:** $313 (High)

Name	Code(s)
Dr Melissa Burak	1
James Saitta	3
Tom Graham	6*
Dr Gerard Beleckas	11,15,69
Joseph Pallotta	20,23
Laurie Mitchell	31*
William Belmont	67
Dr Paul Lynch	2,15,76
Dr Maureen Berman	5,15,79
Arlene Mishanie	7,58,88
Neil Mac Dermott	12*
Amy Cohen	30*
Keri Kelleher	58

Public Schs..Principal	Grd	Prgm	Enr/#Cls	SN	Phone
Lynbrook High Sch 9 Union Ave, Lynbrook 11563 Joseph Rainis	9-12		888 30	18%	516/887-0200 Fax 516/887-8079
Lynbrook Kindergarten Center 111 Atlantic Ave, Lynbrook 11563 Ellen Postman	K-K		198 11	4%	516/887-8065 Fax 516/887-8264
Lynbrook North Middle Sch 529 Merrick Rd, Lynbrook 11563 Seank Fallon	6-8		266 20	22%	516/887-0282 Fax 516/887-0286
Lynbrook South Middle Sch 333 Union Ave, Lynbrook 11563 Joseph Wiener	6-8	G	371	14%	516/887-0266 Fax 516/887-0268
Marion Street Elem Sch 100 Marion St, Lynbrook 11563 Theresa MacChia	1-5		451 24	10%	516/887-0295 Fax 516/887-3350
Waverly Park Elem Sch 320 Waverly Ave, East Rockaway 11518 Allison Banhazl	1-5		205 13	7%	516/887-6589 Fax 516/887-8262
West End Elem Sch 30 Clark Ave, Lynbrook 11563 Cindy Lee	1-5		408 19	16%	516/887-0288 Fax 516/887-8269

• Malverne Union Free Sch Dist   PID: 00737124   516/887-6405
301 Wicks Ln, Malverne 11565   Fax 516/596-2910

Schools: 4 \ **Teachers:** 124 \ **Students:** 1,725 \ **Special Ed Students:** 362 \ **LEP Students:** 35 \ **Ethnic:** Asian 5%, African American 50%, Hispanic 26%, Caucasian 18% \ **Exp:** $529 (High) \ **Poverty:** 6% \ **Title I:** $216,777 \ **Special Education:** $2,250,000 \ **Open-Close:** 09/09 - 06/25 \ **DTBP:** $158 (High) \ 📧

Name	Code(s)
Dr Loran Lewis	1
Dan Balzan	3,5,11,15,79,271
Steven Gilhuley	8,15*
Michael Messina	20,23,29
Rebecca Gottesman	36
Lora Lewis	67
Craig Vella	73
Christopher Caputo	2,15
Micheal Pelan	6,35
Jason Mach	16,41,50
Yvonne Daza	26,57,61*
Meredyth Martini	58
Denise Lawlor	68

Public Schs..Principal	Grd	Prgm	Enr/#Cls	SN	Phone
Davison Ave Elem Sch 49 Davison Ave, Lynbrook 11563 Rachel Gross	3-5	T	375 20	48%	516/887-6462 Fax 516/255-1252
Howard T Herber Middle Sch 75 Ocean Ave, Malverne 11565 Daniel Nehlsen	6-8	T	424 30	52%	516/887-6400 Fax 516/255-1007
Malverne High Sch 80 Ocean Ave, Malverne 11565 Vincent Romano	9-12		532 40	47%	516/887-6400 Fax 516/887-6479
Maurice W Downing Elem Sch 55 Lindner Pl, Malverne 11565 Edward Tallon	K-2		394 23	36%	516/887-6470 Fax 516/887-8620

• Manhasset Union Free Sch Dist   PID: 00737186   516/267-7700
200 Memorial Pl, Manhasset 11030   Fax 516/627-1618

Schools: 4 \ **Teachers:** 273 \ **Students:** 3,250 \ **Special Ed Students:** 440 \ **LEP Students:** 57 \ **College-Bound:** 98% \ **Ethnic:** Asian 23%, African American 3%, Hispanic 7%, Caucasian 67% \ **Exp:** $359 (High) \ **Poverty:** 3% \ **Title I:** $98,057 \ **Special Education:** $3,788,000 \ **Open-Close:** 09/08 - 06/25 \ **DTBP:** $308 (High)

Name	Code(s)
Dr Vincent Butera	1
Frederick Bruder	3,91
James Amen	6,7,35,83,85
Dr Gaurav Passi	8,15,18*
Dr Jean Kendall	15,68
Terisa McGrath	27,35,42
Lauren Tallarine	45
Laurie Lauria	57
Rosemary Johnson	2,15
Kelly Fredrickson	5
Gaurav Passai	8,88
Maryanne Sheilds	11
Sean Adcroft	16,73,82
Mara Steindam	31,39*
Rebecca Chowske	48
Patricia Aitken	67

#	Code	#	Code	#	Code	#	Code	#	Code	#	Code	#	Code
1	Superintendent	8	Curric/Instruct K-12	19	Chief Financial Officer	29	Family/Consumer Science	39	Social Studies K-12	49	English/Lang Arts Elem	59	Special Education Elem	69	Academic Assessment
2	Bus/Finance/Purchasing	9	Curric/Instruct Elem	20	Art K-12	30	Adult Education	40	Social Studies Elem	50	English/Lang Arts Sec	60	Special Education Sec	70	Research/Development
3	Buildings And Grounds	10	Curric/Instruct Sec	21	Art Elem	31	Career/Sch-to-Work K-12	41	Social Studies Sec	51	Reading K-12	61	Foreign/World Lang K-12	71	Public Information
4	Food Service	11	Federal Program	22	Art Sec	32	Career/Sch-to-Work Elem	42	Science K-12	52	Reading Elem	62	Foreign/World Lang Elem	72	Summer School
5	Transportation	12	Title I	23	Music K-12	33	Career/Sch-to-Work Sec	43	Science Elem	53	Reading Sec	63	Foreign/World Lang Sec	73	Instructional Tech
6	Athletic	13	Title V	24	Music Elem	34	Early Childhood Ed	44	Science Sec	54	Remedial Reading K-12	64	Religious Education K-12	74	Inservice Training
7	Health Services	15	Asst Superintendent	25	Music Sec	35	Health/Phys Education	45	Math K-12	55	Remedial Reading Elem	65	Religious Education Elem	75	Marketing/Distributive
		16	Instructional Media Svcs	26	Business Education	36	Guidance Services K-12	46	Math Elem	56	Remedial Reading Sec	66	Religious Education Sec	76	Info Systems
		17	Chief Operations Officer	27	Career & Tech Ed	37	Guidance Services Elem	47	Math Sec	57	Bilingual/ELL	67	School Board President	77	Psychological Assess
		18	Chief Academic Officer	28	Technology Education	38	Guidance Services Sec	48	English/Lang Arts K-12	58	Special Education K-12	68	Teacher Personnel	78	Affirmative Action

NY—124

New York School Directory — Nassau County

Public Schs..Principal	Grd	Prgm	Enr/#Cls	SN	
Manhasset Middle Sch 200 Memorial Pl, Manhasset 11030 Dr Dean Schlanger	7-8		506	4%	516/267-7600 Fax 516/267-7505
Manhasset Secondary Sch 200 Memorial Pl, Manhasset 11030 Dr Dean Schlanger	9-12		1,042	4%	516/267-7600 Fax 516/267-7604
Munsey Park Elem Sch 1 Hunt Ln, Manhasset 11030 Chad Altman	K-6		930	3%	516/267-7400 Fax 516/267-7404
Shelter Rock Elem Sch 27A Shelter Rock Rd, Manhasset 11030 Richard Roder	K-6		684 75	6%	516/267-7450 Fax 516/267-7456

- **Massapequa Union Free SD 23** PID: 00737227   516/308-5000
  4925 Merrick Rd, Massapequa 11758   Fax 516/308-5009

Schools: 9 \ **Teachers:** 613 \ **Students:** 8,000 \
Special Ed Students: 980 \ **LEP Students:** 33 \ **Ethnic:** Asian 2%, Hispanic 6%, Caucasian 92% \ **Exp:** $268 (Med) \ **Poverty:** 2% \ **Title I:** $156,384 \
Special Education: $6,539,000 \ **Open-Close:** 09/03 - 06/25 \ **DTBP:** $317 (High)

Lucille Iconis 1	Alan Adcock 2,15
Timothy O'Donnell 3	Paul Heckelman 4
Keyana Wright 5	John Piropato 6,7,35,83,85*
Dr Thomas Fasano 8,15	Diana Haanraadts 9,288
Bryan Piotrowski 11,73,91,286,298	William Anderson 12,57,69*
Jordan McCaw 13,58,79,88*	Vicent Green 20,23
Brian Trapani 39*	Lisa Caputo 42*
Tonianne Summers 45*	Tina Farrell 48,280*
Kerry Wachter 67	Yvonne Knott 76
Paul Weber 77	

Public Schs..Principal	Grd	Prgm	Enr/#Cls	SN	
Alfred G Berner Middle Sch 50 Carman Mill Rd, Massapequa 11758 Jason Esposito	6-8	GV	1,560	9%	516/308-5700 Fax 516/308-5709
Birch Lane Elem Sch 41 Birch Ln, Massapequa Pk 11762 Stephen Aspetti	K-5		641 51	5%	516/308-5100 Fax 516/308-5109
East Lake Elem Sch 154 Eastlake Ave, Massapequa Pk 11762 Thomas McKillop	K-5		512 36	7%	516/308-5200 Fax 516/308-5209
Fairfield Elem Sch 330 Massapequa Ave, Massapequa 11758 Kristi Gerhard	K-5		514 37	13%	516/308-5300 Fax 516/308-5309
John P McKenna Elem Sch 210A Spruce St, Massapequa Pk 11762 Dr Amanda Lowry	K-5		458 38	8%	516/308-5500 Fax 516/308-5509
Massapequa High Sch 4925 Merrick Rd, Massapequa 11758 Brian Conboy	10-12	AV	1,644	11%	516/308-5900 Fax 516/308-5909
Massapequa HS-Ames Campus 198 Baltimore Ave, Massapequa 11758 Tania Willman	9-9		475	9%	516/308-5800 Fax 516/308-5809
Raymond J Lockhart Elem Sch 199 Pittsburgh Ave, Massapequa 11758 Michael Yannucci	K-5		374 28	10%	516/308-5400 Fax 516/308-5409
Unqua Elem Sch 350 Unqua Rd, Massapequa 11758 Deanna Catapano	K-5		535 38	6%	516/308-5600 Fax 516/308-5609

- **Merrick Union Free School Dist** PID: 00737423   516/992-7200
  21 Babylon Rd, Merrick 11566   Fax 516/378-3904

Schools: 3 \ **Teachers:** 149 \ **Students:** 1,490 \ **Special Ed Students:** 262 \ **LEP Students:** 13 \ **Ethnic:** Asian 4%, African American 2%, Hispanic 6%, Caucasian 88% \ **Exp:** $358 (High) \ **Poverty:** 2% \ **Title I:** $46,493 \
Special Education: $1,143,000 \ **Open-Close:** 09/08 - 06/25 \ **DTBP:** $161 (High)

Dr Dominick Palma 1	Jennifer Buscemi 2,5,15
Thomas Primiano 2	James O'Beirne 3*
Dr Salvatore Dossena 7,59,79	Dr Jill Karp 9,11,15,69,74,288,296,298
Melissa Levine 16,82*	Nancy Kaplan 67
Rose Mary Bonasia 76,286	Mary Feneilius 274

Public Schs..Principal	Grd	Prgm	Enr/#Cls	SN	
Birch Sch 2400 Central Pkwy, Merrick 11566 Kerri Galante	K-6		538 26	6%	516/992-7250 Fax 516/546-0138
Chatterton Sch 108 Merrick Ave, Merrick 11566 Dana Bermas	K-6		395 28	9%	516/992-7270 Fax 516/546-1351
Norman J Levy-Lakeside Sch 21 Babylon Rd, Merrick 11566 Elizabeth Trencheny	K-6		563 34	5%	516/992-7230 Fax 516/546-6592 t

- **Mineola Union Free Sch Dist** PID: 00737461   516/237-2000
  121 Jackson Ave, Mineola 11501   Fax 516/237-2008

Schools: 5 \ **Teachers:** 256 \ **Students:** 2,927 \ **Special Ed Students:** 434 \ **LEP Students:** 307 \ **College-Bound:** 98% \ **Ethnic:** Asian 14%, African American 2%, Hispanic 30%, Caucasian 54% \ **Exp:** $481 (High) \ **Poverty:** 5% \ **Title I:** $229,048 \ **Special Education:** $2,750,000 \
Open-Close: 09/08 - 06/25 \ **DTBP:** $320 (High) \ f t

Dr Michael Nagler 1	Jack Waters 2,15
Dan Romano	William Gilberg 5
Ralph Amitrano 6,35	Matthew Gaven 8,15,58,73,74,81
Nicole Moriarty 57	Christine Napolitano 67
Edward Escobar 68	Catherine Fishman 79

Public Schs..Principal	Grd	Prgm	Enr/#Cls	SN	
Hampton Street Elem Sch 10 Hampton St, Mineola 11501 Margarita Maravel	PK-2		390 10	31%	516/237-2200 Fax 516/237-2208
Jackson Avenue Elem Sch 300 Jackson Ave, Mineola 11501 Janet Gonzalez	3-4		393 17	32%	516/237-2300 Fax 516/237-2308
Meadow Drive Elem Sch 25 Meadow Dr, Albertson 11507 Sara Ortiz	PK-2		398 13	14%	516/237-2400 Fax 516/237-2408
Mineola High Sch 10 Armstrong Rd, New Hyde Park 11040 Dr Whittney Smith	8-12	G	1,100 60	33%	516/237-2600 Fax 516/237-2608
Mineola Middle Sch 200 Emory Rd, Mineola 11501 Andrew Casale	5-7		646 35	34%	516/237-2500 Fax 516/237-2508

---

79 Student Personnel	91 Safety/Security	275 Response To Intervention	298 Grant Writer/Ptnrships	**School Programs**	**Social Media**
80 Driver Ed/Safety	92 Magnet School	277 Remedial Math K-12	750 Chief Innovation Officer	A = Alternative Program	f = Facebook
81 Gifted/Talented	93 Parental Involvement	280 Literacy Coach	751 Chief of Staff	G = Adult Classes	
82 Video Services	95 Tech Prep Program	285 STEM	752 Social Emotional Learning	M = Magnet Program	t = Twitter
83 Substance Abuse Prev	97 Chief Information Officer	286 Digital Learning		T = Title I Schoolwide	
84 Erate	98 Chief Technology Officer	288 Common Core Standards	**Other School Types**	V = Career & Tech Ed Programs	
85 AIDS Education	270 Character Education	294 Accountability	A = Alternative School		
88 Alternative/At Risk	271 Migrant Education	295 Network System	C = Charter School	New Schools are shaded	
89 Multi-Cultural Curriculum	273 Teacher Mentor	296 Title II Programs	M = Magnet School	New Superintendents and Principals are bold	
90 Social Work	274 Before/After Sch	297 Webmaster	Y = Year-Round School	Personnel with email addresses are underscored	

NY—125

Nassau County

Market Data Retrieval

- **New Hyde-Garden City Park UFSD** PID: 00737540   516/434-2305
  1950 Hillside Ave, New Hyde Park 11040   Fax 516/352-6282

  Schools: 4 \ **Teachers:** 136 \ **Students:** 1,785 \
  Special Ed Students: 226 \ **LEP Students:** 109 \ **Ethnic:** Asian 58%, Hispanic 15%, Caucasian 27% \ **Exp:** $344 (High) \ **Poverty:** 4% \
  Title I: $68,471 \ **Special Education:** $1,467,000 \ **Open-Close:** 09/08 - 06/23 \ **DTBP:** $163 (High)

  Dr Jennifer Morrison 1   Michael Frank 2,15
  James Svendsen 9,12,16,73,82,295   Kim Laregina 9*
  Amy Sullivan .... 11*   Terry Davis 35,85*
  Kim Levy 59,79   Jennifer Kerrane 67
  Beth Torreano 274*

Public Schs..Principal	Grd	Prgm	Enr/#Cls	SN
Garden City Park Elem Sch 51 Central Ave, New Hyde Park 11040 Amy Sullivan	K-6		291 16	24% 516/434-2390 Fax 516/873-6368
Hillside Grade Sch 150 Maple Dr W, New Hyde Park 11040 Beth Torreano	K-6		562 22	17% 516/434-2410 Fax 516/352-6081
Manor Oaks Sch 1950 Hillside Ave, New Hyde Park 11040 Jane Ruthkowski	PK-6		399 17	7% 516/434-2350 Fax 516/616-1959
New Hyde Park Road Sch 300 New Hyde Park Rd, New Hyde Park 11040 Kim Laregina	K-6		533 24	22% 516/434-2370 Fax 516/352-6059

- **District 75 City Wide Programs** PID: 00740626
  (Part of New York City Dept of Ed in New York County)

Public Schs..Principal	Grd	Prgm	Enr/#Cls	SN
ⓨ PS 993Q 8515 258th St, Floral Park 11001 Jacqueline Zaretsky	Spec	M	595	78% 718/831-4040 Fax 718/831-4037
ⓨ PS Q256 525 Convent Rd, Syosset 11791 Robert Lopez	Spec	M	442 10	86% 516/921-0450 Fax 516/921-4045

- **North Bellmore Union Free SD** PID: 00737590   516/992-3000
  2616 Martin Ave, Bellmore 11710   Fax 516/992-3020

  Schools: 5 \ **Teachers:** 182 \ **Students:** 2,031 \ **Special Ed Students:** 509 \ **LEP Students:** 53 \ **Ethnic:** Asian 8%, African American 3%, Hispanic 15%, Caucasian 73% \ **Exp:** $304 (High) \ **Poverty:** 3% \ **Title I:** $66,780 \
  Special Education: $2,471,000 \ **Open-Close:** 09/08 - 06/25 \ **DTBP:** $165 (High)

  Marie Testa 1   Jaqueline Rehack 2,5,15,71
  Richard Russo 3   Helina McKenna 4
  Janet Pollitt 9,11,15,57,69,296,298   Tillie McNamara 9,74,280
  Carol Eskew 15,59   Rosemarie Coreless 67
  Jason Ficetti 70,71,73,97,295,750   Kerrie Dejak 77
  Jo Ann Signorelli 83,85,88,270   Linda Mann 273*
  Wade Hamp 295

Public Schs..Principal	Grd	Prgm	Enr/#Cls	SN
John G Dinkelmeyer Elem Sch 2100 Waltoffer Ave, N Bellmore 11710 Danica Brugge	K-6		351 21	14% 516/992-3114 Fax 516/992-3054
Martin Avenue Elem Sch 2616 Martin Ave, N Bellmore 11710 Leyna Malone	K-6		283 18	12% 516/992-3115 Fax 516/992-3164
Newbridge Road Elem Sch 1601 Newbridge Rd, N Bellmore 11710 Denise Fisher	K-6		351 20	14% 516/992-3116 Fax 516/992-3214
Park Avenue Elem Sch 1599 Park Ave, North Merrick 11566 Eileen Speidel	K-6		304 25	7% 516/992-3117 Fax 516/992-3214
Sawmill Road Elem Sch 2801 Saw Mill Rd, N Bellmore 11710 Jeff Rosof	K-6		731 55	10% 516/992-3118 Fax 516/992-3324

- **North Merrick Union Free SD** PID: 00737667   516/292-3694
  1057 Merrick Ave, Merrick 11566   Fax 516/292-3097

  Schools: 3 \ **Teachers:** 87 \ **Students:** 1,177 \ **Special Ed Students:** 224 \ **LEP Students:** 30 \ **Ethnic:** Asian 7%, African American 3%, Hispanic 13%, Caucasian 77% \ **Exp:** $362 (High) \ **Poverty:** 2% \ **Title I:** $29,586 \
  Special Education: $1,119,000 \ **Open-Close:** 09/08 - 06/25 \ **DTBP:** $159 (High)

  Dr Cynthia Seniuk 1   Thomas McDaid 2,15
  Samuel Carder 3   Beth Friedman 9,11,15,68,69
  Dr Edward Murphy 59   Megan Ryan 67

Public Schs..Principal	Grd	Prgm	Enr/#Cls	SN
Camp Avenue Elem Sch 1712 Merrick Ave, Merrick 11566 Hillary Bromberg	K-6		480 25	5% 516/379-3732 Fax 516/379-0200
Harold D Fayette Elem Sch 1057 Merrick Ave, Merrick 11566 Howard Merims	K-6		274 25	13% 516/489-3090 Fax 516/485-6016
Old Mill Road Elem Sch 1775 Old Mill Rd, North Merrick 11566 Laura DeLuca	K-6		423 23	10% 516/379-0945 Fax 516/379-1695

- **North Shore Central SD** PID: 00737708   516/277-7000
  112 Franklin Ave, Sea Cliff 11579   Fax 516/277-7805

  Schools: 5 \ **Teachers:** 295 \ **Students:** 2,548 \ **Special Ed Students:** 467 \ **LEP Students:** 52 \ **College-Bound:** 96% \ **Ethnic:** Asian 6%, Hispanic 12%, Caucasian 82% \ **Exp:** $374 (High) \ **Poverty:** 3% \ **Title I:** $114,118 \
  Special Education: $2,333,000 \ **Open-Close:** 09/08 - 06/25 \ **DTBP:** $318 (High)

  Dr Peter Giarrizzo 1   Olivia Buatsi 2,68
  John Hall 3,91   Lisa Papalia 4*
  Michelle Hall 5   Don Lang 6,35,85*
  Janice Nunziata .... 7*   Robert Chlebicki 8,273
  Janet Bates -Wilkins 11   Christopher Marino 34,58,90*
  Linda Binkin .... 36*   Dave Ludmar
  Shelly Newman 71   Elliot Kaye 73,95
  Peter Segal 88*

Public Schs..Principal	Grd	Prgm	Enr/#Cls	SN
Glen Head Elem Sch 7 School St, Glen Head 11545 Dr Peter Rufa	K-5		358 26	13% 516/277-7700 Fax 516/277-7705
Glenwood Landing Elem Sch 60 Cody Ave, Glen Head 11545 Bridget Finder	K-5		427	7% 516/277-7600 Fax 516/277-7603
North Shore High Sch 450 Glen Cove Ave, Glen Head 11545 Albert Cousins	9-12	AGV	838	12% 516/277-7700 Fax 516/277-7003
North Shore Middle Sch 505 Glen Cove Ave, Glen Head 11545 Robert Dennis	6-8		580	11% 516/277-7300 Fax 516/277-7305

1	Superintendent	8	Curric/Instruct K-12	19	Chief Financial Officer	29	Family/Consumer Science	39	Social Studies K-12	49	English/Lang Arts Elem	59	Special Education Elem	69	Academic Assessment
2	Bus/Finance/Purchasing	9	Curric/Instruct Elem	20	Art K-12	30	Adult Education	40	Social Studies Elem	50	English/Lang Arts Sec	60	Special Education Sec	70	Research/Development
3	Buildings And Grounds	10	Curric/Instruct Sec	21	Art Elem	31	Career/Sch-to-Work K-12	41	Social Studies Sec	51	Reading K-12	61	Foreign/World Lang K-12	71	Public Information
4	Food Service	11	Federal Program	22	Art Sec	32	Career/Sch-to-Work Elem	42	Science K-12	52	Reading Elem	62	Foreign/World Lang Elem	72	Summer School
5	Transportation	12	Title I	23	Music K-12	33	Career/Sch-to-Work Sec	43	Science Elem	53	Reading Sec	63	Foreign/World Lang Sec	73	Instructional Tech
6	Athletic	13	Title V	24	Music Elem	34	Early Childhood Ed	44	Science Sec	54	Remedial Reading K-12	64	Religious Education K-12	74	Inservice Training
7	Health Services	15	Asst Superintendent	25	Music Sec	35	Health/Phys Education	45	Math K-12	55	Remedial Reading Elem	65	Religious Education Elem	75	Marketing/Distributive
		16	Instructional Media Svcs	26	Business Education	36	Guidance Services K-12	46	Math Elem	56	Remedial Reading Sec	66	Religious Education Sec	76	Info Systems
		17	Chief Operations Officer	27	Career & Tech Ed	37	Guidance Services Elem	47	Math Sec	57	Bilingual/ELL	67	School Board President	77	Psychological Assess
		18	Chief Academic Officer	28	Technology Education	38	Guidance Services Sec	48	English/Lang Arts K-12	58	Special Education K-12	68	Teacher Personnel	78	Affirmative Action

New York School Directory — Nassau County

Sea Cliff Elem Sch	K-5	345	7%	516/277-7500
280 Carpenter Ave, Sea Cliff 11579		24		Fax 516/277-7506
Jeanette Wojcik				

• Oceanside Union Free Sch Dist PID: 00737760   516/678-1200
145 Merle Ave, Oceanside 11572   Fax 516/678-6503

Schools: 10 \ **Teachers:** 430 \ **Students:** 5,400 \ **Special Ed Students:** 741 \ **LEP Students:** 224 \ **College-Bound:** 91% \ **Ethnic:** Asian 4%, African American 2%, Hispanic 21%, Caucasian 74% \ **Exp:** $361 (High) \ **Poverty:** 4% \ **Title I:** $221,474 \ **Special Education:** $4,241,000 \ **Open-Close:** 09/08 - 06/25 \ **DTBP:** $3,185 (High)

Dr Phyllis Harrington 1   Christopher Van Cott 2,15
Robert Schloth 3   Jeffrey Risener 6*
Diane Provvido 8,15,70   Dr Jill DeRosa 15,68,79
Mark Sidoti 16   Robert Brase 20,23
Dr David Rose .... 57,61*   Dr Tina Smith 58
Stuart Kaplan 67   Melissa O'Geary 69
Donna Kraus 71   Susan Dwyer 73

Public Schs..Principal	Grd	Prgm	Enr/#Cls	SN	
Ⓐ Oceanside High Sch Castleton 145 Merle Ave, Oceanside 11572 **Brendon Mitchell**	9-12		45	45%	516/678-7593
School 2 Florence A Smith 2745 Terrell Ave, Oceanside 11572 Erin Marone	1-6		414 20	22%	516/678-7557 Fax 516/678-7559
School 3 Oaks Sch 2852 Fortesque Ave, Oceanside 11572 Beth-Ann Castiello	1-6		547 24	17%	516/678-7564 Fax 516/678-6568
School 4 South Oceanside Road 3210 Oceanside Rd, Oceanside 11572 Joanna Kletter	1-6		289 16	19%	516/678-7581 Fax 516/678-6583
School 5 North Oceanside Road 2440 Oceanside Rd, Oceanside 11572 Scott Bullis	1-6		482 24	24%	516/678-7585 Fax 516/678-6597
School 6 Kindergarten Center 25 Castleton Ct, Oceanside 11572 **Lucille McAssey**	K-K		395 28	4%	516/594-2345 Fax 516/678-7330
School 7 Oceanside HS 3160 Skillman Ave, Oceanside 11572 Geraldine DeCarlo	9-12	AGV	1,722	19%	516/678-7526 Fax 516/678-6790
School 8 Fulton Avenue 3252 Fulton Ave, Oceanside 11572 Dr Frank Zangari	1-6	T	412 23	18%	516/678-8503 Fax 516/678-6591
School 9E Walter S Boardman 170 Beatrice Ave, Oceanside 11572 Mr McPherson	1-6		307	10%	516/678-8510 Fax 516/678-7336
School 9M Oceanside Middle Sch 186 Alice Ave, Oceanside 11572 Allison Rogers	7-8	V	893	21%	516/678-8518 Fax 516/594-2365

• Oyster Bay East Norwich Ctl SD PID: 00737863   516/624-6500
1 McCouns Ln, Oyster Bay 11771   Fax 516/624-6520

Schools: 3 \ **Teachers:** 153 \ **Students:** 1,565 \ **Special Ed Students:** 290 \ **LEP Students:** 121 \ **Ethnic:** Asian 4%, African American 3%, Hispanic 24%, Caucasian 69% \ **Exp:** $437 (High) \ **Poverty:** 5% \ **Title I:** $145,882 \ **Special Education:** $984,000 \ **Open-Close:** 09/02 - 06/25 \ **DTBP:** $151 (High)

Dr Laura Seinfeld 1   Michael Cipriani 2,15
Kevin Trentowski 7,35   Dr Lisa Mulhall 8,11,15,288,298
Dr Marisa Bel 57   Ellen Loewy 58*
Laurie Kowalsky 67   Felica Febrizio 71

Janna Ostroff 73,285*

Public Schs..Principal	Grd	Prgm	Enr/#Cls	SN	
James H Vernon Sch 880 Oyster Bay Rd, East Norwich 11732 Valerie Vacchio	3-6		488 23	22%	516/624-6562 Fax 516/624-6522
Oyster Bay High Sch 150 E Main St, Oyster Bay 11771 Sharon Lasher	7-12		730	25%	516/624-6524 Fax 516/624-6684
Theodore Roosevelt Elem Sch 150 W Main St, Oyster Bay 11771 Tami McElwee	PK-2		347 18	16%	516/624-6573 Fax 516/624-6591

• Plainedge Union Free Sch Dist PID: 00737928   516/992-7450
241 Wyngate Dr, N Massapequa 11758   Fax 516/992-7446

Schools: 5 \ **Teachers:** 247 \ **Students:** 2,825 \ **Special Ed Students:** 450 \ **LEP Students:** 57 \ **Ethnic:** Asian 4%, Hispanic 7%, Caucasian 88% \ **Exp:** $411 (High) \ **Poverty:** 3% \ **Title I:** $92,140 \ **Special Education:** $606,000 \ **Open-Close:** 09/01 - 06/25 \ **DTBP:** $313 (High) \ t

Dr Edward Salina 1   Peter Porrazzo 2,15
Joe Jaronczyk 3,91   Jamie LaBelle 6,35,85*
Catherine Honeyman 8,15   Lisa DePaola 8,15,274
Dr Guy Le Vaillant 15,68,286   Veddo Mannino 23
Verdel Jones .... 36*   Bridget Murphy 58
Catherine Flannigan 67   Joe Maisano 83,88*

Public Schs..Principal	Grd	Prgm	Enr/#Cls	SN	
Charles E Schwarting Elem Sch 1 Flower Rd, Massapequa 11758 **Jennifer Thearle**	K-5		504 35	10%	516/992-7400 Fax 516/992-7405
Eastplain Sch 301 N Delaware Ave, N Massapequa 11758 Emily O'Brien	K-5		319 30	6%	516/531-9653 Fax 516/992-7605
John H West Elem Sch 499 Boundary Ave, Bethpage 11714 Joseph Maisano	K-5		461 30	11%	516/992-7500 Fax 516/992-7505
Plainedge High Sch 241 Wyngate Dr, N Massapequa 11758 Robert Amster	9-12		901 75	14%	516/992-7550 Fax 516/992-7545
Plainedge Middle Sch 200 Stewart Ave, Bethpage 11714 Anthony Deriso	6-8		640 70	13%	516/992-7650 Fax 516/992-7645

• Plainview-Old Bethpage Ctl SD PID: 00738013   516/434-3001
106 Washington Ave, Plainview 11803   Fax 516/937-6303

Schools: 7 \ **Teachers:** 459 \ **Students:** 5,000 \ **Special Ed Students:** 760 \ **LEP Students:** 119 \ **College-Bound:** 97% \ **Ethnic:** Asian 24%, Hispanic 6%, Caucasian 70% \ **Exp:** $459 (High) \ **Poverty:** 2% \ **Title I:** $105,665 \ **Special Education:** $5,431,000 \ **Open-Close:** 09/02 - 06/25 \ **DTBP:** $313 (High)

Dr Mary O'Meara 1   Richard Cunningham 2,11,15
Andrew Ward .... 3*   Karen Ball 4
Joseph Braico .... 6,35,83*   Joanne Mannion 8,15,57,69,70
Christopher Dona Rummo 15   Dr Vincent Mulieri 15,68,79
Carolyn Tellone .... 16*   Ben Wiley 20,286*
Michael Rodgers .... 23*   Laurie Lynn 36*
Jeffrey Yagaloff .... 50*   Dolores Espinosa 58,88,752
Debbie Bernstein 67   Bob Zimmerman 71
Guy Lodico .... 73*   Sheri Winick 81*
Cheryl Dender .... 274*   Eileen Annino 280

79	Student Personnel	91	Safety/Security	275	Response To Intervention	298	Grant Writer/Ptnrships	School Programs	Social Media
80	Driver Ed/Safety	92	Magnet School	277	Remedial Math K-12	750	Chief Innovation Officer	A = Alternative Program	
81	Gifted/Talented	93	Parental Involvement	280	Literacy Coach	751	Chief of Staff	G = Adult Classes	f = Facebook
82	Video Services	95	Tech Prep Program	285	STEM	752	Social Emotional Learning	M = Magnet Program	
83	Substance Abuse Prev	97	Chief Information Officer	286	Digital Learning			T = Title I Schoolwide	t = Twitter
84	Erate	98	Chief Technology Officer	288	Common Core Standards			V = Career & Tech Ed Programs	
85	AIDS Education	270	Accountability	294	Accountability		Other School Types		
88	Alternative/At Risk	271	Migrant Education	295	Network System		Ⓐ = Alternative School	New Schools are shaded	
89	Multi-Cultural Curriculum	273	Teacher Mentor	296	Title II Programs		Ⓒ = Charter School	New Superintendents and Principals are bold	
90	Social Work	274	Before/After Sch	297	Webmaster		Ⓜ = Magnet School	Personnel with email addresses are underscored	
								Ⓨ = Year-Round School		

Nassau County — Market Data Retrieval

Public Schs..Principal	Grd	Prgm	Enr/#Cls	SN	
H B Mattlin Middle Sch 100 Washington Ave, Plainview 11803 Joseph Coladonato	5-8		747	5%	516/434-3250 Fax 516/937-6431
John F Kennedy High Sch 50 Kennedy Dr, Plainview 11803 James Murray	9-12		1,554	10%	516/434-3125 Fax 516/937-6433
Old Bethpage Elem Sch 1159 Round Swamp Rd, Old Bethpage 11804 Suzanne Gray	K-4		395 18	6%	516/434-3419 Fax 516/756-3204
Parkway Elem Sch 300 Manetto Hill Rd, Plainview 11803 Gregory Scesney	K-4		398 17	4%	516/434-3358 Fax 516/349-4780
Pasadena Elem Sch 3 Richard Ct, Plainview 11803 Karen Heitner	K-4		445 17	8%	516/434-3451 Fax 516/937-7291
Plainview Old Bethpage Mid Sch 121 Central Park Rd, Plainview 11803 Alice Bowman	5-8		870	12%	516/434-3308 Fax 516/349-4777
Stratford Road Elem Sch 33 Bedford Rd, Plainview 11803 Alison Clark	K-4		547 27	9%	516/434-3389 Fax 516/937-6347

● **Port Washington Union Free SD** PID: 00738130   516/767-5000
100 Campus Dr, Prt Washingtn 11050   Fax 516/767-5007

Schools: 7 \ **Teachers:** 451 \ **Students:** 5,000 \ **Special Ed Students:** 938 \ **LEP Students:** 447 \ **College-Bound:** 99% \ **Ethnic:** Asian 11%, African American 2%, Hispanic 22%, Caucasian 65% \ **Exp:** $329 (High) \ **Poverty:** 8% \ **Title I:** $612,157 \ **Special Education:** $4,446,000 \ **Open-Close:** 09/08 - 06/25 \ **DTBP:** $305 (High)

Dr Michael Hynes 1,288
James Ristano 3,91
Robin Allen 5
Dr Wafa Westervelt 8,11,15,34,69,81,83
Kattie Klein 36,57,88,271
Stephanie Allen 58,79
Elaine Fenick 68
Amity Reiss 76

Mary Callahan 2,4,15
Pam Sanders 4
Stephanie Joannon 6,35*
Dr Christopher Sheilds 15
Shirley Cepero 57*
Nora Johnson 67
Ryan Meloni 73,76,95,286,297

Public Schs..Principal	Grd	Prgm	Enr/#Cls	SN	
Carrie Palmer Weber Middle Sch 52 Campus Dr, Prt Washingtn 11050 Beth Javeline	6-8	V	1,276 85	20%	516/767-5500 Fax 516/767-5507
Guggenheim Elem Sch 38 Poplar Pl, Prt Washingtn 11050 Kimberly Licato	K-5		558 29	20%	516/767-5250 Fax 516/767-5257
John J Daly Elem Sch 36 Rockwood Ave, Prt Washingtn 11050 Sheri Suzzan	PK-5		502 22	24%	516/767-5200 Fax 516/767-5207
John Philip Sousa Elem Sch 101 Sands Point Rd, Prt Washingtn 11050 Dr David Meoli	K-5		549 27	11%	516/767-5350 Fax 516/767-5356
Manorhaven Elem Sch 12 Morewood Oaks, Prt Washingtn 11050 Bonni Cohen	K-5		474 24	33%	516/767-5300 Fax 516/767-5303
Paul D Schreiber High Sch 101 Campus Dr, Prt Washingtn 11050 Dr Ira Pernick	9-12	AV	1,651	20%	516/767-5800 Fax 516/767-5809
South Salem Elem Sch 10 Newbury Rd, Prt Washingtn 11050 Pia Ferrante	K-5		428	13%	516/767-5400 Fax 516/767-5407

● **Rockville Ctr Union Free SD** PID: 00738245   516/255-8957
128 Shepherd St, Rockville CTR 11570   Fax 516/255-8810

Schools: 7 \ **Teachers:** 336 \ **Students:** 3,500 \ **Special Ed Students:** 557 \ **LEP Students:** 57 \ **College-Bound:** 95% \ **Ethnic:** Asian 2%, African American 7%, Hispanic 14%, Caucasian 76% \ **Exp:** $258 (Med) \ **Poverty:** 5% \ **Title I:** $391,640 \ **Special Education:** $2,911,000 \ **Open-Close:** 09/08 - 06/25 \ **DTBP:** $316 (High) \

June Chang 1
John Scalisi 3,91
Carol Roseto 6,7,35*
8,11,69,74,275,277,288,298
Janine Sampino 8
Jade Jacobs 16*
Laurie Levy 31,38*
Michael Anderson 73,286,295

Robert Bartels 2,15,68,78,271
Maryanne Friedermann 4,5
Christopher Pellettieri ....
Dr Noreen Leahy 15,54,58,76,83
Dr Brian Zuar 23*
David Dubner 67

Public Schs..Principal	Grd	Prgm	Enr/#Cls	SN	
Hewitt Elem Sch 446 Demott Ave, Rockville CTR 11570 Elizabeth Pryke	K-5		466 15	7%	516/255-8913 Fax 516/763-1817
Riverside Elem Sch 110 Riverside Dr, Rockville CTR 11570 Patricia Bock	K-5		165 11	21%	516/255-8902 Fax 516/763-1812
South Side High Sch 140 Shepherd St, Rockville CTR 11570 John Murphy	9-12	GV	1,056	15%	516/255-8947 Fax 516/766-7934
South Side Middle Sch 67 Hillside Ave, Rockville CTR 11570 Shelagh McGinn	6-8	V	846 50	12%	516/255-8976 Fax 516/763-0914
Watson Elem Sch 277 N Centre Ave, Rockville CTR 11570 Joan Waldman	K-5		273 19	18%	516/255-8904 Fax 516/763-1808
William S Covert Elem Sch 379 Willow St, S Hempstead 11550 Darren Raymar	K-5		312 15	12%	516/255-8916 Fax 516/538-3165
Wilson Elem Sch 25 Buckingham Rd, Rockville CTR 11570 James Duffy	K-5		430 20	6%	516/255-8910 Fax 516/763-1806

● **Roosevelt Union Free Sch Dist** PID: 00738336   516/345-7000
240 Denton Pl, Roosevelt 11575   Fax 516/345-7326

Schools: 5 \ **Teachers:** 269 \ **Students:** 3,511 \ **Special Ed Students:** 527 \ **LEP Students:** 877 \ **Ethnic:** African American 43%, Hispanic 57%, \ **Exp:** $280 (Med) \ **Poverty:** 19% \ **Title I:** $954,459 \ **Special Education:** $8,303,000 \ **Open-Close:** 09/03 - 06/25 \ **DTBP:** $315 (High)

Dr Deborah Wortham 1
Dan Sadia 3
Gary Gregory 6,35
Michele Van Eyken 9
Dr Shirley Martin 15,68
Dr Dionne Wynn 58,79
Desmond Poyser 73,76,286

Michael Goldberg 2,15,19
Leola Palmer 5
Natesha McVea 8,15,288
Dr Nichelle Rivers 11,296,298
Xiomara Gonzalez 57,61
Charlena Croutch 67

Public Schs..Principal	Grd	Prgm	Enr/#Cls	SN	
ⓨ Centennial Avenue Elem Sch 140 W Centennial Ave, Roosevelt 11575 Barbara Solomon	PK-6	MT	657 32	75%	516/345-7400 Fax 516/345-7490
ⓨ Roosevelt High Sch 516/345-7200 1 Wagner Ave, Roosevelt 11575 Brodrick Spencer	9-12	AGMTV	1,044 68	72%	

1 Superintendent	8 Curric/Instruct K-12	19 Chief Financial Officer	29 Family/Consumer Science	39 Social Studies K-12	49 English/Lang Arts Elem	59 Special Education Elem	69 Academic Assessment
2 Bus/Finance/Purchasing	9 Curric/Instruct Elem	20 Art K-12	30 Adult Education	40 Social Studies Elem	50 English/Lang Arts Sec	60 Special Education Sec	70 Research/Development
3 Buildings And Grounds	10 Curric/Instruct Sec	21 Art Elem	31 Career/Sch-to-Work K-12	41 Social Studies Sec	51 Reading K-12	61 Foreign/World Lang K-12	71 Public Information
4 Food Service	11 Federal Program	22 Art Sec	32 Career/Sch-to-Work Elem	42 Science K-12	52 Reading Elem	62 Foreign/World Lang Elem	72 Summer School
5 Transportation	12 Title I	23 Music K-12	33 Career/Sch-to-Work Sec	43 Science Elem	53 Reading Sec	63 Foreign/World Lang Sec	73 Instructional Tech
6 Athletic	13 Title V	24 Music Elem	34 Early Childhood Ed	44 Science Sec	54 Remedial Reading K-12	64 Religious Education K-12	74 Inservice Training
7 Health Services	15 Asst Superintendent	25 Music Sec	35 Health/Phys Education	45 Math K-12	55 Remedial Reading Elem	65 Religious Education Elem	75 Marketing/Distributive
	16 Instructional Media Svcs	26 Business Education	36 Guidance Services K-12	46 Math Elem	56 Remedial Reading Sec	66 Religious Education Sec	76 Info Systems
	17 Chief Operations Officer	27 Career & Tech Ed	37 Guidance Services Elem	47 Math Sec	57 Bilingual/ELL	67 School Board President	77 Psychological Assess
	18 Chief Academic Officer	28 Technology Education	38 Guidance Services Sec	48 English/Lang Arts K-12	58 Special Education K-12	68 Teacher Personnel	78 Affirmative Action

New York School Directory — Nassau County

	Grd	Prgm	Enr/#Cls	SN		
ⓨ Roosevelt Middle Sch 335 E Clinton Ave, Roosevelt 11575 Dr Jeremiah Sumter	7-8	MT	509	81%	516/345-7700 Fax 516/345-7790	
ⓨ Ulysses Byas Elem Sch 60 Underhill Ave, Roosevelt 11575 Angela Hudson	PK-6	MT	534 19	85%	516/345-7500 Fax 516/345-7590	
ⓨ Washington Rose Elem Sch 2 Rose Ave, Roosevelt 11575 Clyde Brashwell	PK-6	MT	767 60	79%	516/345-7600 Fax 516/345-7690	

- **Roslyn School Dist** PID: 00738403   516/801-5001
  300 Harbor Hill Rd, Roslyn 11576   Fax 516/801-5008

Schools: 5 \ **Teachers:** 265 \ **Students:** 3,150 \ **Special Ed Students:** 344 \ **LEP Students:** 98 \ **College-Bound:** 100% \ **Ethnic:** Asian 18%, African American 3%, Hispanic 8%, Caucasian 70% \ **Exp:** $297 (Med) \ **Poverty:** 4% \ **Title I:** $125,953 \ **Special Education:** $1,804,000 \ **Open-Close:** 09/01 - 06/25 \ **DTBP:** $317 (High)

Allison Brown 1,83	Joseph Dragone 2
Kevin Carpenter 3,91	Dawn Piteo 4*
David Shoob 5	Michael Bruskowski 6
Karina Baez 9,15	Barbara Schwartz 11,58,79*
Michael Goldspiel 15	Greg Wasserman 27,31,36,85*
Barry Edelson 30,71,297,298	Bruce Kahn 67
Jason Lopez 73,286	

Public Schs..Principal	Grd	Prgm	Enr/#Cls	SN	
East Hills Elem Sch 315 Locust Ln, Roslyn HTS 11577 Melissa Krieger	2-5		537 24	19%	516/801-5300 Fax 516/801-5308
Harbor Hill Elem Sch 3 Glen Cove Rd, Greenvale 11548 Jessica Kemler	K-5		508 26	11%	516/801-5400 Fax 516/801-5408
Roslyn Heights Sch 240 Willow St, Roslyn HTS 11577 Mary Wood	PK-1		363 20	15%	516/801-5500 Fax 516/801-5508
Roslyn High Sch 475 Round Hill Rd, Roslyn HTS 11577 Dr Scott Andrews	9-12	AGV	1,068	13%	516/801-5100 Fax 516/801-5108
Roslyn Middle Sch 375 Locust Ln, Roslyn HTS 11577 Craig Johanson	6-8		718 70	13%	516/801-5200 Fax 516/801-5208

- **Seaford Union Free SD** PID: 00738491   516/592-4000
  1600 Washington Ave, Seaford 11783   Fax 516/592-4049

Schools: 4 \ **Teachers:** 209 \ **Students:** 2,249 \ **Special Ed Students:** 436 \ **LEP Students:** 37 \ **College-Bound:** 94% \ **Ethnic:** Asian 3%, African American 1%, Hispanic 8%, Caucasian 89% \ **Exp:** $326 (High) \ **Poverty:** 2% \ **Title I:** $59,172 \ **Special Education:** $2,382,000 \ **Open-Close:** 09/08 - 06/25 \ **DTBP:** $312 (High)

Dr Adele Pecora 1	Marie Donnelly 2,5,15
Russell Costa 3	Elizabeth Fiola 4*
Michael Spreckels 6*	John Striffolino 8,15,69,273,285,288,298
Mary Culella-Sun 11,58,88	Fred Kaden 16,73,76,286,295*
Patricia Foley 57	Bruce Kahn 67
Thomas Lynch 285	

Public Schs..Principal	Grd	Prgm	Enr/#Cls	SN	
Seaford Harbor Elem Sch 3500 Bayview St, Seaford 11783 Thomas Burke	K-5	T	577 29	10%	516/592-4100 Fax 516/592-4101
Seaford High Sch 1575 Seamans Neck Rd, Seaford 11783 Scott Gilbert	9-12	T	713	9%	516/592-4300 Fax 516/592-4399
Seaford Manor Elem Sch 1590 Washington Ave, Seaford 11783 Debra Emmerich	K-5		441 30	4%	516/592-4050 Fax 516/592-4051
Seaford Middle Sch 3940 Sunset Ave, Seaford 11783 Daniel Smith	6-8	T	518 45	9%	516/592-4200 Fax 516/592-4201

- **Sewanhaka Ctl High Sch Dist** PID: 00735554   516/488-9800
  77 Landau Ave, Floral Park 11001   Fax 516/488-7738

Schools: 5 \ **Teachers:** 585 \ **Students:** 8,145 \ **Special Ed Students:** 1,089 \ **LEP Students:** 345 \ **College-Bound:** 94% \ **Ethnic:** Asian 22%, African American 24%, Hispanic 20%, Caucasian 33% \ **Exp:** $158 (Low) \ **Poverty:** 6% \ **Title I:** $834,388 \ **Special Education:** $9,994,000 \ **Open-Close:** 09/08 - 06/25 \ **DTBP:** $311 (High)

Dr James Grossane 1	Christine Byrne 2
Kevin O'Brien 2,3,15	Matt Castelluzzo 3
Suzanne Semler 4	Michael Onufrey 5
Theresa Schmidt 6,35,80,83,85*	Dr Taryn Johnson 10,15
Regina Agrusa 11,38,77,79,90,93,296,298	John Capozzi 15,68
Karen Annunziata 16*	Christine Licastri 26,28*
J Chieffo 27,95*	Diane DeLuca 57*
Mallory Poledro 60	Michael Jaime 67
Christopher Nelson 71,76*	Brian Messinger 73
Daniel Espina 73	Dr Caryl Oris 77

Public Schs..Principal	Grd	Prgm	Enr/#Cls	SN	
Elmont Memorial Jr Sr High Sch 555 Ridge Rd, Elmont 11003 Kevin Dougherty	7-12	TV	1,598	47%	516/488-9200 Fax 516/488-5560
Floral Park Mem Jr Sr High Sch 210 Locust St, Floral Park 11001 Maria Pozzulo	7-12	V	1,406	21%	516/488-9300 Fax 516/394-5079
H Frank Carey Jr Sr High Sch 230 Poppy Ave, Franklin Sq 11010 Christopher Fiore	7-12	V	1,621 80	17%	516/539-9400 Fax 516/538-1791
New Hyde Park Mem Jr Sr HS 500 Leonard Blvd, New Hyde Park 11040 Dr Richard Faccio	7-12	V	1,851 80	23%	516/488-9500 Fax 516/488-9506
Sewanhaka High Sch 500 Tulip Ave, Floral Park 11001 Chris Salinas	7-12	TV	1,669 100	48%	516/488-9600 Fax 516/488-9215

- **Syosset Central School Dist** PID: 00738556   516/364-5600
  99 Pell Ln, Syosset 11791   Fax 516/921-5616

Schools: 10 \ **Teachers:** 620 \ **Students:** 6,500 \ **Special Ed Students:** 793 \ **LEP Students:** 218 \ **Ethnic:** Asian 39%, African American 1%, Hispanic 4%, Caucasian 56% \ **Exp:** $352 (High) \ **Poverty:** 3% \ **Title I:** $204,567 \ **Special Education:** $5,133,000 \ **Open-Close:** 09/08 - 06/25 \ **DTBP:** $316 (High)

Dr Thomas Rogers 1	Dr Patricia Rufo 2,12,15,288
Gregory Hamilton 3,91	Claudia Hardes 5
Adele Bovard 8,15,78	Dr Joseph Lamelza 15,58,79
Tracy Frankel 67	Chrisatine Payne 73,76
Charles Gleason 83*	Jo Jiuffidra 274*

Public Schs..Principal	Grd	Prgm	Enr/#Cls	SN	
Alice P Willits Elem Sch 99 Nana Pl, Syosset 11791 James Connolly	K-5		321 17	6%	516/364-5829 Fax 516/364-3792

79	Student Personnel	91	Safety/Security	275	Response To Intervention	298	Grant Writer/Ptnrships	
80	Driver Ed/Safety	92	Magnet School	277	Remedial Math K-12	750	Chief Innovation Officer	
81	Gifted/Talented	93	Parental Involvement	280	Literacy Coach	751	Chief of Staff	
82	Video Services	95	Tech Prep Program	285	STEM	752	Social Emotional Learning	
83	Substance Abuse Prev	97	Chief Information Officer	286	Digital Learning			
84	Erate	98	Chief Technology Officer	288	Common Core Standards			
85	AIDS Education	270	Character Education	294	Accountability			
88	Alternative/At Risk	271	Migrant Education	295	Network System			
89	Multi-Cultural Curriculum	273	Teacher Mentor	296	Title II Programs			
90	Social Work	274	Before/After Sch	297	Webmaster			

School Programs
A = Alternative Program
G = Adult Classes
M = Magnet Program
T = Title I Schoolwide
V = Career & Tech Ed Programs

Other School Types
Ⓐ = Alternative School
Ⓒ = Charter School
Ⓜ = Magnet School
Ⓨ = Year-Round School

Social Media
 = Facebook
 = Twitter

New Schools are shaded
New Superintendents and Principals are bold
Personnel with email addresses are underscored

NY—129

Nassau County

Market Data Retrieval

Baylis Elem Sch 580 Woodbury Rd, Plainview 11803 Lisa Greiner	K-5		447 19	8%	516/364-5798 Fax 516/364-3357
Berry Hill Elem Sch 181 Cold Spring Rd, Syosset 11791 Mary Kolkhorst	K-5		383 22	4%	516/364-5790 Fax 516/364-3379
H B Thompson Middle Sch 98 Ann Dr, Syosset 11791 Kevin Bonanno	6-8	V	851	6%	516/364-5760 Fax 516/364-3206
Robbins Lane Elem Sch 157 Robbins Ln, Syosset 11791 Thea Pallos	K-5		469 20	7%	516/364-5804 Fax 516/364-3224
South Grove Elem Sch 60 Colony Ln, Syosset 11791 Mi Jung an	K-5		425 19	8%	516/364-5810 Fax 516/364-4261
South Woods Middle Sch 99 Pell Ln, Syosset 11791 Michelle Burget	6-8	V	733	6%	516/364-5621 Fax 516/364-3249
Syosset High Sch 70 Southwoods Rd, Syosset 11791 Dr Giovanni Durante	9-12	AGV	2,234	8%	516/364-5675 Fax 516/921-6032
Village Elem Sch 90 Convent Rd, Syosset 11791 Jeffrey Kasper	K-5	T	399 20	7%	516/364-5817 Fax 516/364-3381
Walt Whitman Elem Sch 482 Woodbury Rd, Woodbury 11797 Chad Snyder	K-5		318 17	2%	516/364-5823 Fax 516/692-9103

● **Uniondale Union Free Sch Dist** PID: 00738697   516/560-8800
933 Goodrich St, Uniondale 11553   Fax 516/918-1271

Schools: 9 \ **Teachers:** 593 \ **Students:** 6,970 \ **Special Ed Students:** 1,059 \ **LEP Students:** 1,442 \ **Ethnic:** Asian 1%, African American 37%, Hispanic 60%, Caucasian 2% \ **Exp:** $243 (Med) \ **Poverty:** 15% \ **Title I:** $1,637,728 \ **Special Education:** $8,617,000 \ **Open-Close:** 09/02 - 06/25 \ **DTBP:** $299 (High)

Dr William Lloyd 1	Steven Epstein 2,4,5,15
John Labare 3,91	Paul Weydig 5
Dr Jonathan Jefferson 6,35,83,85	Sylvia Kallich 7
Rhonda Taylor 8,15,88,270,273	Dr Kimberlee Pierre 11,69,77,81,296
Myrtle Dickson 15,68	Ann Ritter 16,73
Kelvin Jenkins 20,23	Stacie Reid 36
Pierre Rancy 57	Charmise Desire 67
Christine Lopes 298	

Public Schs..Principal	Grd	Prgm	Enr/#Cls	SN	
California Ave Elem Sch 236 California Ave, Uniondale 11553 Bryan Bruno	K-5	T	799 43	68%	516/918-1850 Fax 516/918-1975
Grand Avenue Elem Sch 711 School Dr, Baldwin 11510 Juanita Bryant-Bell	K-5	T	322 19	62%	516/918-2100 Fax 516/918-2124
Lawrence Road Middle Sch 50 Lawrence Rd, Hempstead 11550 Dexter Hodge	6-8	TV	806 32	70%	516/918-1500 Fax 516/918-1506
Northern Parkway Elem Sch 440 Northern Pkwy, Uniondale 11553 Bilal Polson	K-5	T	692	70%	516/918-1700 Fax 516/918-1794
Smith Street Elem Sch 780 Smith St, Uniondale 11553 Lynnda Nadien	K-5		462	66%	516/918-2000 Fax 516/918-2074
Turtle Hook Middle Sch 975 Jerusalem Ave, Uniondale 11553 Donald Humphrey	6-8	TV	802 40	72%	516/918-1301 Fax 516/918-1451
Uniondale High Sch 933 Goodrich St, Uniondale 11553 Edward Thomas	9-12	GTV	2,312	67%	516/560-8800
Uniondale Pre-Kindergarten 835 De Mott Ave, Baldwin 11510 Elaine Debono	PK-PK		100		516/405-8300
Walnut Street Elem Sch 1270 Walnut St, Uniondale 11553 Kevin Bracht	K-5	T	538 26	71%	516/918-2200 Fax 516/918-2275

● **Valley Stream Ctl High SD** PID: 00738790   516/872-5600
1 Kent Rd, Valley Stream 11580   Fax 516/872-5658

Schools: 4 \ **Teachers:** 333 \ **Students:** 4,600 \ **Special Ed Students:** 743 \ **LEP Students:** 171 \ **College-Bound:** 95% \ **Ethnic:** Asian 21%, African American 30%, Hispanic 29%, Caucasian 19% \ **Exp:** $233 (Med) \ **Poverty:** 7% \ **Title I:** $504,450 \ **Special Education:** $7,265,000 \ **Open-Close:** 09/03 - 06/25 \ **DTBP:** $303 (High)

Dr Bill Heidenreich 1	Dr Wayne Loper 2,3,4,5,11,15,78
James Nothel 3,91	Christian Bowen . 10,11,57,69,74,273,288,298
Clifford Odell 15,68	Eva Ouwendijk 16,82*
Kelly Whitney-Rivera 38,71,97	Dr Willam Bushman 60,77,83,90
James Lavery 67	Maureen Henry 88,270*

Public Schs..Principal	Grd	Prgm	Enr/#Cls	SN	
Valley Stream Central High Sch 135 Fletcher Ave, Valley Stream 11580 Dr Joseph Pompilio	10-12	V	964 60	41%	516/561-4400 Fax 516/561-4490
Valley Stream Memorial Jr HS 320 Fletcher Ave, Valley Stream 11580 Bret Strauss	7-9	GT	982 51	37%	516/872-7700 Fax 516/872-7729
Valley Stream North JSHS 750 Herman Ave, Franklin Sq 11010 Rachel Green	7-12		1,347	28%	516/564-5500 Fax 516/564-5539
Valley Stream South JSHS 150 Jedwood Pl, Valley Stream 11581 Maureen Henry	7-12		1,284	30%	516/791-0300 Fax 516/791-0305

● **Valley Stream Union Free SD 13** PID: 00738843   516/568-6100
585 N Corona Ave, Valley Stream 11580   Fax 516/825-2537

Schools: 4 \ **Teachers:** 179 \ **Students:** 1,964 \ **Special Ed Students:** 308 \ **LEP Students:** 105 \ **Ethnic:** Asian 22%, African American 22%, Hispanic 29%, Native American: 1%, Caucasian 26% \ **Exp:** $440 (High) \ **Poverty:** 6% \ **Title I:** $204,507 \ **Special Education:** $2,419,000 \ **Open-Close:** 09/02 - 06/25 \ **DTBP:** $177 (High)

Constance Evelyn 1	Gerard Antoine 2,15,68
Matthew Lukaszewizc 3	Judith LaRocca 9,15,285,288
Lisa Sells-Ash 15,57,78	Andera Dimango 16,73,295
Christine DiDio 21,24	Joanna Land 24
Matthew Spinks 24	Milagros Vicente 67
Mimi Bass 90*	

Public Schs..Principal	Grd	Prgm	Enr/#Cls	SN	
Howell Road Elem Sch 1475 Howell Rd, Valley Stream 11580 Frank Huplosky	K-6	T	480 28	44%	516/568-6130 Fax 516/568-6107
James A Dever Elem Sch 585 N Corona Ave, Valley Stream 11580 Darren Gruen	K-6		431 25	23%	516/568-6120 Fax 516/568-6119
Wheeler Avenue Elem Sch 1 Wheeler Ave W, Valley Stream 11580 John Frias	1-6		584 27	32%	516/568-6140 Fax 516/568-0061

---

1 Superintendent	8 Curric/Instruct K-12	19 Chief Financial Officer	29 Family/Consumer Science	39 Social Studies K-12	49 English/Lang Arts Elem	59 Special Education Elem	69 Academic Assessment
2 Bus/Finance/Purchasing	9 Curric/Instruct Elem	20 Art K-12	30 Adult Education	40 Social Studies Elem	50 English/Lang Arts Sec	60 Special Education Sec	70 Research/Development
3 Buildings And Grounds	10 Curric/Instruct Sec	21 Art Elem	31 Career/Sch-to-Work K-12	41 Social Studies Sec	51 Reading K-12	61 Foreign/World Lang K-12	71 Public Information
4 Food Service	11 Federal Program	22 Art Sec	32 Career/Sch-to-Work Elem	42 Science K-12	52 Reading Elem	62 Foreign/World Lang Elem	72 Summer School
5 Transportation	12 Title I	23 Music K-12	33 Career/Sch-to-Work Sec	43 Science Elem	53 Reading Sec	63 Foreign/World Lang Sec	73 Instructional Tech
6 Athletic	13 Title V	24 Music Elem	34 Early Childhood Ed	44 Science Sec	54 Remedial Reading K-12	64 Religious Education K-12	74 Inservice Training
7 Health Services	15 Asst Superintendent	25 Music Sec	35 Health/Phys Education	45 Math K-12	55 Remedial Reading Elem	65 Religious Education Elem	75 Marketing/Distributive
	16 Instructional Media Svcs	26 Business Education	36 Guidance Services K-12	46 Math Elem	56 Remedial Reading Sec	66 Religious Education Sec	76 Info Systems
	17 Chief Operations Officer	27 Career & Tech Ed	37 Guidance Services Elem	47 Math Sec	57 Bilingual/ELL	67 School Board President	77 Psychological Assess
	18 Chief Academic Officer	28 Technology Education	38 Guidance Services Sec	48 English/Lang Arts K-12	58 Special Education K-12	68 Teacher Personnel	78 Affirmative Action

New York School Directory — Nassau County

Willow Road Elem Sch	K-6		469	21%	516/568-6640
880 Catalpa Dr, Franklin Sq 11010			25		Fax 516/292-2095
Rosalie Ambrosio					

• Valley Stream Union Free SD 24 PID: 00738893   516/434-2825
75 Horton Ave, Valley Stream 11581   Fax 516/256-0163

Schools: 3 \ **Teachers:** 100 \ **Students:** 1,093 \ **Special Ed Students:** 157 \ **LEP Students:** 89 \ **Ethnic:** Asian 16%, African American 23%, Hispanic 42%, Caucasian 19% \ **Exp:** $234 (Med) \ **Poverty:** 9% \ **Title I:** $194,590 \ **Special Education:** $1,512,000 \ **Open-Close:** 09/02 - 06/25 \ **DTBP:** $175 (High)

Dr Don Sturz 1
Charles Brocher 3,91
Dr Scott Comis 12,83,85*
Laura Peterson 58,77,79,88,270,275*
Karen Serro 90*
Jack Mitchell 2,4,5,11,294,298
Dr Lisa Conte 9,15,57,280,288
Mark Onorato 16,73,286,295*
Kimberly Wheeler 67

Public Schs..Principal	Grd	Prgm	Enr/#Cls	SN	
Brooklyn Avenue Elem Sch	K-6	T	337	50%	516/434-2850
24 Brooklyn Ave, Valley Stream 11581			16		Fax 516/256-0169
Dr Scott Comis					
Robert W Carbonaro Elem Sch	K-6		429	38%	516/434-2860
50 Hungry Harbor Rd, Valley Stream 11581			21		Fax 516/791-4573
Rosario Iacono					
William L Buck Elem Sch	K-6		327	34%	516/256-0160
75 Horton Ave, Valley Stream 11581			17		Fax 516/256-0157
Susan Leggett					

• Valley Stream Union Free SD 30 PID: 00738946   516/434-3600
175 N Central Ave Ste 100, Valley Stream 11580   Fax 516/706-1177

Schools: 3 \ **Teachers:** 111 \ **Students:** 1,450 \ **Special Ed Students:** 170 \ **LEP Students:** 131 \ **Ethnic:** Asian 27%, African American 39%, Hispanic 30%, Caucasian 4% \ **Exp:** $709 (High) \ **Poverty:** 11% \ **Title I:** $231,774 \ **Special Education:** $1,436,000 \ **Open-Close:** 09/02 - 06/25 \ **DTBP:** $161 (High)

Dr Nicholas Stirling 1
Brian Phillips 2,5,15
Susan Rodridez 9,16,73,74,76,295
Nicole Schimpf 59
Ashley Tstorner 2
Christopher Malone 3
Jennifer Lewner 15,28,752*
Ingrid Wyllie- Dacon 67

Public Schs..Principal	Grd	Prgm	Enr/#Cls	SN	
Clear Stream Avenue Elem Sch	K-6	T	387	50%	516/434-3550
60 Clearstream Ave, Valley Stream 11580			19		Fax 516/872-1205
John Singleton					
Forest Road Elem Sch	K-6	T	342	44%	516/434-3800
16 Forest Rd, Valley Stream 11581			18		Fax 516/792-2931
Erin Malone					
Shaw Avenue Elem Sch	K-6	T	735	46%	516/434-3700
99 Shaw Ave, Valley Stream 11580			31		Fax 516/568-2436
Christopher Colarossi					

• Wantagh Union Free Sch Dist 23 PID: 00738996   516/781-8000
3301 Beltagh Ave, Wantagh 11793   Fax 516/679-7806

Schools: 5 \ **Teachers:** 244 \ **Students:** 2,770 \ **Special Ed Students:** 469 \ **LEP Students:** 19 \ **College-Bound:** 98% \ **Ethnic:** Asian 3%, Hispanic 8%, Caucasian 89% \ **Exp:** $336 (High) \ **Poverty:** 1% \ **Special Education:** $4,417,000 \ **Open-Close:** 09/08 - 06/25 \ **DTBP:** $322 (High)

John McNamara 1   Anthony Cedrone 2,4,15,90,91

Tom Fucci 3,5
Dr Mark Ferris 8,11,83,285,288,294,296,298
Penny Curry 16,27,28,73,76,286,295,297*
Patricia Calosso 26,61*
Christopher Widmann 39*
John Watson 45*
Jeannie Love 58*
Eric Vonbargen 74*
Jennifer Keane 6,35*
Ryan Alperti 12
Kelly Jones 23*
Frank Muzio 29,36*
Carol Winas 42
Julie Rosslee 48,57
Adam Fisher 67

Public Schs..Principal	Grd	Prgm	Enr/#Cls	SN	
Forest Lake Elem Sch	K-5		381	6%	516/679-6470
3100 Beltagh Ave, Wantagh 11793			20		Fax 516/679-6478
Mrs Zimmer					
Mandalay Elem Sch	K-5		248	7%	516/679-6390
2667 Bayview Ave, Wantagh 11793			14		Fax 516/679-6484
Marie Pisicchio					
Wantagh Elem Sch	K-5		642	6%	516/679-6480
1765 Beech St, Wantagh 11793					Fax 516/679-6365
Randee Bonagura					
Wantagh High Sch	9-12	GV	859	7%	516/679-6402
3297 Beltagh Ave, Wantagh 11793			25		Fax 516/679-6432
Carolyn Breivogel					
Wantagh Middle Sch	6-8	V	640	8%	516/679-6350
3299 Beltagh Ave, Wantagh 11793					Fax 516/679-6311
Anthony Ciuffo					

• West Hempstead School Dist PID: 00739067   516/390-3100
252 Chestnut St, W Hempstead 11552   Fax 516/489-1776

Schools: 5 \ **Teachers:** 165 \ **Students:** 2,300 \ **Special Ed Students:** 456 \ **LEP Students:** 183 \ **College-Bound:** 89% \ **Ethnic:** Asian 8%, African American 21%, Hispanic 46%, Caucasian 26% \ **Exp:** $414 (High) \ **Poverty:** 7% \ **Title I:** $323,121 \ **Special Education:** $2,742,000 \ **Open-Close:** 09/03 - 06/25 \ **DTBP:** $160 (High)

Dan Rehman 1,11,57
William Dworsal 3
Chris Misteretta 6,29,35,80*
Dina Reilly 8,15,18,296,298,752
Vincent Fleck 28,73
Faith Tripp 280*
Joel Press 2,4,5,15,17,91
Gina Gandolfo 5
Bridget Karis 7,58,79,83
Veronsky Mesidor 16,48*
Karen Brohm 67
Joseph Cangemi 285

Public Schs..Principal	Grd	Prgm	Enr/#Cls	SN	
Chestnut Street Sch	K-1		111	33%	516/390-3150
252 Chestnut St, W Hempstead 11552			8		Fax 516/390-3152
Faith Tripp					
Cornwell Ave Elem Sch	1-3	T	361	48%	516/390-3140
250 Cornwell Ave, W Hempstead 11552			15		Fax 516/489-0365
Deanna Sinito					
George Washington Elem Sch	4-6	T	374	52%	516/390-3130
347 William St, W Hempstead 11552			30		Fax 516/489-0068
Michelle Notti					
West Hempstead High Sch	9-12	T	637	47%	516/390-3214
400 Nassau Blvd, W Hempstead 11552					Fax 516/489-1769
James Detommaso					
ⓨ West Hempstead Middle Sch	7-8	MT	278	46%	516/390-3160
450 Nassau Blvd, W Hempstead 11552			50		Fax 516/489-8946
Sean Murray					

---

79 Student Personnel	91 Safety/Security	275 Response To Intervention	298 Grant Writer/Ptnrships
80 Driver Ed/Safety	92 Magnet School	277 Remedial Math K-12	750 Chief Innovation Officer
81 Gifted/Talented	93 Parental Involvement	280 Literacy Coach	751 Chief of Staff
82 Video Services	95 Tech Prep Program	285 STEM	752 Social Emotional Learning
83 Substance Abuse Prev	97 Chief Information Officer	286 Digital Learning	
84 Erate	98 Chief Technology Officer	288 Common Core Standards	
85 AIDS Education	270 Character Education	294 Accountability	
88 Alternative/At Risk	271 Migrant Education	295 Network System	
89 Multi-Cultural Curriculum	273 Teacher Mentor	296 Title II Programs	
90 Social Work	274 Before/After Sch	297 Webmaster	

School Programs
A = Alternative Program
G = Adult Classes
M = Magnet Program
T = Title I Schoolwide
V = Career & Tech Ed Programs

Other School Types
Ⓐ = Alternative School
Ⓒ = Charter School
Ⓜ = Magnet School
Ⓨ = Year-Round School

Social Media
🅕 = Facebook
🅣 = Twitter

New Schools are shaded
New Superintendents and Principals are bold
Personnel with email addresses are underscored

Nassau County

- **Westbury Union Free Sch Dist** PID: 00739122   516/876-5000
  2 Hitchcock Ln, Old Westbury 11568   Fax 516/876-5181

Schools: 6 \ **Teachers:** 370 \ **Students:** 5,000 \ **Special Ed Students:** 761 \ **LEP Students:** 1,544 \ **Ethnic:** Asian 1%, African American 23%, Hispanic 73%, Caucasian 2% \ **Exp:** $326 (High) \ **Poverty:** 17% \ **Title I:** $1,150,446 \ **Special Education:** $9,288,000 \ **Open-Close:** 09/03 - 06/25 \ **DTBP:** $303 (High)

Eudes Budhai	1	Guy Forman	3
Doric Capsis	6,35	Maria Meyer	8,11,69
Roger Bloom	15,68	Jaime Martinez	30
Robert Hassinger	30	Deadra Faulkner	36*
Jorge Santiago	58	Robert Troiano	67
Rocco Varullo	73,76	Carlyle Richards	83,88*

Public Schs..Principal	Grd	Prgm	Enr/#Cls	SN	
Drexel Ave Sch 161 Drexel Ave, Westbury 11590 Dr Wanda Toledo	1-5	T	544 25	80%	516/876-5030 Fax 516/876-5032
Dryden St Sch 545 Dryden St, Westbury 11590 Gloria Dingwall	PK-K	T	589 27	78%	516/876-5039 Fax 516/876-5172
Park Avenue Sch 955 Park Ave, Westbury 11590 Robert Chambers	1-5	T	735 32	85%	516/876-5107 Fax 516/876-5190
Powells Lane Sch 603 Powells Ln, Westbury 11590 Claudia Germain	1-5	T	520 42	77%	516/876-5125 Fax 516/876-5160
Westbury High Sch 1 Post Rd, Old Westbury 11568 David Zimbler	9-12	GTV	1,673 45	76%	516/876-5047 Fax 516/876-5079
Westbury Middle Sch 455 Rockland St, Westbury 11590 Fernando Agramonte	6-8	T	1,166 50	80%	516/876-5082 Fax 516/876-5141

NASSAU CATHOLIC SCHOOLS

- **Diocese of Rockville Ed Office** PID: 00739512   516/678-5800
  128 Cherry Ln, Hicksville 11801   Fax 516/280-2963

Schools: 44 \ **Students:** 32,000

Listing includes only schools located in this county. See District Index for location of Diocesan Offices.

Dr Kathleen Walsh	1	Maureen Hannan	2
Biagio Arpino	15,68	Marian Mingo	15
Vincent Vizzo	15	Emily Guarnieri	73

Catholic Schs..Principal	Grd	Prgm	Enr/#Cls	SN	
Chaminade High Sch 340 Jackson Ave, Mineola 11501 Br Joseph Bellizzi	9-12		1,500 44		516/742-5555 Fax 516/742-1989
Holy Family Sch 17 Fordham Ave, Hicksville 11801 Maryalice Doherty	PK-8		310 20		516/938-3846 Fax 516/938-5041
Holy Name of Mary Sch 90 S Grove St, Valley Stream 11580 Pamela Sanders	PK-8		325 18		516/825-4009 Fax 516/825-2710
Holy Trinity Diocesan High Sch 98 Cherry Ln, Hicksville 11801 Kathleen Moran	9-12		1,000 55		516/433-2900 Fax 516/433-2827
Kellenberg Memorial High Sch 1400 Glenn Curtiss Blvd, Uniondale 11553 Br Kenneth Hoagland	6-12		2,250 72		516/292-0200 Fax 516/292-0877
Long Beach Catholic Reg Sch 735 W Broadway, Long Beach 11561 Kerry Kahn	PK-8		513 17		516/432-8900 Fax 516/432-3841
Maria Regina Elem Sch 4045 Jerusalem Ave, Seaford 11783 Leona Arpino	PK-8	G	410 24		516/541-1229 Fax 516/541-1235
Notre Dame Sch 25 Mayfair Rd, New Hyde Park 11040 Caryn Durkin	PK-8		505 30		516/354-5618 Fax 516/354-5373
Our Lady of Lourdes Sch 76 Park Blvd, Malverne 11565 Kathleen Cotilletta	PK-8		300		516/599-7328 Fax 516/599-3813
Our Lady of Mercy Academy 815 Convent Rd, Syosset 11791 Sandra Betters	9-12		450		516/921-1047 Fax 516/921-3634
Our Lady of Peace Sch 21 Fowler Ave, Lynbrook 11563 Karen Vonbraunsberg	PK-8		295 15		516/593-4884 Fax 516/593-9861
Our Lady of Victory Sch 2 Bellmore St, Floral Park 11001 Peg Augello	PK-8		350 20		516/352-4466 Fax 516/352-2998
Sacred Heart Academy 47 Cathedral Ave, Hempstead 11550 Jean Amore	9-12		801 34		516/483-7383 Fax 516/483-1016
St Agnes Cathedral Sch 70 Clinton Ave, Rockville CTR 11570 Cecilia St John	K-8		638 42		516/678-5550 Fax 516/678-0437
St Aidan Sch 510 Willis Ave, Williston Pk 11596 Julie O'Connell	PK-8		253 10		516/746-6585 Fax 516/746-3086
St Anne Sch 25 Dartmouth St, Garden City 11530 Paul Morisi	PK-8		510 20		516/352-1205 Fax 516/352-5969
St Brigid-Our Lady of Hope Sch 101 Maple Ave, Westbury 11590 Paul Clagnazi	PK-8		500 22		516/333-0580 Fax 516/333-0590
St Christopher Sch 15 Pershing Blvd, Baldwin 11510 Marianne Carberry	PK-8		431 25		516/223-4404 Fax 516/223-1409
St Dominic ES MS 35 School St, Oyster Bay 11771 Ronald Martorelli	PK-8		300 16		516/922-4233 Fax 516/624-7613
St Dominic High Sch 110 Anstice St, Oyster Bay 11771 Ronald Martorelli	9-12		400 25		516/922-4888 Fax 516/922-4898
St Edward the Confessor Sch 2 Teibrook Ave, Syosset 11791 Vincent Albrecht	PK-8		298 22		516/921-7767 Fax 516/496-0001
St Elizabeth A Seton-Bellmore 2341 Washington Ave, Bellmore 11710 Leeann Graziose	PK-8		350 10		516/785-5709 Fax 516/785-4468
St Joseph Sch 450 Franklin Ave, Garden City 11530 Brian Colomban	PK-8		347 18		516/747-2730 Fax 516/747-2854
St Martin Deporres Mrnst Sch 530 Hempstead Blvd, Uniondale 11553 Br Kenneth Hoagland	PK-8		460 20		516/481-3303 Fax 516/483-4138
St Mary Elem Sch 1340 Northern Blvd, Manhasset 11030 Sarah Devenoge	PK-8		270 19		516/627-0184 Fax 516/627-3795
St Mary's High Sch 51 Clapham Ave, Manhasset 11030 Gerard Buckley	9-12		700 35		516/627-2711 Fax 516/627-3209

1 Superintendent	8 Curric/Instruct K-12	19 Chief Financial Officer	29 Family/Consumer Science	39 Social Studies K-12	49 English/Lang Arts Elem	59 Special Education Elem	69 Academic Assessment
2 Bus/Finance/Purchasing	9 Curric/Instruct Elem	20 Art K-12	30 Adult Education	40 Social Studies Elem	50 English/Lang Arts Sec	60 Special Education Sec	70 Research/Development
3 Buildings And Grounds	10 Curric/Instruct Sec	21 Art Elem	31 Career/Sch-to-Work K-12	41 Social Studies Sec	51 Reading K-12	61 Foreign/World Lang K-12	71 Public Information
4 Food Service	11 Federal Program	22 Art Sec	32 Career/Sch-to-Work Elem	42 Science K-12	52 Reading Elem	62 Foreign/World Lang Elem	72 Summer School
5 Transportation	12 Title I	23 Music K-12	33 Career/Sch-to-Work Sec	43 Science Elem	53 Reading Sec	63 Foreign/World Lang Sec	73 Instructional Tech
6 Athletic	13 Title V	24 Music Elem	34 Early Childhood Ed	44 Science Sec	54 Remedial Reading K-12	64 Religious Education K-12	74 Inservice Training
7 Health Services	15 Asst Superintendent	25 Music Sec	35 Health/Phys Education	45 Math K-12	55 Remedial Reading Elem	65 Religious Education Elem	75 Marketing/Distributive
	16 Instructional Media Svcs	26 Business Education	36 Guidance Services K-12	46 Math Elem	56 Remedial Reading Sec	66 Religious Education Sec	76 Info Systems
	17 Chief Operations Officer	27 Career & Tech Ed	37 Guidance Services Elem	47 Math Sec	57 Bilingual/ELL	67 School Board President	77 Psychological Assess
	18 Chief Academic Officer	28 Technology Education	38 Guidance Services Sec	48 English/Lang Arts K-12	58 Special Education K-12	68 Teacher Personnel	78 Affirmative Action

New York School Directory

Nassau County

School	Grade	Enr/#Cls	Phone
St Raymond Sch 263 Atlantic Ave, East Rockaway 11518 Sr Ruthanne Gypalo	PK-8	250 18	516/593-9010 Fax 516/593-0986
St Rose of Lima Sch 4704 Merrick Rd, Massapequa 11758 Brian Jensen	PK-8	500 24	516/541-1546 Fax 516/797-0351
St Thomas the Apostle Sch 12 Westminster Rd, W Hempstead 11552 Valerie Serpe	PK-8	350 20	516/481-9310 Fax 516/481-8769
St William the Abbot Sch 2001 Jackson Ave, Seaford 11783 Elizabeth Bricker	PK-8	500 20	516/785-6784 Fax 516/785-2752

NASSAU PRIVATE SCHOOLS

Private Schs..Principal	Grd	Prgm	Enr/#Cls	SN	Phone
Brandeis Sch 25 Frost Ln, Lawrence 11559 Raz Levin	PK-8		200 23		516/371-4747 Fax 516/371-1572
Brookville Ctr Childrens Srvcs 189 Wheatley Rd, Glen Head 11545 Marianne Klotz	Spec		170 14		516/626-1000 Fax 516/626-2039
Children's Learning Center 380 Washington Ave, Roosevelt 11575 Kevin Loughlin	Spec	G	271 27		516/378-2000 Fax 516/378-3791
Community Academic Prep Sch 45 Rose Ave, Roosevelt 11575 Senkita El	K-12		50 4		516/377-7520 Fax 516/377-7521
Crescent Sch 130 Front St, Hempstead 11550 Iffat Ahmed	PK-12		250 15		516/292-1787 Fax 516/292-1788
De La Salle Sch 87 Pine St, Freeport 11520 Jean Marie Becker	5-8		69 5		516/379-8660 Fax 516/379-8806
East Woods Sch 31 Yellow Cote Rd, Oyster Bay 11771 Matthew Bradley	PK-9		217 30		516/922-4400 Fax 516/922-2589
Freeport Christian Academy 50 N Main St, Freeport 11520 Denise Panucci	K-9		103		516/546-2020
Friends Academy 270 Duck Pond Rd, Locust Valley 11560 Dot Woo \ Christine Saunders \ Mark Schoeffel	PK-12		776		516/676-0393 Fax 516/393-4276
Fusion Academy-Long Island 260 Crossways Park Dr Ste A, Woodbury 11797 Tiffany Belferder	6-12		60		516/364-5414 Fax 516/364-5906
Genesis Sch 600 Newbridge Rd, East Meadow 11554 Hester Bekisz	Spec		30		516/937-1397 Fax 516/937-1463
Gersh Academy-W Hempstead 307 Eagle Ave, W Hempstead 11552 Diana Devivio	Spec		165		516/986-9580
Good Shepherd Lutheran Sch 99 Central Park Rd, Plainview 11803 Stephanie Bribnza	PK-PK		127 6		516/349-1966 Fax 516/349-8434
Grace Christian Academy 36 Smith St, Merrick 11566 Stephen Schultz	K-12		140		516/379-2223
Grace Lutheran Sch 400 Hempstead Ave, Malverne 11565 Wanda Walters	PK-6		300 12		516/599-6557 Fax 516/599-6151
Green Vale Sch 250 Valentines Ln, Glen Head 11545 Dr Jesse Dougherty	PK-8		420		516/621-2420 Fax 516/621-1317
Halb Drs Yeshiva HS for Boys 700 Ibsen St, Woodmere 11598 Dr Hillel Broder	9-12		320		516/295-7700 Fax 516/295-2929
Halb Elementary 523 Church Ave, Long Beach 11561 Richard Altabe \ Uriel Lubetski	PK-8		785 50		516/432-8285 Fax 516/432-6444
Halb Stella K Abraham Girls HS 291 Meadowview Ave, Hewlett 11557 Bluma Drebin	9-12		310		516/374-6851
Hamza Academy 202 Stuart Ave, Valley Stream 11580 Thaslima Thamanna	PK-7		100		516/285-1440 Fax 516/285-8580
Hanc High Sch 215 Oak St, Uniondale 11553 Shlomo Adelman	7-12		290 30		516/538-8161 Fax 516/489-1142
Hanc Middle Sch 215 Oak St, Uniondale 11553 Elliot Hecht	7-8		153		516/538-8161 Fax 516/489-1142
Hanc Plainview Elem Sch 25 Country Dr, Plainview 11803 Kenneth Fogel	PK-6		175 17		516/681-5922 Fax 516/681-8351
Hanc West Hempstead Elem Sch 609 Hempstead Ave, W Hempstead 11552 Yaakov Sadigh	K-6		255 24		516/485-7786 Fax 516/485-0422
Harmony Heights Sch 60 Walnut Ave, East Norwich 11732 Leslei Anesta	Spec		80 15		516/922-6688 Fax 516/922-6126
Hebrew Acad 5 Towns Rockawy ES 33 Washington Ave, Lawrence 11559 Joy Hammer	K-5		1,000		516/569-3043 Fax 516/569-3014
Hebrew Acad 5 Towns Rockawy HS 635 Central Ave, Cedarhurst 11516 Naomi Lippman	9-12		361 25		516/569-3807 Fax 516/374-5761
Hebrew Acad 5 Towns Rockawy MS 44 Frost Ln, Lawrence 11559 Joshua Gold	6-8		250		516/569-6352 Fax 516/569-6457
Henry Viscardi Sch 201 I U Willets Rd, Albertson 11507 Angelo Zegarelli	Spec		401 30		516/465-1560
Holy Child Academy 25 Store Hill Rd, Old Westbury 11568 Kathy Frank \ Pam Gartland	PK-8		225 12		516/626-9300 Fax 516/626-7914
Journey Prep Sch 50 Cherry St, Farmingdale 11735 Monje Moore	K-12		75		631/736-2146 Fax 631/736-2378
Lawrence Woodmere Academy 336 Woodmere Blvd, Woodmere 11598 Sherri Fromowitz \ Marc Hoyle	PK-12		250 40		516/374-9000 Fax 516/374-4707
Little Village Sch 750 Hicksville Rd, Seaford 11783 Patti Pizza	Spec		250 20		516/520-6000 Fax 516/796-6341
Long Island Hebrew Academy 122 Cuttermill Rd, Great Neck 11021 Mrs Shabatian	PK-5		174 9		516/466-3656 Fax 516/466-0774
Long Island Lutheran Sch 131 Brookville Rd, Glen Head 11545 Laura Callahan \ Jessica Raba	6-12		400		516/626-1700 Fax 516/622-7459
Maria Montessori Sch 5 N Village Grn, Levittown 11756 Carolyn Larcy	PK-8		50 5		516/520-0301 Fax 516/520-2935
Martin De Porres Sch 621 Elmont Rd, Elmont 11003 John Galassi	Spec		220		516/502-2840 Fax 516/502-2841
Mesivta Ateres Yaakov 131 Washington Ave, Lawrence 11559 Mordechai Yaffe	9-12		200		516/374-6465 Fax 516/374-1834

---

79 Student Personnel	91 Safety/Security	275 Response To Intervention	298 Grant Writer/Ptnrships
80 Driver Ed/Safety	92 Magnet School	277 Remedial Math K-12	750 Chief Innovation Officer
81 Gifted/Talented	93 Parental Involvement	280 Literacy Coach	751 Chief of Staff
82 Video Services	95 Tech Prep Program	285 STEM	752 Social Emotional Learning
83 Substance Abuse Prev	97 Chief Information Officer	286 Digital Learning	
84 Erate	98 Chief Technology Officer	288 Common Core Standards	Other School Types
85 AIDS Education	270 Character Education	294 Accountability	Ⓐ = Alternative School
88 Alternative/At Risk	271 Migrant Education	295 Network System	Ⓒ = Charter School
89 Multi-Cultural Curriculum	273 Teacher Mentor	296 Title II Programs	Ⓜ = Magnet School
90 Social Work	274 Before/After Sch	297 Webmaster	Ⓨ = Year-Round School

School Programs
A = Alternative Program
G = Adult Classes
M = Magnet Program
T = Title I Schoolwide
V = Career & Tech Ed Programs

Social Media
= Facebook
= Twitter

New Schools are shaded
New Superintendents and Principals are bold
Personnel with email addresses are underscored

NY—133

New York County

Market Data Retrieval

School	Grades	Enrollment	Phone
Mesivta of Long Beach Torah HS 205 W Beech St, Long Beach 11561 Aaron Rosenberg	9-12	150 6	516/255-4700 Fax 516/255-4701
Mesivta Shaarei Pruzdor 120 Long Beach Blvd, Long Beach 11561 Simcha Frishman	9-11	30	516/321-0964
Mill Neck Manor Sch for Deaf 40 Frost Mill Rd, Mill Neck 11765 Kathleen Kerzner	Spec	100 22	516/922-4100 Fax 516/922-4172
Miss Shelley's Upward Prep Sch 66 Nassau Rd, Roosevelt 11575 Shelly Williams	PK-K	55 15	516/378-9206 Fax 516/378-9208
My Spectrum Sch 11 Sintsink Dr E, Prt Washingtn 11050 Dr Linda D'Agostino	PK-1	20	516/883-8035
North Shore Hebrew Acad-Cherry 16 Cherry Ln, Great Neck 11024 Jeffrey Kobrin	PK-5	450 24	516/487-8687 Fax 516/487-8721
North Shore Hebrew Academy 26 Old Mill Rd, Great Neck 11023 Jeffrey Kobrin	6-8	250	516/487-9163 Fax 516/829-3933
North Shore Hebrew Academy HS 400 N Service Rd, Great Neck 11020 Noam Weinberg	9-12	375	516/487-2424 Fax 516/487-6663
Our Lady of Grace Montessori 29 Shelter Rock Rd, Manhasset 11030 Sr Kelly Quinn	PK-3	180 8	516/365-9832 Fax 516/627-5343
Pat Kam Sch 705 Nassau Rd, Uniondale 11553 Ron Clahar	PK-5	80	516/486-7887 Fax 516/486-7905
Portledge Sch 355 Duck Pond Rd, Locust Valley 11560 Simon Owen-Williams	PK-12	400	516/750-3100
Progressive Sch of Long Island 1425 Merrick Ave Ste 2, Merrick 11566 Eric Jacobson	K-8	120	516/868-6835 Fax 516/868-7033
Rambam Mesivta 15 Frost Ln, Lawrence 11559 Yotav Eliach	9-12	160 8	516/371-5824 Fax 516/371-4706
Schechter Day School of Li 1 Barbara Ln, Jericho 11753 Sandi Swerdloff	K-5	409 18	516/935-1441 Fax 516/935-8280
Shulamith School for Girls 305 Cedarhurst Ave, Cedarhurst 11516 Joyce Yarmak \ Rookie Billet \ Sara Munk	PK-12	200	516/569-1713 Fax 516/569-1714
Silverstein Hebrew Academy 117 Cuttermill Rd, Great Neck 11021 Shireen Butman	PK-6	225	516/466-8522 Fax 516/466-3586
Solomon Schechter Sch 6 Cross St, Williston Pk 11596 Eileen Bohrer	K-12	250 35	516/539-3700 Fax 516/539-3685
Tiegerman Middle Sch-Glen Cove 27 Cedar Swamp Rd, Glen Cove 11542 Kristin Lyons	6-8	120	516/801-6915
Tiegerman Sch 100 Glen Cove Ave, Glen Cove 11542 Karen Katzman	Spec	250	516/609-2000
Torah Acad-Lawrence Cedarhurst 26 Columbia Ave, Cedarhurst 11516 Yaakav Jaffee	9-12	15 4	516/295-5700
Trinity Lutheran Sch 40 W Nicholai St, Hicksville 11801 Mary-Elaine Leake	PK-8	354 35	516/931-2211 Fax 516/931-6345
Valley Stream Christian Acad 12 E Fairview Ave, Valley Stream 11580 Sandra Shanhai	K-12	164 13	516/561-6122 Fax 516/284-7270
Vincent Smith Sch 322 Port Washington Blvd, Prt Washingtn 11050 John Baldi	1-12	80 15	516/365-4900 Fax 516/627-5648
Waldorf School of Garden City 225 Cambridge Ave, Garden City 11530 Roland Rothenbucher	PK-12	320 15	516/742-3435 Fax 516/742-3457
Westbury Friends Sch 550 Post Ave, Westbury 11590 Christina Anderson	PK-1	70 6	516/333-3178 Fax 516/333-1353
Whispering Pines SDA Sch 211 Jericho Tpke, Old Westbury 11568 Maurice Grant	PK-10	47 5	516/997-5177 Fax 516/997-2138
Woodward Children Center 201 W Merrick Rd, Freeport 11520 Danielle Colucci	Spec	80 10	516/379-0900 Fax 516/379-0997
Yeshiva Ketana 321 Doughty Blvd, Inwood 11096 Larissa Steele	PK-8 G	400 12	516/791-2800 Fax 516/791-3901
Yeshiva Toras Chaim-S Shore 1170 William St, Hewlett 11557 Leah Girnun \ Daniel Winkler	PK-8 G	650 25	516/374-7363 Fax 516/374-2024

NASSAU REGIONAL CENTERS

• **Nassau BOCES** PID: 00739201   516/396-2500
71 Clinton Rd Ste 100, Garden City 11530   Fax 516/997-8742

Dr Robert Dillon 1   James Widmer 2,15
Anthony Fierro 3   Anthony Carfora 8,73,76
Dr Roxanne France 8,15   Carla Theodorou 27,30,31
Patricia Schwetz 58   Eric Schultz 67
Selma Stoddard 68

NEW YORK COUNTY

NEW YORK PUBLIC SCHOOLS

• **New York City Dept of Ed** PID: 00740626   718/935-4000
52 Chambers St, New York 10007   Fax 718/935-2964

> **Schools:** 1,680 \ **Teachers:** 66,477 \ **Students:** 1,150,000 \
> **Special Ed Students:** 238,607 \ **LEP Students:** 129,927 \ **Ethnic:** Asian 17%, African American 23%, Hispanic 42%, Native American: 1%, Caucasian 16% \ **Exp:** $389 (High) \ **Poverty:** 23% \ **Title I:** $764,391,307
> \ **Special Education:** $2,147,483,647 \ **Open-Close:** 09/15 - 06/25 \
> **DTBP:** $192 (High) \

Richard Carranza 1   Lindsy Oates 2
Kevin Moran 3,5   Ursulina Ramirez 3,17,68
Chris Tricarico 4   Dr Roger Platt 7
Lawrence Pendergast 8,74   Adrienne Austin 15,71,298
Donald Conyers 15   Josh Wallack 15,34
Karin Goldmark 15   Lashawn Robinson 15,79,91,752
Linda Chen 18   Gillian Smith 36
Mirza Sanchez-Medina 57   Christien Foti 58
Lori Podvesker 67   Vicki Bernstein 68
Edie Sharp 70,751   Anuraag Sharma 73,76
Ruby Fernandez 78   Mark Rampersant 91
Mary Wall 751

---

1 Superintendent	8 Curric/Instruct K-12	19 Chief Financial Officer	29 Family/Consumer Science
2 Bus/Finance/Purchasing	9 Curric/Instruct Elem	20 Art K-12	30 Adult Education
3 Buildings And Grounds	10 Curric/Instruct Sec	21 Art Elem	31 Career/Sch-to-Work K-12
4 Food Service	11 Federal Program	22 Art Sec	32 Career/Sch-to-Work Elem
5 Transportation	12 Title I	23 Music K-12	33 Career/Sch-to-Work Sec
6 Athletic	13 Title V	24 Music Elem	34 Early Childhood Ed
7 Health Services	15 Asst Superintendent	25 Music Sec	35 Health/Phys Education
	16 Instructional Media Svcs	26 Business Education	36 Guidance Services K-12
	17 Chief Operations Officer	27 Career & Tech Ed	37 Guidance Services Elem
	18 Chief Academic Officer	28 Technology Education	38 Guidance Services Sec

39 Social Studies K-12	49 English/Lang Arts Elem	59 Special Education Elem	69 Academic Assessment
40 Social Studies Elem	50 English/Lang Arts Sec	60 Special Education Sec	70 Research/Development
41 Social Studies Sec	51 Reading K-12	61 Foreign/World Lang K-12	71 Public Information
42 Science K-12	52 Reading Elem	62 Foreign/World Lang Elem	72 Summer School
43 Science Elem	53 Reading Sec	63 Foreign/World Lang Sec	73 Instructional Tech
44 Science Sec	54 Remedial Reading K-12	64 Religious Education K-12	74 Inservice Training
45 Math K-12	55 Remedial Reading Elem	65 Religious Education Elem	75 Marketing/Distributive
46 Math Elem	56 Remedial Reading Sec	66 Religious Education Sec	76 Info Systems
47 Math Sec	57 Bilingual/ELL	67 School Board President	77 Psychological Assess
48 English/Lang Arts K-12	58 Special Education K-12	68 Teacher Personnel	78 Affirmative Action

New York School Directory — New York County

Community School District 1 PID: 10909565
166 Essex St, New York 10002
212/353-2948 Fax 212/353-2945

Carry Chan 1

Public Schs..Principal	Grd	Prgm	Enr/#Cls	SN	
Bard High School Early College 525 E Houston St, New York 10002 Michael Lerner	9-12		611 25	40%	212/995-8479 Fax 212/777-4702
Ⓐ Cascades High Sch 198 Forsyth St 3rd Fl, New York 10002 Claire Sheehan	9-12	GT	162 12	82%	646/654-1261
Children's Workshop Sch 610 E 12th St, New York 10009 Maria Clarke	PK-5		335 14	48%	212/614-9531 Fax 212/614-9462
Ⓐ Earth Sch 600 E 6th St, New York 10009 Abbe Futterman	PK-5		351 16	56%	212/477-1735 Fax 212/477-2396
East Side Cmty Sch 420 E 12th St, New York 10009 Mark Federman	6-12	GV	681 40	66%	212/460-8467 Fax 212/260-9657
Ⓐ East Village Cmty Sch 610 E 12th St, New York 10009 Bradley Goodman	PK-5		331 9	27%	212/982-0682 Fax 212/260-4012
Forsyth Satellite Acad 198 Forsyth St, New York 10002 Patrick Reimer	9-12	T	161	85%	212/677-8900
Ⓐ Lower East Side Prep High Sch 145 Stanton St Fl 4, New York 10002 Rene Anaya	9-12	T	482	72%	212/505-6366 Fax 212/260-0813
Neighborhood Sch 121 E 3rd St, New York 10009 Dyanthe Spielberg	PK-5		301 13	41%	212/387-0195 Fax 212/387-0198
New Explorations Sci-Tech-Math 111 Columbia St, New York 10002 Mark Berkowitz	K-12		1,801 65	23%	212/677-5190 Fax 212/260-8124
Orchard Collegiate Academy 220 Henry St, New York 10002 Miles Doyle	9-12	T	225	81%	212/406-9411
PS 15 Roberto Clemente 333 E 4th St, New York 10009 Irene Sanchez	PK-5	T	180 14	83%	212/228-8730 Fax 212/477-0931
PS 19 Asher Levy 185 1st Ave, New York 10003 Jacqueline Flanagan	PK-5	T	234 17	72%	212/533-5340 Fax 212/673-1477
PS 20 Anna Silver 166 Essex St, New York 10002 Sarah Pinto	PK-5	T	464 35	65%	212/254-9577 Fax 212/254-3526
PS 34 Franklin D Roosevelt 730 E 12th St, New York 10009 Angeliki Loukatos	PK-8	T	294 24	99%	212/228-4433 Fax 212/353-1973
PS 63 the Star Academy 121 E 3rd St, New York 10009 Darlene Cameron	PK-5	T	233 15	76%	212/674-3180 Fax 212/420-9018
PS 64 Robert Simon 600 E 6th St, New York 10009 Marlon Hosang	PK-5	T	235 15	86%	212/673-6510 Fax 212/477-2369
PS 110 Florence Nightingale 285 Delancey St, New York 10002 Karen Feuer	PK-5		399 21	56%	212/674-2690 Fax 212/475-5835
PS 134 Henrietta Szold 293 E Broadway, New York 10002 Robert Perales	PK-5	T	246 20	92%	212/673-4470 Fax 212/475-6142
PS 140 Nathan Straus 123 Ridge St, New York 10002 Melissa Rodriguez	PK-8	T	371 35	84%	212/677-4680
PS 142 Amalia Castro 100 Attorney St, New York 10002 Daphna Gutman	PK-5	T	325 27	96%	212/598-3800 Fax 212/598-3810
PS 184M Shuang Wen 327 Cherry St, New York 10002 Jeremy Kabinoff	PK-8	T	700 13	68%	212/602-9700 Fax 212/602-9710
PS 188 the Island Sch 442 E Houston St, New York 10002 Suany Ramos	PK-8	T	392 17	94%	212/677-5710 Fax 212/228-3007
School for Global Leaders 145 Stanton St, New York 10002 Keri Ricks	6-8	T	205	84%	212/260-5375 Fax 212/432-5586
Tompkins Square Middle Sch 600 E 6th St, New York 10009 Sonhandso Estwick	6-8	T	359 35	67%	212/995-1430 Fax 212/979-1341
University Neighborhood HS 200 Monroe St, New York 10002 Matthew Willie	9-12	T	499	87%	212/962-4341 Fax 212/267-5611
University Neighborhood MS 220 Henry St, New York 10002 Laura Castro	6-8	T	217 13	84%	212/267-5701 Fax 212/349-8224

Community School District 2 PID: 10909577
333 7th Ave, New York 10001
212/356-3739 Fax 212/356-7514

Donalda Chumney 1

Public Schs..Principal	Grd	Prgm	Enr/#Cls	SN	
Academy Software Engineering 40 Irving Pl, New York 10003 Shawn Raeke	9-12	T	454	67%	212/253-3299 Fax 212/253-3289
Amer Sign Lang-Eng Lwr Sch 47 223 E 23rd St, New York 10010 David Bowell	PK-8	T	182	68%	917/326-6609
American Sign Lang-Eng HS 47 225 E 23rd St, New York 10010 Watfa Shama	Spec	T	198	88%	917/326-6668 Fax 917/326-6688
Art & Design High Sch 245 E 56th St, New York 10022 Maximillian Re-Sugiura	Voc		1,477	56%	212/752-4340 Fax 212/752-4945
Ⓜ Ballet Tech/NYC PS for Dance 890 Broadway Fl 7, New York 10003 Roy Oneill	4-8		140 8	45%	212/254-1803 Fax 212/477-5048
Baruch College Campus High Sch 55 E 25th St, New York 10010 Alicia Perez-Katz	9-12		488 15	39%	212/683-7440 Fax 212/683-7338
Battery Park City Sch 55 Battery Pl, New York 10280 Theresa Ruyter	PK-8		851	15%	212/266-5800
Chelsea Career & Tech HS 131 Avenue of the Americas, New York 10013 Jaivelle Reed	Voc	T	454	78%	212/925-1080 Fax 212/941-7934
East Side Middle Sch 331 E 91st St, New York 10128 David Getz	6-8		457 12	16%	212/360-0114 Fax 212/360-0121
Eleanor Roosevelt High Sch 411 E 76th St, New York 10021 Dimitri Saliani	9-12		540	20%	212/772-1220 Fax 212/772-1440
Ella Baker Sch 317 E 67th St, New York 10065 Joshua Satin	PK-8		332 13	28%	212/717-8809 Fax 212/717-8807
Emma Lazarus High Sch 100 Hester St, New York 10002 Joel Heckethorn	9-12	T	292	93%	212/925-5017 Fax 212/925-5920
Essex Street Academy 350 Grand St, New York 10002 Wallace Simpson	9-12	T	343	68%	212/475-4773 Fax 212/674-2058

---

79 Student Personnel	91 Safety/Security	275 Response To Intervention	296 Grant Writer/Ptnrships	
80 Driver Ed/Safety	92 Magnet School	277 Remedial Math K-12	750 Chief Innovation Officer	
81 Gifted/Talented	93 Parental Involvement	280 Literacy Coach	751 Chief of Staff	
82 Video Services	95 Tech Prep Program	285 STEM	752 Social Emotional Learning	
83 Substance Abuse Prev	97 Chief Infomation Officer	286 Digital Learning		
84 Erate	98 Chief Technology Officer	288 Common Core Standards	**Other School Types**	
85 AIDS Education	270 Character Education	294 Accountability	Ⓐ = Alternative School	
88 Alternative/At Risk	271 Migrant Education	295 Network System	Ⓒ = Charter School	
89 Multi-Cultural Curriculum	273 Teacher Mentor	296 Title II Programs	Ⓜ = Magnet School	
90 Social Work	274 Before/After Sch	297 Webmaster	Ⓨ = Year-Round School	

School Programs
A = Alternative Program
G = Adult Classes
M = Magnet Program
T = Title I Schoolwide
V = Career & Tech Ed Programs

Social Media
= Facebook
= Twitter

New Schools are shaded
New Superintendents and Principals are bold
Personnel with email addresses are underscored

NY—135

New York County

Market Data Retrieval

School	Grades	Type	Enroll	%	Phone
Food and Finance High Sch 525 W 50th St, New York 10019 Roger Turgeon	9-12	T	379 28	82%	212/586-2943 Fax 212/586-4205
Gramercy Arts High Sch 40 Irving Pl, New York 10003 Susan DiCicco	9-12	T	448	79%	212/253-7076 Fax 212/253-8095
Harvest Collegiate High Sch 34 W 14th St, New York 10011 Kate Burch	9-12		449	67%	212/242-3384 Fax 212/242-4173
Harvey Milk High Sch 2 Astor Pl Fl 3, New York 10003 Daphne Perrini	9-12	T	58 5	88%	212/477-1555 Fax 212/674-8650
High Sch of Fashion Industries 225 W 24th St, New York 10011 Daryl Blank	Voc	GT	1,607	81%	212/255-1235 Fax 212/255-4756
ⓐ HS 560-City as Sch 16 Clarkson St, New York 10014 Alan Cheng	10-12	T	565	65%	212/337-6800 Fax 212/337-6875
HS Dual Lang & Asian Studies 350 Grand St 5th Fl, New York 10002 Li Yan	9-12	T	393	89%	212/475-4097 Fax 212/674-1392
ⓜ HS for Environmental Studies 444 W 56th St, New York 10019 Amber Najmi-Shadid	9-12	T	1,144 50	82%	212/262-8113 Fax 212/262-0702
HS for Language & Diplomacy 40 Irving Pl, New York 10003 Sarah Hernandez	9-12	T	275	75%	212/253-2480 Fax 212/253-2539
ⓜ HS Health Prof & Human Serv 345 E 15th St, New York 10003 Robert Gentile	9-12	T	1,827 45	71%	212/780-9175 Fax 212/979-7261
ⓜ HS of Economics & Finance 100 Trinity Pl, New York 10006 Michael Stanzione	9-12	T	745 30	76%	212/346-0708 Fax 212/346-0712
HS of Hospitality Management 525 W 50th St, New York 10019 Yves Mompoint	9-12	T	341	90%	212/586-0963 Fax 212/265-1307
Hudson HS-Lrng Technologies 351 W 18th St, New York 10011 Michael Wilson	9-12	T	464	80%	212/488-3330 Fax 212/488-3335
Humanities Preparatory Academy 351 W 18th St, New York 10011 Jeannie Ferrari	9-12	T	249 12	81%	212/929-4433 Fax 212/929-4445
ⓐ Independence High Sch 850 10th Ave, New York 10019 Ron Smolkin	9-12	T	313 9	85%	212/262-8067 Fax 212/262-8110
Institute for Collaborative Ed 345 E 15th St, New York 10003 Peter Karp	6-12		488 20	27%	212/475-7972 Fax 212/475-0459
International HS-Union Sq 40 Irving Pl, New York 10003 Vadewatie Ramsuchit	9-12	T	346	86%	212/533-2560 Fax 212/228-2946
IS 289 Hudson River Middle Sch 201 Warren St, New York 10282 Zeynep Ozkan	6-8		277 18	53%	212/571-9268 Fax 212/587-6610
Jacqueline Kennedy Onassis HS 120 W 46th St, New York 10036 Edward DeMeo	9-12	T	314 20	77%	212/391-0041 Fax 212/391-1293
James Baldwin Sch Excp Lrng 351 W 18th St, New York 10011 Brady Smith	9-12	T	211	79%	212/627-2812 Fax 212/627-9803
ⓜ JHS 104 Simon Baruch 330 E 21st St, New York 10010 Rocco Macri	6-8		1,098 70	43%	212/674-4545 Fax 212/477-2205
ⓜ JHS 167 Robert F Wagner 220 E 76th St, New York 10021 Jennifer Losquadro	6-8		1,338 68	30%	212/535-8610 Fax 212/472-9385
ⓐ John V Lindsay Wildcat Acad CS © 17 Battery Pl, New York 10004 Ron Tabano	9-12	T	250 6	85%	212/209-6006 Fax 212/635-3874
ⓐ Landmark High Sch 351 W 18th St 5th Fl, New York 10011 Susanna Tenny	9-12	T	338 30	80%	212/647-7410 Fax 212/647-7416
Leadership & Pub Service HS 90 Trinity Pl Lbby 1, New York 10006 Philip Santos	9-12	T	368 28	83%	212/346-0007 Fax 212/346-0612
ⓐ Liberty HS for Newcomers 250 W 18th St, New York 10011 Rhonda Huegel	9-12	T	411 20	76%	212/691-0934 Fax 212/727-1369
Life Sciences Secondary Sch 320 E 96th St, New York 10128 Kimberly Swanson	9-12	T	398	79%	212/348-1694 Fax 212/348-4293
Lower Manhattan Arts Academy 350 Grand St, New York 10002 John Wenk	9-12	T	316	75%	212/505-0143 Fax 212/674-8021
Lower Manhattan Cmty Mid Sch 26 Broadway, New York 10004 Shanna Douglas	6-8		377 8	55%	646/826-8100 Fax 646/826-8101
Manhattan Acad-Arts & Lang 111 E 33rd St, New York 10016 Siv Boletsis	9-12	T	217	97%	212/576-0502 Fax 212/576-0518
Manhattan Bridges High Sch 525 W 50th St, New York 10019 George Lock	9-12	T	517	87%	212/757-5274 Fax 646/557-3926
Manhattan Business Academy 351 W 18th St, New York 10011 Karen Polsonetti	9-12	T	409	87%	212/647-1983 Fax 212/647-1989
ⓐ Manhattan Comp Night & Day HS 240 2nd Ave, New York 10003 Michael Toise	10-12	TV	581 20	89%	212/353-2010 Fax 212/353-1673
Manhattan Early Clg-Advertise 411 Pearl St, New York 10038 Sarah Kaplan	9-12	TV	445	73%	212/225-0880 Fax 212/225-0882
ⓐ Manhattan International HS 317 E 67th St, New York 10065 Gladys Rodriguez	9-12	T	290 16	72%	212/517-6728 Fax 212/517-7147
ⓐ Manhattan Village Academy 43 W 22nd St, New York 10010 Hector Geager	9-12	T	457 25	77%	212/242-8752 Fax 212/242-7630
Mather Bldg Arts & Craftmnp HS 439 W 49th St, New York 10019 Larry Gabbard	Voc	T	424	79%	212/399-3520 Fax 212/245-4669
Millennium High Sch 75 Broad St, New York 10004 Colin McEvoy	9-12		674	49%	212/825-9008 Fax 212/825-9095
MS 131 100 Hester St, New York 10002 Benjamin Geballe	6-8	T	299	89%	212/219-1204 Fax 212/925-6386
MS 177 Yorkville East Mid Sch 1458 York Ave, New York 10075 Christina Riggio	6-8		228	30%	917/432-5413 Fax 917/432-5418
MS 255 Salk School of Science 320 E 20th St, New York 10003 Rhonda Perry	6-8		377 22	14%	212/614-8785 Fax 212/614-0095
MS 297 Morton 75 Morton St Rm 4B12, New York 10014 Jacqueline Getz	6-7		559	27%	212/295-7555 Fax 212/524-4365
MS 933 City Knoll Middle Sch 400 W 53rd St, New York 10019 Kaye Kerr	6-8	T	153	82%	212/695-9115 Fax 212/695-9615
Murray Hill Academy 111 E 33rd St, New York 10016 Anita Felix	9-12	T	271	86%	212/696-0195 Fax 212/696-2498

1 Superintendent	8 Curric/Instruct K-12	19 Chief Financial Officer	29 Family/Consumer Science	39 Social Studies K-12	49 English/Lang Arts Elem	59 Special Education Elem	69 Academic Assessment
2 Bus/Finance/Purchasing	9 Curric/Instruct Elem	20 Art K-12	30 Adult Education	40 Social Studies Elem	50 English/Lang Arts Sec	60 Special Education Sec	70 Research/Development
3 Buildings And Grounds	10 Curric/Instruct Sec	21 Art Elem	31 Career/Sch-to-Work K-12	41 Social Studies Sec	51 Reading K-12	61 Foreign/World Lang K-12	71 Public Information
4 Food Service	11 Federal Program	22 Art Sec	32 Career/Sch-to-Work Elem	42 Science K-12	52 Reading Elem	62 Foreign/World Lang Elem	72 Summer School
5 Transportation	12 Title I	23 Music K-12	33 Career/Sch-to-Work Sec	43 Science Elem	53 Reading Sec	63 Foreign/World Lang Sec	73 Instructional Tech
6 Athletic	13 Title V	24 Music Elem	34 Early Childhood Ed	44 Science Sec	54 Remedial Reading K-12	64 Religious Education K-12	74 Inservice Training
7 Health Services	15 Asst Superintendent	25 Music Sec	35 Health/Phys Education	45 Math K-12	55 Remedial Reading Elem	65 Religious Education Elem	75 Marketing/Distributive
	16 Instructional Media Svcs	26 Business Education	36 Guidance Services K-12	46 Math Elem	56 Remedial Reading Sec	66 Religious Education Sec	76 Info Systems
	17 Chief Operations Officer	27 Career & Tech Ed	37 Guidance Services Elem	47 Math Sec	57 Bilingual/ELL	67 School Board President	77 Psychological Assess
	18 Chief Academic Officer	28 Technology Education	38 Guidance Services Sec	48 English/Lang Arts K-12	58 Special Education K-12	68 Teacher Personnel	78 Affirmative Action

New York School Directory | New York County

School	Grades	Prog	Enroll	%	Phone
Murry Bergtraum HS Business 411 Pearl St, New York 10038 Arleen Liquori	9-12	TV	128	76%	212/964-9610 Fax 212/732-6622
New Design High Sch 350 Grand St, New York 10002 Scott Conti	9-12	T	455	77%	212/475-4148 Fax 212/674-2128
NYC Business of Sports Sch 439 W 49th St, New York 10019 Joshua Solomon	9-12	T	434	72%	212/246-2183 Fax 212/246-2913
NYC Ischool 131 Avenue of the Americas, New York 10013 Isora Bailey	9-12		465	34%	917/237-7300
NYC Lab HS for Coll Studies 333 W 17th St, New York 10011 Brooke Jackson	9-12		518	27%	212/691-6119 Fax 212/691-2147
NYC Lab MS for Coll Studies 333 W 17th St, New York 10011 Megan Adams	6-8		600	35%	212/691-6119 Fax 212/691-6219
NYC Museum Sch 333 W 17th St, New York 10011 Darlene Miller	9-12	T	450 25	56%	212/675-6206 Fax 212/675-6524
Pace High Sch 100 Hester St, New York 10002 Eric Glatz	9-12	T	553	78%	212/334-4663 Fax 212/334-4919
Peck Slip School 343 1 Peck Slip, New York 10038 Margaret Siena	PK-5		457	13%	212/312-6260 Fax 212/312-6265
Professional Perform Arts HS 328 W 48th St, New York 10036 Keith Ryan	6-12		580 15	35%	212/247-8652 Fax 212/247-7514
PS 1 Alfred E Smith 8 Henry St, New York 10038 Amy Hom	PK-5	T	248 30	75%	212/267-4133 Fax 212/267-4469
PS 2 Meyer London 122 Henry St, New York 10002 Silvana Ng	PK-5	T	440	93%	212/964-0350 Fax 212/608-4080
Ⓜ PS 3 Charrette Sch 490 Hudson St, New York 10014 Hilary Casado	PK-5		705 28	22%	212/691-1183 Fax 212/675-5306
PS 6 Lillie D Blake 45 E 81st St Frnt 1, New York 10028 Lauren Fontana	PK-5		649 30	12%	212/452-6650 Fax 212/452-6645
PS 011 William T Harris 320 W 21st St, New York 10011 Robert Bender	PK-5	A	898 35	31%	212/929-1743 Fax 212/989-7816
PS 33 Chelsea Prep 281 9th Ave, New York 10001 Cindy Wang	PK-5		601 20	49%	212/244-6426 Fax 212/629-6893
PS 40 Augustus St Gaudens 320 E 20th St, New York 10003 Susan Felder	PK-5		705 24	12%	212/475-5500 Fax 212/533-5388
PS 41 Greenwich Village 116 W 11th St, New York 10011 Kelly Shannon	PK-5		665 34	7%	212/675-2756 Fax 212/924-0910
PS 42 Benjamin Altman 71 Hester St, New York 10002 May Lee	PK-5	T	553 35	70%	212/226-8410 Fax 212/431-7384
PS 51 Elias Howe 525 W 44th St, New York 10036 Stephanie Lukas	PK-5	T	481 14	56%	212/315-7160 Fax 212/315-7165
PS 59 Beekman Hill Int'l 233 E 56th St, New York 10022 Adele Schroeter	PK-5		637 16	11%	212/888-7870 Fax 212/888-7872
PS 77 Lower Lab Sch 1700 3rd Ave Frnt 2, New York 10128 Sandra Miller	K-5		362 14	11%	212/427-2798 Fax 212/423-0634
PS 89 201 Warren St, New York 10282 Veronica Najjar	PK-5		450 60	9%	212/571-5659 Fax 212/571-0739
PS 111 Adolph S Ochs 440 W 53rd St, New York 10019 Edward Gilligan	PK-5	T	433 50	55%	212/582-7420 Fax 212/245-7236
Ⓜ PS 116 Mary Lindley Murray 210 E 33rd St, New York 10016 Jane Hsu	PK-5		491 32	32%	212/685-4366 Fax 212/696-1009
PS 124 Yung Wing 40 Division St, New York 10002 Alice Hom	PK-5	T	668 50	52%	212/966-7237 Fax 212/219-3069
PS 126 Jacob August Riis 80 Catherine St, New York 10038 Carlos Romero	PK-8	T	717 31	77%	212/962-2188 Fax 212/349-7342
PS 130 Hernando De Soto 143 Baxter St, New York 10013 Renny Fong	PK-5	T	782 45	45%	212/226-8072 Fax 212/431-5524
PS 150 Tribeca Learning Center 334 Greenwich St, New York 10013 Jennifer Bonnet	PK-5		190 7	17%	212/732-4392 Fax 212/766-5895 ⓕⓣ
Ⓜ PS 158 the Bayard Taylor Sch 1458 York Ave, New York 10075 Dina Ercolano	PK-5		803 35	12%	212/744-6562 Fax 212/772-8424
PS 183 Robert L Stevenson 419 E 66th St, New York 10065 Martin Woodard	PK-5		603 35	12%	212/734-7719 Fax 212/861-8314
Ⓜ PS 198 Isador E Ida Straus 1700 3rd Ave, New York 10128 Katharine DeBenedictis	PK-5		489 25	40%	212/289-3702 Fax 212/410-1731
Ⓜ PS 212 Midtown West 328 W 48th St, New York 10036 Kay Loua	PK-5		368 25	20%	212/247-0208 Fax 212/757-4933
PS 234 Independence Sch 292 Greenwich St, New York 10007 Dana Rappaport	K-5		638	10%	212/233-6034 Fax 212/374-1719
PS 267 Eastside Elem Sch 213 E 63rd St, New York 10065 Medea McEvoy	K-5		436	12%	212/888-7848 Fax 212/371-2891
PS 281 the River Sch 425 E 35th St, New York 10016 Jessica Orleans	PK-5		424	30%	212/251-6640 Fax 212/251-6645
Ⓜ PS 290 Manhattan New Sch 311 E 82nd St, New York 10028 Doreen Esposito	PK-5		577 23	13%	212/734-7127 Fax 212/772-8879
PS 340 Sixth Ave Elem Sch 64 W 17th St, New York 10011 Patricia Carney	PK-4		340	8%	917/305-1000 Fax 917/305-1005
PS 527 East Side Sch-Soc Acton 323 E 91st St, New York 10128 Michelle Amato	K-5		478	17%	212/828-2710 Fax 212/828-2712
PS/IS 217 Roosevelt Island 645 Main St, Roosevelt Isl 10044 Mandana Beckman	PK-8		636	33%	212/980-0294 Fax 212/980-1192
Ⓐ Quest to Learn 351 W 18th St 4th Fl, New York 10011 Nicholas Jurman	6-12	T	582	72%	212/488-3645 Fax 212/679-4967
Ⓐ Repertory HS for Theatre Arts 123 W 43rd St, New York 10036 Michael Fram	9-12	T	239 10	68%	212/382-1875 Fax 212/382-2306
Ⓜ Richard R Green HS of Teaching 7 Beaver St, New York 10004 Joan Weaver	9-12	T	355	82%	646/826-8174 Fax 646/826-8175
Ⓐ Satellite Academy High Sch 120 W 30th St Lbby L, New York 10001 Steven Zbaida	9-9	TV	278 50	75%	646/674-2800 Fax 646/674-2829

79 Student Personnel
80 Driver Ed/Safety
81 Gifted/Talented
82 Video Services
83 Substance Abuse Prev
84 Erate
85 AIDS Education
88 Alternative/At Risk
89 Multi-Cultural Curriculum
90 Social Work
91 Safety/Security
92 Magnet School
93 Parental Involvement
95 Tech Prep Program
97 Chief Infomation Officer
98 Chief Technology Officer
270 Character Education
271 Migrant Education
273 Teacher Mentor
274 Before/After Sch
275 Response To Intervention
277 Remedial Math K-12
280 Literacy Coach
285 STEM
286 Digital Learning
288 Common Core Standards
294 Accountability
295 Network System
296 Title II Programs
297 Webmaster
298 Grant Writer/Ptnrships
750 Chief Innovation Officer
751 Chief of Staff
752 Social Emotional Learning

Other School Types
Ⓐ = Alternative School
Ⓒ = Charter School
Ⓜ = Magnet School
Ⓨ = Year-Round School

School Programs
A = Alternative Program
G = Adult Classes
M = Magnet Program
T = Title I Schoolwide
V = Career & Tech Ed Programs

Social Media
ⓕ = Facebook
ⓣ = Twitter

New Schools are shaded
New Superintendents and Principals are bold
Personnel with email addresses are underscored

New York County

Market Data Retrieval

Public Schs..Principal	Grd	Prgm	Enr/#Cls	SN	Phone/Fax
Ⓜ School of the Future 127 E 22nd St, New York 10010 Stacy Goldstein \ John Fanning	6-12		719 43	44%	212/475-8086 Fax 212/475-9273
Spruce Street Sch 12 Spruce St, New York 10038 Nancy Harris	PK-8		560	17%	212/266-4800 Fax 212/266-4805
Ⓜ Stuyvesant High Sch 345 Chambers St, New York 10282 Eric Contreras	9-12	V	3,380	43%	212/312-4800 Fax 212/587-3874
Talent Unlimited High Sch 300 E 68th St, New York 10065 William Gagstetter	9-12		532 20	56%	212/737-1530 Fax 212/737-2863
The Clinton Sch 10 E 15th St, New York 10003 Jonathan Levin	6-12		775 15	16%	212/524-4360 Fax 212/524-4365
The Facing History Sch 525 W 50th St, New York 10019 Dana Panagot	9-12	T	352	79%	212/757-2680 Fax 212/757-2156
Union Sq Acad-Hlth Sciences 40 Irving Pl, New York 10003 Bernardo Ascona	9-12	T	410	83%	212/253-3110 Fax 212/253-3108 ⓕ
Unity Center for Urban Tech 111 E 33rd St, New York 10016 Fausto De La Rosa	9-12	T	271 10	91%	212/576-0530 Fax 212/576-0562
Urban Academy Lab High Sch 317 E 67th St, New York 10065 Adam Grumbach	9-12		131 10	57%	212/570-5284 Fax 212/570-5366
Urban Assembly Academy Gov/Law 350 Grand St Fl 315, New York 10002 Alison Breedy	9-12	T	326 14	82%	212/505-0745 Fax 212/674-8021
Urban Assembly Emergency Mgmt 411 Pearl St Rm B30, New York 10038 Robert Magliaro	9-12	T	256	84%	212/225-0998 Fax 212/225-0996
Urban Assembly Gateway Tech 439 W 49th St, New York 10019 Kristina Dvorakovskaya	9-12	T	453	57%	212/246-1041 Fax 212/246-2654
Urban Assembly Maker Academy 411 Pearl St, New York 10038 Luke Bauer	9-12	T	436	77%	212/225-0890 Fax 212/225-0991
Urban Assembly NY Harbor Sch 10 South St Slip 7, New York 10004 Jeffrey Chetirko	9-12		526 24	54%	212/458-0800 Fax 212/458-0801
Urban Assembly Sch Design/Con 525 W 50th St, New York 10019 Meredith Matson	9-12	T	263 22	80%	212/586-0981 Fax 212/586-1731
Urban Assembly Sch of Business 26 Broadway, New York 10004 Patricia Minaya	9-12	T	178	84%	212/668-0169 Fax 212/668-0635
Ⓐ Vanguard High Sch 317 E 67th St, New York 10065 Erica Doyle	9-12	T	424	72%	212/517-5175 Fax 212/517-5334
Ⓐ Washington Irving YABC 40 Irving Pl, New York 10003 Roger Bradley	10-12		250		212/674-5000
Yorkville Cmty Sch 421 E 88th St, New York 10128 Samantha Kaplan	PK-5		472	38%	212/722-5240 Fax 212/427-8069

● **Community School District 3** PID: 10909589   212/678-5857
154 W 93rd St, New York 10025   Fax 212/678-2804

Ilene Altschul 1

Public Schs..Principal	Grd	Prgm	Enr/#Cls	SN	Phone/Fax
Anderson School PS 334 100 W 77th St, New York 10024 Jodi Hyde	K-8		522	15%	212/595-7193 Fax 212/496-2854
Ⓐ Beacon Sch 522 W 44th St, New York 10036 Ruth Lacey	9-12	V	1,469 31	36%	212/465-4230 Fax 212/465-4235
Community Action School MS 258 154 W 93rd St, New York 10025 Andrew Sullivan	6-8	T	245 12	83%	212/678-5888 Fax 212/531-7351
Ⓐ Edward A Reynolds West Side HS 140 W 102nd St, New York 10025 Lilit Suffet	9-12	GTV	326 39	87%	212/678-7300 Fax 212/678-7380
Fiorello H Laguardia High Sch 100 Amsterdam Ave, New York 10023 Yeou-Jey Vasconcelos	9-12		2,958	28%	212/496-0700 Fax 212/724-5748
Frank McCourt High Sch 145 W 84th St, New York 10024 Danielle Salzberg	9-12		403	53%	212/362-2015 Fax 212/362-5926
Frederick Douglass Academy II 215 W 114th St, New York 10026 Osei Afriyie	6-12	T	323 22	82%	212/865-9260 Fax 212/865-9281
© Future Leaders Institute CS Ⓨ 134 W 122nd St, New York 10027 Jody Flowers	K-8	MT	391 17	86%	212/678-2868 Fax 212/666-2749
Global Learning Collaborative 145 W 84th St, New York 10024 Karla Chiluiza	9-12	T	424	82%	212/877-1103 Fax 212/877-1138
Greene HS Imaginative Inquiry 122 Amsterdam Ave, New York 10023 Stephen Noonan	9-12		286	79%	212/799-4064 Fax 212/799-4171
HS Law Advocacy/Cmty Justice 122 Amsterdam Ave, New York 10023 Doreen Conwell	9-12	T	434 30	89%	212/501-1201 Fax 212/501-1195
HS of Arts & Technology 122 Amsterdam Ave, New York 10023 Mariela Graham	9-12	T	463 28	85%	212/501-1198 Fax 917/441-3693
Ⓐ Innovation Diploma Plus HS 145 W 84th St, New York 10024 Daniel Storchan	10-12	T	170	81%	212/724-2039 Fax 212/724-2765
JHS 54 Booker T Washington 103 W 107th St, New York 10025 Dr Elana Elster	6-8	V	825 44	19%	212/678-2861 Fax 212/316-0883
Lafayette Acad MS 256 154 W 93rd St, New York 10025 Brian Zager	6-8	T	137 9	73%	212/222-2857 Fax 212/531-0586
Manhattan/Hunter Science HS 122 Amsterdam Ave, New York 10023 Kevin Froner	9-12		458	59%	212/501-1235 Fax 212/501-1171
Mott Hall II M 862 234 W 109th St, New York 10025 Marlon Lowe	6-8	T	417 12	65%	212/678-2960 Fax 212/222-0560
MS 243 Center Sch 100 W 84th St, New York 10024 Elaine Schwartz	5-8		247 10	14%	212/799-1477 Fax 212/579-9728
MS 245 the Computer Sch 100 W 77th St, New York 10024 Henry Zymeck	6-8	T	404 26	29%	917/441-0873 Fax 212/678-5908
MS 250 West Side Collaborative 735 W End Ave, New York 10025 Novella Bailey	6-8	T	153 6	69%	212/866-6313 Fax 212/678-5295
MS 291 West End Secondary Sch 227 W 61st St, New York 10023 Jessica Jenkins	6-9		431	18%	212/245-1506 Fax 212/245-1291
MS M247 Dual Lang Middle Sch 100 W 77th St, New York 10024 Kristina Jelinek	6-8	T	232 11	89%	212/496-1050 Fax 212/496-1087
© New York French American CS 311 W 120th St, New York 10027 Marc Maurice	K-6	T	282	71%	212/666-4134 Fax 212/666-4138

1 Superintendent	8 Curric/Instruct K-12	19 Chief Financial Officer	29 Family/Consumer Science	39 Social Studies K-12	49 English/Lang Arts Elem	59 Special Education Elem	69 Academic Assessment
2 Bus/Finance/Purchasing	9 Curric/Instruct Elem	20 Art K-12	30 Adult Education	40 Social Studies Elem	50 English/Lang Arts Sec	60 Special Education Sec	70 Research/Development
3 Buildings And Grounds	10 Curric/Instruct Sec	21 Art Elem	31 Career/Sch-to-Work K-12	41 Social Studies Sec	51 Reading K-12	61 Foreign/World Lang K-12	71 Public Information
4 Food Service	11 Federal Program	22 Art Sec	32 Career/Sch-to-Work Elem	42 Science K-12	52 Reading Elem	62 Foreign/World Lang Elem	72 Summer School
5 Transportation	12 Title I	23 Music K-12	33 Career/Sch-to-Work Sec	43 Science Elem	53 Reading Sec	63 Foreign/World Lang Sec	73 Instructional Tech
6 Athletic	13 Title V	24 Music Elem	34 Early Childhood Ed	44 Science Sec	54 Remedial Reading K-12	64 Religious Education K-12	74 Inservice Training
7 Health Services	15 Asst Superintendent	25 Music Sec	35 Health/Phys Education	45 Math K-12	55 Remedial Reading Elem	65 Religious Education Elem	75 Marketing/Distributive
	16 Instructional Media Svcs	26 Business Education	36 Guidance Services K-12	46 Math Elem	56 Remedial Reading Sec	66 Religious Education Sec	76 Info Systems
	17 Chief Operations Officer	27 Career & Tech Ed	37 Guidance Services Elem	47 Math Sec	57 Bilingual/ELL	67 School Board President	77 Psychological Assess
	18 Chief Academic Officer	28 Technology Education	38 Guidance Services Sec	48 English/Lang Arts K-12	58 Special Education K-12	68 Teacher Personnel	78 Affirmative Action

New York School Directory

New York County

School	Grd	Prgm	Enr/#Cls	SN	Phone
ⓒ Opportunity Charter Sch 240 W 113th St, New York 10026 Sade McCaw \ Jessica Marcu	6-12	T	425 15	87%	212/866-6137 Fax 212/665-7436
PS 9 Sarah Anderson 100 W 84th St, New York 10024 Kate Witzke	PK-5		623 22	22%	212/678-2812 Fax 212/873-4681
PS 75 Emily Dickinson 735 W End Ave, New York 10025 George Georgilakis	K-5	AT	520 32	70%	212/866-5400 Fax 212/866-5543
PS 76 A Philip Randolph 220 W 121st St, New York 10027 Charles DeBerry	PK-8	T	369 40	95%	212/678-2865 Fax 212/678-2867
PS 84 Lillian Weber 32 W 92nd St, New York 10025 Evelyn Lolis	PK-5		691 50	38%	212/799-2534 Fax 212/501-9071
PS 87 William Sherman 160 W 78th St, New York 10024 Monica Berry	PK-5		869 36	10%	212/678-2826 Fax 212/678-5886
PS 145 Bloomingdale Sch 150 W 105th St, New York 10025 Natalia Russo	PK-5	T	394 36	76%	212/678-2857 Fax 212/222-4610
PS 149 Sojourner Truth 41 W 117th St, New York 10026 Claudia Aguirre	PK-8	T	218	98%	646/672-9020 Fax 212/360-5885
PS 163 Alfred E Smith 163 W 97th St, New York 10025 Donny Lopez	PK-5		543 29	49%	212/678-2854 Fax 212/678-2856
PS 165 Robert E Simon 234 W 109th St, New York 10025 Aracelis Castellano	PK-5	T	436	66%	212/678-2873 Fax 212/222-6700
Ⓜ PS 166 Rodgers Sch Arts & Tech 132 W 89th St, New York 10024 Debra Mastriano	K-5		658 26	15%	212/678-2829 Fax 212/579-4542
PS 180 Hugo Newman 370 W 120th St, New York 10027 Jeneca Parker	PK-8	T	506 32	69%	212/678-2849 Fax 212/665-1572
Ⓜ PS 185 Locke Sch Arts & Design 20 W 112th St, New York 10026 Jane Murphy	PK-5		348 18	82%	212/534-7490 Fax 212/831-8613
PS 191 Riverside Sch Makers 300 W 61st St, New York 10023 Stephen Hernon	PK-8	T	530 22	68%	347/478-5228 Fax 347/478-5526
PS 199 Jessie Isador Straus 270 W 70th St, New York 10023 Louise Xerri	K-5		761 33	14%	212/799-1033 Fax 212/799-1179
Ⓜ PS 242 Young Diplomats Magnet 134 W 122nd St, New York 10027 Denise Gomez	PK-5	T	139 12	81%	212/678-2908 Fax 212/678-2927
PS 333 Manhattan Sch for Chldn 154 W 93rd St, New York 10025 Claire Lowenstein	K-8		685	17%	212/222-1450 Fax 212/222-1828
PS 452 210 W 61st St, New York 10023 Scott Parker	PK-5		407	31%	212/259-6222 Fax 212/259-6235
Special Music Sch 129 W 67th St, New York 10023 Katherine Banucci-Smith	K-12		305 10	22%	212/501-3318 Fax 212/501-3339
Ⓨ STEM Institute of Manhattan 240 W 113th St, New York 10026 Marcia Hendricks	K-5	MT	94 22	92%	212/678-2898 Fax 212/678-2975
Urban Assem Sch-Green Careers 145 W 84th St, New York 10024 Madeleine Ciliotta-Young	9-12	T	300 10	85%	212/787-1189 Fax 212/787-1455
Urban Assembly School of Media 122 Amsterdam Ave, New York 10023 Cordelia Veve	9-12	T	413	87%	212/501-1110 Fax 212/580-0156
Ⓜ Wadleigh Performing Arts HS 215 W 114th St, New York 10026 Kyleema Norman	6-12	T	317	79%	212/749-5800 Fax 212/749-6463
West Prep Academy 150 W 105th St, New York 10025 Carland Washington	6-8	T	199	85%	212/280-8502 Fax 212/280-8509

• **Community School District 4** PID: 10909591   212/348-2873
  160 E 120th St, New York 10035

Dr Kristy De La Cruz 1

Public Schs..Principal	Grd	Prgm	Enr/#Cls	SN	Phone
Bilingual Bicultural Sch 182 219 E 109th St, New York 10029 Yazmin Perez	PK-5	T	301 18	96%	212/860-6031 Fax 212/860-4536
Central Park East High Sch 1573 Madison Ave, New York 10029 Bennett Lieberman	9-12	TV	517 20	78%	212/860-5929 Fax 212/860-6043
Central Park East I 1573 Madison Ave, New York 10029 Gabriel Feldberg	PK-5		172 8	43%	212/860-5821 Fax 212/860-6017
Central Park East II 433 E 100th St, New York 10029 Naomi Smith	PK-8	T	471 10	50%	212/860-5992 Fax 212/410-6041
Esperanza Preparatory Academy 240 E 109th St, New York 10029 Luisa Taylor	6-12	T	529	88%	212/722-6507 Fax 212/722-6717
Heritage Sch 1680 Lexington Ave, New York 10029 Dyanand Sugrim	9-12	T	312 20	90%	212/828-2858 Fax 212/828-2861
Isaac Newton MS-Math & Science 260 Pleasant Ave, New York 10029 Florin Purice	6-8	T	280 10	88%	212/860-6006 Fax 212/987-4197
James Weldon Johnson Elem Sch 176 E 115th St, New York 10029 Yaira Jimenez	PK-8	T	690 36	87%	212/876-5522 Fax 212/860-6072
Lexington Academy 131 E 104th St, New York 10029 Antonio Hernandez	PK-8	T	589 38	87%	212/860-5831 Fax 212/860-6094
Ⓜ Manhattan Ctr Science & Math 260 Pleasant Ave, New York 10029 Jimenez David	9-12	TV	1,654	80%	212/876-4639 Fax 212/996-5946
Mosaic Prep Academy 141 E 111th St, New York 10029 Lisette Caesar	PK-5	T	255	95%	212/722-3109 Fax 212/722-3167
MS 224 Manh E Sch Arts & Acad 410 E 100th St, New York 10029 Luis Genao	6-8	T	208 14	68%	212/860-6047 Fax 212/410-0678
Park East High Sch 230 E 105th St 34, New York 10029 Kevin McCarthy	9-12	TV	378 20	80%	212/831-1517 Fax 212/348-6097
PS 7 Samuel Stern 160 E 120th St, New York 10035 Christine Vanzetta	PK-8	T	365 46	92%	212/860-5827 Fax 212/860-6070
PS 38 Roberto Clemente 232 E 103rd St, New York 10029 Carlina Barton	PK-5	T	245 21	94%	212/860-5882
PS 83 Luis Munoz Rivera 219 E 109th St, New York 10029 Frances Castillo	PK-5	T	366 19	87%	212/860-5847
PS 96 Joseph Lanzetta 216 E 120th St, New York 10035 David Pretto	PK-8	T	399 33	94%	212/860-5851 Fax 212/860-6074
PS 102 Jacques Cartier 315 E 113th St, New York 10029 Gaynell Taylor	PK-5	T	234 20	96%	212/860-5834 Fax 212/860-6076

---

79 Student Personnel
80 Driver Ed/Safety
81 Gifted/Talented
82 Video Services
83 Substance Abuse Prev
84 Erate
85 AIDS Education
88 Alternative/At Risk
89 Multi-Cultural Curriculum
90 Social Work
91 Safety/Security
92 Magnet School
93 Parental Involvement
95 Tech Prep Program
97 Chief Information Officer
98 Chief Technology Officer
270 Character Education
271 Migrant Education
273 Teacher Mentor
274 Before/After Sch
275 Response To Intervention
277 Remedial Math K-12
280 Literacy Coach
285 STEM
286 Digital Learning
288 Common Core Standards
294 Accountability
295 Network System
296 Title II Programs
297 Webmaster
298 Grant Writer/Ptnrships
750 Chief Innovation Officer
751 Chief of Staff
752 Social Emotional Learning

School Programs
A = Alternative Program
G = Adult Classes
M = Magnet Program
T = Title I Schoolwide
V = Career & Tech Ed Programs

Other School Types
Ⓐ = Alternative School
ⓒ = Charter School
Ⓜ = Magnet School
Ⓨ = Year-Round School

Social Media
 = Facebook
 = Twitter

New Schools are shaded
New Superintendents and Principals are bold
Personnel with email addresses are underscored

New York County

Market Data Retrieval

School	Grd	Prgm	Enr/#Cls	SN	Phone
PS 108 Assemblyman Angelo Toro 1615 Madison Ave, New York 10029 Bill Gladstone	PK-8	T	462 / 52	86%	212/860-5803 Fax 212/860-6095
PS 112 Jose Celso Barbosa 535 E 119th St, New York 10035 Lisa Velazquez	PK-2	T	306 / 23	76%	212/860-5868 Fax 212/860-6077
PS 146 Ann M Short 421 E 106th St, New York 10029 Mona Silfen	PK-5	T	388 / 36	97%	212/860-5877 Fax 212/860-6078
PS 155 William Paca 319 E 117th St, New York 10035 Marcia Sulit	PK-5	T	240 / 22	97%	212/860-5885 Fax 212/860-5856
PS 171 Patrick Henry 19 E 103rd St, New York 10029 Dimitres Pantelidis	PK-8	T	763 / 30	70%	212/860-5801 Fax 212/860-6079
PS 206 Jose Celso Barbosa 508 E 120th St, New York 10035 Camille Forbes	3-8	T	451 / 20	80%	212/860-5809 Fax 212/860-6080
© Renaissance CHS for Innovation 410 E 100th St, New York 10029 Terence Joseph	9-12	T	402	78%	212/722-5871 Fax 646/430-8555
Renaissance School of the Arts 319 E 117th St, New York 10035 Brian Bradley	6-8	T	199	94%	212/534-6072 Fax 212/534-7418
River East Elem Sch 2351 1st Ave, New York 10035 Michael Panetta	PK-5	T	264 / 12	83%	212/348-2208 Fax 212/289-9231
Tag Young Scholars 240 E 109th St, New York 10029 Janette Cesar	K-8		591 / 16	34%	212/860-6003 Fax 212/831-1842
Young Women's Leadership Sch 105 E 106th St Ste 9, New York 10029 Colleen McGeehan	6-12	T	472 / 28	78%	212/289-7593 Fax 212/289-7728

• Community School District 5   PID: 10909606
123 Morningside Dr, New York 10027   212/222-0473   Fax 212/769-7619

Danika Rux 1

Public Schs..Principal	Grd	Prgm	Enr/#Cls	SN	Phone
Columbia Secondary Sch 425 W 123rd St, New York 10027 Miriam Nightengale	6-12		702	48%	212/666-1278 Fax 212/666-3805
Eagle Academy Young Men-Harlem 6 Edgecombe Ave, New York 10030 Mahaliel Bethea	6-11	T	377	75%	212/694-6051 Fax 212/694-6053
Ⓜ Frederick Douglass Academy 2581 7th Ave, New York 10039 Joseph Gates	6-12	TV	1,092 / 40	78%	212/491-4107 Fax 212/491-4414
© Harlem C Z Promise Academy I 245 W 129th St, New York 10027 Tonya White	K-12	T	1,159	85%	212/534-0700 Fax 212/289-0661
© Harlem C Z Promise Academy II 2005 Madison Ave, New York 10035 Shondell James	K-5	T	600 / 17	82%	917/492-1481 Fax 917/492-1576
Ⓐ Harlem Renaissance High Sch 22 E 128th St, New York 10035 James Caputo	9-12	T	175	87%	212/996-3795 Fax 212/996-4354
HS Math Science & Engr at Ccny 240 Convent Ave, New York 10031 Crystal Bonds	9-12		485 / 9	40%	212/281-6490 Fax 212/281-6918
Mott Hall High Sch 6 Edgecombe Ave 4th Fl, New York 10030 Altagracia Villalona	9-12	T	252	92%	212/694-6020 Fax 212/690-5047
MS 371 Seed Harlem 425 W 130th St, New York 10027 Meredith Hill	6-6		140		212/346-5270
New Design Middle Sch 625 W 133rd St, New York 10027 Francesca Pisa	6-8	T	135	96%	212/281-6339 Fax 212/281-6674
PS 30 Hernandez-Hughes 144 E 128th St 176, New York 10035 Teri Powell	PK-5	T	237 / 42	93%	212/876-1825 Fax 212/876-4034
PS 36 Margaret Douglas 123 Morningside Dr, New York 10027 Heather Jnbaptist	PK-5	T	367 / 62	89%	212/690-5807 Fax 212/690-5811
PS 46 Arthur Tappan 2987 Frederick Douglass Blvd, New York 10039 Kerry Hazell	PK-8	AT	544	93%	212/360-1519 Fax 212/360-1610
PS 92 Mary McLeod Bethune 222 W 134th St, New York 10030 Rosa Davila	PK-5	AT	247 / 27	98%	212/690-5915 Fax 212/690-5920
PS 123 Mahalia Jackson 301 W 140th St, New York 10030 Melitina Paduani	PK-8	AT	441 / 45	94%	212/342-6200 Fax 212/690-5930
PS 125 Ralph Bunche 425 W 123rd St, New York 10027 Reginald Higgins	PK-5	T	303 / 40	68%	212/666-6400 Fax 212/749-1291
PS 129 John H Finley 425 W 130th St, New York 10027 Odelphia Pierre	PK-8	AT	378 / 27	90%	212/690-5932 Fax 212/690-5934
PS 133 Fred R Moore 2121 5th Ave, New York 10037 Nazda Palchik-Medina	PK-5	T	224 / 20	93%	212/690-5936 Fax 212/690-5939
PS 154 Harriet Tubman 250 W 127th St, New York 10027 Elizabeth Jarrett	PK-5	T	277 / 30	95%	212/864-2400
PS 161 Pedro Albizu Campos 499 W 133rd St, New York 10027 Patricia Balbuena	K-8	T	740 / 43	94%	212/690-5945 Fax 917/507-0524
PS 175 Henry Garnet 175 W 134th St, New York 10030 Kavita Jagarnath	PK-5	T	337	92%	212/283-0426 Fax 212/286-6319
PS 194 Countee Cullen 244 W 144th St, New York 10030 Kerianne Citrano	PK-5	AT	188 / 32	98%	212/690-5954 Fax 212/862-5743
PS 197 John B Russwurm 2230 5th Ave, New York 10037 Natasha Spann	PK-5	AT	289 / 30	93%	212/690-5960 Fax 212/690-5959
PS 200 James McCune Smith 2589 7th Ave, New York 10039 Renee Belton	PK-5	T	366 / 60	89%	212/491-6636
© St Hope Leadership Academy CS 222 W 134th St, New York 10030 Meghann Persenaire	6-8	T	295	95%	212/283-1204 Fax 212/283-1207
Teachers College Cmty Sch 168 Morningside Ave, New York 10027 Michelle Verdiner	PK-7		311	49%	212/316-8080 Fax 212/316-8085
Thurgood Marshall Academy 200 W 135th St 214, New York 10030 Maj Fareed	6-12	T	552 / 40	72%	212/283-8055 Fax 212/283-8109
Thurgood Marshall Lower Sch 276 W 151st St, New York 10039 Dawn DeCosta	K-5	T	202 / 11	85%	212/368-8731 Fax 212/368-8641
Urban Assem Sch Performing Art 509 W 129th St, New York 10027 Meghan McMahon	9-12	T	395	83%	212/543-4460 Fax 212/234-4975
Urban Assem-Global Commerce 2005 Madison Ave, New York 10035 Roony Vizcaino	9-12	T	232	83%	212/831-5201 Fax 212/831-5206
Urban Assembly Future Leaders 509 W 129th St, New York 10027 Joseph Gates	6-8	T	100 / 10	87%	212/543-4960 Fax 212/694-4124

1	Superintendent	8	Curric/Instruct K-12	19	Chief Financial Officer	29	Family/Consumer Science
2	Bus/Finance/Purchasing	9	Curric/Instruct Elem	20	Art K-12	30	Adult Education
3	Buildings And Grounds	10	Curric/Instruct Sec	21	Art Elem	31	Career/Sch-to-Work K-12
4	Food Service	11	Federal Program	22	Art Sec	32	Career/Sch-to-Work Elem
5	Transportation	12	Title I	23	Music K-12	33	Career/Sch-to-Work Sec
6	Athletic	13	Title V	24	Music Elem	34	Early Childhood Ed
7	Health Services	15	Asst Superintendent	25	Music Sec	35	Health/Phys Education
		16	Instructional Media Svcs	26	Business Education	36	Guidance Services K-12
		17	Chief Operations Officer	27	Career & Tech Ed	37	Guidance Services Elem
		18	Chief Academic Officer	28	Technology Education	38	Guidance Services Sec
39	Social Studies K-12	49	English/Lang Arts Elem	59	Special Education Elem	69	Academic Assessment
40	Social Studies Elem	50	English/Lang Arts Sec	60	Special Education Sec	70	Research/Development
41	Social Studies Sec	51	Reading K-12	61	Foreign/World Lang K-12	71	Public Information
42	Science K-12	52	Reading Elem	62	Foreign/World Lang Elem	72	Summer School
43	Science Elem	53	Reading Sec	63	Foreign/World Lang Sec	73	Instructional Tech
44	Science Sec	54	Remedial Reading K-12	64	Religious Education K-12	74	Inservice Training
45	Math K-12	55	Remedial Reading Elem	65	Religious Education Elem	75	Marketing/Distributive
46	Math Elem	56	Remedial Reading Sec	66	Religious Education Sec	76	Info Systems
47	Math Sec	57	Bilingual/ELL	67	School Board President	77	Psychological Assess
48	English/Lang Arts K-12	58	Special Education K-12	68	Teacher Personnel	78	Affirmative Action

New York School Directory
New York County

- **Community School District 6** PID: 10909618 917/521-3757
  4360 Broadway, New York 10033 Fax 917/521-3797
  Manuel Ramirez 1

Public Schs..Principal	Grd	Prgm	Enr/#Cls	SN		
A Philip Randolph Campus HS 443 W 135th St, New York 10031 <u>David Fanning</u>	9-12	T	1,454		86%	212/690-6800 Fax 212/690-6805
Amistad Dual Language Sch 4862 Broadway, New York 10034 <u>Robin Edmonds</u>	K-8	T	429 21		78%	212/544-8021 Fax 212/569-7765
Castle Bridge Sch 560 W 169th St, New York 10032 <u>Julia Zuckerman</u>	PK-5	T	188		65%	212/740-4701 Fax 212/740-4706
Community Health Acad Heights 504 W 158th St, New York 10032 <u>Mark House</u>	6-12	T	696		89%	212/342-6600 Fax 212/342-6605
Community Math & Science Prep 401 W 164th St, New York 10032 <u>Olga Quiles</u>	6-8	T	165 16		98%	917/521-2508 Fax 917/521-7797
Dos Puentes Elem Sch 185 Wadsworth Ave, New York 10033 <u>Victoria Hunt</u>	K-5	T	413		65%	212/781-1803 Fax 212/781-1809
Ⓐ George Washington Campus YABC 549 Audubon Ave, New York 10040 <u>Samuel Akel</u>	10-12		250			212/927-1841
Ⓐ Gregorio Luperon HS Sci & Math 501 W 165th St, New York 10032 <u>Yecenia DeLaRosa</u>	9-12	TV	513 20		99%	212/928-1202 Fax 212/928-1309
Hamilton Grange Middle Sch 500 W 138th St, New York 10031 <u>Benjamin Lev</u>	6-8	TV	321		91%	212/281-6184 Fax 212/234-4903
Harbor Heights 306 Fort Washington Ave, New York 10033 <u>Monica Klehr</u>	6-8	T	120 8		98%	212/568-6052 Fax 212/568-7959
HS for Excellence & Innovation 650 Academy St, New York 10034 <u>Tyona Washington</u>	9-12	T	178 14		93%	212/569-1022 Fax 212/569-1190
HS for Health Careers & Sci 549 Audubon Ave, New York 10040 <u>Javier Trejo</u>	9-12	T	405 35		98%	212/927-1841 Fax 212/927-6129
HS for Media & Communications 549 Audubon Ave, New York 10040 <u>Juan Villar</u>	9-12	T	345 20		95%	212/927-1841 Fax 212/927-2326
HS Law & Public Service 549 Audubon Ave, New York 10040 <u>Nicholas Politis</u>	9-12	T	447 23		90%	212/342-6130 Fax 212/781-9516
Ⓒ Inwood Acad for Ldshp Chtr Sch 3896 10th Ave, New York 10034 <u>Valerie Hoekstra</u> \ <u>Mary Hackett</u>	5-12	T	952		87%	646/665-5570 Fax 646/665-5599
Inwood Early Clg Hlth-Info TEC 650 Academy St Fl 4, New York 10034 <u>Samona Tait</u>	9-12	T	452		91%	212/567-1394 Fax 212/567-1825
IS 528 Bea Fuller Rodgers Sch 180 Wadsworth Ave, New York 10033 <u>Carlos Pichardo</u>	6-8	GT	248 11		97%	212/740-4900 Fax 212/781-7302
JHS 52 Harold O Levy Sch 650 Academy St, New York 10034 <u>Lupe Leon</u>	6-8	T	261 100		97%	212/567-9162 Fax 212/942-4952
JHS 143 Eleanor Roosevelt 511 W 182nd St, New York 10033 <u>La Kisha McDaniel</u>	6-8	T	222		91%	212/927-7739 Fax 212/781-5539
Middle School 322 4600 Broadway, New York 10040 <u>Erica Zigelman</u>	6-8	T	321		95%	212/304-0853 Fax 212/567-3016
MS 293 City Clg Acad of Arts 4600 Broadway 4th Fl, New York 10040 <u>Bernadette Drysdale</u>	6-12	T	616		81%	212/567-3164 Fax 212/567-3958
MS 319 Maria Teresa 21 Jumel Pl, New York 10032 <u>Ysidro Abreu</u>	6-8	T	397 18		95%	212/923-3827 Fax 212/740-8012
MS 324 Patria Mirabal 21 Jumel Pl, New York 10032 <u>Janet Heller</u>	6-8	T	310		91%	212/923-4057 Fax 212/923-4626
Muscota New Sch 4862 Broadway, New York 10034 <u>Camille Wallin</u>	K-5		302 12		35%	212/544-0614 Fax 212/544-2678
Ⓒ New Heights Academy CS 1818 Amsterdam Ave, New York 10031 <u>Rinaldo Murray</u> \ <u>Fred Givens</u>	5-12	T	780		92%	212/283-5400 Fax 917/507-9314
Paula Hedbavny Sch 421 W 219th St, New York 10034 <u>Bryanna Velazquez</u>	K-8		517		68%	917/521-2060 Fax 212/942-8177
PS 4 Duke Ellington 500 W 160th St, New York 10032 <u>Adam Stevens</u>	PK-5	T	496 36		87%	212/928-0739 Fax 212/928-4142
PS 5 Ellen Lurie 3703 10th Ave, New York 10034 <u>Christophe Anest</u>	PK-5	GT	544 47		91%	212/567-8109 Fax 212/567-6526
PS 8 Luis Belliard 465 W 167th St, New York 10032 Washington Hernandez	PK-5	T	474 35		97%	212/928-4157 Fax 212/928-4072
PS 18 Park Terrace 4124 9th Ave, New York 10034 <u>Connie Mejia</u>	K-8	T	345 18		92%	917/521-2220 Fax 917/521-2225
PS 28 Wright Brothers 475 W 155th St, New York 10032 Awilda Carde	PK-5	T	537 51		91%	212/690-3014 Fax 212/368-5978
PS 48 Po Michael J Buczek 4360 Broadway 78, New York 10033 Tracy Walsh	PK-5	T	460		92%	917/521-3800 Fax 917/521-3805
PS 98 Shorac Kappock 512 W 212th St, New York 10034 Maritza Rodriguez	PK-5	T	403 45		87%	212/927-7870 Fax 212/569-1827
PS 115 Alexander Humboldt 586 W 177th St, New York 10033 Boris Consuegra	PK-5	T	439 55		97%	212/927-9233 Fax 212/795-4051
PS 128 Audubon 560 W 169th St, New York 10032 Cary Pantaleon	PK-5	T	598 56		91%	212/927-0607 Fax 212/781-8002
PS 132 Juan Pablo Duarte 185 Wadsworth Ave, New York 10033 Jessica Torres	K-5	T	203 54		88%	212/927-7857 Fax 212/568-8163
PS 152 Dyckman Valley 93 Nagle Ave, New York 10040 <u>Julia Pietri</u>	PK-5	T	521 60		91%	212/567-5456 Fax 212/942-6319
PS 153 Adam Clayton Powell 1750 Amsterdam Ave, New York 10031 Karen Bailey	PK-5	T	487 62		90%	212/927-8611 Fax 212/234-4616
PS 173 306 Fort Washington Ave, New York 10033 <u>Rachael Garcia</u>	PK-5	T	506		83%	212/927-7850 Fax 212/740-0905
PS 178M Prof Juan Bosch 12 Ellwood St 18, New York 10040 <u>Deirdre Budd</u>	K-5	T	295 15		67%	212/569-0327 Fax 212/569-0389
PS 189 2580 Amsterdam Ave, New York 10040 Rosalina Perez	PK-5	T	653		93%	212/927-8303 Fax 212/928-7733
PS 192 Jacob H Schiff 500 W 138th St, New York 10031 <u>Hilduara Abreu</u>	PK-5	T	339 20		91%	212/775-9560 Fax 212/862-7129

79 Student Personnel	91 Safety/Security	275 Response To Intervention	298 Grant Writer/Ptnrships	**School Programs**	**Social Media**
80 Driver Ed/Safety	92 Magnet School	277 Remedial Math K-12	750 Chief Innovation Officer	A = Alternative Program	
81 Gifted/Talented	93 Parental Involvement	280 Literacy Coach	751 Chief of Staff	G = Adult Classes	❶ = Facebook
82 Video Services	95 Tech Prep Program	285 STEM	752 Social Emotional Learning	M = Magnet Program	
83 Substance Abuse Prev	97 Chief Information Officer	286 Digital Learning		T = Title I Schoolwide	❷ = Twitter
84 Erate	98 Chief Technology Officer	288 Common Core Standards	**Other School Types**	V = Career & Tech Ed Programs	
85 AIDS Education	270 Accountability	294 Character Education	Ⓐ = Alternative School		
88 Alternative/At Risk	271 Migrant Education	295 Network System	Ⓒ = Charter School	New Schools are shaded	
89 Multi-Cultural Curriculum	273 Teacher Mentor	296 Title II Programs	Ⓜ = Magnet School	New Superintendents and Principals are bold	
90 Social Work	274 Before/After Sch	297 Webmaster	Ⓨ = Year-Round School	Personnel with email addresses are underscored	

NY—141

New York County — Market Data Retrieval

Public Schs..Principal	Grd	Prgm	Enr/#Cls	SN	Phone
PS 368 Hamilton Heights Sch 1750 Amsterdam Ave, New York 10031 Charles Reilly	K-5	T	161 12	68%	212/862-9940 Fax 212/862-9946
PS/IS 187 Hudson Cliffs 349 Cabrini Blvd, New York 10040 Cynthia Chory	PK-8		764 35	40%	212/927-8218 Fax 212/795-9119
PS/IS 210 21st Century Academy 501 W 152nd St 503, New York 10031 Evelyn Linares	PK-8	T	414 20	93%	212/283-0012
© Tep Equity Project Charter ECC 4280 Broadway 2nd Fl, New York 10033 Zeke Vanderhoek	PK-PK		60		212/328-1775
© Tep Equity Project Charter ES 549 Audubon Ave, New York 10040 Zeke Vanderhoek	K-4		450		646/254-6451
© Tep Equity Project Charter MS 153 Sherman Ave, New York 10034 Zeke Vanderhoek	5-8	T	845	86%	347/778-0601 Fax 212/202-3584
The College Academy 549 Audubon Ave, New York 10040 Timothy Sigerson	9-12	T	368	96%	212/927-1841 Fax 212/927-2388
The Mott Hall Sch 71111 Convent Ave, New York 10027 Judith Pena	6-8	T	290 19	77%	212/281-5028 Fax 212/491-3451
Washington Heights Academy 202 Sherman Ave, New York 10034 Renzo Martinez	PK-8	T	583	86%	212/304-3320 Fax 212/304-3322
Washington Hts Exped Lrng Sch 511 W 182nd St, New York 10033 Thomas Rochowicz	PK-12	T	901 22	81%	212/781-0524 Fax 212/781-0742

- **District 75 City Wide Programs** PID: 00750293   212/802-1507   Fax 212/802-1678
  400 1st Ave, New York 10010
  Ketler Louissaint 1

Public Schs..Principal	Grd	Prgm	Enr/#Cls	SN	Phone
ⓨ Manhattan Sch Career Develop 113 E 4th St, New York 10003 Ewa Asterita	Spec	MV	195 21	87%	212/477-2090 Fax 212/228-7095
ⓨ PS 035 317 W 52nd St, New York 10019 Marta Rojo	Spec	M	275 26	84%	212/247-4307 Fax 212/315-2814
ⓨ PS 94M the Spectrum Sch 55 Battery Pl, New York 10280 Jeanne Bradley	Spec	M	417 22	82%	212/266-5810 Fax 212/266-5811
ⓨ PS 138M 144 E 128th St 176, New York 10035 Gregg Soulette	Spec	M	629 52	90%	212/369-2227 Fax 212/427-6608
ⓨ PS 169M Robert F Kennedy 110 E 88th St, New York 10128 Eleyna Rivas	Spec	M	338 15	92%	212/348-6140 Fax 212/996-8245
ⓨ PS 811M Mickey Mantle Sch 466 W End Ave, New York 10024 John McCormick	Spec	M	376 35	90%	212/579-3788 Fax 212/579-3879
ⓨ PS M079 Horan Sch 55 E 120th St, New York 10035 Greer Phillips	Spec	M	275 30	93%	212/369-3134 Fax 212/996-8307
ⓨ PS M226 345 E 15th St Rm 202, New York 10003 M Jardi	Spec	M	400 8	84%	212/477-5017 Fax 212/477-5164
ⓨ PS M721 Occupational Training 250 W Houston St, New York 10014 Sholom Fried	Spec	M	191 20	90%	212/675-7926 Fax 212/255-3227

- **New York Alt High Sch SD 79** PID: 10012045   917/521-3639   Fax 917/521-3649
  4360 Broadway, New York 10033
  Robert Zweig 1

Public Schs..Principal	Grd	Prgm	Enr/#Cls	SN	Phone
Ⓐ Judith S Kaye High Sch 321 E 96th St, New York 10128 Andrew Brown	6-12	T	110	75%	212/369-1509
Ⓐ Pathways to Graduation 269 W 35th St, New York 10018 Marie Polinsky	11-12		190		212/868-7238 Fax 212/967-4565
Ⓐ Restart Academy 448 W 56th St, New York 10019 Joan Indart	6-12		500		212/262-0817
School of Co-op Technical Ed 321 E 96th St, New York 10128 Corey Prober	Voc	G	400 35		212/369-8800 Fax 212/876-9290

NEW YORK CATHOLIC SCHOOLS

- **Archdiocese of New York Ed Off** PID: 00754976   212/371-1011   Fax 212/758-3018
  1011 1st Ave 18th Fl, New York 10022

Schools: 147 \ **Students:** 62,605

Listing includes only schools located in this county. See District Index for location of Diocesan Offices.

Michael Deegan 1
Carmen Leon 10
Frank Viteritti 15,68
John Riley 15
Kathleen Krall 15,70
Mary Jane Daley 15
Dr Noelle Beale 15
Fileen Murtha 58
Patrick Davis 73
Oneeka Jordan 76
James Varay 295
Lori Ziesel 751
Steve Palonetti 4
Cathleen Cassel 15
Joanne Walsh 15,34
Joseph Tweed 15
Linda Dougherty 15
Michael Coppotelli 15,79
Zolita Herrera 15
T J McCormack 71
Lillian Vallentin 76
Christine Cavalucci 83
Kaitlyn Boresky 295

Catholic Schs..Principal	Grd	Prgm	Enr/#Cls	SN	Phone
Academy of St Joseph 111 Washington Pl, New York 10014 Angela Coombs	PK-8		85		212/243-5420 Fax 212/414-4526
Academy of St Paul and St Ann 114 E 118th St, New York 10035 Christian Toala	PK-8		240 17		212/534-0619 Fax 212/534-3990
Ascension Sch 220 W 108th St, New York 10025 Donna Gabella	PK-8		300 15		212/222-5161 Fax 212/280-4690
Cathedral High Sch 350 E 56th St, New York 10022 Maria Spagnuolo	9-12		620 41		212/688-1545 Fax 212/754-2024
Connelly Middle Sch Holy Child 220 E 4th St, New York 10009 Shalonda Gutierrez	4-8	G	90 4		212/982-2287 Fax 212/982-0547
Convent of Sacred Heart Sch 1 E 91st St, New York 10128 Amy Pacula \ Catherine Hubacz \ Margaret Savino	PK-12		657 57		212/722-4745 Fax 212/996-1784
Cooke Center Academy 60 MacDougal St, New York 10012 Mary Clancy	9-12		120		212/477-1297 Fax 212/529-2018

---

1 Superintendent	8 Curric/Instruct K-12	19 Chief Financial Officer	29 Family/Consumer Science	39 Social Studies K-12	49 English/Lang Arts Elem	59 Special Education Elem	69 Academic Assessment
2 Bus/Finance/Purchasing	9 Curric/Instruct Elem	20 Art K-12	30 Adult Education	40 Social Studies Elem	50 English/Lang Arts Sec	60 Special Education Sec	70 Research/Development
3 Buildings And Grounds	10 Curric/Instruct Sec	21 Art Elem	31 Career/Sch-to-Work K-12	41 Social Studies Sec	51 Reading K-12	61 Foreign/World Lang K-12	71 Public Information
4 Food Service	11 Federal Program	22 Art Sec	32 Career/Sch-to-Work Elem	42 Science K-12	52 Reading Elem	62 Foreign/World Lang Elem	72 Summer School
5 Transportation	12 Title I	23 Music K-12	33 Career/Sch-to-Work Sec	43 Science Elem	53 Reading Sec	63 Foreign/World Lang Sec	73 Instructional Tech
6 Athletic	13 Title V	24 Music Elem	34 Early Childhood Ed	44 Science Sec	54 Remedial Reading K-12	64 Religious Education K-12	74 Inservice Training
7 Health Services	15 Asst Superintendent	25 Music Sec	35 Health/Phys Education	45 Math K-12	55 Remedial Reading Elem	65 Religious Education Elem	75 Marketing/Distributive
	16 Instructional Media Svcs	26 Business Education	36 Guidance Services K-12	46 Math Elem	56 Remedial Reading Sec	66 Religious Education Sec	76 Info Systems
	17 Chief Operations Officer	27 Career & Tech Ed	37 Guidance Services Elem	47 Math Sec	57 Bilingual/ELL	67 School Board President	77 Psychological Assess
	18 Chief Academic Officer	28 Technology Education	38 Guidance Services Sec	48 English/Lang Arts K-12	58 Special Education K-12	68 Teacher Personnel	78 Affirmative Action

New York School Directory

New York County

School	Grd	Enr/#Cls	Phone
Cooke Center Grammar Sch 219 Stanton St, New York 10002 Dr Francis Tabone	K-8	117 14	212/995-2020 Fax 212/955-1989
Dominican Academy 44 E 68th St, New York 10065 Leslie Poole-Petit	9-12	235 10	212/744-0195 Fax 212/744-0375 [f]
Good Shepherd Sch 620 Isham St, New York 10034 Geraldine Lavery	PK-8	300 14	212/567-5800 Fax 212/567-5839 [f][t]
Guardian Angel Sch 193 10th Ave, New York 10011 Christie Perez	PK-8	200 10	212/989-8280 Fax 212/352-1467
Immaculate Conception Sch 419 E 13th St, New York 10009 Mary Barry	PK-8	250	212/475-2590 Fax 212/777-2818
Incarnation Sch 570 W 175th St, New York 10033 Nicholas Green	PK-8	540 20	212/795-1030 Fax 212/795-1564
LaSalle Academy 215 E 6th St, New York 10003 Kerry Conroy	9-12	350 14	212/475-8940 Fax 212/529-3598
Loyola Sch 63 E 83rd St, New York 10028 James Lyness	9-12	267 15	212/288-3522 Fax 212/861-1021 [f][t]
Mt Carmel-Holy Rosary Sch 371 Pleasant Ave, New York 10035 Molly Smith	PK-8	184 10	212/876-7555 Fax 212/876-0152
Notre Dame High Sch 327 W 13th St, New York 10014 Jackie Brilliant	9-12	250 20	212/620-5575 Fax 212/620-0432 [f]
Our Lady of Lourdes Sch 468 W 143rd St, New York 10031 Suzanne Kaszynsk	PK-8	324 20	212/926-5820 Fax 212/491-6034
Our Lady Queen of Angels Sch 229 E 112th St, New York 10029 Stephanie Becker	PK-8	309 19	212/722-9277
Our Lady Queen of Martyrs Sch 71 Arden St, New York 10040 Andrew Woods	PK-8	298 12	212/567-3190 Fax 212/304-8587
Regis High Sch 55 E 84th St, New York 10028 Anthony Andreassi	9-12	531 36	212/288-1100 Fax 212/794-1221
Sacred Heart of Jesus Sch 456 W 52nd St, New York 10019 Nick Fargione \ Megan Gonzalez	PK-8	276 10	212/246-4784 Fax 212/707-8382 [f][t]
School of Blessed Sacrament 147 W 70th St, New York 10023 Nick Fargione \ Megan Gonzalez	PK-8	240 12	212/724-7561 Fax 212/724-0735
St Charles Borromeo Sch 214 W 142nd St, New York 10030 Dan Faas	K-8	177 9	212/368-6666 Fax 212/281-1323
St Elizabeth Sch 612 W 187th St, New York 10033 John Frega	PK-8	400 17	212/568-7291 Fax 212/928-2515
St George Academy 215 E 6th St, New York 10003 Andrew Stasiw	9-12	80 4	212/473-3323 Fax 917/534-0819
St Ignatius Loyola Sch 48 E 84th St, New York 10028 Mary Larkin	K-8	525 18	212/861-3820 Fax 212/879-8248
St Jean Baptiste High Sch 173 E 75th St, New York 10021 Sr Maria Cassano	9-12	410 25	212/288-1645 Fax 212/288-6540
St Joseph School-Yorkville 420 E 87th St, New York 10128 Theresa Bernero	PK-8	325 16	212/289-3057 Fax 212/289-7239
St Mark the Evangelist Sch 55 W 138th St, New York 10037 Dominic Fanelli	PK-8	215 8	212/283-4848 Fax 212/283-5909
St Stephen of Hungary Sch 408 E 82nd St, New York 10028 Kelly Burke	PK-8	400 20	212/288-1989 Fax 212/517-5877
St Vincent Ferrer High Sch 151 E 65th St, New York 10065 Sr Gail Morgan	9-12	496 20	212/535-4680 Fax 212/988-3455
The Epiphany Sch 234 E 22nd St, New York 10010 Kate McHugh	PK-8	541 10	212/473-4128 Fax 212/473-4392
Transfiguration Sch 29 Mott St, New York 10013 Michael Lenahan	PK-8	351 8	212/962-5265 Fax 212/964-8965 [f]
Xavier High Sch 30 W 16th St, New York 10011 Michael Livigni	9-12	1,074 43	212/924-7900 Fax 212/924-0303

NEW YORK PRIVATE SCHOOLS

Private Schs..Principal	Grd	Prgm	Enr/#Cls SN	
Aaron Sch 309 E 45th St Rear 1, New York 10017 Debra Schepard	K-7		40	212/867-9594 Fax 212/867-9864
Aaron Sch 42 E 30th St, New York 10016 Roberta Palumbo	Spec		162	212/867-9594 Fax 212/867-5379
Abraham Joshua Heschel Sch 30 W End Ave, New York 10023 Sharon Shorofsky-Mack \ Lori Skopp \ Dr Noam Silverman	PK-12		827	212/595-7087 Fax 212/595-7252
Academics West 37 W 65th St Fl 5, New York 10023 Dr Evan Flamenbaum	Spec		401	212/580-0080
Academy of Thought & Industry 1 Avenue B, New York 10009 Michael Strong	9-12		401	917/338-2820
Alexander Robertson Sch 3 W 95th St, New York 10025 Irwin Shlachter	K-5		70 6	212/663-6441 Fax 212/663-1571
Allen-Stevenson Sch 132 E 78th St, New York 10075 Stephen Warner \ Steven Cohen	K-9		419 35	212/288-6710 Fax 212/288-6802
Altschool Union Square 90 5th Ave, New York 10011 Alex Ragone	5-8		25	866/664-2070
Avenues the World Sch Online 11 E 26th St Fl 17, New York 10010 Ty Tingley	6-12		500	212/935-5000
Avenues the World Sch 259 10th Ave, New York 10001 Eric Ogden \ Todd Shy	PK-12		1,100	212/524-9000 Fax 646/664-0701
Bank St School for Children 610 W 112th St, New York 10025 Jed Lippard	PK-8	G	430 23	212/875-4420 Fax 212/875-4454
Basis Independent Manhattan 795 Columbus Ave, New York 10025 Jesse Rizzo	K-8		151	347/305-4960
Beekman Sch 220 E 50th St, New York 10022 George Higgins	9-12		80 8	212/755-6666 Fax 212/888-6085
Beit Rabban Sch 15 W 86th St, New York 10024 Ingrid Goldfein	PK-5		100 8	212/595-1386 Fax 212/579-7512

79	Student Personnel	91	Safety/Security	275	Response To Intervention	298 Grant Writer/Ptnrships
80	Driver Ed/Safety	92	Magnet School	277	Remedial Math K-12	750 Chief Innovation Officer
81	Gifted/Talented	93	Parental Involvement	280	Literacy Coach	751 Chief of Staff
82	Video Services	95	Tech Prep Program	285	STEM	752 Social Emotional Learning
83	Substance Abuse Prev	97	Chief Information Officer	286	Digital Learning	
84	Erate	98	Chief Technology Officer	288	Common Core Standards	
85	AIDS Education	270	Character Education	294	Accountability	
88	Alternative/At Risk	271	Migrant Education	295	Network System	
89	Multi-Cultural Curriculum	273	Teacher Mentor	296	Title II Programs	
90	Social Work	274	Before/After Sch	297	Webmaster	

School Programs
A = Alternative Program
G = Adult Classes
M = Magnet Program
T = Title I Schoolwide
V = Career & Tech Ed Programs

Other School Types
Ⓐ = Alternative School
Ⓒ = Charter School
Ⓜ = Magnet School
Ⓨ = Year-Round School

Social Media
[f] = Facebook
[t] = Twitter

New Schools are shaded
New Superintendents and Principals are bold
Personnel with email addresses are underscored

New York County

Market Data Retrieval

Beth Jacob Elem Sch — K-8 — 190 — 212/473-4500
142 Broome St, New York 10002 — 10 — Fax 212/460-5317
Rachel Kahn

Birch Wathen Lenox Sch — K-12 — 550 — 212/861-0404
210 E 77th St, New York 10075 — 50 — Fax 212/879-3388
Frank Carnabuci

Blue Sch — PK-5 — 207 — 212/228-6341
241 Water St, New York 10038 — Fax 212/260-3824
Gina Farrar

Brearley Sch — K-12 — 659 — 212/744-8582
610 E 83rd St, New York 10028 — 32 — Fax 212/472-8020
Jane Fried

British Int'l Sch of New York — PK-8 — 254 — 212/481-2700
20 Waterside Plz, New York 10010 — 18 — Fax 646/607-5970
Jason Morrow

Caedmon Montessori Sch — PK-5 — 190 — 212/879-2296
416 E 80th St, New York 10075 — 15 — Fax 212/585-2643
Matthew Stuart

Calhoun Sch — PK-12 V — 500 — 212/497-6500
433 W End Ave, New York 10024 — 35 — Fax 212/497-6530
Steven Solnick

Cathedral Sch-St John Divine — K-8 — 280 — 212/316-7500
1047 Amsterdam Ave, New York 10025 — 21 — Fax 212/316-7558
Laura Higgins \ Dr Worokya Duncan

Child School-Legacy High Sch — K-12 — 300 — 212/223-5055
587 Main St, Roosevelt Isl 10044 — 10 — Fax 212/223-5031
Vishu Grover

Churchill Center & Sch — Spec — 400 — 212/722-0610
301 E 29th St, New York 10016 — 43 — Fax 212/722-1387
Sara Cohen \ Annita Bruna \ Jason Wallin

City & Country Sch — PK-8 — 366 — 212/242-7802
146 W 13th St, New York 10011 — 19 — Fax 212/242-2464
Scott Moran

Collegiate Sch — K-12 — 612 — 212/812-8500
301 Freedom Pl S, New York 10069 — 60 — Fax 212/812-8524
Beth Tashlik \ Jennifer Mitchell \ Benjamin Temple

Columbia Grammar & Prep Sch — PK-12 — 1,204 — 212/749-6200
5 W 93rd St, New York 10025 — Fax 212/865-4278
Simone Hristidis \ Dr Richard Soghoian \ Sue Kilmer

Corlears Sch — PK-5 — 160 — 212/741-2800
324 W 15th St, New York 10011 — 10 — Fax 212/807-1550
David Egolf

Cristo Rey New York High Sch — 9-12 — 383 — 212/996-7000
112 E 106th St Frnt, New York 10029 — Fax 212/427-7444
Dr Frances Clemente

Dalton Lower Sch — K-3 — 385 — 212/423-5431
53 E 91st St, New York 10128
Jim Best

Dalton Sch — K-12 — 1,200 — 212/423-5200
108 E 89th St, New York 10128 — Fax 212/423-5259
James Best

De La Salle Academy — 6-8 — 147 — 212/316-5840
322 W 43rd St, New York 10036 — Fax 212/316-5998
Angel Gonzalez

Dwight Sch — K-12 — 500 — 212/724-6360
291 Central Park W, New York 10024 — 45 — Fax 212/724-2539
Martha Hirschman \ Eric Dale

East Harlem Sch-Exodus House — 4-8 — 140 — 212/876-8775
309 E 103rd St, New York 10029 — 6 — Fax 212/876-8776
Ivan Hageman

Ecole Internationale New York — PK-8 — 140 — 646/410-2238
111 E 22nd St, New York 10010
Yves Rivaud

Ethical Culture Sch — PK-12 — 500 — 212/712-6220
33 Central Park W, New York 10023 — 35 — Fax 212/712-8440
Rob Cousins

Family Sch — PK-6 — 180 — 212/688-5950
323 E 47th St, New York 10017 — 6 — Fax 212/980-2475
Lesley Haberman

Friends Seminary — K-12 — 752 — 212/979-5030
222 E 16th St, New York 10003 — Fax 212/979-5034
John Evans \ Pankti Sevak \ Kate Reynolds

Fusion Academy-Park Avenue — 6-12 — 60 — 212/326-9522
450 Park Ave S Fl 9, New York 10016 — Fax 212/935-4815
Heather Brookman

Fusion Academy-Upper West Side — 7-12 — 150 — 212/362-1014
157 Columbus Ave, New York 10023
Fred Carleton

Geneva School-Manhattan — PK-8 — 275 — 212/754-9988
138 W 90th St, New York 10024
Rim Hinkcley

George Jackson Academy — 4-8 — 135 — 212/228-6789
104 Saint Marks Pl, New York 10009 — 9 — Fax 212/228-8336
Jay Underwood

Gillen Brewer Sch — PK-3 — 90 — 212/831-3667
410 E 92nd St Frnt 3, New York 10128 — Fax 212/831-5254
Donna Kennedy

Grace Church Sch — PK-12 — 560 — 212/475-5609
86 4th Ave, New York 10003 — 34 — Fax 212/475-5015
Barbara Haney \ George Davison \ Hugo Mahabir

Great Tomorrow School USA — K-12 — 50 — 212/427-2839
38 W 123rd St, New York 10027 — 6
Adam LaFleur

Greek Cathedral Sch — PK-8 — 108 — 212/249-2840
319 E 74th St Ste 7, New York 10021 — 15 — Fax 212/249-2847
George Papayannis

Hawthorne Country Day Sch-Manh — Spec — 49 — 212/281-6531
156 William St, New York 10038 — Fax 212/281-6723
Helena Han

Hewitt Sch — K-12 — 500 — 212/288-1919
45 E 75th St, New York 10021 — 26 — Fax 212/472-7531
Frank Patti \ Launa Schweizer \ Elizabeth Stevens

Hudson Way Immersion Sch — PK-5 — 95 — 212/787-8088
525 W 52nd St, New York 10019
Sue Ha

Ideal School of Manhattan — K-5 — 126 — 212/769-1699
314 W 91st St, New York 10024 — Fax 212/769-1698
Angela Bergeson

Islamic Cultural Center Sch — PK-8 — 200 — 212/828-1838
222 E 97 St, New York 10029 — Fax 212/722-5936
Dr Khadijah Pryce

Kennedy Child Study Center — Spec — 150 — 212/988-9500
2212 3rd Ave Frnt 1, New York 10035 — 13 — Fax 212/327-2601
Kristy Chau

La Scuola D'Italia-G Marconi — PK-12 — 230 — 212/369-3290
12 E 96th St, New York 10128 — 17 — Fax 212/369-1164
Dr Maria Palandra

Learning Spring Elem Sch — Spec — 108 — 212/239-4926
247 E 20th St, New York 10003 — Fax 212/239-5226
Margaret Poggi

Leman Manhattan Prep Sch — PK-12 — 750 — 212/232-0266
41 Broad St, New York 10004 — 50 — Fax 212/232-0284
Maria Castelluccio

Little Red Schlhse-Irwin HS — PK-12 — 650 — 212/477-5316
272 Avenue of the Americas, New York 10014 — Fax 212/677-9159
Faith Hunter \ Ana Chaney \ Allison Isbell

Lorge Sch — Spec — 91 — 212/929-8660
353 W 17th St, New York 10011 — 11 — Fax 212/989-8249
Edwin Alexander

Lycee Francais De New York — PK-12 — 1,200 — 212/369-1400
505 E 75th St, New York 10021
Audur Peverelli

---

1 Superintendent	8 Curric/Instruct K-12	19 Chief Financial Officer	29 Family/Consumer Science	39 Social Studies K-12	49 English/Lang Arts Elem	59 Special Education Elem	69 Academic Assessment
2 Bus/Finance/Purchasing	9 Curric/Instruct Elem	20 Art K-12	30 Adult Education	40 Social Studies Elem	50 English/Lang Arts Sec	60 Special Education Sec	70 Research/Development
3 Buildings And Grounds	10 Curric/Instruct Sec	21 Art Elem	31 Career/Sch-to-Work K-12	41 Social Studies Sec	51 Reading K-12	61 Foreign/World Lang K-12	71 Public Information
4 Food Service	11 Federal Program	22 Art Sec	32 Career/Sch-to-Work Elem	42 Science K-12	52 Reading Elem	62 Foreign/World Lang Elem	72 Summer School
5 Transportation	12 Title I	23 Music K-12	33 Career/Sch-to-Work Sec	43 Science Elem	53 Reading Sec	63 Foreign/World Lang Sec	73 Instructional Tech
6 Athletic	13 Title V	24 Music Elem	34 Early Childhood Ed	44 Science Sec	54 Remedial Reading K-12	64 Religious Education K-12	74 Inservice Training
7 Health Services	15 Asst Superintendent	25 Music Sec	35 Health/Phys Education	45 Math K-12	55 Remedial Reading Elem	65 Religious Education Elem	75 Marketing/Distributive
	16 Instructional Media Svcs	26 Business Education	36 Guidance Services K-12	46 Math Elem	56 Remedial Reading Sec	66 Religious Education Sec	76 Info Systems
	17 Chief Operations Officer	27 Career & Tech Ed	37 Guidance Services Elem	47 Math Sec	57 Bilingual/ELL	67 School Board President	77 Psychological Assess
	18 Chief Academic Officer	28 Technology Education	38 Guidance Services Sec	48 English/Lang Arts K-12	58 Special Education K-12	68 Teacher Personnel	78 Affirmative Action

New York School Directory

New York County

School	Grades		Enroll/Staff	Phone
Lyceum Kennedy Sch 225 E 43rd St Fl 4, New York 10017 Claude Bryant	PK-12	G	236 20	212/681-7929 Fax 212/681-1299
Manhattan Christian Academy 401 W 205th St, New York 10034 Manuela Katt	PK-8		279 17	212/567-5521 Fax 212/567-2815
Manhattan Country Sch 150 W 85th St, New York 10024 Mary Trowbridge \ Michelle Sole	PK-8	V	200 10	212/348-0952 Fax 212/348-1621 f t
Manhattan Day Sch 310 W 75th St, New York 10023 Steve Eisenberg	PK-8		500 35	212/376-6800 Fax 212/376-6389
Manhattan HS for Girls 154 E 70th St, New York 10021 Tsivia Yanofsky	9-12		200	212/737-6800 Fax 212/737-0766
Manhattan Star Academy 180 Amsterdam Ave, New York 10023 Rae Eisdorfer	Spec		68	646/795-3850
Marymount School-New York 1026 5th Ave, New York 10028 Katie Bergin \ Jennifer Grogan \ Sabra Hamilton	PK-12		730 30	212/744-4486 Fax 212/744-0163
Mesivta Tifereth Jerusalem 145 E Broadway, New York 10002 Stanley Bronfeld \ Rabbi Ginzberg	K-12		154 20	212/964-2830 Fax 212/349-5213
Metropolitan Montessori Sch 325 W 85th St, New York 10024 Magaly Gamarra	PK-6		195 9	212/579-5525 Fax 212/579-5526
Montessori School of New York 347 E 55th St, New York 10022 Donna Thomas	PK-8		100 3	212/223-4630 Fax 212/644-7051
New York Film Academy 17 Battery Pl Fl 5, New York 10004 David Kline	9-12		3,000	212/966-3488 Fax 212/344-4434
Nord Anglia Int'l Sch-New York 44 E 2nd St, New York 10003 Barrie Scrymgeour \ Matt Payne \ Katherine Clare	PK-12		120	212/600-2010
Northeastern Academy 532 W 215th St, New York 10034 Loris LaBorde	9-12		172 15	212/569-4800 Fax 212/569-6145
Northside Therapeutic ECC 1301 5th Ave, New York 10029 Carolina Laise-Chong	Spec		98 8	212/426-3400 Fax 212/410-7561
Parkside Sch 48 W 74th St, New York 10023 Albina Miller	K-5		85	212/721-8888 Fax 212/721-1547
Polis Mont Columbus Square ES 775 Columbus Ave, New York 10025 Rebecca Simkha	PK-K		11	917/388-1710
Polis Mont Museum Mile ES 12 E 79th St, New York 10075 Erika Somogyi	PK-5		9	917/388-1710
Professional Children's Sch 132 W 60th St, New York 10023 Dania Nauholnyk \ Loryn Evanoff	6-12		180	212/582-3116 Fax 212/956-3295 f t
Quad Preparatory Sch 25 Pine St 4th Fl, New York 10005 Dr Kristin Berman	Spec		50	646/649-3913
Rabbi Samson R Hirsch Yeshiva 8593 Bennett Ave, New York 10033 Yehuda Moller \ Henna Gottesman	PK-8	V	250	212/568-6200
Rabbi Schneier Park E Day Sch 164 E 68th St, New York 10065 Barbara Etra	PK-8		300 25	212/737-6900 Fax 212/639-1568
Ramaz Lower Sch 125 E 85th St, New York 10028 Ruth Gafni	PK-5		400	212/774-8010
Ramaz Sch 60 E 78th St, New York 10075 Sholomo Stochel	9-12	V	400	212/774-8070 Fax 212/774-8099
Rebecca Sch 40 E 30th St Lbby 1, New York 10016 Tina McCourt	Spec		100	212/810-4120 Fax 212/810-4121
Reece Sch 25 E 104th St, New York 10029 Duncan Lester	Spec		80 9	212/289-4872 Fax 212/423-9652
Robert Louis Stevenson Sch 24 W 74th St, New York 10023 Chris Ongaro	8-12		75 10	212/787-6400 Fax 212/873-1872
Rodeph Sholom Elem Sch 168 W 79th St, New York 10024 Colleen Dundon \ Eve Andrias	1-8		180	646/438-8540 Fax 212/362-8069
Rodeph Sholom Sch 10 W 84th St, New York 10024 Colleen Dundon	PK-K		685 70	646/438-8500 Fax 212/362-8069
Rudolf Steiner Lower Sch 15 E 79th St, New York 10075 Jeff Spade	PK-8		298 17	212/535-2130
Rudolf Steiner Upper Sch 15 E 78th St, New York 10075	7-12		83	212/879-1101 Fax 212/794-1554
Saint Albans Sch 317 E 50th St, New York 10022 Meghan Harrington	PK-8		85	212/755-0997
School at Columbia 556 W 110th St, New York 10025 Amani Reed	K-8		328	212/851-4215
School for Young Performers 222 Broadway Fl 21, New York 10038 Iris Evan	K-12		10	212/663-3921 Fax 212/226-7071
Smith Sch 131 W 86th St, New York 10024 Karen Smith	Spec		50 8	212/879-6354 Fax 212/879-0962
Solomon Schechter Sch- Mnhttn 805 Columbus Ave, New York 10025 Gary Pretsfelder	K-8		140	212/427-9500 Fax 212/427-5300
Speyer Sch 925 9th Ave, New York 10019 Larry Donovan	K-8		319	212/581-4000 Fax 866/603-2560
St Bernard's Sch 4 E 98th St, New York 10029 Stuart Johnson	K-9		380	212/289-2878 Fax 212/410-6628
St David's Sch 12 E 89th St, New York 10128 Kim Davidson \ Eric Chapman	PK-8		405 50	212/369-0058 Fax 212/369-5788
St Hilda & St Hugh Sch 619 W 114th St, New York 10025 Virginia Connor	PK-8		380 16	212/932-1980 Fax 212/749-7174
St Luke's Sch 487 Hudson St, New York 10014 Bart Baldwin	PK-8		215	212/924-5960 Fax 212/924-1352
St Thomas Choir Sch 202 W 58th St, New York 10019 Charles Wallace	3-8		36 9	212/247-3311 Fax 212/247-3393
Stephen Gaynor Sch 148 W 90th St, New York 10024 Dr Scott Gaynor	Spec		400 22	212/787-7070 Fax 212/787-3312
Studio Sch 117 W 95th St, New York 10025 Janet Rotter	PK-8		110 8	212/678-2416
The Browning Sch 52 E 62nd St, New York 10065 Laurie Gruhn \ Danielle Passno \ Gene Campbell	K-12		400	212/838-6280 Fax 212/355-5602 f t

79 Student Personnel
80 Driver Ed/Safety
81 Gifted/Talented
82 Video Services
83 Substance Abuse Prev
84 Erate
85 AIDS Education
88 Alternative/At Risk
89 Multi-Cultural Curriculum
90 Social Work
91 Safety/Security
92 Magnet School
93 Parental Involvement
95 Tech Prep Program
97 Chief Information Officer
98 Chief Technology Officer
270 Character Education
271 Migrant Education
273 Teacher Mentor
274 Before/After Sch
275 Response To Intervention
277 Remedial Math K-12
280 Literacy Coach
285 STEM
286 Digital Learning
288 Common Core Standards
294 Accountability
295 Network System
296 Title II Programs
297 Webmaster
298 Grant Writer/Ptnrships
750 Chief Innovation Officer
751 Chief of Staff
752 Social Emotional Learning

Other School Types
Ⓐ = Alternative School
Ⓒ = Charter School
Ⓜ = Magnet School
Ⓨ = Year-Round School

School Programs
A = Alternative Program
G = Adult Classes
M = Magnet Program
T = Title I Schoolwide
V = Career & Tech Ed Programs

Social Media
f = Facebook
t = Twitter

New Schools are shaded
New Superintendents and Principals are bold
Personnel with email addresses are underscored

Niagara County

School	Grade	Enr	Phone
The Buckley Sch 113 E 73rd St, New York 10021 Gregory O'Melia	K-9	361 28	212/452-2203
The Chapin Sch 100 E End Ave, New York 10028 Therese Cruite \ Michael Maloy	K-12	725	212/744-2335 Fax 212/535-8138
The Gateway Sch 211 W 61st St Fl 602, New York 10023 Christy Brockhausen \ Elian Seidel	Spec	143 9	212/777-5966
The King's Academy 2345 3rd Ave, New York 10035 S Streitferdt	PK-11	60 7	212/348-7380 Fax 212/348-0515
The Lang Sch 11 Broadway Ste 300, New York 10004 Micaela Bracamonte	Spec	55	212/977-7777
The Nightingale-Bamford Sch 20 E 92nd St, New York 10128 Dr Rebecca Urciuoli \ Andrea Kassar	K-12	500	212/289-5020 Fax 212/876-1045
The Spence Sch 22 E 91st St, New York 10128 Elizabeth Causey \ Karen Sullivan \ Eric Zahler	K-12	720 15	212/289-5940 Fax 212/996-5689
The Titus Sch 90 John St, New York 10038 Natalie Brandefine	Spec	41	646/756-4103
Town Sch 540 E 76th St, New York 10021 David Wood \ Carole Seeley	PK-8	400 35	212/288-4383 Fax 212/988-5846
Trevor Day School-East 312 E 95th St Frnt 2, New York 10128 Scott Reisinger	PK-12	785	212/426-3300 Fax 212/369-0705
Trevor Day School-West 1 W 88th St, New York 10024 Lisa Alberti \ Rebecca Damas \ Daniel Feigin	6-12	450	212/426-3360 Fax 212/873-8520
Trinity Sch 139 W 91st St, New York 10024 Kristin Crawford \ Jason Ford \ Stephen Kolman	PK-12 G	960	212/873-1650
United Nations Int'l Sch 2450 Fdr Dr, New York 10010 Chad Fairey \ Antoine Delaitre	K-12	1,500	212/684-7400 Fax 212/684-1382
Village Community Sch 272 W 10th St, New York 10014 Eve Kleger	K-8	350 25	212/691-5146 Fax 212/691-9767
West End Day Sch 255 W 71st St, New York 10023 Carrie Catapano	Spec	40	212/873-5708 Fax 212/873-2345
Windward Sch-Manhattan 212 E 93rd St, New York 10128 John Russell	Spec	205	212/222-8628 Fax 212/222-8547
Winston Preparatory Sch 126 W 17th St, New York 10011 William DeHaven	Spec	236 50	212/496-8400 Fax 646/638-2706
Yeshiva Ketana of Manhattan 346 W 89th St, New York 10024 Gidon Goldberg	PK-8	175 12	212/769-1790 Fax 212/874-5706
Yeshiva Univ High Sch for Boys 2540 Amsterdam Ave, New York 10033 Dr Seth Taylor	9-12	352 17	212/960-5337 Fax 212/960-0027
York Preparatory Sch 40 W 68th St, New York 10023 Heather Marshall	6-12	350 10	212/362-0400 Fax 212/362-7106

Market Data Retrieval

NIAGARA COUNTY

NIAGARA COUNTY SCHOOLS

County Schs..Principal	Grd	Prgm	Enr/#Cls	SN
Niagara Academy 3181 Saunders Settlement Rd, Sanborn 14132 Amanda Bennett	Spec	A	190 38	716/731-4176 Fax 585/798-1943
Niagara Educational Center 3181 Saunders Settlement Rd, Sanborn 14132 Leslie Tanner	Voc	AG	1,000 40	716/731-4176

NIAGARA PUBLIC SCHOOLS

• **Barker Central School Dist** PID: 00758960   716/795-3832
1628 Quaker Rd, Barker 14012   Fax 716/795-3394

Schools: 2 \ **Teachers:** 66 \ **Students:** 750 \ **Special Ed Students:** 120 \ **LEP Students:** 5 \ **College-Bound:** 83% \ **Ethnic:** Hispanic 9%, Caucasian 91% \ **Exp:** $167 (Low) \ **Poverty:** 13% \ **Title I:** $178,603 \ **Special Education:** $1,331,000 \ **Open-Close:** 09/08 - 06/24 \ **DTBP:** $420 (High)

Jacob Reimer 1,11		Carol Heiligenthaler 2,5	
Julie Fuerch 4*		Ryan Carberry 6,35*	
Sarah McKee 7*		Mariah Kramer 8,57,58,280,288,296,298	
Janet Morrow 16*		Michael Gendrue 36,88*	
Jeff Rogers 37*		Audra Lakeman 38	
Randall Atwater 67		James Luckman 73,76,286,295*	
Michael Carter 79,83,285*		Leann Briggs 81*	
Jeff Costello 82*			

Public Schs..Principal	Grd	Prgm	Enr/#Cls	SN
Barker Jr Sr High Sch 1628 Quaker Rd, Barker 14012 Michael Carter	7-12	AGTV	349	46% 716/795-3201 Fax 716/795-3911
Pratt Elem Sch 1628 Quaker Rd, Barker 14012 Michael Carter	PK-6	T	386 27	48% 716/795-3237 Fax 716/795-9330

• **Lewiston Porter Ctl Sch Dist** PID: 00758996   716/754-8281
4061 Creek Rd, Youngstown 14174   Fax 716/754-2755

Schools: 4 \ **Teachers:** 165 \ **Students:** 2,187 \ **Special Ed Students:** 401 \ **LEP Students:** 7 \ **College-Bound:** 85% \ **Ethnic:** Asian 2%, African American 1%, Hispanic 3%, Native American: 1%, Caucasian 93% \ **Exp:** $216 (Med) \ **Poverty:** 8% \ **Title I:** $279,493 \ **Special Education:** $3,825,000 \ **Open-Close:** 09/08 - 06/24 \ **DTBP:** $375 (High)

Paul Casseri 1   Patricia Grupka 2,5,15,68
Paul Feathers 3   Brad Halgash 6
Dr Heather Lyon ...8,16,73,79,83,273,288,294   Bradly Hagash 35*
Dr Barbara Godshall 57,58,77,88,271,298   Jodee Riordan 67

Public Schs..Principal	Grd	Prgm	Enr/#Cls	SN
Lewiston Porter High Sch 4061 Creek Rd, Youngstown 14174 Dr Whitney Vantine	9-12	V	666 50	20% 716/754-8281 Fax 716/286-7852

---

1 Superintendent	8 Curric/Instruct K-12	19 Chief Financial Officer	29 Family/Consumer Science	39 Social Studies K-12	49 English/Lang Arts Elem	59 Special Education Elem	69 Academic Assessment
2 Bus/Finance/Purchasing	9 Curric/Instruct Elem	20 Art K-12	30 Adult Education	40 Social Studies Elem	50 English/Lang Arts Sec	60 Special Education Sec	70 Research/Development
3 Buildings And Grounds	10 Curric/Instruct Sec	21 Art Elem	31 Career/Sch-to-Work K-12	41 Social Studies Sec	51 Reading K-12	61 Foreign/World Lang K-12	71 Public Information
4 Food Service	11 Federal Program	22 Art Sec	32 Career/Sch-to-Work Elem	42 Science K-12	52 Reading Elem	62 Foreign/World Lang Elem	72 Summer School
5 Transportation	12 Title I	23 Music K-12	33 Career/Sch-to-Work Sec	43 Science Elem	53 Reading Sec	63 Foreign/World Lang Sec	73 Instructional Tech
6 Athletic	13 Title V	24 Music Elem	34 Early Childhood Ed	44 Science Sec	54 Remedial Reading K-12	64 Religious Education K-12	74 Inservice Training
7 Health Services	14 Instructional Media Svcs	25 Music Sec	35 Health/Phys Education	45 Math K-12	55 Remedial Reading Elem	65 Religious Education Elem	75 Marketing/Distributive
	15 Asst Superintendent	26 Business Education	36 Guidance Services K-12	46 Math Elem	56 Remedial Reading Sec	66 Religious Education Sec	76 Info Systems
	17 Chief Operations Officer	27 Career & Tech Ed	37 Guidance Services Elem	47 Math Sec	57 Bilingual/ELL	67 School Board President	77 Psychological Assess
	18 Chief Academic Officer	28 Technology Education	38 Guidance Services Sec	48 English/Lang Arts K-12	58 Special Education K-12	68 Teacher Personnel	78 Affirmative Action

New York School Directory — Niagara County

Lewiston Porter Interm Ed Ctr 4061 Creek Rd, Youngstown 14174 Tina Rodriguez	3-5		420 23		716/754-8281 Fax 716/286-7854
Lewiston Porter Middle Sch 4061 Creek Rd, Youngstown 14174 Andrew Auer	6-8	G	458 42	25%	716/286-7201 Fax 716/286-7204
Lewiston Porter Primary Ed Ctr 4061 Creek Rd, Youngstown 14174 Tamara Larson	PK-2		450	27%	716/286-7220 Fax 716/286-7855

● **Lockport City School Dist** PID: 00759055 716/478-4811
130 Beattie Ave, Lockport 14094 Fax 716/478-4832

Schools: 9 \ **Teachers:** 369 \ **Students:** 5,100 \ **Special Ed Students:** 1,025 \ **LEP Students:** 59 \ **College-Bound:** 74% \ **Ethnic:** Asian 1%, African American 12%, Hispanic 10%, Native American: 1%, Caucasian 77% \ **Exp:** $204 (Med) \ **Poverty:** 19% \ **Title I:** $1,715,431 \ **Special Education:** $10,122,000 \ **Open-Close:** 09/02 - 06/25 \ **DTBP:** $317 (High)

Michelle Bradley 1		Deborah Coder 2,15,91	
Kevin Guay 3		Timothy Parker 3	
Thomas Heggarty 4		Todd Sukdolak 6,35,85	
Lisa Schroeder 7,15,68		Marianne Currie-Hall 8	
Rosanna Sandell 11,70,298		Dr Robert Lipuma 16,69,71,73,97,295	
Dawn Wylke 58*		Stacey Aliasso 58	
Karen Young 67		Sheila Murphy 79	
Russell Buckley 88*			

Public Schs..Principal	Grd	Prgm	Enr/#Cls	SN	
Anna Merritt Elem Sch 389 Green St, Lockport 14094 Patricia McMahon	K-4	T	313 21	71%	716/478-4725 Fax 716/478-4730
Charles A Upson Elem Sch 28 Harding Ave, Lockport 14094 Jennifer Gilson	K-4	T	458 26	57%	716/478-4400 Fax 716/439-6857
Emmet Belknap Intermediate Sch 491 High St, Lockport 14094 Paul Kowalski	5-6	T	704 50	61%	716/478-4550 Fax 716/478-4535
George Southard Elem Sch 6385 Locust Street Ext, Lockport 14094 Gary Wilson	K-4	T	402 27	51%	716/478-4770 Fax 716/478-4775
John Pound Early Childhood Ctr 51 High St, Lockport 14094 Sharon Peters	PK-PK		169 14		716/478-4751 Fax 716/478-4755
Lockport High Sch 250 Lincoln Ave, Lockport 14094 Dawn Wylke	9-12	T	1,339	49%	716/478-4450 Fax 716/478-4498
Ⓐ Lockport High School West 319 West Ave, Lockport 14094 Russell Buckley	9-12		95 12		716/478-4625 Fax 716/478-4634
North Park Junior High Sch 160 Passaic Ave, Lockport 14094 Bernadette Smith	7-8	T	675 50	57%	716/478-4700 Fax 716/478-4705 🅣
Roy Kelley Elem Sch 610 E High St, Lockport 14094 Heather Walton	K-4	T	434 20	49%	716/478-4670 Fax 716/478-4685 🅣

● **Newfane Central School Dist** PID: 00759172 716/778-6888
6048 Godfrey Rd, Burt 14028 Fax 716/778-6852

Schools: 4 \ **Teachers:** 120 \ **Students:** 1,511 \ **Special Ed Students:** 292 \ **College-Bound:** 79% \ **Ethnic:** African American 1%, Hispanic 3%, Caucasian 95% \ **Exp:** $220 (Med) \ **Poverty:** 11% \ **Title I:** $297,908 \ **Special Education:** $3,192,000 \ **Open-Close:** 09/03 - 06/25 \ **DTBP:** $143 (High)

Michael Baumann 1		Bart Schuler 2,5,11*	
George Noon 3		Joanne Huntington 4*	
Peter Young 8,12,69,73*		Christine Callahan 51	
Jennifer Bower 58,79*		James Schimitt 67	
Jeff Anstett 73			

Public Schs..Principal	Grd	Prgm	Enr/#Cls	SN	
Newfane Early Childhood Center 6048 Godfrey Rd, Burt 14028 Bart Schuler	PK-PK		33 9		716/778-6351 Fax 716/778-6868
Newfane Elem Sch 2909 Transit Rd, Newfane 14108 Holly Staley	K-4	T	436 18	51%	716/778-6376 Fax 716/778-6377
Newfane High Sch 1 Panther Dr, Newfane 14108 Daniel Bedette	9-12	AV	550 38	37%	716/778-6551 Fax 716/778-6578
Newfane Middle Sch 2700 Transit Rd, Newfane 14108 Mark Przybysz	5-8	T	391 45	48%	716/778-6452 Fax 716/778-6460

● **Niagara Falls City Sch Dist** PID: 00759249 716/286-4211
630 66th St, Niagara Falls 14304 Fax 716/286-4283

Schools: 12 \ **Teachers:** 425 \ **Students:** 7,100 \ **Special Ed Students:** 1,548 \ **LEP Students:** 116 \ **College-Bound:** 71% \ **Ethnic:** Asian 2%, African American 40%, Hispanic 9%, Native American: 3%, Caucasian 46% \ **Exp:** $155 (Low) \ **Poverty:** 33% \ **Title I:** $4,736,290 \ **Special Education:** $18,056,000 \ **Open-Close:** 09/04 - 06/22 \ **DTBP:** $223 (High)

Mark Laurrie 1,11		Joseph Giarrizzo 2	
Rebecca Holody 2		Kevin Edwards 4,79	
Annie Carr 5		Joseph Contento 6*	
Jo Silvaroli 7*		Richard Carella 8,74*	
Catherine Sullivan 34,48,275		Bryan Rotella 58	
Vincent Cancemi 67		Alicia Savino 68	
Maria Massaro 68		Marcia Capone 69,71,97,288	
Ray Granieri 76			

Public Schs..Principal	Grd	Prgm	Enr/#Cls	SN	
Cataract Elem Sch 6431 Girard Ave, Niagara Falls 14304 Jeff Showers	PK-6	T	498 26	74%	716/278-9120 Fax 716/278-9122
Community Education Center 6040 Lindbergh Ave, Niagara Falls 14304 Andrew Touma	Adult	A	1,300 10		716/286-0771 Fax 716/278-7933
Gaskill Preparatory Sch 910 Hyde Park Blvd, Niagara Falls 14301 Derek Zimmerman	7-8	TV	529 47	82%	716/278-5820 Fax 716/278-5829
Geraldine J Mann Elem Sch 1330 95th St, Niagara Falls 14304 Tina Smeal	PK-6	T	471 24	55%	716/278-7940 Fax 716/278-7946
Harry F Abate Elem Sch 1625 Lockport St, Niagara Falls 14305 Cynthia Jones	PK-6	T	707 35	82%	716/278-7960 Fax 716/278-7979
Ⓜ Henry J Kalfas Magnet Sch 1800 Beech Ave, Niagara Falls 14305 Italo Baldassarre	PK-6	T	427 20	85%	716/278-9180 Fax 716/278-9173

79	Student Personnel	91	Safety/Security	275	Response To Intervention	298	Grant Writer/Ptnrships
80	Driver Ed/Safety	92	Magnet School	277	Chief Innovation Officer	750	Chief Innovation Officer
81	Gifted/Talented	93	Parental Involvement	280	Literacy Coach	751	Chief of Staff
82	Video Services	95	Tech Prep Program	285	STEM	752	Social Emotional Learning
83	Substance Abuse Prev	97	Chief Information Officer	286	Digital Learning		
84	Erate	98	Chief Technology Officer	288	Common Core Standards		
85	AIDS Education	270	Accountability	294	Accountability		
88	Alternative/At Risk	271	Migrant Education	295	Network System		
89	Multi-Cultural Curriculum	273	Teacher Mentor	296	Title II Programs		
90	Social Work	274	Before/After Sch	297	Webmaster		

School Programs
A = Alternative Program
G = Adult Classes
M = Magnet Program
T = Title I Schoolwide
V = Career & Tech Ed Programs

Other School Types
Ⓐ = Alternative School
Ⓒ = Charter School
Ⓜ = Magnet School
Ⓨ = Year-Round School

Social Media
🅕 = Facebook
🅣 = Twitter

New Schools are shaded
New Superintendents and Principals are bold
Personnel with email addresses are underscored

Niagara County — Market Data Retrieval

School	Grd	Prgm	Enr/#Cls	SN	Phone
Hyde Park Elem Sch 1620 Hyde Park Blvd, Niagara Falls 14305 Mary Kerins	PK-6	T	493 24	85%	716/278-7980 Fax 716/278-7988
LaSalle Preparatory Sch 7436 Buffalo Ave, Niagara Falls 14304 James Spanbauer	7-8	T	511 75	75%	716/278-5880 Fax 716/278-5899
Maple Avenue Elem Sch 952 Maple Ave, Niagara Falls 14305 Maria Chille-Zafuto	PK-6	T	357 18	61%	716/278-9140 Fax 716/278-9156
Niagara Falls High Sch 4455 Porter Rd, Niagara Falls 14305 Cynthia Jones	9-12	AT	1,971 100	72%	716/278-5800 Fax 716/286-7964
Niagara Street Elem Sch 2513 Niagara St, Niagara Falls 14303 Rocco Merino	PK-6	T	629 32	84%	716/278-5860 Fax 716/278-5876
Seventy Ninth Street Elem Sch 551 79th St, Niagara Falls 14304 Diane Coty	PK-6	T	437 20	61%	716/278-7900 Fax 716/278-7901

● **Niagara-Wheatfield Ctl SD** PID: 00759483 716/215-3002 Fax 716/215-3039
6700 Schultz St, Niagara Falls 14304

Schools: 6 \ **Teachers:** 269 \ **Students:** 3,650 \ **Special Ed Students:** 598 \ **LEP Students:** 28 \ **College-Bound:** 79% \ **Ethnic:** Asian 2%, African American 3%, Hispanic 3%, Native American: 5%, Caucasian 86% \ **Exp:** $189 (Low) \ **Poverty:** 10% \ **Title I:** $620,337 \ **Special Education:** $5,654,000 \ **Open-Close:** 09/08 - 06/23 \ **DTBP:** $468 (High)

Daniel Ljiljanich 1
Cono Sammarco 3
Leslie Buczkowski 5
Matt McKenna 6,7*
Mary Jo Casilio 8,73,74
Elena Dzadur 57*
Jessica O'Hern 58
Patrick Phelan 68
John Steel 73
Allison Davis 2
Domenic Barile 4*
Margaret Messer 5
Jim Dailey 8,73
Mary Fortunato 30
Emily Sass 58
Steven Sabo 67
Andrea Tamarazio 73
Jeffery Hazel 76

Public Schs..Principal	Grd	Prgm	Enr/#Cls	SN	Phone
Colonial Village Elem Sch 1456 Saunders Settlement Rd, Niagara Falls 14305 Marissa Vuich	K-5	T	396 32	56%	716/215-3270 Fax 716/215-3290
Edward Town Middle Sch 2292 Saunders Settlement Rd, Sanborn 14132 Jordan Schmidt	6-8		840 70	37%	716/215-3150 Fax 716/215-3160
Errick Road Elem Sch 6839 Errick Rd, N Tonawanda 14120 Nora O'Bryan	K-5		459 36	22%	716/215-3240 Fax 716/215-3260
Niagara-Wheatfield High Sch 2292 Saunders Settlement Rd, Sanborn 14132 Michael Mann	9-12	GV	1,208 102	37%	716/215-3100 Fax 716/215-3125
Tuscarora Indian Sch 2015 Mount Hope Rd, Sanborn 14132 Elizabeth Corieri	PK-6		121 20		716/215-3670 Fax 716/297-5070
West Street Elem Sch 5700 West St, Sanborn 14132 Theron Mong	K-5	T	404 27	45%	716/215-3200 Fax 716/215-3216

● **North Tonawanda City Sch Dist** PID: 00759598 716/807-3655 Fax 716/807-3522
176 Walck Rd, N Tonawanda 14120

Schools: 6 \ **Teachers:** 244 \ **Students:** 3,400 \ **Special Ed Students:** 916 \ **LEP Students:** 48 \ **Ethnic:** Asian 1%, African American 2%, Hispanic 4%, Native American: 1%, Caucasian 92% \ **Exp:** $213 (Med) \ **Poverty:** 13% \ **Title I:** $832,077 \ **Special Education:** $9,206,000 \ **Open-Close:** 09/08 - 06/24 \ **DTBP:** $313 (High) \ facebook

Gregory Woytila 1
James Hart 3
Edward Strasser 5
Mike Tambroni 7,11,36,79,83,90,275
Jane DiVirgilio 28,73,76,295*
Elizabeth Bittar 60
Matthew Kennedy 67
Kristopher Clester 71,97
Anthony Montoro 2,15,91
Ben Glurich 4
Matthew Cook 6
Patrick Holesko 8
Michael Hiller 58
Robert Lucas 63*
Joann Johnston 68,288

Public Schs..Principal	Grd	Prgm	Enr/#Cls	SN	Phone
Drake Elem Sch 380 Drake Dr, N Tonawanda 14120 Janet Matyevich	K-3	T	261 18	45%	716/807-3725 Fax 716/807-3726
North Tonawanda High Sch 405 Meadow Dr, N Tonawanda 14120 James Fisher	9-12	GV	1,028	34%	716/807-3600 Fax 716/807-3639
North Tonawanda Interm Sch 1500 Vanderbilt Ave, N Tonawanda 14120 Katie Smith	4-6	AT	694 21	44%	716/807-3825 Fax 716/807-3835
North Tonawanda Middle Sch 455 Meadow Dr, N Tonawanda 14120 Gregory Burgess	7-8	AT	504	37%	716/807-3700 Fax 716/807-3701
Ohio Elem Sch 625 Ohio Ave, N Tonawanda 14120 John Steckstor	K-3		359 30	26%	716/807-3800 Fax 716/807-3801
Spruce Elem Sch 195 Spruce St, N Tonawanda 14120 Patricia Adler	K-3	T	338 21	53%	716/807-3850 Fax 716/807-3858

● **Royalton Hartland Central SD** PID: 00759720 716/735-2000 Fax 716/735-2036
54 State St, Middleport 14105

Schools: 3 \ **Teachers:** 104 \ **Students:** 1,271 \ **Special Ed Students:** 196 \ **LEP Students:** 6 \ **College-Bound:** 73% \ **Ethnic:** African American 1%, Hispanic 4%, Caucasian 95% \ **Exp:** $180 (Low) \ **Poverty:** 10% \ **Title I:** $223,594 \ **Special Education:** $2,175,000 \ **Open-Close:** 09/04 - 06/25 \ **DTBP:** $359 (High) \ facebook

Hank Stopinski 1
Kathy Polka 2
Julie Fuerch 4
John Grymala 6*
Douglas King 11,58,77,271
Chad Owen 67
Andy Lang 2
Tim Pietrowski 3
Susan Cheasty 5
Jill Heck 8,12,73,285,286,288,296,298
Penny Baize 16*
Danielle Alterio 91

Public Schs..Principal	Grd	Prgm	Enr/#Cls	SN	Phone
Royalton Hartland Elem Sch 4500 Orchard Pl, Gasport 14067 Donna Vanslyke	PK-4		500 25	40%	716/735-2000 Fax 716/735-2066
Royalton Hartland High Sch 54 State St, Middleport 14105 Gary Bell	9-12		396 40	33%	716/735-2000 Fax 716/735-2046
Royalton Hartland Middle Sch 78 State St, Middleport 14105 John Fisgus	5-8	T	375 40	44%	716/735-2000 Fax 716/735-2056

1	Superintendent	8	Curric/Instruct K-12	19	Chief Financial Officer	29	Family/Consumer Science	39	Social Studies K-12	49	English/Lang Arts Elem	59	Special Education Elem	69	Academic Assessment
2	Bus/Finance/Purchasing	9	Curric/Instruct Elem	20	Art K-12	30	Adult Education	40	Social Studies Elem	50	English/Lang Arts Sec	60	Special Education Sec	70	Research/Development
3	Buildings And Grounds	10	Curric/Instruct Sec	21	Art Elem	31	Career/Sch-to-Work K-12	41	Social Studies Sec	51	Reading K-12	61	Foreign/World Lang K-12	71	Public Information
4	Food Service	11	Federal Program	22	Art Sec	32	Career/Sch-to-Work Elem	42	Science K-12	52	Reading Elem	62	Foreign/World Lang Elem	72	Summer School
5	Transportation	12	Title I	23	Music K-12	33	Career/Sch-to-Work Sec	43	Science Elem	53	Reading Sec	63	Foreign/World Lang Sec	73	Instructional Tech
6	Athletic	13	Title V	24	Music Elem	34	Early Childhood Ed	44	Science Sec	54	Remedial Reading K-12	64	Religious Education K-12	74	Inservice Training
7	Health Services	15	Asst Superintendent	25	Music Sec	35	Health/Phys Education	45	Math K-12	55	Remedial Reading Elem	65	Religious Education Elem	75	Marketing/Distributive
		16	Instructional Media Svcs	26	Business Education	36	Guidance Services K-12	46	Math Elem	56	Remedial Reading Sec	66	Religious Education Sec	76	Info Systems
		17	Chief Operations Officer	27	Career & Tech Ed	37	Guidance Services Elem	47	Math Sec	57	Bilingual/ELL	67	School Board President	77	Psychological Assess
		18	Chief Academic Officer	28	Technology Education	38	Guidance Services Sec	48	English/Lang Arts K-12	58	Special Education K-12	68	Teacher Personnel	78	Affirmative Action

New York School Directory
Oneida County

- **Starpoint Central School Dist** PID: 00759768 716/210-2342
  4363 Mapleton Rd, Lockport 14094 Fax 716/210-2355

Schools: 4 \ Teachers: 216 \ Students: 2,931 \ Special Ed Students: 408 \ LEP Students: 28 \ Ethnic: Asian 1%, African American 1%, Hispanic 2%, Caucasian 96% \ Exp: $195 (Low) \ Poverty: 5% \ Title I: $219,504 \ Special Education: $3,726,000 \ Open-Close: 09/02 - 06/24 \ DTBP: $317 (High) \ f

Dr Sean Croft	1,11	John Andrews		2
Tracy Mullen	2	David Ciurczak		3,91
Shar DePriest	5	Vincent Dell'Oso		6,35
Maureen Braunscheidel	8,15,73	Brian Farrell	58,78,79,83,88,271,275	
Michael Zimmerman	67	Gretchen Cercone		68
Roberta Wyner	76	Joe Rozbicki		295

Public Schs..Principal	Grd	Prgm	Enr/#Cls	SN
Douglas J Regan Interm Sch 4363 Mapleton Rd, Lockport 14094 Monica Daigler	3-5		690 29	19% 716/210-2150 Fax 716/210-2158
Fricano Primary Sch 4363 Mapleton Rd, Lockport 14094 Denielle Toth	K-2		644 36	17% 716/210-2100 Fax 716/210-2112
Starpoint High Sch 4363 Mapleton Rd, Lockport 14094 Gil Licata	9-12		874 59	18% 716/210-2300 Fax 716/210-2334
Starpoint Middle Sch 4363 Mapleton Rd, Lockport 14094 Corey Gray	6-8		703 50	20% 716/210-2200 Fax 716/210-2233

- **Wilson Central School Dist** PID: 00759794 716/751-9341
  374 Lake St, Wilson 14172 Fax 716/751-6556

Schools: 2 \ Teachers: 97 \ Students: 1,060 \ Special Ed Students: 198 \ LEP Students: 10 \ College-Bound: 78% \ Ethnic: Hispanic 3%, Native American: 1%, Caucasian 96% \ Exp: $196 (Low) \ Poverty: 12% \ Title I: $222,231 \ Special Education: $2,427,000 \ Open-Close: 09/08 - 06/24 \ DTBP: $361 (High) \ f t

Timothy Carter	1,11	Carolyn Oliveri		2
Robert Clare	3	Todd Harmon		3
Susan Bell	4	Jeffrey Roth		6,57,69*
Amanda Schaus	12,58			

Public Schs..Principal	Grd	Prgm	Enr/#Cls	SN
Wilson Elem Sch 430 Young St, Wilson 14172 John Diodate	PK-5	T	466 33	48% 716/751-9341 Fax 716/751-6558
Wilson Middle High Sch 374 Lake St 380, Wilson 14172 Scott Benton \ Paul Galgovich	6-12	T	594 35	35% 716/751-9341 Fax 716/751-6777

NIAGARA CATHOLIC SCHOOLS

- **Diocese of Buffalo Ed Office** PID: 00725846
  Listing includes only schools located in this county. See District Index for location of Diocesan Offices.

Catholic Schs..Principal	Grd	Prgm	Enr/#Cls	SN
Catholic Acad of Niagara Falls 1055 N Military Rd, Niagara Falls 14304 Jeannine Fortunate	PK-8		200 16	716/283-1455 Fax 716/283-1355 f
DeSales Catholic Sch 6914 Chestnut Ridge Rd, Lockport 14094 Karen Rahill	PK-8		350	716/433-6422 Fax 716/434-4002
Sacred Heart Villa Sch 5269 Lewiston Rd, Lewiston 14092 Sr Elizabeth Domin	PK-5		40 8	716/285-9257
St Peter Roman Catholic Sch 140 N 6th St, Lewiston 14092 Maureen Ingham	PK-8		190 30	716/754-4470 Fax 716/754-0167 f
Stella Niagara Educ Park Sch 4421 Lower River Rd, Stela Niagara 14144 Sr Margaret Sullivan	PK-8		169 10	716/754-4314 Fax 716/754-2964

NIAGARA PRIVATE SCHOOLS

Private Schs..Principal	Grd	Prgm	Enr/#Cls	SN
Christian Acad-Western NY 789 Gilmore Ave, N Tonawanda 14120 Patricia Poeller	PK-12		140 16	716/433-1652
Empower Childen's Academy 9812 Lockport Rd, Niagara Falls 14304 Sherry Kaminski	Spec		138	716/297-1478 Fax 716/205-0044
Henrietta G Lewis Campus Sch 6395 Old Niagara Rd, Lockport 14094 Patricia McMahon	K-12		100 15	716/433-9592 Fax 716/433-3464
Holy Ghost Lutheran Sch 6630 Luther St, Niagara Falls 14304 Kevin Gundell	PK-8		140 11	716/731-3030 Fax 716/731-9449
St John Lutheran Sch 6950 Ward Rd, N Tonawanda 14120 Kaite Gundell	PK-8		175 10	716/693-9677 Fax 716/693-2686
St Paul Lutheran Pre-School 453 Old Falls Blvd, N Tonawanda 14120 Rebecca Orlowski	PK-PK		24 2	716/692-3255 Fax 716/692-3643
St Peter's Lutheran Sch 6168 Walmore Rd, Sanborn 14132 J Michelle Scibetta	PK-8		98 12	716/731-4422 Fax 716/731-1439

ONEIDA COUNTY

ONEIDA COUNTY SCHOOLS

County Schs..Principal	Grd	Prgm	Enr/#Cls	SN
BOCES Career & Tech Ed Center 4747 Middle Settlement Rd, New Hartford 13413 David Statton	Voc	AG	800 45	29% 315/793-8666 Fax 315/793-8540
Rossetti Education Center 4937 Spring Rd, Verona 13478 Erin Noto	Voc	AG	500 20	315/361-5700 Fax 315/361-5880

79 Student Personnel	91 Safety/Security	275 Response To Intervention	298 Grant Writer/Ptnrships	School Programs	Social Media	
80 Driver Ed/Safety	92 Magnet School	277 Remedial Math K-12	750 Chief Innovation Officer	A = Alternative Program	f = Facebook	
81 Gifted/Talented	93 Parental Involvement	280 Literacy Coach	751 Chief of Staff	G = Adult Classes		
82 Video Services	95 Tech Prep Program	285 STEM	752 Social Emotional Learning	M = Magnet Program	t = Twitter	
83 Substance Abuse Prev	97 Chief Information Officer	286 Digital Learning		T = Title I Schoolwide		
84 Erate	98 Chief Technology Officer	288 Common Core Standards	Other School Types	V = Career & Tech Ed Programs		
85 AIDS Education	270 Character Education	294 Accountability	A = Alternative School			
88 Alternative/At Risk	271 Migrant Education	295 Network System	C = Charter School	New Schools are shaded		
89 Multi-Cultural Curriculum	273 Teacher Mentor	296 Title II Programs	M = Magnet School	New Superintendents and Principals are bold		
90 Social Work	274 Before/After Sch	297 Webmaster	Y = Year-Round School	Personnel with email addresses are underscored		

NY—149

Oneida County

ONEIDA PUBLIC SCHOOLS

• **Adirondack Central Sch Dist** PID: 00759885   315/942-9200
110 Ford St, Boonville 13309   Fax 315/942-5522

Schools: 4 \ **Teachers:** 111 \ **Students:** 1,200 \ **Special Ed Students:** 181 \ **LEP Students:** 3 \ **College-Bound:** 62% \ **Ethnic:** Caucasian 99% \ **Exp:** $194 (Low) \ **Poverty:** 15% \ **Title I:** $359,061 \ **Special Education:** $2,456,000 \ **Open-Close:** 09/08 - 06/25 \ **DTBP:** $359 (High)

Ed Niznik 1
Brian Maneen 5
Nadine Medvit 32,36,69*
Michael Kramer 67
Heidi Smith 88,270,271*
Sharon Cihocki 2,296
Wendy Foye 12,60*
Kathy Grenier 33,38*
Jill Schafer 73*
Linda Guernsey 288

Public Schs..Principal	Grd	Prgm	Enr/#Cls	SN	
Adironack High Sch 8181 State Route 294, Boonville 13309 Heidi Smith	9-12	T	351 50	44%	315/942-9200 Fax 315/942-2900
Adirondack Middle Sch 8181 State Route 294, Boonville 13309 Mark Trabucco	6-8	T	286 37	49%	315/942-9200 Fax 315/943-2884
Boonville Elem Sch 110 Ford St, Boonville 13309 Wendy Keefus-Jones	PK-5	T	422 19	46%	315/942-9200 Fax 315/942-5783
West Leyden Elem Sch 1157 Fish Creek Rd, West Leyden 13489 Jill Schafer	PK-5	T	133 10	53%	315/942-9200 Fax 315/943-2864

• **Camden Central School Dist** PID: 00759940   315/245-2500
51 3rd St, Camden 13316   Fax 315/245-1622

Schools: 4 \ **Teachers:** 185 \ **Students:** 2,000 \ **Special Ed Students:** 326 \ **LEP Students:** 5 \ **Ethnic:** Hispanic 2%, Caucasian 97% \ **Exp:** $170 (Low) \ **Poverty:** 12% \ **Title I:** $493,851 \ **Special Education:** $4,948,000 \ **Open-Close:** 09/08 - 06/25 \ **DTBP:** $374 (High)

Dr Ravo Root 1
Randy Bajohr 3,91
Ed Snow 5
Robin Wolzmuth 7*
Craig Ferretti 11*
Matthew Donaleski 23*
Jamie Albrecht 67
Theresa Stowelthouse 83
Karen Jones 2
Tena Omans 4
Stephen Komanecky 6
Louise Rutherford 8,15
Karl Keil 15
Nicholas Pulizzi 58,79
Heather Wieland 73*

Public Schs..Principal	Grd	Prgm	Enr/#Cls	SN	
Camden Elem Sch 1 Oswego St, Camden 13316 Craig Ferretti	PK-4	T	515 29	49%	315/245-2616 Fax 315/245-4194
Camden High Sch 55 Oswego St, Camden 13316 Chris Centner	9-12		625 68	52%	315/245-3168 Fax 315/245-4173
Camden Middle Sch 32 Union St, Camden 13316 Brittany Dercola	5-8	T	660 54	57%	315/245-0080 Fax 315/245-4094
McConnellsville Elem Sch 8564 State Route 13, Blossvale 13308 Shannon Babbie	PK-4	T	265 14	45%	315/245-3412 Fax 315/245-4193

• **Clinton Central School Dist** PID: 00760030   315/557-2253
75 Chenango Ave, Clinton 13323   Fax 315/853-8727

Schools: 3 \ **Teachers:** 100 \ **Students:** 1,258 \ **Special Ed Students:** 161 \ **LEP Students:** 25 \ **College-Bound:** 91% \ **Ethnic:** Asian 2%, African American 2%, Hispanic 3%, Caucasian 93% \ **Exp:** $166 (Low) \ **Poverty:** 10% \ **Title I:** $208,597 \ **Special Education:** $2,014,000 \ **Open-Close:** 09/04 - 06/25 \ **DTBP:** $168 (High)

Dr Stephen Grimm 1
Bradley Preston 3,91
Cynthia Smiegal 7,83*
Ellen Leuthauser 9*
Jennifer Waligory-Lee 12,70,273*
Darcey Cross 35*
Denise Toia-Kramer 57*
Mary Lou Lauchert 67
Joseph Baretta 2,5,11,15,298
Doug Fiore 6*
Deb Van Slyke 8,31,69,286,288
Matthew Lee 10*
Karen Zaleski 16,73*
Jackie Snizek 36,88*
Kathleen Fonda 58
Jordan Ezman 295

Public Schs..Principal	Grd	Prgm	Enr/#Cls	SN	
Clinton Elem Sch 75 Chenango Ave, Clinton 13323 Ellen Leuthauser	K-5		567 27	32%	315/853-5574 Fax 315/557-2331
Clinton Middle Sch 75 Chenango Ave, Clinton 13323 Shaun Carney	6-8		287 38	26%	315/557-2260 Fax 315/557-2216
Clinton Senior High Sch 75 Chenango Ave, Clinton 13323 Matthew Lee	9-12	V	404 50	23%	315/853-5574 Fax 315/853-1424

• **Holland Patent Ctl School Dist** PID: 00760080   315/865-7200
9601 Main St, Holland Patnt 13354   Fax 315/865-4057

Schools: 4 \ **Teachers:** 110 \ **Students:** 1,316 \ **Special Ed Students:** 219 \ **LEP Students:** 4 \ **College-Bound:** 85% \ **Ethnic:** Hispanic 1%, Caucasian 99% \ **Exp:** $308 (High) \ **Poverty:** 12% \ **Title I:** $312,158 \ **Special Education:** $2,415,000 \ **Open-Close:** 09/04 - 06/25 \ **DTBP:** $369 (High)

Jason Evangelist 1
Francesca Zumpano 2
Clifford Casab 4*
Justin Barlow 6
Richard China 23*
Shawna Fox 58*
John Hurteau 73*
Eileen Bates 81*
Cheryl Venettozzi 2,15
Kenneth Smith 3
Christopher Roberts 5
Nancy Nowicki 8,11,15,16,69,296*
Mary Beth Piejko 31,271*
Lydia Berez-Kelly 67
Rebecca Pisani 74,273*

Public Schs..Principal	Grd	Prgm	Enr/#Cls	SN	
General Wm Floyd Elem Sch 8900 State Route 365, Stittville 13469 Kristin Casab	PK-2		273 23	40%	315/865-5721 Fax 315/865-7284
Holland Patent Elem Sch 7940 Elm St, Holland Patnt 13354 Sarah Vergis	3-5	T	289 17	51%	315/865-8151 Fax 315/865-7265
Holland Patent High Sch 8079 Thompson Rd, Holland Patnt 13354 Russell Stevener	9-12		436 50	37%	315/865-7200 Fax 315/865-8154
Holland Patent Middle Sch Route 365, Holland Patnt 13354 Lisa Gentile	6-8		318 40	39%	315/865-8152 Fax 315/865-8978

1	Superintendent	8	Curric/Instruct K-12	19	Chief Financial Officer	29	Family/Consumer Science	39	Social Studies K-12	49	English/Lang Arts Elem	59	Special Education Elem	69	Academic Assessment
2	Bus/Finance/Purchasing	9	Curric/Instruct Elem	20	Art K-12	30	Adult Education	40	Social Studies Elem	50	English/Lang Arts Sec	60	Special Education Sec	70	Research/Development
3	Buildings And Grounds	10	Curric/Instruct Sec	21	Art Elem	31	Career/Sch-to-Work K-12	41	Social Studies Sec	51	Reading K-12	61	Foreign/World Lang K-12	71	Public Information
4	Food Service	11	Federal Program	22	Art Sec	32	Career/Sch-to-Work Elem	42	Science K-12	52	Reading Elem	62	Foreign/World Lang Elem	72	Summer School
5	Transportation	12	Title I	23	Music K-12	33	Career/Sch-to-Work Sec	43	Science Elem	53	Reading Sec	63	Foreign/World Lang Sec	73	Instructional Tech
6	Athletic	13	Title V	24	Music Elem	34	Early Childhood Ed	44	Science Sec	54	Remedial Reading K-12	64	Religious Education K-12	74	Inservice Training
7	Health Services	15	Asst Superintendent	25	Music Sec	35	Health/Phys Education	45	Math K-12	55	Remedial Reading Elem	65	Religious Education Elem	75	Marketing/Distributive
		16	Instructional Media Svcs	26	Business Education	36	Guidance Services K-12	46	Math Elem	56	Remedial Reading Sec	66	Religious Education Sec	76	Info Systems
		17	Chief Operations Officer	27	Career & Tech Ed	37	Guidance Services Elem	47	Math Sec	57	Bilingual/ELL	67	School Board President	77	Psychological Assess
		18	Chief Academic Officer	28	Technology Education	38	Guidance Services Sec	48	English/Lang Arts K-12	58	Special Education K-12	68	Teacher Personnel	78	Affirmative Action

New York School Directory — Oneida County

- **New Hartford Central Sch Dist** PID: 00760145   315/624-1000
  33 Oxford Rd, New Hartford 13413   Fax 315/724-8940

Schools: 5 \ **Teachers:** 207 \ **Students:** 2,553 \ **Special Ed Students:** 336 \ **LEP Students:** 28 \ **College-Bound:** 89% \ **Ethnic:** Asian 6%, African American 1%, Hispanic 5%, Caucasian 88% \ **Exp:** $243 (Med) \ **Poverty:** 5% \ **Title I:** $193,620 \ **Special Education:** $3,102,000 \ **Open-Close:** 09/08 - 06/25 \ **DTBP:** $312 (High)

Robert Nole 1
Marc Elefante 3
Scott Gaffney 5
Jennifer Friedel 7,85*
Carrie Storm 16*
Pamela Smoulcey 58,69,77,79,90*
Cj Amarosa 73
Tina Klar 81*
Mary Mandel 2,15,68
Kate Dorr 4*
John Banek 6,35,91*
Allen Hyde 8,11,15,57,270,273,275,288
Sandy Halpin 30,74*
Pamela King 67
Mark Benson 80*

Public Schs..Principal	Grd	Prgm	Enr/#Cls	SN	
Hughes Elem Sch 340 Higby Rd, New Hartford 13413 Jason Stefanski	K-6		489 23	10%	315/738-9350 Fax 315/724-1899
Myles Elem Sch 100 Clinton Rd, New Hartford 13413 Judeanne Rockford	K-6		390 20	26%	315/738-9600 Fax 315/724-2653
New Hartford Sr High Sch 33 Oxford Rd, New Hartford 13413 Mark Benson	10-12	AGV	546 73	16%	315/624-1214 Fax 315/624-1209
Perry Junior High Sch 9499 Weston Rd, New Hartford 13413 Riccardo Ripa	7-9	GV	651 50	13%	315/738-9300 Fax 315/738-9349
Robert L Bradley Elem Sch 33 Oxford Rd, New Hartford 13413 Maureen Futscher	K-6		477 24	14%	315/624-1220 Fax 315/735-1873

- **New York Mills Union Free SD** PID: 00760212   315/768-8127
  1 Marauder Blvd, New York Mls 13417   Fax 315/768-3521

Schools: 1 \ **Teachers:** 49 \ **Students:** 550 \ **Special Ed Students:** 86 \ **LEP Students:** 4 \ **College-Bound:** 80% \ **Ethnic:** Asian 2%, African American 3%, Hispanic 3%, Caucasian 92% \ **Exp:** $258 (Med) \ **Poverty:** 11% \ **Title I:** $120,077 \ **Special Education:** $1,171,000 \ **Open-Close:** 09/02 - 06/25 \ **DTBP:** $159 (High)

Dr Joanne Shelmidine 1
Mark Santomassino 3
Mary Facci 10,58*
Debra Ellis 36,90*
Eric Sarner 73,295
Lisa Stamboly 2
Joe Palmer 6
Brent Dodge 11,35,296*
Jacquline Edwards 67
Donna Wegrzyn 85*

Public Schs..Principal	Grd	Prgm	Enr/#Cls	SN	
New York Mills Sch 1 Marauder Blvd, New York Mls 13417 Brent Dodge	K-12		550 40	40%	315/768-8124

- **Oriskany Ctl School Dist** PID: 00760248   315/768-2058
  1313 Utica St, Oriskany 13424   Fax 315/768-2057

Schools: 2 \ **Teachers:** 55 \ **Students:** 587 \ **Special Ed Students:** 80 \ **LEP Students:** 3 \ **College-Bound:** 90% \ **Ethnic:** Asian 1%, Hispanic 3%, Caucasian 95% \ **Exp:** $212 (Med) \ **Poverty:** 10% \ **Title I:** $127,328 \ **Special Education:** $1,047,000 \ **Open-Close:** 09/08 - 06/25 \ **DTBP:** $173 (High)

Timothy Gaffney 1
Mark Santomassino 3
Laurie Widman 2,11,298
Al Salisbury 5

Kevin Jones 6
Christopher Williams 31,36,69*
Michelle Anderson 67
Tonya Tamburino 16,82*
Melissa Lowell 58*

Public Schs..Principal	Grd	Prgm	Enr/#Cls	SN	
N A Walbran Elem Sch 8610 State Route 69, Oriskany 13424 Mark Ranieri	PK-6	T	313 16	41%	315/768-2149 Fax 315/768-2137
Oriskany Jr Sr High Sch 1312 Utica St, Oriskany 13424 Julie Thompson	7-12	A	280 40	32%	315/768-2063 Fax 315/768-2046

- **Remsen Central School Dist** PID: 00760298   315/205-4300
  9733 Main St, Remsen 13438   Fax 315/831-2172

Schools: 2 \ **Teachers:** 45 \ **Students:** 400 \ **Special Ed Students:** 60 \ **College-Bound:** 82% \ **Ethnic:** Hispanic 2%, Caucasian 98% \ **Exp:** $251 (Med) \ **Poverty:** 17% \ **Title I:** $158,561 \ **Special Education:** $1,171,000 \ **Open-Close:** 09/08 - 06/25 \ **DTBP:** $378 (High)

Timmothy Jenny 1,11
Adam Degrace 3,5
Dale Dening 6
Fay Harper 58,752*
Lucinda Roberts 2
Kevin Roberts 3,5
Anne Reilly 16*
Marylou Ellen 67

Public Schs..Principal	Grd	Prgm	Enr/#Cls	SN	
Remsen Elem Sch 9733 Main St, Remsen 13438 Gary Winghart	PK-6	T	231 13	61%	315/831-3797
Remsen Jr Sr High Sch 9733 Main St, Remsen 13438 Kristy McGrath	7-12	AT	192 40	56%	315/831-3851 Fax 315/831-4283

- **Rome City School Dist** PID: 00760327   315/338-6500
  409 Bell Rd S, Rome 13440   Fax 315/338-6526

Schools: 10 \ **Teachers:** 462 \ **Students:** 5,300 \ **Special Ed Students:** 1,067 \ **LEP Students:** 65 \ **Ethnic:** Asian 1%, African American 9%, Hispanic 8%, Caucasian 82% \ **Exp:** $164 (Low) \ **Poverty:** 20% \ **Title I:** $2,012,103 \ **Special Education:** $12,210,000 \ **Open-Close:** 09/04 - 06/25

Peter Blake 1
Alex Rodriguez 3
Christopher Whitmore 4*
Mike Stamboly 6,7,35,83,85
James DeAngelo 8,12,57,288
Zachary Snow 16*
Amanda Jones 36
Geoffery Morton 68,79
Patrick Sullivan 73,76,295
Wendy Ahles 76
David Driadel 2
Robert Mezza 3,15
Andrew Thompson 5
Christopher Brewer 8,15,296
Cathy Bragen 11,36,58,77,81,274
Andrea Falvo 20,23,45,285
Paul Fitzpatrick 67
Anneliese Carinci 73,76
Sue Keyser 73,76

Public Schs..Principal	Grd	Prgm	Enr/#Cls	SN	
Bellamy Elem Sch 7118 Brennon Ave, Rome 13440 Molly Mytych	K-6	T	491 25	84%	315/338-5260 Fax 315/334-7472
Gansevoort Elem Sch 758 W Liberty St, Rome 13440 Kathy Bragan	K-6	T	342 23	87%	315/334-5180 Fax 315/334-7352
John E Joy Elem Sch 8194 Bielby Rd, Rome 13440 Andria Lacey	K-6	T	353 14	58%	315/334-1260 Fax 315/334-7362
Louis V Denti Elem Sch 1001 Ruby St, Rome 13440 Sherry Lubey	K-6	T	526	67%	315/338-5360 Fax 315/334-7528

---

79 Student Personnel	91 Safety/Security	275 Response To Intervention	298 Grant Writer/Ptnrships	**School Programs**	**Social Media**
80 Driver Ed/Safety	92 Magnet School	277 Remedial Math K-12	750 Chief Innovation Officer	A = Alternative Program	
81 Gifted/Talented	93 Parental Involvement	280 Literacy Coach	751 Chief of Staff	G = Adult Classes	= Facebook
82 Video Services	95 Tech Prep Program	285 STEM	752 Social Emotional Learning	M = Magnet Program	
83 Substance Abuse Prev	97 Chief Information Officer	286 Digital Learning		T = Title I Schoolwide	= Twitter
84 Erate	98 Chief Technology Officer	288 Common Core Standards	**Other School Types**	V = Career & Tech Ed Programs	
85 AIDS Education	270 Character Education	294 Accountability	Ⓐ = Alternative School		
88 Alternative/At Risk	271 Migrant Education	295 Network System	Ⓒ = Charter School	New Schools are shaded	
89 Multi-Cultural Curriculum	273 Teacher Mentor	296 Title II Programs	Ⓜ = Magnet School	New Superintendents and Principals are bold	
90 Social Work	274 Before/After Sch	297 Webmaster	Ⓨ = Year-Round School	Personnel with email addresses are underscored	

Oneida County

Market Data Retrieval

Lyndon H Strough Middle Sch 801 Laurel St, Rome 13440 Tracy O'Rourke	7-8	TV	824 88	64%	315/338-5200 Fax 315/334-7465
Ridge Mills Elem Sch 7841 Rome Westernville Rd, Rome 13440 Michael Flagg	K-6		356 14	32%	315/334-1280 Fax 315/334-7382
Rome Early Childhood Center 409 Bell Rd S, Rome 13440 Nancy Kristl	PK-PK		122 8		315/334-1250 Fax 315/334-7371
Rome Free Academy 95 Dart Cir, Rome 13441 Brian LeBaron	9-12	TV	1,512	57%	315/334-7200 Fax 315/334-7236
Staley Elem Sch 620 E Bloomfield St, Rome 13440 Julie Kimmel-Gorman	K-6	T	596 100	84%	315/338-5300 Fax 315/338-5306
Stokes Elem Sch 9095 Turin Rd, Rome 13440 Karen Miller	K-6		320 12	38%	315/224-1220 Fax 315/334-7399

● **Sauquoit Valley Central SD** PID: 00760511 315/839-6311
2601 Oneida St, Sauquoit 13456 Fax 315/839-5352

Schools: 3 \ **Teachers:** 76 \ **Students:** 900 \ **Special Ed Students:** 168 \ **LEP Students:** 7 \ **Ethnic:** Asian 1%, African American 1%, Hispanic 2%, Caucasian 96% \ **Exp:** $152 (Low) \ **Poverty:** 13% \ **Title I:** $209,960 \ **Special Education:** $1,735,000 \ **Open-Close:** 09/08 - 06/25 \ **DTBP:** $366 (High)

Ronald Wheelock	1,83	Kimberly Hibbard	2,11
Steve Parker	3	Craig Manderville	5
Douglas Jones	6*	Michele Babbie	16*
Peter Scialdone	38*	Peter Scialbone	38
Tracy Facchini	58*	Dawn Miller	67
Keith Kempney	73*		

Public Schs..Principal	Grd	Prgm	Enr/#Cls	SN
Sauquoit Valley Elem Sch 2640 Sulphur Springs Rd, Sauquoit 13456 Mark Putnam	K-4	T	358 24	43% 315/839-6339 Fax 315/839-6366
Sauquoit Valley High Sch 2601 Oneida St, Sauquoit 13456 Zane Mahar	9-12		270 25	35% 315/839-6316 Fax 315/839-6397
Sauquoit Valley Middle Sch 2648 Sulphur Springs Rd, Sauquoit 13456 Peter Madden	5-8		314 30	43% 315/839-6371 Fax 315/839-6390

● **Utica City School Dist** PID: 00760614 315/792-2210
106 Memorial Pkwy, Utica 13501 Fax 315/792-2200

Schools: 13 \ **Teachers:** 680 \ **Students:** 10,000 \ **Special Ed Students:** 1,764 \ **LEP Students:** 1,721 \ **College-Bound:** 81% \ **Ethnic:** Asian 20%, African American 26%, Hispanic 21%, Caucasian 31% \ **Exp:** $301 (High) \ **Poverty:** 35% \ **Title I:** $8,338,071 \ **Special Education:** $17,588,000 \ **Open-Close:** 09/04 - 06/25 \ **DTBP:** $222 (High)

Bruce Karam	1	Michele Albanese	2,5
Michael Ferraro	3	Mary Kay Vandreason	4
Steven Falchi	8,288*	Michele Lagase	11,298*
Dr Angela Elefante	16,71,82	Alicia Mroz	34
Khinsoe Moe	57,79	Edward Simpson	58
Luis LaPolla	67	Joyce Tencza	68
Steven Davis	73,76,295	Nadia Caleo	74
Anne Lansing	91		

Public Schs..Principal	Grd	Prgm	Enr/#Cls	SN
Albany Elem Sch 1151 Albany St, Utica 13501 Tania Kalavazoff	K-6	T	584 24	79% 315/792-2150 Fax 315/792-2151
Columbus Elem Sch 934 Armory Dr, Utica 13501 Elizabeth Gerling	K-6	T	663	87% 315/792-2011 Fax 315/792-2014
Dr Martin Luther King Jr ES 211 Square St, Utica 13501 Kim Vanduren	K-6	T	350 14	94% 315/792-2175 Fax 315/368-6733
General Herkimer Elem Sch 420 Keyes Rd, Utica 13502 Michele Cotter	K-6	T	738 25	80% 315/792-2160 Fax 315/792-2034
Hugh R Jones Elem Sch 2630 Remington Rd, Utica 13501 Alaine Canestrari	K-6	T	470 38	67% 315/792-2171 Fax 315/792-2154
Jefferson Elem Sch 190 Booth St, Utica 13502 Vanessa Rejrat	K-6	T	567 30	76% 315/792-2163 Fax 315/732-5902
John F Hughes Elem Sch 24 Prospect St, Utica 13501 Mary Belden	K-6	T	429 24	83% 315/368-6620 Fax 315/792-2271
John F Kennedy Middle Sch 500 Deerfield Dr E, Utica 13502 James Van Wormer	7-8	TV	687 75	85% 315/792-2088 Fax 315/792-2084
Kernan Elem Sch 929 York St, Utica 13502 Denise DiSpirito	K-6	T	591 39	87% 315/792-2185 Fax 315/792-2187
Ⓜ Roscoe Conkling Magnet ES 1115 Mohawk St, Utica 13501 Heather Galinski	K-6	T	578	88% 315/368-6800 Fax 315/724-7242
Senator James H Donovan MS 1701 Noyes St, Utica 13502 Annmarie Palldino	7-8	AT	717 70	91% 315/368-6541 Fax 315/792-2077
Thomas R Proctor High Sch 1203 Hilton Ave, Utica 13501 Joshua Gifford	9-12	AGTV	2,691 76	78% 315/368-6400 Fax 315/223-4896
Watson-Williams Elem Sch 107 Elmwood Pl, Utica 13501 Cheryl Minor	K-6	T	672 35	89% 315/792-2167 Fax 315/792-1133

● **Vernon-Verona-Sherrill CSD** PID: 00760547 315/829-2520
5275 State Route 31, Verona 13478 Fax 315/829-4949

Schools: 5 \ **Teachers:** 153 \ **Students:** 1,900 \ **Special Ed Students:** 225 \ **LEP Students:** 4 \ **College-Bound:** 79% \ **Ethnic:** Hispanic 1%, Caucasian 98% \ **Exp:** $250 (Med) \ **Poverty:** 8% \ **Title I:** $258,094 \ **Special Education:** $3,464,000 \ **Open-Close:** 09/08 - 06/24 \ **DTBP:** $368 (High)

Martha Group	1,11	Mark Wixson	2,15,19,34,83,271,295
Ronald Gregory	3,91	Holly Ackerman	4
Mike Peck	5	Randy Thomas	6
Andy Brown	8,15,69	Laura Rouse	8,57
Sandra Whalen	11,76,97	Tina Laramie	16
Christopher LeBlanc	20	Linda Carter	23*
Karen Holton	27,31,36	Gary Oliver	35,85
Brad Myatt	39	Deb Kiskiel	42*
Scott Williams	45	Melanie Miller	48
Rebecca Trevisani	51,54	Patrick Goodman	58
Melissa Palmer	67	Erin Scheemaker	68,79
Sherri Froass	71	Jessica Casamento	77

Public Schs..Principal	Grd	Prgm	Enr/#Cls	SN
E A McAllister Elem Sch 217 Kinsley St, Sherrill 13461 Elisabeth Relyea	PK-6	A	328 21	29% 315/829-2520 Fax 315/361-4783

1	Superintendent	8	Curric/Instruct K-12	19	Chief Financial Officer	29	Family/Consumer Science	39	Social Studies K-12	49	English/Lang Arts Elem	59	Special Education Elem	69	Academic Assessment
2	Bus/Finance/Purchasing	9	Curric/Instruct Elem	20	Art K-12	30	Adult Education	40	Social Studies Elem	50	English/Lang Arts Sec	60	Special Education Sec	70	Research/Development
3	Buildings And Grounds	10	Curric/Instruct Sec	21	Art Elem	31	Career/Sch-to-Work K-12	41	Social Studies Sec	51	Reading K-12	61	Foreign/World Lang K-12	71	Public Information
4	Food Service	11	Federal Program	22	Art Sec	32	Career/Sch-to-Work Elem	42	Science K-12	52	Reading Elem	62	Foreign/World Lang Elem	72	Summer School
5	Transportation	12	Title I	23	Music K-12	33	Career/Sch-to-Work Sec	43	Science Elem	53	Reading Sec	63	Foreign/World Lang Sec	73	Instructional Tech
6	Athletic	13	Title V	24	Music Elem	34	Early Childhood Ed	44	Science Sec	54	Remedial Reading K-12	64	Religious Education K-12	74	Inservice Training
7	Health Services	15	Asst Superintendent	25	Music Sec	35	Health/Phys Education	45	Math K-12	55	Remedial Reading Elem	65	Religious Education Elem	75	Marketing/Distributive
		16	Instructional Media Svcs	26	Business Education	36	Guidance Services K-12	46	Math Elem	56	Remedial Reading Sec	66	Religious Education Sec	76	Info Systems
		17	Chief Operations Officer	27	Career & Tech Ed	37	Guidance Services Elem	47	Math Sec	57	Bilingual/ELL	67	School Board President	77	Psychological Assess
		18	Chief Academic Officer	28	Technology Education	38	Guidance Services Sec	48	English/Lang Arts K-12	58	Special Education K-12	68	Teacher Personnel	78	Affirmative Action

New York School Directory — Oneida County

John D George Elem Sch	PK-6	T	438	45%	315/829-7361
5647 E Main St, Verona 13478			35		Fax 315/361-5895
Gary Bissaillon					
Vernon Verona Sherrill Mid Sch	7-8	AT	303	44%	315/829-2520
5275 State Route 31, Verona 13478			50		
Carrie Hodkinson					
Vernon Verona Sherrill Sr HS	9-12	A	544	37%	315/829-2520
5275 State Route 31, Verona 13478			55		Fax 315/829-4465
Erin Sanchez					
W A Wettel Elem Sch	PK-6	T	269	46%	315/829-7300
4329 Peterboro St, Vernon 13476			20		Fax 315/829-4326
Vincent Pompo					

• **Waterville Central Sch Dist** PID: 00760846 315/841-3900
381 Madison St, Waterville 13480 Fax 315/841-3939

Schools: 2 \ **Teachers:** 68 \ **Students:** 742 \ **Special Ed Students:** 120 \ **LEP Students:** 4 \ **College-Bound:** 70% \ **Ethnic:** Asian 1%, Hispanic 1%, Caucasian 98% \ **Exp:** $179 (Low) \ **Poverty:** 11% \ **Title I:** $162,832 \ **Special Education:** $1,711,000 \ **Open-Close:** 09/04 - 06/25 \ **DTBP:** $340 (High)

Chuck Chafee 1
Maureen Ireland 4
Kimberly Mursch 6,35*
Theresa Stile 16,82*
Julie Tangorra 58*
Steven English 73*
Elizabeth Netzband 270*
Tracy Leone 2,3,11,298
Cynthia Snow 5
Maureen Gray 8*
Robert Gray 36,69,72,81,88*
Stephen Stanton 67
Lisa Corasanti 83*

Public Schs..Principal	Grd	Prgm	Enr/#Cls	SN	
Memorial Park Elem Sch	K-6	T	402		315/841-3700
145 E Bacon St, Waterville 13480			35		Fax 315/841-3718
Maureen Gray					
Waterville Jr Sr High Sch	7-12		340		315/841-3800
381 Madison St, Waterville 13480			40		Fax 315/841-3838
Nicholas Rauch					

• **Westmoreland Central Sch Dist** PID: 00760884 315/557-2600
5176 State Route 233, Westmoreland 13490 Fax 315/853-4602

Schools: 3 \ **Teachers:** 68 \ **Students:** 853 \ **Special Ed Students:** 118 \ **LEP Students:** 3 \ **College-Bound:** 84% \ **Ethnic:** Asian 1%, African American 2%, Hispanic 2%, Caucasian 96% \ **Exp:** $125 (Low) \ **Poverty:** 6% \ **Title I:** $134,028 \ **Special Education:** $1,368,000 \ **Open-Close:** 09/04 - 06/25 \ **DTBP:** $363 (High)

Rocco Migliori 1
Maryann Hawkins 2
Tom Pfisterer 4
Michael Adey 6
Kevin Healy 8,79
Keith Kulpa 36
John Acee 67
David Hoffman 77
Mark Kennedy 2
Randy Rundle 3
Mike Sweeney 5
Joanne Shelmidine 8,12,79
Joshua Saxton 10*
Mary Anne O'Connell 58*
Matt Cieri 73,76,295*

Public Schs..Principal	Grd	Prgm	Enr/#Cls	SN	
Westmoreland Jr Sr High Sch	7-12	T	426	27%	315/557-2616
5176 State Route 233, Westmoreland 13490			34		
Joshua Saxton					
Westmoreland Primary Sch	K-2		180	23%	315/557-2637
5176 State Route 233, Westmoreland 13490			20		Fax 315/853-6597
Mary Anne O'Connell					
Westmoreland Upper Elem Sch	3-6	T	247	28%	315/557-2618
5176 State Route 233, Westmoreland 13490			30		Fax 315/557-2670
David Langone					

• **Whitesboro Ctl School Dist** PID: 00760913 315/266-3303
65 Oriskany Blvd Ste 1, Whitesboro 13492 Fax 315/768-9730

Schools: 7 \ **Teachers:** 241 \ **Students:** 3,135 \ **Special Ed Students:** 563 \ **LEP Students:** 38 \ **College-Bound:** 84% \ **Ethnic:** Asian 1%, African American 1%, Hispanic 4%, Caucasian 94% \ **Exp:** $204 (Med) \ **Poverty:** 8% \ **Title I:** $426,055 \ **Special Education:** $5,468,000 \ **Open-Close:** 09/04 - 06/25 \ **DTBP:** $323 (High)

Brian Bellair 1
Kevin Storsberg 3
Andrew Kirk 5
David Russo 8,15,16,74,273,288,294
Christopher Oneil 12,38
Sean Ryan 42*
Tina Pawloski 57,58
Adam Cleveland 73,76,295*
Kimberly Powers 2
Angela Aguiar 4
Michael Deuel 6,35*
Joseph Mueller 11,15,91,296,298
Jessica Decker 23
Lisa Alexander 45*
Mike Head 67
Garrett Quayle 295

Public Schs..Principal	Grd	Prgm	Enr/#Cls	SN	
Deerfield Elem Sch	K-5		332	36%	315/266-3410
115 Schoolhouse Rd, Deerfield 13502			30		Fax 315/797-7145
Kelli McGowan					
Harts Hill Elem Sch	K-5		354	19%	315/266-3430
8651 Clark Mills Rd, Whitesboro 13492			24		Fax 315/768-9855
Lisa Putnam					
Marcy Elem Sch	K-5		318	31%	315/266-3420
9479 Maynard Dr, Marcy 13403			21		Fax 315/735-3358
Kim Newton					
Parkway Middle Sch	6-6		252	31%	315/266-3175
65 Oriskany Blvd, Whitesboro 13492			20		Fax 315/768-9882
John Egresits					
Westmoreland Road Elem Sch	K-5	T	390	50%	315/266-3440
8596 Westmoreland Rd, Whitesboro 13492			23		Fax 315/768-9789
David Russo					
Whitesboro Middle Sch	7-8		512	35%	315/266-3100
75 Oriskany Blvd, Whitesboro 13492			63		Fax 315/768-9770
John Egresits					
Whitesboro Senior High Sch	9-12	V	985	30%	315/266-3200
6000 State Route 291, Marcy 13403					Fax 315/266-3223
Jeffrey Kuhn					

ONEIDA CATHOLIC SCHOOLS

• **Diocese of Syracuse Ed Office** PID: 00762765
Listing includes only schools located in this county. See District Index for location of Diocesan Offices.

Catholic Schs..Principal	Grd	Prgm	Enr/#Cls	SN	
Notre Dame Elem Sch	PK-6		350		315/732-4374
11 Barton Ave, Utica 13502			17		Fax 315/738-9720
Mary Rossi					
Notre Dame Jr Sr High Sch	7-12	V	322		315/724-5118
2 Notre Dame Ln, Utica 13502			29		Fax 315/724-9460
Roy Kane					
Rome Catholic Sch	PK-6		100		315/336-6190
800 Cypress St, Rome 13440			17		Fax 315/336-6194
Nancy Wilson					

---

79 Student Personnel	91 Safety/Security	275 Response To Intervention	298 Grant Writer/Ptnrships	**School Programs**	**Social Media**
80 Driver Ed/Safety	92 Magnet School	277 Remedial Math K-12	750 Chief Innovation Officer	A = Alternative Program	= Facebook
81 Gifted/Talented	93 Parental Involvement	280 Literacy Coach	751 Chief of Staff	G = Adult Classes	
82 Video Services	95 Tech Prep Program	285 STEM	752 Social Emotional Learning	M = Magnet Program	= Twitter
83 Substance Abuse Prev	97 Chief Infomation Officer	286 Digital Learning		T = Title I Schoolwide	
84 Erate	98 Chief Technology Officer	288 Common Core Standards	**Other School Types**	V = Career & Tech Ed Programs	
85 AIDS Education	270 Accountability	294 Accountability	Ⓐ = Alternative School		
88 Alternative/At Risk	271 Migrant Education	295 Network System	Ⓒ = Charter School	New Schools are shaded	
89 Multi-Cultural Curriculum	273 Teacher Mentor	296 Title II Programs	Ⓜ = Magnet School	New Superintendents and Principals are bold	
90 Social Work	274 Before/After Sch	297 Webmaster	Ⓨ = Year-Round School	Personnel with email addresses are underscored	

Onondaga County

Market Data Retrieval

ONEIDA PRIVATE SCHOOLS

Private Schs..Principal	Grd	Prgm	Enr/#Cls	SN	
Faith Christian Sch 9535 Route 20, Bridgewater 13313 Betty Decker	K-12		18 3		315/822-5233
Tilton Sch 1550 Champlin Ave, Utica 13502 Shannon Perri	2-12		114 20		315/235-7670 Fax 315/236-7769
United Cerebral Palsy Sch 1601 Armory Dr Bldg A, Utica 13501 Leny Giardino	Spec		60		315/798-4006 Fax 315/798-4004

ONEIDA REGIONAL CENTERS

● **Madison-Oneida BOCES** PID: 00761058   315/361-5500
4937 Spring Rd, Verona 13478   Fax 315/361-5595

Jacklin Starks 1	Lisa Decker 2
Scott Budelmann 3,4,5,15,16,68	Todd Vandresser 3
Patricia Vacca 8,15	Susan LeBlanc 16
Kathryn Allen 27,31	Kathleen Rinaldo 30
Colleen Wuest 34	James Weaver 58,88
Suzanne Carvelli 67	Ed Rinaldo 74

● **Oneida-Herkimer-Mad BOCES** PID: 00761046   315/793-8500
4747 Middle Settlement Rd, New Hartford 13413   Fax 315/793-8541

Jacklin Starks 1	Charles Cowen 2,3,5,7,15,68,91
Jack Boak 3,17	Tom Pfisterer 4
Christopher Hill 8,27,30,31,58,72,88,271	Scott Morris 16,295
Elaine Falvo 67	Katie Florian 68
Ann Turner 74	

ONONDAGA COUNTY

ONONDAGA COUNTY SCHOOLS

County Schs..Principal	Grd	Prgm	Enr/#Cls	SN	
ⓐ Bridges Alt Junior High Sch 6400 Schepps Corners Rd, Kirkville 13082 Karen Clark	8-9		60		315/656-6807 Fax 315/656-6809
Lee G Peters Career Center 4500 Crown Rd, Liverpool 13090 Robert Leslie	Adult	AV	500		315/453-4455 Fax 315/451-4676
OCM BOCES-Henry Campus 6820 Thompson Rd, Syracuse 13211 Peter Hunn	Voc	AG	800 18	47%	315/433-2635 Fax 315/431-8445

ONONDAGA PUBLIC SCHOOLS

● **Baldwinsville Central Sch Dist** PID: 00761072   315/638-6043
29 E Oneida St, Baldwinsville 13027   Fax 315/638-6041

> **Schools:** 8 \ **Teachers:** 405 \ **Students:** 5,500 \ **Special Ed Students:** 973 \ **LEP Students:** 27 \ **Ethnic:** Asian 1%, African American 2%, Hispanic 4%, Caucasian 92% \ **Exp:** $176 (Low) \ **Poverty:** 8% \ **Title I:** $702,140 \ **Special Education:** $9,039,000 \ **Open-Close:** 09/09 - 06/25 \ **DTBP:** $313 (High) \

Mathew McDonald 1	James Rodems 2,15,19
Timothy Lynch 2	Richard Foederer 3
Brian Wright 4	Dana Nelson 5
Christopher Campolieta 6,35,85*	Julie Carpenter 7
Joseph DeBarbieri 8,11,36,74,273,288,296	Tony Cardamone 9
Renee Burnett 10,280,285	Richard Delisle 16,73,76,295*
Rocco Nalli 34,57,58,69,77,90,271	Karrie Lamacchia 58,752
Joan Reeves 67	David Kilcourse 68,79
Sean Dunlap 91*	Daniel Nahorney 298

Public Schs..Principal	Grd	Prgm	Enr/#Cls	SN	
Catherine M McNamara Elem Sch 7344 Obrien Rd, Baldwinsville 13027 Jennifer Homeyar	K-5		522 24	25%	315/638-6130 Fax 315/638-5049
Charles W Baker High Sch 29 E Oneida St, Baldwinsville 13027 Kristen Denton	10-12	V	1,257	24%	315/638-6000 Fax 315/635-4575
Donald S Ray Middle Sch 7650 Van Buren Rd, Baldwinsville 13027 Christina Morgan	6-7		888 80	31%	315/638-6106 Fax 315/638-6157
Harry E Elden Elem Sch 29 E Oneida St, Baldwinsville 13027 Thomas Coughlin	K-5		459 19	36%	315/638-6118 Fax 315/638-6171
L Pearl Palmer Elem Sch 7864 Hicks Rd, Baldwinsville 13027 Alex Ewing	K-5		464 22	14%	315/638-6127 Fax 315/638-6275
Mae E Reynolds Elem Sch 222 Deerwood Dr, Baldwinsville 13027 Melissa Chiodo	K-5		448 19	35%	315/638-6124 Fax 315/638-6169
Theodore R Durgee Jr High Sch 29 E Oneida St, Baldwinsville 13027 Thomas Fraher	8-9		832 100	25%	315/638-6086 Fax 315/638-6168
Van Buren Elem Sch 20 Ford St, Baldwinsville 13027 Cynthia Cronin	K-5		519 19	27%	315/638-6121 Fax 315/638-6170

● **East Syracuse Minoa Ctl SD** PID: 00761278   315/434-3000
407 Fremont Rd, East Syracuse 13057   Fax 315/434-3020

> **Schools:** 7 \ **Teachers:** 307 \ **Students:** 3,600 \ **Special Ed Students:** 651 \ **LEP Students:** 94 \ **College-Bound:** 77% \ **Ethnic:** Asian 3%, African American 6%, Hispanic 3%, Native American: 1%, Caucasian 88% \ **Exp:** $258 (Med) \ **Poverty:** 13% \ **Title I:** $572,619 \ **Special Education:** $6,949,000 \ **Open-Close:** 09/04 - 06/25 \ **DTBP:** $216 (High) \

Dr Donna Desiato 1	Katherine Skahen 2
John Young 3,91	Todd Henry 5
Mike Clonan 6*	Pamela Buddendeck 7,34*
Michele Gipe 8	Shane Hacker 8,12,57,69,88,288
Thomas Neveldine 15	Dennis Vasylevskyy 16,295*
Adam Shatraw 23*	Kathleen Colucci 58*
Deb Kolod 67	Rebecca Streib 68,294
Marcia Kelley 71	Kieran O'Connor 73,286,298
Cheryl West 83,275,752	

1 Superintendent	8 Curric/Instruct K-12	19 Chief Financial Officer	29 Family/Consumer Science	39 Social Studies K-12	49 English/Lang Arts Elem	59 Special Education Elem	69 Academic Assessment
2 Bus/Finance/Purchasing	9 Curric/Instruct Elem	20 Art K-12	30 Adult Education	40 Social Studies Elem	50 English/Lang Arts Sec	60 Special Education Sec	70 Research/Development
3 Buildings And Grounds	10 Curric/Instruct Sec	21 Art Elem	31 Career/Sch-to-Work K-12	41 Social Studies Sec	51 Reading K-12	61 Foreign/World Lang K-12	71 Public Information
4 Food Service	11 Federal Program	22 Art Sec	32 Career/Sch-to-Work Elem	42 Science K-12	52 Reading Elem	62 Foreign/World Lang Elem	72 Summer School
5 Transportation	12 Title I	23 Music K-12	33 Career/Sch-to-Work Sec	43 Science Elem	53 Reading Sec	63 Foreign/World Lang Sec	73 Instructional Tech
6 Athletic	13 Title V	24 Music Elem	34 Early Childhood Ed	44 Science Sec	54 Remedial Reading K-12	64 Religious Education K-12	74 Inservice Training
7 Health Services	15 Asst Superintendent	25 Music Sec	35 Health/Phys Education	45 Math K-12	55 Remedial Reading Elem	65 Religious Education Elem	75 Marketing/Distributive
	16 Instructional Media Svcs	26 Business Education	36 Guidance Services K-12	46 Math Elem	56 Remedial Reading Sec	66 Religious Education Sec	76 Info Systems
	17 Chief Operations Officer	27 Career & Tech Ed	37 Guidance Services Elem	47 Math Sec	57 Bilingual/ELL	67 School Board President	77 Psychological Assess
	18 Chief Academic Officer	28 Technology Education	38 Guidance Services Sec	48 English/Lang Arts K-12	58 Special Education K-12	68 Teacher Personnel	78 Affirmative Action

New York School Directory — Onondaga County

Public Schs..Principal	Grd	Prgm	Enr/#Cls	SN	
East Syracuse Elem Sch 230 Kinne St, East Syracuse 13057 Ronald Perry	K-5	T	338 31	64%	315/434-3850 Fax 315/434-3855
East Syracuse Minoa Central HS 6400 Fremont Rd, East Syracuse 13057 Grenardo Avellino	9-12	GV	1,054 60	42%	315/434-3300 Fax 315/434-3335
Fremont Elem Sch 115 W Richmond Rd, East Syracuse 13057 Kelsey DeLany	K-5		338 18	24%	315/434-3480 Fax 315/434-3490
Minoa Elem Sch 501 N Main St, Minoa 13116 Gary Gerst	K-5		371 18	41%	315/434-3420 Fax 315/434-3430
Park Hill Pre-School 303 Roby Ave Ste 1, East Syracuse 13057 Pamela Buddendeck	PK-PK		274 10	29%	315/434-3800 Fax 315/434-3820
Pine Grove Middle Sch 101 Spartan Way, East Syracuse 13057 Doug Mohorter	6-8	T	767 60	42%	315/434-3050 Fax 315/434-3070
Woodland Elem Sch 100 Spartan Way, East Syracuse 13057 Gina Terzini	K-5	T	269 19	48%	315/434-3440 Fax 315/434-3450

● **Fabius Pompey Central SD** PID: 00761371 315/683-5301
1211 Mill St, Fabius 13063 Fax 315/683-5827

Schools: 2 \ **Teachers:** 70 \ **Students:** 611 \ **Special Ed Students:** 74 \ **LEP Students:** 4 \ **College-Bound:** 90% \ **Ethnic:** Asian 1%, African American 1%, Hispanic 2%, Caucasian 96% \ **Exp:** $281 (Med) \ **Poverty:** 15% \ **Title I:** $198,115 \ **Special Education:** $1,082,000 \ **Open-Close:** 09/09 - 06/25 \ **DTBP:** $390 (High)

Timothy Ryan ....1 Peter Mahunik 2,5,11,91
Richard Clancy ....3 Marian Carr 4*
Timothy Wilcox ....6 Patty Feeney 7*
Chantal Corbin ....9,34,58,73,270* Kevin Linck 10,27,57*
Heather Turner ....16,82* Jessica Barnum 36
Jenny Centore ....51,54* Donald Neugebauer 67
Hannah Magej ....77 Cristina Knapp 79
Matthew Heyn 83,85,88*

Public Schs..Principal	Grd	Prgm	Enr/#Cls	SN	
Fabius-Pompey Elem Sch 7800 Main St, Fabius 13063 Chantal Corbin	K-5		278 20	35%	315/683-5857 Fax 315/683-5680
Fabius-Pompey Middle High Sch 1211 Mill St, Fabius 13063 Kevin Linck	6-12	V	333 12	31%	315/683-5811 Fax 315/683-5569

● **Fayetteville-Manlius Ctl SD** PID: 00761773 315/692-1234
8199 E Seneca Tpke, Manlius 13104 Fax 315/692-1227

Schools: 6 \ **Teachers:** 329 \ **Students:** 4,259 \ **Special Ed Students:** 455 \ **LEP Students:** 49 \ **College-Bound:** 94% \ **Ethnic:** Asian 10%, African American 3%, Hispanic 4%, Caucasian 83% \ **Exp:** $224 (Med) \ **Poverty:** 4% \ **Title I:** $183,434 \ **Special Education:** $3,781,000 \ **Open-Close:** 09/08 - 06/24 \ **DTBP:** $317 (High)

Dr Craig Tice ....1 Lynn Frye 2
William Furlong ....2,5,7,15,31,83,85,88 Russ McCarty 3,91
Adam Jerosz ....4* John Cunningham 5
Scott Sugar ....6* Mary Coughlin 8,15,27,54,69,277,288,294
Jeffrey Gordon ....11,15,68 Lisa Dinneen ...11,15,16,57,58,79,275
Heidi Green ....36* Marissa Mims 67
Tracey Noble ....68 Laurel Chiesa 73
Josh Becker 295

Public Schs..Principal	Grd	Prgm	Enr/#Cls	SN	
Eagle Hill Middle Sch 4645 Enders Rd, Manlius 13104 Maureen McCrystal	5-8		670 40	9%	315/692-1400 Fax 315/692-1046
Enders Road Elem Sch 4725 Enders Rd, Manlius 13104 Deborah Capri	K-4		592 28	9%	315/692-1500 Fax 315/692-1053
Fayetteville Elem Sch 704 S Manlius St, Fayetteville 13066 Eileen Lux	K-4		492 40	17%	315/692-1600 Fax 315/692-1055
Fayetteville-Manlius High Sch 8201 E Seneca Tpke, Manlius 13104 Raymond Kilmer	9-12		1,370 100	12%	315/692-1900 Fax 315/692-1028
Mott Road Elem Sch 7173 Mott Rd, Fayetteville 13066 Jonna Johnson	K-4		408 18	15%	315/692-1700 Fax 315/692-1054
Wellwood Middle Sch 700 S Manlius St, Fayetteville 13066 Melissa Corbin	5-8		671 30	16%	315/692-1300 Fax 315/692-1049

● **Jamesville-DeWitt Central SD** PID: 00761412 315/445-8304
6845 Edinger Dr, Fayetteville 13066 Fax 315/445-8477

Schools: 5 \ **Teachers:** 217 \ **Students:** 2,694 \ **Special Ed Students:** 360 \ **LEP Students:** 53 \ **College-Bound:** 94% \ **Ethnic:** Asian 10%, African American 8%, Hispanic 4%, Caucasian 79% \ **Exp:** $166 (Low) \ **Poverty:** 11% \ **Title I:** $488,090 \ **Special Education:** $3,122,000 \ **Open-Close:** 09/04 - 06/25 \ **DTBP:** $124 (High)

Peter Smith ....1,11,83 Timothy Decker 2,5
Jason Crawford ....3,91 Frances Zaryski 4
John Goodson ....6,7,35 Peter Reyes 8
Tracey Menapace ....58,79 Susan Petrosillo 67
Phillip Luckette ....73,95,295 Tim Ristau 79

Public Schs..Principal	Grd	Prgm	Enr/#Cls	SN	
Jamesville Elem Sch 6409 E Seneca Tpke, Jamesville 13078 Marcy Baker	K-4		346 16	26%	315/445-8460 Fax 315/445-8444
Jamesville-DeWitt High Sch 6845 Edinger Dr, Fayetteville 13066 Paul Gasparini	9-12	A	950	19%	315/445-8340 Fax 315/445-8307
Jamesville-DeWitt Middle Sch 6280 Randall Rd, Jamesville 13078 Thomas Eldridge	5-8		845 45	24%	315/445-8360 Fax 315/445-8421
Moses DeWitt Elem Sch 201 Jamesville Rd, De Witt 13214 Mary Sylvester	K-4		260 15	35%	315/445-8370 Fax 315/445-2274
Tecumseh Elem Sch 901 Nottingham Rd, Jamesville 13078 Jill Zerrillo	K-4		293 16	21%	315/445-8320 Fax 315/445-9872

● **Jordan Elbridge Ctl Sch Dist** PID: 00761486 315/689-8500
9 N Chappell St, Jordan 13080 Fax 315/689-0084

Schools: 3 \ **Teachers:** 106 \ **Students:** 1,300 \ **Special Ed Students:** 193 \ **LEP Students:** 10 \ **College-Bound:** 86% \ **Ethnic:** Asian 1%, African American 1%, Hispanic 2%, Caucasian 96% \ **Exp:** $360 (High) \ **Poverty:** 13% \ **Title I:** $312,123 \ **Special Education:** $2,011,000 \ **Open-Close:** 09/08 - 06/24 \ **DTBP:** $377 (High)

James Froio ....1 Roxeanne Miller 2
Vincent Smith ....3 William Vita 4
Diane Miano ....5 Dan Stadtmiller 6,35
Janice Schue ....8,11,15,31,57,69,273,288 Jamie Susino 38*
Colleen Frawley ....58 Karen Guerrette 67

---

79 Student Personnel	91 Safety/Security	275 Response To Intervention	298 Grant Writer/Ptnrshps	**School Programs**	**Social Media**
80 Driver Ed/Safety	92 Magnet School	277 Remedial Math K-12	750 Chief Innovation Officer	A = Alternative Program	= Facebook
81 Gifted/Talented	93 Parental Involvement	280 Literacy Coach	751 Chief of Staff	G = Adult Classes	
82 Video Services	95 Tech Prep Program	285 STEM	752 Social Emotional Learning	M = Magnet Program	= Twitter
83 Substance Abuse Prev	97 Chief Information Officer	286 Digital Learning		T = Title I Schoolwide	
84 Erate	98 Chief Technology Officer	288 Common Core Standards	**Other School Types**	V = Career & Tech Ed Programs	
85 AIDS Education	270 Character Education	294 Accountability	Ⓐ = Alternative School		
88 Alternative/At Risk	271 Migrant Education	295 Network System	Ⓒ = Charter School	New Schools are shaded	
89 Multi-Cultural Curriculum	273 Teacher Mentor	296 Title II Programs	Ⓜ = Magnet School	New Superintendents and Principals are bold	
90 Social Work	274 Before/After Sch	297 Webmaster	Ⓨ = Year-Round School	Personnel with email addresses are underscored	

Onondaga County　　　　　　　　　　　　　　　　　　　　　　　Market Data Retrieval

Steve Mendrek 73,295*
Josh Montgomery 295

Kerry Brogan 83,85*

Public Schs..Principal	Grd	Prgm	Enr/#Cls	SN	
Elbridge Elem Sch 130 E Main St, Elbridge 13060 Rj Hartwell	PK-5	T	400 21	36%	315/689-8540 Fax 315/689-3320
Jordan-Elbridge High Sch 5721 Hamilton Rd, Jordan 13080 Mark Schermerhorn	9-12	GV	381 48	26%	315/689-8510 Fax 315/689-1985
Jordan-Elbridge Middle Sch 9 N Chappell St, Jordan 13080 David Shafer	6-8		499 16	32%	315/689-8520 Fax 315/689-6524

• **La Fayette Central School Dist** PID: 00761527　　　315/677-9728
　5955 US Route 20, La Fayette 13084　　　　　　　　　Fax 315/677-3372

Schools: 4 \ **Teachers:** 101 \ **Students:** 825 \ **Special Ed Students:** 144 \ **College-Bound:** 90% \ **Ethnic:** African American 1%, Hispanic 1%, Native American: 34%, Caucasian 64% \ **Exp:** $367 (High) \ **Poverty:** 12% \ **Title I:** $111,797 \ **Special Education:** $1,411,000 \ **Open-Close:** 09/08 - 06/23 \ **DTBP:** $359 (High)

Jeremie Belfield 1
Ron Cooper 3,5
Jeremiah Kelly 6*
Bill O'Leary 36*
Karen Ocque 58,79*
Sean Zehner 73
Patricia Sandusky 295

Cindy Daley 2
Robert Kennedy 4*
Jennifer Blossey 11*
Rebecca McKenney 36
Stephanie Dow 67
Beverly Oliver 274*

Public Schs..Principal	Grd	Prgm	Enr/#Cls	SN	
C Grant Grimshaw Sch 5957 US Route 20, La Fayette 13084 Jennifer Blossey	PK-6	T	349 23	42%	315/677-3152 Fax 315/677-3154
La Fayette Jr Sr High Sch 3122 US Route 11, La Fayette 13084 Jason Ryan	7-12	V	342 35	43%	315/677-3131 Fax 315/677-3132
Lafayette Big Picture Sch 3122 US Route 11, La Fayette 13084 Susan Osborn	9-12		70		315/504-1000 Fax 315/504-1004
Onondaga Nation Sch Route 11A, Nedrow 13120 John Gizzi	PK-8	TV	130 8	81%	315/469-6991 Fax 315/469-0994

• **Liverpool Ctl School Dist** PID: 00761577　　　315/622-7900
　195 Blackberry Rd, Liverpool 13090

Schools: 14 \ **Teachers:** 551 \ **Students:** 7,000 \ **Special Ed Students:** 1,468 \ **LEP Students:** 156 \ **College-Bound:** 80% \ **Ethnic:** Asian 6%, African American 10%, Hispanic 6%, Native American: 1%, Caucasian 77% \ **Exp:** $207 (Med) \ **Poverty:** 10% \ **Title I:** $1,117,315 \ **Special Education:** $14,252,000 \ **Open-Close:** 09/10 - 06/24 \ **DTBP:** $305 (High) \ f

Dr Mark Potter 1
Darrell Clisson 3
Laura Darcangelis 5
Ari Liberman 6,35
Kasey Dolson 8,69
Jennifer Dibianco 11,79,88
Timothy Manning 15,68
Amy DiVita 58,275
Jennifer Fragola 60*
Karen Humphrey 68,294
Daniel Farscai 73,76
Ronald Richardson 295*

Matthew Enigk 2
Annette Marchbanks 4
Ari Lieberman 6,7,35,83*
Amanda Caldwell 8,288
Richard Chapman 9,57,285
Daniel Henner 15
David Perry 20,25*
Teresa Bowers 59
Craig Dailey 67
Meghan Piper 71
Michael McCarthy 91*

Public Schs..Principal	Grd	Prgm	Enr/#Cls	SN	
Chestnut Hill Elem Sch 200 Saslon Park Dr, Liverpool 13088 Todd Bourcy	K-6	T	384 26	56%	315/453-0242 Fax 315/453-0283
Chestnut Hill Middle Sch 204 Saslon Park Dr, Liverpool 13088 David Hunter	7-8	T	357 32	57%	315/453-0245 Fax 315/453-0278 t
Donlin Drive Elem Sch 299 Donlin Dr, Liverpool 13088 Heather Silvia	K-6	T	447 23	43%	315/453-0249 Fax 315/453-0253
Elmcrest Elem Sch 350 Woodspath Rd, Liverpool 13090 Daphne Valentine	K-6		406 24	30%	315/453-1252 Fax 315/453-1258
Liverpool Elem Sch 910 2nd St, Liverpool 13088 Jessica Ancona	K-6	T	277 16	48%	315/453-0254 Fax 315/453-0286
Liverpool High Sch 4338 Wetzel Rd, Liverpool 13090 Douglas Lawrence	10-12		1,643	36%	315/453-1500 Fax 315/453-1246
Liverpool HS 9th Grade Annex 4340 Wetzel Rd, Liverpool 13090 Judy Campolieta	9-9		540 40		315/453-1275 Fax 315/453-1247
Liverpool Middle Sch 720 7th St, Liverpool 13088 Joseph Mussi	7-8		342 35	43%	315/453-0258 Fax 315/453-0248
Long Branch Elem Sch 4035 Long Branch Rd, Liverpool 13090 Robert McCrone	K-6	T	369 22	49%	315/453-0261 Fax 315/453-0269
Morgan Road Elem Sch 7795 Morgan Rd, Liverpool 13090 Brett Woodcock	K-6		487 21	38%	315/453-1268 Fax 315/453-1287
Nate Perry Elem Sch 7053 Buckley Rd, Liverpool 13088 Dana Ziegler	K-6	T	456 20	47%	315/453-0272 Fax 315/453-0275
Soule Road Elem Sch 8338 Soule Rd, Liverpool 13090 Robert Briggs	K-6		360 21	30%	315/453-1280 Fax 315/453-1260
Soule Road Middle Sch 8340 Soule Rd, Liverpool 13090 Kathleen Beckwith	7-8		429 45	37%	315/453-1283 Fax 315/453-1286
Willow Field Elem Sch 3900 State Route 31, Liverpool 13090 Susan Lohret	K-6		440 24	35%	315/453-1196 Fax 315/453-1255

• **Lyncourt Union Free Sch Dist** PID: 00761759　　　315/455-7571
　2709 Court St, Syracuse 13208　　　　　　　　　　　Fax 315/455-7573

Schools: 1 \ **Teachers:** 37 \ **Students:** 450 \ **Special Ed Students:** 83 \ **LEP Students:** 47 \ **Ethnic:** Asian 18%, African American 16%, Hispanic 9%, Native American: 1%, Caucasian 56% \ **Exp:** $151 (Low) \ **Poverty:** 22% \ **Title I:** $195,487 \ **Special Education:** $751,000 \ **Open-Close:** 09/09 - 06/25 \ **DTBP:** $215 (High)

James Austin 1
Madelynn Wisnowski 2
Katie Mahoney 12,59*
Lawrence Salamino 67
Amy Rotundo 76

Cathryn Marchese 2,5,11
Chris Rehm 6
Diane Sheffield 52,55*
Matthew Dean 73

Public Schs..Principal	Grd	Prgm	Enr/#Cls	SN	
Lyncourt Union Free Sch 2709 Court St, Syracuse 13208 Kimberly Davis	PK-8	T	450 18	60%	315/455-7571

1	Superintendent	8	Curric/Instruct K-12	19	Chief Financial Officer	29	Family/Consumer Science	39	Social Studies K-12
2	Bus/Finance/Purchasing	9	Curric/Instruct Elem	20	Art K-12	30	Adult Education	40	Social Studies Elem
3	Buildings And Grounds	10	Curric/Instruct Sec	21	Art Elem	31	Career/Sch-to-Work K-12	41	Social Studies Sec
4	Food Service	11	Federal Program	22	Art Sec	32	Career/Sch-to-Work Elem	42	Science K-12
5	Transportation	12	Title I	23	Music K-12	33	Career/Sch-to-Work Sec	43	Science Elem
6	Athletic	13	Title V	24	Music Elem	34	Early Childhood Ed	44	Science Sec
7	Health Services	14	Asst Superintendent	25	Music Sec	35	Health/Phys Education	45	Math K-12
		15	Instructional Media Svcs	26	Business Education	36	Guidance Services K-12	46	Math Elem
		16	Chief Operations Officer	27	Career & Tech Ed	37	Guidance Services Elem	47	Math Sec
		17	Chief Academic Officer	28	Technology Education	38	Guidance Services Sec	48	English/Lang Arts K-12

49	English/Lang Arts Elem	59	Special Education Elem	69	Academic Assessment		
50	English/Lang Arts Sec	60	Special Education Sec	70	Research/Development		
51	Reading K-12	61	Foreign/World Lang K-12	71	Public Information		
52	Reading Elem	62	Foreign/World Lang Elem	72	Summer School		
53	Reading Sec	63	Foreign/World Lang Sec	73	Instructional Tech		
54	Remedial Reading K-12	64	Religious Education K-12	74	Inservice Training		
55	Remedial Reading Elem	65	Religious Education Elem	75	Marketing/Distributive		
56	Remedial Reading Sec	66	Religious Education Sec	76	Info Systems		
57	Bilingual/ELL	67	School Board President	77	Psychological Assess		
58	Special Education K-12	68	Teacher Personnel	78	Affirmative Action		

New York School Directory — Onondaga County

- **Marcellus Central School Dist** PID: 00761864   315/673-6000
  2 Reed Pkwy, Marcellus 13108   Fax 315/673-6034

Schools: 3 \ **Teachers:** 141 \ **Students:** 1,507 \ **Special Ed Students:** 225 \ **LEP Students:** 8 \ **College-Bound:** 84% \ **Ethnic:** Asian 2%, African American 1%, Hispanic 1%, Caucasian 96% \ **Exp:** $213 (Med) \ **Poverty:** 7% \ **Title I:** $175,876 \ **Special Education:** $2,148,000 \ **Open-Close:** 09/03 - 06/25

Michelle Brantaer 1,11	Anthony Sonnacchio 2
Larry Allen 3	Donna Rice 4
Susan Stearns 5	Michael Free 6,35*
Jean Sharlow 8,15,69,76	Willard Bryant 35
Kara Lux 58,298	Michael McAuliff 67
Eric Hubbard 70,285	Elena Drescher 73,286*

Public Schs..Principal	Grd	Prgm	Enr/#Cls	SN	
C S Driver Middle Sch 2 Reed Pkwy, Marcellus 13108 Janet O'Mara	4-8		568 55	18%	315/673-6200 Fax 315/673-6202
K C Heffernan Elem Sch 2 Learners Ldg, Marcellus 13108 Robert Montgomery	K-3		398 26	20%	315/673-6100 Fax 315/673-0227
Marcellus Senior High Sch 1 Mustang Hl, Marcellus 13108 John Durkee	9-12		541 20	15%	315/673-6300 Fax 315/673-6327

- **North Syracuse Ctl Sch Dist** PID: 00761917   315/218-2100
  5355 W Taft Rd, N Syracuse 13212   Fax 315/218-2185

Schools: 11 \ **Teachers:** 641 \ **Students:** 8,400 \ **Special Ed Students:** 1,572 \ **LEP Students:** 126 \ **Ethnic:** Asian 3%, African American 5%, Hispanic 5%, Native American: 1%, Caucasian 87% \ **Exp:** $257 (Med) \ **Poverty:** 11% \ **Title I:** $1,621,884 \ **Special Education:** $11,559,000 \ **Open-Close:** 09/08 - 06/24 \ **DTBP:** $354 (High) \ facebook

Daniel Bowles 1	Don Keegan 2,3,5,17,19,73,91,98
Jon Ward 3	Wendy Swift 4*
Matthew Conti 5	Tim Bednarski 6,35,85*
Alicia Pizzuto 8,45,277	Christopher Leahey 8,18,34,51,54,57,271,274
Greg Stone 9,37	Jason Nephew 15,68,78,273
John Rice 16,20,28,29,31,42,73,285	Donna Norton 23,39,61,69,76,88,294*
Lisa Goldberg 36,93,270,752	Lisa Garofalo 58
Valerie Diflorio 58,77,79,90,275	Paul Farfaglia 67
Laurie Cook 71,97	Sally Meyers 286,297

Public Schs..Principal	Grd	Prgm	Enr/#Cls	SN	
Allen Road Elem Sch 803 Allen Rd, N Syracuse 13212 David Lunden	K-4	T	406 20	42%	315/218-2300 Fax 315/218-2385
Cicero Elem Sch 5979 State Route 31, Cicero 13039 Kathleen Wheeler	K-4		575 32	26%	315/218-2500 Fax 315/218-2585
Cicero-N Syracuse High Sch 6002 State Route 31, Cicero 13039 William LaClair	10-12		1,890	33%	315/218-4100 Fax 315/218-4185
Gillette Road Middle Sch 6150 S Bay Rd, Cicero 13039 David Cordone	5-7		1,131 80	29%	315/218-3000 Fax 315/218-3085
Karl Saile Bear Rd Elem Sch 5590 Bear Rd, N Syracuse 13212 John Cole	K-4		575 32	39%	315/218-2400 Fax 315/218-2485
Lakeshore Road Elem Sch 7180 Lakeshore Rd, Cicero 13039 Tina Chmielewski	K-4		480 37	31%	315/218-2600 Fax 315/218-2685
Main Street Sch 205 S Main St, N Syracuse 13212 Dawn Hussein	PK-PK		215 10	26%	315/218-2200 Fax 315/218-2285
North Syracuse Jr High Sch 5353 W Taft Rd, N Syracuse 13212 Constance Turose	8-9		1,322	38%	315/218-3600 Fax 315/218-3685
Roxboro Road Elem Sch 200 Bernard St, Syracuse 13211 Matthew Motala	K-4	T	480 30	71%	315/218-2700 Fax 315/218-2785
Roxboro Road Middle Sch 300 Bernard St, Syracuse 13211 David Shaw	5-7	T	799 55	56%	315/218-3300 Fax 315/218-3385
Smith Road Elem Sch 5959 Smith Rd, N Syracuse 13212 Lyndsey Maloney	K-4	T	518 28	46%	315/218-2800 Fax 315/218-2885

- **Onondaga Central School Dist** PID: 00762052   315/552-5000
  4466 S Onondaga Rd, Nedrow 13120   Fax 315/492-4650

Schools: 3 \ **Teachers:** 81 \ **Students:** 830 \ **Special Ed Students:** 147 \ **LEP Students:** 17 \ **College-Bound:** 92% \ **Ethnic:** Asian 1%, African American 12%, Hispanic 5%, Native American: 4%, Caucasian 78% \ **Exp:** $391 (High) \ **Poverty:** 15% \ **Title I:** $241,045 \ **Special Education:** $1,544,000 \ **Open-Close:** 09/04 - 06/25 \ **DTBP:** $378 (High) \ twitter

Robin Price 1,83	Jennifer Woody 2,3,5,11,296
Patricia Jones 2	Jason Czarny 6
Warren Smith 8,11,57,69,271	Ellen Pristash 16*
Chris Ciereck 38*	Jackie Elias 58*
Maggie Mahoney 67	

Public Schs..Principal	Grd	Prgm	Enr/#Cls	SN	
Onondaga Jr Sr High Sch 4479 S Onondaga Rd, Nedrow 13120 Tim Mumford	7-12		388 40	46%	315/552-5020 Fax 315/552-5027
Rockwell Elem Sch 208 Rockwell Rd, Nedrow 13120 Margaret Hart	PK-2	T	227 12	46%	315/552-5070 Fax 315/469-7732
Wheeler Sch 4543 S Onondaga Rd, Nedrow 13120 Warren Smith	3-6	T	215 14	53%	315/552-5050 Fax 315/552-5054

- **Skaneateles Central Sch Dist** PID: 00762090   315/685-8361
  45 E Elizabeth St, Skaneateles 13152   Fax 315/685-0347

Schools: 4 \ **Teachers:** 124 \ **Students:** 1,200 \ **Special Ed Students:** 121 \ **LEP Students:** 3 \ **College-Bound:** 93% \ **Ethnic:** Asian 2%, Hispanic 2%, Caucasian 96% \ **Exp:** $360 (High) \ **Poverty:** 6% \ **Title I:** $130,884 \ **Special Education:** $908,000 \ **Open-Close:** 09/02 - 06/25 \ **DTBP:** $168 (High)

Eric Knuth 1	Christine Demass 2,15
Ron Moore 3	Emily Cullen 4*
Cherrie Mitchell 5	Deann Sears 6
Stephen Musso 6,7,35*	Brian Cohen 8,27,44,47,285,288*
Francine Grannell 8,48	Jennifer Whipple 8,12,58
Tammy Dudden 16,82*	Mary Ingram 38*
Thomas Lambdin 67	Dr Paul Blair 70,73,286,295*
Gregory Santoro 72*	Brian Hart 77*
Greg Ramsey 295	

Public Schs..Principal	Grd	Prgm	Enr/#Cls	SN	
Belle H Waterman Elem Sch 55 East St, Skaneateles 13152 Pat Brown	K-2	T	230 15	8%	315/291-2351 Fax 315/291-2302

79 Student Personnel	91 Safety/Security	275 Response To Intervention	298 Grant Writer/Ptnrships	**School Programs**	**Social Media**
80 Driver Ed/Safety	92 Magnet School	277 Remedial Math K-12	750 Chief Innovation Officer	A = Alternative Program	= Facebook
81 Gifted/Talented	93 Parental Involvement	280 Literacy Coach	751 Chief of Staff	G = Adult Classes	
82 Video Services	95 Tech Prep Program	285 STEM	752 Social Emotional Learning	M = Magnet Program	= Twitter
83 Substance Abuse Prev	97 Chief Infomation Officer	286 Digital Learning		T = Title I Schoolwide	
84 Erate	98 Chief Technology Officer	288 Common Core Standards	**Other School Types**	V = Career & Tech Ed Programs	
85 AIDS Education	270 Character Education	294 Accountability	Ⓐ = Alternative School		
88 Alternative/At Risk	271 Migrant Education	295 Network System	Ⓒ = Charter School	New Schools are shaded	
89 Multi-Cultural Curriculum	273 Teacher Mentor	296 Title II Programs	Ⓜ = Magnet School	New Superintendents and Principals are bold	
90 Social Work	274 Before/After Sch	297 Webmaster	Ⓨ = Year-Round School	Personnel with email addresses are underscored	

NY—157

Onondaga County

Market Data Retrieval

Skaneateles Middle Sch 35 East St, Skaneateles 13152 Michael Caraccio	6-8		309 20	11%	315/291-2241 Fax 315/291-2267
Skaneateles Senior High Sch 49 E Elizabeth St, Skaneateles 13152 Gregory Santoro	9-12	GV	463 50	10%	315/291-2231 Fax 315/291-2250
State Street Intermediate Sch 72 State St, Skaneateles 13152 John Lawrence	3-5		280 18	14%	315/291-2261 Fax 315/291-2256

- **Solvay Union Free Sch Dist** PID: 00762143 315/468-1111
  299 Bury Dr, Syracuse 13209 Fax 315/468-2755

Schools: 3 \ **Teachers:** 129 \ **Students:** 1,500 \ **Special Ed Students:** 232 \ **LEP Students:** 55 \ **College-Bound:** 83% \ **Ethnic:** Asian 1%, African American 9%, Hispanic 10%, Native American: 1%, Caucasian 80% \ **Exp:** $238 (Med) \ **Poverty:** 19% \ **Title I:** $431,165 \ **Special Education:** $2,693,000 \ **Open-Close:** 09/04 - 06/25 \ **DTBP:** $165 (High)

Jay Tinklepaugh 1		Karen Henry 2,7	
Kevin Vanbeveren 3,91*		Pamela Kinne 4	
Bobbie Jo Eastman 5		John Dippold 6*	
Jessica Hehl 8,11,15,288,296,298		William Guercio 31,36*	
Ellen Sheehan 58		Kristin Sunser-King 67	
Matthew Dean 73		Jill Weston 280*	

Public Schs..Principal	Grd	Prgm	Enr/#Cls	SN	
Solvay Elem Sch 701 Woods Rd, Solvay 13209 Christine Miczan	K-4	T	477 24	62%	315/488-5422 Fax 315/484-1417
Solvay High Sch 600 Gertrude Ave, Solvay 13209 Diane Hagemann	9-12	TV	500 50	61%	315/468-2551 Fax 315/484-1404
Solvay Middle Sch 299 Bury Dr, Syracuse 13209 James Heffron	5-8	T	460	65%	315/487-7061 Fax 315/484-1444

- **Syracuse City School Dist** PID: 00762193 315/435-4499
  725 Harrison St, Syracuse 13210 Fax 315/435-4015

Schools: 37 \ **Teachers:** 1,575 \ **Students:** 21,116 \ **Special Ed Students:** 4,525 \ **LEP Students:** 3,584 \ **College-Bound:** 75% \ **Ethnic:** Asian 8%, African American 53%, Hispanic 14%, Native American: 1%, Caucasian 24% \ **Exp:** $572 (High) \ **Poverty:** 40% \ **Title I:** $18,859,633 \ **Special Education:** $59,261,000 \ **Open-Close:** 09/04 - 06/25 \ **DTBP:** $187 (High) \ 🇫 🇪

Jaime Alicea 1	Mary Habib 2	
Nels Merrill 2	Suzanne Slack 2,19	
Dean DeSantis 3,17	Scott Gates 3	
Thomas Ferrara 3	Carrie Kane 4	
Louis Copani 4	Rachel Murphy 4	
Theresa Kuss 5	Nancy Bailey 7	
Jennifer Harris 8	Nathan Franz 8,15	
Patricia Sawmiller 8	Margaret Wilson 9,15	
Robert Diflorio 9	Anthony Davis 10,15,27*	
Pamela Odom 10	Howard Jackson 11,298	
Rachel Breslin 11	Tiona Rockett 11,298	
Monique Williams 15,751	Sarah Gentile 20,23	
Robert Leslie 27,31*	Dana Corcoran 28,42	
Cindy Watkins 34	Sheila Donahue 36	
Nicholas Stamoulacatos 39	Melanie Cifonelli 45	
Rhonda Zajac 48,54	Jacqueline Leroy 57,61	
Amy Evans 58	Irastina Reid 58	
Karen Williams 58	Kevin Casavant 58	
Michael Puntschenko 58	Sarah Long 58	
Katie Sojewicz 67	Christopher Miller 68	

Jennifer Wells 68			Lisa Wade 68		
Margaret Bailey 69			Michael Henesey 71		
Eric Vogelsang 76			Raymond Stazzone 76		
Marylisa Wade 78,93			Melissa Evans 79		
Anthony Brown 91			Thomas Ristoff 91		
Heidi Feyl-Crane 285			Daniel Burton 294		
Donna Vallese 294			Sonja Aversa 294		
Timothy Moon 294			Gary Daniels 295		
Heather Austin 295			Timothy Marris 295		

Public Schs..Principal	Grd	Prgm	Enr/#Cls	SN	
Bellevue Elem Sch 530 Stolp Ave, Syracuse 13207 Sarah Cupelli	PK-5	T	405 19	84%	315/435-4520 Fax 315/435-6207
Ⓜ Brighton Academy 309 W Brighton Ave, Syracuse 13205 Richard Richardson	6-8	T	347	95%	315/435-4535 Fax 315/435-6208
Ⓜ Clary Middle Sch 100 Amidon Dr, Syracuse 13205 Lisa Costanzo	6-8	TV	399 50	83%	315/435-4411 Fax 315/435-5832
Corcoran High Sch 919 Glenwood Ave, Syracuse 13207 Tara Jennings	9-12	TV	1,243 50	80%	315/435-4321 Fax 315/435-4024
Delaware Primary Sch 900 S Geddes St, Syracuse 13204 Eliezer Hernandez	PK-5	T	59 37	98%	315/435-4540 Fax 315/435-4544
Dr Edwin Weeks Elem Sch 710 Hawley Ave, Syracuse 13203 Diane Vitello	PK-5	T	755 35	87%	315/435-4097 Fax 315/435-6222
Ed Smith PK-8 Sch 1106 Lancaster Ave, Syracuse 13210 Sam Barber	PK-8	T	714 33	70%	315/435-4650 Fax 315/435-6219
Ⓜ Elmcrest Children's Center 960 Salt Springs Rd, Syracuse 13224 Deborah Mastropaolo	1-12		71 14		315/435-6244 Fax 315/445-2667
Ⓜ Expeditionary Learning Mid Sch 4942 S Salina St, Syracuse 13205 Kevin Burns	6-8	T	173	73%	315/435-6416 Fax 315/435-4880
Ⓜ Franklin Magnet Elem Sch 428 S Alvord St, Syracuse 13208 Kimberly Coyne	PK-5	T	751 38	85%	315/435-4550 Fax 315/435-6211
Frazer K-8 Sch 741 Park Ave, Syracuse 13204 Latrina Brumfield	PK-8	T	935 60	91%	315/435-4555 Fax 315/435-4820
Grant Middle Sch 2400 Grant Blvd, Syracuse 13208 Bruno Primerano	6-8	TV	723 40	89%	315/435-4433 Fax 315/435-4856
H W Smith PK-8 Sch 1130 Salt Springs Rd, Syracuse 13224 Theresa Haley	PK-8	T	838 34	79%	315/435-4490 Fax 315/435-6220 🇫 🇪
Henninger High Sch 600 Robinson St, Syracuse 13206 Matthew Williams	9-12	TV	1,733	84%	315/435-4343 Fax 315/435-5867
Huntington PK-8 Sch 400 Sunnycrest Rd, Syracuse 13206 Joanne Harlow	PK-8	T	963 60	75%	315/435-4565 Fax 315/435-6206
Institute of Tech-Central 258 E Adams St, Syracuse 13202 Donna Formica	Voc	T	547 30	73%	315/435-4300 Fax 315/435-5816 🇫
JT Roberts Prek-8 Sch 715 Glenwood Ave, Syracuse 13207 Katrina Allen	PK-8	T	673 27	73%	315/435-4635 Fax 315/435-6217 🇫 🇪
Lemoyne Elem Sch 1528 Lemoyne Ave, Syracuse 13208 Jason Armstrong	2-5	T	360 30	65%	315/435-4590 Fax 315/435-4591 🇫 🇪
Lincoln Middle Sch 1613 James St, Syracuse 13203 Lajuan White	6-8	TV	538 39	90%	315/435-4450 Fax 315/435-4455

1	Superintendent	8	Curric/Instruct K-12	19	Chief Financial Officer	29	Family/Consumer Science
2	Bus/Finance/Purchasing	9	Curric/Instruct Elem	20	Art K-12	30	Adult Education
3	Buildings And Grounds	10	Curric/Instruct Sec	21	Art Elem	31	Career/Sch-to-Work K-12
4	Food Service	11	Federal Program	22	Art Sec	32	Career/Sch-to-Work Elem
5	Transportation	12	Title I	23	Music K-12	33	Career/Sch-to-Work Sec
6	Athletic	13	Title V	24	Music Elem	34	Early Childhood Ed
7	Health Services	15	Asst Superintendent	25	Music Sec	35	Health/Phys Education
		16	Instructional Media Svcs	26	Business Education	36	Guidance Services K-12
		17	Chief Operations Officer	27	Career & Tech Ed	37	Guidance Services Elem
		18	Chief Academic Officer	28	Technology Education	38	Guidance Services Sec

39	Social Studies K-12	49	English/Lang Arts Elem	59	Special Education Elem	69	Academic Assessment
40	Social Studies Elem	50	English/Lang Arts Sec	60	Special Education Sec	70	Research/Development
41	Social Studies Sec	51	Reading K-12	61	Foreign/World Lang K-12	71	Public Information
42	Science K-12	52	Reading Elem	62	Foreign/World Lang Elem	72	Summer School
43	Science Elem	53	Reading Sec	63	Foreign/World Lang Sec	73	Instructional Tech
44	Science Sec	54	Remedial Reading K-12	64	Religious Education K-12	74	Inservice Training
45	Math K-12	55	Remedial Reading Elem	65	Religious Education Elem	75	Marketing/Distributive
46	Math Elem	56	Remedial Reading Sec	66	Religious Education Sec	76	Info Systems
47	Math Sec	57	Bilingual/ELL	67	School Board President	77	Psychological Assess
48	English/Lang Arts K-12	58	Special Education K-12	68	Teacher Personnel	78	Affirmative Action

New York School Directory

Onondaga County

School	Grd	Prgm	Enr/#Cls	SN	Phone
McCarthy School-Beard 220 W Kennedy St, Syracuse 13205 Lisa Upton	Spec		70 10		315/435-5855 Fax 315/435-4601 ⓕⓣ
Ⓜ McKinley-Brighton Magnet Sch 141 W Newell St, Syracuse 13205 Mayra Ortiz	PK-5	T	580 26	85%	315/435-4605 Fax 315/435-4603
Meachem Elem Sch 171 Spaulding Ave, Syracuse 13205 Kathryne Moulton	PK-5	T	369 20	79%	315/435-4610 Fax 315/435-6216 ⓕⓣ
Montessori at Lemoyne 1528 Lemoyne Ave, Syracuse 13208 Jason Armstrong	PK-1		110		315/435-4590
Nottingham High Sch 3100 E Genesee St, Syracuse 13224 Maria Cimino	9-12	GTV	1,318 170	78%	315/435-4380 Fax 315/435-4177 ⓕⓣ
Ⓐ Oasis Academy 1728 South Ave, Syracuse 13207 Nicolle Haynes	K-8		220		315/435-6226
Ⓜ Porter Magnet Elem Sch 512 Emerson Ave, Syracuse 13204 Jennifer King-Reese	PK-5	T	391 29	86%	315/435-4625 Fax 315/435-4897
Ⓐ Promising Futures Ldrshp Acad 573 E Genesee St, Syracuse 13202 Margaret McRobbie Taru	9-12	GV	80		315/435-4135 Fax 315/435-6599
Public Service Ldrshp Academy 227 Magnolia St, Syracuse 13204 Jaime Perez	9-12		1,034		315/435-4376
Public Svc Ldrshp Acad Fowler 227 Magnolia St, Syracuse 13204 Jaime Perez	9-12	GTV	975	88%	315/435-4376 Fax 315/435-6313 ⓕⓣ
Salem-Hyde Elem Sch 450 Durston Ave, Syracuse 13203 Rebecca Groat	PK-6	T	566 26	72%	315/435-4570 Fax 315/435-6212
Ⓜ Seymour Dual Language Acad 108 Shonnard St, Syracuse 13204 James Nieves	PK-5	T	567 20	90%	315/435-4645 Fax 315/435-4646
Ⓜ Steam at Dr King Elem Sch 416 E Raynor Ave, Syracuse 13202 Kuricheses Alexander	PK-5	T	552 29	89%	315/435-4580 Fax 315/435-6213
Syracuse Latin Sch 345 Jamesville Ave, Syracuse 13210 Kelly Manard	PK-5	T	477	39%	315/435-4606
Syracuse STEM at Blodgett MS 312 Oswego St, Syracuse 13204 Dr Harry Valentin	6-8		418		315/435-4386
Van Duyn Elem Sch 401 Loomis Ave, Syracuse 13207 Eva Williams	PK-5	T	460	82%	315/435-4660 Fax 315/435-6221
Webster Elem Sch 500 Wadsworth St, Syracuse 13208 Iverna Minor	PK-5	T	632 32	82%	315/435-4670 Fax 315/435-4021
Westside Academy-Blodgett 312 Oswego St, Syracuse 13204 Harry Valentin	6-8	T	453 35	96%	315/435-4386 Fax 315/435-4539 ⓕⓣ

• **Tully Central School Dist** PID: 00762650　315/696-6204
20 State St, Tully 13159　Fax 315/696-6251

Schools: 2 \ **Teachers:** 80 \ **Students:** 770 \ **Special Ed Students:** 134 \ **LEP Students:** 5 \ **College-Bound:** 74% \ **Ethnic:** Asian 1%, African American 1%, Hispanic 2%, Native American: 1%, Caucasian 96% \ **Exp:** $336 (High) \ **Poverty:** 12% \ **Title I:** $193,600 \ **Special Education:** $1,166,000 \ **Open-Close:** 09/04 - 06/25 \ **DTBP:** $360 (High)

Robert Hughes .... 1　Bradley Corbin 2
Robert Kennedy .... 4　Steve Bailey 5
Don McClure .... 6*　James Paccia 16,82
Cristy Bobbett .... 58*　Denise Cardamone 67
Lee DuVall .... 73　Raymond Herrick 91

Public Schs..Principal	Grd	Prgm	Enr/#Cls	SN	Phone
Tully Elem Sch 20 State St, Tully 13159 Ed Kupiec	PK-6		404 45	35%	315/696-6200 Fax 315/696-6220
Tully Jr Sr High Sch 5850 Route 80, Tully 13159 Maryann Murphy	7-12	A	366 60	25%	315/696-6200 Fax 315/696-6237

• **West Genesee Ctl School Dist** PID: 00761163　315/487-4562
300 Sanderson Dr, Camillus 13031　Fax 315/487-2999

Schools: 7 \ **Teachers:** 354 \ **Students:** 4,600 \ **Special Ed Students:** 787 \ **LEP Students:** 74 \ **College-Bound:** 83% \ **Ethnic:** Asian 1%, African American 3%, Hispanic 5%, Native American: 1%, Caucasian 90% \ **Exp:** $240 (Med) \ **Poverty:** 6% \ **Title I:** $481,273 \ **Special Education:** $6,465,000 \ **Open-Close:** 09/08 - 06/24 \ **DTBP:** $316 (High) \ ⓕ ⓣ

David Bills .... 1　Paul Pelton 2,4,11,15,298
James Dark .... 5　Michael Burns 6,35*
Deb Balcout .... 7　Brian Kesel 8,15,18,83,270,288
Stephen Dunham .... 10*　William Roberge 16,73,286
William Davern .... 20,25,27*　Lynn Magoulis 30
Susan Murray .... 34,58,77*　Darlene Chapin 58
Kimberly Coyne .... 67　David Cirillo 68
Bonnie Russell .... 71　Robert Leo 73,285
Sean Fahey 294

Public Schs..Principal	Grd	Prgm	Enr/#Cls	SN	Phone
Camillus Middle Sch 5525 Ike Dixon Rd, Camillus 13031 Beth Lozier	6-8		405 50	24%	315/672-3159 Fax 315/672-3309
East Hill Elem Sch 401 Blackmore Rd, Camillus 13031 Lisa Craig	K-5		392 21	24%	315/487-4648 Fax 315/487-5499
Onondaga Road Elem Sch 703 S Onondaga Rd, Syracuse 13219 Jeannette Clark	K-5		389	25%	315/487-4653 Fax 315/487-2598
Split Rock Elem Sch 4151 Split Rock Rd, Camillus 13031 Matthew Kimpland	K-5		338 22	30%	315/487-4656 Fax 315/487-5394
Stonehedge Elem Sch 400 Sanderson Dr, Camillus 13031 Amanda Simmons \ Brent Suddaby	K-5		883 43	23%	315/487-4633 Fax 315/487-4599
West Genesee High Sch 5201 W Genesee St, Camillus 13031 Wayne Ackles	9-12	V	1,469	22%	315/487-4592 Fax 315/487-4582
West Genesee Middle Sch 500 Sanderson Dr, Camillus 13031 Stephen Dunham	6-8		607	30%	315/487-4615 Fax 315/487-4618

• **Westhill Central School Dist** PID: 00762686　315/426-3000
400 Walberta Rd, Syracuse 13219　Fax 315/488-6411

Schools: 4 \ **Teachers:** 135 \ **Students:** 1,700 \ **Special Ed Students:** 207 \ **LEP Students:** 20 \ **Ethnic:** Asian 2%, African American 5%, Hispanic 4%, Caucasian 89% \ **Exp:** $319 (High) \ **Poverty:** 6% \ **Title I:** $169,059 \ **Special Education:** $2,694,000 \ **Open-Close:** 09/09 - 06/25 \ **DTBP:** $163 (High)

Casey Barduhn .... 1　Steve Smith 2,15
Ed Wittkowski .... 3　Richard Gunther 4
Jeri Burke .... 5　Jen Smarrelli 6*

---

79 Student Personnel	91 Safety/Security	275 Response To Intervention	298 Grant Writer/Ptnrships
80 Driver Ed/Safety	92 Magnet School	277 Remedial Math K-12	750 Chief Innovation Officer
81 Gifted/Talented	93 Parental Involvement	280 Literacy Coach	751 Chief of Staff
82 Video Services	95 Tech Prep Program	285 STEM	752 Social Emotional Learning
83 Substance Abuse Prev	97 Chief Information Officer	286 Digital Learning	
84 Erate	98 Chief Technology Officer	288 Common Core Standards	**Other School Types**
85 AIDS Education	270 Character Education	294 Accountability	Ⓐ = Alternative School
88 Alternative/At Risk	271 Migrant Education	295 Network System	Ⓒ = Charter School
89 Multi-Cultural Curriculum	273 Teacher Mentor	296 Title II Programs	Ⓜ = Magnet School
90 Social Work	274 Before/After School	297 Webmaster	Ⓨ = Year-Round School

School Programs
A = Alternative Program
G = Adult Classes
M = Magnet Program
T = Title I Schoolwide
V = Career & Tech Ed Programs

Social Media
ⓕ = Facebook
ⓣ = Twitter

New Schools are shaded
New Superintendents and Principals are bold
Personnel with email addresses are underscored

Onondaga County

Darcy Woodcock 8,15,69,274
Mariette Lachenauer 58*
Katie Harmon 73
Jon Dussing 295
Annette Casper 297
Karen Fenner 16*
Lisa Oreilly 67
Jennifer Pisegna 88*
Nate DeVita 295

Public Schs..Principal	Grd	Prgm	Enr/#Cls	SN	
Cherry Road Elem Sch 201 Cherry Rd, Syracuse 13219 Brett King	2-4		402 14	23%	315/426-3300 Fax 315/468-0623
Onondaga Hill Middle Sch 4860 Onondaga Rd, Syracuse 13215 Mark Bednarski	5-8		548 50	20%	315/426-3400 Fax 315/492-0156
Walberta Park Primary Sch 400 Walberta Rd, Syracuse 13219 Beth Kramer	K-1		268 16	17%	315/426-3200 Fax 315/484-9056
Westhill Senior High Sch 4501 Onondaga Blvd, Syracuse 13219 Lee Roscoe	9-12		563 55	17%	315/426-3100 Fax 315/475-0319

ONONDAGA CATHOLIC SCHOOLS

• **Diocese of Syracuse Ed Office** PID: 00762765   315/470-1450
240 E Onondaga St, Syracuse 13202   Fax 315/478-4619

Schools: 22 \ **Students:** 5,100

Listing includes only schools located in this county. See District Index for location of Diocesan Offices.

William Crist 1   Sandy Burgess 2

Catholic Schs..Principal	Grd	Prgm	Enr/#Cls	SN	
Bishop Grimes Jr Sr High Sch 6653 Kirkville Rd, East Syracuse 13057 Debra Brillante	7-12		350 30		315/437-0356 Fax 315/437-0358
Bishop Ludden Jr Sr High Sch 815 Fay Rd, Syracuse 13219 Leo Cosgrove	7-12		340 45		315/468-2591 Fax 315/468-0097
Blessed Sacrament Sch 3129 James St, Syracuse 13206 Lisa Coppola	PK-6		236 16		315/463-1261 Fax 315/463-0253
Cathedral Academy at Pompei 923 N McBride St, Syracuse 13208 Tina Seymour	K-6		86 12		315/422-8548 Fax 315/472-0754
Holy Cross Sch 4200 E Genesee St, De Witt 13214 Martha O'Leary	PK-6		160 8		315/446-4890 Fax 315/446-4799
Holy Family Sch 130 Chapel Dr, Syracuse 13219 Sr Christina Luczynski	PK-6		250 16		315/487-8515 Fax 315/458-4437
Immaculate Conception Sch 400 Salt Springs St, Fayetteville 13066 Donald Mills	PK-6		218 13		315/637-3961 Fax 315/637-2672
Most Holy Rosary Sch 1031 Bellevue Ave, Syracuse 13207 William Bryan	PK-6		115 15		315/476-6035
St Margaret's Sch 201 Roxboro Rd, Mattydale 13211 Michael McAuliff	PK-6		150 15		315/455-5791 Fax 315/455-1250
St Mary's Academy 49 Syracuse St, Baldwinsville 13027 Renae Henderson	PK-6		160 8		315/635-3977 Fax 315/635-8137
St Rose of Lima Sch 411 S Main St, N Syracuse 13212 Mary Crysler	PK-6		263 21		315/458-6036 Fax 315/458-6038

ONONDAGA PRIVATE SCHOOLS

Private Schs..Principal	Grd	Prgm	Enr/#Cls	SN	
AL Ihsan School of Excellence 1406 Park St, Syracuse 13208 Dr Abdelmadjid Mokhtari	PK-8		75 6		315/472-5040
All Saints Elem Sch 112 S Wilbur Ave, Syracuse 13204 Grace Glennon	PK-6		101 8		315/422-3140
Baldwinsville Christian Acad 7312 Van Buren Rd, Baldwinsville 13027 Dave Grey	K-12		104 9		315/638-1069 Fax 315/638-4207
Christian Brothers Academy 6245 Randall Rd, Syracuse 13214 Matthew Keough	7-12		765 40		315/446-5960 Fax 315/446-3393
Faith Heritage Sch 3740 Midland Ave, Syracuse 13205 Neal Capone	K-12		275 30		315/469-7777 Fax 315/492-7440
Living Word Academy 6101 Court Street Rd, Syracuse 13206 Isiaih Rocine	PK-12	V	175 20		315/437-6744 Fax 315/437-6766
Manlius Pebble Hill Sch 5300 Jamesville Rd, Syracuse 13214 Amy Abdo \ Matt Spear \ Fred Montas	PK-12		550 50		315/446-2452 Fax 315/446-2620
Mater Dei Academy 2656 Warners Rd, Warners 13164 Richard Boyle	K-12		180 19		315/320-4085 Fax 315/320-9220
Montessori School of Syracuse 155 Waldorf Pkwy, Syracuse 13224 Mary O'Connor	PK-6		140 5		315/449-9033 Fax 315/449-9867
New Sch 5205 Jamesville Rd, De Witt 13214 Tamara Breed	K-8		30 6		315/475-6453
Parkview Junior Academy 412 S Avery Ave, Syracuse 13219 Kim Kaiser	K-8		70 4		315/468-0117 Fax 315/487-1732
Syracuse Hebrew Day Sch 5655 Thompson Rd, De Witt 13214 Lori Tenenbaum	K-6		80 7		315/446-1900 Fax 315/446-3714
Word of Life Christian Academy 12 E Oneida St, Baldwinsville 13027 Carmen Durst	PK-6		145		315/635-1818 Fax 315/638-2490

ONONDAGA REGIONAL CENTERS

• **Onondaga-Cortland-Madson BOCES** PID: 00762739 315/433-2602
6820 Thompson Rd, Syracuse 13211   Fax 315/431-8555

Dr J Francis Manning 1
John Wisniewski 3
Chris Difulvio 15,16,69,70,74
Phillip Grome 27,31,88
Rosanna Grund 58,77
Joseph Bufano 68
Sherri Kershner 2
Andrew Dibiasi 15
Colleen Viggiano 15,27,58,79,88
Mari Ukleya 30
Ann Wright 67
Pam Mazzaferro 73,76,295

1	Superintendent	8	Curric/Instruct K-12	19	Chief Financial Officer	29	Family/Consumer Science	39	Social Studies K-12	49	English/Lang Arts Elem	59	Special Education Elem	69	Academic Assessment
2	Bus/Finance/Purchasing	9	Curric/Instruct Elem	20	Art K-12	30	Adult Education	40	Social Studies Elem	50	English/Lang Arts Sec	60	Special Education Sec	70	Research/Development
3	Buildings And Grounds	10	Curric/Instruct Sec	21	Art Elem	31	Career/Sch-to-Work K-12	41	Social Studies Sec	51	Reading K-12	61	Foreign/World Lang K-12	71	Public Information
4	Food Service	11	Federal Program	22	Art Sec	32	Career/Sch-to-Work Elem	42	Science K-12	52	Reading Elem	62	Foreign/World Lang Elem	72	Summer School
5	Transportation	12	Title I	23	Music K-12	33	Career/Sch-to-Work Sec	43	Science Elem	53	Reading Sec	63	Foreign/World Lang Sec	73	Instructional Tech
6	Athletic	13	Title V	24	Music Elem	34	Early Childhood Ed	44	Science Sec	54	Remedial Reading K-12	64	Religious Education K-12	74	Inservice Training
7	Health Services	15	Asst Superintendent	25	Music Sec	35	Health/Phys Education	45	Math K-12	55	Remedial Reading Elem	65	Religious Education Elem	75	Marketing/Distributive
		16	Instructional Media Svcs	26	Business Education	36	Guidance Services K-12	46	Math Elem	56	Remedial Reading Sec	66	Religious Education Sec	76	Info Systems
		17	Chief Operations Officer	27	Career & Tech Ed	37	Guidance Services Elem	47	Math Sec	57	Bilingual/ELL	67	School Board President	77	Psychological Assess
		18	Chief Academic Officer	28	Technology Education	38	Guidance Services Sec	48	English/Lang Arts K-12	58	Special Education K-12	68	Teacher Personnel	78	Affirmative Action

New York School Directory   Ontario County

ONTARIO COUNTY

ONTARIO COUNTY SCHOOLS

County Schs..Principal	Grd	Prgm	Enr/#Cls	SN	
Finger Lakes Tech & Career Ctr 3501 County Road 20, Stanley 14561 Matthew Barr	Voc	AG	800 30		585/526-6471 Fax 585/526-4659
Wayne-Fingerlake BOCES Spec Ed 1550 State Route 488, Clifton Spgs 14432 Cindy Parker	Spec		175 10		315/548-6631 Fax 315/548-6639

ONTARIO PUBLIC SCHOOLS

● **Bloomfield Central SD** PID: 00763630   585/657-6121
45 Maple Ave Ste A, Bloomfield 14469   Fax 585/657-4771

Schools: 2 \ **Teachers:** 80 \ **Students:** 850 \ **Special Ed Students:** 118 \ **LEP Students:** 5 \ **College-Bound:** 25% \ **Ethnic:** Asian 1%, African American 1%, Hispanic 4%, Caucasian 95% \ **Exp:** $80 (Low) \ **Poverty:** 7% \ **Title I:** $117,492 \ **Special Education:** $1,700,000 \ **Open-Close:** 09/08 - 06/24 \ **DTBP:** $386 (High)

Andrew Doell 1		Scott Donnelly 2,19,34,68*	
Joseph Flansburg 3,91		Todd Fowler 4*	
Tammy Brace 5		Jonathan Mastin 6,31,35*	
Kathryn Taylor 8,12,51,54,69,288*		Daniel McAlpin 10,27,81,273*	
Kateri Warren 16,36,58,76,79,88		Paul Lubberts 35,83,85*	
Gretchen Fisher 38*		Pamela Nakoski 67	
Karen Soanes 73		Amy Repard 297*	

Public Schs..Principal	Grd	Prgm	Enr/#Cls	SN	
Bloomfield Elem Sch 45 Maple Ave Ste B, Bloomfield 14469 Nicholas Fargnoli	PK-5	T	376 25	34%	585/657-6172 Fax 585/657-6926
Bloomfield Jr Sr High Sch 1 Oakmount Ave, Bloomfield 14469 Daniel McAlpin	6-12	AGV	475 46	29%	585/657-6121

● **Canandaigua City School Dist** PID: 00763666   585/396-3700
143 N Pearl St, Canandaigua 14424   Fax 585/396-7306

Schools: 3 \ **Teachers:** 302 \ **Students:** 3,500 \ **Special Ed Students:** 610 \ **LEP Students:** 38 \ **College-Bound:** 75% \ **Ethnic:** Asian 2%, African American 1%, Hispanic 5%, Caucasian 91% \ **Exp:** $304 (High) \ **Poverty:** 9% \ **Title I:** $488,090 \ **Special Education:** $5,884,000 \ **Open-Close:** 09/09 - 06/25 \ **DTBP:** $317 (High)

Jamie Farr 1	Matthew Fitch 2,15
Michael McClain 3*	Todd Fowler 4
Seth Cleary 5	James Simmons 6*
Matt Schrage 8,12,15,288,296	Stephanie Knapp 11,31,57,58*
Brian Nolan 15,68,78	Eric Bateman 16,82*
Leanne DuCharme 38*	Chris Paige 58
Rachael Schading 58	Jeanie Grimm 67
Carolyn Chapman 71	Daniel Bowman 73
Katie McFarland 74	Cynthia Vanderlee 83*
Jean MacKenzie 275	Vernon Tenney 752

Public Schs..Principal	Grd	Prgm	Enr/#Cls	SN	
Canandaigua Academy 435 East St, Canandaigua 14424 Vernon Tenney	9-12	AV	1,119 	30%	585/396-3800 Fax 585/396-3806 ⓕ
Canandaigua Middle Sch 215 Granger St, Canandaigua 14424 John Arthur	6-8	V	798 100	36%	585/396-3850 Fax 585/396-3885
Canandaigua Prim Elem Sch 96 W Gibson St, Canandaigua 14424 Emily Bonadonna \ Brian Amesbury	PK-5	T	1,531 43	36%	585/396-3900 Fax 585/396-3909

● **Geneva City School Dist** PID: 00763719   315/781-0400
400 W North St, Geneva 14456   Fax 315/781-4193

Schools: 4 \ **Teachers:** 210 \ **Students:** 2,078 \ **Special Ed Students:** 391 \ **LEP Students:** 204 \ **College-Bound:** 76% \ **Ethnic:** Asian 2%, African American 13%, Hispanic 37%, Caucasian 47% \ **Exp:** $398 (High) \ **Poverty:** 18% \ **Title I:** $792,121 \ **Special Education:** $8,930,000 \ **Open-Close:** 09/03 - 06/25 \ **DTBP:** $167 (High)

Dr Patricia Garcia 1	Mary Gere-Penna 2
Timothy Emery 3	Gerald Barker 4
Mike Delrossa 5	Randy Grenier 6
Tricia Budgar 6	Kevin Whitaker 8,11,15,70,294
Stephen Kruger 15	Karissa Schutt 34*
Susan McGowan 37,90*	Michael Gorton 38*
Evelyn Gomez 57*	Jose Canario 67
Tracy Marchionda 70	Heather Swanson 71
Julie Larson 73,76,295	Tonya Russell 79

Public Schs..Principal	Grd	Prgm	Enr/#Cls	SN	
Geneva High Sch 101 Carter Rd, Geneva 14456 Greg Baker	9-12	TV	605 50	54%	315/781-0402 Fax 315/781-0695
Geneva Middle Sch 101 Carter Rd, Geneva 14456 Bob Smith	6-8	TV	456 70	60%	315/781-0404 Fax 315/781-0694
North Street Elem Sch 400 W North St, Geneva 14456 Eric Vaillancourt	3-5	T	617 35	66%	315/781-0489 Fax 315/781-4195
West Street Elem Sch 30 West St, Geneva 14456 Susan Meskos	PK-2	T	430 30	52%	315/781-0406 Fax 315/781-0599

● **Honeoye Central School Dist** PID: 00763783   585/229-4125
8528 Main St, Honeoye 14471   Fax 585/229-5633

Schools: 1 \ **Teachers:** 70 \ **Students:** 251 \ **Special Ed Students:** 93 \ **College-Bound:** 82% \ **Ethnic:** Asian 1%, African American 1%, Hispanic 1%, Caucasian 97% \ **Exp:** $689 (High) \ **Poverty:** 6% \ **Title I:** $67,108 \ **Special Education:** $1,332,000 \ **Open-Close:** 09/04 - 06/25 \ **DTBP:** $368 (High)

Elizabeth Ashton 1	Mike Bastian 2
Sheila Lowe 4*	Melissa Perkowski 8
Keith Stumbo 67	Jessica Green 68
Ryan Arthurton 73	

Public Schs..Principal	Grd	Prgm	Enr/#Cls	SN	
Honeoye Central Sch 8528 Main St, Honeoye 14471 Addie Klaehn \ Margie Wright	K-12		251	33%	585/229-5171

---

79 Student Personnel	91 Safety/Security	275 Response To Intervention	298 Grant Writer/Ptnrships	**School Programs**	**Social Media**
80 Driver Ed/Safety	92 Magnet School	277 Remedial Math K-12	750 Chief Innovation Officer	A = Alternative Program	
81 Gifted/Talented	93 Parental Involvement	280 Literacy Coach	751 Chief of Staff	G = Adult Classes	ⓕ = Facebook
82 Video Services	95 Tech Prep Program	285 STEM	752 Social Emotional Learning	M = Magnet Program	
83 Substance Abuse Prev	97 Chief Information Officer	286 Digital Learning		T = Title I Schoolwide	ⓣ = Twitter
84 Erate	98 Chief Technology Officer	288 Common Core Standards	**Other School Types**	V = Career & Tech Ed Programs	
85 AIDS Education	270 Character Education	294 Accountability	Ⓐ = Alternative School		
88 Alternative/At Risk	271 Migrant Education	295 Network System	Ⓒ = Charter School	New Schools are shaded	
89 Multi-Cultural Curriculum	273 Teacher Mentor	296 Title II Programs	Ⓜ = Magnet School	New Superintendents and Principals are bold	
90 Social Work	274 Before/After Sch	297 Webmaster	Ⓨ = Year-Round School	Personnel with email addresses are underscored	

NY–161

Ontario County
Market Data Retrieval

- **Manchester-Shortsville Ctl SD** PID: 00763939 585/289-2160
  1506 State Route 21, Shortsville 14548 Fax 585/289-2116

Schools: 3 \ **Teachers:** 75 \ **Students:** 800 \ **Special Ed Students:** 125 \ **LEP Students:** 9 \ **College-Bound:** 80% \ **Ethnic:** Asian 1%, Hispanic 6%, Caucasian 93% \ **Exp:** $397 (High) \ **Poverty:** 9% \ **Title I:** $132,205 \ **Special Education:** $1,196,000 \ **Open-Close:** 09/08 - 06/24 \ **DTBP:** $152 (High) \

Charlene Dehn 1
Timothy Burns 2
Rachel Lockman 4
Susan Franceschi 6*
Kathleen Liebentritt 16*
Lori Ryan 36*
Suzanne Bailey 73,295*
Kim Brown 2
Mike Roddenbery 3*
Chris Fairchild 5
Kristine Guererri .. 8,11,58,69,273,275,288,296
Tracy Snieszko 31
Jennifer Speers 67
Rick Yehl 85*

Public Schs..Principal	Grd	Prgm	Enr/#Cls	SN	
Red Jacket Elem Sch 1506 State Route 21, Shortsville 14548 Jeffrey McCarthy	PK-5	T	367 20	52% Fax	585/289-9647 585/289-4499
Red Jacket High Sch 1506 State Route 21, Shortsville 14548 Mark Bracy	9-12	T	250 28	45% Fax	585/289-3966 585/289-4755
Red Jacket Middle Sch 1506 State Route 21, Shortsville 14548 Karen Hall	6-8	T	182 16	46% Fax	585/289-3967 585/289-8715

- **Marcus Whitman Central SD** PID: 00763800 585/554-4848
  4100 Baldwin Rd, Rushville 14544 Fax 585/554-4882

Schools: 3 \ **Teachers:** 118 \ **Students:** 1,227 \ **Special Ed Students:** 242 \ **LEP Students:** 3 \ **College-Bound:** 71% \ **Ethnic:** Hispanic 2%, Caucasian 97% \ **Exp:** $203 (Med) \ **Poverty:** 15% \ **Title I:** $406,960 \ **Special Education:** $3,106,000 \ **Open-Close:** 09/08 - 06/25 \ **DTBP:** $404 (High)

Dr Christopher Brown 1,83
Zoe Kolczynski 2,12,296
Carla Woolston 4*
Paul Lahue 6*
Erica Hasselsterom 8,69
Andrea Smith 57,58,79,752
Brenda Lehman 73,295*
Mark Socola 2
Daniel Blankenberg 3
Leeann Shipman 5
Michelle Rohring 7*
Mike Sullivan 8,18,27,31,36*
Sheila Brown 67

Public Schs..Principal	Grd	Prgm	Enr/#Cls	SN	
Gorham Intermediate Sch 2705 State Route 245, Stanley 14561 Susan Wissick	3-5	T	271 18	51% Fax	585/526-6351 585/526-4435
Marcus Whitman Middle High Sch 4100 Baldwin Rd, Rushville 14544 Dr Clayton Cole \ Jennifer Taft	6-12	AV	602 60	52% Fax	585/554-6442 585/554-3414
Middlesex Valley Primary Sch 149 State Route 245, Rushville 14544 Bonnie Cazer	PK-2	T	297 17	56% Fax	585/554-3115 585/554-6172

- **Naples Central School Dist** PID: 00763848 585/374-7900
  136 N Main St, Naples 14512 Fax 585/374-5859

Schools: 2 \ **Teachers:** 77 \ **Students:** 600 \ **Special Ed Students:** 128 \ **LEP Students:** 3 \ **College-Bound:** 88% \ **Ethnic:** Asian 1%, African American 1%, Hispanic 1%, Caucasian 97% \ **Exp:** $383 (High) \ **Poverty:** 16% \ **Title I:** $210,096 \ **Special Education:** $1,114,000 \ **Open-Close:** 09/08 - 06/24

Matthew Frahm 1
Dr Jeffery Black 2,15,19
Joseph Fleischman 3
Chad Hunt 5,6*
Katherine Piedici 58,79*
Anneke Radin-Snaith 73*
Deena Kingston 4*
Kristina Saucke 8,11*
Jacob Hall 67

Public Schs..Principal	Grd	Prgm	Enr/#Cls	SN	
Naples Elem Sch 2 Academy St, Naples 14512 Kristina Saucke	PK-6	T	344 26	50% Fax	585/374-7900 585/374-2729
Naples Jr Sr High Sch 136 N Main St, Naples 14512 Elizabeth Ashton	7-12	GTV	288	44% Fax	585/374-7900 585/374-9491

- **Phelps-Clifton Springs Ctl SD** PID: 00763874 315/548-6420
  1490 State Route 488, Clifton Spgs 14432 Fax 315/548-6439

Schools: 4 \ **Teachers:** 144 \ **Students:** 1,549 \ **Special Ed Students:** 290 \ **LEP Students:** 31 \ **Ethnic:** Asian 1%, African American 1%, Hispanic 7%, Caucasian 91% \ **Exp:** $502 (High) \ **Poverty:** 10% \ **Title I:** $267,222 \ **Special Education:** $4,292,000 \ **Open-Close:** 09/09 - 06/25 \ **DTBP:** $152 (High)

Matthew Sickles 1
Donald Miller 3
Kathleen Rhow 5
Tammy Wood 7,11,58,81,273,296*
Ryan Davis 67
William Gowan 73,76,295*
Tracy Marshall 2
Jil Swarthout 4
John Lombardi 6,35*
Richard Jones 36*
Mary Joe Peake 68
Kristin Wrobbel 83,88*

Public Schs..Principal	Grd	Prgm	Enr/#Cls	SN	
Midlakes High Sch 1554 State Route 488, Clifton Spgs 14432 Frank Bai-Rossi	9-12		489 50	37% Fax	315/548-6300 315/548-6319
Midlakes Intermediate Sch 1510 State Route 488, Clifton Spgs 14432 Chris Moyer	3-6	T	450 30	46% Fax	315/548-6900 315/548-6909
Midlakes Middle Sch 1550 State Route 488, Clifton Spgs 14432 Frank Bai-Rossi	7-8		245	44% Fax	315/548-6600 315/548-6319
Midlakes Primary Sch 1500 State Route 488, Clifton Spgs 14432 Chris Moyer	K-2	T	365 20	40% Fax	315/548-6700 315/548-6709

- **Victor Central School Dist** PID: 00763977 585/924-3252
  953 High St, Victor 14564 Fax 585/742-7090

Schools: 5 \ **Teachers:** 341 \ **Students:** 4,450 \ **Special Ed Students:** 528 \ **LEP Students:** 96 \ **College-Bound:** 88% \ **Ethnic:** Asian 3%, African American 3%, Hispanic 7%, Caucasian 87% \ **Exp:** $179 (Low) \ **Poverty:** 5% \ **Title I:** $327,211 \ **Special Education:** $3,607,000 \ **Open-Close:** 09/04 - 06/25 \ **DTBP:** $313 (High)

Dr Tim Terranova 1
Christopher Marshall 3,91
Darren Everhart 5
Corrine Fox 7*
James Haugh 15,68,78
Julie Bitely 58
David Henderson 73,295
Ronald Felice 80
Jan Soucier 273*
John Zappia 2,15
Alexandra Tepoel 4*
Duane Weimer 6,35
Kristin Swann 8,11,15,57,79,288,298
Mary Banaszak 27,36,69,88*
Kristin Elliott 67
Veronica Puglisi 79
John Ryan 83,90*
Claire Noonan 280*

Public Schs..Principal	Grd	Prgm	Enr/#Cls	SN	
Early Childhood Sch 953 High St, Victor 14564 Dorothy DiAngelo	PK-1		710 15	18% Fax	585/924-3252 585/742-7033

1	Superintendent	8	Curric/Instruct K-12	19	Chief Financial Officer	29	Family/Consumer Science	39	Social Studies K-12	49	English/Lang Arts Elem	59	Special Education Elem	69	Academic Assessment
2	Bus/Finance/Purchasing	9	Curric/Instruct Elem	20	Art K-12	30	Adult Education	40	Social Studies Elem	50	English/Lang Arts Sec	60	Special Education Sec	70	Research/Development
3	Buildings And Grounds	10	Curric/Instruct Sec	21	Art Elem	31	Career/Sch-to-Work K-12	41	Social Studies Sec	51	Reading K-12	61	Foreign/World Lang K-12	71	Public Information
4	Food Service	11	Federal Program	22	Art Sec	32	Career/Sch-to-Work Elem	42	Science K-12	52	Reading Elem	62	Foreign/World Lang Elem	72	Summer School
5	Transportation	12	Title I	23	Music K-12	33	Career/Sch-to-Work Sec	43	Science Elem	53	Reading Sec	63	Foreign/World Lang Sec	73	Instructional Tech
6	Athletic	13	Title V	24	Music Elem	34	Early Childhood Ed	44	Science Sec	54	Remedial Reading K-12	64	Religious Education K-12	74	Inservice Training
7	Health Services	15	Asst Superintendent	25	Music Sec	35	Health/Phys Education	45	Math K-12	55	Remedial Reading Elem	65	Religious Education Elem	75	Marketing/Distributive
		16	Instructional Media Svcs	26	Business Education	36	Guidance Services K-12	46	Math Elem	56	Remedial Reading Sec	66	Religious Education Sec	76	Info Systems
		17	Chief Operations Officer	27	Career & Tech Ed	37	Guidance Services Elem	47	Math Sec	57	Bilingual/ELL	67	School Board President	77	Psychological Assess
		18	Chief Academic Officer	28	Technology Education	38	Guidance Services Sec	48	English/Lang Arts K-12	58	Special Education K-12	68	Teacher Personnel	78	Affirmative Action

New York School Directory

Orange County

Victor High Sch 953 High St, Victor 14564 Brian Siesto	9-12	V	1,389	20%	585/924-3252 Fax 585/924-9536
Victor Intermediate Sch 953 High St, Victor 14564 Kevin Swartz	4-6		972 43	21%	585/924-3252 Fax 585/742-7055
Victor Junior High Sch 953 High St, Victor 14564 Brian Gee	7-8		654 40	21%	585/924-3252 Fax 585/924-9535
Victor Primary Sch 953 High St, Victor 14564 Jennifer Check	2-3		676	22%	585/924-3252 Fax 585/742-7031

ONTARIO CATHOLIC SCHOOLS

• **Diocese of Rochester Ed Office** PID: 00733623
Listing includes only schools located in this county. See District Index for location of Diocesan Offices.

Catholic Schs..Principal	Grd	Prgm	Enr/#Cls	SN	
SS Francis-Stephen Sch 17 Elmwood Ave, Geneva 14456 Dr Lorraine Williams	PK-8		113 11		315/789-1828 Fax 315/789-9179 f
St Mary Sch 16 Gibson St, Canandaigua 14424 Lisa Milano	PK-8		184 10		585/394-4300 Fax 585/394-3954 f

ONTARIO PRIVATE SCHOOLS

Private Schs..Principal	Grd	Prgm	Enr/#Cls	SN	
Calvary Chapel Christian Sch 1777 Route 332, Farmington 14425 Mark Leckie	K-6		33 6		585/398-3550 Fax 585/398-3250
Clinical Assoc Finger Lakes 590 Fishers Station Dr Ste 130, Victor 14564 Cynthia Tolenian	Spec		500		585/924-7207 Fax 585/924-7049
UCP Happiness House Sch 731 Pre Emption Rd, Geneva 14456 Mary Boatfield	PK-PK		105 6		315/789-6850 Fax 315/789-7750

ORANGE COUNTY

ORANGE COUNTY SCHOOLS

County Schs..Principal	Grd	Prgm	Enr/#Cls	SN	
Ⓐ Hudson Valley Career Academies 3 Maple Ave, Chester 10918 Debbie Brunjes	9-12		150 20		845/469-2270 Fax 845/469-6338
Orange Ulster Sp Ed Ctr 53 Gibson Rd, Goshen 10924 Kerri Stroka	Spec	AGV	930 80		845/291-0200 Fax 845/291-0205
Orange-Ulster BOCES Tech Ctr 53 Gibson Rd, Goshen 10924 Paula Ray	Voc	AG	1,200 50		845/291-0300 Fax 845/291-0308

ORANGE PUBLIC SCHOOLS

• **Chester Union Free School Dist** PID: 00764050 845/469-5052
64 Hambletonian Ave, Chester 10918 Fax 845/469-2377

Schools: 2 \ **Teachers:** 81 \ **Students:** 986 \ **Special Ed Students:** 237 \ **LEP Students:** 37 \ **Ethnic:** Asian 5%, African American 12%, Hispanic 33%, Caucasian 50% \ **Exp:** $309 (High) \ **Poverty:** 8% \ **Title I:** $132,248 \ **Special Education:** $1,919,000 \ **Open-Close:** 09/04 - 06/25 \ **DTBP:** $169 (High)

Denis Petrilak .... 1 Erin Brennan 2,4,5
James Frees .... 3 Muhammad Ali 6
Rolando Aguilar .... 6* Ed Spence 8,16,73,76,286*
Rachel Loftus .... 58 Frank Sambets 67
Lea Morganstein .... 79,752* Lisa Ringel 88

Public Schs..Principal	Grd	Prgm	Enr/#Cls	SN	
Chester Academy 64 Hambletonian Ave, Chester 10918 John Flanagan	6-12		604 35	35%	845/469-2231 Fax 845/469-5831
Chester Elem Sch 2 Herbert Dr, Chester 10918 Cindy Walsh	K-5	T	382 24	35%	845/469-2178 Fax 845/469-2794

• **Cornwall Central School Dist** PID: 00764098 845/534-8009
24 Idlewild Ave, Cornwall HDSN 12520 Fax 845/534-9032

Schools: 5 \ **Teachers:** 224 \ **Students:** 3,122 \ **Special Ed Students:** 450 \ **LEP Students:** 45 \ **College-Bound:** 90% \ **Ethnic:** Asian 5%, African American 6%, Hispanic 20%, Caucasian 68% \ **Exp:** $229 (Med) \ **Poverty:** 4% \ **Title I:** $131,870 \ **Special Education:** $4,903,000 \ **Open-Close:** 09/02 - 06/24 \ **DTBP:** $316 (High)

Terry Dade .... 1,83 Celine Maxwell 2
Harvey Sotland .... 2,5,15 Walter Moran 3
Amy Bishop .... 4 Kayla Renna 5
Michael Kroemer .... 6* John Pinckney 7,91*
Megan Argenio .... 8,11,15,69,88,285,288,295* Nicole Triassi 11,58,79,90,271
Joseph Debold .... 36,270 Nancy Bryan 67
Zigmund Nowicki .... 68 Tina Kakascik 73,76,286
Barbara Marsh .... 77* Cynthia Betters 273*

Public Schs..Principal	Grd	Prgm	Enr/#Cls	SN	
Cornwall Central High Sch 10 Dragon Dr, New Windsor 12553 Emerly Martinez	9-12	V	1,127	14%	845/534-8009 Fax 845/565-2754
Cornwall Central Middle Sch 122 Main St, Cornwall 12518 Kate Polumbo	5-8		939	17%	845/534-8009 Fax 845/534-7809
Cornwall Elem Sch 99 Lee Rd, Cornwall 12518 Robert German	K-4		551 29	17%	845/534-8009 Fax 845/534-0569
Cornwall on Hudson Elem Sch 234 Hudson St, Cornwall HDSN 12520 Darren Corsetti	K-4		226 15	19%	845/534-8009 Fax 845/534-2284
Willow Ave Elem Sch 67 Willow Ave, Cornwall 12518 Greg Schmalz	K-4		259 15	16%	845/534-8009 Fax 845/534-3474

---

79 Student Personnel	91 Safety/Security	275 Response To Intervention	298 Grant Writer/Ptnrships	**School Programs**	**Social Media**		
80 Driver Ed/Safety	92 Magnet School	277 Remedial Math K-12	750 Chief Innovation Officer	A = Alternative Program			
81 Gifted/Talented	93 Parental Involvement	280 Literacy Coach	751 Chief of Staff	G = Adult Classes	f = Facebook		
82 Video Services	95 Tech Prep Program	285 STEM	752 Social Emotional Learning	M = Magnet Program			
83 Substance Abuse Prev	97 Chief Infomation Officer	286 Digital Learning		T = Title I Schoolwide	t = Twitter		
84 Erate	98 Chief Technology Officer	288 Common Core Standards	**Other School Types**	V = Career & Tech Ed Programs			
85 AIDS Education	270 Character Education	294 Accountability	Ⓐ = Alternative School				
88 Alternative/At Risk	271 Migrant Education	295 Network System	Ⓒ = Charter School	New Schools are shaded			
89 Multi-Cultural Curriculum	273 Teacher Mentor	296 Title II Programs	Ⓜ = Magnet School	New Superintendents and Principals are bold			
90 Social Work	274 Before/After Sch	297 Webmaster	Ⓨ = Year-Round School	Personnel with email addresses are underscored			

Orange County

Market Data Retrieval

- **Florida Union Free Sch Dist** PID: 00764907   845/651-3095
51 N Main St, Florida 10921   Fax 845/651-6801

Schools: 2 \ **Teachers:** 73 \ **Students:** 807 \ **Special Ed Students:** 131 \ **LEP Students:** 42 \ **College-Bound:** 72% \ **Ethnic:** Asian 3%, African American 5%, Hispanic 26%, Caucasian 66% \ **Exp:** $193 (Low) \ **Poverty:** 8% \ **Title I:** $103,617 \ **Special Education:** $1,244,000 \ **Open-Close:** 09/03 - 06/24 \ **DTBP:** $165 (High)

Jan Jehring 1	Christopher Slesinski 2
Howard Cohen 2,5,91	Tom Andryshak 3*
Cindy Wood 4*	Joseph Dimattina 6*
Marlene Lysack 7*	Lisa Tiger 8,11,58,83,286,288,296,298
Barbara Scheibling 31*	Greg Geroux 36,79,88,752*
John Redman 67	Dana Castine 73,76,285,295*
Debbie Lisack 274*	

Public Schs..Principal	Grd	Prgm	Enr/#Cls	SN
Golden Hill Elem Sch 478 Round Hill Rd, Florida 10921 Debbie Lisack	PK-5		366 19	28% 845/651-4407 Fax 845/651-7460
SS Seward Institute 53 N Main St, Florida 10921 Michael Rheaume	6-12	V	441 40	24% 845/651-4038 Fax 845/651-7166

- **Goshen Central School Dist** PID: 00764141   845/615-6720
227 Main St, Goshen 10924   Fax 845/615-6725

Schools: 4 \ **Teachers:** 220 \ **Students:** 2,935 \ **Special Ed Students:** 541 \ **LEP Students:** 90 \ **College-Bound:** 88% \ **Ethnic:** Asian 4%, African American 4%, Hispanic 9%, Caucasian 83% \ **Exp:** $347 (High) \ **Poverty:** 7% \ **Title I:** $320,394 \ **Special Education:** $4,352,000 \ **Open-Close:** 09/02 - 06/25 \ **DTBP:** $296 (High) \ 🅵 🅣

Daniel Connor 1	Louise Lynch 2,15
James Riley 3,91	Alan Muhlnickel 4
Karen Wells 5	Matthew Obrien 6*
Nancy Ellesen 7,83	Jason Carter 8,11,15,68,73,288
Heather Hendershot 34,57,58,79,88,271	Deana Lenz 36
Jason Pucci 67	Dr Gregory Voloshin 68
Jonathan Redeker 73	James Sterett 76,286,295

Public Schs..Principal	Grd	Prgm	Enr/#Cls	SN
C J Hooker Middle Sch 41 Lincoln Ave, Goshen 10924 Heather Carman	6-8		721 40	28% 845/615-6300 Fax 845/615-6310
Goshen High Sch 222 Scotchtown Rd, Goshen 10924 Thomas Heinzelman	9-12	AGV	969 50	26% 845/615-6100 Fax 845/615-6116
Goshen Intermediate Sch 13 McNally St, Goshen 10924 Matthew Wentworth	3-5		620 28	27% 845/615-6500 Fax 845/615-6505
Scotchtown Avenue Elem Sch 120 Scotchtown Ave, Goshen 10924 Henry Freedman	K-2		576 29	27% 845/615-6600 Fax 845/615-6610

- **Greenwood Lake Union Free SD** PID: 00764191   845/477-2411
1247 Lakes Rd, Monroe 10950   Fax 845/477-8582

Schools: 2 \ **Teachers:** 56 \ **Students:** 500 \ **Special Ed Students:** 84 \ **LEP Students:** 12 \ **Ethnic:** Asian 3%, African American 3%, Hispanic 26%, Caucasian 67% \ **Exp:** $534 (High) \ **Poverty:** 6% \ **Title I:** $85,893 \ **Special Education:** $1,546,000 \ **Open-Close:** 09/03 - 06/25 \ **DTBP:** $389 (High)

Sarah Hadden 1	Ann Lierow 2,15
Robert Porras 3,91	Alan Muhlnickel 4
Chris Ferry 6	Laura LaRoche 7*
Lina Polchinski 9	Amy Petrassi 11,59,79*
Edna Auerfeld 16,286*	Susan Selser 67
Michael LoPresti 73,76,295	Heather Greenberg 77*
Victor Pignataro 297*	

Public Schs..Principal	Grd	Prgm	Enr/#Cls	SN
Greenwood Lake Elem Sch 80 Waterstone Rd, Greenwood Lk 10925 Dianne Connolly	K-3	T	184 14	27% 845/477-2411 Fax 845/477-3180
Greenwood Lake Middle Sch 1247 Lakes Rd, Monroe 10950 Jeffrey Golubchick	4-8	T	291 40	27% 845/782-8678 Fax 845/782-2004

- **Highland Falls-Ft Montgmry SD** PID: 00764220   845/446-9575
21 Morgan Rd, Highland FLS 10928   Fax 845/446-3321

Schools: 3 \ **Teachers:** 101 \ **Students:** 1,000 \ **Special Ed Students:** 216 \ **LEP Students:** 67 \ **Ethnic:** Asian 1%, African American 12%, Hispanic 25%, Caucasian 62% \ **Exp:** $301 (High) \ **Poverty:** 6% \ **Title I:** $155,425 \ **Special Education:** $1,991,000 \ **Open-Close:** 09/08 - 06/25 \ **DTBP:** $161 (High)

Dr Frank Sheboy 1	Thomas Fargo 3,5,91
Kathryn Coakley 4	Debbie Crowe 6,85*
Andrea Tejedor 10,11,15,73,286*	Beth Hordines 11,57,59,69*
Denise Cedeira 15	Thomas Breitseller 16,31,36,270,271
Anne Lawless 67	Andrea Tejedor 71
Sarah Fitzsimmons 83,88,90	Lucas Patsch 273*

Public Schs..Principal	Grd	Prgm	Enr/#Cls	SN
Fort Montgomery Elem Sch 895 Route 9W, Ft Montgomery 10922 Rachel Adelstein	PK-2		216 9	37% 845/446-1008 Fax 845/446-6608
Highland Falls Interm Sch 52 Mountain Ave, Highland FLS 10928 Michael McElduff	3-8	T	316 30	52% 845/446-4761 Fax 845/446-0858
James I O'Neill High Sch 21 Morgan Rd, Ft Montgomery 10922 Debbie Brand	9-12		477 48	23% 845/446-4914 Fax 845/446-2123

- **Kiryas Joel Union Free SD** PID: 03423956   845/782-2300
48 Bakertown Rd Ste 401, Monroe 10950   Fax 845/782-4176

Schools: 1 \ **Teachers:** 24 \ **Students:** 167 \ **Special Ed Students:** 114 \ **LEP Students:** 90 \ **Ethnic:** Caucasian 100% \ **Exp:** $6,938 (High) \ **Poverty:** 49% \ **Special Education:** $2,746,000 \ **Open-Close:** 09/07 - 06/25 \ **DTBP:** $211 (High)

Joel Petlin 1	Shaye Wercberger 2
Jehuda Halpern 9,59,83,288*	Josh Kamensky 11,15,84,298
Dr Ricki Kramer 12,85,88	Harry Polachak 67
Judah Zelik 73	Moses Witriol 91

Public Schs..Principal	Grd	Prgm	Enr/#Cls	SN
Kiryas Joel Village 1 Dinev Rd, Monroe 10950 Jehuda Halpern	Spec	GT	167 15	84% 845/782-7510 Fax 845/782-5849

1	Superintendent	8	Curric/Instruct K-12	19	Chief Financial Officer	29	Family/Consumer Science
2	Bus/Finance/Purchasing	9	Curric/Instruct Elem	20	Art K-12	30	Adult Education
3	Buildings And Grounds	10	Curric/Instruct Sec	21	Art Elem	31	Career/Sch-to-Work K-12
4	Food Service	11	Federal Program	22	Art Sec	32	Career/Sch-to-Work Elem
5	Transportation	12	Title I	23	Music K-12	33	Career/Sch-to-Work Sec
6	Athletic	13	Title V	24	Music Elem	34	Early Childhood Ed
7	Health Services	15	Asst Superintendent	25	Music Sec	35	Health/Phys Education
		16	Instructional Media Svcs	26	Business Education	36	Guidance Services K-12
		17	Chief Operations Officer	27	Career & Tech Ed	37	Guidance Services Elem
		18	Chief Academic Officer	28	Technology Education	38	Guidance Services Sec

39	Social Studies K-12	49	English/Lang Arts Elem	59	Special Education Elem	69	Academic Assessment
40	Social Studies Elem	50	English/Lang Arts Sec	60	Special Education Sec	70	Research/Development
41	Social Studies Sec	51	Reading K-12	61	Foreign/World Lang K-12	71	Public Information
42	Science K-12	52	Reading Elem	62	Foreign/World Lang Elem	72	Summer School
43	Science Elem	53	Reading Sec	63	Foreign/World Lang Sec	73	Instructional Tech
44	Science Sec	54	Remedial Reading K-12	64	Religious Education K-12	74	Inservice Training
45	Math K-12	55	Remedial Reading Elem	65	Religious Education Elem	75	Marketing/Distributive
46	Math Elem	56	Remedial Reading Sec	66	Religious Education Sec	76	Info Systems
47	Math Sec	57	Bilingual/ELL	67	School Board President	77	Psychological Assess
48	English/Lang Arts K-12	58	Special Education K-12	68	Teacher Personnel	78	Affirmative Action

New York School Directory — Orange County

- **Middletown Enlarged City SD** PID: 00764270   845/326-1134
  223 Wisner Ave, Middletown 10940   Fax 845/326-1225

> **Schools:** 6 \ **Teachers:** 566 \ **Students:** 7,312 \ **Special Ed Students:** 1,371 \ **LEP Students:** 879 \ **College-Bound:** 75% \ **Ethnic:** Asian 3%, African American 24%, Hispanic 59%, Caucasian 14% \ **Exp:** $211 (Med) \ **Poverty:** 19% \ **Title I:** $2,601,028 \ **Special Education:** $18,266,000 \ **Open-Close:** 09/03 - 06/24 \ **DTBP:** $216 (High)

Richard Delmoro 1	Michael Tuttle 2,5,15,73,76
Peter Wilcox 3,15	Thomas Scott 3,91
Debra Donleavy 4	David Coates 6,35*
Amy Creeden 8,15	Liz Boller 11,48,51,54,280,296,298
Catherine Whaley 45	Linda Bradt 57,61,271
Karen Marconi 58	John Williams 67
Rebecca Lloyd 68	Kevin Witt 71
Stacey Atlas 273*	Janet Ferreira 294
Kevin Leonas 295	

Public Schs..Principal	Grd	Prgm	Enr/#Cls	SN	
Maple Hill Elem Sch 491 County Highway 78, Middletown 10940 Susanne Driscoll	K-5	T	1,031 60	81%	845/326-1740 Fax 845/326-1795
Middletown High Sch 30 Gardner Ave Ext, Middletown 10940 Tracey Sorrentino	9-12	ATV	2,332 52	70%	845/326-1600 Fax 845/326-1605
Monhagen Middle Sch 555 County Highway 78, Middletown 10940 Dominick Radogna	6-8	TV	836 190	76%	845/326-1700 Fax 845/326-1701
Presidential Park Elem Sch 50 Roosevelt Ave, Middletown 10940 Susan Short	K-5	T	1,405 35	80%	845/326-1850 Fax 845/326-1851
Twin Towers Middle Sch 112 Grand Ave, Middletown 10940 Gordon Dean	6-8	T	1,019 60	76%	845/326-1650 Fax 845/326-1651
William A Carter Elem Sch 345 Schutt Road Ext, Middletown 10940 Kathleen Jensen	K-5	T	782 40	77%	845/326-1711 Fax 845/326-1723

- **Minisink Valley Central SD** PID: 00764373   845/355-5100
  2320 Route 6, Slate Hill 10973   Fax 845/355-5119

> **Schools:** 5 \ **Teachers:** 298 \ **Students:** 3,493 \ **Special Ed Students:** 695 \ **LEP Students:** 68 \ **Ethnic:** Asian 2%, African American 4%, Hispanic 18%, Caucasian 76% \ **Exp:** $292 (Med) \ **Poverty:** 9% \ **Title I:** $557,622 \ **Special Education:** $9,484,000 \ **Open-Close:** 08/03 - 06/25 \ **DTBP:** $109 (High)

Brian Monahan 1	Patrick Witherow 2,15
David Roda 3	Harold Nicholson 5
Timothy Bult 6,35	Christian Ranaudo 8,11,15,69
Michael Giardina 15,68	Joseph Flaherty 67
Doug Reiser 73,76	Teresia Parker 74
Elizabeth Law 79	

Public Schs..Principal	Grd	Prgm	Enr/#Cls	SN	
Minisink Valley Elem Sch 2320 Route 6, Slate Hill 10973 Coleen Fitzgerald	K-2		447 28	25%	845/355-5270 Fax 845/355-5147
Minisink Valley High Sch 2320 Route 6, Slate Hill 10973 Kenneth Hauck	9-12	AGV	1,217 120	24%	845/355-5150 Fax 845/355-5198
Minisink Valley Interm Sch 2320 Route 6, Slate Hill 10973 Paul Dombal	3-5		468 35	28%	845/355-5254 Fax 845/355-5252
Minisink Valley Middle Sch 2320 Route 6, Slate Hill 10973 Michael Larsen	6-8	V	822 40	27%	845/355-5200 Fax 845/355-5205
Otisville Elem Sch 2525 Mt Hope Rd, Otisville 10963 Vincent Biele	K-5	T	539 17	33%	845/355-5850 Fax 845/355-5853

- **Monroe Woodbury Central SD** PID: 00764426   845/460-6200
  278 Route 32, Central Vly 10917   Fax 845/460-6080

> **Schools:** 7 \ **Teachers:** 486 \ **Students:** 6,900 \ **Special Ed Students:** 1,329 \ **LEP Students:** 297 \ **College-Bound:** 89% \ **Ethnic:** Asian 7%, African American 9%, Hispanic 32%, Caucasian 53% \ **Exp:** $249 (Med) \ **Poverty:** 10% \ **Title I:** $1,099,468 \ **Special Education:** $14,317,000 \ **Open-Close:** 09/02 - 06/25 \ **DTBP:** $330 (High)

Elsie Rodriguez 1	Patrick Cahill 2,15
Peter Quartironi 3	Aldis Ansons 4
Dawn Russell 5	Patricia Batewell 5
Lori Hock 6,35,83,85*	Christine Ricker 7,77,79,90*
Dr Lisa Sassi 7	Dr Eric Hassler 8,15
Karin Morales 11,57*	Karen Morales 12
Bhargav Vyas 15,73,295	Matthew Kravatz 15,68,74*
Wayne Williams 36*	Eric Eulau 58
Karen Jordan 58	Don Beeler 67
Jason McElroy 72*	Kristin Randhare 79
Debra Garling 81*	Frank Squillante 91*

Public Schs..Principal	Grd	Prgm	Enr/#Cls	SN	
Central Valley Elem Sch 45 Route 32, Central Vly 10917 Christine Arlt	2-5		554 30	31%	845/460-6700 Fax 845/460-6047
Monroe Woodbury Middle Sch 199 Dunderberg Rd, Central Vly 10917 Michael Maesano	6-8		1,660	30%	845/460-6400 Fax 845/460-6044
Monroe Woodbury Sr High Sch 155 Dunderberg Rd, Central Vly 10917 John Kaste	9-12		2,329 72	26%	845/460-7000 Fax 845/460-7090
North Main Elem Sch 212 N Main St, Monroe 10950 Joseph Coto	2-5	T	520 26	41%	845/460-6800 Fax 845/460-6048
Pine Tree Elem Sch 156 Pine Tree Rd, Monroe 10950 Bryan Giudice	2-5		846 38	26%	845/460-6900 Fax 845/460-6049
Sapphire Elem Sch 159 Harriman Heights Rd, Harriman 10926 Caitlin Caldwell	K-1		187 18	27%	845/460-6500 Fax 845/460-6045
Smith Clove Elem Sch 21 Smith Clove Rd, Central Vly 10917 Christopher Berger	K-1		385 32	39%	845/460-6300 Fax 845/460-6043

- **Newburgh Enlarged City SD** PID: 00764579   845/563-3400
  124 Grand St, Newburgh 12550   Fax 845/563-3501

> **Schools:** 13 \ **Teachers:** 910 \ **Students:** 11,562 \ **Special Ed Students:** 2,084 \ **LEP Students:** 1,566 \ **Ethnic:** Asian 2%, African American 24%, Hispanic 55%, Caucasian 19% \ **Exp:** $714 (High) \ **Poverty:** 20% \ **Title I:** $4,449,353 \ **Special Education:** $24,320,000 \ **Open-Close:** 09/02 - 06/25 \ **DTBP:** $198 (High)

Dr Roberto Padilla 1	Greg Kern 2,15
Anibal Velez 3	Caitlin Lazarski 4
Patricia Coyne 5	Edgar Glascott 5
Dr James Thomas 7	Sara Feliz 8,15
Sonya Dixon 11,296,298	Chris Bayer 15,36,39,58,79
Ed Forgit 15	Michael McLymore 15,68,88
Theresa Brown 20,23,294	John Etri 27*

79	Student Personnel	91	Safety/Security	275	Response To Intervention	298 Grant Writer/Ptnrships
80	Driver Ed/Safety	92	Magnet School	277	Remedial Math K-12	750 Chief Innovation Officer
81	Gifted/Talented	93	Parental Involvement	280	Literacy Coach	751 Chief of Staff
82	Video Services	95	Tech Prep Program	285	STEM	752 Social Emotional Learning
83	Substance Abuse Prev	97	Chief Information Officer	286	Digital Learning	
84	Erate	98	Chief Technology Officer	288	Common Core Standards	
85	AIDS Education	270	Character Education	294	Accountability	
88	Alternative/At Risk	271	Migrant Education	295	Network System	
89	Multi-Cultural Curriculum	273	Teacher Mentor	296	Title II Programs	
90	Social Work	274	Before/After Sch	297	Webmaster	

School Programs
A = Alternative Program
G = Adult Classes
M = Magnet Program
T = Title I Schoolwide
V = Career & Tech Ed Programs

Other School Types
Ⓐ = Alternative School
Ⓒ = Charter School
Ⓜ = Magnet School
Ⓨ = Year-Round School

Social Media
 = Facebook
 = Twitter

New Schools are shaded
New Superintendents and Principals are bold
Personnel with email addresses are underscored

Orange County

Market Data Retrieval

Alfred Romano 42
Carole Mineo 67
John Krouskoff 73,76,98,295
Lynne Pampel 79
Pamela Peterson 93

Chris Fiorentino 45
Dr Pedro Roman 68
Anne Lytle 76,97
Christina Cloidt 81

Public Schs..Principal	Grd	Prgm	Enr/#Cls	SN	
ⓜ Balmville Elem Sch 5144 Route 9W, Newburgh 12550 Lisa Buon	PK-5	T	451 22	57%	845/563-8550 Fax 845/563-8554
ⓜ Fostertown ETC Magnet Sch 364 Fostertown Rd, Newburgh 12550 Joseph Duffy	K-5	T	642 29	49%	845/568-6425 Fax 845/568-6430
ⓜ Gams Tech Magnet Sch 300 Gidney Ave, Newburgh 12550 Tara Marshall	PK-5	T	811	64%	845/563-8450 Fax 845/563-8459
ⓜ Gardnertown Fund Mag Sch 6 Plattekill Tpke, Newburgh 12550 Lillian Torres	PK-5	T	677 32	54%	845/568-6400 Fax 845/568-6408
Heritage Middle Sch 405 Union Ave, New Windsor 12553 Lynnette Brunger	6-8	AT	943 85	62%	845/563-3750 Fax 845/563-3759
ⓜ Horizons on Hudson Mag Sch 137 Montgomery St, Newburgh 12550 Rob Glowacki	PK-5	T	478 26	66%	845/563-3725 Fax 845/563-3730
ⓜ Meadow Hill Global Sch 124 Meadow Hill Rd, Newburgh 12550 Scott Prokosch	K-8	T	1,057 90	69%	845/568-6600 Fax 845/568-6609
ⓜ New Windsor Sch 175 Quassaick Ave, New Windsor 12553 Dennis Camt	K-5	T	463 30	62%	845/563-3700 Fax 845/563-3709
Newburgh Free Acad-Main Campus 201 Fullerton Ave, Newburgh 12550 Raul Rodriguez	9-12	GTV	3,325 90	60%	845/563-5400 Fax 845/563-5405
Newburgh Free Acad-N Campus 301 Robinson Ave, Newburgh 12550 Matteo Doddo	9-12		1,000 120		845/563-8400 Fax 845/563-8409
ⓜ South Middle Sch 33 Monument St 63, Newburgh 12550 Chante Brooks	6-8	T	934 80	65%	845/563-7000 Fax 845/563-7019
ⓜ Temple Hill Academy 525 Union Ave, New Windsor 12553 Ventura Lopez	K-8	T	982 60	79%	845/568-6450 Fax 845/568-6470
ⓜ Vails Gate High Tech Magnet ES 400 Old Forge Hill Rd, New Windsor 12553 Ciria Briscoe-Perez	K-5	T	552 50	73%	845/563-7900 Fax 845/563-7909

● **Pine Bush Central School Dist** PID: 00764799
156 State Route 302, Pine Bush 12566
845/744-2031
Fax 845/744-6189

Schools: 8 \ **Teachers:** 384 \ **Students:** 5,000 \ **Special Ed Students:** 973
\ **LEP Students:** 182 \ **College-Bound:** 84% \ **Ethnic:** Asian 2%, African
American 10%, Hispanic 17%, Caucasian 70% \ **Exp:** $207 (Med) \
Poverty: 12% \ **Title I:** $977,788 \ **Special Education:** $12,500,000 \
Open-Close: 09/08 - 06/25 \ **DTBP:** $224 (High)

Tim Mains 1,11
Jenn Byrne 2
James Licardi 3
Kurt Wickham 5
Amy Brockner 8,13,15,288
Ruth Holt 30
Gretchen Meier 67
Alex Tremper 91

Dawn Loechner 2
Michael Pacella 2,5,15
Lyn Prestia 4
Micheal Gillespie 6,35*
John Hicks 16,73,82,95,295*
Rosemary Mannino 58
Angela Wise 68,76

Public Schs..Principal	Grd	Prgm	Enr/#Cls	SN	
Circleville Elem Sch 2000 Route 302, Circleville 10919 Amy Brockner	PK-5	T	454 30	49%	845/744-2031 Fax 845/361-2136
Circleville Middle Sch 1951 Route 302, Circleville 10919 Lisa Hankinson	6-8	T	565	57%	845/744-2031 Fax 845/361-3811
Crispell Middle Sch 77 Maple Ave, Pine Bush 12566 John Boyle	6-8	T	693 56	41%	845/744-2031 Fax 845/744-2261
E J Russell Elem Sch 78 Holland Ave, Pine Bush 12566 Elizabeth Sproul	PK-5	T	570 30	36%	845/744-2031 Fax 845/744-3308
Pakanasink Elem Sch 1953 Route 302, Circleville 10919 Brian Breheny	PK-5	T	455 24	67%	845/744-2031 Fax 845/361-3816
Pine Bush Elem Sch 21 Ulsterville Rd, Pine Bush 12566 Eric Winter	PK-5	T	658 34	44%	845/744-2031 Fax 845/744-8092
Pine Bush High Sch 118 State Route 302, Pine Bush 12566 Aaron Hopmayer	9-12	T	1,666	43%	845/744-2031 Fax 845/744-3488
ⓐ Stars Academy 118 State Route 302, Pine Bush 12566 Andre Spinelli	9-12		20		845/744-2031

● **Port Jervis City School Dist** PID: 00764854
9 Thompson St, Port Jervis 12771
845/858-3100
Fax 845/856-1885

Schools: 4 \ **Teachers:** 222 \ **Students:** 2,332 \ **Special Ed Students:** 634
\ **LEP Students:** 31 \ **College-Bound:** 69% \ **Ethnic:** Asian 2%, African
American 9%, Hispanic 18%, Caucasian 72% \ **Exp:** $320 (High) \
Poverty: 21% \ **Title I:** $1,067,698 \ **Special Education:** $8,337,000 \
Open-Close: 09/04 - 06/25 \ **DTBP:** $231 (High) \

Mike Rydell 1,11,57,83
Don Preiss 3
Ray Holyk 6,7,35,85*
Lisa Perkowski 16*
Debroah Lasch 67

Jospeh Lenz 2,15
Deahbra Mills 4
Nicholas Pantaleone 8,15,288,296
Meagan Sullivan 58
Emerson Segara 73

Public Schs..Principal	Grd	Prgm	Enr/#Cls	SN	
Anna S Kuhl Elem Sch 10 Route 209, Port Jervis 12771 Brett Cancredi	K-6	T	877 47	63%	845/858-3100 Fax 845/858-2894
Hamilton Bicentennial Elem Sch 929 US Route 209, Cuddebackvlle 12729 Jared Kahmar	K-6	T	427 30	51%	845/858-3100 Fax 845/754-7355
Port Jervis High Sch 10 Route 209, Port Jervis 12771 Andrew Marotta	9-12	AV	751 40	51%	845/858-3100 Fax 845/858-2895
Port Jervis Middle Sch 118 E Main St, Port Jervis 12771 Jean Lain	7-8	TV	390 44	60%	845/858-3100 Fax 845/858-2893

● **Tuxedo Union Free Sch Dist** PID: 00764921
1 Tornado Dr, Tuxedo Park 10987
845/351-4786
Fax 845/351-5296

Schools: 2 \ **Teachers:** 30 \ **Students:** 225 \ **Special Ed Students:** 61
\ **LEP Students:** 10 \ **College-Bound:** 99% \ **Ethnic:** Asian 3%,
African American 6%, Hispanic 15%, Caucasian 75% \ **Exp:** $626 (High)
\ **Poverty:** 5% \ **Title I:** $29,994 \ **Special Education:** $524,000 \
Open-Close: 09/03 - 06/25 \ **DTBP:** $359 (High)

Timothy Bohlke 1   Kevin Ziemba 2,4,11,296

1 Superintendent	8 Curric/Instruct K-12	19 Chief Financial Officer	29 Family/Consumer Science
2 Bus/Finance/Purchasing	9 Curric/Instruct Elem	20 Art K-12	30 Adult Education
3 Buildings And Grounds	10 Curric/Instruct Sec	21 Art Elem	31 Career/Sch-to-Work K-12
4 Food Service	11 Federal Program	22 Art Sec	32 Career/Sch-to-Work Elem
5 Transportation	12 Title I	23 Music K-12	33 Career/Sch-to-Work Sec
6 Athletic	13 Title V	24 Music Elem	34 Early Childhood Ed
7 Health Services	15 Asst Superintendent	25 Music Sec	35 Health/Phys Education
	16 Instructional Media Svcs	26 Business Education	36 Guidance Services K-12
	17 Chief Operations Officer	27 Career & Tech Ed	37 Guidance Services Elem
	18 Chief Academic Officer	28 Technology Education	38 Guidance Services Sec

39 Social Studies K-12	49 English/Lang Arts Elem	59 Special Education Elem	69 Academic Assessment
40 Social Studies Elem	50 English/Lang Arts Sec	60 Special Education Sec	70 Research/Development
41 Social Studies Sec	51 Reading K-12	61 Foreign/World Lang K-12	71 Public Information
42 Science K-12	52 Reading Elem	62 Foreign/World Lang Elem	72 Summer School
43 Science Elem	53 Reading Sec	63 Foreign/World Lang Sec	73 Instructional Tech
44 Science Sec	54 Remedial Reading K-12	64 Religious Education K-12	74 Inservice Training
45 Math K-12	55 Remedial Reading Elem	65 Religious Education Elem	75 Marketing/Distributive
46 Math Elem	56 Remedial Reading Sec	66 Religious Education Sec	76 Info Systems
47 Math Sec	57 Bilingual/ELL	67 School Board President	77 Psychological Assess
48 English/Lang Arts K-12	58 Special Education K-12	68 Teacher Personnel	78 Affirmative Action

New York School Directory — Orange County

Brendon Eirind	3
John Landro	6*
Dorothy Ziegelbauer	67
Arlene Dyba	76
Marco Margata	285
Joann Martin	5
Christine Oliva	36*
Paul Brown	73
Nicole Scarunio	77,79

Public Schs..Principal	Grd	Prgm	Enr/#Cls	SN	
George F Baker High Sch PO Box 2002, Tuxedo Park 10987 Timothy Bohkle	7-12	V	101 30	17%	845/351-4786 Fax 845/351-4823
George Grant Mason Elem Sch 11 Hillside Ave, Tuxedo Park 10987 Jason Schrammel	K-6	T	122 13	25%	845/351-4797 Fax 845/351-3402

• **Valley Central School Dist** PID: 00764490   845/457-2400
  944 State Route 17K, Montgomery 12549   Fax 845/457-4319

> **Schools:** 7 \ **Teachers:** 368 \ **Students:** 4,200 \ **Special Ed Students:** 937 \ **LEP Students:** 51 \ **College-Bound:** 80% \ **Ethnic:** Asian 2%, African American 8%, Hispanic 25%, Caucasian 65% \ **Exp:** $220 (Med) \ **Poverty:** 9% \ **Title I:** $638,061 \ **Special Education:** $13,461,000 \ **Open-Close:** 09/02 - 06/25 \ **DTBP:** $224 (High)

John Xanthis	1
Eleanore Mills	4*
Marianne Serratore	8,15
Tammy Coleman	34
Georgia Patchen	58
Christopher Mohr	73
Brad Conklin	2
William Miller	6,35*
Michael Bellarosa	15,68
Barbra Butler	58*
Joseph Bond	67

Public Schs..Principal	Grd	Prgm	Enr/#Cls	SN	
ⓐ Alternative Learning Center 120 Broadway, Maybrook 12543 Barbra Butler	K-12		30		845/457-2400 Fax 845/427-5119
Berea Elem Sch 946 State Route 17K, Montgomery 12549 John Solimando	K-5	T	487	41%	845/457-2400 Fax 845/457-4442
East Coldenham Elem Sch 286 Route 17K, Newburgh 12550 Dan McDonald	K-5	T	316 12	42%	845/457-2400 Fax 845/564-1554
Montgomery Elem Sch 141 Union St, Montgomery 12549 Matthew Canino	K-5	T	550 44	30%	845/457-2400 Fax 845/457-9120
Valley Central High Sch 1175 State Route 17K, Montgomery 12549 Jayme Baxter	9-12		1,383 100	36%	845/457-2400 Fax 845/457-4056
Valley Central Middle Sch 1189 State Route 17K, Montgomery 12549 Russel Burns	6-8	A	963 86	38%	845/457-2400 Fax 845/457-4311
Walden Elem Sch 75 Orchard St, Walden 12586 Gregory Heidemann	K-5	T	432 25	48%	845/457-2400 Fax 845/778-7110

• **Warwick Valley Central SD** PID: 00764945   845/987-3000
  225 W Street Ext, Warwick 10990   Fax 845/987-1147

> **Schools:** 4 \ **Teachers:** 264 \ **Students:** 3,569 \ **Special Ed Students:** 688 \ **LEP Students:** 47 \ **College-Bound:** 90% \ **Ethnic:** Asian 2%, African American 4%, Hispanic 15%, Caucasian 78% \ **Exp:** $492 (High) \ **Poverty:** 5% \ **Title I:** $324,484 \ **Special Education:** $5,181,000 \ **Open-Close:** 09/04 - 06/25 \ **DTBP:** $224 (High) \ 🅵 🆃

Dr David Leach	1
Timothy Holmes	2,11,15
Debbie Weissman	5
James Yap	8,15,329
Jennifer Bengel	2
Steven Salvato	3
Gregory Sirico	6*
Cindy Leandro	15,91
Kathleen Turner	16,82*
Meghan McGourty	58,79
Mary Fox	31,36*
Sharon Davis	67

Public Schs..Principal	Grd	Prgm	Enr/#Cls	SN	
Park Ave Elem Sch 10 Park Ave, Warwick 10990 Sandra Wood	K-4		484	17%	845/987-3170 Fax 845/988-5893 🅵 🆃
Sanfordville Elem Sch 144 Sanfordville Rd, Warwick 10990 Johnna Maraia	K-4		703	18%	845/987-3300 Fax 845/986-7287
Warwick Valley High Sch 89 Sanfordville Rd, Warwick 10990 Marguerite Fusco	9-12	GV	1,326	16%	845/987-3050 Fax 845/987-2061 🅵 🆃
Warwick Valley Middle Sch 225 W Street Ext, Warwick 10990 Georgianna Diopoulos	5-8	GV	1,056 150	18%	845/987-3100 Fax 845/986-6942 🅵 🆃

• **Washingtonville Central SD** PID: 00765004   845/497-4000
  52 W Main St, Washingtonvle 10992   Fax 845/497-4030

> **Schools:** 5 \ **Teachers:** 302 \ **Students:** 3,793 \ **Special Ed Students:** 633 \ **LEP Students:** 87 \ **Ethnic:** Asian 3%, African American 9%, Hispanic 25%, Caucasian 63% \ **Exp:** $140 (Low) \ **Poverty:** 8% \ **Title I:** $593,070 \ **Special Education:** $6,888,000 \ **Open-Close:** 09/03 - 06/25 \ **DTBP:** $326 (High)

Dr Larry Washington	1
Paul Nienstadt	3,15,91
Ralph Perez	5
Dr Michael Cogliano	15,57,58,79
Scott Lerner	36,285*
Katrina Kiernan	42,45*
Lynn Imperato	68
Arielle Sikora	77
Lorine Lamerand	2,11,15,97
Robert Gellman	4
Barbara Quinn	8,15,296,298
Margo Hadley-Bell	34,58*
William Ormiston	41,50*
Jennifer Dellova	67
Joseph Catania	76,295
Carla Sansone	273*

Public Schs..Principal	Grd	Prgm	Enr/#Cls	SN	
Little Britain Elem Sch Rt 207, New Windsor 12553 Sagrario O'Neill	1-5	T	408 30	12%	845/497-4000 Fax 845/497-4003
Round Hill Elem Sch 1314 Route 208, Washingtonvle 10992 Steve Kiel	PK-5	T	648 42	34%	845/497-4000 Fax 845/497-4005
Taft Elem Sch 20 Toleman Rd, Washingtonvle 10992 Christine Williams	K-5	T	716 34	18%	845/497-4000 Fax 845/497-4002
Washingtonville Middle Sch 38 W Main St, Washingtonvle 10992 Teresa Thompson	6-8	TV	952	26%	845/497-4000 Fax 845/497-4001
Washingtonville Sr High Sch 54 W Main St, Washingtonvle 10992 Brian Connolly	9-12	AGTV	1,337	22%	845/497-4000 Fax 845/497-4004

• **West Point School Dist** PID: 03179765   845/938-2923
  705A Barry Rd, West Point 10996

> **Schools:** 2 \ **Students:** 629 \ **Open-Close:** 08/24 - 06/11 \ **DTBP:** $161 (High)

Helen Balilo	1

Public Schs..Principal	Grd	Prgm	Enr/#Cls	SN	
West Point Elem Sch 705A Barry Rd, West Point 10996 Denise DeMarco	PK-5		430 25		845/839-7500 Fax 845/839-7518

79	Student Personnel	91	Safety/Security	275	Response To Intervention	298	Grant Writer/Ptnrships
80	Driver Ed/Safety	92	Magnet School	277	Remedial Math K-12	750	Chief Innovation Officer
81	Gifted/Talented	93	Parental Involvement	280	Literacy Coach	751	Chief of Staff
82	Video Services	95	Tech Prep Program	285	STEM	752	Social Emotional Learning
83	Substance Abuse Prev	97	Chief Information Officer	286	Digital Learning		
84	Erate	98	Chief Technology Officer	288	Common Core Standards		
85	AIDS Education	270	Character Education	294	Accountability		
88	Alternative/At Risk	271	Migrant Education	295	Network System		
89	Multi-Cultural Curriculum	273	Teacher Mentor	296	Title II Programs		
90	Social Work	274	Before/After Sch	297	Webmaster		

School Programs
A = Alternative Program
G = Adult Classes
M = Magnet Program
T = Title I Schoolwide
V = Career & Tech Ed Programs

Other School Types
Ⓐ = Alternative School
Ⓒ = Charter School
Ⓜ = Magnet School
Ⓨ = Year-Round School

Social Media
🅵 = Facebook
🆃 = Twitter

New Schools are shaded
New Superintendents and Principals are bold
Personnel with email addresses are underscored

Orleans County

Market Data Retrieval

West Point Middle Sch 705 Barry Rd, West Point 10996 Miles Shea	6-8	199 25	845/938-2923 Fax 845/938-2568

ORANGE CATHOLIC SCHOOLS

• **Archdiocese of New York Ed Off** PID: 00754976
Listing includes only schools located in this county. See District Index for location of Diocesan Offices.

Catholic Schs..Principal	Grd	Prgm	Enr/#Cls	SN
Bishop Dunn Memorial Sch 50 Gidney Ave, Newburgh 12550 Nancy Benfer	PK-8		215 14	845/569-3494 Fax 845/569-3303
John S Burke Catholic High Sch 80 Fletcher St, Goshen 10924 Janet Clark	9-12		400 30	845/294-5481 Fax 845/294-0817
Most Precious Blood Sch 180 Ulster Ave, Walden 12586 Woodrow Hallaway	PK-8		140 9	845/778-3028 Fax 845/778-3785
Our Lady of Mt Carmel Sch 205 Wawayanda Ave, Middletown 10940 Jennifer Langford	1-8		269 15	845/343-8836 Fax 845/342-1404
Sacred Heart Sch 26 Still Rd, Monroe 10950 Catherine Muenkel	PK-8		223 10	845/783-0365 Fax 845/782-0354
St John Sch 77 Murray Ave, Goshen 10924 Linda Power	PK-8		175 8	845/294-6434 Fax 845/294-7303
St Stephen & St Edward Sch 75 Sanfordville Rd, Warwick 10990 Bethany Negersmith	PK-8		300 12	845/986-3533 Fax 845/987-7023

ORANGE PRIVATE SCHOOLS

Private Schs..Principal	Grd	Prgm	Enr/#Cls	SN
Blooming Grove Academy 422 Blooming Grove Tpke, New Windsor 12553 Lisa Rinaldo	Spec		401	845/863-3334
Bnei Yoel Sch 156 Acres Rd, Monroe 10950 Yitchok Tyrnaver	PK-12		411	845/783-8036 Fax 845/782-7039
Chapel Field Christian Sch 211 Fleury Rd, Pine Bush 12566 Cindy Schoch \ David Stein	PK-12		280	845/778-1881 Fax 845/778-5841
Cong Mesifta Ohr Hatalmud 701 Blooming Grove Tpke, New Windsor 12553 Moshe Silberberg	9-12		100	845/784-4020 Fax 845/784-4028
Fei Tian Academy of the Arts 140 Galley Hill Rd, Cuddebackvlle 12729 Huaping Guo	6-12		200	845/754-4226 Fax 845/977-0481
Goshen Christian Sch 2430 State Route 17A, Goshen 10924 Sharon Vogel	PK-PK		40 10	845/294-6365
Harmony Christian Sch 1790 Route 211 E, Middletown 10941 Kevin Barry \ Vanessa Veras \ Penny Garr	PK-12	GV	204 18	845/692-5353 Fax 845/692-7140
Middletown Christian Sch 70 Highland Ave, Middletown 10940 Lionel Jean Jacques	PK-8		63 5	845/343-3775 Fax 845/343-6633
Montgomery Montessori Sch 136 Clinton St, Montgomery 12549 Parinaz Mokhtari	PK-8		45	845/401-9232
New Beginnings Montessori Sch 33 Albert St, Middletown 10940 Frank Tramontano	PK-2		168 8	845/342-0051 Fax 845/342-1719
New York Military Academy 78 Academy Ave, Cornwall HDSN 12520 Jeffery Coverdale	7-12		62 20	888/275-6962 Fax 845/534-7891
Nora Cronin Presentation Acad 69 Bay View Ter, Newburgh 12550 Sr Yliana Hernndez	5-8		60	845/567-0708 Fax 845/567-0709
Northern Academy 1 Ashley Ave, Middletown 10940 Dr Marilyn Torley	6-12		41	845/779-0808
San Miguel Academy of Newburgh 245 Renwick St, Newburgh 12550 Kerry DiMeo	5-8		60	845/561-2822 Fax 845/561-0312
Storm King Sch 314 Mountain Rd, Cornwall HDSN 12520 Jonathan Lamb	8-12		140 12	845/534-7892 Fax 845/534-2709
Thevenet Montessori Sch 21 Bethany Dr, Highland Mls 10930 Sr Joan Faraone	PK-6		120 4	845/928-6981 Fax 845/928-3179
Tuxedo Park Sch 1 Mountain Farm Rd, Tuxedo Park 10987 Todd Stansbery	PK-9		250 16	845/351-4737
United Talmudical Bais Rachel 7 Israel Zupnick Dr, Monroe 10950 Elliott Cohen	PK-12		1,800	845/783-5820 Fax 845/782-7302
Windsor Academy 271 Quassaick Ave, New Windsor 12553 Rita Epstein	PK-6		200	845/562-3711 Fax 845/562-2222

ORANGE REGIONAL CENTERS

• **Orange-Ulster BOCES** PID: 00765066   845/291-0100
53 Gibson Rd, Goshen 10924   Fax 845/291-0138

William Hecht 1	Deborah McBride-Heppes 2,4,15
Mark Coleman 3	Patricia Milburn 5
Theresa Reynolds 8,15,298	Orande Daring 27,31
Andrew Carnright 30	Kerri Stroka 58,88
Eugenia Pavek 67	Forrest Addor 73,76
Dr Diane Lang 74	

ORLEANS COUNTY

ORLEANS COUNTY SCHOOLS

County Schs..Principal	Grd	Prgm	Enr/#Cls	SN
Orleans-Niagara BOCES Sch 4232 Shelby Basin Rd, Medina 14103 Michael Mann	Voc	AG	500 18	14% 716/731-6800 Fax 585/798-1317

1 Superintendent	8 Curric/Instruct K-12	19 Chief Financial Officer	29 Family/Consumer Science	39 Social Studies K-12	49 English/Lang Arts Elem	59 Special Education Elem	69 Academic Assessment
2 Bus/Finance/Purchasing	9 Curric/Instruct Elem	20 Art K-12	30 Adult Education	40 Social Studies Elem	50 English/Lang Arts Sec	60 Special Education Sec	70 Research/Development
3 Buildings And Grounds	10 Curric/Instruct Sec	21 Art Elem	31 Career/Sch-to-Work K-12	41 Social Studies Sec	51 Reading K-12	61 Foreign/World Lang K-12	71 Public Information
4 Food Service	11 Federal Program	22 Art Sec	32 Career/Sch-to-Work Elem	42 Science K-12	52 Reading Elem	62 Foreign/World Lang Elem	72 Summer School
5 Transportation	12 Title I	23 Music K-12	33 Career/Sch-to-Work Sec	43 Science Elem	53 Reading Sec	63 Foreign/World Lang Sec	73 Instructional Tech
6 Athletic	13 Title V	24 Music Elem	34 Early Childhood Ed	44 Science Sec	54 Remedial Reading K-12	64 Religious Education K-12	74 Inservice Training
7 Health Services	15 Asst Superintendent	25 Music Sec	35 Health/Phys Education	45 Math K-12	55 Remedial Reading Elem	65 Religious Education Elem	75 Marketing/Distributive
	16 Instructional Media Svcs	26 Business Education	36 Guidance Services K-12	46 Math Elem	56 Remedial Reading Sec	66 Religious Education Sec	76 Info Systems
	17 Chief Operations Officer	27 Career & Tech Ed	37 Guidance Services Elem	47 Math Sec	57 Bilingual/ELL	67 School Board President	77 Psychological Assess
	18 Chief Academic Officer	28 Technology Education	38 Guidance Services Sec	48 English/Lang Arts K-12	58 Special Education K-12	68 Teacher Personnel	78 Affirmative Action

New York School Directory — Orleans County

ORLEANS PUBLIC SCHOOLS

• **Albion Central School Dist** PID: 00765133 — 585/589-2056
324 East Ave, Albion 14411 — Fax 585/589-2059

Schools: 3 \ **Teachers:** 146 \ **Students:** 1,860 \ **Special Ed Students:** 256 \ **LEP Students:** 46 \ **College-Bound:** 73% \ **Ethnic:** Asian 1%, African American 12%, Hispanic 11%, Native American: 1%, Caucasian 76% \ **Exp:** $424 (High) \ **Poverty:** 15% \ **Title I:** $626,062 \ **Special Education:** $3,398,000 \ **Open-Close:** 09/09 - 06/25 \ **DTBP:** $166 (High)

Michael Bonnewell 1,83
Tim Mercer 3
Lea Olles 5
Mary Leto 8,11,16,69,74,271,296,298
Jenna George 37
Jessica Beal 58
James Wood 68
Mark Vanacore 73,295
Amy Castricone 79
Shawn Liddle 2,5,15,91
Maevonne Luckman 4
Randy Knaak 6
Della Morales 16*
Carmen Rosebrittan 57
Kathy Harling 67
Sue Miller 71*
Eric Christiansen 77*
Elizabeth Marquette 273*

Public Schs..Principal	Grd	Prgm	Enr/#Cls	SN	
Carl I Bergerson Middle Sch 254 East Ave, Albion 14411 Bradley Pritchard	6-8	T	427 55	64%	585/589-2020 Fax 585/589-2029
Charles C D'Amico High Sch 302 East Ave, Albion 14411 Matthew Peterson	9-12		545 60	56%	585/589-2040 Fax 585/589-2049
Ronald L Sodoma Elem Sch 324 East Ave, Albion 14411 Rachel Curtin	PK-5	T	888 53	58%	585/589-2030

• **Holley Central School Dist** PID: 00765183 — 585/638-6316
3800 N Main Street Rd, Holley 14470 — Fax 585/638-7409

Schools: 2 \ **Teachers:** 89 \ **Students:** 1,200 \ **Special Ed Students:** 150 \ **LEP Students:** 12 \ **Ethnic:** Asian 1%, African American 2%, Hispanic 9%, Caucasian 89% \ **Exp:** $154 (Low) \ **Poverty:** 14% \ **Title I:** $338,116 \ **Special Education:** $2,625,000 \ **Open-Close:** 09/09 - 06/24 \ **DTBP:** $359 (High) \

Brian Bartalo 1
John Sherman 3
Tammy Beaney 5
Orissa Hill 7*
Susan Cory 10,12,69,79*
Lisa Osur 16*
Robin Silvis 67
Karen Gaylord 2,71,97
Vickie Scroger 4*
Dan Courtney 6*
Rose Porter 7*
Sharon Zacher 15
Stephanie Sanchez 58*

Public Schs..Principal	Grd	Prgm	Enr/#Cls	SN	
Holley Elem Sch 3800 N Main Street Rd, Holley 14470 Karrie Schiavone	PK-6	T	549 35	60%	585/638-6318 Fax 585/638-0706
Holley Middle High Sch 16848 Lynch Rd, Holley 14470 Susan Cory	7-12	TV	422 45	55%	585/638-6318 Fax 585/638-7925

• **Kendall Central School Dist** PID: 00765212 — 585/659-2741
1932 Kendall Rd, Kendall 14476 — Fax 585/659-8903

Schools: 2 \ **Teachers:** 69 \ **Students:** 710 \ **Special Ed Students:** 129 \ **LEP Students:** 3 \ **Ethnic:** African American 1%, Hispanic 6%, Caucasian 93% \ **Exp:** $298 (Med) \ **Poverty:** 13% \ **Title I:** $180,956 \ **Special Education:** $1,960,000 \ **Open-Close:** 09/08 - 06/25 \ **DTBP:** $363 (High)

Julie Christensen 1,11
Dan Brundage 3,91
Robert Ryan 5
Marjorie Lapp 7*
Carol D'Agostino 10*
Justin Laurenau 35,83,85
Richard Hancy 73,295
Jackie Nielsen 286
Deb Ryan 2,19
Donna Faulkner 4
Nick Picardo 6,58*
Heather Eysaman 8,270,273,274
Ari Aranov 31,38,77,90
Lisa Levett 67
Melisa Rath 77*
Tracie Heise 298*

Public Schs..Principal	Grd	Prgm	Enr/#Cls	SN	
Kendall Elem Sch 1932 Kendall Rd, Kendall 14476 Kevin Watson	PK-6	T	377 30	51%	585/659-8317 Fax 585/659-8940
Kendall Jr Sr High Sch 16887 Roosevelt Hwy, Kendall 14476 Kevin Watson \ Carol D'Agostino	7-12	AT	338 50	44%	585/659-2706 Fax 585/659-8988

• **Lyndonville Central Sch Dist** PID: 00765248 — 585/765-2251
25 Housel Ave, Lyndonville 14098 — Fax 585/765-3190

Schools: 2 \ **Teachers:** 60 \ **Students:** 700 \ **Special Ed Students:** 117 \ **LEP Students:** 6 \ **Ethnic:** Asian 1%, African American 1%, Hispanic 5%, Native American: 1%, Caucasian 93% \ **Exp:** $359 (High) \ **Poverty:** 14% \ **Title I:** $186,929 \ **Special Education:** $830,000 \ **Open-Close:** 09/08 - 06/25 \ **DTBP:** $377 (High) \

Jason Smith 1
Kevin Czaja 3
Lynne Fetzner 5
Mary Kurz 7*
Aaron Slack 10*
Jeffrey Kingsbury 38,69*
Theodore Lewis 67
Penny Barry 77*
Joseph Dipassio 2,11,19,296
Michelle Higgins 4
James Zeliff 6
Sharon Smith 8,36,58,88,97
Todd Wolford 16,73,82*
Kimberlyann Meal 57
Jason Wilhelm 73*
Shane Phillips 85*

Public Schs..Principal	Grd	Prgm	Enr/#Cls	SN	
L A Webber Middle High Sch 25 Housel Ave, Lyndonville 14098 Aaron Slack	7-12	TV	280 40	39%	585/765-3164
Lyndonville Elem Sch 25 Housel Ave, Lyndonville 14098 Elissa Smith	PK-6	T	339 21	32%	585/765-3122 Fax 585/765-3120

• **Medina Central School Dist** PID: 00765274 — 585/798-2700
1 Mustang Dr, Medina 14103 — Fax 585/798-5676

Schools: 3 \ **Teachers:** 121 \ **Students:** 1,475 \ **Special Ed Students:** 213 \ **LEP Students:** 20 \ **College-Bound:** 66% \ **Ethnic:** African American 5%, Hispanic 8%, Native American: 1%, Caucasian 85% \ **Exp:** $184 (Low) \ **Poverty:** 16% \ **Title I:** $500,677 \ **Special Education:** $3,927,000 \ **Open-Close:** 09/09 - 06/25 \ **DTBP:** $121 (High) \

Mark Kruzynski 1,11
Marc Graff 2,15,68
Maria Heagerty 4*
Eric Valley 6*
Gordon Luthart 35,83,85*
Alexandra DiLaura 58
Christine Griffin 2
Gerhard Leuer 3
Robert Dennis 5
Sarah Stalker 7
Tina DeSimone 36,90*
Arlene Pawlaczyk 67

---

79 Student Personnel
80 Driver Ed/Safety
81 Gifted/Talented
82 Video Services
83 Substance Abuse Prev
84 Erate
85 AIDS Education
88 Alternative/At Risk
89 Multi-Cultural Curriculum
90 Social Work
91 Safety/Security
92 Magnet School
93 Parental Involvement
95 Tech Prep Program
97 Chief Infomation Officer
98 Chief Technology Officer
270 Character Education
271 Migrant Education
273 Teacher Mentor
274 Before/After Sch
275 Response To Intervention
277 Remedial Math K-12
280 Literacy Coach
285 STEM
286 Digital Learning
288 Common Core Standards
294 Accountability
295 Network System
296 Title II Programs
297 Webmaster
298 Grant Writer/Ptnrships
750 Chief Innovation Officer
751 Chief of Staff
752 Social Emotional Learning

School Programs
A = Alternative Program
G = Adult Classes
M = Magnet Program
T = Title I Schoolwide
V = Career & Tech Ed Programs

Other School Types
Ⓐ = Alternative School
Ⓒ = Charter School
Ⓜ = Magnet School
Ⓨ = Year-Round School

Social Media
 = Facebook
 = Twitter

New Schools are shaded
New Superintendents and Principals are bold
Personnel with email addresses are underscored

Oswego County

Anthony Moreno 73

Public Schs..Principal	Grd	Prgm	Enr/#Cls	SN		
Clifford Wise Mid Interm Sch 1016 Gwinn St, Medina 14103 Chris Hughes	4-7	T	445 35	59%	585/798-2700 Fax 585/798-6917	
Medina High Sch 2 Mustang Dr, Medina 14103 Michael Cavanagh	8-12	ATV	588 42	52%	585/798-2700 Fax 585/318-1280	
Oak Orchard Elem Sch 335 W Oak Orchard St, Medina 14103 Julie Webber	PK-3	T	458 22	54%	585/798-2700 Fax 585/798-2352	

ORLEANS PRIVATE SCHOOLS

Private Schs..Principal	Grd	Prgm	Enr/#Cls	SN	
Orleans County Christian Sch 324 Catherine St, Medina 14103 Linda Strickland	K-12		21 4		585/798-2992 Fax 585/798-3766

ORLEANS REGIONAL CENTERS

• **Orleans-Niagara BOCES** PID: 00765327 716/731-6800
4232 Shelby Basin Rd, Medina 14103 Fax 585/798-1317

Dr Clark Godshall 1
Dan Connolly 3
Lindsey DeLaney 16
Ron Barstys 58
Sheldon Soman 295
Melanie Conley 2
Joseph Steinmetz 8,27,30,31,73,74
Cassandra Barnes 57
Wendy Swearingen 67

OSWEGO COUNTY

OSWEGO COUNTY SCHOOLS

County Schs..Principal	Grd	Prgm	Enr/#Cls	SN	
Oswego BOCES-Exceptional Ed 179 County Route 64, Mexico 13114 Julie Landy	Spec	AG	600 8	54%	315/963-4315 Fax 315/963-4316
Technical Career Center 179 County Route 64, Mexico 13114 Marla Berlin		Voc	950 20		315/963-4313 Fax 315/963-7882

OSWEGO PUBLIC SCHOOLS

• **Altmar-Parish-Williamstown SD** PID: 00765353 315/625-5251
639 County Route 22, Parish 13131 Fax 315/625-7952

Schools: 2 \ **Teachers:** 91 \ **Students:** 1,500 \ **Special Ed Students:** 270 \ **College-Bound:** 64% \ **Ethnic:** African American 1%, Hispanic 2%, Caucasian 97% \ **Exp:** $175 (Low) \ **Poverty:** 18% \ **Title I:** $391,737 \ **Special Education:** $3,374,000 \ **Open-Close:** 09/02 - 06/25 \ **DTBP:** $378 (High)

Eric Knuth 1
David Poore 3
Nate Metcalf 5
Naomi Ryfun 8,15,76
Mark Mattison 67
Danielle DeBiase 2
David Bartholomew 4
Jamie Coppola 6
Meredith Furlong 11,58*

Public Schs..Principal	Grd	Prgm	Enr/#Cls	SN	
Altmar-Parish-Williamstown ES 640 County Route 22, Parish 13131 Julie Woolson	PK-6	T	578 16	62%	315/625-5270 Fax 315/625-4937
Altmar-Parish-Williamstown HS 639 County Route 22, Parish 13131 Joseph Olsen	7-12	TV	553 25	59%	315/625-5220 Fax 315/625-4638

• **Central Square Central SD** PID: 00765406 315/668-4220
44 School Dr, Central Sq 13036 Fax 315/676-4437

Schools: 6 \ **Teachers:** 285 \ **Students:** 3,800 \ **Special Ed Students:** 561 \ **College-Bound:** 66% \ **Ethnic:** Asian 1%, African American 1%, Hispanic 2%, Caucasian 96% \ **Exp:** $178 (Low) \ **Poverty:** 15% \ **Title I:** $1,019,297 \ **Special Education:** $8,434,000 \ **Open-Close:** 09/08 - 06/25 \ **DTBP:** $232 (High)

Thomas Colabufo 1
Iraina Gerchman 3,295
David Bartholomew 4
James Drancsak 6,7,35,85*
Erin Phillips 9
Andrew Martin 67
Jennifer Dibianco 79,275
Maureen Ladd 2,91
Paul Brissette 3
John Pierce 5
Concetta Galvan 8,11,15,68,296,298
Michelle Alagna 58*
Teresa Ross 77,79,81,275*

Public Schs..Principal	Grd	Prgm	Enr/#Cls	SN	
Aura A Cole Elem Sch 1683 State Route 49, Constantia 13044 Michael Smolnik	PK-5	T	395 13	49%	315/668-4030 Fax 315/623-7209
Brewerton Elem Sch 9530 Brewerton Rd, Brewerton 13029 Brent Bowden	PK-5		450 23	31%	315/668-4201 Fax 315/668-8175
Central Square Middle Sch 248 US Route 11, Central Sq 13036 Mathew Penrod	6-8	T	859	44%	315/668-4218 Fax 315/668-7181
Hastings-Mallory Elem Sch 93 Barker Rd, Central Sq 13036 Lawrence Wink	PK-5	T	402 12	60%	315/668-4252 Fax 315/668-4299
Millard Hawk Elem Sch 74 School Dr, Central Sq 13036 Amanda Viel	PK-5	T	483 16	49%	315/668-4310 Fax 315/668-4356
Paul V Moore High Sch 44 School Dr, Central Sq 13036 Kristin Enright	9-12	T	1,111 75	40%	315/668-4231 Fax 315/668-4346

• **Fulton City School Dist** PID: 00765482 315/593-5500
129 Curtis St, Fulton 13069 Fax 315/598-6351

Schools: 6 \ **Teachers:** 262 \ **Students:** 3,500 \ **Special Ed Students:** 652 \ **LEP Students:** 44 \ **College-Bound:** 63% \ **Ethnic:** Asian 1%, African American 2%, Hispanic 5%, Caucasian 92% \ **Exp:** $314 (High) \ **Poverty:** 27% \ **Title I:** $1,661,196 \ **Special Education:** $7,824,000 \ **Open-Close:** 09/07 - 06/25 \ **DTBP:** $313 (High)

Brian Pulvino 1
Al Crump 3,5,91
Greg Henrie 5
Elizabeth Conners 8,11,54,57,69,88,285,288
Dominic Lisi 16,73
Kathy Adams 58,79
Thomas Greer 68
Kathy Nichols 2
Terry Warwick 4
Christopher Ells 6,7,35,83
Geri Geitner 11,36,79,275
Heather Witter 34,280
Robbin Griffin 67
Daniel Carroll 79

1	Superintendent	8	Curric/Instruct K-12	19	Chief Financial Officer	29	Family/Consumer Science	39	Social Studies K-12	49	English/Lang Arts Elem	59	Special Education Elem	69	Academic Assessment
2	Bus/Finance/Purchasing	9	Curric/Instruct Elem	20	Art K-12	30	Adult Education	40	Social Studies Elem	50	English/Lang Arts Sec	60	Special Education Sec	70	Research/Development
3	Buildings And Grounds	10	Curric/Instruct Sec	21	Art Elem	31	Career/Sch-to-Work K-12	41	Social Studies Sec	51	Reading K-12	61	Foreign/World Lang K-12	71	Public Information
4	Food Service	11	Federal Program	22	Art Sec	32	Career/Sch-to-Work Elem	42	Science K-12	52	Reading Elem	62	Foreign/World Lang Elem	72	Summer School
5	Transportation	12	Title I	23	Music K-12	33	Career/Sch-to-Work Sec	43	Science Elem	53	Reading Sec	63	Foreign/World Lang Sec	73	Instructional Tech
6	Athletic	13	Title V	24	Music Elem	34	Early Childhood Ed	44	Science Sec	54	Remedial Reading K-12	64	Religious Education K-12	74	Inservice Training
7	Health Services	15	Asst Superintendent	25	Music Sec	35	Health/Phys Education	45	Math K-12	55	Remedial Reading Elem	65	Religious Education Elem	75	Marketing/Distributive
		16	Instructional Media Svcs	26	Business Education	36	Guidance Services K-12	46	Math Elem	56	Remedial Reading Sec	66	Religious Education Sec	76	Info Systems
		17	Chief Operations Officer	27	Career & Tech Ed	37	Guidance Services Elem	47	Math Sec	57	Bilingual/ELL	67	School Board President	77	Psychological Assess
		18	Chief Academic Officer	28	Technology Education	38	Guidance Services Sec	48	English/Lang Arts K-12	58	Special Education K-12	68	Teacher Personnel	78	Affirmative Action

New York School Directory — Oswego County

Public Schs..Principal	Grd	Prgm	Enr/#Cls	SN	
Fairgrieve Elem Sch 716 Academy St, Fulton 13069 Jean Sampsell	K-6	T	454 26	71%	315/593-5550 Fax 315/593-5561
Fulton Junior High Sch 129 Curtis St, Fulton 13069 Copani Marc	7-8	ATV	522 75	52%	315/593-5440 Fax 315/593-5459
G Ray Bodley High Sch 6 William Gillard Dr, Fulton 13069 Donna Parkhurst	9-12	ATV	955 68	53%	315/593-5400 Fax 315/593-5427
Granby Elem Sch 400 W 7th St N, Fulton 13069 Gina Salerno	K-6	T	476 26	60%	315/593-5480 Fax 315/593-5492
J E Lanigan Elem Sch 59 Bakeman St, Fulton 13069 Jeffrey Hendrickson	K-6	T	456 20	48%	315/593-5470 Fax 315/593-5599
Volney Elem Sch 2592 State Route 3, Fulton 13069 Elizabeth Stoddard	K-6	T	337 26	46%	315/593-5570 Fax 315/593-5579

● **Hannibal Central School Dist** PID: 00765602   315/564-8100
928 Cayuga St, Hannibal 13074   Fax 315/564-7263

Schools: 3 \ **Teachers:** 117 \ **Students:** 1,310 \ **Special Ed Students:** 230 \ **LEP Students:** 5 \ **College-Bound:** 67% \ **Ethnic:** African American 1%, Hispanic 2%, Caucasian 97% \ **Exp:** $271 (Med) \ **Poverty:** 24% \ **Title I:** $627,332 \ **Special Education:** $3,214,000 \ **Open-Close:** 09/08 - 06/25 \ **DTBP:** $359 (High)

Dee Froio 8,288   Joseph Musa 11,58,79
Andrew Tyner 82

Public Schs..Principal	Grd	Prgm	Enr/#Cls	SN	
Dennis M Kenney Middle Sch 846 Cayuga St, Hannibal 13074 Shawn Morgan	5-8	T	373 27	73%	315/564-8120 Fax 315/564-7509
Fairley Elem Sch 953 Auburn St, Hannibal 13074 Amy Bird	PK-4	T	519 29	62%	315/564-8110 Fax 315/564-7951
Hannibal Senior High Sch 928 Cayuga St, Hannibal 13074 Stephen Dunn	9-12	ATV	418 50	68%	315/564-8130 Fax 315/564-7973

● **Mexico Central School Dist** PID: 00765640   315/963-8400
16 Fravor Rd Ste A, Mexico 13114   Fax 315/963-5801

Schools: 5 \ **Teachers:** 190 \ **Students:** 2,055 \ **Special Ed Students:** 352 \ **LEP Students:** 3 \ **College-Bound:** 50% \ **Ethnic:** African American 1%, Hispanic 2%, Caucasian 97% \ **Exp:** $351 (High) \ **Poverty:** 17% \ **Title I:** $595,622 \ **Special Education:** $5,042,000 \ **Open-Close:** 09/08 - 06/25 \ **DTBP:** $359 (High) \ f

Michael Schiedo 1   Sheila Roth 2
Micheal Wood 3   Brenda Thomas 4
Julie Bradish 5   Andrew Gates 6,27,31,83
Coleen Root 8,11,57,280,285,286,288,296   Colleen Root 15,76*
Elizabeth Dicosimo 15,68   Patricia Meaker 36*
Jennifer Stanton 58,79   James Emery 67
Anthony Murabito ....273*   Bradley Fox 295

Public Schs..Principal	Grd	Prgm	Enr/#Cls	SN	
Mexico Elem Sch 26 Academy St, Mexico 13114 Elizabeth Voegler	PK-4	T	366 20	48%	315/963-8400 Fax 315/963-8992
Mexico High Sch 3338 Main St, Mexico 13114 Ryan Lanigan	9-12	A	575 80	48%	315/963-8400 Fax 315/963-8887 f
Mexico Middle Sch 16 Fravor Rd, Mexico 13114 Kimberly Holliday	5-8	T	615	57%	315/963-8400 Fax 315/963-3848
New Haven Elem Sch 4320 State Route 104, New Haven 13121 Jennifer Granholm	PK-4	T	278 13	55%	315/963-8400 Fax 315/963-8813
Palermo Elem Sch 1638 County Route 45, Fulton 13069 Margaret Scorzelli	PK-4	T	221 13	53%	315/963-8400 Fax 315/963-3199

● **Oswego City School Dist** PID: 00765705   315/341-2001
1 Buccaneer Blvd, Oswego 13126   Fax 315/341-2910

Schools: 7 \ **Teachers:** 298 \ **Students:** 3,669 \ **Special Ed Students:** 721 \ **LEP Students:** 61 \ **College-Bound:** 62% \ **Ethnic:** Asian 1%, African American 2%, Hispanic 5%, Caucasian 92% \ **Exp:** $180 (Low) \ **Poverty:** 21% \ **Title I:** $1,420,018 \ **Special Education:** $5,540,000 \ **Open-Close:** 09/04 - 06/25 \ **DTBP:** $329 (High)

Dr Mathis Calvin 1   Nancy Squires 2
David Crisafulli 3   Thomas Gunn 5
Rhonda Bullard 6,35   Christina Chamberlain 7
Carrie Plasse ....9,11,34,294,296,298*   Dr Heidi Sweeney 10,68
Robert Duffy 57,77,79,83,88,90,271   Lisa-Marie Carter 58
Heather DelConte 67   Jaime Sykut 73,76,286,295

Public Schs..Principal	Grd	Prgm	Enr/#Cls	SN	
Charles E Riley Elem Sch 269 E 8th St, Oswego 13126 Linda Doty	K-6	T	422 38	1%	315/341-2800 Fax 315/341-2980
Fitzhugh Park Elem Sch 195 E Bridge St, Oswego 13126 Donna Simmons	K-6	T	417	1%	315/341-2400 Fax 315/341-2940
Kingsford Park Elem Sch 275 W 5th St, Oswego 13126 Mary Volkomer	K-6	T	443 21	1%	315/341-2500 Fax 315/341-2950
Leighton Elem Sch 1 Buccaneer Blvd, Oswego 13126 Kara Shore	K-6	T	281	2%	315/341-2700 Fax 315/341-2970
Minetto Elem Sch 2411 County Route 8, Minetto 13115 Jennifer Sullivan	K-6	T	429 17	1%	315/341-2600 Fax 315/341-2960
Oswego High Sch 2 Buccaneer Blvd, Oswego 13126 Patrick Wallace	9-12	GT	1,113	1%	315/341-2200 Fax 315/341-2920
Oswego Middle Sch 20 Mark Fitzgibbons Dr, Oswego 13126 Mary Beth Fierro	7-8	T	557 75	1%	315/341-2300 Fax 315/341-2930

● **Phoenix Central School Dist** PID: 00765781   315/695-1555
116 Volney St, Phoenix 13135   Fax 315/695-1201

Schools: 3 \ **Teachers:** 152 \ **Students:** 1,684 \ **Special Ed Students:** 208 \ **LEP Students:** 3 \ **College-Bound:** 66% \ **Ethnic:** African American 1%, Hispanic 1%, Caucasian 97% \ **Exp:** $269 (Med) \ **Poverty:** 17% \ **Title I:** $561,612 \ **Special Education:** $4,243,000 \ **Open-Close:** 09/08 - 06/25 \ **DTBP:** $171 (High) \ f t

Christopher Byrne 1   Karl Seckner 2,15
Jason Godkin 3,91   Patty Barber 4
Deborah Gerace 5   John Jeffries 6,35
Stacie Shaffer ....9,285*   Bob Edwards 11,16,57,68,288,294,296
Chelsea Powell ....16*   Thomas Bailer 33*

79	Student Personnel	91	Safety/Security	275	Response To Intervention	298	Grant Writer/Ptnrships	**School Programs**
80	Driver Ed/Safety	92	Magnet School	277	Remedial Math K-12	750	Chief Innovation Officer	A = Alternative Program
81	Gifted/Talented	93	Parental Involvement	280	Literacy Coach	751	Chief of Staff	G = Adult Classes
82	Video Services	95	Tech Prep Program	285	STEM	752	Social Emotional Learning	M = Magnet Program
83	Substance Abuse Prev	97	Chief Infomation Officer	286	Digital Learning			T = Title I Schoolwide
84	Erate	98	Chief Technology Officer	288	Common Core Standards			V = Career & Tech Ed Programs
85	AIDS Education	270	Character Education	294	Accountability		**Other School Types**	
88	Alternative/At Risk	271	Migrant Education	295	Network System		Ⓐ = Alternative School	**Social Media**
89	Multi-Cultural Curriculum	273	Teacher Mentor	296	Title II Programs		Ⓒ = Charter School	f = Facebook
90	Social Work	274	Before/After Sch	297	Webmaster		Ⓜ = Magnet School	t = Twitter
							Ⓨ = Year-Round School	

New Schools are shaded
New Superintendents and Principals are bold
Personnel with email addresses are underscored

Otsego County

Kathie Palladino .... 36,58,79,271*   Brett Doody 55,270,274*
Earl Rudy 67   Nicole Covell 73,76,275,286,295

Public Schs..Principal	Grd	Prgm	Enr/#Cls	SN
Emerson Dillon Middle Sch 116 Volney St, Phoenix 13135 Susan Anderson	5-8	TV	520 54	52% 315/695-1521 Fax 315/695-1544
John C Birdlebough High Sch 552 Main St, Phoenix 13135 Thomas Bailer	9-12	V	490 40	51% 315/695-1631 Fax 315/695-1694
Michael A Maroun Elem Sch 11 Elm St, Phoenix 13135 Brett Doody	PK-4	T	674 65	53% 315/695-1561 Fax 315/695-1620

- **Pulaski Central School Dist** PID: 00765846   315/298-5188
  2 Hinman Rd, Pulaski 13142   Fax 315/298-4390

Schools: 2 \ **Teachers:** 85 \ **Students:** 971 \ **Special Ed Students:** 157 \
Ethnic: Hispanic 1%, Caucasian 98% \ **Exp:** $233 (Med) \ **Poverty:** 18% \
Title I: $289,354 \ **Special Education:** $2,607,000 \ **Open-Close:** 09/08 - 06/25 \ **DTBP:** $359 (High)

Tom Jennings 1   Sarah Starbird 2
James Sheeley 3   Dave Barthokmbu 4
Bryan Philips 5   Jim Karcz 6
Michael Bateson ....8,11,31,36,57*   Joel Southwell 67
Mike Davis 73,295   Scott Jones 83,85

Public Schs..Principal	Grd	Prgm	Enr/#Cls	SN
Lura Sharp Elem Sch 2 Hinman Rd, Pulaski 13142 Joelle Hendry	PK-5	T	435 29	54% 315/298-2412 Fax 315/298-7464
Pulaski Middle High Sch 4624 Salina St, Pulaski 13142 Patrick Vrooman	6-12		536 70	47% 315/298-5103 Fax 315/298-2371

- **Sandy Creek Central Sch Dist** PID: 00765872   315/387-3445
  124 Salisbury St, Sandy Creek 13145   Fax 315/387-2196

Schools: 1 \ **Teachers:** 87 \ **Students:** 800 \ **Special Ed Students:** 115
\ **LEP Students:** 3 \ **College-Bound:** 60% \ **Ethnic:** Asian 1%, African
American 2%, Hispanic 2%, Caucasian 95% \ **Exp:** $413 (High) \
Poverty: 15% \ **Title I:** $217,867 \ **Special Education:** $2,717,000 \
Open-Close: 09/04 - 06/25 \ **DTBP:** $396 (High)

Kyle Faulkner 1   Shelley Fitzpatrick 2,11
Andy Ridgeway ....3*   Tracy Sullivan 4
Robin Cashel 5   Michael Stevens 6,35*
Laurie Crast ....7,85*   Amy McCormack 8,12,51,54,69*
Theresa Crast ....16*   Danielle James 36*
Theodore Krenrich ....42*   Katie Soluri 45*
Kim Manfredi ....58*   John Schelmidine 67
Christopher Grieco 73*

Public Schs..Principal	Grd	Prgm	Enr/#Cls	SN
Sandy Creek Sch 124 Salisbury St, Sandy Creek 13145 Timothy Filiatrault \ Amy Molloy \ Kevin Seymour	PK-12		800 72	52% 315/387-3465

OSWEGO CATHOLIC SCHOOLS

- **Diocese of Syracuse Ed Office** PID: 00762765
  Listing includes only schools located in this county. See District Index for location of Diocesan Offices.

Catholic Schs..Principal	Grd	Prgm	Enr/#Cls	SN
Trinity Catholic Sch 115 E 5th St, Oswego 13126 Barbara Sugar	PK-6		200 16	315/343-6700 Fax 315/342-9471

OSWEGO PRIVATE SCHOOLS

Private Schs..Principal	Grd	Prgm	Enr/#Cls	SN
Oswego Cmty Christian Sch 400 E Albany St, Oswego 13126 David Proietti	PK-12		80 12	315/342-9322 Fax 315/342-0268

OSWEGO REGIONAL CENTERS

- **Ctr for Instruct Tech Innov** PID: 00765913   315/963-4251
  179 County Route 64, Mexico 13114   Fax 315/963-4475

Christoper Todd 1,11   Wayne Wideman 3
John Ramin 8   Roseann Bayne 8,15
Mark LaFountain 15,68   Michael Sheperd 15
Marla Berlin 27,31   Julie Landy 58,88
John Shelmidine 67   Kristen Roland 69
Stehanie Maturo 73   Tracy Fleming 76
Paul Gugel 271

OTSEGO COUNTY

OTSEGO COUNTY SCHOOLS

County Schs..Principal	Grd	Prgm	Enr/#Cls	SN
Otsego Area Occupation Center 1914 County Route 35, Milford 13807 Ryan DeMars	Voc	AG	300 20	607/286-7715 Fax 607/286-9603

OTSEGO PUBLIC SCHOOLS

- **Cherry Valley-Springfield SD** PID: 00765963   607/264-3265
  597 County Highway 54, Cherry Valley 13320   Fax 607/264-9023

Schools: 1 \ **Teachers:** 47 \ **Students:** 449 \ **Special Ed Students:** 78
\ **College-Bound:** 70% \ **Ethnic:** African American 1%, Hispanic 1%,
Caucasian 97% \ **Exp:** $198 (Low) \ **Poverty:** 15% \ **Title I:** $182,031 \
Special Education: $715,000 \ **Open-Close:** 09/08 - 06/25 \ **DTBP:** $392
(High)

---

1 Superintendent	8 Curric/Instruct K-12	19 Chief Financial Officer	29 Family/Consumer Science	39 Social Studies K-12	49 English/Lang Arts Elem	59 Special Education Elem	69 Academic Assessment
2 Bus/Finance/Purchasing	9 Curric/Instruct Elem	20 Art K-12	30 Adult Education	40 Social Studies Elem	50 English/Lang Arts Sec	60 Special Education Sec	70 Research/Development
3 Buildings And Grounds	10 Curric/Instruct Sec	21 Art Elem	31 Career/Sch-to-Work K-12	41 Social Studies Sec	51 Reading K-12	61 Foreign/World Lang K-12	71 Public Information
4 Food Service	11 Federal Program	22 Art Sec	32 Career/Sch-to-Work Elem	42 Science K-12	52 Reading Elem	62 Foreign/World Lang Elem	72 Summer School
5 Transportation	12 Title I	23 Music K-12	33 Career/Sch-to-Work Sec	43 Science Elem	53 Reading Sec	63 Foreign/World Lang Sec	73 Instructional Tech
6 Athletic	13 Title V	24 Music Elem	34 Early Childhood Ed	44 Science Sec	54 Remedial Reading K-12	64 Religious Education K-12	74 Inservice Training
7 Health Services	15 Asst Superintendent	25 Music Sec	35 Health/Phys Education	45 Math K-12	55 Remedial Reading Elem	65 Religious Education Elem	75 Marketing/Distributive
	16 Instructional Media Svcs	26 Business Education	36 Guidance Services K-12	46 Math Elem	56 Remedial Reading Sec	66 Religious Education Sec	76 Info Systems
	17 Chief Operations Officer	27 Career & Tech Ed	37 Guidance Services Elem	47 Math Sec	57 Bilingual/ELL	67 School Board President	77 Psychological Assess
	18 Chief Academic Officer	28 Technology Education	38 Guidance Services Sec	48 English/Lang Arts K-12	58 Special Education K-12	68 Teacher Personnel	78 Affirmative Action

New York School Directory — Otsego County

Therijo Climenhaga	1	Denise Wist	2*
David Mayton	3,5*	Melissa Davidson	4
Kevin Keane	6*	Jim Brophy	12*
Audrey Maldonado	16*	Angeline Conte	38*
Bonnie Georgi	58,77*	Robert Tabor	67

Public Schs..Principal	Grd	Prgm	Enr/#Cls	SN	
Cherry Valley-Springfield Sch 597 County Highway 54, Cherry Valley 13320 Nicole Knapp \ Kevin Keane	PK-12	T	449 60	54%	607/264-3265

- **Cooperstown Ctl School Dist** PID: 00765987   607/547-5364
  39 Linden Ave, Cooperstown 13326   Fax 607/547-5100

Schools: 2 \ **Teachers:** 70 \ **Students:** 818 \ **Special Ed Students:** 97 \ **LEP Students:** 3 \ **College-Bound:** 82% \ **Ethnic:** Asian 4%, African American 2%, Hispanic 4%, Caucasian 90% \ **Exp:** $304 (High) \ **Poverty:** 10% \ **Title I:** $180,963 \ **Special Education:** $848,000 \ **Open-Close:** 09/04 - 06/25 \ **DTBP:** $120 (High)

Dr William Crankshaw	1	Amy Kukenberger	2,11
Matthew Murphy	3	Melissa Rathbun	4*
Joseph Kukenberger	5	David Bertram	6
Kristin Butler	8,11,285,288,298	Michelle Hitchcock	16*
Eric Carr	31,36,69,88*	Laura Lamb	58*
Timothy Hayes	67	Jason Burke	295

Public Schs..Principal	Grd	Prgm	Enr/#Cls	SN	
Cooperstown Elem Sch 21 Walnut St, Cooperstown 13326 Ann Meccariello	K-6		416 23	19%	607/547-9976 Fax 607/547-4427
Cooperstown Junior-Senior High 39 Linden Ave, Cooperstown 13326 Kristin Butler	7-12	V	402 42	17%	607/547-8181

- **Edmeston Ctl School Dist** PID: 00766022   607/965-8931
  11 North St, Edmeston 13335   Fax 607/965-8942

Schools: 1 \ **Teachers:** 43 \ **Students:** 390 \ **Special Ed Students:** 52 \ **College-Bound:** 50% \ **Ethnic:** Asian 2%, African American 1%, Hispanic 1%, Caucasian 96% \ **Exp:** $410 (High) \ **Poverty:** 21% \ **Title I:** $141,124 \ **Special Education:** $894,000 \ **Open-Close:** 09/08 - 06/25 \ **DTBP:** $404 (High)

Dr Gary Furman	1,11	Sonja Rosweiler	2
Darren Balden	3	Brian Belknap	4*
Julie Glassman	6	Pamela Grimm	8,58*
Amanda Conklin	31*	Jaime Reisen	54*
John Holdorf	67	Christine Nichols	69,273,288*
Kathleen Russell	83,85,88*		

Public Schs..Principal	Grd	Prgm	Enr/#Cls	SN	
Edmeston Central Sch 11 North St, Edmeston 13335 Christine Nichols	PK-12		390 35	38%	607/965-8931

- **Gilbertsville-Mt Upton SD** PID: 00766046   607/783-2207
  693 State Highway 51, Gilbertsville 13776   Fax 607/783-2254

Schools: 1 \ **Teachers:** 40 \ **Students:** 350 \ **Special Ed Students:** 73 \ **LEP Students:** 3 \ **College-Bound:** 68% \ **Ethnic:** African American 1%, Hispanic 1%, Caucasian 98% \ **Exp:** $262 (Med) \ **Poverty:** 17% \ **Title I:** $134,550 \ **Special Education:** $659,000 \ **Open-Close:** 09/09 - 06/24 \ **DTBP:** $383 (High)

| Annette Hammond | 1 | Dorothy Ianello | 2,11* |

Alan Digsby	3	Susan Sebeck	4*
Joe Zaczek	5*	Greg Bonzkowski	6,85*
Kelly Ingham	7*	Raquel Norton	16*
Clara Tanner	31,83*	Lisa Ruland	37,270*
Heather Wilcox	58,274*	Jeremy Pain	67
Annette Hammond	69,273,288*	Eric Voorhees	73,74,76,295
Theresa Yantz	77	Mark Seigers	285

Public Schs..Principal	Grd	Prgm	Enr/#Cls	SN	
Gilbertsville-Mt Upton Sch 693 State Highway 51, Gilbertsville 13776 Heather Wilcox	PK-12	T	350 30	60%	607/783-2207

- **Laurens Central School Dist** PID: 00766060   607/432-2050
  55 Main St, Laurens 13796   Fax 607/432-4388

Schools: 1 \ **Teachers:** 36 \ **Students:** 300 \ **Special Ed Students:** 63 \ **LEP Students:** 3 \ **College-Bound:** 75% \ **Ethnic:** Asian 1%, African American 3%, Hispanic 9%, Caucasian 88% \ **Exp:** $235 (Med) \ **Poverty:** 13% \ **Title I:** $151,816 \ **Special Education:** $1,062,000 \ **Open-Close:** 09/08 - 06/25 \ **DTBP:** $77 (Low)

William Dorritie	1,288	Kristyn Degroat	2
Jason Stone	5	Steven West	6
Mary Rokhvadze	16*	Danielle Dennett	38,83,88
Lindsey Gifford	58,69,288,752*	Cindy Struckle	67
Charles Walker	73,295*	John Mushtare	76
Jean Barry	274		

Public Schs..Principal	Grd	Prgm	Enr/#Cls	SN	
Laurens Central Sch 55 Main Street, Laurens 13796 William Dorritie	K-12	ATV	300 30	52%	607/432-2050

- **Milford Central School Dist** PID: 00766084   607/286-3349
  42 W Main St, Milford 13807   Fax 607/286-7879

Schools: 1 \ **Teachers:** 40 \ **Students:** 361 \ **Special Ed Students:** 60 \ **College-Bound:** 78% \ **Ethnic:** Asian 1%, African American 2%, Hispanic 1%, Caucasian 96% \ **Exp:** $466 (High) \ **Poverty:** 10% \ **Title I:** $66,620 \ **Special Education:** $936,000 \ **Open-Close:** 09/08 - 06/25 \ **DTBP:** $334 (High)

Mark Place	1	Marissa Christensen	2
Donald Harvey	3,5,91*	Cynthia Marino	4
Jolene Chase	7,85	Teresa Glavin	8,275,285*
Michelle Dibble	11,69*	Daniel Blake	16,73,82,295*
Jennifer Carr	31*	Alicia Flint	35,83*
Nicole Lippitt	58*	Marion Mossman	67
Lorre Gregory	298*		

Public Schs..Principal	Grd	Prgm	Enr/#Cls	SN	
Milford Central Sch 42 W Main St, Milford 13807 Brenda Lang	PK-12	T	361 53	47%	607/286-7721

- **Morris Central School Dist** PID: 00766101   607/263-6100
  65 Main St, Morris 13808   Fax 607/263-2483

Schools: 1 \ **Teachers:** 42 \ **Students:** 322 \ **Special Ed Students:** 91 \ **College-Bound:** 63% \ **Ethnic:** Asian 2%, Hispanic 4%, Caucasian 94% \ **Exp:** $483 (High) \ **Poverty:** 11% \ **Title I:** $66,806 \ **Special Education:** $952,000 \ **Open-Close:** 09/08 - 06/25 \ **DTBP:** $383 (High)

| Matthew Sheldon | 1 | Kristina Hand | 2* |

---

79 Student Personnel	91 Safety/Security	275 Response To Intervention	298 Grant Writer/Ptnrships	**School Programs**	**Social Media**		
80 Driver Ed/Safety	92 Magnet School	277 Remedial Math K-12	750 Chief Innovation Officer	A = Alternative Program			
81 Gifted/Talented	93 Parental Involvement	280 Literacy Coach	751 Chief of Staff	G = Adult Classes	= Facebook		
82 Video Services	95 Tech Prep Program	285 STEM	752 Social Emotional Learning	M = Magnet Program			
83 Substance Abuse Prev	97 Chief Infomation Officer	286 Digital Learning		T = Title I Schoolwide	= Twitter		
84 Erate	98 Chief Technology Officer	288 Common Core Standards	**Other School Types**	V = Career & Tech Ed Programs			
85 AIDS Education	270 Character Education	294 Accountability	Ⓐ = Alternative School				
88 Alternative/At Risk	271 Migrant Education	295 Network System	Ⓒ = Charter School	New Schools are shaded			
89 Multi-Cultural Curriculum	273 Teacher Mentor	296 Title II Programs	Ⓜ = Magnet School	New Superintendents and Principals are bold			
90 Social Work	274 Before/After Sch	297 Webmaster	Ⓨ = Year-Round School	Personnel with email addresses are underscored			

Otsego County

Market Data Retrieval

John Tol	3*
Mallory Jorgensen	5
Katarzyna Baker	7,83,85*
Kim Murray	11,58,296,298*
Lorraine Miller	37*
Joanne Telfer	57*
Greg Thom	73,76,286*
Jill Forester	4
Michael Iannelli	6*
Kathy Smith	8,11,69,270,271,273*
Morgan Brashear	16,82*
Diane Walling	51,280*
Wendy Moore	67

Public Schs..Principal	Grd	Prgm	Enr/#Cls	SN	
Morris Central Sch 65 Main St, Morris 13808 Kathy Smith	PK-12	ATV	322 50	52%	607/263-6100

● Oneonta City School Dist PID: 00766125
31 Center St, Oneonta 13820
607/433-8200
Fax 607/433-8290

Schools: 5 \ **Teachers:** 160 \ **Students:** 1,736 \ **Special Ed Students:** 334 \ **LEP Students:** 22 \ **College-Bound:** 77% \ **Ethnic:** Asian 4%, African American 6%, Hispanic 9%, Caucasian 82% \ **Exp:** $274 (Med) \ **Poverty:** 15% \ **Title I:** $404,965 \ **Special Education:** $4,303,000 \ **Open-Close:** 09/09 - 06/25 \ **DTBP:** $359 (High)

Thomas Brindley	1
Gerald Mackey	6*
Lisa Weeks	12
Cheryl Holt	30
Steven Currie	295
Karen Czerkies	2
Timothy Gracy	11,58
Bonnie Nobiling	16,73,76,297*
Bill Grau	67

Public Schs..Principal	Grd	Prgm	Enr/#Cls	SN	
Greater Plains Elem Sch 60 W End Ave, Oneonta 13820 Nancy Osburne	K-5		288 16	24%	607/433-8272 Fax 607/433-8207
Oneonta Middle Sch 130 East St, Oneonta 13820 Thomas Molle	6-8		402 28	30%	607/433-8262 Fax 607/433-8203
Oneonta Senior High Sch 130 East St, Oneonta 13820 Anne Wolstenholme	9-12		496 50	22%	607/433-8243 Fax 607/433-8204
Riverside Elem Sch 39 House St, Oneonta 13820 Melinda Murdock	K-5		258 11	31%	607/433-8273 Fax 607/433-8210
Valleyview Elem Sch 40 Valleyview St 46, Oneonta 13820 Walter Baskin	K-5		292 20	21%	607/433-8252 Fax 607/433-8211

● Richfield Springs Central SD PID: 00766199
93 Main St, Richfld Spgs 13439
315/858-0610
Fax 315/858-0582

Schools: 1 \ **Teachers:** 51 \ **Students:** 450 \ **Special Ed Students:** 101 \ **College-Bound:** 50% \ **Ethnic:** African American 3%, Hispanic 2%, Caucasian 95% \ **Exp:** $364 (High) \ **Poverty:** 14% \ **Title I:** $125,441 \ **Special Education:** $908,000 \ **Open-Close:** 09/03 - 06/30 \ **DTBP:** $400 (High)

Thomas Piatti	1
Rob Walker	3*
Stan Gross	5
Vicky Greenman	16*
Amy Ambrose	37*
Scott Mondore	67
Kurt Sunderland	2
Chris Abbruzzese	4*
Rene Wilson	11,69*
Terry Havens	35,85*
Linda Trimble	58*
Jim Lavere	73,295*

Public Schs..Principal	Grd	Prgm	Enr/#Cls	SN	
Richfield Springs Ctl Sch 93 Main St, Richfld Spgs 13439 Joe D'Apice \ Rene Wilson	PK-12	GTV	450 35	52%	315/858-0610

● Schenevus Ctl School Dist PID: 00765949
159 Main St, Schenevus 12155
607/638-5530
Fax 607/638-5600

Schools: 1 \ **Teachers:** 36 \ **Students:** 350 \ **Special Ed Students:** 67 \ **College-Bound:** 60% \ **Ethnic:** African American 2%, Hispanic 3%, Caucasian 95% \ **Exp:** $233 (Med) \ **Poverty:** 7% \ **Title I:** $80,811 \ **Special Education:** $736,000 \ **Open-Close:** 09/08 - 06/25 \ **DTBP:** $367 (High)

Theresa Carlin	1
Tom Hunt	3,5,73,91
Kimberly Matthews	8,11,58*
Collin Begnoche	98
Greg Beall	2
Vinny Calleja	4
Terri Korba	36

Public Schs..Principal	Grd	Prgm	Enr/#Cls	SN	
Schenevus Central Sch 159 Main St, Schenevus 12155 Kimberly Matthews	PK-12	T	350 40	49%	607/638-5881

● Unatego Unadilla Central SD PID: 00766254
2641 State Highway 7, Otego 13825
607/988-5000
Fax 607/988-1039

Schools: 3 \ **Teachers:** 69 \ **Students:** 716 \ **Special Ed Students:** 142 \ **LEP Students:** 6 \ **College-Bound:** 55% \ **Ethnic:** Asian 1%, African American 2%, Hispanic 6%, Caucasian 92% \ **Exp:** $127 (Low) \ **Poverty:** 14% \ **Title I:** $207,351 \ **Special Education:** $372,000 \ **Open-Close:** 09/04 - 06/15 \ **DTBP:** $859 (High)

Dr David Richards	1
Brian Trask	3,5,73
Luci Hopps	4
Matthew Hafele	6
Cheryl Nages	23
James Salisbury	67
Patricia Loker	2
Kim Corcoran	4
Patricia Walker	4
Julie Lambiaso	10,69,273*
Katherine Mazourek	58
Carrie Hewett	274

Public Schs..Principal	Grd	Prgm	Enr/#Cls	SN	
Unatego Elem Sch 265 Main St, Unadilla 13849 Mike Snider	K-5	T	332 14	51%	607/369-6200 Fax 607/369-6222
Unatego High Sch 2641 State Highway 7, Otego 13825 Patricia Hoyt \ Julie Lambiaso	9-12	TV	208 61	52%	607/988-5000 Fax 607/988-1050
Unatego Middle Sch 2641 State Highway 7, Otego 13825 Patricia Hoyt	6-8	T	176	55%	607/988-5000

● Worcester Ctl School Dist PID: 00766292
198 Main St, Worcester 12197
607/397-8785
Fax 607/397-9454

Schools: 1 \ **Teachers:** 38 \ **Students:** 350 \ **Special Ed Students:** 79 \ **College-Bound:** 65% \ **Ethnic:** African American 1%, Hispanic 2%, Caucasian 97% \ **Exp:** $252 (Med) \ **Poverty:** 16% \ **Title I:** $157,527 \ **Special Education:** $1,095,000 \ **Open-Close:** 09/08 - 06/25 \ **DTBP:** $376 (High)

Timothy Gonzales	1,11
Glenn Jaquish	3*
Eric Haley	5
Poletta Louis	36,83,85,88,271*
Winsome Zinkievich	58
Gary Pochkar	2
Joseph Calleja	4*
James Kenyon	6*
Karryann Sanders	57*
William Fisher	67

Public Schs..Principal	Grd	Prgm	Enr/#Cls	SN	
Worcester Central Sch 198 Main St, Worcester 12197 Jessie Westfall \ Melissa Leonard	PK-12	ATV	350 30	53%	607/397-8785

1	Superintendent	8	Curric/Instruct K-12	19	Chief Financial Officer	29	Family/Consumer Science	39	Social Studies K-12	49	English/Lang Arts Elem	59	Special Education Elem	69	Academic Assessment
2	Bus/Finance/Purchasing	9	Curric/Instruct Elem	20	Art K-12	30	Adult Education	40	Social Studies Elem	50	English/Lang Arts Sec	60	Special Education Sec	70	Research/Development
3	Buildings And Grounds	10	Curric/Instruct Sec	21	Art Elem	31	Career/Sch-to-Work K-12	41	Social Studies Sec	51	Reading K-12	61	Foreign/World Lang K-12	71	Public Information
4	Food Service	11	Federal Program	22	Art Sec	32	Career/Sch-to-Work Elem	42	Science K-12	52	Reading Elem	62	Foreign/World Lang Elem	72	Summer School
5	Transportation	12	Title I	23	Music K-12	33	Career/Sch-to-Work Sec	43	Science Elem	53	Reading Sec	63	Foreign/World Lang Sec	73	Instructional Tech
6	Athletic	13	Title V	24	Music Elem	34	Early Childhood Ed	44	Science Sec	54	Remedial Reading K-12	64	Religious Education K-12	74	Inservice Training
7	Health Services	15	Asst Superintendent	25	Music Sec	35	Health/Phys Education	45	Math K-12	55	Remedial Reading Elem	65	Religious Education Elem	75	Marketing/Distributive
		16	Instructional Media Svcs	26	Business Education	36	Guidance Services K-12	46	Math Elem	56	Remedial Reading Sec	66	Religious Education Sec	76	Info Systems
		17	Chief Operations Officer	27	Career & Tech Ed	37	Guidance Services Elem	47	Math Sec	57	Bilingual/ELL	67	School Board President	77	Psychological Assess
		18	Chief Academic Officer	28	Technology Education	38	Guidance Services Sec	48	English/Lang Arts K-12	58	Special Education K-12	68	Teacher Personnel	78	Affirmative Action

New York School Directory
Putnam County

OTSEGO PRIVATE SCHOOLS

Private Schs..Principal	Grd	Prgm	Enr/#Cls	SN	
Brookwood Sch 687 County Highway 59, Cooperstown 13326 Gina Reeves	PK-K		40 5		607/547-4060 Fax 607/547-2835 f
Lighthouse Christian Academy 12 Grove St, Oneonta 13820 Chris Cleveland	PK-12		45 9		607/432-2031
Oneonta Christian Academy 158 River St, Oneonta 13820 Chris Cleveland	PK-12		97 10		607/432-0383 Fax 607/436-9137
Pathfinder Village Sch Route 80, Edmeston 13335 Mauro Iorio	Spec	G	16 4		607/965-8121 Fax 607/965-8031

PUTNAM COUNTY

PUTNAM PUBLIC SCHOOLS

• **Brewster Central School Dist** PID: 00766319   845/279-8000
30 Farm to Market Rd, Brewster 10509   Fax 845/279-6921

Schools: 4 \ **Teachers:** 237 \ **Students:** 3,066 \ **Special Ed Students:** 450 \ **LEP Students:** 299 \ **College-Bound:** 90% \ **Ethnic:** Asian 3%, African American 2%, Hispanic 39%, Caucasian 56% \ **Exp:** $247 (Med) \ **Poverty:** 8% \ **Title I:** $498,997 \ **Special Education:** $3,837,000 \ **Open-Close:** 09/08 - 06/25 \ **DTBP:** $319 (High) \ f t

Dr Lorie Bandlow 1		Elena Nash-Graham 2	
Victor Karlsson 2,3,11,15		Glen Freyer 3,88	
Cathy Hancock 4*		Mary Smith 5	
Dean Berardo 6,83*		Michelle Gosh 8,15,69	
James Treloar 28,73,76,286,295		Elizabeth Kennedy 58,79	
Sonia Mesika 67		Dr Brent Harrington 68	

Public Schs..Principal	Grd	Prgm	Enr/#Cls	SN	
Brewster High Sch 50 Fogintown Rd, Brewster 10509 Nichole Horler	9-12		1,029	30%	845/279-5051 Fax 845/279-6730
C V Starr Intermediate Sch 20 Farm to Market Rd, Brewster 10509 Maggie Andriello	3-5	T	661 24	41%	845/279-4018 Fax 845/279-8154
Henry H Wells Middle Sch 570 Route 312, Brewster 10509 John Clark	6-8		745 45	36%	845/279-3702 Fax 845/279-3192
John F Kennedy Elem Sch 31 Fogintown Rd, Brewster 10509 Frank Zamperlin	K-2	T	631 50	38%	845/279-2087 Fax 845/279-7638

• **Carmel Central School Dist** PID: 00766369   845/878-2094
81 South St, Patterson 12563   Fax 845/878-4337

Schools: 5 \ **Teachers:** 322 \ **Students:** 3,973 \ **Special Ed Students:** 684 \ **LEP Students:** 149 \ **College-Bound:** 90% \ **Ethnic:** Asian 3%, African American 3%, Hispanic 29%, Caucasian 66% \ **Exp:** $297 (Med) \ **Poverty:** 7% \ **Title I:** $417,194 \ **Special Education:** $6,187,000 \ **Open-Close:** 09/02 - 06/25 \ **DTBP:** $327 (High)

Andy Irvin 1		Eric Stark 2,15	
John Weise 3		Pat Rodia 4	
Pat Payne 5		Susan Dullea 6,35	
Janet Warden 8,11,15,57,273,274,288		Rosey Mitchell 30*	
Joseph Simoni 58,79		John Cody 67	
Joseph Keenan 71,97,285,295		Susan Dieck 71,298	
Scott Clark 73			

Public Schs..Principal	Grd	Prgm	Enr/#Cls	SN	
Carmel High Sch 30 Fair St, Carmel 10512 John Fink	9-12	AV	1,422 73	28%	845/225-8441 Fax 845/228-2308
George Fischer Middle Sch 281 Fair St, Carmel 10512 John Piscitella	5-8	V	1,236 75	30%	845/228-2300 Fax 845/228-2304
Kent Elem Sch 1091 Route 52, Carmel 10512 Kathryn White	K-4		411 21	27%	845/225-5029 Fax 845/225-1849
Kent Primary Sch 1065 Route 52, Carmel 10512 Daniel Brown	K-4		421 26	35%	845/225-5025 Fax 845/228-4824
Matthew Paterson Elem Sch 100 South St, Patterson 12563 Michael Kirk	K-4		483 31	28%	845/878-3211 Fax 845/878-3964

• **Garrison Union Free Sch Dist** PID: 00766424   845/424-3689
1100 Route 9D, Garrison 10524   Fax 845/424-4733

Schools: 1 \ **Teachers:** 23 \ **Students:** 207 \ **Special Ed Students:** 39 \ **LEP Students:** 3 \ **Ethnic:** Asian 2%, African American 1%, Hispanic 17%, Caucasian 79% \ **Exp:** $597 (High) \ **Poverty:** 3% \ **Title I:** $34,084 \ **Special Education:** $220,000 \ **Open-Close:** 09/02 - 06/25 \ **DTBP:** $380 (High)

Laura Mitchell 1,11,288		Sue Huetter 2	
Mike Twardy 3,5		Patrick Beckley 6*	
Alex Lavine 9,270		Krista DiDiego 37	
Sarah Tormey 67		Nancy Romano 73,295*	
Jessica Vandekker 83,88,90*			

Public Schs..Principal	Grd	Prgm	Enr/#Cls	SN	
Garrison Elem Sch 1100 Route 9D, Garrison 10524 Alex Levine	K-8		207 20	1%	845/424-3689

• **Haldane Central School Dist** PID: 00766448   845/265-9254
15 Craigside Dr, Cold Spring 10516   Fax 845/265-9213

Schools: 1 \ **Teachers:** 74 \ **Students:** 794 \ **Special Ed Students:** 119 \ **LEP Students:** 12 \ **College-Bound:** 85% \ **Ethnic:** Asian 3%, African American 2%, Hispanic 7%, Caucasian 88% \ **Exp:** $322 (High) \ **Poverty:** 3% \ **Title I:** $26,657 \ **Special Education:** $535,000 \ **Open-Close:** 09/03 - 06/24 \ **DTBP:** $162 (High)

Dr Phillip Benante 1		Anne Dinio 2,4	
Nancy Norton 4		Christopher Salum 6,7,35*	
Anthony Showah 11,58,69,295,296		Carol Storey 37,93*	

79 Student Personnel	91 Safety/Security	275 Response To Intervention	298 Grant Writer/Ptnrships	**School Programs**	**Social Media**
80 Driver Ed/Safety	92 Magnet School	277 Remedial Math K-12	750 Chief Innovation Officer	A = Alternative Program	f = Facebook
81 Gifted/Talented	93 Parental Involvement	280 Literacy Coach	751 Chief of Staff	G = Adult Classes	t = Twitter
82 Video Services	95 Tech Prep Program	285 STEM	752 Social Emotional Learning	M = Magnet Program	
83 Substance Abuse Prev	97 Chief Infomation Officer	286 Digital Learning		T = Title I Schoolwide	
84 Erate	98 Chief Technology Officer	288 Common Core Standards	**Other School Types**	V = Career & Tech Ed Programs	
85 AIDS Education	270 Accountability	294 Accountability	Ⓐ = Alternative Program		
88 Alternative/At Risk	271 Migrant Education	295 Network System	Ⓒ = Charter School	New Schools are shaded	
89 Multi-Cultural Curriculum	273 Teacher Mentor	296 Title II Programs	Ⓜ = Magnet School	New Superintendents and Principals are bold	
90 Social Work	274 Before/After Sch	297 Webmaster	Ⓨ = Year-Round School	Personnel with email addresses are underscored	

NY–175

Queens County Market Data Retrieval

Kristen Mosco 38*	Andrea Saunders 51,54*
Jen Daly 67	Leah Horn 76*
Tara Rounds 79	Scott Many 83,90*
Paul Piazza 91*	Tim Donaghy 273
Tom Virgadamo 273	

Public Schs..Principal	Grd	Prgm	Enr/#Cls	SN
Haldane Sch 15 Craigside Dr, Cold Spring 10516 Christine Jamin \ Mary Ann Seelke \ Julia Sniffen	K-12		794 22	17% 845/265-9254 Fax 845/265-3510

• **Mahopac Ctl School Dist** PID: 00766474 845/628-3415
179 E Lake Blvd, Mahopac 10541 Fax 845/628-5502

Schools: 5 \ **Teachers:** 371 \ **Students:** 3,968 \ **Special Ed Students:** 797 \ **LEP Students:** 120 \ **College-Bound:** 90% \ **Ethnic:** Asian 2%, African American 2%, Hispanic 21%, Caucasian 75% \ **Exp:** $203 (Med) \ **Poverty:** 4% \ **Title I:** $171,600 \ **Special Education:** $10,696,000 \ **Open-Close:** 09/04 - 06/25 \ **DTBP:** $322 (High) \

Anthony Di Carlo 1	Harvey Sotland 2,15
Robert Campisi 4	Pamela Romeo 5
John Augusta 6	Andrea Hughes 8,15
Joanne Sullivan 8,15	Michael Tromblee 8,15
Adam Pease 11,85,298*	Debra Legato 15,68
Dr Gregory Stowell 15,79	Gregory Sullivan 15
Marguerite Morales 15	Elsa Petix 30*
Jeffrey Finton 58	Meghan Febbie 58
Michael Mongon 67	Dr Dennis Creedon 288

Public Schs..Principal	Grd	Prgm	Enr/#Cls	SN
Austin Road Elem Sch 390 Austin Rd, Mahopac 10541 James Gardineer	K-5	T	602 31	15% 845/628-1346 Fax 845/628-5521
Fulmar Road Elem Sch 55 Fulmar Rd, Mahopac 10541 Gary Chadwick	K-5	T	500 25	13% 845/628-0440 Fax 845/628-5714
Lakeview Elem Sch 112 Lakeview Dr, Mahopac 10541 Jennifer Pontillo	K-5	T	568 30	23% 845/628-3331 Fax 845/628-5849
Mahopac High Sch 421 Baldwin Place Rd, Mahopac 10541 Matthew Lawrence	9-12	AGV	1,387	13% 845/628-3256 Fax 845/628-4380
Mahopac Middle Sch 425 Baldwin Place Rd, Mahopac 10541 Thomas Cozzocrea	6-8	T	911 53	15% 845/621-1330 Fax 845/628-5847

• **Putnam Valley Ctl School Dist** PID: 00766541 845/528-8143
171 Oscawana Lake Rd, Putnam Valley 10579 Fax 845/528-8386

Schools: 3 \ **Teachers:** 145 \ **Students:** 1,587 \ **Special Ed Students:** 264 \ **LEP Students:** 50 \ **College-Bound:** 92% \ **Ethnic:** Asian 1%, African American 3%, Hispanic 21%, Caucasian 74% \ **Exp:** $379 (High) \ **Poverty:** 7% \ **Title I:** $163,605 \ **Special Education:** $2,264,000 \ **Open-Close:** 09/08 - 06/25 \ **DTBP:** $164 (High)

Dr Jeremy Luft 1	Jill Figarella 2
David Spittal 3,5	Brian Burrow 6,35
Jenette Mistretta 8	Natalie Doherty 12,15
Jeanine Rufo 67	Michael Lee 71,97

Public Schs..Principal	Grd	Prgm	Enr/#Cls	SN
Putnam Valley Elem Sch 171 Oscawana Lake Rd, Putnam Valley 10579 Margaret Podesta	K-4	T	528	16% 845/528-8092 Fax 845/528-8171
Putnam Valley High Sch 146 Peekskill Hollow Rd, Putnam Valley 10579 Sandra Intrieri	9-12	A	569	18% 845/528-4456 Fax 845/528-4466
Putnam Valley Middle Sch 142 Peekskill Hollow Rd, Putnam Valley 10579 Travis McCarty	5-8	T	490 25	20% 845/528-8101 Fax 845/528-8145

PUTNAM CATHOLIC SCHOOLS

• **Archdiocese of New York Ed Off** PID: 00754976
Listing includes only schools located in this county. See District Index for location of Diocesan Offices.

Catholic Schs..Principal	Grd	Prgm	Enr/#Cls	SN
St James the Apostle Sch 12 Gleneida Ave, Carmel 10512 Maura Crawford	PK-8		150 15	845/225-9365 Fax 845/228-2859

PUTNAM PRIVATE SCHOOLS

Private Schs..Principal	Grd	Prgm	Enr/#Cls	SN
Green Chimneys Sch 400 Doansburg Rd, Brewster 10509 Jerry Newell	Spec	V	200 20	845/279-2995 Fax 845/230-9505
Hudson Valley Christian Acad 531 Route 6 N, Mahopac Falls 10542 Maija Murry	PK-5		38 8	845/628-2775 Fax 845/621-9135
Manitou Sch 1656 Route 9D, Cold Spring 10516 Maria Stein-Marrison	PK-8		100	845/809-5695
Temple Beth Shalom Sch 760 Route 6, Mahopac 10541 Libby Spitzer	PK-12		62	845/628-6133

QUEENS COUNTY

QUEENS PUBLIC SCHOOLS

• **Community School District 24** PID: 10909840 718/592-3357
9850 50th Ave, Corona 11368 Fax 718/592-3770

(Part of New York City Dept of Ed in New York County)
Madelene Taub 1

Public Schs..Principal	Grd	Prgm	Enr/#Cls	SN
Academy of Finance Enterprise 3020 Thomson Ave Fl 4, Long Is City 11101 Victoria Armano	9-12	T	677	80% 718/389-3623 Fax 718/389-3724
Aviation Career & Tech Ed HS 4530 36th St, Long Is City 11101 Steven Jackson	Voc	GT	2,076	62% 718/361-2032 Fax 718/784-8654
Bard HS Early College Queens 3020 Thomson Ave, Long Is City 11101 Valeri Thomson	9-12		636	43% 718/361-3133 Fax 718/361-6742

1 Superintendent	8 Curric/Instruct K-12	19 Chief Financial Officer	29 Family/Consumer Science	39 Social Studies K-12	49 English/Lang Arts Elem	59 Special Education Elem	69 Academic Assessment
2 Bus/Finance/Purchasing	9 Curric/Instruct Elem	20 Art K-12	30 Adult Education	40 Social Studies Elem	50 English/Lang Arts Sec	60 Special Education Sec	70 Research/Development
3 Buildings And Grounds	10 Curric/Instruct Sec	21 Art Elem	31 Career/Sch-to-Work K-12	41 Social Studies Sec	51 Reading K-12	61 Foreign/World Lang K-12	71 Public Information
4 Food Service	11 Federal Program	22 Art Sec	32 Career/Sch-to-Work Elem	42 Science K-12	52 Reading Elem	62 Foreign/World Lang Elem	72 Summer School
5 Transportation	12 Title I	23 Music K-12	33 Career/Sch-to-Work Sec	43 Science Elem	53 Reading Sec	63 Foreign/World Lang Sec	73 Instructional Tech
6 Athletic	13 Title V	24 Music Elem	34 Early Childhood Ed	44 Science Sec	54 Remedial Reading K-12	64 Religious Education K-12	74 Inservice Training
7 Health Services	15 Asst Superintendent	25 Music Sec	35 Health/Phys Education	45 Math K-12	55 Remedial Reading Elem	65 Religious Education Elem	75 Marketing/Distributive
	16 Instructional Media Svcs	26 Business Education	36 Guidance Services K-12	46 Math Elem	56 Remedial Reading Sec	66 Religious Education Sec	76 Info Systems
	17 Chief Operations Officer	27 Career & Tech Ed	37 Guidance Services Elem	47 Math Sec	57 Bilingual/ELL	67 School Board President	77 Psychological Assess
	18 Chief Academic Officer	28 Technology Education	38 Guidance Services Sec	48 English/Lang Arts K-12	58 Special Education K-12	68 Teacher Personnel	78 Affirmative Action

New York School Directory

Queens County

School	Grades	Prog	Enroll	%	Phone
Children's Lab Sch 4545 42nd St, Sunnyside 11104 Brooke Barr	PK-4	T	427	82%	718/361-3300 Fax 718/361-3305
Civic Leadership Academy 4510 94th St 4th Fl, Elmhurst 11373 Phuong Nguyen	9-12	T	643	76%	718/271-1487 Fax 718/271-3408
Corona Arts & Sciences Acad 9811 44th Ave, Corona 11368 Beth Garelick	6-8	T	764	97%	718/507-3820 Fax 718/507-3828
Grover Cleveland High Sch 2127 Himrod St, Ridgewood 11385 Marc Pascente	9-12	TV	1,700 120	70%	718/381-9600
Helen M Marshall Sch 11008 Northern Blvd, Corona 11368 Deborah Rudolph	K-5	T	492	93%	718/505-5110 Fax 718/505-5115
Ⓐ High School Arts & Bus YABC 10525 Horace Harding Expy, Corona 11368 Jimmy Liu	9-12		250		718/271-8383
High School Arts & Business 10525 Horace Harding Expy, Corona 11368 Ana Burakov	9-12	GT	788 40	68%	718/271-8383 Fax 718/271-7196
HS of Applied Communications 3020 Thomson Ave Fl 5, Long Is City 11101 Michael Weinstein	9-12	T	414	75%	718/389-3163 Fax 718/389-3427
Int'l HS-Health Sciences 4801 90th St, Elmhurst 11373 Carl Finney	9-12	T	282	91%	718/595-8600 Fax 718/595-8605
International High Sch 4535 Van Dam St, Long Is City 11101 Jaclyn Valane	9-12	TV	520 36	67%	718/392-3433 Fax 718/392-3443
IS 5 Walter H Crowley 5040 Jacobus St, Elmhurst 11373 Kelly Nepogoda	6-8	TV	1,749	76%	718/205-6788 Fax 718/429-6518
IS 61 Leonardo Da Vinci 9850 50th Ave, Corona 11368 Joseph Lisa	6-8	TV	2,268 80	93%	718/760-3233 Fax 718/760-5220
IS 73 Frank Sansivieri 7002 54th Ave, Maspeth 11378 Michael Casale	6-8	TV	2,002	66%	718/639-3817 Fax 718/429-5162
IS 77 Queens 976 Seneca Ave, Ridgewood 11385 Joseph Miller	6-8	TV	878	90%	718/366-7120 Fax 718/456-9512
IS 93 Ridgewood 6656 Forest Ave, Ridgewood 11385 Edward Santos	6-8	TV	1,154 57	90%	718/821-4882 Fax 718/456-9521
IS 125 Thomas McCann-Woodside 4602 47th Ave, Woodside 11377 Judy Mittler	6-8	AT	1,454 100	74%	718/937-0320 Fax 718/361-2451
Learners & Leaders 378 Seneca Ave, Ridgewood 11385 Lynn Botfeld	PK-5	T	560	84%	718/366-1061 Fax 718/366-4301
Maspeth High Sch 5440 74th St, Elmhurst 11373 Khurshid Mutakabbi	9-12		1,222	55%	718/803-7100 Fax 718/803-7105
Middle College High Sch 4535 Van Dam St, Long Is City 11101 Socrates Ortiz	9-12	T	508 50	69%	718/392-3330 Fax 718/392-3315
Mosaic Pre-K Center at 47 Ave 10910 47th Ave, Corona 11368 Beth Useloff	PK-PK		72		718/271-7364
Mosaic Pre-K Center at 101 St 5425 101st St, Corona 11368 Beth Tekverk	PK-PK		54		718/326-8170
Mosaic Pre-K Center Myrtle Ave 6820 Myrtle Ave, Ridgewood 11385	PK-PK		401		718/592-3357
Newtown High Sch 4801 90th St, Elmhurst 11373 John Ficalora	9-12	TV	1,663	76%	718/595-8400 Fax 718/699-8584
Pan American International HS 4510 94th St, Elmhurst 11373 George Badia	9-12	T	433	84%	718/271-3602 Fax 718/271-4041
PS 7 Louis Simeone 8055 Cornish Ave, Elmhurst 11373 Jason Chin	PK-5	T	1,347	82%	718/446-2726 Fax 718/397-7916
PS 12 James B Colgate 4200 72nd St, Woodside 11377 Stephanie Moskos	K-5	T	1,125 47	86%	718/424-5905 Fax 718/424-0207
PS 13 Clement C Moore 5501 94th St, Elmhurst 11373 Evelyn Velez	K-5	T	1,392	72%	718/271-1021 Fax 718/699-3008
PS 14 Fairview 10701 Otis Ave, Corona 11368 Heather Benson	K-5	T	1,388 50	81%	718/699-6071 Fax 718/699-3224
PS 19 Marino P Jeantet 4010 99 St, Corona 11368 Genie Calibar	PK-5	GT	1,844 95	88%	718/424-5859
PS 28 Thomas Emanuel ECC 10910 47th Ave, Corona 11368 Robert Quintana	PK-2	T	466 22	79%	718/271-4971 Fax 718/271-2576
PS 49 Dorothy Bonawit Kole 6360 80th St, Middle Vlg 11379 Thomas Carty	K-8		1,201 22	51%	718/326-2111 Fax 718/894-3026
PS 58 School of Heroes 7224 Grand Ave, Maspeth 11378 Adeline Tripoli	PK-6	T	968	73%	718/533-6712 Fax 718/533-6794
PS 68 Cambridge 5909 Saint Felix Ave, Ridgewood 11385 Anne-Marie Scalfaro	PK-5	T	541 42	65%	718/821-7246 Fax 718/497-8945
PS 71 Forest Elem Sch 6285 Forest Ave, Ridgewood 11385 Indiana Soto	PK-5	T	672	84%	718/821-7772 Fax 718/386-7088
PS 81 Jean Paul Richter 559 Cypress Ave, Ridgewood 11385 Romy Diamond	PK-5	T	619 54	79%	718/821-9800 Fax 718/386-7203
PS 87 Middle Village 6754 80th St, Middle Vlg 11379 Caryn Michaeli	PK-8		604 26	56%	718/326-8243 Fax 718/894-3797
PS 88 Seneca 6085 Catalpa Ave, Ridgewood 11385 Linda O'Shaughnessy	PK-5	T	789	74%	718/821-8121 Fax 718/386-7214
PS 89 Elmhurst 8528 Britton Ave, Elmhurst 11373 Laura La Sala	K-5	T	1,709	75%	718/898-2230 Fax 718/672-3066
PS 91 Richard Arkwright 6810 Central Ave, Glendale 11385 Gregory Filippi	PK-5	T	773	64%	718/821-6880 Fax 718/386-0216
PS 102 Bayview 5524 Van Horn St, Elmhurst 11373 Catherine Weinstein	PK-8	T	1,270 40	83%	718/446-3308 Fax 718/672-3101
PS 110 4318 97th Pl, Corona 11368 Elisa Gomez	K-5	T	974	92%	718/424-8278 Fax 718/424-8345
PS 128 Juniper Valley 6910 65th Dr, Middle Vlg 11379 Camillo Turriciano	K-8		958 13	27%	718/326-6210 Fax 718/326-6080
PS 143 Louis Armstrong 3474 113th St, Corona 11368 Justine Lucas	K-5	T	1,286 59	94%	718/429-5700 Fax 718/478-8306
PS 153 Maspeth 6002 60th Ln, Maspeth 11378 David Berkowitz	PK-6	T	1,062	64%	718/821-7850 Fax 718/386-7392

---

79 Student Personnel
80 Driver Ed/Safety
81 Gifted/Talented
82 Video Services
83 Substance Abuse Prev
84 Erate
85 AIDS Education
88 Alternative/At Risk
89 Multi-Cultural Curriculum
90 Social Work
91 Safety/Security
92 Magnet School
93 Parental Involvement
95 Tech Prep Program
97 Chief Infomation Officer
98 Chief Technology Officer
270 Character Education
271 Migrant Education
273 Teacher Mentor
274 Before/After Sch
275 Response To Intervention
277 Remedial Math K-12
280 Literacy Coach
285 STEM
286 Digital Learning
288 Common Core Standards
294 Accountability
295 Network System
296 Title II Programs
297 Webmaster
298 Grant Writer/Ptnrships
750 Chief Innovation Officer
751 Chief of Staff
752 Social Emotional Learning

School Programs
A = Alternative Program
G = Adult Classes
M = Magnet Program
T = Title I Schoolwide
V = Career & Tech Ed Programs

Other School Types
Ⓐ = Alternative School
Ⓒ = Charter School
Ⓜ = Magnet School
Ⓨ = Year-Round School

Social Media
❑ = Facebook
❑ = Twitter

New Schools are shaded
New Superintendents and Principals are bold
Personnel with email addresses are underscored

NY-177

Queens County   Market Data Retrieval

Public Schs..Principal	Grd	Prgm	Enr/#Cls	SN		
PS 199 Maurice Fitzgerald 3920 48th Ave, Long Is City 11104 Anthony Inzerillo	PK-5	T	690		68%	718/784-3431 Fax 718/786-1375
PS 211Q Elm Tree Elem Sch 5051 98th St, Corona 11368 Kristen Niven	PK-5	T	661		93%	929/208-4680 Fax 929/208-4862
PS 229 Emmanuel Kaplan 6725 51st Rd, Woodside 11377 Seth Berger	PK-5	T	1,391		70%	718/446-2120 Fax 718/672-3117
PS 239 1715 Weirfield St, Ridgewood 11385 Michele Dzwonek	PK-5	T	510 35		86%	718/417-2840 Fax 718/417-2845
PS 290 Ace Acad for Scholars 5520 Metropolitan Ave, Ridgewood 11385 Jose Jimenez	PK-5		582		65%	718/571-6900 Fax 718/571-6920
PS 307 Pioneer Academy 4020 100th St, Corona 11368 Cecilia Jackson	K-5	T	867		95%	718/779-5068 Fax 718/779-5109
PS Q016 Nancy Debenedittis 4115 104th St, Corona 11368 Elaine Iodice	K-5	T	1,404		85%	718/505-0140 Fax 718/505-0141
PS/IS 113 Anthony J Pranzo 7823 87th St, Glendale 11385 Alejandro Megias	PK-8		869 22		47%	718/847-0724 Fax 718/805-0737
PS/IS 119 the Glendale 7401 78th Ave, Glendale 11385 Dr Jeanne Fagan	K-8	TV	1,319 30		73%	718/326-8261 Fax 718/456-9523
Queens Technical High Sch 3702 47th Ave, Long Is City 11101 Melissa Burg	Voc	GT	1,472 66		86%	718/937-3010 Fax 718/392-8397
ⓐ Robert Wagner Jr Sch Arts-Tech 4707 30th Pl, Long Is City 11101 Dr Stephania Goel	6-12	T	654 25		73%	718/472-5671 Fax 718/472-9117
Voyages Preparatory Sch 4510 94th St, Elmhurst 11373 Nicholas Bleiberg	9-9	T	236		69%	718/271-7851 Fax 718/271-8549

- **Community School District 25** PID: 10909852 718/281-7605
  3048 Linden Pl, Flushing 11354 Fax 718/281-7690

  (Part of New York City Dept of Ed in New York County)
  Danielle Dimango 1

Public Schs..Principal	Grd	Prgm	Enr/#Cls	SN		
Active Learning Elem Sch 13720 Franklin Ave, Flushing 11355 Robert Groff	PK-3	T	470		79%	718/445-5730 Fax 718/445-5856
Bell Academy 1825 212th St, Bayside 11360 David Abbott	6-8		362		42%	718/428-0587 Fax 718/428-0237
East-West Sch of Int'l Studies 4621 Colden St, Flushing 11355 Anthony Cromer	6-12	T	665		82%	718/353-0009 Fax 718/353-3772
Flushing High Sch 3501 Union St, Flushing 11354 Ignazio Accardi	9-12	TV	1,512		78%	718/888-7500 Fax 718/886-4255
Flushing International HS 14480 Barclay Ave, Flushing 11355 Lara Evangelista	9-12	T	441		92%	718/463-2348 Fax 718/463-3514
ⓐ Flushing YABC 3501 Union St, Flushing 11354 Andy Siu Hei Szeto	10-12		250			718/888-7500
ⓜ IS 25 Adrien Block 3465 192nd St, Flushing 11358 Mary Ellen Beirne	6-8		1,074 38		54%	718/961-3480 Fax 718/358-1563
IS 237 Rachel Carson Magnet 4621 Colden St, Flushing 11355 Judith Friedman	6-8	T	1,348		79%	718/353-6464 Fax 718/460-6427
ⓜ IS 250 Robert F Kennedy 15840 76th Rd, Flushing 11366 Tara Mrwik	6-8	T	354 25		87%	718/591-9000 Fax 718/591-2340
JHS 185 Edward Bleeker 14726 25th Dr, Flushing 11354 Theresa Mshar	6-8	GT	1,472 45		74%	718/445-3232 Fax 718/359-5352
JHS 189 Daniel Carter Beard 14480 Barclay Ave, Flushing 11355 Magdalen Radovich	6-8	T	730 40		76%	718/359-6676 Fax 718/358-0155
JHS 194 William H Carr 15460 17th Ave, Whitestone 11357 Jennifer Miller	6-8	G	1,289		54%	718/746-0818 Fax 718/746-7618
John Bowne High Sch 6325 Main St, Flushing 11367 Laura Izzo Iannelli	9-12	TV	3,451 110		72%	718/263-1919 Fax 718/575-4069
MS 379 Clg Point Collaborative 12406 14th Ave, College Point 11356 Renee Klager	6-6	T	507		77%	929/362-3300
North Queens Cmty High Sch 14125 77th Rd, Flushing 11367 Winston McCarthy	9-12	T	159		75%	718/380-1650 Fax 718/380-2189
Pre-K Center at 14-45 1445 143rd St, Whitestone 11357 L Thompson	PK-PK		108			718/357-2840
PS 20 John Bowne 14230 Barclay Ave, Flushing 11355 Victoria Hart	PK-5	T	1,171		89%	718/359-0321 Fax 718/358-0762
PS 21 Edward Hart 14736 26th Ave, Flushing 11354 Michael Swirsky	PK-5	T	1,334 50		76%	718/445-8833 Fax 718/358-0891
PS 22 Thomas Jefferson 15333 Sanford Ave, Flushing 11355 Jennifer Meyer	PK-5	T	861 33		89%	718/762-4141 Fax 718/358-1260
PS 24 Andrew Jackson 4557 Union St, Flushing 11355 Debra Cassidy	PK-5	T	1,080 32		66%	718/359-2288 Fax 718/460-3251
ⓜ PS 29 Queens 12510 23rd Ave, College Point 11356 Jill Leakey	PK-5	T	706 30		82%	718/886-5111 Fax 718/461-6812
PS 32 State Street 17111 35th Ave, Flushing 11358 Debra Errico	PK-5	T	1,031 34		64%	718/463-3747 Fax 718/358-1622
ⓜ PS 79 Francis Lewis 14727 15th Dr, Whitestone 11357 George Carter	PK-5	T	1,096 37		50%	718/746-0396 Fax 718/746-3103
PS 107 Thomas A Dooley 16702 45th Ave, Flushing 11358 Lori Cummings	PK-5	T	940		75%	718/762-5995 Fax 718/461-4989
PS 120 Queens 5801 136th St, Flushing 11355 Robert Marino	PK-5	T	896 33		71%	718/359-3390 Fax 718/460-4513
PS 129 Patricia A Larkin 12802 7th Ave, College Point 11356 Marilyn Alesi	K-5	T	1,108 26		76%	718/353-3150 Fax 718/321-2476
ⓜ PS 130 20001 42nd Ave, Bayside 11361 Michelle Contratti	PK-5		402 14		44%	718/819-2230 Fax 718/819-2238
PS 154 Queens 7502 162nd St, Flushing 11366 Pamela Gathers	PK-5	T	649 28		79%	718/591-1500 Fax 718/591-8751
ⓜ PS 163 Flushing Heights 15901 59th Ave, Flushing 11365 Francine Marsaggi	PK-5	T	802 23		80%	718/353-2514 Fax 718/460-4244

1	Superintendent	8	Curric/Instruct K-12	19	Chief Financial Officer	29	Family/Consumer Science	39 Social Studies K-12
2	Bus/Finance/Purchasing	9	Curric/Instruct Elem	20	Art K-12	30	Adult Education	40 Social Studies Elem
3	Buildings And Grounds	10	Curric/Instruct Sec	21	Art Elem	31	Career/Sch-to-Work K-12	41 Social Studies Sec
4	Food Service	11	Federal Program	22	Art Sec	32	Career/Sch-to-Work Elem	42 Science K-12
5	Transportation	12	Title I	23	Music K-12	33	Career/Sch-to-Work Sec	43 Science Elem
6	Athletic	13	Title V	24	Music Elem	34	Early Childhood Ed	44 Science Sec
7	Health Services	14	Asst Superintendent	25	Music Sec	35	Health/Phys Education	45 Math K-12
		15	Instructional Media Svcs	26	Business Education	36	Guidance Services K-12	46 Math Elem
		16	Chief Operations Officer	27	Career & Tech Ed	37	Guidance Services Elem	47 Math Sec
		18	Chief Academic Officer	28	Technology Education	38	Guidance Services Sec	48 English/Lang Arts K-12

49 English/Lang Arts Elem	59 Special Education K-12	69 Academic Assessment
50 English/Lang Arts Sec	60 Special Education Sec	70 Research/Development
51 Reading K-12	61 Foreign/World Lang K-12	71 Public Information
52 Reading Elem	62 Foreign/World Lang Elem	72 Summer School
53 Reading Sec	63 Foreign/World Lang Sec	73 Instructional Tech
54 Remedial Reading K-12	64 Religious Education K-12	74 Inservice Training
55 Remedial Reading Elem	65 Religious Education Elem	75 Marketing/Distributive
56 Remedial Reading Sec	66 Religious Education Sec	76 Info Systems
57 Bilingual/ELL	67 School Board President	77 Psychological Assess
58 Special Education K-12	68 Teacher Personnel	78 Affirmative Action

New York School Directory

Queens County

School	Grd	Prgm	Enr/#Cls	SN	Phone
Ⓜ PS 164 Queens Valley 13801 77th Ave, Flushing 11367 Lisa Liatto	PK-8	T	671 28	73%	718/544-1083 Fax 718/544-2042
PS 165 Edith K Bergtraum 7035 150th St, Flushing 11367 Tiffany Davis	PK-5	T	715 38	67%	718/263-4004 Fax 718/793-9812
Ⓜ PS 169 Bay Terrace 1825 212th St, Bayside 11360 Vanessa Rosa	K-5		382	35%	718/428-6160 Fax 718/224-1013
Ⓜ PS 184 Flushing Manor 16315 21st Rd, Whitestone 11357 Anna Dimilta	PK-5		528 21	47%	718/352-7800 Fax 718/352-0311
Ⓜ PS 193 Alfred J Kennedy 15220 11th Ave, Whitestone 11357 Diane Tratner	PK-5		573 10	33%	718/767-8810 Fax 718/746-7617
PS 201 Discovery Sch 6511 155th St, Flushing 11367 Umit Serin	PK-5	T	469 23	71%	718/359-0620 Fax 718/321-2081
PS 209 Clearview Gardens 1610 Utopia Pkwy, Whitestone 11357 Dr Mary McDonnell	PK-5		553 25	39%	718/352-3939 Fax 718/352-0367
PS 214 Cadwallader Colden 3115 140th St, Flushing 11354 Denise Fuccillo	PK-5	T	410 20	77%	718/461-4055 Fax 718/460-6841
Ⓜ PS 219 Paul Klapper 14439 Gravett Rd, Flushing 11367 Frederick Wright	PK-8	T	630 35	72%	718/793-2130 Fax 718/793-1039
PS 242 Leonard P Stavisky 2966 137th St, Flushing 11354 Jill Pritchard	PK-3		402 17	67%	718/445-2902 Fax 718/939-7751
Ⓜ PS/MS 200 Global Studies/ 7010 164th St, Flushing 11365 Kevin McAuliffe	PK-8	T	542 35	72%	718/969-7780 Fax 718/380-2615
Ⓐ Queens Academy High Sch 13811 35th Ave, Flushing 11354 James Memola	10-12	T	324 25	69%	718/463-3111 Fax 718/886-5015
Queens College Sch Math & Sci 14820 Reeves Ave, Flushing 11367 Simi Minhas	PK-8		515 8	45%	718/461-7462 Fax 718/461-7244
Queens High Sch-Lang Studies 3501 Union St, Flushing 11354 Melanie Lee	9-12	T	443	77%	718/888-7530 Fax 718/888-7526
Queens School of Inquiry 15840 76th Rd, Flushing 11366 M Inbal	6-12		597	54%	718/380-6929 Fax 718/380-6809
Robert F Kennedy Cmty High Sch 7540 Parsons Blvd, Flushing 11366 Anthony Barbetta	9-12	T	682 25	80%	718/969-5510 Fax 718/969-5524
Townsend Harris High Sch 14911 Melbourne Ave, Flushing 11367 Brian Condon	9-12	V	1,219	48%	718/575-5580 Fax 718/575-1366
Veritas Academy 3501 Union St, Flushing 11354 Mr Vanderwalker	9-12	T	607	69%	718/888-7520 Fax 718/888-7524
World Journalism Prep Sch 3465 192nd St, Flushing 11358 Dr Janine Werner	6-12		607 26	60%	718/461-2219 Fax 718/461-2633

● **Community School District 26** PID: 10909864   718/631-6943
6115 Oceania St, Bayside 11364

(Part of New York City Dept of Ed in New York County)
Danielle Giunta 1

Public Schs..Principal	Grd	Prgm	Enr/#Cls	SN	Phone
Bayside High Sch 3224 Corporal Kennedy St, Bayside 11361 Michael Athy	9-12	TV	2,882	71%	718/229-7600 Fax 718/423-9566
Benjamin N Cardozo High Sch 5700 223rd St, Bayside 11364 Meagan Colby	9-12	V	3,455	62%	718/279-6500 Fax 718/631-7880 f
Business Tech Early Clg HS 23017 Hillside Ave, Queens Vlg 11427 Patrice Henry	9-12	T	563	66%	718/217-3613 Fax 718/217-3616
Francis Lewis High Sch 5820 Utopia Pkwy, Fresh Meadows 11365 David Marmor	9-12	TV	4,472 144	69%	718/281-8200 Fax 718/746-2017
Irwin Altman Middle School 172 8114 257th St, Floral Park 11004 Jeffrey Slivko	6-8	V	1,003	60%	718/831-4000 Fax 718/831-4008
JHS 67 Louis Pasteur Sch 5160 Marathon Pkwy, Little Neck 11362 Brian Annello	6-8	V	1,042	43%	718/423-8138 Fax 718/423-8281
JHS 74 Nathaniel Hawthorne 6115 Oceania St, Bayside 11364 Anthony Armstrong	6-8	V	1,159	46%	718/631-6800 Fax 718/631-6899
JHS 216 George J Ryan 6420 175th St, Fresh Meadows 11365 Reginald Landeau	6-8	V	1,575 44	69%	718/358-2005 Fax 718/358-2070
Martin Van Buren High Sch 23017 Hillside Ave, Queens Vlg 11427 Sam Sochet	9-12	TV	1,157 142	73%	718/776-4728 Fax 718/217-6287
MS 158 Marie Curie 4635 Oceania St, Bayside 11361 Henry Schandel	6-8	V	1,070 44	55%	718/423-8100 Fax 718/423-8135
PS 18 Winchester 8635 235th Ct, Queens Vlg 11427 Laurie Careddu	PK-5		510 21	58%	718/464-4167 Fax 718/464-4273
PS 26 Rufus King 19502 69th Ave, Flushing 11365 Andrew Pecorella	PK-5	T	702 23	66%	718/464-4505 Fax 718/464-4644
PS 31 Bayside 21145 46th Rd, Bayside 11361 Terri Graybow	PK-5		507 26	58%	718/423-8289 Fax 718/746-3619
PS 41 Crocheron 21443 35th Ave, Bayside 11361 Joseph Ferrara	K-5		469 21	37%	718/423-8333 Fax 718/423-8362
PS 46 Alley Pond 6445 218th St, Oakland GDNS 11364 Stamo Karalazarides	PK-5		541 24	47%	718/423-8395 Fax 718/423-8472
PS 94 David D Porter 4177 Little Neck Pkwy, Little Neck 11363 Laura Avakians	PK-5		342 16	45%	718/423-8491 Fax 718/423-8531
PS 098 the Douglaston Sch 4020 235th St, Douglaston 11363 Lena Kim	PK-5		284 12	20%	718/423-8535 Fax 718/423-8550
PS 115 James J Ambrose Sch 8051 261st St, Floral Park 11004 Danielle LaPorte	PK-5		773 25	38%	718/831-4010 Fax 718/831-4014
PS 133 Queens 24805 86th Ave, Bellerose 11426 Nicole Colon	PK-5		607 30	57%	718/831-4016 Fax 718/831-4020
PS 159 20501 33rd Ave, Bayside 11361 Paul DiDio	PK-5		662	46%	718/423-8553 Fax 718/423-8583
PS 162 John Golden 20102 53rd Ave, Bayside 11364 Pamela Lee	PK-5		649	61%	718/423-8621 Fax 718/423-8647
PS 173 Fresh Meadows 17410 67th Ave, Flushing 11365 Molly Wang	PK-5	A	948 56	55%	718/358-2243 Fax 718/358-2989

79 Student Personnel	91 Safety/Security	275 Response To Intervention
80 Driver Ed/Safety	92 Magnet School	277 Remedial Math K-12
81 Gifted/Talented	93 Parental Involvement	280 Literacy Coach
82 Video Services	95 Tech Prep Program	285 STEM
83 Substance Abuse Prev	97 Chief Information Officer	286 Digital Learning
84 Erate	98 Chief Technology Officer	288 Common Core Standards
85 AIDS Education	270 Character Education	294 Accountability
88 Alternative/At Risk	271 Migrant Education	295 Network System
89 Multi-Cultural Curriculum	273 Teacher Mentor	296 Title II Programs
90 Social Work	274 Before/After Sch	297 Webmaster

298 Grant Writer/Ptnrships	**School Programs**
750 Chief Innovation Officer	A = Alternative Program
751 Chief of Staff	G = Adult Classes
752 Social Emotional Learning	M = Magnet Program
	T = Title I Schoolwide
Other School Types	V = Career & Tech Ed Programs
Ⓐ = Alternative School	
Ⓒ = Charter School	New Schools are shaded
Ⓜ = Magnet School	New Superintendents and Principals are bold
Ⓨ = Year-Round School	Personnel with email addresses are underscored

Social Media
f = Facebook
t = Twitter

NY—179

Queens County

Market Data Retrieval

PS 186 Castlewood 25212 72nd Ave, Bellerose 11426 Melissa Haidary	PK-5	371 25	34%	718/831-4021 Fax 718/831-4029
PS 188 Kingsbury 21812 Hartland Ave, Bayside 11364 Janet Caraisco	PK-5	712 30	25%	929/600-5683 Fax 929/600-5685
PS 191 Mayflower 8515 258th St, Floral Park 11001 Michael Ranieri	PK-5	384 35	65%	718/831-4032 Fax 718/831-4036
PS 203 Oakland Gardens 5311 Springfield Blvd, Bayside 11364 Deborah Florio	PK-5	855 32	42%	718/423-8652 Fax 718/423-8713
PS 205 Alexander Graham Bell 7525 Bell Blvd, Bayside 11364 Karen Piazza	PK-5	301 20	27%	718/464-5773 Fax 718/464-5875
PS 213 Carl Ullman 23102 67th Ave, Bayside 11364 Megan McCauley	PK-5	450 25	55%	718/423-8747 Fax 718/423-8805
PS 221 North Hills Sch 5740 Marathon Pkwy, Little Neck 11362 Patricia Bullard	PK-5	637 27	37%	718/225-7029 Fax 718/225-7030
PS 376Q 21021 48th Ave, Oakland GDNS 11364 Clara Kang	PK-1	170	46%	929/267-5900 Fax 929/267-5910
PS 390Q Civic ES Bayside Hills 5610 214th St, Oakland GDNS 11364 Melody Leib	PK-K	61		
PS/IS 178 Holliswood 18910 Radnor Rd, Jamaica 11423 Jessica Cruz	PK-8	571	37%	718/464-5763 Fax 718/464-5766
PS/IS 266 7410 Commonwealth Blvd, Bellerose 11426 Ayanna Greenidge	PK-8	623 30	49%	718/479-3920 Fax 718/479-2482
Queens High School of Teaching 7420 Commonwealth Blvd, Bellerose 11426 Ean Corrado	9-12	1,030	58%	718/736-7100 Fax 718/736-7117

• **Community School District 27** PID: 10909876   718/642-5770
  8201 Rockaway Blvd, Ozone Park 11416   Fax 718/642-5705
  (Part of New York City Dept of Ed in New York County)
  Jennifer Ambert 1   Patricia Finn 34*

Public Schs..Principal	Grd	Prgm	Enr/#Cls	SN	
Acad of Med Tech-College Board 821 Bay 25th St, Far Rockaway 11691 William Johnson	6-12	T	679	82%	718/471-3571 Fax 718/471-0314
August Martin High Sch 15610 Baisley Blvd, Jamaica 11434 Rory Parnell	9-12	TV	371	77%	718/528-2920 Fax 718/276-1846
© Challenge Charter Middle Sch 1279 Redfern Ave, Far Rockaway 11691 Mavgar Gordon	6-8		190		347/990-1875
© Challenge Prep Charter Sch 710 Hartman Ln, Far Rockaway 11691 Nicole Griffin	K-5	T	601	86%	718/327-1352 Fax 718/583-6238
Channel View Sch for Research 10000 Beach Channel Dr, Rockaway Park 11694 Denise Richardson	6-12	T	1,082	72%	718/634-1970 Fax 718/734-3296
Curious Young Learners PK Ctr 13340 79th St, Howard Beach 11414 Tracy Keane	PK-PK		379		
Epic High School-North 9425 117th St, S Richmond HI 11419 Kristen Breen	9-12	TV	452	73%	718/570-8230 Fax 718/570-8231
Epic High School-South 12110 Rockaway Blvd, S Ozone Park 11420 Subhas Mohan	9-12	TV	409	64%	718/845-1290 Fax 718/843-2072
Frederick Douglass Acad VI HS 821 Bay 25th St, Far Rockaway 11691 Deborah Burnett	9-12	T	305 8	75%	718/471-2154 Fax 718/471-2890
Goddard HS of Comm Arts & Tech 13830 Lafayette St, Ozone Park 11417 Joseph Birgeles	9-12	T	611	74%	718/848-8357 Fax 718/848-8579
Goldie Maple Academy 365 Beach 56th St, Arverne 11692 Angela Logan-Smith	PK-8	T	421	67%	718/945-3300 Fax 718/945-3303
HS Construct Trades Eng & Arch 9406 104th St, Ozone Park 11416 Lakeisha Gordon	9-12		1,092	61%	718/846-6280 Fax 718/846-6283
Ⓜ JHS 202 Robert H Goddard 13830 Lafayette St, Ozone Park 11417 William Fitzgerald	6-8	T	1,100	76%	718/848-0001 Fax 718/848-8082
JHS 210 Elizabeth Blackwell 9311 101st Ave, Ozone Park 11416 Kuljit Singh	6-8	T	1,803	81%	718/845-5942 Fax 718/845-4037
JHS 226 Virgil I Grissom 12110 Rockaway Blvd, S Ozone Park 11420 Rushell White	6-8	T	903 62	85%	718/843-2260 Fax 718/835-6317
John Adams High Sch 10101 Rockaway Blvd, Ozone Park 11417 Daniel Scanlon	9-12	TV	2,517	74%	718/322-0500 Fax 718/738-9077
Ⓐ John Adams YABC 10101 Rockaway Blvd, Ozone Park 11417 Edita Volovodovskaya	10-12		250		718/322-0500
Knowledge & Power Prep Acad VI 821 Bay 25th St, Far Rockaway 11691 Gary Dumornay	6-8	T	279	84%	718/471-6934 Fax 718/471-6938
MS 53 Brian Piccolo 1045 Nameoke St, Far Rockaway 11691 Zoanne Wilkins	6-8	T	169 50	86%	718/471-6900 Fax 718/471-6955
Ⓜ MS 137 America's Sch of Heroes 10915 98th St, Ozone Park 11417 Laura Mastrogiovanni	6-8	T	1,956	82%	718/659-0471 Fax 718/659-4594
MS 297 Hawtree Creek Mid Sch 12110 Rockaway Blvd, S Ozone Park 11420 Dr Maureen Hussey	6-8	T	388	89%	718/659-3792 Fax 718/659-3798
New York City Acad-Discovery 9516 89th Ave, Woodhaven 11421 Cheryl-Ann Leone	PK-5		373	83%	718/441-2165 Fax 718/441-5923
© Peninsula Prep Academy CS 611 Beach 19th St, Far Rockaway 11691 Karen Jones	K-5		318 12	83%	347/403-9231 Fax 718/318-4561
PS 43 160 Beach 29th St, Far Rockaway 11691 Simone Nicholas	PK-8	T	855	93%	718/327-5860 Fax 718/327-6925
PS 45 Clarence Witherspoon 12628 150th St, S Ozone Park 11436 Samantha Severin	PK-5	T	327 23	84%	718/480-2500
PS 47 Chris Galas 140 Beach 112th St, Rockaway Park 11694 Heather Lorenz	PK-8		257 12	43%	718/634-7167 Fax 718/945-5394
PS 51 8745 117th St, Richmond Hill 11418 Magdaly Saint Juste	PK-1	T	213 5	77%	718/850-0738 Fax 718/850-0830
PS 56 Harry Eichler 8610 114th St, Richmond Hill 11418 Ann Leiter	2-5	T	372 22	79%	718/441-4448 Fax 718/805-1538
PS 60 Woodhaven 9102 88th Ave, Woodhaven 11421 Frank DeSario	PK-5	T	1,139 52	82%	718/441-5046 Fax 718/805-1487

1	Superintendent	8	Curric/Instruct K-12	19	Chief Financial Officer	29	Family/Consumer Science	39 Social Studies K-12
2	Bus/Finance/Purchasing	9	Curric/Instruct Elem	20	Art K-12	30	Adult Education	40 Social Studies Elem
3	Buildings And Grounds	10	Curric/Instruct Sec	21	Art Elem	31	Career/Sch-to-Work K-12	41 Social Studies Sec
4	Food Service	11	Federal Program	22	Art Sec	32	Career/Sch-to-Work Elem	42 Science K-12
5	Transportation	12	Title I	23	Music K-12	33	Career/Sch-to-Work Sec	43 Science Elem
6	Athletic	13	Title V	24	Music Elem	34	Early Childhood Ed	44 Science Sec
7	Health Services	14	Instructional Media Svcs	25	Music Sec	35	Health/Phys Education	45 Math K-12
		15	Asst Superintendent	26	Business Education	36	Guidance Services K-12	46 Math Elem
		16	Chief Operations Officer	27	Career & Tech Ed	37	Guidance Services Elem	47 Math Sec
		17	Chief Academic Officer	28	Technology Education	38	Guidance Services Sec	48 English/Lang Arts K-12

49 English/Lang Arts Elem	59 Special Education Elem	69 Academic Assessment
50 English/Lang Arts Sec	60 Special Education Sec	70 Research/Development
51 Reading K-12	61 Foreign/World Lang K-12	71 Public Information
52 Reading Elem	62 Foreign/World Lang Elem	72 Summer School
53 Reading Sec	63 Foreign/World Lang Sec	73 Instructional Tech
54 Remedial Reading K-12	64 Religious Education K-12	74 Inservice Training
55 Remedial Reading Elem	65 Religious Education Elem	75 Marketing/Distributive
56 Remedial Reading Sec	66 Religious Education Sec	76 Info Systems
57 Bilingual/ELL	67 School Board President	77 Psychological Assess
58 Special Education K-12	68 Teacher Personnel	78 Affirmative Action

NY—180

New York School Directory — Queens County

School	Grades	Prgm	Enr/#Cls	SN	Phone
PS 62 Chester Park 9725 108th St, S Richmond Hl 11419 Angela Odowd	PK-5	T	926 44	66%	718/286-4460 Fax 718/286-4465
PS 63 Old South 9015 Sutter Ave, Ozone Park 11417 Diane Marino	PK-5	T	1,166 61	79%	718/845-7560 Fax 718/845-7269
PS 64 Joseph P Addabbo 8201 101st Ave, Ozone Park 11416 Elizabeth Mitchell	PK-5	T	521	72%	718/845-8290 Fax 718/848-0052
PS 65 Raymond York ES 10322 99th St, Ozone Park 11417 Rafael Morales	PK-5	T	472 20	66%	718/323-1685 Fax 718/323-1785
PS 66 J Kennedy Onasiss 8511 102nd St, Richmond Hill 11418 Helen DeSario	PK-5	T	477 19	81%	718/849-0184 Fax 718/846-6889
PS 90 Horace Mann 8650 109th St, Richmond Hill 11418 Adrienne Ubertini	PK-5	T	754 43	89%	718/847-3370 Fax 718/847-2965
PS 96 13001 Rockaway Blvd, S Ozone Park 11420 Vivian Eweka	PK-5	T	307 14	83%	718/529-2547 Fax 718/659-0113
PS 97 Forest Park 8552 85th St, Woodhaven 11421 Marilyn Custodio	PK-5	T	676 33	83%	718/849-4870 Fax 718/849-5356
PS 100 Glen Morris 11111 118th St, S Ozone Park 11420 Laureen Fromberg	PK-5	T	891 53	59%	718/558-1510
PS 104 the Bays Water 2601 Mott Ave, Far Rockaway 11691 Katie Grady	PK-5	T	613 30	78%	718/327-1910 Fax 718/337-2146
PS 105 Bay Sch 420 Beach 51st St, Far Rockaway 11691 Laurie Shapiro	PK-8	T	822 48	88%	718/474-8615 Fax 718/474-8841
PS 106 Lighthouse Elem Sch 180 Beach 35th St, Far Rockaway 11691 Rachelle Legions	PK-5	T	188 25	96%	718/327-5828 Fax 718/327-5956
PS 108 Capt Vincent G Fowler 10810 109th Ave, S Ozone Park 11420 Jennifer Iovine	PK-5	T	1,365 51	81%	718/558-2700 Fax 718/558-2701
PS 123 14501 119th Ave, S Ozone Park 11436 Anthony Hooks	PK-5	T	653 41	83%	718/529-4300 Fax 718/529-4290
Ⓜ PS 124 Osmond A Church 12915 150th Ave, S Ozone Park 11420 Maritza Jones	K-8	T	1,119 48	59%	718/529-2580 Fax 718/322-4039
PS 146 Howard Beach 9801 159th Ave, Howard Beach 11414 Mary Keegan	PK-8		588 29	47%	718/659-3140 Fax 718/641-0901
PS 155 13002 115th Ave, S Ozone Park 11420 Jacobs Gregory	PK-5	T	546 38	87%	718/558-1310 Fax 718/558-1311
Ⓜ PS 183 Dr Richard R Green 245 Beach 79th St, Far Rockaway 11693 Maureen Campbell	PK-8	T	463 35	91%	718/634-9459 Fax 718/634-9458
PS 197 Ocean Sch 825 Hicksville Rd, Far Rockaway 11691 Christina Villavicencio	PK-5	T	519 43	94%	718/327-1083 Fax 718/327-3518
PS 207 Rockwood Park 15915 88th St, Howard Beach 11414 Eileen Davies	PK-8		685	29%	718/848-2700 Fax 718/848-4226
PS 223 Lyndon Baines Johnson 12520 Sutphin Blvd, Jamaica 11434 Deborah Otto	PK-5	T	532 47	89%	718/558-2900 Fax 718/925-9020
PS 232 Lindenwood 15323 83rd St, Howard Beach 11414 Lisa Josephson	PK-8		943 32	56%	718/848-9247 Fax 718/738-8505
PS 253 1307 Central Ave, Far Rockaway 11691 Phoebe Robinson	PK-5	T	544	97%	718/327-0895 Fax 718/327-3964
PS 254 Rosa Parks ES 8440 101st St, Richmond Hill 11418 Pamela Tavernier	PK-5	T	624	75%	718/520-7878 Fax 718/846-7404
PS 273 8807 102nd St, Richmond Hill 11418 Brenda Ward	PK-5	T	308	91%	718/286-8300 Fax 718/286-8310
PS 377 15015 Raleigh St, Ozone Park 11417 Tracy Keane	PK-1		290	64%	929/398-3215 Fax 929/398-3218
PS/MS 42 R Vernam 488 Beach 66th St, Arverne 11692 Patricia Finn	PK-8	T	635	95%	718/634-7914 Fax 718/474-7591
PS/MS 114 Belle Harbor 13401 Cronston Ave, Rockaway Park 11694 Elizabeth Welson	PK-8		709 35	26%	718/634-3382 Fax 718/945-4510
Queens Explorers Elem Sch 9007 101st Ave, Ozone Park 11416 Melissa Compson	PK-4	T	399	76%	718/558-7088 Fax 718/558-7091
Queens HS for Info Rsch & Tech 821 Bay 25th St, Far Rockaway 11691 Carl Manalo	9-12	T	487	69%	718/868-2978 Fax 718/868-1653
Richmond Hill High Sch 8930 114th St, Richmond Hill 11418 Neil Ganesh	9-12	TV	1,615	81%	718/846-3335 Fax 718/847-0980
Rockaway Collegiate High Sch 10000 Beach Channel Dr, Rockaway Park 11694 Hassan Fuller	9-12	T	324	81%	718/734-3290 Fax 718/734-3276
Rockaway Park High Sch 10000 Beach Channel Dr, Rockaway Park 11694 Miriam Lamhaouhi	9-12	T	281	90%	718/734-3280 Fax 718/734-3286
Scholars Academy 320 Beach 104th St, Rockaway Park 11694 Brian Oconnell	6-12		1,311	47%	718/474-6918 Fax 718/945-8958
Village Academy 1045 Nameoke St, Far Rockaway 11691 Doris Lee	6-8	T	370	81%	718/471-6042 Fax 718/471-6243
Voyages Prep-South Queens 15610 Baisley Blvd, Jamaica 11434 Christopher Losurdo	9-12		283	64%	718/276-1946 Fax 718/276-2784
Waterside Children's Studio 190 Beach 110th St, Rockaway Park 11694 Dana Gerendasi	PK-5		501	70%	718/634-1344 Fax 718/634-3884
Waterside Sch for Leadership 190 Beach 110th St, Rockaway Park 11694 Linda Munro	6-8	T	224	88%	718/634-1128 Fax 718/634-1185
Wave Prep Elem Sch 535 Briar Pl, Far Rockaway 11691 Gemma Ferguson	PK-5		514	88%	718/327-7091 Fax 718/327-7097

• **Community School District 28** PID: 10909888   718/557-2618
9027 Sutphin Blvd, Jamaica 11435

(Part of New York City Dept of Ed in New York County)

Dr Tammy Pate 1

Public Schs..Principal	Grd	Prgm	Enr/#Cls	SN	
Acad for Excellence Thru Arts 6860 110th St, Forest Hills 11375 Barbara Leto	PK-5		209	24%	929/467-6200 Fax 929/467-6201
Catherine & Count Basie MS 72 13325 Guy R Brewer Blvd, Jamaica 11434 Omotayo Cineus	6-8	AGTV	275 65	81%	718/723-6200 Fax 718/527-1675

79 Student Personnel	91 Safety/Security	275 Response To Intervention	298 Grant Writer/Ptnrships
80 Driver Ed/Safety	92 Magnet School	277 Remedial Math K-12	750 Chief Innovation Officer
81 Gifted/Talented	93 Parental Involvement	280 Literacy Coach	751 Chief of Staff
82 Video Services	95 Tech Prep Program	285 STEM	752 Social Emotional Learning
83 Substance Abuse Prev	97 Chief Infomation Officer	286 Digital Learning	
84 Erate	98 Chief Technology Officer	288 Common Core Standards	**Other School Types**
85 AIDS Education	270 Accountability	294 Accountability	Ⓐ = Alternative School
88 Alternative/At Risk	271 Migrant Education	295 Network System	Ⓒ = Charter School
89 Multi-Cultural Curriculum	273 Teacher Mentor	296 Title II Programs	Ⓜ = Magnet School
90 Social Work	274 Before/After Sch	297 Webmaster	Ⓨ = Year-Round School

School Programs
A = Alternative Program
G = Adult Classes
M = Magnet Program
T = Title I Schoolwide
V = Career & Tech Ed Programs

Social Media
 = Facebook
 = Twitter

New Schools are shaded
New Superintendents and Principals are bold
Personnel with email addresses are underscored

NY—181

Queens County

Market Data Retrieval

School	Grades		Enroll	%	Phone
Emerson Sch 10835 167th St, Jamaica 11433 Jakub Lau	6-8	T	359	81%	718/657-4801 Fax 718/657-4807
Forest Hills High Sch 6701 110th St, Forest Hills 11375 Paul Wilbur	9-12	GTV	3,754	78%	718/268-3137 Fax 718/793-7850
Hillcrest High Sch 16005 Highland Ave, Jamaica 11432 David Morrison	9-12	TV	3,125 100	82%	718/658-5407 Fax 718/739-5137
Hillside Arts & Letters Acad 16701 Gothic Dr, Jamaica 11432 Raquel Nolasco	9-12	T	450	73%	718/658-1249 Fax 718/658-1613
HS for Community Leadership 16701 Gothic Dr, Jamaica 11432 Carlos Borrero	9-12	T	449	77%	718/558-9801 Fax 718/558-9807
HS Law Enforcement Pub Safety 11625 Guy R Brewer Blvd, Jamaica 11434 Laura Van Deren	9-12	T	405	69%	718/977-4800 Fax 718/977-4802
Jamaica Gateway to Sciences 16701 Gothic Dr, Jamaica 11432 Caren Taylor	9-12	T	485	74%	718/480-2689 Fax 718/480-2697
Jamaican Children's Sch 10920 Union Hall St, Jamaica 11433 Valerie Paul	K-4	T	198	89%	718/526-0160 Fax 718/526-0703
JHS 8 Richard S Grossley 10835 167th St, Jamaica 11433 Katiana Louissaint	6-8	AGTV	441 22	85%	718/739-6883
JHS 157 Stephen A Halsey 6355 102nd St, Rego Park 11374 Vincent Suraci	6-9		1,695 55	54%	718/830-4910 Fax 718/830-4993
JHS 190 Russell Sage 6817 Austin St, Forest Hills 11375 John Greggo	6-8	V	1,123	42%	718/830-4970 Fax 718/830-3566
JHS 217 Robert A Van Wyck 8505 144th St, Jamaica 11435 Patrick Burns	6-8	AT	1,703	70%	718/657-1120 Fax 718/291-3668
Metropolitan Exped Lrng Sch 9130 Metropolitan Ave, Flushing 11375 Patrick Finley	6-12	T	825	71%	718/286-3500 Fax 718/286-3501
MS 358 8808 164th St, Jamaica 11432 Brendan Mims	6-8	T	361	86%	718/558-6240
PS 40 Samuel Huntington 10920 Union Hall St, Jamaica 11433 Alison Branker	PK-5	T	366 40	88%	718/526-1906
PS 48 William Wordsworth 108-29 155th St, Jamaica 11433 Patricia Mitchell	PK-5	AT	544 30	89%	718/558-6700 Fax 718/558-6710
PS 50 Talfourd Lawn Elem Sch 14326 101st Ave, Jamaica 11435 Rina Manjarrez	PK-5	T	844 38	90%	718/526-5336 Fax 718/526-7261
PS 54 Hillside 8602 127th St, Richmond Hill 11418 Anita Prashad	K-5	T	511 28	77%	718/849-0962 Fax 718/847-4629
PS 55 Maure 13110 97th Ave, S Richmond Hl 11419 Ralph Honore	PK-5	T	496 45	79%	718/849-3845
ⓜ PS 80 Thurgood Marshall Magnet 17105 137th Ave, Jamaica 11434 Kersandra Cox	PK-5	T	466	75%	718/528-7070 Fax 718/949-0963
PS 82 Hammond 8802 144th St, Jamaica 11435 Grisel Rodriguez	K-5	T	602	80%	718/526-4139 Fax 718/297-0290
PS 99 Kew Gardens 8237 Kew Gardens Rd, Kew Gardens 11415 Paulette Foglio	K-6	T	706 41	61%	718/544-4343 Fax 718/544-5992
PS 101 School In the Gardens 2 Russell Pl, Forest Hills 11375 Monique Paniagua	PK-6		669 27	14%	718/268-7231 Fax 718/575-3571
PS 117 J Keld/Briarwood Sch 8515 143rd St, Briarwood 11435 Paula Holsey	PK-5	T	930	67%	718/526-4780 Fax 718/297-1796
PS 121 Queens 12610 109th Ave, S Ozone Park 11420 Evelyn Vadi	PK-5	T	826	78%	718/558-1560 Fax 718/558-1565
PS 139 Rego Park 9306 63rd Dr, Rego Park 11374 Natalie Perez	K-5		711 34	60%	718/459-1044 Fax 718/997-8639
PS 140 Edward K Ellington 16601 116th Ave, Jamaica 11434 Robbyn Signal	PK-5	AT	442 37	90%	718/657-4760 Fax 718/526-1051
PS 144 Col Jeromus Remsen 6920 Juno St, Forest Hills 11375 Reva Schneider	PK-5		939 30	22%	718/268-2775 Fax 718/575-3734
PS 160 Walter Francis Bishop 10959 Inwood St, Jamaica 11435 Tiffany Hicks	PK-5	T	600	79%	929/398-3140 Fax 929/398-3142
PS 161 Arthur Ashe Sch 10133 124th St, S Richmond Hl 11419 Jill Hoder	PK-5	T	584 28	85%	718/441-5493 Fax 718/441-6202
PS 174 William Sidney Mount 6510 Dieterle Cres, Rego Park 11374 Karin Kelly	PK-5		658 28	33%	718/897-7006 Fax 718/897-7254
PS 175 Lynn Gross Discovery 6435 102nd St, Rego Park 11374 Angela Tuetschman	PK-5		807 31	56%	718/897-8600 Fax 718/997-8644
PS 182 Samantha Smith 15327 88th Ave, Jamaica 11432 Andrew Topol	PK-5	T	683 25	95%	718/298-7700 Fax 718/298-7706
PS 196 Grand Central Parkway 7125 113th St, Forest Hills 11375 Susan Migliano	PK-5	T	1,062 30	26%	718/263-9770 Fax 718/575-3934
PS 206 the Horace Harding Sch 6102 98th St, Rego Park 11374 Joan Thomas	PK-5	T	572 32	74%	718/592-0300 Fax 718/271-7011
PS 220 Edward Mandel 6210 108th St, Forest Hills 11375 Josette Pizarro	PK-5	T	670 22	70%	718/592-3030 Fax 718/271-7642
PS 354 J L Green STEM Inst 12610 Bedell St, Jamaica 11434 Raevan Askew	PK-5	T	534	79%	718/276-1348 Fax 718/276-2498
PS Q086 8741 Parsons Blvd, Jamaica 11432 Rosita Rivera	PK-5	T	770 38	78%	718/291-6264 Fax 718/297-0298
Queens Collegiate-College Brd 16701 Gothic Dr, Jamaica 11432 Jaime Dubei	6-12	T	664	86%	718/658-4016 Fax 718/658-5149
Queens Gateway Hlth Sciences 16020 Goethals Ave, Jamaica 11432 Judy Henry	6-12		696 20	55%	718/969-3155 Fax 718/969-3552
Queens HS for Sciences at York 9450 159th St, Jamaica 11433 Ana De Jesus	9-12		479 15		718/657-3181 Fax 718/657-2579
Queens Metropolitan HS 9130 Metropolitan Ave, Flushing 11375 Saida Tabone	9-12		1,147	61%	718/286-3600 Fax 718/286-3601
Queens Satellite HS-Oppor 16202 Hillside Ave, Jamaica 11432 Mark Melkonian	9-12	T	222	90%	718/657-3920 Fax 718/658-2309
Queens Sch Ldrshp Excellence 8808 164th St, Jamaica 11432 Tanya Howell	PK-4	T	513	84%	718/558-6220 Fax 718/558-6225

1	Superintendent	8	Curric/Instruct K-12	19	Chief Financial Officer	29	Family/Consumer Science	39	Social Studies K-12
2	Bus/Finance/Purchasing	9	Curric/Instruct Elem	20	Art K-12	30	Adult Education	40	Social Studies Elem
3	Buildings And Grounds	10	Curric/Instruct Sec	21	Art Elem	31	Career/Sch-to-Work K-12	41	Social Studies Sec
4	Food Service	11	Federal Program	22	Art Sec	32	Career/Sch-to-Work Elem	42	Science K-12
5	Transportation	12	Title I	23	Music K-12	33	Career/Sch-to-Work Sec	43	Science Elem
6	Athletic	13	Title V	24	Music Elem	34	Early Childhood Ed	44	Science Sec
7	Health Services	14	Instructional Media Svcs	25	Music Sec	35	Health/Phys Education	45	Math K-12
		15	Asst Superintendent	26	Business Education	36	Guidance Services K-12	46	Math Elem
		16	Instructional Media Svcs	27	Career & Tech Ed	37	Guidance Services Elem	47	Math Sec
		17	Chief Operations Officer	28	Technology Education	38	Guidance Services Sec	48	English/Lang Arts K-12
		18	Chief Academic Officer						

49	English/Lang Arts Elem	59	Special Education Elem	69	Academic Assessment
50	English/Lang Arts Sec	60	Special Education Sec	70	Research/Development
51	Reading K-12	61	Foreign/World Lang K-12	71	Public Information
52	Reading Elem	62	Foreign/World Lang Elem	72	Summer School
53	Reading Sec	63	Foreign/World Lang Sec	73	Instructional Tech
54	Remedial Reading K-12	64	Religious Education K-12	74	Inservice Training
55	Remedial Reading Elem	65	Religious Education Elem	75	Marketing/Distributive
56	Remedial Reading Sec	66	Religious Education Sec	76	Info Systems
57	Bilingual/ELL	67	School Board President	77	Psychological Assess
58	Special Education K-12	68	Teacher Personnel	78	Affirmative Action

New York School Directory — Queens County

School	Grd	Prgm	Enr/#Cls	SN	Phone
Redwood Middle Sch 13325 Guy R Brewer Blvd, Jamaica 11434 Judson Hamilton	6-8	TV	276	65%	718/276-4540
© Rochdale Early Advantage CS 12205 Smith St, Jamaica 11434 Dr Knight	K-7	T	286	68%	718/978-0075 Fax 718/978-0110
Thomas Edison Career & Tech HS 16565 84th Ave, Jamaica 11432 Moses Ojeda	Voc	GT	2,211 120	76%	718/297-6580 Fax 718/658-0365
York Early College Academy 10835 167th St, Jamaica 11433 Noah Angeles	6-12	T	637	69%	718/262-8547 Fax 718/558-4257
Young Women's Leadership HS 15091 87th Rd, Jamaica 11432 Mala Panday	6-12	T	567	71%	718/725-0402 Fax 718/725-0390

● **Community School District 29** PID: 10909890   718/217-7740
22214 Jamaica Ave, Queens Vlg 11428   Fax 718/264-3148
(Part of New York City Dept of Ed in New York County)
Beverly Mitchell 1

Public Schs..Principal	Grd	Prgm	Enr/#Cls	SN	Phone
Bellaire Sch 20711 89th Ave, Queens Vlg 11427 Diana Lagnese	PK-5	T	879 45	56%	718/464-2119
Ben Franklin HS Finance & It 20701 116th Ave, Cambria HTS 11411 Dudrige Brenord	9-12	T	420	85%	718/276-0150 Fax 718/276-4725
Cambria Heights Academy 18804 91st Ave, Hollis 11423 Melissa Menake	9-12	T	368	73%	718/736-7320 Fax 718/736-7325
Collaborative Arts Middle Sch 14500 Springfield Blvd, Sprngfld GDNS 11413 Tammy Holloway	6-8	T	336	79%	718/977-6181 Fax 718/977-6183
Community Voices Middle Sch 14500 Springfield Blvd, Sprngfld GDNS 11413 Ryan Branch	6-8	T	342	73%	718/977-6180 Fax 718/977-6182
Cynthia Jenkins Elem Sch 17937 137th Ave, Jamaica 11434 Pascale Pereira	PK-5	T	357 27	80%	718/528-5399 Fax 718/949-0887
Eagle Acad Young Men III 17110 Linden Blvd, Jamaica 11434 Cedric Hall	6-12	T	426	68%	718/480-2600 Fax 718/480-2610
Excelsior Preparatory High Sch 14310 Springfield Blvd, Sprngfld GDNS 11413 Lilly Lucas	9-12	T	424 20	84%	718/525-6507 Fax 718/525-6276
G W Carver HS for Science 14310 Springfield Blvd, Sprngfld GDNS 11413 Dr Janice Sutton	9-12	T	389	71%	718/525-6439 Fax 718/525-6482
Ⓜ Humanities & Arts High Sch 20701 116th Ave, Cambria HTS 11411 Kayode Ayetiwa	9-12	T	369 25	82%	718/978-2135 Fax 718/978-2309
Institute Health Professionals 20701 116th Ave, Cambria HTS 11411 Gareth Robinson	9-12	T	449	82%	718/723-7301 Fax 718/723-7306
IS 59 Springfield Gardens 13255 Ridgedale St, Sprngfld GDNS 11413 Kimlyn Greig	6-8	TV	578	65%	718/527-3501 Fax 718/276-1364
IS 192 Linden 10989 204th St, Saint Albans 11412 Harriett Diaz	6-8	TV	464 80	69%	718/479-5540 Fax 718/217-4645
IS 238 Susan B Anthony 8815 182nd St, Hollis 11423 Peter Leddy	6-8	TV	1,243	83%	718/297-9821 Fax 718/658-5288
Jean Nuzzi Intermediate Sch 21310 92nd Ave, Queens Vlg 11428 Karleen Comrie	6-8	TV	1,166 60	65%	718/465-0651 Fax 718/264-1246
Ⓜ Math Science Research Tech HS 20701 116th Ave, Cambria HTS 11411 Allika Thompson	9-12	T	388	73%	718/978-1837 Fax 718/978-2063
Pathways College Prep Sch 10989 204th St, Saint Albans 11412 Fia Davis	6-12	T	583 30	76%	718/454-4957
Prep Academy for Writers 14310 Springfield Blvd, Sprngfld GDNS 11413 Charles Anderson	6-12	T	562	71%	718/949-8405 Fax 718/525-8495
PS 15 Jackie Robinson Sch 12115 Lucas St, Sprngfld GDNS 11413 Anthony Pignataro	PK-5	T	380 24	73%	718/525-1670 Fax 718/723-7613
PS 33 Edward M Funk 9137 222nd St, Queens Vlg 11428 Vincent Gatto	PK-5	T	943	76%	718/465-6283 Fax 718/464-7588
PS 34 John Harvard 10412 Springfield Blvd, Queens Vlg 11429 Pauline Shakespeare	PK-5	T	576 32	87%	718/465-6818 Fax 718/464-9073
PS 35 Nathaniel Woodhull 19102 90th Ave, Hollis 11423 Mia Peebles-Davis	PK-5	T	686 33	83%	718/465-6820 Fax 718/217-4314
PS 36 St Albans Sch 18701 Foch Blvd, Saint Albans 11412 Lynn Staton	PK-5	T	362 15	68%	718/528-1862 Fax 718/723-6928
PS 38 Rosedale 13521 241st St, Rosedale 11422 Julia Soussis	K-5	T	265 13	70%	718/528-2276 Fax 718/712-1598
PS 52 Queens 17837 146th Ter, Jamaica 11434 Ms Salaurante	PK-5	T	372 41	80%	718/528-2238
PS 95 Eastwood 17901 90th Ave, Jamaica 11432 Kim Hill	K-5	T	1,422	68%	718/739-0007 Fax 718/658-5271
PS 116 William Hughley 10725 Wren Pl, Jamaica 11433 Debra Farrow	PK-8	T	825 50	76%	718/526-4884 Fax 718/658-5663
PS 118 Lorraine Hansberry 19020 109th Rd, Saint Albans 11412 Michelle Soussoudis	PK-5	T	424 42	70%	718/465-5538 Fax 718/264-9178
PS 131 Abigail Adams 17045 84th Ave, Jamaica 11432 Veronica DePaolo	K-5	T	703 45	90%	718/480-2840 Fax 718/658-5690
PS 132 Ralph Bunche 13215 218th St, Sprngfld GDNS 11413 Alicia Davis	PK-5	T	323 21	75%	718/528-5734 Fax 718/723-6931
PS 134 Hollis 20306 109th Ave, Saint Albans 11412 Randi Posner Marino	PK-5	T	308 28	68%	718/464-5544 Fax 718/464-7779
PS 136 Roy Wilkins 20115 115th Ave, Saint Albans 11412 Tanya Walker	PK-5	T	504	70%	718/465-2286 Fax 718/464-0040
PS 156 Laurelton 22902 137th Ave, Sprngfld GDNS 11413 Estelle Moore	PK-5	T	204 40	65%	718/528-9173
PS 176 Cambria Heights 12045 235th St, Cambria HTS 11411 Marisa Castello	PK-5	T	729 40	65%	718/525-4057
PS 181 Brookfield 14815 230th St, Sprngfld GDNS 11413 Dina Wheeler	PK-5	T	319 30	66%	718/528-5807 Fax 718/723-7825
PS 195 William Haberle 25350 149th Ave, Rosedale 11422 Beryl Bailey	PK-5	T	463 27	83%	718/723-0313

---

79 Student Personnel	91 Safety/Security	275 Response To Intervention	298 Grant Writer/Ptnrships	**School Programs**
80 Driver Ed/Safety	92 Magnet School	277 Remedial Math K-12	750 Chief Innovation Officer	A = Alternative Program
81 Gifted/Talented	93 Parental Involvement	280 Literacy Coach	751 Chief of Staff	G = Adult Classes
82 Video Services	95 Tech Prep Program	285 STEM	752 Social Emotional Learning	M = Magnet Program
83 Substance Abuse Prev	97 Chief Infomation Officer	286 Digital Learning		T = Title I Schoolwide
84 Erate	98 Chief Technology Officer	288 Common Core Standards	**Other School Types**	V = Career & Tech Ed Programs
85 AIDS Education	270 Character Education	294 Accountability	Ⓐ = Alternative School	
88 Alternative/At Risk	271 Migrant Education	295 Network System	Ⓒ = Charter School	New Schools are shaded
89 Multi-Cultural Curriculum	273 Teacher Mentor	296 Title II Programs	Ⓜ = Magnet School	New Superintendents and Principals are bold
90 Social Work	274 Before/After Sch	297 Webmaster	Ⓨ = Year-Round School	Personnel with email addresses are underscored

Social Media
 = Facebook
 = Twitter

Queens County

Market Data Retrieval

Public Schs..Principal	Grd	Prgm	Enr/#Cls	SN	Phone/Fax
Ⓜ PS 251 Queens 14451 Arthur St, Sprngfld GDNS 11413 Relda Barry-Grant	PK-5	T	333 18	72%	718/276-2745 Fax 718/723-7822
PS 360 New Choice ES 19910 112th Ave, Saint Albans 11412 Rachel Thomas	PK-3	T	208	60%	718/776-7370 Fax 718/776-7380
PS/IS 208 7430 Commonwealth Blvd, Bellerose 11426 James Philemy	K-8		748	41%	718/468-6420 Fax 718/468-5054
PS/IS 268 9207 175th St, Jamaica 11433 Lissa Grantstewart	K-8	T	642 24	70%	718/206-3240 Fax 718/206-2938
PS/IS 270Q Gordon Parks Sch 23315 Merrick Blvd, Rosedale 11422 Chayvonne Harper	PK-8	T	756 24	71%	718/341-8280 Fax 718/341-5589
PS/IS 295Q 22214 Jamaica Ave, Queens Vlg 11428 Deon Lavigne-Jones	PK-8	T	516	72%	718/464-1433 Fax 718/464-1439
PS/MS 138 Sunrise 25111 Weller Ave, Rosedale 11422 James McEnaney	PK-8	T	623	76%	929/600-5777 Fax 929/600-5779
PS/MS 147 Ronald McNair 21801 116th Ave, Cambria HTS 11411 Afua Hill	PK-8	T	559 40	69%	718/528-2420 Fax 718/723-7819
Queens Preparatory Academy 14310 Springfield Blvd, Sprngfld GDNS 11413 Tashon Haywood	9-12	T	288	79%	718/712-2304 Fax 718/712-3273
Queens United Middle Sch 289 22902 137th Ave, Sprngfld GDNS 11413 Toshalyn Francis	6-8	T	181	69%	718/723-3501 Fax 718/723-3507
© Riverton Street Charter Sch [210] 11834 Riverton St, Saint Albans 11412 Verone Kennedy	K-8	T	990	77%	718/481-8200 Fax 347/923-3315

● Community School District 30   PID: 10909905
2811 Queens Plz N, Long Is City 11101   718/391-6122   Fax 718/391-6511

(Part of New York City Dept of Ed in New York County)
Dr Philip Composto 1   Blanca Quinones 11*

Public Schs..Principal	Grd	Prgm	Enr/#Cls	SN	Phone/Fax
Academy for Careers-TV & Film 150 51st Ave, Long Is City 11101 Edgar Rodriguez	9-12		545	56%	718/609-3330 Fax 718/609-3339
Academy for New Americans 3014 30th St, Astoria 11102 Betty Cartagena	6-8	T	83 10	92%	718/956-4140 Fax 718/956-4145
Ⓜ Academy of American Studies 2804 41st Ave, Long Is City 11101 William Bassell	9-12		1,024 20	62%	718/361-8786 Fax 718/361-8832
Baccalaureate Sch-Global Educ 3412 36th Ave, Long Is City 11106 Kelly Joan Johnson	7-12		560	36%	718/361-5275 Fax 718/361-5395
East Elmhurst Community Sch 2625 97th St, East Elmhurst 11369 Rachel Hallenbeck	K-5	T	449	91%	718/505-6050 Fax 718/505-6055
Energy Tech High Sch 3641 28th St, Astoria 11106 Hope Barter	9-12		508	73%	718/472-0536 Fax 718/472-0490
Frank Sinatra HS of the Arts 3512 35th Ave, Astoria 11106 Gideon Frankel	9-12		859 18	39%	718/361-9920 Fax 718/361-9995
© Growing Up Green Charter ES 3927 28th St, Long Is City 11101 Aris Colgan	K-5	T	552	53%	347/642-4306 Fax 347/642-4310
© Growing Up Green Middle Sch 3649 11th St, Long Is City 11106 Jennifer Slutak	6-8		275		347/642-4306 Fax 347/642-4310
Hunters Point Cmty Middle Sch 150 51st Ave, Astoria 11101 Sarah Goodman	6-8		422	54%	718/609-3300 Fax 718/609-3319
Information Technology HS 2116 44th Rd, Long Is City 11101 Jean Woods-Powell	9-12	TV	994	74%	718/937-4270 Fax 718/937-5236
Ⓜ IS 10 Horace Greeley 4511 31st Ave, Long Is City 11103 Clemente Lopes	6-8	AGT	801	75%	718/278-7054 Fax 718/274-1578
Ⓜ IS 141 the Steinway 3711 21st Ave, Long Is City 11105 Vanessa Williams	6-8	AT	1,186 70	57%	718/278-6403 Fax 718/278-2884
Ⓜ IS 145 Joseph Pulitzer 3334 80th St, Jackson HTS 11372 Ivan Rodriguez	6-8	AGT	1,659 75	90%	718/457-1242 Fax 718/335-0601
Ⓜ IS 204 Oliver Wendell Holmes 3641 28th St, Long Is City 11106 Faye Erstejn-Kotzer	6-8	AGT	448 79	88%	718/937-1463 Fax 718/937-7964
Ⓜ IS 227 Louis Armstrong 3202 Junction Blvd, East Elmhurst 11369 Helen Ponella	5-8	T	1,571 80	69%	718/335-7500 Fax 718/779-7186 f t
Ⓜ IS 230Q Sch for Civics In Cmty 7310 34th Ave, Jackson HTS 11372 Ronald Zirin	6-8	T	1,189 40	75%	718/335-7648 Fax 718/335-7513
Long Island City High Sch 1430 Broadway, Long Is City 11106 Vivian Selenikas	9-12	TV	2,231	83%	718/545-7095 Fax 718/545-2980
Newcomers High Sch 2801 41st Ave, Long Is City 11101 Lilliam Katcher	9-12	T	786 30	87%	718/937-6005
PS 2 Alfred Zimberg 7510 21st Ave, East Elmhurst 11370 Amy Goldman	K-5	GT	525 30	72%	718/728-1459 Fax 718/274-4332
PS 11 Kathryn Phelan 5425 Skillman Ave, Woodside 11377 Elizabeth Pena	PK-6	T	929 51	64%	718/779-2090 Fax 718/458-6362
PS 17 Henry David Thoreau 2837 29th St, Long Is City 11102 Rebecca Heyward	PK-5	GT	582 52	69%	718/278-1220 Fax 718/278-8257
PS 69 Jackson Heights 7702 37th Ave, Jackson HTS 11372 Martha Vazquez	PK-5	T	967	60%	718/424-7700 Fax 718/458-6567
PS 70 Queens 3045 42nd St, Long Is City 11103 Donna Geller	PK-5	GT	799	78%	718/728-4646 Fax 718/728-5817
Ⓜ PS 76 William Hallet 3636 10th St, Long Is City 11106 Timothy Miller	PK-5	GT	429 45	79%	718/361-7464 Fax 718/361-8014
PS 84 Steinway 2245 41st St, Astoria 11105 John Buffa	PK-5	T	262 19	54%	718/278-1915 Fax 718/932-4649
PS 85 Judge Charles Vallone 2370 31st St, Long Is City 11105 Ann Chang	PK-5	T	656 31	40%	718/278-3630 Fax 718/278-8312
Ⓜ PS 92 Harry T Stewart Sr 9901 34th Ave, Corona 11368 Pasquale Baratta	PK-5	GT	896 28	80%	718/533-1013 Fax 718/533-1083
Ⓜ PS 111 Jacob Blackwell 3715 13th St, Long Is City 11101 Dionne Jaggon	PK-8	GT	330 30	91%	718/786-2073 Fax 718/729-7102
PS 112 Dutch Kills 2505 37th Ave, Long Is City 11101 Dov Witkes	PK-5	GT	413 24	82%	718/784-5250 Fax 718/784-5681

1 Superintendent	8 Curric/Instruct K-12	19 Chief Financial Officer	29 Family/Consumer Science	39 Social Studies K-12	49 English/Lang Arts Elem	59 Special Education Elem	69 Academic Assessment
2 Bus/Finance/Purchasing	9 Curric/Instruct Elem	20 Art K-12	30 Adult Education	40 Social Studies Elem	50 English/Lang Arts Sec	60 Special Education Sec	70 Research/Development
3 Buildings And Grounds	10 Curric/Instruct Sec	21 Art Elem	31 Career/Sch-to-Work K-12	41 Social Studies Sec	51 Reading K-12	61 Foreign/World Lang K-12	71 Public Information
4 Food Service	11 Federal Program	22 Art Sec	32 Career/Sch-to-Work Elem	42 Science K-12	52 Reading Elem	62 Foreign/World Lang Elem	72 Summer School
5 Transportation	12 Title I	23 Music K-12	33 Career/Sch-to-Work Sec	43 Science Elem	53 Reading Sec	63 Foreign/World Lang Sec	73 Instructional Tech
6 Athletic	13 Title V	24 Music Elem	34 Early Childhood Ed	44 Science Sec	54 Remedial Reading K-12	64 Religious Education K-12	74 Inservice Training
7 Health Services	15 Asst Superintendent	25 Music Sec	35 Health/Phys Education	45 Math K-12	55 Remedial Reading Elem	65 Religious Education Elem	75 Marketing/Distributive
	16 Instructional Media Svcs	26 Business Education	36 Guidance Services K-12	46 Math Elem	56 Remedial Reading Sec	66 Religious Education Sec	76 Info Systems
	17 Chief Operations Officer	27 Career & Tech Ed	37 Guidance Services Elem	47 Math Sec	57 Bilingual/ELL	67 School Board President	77 Psychological Assess
	18 Chief Academic Officer	28 Technology Education	38 Guidance Services Sec	48 English/Lang Arts K-12	58 Special Education K-12	68 Teacher Personnel	78 Affirmative Action

New York School Directory — Queens County

Public Schs..Principal	Grd	Prgm	Enr/#Cls	SN	Phone
Ⓜ PS 122 Mamie Fay 2121 Ditmars Blvd, Astoria 11105 Anna Aprea	PK-8	G	1,365 50	48%	718/721-6410 Fax 718/726-0016
PS 127 Aerospace Science Acad 9801 25th Ave, East Elmhurst 11369 Evita Sanabria	PK-8	GT	1,215	85%	718/446-4700 Fax 718/397-7645
Ⓜ PS 148 Queens 8902 32nd Ave, East Elmhurst 11369 Yolanda Harvey	PK-5	GT	769 55	75%	718/898-8181
Ⓜ PS 149 Christa McAuliffe 9311 34th Ave, Jackson HTS 11372 Onalis Hernandez	K-5	GT	943	75%	718/898-3630 Fax 718/476-1976
PS 150 Queens 4001 43rd Ave, Long Is City 11104 Carmen Parache	PK-6	GT	1,013 60	51%	718/784-2252 Fax 718/729-7823
PS 151 Mary D Carter 5005 31st Ave, Woodside 11377 Samantha Maisonet	PK-5	T	314	92%	718/728-2676 Fax 718/545-2028
Ⓜ PS 152 Gwendoline N Alleyne 3352 62nd St, Woodside 11377 Vincent Vitolo	PK-5	GT	930 68	74%	718/429-3141 Fax 718/779-7532
PS 166 Henry Gradstein 3309 35th Ave, Long Is City 11106 Jessica Geller	PK-5	GT	947 54	67%	718/786-6703 Fax 718/729-7443
Ⓜ PS 171 Peter G Van Alst 1414 29th Ave, Long Is City 11102 Lisa Stone	PK-5	GT	429	92%	718/932-0909 Fax 718/932-6749
Ⓜ PS 212 3425 82nd St, Jackson HTS 11372 Carin Ilene Ellis	PK-5	T	763 31	55%	718/898-6973 Fax 718/898-7068
Ⓜ PS 228 Lafayette Sch of Arts 3263 93rd St, East Elmhurst 11369 Olga Guzman	PK-2	T	293 13	85%	718/899-5799
PS 234 3015 29th St, Astoria 11102 Dora Danner	PK-5	T	455 36	79%	718/956-2760 Fax 718/956-2765
PS 280 3420 94th St, Jackson HTS 11372 Lisa Nieves	K-5	T	578	95%	718/424-9031 Fax 718/424-9093
PS 384 2735 Jackson Ave Fl 2, Long Is City 11101 Christine Britton	K-K	T	35	43%	718/391-4667
PS 398Q Hector Figueroa Sch 6901 34th Ave, Woodside 11377 Erica Urena-Thus	PK-K		118		929/463-7200
Ⓜ PS Q222-Christopher A Santora 8615 37th Ave, Jackson HTS 11372 Yvonne Marrero	PK-2	T	273 11	67%	718/429-2563 Fax 718/429-3484
PS/IS 78Q Robert F Wagner 4809 Center Blvd, Long Is City 11109 Louis Pavone	PK-8		747 14	23%	718/392-5402 Fax 718/392-5434
Q300 Citywide Gifted Talented 2837 29th St, Astoria 11102 Vasilios Biniaris	K-8		542	25%	718/626-8502 Fax 718/626-8508
Ⓒ Renaissance Charter Sch 3559 81st St, Jackson HTS 11372 Stacey Gauthier	K-12	T	591 18	67%	718/803-0060 Fax 718/803-3785
Ⓜ Shanker Sch Visual Perf Arts 3151 21st St, Long Is City 11106 Alexander Angueira	6-8	AGT	625 60	84%	718/274-8316 Fax 718/278-6512
Ⓒ Voice Charter Sch 3624 12th St, Long Is City 11106 Frank Headley	K-8	T	653	75%	718/786-6213 Fax 646/537-1703
William C Bryant High Sch 4810 31st Ave, Long Is City 11103 Namita Dwarka	9-12	TV	2,290	83%	718/721-5404 Fax 718/728-3478
Woodside Cmty School 361Q 3907 57th St, Woodside 11377 Nayeon Hwang	PK-3	T	345	76%	718/592-3300 Fax 718/592-3310
Young Women's Leadership Sch 2315 Newtown Ave, Astoria 11102 Allison Persad	6-12	T	584	79%	718/267-2839 Fax 718/728-0218

- **District 75 City Wide Programs** PID: 00740626
  (Part of New York City Dept of Ed in New York County)

Public Schs..Principal	Grd	Prgm	Enr/#Cls	SN	Phone
John F Kennedy Jr Sch 5712 94th St, Elmhurst 11373 Henry Renelus	Spec		471	86%	718/760-1083
Ⓨ PS 009 5874 57th St, Maspeth 11378 Robert Wojnarowski	Spec	M	621	82%	718/456-7105 Fax 718/456-5977
Ⓨ PS 75Q Robert E Peary 1666 Hancock St, Ridgewood 11385 James Thorbs	Spec	M	541 20	80%	718/456-7588 Fax 718/628-0491
PS 277Q the Riverview Sch 5011 44th St, Sunnyside 11104 Annette Beale	Spec		200		718/361-3567 Fax 718/361-3568
Ⓨ PS Q004 19625 Peck Ave, Fresh Meadows 11365 Alison Quinlan	Spec	M	459 12	71%	718/264-0916 Fax 718/264-1205
Ⓨ PS Q023-Queens Childrens Ctr 7403 Commonwealth Blvd, Bellerose 11426 Jacqueline Jones	Spec	M	358	89%	718/264-4880 Fax 718/264-4836
Ⓨ PS Q177 5637 188th St, Flushing 11365 Christopher Duffy	Spec	M	487 50	79%	718/357-4650 Fax 718/357-3507
Ⓨ PS Q224 25212 72nd Ave, Bellerose 11426 Desmond Park	Spec	M	394 12	69%	718/831-4024 Fax 718/831-4026
Ⓨ PS Q233 9130 Metropolitan Ave, Forest Hills 11375 Debbie Edmonds	Spec	M	559	85%	718/286-4700 Fax 718/286-4701
Ⓨ PS Q255 15840 76th Rd, Flushing 11366 Gregg Lopez	Spec	M	411 24	78%	718/380-1247 Fax 718/380-2295
Ⓨ PS Q811 6125 Marathon Pkwy, Little Neck 11362 Nicole Avila	Spec	M	426 20	81%	718/224-8060 Fax 718/224-5914
Queens Transition Center 14210 Linden Blvd, Jamaica 11436 Fritzy Brown	Spec	M	395 32	84%	718/558-2060 Fax 718/558-2036

- **New York Alt High Sch SD 79** PID: 00740626
  (Part of New York City Dept of Ed in New York County)

Public Schs..Principal	Grd	Prgm	Enr/#Cls	SN	Phone
Ⓐ East River Academy-Rikers 1010 Hazen St, East Elmhurst 11370 Tanya Threadgill	9-12	GV	575 22		718/546-6200 Fax 718/546-6230
Ⓐ Passages Acad-South Ozone Park 133 127th St #23, S Ozone Park 11420 Ron Carter	9-12		401		718/927-1228

---

79 Student Personnel	91 Safety/Security	275 Response To Intervention	298 Grant Writer/Ptnrships
80 Driver Ed/Safety	92 Magnet School	277 Remedial Math K-12	750 Chief Innovation Officer
81 Gifted/Talented	93 Parental Involvement	280 Literacy Coach	751 Chief of Staff
82 Video Services	95 Tech Prep Program	285 STEM	752 Social Emotional Learning
83 Substance Abuse Prev	97 Chief Infomation Officer	286 Digital Learning	
84 Erate	98 Chief Technology Officer	288 Common Core Standards	
85 AIDS Education	270 Character Education	294 Accountability	
88 Alternative/At Risk	271 Migrant Education	295 Network System	
89 Multi-Cultural Curriculum	273 Teacher Mentor	296 Title II Programs	
90 Social Work	274 Before/After Sch	297 Webmaster	

School Programs
A = Alternative Program
G = Adult Classes
M = Magnet Program
T = Title I Schoolwide
V = Career & Tech Ed Programs

Other School Types
Ⓐ = Alternative School
Ⓒ = Charter School
Ⓜ = Magnet School
Ⓨ = Year-Round School

New Schools are shaded
New Superintendents and Principals are bold
Personnel with email addresses are underscored

Social Media
 = Facebook
 = Twitter

Queens County

Market Data Retrieval

QUEENS CATHOLIC SCHOOLS

- **Diocese of Brooklyn Ed Office** PID: 00752801
  Listing includes only schools located in this county. See District Index for location of Diocesan Offices.

Catholic Schs..Principal	Grd	Prgm	Enr/#Cls	SN		
Archbishop Molloy High Sch 8353 Manton St, Briarwood 11435 Darius Penikas	9-12		1,596 42		718/441-2100 Fax 718/849-8251	
Cathedral Preparatory Seminary 5625 92nd St, Elmhurst 11373 Richie Diaz	9-12		160 15		718/592-6800 Fax 718/592-5574	
Christ the King Regional HS 6802 Metropolitan Ave, Middle Vlg 11379 Geri Martinez	9-12		1,000 75		718/366-7400 Fax 718/417-8830	
Divine Mercy Catholic Academy 10160 92nd St, Ozone Park 11416 Francis Marie	PK-8		216 15		718/845-3074 Fax 718/845-5068	
Divine Wisdom Acad-Douglaston 4511 245th St, Douglaston 11362 Miriam Bonici	PK-8		210 27		718/631-3153 Fax 718/631-3945	
Holy Child Jesus Catholic Acad 11102 86th Ave, Richmond Hill 11418 Patricia Winters	PK-8		350		718/849-3988 Fax 718/850-2842	
Holy Cross High Sch 2620 Francis Lewis Blvd, Flushing 11358 Edward Burns	9-12		900		718/886-7250 Fax 718/886-7257	
Holy Family Catholic Academy 7415 175th St, Fresh Meadows 11366 Mary Scheer	PK-8		263 16		718/969-2124 Fax 718/380-2183	
Immaculate Conception Academy 17914 Dalny Rd, Jamaica 11432 Dorothea Breen	PK-8		406 32		718/739-5933 Fax 718/523-7436	
Immaculate Conception Sch 2163 29th St, Astoria 11105 Eileen Harnischfeger	PK-8		275		718/728-1969 Fax 718/728-3374	
Incarnation Sch 8915 Francis Lewis Blvd, Queens Vlg 11427 Mary Bellone	PK-8		280 16		718/465-5066 Fax 718/464-4128	
Mary Louis Academy 17621 Wexford Ter, Jamaica 11432 Ann O'Hagan Cordes	9-12		950 100		718/297-2120 Fax 718/739-0037	
Monsignor McClancy Memorial HS 7106 31st Ave, East Elmhurst 11370 James Castrataro	9-12		650 21		718/898-3800 Fax 718/898-3929	
Notre Dame Catholic Academy 6232 61st St, Ridgewood 11385 Jennifer Dilornezo	PK-8		360 18		718/821-2221 Fax 718/821-1058	
Our Lady Blessed Sacrament Sch 3445 202nd St, Bayside 11361 Joan Kane	PK-8		399 25		718/229-4434 Fax 718/229-5820	
Our Lady of Fatima Sch 2538 80th St, East Elmhurst 11370 Margaret Rogers	PK-8		450 23		718/429-7031 Fax 718/899-2811	
Our Lady of Hope Sch 6121 71st St, Middle Vlg 11379 Giuseppe Campailla	PK-8		503 23		718/458-3535 Fax 718/458-9031	
Our Lady of Mercy Sch 7025 Kessel St, Forest Hills 11375 Dana McCann	PK-8		320 21		718/793-2086 Fax 718/897-2144	
Our Lady of Sorrows Sch 3534 105th St, Corona 11368 Dr Cristina Cruz	PK-8		280 11		718/426-5517 Fax 718/651-5585	
Our Lady of the Snows Sch 7933 258th St, Floral Park 11004 Joseph Venticinque	PK-8		495 23		718/343-1346 Fax 718/343-7303	
Our Lady Perpetual Help Acad 11110 115th St, S Ozone Park 11420 Frances DeLuca	PK-8		550 23		718/843-4184 Fax 718/843-6838	
Our Lady Queen of Martyrs Acad 7255 Austin St, Forest Hills 11375 Anne Zuschlag	PK-8		358 14		718/263-2622 Fax 718/263-0063	
Our Lady's Catholic Academy 10955 128th St, S Ozone Park 11420 Satti Marchen	PK-8		267 15		718/641-1316 Fax 718/843-0769	
Resurrection Ascension Sch 8525 61st Rd, Rego Park 11374 Joanne Heppt	PK-8		350 10		718/426-4963 Fax 718/426-0940	
Sacred Heart Catholic Academy 11550 221st St, Cambria HTS 11411 Yvonne Russell-Smith	PK-8		298 15		718/527-0123 Fax 718/527-1204	
Sacred Heart Sch 8405 78th Ave, Glendale 11385 Joanne Gangi	PK-8		297 18		718/456-6636 Fax 718/456-0286	
Sacred Heart Sch 21601 38th Ave, Bayside 11361 Alexandra Conlan	PK-8		400 24		718/631-4804 Fax 718/631-5738	
SS Joachim & Anne Sch 21819 105th Ave, Queens Vlg 11429 Linda Freebes	PK-8		490 22		718/465-2230 Fax 718/468-5698	
St Adalbert Sch 5217 83rd St, Elmhurst 11373 Thomas Morris	PK-8		333 23		718/424-2376 Fax 718/898-7852	
St Agnes Academic High Sch 1320 124th St, College Point 11356 Susan Nicoletti	9-12		300 26		718/353-6276 Fax 718/353-6068	
St Andrew Avellino Cath Acad 3550 158th St, Flushing 11358 Debora Hanna	PK-8		300 35		718/359-7887 Fax 718/359-2295	
St Bartholomew Sch 4415 Judge St, Elmhurst 11373 Denise Gonzalez	K-8		170 11		718/446-7575 Fax 718/446-7743	
St Camillus Catholic Academy 185 Beach 99th St, Rockaway Park 11694 Raffaele Corso	PK-8		151 9		718/634-5260 Fax 718/634-8353	
St Clare Catholic Academy 13725 Brookville Blvd, Rosedale 11422 Mary Basile	PK-8		295 11		718/528-7174 Fax 718/528-4389	
St Elizabeth Catholic Academy 9401 85th St, Ozone Park 11416 Jeanne Shannon	PK-8		375 10		718/641-6990 Fax 718/323-5010	
St Francis DeSales Sch 219 Beach 129th St, Rockaway Park 11694 Chris Scharbach	PK-8		780 26		718/634-2775 Fax 718/634-6673	
St Francis of Assisi Sch 2118 46th St, Astoria 11105 Anne Stefano	PK-8		340 12		718/726-9405 Fax 718/721-2577	
St Francis Preparatory Sch 6100 Francis Lewis Blvd, Fresh Meadows 11365 Patrick McLaughlin	9-12		2,700 81		718/423-8810 Fax 718/224-2108	
St Gregory the Great Sch 24444 87th Ave, Bellerose 11426 Lynn Alaimo	PK-8		340 25		718/343-5053 Fax 718/347-1142	
St Helen Catholic Academy 8309 157th Ave, Howard Beach 11414 Frederick Tudda	PK-8		250 20		718/835-4155 Fax 718/738-0580	
St Joan of Arc Sch 3527 82nd St, Jackson HTS 11372 Raffaele Corso	PK-8		485 19		718/639-9020 Fax 718/639-5428	

1	Superintendent	8	Curric/Instruct K-12	19	Chief Financial Officer	29	Family/Consumer Science	39	Social Studies K-12	49	English/Lang Arts Elem	59	Special Education Elem	69	Academic Assessment
2	Bus/Finance/Purchasing	9	Curric/Instruct Elem	20	Art K-12	30	Adult Education	40	Social Studies Elem	50	English/Lang Arts Sec	60	Special Education Sec	70	Research/Development
3	Buildings And Grounds	10	Curric/Instruct Sec	21	Art Elem	31	Career/Sch-to-Work K-12	41	Social Studies Sec	51	Reading K-12	61	Foreign/World Lang K-12	71	Public Information
4	Food Service	11	Federal Program	22	Art Sec	32	Career/Sch-to-Work Elem	42	Science K-12	52	Reading Elem	62	Foreign/World Lang Elem	72	Summer School
5	Transportation	12	Title I	23	Music K-12	33	Career/Sch-to-Work Sec	43	Science Elem	53	Reading Sec	63	Foreign/World Lang Sec	73	Instructional Tech
6	Athletic	13	Title V	24	Music Elem	34	Early Childhood Ed	44	Science Sec	54	Remedial Reading K-12	64	Religious Education K-12	74	Inservice Training
7	Health Services	15	Asst Superintendent	25	Music Sec	35	Health/Phys Education	45	Math K-12	55	Remedial Reading Elem	65	Religious Education Elem	75	Marketing/Distributive
		16	Instructional Media Svcs	26	Business Education	36	Guidance Services K-12	46	Math Elem	56	Remedial Reading Sec	66	Religious Education Sec	76	Info Systems
		17	Chief Operations Officer	27	Career & Tech Ed	37	Guidance Services Elem	47	Math Sec	57	Bilingual/ELL	67	School Board President	77	Psychological Assess
		18	Chief Academic Officer	28	Technology Education	38	Guidance Services Sec	48	English/Lang Arts K-12	58	Special Education K-12	68	Teacher Personnel	78	Affirmative Action

New York School Directory — Queens County

School	Grd	Enr/#Cls SN	Phone/Fax
St John's Preparatory Sch 2121 Crescent St, Astoria 11105 Sheila Halpin	9-12	585	718/721-7200 Fax 718/545-9385
St Joseph Catholic Academy 2846 44th St, Long Is City 11103 Luke Nawrocki	PK-8	450 21	718/728-0724 Fax 718/728-6142
St Kevin Catholic Academy 4550 195th St, Flushing 11358 Allison Murphy	PK-8	300 9	718/357-8110 Fax 718/357-2519
St Leo Catholic Academy 10419 49th Ave, Corona 11368 Jennifer Hernandez	PK-8	400 20	718/592-7050 Fax 718/592-0787
St Luke Sch 1601 150th Pl, Whitestone 11357 Jan Brunswick	PK-8	500 20	718/746-3833 Fax 718/747-2101
St Margaret Sch 6610 80th St, Middle Vlg 11379 Victoria Richardson	PK-8	325 22	718/326-0922 Fax 718/326-3308 f t
St Mary Gate of Heaven Sch 10406 101st Ave, Ozone Park 11416 Philip Heide	PK-8	350	718/846-0689 Fax 718/846-1059 f
St Matthias Sch 5825 Catalpa Ave, Ridgewood 11385 Maria Cuomo	PK-8	400 20	718/381-8003 Fax 718/381-3519
St Mel Sch 15424 26th Ave, Flushing 11354 Amy Barron	PK-8	492 20	718/539-8211 Fax 718/539-6563 f
St Michaels Catholic Academy 13658 41st Ave, Flushing 11355 Maureen Rogone	PK-8	300 20	718/961-0246 Fax 718/961-2013
St Nicholas of Tolentine Sch 8022 Parsons Blvd, Jamaica 11432 Robert Lowenberg	PK-8	375 20	718/380-1900 Fax 718/591-6977
St Rose of Lima Catholic Acad 154 Beach 84th St, Far Rockaway 11693 Theresa Andersen	PK-8	374 15	718/474-7079 Fax 718/634-0524
St Sebastian Sch 3976 58th St, Woodside 11377 Michelle Picarello	PK-8	442 20	718/429-1982 Fax 718/446-7225
St Stanislaus Kostka Sch 6117 Grand Ave, Maspeth 11378 Catherine Mangone	PK-8	270	718/326-1585 Fax 718/326-1745
St Thomas Apostle CA 8749 87th St, Woodhaven 11421 Thomas Piro	PK-8	280 15	718/847-3904 Fax 718/847-3513

QUEENS PRIVATE SCHOOLS

Private Schs..Principal	Grd	Prgm	Enr/#Cls SN	Phone
A B C Math Academy 43 Kissna Blvd, Flushing 11355 Victor Lou	7-12		100	718/888-7866
A Childs Place Day Sch 3220 108th St, East Elmhurst 11369 Denice Coles	PK-5		275	718/424-7949 Fax 718/779-8102
AL Iman Sch 8989 Van Wyck Expy, Jamaica 11435 Sr Iman Dakmak-Rakka	PK-12		250	718/297-6520 Fax 718/785-4226
Al-Ihsan Academy 13008 Rockaway Blvd, S Ozone Park 11420 Shaykh Mohamed	PK-12		450 25	718/322-3154 Fax 718/322-7069 f t
Al-Mamoor Sch 7831 Parsons Blvd, Fresh Meadows 11366 Dr Ismael Khalil	PK-12		138 7	718/739-0902 Fax 718/739-3211
Allen Christian Sch 11432 Merrick Blvd, Jamaica 11434 Linda Morant	PK-1		300 30	718/657-1676 Fax 718/291-7751
Bais Yaakov Academy of Queens 12450 Metropolitan Ave, Kew Gardens 11415 Morde Chai Gewirtz	K-8		750 30	718/847-5352 Fax 718/847-5128
Bethel Christian Learning Ctr 21532 Jamaica Ave, Queens Vlg 11428 Dr Gail Johnson	K-12		71 7	718/740-4357 Fax 718/740-7056
Bnos Bais Yaakov 613 Beach 9th St, Far Rockaway 11691 Deborah Kurland \ Sara Koening \ Adina Mandel	PK-12		1,000 25	718/337-6000 Fax 718/337-9160
Bnos Bais Yaakov High Sch 613 Beach 9th St, Far Rockaway 11691 Adina Mandell	9-12		100	718/337-6000
Bnos Malka Academy 7102 113th St, Forest Hills 11375 Michael Salzbank	PK-8		316 25	718/268-2667 Fax 718/228-9159
C C B School of Douglaston 4514 251st St Ste 203, Little Neck 11362 Shirley Zhang	K-12		101	718/281-3333
Cambria Ctr for Gifted Child 23310 Linden Blvd, Cambria HTS 11411 Sheree Palmer	PK-8		320 19	718/341-1991 Fax 718/341-2395
Chabad Acad of Arts & Sciences 21212 26th Ave, Bayside 11360 Dina Blesofsky	K-8		90	718/279-1457
Christ Lutheran Sch 24801 Francis Lewis Blvd, Rosedale 11422 Richard Liescheidt	K-8		40 5	718/525-6884 Fax 718/525-0456
Church of God Christian Acad 1332 Central Ave, Far Rockaway 11691 Charmaine Jean-Baptiste	K-12		100 6	718/327-9590 Fax 718/327-0988
Clara Muhammad School Queens 10302 Northern Blvd, Corona 11368 Sharifa Dye	1-6		49	646/939-2670
El Ber Islamic Sch 2542 49th St, Long Is City 11103 Solafa Mohamed	PK-4		24	718/274-9060
Evangel Christian Sch 3921 Crescent St, Long Is City 11101 Carmen Perez	PK-12		520 30	718/937-9600 Fax 718/937-1613
Ezra Academy 11945 Union Tpke, Forest Hills 11375 Francine Hirschman	7-12		130 15	718/263-5500 Fax 718/520-9424
Flushing Christian Sch 4154 Murray St, Flushing 11355 Karen Blatt	K-8		133 9	718/445-3533 Fax 718/445-7546
Forest Hills Montessori Sch 6704 Austin St, Forest Hills 11375 Sunila Tejpaul	PK-1		120 7	718/275-0173 Fax 718/275-0176
Garden Sch 3316 79th St, Jackson HTS 11372 Dr Richard Marotta	K-12		325 35	718/335-6363 Fax 718/565-1169
Greater New York Academy 4132 58th St, Woodside 11377 Jacques Patterson	9-12		210 13	718/639-1752 Fax 718/639-8992
Highland Elem Sch 19310 Peck Ave, Fresh Meadows 11365 Shelly Singh	K-8		120 9	718/357-4747 Fax 718/357-4323
Holy Martyrs Armenian Day Sch 20915 Horace Harding Expy, Oakland GDNS 11364 Seta Megherian	PK-6		100 9	718/225-4826 Fax 718/225-4837
Ideal Islamic Sch 3129 12th St, Long Is City 11106 Somai Ferozi	PK-7		30 7	718/728-5307

---

79 Student Personnel
80 Driver Ed/Safety
81 Gifted/Talented
82 Video Services
83 Substance Abuse Prev
84 Erate
85 AIDS Education
88 Alternative/At Risk
89 Multi-Cultural Curriculum
90 Social Work
91 Safety/Security
92 Magnet School
93 Parental Involvement
95 Tech Prep Program
97 Chief Information Officer
98 Chief Technology Officer
270 Character Education
271 Migrant Education
273 Teacher Mentor
274 Before/After Sch
275 Response To Intervention
277 Remedial Math K-12
280 Literacy Coach
285 STEM
286 Digital Learning
288 Common Core Standards
294 Accountability
295 Network System
296 Title II Programs
297 Webmaster
298 Grant Writer/Ptnrships
750 Chief Innovation Officer
751 Chief of Staff
752 Social Emotional Learning

School Programs
A = Alternative Program
G = Adult Classes
M = Magnet Program
T = Title I Schoolwide
V = Career & Tech Ed Programs

Other School Types
Ⓐ = Alternative School
Ⓒ = Charter School
Ⓜ = Magnet School
Ⓨ = Year-Round School

Social Media
f = Facebook
t = Twitter

New Schools are shaded
New Superintendents and Principals are bold
Personnel with email addresses are underscored

Queens County

Market Data Retrieval

School	Grades		Enroll	Phone
Jackson Heights SDA Elem Sch 7225 Woodside Ave, Woodside 11377 Marissa Gentles	PK-8		88 6	718/426-5729 Fax 718/426-0079
Jamaica SDA Elem Sch 8828 163rd St, Jamaica 11432 Dorrett Francis	PK-8		64	718/297-3491
Jewish Institue of Queens 6005 Woodhaven Blvd, Elmhurst 11373 Jennifer Seideman \ Mrs Aminov	PK-12		500	718/426-9369 Fax 718/446-2071
Kew-Forest Sch 11917 Union Tpke, Forest Hills 11375 Tiffany Trotter	PK-12		250 30	718/268-4667 Fax 718/268-9121
Learning Tree STEM-Arts Sch 10302 Northern Blvd, Corona 11368 Nicole Bailey	K-8		66	718/397-5446 Fax 718/397-3302
Lexington School for Deaf 2526 75th St, East Elmhurst 11370 Dr Regina Carroll	Spec	G	330 35	718/899-8800 Fax 718/899-9846
Lifeline Center for Child Dev 8009 Winchester Blvd, Queens Vlg 11427 Amy Levine	Spec		100	718/740-4300 Fax 718/217-9566
Linden SDA Sch 13701 228th St, Laurelton 11413 Laurene Richards-Usher	1-8		162 12	718/527-6868 Fax 718/527-6650
Little Meadow Early Chldhd Ctr 6725 188th St, Fresh Meadows 11365 Linda Silver	Spec		100 7	718/454-6460 Fax 718/454-0661
Lowell Sch 2420 Parsons Blvd, Whitestone 11357 Irene Psilakis	9-12		240	718/352-2100 Fax 718/352-3654
Lowell Sch 14245 58th Rd, Flushing 11355 Irene Tsialikis	Spec	V	140 7	718/445-4222 Fax 718/353-6942
Lutheran Sch-Flushing Bayside 3601 Bell Blvd, Bayside 11361 Pia Haselbach	PK-8		125 8	718/225-5502 Fax 718/225-7446
Martin Luther High Sch 6002 Maspeth Ave, Maspeth 11378 Donna Younghese	6-12		250 25	718/894-4000 Fax 718/894-1469
Mesivta Ohr Torah 8606 135th St, Richmond Hill 11418 Rabbi Kashani	PK-8	V	300 10	718/658-7066 Fax 718/618-1022
Midrash L'Man Achai High Sch 9730 Queens Blvd, Rego Park 11374 Daniel Baybachayev	9-12		401	718/544-4875
Muslim Center Elem Mid Sch 13758 Geranium Ave, Flushing 11355 Nahid Farooqi	PK-8		170 10	718/460-2127 Fax 718/460-9727
New World Education Center 13737 Farmers Blvd, Jamaica 11434 April Patterson	PK-PK		32 3	718/528-8751 Fax 718/528-8752
North Side Sch 1650 Utopia Pkwy, Whitestone 11357 Irene Kouba	PK-PK		108 8	718/229-5050
Nurturing Center and Academy 11218 Springfield Blvd, Queens Vlg 11429 Beverly Davis	PK-5		150	718/527-5932 Fax 718/527-3361
Our Saviour Lutheran Sch 6433 Woodhaven Blvd, Rego Park 11374 Warren Castellani	PK-PK		120 7	718/897-4343 Fax 718/830-9275
Phyllilsuster Birch Sch 7164 168th St, Flushing 11365 Michael Claus	Spec		85	718/591-8100 Fax 718/969-2941
Phyllis L Susser Sch 7164 168th St, Flushing 11365 Michael Clause	Spec		82 10	718/591-8100 Fax 718/969-2941
Promise Christian Academy 13030 31st Ave Ste 724, Flushing 11354 Janice Catapano	PK-8		200	718/461-4409 Fax 718/461-7368
Queens Lutheran Sch 3120 21st Ave, Astoria 11105 Robert Alovisetti	PK-6		120 8	718/721-4313 Fax 718/721-7662
Rabbinical Seminary High Sch 7601 147th St, Flushing 11367 Yosef Singer	9-12		100 8	718/263-1445 Fax 718/263-4918
Razi Sch 5511 Queens Blvd, Woodside 11377 Ghassan Elcheikhali	K-12		308 18	718/779-0711
Redeemer Lutheran Sch 6926 Cooper Ave, Glendale 11385 Michael Williams	PK-8		200 14	718/821-6670 Fax 718/366-0338
Rising Stars Islamic Sch 16626 89th Ave, Jamaica 11432 Fauzia Khondker	PK-6		123	646/243-5895
Shaarei Zion Ohel Bracha Sch 7524 Grand Central Pkwy, Forest Hills 11375 Label Lam	K-8		200	718/897-6771 Fax 718/268-3447
Shevach High Sch 7509 Main St, Flushing 11367 Rochelle Hirtz	9-12		200 13	718/263-0525 Fax 718/263-3759
Shield Institute of Flushing 14461 Roosevelt Ave, Flushing 11354 Leah O'Malley	Spec		220 7	718/939-8700 Fax 718/939-8364
Slcd Sch 7024 47th Ave, Woodside 11377 Lauren Leonrdi	Spec		125	718/476-7163 Fax 718/476-7051
Solomon Schechter Sch- Queens 7616 Parsons Blvd, Fresh Meadows 11366 Sheldon Naparstek	PK-8		400 30	718/591-9800 Fax 718/591-8464
St Albans Christian Academy 20512 Hollis Ave, Saint Albans 11412 Joanne Johnson	PK-8		10 11	718/468-6060 Fax 718/465-7173
St Demetrios Elem Sch 2230 33rd St, Astoria 11105 Anastasios Koularmanis	PK-3		305 14	718/728-1100 Fax 718/728-1350
St Demetrios Mid High Sch 3003 30th Dr, Astoria 11102 Anastasios Koularmanis	4-12		600 40	718/728-1754 Fax 718/726-3482
St Joseph's Parish Day Sch 21755 100th Ave, Queens Vlg 11429 Marlon Brown	PK-8		80 15	718/464-8913 Fax 718/464-2366
Stepping Stone Pre & Grade Sch 11428 Francis Lewis Blvd, Jamaica 11411 Madge Warren	PK-3		75	718/465-2344 Fax 718/465-0114
Summit Sch 18730 Grand Central Pkwy, Jamaica 11432 Richard Sitman	9-12		210	718/264-2931 Fax 718/264-2935
Summitt School Annex 18302 Union Tpke, Flushing 11366 Karen Frigenti	Spec		125	718/969-3944 Fax 718/969-4073
Talmud Torah Siach Yitzchok 1513 Central Ave, Far Rockaway 11691 David Sitnick	PK-8		325 11	718/327-6247 Fax 718/471-0925
Theatre Street Sch 8761 111th St, Richmond Hill 11418 Teresa Aubel	1-8		12 9	718/846-9182 Fax 718/849-7537
Theresa Paplin Sch 8570 148th St, Jamaica 11435 Shante Spiezy	Spec	V	60 9	718/658-8180 Fax 718/291-4279
Torah Academy for Girls 444 Beach 6th St, Far Rockaway 11691 Temima Felma \ Cecille Wieder \ Michoel Sheppard	PK-12	GV	1,600	718/471-8444 Fax 718/868-4612

1 Superintendent	8 Curric/Instruct K-12	19 Chief Financial Officer	29 Family/Consumer Science	39 Social Studies K-12	49 English/Lang Arts Elem	59 Special Education Elem	69 Academic Assessment
2 Bus/Finance/Purchasing	9 Curric/Instruct Elem	20 Art K-12	30 Adult Education	40 Social Studies Elem	50 English/Lang Arts Sec	60 Special Education Sec	70 Research/Development
3 Buildings And Grounds	10 Curric/Instruct Sec	21 Art Elem	31 Career/Sch-to-Work K-12	41 Social Studies Sec	51 Reading K-12	61 Foreign/World Lang K-12	71 Public Information
4 Food Service	11 Federal Program	22 Art Sec	32 Career/Sch-to-Work Elem	42 Science K-12	52 Reading Elem	62 Foreign/World Lang Elem	72 Summer School
5 Transportation	12 Title I	23 Music K-12	33 Career/Sch-to-Work Sec	43 Science Elem	53 Reading Sec	63 Foreign/World Lang Sec	73 Instructional Tech
6 Athletic	13 Title V	24 Music Elem	34 Early Childhood Ed	44 Science Sec	54 Remedial Reading K-12	64 Religious Education K-12	74 Inservice Training
7 Health Services	15 Asst Superintendent	25 Music Sec	35 Health/Phys Education	45 Math K-12	55 Remedial Reading Elem	65 Religious Education Elem	75 Marketing/Distributive
	16 Instructional Media Svcs	26 Business Education	36 Guidance Services K-12	46 Math Elem	56 Remedial Reading Sec	66 Religious Education Sec	76 Info Systems
	17 Chief Operations Officer	27 Career & Tech Ed	37 Guidance Services Elem	47 Math Sec	57 Bilingual/ELL	67 School Board President	77 Psychological Assess
	18 Chief Academic Officer	28 Technology Education	38 Guidance Services Sec	48 English/Lang Arts K-12	58 Special Education K-12	68 Teacher Personnel	78 Affirmative Action

New York School Directory

School	Grd	Prgm	Enr/#Cls	SN	Phone
UCP of Queens Children's Ctr 8225 164th St, Jamaica 11432 Nancy Glass	Spec		100		718/374-0002
United Nations Int'l Sch 17353 Croydon Rd, Jamaica 11432 Barbara Kennedy	K-8		132 15		718/658-6166 Fax 718/658-5742
Wellspring Sch 9020 191st St, Hollis 11423 Radeyah Ishmael \ Rozina Begum \ Assad Nasrullah	PK-12		153		718/721-3523 Fax 888/776-6912
Whitestone Academy 15034 12th Ave, Whitestone 11357 Francis Ottaviano	7-12		111 11		718/767-0773 Fax 718/767-4426
William Spyropoulos Sch 4315 196th St, Flushing 11358 Mary Tzallas	K-8		450 25		718/357-5583 Fax 718/428-3051
Windsor Sch 3702 Main St 4th Fl, Flushing 11354 James DeFeo	7-12		150		718/359-8300 Fax 718/359-1876
Yeshiva Dar HEI Torah 257 Beach 17th St, Far Rockaway 11691 Ariella Kelman	K-12		2,100 30		718/868-2300
Yeshiva Har Torah Sch 25010 Grand Central Pkwy, Bellerose 11426 Pesha Kletenik	PK-8		580 18		718/343-2533 Fax 718/631-2513
Yeshiva Ketana of Queens 7815 Parsons Blvd, Flushing 11366 Rasha Grossman	K-8		415		718/969-1000 Fax 718/969-9600
Yeshiva Mercaz Hatorah 505 Beach 129th St, Rockaway Park 11694 Shmuelzev Dicker	9-12	G	75 5		718/474-3064 Fax 718/634-4510
Yeshiva of Central Queens 14737 70th Rd, Flushing 11367 Mark Landsman	PK-8		910 38		718/793-8500 Fax 718/793-8504
Yeshiva of Far Rockaway 802 Hicksville Rd, Far Rockaway 11691 Mordechai Miller	9-12		115 12		718/327-7600 Fax 718/327-1430
Yeshiva Tifereth Moshe 8306 Abingdon Rd, Kew Gardens 11415 Yakov May	K-8		450 7		718/846-7300 Fax 718/441-3962
Yeshiva Univ HS-Girls 8686 Palo Alto St, Hollis 11423 Cb Neugroschl	9-12		270 25		718/479-8550 Fax 718/479-8686
Yeshivat Ohr Haiim 8606 135th St, Richmond Hill 11418 Mordechai Kashani	PK-8		300 20		718/658-7066 Fax 718/658-1022

RENSSELAER COUNTY

RENSSELAER COUNTY SCHOOLS

County Schs..Principal	Grd	Prgm	Enr/#Cls	SN	Phone
George Washington Sch 344 Menemsha Ln, Troy 12180 Danielle Remillard	Spec		56		518/283-5752 Fax 518/283-5621
Questar 3-Rensselaer Ed Ctr 35 Colleen Rd, Troy 12180 Anthony DeFazio	Voc	AG	325 30		518/273-2264 Fax 518/273-4129

RENSSELAER PUBLIC SCHOOLS

• **Averill Park Central Sch Dist** PID: 00766591   518/674-7050
146 Gettle Rd 1, Averill Park 12018   Fax 518/674-3802

Schools: 5 \ **Teachers:** 219 \ **Students:** 2,665 \ **Special Ed Students:** 526 \ **LEP Students:** 12 \ **Ethnic:** Asian 1%, African American 1%, Hispanic 3%, Caucasian 95% \ **Exp:** $234 (Med) \ **Poverty:** 5% \ **Title I:** $229,048 \ **Special Education:** $6,100,000 \ **Open-Close:** 09/08 - 06/25 \ **DTBP:** $226 (High)

Dr James Franchanni 1
Aaron Heffner 3,91
Mark Premo 5
Anne Lanoue 7
Tim Herbs 9,270*
Jennifer Yost 16*
Nancy Bush 30*
Kate Dorgan 58*
Kimberly Nugent 68
Lynn Burdick 73,295,297
Elizabeth Magill 273
Brian Rhode 280
Catina Riley 2
Coleen Wise 4
Mark Bubniak 6,35
Matthew Hladun . 8,11,18,83,285,286,288,296
Micheal Ouimet 15,76,78
Julie Ernest 30
Laura Schmidt 57*
Jessica Zweig 67
Kristin Card 69,294*
Tracy Hacker 77*
Tom Ladd 277*

Public Schs..Principal	Grd	Prgm	Enr/#Cls	SN	Phone
Algonquin Middle Sch 333 NY Highway 351, Averill Park 12018 Robert Messia	6-8		671 36	26%	518/674-7100 Fax 518/674-0671
Averill Park High Sch 146 Gettle Rd, Averill Park 12018 Heath Quiles	9-12	GV	879 60	18%	518/674-7000 Fax 518/674-7046
Miller Hill-Sand Lake Elem Sch 8439 Miller Hill Rd, Averill Park 12018 Denis Sibson	K-5		383 25	28%	518/674-7075 Fax 518/674-8003
Poestenkill Elem Sch 1 School Rd, Poestenkill 12140 John Bishop	K-5		339 19	22%	518/674-7125 Fax 518/286-1971
West Sand Lake Elem Sch 24 Meeler Rd, W Sand Lake 12196 Laura Kyer	K-5		393 23	25%	518/674-7175 Fax 518/674-3225

• **Berlin Central School Dist** PID: 00766668   518/658-1500
17400 State Rte 22, Cherry Plain 12040

Schools: 2 \ **Teachers:** 81 \ **Students:** 800 \ **Special Ed Students:** 126 \ **College-Bound:** 70% \ **Ethnic:** African American 2%, Hispanic 1%, Caucasian 97% \ **Exp:** $265 (Med) \ **Poverty:** 11% \ **Title I:** $151,335 \ **Special Education:** $1,941,000 \ **Open-Close:** 09/08 - 06/25 \ **DTBP:** $381 (High)

Dr Stephen Young 1
Cyril Grant 3
Joshua Weaver 6*
Tracy Kent 9,11*
Ann Lazarony 31,36,69,83*
Samantha Brewer 58,81
Tammy Dunlop 73*
Karen Capozzi 2,5,71,97
Tammy Whitman 4
Michelle Corsey 7*
Dr Cathie Allian 10*
Sandra Honsinger 35,85*
Frank Zwack 67
Brenda Dixon 270*

Public Schs..Principal	Grd	Prgm	Enr/#Cls	SN	Phone
Berlin Elem Sch 53 School St, Berlin 12022 Tracy Kent	K-5	T	296 20	52%	518/658-2127 Fax 518/658-0482
Berlin Middle High Sch 17400 New York 22, Cherry Plain 12040 Dr Cathie Allian	6-12		377 30		518/658-2515 Fax 518/658-2535

79 Student Personnel	91 Safety/Security	275 Response To Intervention	298 Grant Writer/Ptnrships	**School Programs**	**Social Media**	
80 Driver Ed/Safety	92 Magnet School	277 Remedial Math K-12	750 Chief Innovation Officer	A = Alternative Program		
81 Gifted/Talented	93 Parental Involvement	280 Literacy Coach	751 Chief of Staff	G = Adult Classes	▌▌ = Facebook	
82 Video Services	95 Tech Prep Program	285 STEM	752 Social Emotional Learning	M = Magnet Program		
83 Substance Abuse Prev	97 Chief Infomation Officer	286 Digital Learning		T = Title I Schoolwide	▌▌ = Twitter	
84 Erate	98 Chief Technology Officer	288 Common Core Standards	**Other School Types**	V = Career & Tech Ed Programs		
85 AIDS Education	270 Accountability	294 Accountability	Ⓐ = Alternative School			
88 Alternative/At Risk	271 Migrant Education	295 Network System	Ⓒ = Charter School	New Schools are shaded		
89 Multi-Cultural Curriculum	273 Teacher Mentor	296 Title II Programs	Ⓜ = Magnet School	**New Superintendents and Principals are bold**		
90 Social Work	274 Before/After Sch	297 Webmaster	Ⓨ = Year-Round School	Personnel with email addresses are underscored		

Rensselaer County

Market Data Retrieval

- **Brunswick Central School Dist** PID: 00766723   518/279-4600
  3992 State Highway 2, Troy 12180   Fax 518/279-1918

Schools: 2 \ **Teachers:** 108 \ **Students:** 1,200 \ **Special Ed Students:** 162 \ **LEP Students:** 8 \ **College-Bound:** 92% \ **Ethnic:** Asian 1%, African American 1%, Hispanic 4%, Caucasian 93% \ **Exp:** $349 (High) \ **Poverty:** 8% \ **Title I:** $154,062 \ **Special Education:** $1,696,000 \ **Open-Close:** 09/09 - 06/25 \ **DTBP:** $221 (High) \ f

Dr Angelina Maloney	1	Stephanie Steinhart	2,15
Whitney Colvin	3,5	Joy Wright	4*
Donna VanZandt	6	Patricia Poupore	38,273
Rochelle Hoot	58	Jack Roddy	67
Shannon Dankwerth	71	Michelle Furlong	73*
Carol Galbraith	274	Eric Wetmore	295

Public Schs..Principal	Grd	Prgm	Enr/#Cls	SN	
Tamarac Elem Sch 3992 State Highway 2, Troy 12180 Richard Pogue	PK-5		505 37	34% Fax	518/279-4600 518/279-0612 f
Tamarac Secondary Sch 3992 State Highway 2, Troy 12180 Richard Pogue	6-12	V	658 60	31% Fax	518/279-4600 518/279-3888 f

- **East Greenbush Central SD** PID: 00766773   518/207-2500
  29 Englewood Ave, E Greenbush 12061   Fax 518/477-4833

Schools: 7 \ **Teachers:** 324 \ **Students:** 5,042 \ **Special Ed Students:** 728 \ **LEP Students:** 40 \ **Ethnic:** Asian 7%, African American 3%, Hispanic 6%, Caucasian 84% \ **Exp:** $185 (Low) \ **Poverty:** 6% \ **Title I:** $415,830 \ **Special Education:** $6,923,000 \ **Open-Close:** 09/08 - 05/21 \ **DTBP:** $326 (High) \ f

Jeffrey Simons	1	Larry Edson	2,15
Paul Bickel	3	Phyllis Sanford-Krug	4*
Mark Noeth	5	Molly McGrath	7,34,58,79
James McHugh	8,11,57,77,275,285,288,296	Michael Buono	67
Marissa Cannon	68,74,91	Peter Goodwin	73,76,286,295

Public Schs..Principal	Grd	Prgm	Enr/#Cls	SN	
Bell Top Elem Sch 39 Reynolds Rd, Troy 12180 Martin Mahar	K-5		321 17	14% Fax	518/207-2600 518/283-1184
Citizen Edmond Genet Elem Sch 29 Englewood Ave, E Greenbush 12061 Wayne Grignon	K-5		430 19	22% Fax	518/207-2680 518/477-4466 f
Columbia High Sch 962 Luther Rd, E Greenbush 12061 Michael Harkin	9-12	AGV	1,312	22% Fax	518/207-2000 518/207-2009 f
Donald P Sutherland Elem Sch 4 John St, Nassau 12123 Jack Alvey	K-5		294 16	35% Fax	518/207-2620 518/766-9548
Green Meadow Elem Sch 234 Schuurman Rd, Castleton 12033 Daniel Garab	K-5		380 30	19% Fax	518/207-2640 518/479-7954
Howard L Goff Middle Sch 35 Gilligan Rd, E Greenbush 12061 Jill Barker	6-8	V	934 100	25% Fax	518/207-2430 518/477-2667 f t
Red Mill Elem Sch 225 McCullough Pl, Rensselaer 12144 Helen Squillace	K-5		417 21	28% Fax	518/207-2660 518/449-2480 f

- **Hoosic Valley Central Sch Dist** PID: 00766876   518/753-4458
  2 Pleasant Ave, Schaghticoke 12154   Fax 518/753-7665

Schools: 2 \ **Teachers:** 81 \ **Students:** 931 \ **Special Ed Students:** 176 \ **LEP Students:** 3 \ **College-Bound:** 69% \ **Ethnic:** African American 1%, Hispanic 1%, Caucasian 98% \ **Exp:** $368 (High) \ **Poverty:** 8% \ **Title I:** $151,567 \ **Special Education:** $1,893,000 \ **Open-Close:** 09/04 - 06/25 \ **DTBP:** $417 (High)

G Michael Apostol	1	Anthony Cammarata	2
Michael Corlen	4	Wayne Akin	5
Paula Lanoue	6*	Debra Ellett	7,85*
Julie Adams	10*	Mark Foti	11*
Jeff Hoag	16,73,286*	Patti Sawyer	58*
Chris Pepe	67		

Public Schs..Principal	Grd	Prgm	Enr/#Cls	SN	
Hoosic Valley Elem Sch 22 Pleasant Ave, Schaghticoke 12154 Mark Foti	K-6		487 31	38% Fax	518/753-4491 518/753-7576
Hoosic Valley High Sch 1548 State Route 67, Schaghticoke 12154 Eric Papandrea	7-12	AV	444 40	32% Fax	518/753-4432 518/753-7491

- **Hoosick Falls Central Sch Dist** PID: 00766905   518/686-7012
  21187 State Route 22, Hoosick Falls 12090   Fax 518/686-9060

Schools: 2 \ **Teachers:** 103 \ **Students:** 1,200 \ **Special Ed Students:** 179 \ **LEP Students:** 6 \ **College-Bound:** 78% \ **Ethnic:** Hispanic 2%, Native American 1%, Caucasian 97% \ **Exp:** $245 (Med) \ **Poverty:** 19% \ **Title I:** $429,930 \ **Special Education:** $1,998,000 \ **Open-Close:** 09/08 - 06/25 \ **DTBP:** $402 (High)

Ken Facin	1,11	Emily Sanders	2,84
Paul Baker	3*	Kenneth Fleming	4*
Joe Steller	5	Tom Husser	6*
Patrick Bailey	12	Jennifer Berry	37*
Kristin Philpott	58*	John Helft	67
David Breese	73*		

Public Schs..Principal	Grd	Prgm	Enr/#Cls	SN	
Hoosick Falls Elem Sch 21187 State Route 22, Hoosick Falls 12090 Amy Netti	PK-6	T	564	50% Fax	518/686-9492 518/686-7496
Hoosick Falls High Sch 21187 State Route 22, Hoosick Falls 12090 Michael Hall	7-12	T	519	45% Fax	518/686-7321 518/686-7452

- **Lansingburgh Central Sch Dist** PID: 00766931   518/233-6850
  55 New Turnpike Rd, Troy 12182   Fax 518/235-7436

Schools: 4 \ **Teachers:** 204 \ **Students:** 2,335 \ **Special Ed Students:** 502 \ **LEP Students:** 52 \ **Ethnic:** African American 21%, Hispanic 16%, Caucasian 63% \ **Exp:** $202 (Med) \ **Poverty:** 23% \ **Title I:** $1,050,255 \ **Special Education:** $5,876,000 \ **Open-Close:** 09/03 - 06/25 \ **DTBP:** $232 (High)

Dr Antonio Abitabile	1	Linda Klime	2,73,91
Robert Schongar	3	Kevin Darigo	4
David Greklek	5	Sean Colfer	6,7,35
Kelly Smith	8,12	Cynthia Dedominick	11
Gregory Rashford	38,83,88*	Shaun Paolino	57,58
Jason Shover	67	Lisa Kyer	68
Dana Roman	71	Mary Sweeney	71
Lucas Larkin	76	Lori Filarecki	273*
Mary Hadock	273*	Paul Brown	295

---

1 Superintendent	8 Curric/Instruct K-12	19 Chief Financial Officer	29 Family/Consumer Science	39 Social Studies K-12	49 English/Lang Arts Elem	59 Special Education Elem	69 Academic Assessment
2 Bus/Finance/Purchasing	9 Curric/Instruct Elem	20 Art K-12	30 Adult Education	40 Social Studies Elem	50 English/Lang Arts Sec	60 Special Education Sec	70 Research/Development
3 Buildings And Grounds	10 Curric/Instruct Sec	21 Art Elem	31 Career/Sch-to-Work K-12	41 Social Studies Sec	51 Reading K-12	61 Foreign/World Lang K-12	71 Public Information
4 Food Service	11 Federal Program	22 Art Sec	32 Career/Sch-to-Work Elem	42 Science K-12	52 Reading Elem	62 Foreign/World Lang Elem	72 Summer School
5 Transportation	12 Title I	23 Music K-12	33 Career/Sch-to-Work Sec	43 Science Elem	53 Reading Sec	63 Foreign/World Lang Sec	73 Instructional Tech
6 Athletic	13 Title V	24 Music Elem	34 Early Childhood Ed	44 Science Sec	54 Remedial Reading K-12	64 Religious Education K-12	74 Inservice Training
7 Health Services	15 Asst Superintendent	25 Music Sec	35 Health/Phys Education	45 Math K-12	55 Remedial Reading Elem	65 Religious Education Elem	75 Marketing/Distributive
	16 Instructional Media Svcs	26 Business Education	36 Guidance Services K-12	46 Math Elem	56 Remedial Reading Sec	66 Religious Education Sec	76 Info Systems
	17 Chief Operations Officer	27 Career & Tech Ed	37 Guidance Services Elem	47 Math Sec	57 Bilingual/ELL	67 School Board President	77 Psychological Assess
	18 Chief Academic Officer	28 Technology Education	38 Guidance Services Sec	48 English/Lang Arts K-12	58 Special Education K-12	68 Teacher Personnel	78 Affirmative Action

New York School Directory

Rensselaer County

Public Schs..Principal	Grd	Prgm	Enr/#Cls	SN	
Knickerbacker Middle Sch 320 7th Ave, Troy 12182 Carrie Phelan	6-8	T	477 40	65%	518/233-6811 Fax 518/237-2917
Lansingburgh High Sch 320 7th Ave, Troy 12182 Matt Van Dervoort	9-12	TV	646 60	57%	518/233-6806 Fax 518/233-6826
Rensselaer Park Elem Sch 70 110th St, Troy 12182 Thomas Hopkins	3-5	T	543 30	71%	518/233-6823 Fax 518/238-1708
Turnpike Elem Sch 55 New Turnpike Rd, Troy 12182 Ian Knox	PK-2	T	595 27	56%	518/233-6822 Fax 518/235-3593

• **North Greenbush Common SD** PID: 00767210 518/283-6748
48 N Greenbush Rd Unit B, Troy 12180 Fax 518/283-6609

Schools: 1 \ **Teachers:** 2 \ **Students:** 13 \ **Special Ed Students:** 18 \
LEP Students: 3 \ **Ethnic:** Asian 5%, African American 5%, Hispanic 5%, Caucasian 85% \ **Exp:** $848 (High) \ **Poverty:** 8% \ **Title I:** $21,077 \
Special Education: $67,000 \ **Open-Close:** 09/04 - 06/25 \ **DTBP:** $140 (High)

Christine Hamill 1,11,83,288   Monica Bentley 7*
Lorraine Thompson 59   Susan O'Connell 67

Public Schs..Principal	Grd	Prgm	Enr/#Cls	SN	
Little Red Schoolhouse 49 N Greenbush Rd, Troy 12180 Christine Hamill	K-1		13 1		518/283-6748

• **Rensselaer City School Dist** PID: 00767014 518/465-7509
25 Van Rensselaer Dr, Rensselaer 12144 Fax 518/436-0479

Schools: 2 \ **Teachers:** 98 \ **Students:** 1,060 \ **Special Ed Students:** 239 \ **LEP Students:** 68 \ **Ethnic:** Asian 15%, African American 15%, Hispanic 11%, Caucasian 59% \ **Exp:** $146 (Low) \ **Poverty:** 20% \ **Title I:** $377,602 \
Special Education: $2,806,000 \ **Open-Close:** 09/02 - 06/25 \ **DTBP:** $168 (High)

Joseph Kardash 1   Megan Heimroth 2,19
Charles Thomas .... 3*   Theresa Hopper 4*
Rhonda Greenway 5   William Stath 6*
Colleen Multer .... 27,58,76*   Brandy Cenci 36*
Brendan Dilello 37   John Mooney 67
David Howell .... 73*   Heather Staszak 90*
Tracy Foust 97   Justin Darling 295

Public Schs..Principal	Grd	Prgm	Enr/#Cls	SN	
Rensselaer Jr Sr High Sch 25 Van Rensselaer Dr, Rensselaer 12144 Dom Pitaniello	7-12	AT	445 40		518/436-8561 Fax 518/436-8563
Van Rensselaer Elem Sch 25 Van Rensselaer Dr, Rensselaer 12144 Jeff Palmer	PK-6	T	615 35		518/436-4618 Fax 518/436-4692

• **Schodack Central School Dist** PID: 00767052 518/732-2297
1477 S Schodack Rd, Castleton 12033 Fax 518/732-2418

Schools: 2 \ **Teachers:** 78 \ **Students:** 900 \ **Special Ed Students:** 173 \ **LEP Students:** 4 \ **College-Bound:** 80% \ **Ethnic:** Asian 1%, African American 1%, Hispanic 4%, Caucasian 95% \ **Exp:** $247 (Med) \ **Poverty:** 4% \ **Title I:** $41,421 \ **Special Education:** $1,883,000 \ **Open-Close:** 09/10 - 06/25 \ **DTBP:** $160 (High) \

Jason Chevrier 1   Brian Carey 2
Matt LaClair .... 3,91*   Tom McNay 4
Rhonda Greenway 5   Michael Bennett 8,11,57,58,77,280,288,296
Lisa Smith Auer 30   Michael Tuttle 67
Brian Radbwitz 71   Jim Yox 73,76,295*

Public Schs..Principal	Grd	Prgm	Enr/#Cls	SN	
Castleton Elem Sch 1477 S Schodack Rd, Castleton 12033 James Derby	K-6		505 31	21%	518/732-7755 Fax 518/732-0495
Maple Hill Jr Sr High Sch 1216 Maple Hill Rd, Castleton 12033 Jacqueline Hill	7-12	GV	395 40	21%	518/732-7701 Fax 518/732-0494

• **Troy City School Dsitrict** PID: 00767090 518/328-5052
475 1st St, Troy 12180 Fax 518/271-5229

Schools: 7 \ **Teachers:** 346 \ **Students:** 4,090 \ **Special Ed Students:** 918 \ **LEP Students:** 123 \ **College-Bound:** 83% \ **Ethnic:** Asian 1%, African American 34%, Hispanic 19%, Caucasian 45% \ **Exp:** $365 (High) \
Poverty: 27% \ **Title I:** $2,390,693 \ **Special Education:** $13,737,000 \
Open-Close: 09/09 - 06/25 \ **DTBP:** $223 (High) \

John Carmello 1   Adam Hotaling 2,15
Samantha Schweizer 2   Bob Garland 3,91
Mario Loccisano 5   Paul Reinisch 6,7,35,78*
Dr Donna Watson 8,15,288   Julianna Currey 11,296,298
James Canfield 36,88   Donna Fitzgerald 58,79
Thomas Mayo 67   Kristen Miaski 68
Erin Sheevers .... 73,285,286*   Barbara Paulsen 76
Jennifer DeMarco .... 275*   Jennifer DeMarco 275

Public Schs..Principal	Grd	Prgm	Enr/#Cls	SN	
Carroll Hill Elem Sch 112 Delaware Ave, Troy 12180 Roy Stiles	K-5	T	393 22	85%	518/328-5701 Fax 518/274-4587
PS 2 470 10th St, Troy 12180 Natelege Turner-Hassell	K-5	T	298	95%	518/328-5410 Fax 518/271-5205
PS 14 1700 Tibbits Ave, Troy 12180 Karen Cloutier	PK-5	T	533 8	82%	518/328-5801 Fax 518/274-0371
PS 16 40 Collins Ave, Troy 12180 Tracy Ford	K-5	T	286 16	64%	518/328-5101 Fax 518/274-4585
PS 18 412 Hoosick St, Troy 12180 Virginia MacPhee	K-5	T	322 16	51%	518/328-5501 Fax 518/274-4374
Troy High Sch 1950 Burdett Ave, Troy 12180 Joseph Mariano	9-12	GV	1,150 80	72%	518/328-5401 Fax 518/274-2341
Troy Middle Sch 1976 Burdett Ave, Troy 12180 Ian McShane	6-8	TV	891 50	83%	518/328-5301 Fax 518/271-8160

• **Wynantskill Union Free SD** PID: 00767234 518/283-4679
25 East Ave, Troy 12180 Fax 518/283-3799

Schools: 1 \ **Teachers:** 32 \ **Students:** 400 \ **Special Ed Students:** 64 \ **LEP Students:** 5 \ **Ethnic:** Asian 3%, African American 2%, Hispanic 2%, Caucasian 94% \ **Exp:** $293 (Med) \ **Poverty:** 8% \ **Title I:** $54,535 \
Special Education: $662,000 \ **Open-Close:** 09/08 - 06/24 \ **DTBP:** $174 (High)

Andy Deguire .... 3*   Lori Audi 4*
James Goyer 5   Daniel Disotto 6*

---

79 Student Personnel
80 Driver Ed/Safety
81 Gifted/Talented
82 Video Services
83 Substance Abuse Prev
84 Erate
85 AIDS Education
88 Alternative/At Risk
89 Multi-Cultural Curriculum
90 Social Work

91 Safety/Security
92 Magnet School
93 Parental Involvement
95 Tech Prep Program
97 Chief Infomation Officer
98 Chief Technology Officer
270 Character Education
271 Migrant Education
273 Teacher Mentor
274 Before/After Sch

275 Response To Intervention
277 Remedial Math K-12
280 Literacy Coach
285 STEM
286 Digital Learning
288 Common Core Standards
294 Accountability
295 Network System
296 Title II Programs
297 Webmaster

298 Grant Writer/Ptnrships
750 Chief Innovation Officer
751 Chief of Staff
752 Social Emotional Learning

School Programs
A = Alternative Program
G = Adult Classes
M = Magnet Program
T = Title I Schoolwide
V = Career & Tech Ed Programs

Other School Types
Ⓐ = Alternative School
Ⓒ = Charter School
Ⓜ = Magnet School
Ⓨ = Year-Round School

Social Media
🄵 = Facebook
🆃 = Twitter

New Schools are shaded
New Superintendents and Principals are bold
Personnel with email addresses are underscored

NY—191

Richmond County

Market Data Retrieval

Mary Yodis 9,71,88,270,273*
Rebecca Davis 59
Mathew Lutz 73*
Linda Fecura 16*
Andrew Lanesey 67
Amy Murphy 83*

Public Schs..Principal	Grd	Prgm	Enr/#Cls	SN	
Gardner Dickinson Elem Sch 25 East Ave, Troy 12180 Mary Yodis	PK-8	T	400 20	24%	518/283-4600 Fax 518/283-3684

RENSSELAER CATHOLIC SCHOOLS

- **Diocese of Albany Ed Office** PID: 00715059
  Listing includes only schools located in this county. See District Index for location of Diocesan Offices.

Catholic Schs..Principal	Grd	Prgm	Enr/#Cls	SN	
Catholic Central High Sch 625 7th Ave, Troy 12182 Christopher Signor	7-12		465 50		518/235-7100 Fax 518/237-1796
Holy Spirit Sch 54 Highland Dr, E Greenbush 12061 Michael Kosar	PK-8		206 10		518/477-5739 Fax 518/477-5743
Sacred Heart Sch 308 Spring Ave, Troy 12180 Amanda Goyer	PK-6		204 10		518/274-3655 Fax 518/274-8720
St Jude the Apostle Sch 42 Dana Ave, Wynantskill 12198 Danielle Cox	PK-6		266 10		518/283-0333 Fax 518/283-0475

RENSSELAER PRIVATE SCHOOLS

Private Schs..Principal	Grd	Prgm	Enr/#Cls	SN	
Doane Stuart Sch 199 Washington Ave, Rensselaer 12144 Sandy Cassant \ Seamus Hodgkinson \ James Wheaton	PK-12		252 21		518/465-5222 Fax 518/465-5230
Emma Willard Sch 285 Pawling Ave, Troy 12180 Jenny Rao	9-12		356 45		518/833-1300 Fax 518/833-1815
Hoosac Sch Pine Valley Road, Hoosick 12089 Dean Foster	8-12		120 15		518/686-7331 Fax 518/686-3370
La Salle Institute 174 Williams Rd, Troy 12180 Joseph Raczkowski	6-12		395 35		518/283-2500 Fax 518/283-6265
Oakwood Christian Sch 260 Oakwood Ave, Troy 12182 Sharyn Hine	PK-10		100 20		518/271-0526 Fax 518/270-1659
Redemption Christian Academy 192 9th St, Troy 12180 Joan Massey	PK-12		110 9		518/272-6679 Fax 518/270-8039
Robert C Parker Sch 4254 NY Route 43, Wynantskill 12198 Laura Graceffa	PK-8		105 12		518/286-3449 Fax 518/286-3452
Susan Odell Taylor Sch 116 Pinewoods Ave, Troy 12180 Kelly Magoolaghan	PK-8		100		518/274-4994 Fax 518/266-1343
Unity Sunshine Sch 435 4th St, Troy 12180 Suzanne Rimkunas	Spec		200 11		518/271-6777 Fax 518/274-5438
Vanderheyden Hall Sch Route 355, Wynantskill 12198 Frank Dembo	Spec		80		518/283-6500 Fax 518/283-3013

Woodland Hill Montessori Sch 100 Montessori Pl, Rensselaer 12144 Susan Kambrich	PK-8	260		518/283-5400 Fax 518/283-4861

RENSSELAER REGIONAL CENTERS

- **Questar III BOCES** PID: 00767260   518/477-8771
  10 Empire State Blvd, Castleton 12033   Fax 518/477-9833

Dr Gladys Cruz 1
Kenneth Ziobrowski 2
Kerri Burch 16
James Church 27,31,70
Kimberly Rockenstyre 58
Michael Buono 68
Jeffrey Baker 71,97
Jake Stomieroski 88
Charalambos Hadjioannou 2,15
Craig Hansen 3,7,91
Diane Bolton-Wales 27
Chris Foster 30
John Hill 67
Daniel Sherman 71
Chad Goodfellow 73,76

RICHMOND COUNTY

RICHMOND PUBLIC SCHOOLS

- **Community School District 31** PID: 10909917   718/420-5667
  715 Ocean Ter Bldg A, Staten Island 10301

  (Part of New York City Dept of Ed in New York County)
  Vincenza Gallassio 1

Public Schs..Principal	Grd	Prgm	Enr/#Cls	SN	
Ⓐ Concord High Sch 109 Rhine Ave, Staten Island 10304 Christopher Anzalone	9-12	TV	166 10	77%	718/447-1274 Fax 718/442-6276
CSI HS-International Studies 100 Essex Dr, Staten Island 10314 Joseph Canale	9-12		490	48%	718/370-6900 Fax 718/370-6915
Curtis High Sch 105 Hamilton Ave, Staten Island 10301 Greg Jaenicke	9-12	TV	2,604	74%	718/390-1800 Fax 718/556-4800
Eagle Acad Young Men-Staten IS 101 Warren St, Staten Island 10304 Jermaine Cameron	6-11	T	310	79%	718/727-6201 Fax 718/727-6207
IS 002 George L Egbert 333 Midland Ave, Staten Island 10306 Adrienne Stallone	6-8	TV	1,054	69%	718/987-5336 Fax 718/987-6937
IS 7 Elias Bernstein 1270 Huguenot Ave, Staten Island 10312 Nora Karby	6-8	V	1,180	37%	718/697-8488 Fax 718/967-0809
IS 24 Myra S Barnes 750 Durant Ave, Staten Island 10308 Leonard Santamaria	6-8	V	1,359 48	45%	718/982-4700 Fax 718/356-5834
IS 27 Anning S Prall 11 Clove Lake Pl, Staten Island 10310 Matthew Barone	6-8	TV	1,066	73%	718/981-8800 Fax 718/815-4677
IS 34 Tottenville 528 Academy Ave, Staten Island 10307 John Boyle	6-8	V	1,038 120	38%	718/477-4500 Fax 718/227-4074
IS 49 Berta A Dreyfus 101 Warren St, Staten Island 10304 James De Francesco	6-8	TV	558 50	90%	718/727-6040 Fax 718/876-8207

1	Superintendent	8	Curric/Instruct K-12	19	Chief Financial Officer	29	Family/Consumer Science
2	Bus/Finance/Purchasing	9	Curric/Instruct Elem	20	Art K-12	30	Adult Education
3	Buildings And Grounds	10	Curric/Instruct Sec	21	Art Elem	31	Career/Sch-to-Work K-12
4	Food Service	11	Federal Program	22	Art Sec	32	Career/Sch-to-Work Elem
5	Transportation	12	Title I	23	Music K-12	33	Career/Sch-to-Work Sec
6	Athletic	13	Title V	24	Music Elem	34	Early Childhood Ed
7	Health Services	15	Asst Superintendent	25	Music Sec	35	Health/Phys Education
		16	Instructional Media Svcs	26	Business Education	36	Guidance Services K-12
		17	Chief Operations Officer	27	Career & Tech Ed	37	Guidance Services Elem
		18	Chief Academic Officer	28	Technology Education	38	Guidance Services Sec

39	Social Studies K-12	49	English/Lang Arts Elem	59	Special Education Elem	69	Academic Assessment
40	Social Studies Elem	50	English/Lang Arts Sec	60	Special Education Sec	70	Research/Development
41	Social Studies Sec	51	Reading K-12	61	Foreign/World Lang K-12	71	Public Information
42	Science K-12	52	Reading Elem	62	Foreign/World Lang Elem	72	Summer School
43	Science Elem	53	Reading Sec	63	Foreign/World Lang Sec	73	Instructional Tech
44	Science Sec	54	Remedial Reading K-12	64	Religious Education K-12	74	Inservice Training
45	Math K-12	55	Remedial Reading Elem	65	Religious Education Elem	75	Marketing/Distributive
46	Math Elem	56	Remedial Reading Sec	66	Religious Education Sec	76	Info Systems
47	Math Sec	57	Bilingual/ELL	67	School Board President	77	Psychological Assess
48	English/Lang Arts K-12	58	Special Education K-12	68	Teacher Personnel	78	Affirmative Action

New York School Directory — Richmond County

School	Grades	Programs	Enroll	%	Phone
IS 51 Edwin Markham 80 Willowbrook Rd, Staten Island 10302 Nicholas Mele	6-8	T,V	1,311	78%	718/981-0502 Fax 718/815-3957
Ⓜ IS 61 William A Morris 445 Castleton Ave, Staten Island 10301 Susan Tronolone	6-8	T,V	973 45	78%	718/727-8481 Fax 718/447-2112
IS 72 Rocco Laurie 33 Ferndale Ave, Staten Island 10314 Jessica Jackson	6-8	T,V	1,578 100	63%	718/698-5757 Fax 718/761-5928
IS 75 Frank D Paulo 455 Huguenot Ave, Staten Island 10312 Kenneth Zapata	6-8	V	1,445 80	41%	718/701-6343 Fax 718/701-6351
Marsh Ave Sch Expditionry Lrng 100 Essex Dr, Staten Island 10314 Cara De Angelo	6-8		453	46%	718/370-6850 Fax 718/370-6860
McCown Expeditionary Lrng Sch 100 Essex Dr, Staten Island 10314 Maggie Tang	9-12		424 30	43%	718/370-6950 Fax 718/370-6960
Michael J Petrides Sch 715 Ocean Ter, Staten Island 10301 Joanne Buckheit	PK-12		1,327	44%	718/815-0186 Fax 718/815-9638
New Dorp High Sch 465 New Dorp Ln, Staten Island 10306 Deirdre DeAngelis	9-12	T,V	3,113	62%	718/667-8686 Fax 718/987-4889
Port Richmond High Sch 85 Saint Josephs Ave, Staten Island 10302 Andrew Greenfield	9-12	T,V	1,545	76%	718/420-2100 Fax 718/981-6203
PS 1 Tottenville 58 Summit St, Staten Island 10307 Graziella Pietrangelo	PK-5		435 24	40%	718/984-0960 Fax 718/984-3389
PS 3 Margaret Gioiosa Sch 80 S Goff Ave, Staten Island 10309 Elmer Myers	PK-5		667 30	33%	718/984-1021 Fax 718/984-3628
PS 4 Maurice Wollin 200 Nedra Pl, Staten Island 10312 Suzanne Dimitri	PK-5		743 50	38%	718/984-1197 Fax 718/984-2324
PS 5 Huguenot 348 Deisius St, Staten Island 10312 Lisa Arcuri	K-5		316 12	22%	718/668-3270 Fax 718/984-4761
PS 6 Cpl Allan F Kivlehan Sch 555 Page Ave, Staten Island 10307 Elizabeth Waters	PK-5		527	41%	718/697-3760 Fax 718/697-3761
PS 8 Shirlee Solomon 112 Lindenwood Rd, Staten Island 10308 Lisa Esposito	PK-5		586 43	36%	718/356-2800 Fax 718/356-2065
PS 9 Naples St Elem Sch 1055 Targee St, Staten Island 10304 Deanna Marco	PK-5		318	37%	718/876-4610 Fax 718/876-4611
PS 10 Ft Hill Collaborative ES 195 Daniel Low Ter, Staten Island 10301 Jennifer Funes	K-4	T	183	94%	718/420-5115 Fax 718/420-5118
PS 11 Thomas Dongan 51 Jefferson St, Staten Island 10304 Erica Mattera	PK-5	T	320 25	77%	718/979-1030 Fax 718/979-0259
PS 13 M L Lindemeyer 191 Vermont Ave, Staten Island 10305 Paul Martuccio	PK-5	T	860 25	71%	718/447-1462 Fax 718/447-8681
PS 16 John J Driscoll 195 Daniel Low Ter, Staten Island 10301 Michele Ramos	PK-5	T	437 35	98%	718/447-0124 Fax 718/447-5398
PS 18 John G Whittier 221 Broadway, Staten Island 10310 Robert Rodriguez	PK-5	T	462 45	91%	718/442-0216 Fax 718/720-1558
PS 19 the Curtis Sch 780 Post Ave, Staten Island 10310 Lynette Cartagena	PK-5	T	559 27	85%	718/442-3860 Fax 718/815-2862
PS 20 Port Richmond 161 Park Ave, Staten Island 10302 Marie Munoz	K-5	T	423	94%	718/442-4110 Fax 718/815-2228
PS 21 Margaret Emery Elm Park 168 Hooker Pl, Staten Island 10302 Anthony Cosentino	PK-5	T	387 20	84%	718/816-3300 Fax 718/816-3305
PS 22 Graniteville 1860 Forest Ave, Staten Island 10303 Melissa Donath	PK-5	T	926	86%	718/442-2219 Fax 718/815-3104
PS 23 Richmondtown 30 Natick St, Staten Island 10306 Paul Proscia	PK-5		568 29	35%	718/351-1155 Fax 718/667-4958
PS 26 Carteret Sch 4108 Victory Blvd, Staten Island 10314 Laura Kump	PK-5		292 10	45%	718/698-1530 Fax 718/494-2907
PS 29 Bardwell 1581 Victory Blvd, Staten Island 10314 Linda Manfredi	PK-5		634	53%	718/556-4400 Fax 718/556-4429
PS 30 Westerleigh 200 Wardwell Ave, Staten Island 10314 Alan Ihne	PK-5		814	38%	718/442-0462 Fax 718/442-4265
PS 31 William T Davis 55 Layton Ave, Staten Island 10301 Daniel Singleton	PK-5	T	392	92%	718/273-3500 Fax 718/815-4826
PS 32 Gifford Sch 232 Barlow Ave, Staten Island 10308 Nancy Spataro	PK-5		663 50	34%	718/984-1688 Fax 718/227-5736
PS 35 Clove Valley 60 Foote Ave, Staten Island 10301 Melissa Garofalo	K-5		424 16	36%	718/442-3037
PS 36 J C Drumgoole 255 Ionia Ave, Staten Island 10312 Barbara Bellafatto	PK-5		882 45	37%	718/984-1422 Fax 718/227-6354
PS 38 George Cromwell 421 Lincoln Ave, Staten Island 10306 Nancy Murillo	PK-5	T	387 20	69%	718/351-1225 Fax 718/979-2487
PS 39 Francis J Murphy Jr 99 MacFarland Ave, Staten Island 10305 Tracey Wright	K-5	T	518 19	63%	718/447-4543 Fax 718/447-0500
PS 41 Stephanie A Vierno Sch 216 Clawson St, Staten Island 10306 Jennifer Logan	PK-5		695	65%	718/351-6777 Fax 718/667-8200
PS 42 Eltingville 380 Genesee Ave, Staten Island 10312 Brian Sharkey	PK-5		1,081	32%	718/984-3800 Fax 718/227-6358
PS 44 Thomas C Brown 80 Maple Pkwy, Staten Island 10303 Kasandra Lopez-Garcia	PK-5		686 40	94%	718/442-0433 Fax 718/442-2323
PS 45 John Tyler 58 Lawrence Ave, Staten Island 10310 Christine Chavez	PK-5		842 49	70%	718/442-6123
PS 46 Albert V Maniscalco 41 Reid Ave, Staten Island 10305 Andrea Maffeo	PK-5		254 25	85%	718/987-5155 Fax 718/987-1703
PS 48 William C Wilcox 1050 Targee St, Staten Island 10304 Allison Odonnell	PK-8		1,001 20	44%	718/447-8323
PS 50 Frank Hankinson 200 Adelaide Ave, Staten Island 10306 Joseph Santello	PK-5		707 36	50%	718/987-0396 Fax 718/987-1925
PS 52 John C Thompson 450 Buel Ave, Staten Island 10305 Jane McCord	PK-5	T	587 32	62%	718/351-5454 Fax 718/667-8900
PS 53 Barbara Esselborn Sch 330 Durant Ave, Staten Island 10308 Beth Albano	PK-5		847 34	37%	718/987-8020 Fax 718/987-3675

Legend:

#	Category	#	Category	#	Category	#	Category
79	Student Personnel	91	Safety/Security	275	Response To Intervention	298	Grant Writer/Ptnrships
80	Driver Ed/Safety	92	Magnet School	277	Remedial Math K-12	750	Chief Innovation Officer
81	Gifted/Talented	93	Parental Involvement	280	Literacy Coach	751	Chief of Staff
82	Video Services	95	Tech Prep Program	285	STEM	752	Social Emotional Learning
83	Substance Abuse Prev	97	Chief Infomation Officer	286	Digital Learning		
84	Erate	98	Chief Technology Officer	288	Common Core Standards		
85	AIDS Education	270	Character Education	294	Accountability		
88	Alternative/At Risk	271	Migrant Education	295	Network System		
89	Multi-Cultural Curriculum	273	Teacher Mentor	296	Title II Programs		
90	Social Work	274	Before/After Sch	297	Webmaster		

School Programs
- A = Alternative Program
- G = Adult Classes
- M = Magnet Program
- T = Title I Schoolwide
- V = Career & Tech Ed Programs

Other School Types
- Ⓐ = Alternative School
- Ⓒ = Charter School
- Ⓜ = Magnet School
- Ⓨ = Year-Round School

Social Media
- 🅵 = Facebook
- 🆃 = Twitter

New Schools are shaded
New Superintendents and Principals are bold
Personnel with email addresses are underscored

Richmond County

School	Grd	Prgm	Enr/#Cls	%	Phone
PS 54 Charles W Leng 1060 Willowbrook Rd, Staten Island 10314 Karen Catanzaro	PK-5		821 35	62%	718/698-0600 Fax 718/698-1736
PS 55 Henry M Boehm 54 Osborne St, Staten Island 10312 Sharon Fishman	PK-5		580 35	34%	718/697-5200 Fax 718/356-0114
PS 56 Louis DeSario Sch 250 Kramer Ave, Staten Island 10309 Philip Carollo	PK-5		596	31%	718/605-1189 Fax 718/605-1195
PS 57 Hubert H Humphrey 140 Palma Dr, Staten Island 10304 Karyn Polanco	PK-5	T	653 41	88%	718/447-1191 Fax 718/720-0747
PS 59 Harbor View Sch 300 Richmond Ter, Staten Island 10301 Carol Mongiello	PK-5	T	300	60%	718/390-2190 Fax 718/390-2195
PS 60 Alice Austen 55 Merrill Ave, Staten Island 10314 Donna Dinaso	PK-5		795 45	59%	718/761-3325 Fax 718/983-8534
PS 62 Kathleen Grimm 644 Bloomingdale Rd, Staten Island 10309 Lisa Sarnicola	PK-3		281	28%	718/668-8640 Fax 718/668-8645
PS 65 Academy-Innovative Lrng 155 St Pauls Ave, Staten Island 10301 Sophie Scamardella	PK-5	T	425	64%	718/981-5034
PS 68 Port Richmond Vis Lrng 1625 Forest Ave, Staten Island 10302 Lorrie Brown	PK-2	T	235	78%	718/816-3377 Fax 718/816-3378
PS 69 Daniel D Tompkins 144 Keating Pl, Staten Island 10314 Doreen Murphy	PK-5		894 44	58%	718/698-6661 Fax 718/698-1903
PS 74 Future Leaders ES 211 Daniel Low Ter, Staten Island 10301 Hanin Hasweh	PK-5	T	280	88%	718/727-5380 Fax 718/727-5386
PS 78 100 Tompkins Ave, Staten Island 10304 Jodi Contento	PK-5	T	716	96%	718/442-3094 Fax 718/442-3904
Ralph McKee Career & Tech HS 290 Saint Marks Pl, Staten Island 10301 Sharon Henry	Voc	GT	840 40	70%	718/420-2600 Fax 718/981-8776
Richmond Pre K Ctr Forest Ave 1625 Forest Ave, Staten Island 10302 Edele Williams	PK-PK		50		718/816-3370
Richmond Pre K Ctr Stuyvesant 120 Stuyvesant Pl, Staten Island 10301 Edele Williams	PK-PK		50		718/816-3340
Richmond Pre K Ctr Teleport Dr 1 Teleport Dr, Staten Island 10311 Edele Williams	PK-PK		144		718/477-8980
Space Shuttle Columbia Sch 77 Marsh Ave, Staten Island 10314 Michael La Morte	PK-5		684	52%	718/761-2155 Fax 718/761-7384
Staten Island Sch-Civic Ldrshp 280 Regis Dr, Staten Island 10314 Donna Nilsen	PK-8	T	865	72%	718/697-5250 Fax 718/697-5260
Staten Island Technical HS 485 Clawson St, Staten Island 10306 Mark Erlenwein	9-12	V	1,334	42%	718/667-3222 Fax 718/987-5872
Susan E Wagner High Sch 1200 Manor Rd, Staten Island 10314 David Cugini	9-12	V	3,436	55%	718/698-4200 Fax 718/698-5213
Tottenville High Sch 100 Luten Ave, Staten Island 10312 Jospeh Scarmato	9-12	V	3,697	34%	718/668-8800 Fax 718/317-0962
Ⓐ Tottenville YABC 100 Luten Ave, Staten Island 10312 Michael Noto	10-12		250		718/668-8800

- **District 75 City Wide Programs** PID: 00740626
  (Part of New York City Dept of Ed in New York County)

Public Schs..Principal	Grd	Prgm	Enr/#Cls	SN	Phone
ⓨ IS/PS 25-S Richmond HS 6581 Hylan Blvd, Staten Island 10309 James McKeon	Spec	M	580 48	82%	718/984-1526 Fax 718/356-8905
ⓨ PS R037 Marquis Sch of Arts 15 Fairfield St, Staten Island 10308 Deborah Evans	Spec	M	390 40	78%	718/984-9800 Fax 718/356-8712
ⓨ PS R373 91 Henderson Ave, Staten Island 10301 Paulette Benevento	Spec	M	592 29	80%	718/816-8897 Fax 718/727-6867
ⓨ Richard H Hungerford Sch 155 Tompkins Ave, Staten Island 10304 Kristin McHugh	Spec	M	445 25	91%	718/273-8622 Fax 718/727-6994

- **New York Alt High Sch SD 79** PID: 00740626
  (Part of New York City Dept of Ed in New York County)

Public Schs..Principal	Grd	Prgm	Enr/#Cls	SN	Phone
Ⓐ Passages Acad-Staten Island 1133 Forest Hill Rd, Staten Island 10314 Chrystal Stewart	9-12		401		718/304-2037

RICHMOND CATHOLIC SCHOOLS

- **Archdiocese of New York Ed Off** PID: 00754976
  Listing includes only schools located in this county. See District Index for location of Diocesan Offices.

Catholic Schs..Principal	Grd	Prgm	Enr/#Cls	SN	Phone
Academy of St Dorothy 1305 Hylan Blvd, Staten Island 10305 Sr Sharon McCarthy	PK-8		326 10		718/351-0939 Fax 718/351-0661
Blessed Sacrament Sch 830 Delafield Ave, Staten Island 10310 Joseph Cocozello	PK-8		678 20		718/442-3090 Fax 718/442-9654
FR Vincent Capodanno Cath Acad 100 Jerome Ave, Staten Island 10305 Diane Hesterhagen	PK-8		275 12		718/447-1195 Fax 718/815-5862
Monsignor Farrell High Sch 2900 Amboy Rd, Staten Island 10306 Lawrence Musanti	9-12		900 50		718/987-2900 Fax 718/987-4241
Moore Catholic High Sch 100 Merrill Ave, Staten Island 10314 Gina DeSantis	9-12		1,000 30		718/761-9200 Fax 718/370-4148
Notre Dame Academy High Sch 134 Howard Ave, Staten Island 10301 Jann Amato	9-12		472 16		718/447-8878 Fax 718/447-2926
Notre Dame Elem Academy 78 Howard Ave, Staten Island 10301 Rebecca Giaccio	PK-8		200 12		718/273-9096 Fax 718/273-1093
Our Lady of Good Counsel Sch 42 Austin Pl, Staten Island 10304 Tara Hynes	PK-8		325 10		718/447-7260 Fax 718/447-8639
Our Lady Queen of Peace Sch 22 Steele Ave, Staten Island 10306 Margaret O'Connor	PK-8		500 20		718/351-0370 Fax 718/351-0950
Our Lady Star of the Sea Sch 5411 Amboy Rd, Staten Island 10312 Jeannine Roland	PK-8		795 20		718/984-5750 Fax 718/948-1346

#		#		#		#		#		#		#	
1	Superintendent	8	Curric/Instruct K-12	19	Chief Financial Officer	29	Family/Consumer Science	39	Social Studies K-12	49	English/Lang Arts Elem	59	Special Education Elem	69	Academic Assessment
2	Bus/Finance/Purchasing	9	Curric/Instruct Elem	20	Art K-12	30	Adult Education	40	Social Studies Elem	50	English/Lang Arts Sec	60	Special Education Sec	70	Research/Development
3	Buildings And Grounds	10	Curric/Instruct Sec	21	Art Elem	31	Career/Sch-to-Work K-12	41	Social Studies Sec	51	Reading K-12	61	Foreign/World Lang K-12	71	Public Information
4	Food Service	11	Federal Program	22	Art Sec	32	Career/Sch-to-Work Elem	42	Science K-12	52	Reading Elem	62	Foreign/World Lang Elem	72	Summer School
5	Transportation	12	Title I	23	Music K-12	33	Career/Sch-to-Work Sec	43	Science Elem	53	Reading Sec	63	Foreign/World Lang Sec	73	Instructional Tech
6	Athletic	13	Title V	24	Music Elem	34	Early Childhood Ed	44	Science Sec	54	Remedial Reading K-12	64	Religious Education K-12	74	Inservice Training
7	Health Services	14	Asst Superintendent	25	Music Sec	35	Health/Phys Education	45	Math K-12	55	Remedial Reading Elem	65	Religious Education Elem	75	Marketing/Distributive
		15	Instructional Media Svcs	26	Business Education	36	Guidance Services K-12	46	Math Elem	56	Remedial Reading Sec	66	Religious Education Sec	76	Info Systems
		16	Chief Operations Officer	27	Career & Tech Ed	37	Guidance Services Elem	47	Math Sec	57	Bilingual/ELL	67	School Board President	77	Psychological Assess
		17	Chief Academic Officer	28	Technology Education	38	Guidance Services Sec	48	English/Lang Arts K-12	58	Special Education K-12	68	Teacher Personnel	78	Affirmative Action

New York School Directory

Rockland County

School	Grd		Enr/#Cls	Phone
Sacred Heart Elem Sch 301 N Burgher Ave, Staten Island 10310 Celeste Catalano	PK-8		250 18	718/442-0347 Fax 718/442-6978
St Ann Sch 125 Cromwell Ave, Staten Island 10304 Bernadette Ficchi	K-8		250 10	718/351-4343 Fax 718/987-3117
St Charles Sch 200 Penn Ave, Staten Island 10306 Jc Kiernan	PK-8		688 20	718/987-0200 Fax 718/987-8158
St Christopher Parochial Sch 15 Lisbon Pl, Staten Island 10306 Catherine Falabella	PK-8		305 10	718/351-0902 Fax 718/351-0975 f
St Clare Sch 151 Lindenwood Rd, Staten Island 10308 Theresa Signorile	PK-8		645 21	718/984-7091 Fax 718/227-5052
St Joseph by the Sea High Sch 5150 Hylan Blvd, Staten Island 10312 Michael Reilly	9-12		1,200 50	718/984-6500 Fax 718/984-6503
St Joseph Hill Academy ES 850 Hylan Blvd, Staten Island 10305 Lawrence Hansen	PK-8		512 23	718/981-1187 Fax 718/448-7016
St Joseph Hill Academy HS 850 Hylan Blvd, Staten Island 10305 Maria Molluzzo	9-12		422 19	718/447-1374 Fax 718/447-3041
St Patrick School-Richmond 3560 Richmond Rd, Staten Island 10306 Vincent Sadowski	PK-8		400	718/979-8815 Fax 718/979-4984
St Peter's High Sch for Boys 200 Clinton Ave, Staten Island 10301 Michael Cosentino	9-12		600 34	718/447-1676 Fax 718/447-4027
St Teresa St Rita Stream Acad 1632 Victory Blvd, Staten Island 10314 Nicole Fresca	PK-8		240 18	718/448-9650 Fax 718/447-6426

RICHMOND PRIVATE SCHOOLS

Private Schs..Principal	Grd	Prgm	Enr/#Cls SN	
Building Blocks Montessori Sch 55 Forest Ave, Staten Island 10301 Slivana Frasier	PK-5		75 5	718/448-2992 Fax 718/448-2882
Eden II Sch-Autistic Chldrn 15 Beach St, Staten Island 10304 Jamie Arnold	Spec	G	68 13	718/816-1422 Fax 718/816-1428
Eltingville Lutheran Sch 300 Genesee Ave, Staten Island 10312 Deborah Cortez	PK-8		75 9	718/356-7811 Fax 718/967-8892
Gateway Academy 200 Boscombe Ave, Staten Island 10309 Christopher DeSanctis	PK-8		120 10	718/966-8695 Fax 718/948-2241
Jewish Fndtn Sch-Staten Island 400 Caswell Ave, Staten Island 10314 Netanel Gralla	1-8		145 50	718/983-6042 f t
Miraj Islamic Sch 307 Victory Blvd, Staten Island 10301 Lamiaa Refaey	PK-12		270 14	718/816-9865 Fax 718/816-5829
New Dorp Christian Academy 259 Rose Ave, Staten Island 10306 Mark Rawnsley	PK-8		211 9	718/351-4442 Fax 718/351-1765
Rabbi Jacob Joseph School-Boys 4280 Amboy Rd, Staten Island 10308 Sharir Yavlonsky	PK-8		180 9	718/979-6333 Fax 718/979-5152
Rabbi Jacob Joseph-Girls 400 Caswell Ave, Staten Island 10314 Esther Ackerman	PK-8		250 9	718/982-8745 Fax 718/698-3024

School	Grd		Enr/#Cls	Phone
St John's Lutheran Sch 663 Manor Rd, Staten Island 10314 Mrs Speiser	PK-8		285 11	718/761-1858 Fax 718/761-4962
Staten Island Academy 715 Todt Hill Rd, Staten Island 10304 Lea Prendergast \ Eileen Corigliano \ Frank Crane	PK-12		340 40	718/987-8100 Fax 718/979-7641
Yeshiva of Staten Island 1870 Drumgoole Rd E, Staten Island 10309 Schlomo Eidelem	9-12	V	120 5	718/356-4323 Fax 718/356-5200

ROCKLAND COUNTY

ROCKLAND COUNTY SCHOOLS

County Schs..Principal	Grd	Prgm	Enr/#Cls SN	
Cbi Tech-Gateway 65 Parrott Rd, West Nyack 10994 Pamela Charles	Spec		80	845/624-5566 Fax 845/624-5699
Jessie J Kaplan Spec Sch 65 Parrott Rd Bldg 9, West Nyack 10994 Gianluca Dimuccio	Spec	V	260 20	845/627-4797 Fax 845/623-2730
Ⓐ Riverview High Sch 131 N Midland Ave, Nyack 10960 Joycer Mucci	9-12		110 8	845/348-3518 Fax 845/358-9224

ROCKLAND PUBLIC SCHOOLS

• **Clarkstown Central School Dist** PID: 00767301 845/639-6300
62 Old Middletown Rd, New City 10956 Fax 845/639-6488

Schools: 13 \ **Teachers:** 651 \ **Students:** 7,907 \ **Special Ed Students:** 1,455 \ **LEP Students:** 262 \ **Ethnic:** Asian 14%, African American 4%, Hispanic 20%, Caucasian 62% \ **Exp:** $366 (High) \ **Poverty:** 6% \ **Title I:** $797,576 \ **Special Education:** $9,035,000 \ **Open-Close:** 09/02 - 06/25 \ **DTBP:** $309 (High)

Martin Cox 1		Maureen Sullivan 2,91	
Anthony Valenti 3		Julian Febres 3	
Russell Carrasquillo 3		Robert Preiss 4	
Nicole Dolce 5		Dr Christopher Serra 6,35	
Susan Sherlock 7*		Dr Liz Vonwurmb 8,16,20,23	
Bill Malloy 11		David Carlson 15,58,79	
Sandra Condon 34		Tamara Bierker 67	
Neena Shaji 69		Richard Hernandez 73,286	
Marianna Dougherty 77		Teresa Carroll 84	
Matthew Schuchman 285*			

Public Schs..Principal	Grd	Prgm	Enr/#Cls SN	
Bardonia Elem Sch 31 Bardonia Rd, Bardonia 10954 Michelle Zernone	K-5		388 19	17% 845/639-6460 Fax 845/627-7633
Ⓐ Birchwood Sch 214 Sickletown Rd, West Nyack 10994 Jonathan Slaybaugh	K-12		88 11	31% 845/639-6480 Fax 845/353-9334
Clarkstown North High Sch 151 Congers Rd, New City 10956 Dr Harry Leonardatos	9-12	GV	1,275 100	18% 845/639-6501 Fax 845/639-9635

---

79 Student Personnel	91 Safety/Security	275 Response To Intervention	298 Grant Writer/Ptnrships
80 Driver Ed/Safety	92 Magnet School	277 Remedial Math K-12	750 Chief Innovation Officer
81 Gifted/Talented	93 Parental Involvement	280 Literacy Coach	751 Chief of Staff
82 Video Services	95 Tech Prep Program	285 STEM	752 Social Emotional Learning
83 Substance Abuse Prev	97 Chief Information Officer	286 Digital Learning	
84 Erate	98 Chief Technology Officer	288 Common Core Standards	Other School Types
85 AIDS Education	270 Character Education	294 Accountability	Ⓐ = Alternative School
88 Alternative/At Risk	271 Migrant Education	295 Network System	Ⓒ = Charter School
89 Multi-Cultural Curriculum	273 Teacher Mentor	296 Title II Programs	Ⓜ = Magnet School
90 Social Work	274 Before/After Sch	297 Webmaster	Ⓨ = Year-Round School

School Programs
A = Alternative Program
G = Adult Classes
M = Magnet Program
T = Title I Schoolwide
V = Career & Tech Ed Programs

Social Media
f = Facebook
t = Twitter

New Schools are shaded
New Superintendents and Principals are bold
Personnel with email addresses are underscored

NY—195

Rockland County

Market Data Retrieval

Clarkstown South High Sch 31 Demarest Mill Rd, West Nyack 10994 Debra Tarantino	9-12	V	1,334 100	13%	845/624-3410 Fax 845/623-5470
Felix Festa Middle Sch 30 Parrott Rd, West Nyack 10994 Jonathan Schatz	6-8		1,846 80	16%	845/624-3970 Fax 845/639-6388
Lakewood Elem Sch 77 Lakeland Ave, Congers 10920 Deborah Mariniello	K-5		409 30	24%	845/639-6320 Fax 845/268-5011
Laurel Plains Elem Sch 14 Teakwood Ln, New City 10956 Carol Pilla	K-5		344 18	13%	845/639-6350 Fax 845/639-4206
Link IB World Sch 51 Red Hill Rd, New City 10956 Francine Cuccia	K-5		368 20	11%	845/624-3494 Fax 845/638-1615
Little TOR Elem Sch 56 Gregory St, New City 10956 Matthew Younghans	K-5		297 15	9%	845/624-3471 Fax 845/638-0807
New City Elem Sch 60 Crestwood Dr, New City 10956 Debra Forman	K-5		403 35	12%	845/624-3467 Fax 845/638-0504
Strawtown Elem Sch 413 Strawtown Rd, West Nyack 10994 Mary Ryan	K-5		292 17	9%	845/624-3473 Fax 845/348-0118
West Nyack Elem Sch 661 W Nyack Rd, West Nyack 10994 Annie Streiff	K-5		342 15	19%	845/624-3474 Fax 845/348-0115
Woodglen Elem Sch 121 Phillips Hill Rd, New City 10956 Lisa Maher	K-5		435 24	21%	845/624-3417 Fax 845/639-6017

• **East Ramapo Central Sch Dist** PID: 00767911 845/577-6000
105 S Madison Ave, Spring Valley 10977   Fax 845/577-6038

Schools: 14 \ **Teachers:** 691 \ **Students:** 8,843 \ **Special Ed Students:** 2,820 \ **LEP Students:** 3,289 \ **College-Bound:** 94% \ **Ethnic:** Asian 4%, African American 30%, Hispanic 62%, Caucasian 4% \ **Exp:** $552 (High) \ **Poverty:** 38% \ **Title I:** $23,781,182 \ **Special Education:** $17,997,000 \ **Open-Close:** 09/09 - 06/25 \ **DTBP:** $313 (High)

Dr Deborah Wortham 1	Valter Paci 2,15	
Obi Ifedigbo 3,91	Carmella Cemaro 4	
Douglas Schwegler 5	Brad Gitlen 6,35*	
Christine Healy 7	Nateasha McVea 8,15	
Dr Daniel Shanahan 11,15,296,298	Alex Marrero 15	
Mary Sculnick 15,68	Ogechi Iwouha 15,74	
Tamar Walker 15,58	Michael Smith 20,23	
Melissa Barrow 57,61	Harry Grossman 67	
Gail Piscatelli 71,97	Azhar Ahmad 73,76,286	
Dr Dovid Berkowitz 77*		

Public Schs..Principal	Grd	Prgm	Enr/#Cls	SN	
Chestnut Ridge Middle Sch 892 Chestnut Ridge Rd, Chestnut RDG 10977 Holly Zuber-Banks	7-8	T	588	90%	845/577-6301 Fax 845/577-6333
East Ramapo Early Chldhd Ctr 465 Viola Rd, Spring Valley 10977 Jacqueline Fernandez	K-K	T	371	72%	845/577-6585
Eldorado Elem Sch 5 Eldorado Dr, Chestnut RDG 10977 Astrid Johnson	4-6	T	519 30	89%	845/577-6150 Fax 845/426-0850
Elmwood Elem Sch 43 Robert Pitt Dr, Monsey 10952 Ellen Andriello	K-6	T	553 17	91%	845/577-6160 Fax 845/426-0852
Fleetwood Elem Sch 22 Fleetwood Ave, Chestnut RDG 10977 Carolyn Fields	K-3	T	596 27	82%	845/577-6170 Fax 845/426-1807
Grandview Elem Sch 151 Grandview Ave, Monsey 10952 Patricia Smith	K-3	T	592 25	85%	845/577-6260 Fax 845/362-0646
Hempstead Elem Sch 80 Brick Church Rd, Spring Valley 10977 Hazel Ortiz	K-6	T	445	85%	845/577-6270 Fax 845/362-0627
Kakiat Steam Academy 465 Viola Rd, Spring Valley 10977 Jennifer Wilmoth	4-8	T	628	86%	845/577-6100 Fax 845/426-1059
Lime Kiln Elem Sch 35 Lime Kiln Rd, Suffern 10901 Laura Latronica	4-6	T	532	91%	845/577-6280 Fax 845/362-3570
Margetts Elem Sch 25 Margetts Rd, Monsey 10952 Barbara Knecht	K-3	T	577 26	84%	845/577-6190 Fax 845/426-0958
Pomona Middle Sch 101 Pomona Rd, Suffern 10901 **Angela Alexander**	7-8	T	573	89%	845/577-6200 Fax 845/577-6245
Ramapo High Sch 400 Viola Rd, Spring Valley 10977 Michael Phillips	9-12	AT	1,460	79%	845/577-6400 Fax 845/577-6567
Spring Valley High Sch 361 W Route 59, Spring Valley 10977 Karen Pinel	9-12	AT	1,347 45	84%	845/577-6500 Fax 845/577-6526
Summit Park Elem Sch 925 Route 45, New City 10956 Kim Hewlett	PK-5	T	600 29	81%	845/577-6290 Fax 845/362-0920

• **Nanuet Union Free School Dist** PID: 00767519 845/627-9880
101 Church St, Nanuet 10954   Fax 845/624-5338

Schools: 5 \ **Teachers:** 181 \ **Students:** 2,220 \ **Special Ed Students:** 298 \ **LEP Students:** 147 \ **College-Bound:** 95% \ **Ethnic:** Asian 16%, African American 7%, Hispanic 25%, Caucasian 52% \ **Exp:** $293 (Med) \ **Poverty:** 7% \ **Title I:** $239,955 \ **Special Education:** $1,981,000 \ **Open-Close:** 09/04 - 06/25 \ **DTBP:** $352 (High)

Kevin McCahill 1	Mario Spagnuolo 2,15
Rudy Villanyi 3,91	Mary Ann Gregor 4
Jill Russo 5	Frank Mazzuca 6,7,77*
Christoph Polizzi 9,70,285*	Meredith Fox 11,15,286,288,296,298
Ursula Carbone 16,71,73,76,97*	Melissa Lipson 37*
Jacqueline Laurenzano 38*	Judith Henaey 58,79
Amy Chiapperino 61*	Ann Byrne 67
Kathleen Maier 71	Alllison Kersh 83,88
Heather Grymes 273*	Rose Ann Mercado 274
Boces Boces 295	

Public Schs..Principal	Grd	Prgm	Enr/#Cls	SN	
A MacArthur Barr 5-6 Academy 143 Church St, Nanuet 10954 Anne Chen	5-6		340	25%	845/627-4040 Fax 845/624-3138
A MacArthur Barr Middle Sch 143 Church St, Nanuet 10954 Roger Guccione	7-8		391 70	23%	845/627-4040 Fax 845/624-3138
George W Miller Elem Sch 50 Blauvelt Rd, Nanuet 10954 Maryellen Griffin	K-2		427 34	25%	845/627-4860 Fax 845/624-1534
Highview Elem Sch 24 Highview Ave, Nanuet 10954 Nancy Bonner	3-4		311 16	26%	845/627-3460 Fax 845/627-0340
Nanuet High Sch 103 Church St, Nanuet 10954 Michael Mahoney	9-12	AGV	751 58	19%	845/627-9800 Fax 845/624-5520

1 Superintendent	8 Curric/Instruct K-12	19 Chief Financial Officer	29 Family/Consumer Science	39 Social Studies K-12	49 English/Lang Arts Elem	59 Special Education Elem	69 Academic Assessment
2 Bus/Finance/Purchasing	9 Curric/Instruct Elem	20 Art K-12	30 Adult Education	40 Social Studies Elem	50 English/Lang Arts Sec	60 Special Education Sec	70 Research/Development
3 Buildings And Grounds	10 Curric/Instruct Sec	21 Art Elem	31 Career/Sch-to-Work K-12	41 Social Studies Sec	51 Reading K-12	61 Foreign/World Lang K-12	71 Public Information
4 Food Service	11 Federal Program	22 Art Sec	32 Career/Sch-to-Work Elem	42 Science K-12	52 Reading Elem	62 Foreign/World Lang Elem	72 Summer School
5 Transportation	12 Title I	23 Music K-12	33 Career/Sch-to-Work Sec	43 Science Elem	53 Reading Sec	63 Foreign/World Lang Sec	73 Instructional Tech
6 Athletic	13 Title V	24 Music Elem	34 Early Childhood Ed	44 Science Sec	54 Remedial Reading K-12	64 Religious Education K-12	74 Inservice Training
7 Health Services	15 Asst Superintendent	25 Music Sec	35 Health/Phys Education	45 Math K-12	55 Remedial Reading Elem	65 Religious Education Elem	75 Marketing/Distributive
	16 Instructional Media Svcs	26 Business Education	36 Guidance Services K-12	46 Math Elem	56 Remedial Reading Sec	66 Religious Education Sec	76 Info Systems
	17 Chief Operations Officer	27 Career & Tech Ed	37 Guidance Services Elem	47 Math Sec	57 Bilingual/ELL	67 School Board President	77 Psychological Assess
	18 Chief Academic Officer	28 Technology Education	38 Guidance Services Sec	48 English/Lang Arts K-12	58 Special Education K-12	68 Teacher Personnel	78 Affirmative Action

New York School Directory

Rockland County

- **North Rockland Central SD** PID: 00767569   845/942-3000
  65 Chapel St, Garnerville 10923   Fax 845/942-3175

Schools: 8 \ Teachers: 548 \ Students: 8,000 \ Special Ed Students: 1,493 \ LEP Students: 1,077 \ College-Bound: 89% \ Ethnic: Asian 4%, African American 13%, Hispanic 59%, Caucasian 24% \ Exp: $364 (High) \ Poverty: 14% \ Title I: $1,918,784 \ Special Education: $14,359,000 \ Open-Close: 09/08 - 06/25 \ DTBP: $313 (High)

Name	Code
Dr Kris Felicello	1
Rooney Paul	3
Teresa Samuels	5,91
Kathy Varieur	7
Baird Eric	15,68
Laura Grant	16*
Taren Soto	58
Edward Hoffman	73*
Maltbie Edward	76
Senno Michael	2,15
Posillipo Raymond	4
Joe Casarella	6
Miguelina Lopez	9,11,57
Eric Baird	15,68
Lauren Dapenta	30
Richard Fernandez	67
Ed Maltbie	76

Public Schs..Principal	Grd	Prgm	Enr/#Cls	SN	Phone
Fieldstone Middle Sch 100 Fieldstone Dr, Thiells 10984 Anthony Zollo	7-8		1,323	51%	845/942-7900 Fax 845/942-7910
Haverstraw Elem Sch 16 Grant St, Haverstraw 10927 Benito Herrero	4-6	V	629 35	67%	845/942-3400 Fax 845/942-3403
James A Farley Elem Sch 140 Route 210, Stony Point 10980 Avis Shelby	4-6	V	569 35	44%	845/942-3200 Fax 845/942-3207
North Rockland High Sch 106 Hammond Rd, Thiells 10984 Dr Michael Gill	9-12	AGV	2,654	51%	845/942-3300 Fax 845/942-3365 t
Stony Point Elem Sch 7 Gurnee Dr, Stony Point 10980 Farid Johnson	K-3	T	607 27	48%	845/942-3140 Fax 845/942-3083
Thiells Elem Sch 78 Rosman Rd, Thiells 10984 Peter Dibernardi	K-3	T	739 40	53%	845/942-3160 Fax 845/429-4419
West Haverstraw Elem Sch 71 Blauvelt Ave, W Haverstraw 10993 Mary Esposito	K-3	T	780 55	63%	845/942-3181 Fax 845/942-3084
Willow Grove Elem Sch 153 Storrs Rd, Thiells 10984 Michael Roth	4-6	V	586 54	45%	845/942-8000 Fax 845/942-8009

- **Nyack Union Free School Dist** PID: 00767686   845/353-7000
  13A Dickinson Ave, Nyack 10960   Fax 845/353-7019

Schools: 5 \ Teachers: 260 \ Students: 3,000 \ Special Ed Students: 480 \ LEP Students: 233 \ College-Bound: 90% \ Ethnic: Asian 7%, African American 19%, Hispanic 28%, Caucasian 47% \ Exp: $439 (High) \ Poverty: 9% \ Title I: $472,476 \ Special Education: $3,015,000 \ Open-Close: 09/08 - 06/25 \ DTBP: $313 (High)

Name	Code
Dr James Monpesano	1,11
Kevin Heaton	3
Karen Sher	5
Dr Winsome Gregory	8,12,15,68,69,288
Lorraine Longing	36,752*
Leo Macias	58,79,91
Lisa Retallack	71
Dornzella Milligan	83*
Carol Mayewksi	2
Steve Wilson	4
Joseph Sigillo	6,7*
Gloria Menoutis	11
Audrey Cabbell	57
Michael Mark	67
Darlene Nicolosi	73,76
Jocyln Abraham	271

Public Schs..Principal	Grd	Prgm	Enr/#Cls	SN	Phone
Liberty Elem Sch 142 Lake Rd, Vly Cottage 10989 Ellen Rechenberger	K-5	T	461 23	45%	845/353-7240 Fax 845/353-7243
Nyack High Sch 360 Christian Herald Rd, Nyack 10960 Nicole Saieva	9-12		925 55	32%	845/353-7100 Fax 845/353-7197
Nyack Middle Sch 98 S Highland Ave, Nyack 10960 David Johnson	6-8		668 43	35%	845/353-7200 Fax 845/353-0506
Upper Nyack Elem Sch 336 N Broadway, Nyack 10960 Joe Mercora	K-5		398 24	25%	845/353-7260 Fax 845/353-7262
Valley Cottage Elem Sch 26 Lake Rd, Vly Cottage 10989 Lucresha Addison-Harris	K-5		413 22	37%	845/353-7280 Fax 845/353-7287

- **Pearl River School Dist** PID: 00767753   845/620-3900
  135 W Crooked Hill Rd, Pearl River 10965   Fax 845/620-3927

Schools: 5 \ Teachers: 195 \ Students: 2,360 \ Special Ed Students: 379 \ LEP Students: 63 \ College-Bound: 92% \ Ethnic: Asian 5%, African American 1%, Hispanic 13%, Caucasian 80% \ Exp: $188 (Low) \ Poverty: 8% \ Title I: $335,391 \ Special Education: $2,833,000 \ Open-Close: 09/04 - 06/25 \ DTBP: $154 (High)

Name	Code
Marco Pochintesta	1
Robert Nelan	3,91
Artie McCormack	6,35
Diana Musich	15,30,68,71,80
Bruce Bond	67
Annmarie Tromer	2,15
Mary Cinelli	5
Dr Robert Roelle	8,11,57,76,88,286,288,298
Carolyn Moffa	34,36,58,79,83,85,90
Eric Coronado	73

Public Schs..Principal	Grd	Prgm	Enr/#Cls	SN	Phone
Evans Park Elem Sch 40 Marion Pl, Pearl River 10965 Peggy Lynch	K-4	A	309 28	11%	845/620-3950 Fax 845/620-7570
Franklin Ave Elem Sch 48 Franklin Ave, Pearl River 10965 Kristin Talleyrand	K-4	A	286 14	18%	845/620-3965 Fax 845/620-3981
Lincoln Avenue Elem Sch 115 Lincoln Ave, Pearl River 10965 Kathleenann Cool	K-4	A	204 16	11%	845/620-3850 Fax 845/620-3975
Pearl River High Sch 275 E Central Ave, Pearl River 10965 Michael Murphy	8-12	AGV	981 60	13%	845/620-3800 Fax 845/620-3904
Pearl River Middle Sch 520 Gilbert Ave, Pearl River 10965 Maria Paese	5-7	A	580 40	13%	845/620-3870 Fax 845/620-3894

- **South Orangetown Central SD** PID: 00767820   845/680-1000
  160 Van Wyck Rd, Blauvelt 10913   Fax 845/680-1900

Schools: 4 \ Teachers: 258 \ Students: 2,911 \ Special Ed Students: 382 \ LEP Students: 152 \ College-Bound: 94% \ Ethnic: Asian 8%, African American 2%, Hispanic 18%, Caucasian 72% \ Exp: $447 (High) \ Poverty: 4% \ Title I: $168,262 \ Special Education: $3,222,000 \ Open-Close: 09/08 - 06/25 \ DTBP: $304 (High) \ t

Name	Code
Dr Robert Pritchard	1
Laura Zarcone	2
Catherine Wisbeski	4
William Pilla	6,35
Terry Campanella	30
Dan Lamadrid	67
George Brady	73,295
Alicia Koster	2
Jack Rallo	3
Paul Guglielmo	5
Dr Brian Culot	8,11,57,69,83,280,288,298
Karen Tesik	58,79,88,275*
Joseph Lloyd	68

Public Schs..Principal	Grd	Prgm	Enr/#Cls	SN	Phone
Cottage Lane Elem Sch 120 Cottage Ln, Blauvelt 10913 Karen Ramirez	3-5		582 21	14%	845/680-1500 Fax 845/680-1940

Code	Description	Code	Description	Code	Description	Code	Description
79	Student Personnel	91	Safety/Security	275	Response To Intervention	298	Grant Writer/Ptnrships
80	Driver Ed/Safety	92	Magnet School	277	Remedial Math K-12	750	Chief Innovation Officer
81	Gifted/Talented	93	Parental Involvement	280	Literacy Coach	751	Chief of Staff
82	Video Services	95	Tech Prep Program	285	STEM	752	Social Emotional Learning
83	Substance Abuse Prev	97	Chief Infomation Officer	286	Digital Learning		
84	Erate	98	Chief Technology Officer	288	Common Core Standards		
85	AIDS Education	270	Character Education	294	Accountability		
88	Alternative/At Risk	271	Migrant Education	295	Network System		
89	Multi-Cultural Curriculum	273	Teacher Mentor	296	Title II Programs		
90	Social Work	274	Before/After Sch	297	Webmaster		

School Programs
A = Alternative Program
G = Adult Classes
M = Magnet Program
T = Title I Schoolwide
V = Career & Tech Ed Programs

Other School Types
Ⓐ = Alternative School
Ⓒ = Charter School
Ⓜ = Magnet School
Ⓨ = Year-Round School

Social Media
f = Facebook
t = Twitter

New Schools are shaded
New Superintendents and Principals are bold
Personnel with email addresses are underscored

Rockland County
Market Data Retrieval

School	Grd	Prgm	Enr/#Cls	SN	Phone	Fax
South Orangetown Middle Sch 160 Van Wyck Rd, Blauvelt 10913 Chad Corey	6-8		694	15%	845/680-1100	Fax 845/680-1905
Tappan Zee High Sch 15 Dutch Hill Rd, Orangeburg 10962 Rudy Arietta	9-12	AGV	1,029 83	16%	845/680-1600	Fax 845/680-1950
W O Schaefer Elem Sch 140 Lester Dr, Tappan 10983 Sheila Beglin	K-2		606 25	13%	845/680-1301	Fax 845/680-1920

• **Suffern Central School Dist** PID: 00768123   845/357-7783
   45 Mountain Ave, Hillburn 10931   Fax 845/357-5707

Schools: 7 \ **Teachers:** 372 \ **Students:** 4,283 \ **Special Ed Students:** 750 \ **LEP Students:** 333 \ **College-Bound:** 95% \ **Ethnic:** Asian 8%, African American 7%, Hispanic 28%, Caucasian 57% \ **Exp:** $337 (High) \ **Poverty:** 9% \ **Title I:** $749,858 \ **Special Education:** $5,071,000 \ **Open-Close:** 09/09 - 06/25 \ **DTBP:** $320 (High)

Dr Lisa Weber 1
Theresa Isoldi 2
Alexis Fibble 12
Sarah Kern 38*
Courtney Violetti 60*
Matthew Kern 67
Robert Carella 295
Rena Gesner 2
Andrew Guccione 6,35*
Lawrence Mautone 15,68
Joanne McDonough 59
Sybil Jeffs 60
Lillian Rinchiera 76,97

Public Schs..Principal	Grd	Prgm	Enr/#Cls	SN	Phone	Fax
Cherry Lane Elem Sch 1 Heather Dr, Suffern 10901 Angela Aguilar	K-5		231 20	37%	845/357-3988	Fax 845/357-2191
Montebello Elem Sch 50 Montebello Rd, Suffern 10901 Dr Teresa Ivey	K-5		364 27	40%	845/357-4466	Fax 845/368-4161
Richard P Connor Elem Sch 13 Cypress Rd, Suffern 10901 Kelly Benadi	K-5	T	432 24	43%	845/357-2858	Fax 845/357-8657
Sloatsburg Elem Sch 11 2nd St, Sloatsburg 10974 Dr William Castellane	K-5	T	188 20	33%	845/753-2720	Fax 845/753-6636
Suffern High Sch 49 Viola Rd, Suffern 10901 Patrick Breen	9-12		1,495 103	26%	845/357-3800	Fax 845/357-5035
Suffern Middle Sch 80 Hemion Rd, Suffern 10901 Brian Fox	6-8		1,007 68	30%	845/357-7400	Fax 845/357-4563
Viola Elem Sch 557 Haverstraw Rd, Suffern 10901 Christine Druss	PK-5		321 25	21%	845/357-8315	Fax 845/357-2230

ROCKLAND CATHOLIC SCHOOLS

• **Archdiocese of New York Ed Off** PID: 00754976
   Listing includes only schools located in this county. See District Index for location of Diocesan Offices.

Catholic Schs..Principal	Grd	Prgm	Enr/#Cls	SN	Phone	Fax
Albertus Magnus High Sch 798 Route 304, Bardonia 10954 Christopher Power	9-12		460 24		845/623-8842	Fax 845/623-0009
St Anthony St Paul Sch 365 Kings Hwy, Vly Cottage 10989 Michelle Powrie	PK-2		165 10		845/268-6506	Fax 845/268-1809
St Anthony St Paul Sch 34 W Nyack Rd, Nanuet 10954 Dr Anna Adam	3-8		170 15		845/623-2311	Fax 845/623-0055
St Gregory Barbarigo Sch 29 Cinder Rd, Garnerville 10923 Dana Spicer	K-8		200 11		845/947-1330	Fax 845/947-4392
St Margaret Sch 34 N Magnolia St, Pearl River 10965 Patricia Maldonado	PK-8		230 10		845/735-2855	Fax 845/735-0131

ROCKLAND PRIVATE SCHOOLS

Private Schs..Principal	Grd	Prgm	Enr/#Cls	SN	Phone	Fax
Ashar Sch 360 New Hempstead Rd, New City 10956 Jacqueline Borgen \ Debby Jacobson	PK-8		340 30		845/357-1515	Fax 845/357-1516
Ateres Bais Yaakov 200 Summit Park Rd, Spring Valley 10977 Jenny Samet \ Kayla Stimmel \ Chana Lewenstein	PK-12		406 14		845/368-2200	Fax 845/368-2210
Bais Malka Sch 48 Grandview Ave, Spring Valley 10977 Yocheved Fisher \ Mrs Laser	PK-12		700 26		845/371-0500	Fax 845/354-2864
Bais Mikroh Boys Sch 221 Viola Rd, Monsey 10952 Chaim Bodenheimer	PK-8		620 22		845/425-4880	Fax 845/425-1062
Bais Shifra Miriam 70 Highview Rd, Monsey 10952 Gabriel Kramarski	K-12		300		845/356-0061	Fax 845/356-0223
Bais Yaakov Chofetz Chaim 44 Camp Hill Rd, Pomona 10970 Leah Zaks	PK-8		380 20		845/362-3166	Fax 845/354-6682
Bais Yaakov D'Rav Hirsch 235 N Main St, Spring Valley 10977 Steven Rosenstock	9-12		155 8		845/371-6750	Fax 845/371-6618
Bais Yaakov High Sch 11 Smolley Dr, Monsey 10952 Gitty Eisenberg	9-12		375		845/356-3113	Fax 845/356-3132
Bais Yaakov Ramapo Sch 16 Hershel Ter, Monsey 10952 J Gitty-Kramer	9-12		350		845/362-7262	Fax 845/362-7260
Bas Mikroh Girls Sch 381 Viola Rd, Spring Valley 10977 Deborah Ribiat	K-8		500 15		845/352-5296	Fax 845/425-5163
Beth Rochel School for Girls 145 Saddle River Rd, Monsey 10952 D Weizberg \ S Herzberg	K-12	G	900		845/352-5000	Fax 845/352-6571
Blue Rock Sch 110 Demarest Mill Rd, West Nyack 10994 Caty Laignel	K-8		90 9		845/627-0234	Fax 845/627-0208
Bnei Yakov Yosef of Monsey 23 Union Rd, Spring Valley 10977 Mosha Weber	PK-5		150		845/573-9400	
Bnos Esther Pupa Sch 15 Widman Ct, Spring Valley 10977 Abraham Schmidt	PK-5		191 11		845/371-1220	
Bnos Yisroel Girls Sch 1 School Ter, Monsey 10952 Hershy Moskowitz \ Marium Lea Tenenhause	PK-12		1,000		845/356-2322	Fax 845/356-7359
Cheder Chabad Sch-Monsey 25 S Monsey Rd, Airmont 10952 Moshe Wiener	PK-8		300		845/356-1213	Fax 845/503-2322
Cong Bais Chinuch Ateres Bnos 246 N Main St, Spring Valley 10977 Chaim Itzkowitz	9-12		300		845/675-8200	

New York School Directory

Rockland County

School	Grades	Enroll	Phone
Cong Yeshuos Moshe Viznitz 49 S Main St, Spring Valley 10977 Abraham Lowy	K-6	50	845/579-6363
Congregation Bais Chana Malka 185 N Main St, Spring Valley 10977 Martin Grenwald	K-12	100	845/352-1300
Congregation Belz Sch 3 N Cole Ave, Spring Valley 10977	PK-8	500	845/425-0909 Fax 845/425-5590
Congregation Yeshiva GR Monsey 667 New Hempstead Rd, Spring Valley 10977 Rena Levine	K-8	434	845/440-7976
Green Meadow Waldorf Sch 307 Hungry Hollow Rd, Spring Valley 10977 Treeanne McEnery	PK-12	300	845/356-2514
Hebrew Academy 315 N Main St, New City 10956 Avremel Kotlarsky	PK-8	88 12	845/634-0951 Fax 845/634-7704
Kolel Chasidei Rachmistrivka 97 Highview Rd, Suffern 10901 David Kalisch	PK-8	320	845/357-5550
Mesifta Ohel Torah 91 College Rd, Monsey 10952 Rabbi Rosengarden	9-12	140	845/371-3740
Mesivta Ahavas Hatorah 720 Union Rd, Spring Valley 10977	9-12	57	845/426-7400
Mesivta Beth Shraga for Boys 28 N Saddle River Rd, Monsey 10952 Feivel Mendlowitz	9-12	100 6	845/356-1980 Fax 845/425-2604
Mesivta Ziev Hatorah 4 Rita Ave, Monsey 10952 Rabbi Geldman	8-10	42	845/426-6868 Fax 845/356-5651
Ohr Reuven Sch 259 Grandview Ave, Suffern 10901 Boruch Rudinsky	9-12	73 6	845/362-8362 Fax 845/354-4830
Prime Time for Kids 70 Phillips Hill Rd, New City 10956 Dr Janet Masotti	Spec	110 13	845/639-2425 Fax 845/639-2433
Rockland Institute for Spec Ed 972 Chestnut Ridge Rd, Spring Valley 10977 Robert Kelderhouse	Spec	55 8	845/352-3307 Fax 845/352-3375
St Dominic Sch 488 Western Hwy, Blauvelt 10913 Heather Cahill	Spec	96 10	845/359-3400 Fax 845/359-5286
Sterling East-Pascack Lrng Ctr 27 Church Rd, Monsey 10952 Michael Jarvis	3-12	112	845/357-0980
Summit School at Nyack 339 N Broadway, Nyack 10960 Deborah Sherwood	Spec V	140 14	845/358-7772 Fax 845/358-2487
Talmud Torah D'Khal Adas Yerei 33 Union Rd, Spring Valley 10977 Rabbi Samuel	K-8	270 11	845/425-5678 Fax 845/208-0440
Talmud Torah Darkei Avos ES 15 Widman Ct, Spring Valley 10977 David Mashinsky	2-4	90	845/612-1027
Talmud Torah Darkei Avos PK-1 235 N Pascack Rd, Spring Valley 10977 David Mashinsky	PK-1	103	845/371-2476
Torah United Talmudical Boys 89 S Main St, Spring Valley 10977 David Jungreis	PK-12	1,464	845/425-0392 Fax 845/352-7253
United Talmudical Acad Boys HS 214 Maple Ave, Monsey 10952 Yidel Spitzer	9-12	41	845/425-0392
United Talmudical Acad-Madison 106 S Madison Ave, Spring Valley 10977	K-12	41	845/425-0392
United Talmudical Acad-Viola 415 Viola Rd, Spring Valley 10977 Jacob Lebovitz	K-12	41	845/425-0392
V'Yoel Moshe D'Satmar-Uta 89 S Main St, Spring Valley 10977 Martin Deutsch	K-12	360	845/425-0392 Fax 845/352-7253
Yeshiva Ahavath Israel Sch 15 Elyon Rd, Monsey 10952 Hershel Moskowitz	K-12	2,561	845/356-1010 Fax 845/356-7359
Yeshiva Avir Yakov Girls Sch 15 Roosevelt Ave, Spring Valley 10977 Ziaty Hoffman	PK-12 V	988	845/354-0874 Fax 845/354-5920
Yeshiva Bais Hachinuch 50 S Main St, Spring Valley 10977 Jordan Most	3-8	70	845/354-3805
Yeshiva Beth David 22 W Maple Ave, Monsey 10952 Shraga Gold	K-9	900	845/352-3100 Fax 845/352-0153
Yeshiva Darkei Emunah 201 Route 306, Monsey 10952 Abraham Felberbaum	PK-8	202	845/356-2761
Yeshiva Degel Hatorah 111 Maple Ave, Spring Valley 10977 Moshe Schwab	PK-12	250 13	845/356-4610 Fax 845/356-4507
Yeshiva Eitz Chaim-Skill Ctr 15 Widman Ct, Spring Valley 10977 Sarah Eidlitz	PK-8	70	845/425-3623 Fax 845/517-5488
Yeshiva High Sch of Monsey 58 Parker Blvd, Monsey 10952 David Rubin	9-12	100 4	845/406-6670 Fax 845/425-1062
Yeshiva of Spring Valley 121 College Rd, Suffern 10901 Yehudi Frankel	PK-8	1,700	845/356-1400 Fax 845/356-8551
Yeshiva Shaar Ephraim 5 Acer Ct, Monsey 10952 Asher Greenberg	9-12	200	845/426-3110 Fax 845/425-4721
Yeshiva Shaarei Torah 91 Carlton Rd W, Suffern 10901 Abraham Posner	9-12	75 15	845/352-3431 Fax 845/352-3433
Yeshiva Viznitz Boys High Sch 20 Ashel Ln, Monsey 10952 Yosef Gruber	9-12	300 8	845/356-1010 Fax 845/356-7359

ROCKLAND REGIONAL CENTERS

- **Rockland BOCES** PID: 00768226   845/627-4700
  65 Parrott Rd, West Nyack 10994   Fax 845/627-6124

David Gleason	2,15	Catherine O'Brien	7,15,27
Dr Amy Albers	15,79	Yasmin Helou-Care	15,68
Christopher D'Ambrese	30	Julie Larsen	58
Peggy Zugibe	67	Sarah Chauncey	73
Lisa Collopy	74	Kaushika Patel	295

79	Student Personnel	91	Safety/Security	275	Response To Intervention
80	Driver Ed/Safety	92	Magnet School	277	Remedial Math K-12
81	Gifted/Talented	93	Parental Involvement	280	Literacy Coach
82	Video Services	95	Tech Prep Program	285	STEM
83	Substance Abuse Prev	97	Chief Infomation Officer	286	Digital Learning
84	Erate	98	Chief Technology Officer	288	Common Core Standards
85	AIDS Education	270	Character Education	294	Accountability
88	Alternative/At Risk	271	Migrant Education	295	Network System
89	Multi-Cultural Curriculum	273	Teacher Mentor	296	Title II Programs
90	Social Work	274	Before/After Sch	297	Webmaster

298	Grant Writer/Ptnrships	**School Programs**	
750	Chief Innovation Officer	A = Alternative Program	
751	Chief of Staff	G = Adult Classes	
752	Social Emotional Learning	M = Magnet Program	
		T = Title I Schoolwide	
Other School Types		V = Career & Tech Ed Programs	
Ⓐ = Alternative School			
Ⓒ = Charter School		New Schools are shaded	
Ⓜ = Magnet School		New Superintendents and Principals are bold	
Ⓨ = Year-Round School		Personnel with email addresses are underscored	

Social Media
- ▌f = Facebook
- ▌t = Twitter

Saratoga County

Market Data Retrieval

SARATOGA COUNTY

SARATOGA COUNTY SCHOOLS

County Schs..Principal	Grd	Prgm	Enr/#Cls	SN
F Donald Myers Education Ctr 15 Henning Rd, Saratoga Spgs 12866 Shawn Hunziker	Voc	AG	800 30	518/581-3600 Fax 518/581-3609

SARATOGA PUBLIC SCHOOLS

• **Ballston Spa Ctl School Dist** PID: 00769402 518/884-7195
70 Malta Ave, Ballston Spa 12020 Fax 518/884-7101

Schools: 6 \ **Teachers:** 331 \ **Students:** 4,200 \ **Special Ed Students:** 776 \ **LEP Students:** 29 \ **College-Bound:** 80% \ **Ethnic:** Asian 2%, African American 2%, Hispanic 3%, Caucasian 94% \ **Exp:** $358 (High) \ **Poverty:** 7% \ **Title I:** $492,180 \ **Special Education:** $6,573,000 \ **Open-Close:** 09/08 - 06/25 \ **DTBP:** $321 (High)

Kenneth Slentz 1	Brian Sirianni 2,4,15	
Candy Staulters 2	Melissa Lovelass 2	
Edwin Martin 3,91	Sherry Demers 5	
David Sunkes 6*	Laurel Logan-King 8,11,30,57,69,79,83,90	
Brian Merchant 16,295	Diane Irwin 42	
Kristi Jensen 58*	Angela Nagle 59*	
Daniella Lans 60	Dottie Sellers 67	
Gail Mathias 71	Stuart Williams 71	

Public Schs..Principal	Grd	Prgm	Enr/#Cls	SN
Ballston Spa High Sch 220 Ballston Ave, Ballston Spa 12020 Gianleo Duca	9-12	AGV	1,259 85	31% 518/884-7150 Fax 518/884-7199
Ballston Spa Middle Sch 210 Ballston Ave, Ballston Spa 12020 Ann Laszewski	6-8	V	987 80	35% 518/884-7200 Fax 518/884-7234
Gordon Creek Elem Sch 50 Wood Rd, Ballston Spa 12020 Celeste Keane	K-5		499 55	27% 518/884-7270 Fax 518/884-7268
Malta Avenue Elem Sch 100 Wood Rd, Ballston Spa 12020 Sharon Dagostino	K-5		321 21	20% 518/884-7250 Fax 518/884-7258
Milton Terrace North Elem Sch 200 Wood Rd, Ballston Spa 12020 Kathleen Chaucer	K-5		458	34% 518/884-7210 Fax 518/884-7219
Wood Road Elem Sch 300 Wood Rd, Ballston Spa 12020 Anders Rasmussen	K-5	T	552 28	41% 518/884-7290 Fax 518/884-7286

• **Burnt Hills Ballston Lake SD** PID: 00769488 518/399-9141
88 Lake Hill Rd, Burnt Hills 12027 Fax 518/399-1882

Schools: 5 \ **Teachers:** 252 \ **Students:** 3,000 \ **Special Ed Students:** 491 \ **LEP Students:** 11 \ **Ethnic:** Asian 2%, African American 1%, Hispanic 2%, Caucasian 95% \ **Exp:** $238 (Med) \ **Poverty:** 4% \ **Title I:** $143,542 \ **Special Education:** $5,256,000 \ **Open-Close:** 09/09 - 06/25 \ **DTBP:** $316 (High) \

Patrick McGrath 1	Brenda Kane 2
Christopher Abdoo 2,15,91	Dan Diggins 3,91
Nicky Boehm 4	Joseph Czub 5
Joseph Scalise 6,7,35*	David Collins 8,11,15,69,285*
Sharon McTygue 12,34,58,90,271*	Tracy Salvo 16,73
Peter Giroux 23*	Dacey Bonney 30
Stephanie Andrejcak 31*	Russell Weinlein 36*
William McQuay 45*	Kate Gurley 48,51,54,68,74,275*
Suzanne Rayome 57,61,82*	Don Marshall 67
Michael Nickson 68	Tara Mitchell 71
Tracy Falvo 76,97	Daniel LeClaire 80,88,286*

Public Schs..Principal	Grd	Prgm	Enr/#Cls	SN
Burnt Hills Ballston Lake HS 88 Lake Hill Rd, Burnt Hills 12027 Tim Brunson	9-12	AGV	1,006 95	17% 518/399-9141 Fax 518/399-4341
Charlton Heights Elem Sch 170 Stage Rd, Ballston Lake 12019 Tim Sinnenberg	K-5		451 23	11% 518/399-9141 Fax 518/399-0227
Francis L Stevens Elem Sch 25 Lakehill Rd, Ballston Lake 12019 Dr Richard Evans	K-5	T	463 24	19% 518/399-9141 Fax 518/399-0343
Pashley Elem Sch 30 Pashley Rd, Glenville 12302 Jill Bonacio	K-5	T	441 26	18% 518/399-9141 Fax 518/399-0534
Richard H O'Rourke Middle Sch 173 Lake Hill Rd, Burnt Hills 12027 Colleen Wolff	6-8	AGTV	721 60	17% 518/399-9141 Fax 518/384-2588

• **Corinth Central School Dist** PID: 00769555 518/654-9005
105 Oak St, Corinth 12822 Fax 518/654-6266

Schools: 3 \ **Teachers:** 98 \ **Students:** 1,139 \ **Special Ed Students:** 160 \ **LEP Students:** 3 \ **College-Bound:** 68% \ **Ethnic:** Asian 1%, Hispanic 2%, Caucasian 97% \ **Exp:** $222 (Med) \ **Poverty:** 12% \ **Title I:** $228,273 \ **Special Education:** $1,943,000 \ **Open-Close:** 09/08 - 06/25 \ **DTBP:** $215 (High) \

Dr Mark Stratton 1	Susan Foloy 2,11,19,91,294
Daniel Miller 3	Lisa Tevendale 4
Cathleen Wardell 5	Hilary Haskell 6,35*
Donna Briner 7*	Eric Schenone 8,288*
Jill Cheney-Bovee 11,15,58,275	Lynne Jenkins 27,36*
Christopher Castrio 37*	Sayde Whitman 38*
Patricia Saunders 56*	Patricia Siano 63*
Arthur Lozier 67	Sarah Giaculli 82*
De Nolett 295	

Public Schs..Principal	Grd	Prgm	Enr/#Cls	SN
Corinth Elem Sch 356 Center St, Corinth 12822 Renee Young	K-5	T	521 27	54% 518/654-2960 Fax 518/654-6235
Corinth High Sch 105 Oak St, Corinth 12822 Brian Testani	9-12	GV	340	47% 518/654-9005
Corinth Middle Sch 105 Oak St, Corinth 12822 Eric Schenone	6-8	T	278	46% 518/654-9005

• **Edinburg Common School Dist** PID: 00769610 518/863-8412
4 Johnson Rd, Northville 12134 Fax 518/863-2564

Schools: 1 \ **Teachers:** 10 \ **Students:** 65 \ **Special Ed Students:** 8 \ **Ethnic:** Hispanic 1%, Caucasian 99% \ **Exp:** $597 (High) \ **Poverty:** 12% \ **Title I:** $27,236 \ **Special Education:** $154,000 \ **Open-Close:** 09/08 - 06/29 \ **DTBP:** $385 (High)

---

1 Superintendent	8 Curric/Instruct K-12	19 Chief Financial Officer	29 Family/Consumer Science	39 Social Studies K-12	49 English/Lang Arts Elem	59 Special Education Elem	69 Academic Assessment
2 Bus/Finance/Purchasing	9 Curric/Instruct Elem	20 Art K-12	30 Adult Education	40 Social Studies Elem	50 English/Lang Arts Sec	60 Special Education Sec	70 Research/Development
3 Buildings And Grounds	10 Curric/Instruct Sec	21 Art Elem	31 Career/Sch-to-Work K-12	41 Social Studies Sec	51 Reading K-12	61 Foreign/World Lang K-12	71 Public Information
4 Food Service	11 Federal Program	22 Art Sec	32 Career/Sch-to-Work Elem	42 Science K-12	52 Reading Elem	62 Foreign/World Lang Elem	72 Summer School
5 Transportation	12 Title I	23 Music K-12	33 Career/Sch-to-Work Sec	43 Science Elem	53 Reading Sec	63 Foreign/World Lang Sec	73 Instructional Tech
6 Athletic	13 Title V	24 Music Elem	34 Early Childhood Ed	44 Science Sec	54 Remedial Reading K-12	64 Religious Education K-12	74 Inservice Training
7 Health Services	15 Asst Superintendent	25 Music Sec	35 Health/Phys Education	45 Math K-12	55 Remedial Reading Elem	65 Religious Education Elem	75 Marketing/Distributive
	16 Instructional Media Svcs	26 Business Education	36 Guidance Services K-12	46 Math Elem	56 Remedial Reading Sec	66 Religious Education Sec	76 Info Systems
	17 Chief Operations Officer	27 Career & Tech Ed	37 Guidance Services Elem	47 Math Sec	57 Bilingual/ELL	67 School Board President	77 Psychological Assess
	18 Chief Academic Officer	28 Technology Education	38 Guidance Services Sec	48 English/Lang Arts K-12	58 Special Education K-12	68 Teacher Personnel	78 Affirmative Action

New York School Directory — Saratoga County

Michelle Ellis	1,73	Sandy Moore	2,19,298
Michael Sherman	3,5	Constance Breda	4
Ashlee Weddell	7	Thomas Moore	16,73,295*
Erin Gurdineer	59	Michael Evans	67

Public Schs..Principal	Grd	Prgm	Enr/#Cls	SN	
Edinburg Common Sch 4 Johnson Rd, Northville 12134 Michelle Ellis	PK-6	T	65 9	49%	518/863-8412

• Galway Central School Dist PID: 00769634
5317 Sacandaga Rd, Galway 12074
518/882-1033 Fax 518/882-5250

Schools: 2 \ **Teachers:** 80 \ **Students:** 837 \ **Special Ed Students:** 115 \ **College-Bound:** 78% \ **Ethnic:** Caucasian 99% \ **Exp:** $317 (High) \ **Poverty:** 5% \ **Title I:** $101,906 \ **Special Education:** $1,042,000 \ **Open-Close:** 09/07 - 06/22 \ **DTBP:** $359 (High)

Brita Donovan	1	Jeannine Yates	2
Christopher Cook	3	Amy Thompson	4
William Clark	5	Jennifer Gerber	35*
Kathy Morck	38*	Jennifer Hall	58,79
Jay Anderson	67	Scot Carpenter	73*

Public Schs..Principal	Grd	Prgm	Enr/#Cls	SN	
Galway Jr Sr High Sch 5317 Sacandaga Rd, Galway 12074 Michael Miller	7-12	AGV	372 35	29%	518/882-1221
Joseph Henry Elem Sch 5317 Sacandaga Rd, Galway 12074 Michelle McDougall	PK-6		465 23	35%	518/882-1291 Fax 518/882-9430

• Mechanicville City Sch Dist PID: 00769660
25 Kniskern Ave, Mechanicville 12118
518/664-5727 Fax 518/514-2102

Schools: 2 \ **Teachers:** 104 \ **Students:** 1,345 \ **Special Ed Students:** 249 \ **LEP Students:** 4 \ **College-Bound:** 77% \ **Ethnic:** Asian 2%, African American 2%, Hispanic 3%, Caucasian 93% \ **Exp:** $164 (Low) \ **Poverty:** 12% \ **Title I:** $242,681 \ **Special Education:** $2,428,000 \ **Open-Close:** 09/04 - 06/25

Bruce Potter	1	Jodi Birch	2
Sandra Fishbough	4*	Michael Pratt	5
Yvonne Lajeunesse	7,85	Kevin Kolakowski	10,27,31,83,88*
Jennifer LaFleche	36,57,72,77*	Mary Alice Hipwell	58
Marlene Tierney	67	Margaret Giller	71,97

Public Schs..Principal	Grd	Prgm	Enr/#Cls	SN	
Mechanicville Elem Sch 25 Kniskern Ave, Mechanicville 12118 Craig Forth	K-5		615 32	37%	518/664-7336 Fax 518/514-2119
Mechanicville Jr Sr High Sch 25 Kniskern Ave, Mechanicville 12118 Kevin Kolakowski	6-12	V	730 30	38%	518/664-9888 Fax 518/514-2107

• Saratoga Springs City Sch Dist PID: 00769696
3 Blue Streak Blvd, Saratoga Spgs 12866
518/583-4700 Fax 518/584-6624

Schools: 8 \ **Teachers:** 482 \ **Students:** 6,375 \ **Special Ed Students:** 859 \ **LEP Students:** 78 \ **College-Bound:** 87% \ **Ethnic:** Asian 2%, African American 2%, Hispanic 4%, Caucasian 92% \ **Exp:** $180 (Low) \ **Poverty:** 6% \ **Title I:** $571,256 \ **Special Education:** $7,849,000 \ **Open-Close:** 09/09 - 06/25 \ **DTBP:** $313 (High) 🅵 🅣

Dr Michael Patton	1	Dr Joseph Greco	2

Tim Hilker	2,15	Dr Stephen Verral	3
Margaret Sullivan	4	Cheryl Dalton	5
Nicholas McPartland	6	Darlene King	7,57,58,79
Lisa Cutting	8,11,15	Jennifer Steimle	12,48,51,81,288
David L'Hommedieu	15,295*	Melissa Allen	38*
Anjeanette Emeka	67	Dr Hillary Brewer	68,78,273
Melissa Kerrick	68,74	Maura Manny	71
Benjamin Peck	73	Kathy Goodwin	76
Laurie Newcomer	77	Madeline Daley	85
Timothy Harris	88*	Judy Kahn	91

Public Schs..Principal	Grd	Prgm	Enr/#Cls	SN	
Caroline Street Elem Sch 310 Caroline St, Saratoga Spgs 12866 Daniel Packard	K-5		358 21	20%	518/584-7612 Fax 518/583-4768
Division Street Elem Sch 220 Division St, Saratoga Spgs 12866 Dr Greer Miller	K-5		448 30	18%	518/583-4794 Fax 518/583-4722
Dorothy Nolan Elem Sch 221 Jones Rd, Saratoga Spgs 12866 Dana Bush	K-5		757 41	17%	518/584-7383 Fax 518/583-4726
Geyser Road Elem Sch 61 Geyser Rd, Saratoga Spgs 12866 Michele Whitley	K-5		387 20	24%	518/584-7699 Fax 518/583-4733
Greenfield Elem Sch 3180 Route 9N, Greenfld CTR 12833 Tina Davis	K-5		385 21	27%	518/893-7402 Fax 518/893-7408
Lake Avenue Elem Sch 126 Lake Ave, Saratoga Spgs 12866 Dr Barbara Messier	K-5		406 30	7%	518/584-3678 Fax 518/583-4778
Maple Avenue Middle Sch 515 Maple Ave, Saratoga Spgs 12866 Bruce Ballan	6-8		1,467 75	21%	518/587-4551 Fax 518/587-5759
Saratoga Springs High Sch 1 Blue Streak Blvd, Saratoga Spgs 12866 Michelle Tsao	9-12	AGTV	2,040	17%	518/587-6690 Fax 518/583-1671

• Schuylerville Central Sch Dist PID: 00769787
14 Spring St, Schuylerville 12871
518/695-3255 Fax 518/695-6491

Schools: 3 \ **Teachers:** 131 \ **Students:** 1,500 \ **Special Ed Students:** 188 \ **LEP Students:** 11 \ **Ethnic:** African American 1%, Hispanic 3%, Caucasian 96% \ **Exp:** $231 (Med) \ **Poverty:** 6% \ **Title I:** $157,104 \ **Special Education:** $3,088,000 \ **Open-Close:** 09/10 - 06/25 \ **DTBP:** $368 (High)

Ryan Sherman	1,83	Mariann Christman	2
Peter Riggi	3	Sarah Keen	4
Charles Barrs	5	Pam Driscoll	7*
Jorden Tasendos	8,74	Greg Barthelmess	11,27,36,57,58,69,79,88
Genene Obrian	31	Michael Bodnar	67
Karen Kane	71,97	Jason Megan	73
James DuCharme	273		

Public Schs..Principal	Grd	Prgm	Enr/#Cls	SN	
Schuylerville Elem Sch 14 Spring St, Schuylerville 12871 Gregg Barthelmas	K-5		652 47	28%	518/695-3255 Fax 518/695-6405
Schuylerville High Sch 14 Spring St, Schuylerville 12871 James DuCharme	9-12	V	484 50	26%	518/695-3255
Schuylerville Middle Sch 14 Spring St, Schuylerville 12871 Mary Kate Elsworth	6-8		380	31%	518/695-3255

79	Student Personnel	91	Safety/Security	275	Response To Intervention	298	Grant Writer/Ptnrships
80	Driver Ed/Safety	92	Magnet School	277	Remedial Math K-12	750	Chief Innovation Officer
81	Gifted/Talented	93	Parental Involvement	280	Literacy Coach	751	Chief of Staff
82	Video Services	95	Tech Prep Program	285	STEM	752	Social Emotional Learning
83	Substance Abuse Prev	97	Chief Information Officer	286	Digital Learning		
84	Erate	98	Chief Technology Officer	288	Common Core Standards		
85	AIDS Education	270	Character Education	294	Accountability		
88	Alternative/At Risk	271	Migrant Education	295	Network System		
89	Multi-Cultural Curriculum	273	Teacher Mentor	296	Title II Programs		
90	Social Work	274	Before/After Sch	297	Webmaster		

School Programs
A = Alternative Program
G = Adult Classes
M = Magnet Program
T = Title I Schoolwide
V = Career & Tech Ed Programs

Other School Types
Ⓐ = Alternative School
Ⓒ = Charter School
Ⓜ = Magnet School
Ⓨ = Year-Round School

Social Media
🅵 = Facebook
🅣 = Twitter

New Schools are shaded
New Superintendents and Principals are bold
Personnel with email addresses are underscored

Saratoga County

Market Data Retrieval

• **Shenendehowa Central Sch Dist** PID: 00769828   518/881-0600
5 Chelsea Pl, Clifton Park 12065   Fax 518/371-9393

Schools: 12 \ **Teachers:** 666 \ **Students:** 9,499 \ **Special Ed Students:** 1,240 \ **LEP Students:** 221 \ **College-Bound:** 67% \ **Ethnic:** Asian 12%, African American 3%, Hispanic 7%, Caucasian 79% \ **Exp:** $201 (Med) \ **Poverty:** 3% \ **Title I:** $358,348 \ **Special Education:** $9,237,000 \ **Open-Close:** 09/09 - 06/25 \ **DTBP:** $313 (High) \ 🇫 🇹

Dr L Oliver Robinson 1	Kathleen Wetmore-Chase 2,15
Katy Headwell 4	Alfred Karam 5
Chris Culnan 6,35*	Rose Barra 7,29
Dr Elizabeth Wood ..8,11,15,40,69,78,286,288	Michelle Mylod 12,58,79
Jill Bush 15	Robert Melia 15
Frank Rosselli 20,23	Lucas LaBarre 38
Lisa Kissinger 41	Michelle Gabree-Huba 43
Jean Lorch 44	Kathleen Sherwin 48,280
Sarah Cioffi 57,61	Deanna Stephenson 67
Rebecca Carman 70	Kelly Defeciani 71
Ken McDermith 73,76,295*	Anna Sugarman 74
Steve West 91	

Public Schs..Principal	Grd	Prgm	Enr/#Cls	SN	
Acadia Middle Sch 970 Route 146, Clifton Park 12065 John Burns	6-8		747 100	19%	518/881-0450 Fax 518/371-3981
Arongen Elem Sch 489 Clifton Park Ctr Rd, Clifton Park 12065 Andrew Hills	K-5		648 32	23%	518/881-0510 Fax 518/371-8177
Chango Elem Sch 100 Chango Dr, Ballston Lake 12019 Karin Skarka	K-5		568 23	11%	518/881-0520 Fax 518/899-5971
Gowana Middle Sch 970 Route 146, Clifton Park 12065 Robin Gawrys	6-8		701	16%	518/881-0460 Fax 518/383-1490
Karigon Elem Sch 970 Route 146, Clifton Park 12065 Malik Jones	K-5		468 25	8%	518/881-0530 Fax 518/383-1176
Koda Middle Sch 970 Route 146, Clifton Park 12065 Sean Gnat	6-8		743 40	23%	518/881-0470 Fax 518/383-1532
Okte Elem Sch 1581 Crescent Rd, Clifton Park 12065 Lisa Mickle	K-5		490 23	19%	518/881-0540 Fax 518/383-1964
Orenda Elem Sch 970 Route 146, Clifton Park 12065 Todd Giagni	K-5	T	536 28	16%	518/881-0550 Fax 518/383-1219
Shatekon Elem Sch 35 Maxwell Dr, Clifton Park 12065 Erica Ryan	K-5		505	24%	518/881-0580 Fax 518/371-1762
Shenendehowa High Sch 970 Route 146, Clifton Park 12065 Ron Agostinoni	9-12	G	3,163	18%	518/881-0310 Fax 518/383-1670
Skano Elem Sch 970 Route 146, Clifton Park 12065 Jill Florio	K-5		579 27	13%	518/881-0560 Fax 518/383-1260
Tesago Elem Sch 970 Route 146, Clifton Park 12065 Gregory Pace	K-5		386 30	9%	518/881-0570 Fax 518/383-1486

• **South Glens Falls Ctl Sch Dist** PID: 00769933   518/793-9617
42 Merritt Rd A, S Glens Falls 12803   Fax 518/761-0723

Schools: 6 \ **Teachers:** 225 \ **Students:** 3,000 \ **Special Ed Students:** 489 \ **LEP Students:** 10 \ **College-Bound:** 73% \ **Ethnic:** Asian 1%, African American 1%, Hispanic 4%, Caucasian 94% \ **Exp:** $152 (Low) \ **Poverty:** 7% \ **Title I:** $306,760 \ **Special Education:** $4,395,000 \ **Open-Close:** 09/08 - 06/25 \ **DTBP:** $308 (High)

Kristine Orr 1,11	Tammi Edwards 2
Ronald Gorham 3,91	Robert Defrancisco 4*
Fred Strassburg 5	Matthew Griep 6,7,35,85*
Bristie Tracy 7	Tim Dawkins 8,15
Michael Davies 16,82*	Jessica Spellburg 58
William Elder 67	Flora Covey 71,76,97
Monica Lester 71	Alex Spada 73,295
Shelly Finton 280*	

Public Schs..Principal	Grd	Prgm	Enr/#Cls	SN	
Ballard Elem Sch 300 Ballard Rd, Wilton 12831 Michael Huchro	K-5		340 18	28%	518/587-0600 Fax 518/587-2248
Harrison Avenue Elem Sch 76 Harrison Ave, S Glens Falls 12803 Carla Biviano	K-5	T	256 30	54%	518/793-9048 Fax 518/824-2229
Moreau Elem Sch 76 Bluebird Rd, S Glens Falls 12803 Robert McGough	K-5	T	251 16	35%	518/793-9644 Fax 518/824-2262 🇫🇹
Oliver W Winch Middle Sch 99 Hudson St, S Glens Falls 12803 Raymond Ruby	6-8		734 80	34%	518/792-5891 Fax 518/824-2267 🇫
South Glens Falls Sr High Sch 42 Merritt Rd, S Glens Falls 12803 Peter Mody	9-12	AV	907 25	32%	518/792-9987 Fax 518/824-2261 🇫🇹
Tanglewood Elem Sch 60 Tanglewood Dr, S Glens Falls 12803 Matthew Conrick	K-5	T	429 24	34%	518/793-5631 Fax 518/793-9241

• **Stillwater Central Sch Dist** PID: 00770009   518/373-6100
1068 Hudson Ave, Stillwater 12170   Fax 518/664-9134

Schools: 3 \ **Teachers:** 101 \ **Students:** 1,035 \ **Special Ed Students:** 151 \ **LEP Students:** 3 \ **College-Bound:** 77% \ **Ethnic:** Asian 1%, African American 1%, Hispanic 3%, Caucasian 95% \ **Exp:** $236 (Med) \ **Poverty:** 6% \ **Title I:** $111,739 \ **Special Education:** $1,883,000 \ **Open-Close:** 09/10 - 06/25 \ **DTBP:** $165 (High) \ 🇫 🇹

Patricia Morris 1,83	Scott Messineo 2
Joan Hopeck 4	Thomas Murphy 5
Mike Kinney 6*	Tim Hulihan 12,298
Carolyn Manzella 58,79	Valerie Masterson 67
Chris Lynch 73*	Mikal Benamati 77*

Public Schs..Principal	Grd	Prgm	Enr/#Cls	SN	
Stillwater Central High Sch 1068 Hudson Ave, Stillwater 12170 Michael Johnson	9-12	V	352 50	28%	518/373-6100 🇫🇹
Stillwater Elem Sch 1068 Hudson Ave, Stillwater 12170 Rebecca Toleman	PK-5		461 29	29%	518/373-6100 Fax 518/373-6194 🇫🇹
Stillwater Middle Sch 1068 Hudson Ave, Stillwater 12170 Timothy Hulihan	6-8		264		518/373-6100 Fax 518/373-6164

1	Superintendent	8	Curric/Instruct K-12	19	Chief Financial Officer	29	Family/Consumer Science	39	Social Studies K-12
2	Bus/Finance/Purchasing	9	Curric/Instruct Elem	20	Art K-12	30	Adult Education	40	Social Studies Elem
3	Buildings And Grounds	10	Curric/Instruct Sec	21	Art Elem	31	Career/Sch-to-Work K-12	41	Social Studies Sec
4	Food Service	11	Federal Program	22	Art Sec	32	Career/Sch-to-Work Elem	42	Science K-12
5	Transportation	12	Title I	23	Music K-12	33	Career/Sch-to-Work Sec	43	Science Elem
6	Athletic	13	Title V	24	Music Elem	34	Early Childhood Ed	44	Science Sec
7	Health Services	15	Asst Superintendent	25	Music Sec	35	Health/Phys Education	45	Math K-12
		16	Instructional Media Svcs	26	Business Education	36	Guidance Services K-12	46	Math Elem
		17	Chief Operations Officer	27	Career & Tech Ed	37	Guidance Services Elem	47	Math Sec
		18	Chief Academic Officer	28	Technology Education	38	Guidance Services Sec	48	English/Lang Arts K-12

49	English/Lang Arts Elem	59	Special Education Elem	69	Academic Assessment
50	English/Lang Arts Sec	60	Special Education Sec	70	Research/Development
51	Reading K-12	61	Foreign/World Lang K-12	71	Public Information
52	Reading Elem	62	Foreign/World Lang Elem	72	Summer School
53	Reading Sec	63	Foreign/World Lang Sec	73	Instructional Tech
54	Remedial Reading K-12	64	Religious Education K-12	74	Inservice Training
55	Remedial Reading Elem	65	Religious Education Elem	75	Marketing/Distributive
56	Remedial Reading Sec	66	Religious Education Sec	76	Info Systems
57	Bilingual/ELL	67	School Board President	77	Psychological Assess
58	Special Education K-12	68	Teacher Personnel	78	Affirmative Action

New York School Directory — Schenectady County

- **Waterford Halfmoon School Dist** PID: 00770035 518/237-0800
  125 Middletown Rd, Waterford 12188 Fax 518/237-7335

Schools: 2 \ **Teachers:** 75 \ **Students:** 800 \ **Special Ed Students:** 129 \ **LEP Students:** 5 \ **College-Bound:** 90% \ **Ethnic:** Asian 1%, African American 1%, Hispanic 2%, Caucasian 95% \ **Exp:** $237 (Med) \ **Poverty:** 8% \ **Title I:** $134,717 \ **Special Education:** $1,627,000 \ **Open-Close:** 09/04 - 06/25 \ **DTBP:** $161 (High)

Patrick Pomerville 1	Rachel Schwendinger 2,5
Mike Robbins 6*	Jennifer Mead 7,35,85*
Jennifer Bull 11,58*	Cynthia Viola 53,56
Marsha Ricci 67	Joel Richardson 69*
Joseph Spretty 73	Karen Grimes 77*
Nicole Spulnick 273*	

Public Schs..Principal	Grd	Prgm	Enr/#Cls	SN	
Waterford Elem Sch 125 Middletown Rd, Waterford 12188 Joseph Siracuse	K-6	GT	412 19	42%	518/237-0800 Fax 518/237-7083
Waterford Jr Sr High Sch 125 Middletown Rd, Waterford 12188 Christopher Scanlan	7-12	G	340	38%	518/237-0800

SARATOGA CATHOLIC SCHOOLS

- **Diocese of Albany Ed Office** PID: 00715059
  Listing includes only schools located in this county. See District Index for location of Diocesan Offices.

Catholic Schs..Principal	Grd	Prgm	Enr/#Cls	SN	
Saratoga Central Catholic HS 247 Broadway, Saratoga Spgs 12866 Joe Kilmade	6-12		250 18		518/587-7070 Fax 518/587-0678
St Clement's Regional Cath Sch 231 Lake Ave, Saratoga Spgs 12866 Jane Kromm	PK-5		299 13		518/584-7350 Fax 518/587-2623
St Mary's Sch 40 Thompson St, Ballston Spa 12020 Lynn Fitzgerald	K-5		226 10		518/885-7300 Fax 518/885-7378 t
St Mary's Sch 12 6th St, Waterford 12188 Matthew Rucinski	PK-8	G	259 19		518/237-0652 Fax 518/233-0898

SARATOGA PRIVATE SCHOOLS

Private Schs..Principal	Grd	Prgm	Enr/#Cls	SN	
Augustine Classical Academy 7 N Main St, Mechanicville 12118 Matt Hopkins	K-12		65		518/541-2089
Ketchum-Grande Memorial Sch 322 Lake Hill Rd, Burnt Hills 12027 Tina Crego	Spec		35 9		518/399-8182 Fax 518/399-8195
Mother Teresa Academy 1 Executive Park Dr, Clifton Park 12065 Debbie Maddalone	PK-1		60		518/280-4227
Newmeadow Saratoga Sch 23 Sitterly Rd, Clifton Park 12065 Andrew McKenzie	Spec		140		518/899-9235 Fax 518/899-9315

	Grd	Enr/#Cls		
Saratoga Independent Sch 459 Lake Ave, Saratoga Spgs 12866 Lisa Brown	PK-6	63 6		518/583-0841 Fax 518/587-6831
Spa Christian Sch 206 Greenfield Ave, Ballston Spa 12020 Amanda Klint	PK-6	75 8		518/885-0508
The Kings Sch 6087 Route 9 N, Hadley 12835 Kellie Girling	PK-12	125 15		518/654-6230 Fax 518/654-7310 f t
Waldorf Sch-Saratota Springs 62 York Ave, Saratoga Spgs 12866 Katherine Scharff	PK-12	253 18		518/584-7643 Fax 518/581-1682
Wilton Baptist Academy 755 Saratoga Rd, Gansevoort 12831 Steve Harness	K-12	27		518/583-2736

SCHENECTADY COUNTY

SCHENECTADY PUBLIC SCHOOLS

- **Duanesburg Central Sch Dist** PID: 00770126 518/895-2279
  133 School Dr, Delanson 12053 Fax 518/895-2626

Schools: 2 \ **Teachers:** 65 \ **Students:** 770 \ **Special Ed Students:** 87 \ **College-Bound:** 90% \ **Ethnic:** Asian 1%, African American 1%, Hispanic 4%, Caucasian 94% \ **Exp:** $362 (High) \ **Poverty:** 5% \ **Title I:** $105,101 \ **Special Education:** $1,657,000 \ **Open-Close:** 09/08 - 06/25 \ **DTBP:** $387 (High) \ f t

Dr James Niedermeier 1	Jeff Rivenburg 2,11
Aanen Aanensen 3	Mary Jewell 4*
Dan McConnely 5	Penny Hardenstine 6,8*
Andrea Conover 9,34,58,69,275,288*	Aimee Skiff 11,298
Donna Wilkes 16*	Kristina Goebel 31,36,83*
Camille Siano Enders 67	Karen Lancto 68
Joseph O'Neill 73,76,286,295*	Laural Halberg 77*
David Presson 90*	Jim Nesbitt 91*
Polly Benjamin 273	Melissa Gregory 285*
Monique Jacobs 297*	

Public Schs..Principal	Grd	Prgm	Enr/#Cls	SN	
Duanesburg Elem Sch 165 Chadwick Rd, Delanson 12053 Andrea Conover	PK-6		331 18	27%	518/895-2580 Fax 518/895-2957 f
Duanesburg Jr Sr High Sch 163 School Dr, Delanson 12053 Jodi Marvin	7-12	G	338 34	25%	518/895-3000 Fax 518/895-9971

- **Mohonasen Central Sch Dist** PID: 00770152 518/356-8200
  2072 Curry Rd, Schenectady 12303 Fax 518/356-8247

Schools: 4 \ **Teachers:** 206 \ **Students:** 2,799 \ **Special Ed Students:** 433 \ **LEP Students:** 37 \ **College-Bound:** 79% \ **Ethnic:** Asian 3%, African American 4%, Hispanic 9%, Caucasian 84% \ **Exp:** $167 (Low) \ **Poverty:** 9% \ **Title I:** $379,019 \ **Special Education:** $3,768,000 \ **Open-Close:** 09/04 - 06/25 \ **DTBP:** $326 (High) \ f

Shannon Shine 1	Christopher Ruberti 2,15,19
Joe Mayo 3	Kimberly Gagnon 4*
Randy Jerreld 5	David Bertram 6,7,35
Laurel Logan King 8,11,15,286,296	James Dilbone 16,73

79 Student Personnel	91 Safety/Security	275 Response To Intervention	298 Grant Writer/Ptnrships	**School Programs**
80 Driver Ed/Safety	92 Magnet School	277 Remedial Math K-12	750 Chief Innovation Officer	A = Alternative Program
81 Gifted/Talented	93 Parental Involvement	280 Literacy Coach	751 Chief of Staff	G = Adult Classes
82 Video Services	95 Tech Prep Program	285 STEM	752 Social Emotional Learning	M = Magnet Program
83 Substance Abuse Prev	97 Chief Infomation Officer	286 Digital Learning		T = Title I Schoolwide
84 Erate	98 Chief Technology Officer	288 Common Core Standards	**Other School Types**	V = Career & Tech Ed Programs
85 AIDS Education	270 Accountability	294 Accountability	Ⓐ = Alternative School	
88 Alternative/At Risk	271 Migrant Education	295 Network System	Ⓒ = Charter School	New Schools are shaded
89 Multi-Cultural Curriculum	273 Teacher Mentor	296 Title II Programs	Ⓜ = Magnet School	New Superintendents and Principals are bold
90 Social Work	274 Before/After Sch	297 Webmaster	Ⓨ = Year-Round School	Personnel with email addresses are underscored

Social Media
f = Facebook
t = Twitter

Schenectady County

Market Data Retrieval

Rebecca Pauley 36*
Lisa Gaglioti 67
Matthew Hubbell 285
Sara Lewis 58,275
Alissa Scott 71,76
Tasha Anderson 295

Public Schs..Principal	Grd	Prgm	Enr/#Cls	SN
Draper Middle Sch 2070 Curry Rd, Schenectady 12303 Richard Arket	6-8	AT	699 44	42% 518/356-8350 Fax 518/356-8359
Herman L Bradt Primary Sch 2719 Hamburg St, Schenectady 12303 Leslie Smith	K-2	T	630 26	42% 518/356-8400 Fax 518/356-8404
Mohonasen High Sch 2072 Curry Rd, Schenectady 12303 Craig Chandler	9-12	AGV	843 45	39% 518/356-8300 Fax 518/356-8309
Pinewood Intermediate Sch 901 Kings Rd, Schenectady 12303 Jason Thompson	3-5	T	627 44	42% 518/356-8430 Fax 518/356-8434

- **Niskayuna Central School Dist** PID: 00770217 518/377-4666
  1239 Van Antwerp Rd, Niskayuna 12309 Fax 518/377-4074

Schools: 8 \ **Teachers:** 326 \ **Students:** 4,240 \ **Special Ed Students:** 530 \ **LEP Students:** 135 \ **College-Bound:** 92% \ **Ethnic:** Asian 17%, African American 5%, Hispanic 5%, Caucasian 73% \ **Exp:** $174 (Low) \ **Poverty:** 3% \ **Title I:** $174,598 \ **Special Education:** $4,660,000 \ **Open-Close:** 09/14 - 06/24 \ **DTBP:** $328 (High)

Dr Cosimo Tangorra 1
Jefferey Bradt 4
Larry Gillooley 35*
Howard Schlossberg 67
Jacquelin Carrese 285
Carrie Nyc Chevrier 2,15
Marie DiGirolamo 8,11,15,18,57,288,296
William Wales 45
Henry Geidel 73,286

Public Schs..Principal	Grd	Prgm	Enr/#Cls	SN
Birchwood Elem Sch 897 Birchwood Ln, Schenectady 12309 Deborah Berndt	K-5		379 15	10% 518/344-2910 Fax 518/344-5610
Craig Elem Sch 2566 Balltown Rd, Niskayuna 12309 William Anders	K-5	T	408 19	15% 518/377-0156 Fax 518/377-1075
Glencliff Elem Sch 961 Riverview Rd, Rexford 12148 Shelley Baldwin	K-5	T	370 15	16% 518/399-2323 Fax 518/399-4072
Hillside Elem Sch 1100 Cornelius Ave, Schenectady 12309 Dr Shireen Fasciglione	K-5	T	397 18	12% 518/377-1856 Fax 518/377-1099
Iroquois Middle Sch 2495 Rosendale Rd, Schenectady 12309 Victoria Wyld	6-8	T	517 60	14% 518/377-2233 Fax 518/377-0655
Niskayuna High Sch 1626 Balltown Rd, Niskayuna 12309 John Rickert	9-12	T	1,377 80	13% 518/382-2511 Fax 518/382-2539
Rosendale Elem Sch 2445 Rosendale Rd, Schenectady 12309 Joseph Dicaprio	K-5	T	384 17	12% 518/377-3123 Fax 518/377-1098
Van Antwerp Middle Sch 2253 Story Ave, Schenectady 12309 Luke Rakoczy	6-8		454 32	11% 518/370-1243 Fax 518/370-4610

- **Schalmont Central School Dist** PID: 00770308 518/355-9200
  4 Sabre Dr, Schenectady 12306 Fax 518/355-9203

Schools: 3 \ **Teachers:** 142 \ **Students:** 1,798 \ **Special Ed Students:** 298 \ **LEP Students:** 9 \ **College-Bound:** 83% \ **Ethnic:** Asian 2%, African American 2%, Hispanic 6%, Caucasian 91% \ **Exp:** $297 (Med) \ **Poverty:** 6% \ **Title I:** $209,096 \ **Special Education:** $3,584,000 \ **Open-Close:** 09/09 - 06/25 \ **DTBP:** $229 (High)

Thomas Reardon 1
John Odonell 3
Joe Hilts 5
Bronson Knaggs 7,8,288*
Mary Shands 16*
Angelo Santabarbara 67
William DeVoe 71
Jason Beck 85*
Joseph Karas 2
Renee Heller 4
Matthew Ranca 6
Shari Lontrato 11,58,79,275
Donna Notar 30
Debbie Falcone 71,97
Anthony Cassale 73*
Teresa McCreadle 295

Public Schs..Principal	Grd	Prgm	Enr/#Cls	SN
Jefferson Elem Sch 100 Princetown Rd, Schenectady 12306 Joby Gifford	K-4		657 39	26% 518/355-1342 Fax 518/357-0293
Schalmont High Sch 1 Sabre Dr, Schenectady 12306 Maureen Avione	9-12	AV	612 40	25% 518/355-6110 Fax 518/355-8720
Schalmont Middle Sch 2 Sabre Dr, Schenectady 12306 Scott Ziomek	5-8		529 25	30% 518/355-6255 Fax 518/355-5329

- **Schenectady City School Dist** PID: 00770396 518/370-8100
  108 Education Dr, Schenectady 12303 Fax 518/370-8173

Schools: 17 \ **Teachers:** 786 \ **Students:** 9,921 \ **Special Ed Students:** 1,932 \ **LEP Students:** 443 \ **College-Bound:** 81% \ **Ethnic:** Asian 20%, African American 33%, Hispanic 23%, Caucasian 23% \ **Exp:** $268 (Med) \ **Poverty:** 26% \ **Title I:** $5,470,436 \ **Special Education:** $23,924,000 \ **Open-Close:** 09/07 - 06/22 \ **DTBP:** $307 (High)

Laurence Spring 1
Kimberly Lewis 2
Brian Hoffman 3
Elaine Reynolds 4
Steven Boynton 6*
Erika McFarlane 8,30
Aaron Bochniak 11,294
Kerri Messler 16,48,51,54*
Kathleen Beck 20,23*
Sue Gorman 34*
Jane O'Shea 52,280
Jessica Karn 58
Christina Mahoney 68,74,78
Sara Schneller 70,294
Chris Pietrantonio 73
Jim Leupold 76
Kari Girard 77,83*
Kristen Shearer 79
Beth Carusone 2
Taryn Breen 2
Mike Barry 3
Al Valachovic 5
Holly Vacca 7
Tonda Dunbar 8,57,288
Patricia Paser 15*
Peter Goodwin 16,95,295*
Carmella Parente 29,39,61*
Kurt Redman 42,45*
Donna Fowler 58
John Foley 67
Kimberly Hughes 68
Karen Corona 71
Abigail Anderson 76
Michele LaCorte 76
Andrea Tote 79
Joseph Palmer 294

Public Schs..Principal	Grd	Prgm	Enr/#Cls	SN
ⓜ Central Park Int'l Magnet Sch 421 Elm St, Schenectady 12304 Jason Rogers	6-8	TV	715 35	69% 518/370-8250 Fax 518/881-3662
Hamilton Elem Sch 1091 Webster St, Schenectady 12303 Renee Beaulieu	PK-5	T	417 20	80% 518/881-3720 Fax 518/881-3722
ⓜ Howe Elem Sch 1065 Baker Ave, Schenectady 12309 Sue Gorman	PK-5	T	431 15	58% 518/370-8295 Fax 518/881-3762

1 Superintendent	8 Curric/Instruct K-12	19 Chief Financial Officer	29 Family/Consumer Science	39 Social Studies K-12	49 English/Lang Arts Elem	59 Special Education Elem	69 Academic Assessment
2 Bus/Finance/Purchasing	9 Curric/Instruct Elem	20 Art K-12	30 Adult Education	40 Social Studies Elem	50 English/Lang Arts Sec	60 Special Education Sec	70 Research/Development
3 Buildings And Grounds	10 Curric/Instruct Sec	21 Art Elem	31 Career/Sch-to-Work K-12	41 Social Studies Sec	51 Reading K-12	61 Foreign/World Lang K-12	71 Public Information
4 Food Service	11 Federal Program	22 Art Sec	32 Career/Sch-to-Work Elem	42 Science K-12	52 Reading Elem	62 Foreign/World Lang Elem	72 Summer School
5 Transportation	12 Title I	23 Music K-12	33 Career/Sch-to-Work Sec	43 Science Elem	53 Reading Sec	63 Foreign/World Lang Sec	73 Instructional Tech
6 Athletic	13 Title V	24 Music Elem	34 Early Childhood Ed	44 Science Sec	54 Remedial Reading K-12	64 Religious Education K-12	74 Inservice Training
7 Health Services	15 Asst Superintendent	25 Music Sec	35 Health/Phys Education	45 Math K-12	55 Remedial Reading Elem	65 Religious Education Elem	75 Marketing/Distributive
	16 Instructional Media Svcs	26 Business Education	36 Guidance Services K-12	46 Math Elem	56 Remedial Reading Sec	66 Religious Education Sec	76 Info Systems
	17 Chief Operations Officer	27 Career & Tech Ed	37 Guidance Services Elem	47 Math Sec	57 Bilingual/ELL	67 School Board President	77 Psychological Assess
	18 Chief Academic Officer	28 Technology Education	38 Guidance Services Sec	48 English/Lang Arts K-12	58 Special Education K-12	68 Teacher Personnel	78 Affirmative Action

New York School Directory

Schenectady County

Public Schs..Principal	Grd	Prgm	Enr/#Cls	SN	
Jessie T Zoller Elem Sch 1880 Lancaster St, Schenectady 12308 Patricia Doyle	PK-5	T	467 22	61%	518/370-8290 Fax 518/881-3882 f t
Lincoln Elem Cmty Sch 2 Robinson St, Schenectady 12304 Job Thomas	PK-5	T	338 17	82%	518/370-8355 Fax 518/395-3576 f t
ⓜ Martin L King Magnet Sch 918 Stanley St, Schenectady 12307 Michelle Vanderlinden	PK-5	T	480 30	83%	518/370-8360 Fax 518/370-8363
Mont Pleasant Middle Sch 1121 Forest Rd, Schenectady 12303 Jeffrey Bennett	6-8	TV	761 70	60%	518/370-8160 Fax 518/881-3562
Oneida Middle Sch 1529 Oneida St, Schenectady 12308 Antonio Farina	6-8	T	714	76%	518/370-8260
Paige Elem Sch 104 Elliot Ave, Schenectady 12304 Matthew Berkshire	PK-5	T	468 24	62%	518/370-8300 Fax 518/881-3522
ⓜ Pleasant Valley Elem Sch 1097 Forest Rd, Schenectady 12303 Sean Inglee	PK-5	T	428 20	80%	518/881-3640 Fax 518/881-3642 f t
Schenectady High Sch 1445 the Plz, Schenectady 12308 Diane Wilkinson	9-12	TV	2,737	70%	518/881-2044 Fax 518/881-3802 f t
Steinmetz Career Leadrshp Acad 880 Oakwood Ave, Schenectady 12303 Gregory Fields	Voc		230 20		518/881-2030 Fax 518/881-3602
Van Corlaer Elem Sch 2300 Guilderland Ave, Schenectady 12306 Marianne Bellai	PK-5	T	415 19	69%	518/370-8270 Fax 518/881-3742
Washington Irving Ed Center 422 Mumford St, Schenectady 12307 Jesse Roylance	Adult		200		518/370-8220
William Keane Elem Sch 1252 Albany St, Schenectady 12304 John Sardos	PK-5	T	323 16	66%	518/881-3960 Fax 518/881-3962
Woodlawn Elem Sch 3311 Wells Ave, Schenectady 12304 John Perreault	PK-5	T	437 23	69%	518/370-8280 Fax 518/370-8283 f t
ⓜ Yates Magnet Sch 725 Salina St, Schenectady 12308 Robert Flanders	PK-5	T	379 18	86%	518/370-8320 Fax 518/881-3862 f t

- **Scotia Glenville Ctl Sch Dist** PID: 00770645   518/347-3600
  900 Preddice Pkwy, Scotia 12302   Fax 518/386-4336

Schools: 6 \ **Teachers:** 193 \ **Students:** 2,600 \ **Special Ed Students:** 452 \ **LEP Students:** 15 \ **College-Bound:** 79% \ **Ethnic:** Asian 1%, African American 4%, Hispanic 4%, Caucasian 91% \ **Exp:** $189 (Low) \ **Poverty:** 11% \ **Title I:** $439,008 \ **Special Education:** $5,302,000 \ **Open-Close:** 09/08 - 06/24 \ **DTBP:** $323 (High)

Susan Swartz 1	Andrew Giaquinto 2
Mark Cary 3,91	Pete Zwack 3
Clara Bisaillon 5	Jamian Rockhill 6
Kenneth Handin 7,58,79,90*	Karen Swain 8,11,15,288
Peter Bednarek 8*	Robert Hanlon 16,71
Cynthia Shipley 30	Thomas Fyvie 36*
Susan Vachris 39,48	Megan Johnson 42
Anthony Peconie 60,72*	David Bucciferro 67
Jan Tunison 73,286	Dean Mays 76

Public Schs..Principal	Grd	Prgm	Enr/#Cls	SN	
Glen Worden Elem Sch 30 Worden Rd, Scotia 12302 Nicholas Criscone	K-5		239 12	25%	518/347-3600 Fax 518/346-0855
Glendaal Elem Sch 774 Sacandaga Rd, Scotia 12302 Thomas Eagan	K-5		208 15	12%	518/382-1201 Fax 518/382-1203
Lincoln Elem Sch 40 Albion St, Scotia 12302 John Geniti	K-5	T	249 13	42%	518/382-1296 Fax 518/386-2808
Sacandaga Elem Sch 300 Wren St, Scotia 12302 Tonya Federico	K-5		330 24	34%	518/382-1282 Fax 518/386-4311
Scotia Glenville High Sch 1 Tartan Way, Scotia 12302 Peter Bednarek	9-12		774 40	30%	518/382-1231 Fax 518/386-4350
Scotia Middle Sch 10 Prestige Pkwy, Scotia 12302 Robert Cosmer	6-8		572 60	30%	518/382-1263 Fax 518/386-4303

SCHENECTADY CATHOLIC SCHOOLS

- **Diocese of Albany Ed Office** PID: 00715059
  Listing includes only schools located in this county. See District Index for location of Diocesan Offices.

Catholic Schs..Principal	Grd	Prgm	Enr/#Cls	SN	
Notre Dame-Bishop Gibbons Sch 2600 Albany St, Schenectady 12304 Kiante Jones	6-12		274 25		518/393-3131 Fax 518/370-3817
St Kateri Tekakwitha Sch 1801 Union St, Niskayuna 12309 Tosha Grimmer	PK-5		330 17		518/382-8225 Fax 518/374-8522 f t
St Madeleine Sophie Sch 3510 Carman Rd, Schenectady 12303 Kelly Sloan	PK-5		200 8		518/355-3080 Fax 518/355-3106

SCHENECTADY PRIVATE SCHOOLS

Private Schs..Principal	Grd	Prgm	Enr/#Cls	SN	
An Nur Islamic Sch 2195 Central Ave, Schenectady 12304 Dr Sohaib Chekima	PK-12		200 9		518/395-9866
Brown Sch 150 Corlaer Ave, Schenectady 12304 Patti Vitale	PK-8		189 30		518/370-0366 Fax 518/370-1514
Clover Patch Camp 55 Helping Hand Ln, Glenville 12302 Dani-Leigh Ross	Spec		40 4		518/384-3042 Fax 518/384-3001
Mekeel Christian Academy 36-38 Sacandaga Rd, Scotia 12302 Chad Bowman	K-12		320 35		518/370-4272 Fax 518/370-4778 t
Oak Hill Sch 39 Charlton Rd, Scotia 12302 J Stubing	Spec		24 5		518/399-5048 Fax 518/399-6140
School at Northeast 1821 Hamburg St, Schenectady 12304 Richard Danson	Spec		165 30		518/346-1273 Fax 518/370-3705
Wildwood Sch 2995 Curry Rd Ext, Schenectady 12303 Wilford Laforester	Spec	G	216 21		518/836-2200 Fax 518/836-2201

79 Student Personnel	91 Safety/Security	275 Response To Intervention	298 Grant Writer/Ptnrships
80 Driver Ed/Safety	92 Magnet School	277 Remedial Math K-12	750 Chief Innovation Officer
81 Gifted/Talented	93 Parental Involvement	280 Literacy Coach	751 Chief of Staff
82 Video Services	95 Tech Prep Program	285 STEM	752 Social Emotional Learning
83 Substance Abuse Prev	97 Chief Infomation Officer	286 Digital Learning	
84 Erate	98 Chief Technology Officer	288 Common Core Standards	**Other School Types**
85 AIDS Education	270 Accountability	294 Character Education	Ⓐ = Alternative School
88 Alternative/At Risk	271 Migrant Education	295 Network System	Ⓒ = Charter School
89 Multi-Cultural Curriculum	273 Teacher Mentor	296 Title II Programs	Ⓜ = Magnet School
90 Social Work	274 Before/After Sch	297 Webmaster	Ⓨ = Year-Round School

School Programs
A = Alternative Program
G = Adult Classes
M = Magnet Program
T = Title I Schoolwide
V = Career & Tech Ed Programs

Social Media
f = Facebook
t = Twitter

New Schools are shaded
New Superintendents and Principals are bold
Personnel with email addresses are underscored

Schoharie County

Market Data Retrieval

SCHOHARIE COUNTY

SCHOHARIE COUNTY SCHOOLS

County Schs..Principal	Grd	Prgm	Enr/#Cls	SN
Career & Tech Sch-Schoharie 174 State Route 30A, Schoharie 12157 Mindy Iannotti	Voc	AG	195 11	518/295-3000 Fax 518/295-3075

SCHOHARIE PUBLIC SCHOOLS

• **Cobleskill Richmondville SD** PID: 00770736   518/234-4032
155 Washington Ave, Cobleskill 12043   Fax 518/234-7721

Schools: 4 \ **Teachers:** 155 \ **Students:** 1,700 \ **Special Ed Students:** 183 \ **LEP Students:** 6 \ **Ethnic:** Asian 1%, African American 1%, Hispanic 5%, Caucasian 92% \ **Exp:** $180 (Low) \ **Poverty:** 13% \ **Title I:** $388,130 \ **Special Education:** $3,755,000 \ **Open-Close:** 09/08 - 06/25 \ **DTBP:** $159 (High) \ 🇫 🇹

Carl Mummenthey	1	Tracy Fraleigh	2
Bill Himme	3,5	Amy Stuart	4*
John Henry	6,7,42,83,85*	Scott McDonald	8
Mel Ausfeld	11,79,270*	Mary Bristol	26*
Edie Schultz	31,36,83*	Lynn Bramski	58
Bruce Tryon	67	Jeff Klenk	72*
David Sander	73*		

Public Schs..Principal	Grd	Prgm	Enr/#Cls	SN
Cobleskill-Richmondville HS 1353 State Route 7, Richmondville 12149 Brett Barr	9-12	AV	568 60	40% 518/234-3565 Fax 518/234-9006 🇫🇹
George D Ryder Elem Sch 143 Golding Dr, Cobleskill 12043 Kevin Kelly	PK-2		424 19	40% 518/234-2585 Fax 518/234-7956 🇫🇹
Joseph B Radez Elem Sch 319 Main St, Richmondville 12149 Eric Whipple	3-5	T	370 18	55% 518/294-6621 Fax 518/294-6425
William H Golding Middle Sch 193 Golding Dr, Cobleskill 12043 Scott McDonald	6-8	T	357 50	54% 518/234-8368 Fax 518/234-4114 🇫🇹

• **Gilboa-Conesville Central SD** PID: 00770774   607/588-7541
132 Wyckoff Rd, Gilboa 12076   Fax 607/588-6820

Schools: 1 \ **Teachers:** 36 \ **Students:** 312 \ **Special Ed Students:** 53 \ **College-Bound:** 58% \ **Ethnic:** Asian 1%, African American 1%, Hispanic 2%, Caucasian 97% \ **Exp:** $266 (Med) \ **Poverty:** 15% \ **Title I:** $94,321 \ **Special Education:** $746,000 \ **Open-Close:** 09/08 - 06/25 \ **DTBP:** $359 (High)

John Etter	1,83	Lester Chase	3,91
Danielle Proudman	4*	Carl Fancher	5*
Daniel McGlynn	6*	Allissa CO	7
Michelle Dumas	11,298*	Daniel Ringuette	31,36,57,81,88*
Janice Cashman	58*	Michael Fleischman	67
Brett Maury	73	Jack Etter	288*

Public Schs..Principal	Grd	Prgm	Enr/#Cls	SN
Gilboa-Conesville Central Sch 132 Wyckoff Rd, Gilboa 12076 Thomas Cervola	PK-12	T	312 13	1% 607/588-7541

• **Jefferson Central Sch Dist** PID: 00770798   607/652-7821
1332 State Route 10, Jefferson 12093   Fax 607/652-7806

Schools: 1 \ **Teachers:** 29 \ **Students:** 195 \ **Special Ed Students:** 41 \ **College-Bound:** 48% \ **Ethnic:** Hispanic 3%, Caucasian 97% \ **Exp:** $228 (Med) \ **Poverty:** 19% \ **Title I:** $99,771 \ **Special Education:** $461,000 \ **Open-Close:** 09/08 - 06/15 \ **DTBP:** $359 (High)

Tarkan Ceng	1,11	Fred Loveless	3
Alesia Eppich	4*	Russell Brovetto	5
Rick Cammer	6,35*	Alissa Chung	36
Sara Schulz	67	Thomas Jory	73,286,295*

Public Schs..Principal	Grd	Prgm	Enr/#Cls	SN
Jefferson Central Sch 1332 State Route 10, Jefferson 12093 William Clooney	PK-12		195 60	18% 607/652-7821

• **Middleburgh Ctl School Dist** PID: 00770815   518/827-3625
291 Main St, Middleburgh 12122   Fax 518/827-6632

Schools: 2 \ **Teachers:** 68 \ **Students:** 750 \ **Special Ed Students:** 133 \ **LEP Students:** 3 \ **Ethnic:** Asian 1%, African American 1%, Hispanic 1%, Caucasian 97% \ **Exp:** $246 (Med) \ **Poverty:** 11% \ **Title I:** $141,566 \ **Special Education:** $1,854,000 \ **Open-Close:** 09/08 - 06/25 \ 🇫

Brian Dunn	1	Terry Gillooley	2
Steven Weinhofer	3	Rock Loiselle	5
Paul Pierce	6	Jennifer Adams	7*
Mathew Sloan	8	Maura Green	31,36,57,58,79,88
Kelly Pacatte	38*	Alex Johnson	50*
Pamela Standhart	67	Frank Cossu	73,76
Heather Howe	270*		

Public Schs..Principal	Grd	Prgm	Enr/#Cls	SN
Middleburgh Elem Sch 245 Main St 1, Middleburgh 12122 Amy Irwin	PK-6	T	370 30	57% 518/827-3677 Fax 518/827-5321
Middleburgh Jr Sr High Sch 291 Main St, Middleburgh 12122 Matthew Sloane	7-12	TV	320 24	49% 518/827-3605 Fax 518/827-5192

• **Schoharie Central SD** PID: 00770865   518/295-6600
136 Academy Dr, Schoharie 12157   Fax 518/295-9510

Schools: 2 \ **Teachers:** 85 \ **Students:** 875 \ **Special Ed Students:** 130 \ **Ethnic:** Hispanic 2%, Caucasian 97% \ **Exp:** $237 (Med) \ **Poverty:** 13% \ **Title I:** $216,928 \ **Special Education:** $2,413,000 \ **Open-Close:** 09/14 - 06/25 \ **DTBP:** $373 (High)

David Blanchard	1	Robert Bonaker	2,73,82
Shawn Gathen	3	Eric Bush	4
Amy Crewell	5	Shane Barton	6
Matthew Wright	8,58,79	Wendy Molle	16*
Terry Burton	67	Jake Palmateer	71,297

Public Schs..Principal	Grd	Prgm	Enr/#Cls	SN
Schoharie Elem Sch 136 Academy Dr, Schoharie 12157 Andrea Polikoski	K-6	T	503 28	51% 518/295-6651 Fax 518/295-9506

---

1 Superintendent	8 Curric/Instruct K-12	19 Chief Financial Officer	29 Family/Consumer Science	39 Social Studies K-12	49 English/Lang Arts Elem	59 Special Education Elem	69 Academic Assessment
2 Bus/Finance/Purchasing	9 Curric/Instruct Elem	20 Art K-12	30 Adult Education	40 Social Studies Elem	50 English/Lang Arts Sec	60 Special Education Sec	70 Research/Development
3 Buildings And Grounds	10 Curric/Instruct Sec	21 Art Elem	31 Career/Sch-to-Work K-12	41 Social Studies Sec	51 Reading K-12	61 Foreign/World Lang K-12	71 Public Information
4 Food Service	11 Federal Program	22 Art Sec	32 Career/Sch-to-Work Elem	42 Science K-12	52 Reading Elem	62 Foreign/World Lang Elem	72 Summer School
5 Transportation	12 Title I	23 Music K-12	33 Career/Sch-to-Work Sec	43 Science Elem	53 Reading Sec	63 Foreign/World Lang Sec	73 Instructional Tech
6 Athletic	13 Title V	24 Music Elem	34 Early Childhood Ed	44 Science Sec	54 Remedial Reading K-12	64 Religious Education K-12	74 Inservice Training
7 Health Services	15 Asst Superintendent	25 Music Sec	35 Health/Phys Education	45 Math K-12	55 Remedial Reading Elem	65 Religious Education Elem	75 Marketing/Distributive
	16 Instructional Media Svcs	26 Business Education	36 Guidance Services K-12	46 Math Elem	56 Remedial Reading Sec	66 Religious Education Sec	76 Info Systems
	17 Chief Operations Officer	27 Career & Tech Ed	37 Guidance Services Elem	47 Math Sec	57 Bilingual/ELL	67 School Board President	77 Psychological Assess
	18 Chief Academic Officer	28 Technology Education	38 Guidance Services Sec	48 English/Lang Arts K-12	58 Special Education K-12	68 Teacher Personnel	78 Affirmative Action

New York School Directory

Schuyler County

Schoharie High Sch	7-12	T	385	41%	518/295-6601
136 Academy Dr, Schoharie 12157			45		Fax 518/295-8161
Kevin Calacone					

• **Sharon Springs Ctl SD** PID: 00770891   518/284-2266
514 Highway Route 20, Sharon Spgs 13459   Fax 518/284-9033

Schools: 1 \ **Teachers:** 31 \ **Students:** 226 \ **Special Ed Students:** 49 \ **LEP Students:** 3 \ **Ethnic:** Asian 1%, African American 1%, Hispanic 5%, Caucasian 92% \ **Exp:** $459 (High) \ **Poverty:** 19% \ **Title I:** $153,782 \ **Special Education:** $903,000 \ **Open-Close:** 09/04 - 06/29 \ **DTBP:** $423 (High)

Patterson Green 1		Anthony DiPace 2	
Chris Gray 5		Chris Smith 6*	
Russell Scimeca 11,58,271,296*		Heather Bivins 16,82*	
Liz Schlenke 31,36,83,88*		Tammy Behr 35*	
Danielle Connors 57*		Laura Jackson 67	
Christopher Grey 73*		Thomas Reynolds 97,295*	

Public Schs..Principal	Grd	Prgm	Enr/#Cls	SN	
Sharon Springs Central Sch	K-12	TV	226	52%	518/284-2267
514 Great Western Tpke, Sharon Spgs 13459			35		Fax 518/284-9075
Tom Yorke					

SCHOHARIE PRIVATE SCHOOLS

Private Schs..Principal	Grd	Prgm	Enr/#Cls	SN	
Cornerstone Christian Academy	3-12		6		518/868-2268
133 Sprakers, Sloansville 12160			2		
Arlene Lent					

SCHUYLER COUNTY

SCHUYLER PUBLIC SCHOOLS

• **Bradford Central Sch Dist** PID: 00771285   607/583-4616
2820 State Route 226, Bradford 14815   Fax 607/583-4013

Schools: 1 \ **Teachers:** 30 \ **Students:** 265 \ **Special Ed Students:** 66 \ **Ethnic:** Hispanic 1%, Caucasian 99% \ **Exp:** $330 (High) \ **Poverty:** 18% \ **Title I:** $93,222 \ **Special Education:** $809,000 \ **Open-Close:** 09/04 - 06/25 \ **DTBP:** $372 (High)

John Marshall 1,11,57		Lisa Kuhnel 2,19	
Faron Rogers 3,91*		Pam Drumm 4*	
David Lewis 5		Jeff Rutlugde 6	
Karen Miller 7,83,85		Katheryn Ellison 8,11,74,288,296	
Erica Sparks 36,271		Nicole Keefer 58*	
Melissa Nowicki 61*		Joe Miller 67	
Jeff Tham 73,76,286,295*		Rebecca Schrader 81*	
Christa Coats 270,274*			

Public Schs..Principal	Grd	Prgm	Enr/#Cls	SN	
Bradford Central Sch	PK-12	ATV	265	58%	607/583-4616
2820 State Route 226, Bradford 14815			25		
Katheryn Ellison					

• **Odessa Montour Ctl Sch Dist** PID: 00770918   607/594-3341
300 College Ave, Odessa 14869   Fax 607/594-3976

Schools: 3 \ **Teachers:** 72 \ **Students:** 733 \ **Special Ed Students:** 123 \ **LEP Students:** 3 \ **College-Bound:** 57% \ **Ethnic:** Asian 1%, African American 1%, Hispanic 2%, Caucasian 97% \ **Exp:** $213 (Med) \ **Poverty:** 18% \ **Title I:** $245,343 \ **Special Education:** $1,165,000 \ **Open-Close:** 09/04 - 06/25 \ **DTBP:** $355 (High)

Christopher Wood 1		Lisa Kuhnel 2,19	
Kelly Cain 3		Ann Overhiser 4*	
Rob Cole 4*		Michelle Clark 5	
Jane O'Neil 7,83,85*		Veronica Lewis 8,11,58,271,298	
Colleen Coolican 36*		Robert Halpin 67	
Kay Collins 68		Erin Edger 71	
James Nolan 73,295*			

Public Schs..Principal	Grd	Prgm	Enr/#Cls	SN	
B C Cate Elem Sch	PK-2	T	242	42%	607/535-7267
262 Canal St, Montour Falls 14865			10		Fax 607/535-7802
James Nolan					
Howard A Hanlon Elem Sch	3-6	T	219	55%	607/594-3341
300 College Ave, Odessa 14869			10		Fax 607/594-3434
Veronica Lewis \ Rob Francischelli					
Odessa Montour Jr Sr High Sch	7-12	T	314	46%	607/594-3341
300 College Ave, Odessa 14869			22		Fax 607/594-3438
James Nolan \ Skip McCarty					

• **Watkins Glen Central Sch Dist** PID: 00770956   607/535-3219
303 12th St, Watkins Glen 14891   Fax 607/535-4629

Schools: 2 \ **Teachers:** 88 \ **Students:** 1,040 \ **Special Ed Students:** 179 \ **LEP Students:** 3 \ **Ethnic:** Asian 1%, African American 1%, Hispanic 3%, Native American: 1%, Caucasian 94% \ **Exp:** $490 (High) \ **Poverty:** 16% \ **Title I:** $286,787 \ **Special Education:** $2,068,000 \ **Open-Close:** 09/08 - 06/24 \ **DTBP:** $351 (High)

Gregory Kelahan 1,11		Dan Delano 3	
Rob Cole 4		Michelle Clark 5	
Kristine Somerville 8,15,34,58,69,74,288		Maggie Field 16,82*	
Jason Westervelt 35,83,85		Gloria Brubaker 67	
Melanie Chandler 73,295		Christin Bresett 88	

Public Schs..Principal	Grd	Prgm	Enr/#Cls	SN	
Watkins Glen Central High Sch	7-12	GT	486	46%	607/535-3210
301 12th St, Watkins Glen 14891			50		Fax 607/535-3283
Kai D'Alleva					
Watkins Glen Elem Sch	PK-6	T	554	50%	607/535-3250
612 S Decatur St, Watkins Glen 14891			28		Fax 607/535-7012
Jeremy LeRoux					

---

79 Student Personnel	91 Safety/Security	275 Response To Intervention	298 Grant Writer/Ptnrships	**School Programs**	**Social Media**
80 Driver Ed/Safety	92 Magnet School	277 Remedial Math K-12	750 Chief Innovation Officer	A = Alternative Program	
81 Gifted/Talented	93 Parental Involvement	280 Literacy Coach	751 Chief of Staff	G = Adult Classes	▇ = Facebook
82 Video Services	95 Tech Prep Program	285 STEM	752 Social Emotional Learning	M = Magnet Program	
83 Substance Abuse Prev	97 Chief Infomation Officer	286 Digital Learning		T = Title I Schoolwide	▇ = Twitter
84 Erate	98 Chief Technology Officer	288 Common Core Standards	**Other School Types**	V = Career & Tech Ed Programs	
85 AIDS Education	270 Character Education	294 Accountability	Ⓐ = Alternative School		
88 Alternative/At Risk	271 Migrant Education	295 Network System	Ⓒ = Charter School	New Schools are shaded	
89 Multi-Cultural Curriculum	273 Teacher Mentor	296 Title II Programs	Ⓜ = Magnet School	New Superintendents and Principals are bold	
90 Social Work	274 Before/After Sch	297 Webmaster	Ⓨ = Year-Round School	Personnel with email addresses are underscored	

NY–207

Seneca County

Market Data Retrieval

SENECA COUNTY

SENECA PUBLIC SCHOOLS

- **Romulus Ctl School Dist** PID: 00771027 607/869-5391
  5705 State Route 96, Romulus 14541 Fax 607/869-5961

Schools: 1 \ **Teachers:** 44 \ **Students:** 420 \ **Special Ed Students:** 57 \ **College-Bound:** 81% \ **Ethnic:** African American 1%, Hispanic 4%, Caucasian 96% \ **Exp:** $285 (Med) \ **Poverty:** 17% \ **Title I:** $207,256 \ **Special Education:** $851,000 \ **Open-Close:** 09/08 - 06/24 \ **DTBP:** $1,158 (High)

Marty Rotz 1	Ed Ninestine 2*
Edward Oldfield 3,91*	Christopher Puylara 8*
Jen Bartlett Prati 11,286,288,296*	Stacy Merrill 16*
Kathy Stuck 58*	Robert McCann 67
Sue Fegley 73*	Katie Harris Maxwell 752

Public Schs..Principal	Grd	Prgm	Enr/#Cls	SN	
Romulus Central Sch 5705 State Route 96, Romulus 14541 Christopher Puylara	PK-12	TV	420 50	55%	607/869-5391 Fax 607/869-2121

- **Seneca Falls Central Sch Dist** PID: 00771053 315/568-5818
  98 Clinton St, Seneca Falls 13148 Fax 315/712-0535

Schools: 4 \ **Teachers:** 113 \ **Students:** 1,173 \ **Special Ed Students:** 205 \ **LEP Students:** 10 \ **Ethnic:** Asian 2%, African American 3%, Hispanic 5%, Native American: 1%, Caucasian 88% \ **Exp:** $236 (Med) \ **Poverty:** 14% \ **Title I:** $312,472 \ **Special Education:** $3,428,000 \ **Open-Close:** 09/08 - 06/24 \ **DTBP:** $367 (High) \

Jeremy Clingerman 1,11,83	James Bruni 2,19,73,97,295,296
Jack Rowles 3,91	Stephanie Lyons-Lawrence 4
Debra Burnham 5	Anthony Ferrara 6
Victoria Burm 7*	Jodie Verky 8,273,288
Carleen Mull 12,275*	Nancy Galusha 16
Jessica Taylor 38*	Karissa Blamble 58,79
Cara Lajewski 67	

Public Schs..Principal	Grd	Prgm	Enr/#Cls	SN	
Elizabeth Cady Stanton ES 38 Garden St, Seneca Falls 13148 Amy Hibbard	3-5	T	280 16	53%	315/568-5834 Fax 315/712-0551
Frank M Knight Elem Sch 98 Clinton St, Seneca Falls 13148 Janet Clendenen	K-2	T	254 25	51%	315/568-5500 Fax 315/712-0527
Mynderse Academy High Sch 105 Troy St, Seneca Falls 13148 Faith Lewis	9-12		367 33	40%	315/568-5500 Fax 315/712-0523
Seneca Falls Middle Sch 95 Troy St, Seneca Falls 13148 Kevin Rhinehart	6-8	T	297 34	48%	315/568-5500 Fax 315/712-0524

- **South Seneca Ctl Sch Dist** PID: 00771118 607/869-9636
  7263 Main St, Ovid 14521 Fax 607/869-2529

Schools: 2 \ **Teachers:** 76 \ **Students:** 700 \ **Special Ed Students:** 136 \ **LEP Students:** 3 \ **College-Bound:** 78% \ **Ethnic:** Asian 1%, African American 1%, Hispanic 1%, Caucasian 96% \ **Exp:** $349 (High) \ **Poverty:** 22% \ **Title I:** $380,023 \ **Special Education:** $2,396,000 \ **Open-Close:** 09/09 - 06/25 \ **DTBP:** $359 (High)

Stephen Zielinski 1	Naomi Zuckerman 2,4,83,88,91
Lance Heitmann 3,5	Heather Mott 6*
Dina Ganoug 7*	Stacy Clarke 11,58*
Liz McCheyne 16,82*	Cathy Flanders 35*
Kevin Webster 37*	Sean Green 38,83*
Peter Jennings 67	Mike Pliss 73*
Daniel Schanck 77*	Michele Wolff 273*
Emily Sturidvant 274	Robert Hermanet 286*

Public Schs..Principal	Grd	Prgm	Enr/#Cls	SN	
South Seneca Central Elem Sch 8326 Main St, Interlaken 14847 Adam Rundell	PK-5	T	317 31	45%	607/869-9636 Fax 607/532-8540
South Seneca Middle High Sch 7263 Main St, Ovid 14521 Tim Houseknecht	6-12	T	342 40	47%	607/869-9636 Fax 607/869-9553

- **Waterloo Central School Dist** PID: 00771156 315/539-1500
  109 Washington St, Waterloo 13165 Fax 315/539-1504

Schools: 4 \ **Teachers:** 143 \ **Students:** 1,538 \ **Special Ed Students:** 304 \ **LEP Students:** 15 \ **Ethnic:** Asian 1%, African American 4%, Hispanic 5%, Caucasian 90% \ **Exp:** $676 (High) \ **Poverty:** 17% \ **Title I:** $518,742 \ **Special Education:** $3,856,000 \ **Open-Close:** 09/02 - 06/24 \ **DTBP:** $379 (High)

Terri Bavis 1	Mark Socola 2
Jeffery Mochan 3,91	Brian Corey 4*
Dallah Lasson 5	Christal Kent 6,35
Sherri Monell 7,58,79	Jennifer Hayden ... 8,11,15,31,57,69,271,288
Tim Lincoln 28	Katie Wright 36*
Ellen Hughes 67	Todd Conrow 76
Kathleen Bremer 90*	

Public Schs..Principal	Grd	Prgm	Enr/#Cls	SN	
Lafayette Intermediate Sch 71 Inslee St, Waterloo 13165 Shaun Merrill	3-5	T	366 18	59%	315/539-1530 Fax 315/539-1529
Skoi Yase Primary Sch 65 Fayette St, Waterloo 13165 Elizabeth Springer	K-2	T	331 19	57%	315/539-1520 Fax 315/539-1527
Waterloo High Sch 96 Stark St, Waterloo 13165 Mary Thomas-Madonna	9-12	ATV	488 50	55%	315/539-1550 Fax 315/539-1536
Waterloo Middle Sch 65 Center St, Waterloo 13165 Vince Vitale	6-8	T	353 55	56%	315/539-1540 Fax 315/539-1534

SENECA PRIVATE SCHOOLS

Private Schs..Principal	Grd	Prgm	Enr/#Cls	SN
Fayette Mennonite Sch 1468 Leader Rd, Waterloo 13165 Lee Vimmerman	1-8		40 2	315/277-0454

---

1 Superintendent	8 Curric/Instruct K-12	19 Chief Financial Officer	29 Family/Consumer Science	39 Social Studies K-12	49 English/Lang Arts Elem	59 Special Education Elem	69 Academic Assessment
2 Bus/Finance/Purchasing	9 Curric/Instruct Elem	20 Art K-12	30 Adult Education	40 Social Studies Elem	50 English/Lang Arts Sec	60 Special Education Sec	70 Research/Development
3 Buildings And Grounds	10 Curric/Instruct Sec	21 Art Elem	31 Career/Sch-to-Work K-12	41 Social Studies Sec	51 Reading K-12	61 Foreign/World Lang K-12	71 Public Information
4 Food Service	11 Federal Program	22 Art Sec	32 Career/Sch-to-Work Elem	42 Science K-12	52 Reading Elem	62 Foreign/World Lang Elem	72 Summer School
5 Transportation	12 Title I	23 Music K-12	33 Career/Sch-to-Work Sec	43 Science Elem	53 Reading Sec	63 Foreign/World Lang Sec	73 Instructional Tech
6 Athletic	13 Title V	24 Music Elem	34 Early Childhood Ed	44 Science Sec	54 Remedial Reading K-12	64 Religious Education K-12	74 Inservice Training
7 Health Services	14 Instructional Media Svcs	25 Music Sec	35 Health/Phys Education	45 Math K-12	55 Remedial Reading Elem	65 Religious Education Elem	75 Marketing/Distributive
	15 Asst Superintendent	26 Business Education	36 Guidance Services K-12	46 Math Elem	56 Remedial Reading Sec	66 Religious Education Sec	76 Info Systems
	16 Instructional Media Svcs	27 Career & Tech Ed	37 Guidance Services Elem	47 Math Sec	57 Bilingual/ELL	67 School Board President	77 Psychological Assess
	17 Chief Operations Officer	28 Technology Education	38 Guidance Services Sec	48 English/Lang Arts K-12	58 Special Education K-12	68 Teacher Personnel	78 Affirmative Action
	18 Chief Academic Officer						

New York School Directory

St Lawrence County

Finger Lakes Christian Sch	PK-12	65	315/568-2216
2291 State Route 89, Seneca Falls 13148		8	Fax 315/568-6638
Scott VanKirk			
Seneca Bible Bapt Chrn Academy	K-12	15	315/568-9100
1859 US Route 20, Seneca Falls 13148		4	Fax 315/257-0228
Terry Fenton			

ST LAWRENCE COUNTY

ST LAWRENCE COUNTY SCHOOLS

County Schs..Principal	Grd	Prgm	Enr/#Cls	SN	
Northwest Career Tech Ed Ctr	Voc	AG	200		315/393-4570
1000 Park St, Ogdensburg 13669			10		Fax 315/393-4724
Larry Jenne					
Seaway Area Tech Center	Voc	AG	500		315/353-2293
7225 State Highway 56, Norwood 13668			20		Fax 315/353-7334
Stephen Putman					
Southwest Technical Center	Voc	AG	250		315/287-3590
3606 State Highway 58, Gouverneur 13642			12		Fax 315/287-2720
Lori Sheffield					

ST LAWRENCE PUBLIC SCHOOLS

• **Brasher Falls School Dist** PID: 00768989   315/389-5131
34 George St, Brasher Falls 13613   Fax 315/389-5245

Schools: 3 \ **Teachers:** 82 \ **Students:** 1,000 \ **Special Ed Students:** 147 \ **Ethnic:** African American 1%, Hispanic 2%, Native American: 2%, Caucasian 95% \ **Exp:** $155 (Low) \ **Poverty:** 18% \ **Title I:** $410,651 \ **Special Education:** $1,601,000 \ **Open-Close:** 09/04 - 06/25 \ **DTBP:** $341 (High)

Robert Stewart 1		Cynthia Fraser 2	
Timothy Redmond 3,5		Melanie Cline 4*	
Joey Reome 6		Carol Hallahan 7,85*	
Karen Locey 11		Johnathan Hirschey 12,73,295*	
Rebecca Dullea 16*		Rachel Baxter 38,83*	
Katherine Levigne 58		Seth Belt 67	
Cindy Delisle 271			

Public Schs..Principal	Grd	Prgm	Enr/#Cls	SN	
St Lawrence Elem Sch	PK-4	T	402	58%	315/389-5131
1039 State Highway 11C, Brasher Falls 13613			35		Fax 315/389-4651
Johnathan Hirschey					
St Lawrence Middle Sch	5-8	TV	312	56%	315/389-5131
1039 State Highway 11C, Brasher Falls 13613					Fax 315/389-4185
Christopher Rose					
St Lawrence Senior High Sch	9-12	TV	286	52%	315/389-5131
1039 State Highway 11C, Brasher Falls 13613			50		Fax 315/389-4600
Kristen Zender					

• **Canton Central School Dist** PID: 00768355   315/386-8561
99 State St, Canton 13617   Fax 315/386-1323

Schools: 3 \ **Teachers:** 103 \ **Students:** 1,000 \ **Special Ed Students:** 229 \ **LEP Students:** 5 \ **Ethnic:** Asian 1%, African American 1%, Hispanic 2%, Caucasian 96% \ **Exp:** $287 (Med) \ **Poverty:** 13% \ **Title I:** $349,455 \ **Special Education:** $3,296,000 \ **Open-Close:** 09/03 - 06/24 \ **DTBP:** $394 (High)

Ronald Burke 1		Denise Folsom 2	
Scott Sanderson 3*		Bluejay Fenlong 4	
Tawn Evans 5		William Porter 6*	
Joseph McDonough 9*		Kelly Finnerty 11,34,58	
Jeff Kelly 16,73,82,295*		Julia Bailey 16*	
Victor Rycroft 67		Maryjo Furnia 294	

Public Schs..Principal	Grd	Prgm	Enr/#Cls	SN	
F S Banford Elem Sch	PK-4	T	505	45%	315/386-8561
99 State St, Canton 13617			20		
Viola Schmid-Doyle					
H C Williams High Sch	9-12	TV	373	38%	315/386-8561
99 State St, Canton 13617			40		Fax 315/379-1239
Doug Dominy					
J M McKenney Middle Sch	5-8	TV	359	50%	315/386-8561
99 State St, Canton 13617			24		
Joseph McDonough					

• **Clifton-Fine Central Sch Dist** PID: 00768408   315/848-3333
11 Hall Ave, Star Lake 13690   Fax 315/848-3378

Schools: 1 \ **Teachers:** 35 \ **Students:** 295 \ **Special Ed Students:** 57 \ **Ethnic:** Asian 1%, African American 1%, Hispanic 1%, Native American: 2%, Caucasian 96% \ **Exp:** $258 (Med) \ **Poverty:** 19% \ **Title I:** $142,626 \ **Special Education:** $484,000 \ **Open-Close:** 09/08 - 06/24 \ **DTBP:** $381 (High)

Matthew Southwick 1		Colleen Hayers 2	
Randy Collins 4*		James McCaul 6	
Rebecca Bascom 11,73*		Traci Southwick 31,36,69,83,274*	
Trent Curry 35		Joseph Ruddy 58*	
Jeremy Thompson 67		Angela Oliver 71,97	
Cathy Lelemer 752			

Public Schs..Principal	Grd	Prgm	Enr/#Cls	SN	
Clifton-Fine Central Sch	PK-12	T	295	70%	315/848-3333
11 Hall Ave, Star Lake 13690			30		
Rebecca Bascom					

• **Colton Pierrepont School Dist** PID: 00768422   315/262-2100
4921 State Highway 56, Colton 13625   Fax 315/262-2644

Schools: 1 \ **Teachers:** 38 \ **Students:** 368 \ **Special Ed Students:** 48 \ **College-Bound:** 25% \ **Ethnic:** Caucasian 100% \ **Exp:** $406 (High) \ **Poverty:** 15% \ **Title I:** $82,297 \ **Special Education:** $116,000 \ **Open-Close:** 09/03 - 06/25

James Nee 1,288		Dale Munn 2,11,19	
Craig Bogart 6*		Sarah Long 7*	
Lianne Knight 12,58,77,79,296,298		Melinda Miller 16*	
Heather Rousell 36*		Danelle Edwards 57	
Cindy McLean 67		Peter Edwards 73	
Nancy McKinley 273*			

---

79 Student Personnel	91 Safety/Security	275 Response To Intervention	298 Grant Writer/Ptnrships	**School Programs**	**Social Media**
80 Driver Ed/Safety	92 Magnet School	277 Remedial Math K-12	750 Chief Innovation Officer	A = Alternative Program	
81 Gifted/Talented	93 Parental Involvement	280 Literacy Coach	751 Chief of Staff	G = Adult Classes	![f] = Facebook
82 Video Services	95 Tech Prep Program	285 STEM	752 Social Emotional Learning	M = Magnet Program	
83 Substance Abuse Prev	97 Chief Infomation Officer	286 Digital Learning		T = Title I Schoolwide	![t] = Twitter
84 Erate	98 Chief Technology Officer	288 Common Core Standards	**Other School Types**	V = Career & Tech Ed Programs	
85 AIDS Education	270 Accountability	294 Character Education	Ⓐ = Alternative School		
88 Alternative/At Risk	271 Migrant Education	295 Network System	Ⓒ = Charter School	New Schools are shaded	
89 Multi-Cultural Curriculum	273 Teacher Mentor	296 Title II Programs	Ⓜ = Magnet School	New Superintendents and Principals are bold	
90 Social Work	274 Before/After Sch	297 Webmaster	Ⓨ = Year-Round School	Personnel with email addresses are underscored	

NY-209

St Lawrence County

Market Data Retrieval

Public Schs..Principal	Grd	Prgm	Enr/#Cls	SN	
Colton Pierrepont Ctl Sch 4921 State Highway 56, Colton 13625 James Nee	PK-12	T	368 30	37%	315/262-2100

• Edwards-Knox Central Sch Dist PID: 00768604   315/562-8131
2512 County Route 24, Hermon 13652   Fax 315/562-2477

Schools: 1 \ **Teachers:** 46 \ **Students:** 537 \ **Special Ed Students:** 119 \ **College-Bound:** 66% \ **Ethnic:** Hispanic 2%, Native American: 1%, Caucasian 96% \ **Exp:** $264 (Med) \ **Poverty:** 18% \ **Title I:** $220,213 \ **Special Education:** $1,433,000 \ **Open-Close:** 09/08 - 06/25 \ **DTBP:** $360 (High) \

Erin Woods 1,11	Glenda Morales-Hanley 2*
Christopher Harris 3	Rob White 6*
Amy Sykes 10,274	Lura Hughes 12,288*
Megan McGrath 13,16*	Samantha Deleel 37,270*
Linda Alford 38,69*	Sherry White 58*
Penny Allen 67,83	Caleb Fuller 71,97
Kristin Grant 73*	Steve Szczepanski 85*
Jaime Gotham 93*	Rod Hooper 286*

Public Schs..Principal	Grd	Prgm	Enr/#Cls	SN	
Edwards-Knox Central Sch 2512 County Route 24, Hermon 13652 Amy Sykes \ Lura Hughes	PK-12	TV	537 39	51%	315/562-8131

• Gouverneur Ctl School Dist PID: 00768460   315/287-4870
133 E Barney St, Gouverneur 13642   Fax 315/287-4736

Schools: 3 \ **Teachers:** 125 \ **Students:** 1,515 \ **Special Ed Students:** 277 \ **LEP Students:** 8 \ **College-Bound:** 58% \ **Ethnic:** African American 1%, Hispanic 2%, Caucasian 97% \ **Exp:** $428 (High) \ **Poverty:** 19% \ **Title I:** $816,449 \ **Special Education:** $4,196,000 \ **Open-Close:** 09/08 - 06/25 \ **DTBP:** $359 (High)

Lauren French 1	Carol LaSala 2,78
Harold Simmons 3	Christine Bristol 4*
Kelley Moore 5	Christopher Marshall 6,35
Beth Martin 7,83	Dr Donna Runner 8,11,288,296,298
Kelly Wilson 16*	Patricia Bush 31,36,69*
Mandi Sanchez 57	Robyn Knowlton 58,77
David Fenlong 67	Shannon Mattice 71,73,76,97,295
Cory Wood 88,270*	

Public Schs..Principal	Grd	Prgm	Enr/#Cls	SN	
Gouverneur Elem Sch 111 Gleason St, Gouverneur 13642 **Charity Zawatski**	PK-4	T	620 20	65%	315/287-2260 Fax 315/287-0073
Gouverneur High Sch 113 E Barney St, Gouverneur 13642 Cory Wood	9-12	GTV	435 51	55%	315/287-1900 Fax 315/287-5513
Gouverneur Middle Sch 25 Wilson St, Gouverneur 13642 Jessica Sullivan	5-8	T	460	66%	315/287-3200

• Hammond Central School Distict PID: 00768537   315/324-5931
51 S Main St, Hammond 13646   Fax 315/324-6057

Schools: 1 \ **Teachers:** 26 \ **Students:** 257 \ **Special Ed Students:** 40 \ **College-Bound:** 50% \ **Ethnic:** African American 1%, Caucasian 99% \ **Exp:** $336 (High) \ **Poverty:** 20% \ **Title I:** $142,004 \ **Special Education:** $385,000 \ **Open-Close:** 09/08 - 06/25 \ **DTBP:** $349 (High)

Douglas McQueer 1	Tammy Gallagher 2*
Lenny Bickelhaupt 3,5	Diane Ayotte 6,11
Trisha Storie 8,36,57,58,69,88,271	Penny Slate 16,73,295*
Jennifer Gardner 67	Timm Scagel 77
Kristin Towne 280,285,288,296,298	

Public Schs..Principal	Grd	Prgm	Enr/#Cls	SN	
Hammond Central Sch 51 S Main St, Hammond 13646 Kristin Towne	PK-12	ATV	257 33	53%	315/324-5931

• Hermon-DeKalb Central Sch Dist PID: 00768551   315/347-3442
709 E DeKalb Rd, De Kalb Jct 13630   Fax 315/347-3817

Schools: 1 \ **Teachers:** 37 \ **Students:** 430 \ **Special Ed Students:** 75 \ **LEP Students:** 3 \ **College-Bound:** 61% \ **Ethnic:** African American 2%, Hispanic 2%, Caucasian 96% \ **Exp:** $413 (High) \ **Poverty:** 15% \ **Title I:** $185,361 \ **Special Education:** $973,000 \ **Open-Close:** 09/04 - 06/25 \ **DTBP:** $359 (High)

Mark White 1	Janet Boyd 2
Thomas Fetcie 4*	Megan Foster 5,57,296*
Shelley Arno 6	Jill Morrill 7,83*
Edith Seymour 11,69,73,76*	Andrew Gillie 58,77*
Ronald Smith 67	

Public Schs..Principal	Grd	Prgm	Enr/#Cls	SN	
Hermon-DeKalb Ctl Sch 709 E DeKalb Rd, De Kalb Jct 13630 Megan Foster	PK-12	T	430 35	64%	315/347-3442

• Heuvelton Central School Dist PID: 00768587   315/344-2414
87 Washington St, Heuvelton 13654   Fax 315/344-2349

Schools: 1 \ **Teachers:** 47 \ **Students:** 580 \ **Special Ed Students:** 70 \ **College-Bound:** 77% \ **Ethnic:** African American 1%, Hispanic 1%, Caucasian 98% \ **Exp:** $276 (Med) \ **Poverty:** 19% \ **Title I:** $500,042 \ **Special Education:** $1,052,000 \ **Open-Close:** 09/08 - 06/25 \ **DTBP:** $351 (High) \

Jesse Coburn 1	Michael Robinson 2
Kevin Gamble 3	Bill Rupp 5
David Steele 6*	Maryann Weldon 7,35,83,85*
Nicole LeBeau 8*	Roberta Stillan-Dowman 12
Joan Fischer 16,274*	Kendra Quinlan 31,36,69,271,294*
Michelle Desormeaux 51,54*	Andrew Martin 67
Andrew Bigelow 73,295*	Stephanie Gilbert 77*

Public Schs..Principal	Grd	Prgm	Enr/#Cls	SN	
Heuvelton Central Sch 87 Washington St, Heuvelton 13654 Nicole LeBeau \ Shannon Jordan	PK-12	T	580 25	48%	315/344-2414

• Lisbon Central School Dist PID: 00768628   315/393-4951
6866 County Route 10, Lisbon 13658   Fax 315/393-7666

Schools: 1 \ **Teachers:** 51 \ **Students:** 587 \ **Special Ed Students:** 75 \ **LEP Students:** 4 \ **Ethnic:** Asian 1%, Hispanic 1%, Caucasian 98% \ **Exp:** $185 (Low) \ **Poverty:** 10% \ **Title I:** $146,526 \ **Special Education:** $295,000 \ **Open-Close:** 09/08 - 06/25 \ **DTBP:** $347 (High)

Patrick Farrand 1	Mike Robinson 2,11
Timothy Gerome 3*	Rick Anderson 4*
Julia Morse 8,31,36,69*	Liz Hafer 9,58
Tina Bush 9,58	Rachel Mouthrop 16*

1	Superintendent	8	Curric/Instruct K-12	19	Chief Financial Officer	29	Family/Consumer Science	39	Social Studies K-12	49 English/Lang Arts K-12	59 Special Education Elem	69 Academic Assessment
2	Bus/Finance/Purchasing	9	Curric/Instruct Elem	20	Art K-12	30	Adult Education	40	Social Studies Elem	50 English/Lang Arts Sec	60 Special Education Sec	70 Research/Development
3	Buildings And Grounds	10	Curric/Instruct Sec	21	Art Elem	31	Career/Sch-to-Work K-12	41	Social Studies Sec	51 Reading K-12	61 Foreign/World Lang K-12	71 Public Information
4	Food Service	11	Federal Program	22	Art Sec	32	Career/Sch-to-Work Elem	42	Science K-12	52 Reading Elem	62 Foreign/World Lang Elem	72 Summer School
5	Transportation	12	Title I	23	Music K-12	33	Career/Sch-to-Work Sec	43	Science Elem	53 Reading Sec	63 Foreign/World Lang Sec	73 Instructional Tech
6	Athletic	13	Title V	24	Music Elem	34	Early Childhood Ed	44	Science Sec	54 Remedial Reading K-12	64 Religious Education K-12	74 Inservice Training
7	Health Services	14	Instructional Media Svcs	25	Music Sec	35	Health/Phys Education	45	Math K-12	55 Remedial Reading Elem	65 Religious Education Elem	75 Marketing/Distributive
		15	Asst Superintendent	26	Business Education	36	Guidance Services K-12	46	Math Elem	56 Remedial Reading Sec	66 Religious Education Sec	76 Info Systems
		16	Instructional Media Svcs	27	Career & Tech Ed	37	Guidance Services Elem	47	Math Sec	57 Bilingual/ELL	67 School Board President	77 Psychological Assess
		17	Chief Operations Officer	28	Technology Education	38	Guidance Services Sec	48	English/Lang Arts K-12	58 Special Education K-12	68 Teacher Personnel	78 Affirmative Action

New York School Directory
St Lawrence County

Lauren Morley .... 28,57,88*   Andrea Randle 67

Public Schs..Principal	Grd	Prgm	Enr/#Cls	SN	
Lisbon Central Sch 6866 County Route 10, Lisbon 13658 Staci Vaughn \ Lauren Morley	PK-12	T	587 50	40%	315/393-4951

● **Madrid-Waddington Central SD** PID: 00768654   315/322-5746
2582 State Highway 345, Madrid 13660   Fax 315/322-4462

> **Schools:** 1 \ **Teachers:** 57 \ **Students:** 647 \ **Special Ed Students:** 109 \ **LEP Students:** 3 \ **College-Bound:** 74% \ **Ethnic:** Hispanic 2%, Caucasian 98% \ **Exp:** $209 (Med) \ **Poverty:** 17% \ **Title I:** $255,240 \ **Special Education:** $1,394,000 \ **Open-Close:** 09/03 - 06/25 \ f

Eric Burke 1,11	Julie Bresett 2
Lori McIntosh 2	James Murry 3
Steve Adams 4	Craig Ashley 5
Bryan Harmer 6	Amber Murphy 7
Matthew Daley 9,34,52,55,57*	Joseph Binion 10,12
Meghan Gabri 16,82	Toni Siddon 31,36,58,69,88,271,752
Tina Wilson- Bush 67	Michelle Burke 73,295
Jen Nichols 77	

Public Schs..Principal	Grd	Prgm	Enr/#Cls	SN	
Madrid-Waddington Central Sch 2582 State Highway 345, Madrid 13660 Joseph Binion \ Matthew Daley	PK-12	V	647 36	39%	315/322-5746 f

● **Massena Central School Dist** PID: 00768692   315/764-3700
84 Nightengale Ave, Massena 13662   Fax 315/764-3701

> **Schools:** 5 \ **Teachers:** 201 \ **Students:** 2,500 \ **Special Ed Students:** 500 \ **LEP Students:** 3 \ **College-Bound:** 71% \ **Ethnic:** Asian 1%, African American 2%, Hispanic 2%, Native American: 9%, Caucasian 87% \ **Exp:** $167 (Low) \ **Poverty:** 20% \ **Title I:** $1,243,663 \ **Special Education:** $5,227,000 \ **Open-Close:** 09/08 - 06/25 \ **DTBP:** $215 (High)

Patrick Brady 1	Cindy Myers 2
Greg Tessier 3	Peter Bertrand 4
Allen Rowledge 5	Timothy Hayes 6,35
Judy Gilman 7*	Evelyn Fiske 12,69,288,298
Jonathan Hunkins 25*	Robert Jordan 36*
Susan Lambert 58,79,271	Patrick Bronchetti 67
Erin Covell 83,88*	William Seguin 91*

Public Schs..Principal	Grd	Prgm	Enr/#Cls	SN	
J W Leary Junior High Sch 1 School St, Massena 13662 Alan Oliver	7-8	TV	425 30	56%	315/764-3720 Fax 315/764-3723
Jefferson Elem Sch 84 Nightengale Ave, Massena 13662 Duane Richards	PK-6	T	435 21	66%	315/764-3730 Fax 315/764-3739
Madison Elem Sch 25 Owl Ave, Massena 13662 Danielle Chapman	PK-6	T	465 18	65%	315/764-3740 Fax 315/764-3743
Massena High Sch 84 Nightengale Ave, Massena 13662 Sarah Boyce	9-12	TV	809 54	56%	315/764-3710 Fax 315/764-3752
Nightengale Elem Sch 84 Nightengale Ave, Massena 13662 Amy Hornung	PK-6	T	431 22	50%	315/764-3750 Fax 315/764-3753

● **Morristown Ctl School Dist** PID: 00768783   315/375-8814
408 Gouverneur St, Morristown 13664   Fax 315/375-8604

> **Schools:** 1 \ **Teachers:** 34 \ **Students:** 333 \ **Special Ed Students:** 50 \ **Ethnic:** Caucasian 100% \ **Exp:** $242 (Med) \ **Poverty:** 19% \ **Title I:** $164,591 \ **Special Education:** $414,000 \ **Open-Close:** 09/08 - 06/25 \ **DTBP:** $369 (High)

Staci Vaughn 1,11,288	Kimberly Fuller 2
John Barse 3,5	Richard Anderson 4
David Doe 8,88,294*	Roberta Stillin-Dowman 12
Nicki Odonell 58	Dr Lawrence Kring 67
Foster Champine 73	

Public Schs..Principal	Grd	Prgm	Enr/#Cls	SN	
Morristown Central Sch 408 Gouverneur St, Morristown 13664 David Doe	PK-12	T	333 22	60%	315/375-8814

● **Norwood-Norfolk Ctl SD** PID: 00768800   315/353-9951
7852 State Highway 56, Norwood 13668   Fax 315/353-2467

> **Schools:** 3 \ **Teachers:** 84 \ **Students:** 987 \ **Special Ed Students:** 156 \ **Ethnic:** Asian 1%, Hispanic 1%, Native American: 1%, Caucasian 97% \ **Exp:** $310 (High) \ **Poverty:** 16% \ **Title I:** $411,597 \ **Special Education:** $2,694,000 \ **Open-Close:** 09/04 - 06/25 \ **DTBP:** $431 (High) \ f

James Cruikshank 1	Lisa Mitras 2,11
Bluejay Fenlong 4	Kim Brown 7
Carrie French 37*	Jordan Hellmer 38
Vicky Derouchie 57*	Cassidy Mattimore 58
Artie Frego 67	Dave Coffey 73

Public Schs..Principal	Grd	Prgm	Enr/#Cls	SN	
Norwood-Norfolk Elem Sch 7852 State Highway 56, Norwood 13668 Rebecca Kingsley	PK-4	T	381 30	58%	315/353-6674 Fax 315/353-2408
Norwood-Norfolk Middle Sch 7852 State Highway 56, Norwood 13668 William Lint	5-8	T	312	60%	315/353-6631
Norwood-Norfolk Sr High Sch 7852 State Highway 56, Norwood 13668 Robin Fetter	9-12	T	294 60	50%	315/353-6631 Fax 315/353-2480

● **Ogdensburg City School Dist** PID: 00768848   315/393-0900
1100 State St, Ogdensburg 13669   Fax 315/393-2767

> **Schools:** 3 \ **Teachers:** 134 \ **Students:** 1,535 \ **Special Ed Students:** 323 \ **LEP Students:** 3 \ **College-Bound:** 73% \ **Ethnic:** African American 1%, Hispanic 1%, Caucasian 98% \ **Exp:** $231 (Med) \ **Poverty:** 20% \ **Title I:** $651,622 \ **Special Education:** $4,498,000 \ **Open-Close:** 09/03 - 06/25 \ **DTBP:** $305 (High)

Kevin Kendall 1,11	Patricia Smithers 2
James McCarthy 3,91*	Brian Mitchell 4*
Sabrina Charleston 5	Anthony Bjork 6*
Jacquelyn Kelly 8,15,58	Kimberly Richards 58
Ronald Johnson 67	Katrina Putman 69

Public Schs..Principal	Grd	Prgm	Enr/#Cls	SN	
John F Kennedy Elem Sch 801-809 Park St, Ogdensburg 13669 Christina Frank \ Sueellen Bouchard	PK-6	T	534 45	57%	315/393-4264 Fax 315/394-0480

---

79 Student Personnel	91 Safety/Security	275 Response To Intervention	298 Grant Writer/Ptnrships	**School Programs**	**Social Media**		
80 Driver Ed/Safety	92 Magnet School	277 Remedial Math K-12	750 Chief Innovation Officer	A = Alternative Program	f = Facebook		
81 Gifted/Talented	93 Parental Involvement	280 Literacy Coach	751 Chief of Staff	G = Adult Classes			
82 Video Services	95 Tech Prep Program	285 STEM	752 Social Emotional Learning	M = Magnet Program	t = Twitter		
83 Substance Abuse Prev	97 Chief Infomation Officer	286 Digital Learning		T = Title I Schoolwide			
84 Erate	98 Chief Technology Officer	288 Common Core Standards	**Other School Types**	V = Career & Tech Ed Programs			
85 AIDS Education	270 Accountability	294 Character Education	Ⓐ = Alternative School				
88 Alternative/At Risk	271 Migrant Education	295 Network System	Ⓒ = Charter School	New Schools are shaded			
89 Multi-Cultural Curriculum	273 Teacher Mentor	296 Title II Programs	Ⓜ = Magnet School	New Superintendents and Principals are bold			
90 Social Work	274 Before/After Sch	297 Webmaster	Ⓨ = Year-Round School	Personnel with email addresses are underscored			

NY-211

Steuben County

Market Data Retrieval

Madill Elem Sch 800 Jefferson Ave, Ogdensburg 13669 Amy DiSalvo	PK-6	T	298 20	61%	315/393-7729 Fax 315/393-0419
Ogdensburg Free Academy 1100 State St, Ogdensburg 13669 David Price \ Cynthia Tuttle	7-12	TV	703	54%	315/393-0900

• **Parishville Hopkinton Sch Dist** PID: 00768915   315/265-4642
12 County Route 47, Parishville 13672   Fax 315/268-1309

Schools: 1 \ **Teachers:** 36 \ **Students:** 420 \ **Special Ed Students:** 71 \ **College-Bound:** 75% \ **Ethnic:** Caucasian 99% \ **Exp:** $252 (Med) \ **Poverty:** 13% \ **Title I:** $116,353 \ **Special Education:** $822,000 \ **Open-Close:** 09/08 - 06/24 \ **DTBP:** $363 (High)

Dr William Collins 1	Collene Aires 2
Francis Barney 3,5	Melany Kline 4
Steven Coffin 6,10,31,74,83,275*	Brooke Reid 8,11,58,270,298*
Kimberly Scott 16,82*	Melissa Scudder 33,36,69,88,271,296*
Erin Casey 55*	Timothy Zellweger 67
Melissa Lovely 73,76,295	April Fullerton 752

Public Schs..Principal	Grd	Prgm	Enr/#Cls	SN	
Parishville Hopkinton Ctl Sch 12 County Route 47, Parishville 13672 Steven Coffin \ Brooke Reid	PK-12	T	420 48	35%	315/265-4642

• **Potsdam Central School Dist** PID: 00768941   315/265-2000
29 Leroy St, Potsdam 13676   Fax 315/265-2048

Schools: 3 \ **Teachers:** 105 \ **Students:** 1,200 \ **Special Ed Students:** 214 \ **LEP Students:** 23 \ **College-Bound:** 95% \ **Ethnic:** Asian 3%, African American 1%, Hispanic 2%, Caucasian 93% \ **Exp:** $182 (Low) \ **Poverty:** 12% \ **Title I:** $339,350 \ **Special Education:** $3,106,000 \ **Open-Close:** 09/03 - 06/24 \ **DTBP:** $344 (High)

Joann Chambers 1,11	Laura Hart 2
Patrick McLaughlin 3*	David Gravlin 4*
Kevin Kingsley 5	Mark Wilson 6*
Nichole Weakfall . 8,76,83,88,286,288,296,752	Jennifer Neaton 12,58
Robert Best 16,73*	Amy Stevenson 57*
James Hubbard 67	Joanna Cross 298

Public Schs..Principal	Grd	Prgm	Enr/#Cls	SN	
A A Kingston Middle Sch Outer Lawrence Ave, Potsdam 13676 Mark Bennett	5-8	T	409 24	39%	315/265-2000 Fax 315/265-8103
Lawrence Ave Elem Sch 46 Lawrence Ave, Potsdam 13676 Jennifer Gray	PK-4	T	522 40	39%	315/265-2000 Fax 315/265-5458
Potsdam High Sch 29 Leroy St, Potsdam 13676 Mark Bennett	8-12		400 57	30%	315/265-2000 Fax 315/265-8134

ST LAWRENCE CATHOLIC SCHOOLS

• **Diocese of Ogdensburg Ed Off** PID: 00769050   315/393-2920
622 Washington St, Ogdensburg 13669   Fax 866/314-7296

Schools: 9 \ **Students:** 1,293

Listing includes only schools located in this county. See District Index for location of Diocesan Offices.

Sr Ellen Rose Coughlin 1   Karen Donahue 8,11,15

Catholic Schs..Principal	Grd	Prgm	Enr/#Cls	SN	
St James Elem Sch 20 S Gordon St, Gouverneur 13642 Michele Lallier	PK-6		110 11		315/287-0130 Fax 315/287-0111
Trinity Catholic Sch 188 Main St, Massena 13662 Joyce Giroux	PK-6		187 18		315/769-5911 Fax 315/769-1185

ST LAWRENCE PRIVATE SCHOOLS

Private Schs..Principal	Grd	Prgm	Enr/#Cls	SN	
Akwesasne Freedom Sch 31 Indian Village Rd, Rooseveltown 13683 Tara Skidders	PK-9		75		518/358-2073
Holy Name of Jesus Academy 337 Trippany Rd, Massena 13662 Sr Prioress	PK-12		130		315/769-6030 Fax 315/769-6057
Little River Community Sch 1227 County Route 25, Canton 13617 Steve Molnar	K-12	A	34		315/379-9474
St Therese's Academy 68 County Rd 55, Nicholville 12965 Steven Soos	K-8		30 7		315/328-4027

ST LAWRENCE REGIONAL CENTERS

• **St Lawrence-Lewis BOCES** PID: 00769012   315/386-4504
40 W Main St, Canton 13617   Fax 315/386-3395

Thomas Burns 1	Amy Pastuf 2
Ginger Tebo 16	Larry Jenne 27,31
Roger Bennett 67	Rafael Olazagasti 68
Craig LaLonde 73	

STEUBEN COUNTY

STEUBEN COUNTY SCHOOLS

County Schs..Principal	Grd	Prgm	Enr/#Cls	SN	
Coopers Campus Cte 9579 Vocational Dr, Painted Post 14870 Richard Perkins	Voc	AG	400 18		607/962-3175 Fax 607/962-1579

1	Superintendent	8	Curric/Instruct K-12	19	Chief Financial Officer	29	Family/Consumer Science	39	Social Studies K-12
2	Bus/Finance/Purchasing	9	Curric/Instruct Elem	20	Art K-12	30	Adult Education	40	Social Studies Elem
3	Buildings And Grounds	10	Curric/Instruct Sec	21	Art Elem	31	Career/Sch-to-Work K-12	41	Social Studies Sec
4	Food Service	11	Federal Program	22	Art Sec	32	Career/Sch-to-Work Elem	42	Science K-12
5	Transportation	12	Title I	23	Music K-12	33	Career/Sch-to-Work Sec	43	Science Elem
6	Athletic	13	Title V	24	Music Elem	34	Early Childhood Ed	44	Science Sec
7	Health Services	14	Instructional Media Svcs	25	Music Sec	35	Health/Phys Education	45	Math K-12
		15	Asst Superintendent	26	Business Education	36	Guidance Services K-12	46	Math Elem
		16	Instructional Media Svcs	27	Career & Tech Ed	37	Guidance Services Elem	47	Math Sec
		17	Chief Operations Officer	28	Technology Education	38	Guidance Services Sec	48	English/Lang Arts K-12
		18	Chief Academic Officer						

49	English/Lang Arts Elem	59	Special Education Elem	69	Academic Assessment
50	English/Lang Arts Sec	60	Special Education Sec	70	Research/Development
51	Reading K-12	61	Foreign/World Lang K-12	71	Public Information
52	Reading Elem	62	Foreign/World Lang Elem	72	Summer School
53	Reading Sec	63	Foreign/World Lang Sec	73	Instructional Tech
54	Remedial Reading K-12	64	Religious Education K-12	74	Inservice Training
55	Remedial Reading Elem	65	Religious Education Elem	75	Marketing/Distributive
56	Remedial Reading Sec	66	Religious Education Sec	76	Info Systems
57	Bilingual/ELL	67	School Board President	77	Psychological Assess
58	Special Education K-12	68	Teacher Personnel	78	Affirmative Action

New York School Directory — Steuben County

Wildwood Campus Cte Voc AG 550 607/324-7880
1126 Bald Hill Rd, Hornell 14843   22   Fax 607/324-3842
Sally Deane Moshier

STEUBEN PUBLIC SCHOOLS

• **Addison Central School Dist** PID: 00771209 607/359-2245
7 Cleveland Dr Ste 101, Addison 14801 Fax 607/359-4480

Schools: 3 \ **Teachers:** 93 \ **Students:** 1,100 \ **Special Ed Students:** 184 \ **LEP Students:** 3 \ **Ethnic:** Asian 1%, African American 1%, Hispanic 1%, Caucasian 97% \ **Exp:** $245 (Med) \ **Poverty:** 22% \ **Title I:** $500,540 \ **Special Education:** $2,588,000 \ **Open-Close:** 09/08 - 06/24 \ **DTBP:** $359 (High)

Joseph Dioguardi	1	Rich Everly	2,298
James Smith	3,91	Pam Drumm	4*
Doug Lewis	5	Michael Makowiec	6
William Howe	8,11,286	Georgia Weed	9*
Angela Ingles	16*	Tanya Loomis	58,77,85,88*
Michelle Terwilliger	67	Scott Vang	73
Mary Clark	83		

Public Schs..Principal	Grd	Prgm	Enr/#Cls	SN	
Addison Jr Sr High Sch 1 Colwell St, Addison 14801 Kris Benton \ Jennifer Crane	6-12	ATV	553 40	51%	607/359-2241 Fax 607/359-3443
Tuscarora Elem Sch 7 Cleveland Dr, Addison 14801 Georgia Weed	K-5	T	424 35	57%	607/359-2262 Fax 607/359-4507
Valley Early Childhood Center 6786 County Route 119, Cameron Mills 14820 Tanya Loomis	PK-PK		74 8	48%	607/695-2636 Fax 607/695-2429

• **Arkport Central School Dist** PID: 00771247 607/295-7471
35 East Ave, Arkport 14807 Fax 607/295-7473

Schools: 1 \ **Teachers:** 43 \ **Students:** 475 \ **Special Ed Students:** 53 \ **LEP Students:** 11 \ **College-Bound:** 72% \ **Ethnic:** Asian 1%, Hispanic 4%, Caucasian 94% \ **Exp:** $396 (High) \ **Poverty:** 15% \ **Title I:** $119,963 \ **Special Education:** $764,000 \ **Open-Close:** 09/08 - 06/25

Jesse Harper	1,288	Traci McCarthy	4
Dale Steiner	6	Trica Smith	7,85*
Claire Smith	8,11,54,57,83,296,298	Christina Ferris	16,82*
Sarah Eggleston	36*	Patrick Flaitz	67

Public Schs..Principal	Grd	Prgm	Enr/#Cls	SN	
Arkport Central Sch 35 East Ave, Arkport 14807 Caiti Dewey	PK-12	T	475 35	40%	607/295-7471

• **Avoca Central School Dist** PID: 00771261 607/566-2221
17 Oliver St 29, Avoca 14809 Fax 607/566-2398

Schools: 1 \ **Teachers:** 47 \ **Students:** 440 \ **Special Ed Students:** 65 \ **Ethnic:** African American 1%, Hispanic 2%, Caucasian 96% \ **Exp:** $410 (High) \ **Poverty:** 15% \ **Title I:** $143,083 \ **Special Education:** $1,070,000 \ **Open-Close:** 09/08 - 06/30

Stephen Saxton	1,11	Michael Oyer	3
David Schubmehal	5	Stephanie Helgeland	9*
Steven Denaker	10,27*	Kelly Buisch	12,58,77

Megan Hubbard	67	Matthew Pfleegor	73

Public Schs..Principal	Grd	Prgm	Enr/#Cls	SN	
Avoca Central Sch 17 Oliver St 29, Avoca 14809 Steven Denaker \ Stephanie Helgeland	K-12	T	440 58	50%	607/566-2221

• **Bath Central School Dist** PID: 00771613 607/776-3301
25 Ellas Ave, Bath 14810 Fax 607/776-5021

Schools: 3 \ **Teachers:** 136 \ **Students:** 1,500 \ **Special Ed Students:** 220 \ **LEP Students:** 3 \ **College-Bound:** 64% \ **Ethnic:** African American 2%, Hispanic 1%, Caucasian 96% \ **Exp:** $239 (Med) \ **Poverty:** 19% \ **Title I:** $506,432 \ **Special Education:** $1,442,000 \ **Open-Close:** 09/08 - 06/24 \ **DTBP:** $361 (High)

Joseph Rumsey	1,11,83	Theresa McKinna	2
Anthony Colomaio	3,91	Derek Ortiz	5
Randy Abrams	6*	Randy Brezezski	11,71,286,288,296
Sheri Neu	35	Christina Snavely	57
Michelle Sincerbox	58	Michael Mishook	67
Christopher Smith	73,84	Ryan Finney	295

Public Schs..Principal	Grd	Prgm	Enr/#Cls	SN	
Dana L Lyon Middle Sch 25 Ellas Ave, Bath 14810 Jennifer Dabbracci	4-8	T	541 32	58%	607/776-4110 Fax 607/776-5625
Haverling High Sch 25 Ellas Ave, Bath 14810 Michael Siebert	9-12	GTV	443 45	46%	607/776-4107 Fax 607/776-1458
V E Wightman Primary Sch 216 Maple Hts, Bath 14810 Deborah Barlow	PK-3	T	518 48	54%	607/776-3301 Fax 607/776-4124

• **Campbell-Savona Ctl Sch Dist** PID: 00771302 607/527-9800
8455 County Route 125, Campbell 14821 Fax 607/527-9863

Schools: 2 \ **Teachers:** 77 \ **Students:** 829 \ **Special Ed Students:** 166 \ **LEP Students:** 3 \ **College-Bound:** 62% \ **Ethnic:** Asian 1%, Hispanic 2%, Caucasian 97% \ **Exp:** $257 (Med) \ **Poverty:** 17% \ **Title I:** $276,979 \ **Special Education:** $2,397,000 \ **Open-Close:** 09/08 - 06/25 \ **DTBP:** $359 (High)

Kathy Hagenbuch	1,11	Jason Rosno	2,15,78
Bob Wilson	3,91*	Pam Drumm	4*
Sarah Burgess	5	Caitlyn Bughan	6
Kim Mullikin	7	Chris Gill	8,69,273
Monique Knapp	35*	Angela Pavlick	57,58,77,79,270,271,275
Tom Hauryski	67	Lucinda Adams	73
Ronda Strawser	83,88*		

Public Schs..Principal	Grd	Prgm	Enr/#Cls	SN	
Campbell-Savona Elem Sch 64 E Lamoka Ave, Savona 14879 James Anderson	PK-6	T	442 50	49%	607/527-9800 Fax 607/527-9866
Campbell-Savona Jr Sr HS 8455 County Route 125, Campbell 14821 Kelley Meade	7-12	AT	387 50	52%	607/527-9800

---

79 Student Personnel	91 Safety/Security	275 Response To Intervention	298 Grant Writer/Ptnrships
80 Driver Ed/Safety	92 Magnet School	277 Remedial Math K-12	750 Chief Innovation Officer
81 Gifted/Talented	93 Parental Involvement	280 Literacy Coach	751 Chief of Staff
82 Video Services	95 Tech Prep Education	285 STEM	752 Social Emotional Learning
83 Substance Abuse Prev	97 Chief Information Officer	286 Digital Learning	
84 Erate	98 Chief Technology Officer	288 Common Core Standards	
85 AIDS Education	270 Character Education	294 Accountability	
88 Alternative/At Risk	271 Migrant Education	295 Network System	
89 Multi-Cultural Curriculum	273 Teacher Mentor	296 Title II Programs	
90 Social Work	274 Before/After Sch	297 Webmaster	

School Programs
A = Alternative Program
G = Adult Classes
M = Magnet Program
T = Title I Schoolwide
V = Career & Tech Ed Programs

Other School Types
Ⓐ = Alternative School
Ⓒ = Charter School
Ⓜ = Magnet School
Ⓨ = Year-Round School

Social Media
f = Facebook
t = Twitter

New Schools are shaded
New Superintendents and Principals are bold
Personnel with email addresses are underscored

Steuben County

Canisteo-Greenwood Central SD PID: 00771326
84 Greenwood St, Canisteo 14823
607/698-4225
Fax 607/698-2833

Schools: 2 \ **Teachers:** 88 \ **Students:** 1,000 \ **Special Ed Students:** 156 \ **College-Bound:** 60% \ **Ethnic:** Asian 1%, African American 1%, Hispanic 2%, Caucasian 97% \ **Exp:** $316 (High) \ **Poverty:** 14% \ **Title I:** $224,760 \ **Special Education:** $2,165,000 \ **Open-Close:** 09/08 - 06/25 \ **DTBP:** $359 (High) \ 📘

Tom Crook 1	Theresa McKenna 2*
Michelle Miller 4	Heidi Beecher 5
Chris Koehler 6	Teffenie Duschen 12,73,288*
Tricia Dodge 58*	Michael Nisbit 67

Public Schs..Principal	Grd	Prgm	Enr/#Cls	SN	
Canisteo-Greenwood Elem Sch 120 Greenwood St, Canisteo 14823 Colleen Brownell	PK-6	T	576 40	58%	607/698-4225 Fax 607/698-2345
Canisteo-Greenwood High Sch 84 Greenwood St, Canisteo 14823 Peter Reynolds	7-12	AT	453 55	50%	607/698-4225 Fax 607/698-2776

Corning-Painted Post Area SD PID: 00771376
165 Charles St, Painted Post 14870
607/936-3704
Fax 607/654-2727

Schools: 9 \ **Teachers:** 403 \ **Students:** 4,500 \ **Special Ed Students:** 910 \ **LEP Students:** 33 \ **Ethnic:** Asian 4%, African American 2%, Hispanic 3%, Caucasian 91% \ **Exp:** $290 (Med) \ **Poverty:** 11% \ **Title I:** $796,213 \ **Special Education:** $8,006,000 \ **Open-Close:** 09/08 - 06/25 \ **DTBP:** $236 (High) \ 📘

Michelle Caulfield 1	Paul Webster 2
William Pierce 3	Joseph Kilmer 4
Larry Eccleston 5	Damian Saks 6
Linda Perry 8,11,73,285,286,288	Jennifer Batzing 12,58
Jeff Delorme 15	Kerry Elsasser 15
Becky Henderson 58	Dr Dale Wexell 67
Bill Cameron 71	

Public Schs..Principal	Grd	Prgm	Enr/#Cls	SN	
Calvin U Smith Elem Sch 3414 Stanton St, Painted Post 14870 Heather Wolfe	K-5	T	281 23	51%	607/936-4156
Corning-Painted Post High Sch 201 Cantigney St, Corning 14830 Robin Sheehan	9-12		1,464 60	32%	607/654-2988
Corning-Painted Post Mid Sch 35 Victory Hwy, Painted Post 14870 Rick Kimble	6-8	T	986 50	42%	607/654-2966 Fax 607/654-2908
Erwin Valley Elem Sch 16 Beartown Rd, Painted Post 14870 Kate Merrill	K-5		436 20	28%	607/936-6514 Fax 607/654-2878
Frederick Carder Elem Sch 289 State St, Corning 14830 Dan Davis	K-5		479 25	37%	607/962-2454 Fax 607/654-2829
ⓐ High School Lrng Ctr-CCC 1 Academic Dr, Corning 14830 Frank Barber	10-12		30	63%	607/962-9283 Fax 607/962-9534
Hugh W Gregg Elem Sch 164 Flint Ave, Corning 14830 Ann Collins	K-5	T	228 13	46%	607/962-1514 Fax 607/654-2815
William E Severn Elem Sch 1 McMahon Ave, Corning 14830 John Whaley	K-5	T	437 22	53%	607/962-6844 Fax 607/654-2869

Winfield Street Elem Sch 193 Winfield St, Corning 14830 Michele Wright	K-5	T	216 14	61%	607/962-6706

Hammondsport Ctl School Dist PID: 00771584
8272 Main Street Ext, Hammondsport 14840
607/569-5200
Fax 607/569-5212

Schools: 2 \ **Teachers:** 54 \ **Students:** 450 \ **Special Ed Students:** 65 \ **College-Bound:** 55% \ **Ethnic:** African American 1%, Hispanic 3%, Caucasian 95% \ **Exp:** $445 (High) \ **Poverty:** 15% \ **Title I:** $125,449 \ **Special Education:** $532,000 \ **Open-Close:** 09/08 - 06/25 \ **DTBP:** $388 (High)

Kyle Bower 1	Cheryl Berlin 2
Emery Cummings 5	Daniel Conley 6*
Joni Makowiec 8	Joe Kohler 12
James Derr 38*	Katie Boyer 58,77*
Dennis Carlson 67	Michael Wooldrige 73,286
John Lowin 285	

Public Schs..Principal	Grd	Prgm	Enr/#Cls	SN	
Glenn Curtiss Elem Sch 8272 Main Street Ext, Hammondsport 14840 Joe Koehler	PK-6	T	237	51%	607/569-5200
Hammondsport Jr Sr High Sch 8272 Main Street Ext, Hammondsport 14840 Tad Rounds	7-12	ATV	189 60	45%	607/569-5200

Hornell City School Dist PID: 00771651
120 Raider Rd, Hornell 14843
607/324-1302
Fax 607/324-4060

Schools: 4 \ **Teachers:** 137 \ **Students:** 1,700 \ **Special Ed Students:** 306 \ **LEP Students:** 22 \ **College-Bound:** 65% \ **Ethnic:** Asian 1%, African American 3%, Hispanic 3%, Caucasian 93% \ **Exp:** $634 (High) \ **Poverty:** 23% \ **Title I:** $672,235 \ **Special Education:** $3,378,000 \ **Open-Close:** 09/08 - 06/25 \ **DTBP:** $375 (High)

Jeremy Palotti 1	Patrick Haitz 2
Shannon Davis 3,91	Tracie McCarthy 4
Steve Sleight 5	Erica Seibert 8,11
Amy Feeley 57,58,79,275	Kerry Davis 67
Nancy Shedlock 83*	Colby Moore 97
Jennifer Sorochin 285	

Public Schs..Principal	Grd	Prgm	Enr/#Cls	SN	
Bryant Elem Sch 173 Terry St, Hornell 14843 Jennifer Sorochin	2-3	T	249 10	58%	607/324-2171 Fax 607/324-5588
Hornell High Sch 134 Seneca St, Hornell 14843 Scott Carroll	7-12	T	726	47%	607/324-1303 Fax 607/324-6378
Hornell Intermediate Sch 71 Buffalo St, Hornell 14843 Sean Gaffney	4-6	T	351 31	58%	607/324-1304 Fax 607/324-1301
North Hornell Elem Sch 1 Avondale Ave, Hornell 14843 Barbara Kramer	PK-1	T	287 17	59%	607/324-0014 Fax 607/324-7478

Jasper Troupsburg Central SD PID: 00771742
3769 State Route 417, Jasper 14855
607/792-3675
Fax 607/792-3749

Schools: 2 \ **Teachers:** 46 \ **Students:** 450 \ **Special Ed Students:** 92 \ **Ethnic:** Asian 1%, Caucasian 98% \ **Exp:** $218 (Med) \ **Poverty:** 28% \ **Title I:** $427,467 \ **Special Education:** $813,000 \ **Open-Close:** 09/08 - 06/25 \ **DTBP:** $413 (High)

---

1 Superintendent	8 Curric/Instruct K-12	19 Chief Financial Officer	29 Family/Consumer Science	39 Social Studies K-12	49 English/Lang Arts Elem	59 Special Education Elem	69 Academic Assessment
2 Bus/Finance/Purchasing	9 Curric/Instruct Elem	20 Art K-12	30 Adult Education	40 Social Studies Elem	50 English/Lang Arts Sec	60 Special Education Sec	70 Research/Development
3 Buildings And Grounds	10 Curric/Instruct Sec	21 Art Elem	31 Career/Sch-to-Work K-12	41 Social Studies Sec	51 Reading K-12	61 Foreign/World Lang K-12	71 Public Information
4 Food Service	11 Federal Program	22 Art Sec	32 Career/Sch-to-Work Elem	42 Science K-12	52 Reading Elem	62 Foreign/World Lang Elem	72 Summer School
5 Transportation	12 Title I	23 Music K-12	33 Career/Sch-to-Work Sec	43 Science Elem	53 Reading Sec	63 Foreign/World Lang Sec	73 Instructional Tech
6 Athletic	13 Title V	24 Music Elem	34 Early Childhood Ed	44 Science Sec	54 Remedial Reading K-12	64 Religious Education K-12	74 Inservice Training
7 Health Services	15 Asst Superintendent	25 Music Sec	35 Health/Phys Education	45 Math K-12	55 Remedial Reading Elem	65 Religious Education Elem	75 Marketing/Distributive
	16 Instructional Media Svcs	26 Business Education	36 Guidance Services K-12	46 Math Elem	56 Remedial Reading Sec	66 Religious Education Sec	76 Info Systems
	17 Chief Operations Officer	27 Career & Tech Ed	37 Guidance Services Elem	47 Math Sec	57 Bilingual/ELL	67 School Board President	77 Psychological Assess
	18 Chief Academic Officer	28 Technology Education	38 Guidance Services Sec	48 English/Lang Arts K-12	58 Special Education K-12	68 Teacher Personnel	78 Affirmative Action

New York School Directory

Suffolk County

Michael Mead 1,11	Stephen Miskell 2
Robert Cornish 5	Jean Green 6
Lisa Howell 16*	Keith Krause 67
Christopher Parker 88*	

Public Schs..Principal	Grd	Prgm	Enr/#Cls	SN	
Jasper Troupsburg Elem Sch 908 State Route 36, Troupsburg 14885 Leeanne Jordan	K-6	T	200 15	58%	607/525-6301 Fax 607/525-6309
Jasper Troupsburg Jr Sr HS 3769 State Route 417, Jasper 14855 Christopher Parker	7-12	TV	201 30	50%	607/792-3690

• **Prattsburgh Central Sch Dist** PID: 00771766   607/522-3795
1 Academy St, Prattsburgh 14873   Fax 607/522-6221

Schools: 1 \ **Teachers:** 33 \ **Students:** 388 \ **Special Ed Students:** 67 \ **College-Bound:** 76% \ **Ethnic:** Asian 1%, African American 2%, Hispanic 1%, Caucasian 97% \ **Exp:** $198 (Low) \ **Poverty:** 23% \ **Title I:** $178,586 \ **Special Education:** $99,000 \ **Open-Close:** 09/04 - 06/25 \ **DTBP:** $347 (High)

Kory Bay 1	Greg Elliott 4*
Charlene Wilson 5	James Burke 6
Erin Peck 8*	Jeffrey Black 11
Amanda Mullen 16,82*	Aimee Bristol 36*
Brian Fleet 58*	Amy Dlugos 67

Public Schs..Principal	Grd	Prgm	Enr/#Cls	SN	
Prattsburgh Central Sch 1 Academy St, Prattsburgh 14873 Erin Peck \ Penny Kephart	PK-12	T	388 45	48%	607/522-3795 Fax 607/522-6230

• **Wayland-Cohocton Central SD** PID: 00771821   585/728-2211
2350 State Route 63, Wayland 14572   Fax 585/728-3566

Schools: 4 \ **Teachers:** 134 \ **Students:** 1,246 \ **Special Ed Students:** 163 \ **LEP Students:** 3 \ **Ethnic:** African American 1%, Caucasian 98% \ **Exp:** $367 (High) \ **Poverty:** 14% \ **Title I:** $316,847 \ **Special Education:** $3,667,000 \ **Open-Close:** 09/14 - 06/23 \ **DTBP:** $353 (High)

Eileen Feinman 1	Mary Briggs 2
Mike Donovan 3,91*	Rebecca Schorer 4
Tracey Proctor 5	James Brownell 6
Rebecca Wager 8,288,296	Katherine Wolcott 11,34,58*
Flo Cappiello 16,73,82*	Jennifer Billotte 27,36,69,75*
Deedee Kuhn 30*	Eileen Feinman 38*
Eric Joyner 57	Rich Rizzieri 67
Fred Grambs 76	Tanya Denee 93*
Allison Lana 273*	Sharon Manley 273,280*
Kristy Shafer 285	

Public Schs..Principal	Grd	Prgm	Enr/#Cls	SN	
Cohocton Elem Sch 30 Park Ave, Cohocton 14826 Adam Button	K-4	T	273 13	49%	585/384-5234 Fax 585/384-5677
Wayland Elem Sch 2350 State Route 63, Wayland 14572 Adam Button	PK-4	T	228	56%	585/728-2211
Wayland-Cohocton High Sch 2350 State Route 63, Wayland 14572 Josie Steiner	9-12		375	54%	585/728-2366
Wayland-Cohocton Middle Sch 2350 State Route 63, Wayland 14572 Scott Manne	5-8	GTV	405	56%	585/728-2551 Fax 585/728-2425

STEUBEN CATHOLIC SCHOOLS

• **Diocese of Rochester Ed Office** PID: 00733623
Listing includes only schools located in this county. See District Index for location of Diocesan Offices.

Catholic Schs..Principal	Grd	Prgm	Enr/#Cls	SN	
All Saints Academy 158 State St, Corning 14830 Tj Verzillo	PK-8		120 8		607/936-9234 Fax 607/936-1797

STEUBEN PRIVATE SCHOOLS

Private Schs..Principal	Grd	Prgm	Enr/#Cls	SN	
Alternative Sch for Math & Sci 291 E 1st St, Corning 14830 Linda Cole	6-8		133		607/962-0011 Fax 607/962-4866
Corning Christian Academy 11 Aisne St, Corning 14830 Richard Cornfield	PK-12		200 16		607/962-4220 Fax 607/962-4410
Hope Christian Academy 22 John St, Painted Post 14870 Melissa Hughes	K-8		65 8		607/936-4656 Fax 607/936-4673
St Ann's Academy 41 Genesee St, Hornell 14843 Sr Dolores Ann Stein	PK-6		85		607/281-1010

STEUBEN REGIONAL CENTERS

• **Greater Southern Tier BOCES** PID: 00771845   607/962-3581
9579 Vocational Dr Bldg 8, Painted Post 14870   Fax 607/654-5304

James Frame 1	Margaret Munson 2,15
Brian Bentley 3	Sarah Vakkas 8,15
Stephanie Wilson 16	Matthew Talada 27
Stacy Saglibene 58,77	Donald Keddell 67
C Douglas Johnson 68	Linda Perry 69,70
Betty Denardo 74	Angela Olkey 285

SUFFOLK COUNTY

SUFFOLK COUNTY SCHOOLS

County Schs..Principal	Grd	Prgm	Enr/#Cls	SN	
Bellport Academic Center 350 B Martha Ave, Bellport 11713 Anthony Coggiano	9-12		250 23		631/286-6900 Fax 631/286-6955
Brennan Middle Sch 550 Mount Ave, West Babylon 11704 Chandra Rivera	Spec		90		631/491-4149 Fax 631/623-4937
Brookhaven Learning Center 353 Martha Ave, Bellport 11713 Nicole Drinkwater	Spec		200 14		631/286-6750 Fax 631/286-1473

---

79 Student Personnel	91 Safety/Security	275 Response To Intervention	298 Grant Writer/Ptnrships	**School Programs**
80 Driver Ed/Safety	92 Magnet School	277 Remedial Math K-12	750 Chief Innovation Officer	A = **Alternative Program**
81 Gifted/Talented	93 Parental Involvement	280 Literacy Coach	751 Chief of Staff	G = **Adult Classes**
82 Video Services	95 Tech Prep Program	285 STEM	752 Social Emotional Learning	M = **Magnet Program**
83 Substance Abuse Prev	97 Chief Information Officer	286 Digital Learning		T = **Title I Schoolwide**
84 Erate	98 Chief Technology Officer	288 Common Core Standards	**Other School Types**	V = **Career & Tech Ed Programs**
85 AIDS Education	270 Character Education	294 Accountability	Ⓐ = Alternative School	
88 Alternative/At Risk	271 Migrant Education	295 Network System	Ⓒ = Charter School	New Schools are shaded
89 Multi-Cultural Curriculum	273 Teacher Mentor	296 Title II Programs	Ⓜ = Magnet School	New Superintendents and Principals are bold
90 Social Work	274 Before/After Sch	297 Webmaster	Ⓨ = Year-Round School	Personnel with email addresses are underscored

Social Media

 = Facebook

 = Twitter

Suffolk County

Edward J Milliken Tech Center 375 Locust Ave, Oakdale 11769 Thomas McGrath	Voc	G	700 40	631/244-5806 Fax 631/244-5814	
Gary D Bixhorn Tech Center 350 Martha Ave, Bellport 11713 Sam McAleese	Voc	G	800 26	631/286-6500 Fax 631/286-6524	
Harry B Ward Technical Center 970 N Griffing Ave, Riverhead 11901 Marie Davis	Voc	AG	500 20	631/369-8100 Fax 631/369-5375	
Islip Academic Center 371 Locust Ave, Oakdale 11769 Susan Goltz	Spec		100 12	631/244-5950 Fax 631/244-7360	
ⓐ James Allen Alternative Sch 31 Lee Ave, Wheatley HTS 11798 Thomas Logatto	7-12		60	631/586-1300 Fax 631/623-4944	
James E Allen Elem Sch 762 Deer Park Rd, Dix Hills 11746 Kimberly Cooper	Spec		284	631/254-0094 Fax 631/623-4930	
James E Allen Jr-Sr HS 35 Carman Rd, Dix Hills 11746 Martin Hearny	Spec		300 37	631/549-5580 Fax 631/623-4933	
Jefferson Academic Center 118 Spring St, Prt Jefferson 11777 Holly Iuliucci	Spec	A	190 24	631/476-0564 Fax 631/476-9322	
Manor Plains High Sch 200 Little Plains Rd, Huntington 11743 Karen Bowden	Voc	AG	400 30	631/754-2900 Fax 631/623-4909	
Peter J Brennan High Sch 550 Mount Ave, West Babylon 11704 Chandra Rivera	Spec	A	200 22	631/491-4390 Fax 631/623-4940	
Premm Learning Center 1200 Montauk Hwy, Oakdale 11769 Carolyn Hansen	Spec		140 13	631/567-4901 Fax 631/563-8217	
Sayville Elementary 100 Greene Ave, Sayville 11782 Michele Carpenter	Spec		140 13	631/422-1570 Fax 631/422-1613	
Sequoya High Sch 750 Waverly Ave, Holtsville 11742 Steven Repperger	Spec	V	50	631/622-1200	
Tecumseh Elem Sch 179 Granny Rd, Farmingville 11738 Sue Peterson	Spec		150 12	631/775-1700	
Westhampton Beach Lrng Center 215 Riverhead Rd, W Hampton Bch 11978 James Crenshaw	Spec		250 50	631/288-6400 Fax 631/288-6596	
Wilson Tech Dix Hills 17 Westminster Ave, Dix Hills 11746 Ann Joseph	Voc	AG	600	631/667-6000 Fax 631/623-1904	
Wilson Tech Northport 152 Laurel Hill Rd, Northport 11768 Debra Montaruli	Voc	G	100	631/261-3600 Fax 631/623-4907	

SUFFOLK PUBLIC SCHOOLS

● **Amagansett Union Free Sch Dist** PID: 00771871 631/267-3572
320 Main St, Amagansett 11930 Fax 631/267-3046

Schools: 1 \ **Teachers:** 21 \ **Students:** 79 \ **Special Ed Students:** 10 \
LEP Students: 6 \ **Ethnic:** African American 1%, Hispanic 27%, Caucasian
71% \ **Exp:** $1,597 (High) \ **Poverty:** 5% \ **Special Education:** $64,000 \
Open-Close: 09/09 - 06/25 \ **DTBP:** $155 (High)

Seth Turner 1   Roxanne Ecker 2
Kerry Griffiths .... 3,5*   Michael Rodgers 6*

Maria Dorr ....11,57,88,274,285,288,298*   Jennifer Miller 16,73,76,82,295*
Kristen Peterson 67   Kaitlin Hamilton 90,270*

Public Schs..Principal	Grd	Prgm	Enr/#Cls	SN	
Amagansett Sch 320 Main St, Amagansett 11930 Maria Dorr	PK-6		79 10		631/267-3572

● **Amityville Union Free Sch Dist** PID: 00771895 631/565-6000
150 Park Ave, Amityville 11701 Fax 631/598-6516

Schools: 5 \ **Teachers:** 273 \ **Students:** 3,100 \
Special Ed Students: 470 \ **LEP Students:** 614 \ **College-Bound:** 75% \
Ethnic: Asian 1%, African American 39%, Hispanic 54%, Native American:
1%, Caucasian 5% \ **Exp:** $411 (High) \ **Poverty:** 14% \ **Title I:** $791,443 \
Special Education: $7,477,000 \ **Open-Close:** 09/09 - 06/25 \ **DTBP:** $313
(High)

Dr Mary Kelly 1   Evan Farkas 6,35
Andrea Pekar 8,12,15,296,298   Thomas DeNicola 15,73
Frances Fernandez .... 20*   Mary Stephens 48,57,61
Peter Paternostro 58,79   Dr Terry Fulton 67

Public Schs..Principal	Grd	Prgm	Enr/#Cls	SN	
Amityville Memorial High Sch 250 Merrick Rd, Amityville 11701 Edward Plaia	10-12	TV	740 70	75%	631/565-6100 Fax 631/264-4489 f t
Edmund W Miles Middle Sch 501 Route 110, Amityville 11701 Earl Mitchell	7-9	TV	656 70	82%	631/565-6200 Fax 631/789-1655
Northeast Elem Sch 420 Albany Ave, Amityville 11701 Dr Pauline Collins	PK-K	T	318 14	59%	631/565-6400 Fax 631/789-6225
Northwest Elem Sch 450 County Line Rd, Amityville 11701 Kathleen Hyland	1-3	T	656 21	81%	631/565-6500 Fax 631/789-6235
Park Avenue Memorial Elem Sch 140 Park Ave, Amityville 11701 Robyn Santiago	4-6	T	697 24	81%	631/565-6300 Fax 631/598-4124

● **Babylon Union Free Sch Dist** PID: 00771950 631/893-7923
50 Railroad Ave, Babylon 11702 Fax 631/893-7935

Schools: 3 \ **Teachers:** 144 \ **Students:** 1,554 \ **Special Ed Students:** 248
\ **LEP Students:** 37 \ **College-Bound:** 89% \ **Ethnic:** Asian 4%,
African American 3%, Hispanic 14%, Caucasian 80% \ **Exp:** $312 (High) \
\ **Poverty:** 4% \ **Title I:** $70,162 \ **Special Education:** $2,086,000 \
Open-Close: 09/08 - 06/25 \ **DTBP:** $184 (High)

Linda Rozzi 1   Peter Daly 2,15,91
Kevin Warren 3   Nancy Padrone 4*
Karen Bustamante 5   Michael DeJoseph 6
Daniel D'Amico .... 8,11,15,294*   Dennis Murphy 31,36*
John Michele .... 45*   Theresa Collins 48*
Lisa Consolo 58   Elizabeth O'Brien 67
David DiLeo 73,95,295   Dennis McGovern 88*
Steven Goldberg 274*

Public Schs..Principal	Grd	Prgm	Enr/#Cls	SN	
Babylon Elem Sch 171 Ralph Ave, Babylon 11702 Travis Davey	K-2		333 20	13%	631/893-7960 Fax 631/893-7930
Babylon Jr Sr High Sch 50 Railroad Ave, Babylon 11702 Al Cirone	7-12	V	740 75	18%	631/893-7910 Fax 631/893-7936

1	Superintendent	8	Curric/Instruct K-12	19	Chief Financial Officer	29	Family/Consumer Science
2	Bus/Finance/Purchasing	9	Curric/Instruct Elem	20	Art K-12	30	Adult Education
3	Buildings And Grounds	10	Curric/Instruct Sec	21	Art Elem	31	Career/Sch-to-Work K-12
4	Food Service	11	Federal Program	22	Art Sec	32	Career/Sch-to-Work Elem
5	Transportation	12	Title I	23	Music K-12	33	Career/Sch-to-Work Sec
6	Athletic	13	Title V	24	Music Elem	34	Early Childhood Ed
7	Health Services	15	Asst Superintendent	25	Music Sec	35	Health/Phys Education
		16	Instructional Media Svcs	26	Business Education	36	Guidance Services K-12
		17	Chief Operations Officer	27	Career & Tech Ed	37	Guidance Services Elem
		18	Chief Academic Officer	28	Technology Education	38	Guidance Services Sec

39	Social Studies K-12	49	English/Lang Arts Elem	59	Special Education Elem	69	Academic Assessment
40	Social Studies Elem	50	English/Lang Arts Sec	60	Special Education Sec	70	Research/Development
41	Social Studies Sec	51	Reading K-12	61	Foreign/World Lang K-12	71	Public Information
42	Science K-12	52	Reading Elem	62	Foreign/World Lang Elem	72	Summer School
43	Science Elem	53	Reading Sec	63	Foreign/World Lang Sec	73	Instructional Tech
44	Science Sec	54	Remedial Reading K-12	64	Religious Education K-12	74	Inservice Training
45	Math K-12	55	Remedial Reading Elem	65	Religious Education Elem	75	Marketing/Distributive
46	Math Elem	56	Remedial Reading Sec	66	Religious Education Sec	76	Info Systems
47	Math Sec	57	Bilingual/ELL	67	School Board President	77	Psychological Assess
48	English/Lang Arts K-12	58	Special Education K-12	68	Teacher Personnel	78	Affirmative Action

New York School Directory — Suffolk County

Babylon Memorial Grade Sch 169 Park Ave, Babylon 11702 Steven Goldberg	3-6		481	17%	631/893-7980 Fax 631/893-7990

- **Bay Shore Union Free Sch Dist** PID: 00771998   631/968-1252
  75 W Perkal St, Bay Shore 11706   Fax 631/968-4131

Schools: 7 \ **Teachers:** 473 \ **Students:** 6,000 \ **Special Ed Students:** 1,032 \ **LEP Students:** 653 \ **College-Bound:** 83% \ **Ethnic:** Asian 5%, African American 19%, Hispanic 47%, Caucasian 29% \ **Exp:** $286 (Med) \ **Poverty:** 10% \ **Title I:** $790,760 \ **Special Education:** $9,335,000 \ **Open-Close:** 09/09 - 06/30 \ **DTBP:** $313 (High) \ f t

Joseph Bond 1
Joseph Hodosky 3,91
Richard Gallagher 5
Dr Steven Maloney ... 8,11,15,69,270,288,296
Michael Rotello 20,23
Jacqueline Ribera 34
Maddie Padilla 39
Patricia Rogers 57*
Patricia Rogers 61
Krystyna Baumgartner 71
Robert Torres 79
Chris Kauter 286
Maureen Virsinger 2,15
Jeanine Quicker 4
Robert Panariello 6,35
Lisa Giacoia 15,68
Christopher Mentz 26,45
Louis Balsamo 36*
Donna Bettinelli 42,285
Dr Russell Endes 58,79,90
Susan Garsan 67
Michael Versinger 73,76,295,297*
Katie Kelly 83,88,275*

Public Schs..Principal	Grd	Prgm	Enr/#Cls	SN	
Bay Shore High Sch 155 3rd Ave, Bay Shore 11706 Robert Pashkin	9-12	AV	1,956 60	57%	631/968-1157 Fax 631/968-2332 f t
Bay Shore Middle Sch 393 Brook Ave, Bay Shore 11706 Dr Laquita Outlaw	6-8	V	1,394 100	59%	631/968-1210 Fax 631/968-2342 f
Brook Avenue Elem Sch 45 Brook Ave, Bay Shore 11706 Joseph Lemke	K-2	T	349 21	67%	631/968-1130 Fax 631/968-2439
Fifth Avenue Sch 217 5th Ave, Bay Shore 11706 Kristina Cope	K-2	T	373 19	54%	631/968-1140 Fax 631/968-2463 f t
Gardiner Manor Sch 125 Wohseepee Dr, Bay Shore 11706 Carlton Brown	3-5		754 32	61%	631/968-1150 Fax 631/968-2487
Mary G Clarkson Sch 1415 E 3rd Ave, Bay Shore 11706 Leticia Garcia	K-2	T	495 28	53%	631/968-1205 Fax 631/968-2461
South Country Sch 885 Hampshire Rd, Bay Shore 11706 Johnna Grasso	3-5		529 28	56%	631/968-1250 Fax 631/968-2499

- **Bayport- Blue Point USD** PID: 00772071   631/472-7860
  189 Academy St, Bayport 11705   Fax 631/472-7873

Schools: 5 \ **Teachers:** 216 \ **Students:** 2,080 \ **Special Ed Students:** 391 \ **LEP Students:** 23 \ **College-Bound:** 90% \ **Ethnic:** Asian 2%, African American 2%, Hispanic 8%, Caucasian 88% \ **Exp:** $271 (Med) \ **Poverty:** 4% \ **Title I:** $107,763 \ **Special Education:** $2,942,000 \ **Open-Close:** 09/04 - 06/25 \ **DTBP:** $309 (High)

Dr Timothy Hearney 1
Timothy Mullins 6,35
Natalie Doyle 58
Caroline Kipfer 73,286
Richard Snyder 2,3,15
Dr Theodore Fulton 8,12,15
Michael Miller 67

Public Schs..Principal	Grd	Prgm	Enr/#Cls	SN	
Academy Street Elem Sch 150 Academy St, Bayport 11705 Kerry Vann	K-5		313 21	9%	631/472-7850 Fax 631/472-7858
Bayport Blue Point High Sch 200 Snedecor Ave, Bayport 11705 Robert Haas	9-12		726 70	13%	631/472-7800 Fax 631/472-7814
Blue Point Elem Sch 212 Blue Point Ave, Blue Point 11715 Tara Falasco	K-5		227 18	11%	631/472-6100 Fax 631/472-6110
James Wilson Young Middle Sch 602 Sylvan Ave, Bayport 11705 John Andruszkiewicz	6-8		517 35	15%	631/472-7820 Fax 631/472-7849
Sylvan Ave Elem Sch 600 Sylvan Ave, Bayport 11705 Alane Dugan	K-5		297 21	20%	631/472-7840 Fax 631/472-7857

- **Brentwood Union Free Sch Dist** PID: 00772203   631/434-2123
  52 3rd Ave, Brentwood 11717   Fax 631/273-6575

Schools: 17 \ **Teachers:** 1,167 \ **Students:** 20,000 \ **Special Ed Students:** 2,965 \ **LEP Students:** 6,053 \ **College-Bound:** 86% \ **Ethnic:** Asian 2%, African American 9%, Hispanic 85%, Caucasian 3% \ **Exp:** $332 (High) \ **Poverty:** 16% \ **Title I:** $4,239,630 \ **Special Education:** $42,200,000 \ **Open-Close:** 09/04 - 06/25 \ **DTBP:** $236 (High)

Richard Loeschner 1
Stacy O'Connor 2,15
Miguel Cruz 3
Karen Harris 5
Sean Coffin 7,77,90
Dr Monique Darrisaw-Akil 10,15
Steven Guarino 20,23
Wayne Abenes 36,93*
Eileen Welch-Chestaro 42,45*
Robert Feliciano 67
Guy Nelson 73,76,295
Carlos Sanchez 91
Frank Hark 2
Erik Karlund 3
Carol-Anne Gradoski 4
Kevin O'Reilly 6,35,85
Ann Palmer 9,15
Wanda Ortiz-Rivera 15,57
Lisa Rodriguez 30,72*
Trish Brockbank 39,48
Kim Fauci 58
Alice Vandervelt 68,273
Candice Cheng 76
Jerry Cheng 97

Public Schs..Principal	Grd	Prgm	Enr/#Cls	SN	
Brentwood High Sch 2 6th Ave, Brentwood 11717 John Callan	9-12	AGTV	4,707 200	76%	631/434-2204 Fax 631/434-2206
East Kindergarten Center 50 Timberline Dr, Brentwood 11717 Minerva Feliciano	PK-K	T	485 22	65%	631/434-2525 Fax 631/434-2186
East Middle Sch 70 Hilltop Dr, Brentwood 11717 Barry Mohammed	6-8	TV	1,171 63	88%	631/434-2473 Fax 631/434-2171
Fjc Southeast Elem Sch 1 Melody Ln, Brentwood 11717 Lisa Calderaro	1-5	T	662 26	83%	631/434-2265 Fax 631/434-2170
Freshman Center 33 Leahy Ave, Brentwood 11717 Vincent Autera	9-9	T	1,211	83%	631/434-2541 Fax 631/434-2549
Hemlock Park Elem Sch 19 Hemlock Dr, Bay Shore 11706 Dr Chris Dalley	K-5	T	666 29	81%	631/434-2451 Fax 631/434-2191
Laurel Park Elem Sch 48 Swan Pl, Brentwood 11717 Eric Snell	1-5	T	660	88%	631/434-2464 Fax 631/434-2190
Loretta Park Elem Sch 77 Stahley St, Brentwood 11717 Robert McCarthy	1-5	T	721 31	89%	631/434-2246 Fax 631/434-2189
North Elem Sch 50 W White St, Brentwood 11717 Patrick Morris	1-5	T	926 41	86%	631/434-2275 Fax 631/434-2181
North Middle Sch 350 Wicks Rd, Brentwood 11717 Matt Gengler	6-8	TV	1,205 110	86%	631/434-2356 Fax 631/952-9249

---

79 Student Personnel
80 Driver Ed/Safety
81 Gifted/Talented
82 Video Services
83 Substance Abuse Prev
84 Erate
85 AIDS Education
88 Alternative/At Risk
89 Multi-Cultural Curriculum
90 Social Work
91 Safety/Security
92 Magnet School
93 Parental Involvement
95 Tech Prep Program
97 Chief Infomation Officer
98 Chief Technology Officer
270 Character Education
271 Migrant Education
273 Teacher Mentor
274 Before/After Sch
275 Response To Intervention
277 Remedial Math K-12
280 Literacy Coach
285 STEM
286 Digital Learning
288 Common Core Standards
294 Accountability
295 Network System
296 Title II Programs
297 Webmaster
298 Grant Writer/Ptnrships
750 Chief Innovation Officer
751 Chief of Staff
752 Social Emotional Learning

School Programs
A = Alternative Program
G = Adult Classes
M = Magnet Program
T = Title I Schoolwide
V = Career & Tech Ed Programs

Other School Types
Ⓐ = Alternative School
Ⓒ = Charter School
Ⓜ = Magnet School
Ⓨ = Year-Round School

Social Media
f = Facebook
t = Twitter

New Schools are shaded
New Superintendents and Principals are bold
Personnel with email addresses are underscored

Suffolk County

Market Data Retrieval

Northeast Elem Sch 2 Devon Rd, Brentwood 11717 Marilyn Friend-Ituarte	1-5	T	1,073 43	86%	631/434-2435 Fax 631/434-2188
Oak Park Elem Sch 775 Wisconsin Ave, Bay Shore 11706 Lisa Catandella	K-5	T	779 33	82%	631/434-2255 Fax 631/434-2183
Pine Park Elem Sch 1 Mur Pl, Brentwood 11717 Ann Weishahn	K-1	T	600 31	70%	631/434-2251 Fax 631/434-2168
South Middle Sch 785 Candlewood Rd, Brentwood 11717 Bergre Escorbores	6-8	TV	1,107 80	86%	631/434-2341 Fax 631/434-2560
Southwest Elem Sch 1095 Joselson Ave, Bay Shore 11706 Michele Rogers	PK-5	T	1,093 52	71%	631/434-2261 Fax 631/434-2196
Twin Pines Elem Sch 2 Mur Pl, Brentwood 11717 Gloria Jackson	1-5	T	857 34	85%	631/434-2457 Fax 631/434-2187
West Middle Sch 2030 Udall Rd, Bay Shore 11706 Felicia Thomas	6-8	TV	938 70	83%	631/434-2371 Fax 631/242-3992

● **Bridgehampton Union Free SD** PID: 00772394 631/537-0271
2685 Montauk Hwy, Bridgehampton 11932 Fax 631/537-1030

Schools: 1 \ **Teachers:** 29 \ **Students:** 227 \ **Special Ed Students:** 48 \ **LEP Students:** 51 \ **College-Bound:** 93% \ **Ethnic:** Asian 1%, African American 24%, Hispanic 49%, Caucasian 26% \ **Exp:** $885 (High) \ **Poverty:** 2% \ **Special Education:** $289,000 \ **Open-Close:** 09/10 - 06/25 \ **DTBP:** $342 (High) \

Robert Hauser 1		Melissa Styles 2,15	
Michael DeRosa 6		Elizabeth Flanagan 7*	
Ken Giosi 12,58*		Michael Miller 35*	
Danielle Doscher 36,69*		Dr Angela Austin 57,79	
Ronald White 67		Lauren Sebor 83,88*	

Public Schs..Principal	Grd	Prgm	Enr/#Cls	SN	
Bridgehampton Sch 2685 Montauk Hwy, Bridgehampton 11932 Michael Miller	PK-12	TV	227 14	1%	631/537-0271

● **Brookhaven Comsewogue Unif SD** PID: 00772784 631/474-8100
290 Norwood Ave, Port Jeff Sta 11776 Fax 631/474-3568

Schools: 6 \ **Teachers:** 262 \ **Students:** 3,702 \ **Special Ed Students:** 658 \ **LEP Students:** 250 \ **College-Bound:** 91% \ **Ethnic:** Asian 3%, African American 3%, Hispanic 32%, Caucasian 61% \ **Exp:** $190 (Low) \ **Poverty:** 9% \ **Title I:** $473,092 \ **Special Education:** $6,602,000 \ **Open-Close:** 09/08 - 06/25 \ **DTBP:** $326 (High) \

Jennifer Quinn 1	Susan Casali 2,91,274
Stephanie Popky 3	Doreen Burke 4*
Debra Meaney 5	Matt DeVincenzo 6
Dr Jennifer Polychronakos 8,12	Dr Jennifer Quinn 15,73*
Audrey Nilsen 34,58,77,79,83,88,90	John Swenning 67
Michelle Lautato 68	Natasha Zublionis 295,296*

Public Schs..Principal	Grd	Prgm	Enr/#Cls	SN	
Boyle Road Elem Sch 424 Boyle Rd, Port Jeff Sta 11776 Robert Pearl	3-5		334 25	22%	631/474-8140 Fax 631/474-8498
Clinton Avenue Elem Sch 140 Clinton Ave, Port Jeff Sta 11776 Toni Bifalco	K-2		437 25	24%	631/474-8150 Fax 631/474-8499
Comsewogue High Sch 565 Bicycle Path, Port Jeff Sta 11776 Mike Mosca	9-12	T	1,219 60	28%	631/474-8179 Fax 631/474-8175
John F Kennedy Middle Sch 200 Jayne Blvd, Port Jeff Sta 11776 Michael Fama	6-8	T	835 54	26%	631/474-8160 Fax 631/476-8176
Norwood Avenue Elem Sch 290 Norwood Ave, Port Jeff Sta 11776 Theresa Etts	K-2		360 18	14%	631/474-8130 Fax 631/474-8385
Terryville Road Elem Sch 401 Terryville Rd, Port Jeff Sta 11776 Annemarie Sciove	3-5	T	484 35	34%	631/474-2834 Fax 631/474-2846

● **Center Moriches Union Free SD** PID: 00772411 631/878-0052
529 Main St, CTR Moriches 11934 Fax 631/878-4326

Schools: 3 \ **Teachers:** 117 \ **Students:** 1,400 \ **Special Ed Students:** 313 \ **LEP Students:** 90 \ **College-Bound:** 82% \ **Ethnic:** Asian 1%, African American 5%, Hispanic 15%, Native American: 4%, Caucasian 75% \ **Exp:** $347 (High) \ **Poverty:** 6% \ **Title I:** $110,434 \ **Special Education:** $2,725,000 \ **Open-Close:** 09/08 - 06/25

Ron Masera 1	Keri Loughlin 2
Raina Ingolia 3,8,11,15,76,288	Jeremy Thode 6,35*
Ricardo Soto 15,68,73,79,296	George Maxwell 67
Joseph Townsend 91	Courtney Fabian 298

Public Schs..Principal	Grd	Prgm	Enr/#Cls	SN	
Center Moriches High Sch 311 Frowein Rd, CTR Moriches 11934 Edward Casswell	9-12	GV	574 50	20%	631/878-0092 Fax 631/878-1796
Center Moriches Middle Sch 311 Frowein Rd, CTR Moriches 11934 Melissa Reggio	6-8		381 17	21%	631/878-2519 Fax 631/878-0362
Clayton Huey Elem Sch 511 Main St, CTR Moriches 11934 Dennis Ricci	K-5		583 32	24%	631/878-9780 Fax 631/878-0238

● **Central Islip Union Free SD** PID: 00772435 631/348-5112
50 Wheeler Rd, Central Islip 11722 Fax 631/348-0366

Schools: 8 \ **Teachers:** 530 \ **Students:** 7,400 \ **Special Ed Students:** 1,084 \ **LEP Students:** 2,331 \ **College-Bound:** 71% \ **Ethnic:** Asian 2%, African American 16%, Hispanic 77%, Caucasian 4% \ **Exp:** $225 (Med) \ **Poverty:** 16% \ **Title I:** $1,650,548 \ **Special Education:** $15,821,000 \ **Open-Close:** 09/08 - 06/25 \ **DTBP:** $287 (High)

Sharon Dungee 1	Sharon Morgan 2
Matthew Providente 3	Paul Carlozzo 4
Christopher Brown 5,15,68,69	Lawrence Philips 6,7*
Dr Stacey Morgan 11,296,298	Elaine Medin 30
Dr Rosa Lien 57	Sheldon Steinfeld 58,77
Norman Wagner 67	Phillip Voight 76,98
Jacqueline Fagan 79	Thomas Weiner 91

Public Schs..Principal	Grd	Prgm	Enr/#Cls	SN	
Andrew T Morrow Elem Sch 299 Sycamore Ln, Central Islip 11749 Dr Neema Coker	K-6	T	766 33	59%	631/348-5037 Fax 631/348-5163
Anthony Alfano Elem Sch 50 Wheeler Rd, Central Islip 11722 Ann Bucco	PK-6	T	599 26	52%	631/348-5139 Fax 631/348-5184
Central Islip High Sch 85 Wheeler Rd, Central Islip 11722 Brett Macmonigle	9-12	GTV	2,375	55%	631/348-5079 Fax 631/348-0161

1	Superintendent	8	Curric/Instruct K-12	19	Chief Financial Officer	29	Family/Consumer Science
2	Bus/Finance/Purchasing	9	Curric/Instruct Elem	20	Art K-12	30	Adult Education
3	Buildings And Grounds	10	Curric/Instruct Sec	21	Art Elem	31	Career/Sch-to-Work K-12
4	Food Service	11	Federal Program	22	Art Sec	32	Career/Sch-to-Work Elem
5	Transportation	12	Title I	23	Music K-12	33	Career/Sch-to-Work Sec
6	Athletic	13	Title V	24	Music Elem	34	Early Childhood Ed
7	Health Services	15	Asst Superintendent	25	Music Sec	35	Health/Phys Education
		16	Instructional Media Svcs	26	Business Education	36	Guidance Services K-12
		17	Chief Operations Officer	27	Career & Tech Ed	37	Guidance Services Elem
		18	Chief Academic Officer	28	Technology Education	38	Guidance Services Sec

39	Social Studies K-12	49	English/Lang Arts Elem	59	Special Education Elem	69	Academic Assessment
40	Social Studies Elem	50	English/Lang Arts Sec	60	Special Education Sec	70	Research/Development
41	Social Studies Sec	51	Reading K-12	61	Foreign/World Lang K-12	71	Public Information
42	Science K-12	52	Reading Elem	62	Foreign/World Lang Elem	72	Summer School
43	Science Elem	53	Reading Sec	63	Foreign/World Lang Sec	73	Instructional Tech
44	Science Sec	54	Remedial Reading K-12	64	Religious Education K-12	74	Inservice Training
45	Math K-12	55	Remedial Reading Elem	65	Religious Education Elem	75	Marketing/Distributive
46	Math Elem	56	Remedial Reading Sec	66	Religious Education Sec	76	Info Systems
47	Math Sec	57	Bilingual/ELL	67	School Board President	77	Psychological Assess
48	English/Lang Arts K-12	58	Special Education K-12	68	Teacher Personnel	78	Affirmative Action

New York School Directory — Suffolk County

Charles A Mulligan Elem Sch 1 Broadway Ave, Central Islip 11722 Tracy Hudson	K-6	T	1,030 80	58%	631/348-5041 Fax 631/348-5164
Cordello Ave Elem Sch 51 Cordello Ave, Central Islip 11722 Brenda Jackson	K-6	T	567	58%	631/348-4189 Fax 631/348-7712
Francis J O'Neill Elem Sch 545 Clayton St, Central Islip 11722 Kristine Locascio	K-6	T	591	57%	631/348-5060 Fax 631/348-5162
Marguerite L Mulvey Elem Sch 44 E Cherry St, Central Islip 11722 Jessica Iafrate	K-6	T	592 60	63%	631/348-5059 Fax 631/348-1532
Ralph Reed Middle Sch 200 Half Mile Rd, Central Islip 11722 Matthew Matera	7-8	T	1,227 45	59%	631/348-5066 Fax 631/348-5159

● **Cold Spring Harbor Central SD** PID: 00772526 631/367-5900
75 Goose Hill Rd, Cold SPG HBR 11724 Fax 631/367-3108

Schools: 4 \ **Teachers:** 151 \ **Students:** 1,650 \ **Special Ed Students:** 206 \ **LEP Students:** 10 \ **College-Bound:** 98% \ **Ethnic:** Asian 5%, African American 1%, Hispanic 5%, Caucasian 89% \ **Exp:** $582 (High) \ **Poverty:** 5% \ **Title I:** $148,608 \ **Special Education:** $944,000 \ **Open-Close:** 09/08 - 06/25 \ **DTBP:** $168 (High)

Robert Fenter 1	James Stucchio 2,11,15	
John Marreck 3	Gerri Tiger 4*	
Jean Luna 5	Michael Bongino 6	
Dr Lydia Bellino 8,15,296	Denise Campbell 15,58,90,288	
Joseph Monastero 16,73*	Justin Arini 36	
Justin Arini 36*	Amelia Brogan 67	
Christopher Horner 83,88*	Kimberly Libertini 285	

Public Schs..Principal	Grd	Prgm	Enr/#Cls	SN	
Cold Spring Harbor Jr Sr HS 82 Turkey Ln, Cold SPG HBR 11724 James Bolen	7-12	TV	865 45	3%	631/367-6900 Fax 631/692-7079
Goose Hill Primary Sch 75 Goose Hill Rd Ste C, Cold SPG HBR 11724 Lynn Herschlein	K-1	T	207 15	1%	631/367-5940 Fax 631/367-2157
Lloyd Harbor Elem Sch 7 School Ln, Huntington 11743 Valerie Massimo	2-6	T	347 27	3%	631/367-8800 Fax 631/421-4229
West Side Elem Sch 1597 Laurel Hollow Rd, Syosset 11791 Alison Hazut	2-6	T	215 15	2%	516/692-7900 Fax 516/692-4845

● **Commack Union Free School Dist** PID: 00772576 631/912-2000
480 Clay Pitts Rd, E Northport 11731 Fax 631/912-2240

Schools: 8 \ **Teachers:** 511 \ **Students:** 5,889 \ **Special Ed Students:** 1,208 \ **LEP Students:** 65 \ **College-Bound:** 93% \ **Ethnic:** Asian 9%, African American 1%, Hispanic 9%, Caucasian 81% \ **Exp:** $205 (Med) \ **Poverty:** 3% \ **Title I:** $213,021 \ **Special Education:** $7,864,000 \ **Open-Close:** 09/14 - 06/25 \ **DTBP:** $313 (High)

Dr Donald James 1	Laura Newman 2,4,5,11,15,76,80,91
Richard Schramm 3	Amanda Kalvana 5,80
Patrick Friel 6,35,83*	Jordan Cox 8,34,77
Micheal Inforna 15	Paul Giordano 16,73,76
Jeffrey Sautner 39*	Alison Celentano 42*
Barbara Gerson 45*	Kristi Keingstein 58
Steven Hartman 67	Brenda Lentsch 71,297*
Brenda Lentsch 297	

Public Schs..Principal	Grd	Prgm	Enr/#Cls	SN	
Burr Intermediate Sch 235 Burr Rd, Commack 11725 Paul Schmelter	3-5		674 43	12%	631/858-3636 Fax 631/858-3643
Commack High Sch 1 Scholar Ln, Commack 11725 Eslie Boritz	9-12	AGV	2,113	12%	631/912-2100 Fax 631/912-2250
Commack Middle Sch 700 Vanderbilt Pkwy, Commack 11725 Michael Larson	6-8		1,381	10%	631/858-3500 Fax 631/858-3647
Indian Hollow Primary Sch 151 Kings Park Rd, Commack 11725 Brian Simpson	K-2		269 17	7%	631/858-3590 Fax 631/493-0465
Mandracchia-Sawmill Interm Sch 103 New Hwy, Commack 11725 Michelle Tancredi	3-5		556	13%	631/858-3650 Fax 631/912-2243
North Ridge Primary Sch 300 Townline Rd, Commack 11725 Katherine Rihm	K-2		362	8%	631/912-2190 Fax 631/912-2260
Rolling Hills Elem Sch 25 McCulloch Dr, Dix Hills 11746 Jessica Santarpia	K-2		215 17	11%	631/858-3570 Fax 631/493-1219
Wood Park Primary Sch 15 New Hwy, Commack 11725 Michelle Collison	K-2		316	9%	631/858-3680 Fax 631/493-0467

● **Connetquot Central School Dist** PID: 00772863 631/244-2215
780 Ocean Ave, Bohemia 11716 Fax 631/589-0683

Schools: 11 \ **Teachers:** 512 \ **Students:** 5,653 \ **Special Ed Students:** 1,054 \ **LEP Students:** 143 \ **College-Bound:** 84% \ **Ethnic:** Asian 6%, African American 2%, Hispanic 15%, Caucasian 76% \ **Exp:** $313 (High) \ **Poverty:** 4% \ **Title I:** $250,215 \ **Special Education:** $11,863,000 \ **Open-Close:** 09/08 - 06/25 \ **DTBP:** $322 (High)

Dr Lynda Adams 1	Jacqueine Scrio 2,15
Joanne Sharrott 2	Tim Dungate 3
John Garverick 5	Peter Melore 6,35
Peter Melore 6*	Dean Mittleman 8,11,15,16,285
Laura Kinball 9*	John Allen 15
Monica Manzi 15,58	Carole Polney 16,28,73,76,84,286
George Rockwin 20,23	Margaret Ronai 26,39
Jonathan MacAluso 36	Louise Burger 45
Christina Poppe 48	Gail Santo 57,79,83,88
Louis Bonadonna 58	Denise Hannaoui 61
Eileen Panico 67	Don Flynn 91
Bethany Rizzo 285	

Public Schs..Principal	Grd	Prgm	Enr/#Cls	SN	
Cherokee Street Elem Sch 130 Cherokee St, Ronkonkoma 11779 Jill Lahey	K-5		562 34	29%	631/467-6027 Fax 631/467-6166
Connetquot Alternative Pre-Sch 50 Bourne Blvd, Bohemia 11716 Gail Holden	PK-PK		72 3		631/563-9833 Fax 631/563-9659
Connetquot Senior High Sch 190 7th St, Bohemia 11716 Kenneth Costa	9-12	TV	1,923	22%	631/244-2228 Fax 631/244-2287
Edith L Slocum Elem Sch 2460 Sycamore Ave, Ronkonkoma 11779 John Delio	K-5		279 19	32%	631/467-6040 Fax 631/467-6446
Edward J Bosti Elem Sch 50 Bourne Blvd, Bohemia 11716 Laura Kimball	K-5		299 26	17%	631/244-2291 Fax 631/244-2290
Helen B Duffield Elem Sch 600 1st St, Ronkonkoma 11779 Lisa Farrell	K-5		375 23	21%	631/467-6010 Fax 631/467-6326

---

79 Student Personnel	91 Safety/Security	275 Response To Intervention	298 Grant Writer/Ptnrships	**School Programs**	**Social Media**
80 Driver Ed/Safety	92 Magnet School	277 Remedial Math K-12	750 Chief Innovation Officer	A = Alternative Program	▯ = Facebook
81 Gifted/Talented	93 Parental Involvement	280 Literacy Coach	751 Chief of Staff	G = Adult Classes	
82 Video Services	95 Tech Prep Program	285 STEM	752 Social Emotional Learning	M = Magnet Program	▯ = Twitter
83 Substance Abuse Prev	97 Chief Infomation Officer	286 Digital Learning		T = Title I Schoolwide	
84 Erate	98 Chief Technology Officer	288 Common Core Standards	**Other School Types**	V = Career & Tech Ed Programs	
85 AIDS Education	270 Accountability	294 Accountability	Ⓐ = Alternative School		
88 Alternative/At Risk	271 Migrant Education	295 Network System	Ⓒ = Charter School	New Schools are shaded	
89 Multi-Cultural Curriculum	273 Teacher Mentor	296 Title II Programs	Ⓜ = Magnet School	New Superintendents and Principals are bold	
90 Social Work	274 Before/After Sch	297 Webmaster	Ⓨ = Year-Round School	Personnel with email addresses are underscored	

Suffolk County

Market Data Retrieval

Idle Hour Elem Sch 334 Idle Hour Blvd, Oakdale 11769 Sandra Rubin	K-5		228 37	11% 631/244-2306 Fax 631/244-2305
John Pearl Elem Sch 1070 Smithtown Ave, Bohemia 11716 Susan White	K-5		211 20	26% 631/244-2300
Oakdale-Bohemia Middle Sch 60 Oakdale Bohemia Rd, Oakdale 11769 Susanne Bailey	6-8		613 150	19% 631/244-2268 Fax 631/563-6167
Ronkonkoma Middle Sch 501 Peconic St, Ronkonkoma 11779 Joseph Licato	6-8	T	701 59	27% 631/467-6000 Fax 631/467-6003
Sycamore Avenue Elem Sch 745 Sycamore Ave, Bohemia 11716 Stuart Pollak	K-5		415 28	20% 631/244-2261 Fax 631/244-2260

• **Copiague Union Free Sch Dist** PID: 00772980 631/842-4015
  2650 Great Neck Rd, Copiague 11726 Fax 631/841-4614

Schools: 6 \ **Teachers:** 323 \ **Students:** 4,864 \ **Special Ed Students:** 911 \ **LEP Students:** 775 \ **Ethnic:** Asian 2%, African American 23%, Hispanic 62%, Caucasian 14% \ **Exp:** $252 (Med) \ **Poverty:** 15% \ **Title I:** $1,098,322 \ **Special Education:** $15,221,000 \ **Open-Close:** 09/08 - 06/25 \ **DTBP:** $313 (High) \

Dr Kathleen Bannon ....1,11 Jeffery White 2,5,15
Angelo Lisa ....3 Maryanne Matzak 4
William Bennett ....6 Karen Sheridan 7,15,36,58,79,88,90
Dr Jeanette Altruda ....8 Todd Andrews 15,68
Lisa Dunn ....30* Michelle Passeggiata 57*
Brian Sales ....67 Bonnie Burton 69
Kelly Urraro 73

Public Schs..Principal	Grd	Prgm	Enr/#Cls	SN
Copiague Middle Sch 2650 Great Neck Rd, Copiague 11726 Andrew Lagnado	6-8	AV	1,151 45	75% 631/842-4011 Fax 631/841-4630
Deauville Gardens East ES 100 Deauville Blvd, Copiague 11726 Joseph Buccello	K-5	T	485	64% 631/842-3320
Deauville Gardens West ES 100 Deauville Blvd, Copiague 11726 Kristina Biamonte	K-5	T	504 50	67% 631/842-4012 Fax 631/841-4656
Great Neck Road Elem Sch 1400 Great Neck Rd, Copiague 11726 Karla Cangelosi	K-5	T	510 23	70% 631/842-4013 Fax 631/841-4676
Susan E Wiley Elem Sch 365 Scudder Ave, Copiague 11726 Cynthia Florio	K-5	T	766 33	69% 631/842-4014 Fax 631/841-4670
Walter G O'Connell Copiague HS 1100 Dixon Ave, Copiague 11726 Joseph Agosta	9-12	AGV	1,549	69% 631/842-4010 Fax 631/841-4642

• **Deer Park Union Free Sch Dist** PID: 00773051 631/274-4000
  1881 Deer Park Ave, Deer Park 11729 Fax 631/242-6762

Schools: 5 \ **Teachers:** 372 \ **Students:** 4,015 \ **Special Ed Students:** 757 \ **LEP Students:** 267 \ **College-Bound:** 87% \ **Ethnic:** Asian 13%, African American 19%, Hispanic 27%, Caucasian 40% \ **Exp:** $235 (Med) \ **Poverty:** 8% \ **Title I:** $490,816 \ **Special Education:** $5,559,000 \ **Open-Close:** 09/08 - 06/25 \ **DTBP:** $321 (High)

James Cummings ....1 Marguerite Jimenez 2,4,15
Robert Woolsey ....3,91* Dominick Fontana 6*
Dr Danielle Sheridan ....9,12,288 Jeanne Kozlowsky 10
Mary Reynolds ....11,68,296,298 Alicia Konecki 15

Jay Murphy ....16,73,76,286* Bradley Murphy 20,23*
Ashley Rosenberg ....57* Sean O'Brien 58*
David Renahan ....59* Donna Elliott 67
Theresa Ceruti 77*

Public Schs..Principal	Grd	Prgm	Enr/#Cls	SN
Deer Park High Sch 1 Falcon Pl, Deer Park 11729 Charles Cobb	9-12	AV	1,294	43% 631/274-4110 Fax 631/254-0237
John F Kennedy Interm Sch 101 Lake Ave, Deer Park 11729 Kelly Benson	3-5	T	824	46% 631/274-4310 Fax 631/274-4301
John Quincy Adams Primary Sch 172 Old Country Rd, Deer Park 11729 Christopher Molinelli	PK-2	T	473 26	40% 631/274-4410 Fax 631/274-4439
May Moore Primary Sch 239 Central Ave, Deer Park 11729 Philip Paniccia	PK-2	T	454 26	41% 631/274-4460 Fax 631/242-6575
Robert Frost Middle Sch 450 Half Hollow Rd, Deer Park 11729 Eliana Levey	6-8		970	47% 631/274-4210 Fax 631/242-0035

• **East Hampton Union Free SD** PID: 00773142 631/329-4100
  4 Long Ln, East Hampton 11937 Fax 631/324-0109

Schools: 3 \ **Teachers:** 182 \ **Students:** 1,781 \ **Special Ed Students:** 219 \ **LEP Students:** 318 \ **College-Bound:** 87% \ **Ethnic:** Asian 3%, African American 3%, Hispanic 56%, Native American: 1%, Caucasian 38% \ **Exp:** $433 (High) \ **Poverty:** 9% \ **Title I:** $140,428 \ **Special Education:** $1,553,000 \ **Open-Close:** 09/09 - 06/25 \ **DTBP:** $161 (High)

Richard Burns ....1 Jerel Cokley 2,3,11
Melissa Curran ....4* Joseph Lipani 5
Joseph Vasile-Cozzo ....6,35,83,85* Robert Tymann 8,34,69,72,85,270,273,288
Cindy Allentuck ....11,58,77,79,285 Charles Westergard 16,73,286,295*
Debbie Mansir ....30* Elizabeth Reveiz 57*
James Foster 67

Public Schs..Principal	Grd	Prgm	Enr/#Cls	SN
East Hampton High Sch 2 Long Ln, East Hampton 11937 Adam Fine	9-12	AGTV	921	40% 631/329-4130 Fax 631/329-4210
East Hampton Middle Sch 76 Newtown Ln, East Hampton 11937 Dr Charles Soriano	6-8	T	342 40	47% 631/329-4112 Fax 631/329-4187
John M Marshall Elem Sch 3 Gingerbread Ln, East Hampton 11937 Elizabeth Doyle	PK-5	T	518 25	52% 631/329-4155 Fax 631/329-4157

• **East Islip Union Free SD** PID: 00773180 631/224-2000
  1 Craig B Gariepy Ave, Islip Terrace 11752 Fax 631/581-1617

Schools: 6 \ **Teachers:** 309 \ **Students:** 3,782 \ **Special Ed Students:** 659 \ **LEP Students:** 76 \ **College-Bound:** 87% \ **Ethnic:** Asian 3%, African American 3%, Hispanic 19%, Caucasian 75% \ **Exp:** $236 (Med) \ **Poverty:** 4% \ **Title I:** $166,528 \ **Special Education:** $7,464,000 \ **Open-Close:** 09/03 - 06/25 \ **DTBP:** $124 (High)

John Dolan ....1 Stephen Harrison 2,4,5,15,84
Eric Woellhof ....3,91 Stephen Restivo 6,7,78*
Paul Manzo ....8,15,57,68,69,294,298 Lisa Belz 11,58,79,88
Robert Wottawa ....20,23* Israel Malinowitzer 27,31,36*
Sarajean Anderson ....39,48* Frank Pillitteri 45,285
Aileen O'Rourke ....58,79 Jessica Carney 67
Carol Feudi ....68 Greg Fasolino 71
Richard Zwycewicz ....73 Rochelle Stapleton 74,273

1	Superintendent	8	Curric/Instruct K-12	19	Chief Financial Officer	29	Family/Consumer Science	39	Social Studies K-12	49	English/Lang Arts Elem	59	Special Education Elem	69	Academic Assessment
2	Bus/Finance/Purchasing	9	Curric/Instruct Elem	20	Art K-12	30	Adult Education	40	Social Studies Elem	50	English/Lang Arts Sec	60	Special Education Sec	70	Research/Development
3	Buildings And Grounds	10	Curric/Instruct Sec	21	Art Elem	31	Career/Sch-to-Work K-12	41	Social Studies Sec	51	Reading K-12	61	Foreign/World Lang K-12	71	Public Information
4	Food Service	11	Federal Program	22	Art Sec	32	Career/Sch-to-Work Elem	42	Science K-12	52	Reading Elem	62	Foreign/World Lang Elem	72	Summer School
5	Transportation	12	Title I	23	Music K-12	33	Career/Sch-to-Work Sec	43	Science Elem	53	Reading Sec	63	Foreign/World Lang Sec	73	Instructional Tech
6	Athletic	13	Title V	24	Music Elem	34	Early Childhood Ed	44	Science Sec	54	Remedial Reading K-12	64	Religious Education K-12	74	Inservice Training
7	Health Services	14	Instructional Media Svcs	25	Music Sec	35	Health/Phys Education	45	Math K-12	55	Remedial Reading Elem	65	Religious Education Elem	75	Marketing/Distributive
		15	Asst Superintendent	26	Business Education	36	Guidance Services K-12	46	Math Elem	56	Remedial Reading Sec	66	Religious Education Sec	76	Info Systems
		16	Instructional Media Svcs	27	Career & Tech Ed	37	Guidance Services Elem	47	Math Sec	57	Bilingual/ELL	67	School Board President	77	Psychological Assess
		18	Chief Academic Officer	28	Technology Education	38	Guidance Services Sec	48	English/Lang Arts K-12	58	Special Education K-12	68	Teacher Personnel	78	Affirmative Action

NY-220

New York School Directory — Suffolk County

Public Schs..Principal	Grd	Prgm	Enr/#Cls	SN		
Connetquot Elem Sch 1 Merrick St, Islip Terrace 11752 Nicholas Bilotti	K-2		339 21	26%	631/224-2001 Fax 631/581-5315	
East Islip High Sch 1 Redmen St, Islip Terrace 11752 Mark Bernard	9-12		1,194 50	23%	631/224-2006 Fax 631/581-4410	
East Islip Middle Sch 100 Redmen St, Islip Terrace 11752 Brennen William	6-8		853	23%	631/224-2008 Fax 631/859-3745	
John F Kennedy Elem Sch 94 Woodland Dr, East Islip 11730 Deborah Smith	3-5		431 24	17%	631/224-2003 Fax 631/581-1354	
Ruth C Kinney Elem Sch 1 Spur Dr S, Islip Terrace 11752 Janet Jones	3-5		352 17	31%	631/224-2007 Fax 631/581-0969	
Timber Point Elem Sch 200 Timberpoint Rd, East Islip 11730 Danielle Naccarato	K-2		380 19	15%	631/224-2004 Fax 631/581-4078	

● **East Moriches Union Free SD** PID: 00773271   631/878-0162
9 Adelaide Ave, East Moriches 11940   Fax 631/909-1379

Schools: 2 \ **Teachers:** 54 \ **Students:** 750 \ **Special Ed Students:** 112 \ **LEP Students:** 25 \ **Ethnic:** Asian 1%, African American 3%, Hispanic 12%, Caucasian 84% \ **Exp:** $264 (Med) \ **Poverty:** 4% \ **Title I:** $32,967 \ **Special Education:** $1,783,000 \ **Open-Close:** 09/08 - 06/25 \ **DTBP:** $161 (High) \ t

Daniel McKeon 1   Bart Stewart 3
Muriel Rountos 9,12   Michele Pepey 59,296,298
Greg Menegio 67   Dr Charles Russo 84

Public Schs..Principal	Grd	Prgm	Enr/#Cls	SN		
East Moriches Elem Sch 523 Montauk Hwy, East Moriches 11940 Edward Schneyer	K-4	T	360 30	1%	631/878-0162 Fax 631/909-7505	
East Moriches Middle Sch 9 Adelaide Ave, East Moriches 11940	5-8		325		631/878-0162	

● **East Quogue Union Free SD** PID: 00773295   631/653-5210
6 Central Ave, East Quogue 11942   Fax 631/653-8644

Schools: 1 \ **Teachers:** 40 \ **Students:** 390 \ **Special Ed Students:** 59 \ **LEP Students:** 75 \ **Ethnic:** Asian 1%, African American 1%, Hispanic 29%, Caucasian 70% \ **Exp:** $719 (High) \ **Poverty:** 6% \ **Title I:** $61,352 \ **Special Education:** $446,000 \ **Open-Close:** 09/03 - 06/25 \ **DTBP:** $172 (High)

Robert Long 1   Eric Gomez 3
Allen Faricatore .... 4*   John Moran 5,91
Robert Long .... 9,11,16,69,83,270,288*   Michelle Diveris 12,296*
Christopher Hudson 67

Public Schs..Principal	Grd	Prgm	Enr/#Cls	SN		
East Quogue Elem Sch 6 Central Ave, East Quogue 11942 Robert Long	K-6		390 20	28%	631/653-5210	

● **Eastport-South Manor Ctrl SD** PID: 00775853   631/801-3013
149 Dayton Ave, Manorville 11949   Fax 631/874-6750

Schools: 6 \ **Teachers:** 234 \ **Students:** 3,294 \ **Special Ed Students:** 568 \ **LEP Students:** 80 \ **Ethnic:** Asian 1%, African American 2%, Hispanic 8%, Caucasian 88% \ **Exp:** $198 (Low) \ **Poverty:** 6% \ **Title I:** $299,943 \ **Special Education:** $6,513,000 \ **Open-Close:** 09/03 - 06/25 \ **DTBP:** $316 (High)

Joseph Steimel 1   Timothy Laube 2,15
Michael Bergin 3   Michael Bergin 3*
William Madsen 6   Linda Weiss 15,78,273
Christine Duffy .... 31,36*   Michael Byrnes 67

Public Schs..Principal	Grd	Prgm	Enr/#Cls	SN		
Ⓐ Alternative High Sch 543 Moriches Middle Island Rd, Manorville 11949 Ethan Wivietsky	9-12		25		631/801-3292 Fax 631/874-6788	
Dayton Avenue Elem Sch 151 Dayton Ave, Manorville 11949 Shelita Watkis	3-6	T	479 27	23%	631/801-3085 Fax 631/878-6404	
Eastport Elem Sch 390 Montauk Hwy, Eastport 11941 William Hender	3-6		443	18%	631/801-3170 Fax 631/325-1066	
Ⓐ Eastport South Manor Jr Sr HS 543 Moriches Middle Island Rd, Manorville 11949 Sal Alaimo	7-12		1,763	18%	631/801-3250 Fax 631/874-6787	
South Street Elem Sch 130 South St, Manorville 11949 John-Michael Jackson	K-2	T	305 20	24%	631/801-3140 Fax 631/878-4954	
Tuttle Avenue Sch 1 Tuttle Ave, Eastport 11941 Jeanmarie Zambelli	K-2		242	18%	631/801-3058 Fax 631/325-1952	

● **Elwood Union Free School Dist** PID: 00773336   631/266-5400
100 Kenneth Ave, Greenlawn 11740   Fax 631/266-3834

Schools: 4 \ **Teachers:** 176 \ **Students:** 2,049 \ **Special Ed Students:** 280 \ **LEP Students:** 81 \ **College-Bound:** 93% \ **Ethnic:** Asian 9%, African American 6%, Hispanic 19%, Caucasian 66% \ **Exp:** $251 (Med) \ **Poverty:** 5% \ **Title I:** $260,909 \ **Special Education:** $2,323,000 \ **Open-Close:** 09/08 - 06/25 \ **DTBP:** $306 (High)

Dr Kenneth Bossert 1   Lorraine Dunkel 2,15,84,91
John McDonald 3   Mara Pugh 4
Gene Tranchino 5,16,73,76,286,295   David Shanahan 6,35,83*
Dr Maureen Hull 8,288,298   Eileen Kelly - Gorman 11,57,58,88,296
James Tomeo 67   Thomas Colletti 68*
Beth Izzo 71   Pamela Fine 275,280

Public Schs..Principal	Grd	Prgm	Enr/#Cls	SN		
Elwood Middle Sch 100 Kenneth Ave, Greenlawn 11740 Dr Christina Sapienza	6-8		515 40	23%	631/266-5420 Fax 631/266-3987	
Elwood-John Glenn High Sch 478 Elwood Rd, Elwood 11731 C Burzynski	9-12	A	692 70	19%	631/266-5410 Fax 631/266-6280	
Harley Avenue Primary Sch 30 Harley Ave, E Northport 11731 Elissa Millan	K-2		409 30	21%	631/266-5445 Fax 631/266-3985	
James H Boyd Intermediate Sch 286 Cuba Hill Rd, Huntington 11743 Denise Toscano	3-5	V	433 27	25%	631/266-5430 Fax 631/266-6265 f	

---

79 Student Personnel	91 Safety/Security	275 Response To Intervention	298 Grant Writer/Ptnrships	**School Programs**	**Social Media**
80 Driver Ed/Safety	92 Magnet School	277 Remedial Math K-12	750 Chief Innovation Officer	A = Alternative Program	
81 Gifted/Talented	93 Parental Involvement	280 Literacy Coach	751 Chief of Staff	G = Adult Classes	f = Facebook
82 Video Services	95 Tech Prep Program	285 STEM	752 Social Emotional Learning	M = Magnet Program	
83 Substance Abuse Prev	97 Chief Infomation Officer	286 Digital Learning		T = Title I Schoolwide	t = Twitter
84 Erate	98 Chief Technology Officer	288 Common Core Standards	**Other School Types**	V = Career & Tech Ed Programs	
85 AIDS Education	270 Character Education	294 Accountability	Ⓐ = Alternative School		
88 Alternative/At Risk	271 Migrant Education	295 Network System	Ⓒ = Charter School	New Schools are shaded	
89 Multi-Cultural Curriculum	273 Teacher Mentor	296 Title II Programs	Ⓜ = Magnet School	New Superintendents and Principals are bold	
90 Social Work	274 Before/After Sch	297 Webmaster	Ⓨ = Year-Round School	Personnel with email addresses are underscored	

Suffolk County

Market Data Retrieval

• Fire Island Union Free SD PID: 00774770
Surf Rd & Midway, Ocean Beach 11770
631/583-5626
Fax 631/583-5167

Schools: 1 \ **Teachers:** 8 \ **Students:** 32 \ **Special Ed Students:** 3 \ **LEP Students:** 3 \ **Ethnic:** Asian 6%, African American 3%, Hispanic 16%, Caucasian 75% \ **Exp:** $863 (High) \ **Poverty:** 15% \ **Title I:** $1,448 \ **Special Education:** $35,000 \ **Open-Close:** 09/08 - 06/24 \ **DTBP:** $182 (High)

Loretta Ferraro 1,11,73
James Fitz 3
Anna Bainbridge 6,35
Jay Lippert 67
Christopher Forget 295
Kevin Wurtz 2
Michael DiDio 5
Janet Laviolette 7,83,85
Philip Tamberino 78

Public Schs..Principal	Grd	Prgm	Enr/#Cls	SN	
Woodhull Elem Sch Surf Road 1, Ocean Beach 11770 Loretta Ferraro	PK-6	GT	32 5		631/583-5626

• Fishers Island Union Free SD PID: 00773398
78 Greenwood Rd, Fishers Isle 06390
631/788-7444
Fax 631/788-5532

Schools: 1 \ **Teachers:** 16 \ **Students:** 65 \ **Special Ed Students:** 8 \ **College-Bound:** 83% \ **Ethnic:** African American 3%, Hispanic 7%, Caucasian 90% \ **Exp:** $1,113 (High) \ **Poverty:** 10% \ **Open-Close:** 09/04 - 06/22 \ **DTBP:** $364 (High)

Karen Goodwin 1,11,288
Carol Doherty 5*
Allie Mesite 16,58*
Carol Giles 29*
Jamie Doucette 67
James Eagan 2
Adam Baber 6,35,83*
Allie Mesite 16,58
Julie Arcelus 36,69,275*
Linda Bean 73,286,295*

Public Schs..Principal	Grd	Prgm	Enr/#Cls	SN	
Fishers Island Sch 78 Greenwood Rd, Fishers Isle 06390 Christian Arsenault	PK-12		65 13		631/788-7444

• Greenport Union Free Sch Dist PID: 00773415
720 Front St, Greenport 11944
631/477-1950
Fax 631/593-8951

Schools: 1 \ **Teachers:** 63 \ **Students:** 627 \ **Special Ed Students:** 63 \ **LEP Students:** 123 \ **College-Bound:** 68% \ **Ethnic:** Asian 1%, African American 8%, Hispanic 52%, Caucasian 39% \ **Exp:** $431 (High) \ **Poverty:** 15% \ **Title I:** $102,391 \ **Special Education:** $566,000 \ **Open-Close:** 09/04 - 06/25 \ **DTBP:** $143 (High)

Marlon Small 1,11
Joseph Tsavaras 58,69
Ryan Case 73,286
Charles Scheid 2
Daniel Creedon 67
Brandy Hopkins 88

Public Schs..Principal	Grd	Prgm	Enr/#Cls	SN	
Greenport Sch 720 Front St, Greenport 11944 Joseph Tsavaras \ Gary Kalish	K-12	V	627 60	60%	631/477-1950

• Half Hollow Hills Central SD PID: 00773439
525 Half Hollow Rd, Dix Hills 11746
631/592-3030
Fax 631/592-3900

Schools: 9 \ **Teachers:** 661 \ **Students:** 8,017 \ **Special Ed Students:** 1,674 \ **LEP Students:** 251 \ **Ethnic:** Asian 18%, African American 12%, Hispanic 12%, Caucasian 57% \ **Exp:** $372 (High) \ **Poverty:** 4% \ **Title I:** $358,416 \ **Special Education:** $9,056,000 \ **Open-Close:** 09/08 - 06/25 \ **DTBP:** $228 (High)

Dr Patrick Harrigan 1
Bonnie Scally 4
Debra Ferry 6
John O'Farrell 10,11,15,298
Dr Darlene Lilla 20,23
Nicole Alexander 26,73
Patrick Murphy 29,35,80,83,85
Lorraine Lupinskie 39
Ian Dunst 45
Love Karima Foy 50,53,288
Lisa Zito 59
Eric Geringswald 67
Sunil John 76,84
David Spera 91
Anne Marie Caliendo 2,3,15
Maurita Simpson 5
Diana Ketcham 9,15
Dr Jeffrey Woodbury 15
Jolynn Sapia 26,73*
Allison Strand 27,31,58,69,88,273
Daniel Giglio Blanco 34
Christian Fogarazzo 42,285
Lisa DeRienzo 49,52
Lori Campbell 57,61
Michelle Melfi 60
Dr Mike Lake 70
Julia Gallo 90

Public Schs..Principal	Grd	Prgm	Enr/#Cls	SN	
Candlewood Middle Sch 1200 Carlls Straight Path, Dix Hills 11746 Pamela Higgins	6-8	GV	774 50	19%	631/592-3300 Fax 631/592-3921
Half Hollow Hills High Sch E 50 Vanderbilt Pkwy, Dix Hills 11746 Milton Strong	9-12	GV	1,618	18%	631/592-3100 Fax 631/592-3907
Half Hollow Hills High Sch W 375 Wolf Hill Rd, Dix Hills 11746 Dr Michael Catapano	9-12	V	1,198 50	19%	631/592-3200 Fax 631/592-3923
Otsego Elem Sch 55 Otsego Ave, Dix Hills 11746 Dr Stacey Gillespie	K-5		573 37	23%	631/592-3600 Fax 631/592-3915
Paumanok Elem Sch 1 Seaman Neck Rd, Dix Hills 11746 Kendra Cooper	K-5		539 33	23%	631/592-3650 Fax 631/592-3916
Signal Hill Elem Sch 670 Caledonia Rd, Dix Hills 11746 Maryann Fasciana	K-5		689	17%	631/592-3700 Fax 631/592-3917
Sunquam Elem Sch 515 Sweet Hollow Rd, Melville 11747 Karen Littell	K-5		527 34	17%	631/592-3750 Fax 631/592-3920
Vanderbilt Elem Sch 350 Deer Park Rd, Dix Hills 11746 Martin Boettcher	K-5		696 60	17%	631/592-3800 Fax 631/592-3918
West Hollow Middle Sch 250 Old East Neck Rd, Melville 11747 Steven Hauk	6-8		1,094 90	19%	631/592-3400 Fax 631/592-3400

• Hampton Bays Union Free SD PID: 00773594
86 Argonne Rd E, Hampton Bays 11946
631/723-2100
Fax 631/723-2109

Schools: 3 \ **Teachers:** 164 \ **Students:** 2,060 \ **Special Ed Students:** 255 \ **LEP Students:** 505 \ **Ethnic:** Asian 1%, African American 1%, Hispanic 57%, Caucasian 41% \ **Exp:** $315 (High) \ **Poverty:** 11% \ **Title I:** $293,126 \ **Special Education:** $2,309,000 \ **Open-Close:** 09/08 - 06/25 \ **DTBP:** $165 (High)

Lars Clemensen 1
John Moran 5
Micheal Carlson 8,15,69,270,288
Jennifer Spota 16*
Marion Lawson 68
Lawrence Luce 2,15
Drew Walker 6,35*
Mark Pagano 11,15,58,296
Kevin Springer 67
Micheal Llyod 295

1	Superintendent	8	Curric/Instruct K-12	19	Chief Financial Officer	29	Family/Consumer Science	39	Social Studies K-12	49	English/Lang Arts Elem	59	Special Education Elem	69	Academic Assessment
2	Bus/Finance/Purchasing	9	Curric/Instruct Elem	20	Art K-12	30	Adult Education	40	Social Studies Elem	50	English/Lang Arts Sec	60	Special Education Sec	70	Research/Development
3	Buildings And Grounds	10	Curric/Instruct Sec	21	Art Elem	31	Career/Sch-to-Work K-12	41	Social Studies Sec	51	Reading K-12	61	Foreign/World Lang K-12	71	Public Information
4	Food Service	11	Federal Program	22	Art Sec	32	Career/Sch-to-Work Elem	42	Science K-12	52	Reading Elem	62	Foreign/World Lang Elem	72	Summer School
5	Transportation	12	Title I	23	Music K-12	33	Career/Sch-to-Work Sec	43	Science Elem	53	Reading Sec	63	Foreign/World Lang Sec	73	Instructional Tech
6	Athletic	13	Title V	24	Music Elem	34	Early Childhood Ed	44	Science Sec	54	Remedial Reading K-12	64	Religious Education K-12	74	Inservice Training
7	Health Services	15	Asst Superintendent	25	Music Sec	35	Health/Phys Education	45	Math K-12	55	Remedial Reading Elem	65	Religious Education Elem	75	Marketing/Distributive
		16	Instructional Media Svcs	26	Business Education	36	Guidance Services K-12	46	Math Elem	56	Remedial Reading Sec	66	Religious Education Sec	76	Info Systems
		17	Chief Operations Officer	27	Career & Tech Ed	37	Guidance Services Elem	47	Math Sec	57	Bilingual/ELL	67	School Board President	77	Psychological Assess
		18	Chief Academic Officer	28	Technology Education	38	Guidance Services Sec	48	English/Lang Arts K-12	58	Special Education K-12	68	Teacher Personnel	78	Affirmative Action

New York School Directory

Suffolk County

Public Schs..Principal	Grd	Prgm	Enr/#Cls	SN	
Hampton Bays Elem Sch 72 Ponquogue Ave, Hampton Bays 11946 Mark Meyer	K-4	T	655 45	63%	631/723-2121 Fax 631/723-2840
Hampton Bays High Sch 88 Argonne Rd E, Hampton Bays 11946 Christoph Richardt	9-12	AG	690 45	56%	631/723-2110 Fax 631/723-2120
Hampton Bays Middle Sch 70 Ponquogue Ave, Hampton Bays 11946 Dennis Schug	5-8	T	665	62%	631/723-4700 Fax 631/723-4900 🇹

● Harborfields Ctl School Dist PID: 00773623
2 Oldfield Rd, Greenlawn 11740

631/754-5320
Fax 631/261-0068

Schools: 4 \ **Teachers:** 257 \ **Students:** 2,965 \ **Special Ed Students:** 538
\ **LEP Students:** 104 \ **College-Bound:** 89% \ **Ethnic:** Asian 5%,
African American 4%, Hispanic 14%, Caucasian 76% \ **Exp:** $244 (Med)
\ **Poverty:** 2% \ **Title I:** $82,357 \ **Special Education:** $4,182,000 \
Open-Close: 09/08 - 06/25 \ **DTBP:** $304 (High)

Dr Francesco Ianni 1,11	Sharon Donnelly 2,4,5,15
Richard LaFountain 3,91	Gail Sanders 4
Marianna Price 5	John Valente 6,7,35
Dr Rory Manning 8,73	Theresa McGuire 58,79
Susie Lustig 67	Maureen Raynor 68

Public Schs..Principal	Grd	Prgm	Enr/#Cls	SN	
Harborfields High Sch 98 Taylor Ave, Greenlawn 11740 Timothy Russo	9-12	AV	1,024 25	14%	631/754-5360 Fax 631/261-7557
Oldfield Middle Sch 2 Oldfield Rd, Greenlawn 11740 Joanne Giordano	6-8	V	759 40	15%	631/754-5310 Fax 631/754-2677 🇫
Thomas J Lahey Elem Sch 625 Pulaski Rd, Greenlawn 11740 Mary Williams	3-5		637 36	17%	631/754-5400 Fax 631/754-5412
Washington Drive Primary Sch 95 Washington Dr, Centerport 11721 Kathryn McNally	K-2		545 25	11%	631/754-5592 Fax 631/754-3346

● Hauppauge Union Free Sch Dist PID: 00773697
495 Hoffman Ln Ste 1, Hauppauge 11788

631/761-8300
Fax 631/265-3649

Schools: 5 \ **Teachers:** 307 \ **Students:** 3,200 \ **Special Ed Students:** 557
\ **LEP Students:** 103 \ **College-Bound:** 93% \ **Ethnic:** Asian 10%,
African American 4%, Hispanic 11%, Caucasian 76% \ **Exp:** $412 (High)
\ **Poverty:** 4% \ **Title I:** $150,467 \ **Special Education:** $4,251,000 \
Open-Close: 09/02 - 06/25 \ **DTBP:** $321 (High)

Dr Dennis Ohara 1	Jacqueline Pirro 2,3,15
Gerald Kinsley 5	Daniel Butler 6,29,35
Dr Donald Murphy 8,11,15,73,295,752	Joseph Tasman 15,68
Dr Christopher Michael 16,48,51*	Dr Laura Landor 20,23*
Doreen Gordon 26,39	Dr Robert Wankmuller 42,73
Meridyth Hansen 45	Dr Tim McCarthy 57,61,73
Rebecca Bilski 58,79	David Barshay 67
Daniel Wald 76	Patrick Caffrey 91

Public Schs..Principal	Grd	Prgm	Enr/#Cls	SN	
Bretton Woods Elem Sch 1 Club Ln, Hauppauge 11788 George Gagliardi	K-5		574	14%	631/582-6633 Fax 631/582-1136
Forest Brook Elem Sch 299 Lilac Ln, Smithtown 11787 Kristen Reingold	K-5		337 25	7%	631/265-3265 Fax 631/265-3673
Hauppauge High Sch 500 Lincoln Blvd, Hauppauge 11788 Christopher Cook	9-12	V	1,189 95	13%	631/761-8302 Fax 631/265-8679
Hauppauge Middle Sch 600 Townline Rd, Hauppauge 11788 Christine O'Connor	6-8		765	12%	631/761-8230 Fax 631/366-1299
Pines Elem Sch 22 Holly Dr, Smithtown 11787 Claudine Dimuzio	K-5		415 30	7%	631/543-8700 Fax 631/543-3632

● Huntington Union Free Sch Dist PID: 00773776
50 Tower St, Huntingtn Sta 11746

631/673-2038
Fax 631/423-3447

Schools: 8 \ **Teachers:** 369 \ **Students:** 4,545 \ **Special Ed Students:** 799
\ **LEP Students:** 941 \ **College-Bound:** 86% \ **Ethnic:** Asian 2%,
African American 8%, Hispanic 52%, Caucasian 38% \ **Exp:** $520 (High)
\ **Poverty:** 10% \ **Title I:** $805,021 \ **Special Education:** $5,635,000 \
Open-Close: 09/08 - 06/25 \ **DTBP:** $316 (High)

James Polansky 1	Kathleen Acker 2,15
Alvin White 3	Thomas Desmond 3
Vita Virgilio 5	Georgia McCarthy 6,35*
Beth McCoy 8,15,30	Nancy Allard 12
Georganne White 16*	Eric Reynolds 20,23*
Camille Decanio 27	Kitty Klein 36,69*
Marybeth Robinette 46,69,73	Kathleen Aufiero 47
Angela Berner 48*	Judy Moroff 57,61*
Diana Rich 58	Valerie Monforte 59
Linda Costello-Roth 60*	Christine Biernacki 67
Christopher Hender 68	James Hoops 71*
Maryann Daley 81	Jill Johanson 285

Public Schs..Principal	Grd	Prgm	Enr/#Cls	SN	
Flower Hill Primary Sch 98 Flower Hill Rd, Huntington 11743 Lucia Laguarda	K-3	T	300 19	51%	631/673-2050 Fax 631/425-6255
Huntington High Sch 188 Oakwood Rd, Huntington 11743 Brenden Cusack	9-12		1,536 75	53%	631/673-2001 Fax 631/425-4730
J Taylor Finley Middle Sch 20 Greenlawn Rd, Huntington 11743 Traci Roethel	7-8		700 30	54%	631/673-2020 Fax 631/425-4746
Ⓜ Jack Abrams STEM Magnet Sch 155 Lowndes Ave, Huntingtn Sta 11746 Donna Moro	4-6		500	49%	631/673-2060 Fax 631/421-7178
Jefferson Primary Sch 253 Oakwood Rd, Huntington 11743 Valerie Catitulo-Saide	K-3	T	304 15	55%	631/673-2070 Fax 631/425-6257
Southdown Primary Sch 125 Browns Rd, Huntington 11743 Scott Oshrin	K-3	T	283 23	53%	631/673-2080 Fax 631/425-6258
Washington Primary Sch 78 Whitson Rd, Huntingtn Sta 11746 Michelle Richards	K-3	T	345	57%	631/673-2090 Fax 631/425-6259
Woodhull Intermediate Sch 140 Woodhull Rd, Huntington 11743 Lara Gonzalez	4-6	T	514 27	66%	631/673-2030 Fax 631/425-4718

● Islip Union Free School Dist PID: 00773881
215 Main St, Islip 11751

631/650-8200
Fax 631/650-8218

Schools: 5 \ **Teachers:** 243 \ **Students:** 2,726 \ **Special Ed Students:** 458
\ **LEP Students:** 179 \ **College-Bound:** 87% \ **Ethnic:** Asian 4%,
African American 6%, Hispanic 29%, Caucasian 61% \ **Exp:** $304 (High)
\ **Poverty:** 5% \ **Title I:** $235,864 \ **Special Education:** $4,365,000 \
Open-Close: 09/08 - 06/25 \ **DTBP:** $337 (High)

---

79 Student Personnel	91 Safety/Security	275 Response To Intervention	298 Grant Writer/Ptnrships	**School Programs**	**Social Media**	
80 Driver Ed/Safety	92 Magnet School	277 Remedial Math K-12	750 Chief Innovation Officer	A = Alternative Program	🇫 = Facebook	
81 Gifted/Talented	93 Parental Involvement	280 Literacy Coach	751 Chief of Staff	G = Adult Classes		
82 Video Services	95 Tech Prep Program	285 STEM	752 Social Emotional Learning	M = Magnet Program	🇹 = Twitter	
83 Substance Abuse Prev	97 Chief Information Officer	286 Digital Learning		T = Title I Schoolwide		
84 Erate	98 Chief Technology Officer	288 Common Core Standards	**Other School Types**	V = Career & Tech Ed Programs		
85 AIDS Education	270 Character Education	294 Accountability	Ⓐ = Alternative School			
88 Alternative/At Risk	271 Migrant Education	295 Network System	Ⓒ = Charter School	New Schools are shaded		
89 Multi-Cultural Curriculum	273 Teacher Mentor	296 Title II Programs	Ⓜ = Magnet School	New Superintendents and Principals are bold		
90 Social Work	274 Before/After Sch	297 Webmaster	Ⓨ = Year-Round School	Personnel with email addresses are underscored		

Suffolk County — Market Data Retrieval

Dr Ellen Semel	1
Brian Graham	3
Cynthia Fitzgerald	15,68
Kate O'Callaghan	58,79
Michele Finlay	71,97
Michael Zeterberg	2,5,15
Andrew Bromm	4
John Sparacio	35
Philip Dineen	67
James Prudente	73,286,295

Public Schs..Principal	Grd	Prgm	Enr/#Cls	SN	
Commack Road Elem Sch 300 Commack Rd, Islip 11751 James Cameron	2-5		455 27	37%	631/650-8600 Fax 631/650-8608
Islip High Sch 2508 Union Blvd, Islip 11751 Jon Larochester	9-12	V	964 50	29%	631/650-8301 Fax 631/650-8308
Islip Middle Sch 211 Main St, Islip 11751 Dr Tim Martin	6-8		638 76	32%	631/650-8500 Fax 631/650-8508
Maud S Sherwood Elem Sch 301 Smith Ave, Islip 11751 Chad Walerstein	2-5		302 20	28%	631/650-8650 Fax 631/650-8658
Wing Elem Sch 1 Winganhauppauge Rd, Islip 11751 Michael Giacchetto	K-1		367 21	28%	631/650-8450 Fax 631/650-8458

- **Kings Park Ctl School Dist** PID: 00773946 631/269-3310
  180 Lawrence Rd Rm 208, Kings Park 11754 Fax 631/269-0750

Schools: 5 \ **Teachers:** 268 \ **Students:** 2,888 \ **Special Ed Students:** 621 \ **LEP Students:** 53 \ **College-Bound:** 97% \ **Ethnic:** Asian 3%, Hispanic 9%, Caucasian 88% \ **Exp:** $272 (Med) \ **Poverty:** 4% \ **Title I:** $148,449 \ **Special Education:** $4,877,000 \ **Open-Close:** 09/08 - 06/25 \ **DTBP:** $313 (High)

Dr Timothy Eagen	1
John Craig	3,68
Steven Lee	5
Dr Ralph Cartisano	8,13,15,69,88
Nicole Zito	58
Dr Sharon Macken	73*
Dr Sharon Macken	76
Shannon Meehan	2
Kathleen Weinberger	4
Bill Denniston	6
Dr Danielle Colby-Rooney	12,34,79,298
Diane Nally	67
Steven Weisse	73,91

Public Schs..Principal	Grd	Prgm	Enr/#Cls	SN	
Ft Salonga Elem Sch 39 Sunken Meadow Rd, Northport 11768 Stephanie Montecalvo	K-3		393 32	12%	631/269-3365 Fax 631/269-2190
Kings Park High Sch 200 Route 25A, Kings Park 11754 Jason Huntsman	9-12	AV	1,042	8%	631/269-3345 Fax 631/269-7472
Parkview Elem Sch 23 Roundtree Dr, Kings Park 11754 Kevin Storch	K-3		341 30	8%	631/269-3770 Fax 631/361-6590
Rjo Intermediate Sch 99 Old Dock Rd, Kings Park 11754 Rudy Massimo	4-5		432 32	10%	631/269-3798 Fax 631/269-3222
William T Rogers Middle Sch 97 Old Dock Rd, Kings Park 11754 Lauren Moreno	6-8	T	680 80	10%	631/269-3369 Fax 631/269-3282

- **Lindenhurst Union Free SD** PID: 00774043 631/867-3000
  350 Daniel St, Lindenhurst 11757 Fax 631/867-3008

Schools: 8 \ **Teachers:** 482 \ **Students:** 5,694 \ **Special Ed Students:** 1,063 \ **LEP Students:** 298 \ **College-Bound:** 76% \ **Ethnic:** Asian 3%, African American 3%, Hispanic 25%, Caucasian 69% \ **Exp:** $295 (Med) \ **Poverty:** 7% \ **Title I:** $636,698 \ **Special Education:** $13,543,000 \ **Open-Close:** 09/09 - 06/18 \ **DTBP:** $322 (High)

Daniel Giordano	1
Zachary Nyberg	2
Maureen Ciaci	5
Bret Kearney	7,15,58,79,90
Vincent Caravana	8,11,15,69,70,72,81
Dr Lisa Omeis	15,79
Jon Trapani	20,23
Richard Finder	39
Trecia Wong	45
Jill Schilling	57,61
Donna Hochman	67
Jennifer Bova	74
Dr Grace Chan	2,15
Robert Cozzetto	3,91
Anthony Amesti	6,35
Aileen Cavlieri	8,73
Irene DeNisco	12
Steve Mazza	16,73
Andrea Judge	36*
Dr Matthew Linger	42
Kimberly Boccanfuso	48
Shelita Watkis	57,61,89*
Alison De Maria	71

Public Schs..Principal	Grd	Prgm	Enr/#Cls	SN	
Albany Avenue Elem Sch 180 Albany Ave, Lindenhurst 11757 Marcy Miller	K-5		451 22	40%	631/867-3150 Fax 631/867-3158
Alleghany Avenue Elem Sch 250 S Alleghany Ave, Lindenhurst 11757 Valerie Filbry	K-5		303 17	43%	631/867-3200 Fax 631/867-3208
Daniel Street Elem Sch 289 Daniel St, Lindenhurst 11757 Linda Domanico	K-5		515 29	36%	631/867-3300 Fax 631/867-3308
Harding Avenue Elem Sch 2 Harding Ave, Lindenhurst 11757 Brian Chamberlin	K-5		301 15	28%	631/867-3350
Lindenhurst Middle Sch 350 S Wellwood Ave, Lindenhurst 11757 Frank Naccarato	6-8	TV	1,346	40%	631/867-3500 Fax 631/867-3508
Lindenhurst Senior High Sch 300 Charles St, Lindenhurst 11757 Dr Candice Brodie	9-12	AGV	1,906 110	37%	631/867-3700 Fax 631/867-3708
West Gates Avenue Elem Sch 175 W Gates Ave, Lindenhurst 11757 Donna Smawley	K-5		318 18	35%	631/867-3400 Fax 631/867-3408
William Rall Elem Sch 761 Wellwood Ave, Lindenhurst 11757 Farrah McKenna	K-5		531 30	48%	631/867-3450 Fax 631/867-3458

- **Little Flower Union Free SD** PID: 01854713 631/929-4300
  2460 N Wading River Rd, Wading River 11792 Fax 631/929-0303

Schools: 1 \ **Teachers:** 21 \ **Students:** 96 \ **Special Ed Students:** 16 \ **Ethnic:** Asian 1%, African American 30%, Hispanic 15%, Caucasian 55% \ **Exp:** $671 (High) \ **Open-Close:** 09/04 - 06/25 \ **DTBP:** $154 (High)

Harold Dean	1
Robert Scappatore	8,73*
Dr Charles Drexel	67
Ann Romeo	2,15
Michael Gordon	58*

Public Schs..Principal	Grd	Prgm	Enr/#Cls	SN	
Little Flower Sch 2460 N Wading River Rd, Wading River 11792 Robert Scappatore	Spec	T	96 11	13%	631/929-4300

- **Longwood Central School Dist** PID: 00774378 631/345-2172
  35 Yaphank Middle Island Rd, Middle Island 11953 Fax 631/345-2166

Schools: 7 \ **Teachers:** 639 \ **Students:** 9,150 \ **Special Ed Students:** 1,730 \ **LEP Students:** 541 \ **College-Bound:** 82% \ **Ethnic:** Asian 4%, African American 20%, Hispanic 28%, Caucasian 48% \ **Exp:** $258 (Med) \ **Poverty:** 10% \ **Title I:** $1,320,116 \ **Special Education:** $24,476,000 \ **Open-Close:** 09/08 - 06/24 \ **DTBP:** $308 (High)

Dr Michael Lonergan	1
Janet Bryan	2,3,15
Thomas Murphy	4
Bonnie Massetti	2
Nancy Kavanaugh	2
John Ryan	5

---

1 Superintendent	8 Curric/Instruct K-12	19 Chief Financial Officer	29 Family/Consumer Science	39 Social Studies K-12	49 English/Lang Arts K-12	59 Special Education Elem	69 Academic Assessment
2 Bus/Finance/Purchasing	9 Curric/Instruct Elem	20 Art K-12	30 Adult Education	40 Social Studies Elem	50 English/Lang Arts Sec	60 Special Education Sec	70 Research/Development
3 Buildings And Grounds	10 Curric/Instruct Sec	21 Art Elem	31 Career/Sch-to-Work K-12	41 Social Studies Sec	51 Reading K-12	61 Foreign/World Lang K-12	71 Public Information
4 Food Service	11 Federal Program	22 Art Sec	32 Career/Sch-to-Work Elem	42 Science K-12	52 Reading Elem	62 Foreign/World Lang Elem	72 Summer School
5 Transportation	12 Title I	23 Music K-12	33 Career/Sch-to-Work Sec	43 Science Elem	53 Reading Sec	63 Foreign/World Lang Sec	73 Instructional Tech
6 Athletic	13 Title V	24 Music Elem	34 Early Childhood Ed	44 Science Sec	54 Remedial Reading K-12	64 Religious Education K-12	74 Inservice Training
7 Health Services	15 Asst Superintendent	25 Music Sec	35 Health/Phys Education	45 Math K-12	55 Remedial Reading Elem	65 Religious Education Elem	75 Marketing/Distributive
	16 Instructional Media Svcs	26 Business Education	36 Guidance Services K-12	46 Math Elem	56 Remedial Reading Sec	66 Religious Education Sec	76 Info Systems
	17 Chief Operations Officer	27 Career & Tech Ed	37 Guidance Services Elem	47 Math Sec	57 Bilingual/ELL	67 School Board President	77 Psychological Assess
	18 Chief Academic Officer	28 Technology Education	38 Guidance Services Sec	48 English/Lang Arts K-12	58 Special Education K-12	68 Teacher Personnel	78 Affirmative Action

New York School Directory — Suffolk County

Gina Curiale	6,35
Maria Castro	8,15
Lance Lohman	9,12,34,54*
Richard Kollar	15,68,80,83
John Gallagher	20,23
Janine Villez	59
Penelope McGrath	67
Pierre Gay	73,76
Steve Harding	91
Stephanie Columbia	7
Dr Tracy Poulton	8,39
Lisa Mato	11,69
Vaughn Denton	15,79
Von Genton	30
Jennifer McCarthy	60
Pamela Donovan	71
Joseph Scarpinato	76
Mary Richardson	298

Public Schs..Principal	Grd	Prgm	Enr/#Cls	SN
Charles E Walters Elem Sch 15 Everett Dr, Yaphank 11980 Brian Foster	K-4	T	741 49	54% 631/345-2758 Fax 631/345-2849
Coram Elem Sch 61 Coram Mount Sinai Rd, Coram 11727 Susan Connolly	K-4	T	1,013 30	54% 631/698-0077 Fax 631/698-0807
Longwood High Sch 100 Longwood Rd, Middle Island 11953 Scott Schuster	9-12	ATV	2,917 100	49% 631/345-9200 Fax 631/345-9279
Longwood Junior High Sch 198 Longwood Rd, Middle Island 11953 Adam DeWitt	7-8	GTV	1,541 70	50% 631/345-2700 Fax 631/345-9281
Longwood Middle Sch 41 Yaphank Middle Island Rd, Middle Island 11953 Yvette Mercado-Tilley	5-6	GT	1,387	51% 631/345-2735 Fax 631/345-9296
Ridge Elem Sch 105 Ridge Rd, Ridge 11961 Janine Rozycki	K-4	T	769 40	43% 631/345-2765 Fax 631/345-9289
West Middle Island Elem Sch 30 Swezey Ln, Middle Island 11953 Gretchen Schaentzler	K-4	T	676 80	52% 631/345-2160 Fax 631/345-3518

• **Mattituck-Cutchogue UFSD** PID: 00774160   631/298-4242
385 Depot Ln, Cutchogue 11935   Fax 631/298-8573

Schools: 2 \ **Teachers:** 118 \ **Students:** 1,100 \ **Special Ed Students:** 178 \ **LEP Students:** 79 \ **College-Bound:** 89% \ **Ethnic:** Asian 1%, African American 2%, Hispanic 17%, Caucasian 80% \ **Exp:** $392 (High) \ **Poverty:** 4% \ **Title I:** $50,719 \ **Special Education:** $944,000 \ **Open-Close:** 09/08 - 06/25 \ **DTBP:** $177 (High)

Jill Gierasch	1
Eugene Pacholk	3
Gregory Wormuth	6,7,35,83*
Tricia Desiderio	57,58,79
Gerri Doherty	73,76,295
Kevin Coffey	2,68
Judi Passiglia	5
Deborah Guryn	11,58,72,296,298*
Barbara Wheaton	67
Bill Haining	295

Public Schs..Principal	Grd	Prgm	Enr/#Cls	SN
Cutchogue East Elem Sch 34900 Main Rd, Cutchogue 11935 Kathleen DeVine	K-6		491 52	30% 631/734-6049 Fax 631/734-4299
Mattituck Jr Sr High Sch 15125 Main Rd, Mattituck 11952 Shawn Petretti	7-12		609 30	26% 631/298-8471 Fax 631/298-8544 f

• **Middle Country Ctl Sch Dist** PID: 00774201   631/285-8000
8 43rd St, Centereach 11720   Fax 631/738-2719

Schools: 14 \ **Teachers:** 698 \ **Students:** 9,860 \ **Special Ed Students:** 1,648 \ **LEP Students:** 475 \ **College-Bound:** 83% \ **Ethnic:** Asian 8%, African American 4%, Hispanic 24%, Caucasian 64% \ **Exp:** $401 (High) \ **Poverty:** 7% \ **Title I:** $1,013,481 \ **Special Education:** $20,300,000 \ **Open-Close:** 09/10 - 06/25 \ **DTBP:** $78 (Low)

Dr Roberta Gerold	1
Dr Beth Rella	2,15,19

Frank Fiorino	3,91
Lisa Myers	5
Francine McMann	8,15,51,274
Brook Licker	10,11
Diana Cook	20,23,270
Nick Cangero	31
Rachel Ndembera	42
Jonathan Singer	57,285,288*
Adele Cullen	60
Stephanie Larkin	71
Dr Vincent Raicovi	73,76,286
Trish Damato	273
Denise Ferrera	298
Bill Kidd	4
Joseph Mercado	6,35,83,85
Kayria Siegel	9,48,54
James Donovan	15,68
Nicole Peterson	30
Mark Palios	36
Ryan Milano	45
Dr Jennifer Harrison	58,77,88*
Dr Karen Lesser	67
Jennifer Haynia	73
Nadia Resnikoff	74,78
Ed Katuna	295

Public Schs..Principal	Grd	Prgm	Enr/#Cls	SN
Bicycle Path Pre-K & Kdgn Ctr 27 N Bicycle Path, Selden 11784 Lisa Marie Contarino	PK-K		442 25	21% 631/285-8800 Fax 631/285-8801
Centereach High Sch 14 43rd St, Centereach 11720 Tom Bell	9-12	AGV	1,541 80	22% 631/285-8100 Fax 631/285-8101
Dawnwood Middle Sch 10 43rd St, Centereach 11720 Daniel Katchihtes	6-8	V	1,043 68	28% 631/285-8200 Fax 631/285-8201
Eugene Auer Memorial Elem Sch 17 Wing St, Lake Grove 11755 Kenneth Gutmann	1-5		267 20	21% 631/285-8500 Fax 631/285-8501
Hawkins Path Elem Sch 485 Hawkins Rd, Selden 11784 Kristi Leonard	1-5		279 19	28% 631/285-8530 Fax 631/285-8531
Holbrook Road Elem Sch 170 Holbrook Rd, Centereach 11720 Dr Craig Unkenholz	1-5		375 18	17% 631/285-8560 Fax 631/285-8561
Jericho Elem Sch 34 N Coleman Rd, Centereach 11720 Glen Rogers	1-5		380 23	27% 631/285-8600 Fax 631/285-8601
New Lane Memorial Elem Sch 15 New Ln, Selden 11784 Phyllis Saltz	1-5		820 54	28% 631/285-8900 Fax 631/285-8901
Newfield High Sch 145 Marshall Dr, Selden 11784 Scott Graviano	9-12	V	1,559 45	26% 631/285-8300 Fax 631/285-8301
North Coleman Road Elem Sch 197 N Coleman Rd, Centereach 11720 Gretchen Rodney	PK-5		397 19	21% 631/285-8660 Fax 631/285-8661
Oxhead Road Elem Sch 144 Oxhead Rd, Centereach 11720 Corinne Seeh	1-5		420 24	33% 631/285-8700 Fax 631/285-8701
Selden Middle Sch 22 Jefferson Ave, Centereach 11720 Andrew Bennett	6-8	V	1,053	26% 631/285-8400 Fax 631/285-8401
Stagecoach Elem Sch 205 Dare Rd, Selden 11784 Shaun Rothberg	1-5		414 25	35% 631/285-8730 Fax 631/285-8731
Unity Drive Pre-K Kdgn Center 11 Unity Dr, Centereach 11720 Deborah Wolfe	PK-K		526 26	17% 631/285-8760

• **Miller Place Union Free SD** PID: 00774445   631/474-2700
7 Memorial Dr, Miller Place 11764   Fax 631/331-8832

Schools: 4 \ **Teachers:** 200 \ **Students:** 2,489 \ **Special Ed Students:** 442 \ **LEP Students:** 46 \ **College-Bound:** 90% \ **Ethnic:** Asian 2%, African American 1%, Hispanic 8%, Caucasian 89% \ **Exp:** $244 (Med) \ **Poverty:** 3% \ **Title I:** $168,350 \ **Special Education:** $3,974,000 \ **Open-Close:** 09/02 - 06/24 \ **DTBP:** $337 (High)

---

79 Student Personnel	91 Safety/Security	275 Response To Intervention	298 Grant Writer/Ptnrships
80 Driver Ed/Safety	92 Magnet School	277 Remedial Math K-12	750 Chief Innovation Officer
81 Gifted/Talented	93 Parental Involvement	280 Literacy Coach	751 Chief of Staff
82 Video Services	95 Tech Prep Program	285 STEM	752 Social Emotional Learning
83 Substance Abuse Prev	97 Chief Infomation Officer	286 Digital Learning	
84 Erate	98 Chief Technology Officer	288 Common Core Standards	
85 AIDS Education	270 Character Education	294 Accountability	
88 Alternative/At Risk	271 Migrant Education	295 Network System	
89 Multi-Cultural Curriculum	273 Teacher Mentor	296 Title II Programs	
90 Social Work	274 Before/After Sch	297 Webmaster	

School Programs
A = Alternative Program
G = Adult Classes
M = Magnet Program
T = Title I Schoolwide
V = Career & Tech Ed Programs

Other School Types
Ⓐ = Alternative School
Ⓒ = Charter School
Ⓜ = Magnet School
Ⓨ = Year-Round School

Social Media
f = Facebook
t = Twitter

New Schools are shaded
New Superintendents and Principals are bold
Personnel with email addresses are underscored

Suffolk County

Market Data Retrieval

Dr Marianne Cartisano 1
Dennis Warsaw 3
Regina Tambasco 5
Sandra Wojnowski 10,12,58,296*
Susan Craddock 15
Sean White 36*
Barbara Weir 73,84,295

Colleen Card 2
Cathy Schretzmayer 4
Ron Petrie 6,58,85*
Seth Lipshie 15
Kate Lynch 16,82*
Johonna Testa 67
Jeremy Koch 79

Public Schs..Principal	Grd	Prgm	Enr/#Cls	SN
Andrew Muller Primary Sch 65 Lower Rocky Point Rd, Miller Place 11764 Laura Gewurz	K-2		470 30	14% 631/474-2715 Fax 631/474-4738
Laddie Decker Sound Beach Sch 197 N Country Rd, Miller Place 11764 Catherine Honeyman	3-5		510 30	15% 631/474-2719 Fax 631/474-2497
Miller Place High Sch 15 Memorial Dr, Miller Place 11764 Kevin Slavin	9-12	V	870 110	15% 631/474-2723 Fax 631/474-1734
North Country Rd Middle Sch 191 N Country Rd, Miller Place 11764 Matthew Clark	6-8		639 46	13% 631/474-2710 Fax 631/474-5178

- **Montauk Union Free School Dist** PID: 00774483   631/668-2474
  50 S Dorset Dr, Montauk 11954   Fax 631/668-1107

  Schools: 1 \ **Teachers:** 37 \ **Students:** 320 \ **Special Ed Students:** 56 \ **LEP Students:** 23 \ **Ethnic:** Asian 1%, African American 4%, Hispanic 30%, Caucasian 65% \ **Exp:** $424 (High) \ **Poverty:** 8% \ **Title I:** $80,810 \ **Special Education:** $315,000 \ **Open-Close:** 09/04 - 06/25 \ **DTBP:** $366 (High)

J Philip Perna 1,11
William Collins 6,35,83,85
Bridget Collins 12,69,270,286,288,298
Adriana Proctor 57,271
Tyler Van Slyke 73,76
Joseph Malave 285
Michael Adelson 752

Mathew Neuschwender 2
J Philip Perna 11,88*
Rachel Kleinberg 16,82
Diane Hausman 67
Sara McGuirre 88,275
Brigid Collins 298*

Public Schs..Principal	Grd	Prgm	Enr/#Cls	SN
Montauk Public Sch 50 S Dorset Dr, Montauk 11954 J Philip Perna	PK-8	GT	320 30	631/668-2474

- **Mt Sinai Union Free SD** PID: 00774500   631/870-2500
  118 N Country Rd, Mount Sinai 11766   Fax 631/473-0905

  Schools: 3 \ **Teachers:** 172 \ **Students:** 2,100 \ **Special Ed Students:** 317 \ **LEP Students:** 16 \ **College-Bound:** 80% \ **Ethnic:** Asian 6%, African American 1%, Hispanic 8%, Caucasian 85% \ **Exp:** $245 (Med) \ **Poverty:** 6% \ **Title I:** $212,687 \ **Special Education:** $2,599,000 \ **Open-Close:** 09/08 - 06/25 \ **DTBP:** $325 (High)

Gordon Brosdal 1
Scott Reh 3,6*
Peter Pramataris 8*
Doris Stangev 58
Ken Jockers 76,295
Andy Matthews 285

Linda Jensen 2,5
Deena Timo 8,11,16,69,73,77,288*
Matt Dyroff 36*
Robert Sweeney 67
Rob Catlin 274*

Public Schs..Principal	Grd	Prgm	Enr/#Cls	SN
Mt Sinai Elem Sch 118 N Country Rd, Mount Sinai 11766 Rob Catlin	K-4		716 60	9% 631/870-2600 Fax 631/928-3860
Mt Sinai High Sch 110 N Country Rd, Mount Sinai 11766 Peter Pramataris	9-12	GV	797 50	8% 631/870-2800 Fax 631/928-3668
Mt Sinai Middle Sch 150 N Country Rd, Mount Sinai 11766 Elizabeth Hine	5-8		654 53	11% 631/870-2800 Fax 631/928-3129

- **New Suffolk Common School Dist** PID: 00774524   631/734-6940
  1295 4th St, New Suffolk 11956

  Schools: 1 \ **Teachers:** 7 \ **Students:** 13 \ **Special Ed Students:** 3 \ **LEP Students:** 3 \ **Ethnic:** Hispanic 13%, Caucasian 87% \ **Exp:** $602 (High) \ **Open-Close:** 09/08 - 06/25 \ **DTBP:** $161 (High)

Phill Kent 1,11
Sara Campbell 9,69,286,752
Michelle Feeley 71

Angela Kohl 2
Tony Dill 67
Joe Wiederman 73

Public Schs..Principal	Grd	Prgm	Enr/#Cls	SN
New Suffolk Common Sch 1295 4th St, New Suffolk 11956 Phil Kent	PK-6		13 2	631/734-6940

- **North Babylon Union Free SD** PID: 00774548   631/620-7000
  5 Jardine Pl, North Babylon 11703   Fax 631/321-3295

  Schools: 7 \ **Teachers:** 359 \ **Students:** 4,491 \ **Special Ed Students:** 802 \ **LEP Students:** 295 \ **College-Bound:** 80% \ **Ethnic:** Asian 6%, African American 24%, Hispanic 30%, Caucasian 40% \ **Exp:** $226 (Med) \ **Poverty:** 7% \ **Title I:** $490,816 \ **Special Education:** $10,942,000 \ **Open-Close:** 09/08 - 06/25 \ **DTBP:** $316 (High)

Glen Eschbach 1
Mark Savella 4
Jason Friesen 6,7,83*
Barbara Butler 15,68
Dennis McElheron 58
Daniel Rose 73,79,295*

Salvatore Carambia 2
Allen Miller 5
Kimberly Skillen 8,15,288
Dr Kim Coyne 20,23*
Daniel Caroleo 67
Joseph Vereline 91

Public Schs..Principal	Grd	Prgm	Enr/#Cls	SN
Belmont Elem Sch 108 Barnum St, West Babylon 11704 Valerie Jackson	K-5	A	402 21	36% 631/620-7500 Fax 631/376-0278
Marion G Vedder Elem Sch 794 Deer Park Ave, North Babylon 11703 Kerry Larke	K-5	A	325 25	32% 631/620-7600 Fax 631/587-2480
North Babylon High Sch 1 Phelps Ln, North Babylon 11703 Jonathan Klomp	9-12	AGV	1,457 23	38% 631/620-7100 Fax 631/321-3327
Parliament Place Elem Sch 80 Parliament Pl, North Babylon 11703 Drew Olson	K-5	A	476 21	36% 631/620-7900 Fax 631/254-2318
Robert Moses Middle Sch 250 Phelps Ln, North Babylon 11703 John Ruggero	6-8	ATV	1,094 50	40% 631/620-7302 Fax 631/587-2372
William E DeLuca Jr Elem Sch 223 Phelps Ln, North Babylon 11703 Vincent Fantauzzi	K-5	A	395 21	32% 631/620-7700 Fax 631/321-3331
Woods Road Elem Sch 110 Woods Rd, North Babylon 11703 Celeste Archer	K-5	A	400 21	31% 631/620-7800 Fax 631/243-5492

1	Superintendent	8	Curric/Instruct K-12	19	Chief Financial Officer	29	Family/Consumer Science	39	Social Studies K-12	49	English/Lang Arts Elem	59	Special Education Elem	69	Academic Assessment
2	Bus/Finance/Purchasing	9	Curric/Instruct Elem	20	Art K-12	30	Adult Education	40	Social Studies Elem	50	English/Lang Arts Sec	60	Special Education Sec	70	Research/Development
3	Buildings And Grounds	10	Curric/Instruct Sec	21	Art Elem	31	Career/Sch-to-Work K-12	41	Social Studies Sec	51	Reading K-12	61	Foreign/World Lang K-12	71	Public Information
4	Food Service	11	Federal Program	22	Art Sec	32	Career/Sch-to-Work Elem	42	Science K-12	52	Reading Elem	62	Foreign/World Lang Elem	72	Summer School
5	Transportation	12	Title I	23	Music K-12	33	Career/Sch-to-Work Sec	43	Science Elem	53	Reading Sec	63	Foreign/World Lang Sec	73	Instructional Tech
6	Athletic	13	Title V	24	Music Elem	34	Early Childhood Ed	44	Science Sec	54	Remedial Reading K-12	64	Religious Education K-12	74	Inservice Training
7	Health Services	15	Asst Superintendent	25	Music Sec	35	Health/Phys Education	45	Math K-12	55	Remedial Reading Elem	65	Religious Education Elem	75	Marketing/Distributive
		16	Instructional Media Svcs	26	Business Education	36	Guidance Services K-12	46	Math Elem	56	Remedial Reading Sec	66	Religious Education Sec	76	Info Systems
		17	Chief Operations Officer	27	Career & Tech Ed	37	Guidance Services Elem	47	Math Sec	57	Bilingual/ELL	67	School Board President	77	Psychological Assess
		18	Chief Academic Officer	28	Technology Education	38	Guidance Services Sec	48	English/Lang Arts K-12	58	Special Education K-12	68	Teacher Personnel	78	Affirmative Action

New York School Directory — Suffolk County

• Northport-East Northport UFSD PID: 00774653   631/262-6600
158 Laurel Ave, Northport 11768   Fax 631/262-6607

Schools: 9 \ **Teachers:** 489 \ **Students:** 5,141 \ **Special Ed Students:** 939 \ **LEP Students:** 139 \ **College-Bound:** 91% \ **Ethnic:** Asian 3%, African American 1%, Hispanic 11%, Caucasian 85% \ **Exp:** $303 (High) \ **Poverty:** 3% \ **Title I:** $175,827 \ **Special Education:** $5,923,000 \ **Open-Close:** 09/08 - 06/25 \ **DTBP:** $321 (High)

Robert Banzer ...1	Robert Howard ...2,15
John Lackner ...3	Danielle Tiecher ...4
Trish McGrane ...5	Mark Dantuono ...6,35
Mark Dantuono ...6,35*	Dr Dana Boshnack ...8
Irene McLaughlin ...15,68	Dr Izzet Mergen ...20,23
Mary Mathers ...30	Shannon Danturno ...36,79
Sean Hurley ...39	David Storch ...42*
Robin Rann ...45	Patricia Schmitt ...48*
Tara Gaiss ...51	David Badanes ...67
Judy Proscia ...73	

Public Schs..Principal	Grd	Prgm	Enr/#Cls	SN	
Bellerose Elem Sch 253 Bellerose Ave, E Northport 11731 Lori Beekman	K-5		306 24	11%	631/262-6800 Fax 631/262-6805
Dickinson Avenue Elem Sch 120 Dickinson Ave, E Northport 11731 Laurie Storch	K-5	T	374 30	18%	631/262-6810 Fax 631/262-6815
East Northport Middle Sch 1075 5th Ave, E Northport 11731 Pasquale DeStefano	6-8	V	559 50	17%	631/262-6770 Fax 631/262-6773
Fifth Avenue Elem Sch 1157 5th Ave, E Northport 11731 Thomas Harrison	K-5		357 26	8%	631/262-6820 Fax 631/262-2825
Northport High Sch 154 Laurel Hill Rd, Northport 11768 Daniel Danbusky	9-12	AV	1,871	14%	631/262-6654 Fax 631/262-6880
Northport Middle Sch 11 Middleville Rd, Northport 11768 Tim Hoss	6-8	V	602 50	10%	631/262-6750 Fax 631/262-6793
Norwood Avenue Elem Sch 25 Norwood Rd, Northport 11768 Michael Genovese	K-5		304 35	5%	631/262-6830 Fax 631/262-6835
Ocean Avenue Elem Sch 100 Ocean Ave, Northport 11768 Sabina Larkin	K-5		304 26	8%	631/262-6840 Fax 631/262-6845
Pulaski Road Elem Sch 623 9th Ave, E Northport 11731 Jeffrey Haubrich	K-5	T	377 26	25%	631/262-6850 Fax 631/262-6855

• Oysterponds Union Free SD PID: 00774794   631/323-2410
23405 Main Rd, Orient 11957   Fax 631/323-3713

Schools: 1 \ **Teachers:** 15 \ **Students:** 104 \ **Special Ed Students:** 12 \ **LEP Students:** 7 \ **Ethnic:** African American 1%, Hispanic 26%, Caucasian 73% \ **Exp:** $233 (Med) \ **Poverty:** 4% \ **Special Education:** $109,000 \ **Open-Close:** 09/09 - 06/25 \ **DTBP:** $359 (High)

Richard Malone ...1,288	Melissa Palermo ...2
Harmon Cohen ...59	Thomas Stevenson ...67
Amy Bennett ...73	

Public Schs..Principal	Grd	Prgm	Enr/#Cls	SN	
Oysterponds Elem Sch 23405 Main Rd, Orient 11957 Jennifer Wissemann	PK-6		104 12		631/323-2410

• Patchogue-Medford Unified SD PID: 00774811   631/687-6300
241 S Ocean Ave, Patchogue 11772   Fax 631/687-6389

Schools: 11 \ **Teachers:** 528 \ **Students:** 7,503 \ **Special Ed Students:** 1,271 \ **LEP Students:** 979 \ **Ethnic:** Asian 2%, African American 5%, Hispanic 45%, Caucasian 47% \ **Exp:** $260 (Med) \ **Poverty:** 9% \ **Title I:** $998,879 \ **Special Education:** $15,298,000 \ **Open-Close:** 09/09 - 06/25 \ **DTBP:** $313 (High)

Donna Jones ...1	Doreen Lamm ...2
Frank Mazzie ...2	Nicole Ciminiello ...2
Paul Noonan ...3	Daniel Erwin ...4*
Carol Sicignano ...5	Ryan Cox ...6,7,35*
Lori Cannetti ...8,11,15,288	Jessica Lukas ...15,58
Dr Joey Cohen ...15,68	Sharon Deland ...16,40,49,51
Mark Stuckey ...20,23*	Raymond Ruiz ...31
Michael Zanfardino ...36,69,73	Gloria Sesso ...41
Dalimar Rastello ...49,57,62*	Michelle Marrone ...57,61
Kristin Pucilowski ...58	Lori Goldstein ...59*
Debra Ciccarelli ...60	Kelli Jennings ...67
James Richroath ...76,295*	Catherine Carella-Dean ...79
Dharminder Sohal ...285	Louis Stellato ...285*

Public Schs..Principal	Grd	Prgm	Enr/#Cls	SN	
Barton Elem Sch 199 Barton Ave, Patchogue 11772 Matthew Hanley	K-5		456 35	40%	631/687-6900 Fax 631/687-6940
Bay Elem Sch 114 Bay Ave, Patchogue 11772 Rui Mendes	K-5	T	360 30	55%	631/687-6950 Fax 631/687-6990
Canaan Elem Sch 59 Fry Blvd, Patchogue 11772 Robert Epstein	K-5	T	521 30	55%	631/687-8100 Fax 631/687-8140
Eagle Elem Sch 1000 Wave Ave, Medford 11763 Erin Skahill	K-5		570 26	53%	631/687-8150 Fax 631/687-8190
Medford Elem Sch 281 Medford Ave, Patchogue 11772 Margherit Proscia	K-5	T	502 35	56%	631/687-8300 Fax 631/687-8340
Oregon Middle Sch 109 Oregon Ave, Medford 11763 Bryan Lake	6-8		573 50	48%	631/687-6800 Fax 631/687-6840
Patchogue Medford Sr High Sch 181 Buffalo Ave, Medford 11763 Randy Rusielewicz	9-12	G	2,424	51%	631/687-6500 Fax 631/687-6599
River Elem Sch 46 River Ave, Patchogue 11772 Tania Dalley	K-5	T	307 16	61%	631/687-8350 Fax 631/687-8370
Saxton Middle Sch 121 Saxton St, Patchogue 11772 Manuel Sanzone	6-8		566 52	58%	631/687-6700 Fax 631/687-6740
South Ocean Middle Sch 225 S Ocean Ave, Patchogue 11772 Timothy Piciullo	6-8		587 60	61%	631/687-6600 Fax 631/687-6640
Tremont Elem Sch 143 Tremont Ave, Medford 11763 Emily Wernau	K-5		488 30	34%	631/687-8700 Fax 631/687-8740

• Port Jefferson Union Free SD 6 PID: 00774938   631/791-4500
550 Scraggy Hill Rd, Prt Jefferson 11777   Fax 631/476-4467

Schools: 3 \ **Teachers:** 119 \ **Students:** 1,048 \ **Special Ed Students:** 200 \ **LEP Students:** 38 \ **College-Bound:** 98% \ **Ethnic:** Asian 8%, African American 1%, Hispanic 10%, Caucasian 81% \ **Exp:** $514 (High) \ **Poverty:** 3% \ **Title I:** $34,598 \ **Special Education:** $836,000 \ **Open-Close:** 09/08 - 06/25 \ **DTBP:** $166 (High)

---

79 Student Personnel	91 Safety/Security	275 Response To Intervention	298 Grant Writer/Ptnrships	**School Programs**
80 Driver Ed/Safety	92 Magnet School	277 Remedial Math K-12	750 Chief Innovation Officer	A = Alternative Program
81 Gifted/Talented	93 Parental Involvement	280 Literacy Coach	751 Chief of Staff	G = Adult Classes
82 Video Services	95 Tech Prep Program	285 STEM	752 Social Emotional Learning	M = Magnet Program
83 Substance Abuse Prev	97 Chief Information Officer	286 Digital Learning		T = Title I Schoolwide
84 Erate	98 Chief Technology Officer	288 Common Core Standards	**Other School Types**	V = Career & Tech Ed Programs
85 AIDS Education	270 Character Education	294 Accountability	Ⓐ = Alternative School	
88 Alternative/At Risk	271 Migrant Education	295 Network System	Ⓒ = Charter School	**Social Media**
89 Multi-Cultural Curriculum	273 Teacher Mentor	296 Title II Programs	Ⓜ = Magnet School	f = Facebook
90 Social Work	274 Before/After Sch	297 Webmaster	Ⓨ = Year-Round School	t = Twitter

New Schools are shaded
New Superintendents and Principals are bold
Personnel with email addresses are underscored

Suffolk County

Market Data Retrieval

Jessica Schmettan	1	Sean Leister	2,11,15,76	Ryan Jacobellis	3	Keith Graham	4
Fred Koelbel	3,5	Adam Sherrard	6*	Colette Furcht	5	Let Moore	5
Christine Austin	18,298	Jody Cahill	58,78	Brian Sacks	6,35,80	Jeane-Marie Mazzaferro	7,58,79,83,85,88,90,274
Ellen Boehm	67	Brian Sandak	73,84	Robert Hines	16,73,76,84,286,295	Jason Rottcamp	20,23
				Charles Gassar	36	Maria Cassamassa	48,280
				Elizabeth Scaduto	57*	Laurie Downs	67
				Arlene Durkalski	68	Collene Richardson	80*
				Terry Culhane	91	Christopher Amato	294

Public Schs..Principal	Grd	Prgm	Enr/#Cls	SN
Earl Van Dermuelen High Sch 350 Old Post Rd, Prt Jefferson 11777 Eric Haruthunian	9-12		357 30	7% 631/476-4400 Fax 631/476-4408
Edna Louise Spear Elem Sch 500 Scraggy Hill Rd, Prt Jefferson 11777 Thomas Meehan	PK-5		433 34	9% 631/791-4300 Fax 631/476-4419
Port Jefferson Middle Sch 350 Old Post Rd, Prt Jefferson 11777 Dr Robert Neidig	6-8		258 24	7% 631/476-4440 Fax 631/476-4430

● **Quogue Union Free School Dist** PID: 00774976   631/653-4285
10 Edgewood Rd, Quogue 11959   Fax 631/996-4600

Schools: 1 \ **Teachers:** 18 \ **Students:** 130 \ **Special Ed Students:** 16
\ **LEP Students:** 3 \ **Ethnic:** Asian 1%, Hispanic 15%, Caucasian 84% \
Exp: $1,331 (High) \ **Poverty:** 2% \ **Special Education:** $84,000 \
Open-Close: 09/09 - 06/25 \ **DTBP:** $345 (High)

Jeffrey Ryvicker	1	Micheal Zuccaro	2
Ryan Fay	6,35,85*	Dawn Hine	16,82*
Laura Meyer	57*	Lauren Battista	67
Colleen McGreevy	73,295*		

Public Schs..Principal	Grd	Prgm	Enr/#Cls	SN
Quogue Elem Sch 10 Edgewood Rd, Quogue 11959 Jeffrey Ryvicker	PK-6		130 7	4% 631/653-4285

● **Remsenburg-Speonk UFSD** PID: 00774990   631/325-0203
11 Mill Rd, Remsenburg 11960   Fax 631/325-8439

Schools: 1 \ **Teachers:** 25 \ **Students:** 132 \
Special Ed Students: 22 \ **LEP Students:** 11 \ **Ethnic:** Asian 2%,
African American 1%, Hispanic 15%, Caucasian 82% \ **Exp:** $850 (High) \
Poverty: 2% \ **Special Education:** $228,000 \ **Open-Close:** 09/04 - 06/25 \
DTBP: $377 (High)

Denise Sullivan	1,83	Jamie Reed	2,71
Ron Senn	3*	Lisa Senn	4*
Guy Napolitano	6*	Adrienne Cirone	11,296,752*
Laureen Andrea	16,82*	Kate Sears	57*
John Barry	67	Christina Patsos	73,76*
Ryan Curtis	73,295		

Public Schs..Principal	Grd	Prgm	Enr/#Cls	SN
Remsenburg-Speonk Elem Sch 11 Mill Rd, Remsenburg 11960 Denise Sullivan	K-6		132 10	20% 631/325-0203

● **Riverhead Central School Dist** PID: 00775011   631/369-6700
700 Osborn Ave, Riverhead 11901   Fax 631/369-6816

Schools: 7 \ **Teachers:** 383 \ **Students:** 5,600 \ **Special Ed Students:** 956
\ **LEP Students:** 1,538 \ **College-Bound:** 83% \ **Ethnic:** Asian 1%,
African American 10%, Hispanic 51%, Caucasian 38% \ **Exp:** $310 (High)
\ **Poverty:** 15% \ **Title I:** $1,267,792 \ **Special Education:** $7,197,000 \
Open-Close: 09/03 - 06/25 \ **DTBP:** $407 (High)

Christine Tona	1,11,288	Sam Schneider	2,15,68

Public Schs..Principal	Grd	Prgm	Enr/#Cls	SN
Aquebogue Elem Sch 499 Main Rd, Aquebogue 11931 Bryan Miltenberg	K-4	T	497 23	41% 631/369-6780 Fax 631/369-0543
Phillips Avenue Elem Sch 141 Phillips Ave, Riverhead 11901 Debra Rodgers	K-4	T	566 25	57% 631/369-6787 Fax 631/369-6833
Pulaski Street Elem Sch 300 Pulaski St, Riverhead 11901 David Densieski	5-6	T	866 32	60% 631/369-6794 Fax 631/369-7795
Riley Avenue Elem Sch 374 Riley Ave, Calverton 11933 David Enos	K-4	T	554	40% 631/369-6804 Fax 631/369-6807
Riverhead High Sch 700 Harrison Ave, Riverhead 11901 Sean O'Hara	9-12	GTV	2,067	49% 631/369-6723 Fax 631/369-5164
Riverhead Middle Sch 600 Harrison Ave, Riverhead 11901 Stephen Hudson	7-8	TV	897 60	57% 631/369-6759 Fax 631/369-6829
Roanoke Avenue Elem Sch 549 Roanoke Ave, Riverhead 11901 Thomas Payton	K-4	T	387 18	58% 631/369-6813 Fax 631/369-6830

● **Rocky Point Union Free SD** PID: 00775102   631/744-1600
90 Rocky Point-Yaphank Rd, Rocky Point 11778   Fax 631/849-7558

Schools: 4 \ **Teachers:** 234 \ **Students:** 2,947 \ **Special Ed Students:** 559
\ **LEP Students:** 112 \ **College-Bound:** 84% \ **Ethnic:** Asian 1%,
African American 1%, Hispanic 15%, Caucasian 82% \ **Exp:** $384 (High)
\ **Poverty:** 6% \ **Title I:** $283,583 \ **Special Education:** $7,514,000 \
Open-Close: 09/02 - 06/25 \ **DTBP:** $313 (High)

Dr Scott O'Brien	1	Debra Hoffman	2
Paul Martinez	3	Maureen Branagan	4*
Greg Hilton	5	Charles Delargy	6,7,35,80
Aaron Factor	8	Anja Groth	8,11,69,280,298*
Susan Wilson	8,16,34,73,76,273,295*	Dr Deborah DeLuca	13,88,275,277,285,294,296
Melinda Brooke	16,20,39,48,57	Lori Kauhn	30,80
Andrea Mosciatello	58	Susan Sullivan	67
Kristen White	79		

Public Schs..Principal	Grd	Prgm	Enr/#Cls	SN
Frank J Carasiti Elem Sch 90 Rocky Point Yaphank Rd, Rocky Point 11778 Virginia Kellygibbons	K-2		587 41	30% 631/744-1601 Fax 631/744-1396
Joseph A Edgar Interm Sch 525 Route 25A, Rocky Point 11778 Linda Murphy	3-5		643 53	35% 631/744-1600 Fax 631/744-4898
Ⓐ Rocky Point High Sch 82 Rocky Point Yaphank Rd, Rocky Point 11778 Jonathan Hart	9-12	G	999 59	30% 631/744-1604 Fax 631/591-0220
Rocky Point Middle Sch 76 Rocky Point Yaphank Rd, Rocky Point 11778 James Moeller	6-8	V	697	30% 631/744-1603 Fax 631/886-0000

1	Superintendent	8	Curric/Instruct K-12	19	Chief Financial Officer	29	Family/Consumer Science	39	Social Studies K-12	49	English/Lang Arts Elem	59	Special Education Elem	69	Academic Assessment
2	Bus/Finance/Purchasing	9	Curric/Instruct Elem	20	Art K-12	30	Adult Education	40	Social Studies Elem	50	English/Lang Arts Sec	60	Special Education Sec	70	Research/Development
3	Buildings And Grounds	10	Curric/Instruct Sec	21	Art Elem	31	Career/Sch-to-Work K-12	41	Social Studies Sec	51	Reading K-12	61	Foreign/World Lang K-12	71	Public Information
4	Food Service	11	Federal Program	22	Art Sec	32	Career/Sch-to-Work Elem	42	Science K-12	52	Reading Elem	62	Foreign/World Lang Elem	72	Summer School
5	Transportation	12	Title I	23	Music K-12	33	Career/Sch-to-Work Sec	43	Science Elem	53	Reading Sec	63	Foreign/World Lang Sec	73	Instructional Tech
6	Athletic	13	Title V	24	Music Elem	34	Early Childhood Ed	44	Science Sec	54	Remedial Reading K-12	64	Religious Education K-12	74	Inservice Training
7	Health Services	14	Instructional Media Svcs	25	Music Sec	35	Health/Phys Education	45	Math K-12	55	Remedial Reading Elem	65	Religious Education Elem	75	Marketing/Distributive
		15	Asst Superintendent	26	Business Education	36	Guidance Services K-12	46	Math Elem	56	Remedial Reading Sec	66	Religious Education Sec	76	Info Systems
		16	Chief Operations Officer	27	Career & Tech Ed	37	Guidance Services Elem	47	Math Sec	57	Bilingual/ELL	67	School Board President	77	Psychological Assess
		17	Chief Academic Officer	28	Technology Education	38	Guidance Services Sec	48	English/Lang Arts K-12	58	Special Education K-12	68	Teacher Personnel	78	Affirmative Action

New York School Directory — Suffolk County

• **Sachem Central School Dist** PID: 00775138 631/471-1300
51 School St, Lk Ronkonkoma 11779   Fax 631/471-1318

Schools: 15 \ **Teachers:** 944 \ **Students:** 13,500 \
Special Ed Students: 2,357 \ **LEP Students:** 301 \ **Ethnic:** Asian 6%, African American 3%, Hispanic 17%, Caucasian 74% \ **Exp:** $430 (High) \ **Poverty:** 5% \ **Title I:** $974,543 \ **Special Education:** $26,990,000 \
Open-Close: 09/08 - 06/25 \ **DTBP:** $676 (High) \ t

John O'Keefe	2,15	Ron Sacks	2,84
Ed Miller	3	Scott Ptaszynski	3
Lisa Zdenek	4	Joseph Cervone	5
Gary Beutel	6,7,35	Shannon McEntee	6,35
Erin Hynes	8,15,280	Jack Renda	9,16,27,73,81,295
Kristin Capel-Eden	15,68,74	Mary Faller	29*
Marie O'Doherty	43	Suzanne Groe	63*
Alex Piccirillo	67	Wayne Wilson	91

Public Schs..Principal	Grd	Prgm	Enr/#Cls	SN	
Cayuga Elem Sch 865 Hawkins Ave, Lake Grove 11755 Matthew Wells	K-5		528 40	32%	631/471-1800 Fax 631/467-2486
Chippewa Elem Sch 31 Morris Ave, Holtsville 11742 Patricia Aubrey	K-5		549 26	24%	631/696-8640 Fax 631/696-8645
Grundy Avenue Elem Sch 950 Grundy Ave, Holbrook 11741 Laura Amato	K-5		495	19%	631/471-1820 Fax 631/467-3867
Hiawatha Elem Sch 97 Patchogue Rd, Lk Ronkonkoma 11779 Andrew Larson	K-5		563 35	34%	631/471-1830 Fax 631/467-3861
Lynwood Avenue Elem Sch 50 Lynwood Ave, Farmingville 11738 Dr Danielle DeLorenzo	K-5		630 22	34%	631/696-8650 Fax 631/736-9478
Merrimac Elem Sch 1090 Broadway Ave, Holbrook 11741 Veronica Decicco	K-5		461 30	24%	631/244-5670 Fax 631/563-3369
Nokomis Elem Sch 151 Holbrook Rd, Holbrook 11741 Denise Kleinman	K-5		514 23	24%	631/471-1840 Fax 631/467-3894
Sachem High School East 177 Granny Rd, Farmingville 11738 Louis Antonetti	9-12	AV	2,152	22%	631/716-8200 Fax 631/716-8208 t
Sachem High School North 212 Smith Rd, Lk Ronkonkoma 11779 Patricia Trombetta	9-12	AV	2,103	25%	631/471-1400 Fax 631/471-1408
Sagamore Middle Sch 57 Division St, Holtsville 11742 Frank Panasci	6-8	V	1,015 70	29%	631/696-8600 Fax 631/696-8620
Samoset Middle Sch 51 School St, Lk Ronkonkoma 11779 James Horan	6-8		897	26%	631/471-1700 Fax 631/471-1706
Seneca Middle Sch 850 Main St, Holbrook 11741 Gemma Salvia	6-8	V	1,033 65	22%	631/471-1850 Fax 631/471-1849
Tamarac Elem Sch 50 Spence Ave, Holtsville 11742 Michael Saidens	K-5		454	18%	631/244-5680 Fax 631/244-5685
Waverly Avenue Elem Sch 1111 Waverly Ave, Holtsville 11742 John Ruggero	K-5		473	25%	631/654-8690 Fax 631/475-3970
Wenonah Elem Sch 251 Hudson Ave, Lake Grove 11755 Thomas Desmond	K-5		484 60	17%	631/471-1880 Fax 631/471-1886

• **Sag Harbor Union Free Sch Dist** PID: 00775310 631/725-5300
200 Jermain Ave, Sag Harbor 11963   Fax 631/725-5307

Schools: 2 \ **Teachers:** 109 \ **Students:** 953 \ **Special Ed Students:** 119 \ **LEP Students:** 71 \ **College-Bound:** 88% \ **Ethnic:** Asian 3%, African American 3%, Hispanic 22%, Caucasian 73% \ **Exp:** $389 (High) \ **Poverty:** 7% \ **Title I:** $98,163 \ **Special Education:** $1,121,000 \
Open-Close: 09/09 - 06/25 \ **DTBP:** $151 (High)

Jeff Nichols	1	Christine Schnell	2
Paul Wilken	3	Eric Bramoff	6
Susan Denis	7,83,85*	Barbara Bekermus	11,58*
Jennifer Buscemi	11	Kira McLaughlin	16*
Michelle Grant	37*	Margrett Motto	38*
Kate Berkoski	54*	Juliette Rendon	57*
Brian DeSesa	67	Scott Fisher	73,295*
Lindsay Reilly	271*	Nina Landi	273*

Public Schs..Principal	Grd	Prgm	Enr/#Cls	SN	
Pierson Middle High Sch 200 Jermain Ave, Sag Harbor 11963 Brittany Carriero \ Jeff Nichols	6-12		536 25	17%	631/725-5302 Fax 631/725-5314
Sag Harbor Elem Sch 68 Hampton St, Sag Harbor 11963 Matt Malone	PK-5		417 24	15%	631/725-5301 Fax 631/899-3744

• **Sagaponack Common School Dist** PID: 00775346 631/537-0651
400 Main St, Sagaponack 11962   Fax 631/537-2342

Schools: 1 \ **Teachers:** 2 \ **Students:** 16 \ **Ethnic:** Hispanic 7%, Caucasian 93% \ **Exp:** $1,108 (High) \ **Special Education:** $4,000 \ **Open-Close:** 09/09 - 06/25 \ **DTBP:** $308 (High)

Alan Van Cott	1	Eileen Tuohy	2,12,296
Fred Wilford	3	Terry Scammell	9,11,69,271,275*
Katherine Lombardo	16,73*	Yvonne Velasquez	57
Cathy Hatgistavrou	67	Jeanette Krempler	76
Angela Kiang	286	Dr Edward Vinski	752

Public Schs..Principal	Grd	Prgm	Enr/#Cls	SN	
Sagaponack Elem Sch 400 Main St, Sagaponack 11962 Alan Van Cott	K-3		16 1		631/537-0651

• **Sayville Union Free Sch Dist** PID: 00775360 631/244-6510
99 Greeley Ave, Sayville 11782   Fax 631/244-6504

Schools: 5 \ **Teachers:** 237 \ **Students:** 2,823 \ **Special Ed Students:** 410 \ **LEP Students:** 11 \ **College-Bound:** 93% \ **Ethnic:** Asian 2%, African American 1%, Hispanic 7%, Caucasian 90% \ **Exp:** $598 (High) \ **Poverty:** 7% \ **Title I:** $283,583 \ **Special Education:** $4,040,000 \ **Open-Close:** 09/04 - 06/25 \ **DTBP:** $311 (High)

Dr John Stimmel	1	John Belmonte	2,3,15,71,91
Keith Filosa	4	Dennis Maloney	6,35*
Dr Cristine Criscione	8,15	William Seus	16,73,76,82,295
Michael Baio	30*	Edward Schmieder	48*
Tracey Von-Eschen	58*	Keith Kolar	67
Dr Peter Branscombe	68	Jill Makras	73
Kelly Cummings	81*		

Public Schs..Principal	Grd	Prgm	Enr/#Cls	SN	
Cherry Avenue Elem Sch 155 Cherry Ave, West Sayville 11796 Dr Lisa Ihne	K-5		418 22	6%	631/244-6700 Fax 631/244-6707

79 Student Personnel	91 Safety/Security	275 Response To Intervention	298 Grant Writer/Ptnrships
80 Driver Ed/Safety	92 Magnet School	277 Remedial Math K-12	750 Chief Innovation Officer
81 Gifted/Talented	93 Parental Involvement	280 Literacy Coach	751 Chief of Staff
82 Video Services	95 Tech Prep Program	285 STEM	752 Social Emotional Learning
83 Substance Abuse Prev	97 Chief Infomation Officer	286 Digital Learning	
84 Erate	98 Chief Technology Officer	288 Common Core Standards	
85 AIDS Education	270 Character Education	294 Accountability	
88 Alternative/At Risk	271 Migrant Education	295 Network System	
89 Multi-Cultural Curriculum	273 Teacher Mentor	296 Title II Programs	
90 Social Work	274 Before/After Sch	297 Webmaster	

School Programs
A = Alternative Program
G = Adult Classes
M = Magnet Program
T = Title I Schoolwide
V = Career & Tech Ed Programs

Other School Types
Ⓐ = Alternative School
Ⓒ = Charter School
Ⓜ = Magnet School
Ⓨ = Year-Round School

Social Media
f = Facebook
t = Twitter

New Schools are shaded
New Superintendents and Principals are bold
Personnel with email addresses are underscored

NY—229

Suffolk County

Market Data Retrieval

Lincoln Avenue Elem Sch 440 Lincoln Ave, Sayville 11782 Christine Carlson	K-5	T	393 27	13%	631/244-6725 Fax 631/244-6507
Sayville High Sch 20 Brook St, West Sayville 11796 Ronald Hoffer	9-12	GV	969 50	10%	631/244-6600 Fax 631/244-6779
Sayville Middle Sch 291 Johnson Ave, Sayville 11782 Thomas Murray	6-8	GV	679	10%	631/244-6650 Fax 631/244-6655
Sunrise Drive Elem Sch 320 Sunrise Dr, Sayville 11782 James Foy	K-5		364 27	7%	631/244-6750 Fax 631/244-6509

- **Shelter Island Union Free SD** PID: 00775437   631/749-0302
  33 N Ferry Rd, Shelter Is 11964   Fax 631/749-1262

Schools: 1 \ **Teachers:** 34 \ **Students:** 202 \ **Special Ed Students:** 33 \ **LEP Students:** 18 \ **College-Bound:** 89% \ **Ethnic:** Asian 1%, African American 2%, Hispanic 22%, Caucasian 74% \ **Exp:** $614 (High) \ **Poverty:** 3% \ **Title I:** $9,299 \ **Special Education:** $192,000 \ **Open-Close:** 09/08 - 06/25 \ **DTBP:** $353 (High)

Brian Doelger 1   Deborah Vecchio 2
Michael Dunning 3   Helene Starzee 4
Todd Gulluscio .... 6,35,83*   Mary Kanarvogel 7*
Jennifer Rylott .... 8,288*   Kathleen Lynch 67
Walter Brigham 73

Public Schs..Principal	Grd	Prgm	Enr/#Cls	SN	
Shelter Island Sch 33 N Ferry Road, Shelter Is 11964 Christine Finn	PK-12	AV	202 25	33%	631/749-0302

- **Shoreham-Wading River Ctl SD** PID: 00775451   631/821-8100
  250B Route 25A, Shoreham 11786   Fax 631/929-3001

Schools: 4 \ **Teachers:** 186 \ **Students:** 2,000 \ **Special Ed Students:** 379 \ **LEP Students:** 10 \ **College-Bound:** 94% \ **Ethnic:** Asian 2%, African American 1%, Hispanic 8%, Caucasian 89% \ **Exp:** $320 (High) \ **Poverty:** 4% \ **Title I:** $99,748 \ **Special Education:** $3,232,000 \ **Open-Close:** 09/01 - 06/25 \ **DTBP:** $313 (High)

Gerard Poole 1   Glen Arcuri 2,4,15
Angelo Andreotti 3,91   Patricia Rogers 5
Mark Passamonte 6,35   Alan Meinster 8,16,27,54,69,277,288,298
Brian Heyward 15   Paul Koretzki 30
Nicole Walvbauer 57   Charles Althoff 58,88
Michael Lewis 67   Peter Esposito 73,95,295

Public Schs..Principal	Grd	Prgm	Enr/#Cls	SN	
Albert G Prodell Middle Sch 100 Randall Rd, Shoreham 11786 Kevin Vann	6-8		479	4%	631/821-8210 Fax 631/821-8275
Miller Avenue Elem Sch 3 Miller Ave, Shoreham 11786 Claudia Smith	K-2		354 21	3%	631/821-8231 Fax 631/821-8249
Shoreham Wading River High Sch 250A Route 25A, Shoreham 11786 Frank Pugliese	9-12	GV	775	3%	631/821-8140 Fax 631/821-8145
Wading River Elem Sch 1900 Wading River Manor Rd, Wading River 11792 Louis Parrinello	3-5		417 20	3%	631/821-8254 Fax 631/821-8258

- **Smithtown Central Sch Dist** PID: 00775504   631/382-2000
  26 New York Ave, Smithtown 11787   Fax 631/382-2010

Schools: 12 \ **Teachers:** 742 \ **Students:** 8,946 \ **Special Ed Students:** 1,647 \ **LEP Students:** 132 \ **College-Bound:** 93% \ **Ethnic:** Asian 6%, African American 1%, Hispanic 9%, Caucasian 83% \ **Exp:** $355 (High) \ **Poverty:** 3% \ **Title I:** $262,894 \ **Special Education:** $10,790,000 \ **Open-Close:** 09/08 - 06/25 \ **DTBP:** $230 (High)

Russell Stewart 1   Andrew Tobin 2,3,15
Dan Leddy 3   Regina Dunne 4
Mary Augugliaro 5   Patrick Smith 6,35,83*
Jennifer Bradshaw 8,15,288   Paul Strader 8
Daniel Helms 15,58,79   Neil Katz 15,68
Christine Lofrese .... 26,28*   Patricia Russo 30
Kevin Colon 36   Bryon Frank 39*
Laura Snell .... 42*   Angelica Babino 45*
Vincenza Graham .... 57,63*   Dr Brenda Clark 59
Matthew Prahl 60   Matthew Gribbin 67
John Nolan 73,76,286   Kristen Andriaccio 298

Public Schs..Principal	Grd	Prgm	Enr/#Cls	SN	
Accompsett Elem Sch 1 Lincoln St, Smithtown 11787 B Frank	PK-5		570 50	9%	631/382-4155 Fax 631/382-4157
Accompsett Middle Sch 660 Meadow Rd, Smithtown 11787 Paul McNeil	6-8	V	569 42	10%	631/382-2300 Fax 631/382-2307
Dogwood Elem Sch 50 Dogwood Dr, Smithtown 11787 Renee Carpenter	K-5		369	8%	631/382-4255 Fax 631/382-4256
Great Hollow Middle Sch 150 Southern Blvd Bldg 1, Nesconset 11767 John Scomillio	6-8		917 30	8%	631/382-2805 Fax 631/382-2807
Mills Pond Elem Sch 246 Moriches Rd, Saint James 11780 Ireen Westrack	K-5		402 24	7%	631/382-4305 Fax 631/382-4304
Mt Pleasant Elem Sch 33 Plaisted Ave, Smithtown 11787 Joeseph Ierano	K-5		535 23	9%	631/382-4355 Fax 631/382-4356
Nesaquake Middle Sch 479 Edgewood Ave, Saint James 11780 Daniel McCabe	6-8		559	7%	631/382-5105 Fax 631/382-5107
Smithtown Elem Sch 51 Lawrence Ave, Smithtown 11787 Janine Lavery	K-5		430 30	14%	631/382-4505 Fax 631/382-4507
Smithtown High School-East 10 School St, Saint James 11780 Kevin Simmons	9-12	V	1,523	7%	631/382-2705 Fax 631/382-2707
Smithtown High School-West 100 Central Rd, Smithtown 11787 John Coady	9-12	AV	1,496	10%	631/382-2905 Fax 631/382-2910
St James Elem Sch 580 Lake Ave, Saint James 11780 Mary Grace Lynch	K-5		479 26	10%	631/382-4455 Fax 631/382-4456
Tackan Elem Sch 99 Midwood Ave, Nesconset 11767 Dr Allyn Leeds	K-5		545 25	15%	631/382-2670 Fax 631/382-2676

1 Superintendent	8 Curric/Instruct K-12	19 Chief Financial Officer	29 Family/Consumer Science	39 Social Studies K-12	49 English/Lang Arts Elem	59 Special Education Elem	69 Academic Assessment
2 Bus/Finance/Purchasing	9 Curric/Instruct Elem	20 Art K-12	30 Adult Education	40 Social Studies Elem	50 English/Lang Arts Sec	60 Special Education Sec	70 Research/Development
3 Buildings And Grounds	10 Curric/Instruct Sec	21 Art Elem	31 Career/Sch-to-Work K-12	41 Social Studies Sec	51 Reading K-12	61 Foreign/World Lang K-12	71 Public Information
4 Food Service	11 Federal Program	22 Art Sec	32 Career/Sch-to-Work Elem	42 Science K-12	52 Reading Elem	62 Foreign/World Lang Elem	72 Summer School
5 Transportation	12 Title I	23 Music K-12	33 Career/Sch-to-Work Sec	43 Science Elem	53 Reading Sec	63 Foreign/World Lang Sec	73 Instructional Tech
6 Athletic	13 Title V	24 Music Elem	34 Early Childhood Ed	44 Science Sec	54 Remedial Reading K-12	64 Religious Education K-12	74 Inservice Training
7 Health Services	15 Asst Superintendent	25 Music Sec	35 Health/Phys Education	45 Math K-12	55 Remedial Reading Elem	65 Religious Education Elem	75 Marketing/Distributive
	16 Instructional Media Svcs	26 Business Education	36 Guidance Services K-12	46 Math Elem	56 Remedial Reading Sec	66 Religious Education Sec	76 Info Systems
	17 Chief Operations Officer	27 Career & Tech Ed	37 Guidance Services Elem	47 Math Sec	57 Bilingual/ELL	67 School Board President	77 Psychological Assess
	18 Chief Academic Officer	28 Technology Education	38 Guidance Services Sec	48 English/Lang Arts K-12	58 Special Education K-12	68 Teacher Personnel	78 Affirmative Action

New York School Directory — Suffolk County

• South Country Central Sch Dist PID: 00772136 631/730-1500
189 Dunton Ave, Patchogue 11772   Fax 631/286-5518

Schools: 7 \ **Teachers:** 396 \ **Students:** 4,400 \ **Special Ed Students:** 731 \ **LEP Students:** 490 \ **College-Bound:** 75% \ **Ethnic:** Asian 2%, African American 18%, Hispanic 40%, Caucasian 40% \ **Exp:** $242 (Med) \ **Poverty:** 14% \ **Title I:** $1,001,978 \ **Special Education:** $10,262,000 \ **Open-Close:** 09/08 - 06/25 \ **DTBP:** $346 (High)

Dr Joseph Giani	1	Dr Sam Gergis	2,15
Debbie Tomasello	4	Robert McIntyre	6,7,35*
Laurie O'Hara	8	Marlon Small	8,15,294
Amy Brennan	9	Nelson Briggs	15,68
Ingrid Hrvatin	36	Jaclyn O'Hagan	48
Monica Pullows Tetuan	57,61	Kerry Carson	58,79,81
E Anne Hayes	67	Jenna Restivo	77
Ann Haddad	90	Jack Burke	285

Public Schs..Principal	Grd	Prgm	Enr/#Cls	SN	
Bellport High Sch 205 Beaver Dam Rd, Brookhaven 11719 Timothy Hogan	9-12	T	1,362	55%	631/730-1575 Fax 631/286-5336
Bellport Middle Sch 35 Kreamer St, Bellport 11713 Dr Jamal Colson	6-8	T	1,024 75	56%	631/730-1626 Fax 631/286-4460
Brookhaven Elem Sch 101 Fireplace Neck Rd, Brookhaven 11719 Dr Rebecca Raymond	PK-3	T	558 31	52%	631/730-1700 Fax 631/286-6210
Frank P Long Intermediate Sch 599 Brookhaven Ave, Bellport 11713 Stefanie Rucinski	4-5	T	579 32	62%	631/730-1725 Fax 631/286-0276
Kreamer Street Elem Sch 37 Kreamer St, Bellport 11713 Sean Clark	K-3	T	337 19	52%	631/730-1650 Fax 631/776-0903
South Haven Early Chldhd Ctr 2714 Montauk Hwy, Brookhaven 11719 Brian Ginty	PK-PK		63		631/730-2180 Fax 631/286-9405
Verne W Critz Primary Sch 185 N Dunton Ave, E Patchogue 11772 Mandy Mazziotti	K-3	T	293 50	55%	631/730-1675 Fax 631/286-2918

• South Huntington Union Free SD PID: 00775736 631/812-3000
60 Weston St, Huntingtn Sta 11746   Fax 631/812-3075

Schools: 7 \ **Teachers:** 495 \ **Students:** 5,900 \ **Special Ed Students:** 1,178 \ **LEP Students:** 995 \ **College-Bound:** 96% \ **Ethnic:** Asian 6%, African American 7%, Hispanic 45%, Caucasian 42% \ **Exp:** $233 (Med) \ **Poverty:** 9% \ **Title I:** $775,762 \ **Special Education:** $8,198,000 \ **Open-Close:** 09/01 - 06/25 \ **DTBP:** $308 (High)

Dr David Bennardo	1	Dr Vito D'Elia	2,15,78,79
Carlo Giodinao	3,91	Sheila Buhse	4
Michael Trelfa	5	Dr Jim Wright	6*
April Poprilo	7	Allison Bruno	8,11,83,285,288,296
Dr Joseph Centamore	11,15,69,73,76,286,298	Dr Matt Krivoshey	58
Nicholas Ciappetta	67	Elizabeth Demonte	71
Robert Cangero	273	Louis Mangieri	295

Public Schs..Principal	Grd	Prgm	Enr/#Cls	SN	
Birchwood Intermediate Sch 121 Wolf Hill Rd, Melville 11747 Anthony Ciccarelli	3-5	T	635 31	57%	631/812-3200 Fax 631/812-3232
Countrywood Primary Center 499 Old Country Rd, Huntingtn Sta 11746 Mitchell Levy	K-2	T	603 25	45%	631/812-3300
Maplewood Intermediate Sch 19 School Ln, Huntingtn Sta 11746 Gayle Steele	3-5	T	597 32	51%	631/812-3400 Fax 631/812-3434
Oakwood Primary Center 264 W 22nd St, Huntington 11743 Annie Michaelian	PK-2	T	635 35	51%	631/812-3500 Fax 631/812-3535
Silas Wood 6th Grade Center 23 Harding Pl, Huntingtn Sta 11746 Stephen Toto	6-6	T	453	51%	631/812-3600 Fax 631/812-3636
Stimson Middle Sch 401 Oakwood Rd, Huntingtn Sta 11746 Edwin Smith	7-8	T	974 52	49%	631/812-3700 Fax 631/812-3737
Walt Whitman High Sch 301 W Hills Rd, Huntingtn Sta 11746 John Murphy	9-12	AGTV	1,979	50%	631/812-3800 Fax 631/812-3838

• Southampton Union Free SD PID: 00775877 631/591-4510
70 Leland Ln, Southampton 11968   Fax 631/287-2870

Schools: 3 \ **Teachers:** 174 \ **Students:** 1,575 \ **Special Ed Students:** 256 \ **LEP Students:** 260 \ **Ethnic:** Asian 2%, African American 3%, Hispanic 41%, Native American: 8%, Caucasian 46% \ **Exp:** $716 (High) \ **Poverty:** 9% \ **Title I:** $169,059 \ **Special Education:** $1,428,000 \ **Open-Close:** 09/08 - 06/25 \ **DTBP:** $166 (High) \

Dr Nicholas Dyno	1	Danielle Leef	2
Jean Mingot	2,15,298	Marcus DaSilva	3
Regan Kiembock	4*	Darren Phillips	6,83,85*
Julieann Purcell	16,286	Dr Kim Rodriguez	38,88*
Ana Martinez	57*	Jeanne-Marie Mazzaferro	58
Jacqueline Robinson	67	Peter Wolter	73,76,295*
Sean Brand	273*	Larriee Jerniola	294*

Public Schs..Principal	Grd	Prgm	Enr/#Cls	SN	
Southampton Elem Sch 30 Pine St, Southampton 11968 Jaime Bottcher	PK-4	T	488 31	53%	631/591-4800 Fax 631/283-6891
Southampton High Sch 141 Narrow Ln, Southampton 11968 Dr Brian Zahn	9-12	AV	641 50	43%	631/591-4600 Fax 631/283-6313
Southampton Intermediate Sch 70 Leland Ln, Southampton 11968 Timothy Frazier	5-8	V	432 40	46%	631/591-4700 Fax 631/283-6899

• Southold Union Free Sch Dist PID: 00775918 631/765-5400
420 Oaklawn Ave, Southold 11971   Fax 631/765-5086

Schools: 2 \ **Teachers:** 78 \ **Students:** 750 \ **Special Ed Students:** 113 \ **LEP Students:** 128 \ **College-Bound:** 80% \ **Ethnic:** Asian 2%, African American 2%, Hispanic 31%, Caucasian 66% \ **Exp:** $448 (High) \ **Poverty:** 15% \ **Title I:** $204,404 \ **Special Education:** $901,000 \ **Open-Close:** 09/04 - 06/25 \ **DTBP:** $161 (High)

Anthony Mauro	1	Charles Scheid	2,15,84
Erica Frank	2	Anthony Dragone	3,91
Christopher Campos	4,5	Steven Flanagan	6*
Patricia O'Day	7*	Ellen Waldron-Oneill	9*
Terrence Ruch	10	Dr Lisa Simonitti	11,36,57,58,79,275,296,298
Paulette Ofrias	67	Patricia DiGregorio	68
Marlene Bufkins	69*	Ryan Case	73,76,285,295
Eric Kehl	82*		

Public Schs..Principal	Grd	Prgm	Enr/#Cls	SN	
Southold Elem Sch 1120 Oaklawn Ave, Southold 11971 Ellen Waldron-Oneill	PK-6	T	321 22	27%	631/765-5208 Fax 631/765-6893

---

79 Student Personnel	91 Safety/Security	275 Response To Intervention	298 Grant Writer/Ptnrships	**School Programs**	**Social Media**
80 Driver Ed/Safety	92 Magnet School	277 Remedial Math K-12	750 Chief Innovation Officer	A = Alternative Program	= Facebook
81 Gifted/Talented	93 Parental Involvement	280 Literacy Coach	751 Chief of Staff	G = Adult Classes	
82 Video Services	95 Tech Prep Program	285 STEM	752 Social Emotional Learning	M = Magnet Program	= Twitter
83 Substance Abuse Prev	97 Chief Information Officer	286 Digital Learning		T = Title I Schoolwide	
84 Erate	98 Chief Technology Officer	288 Common Core Standards	**Other School Types**	V = Career & Tech Ed Programs	
85 AIDS Education	270 Character Education	294 Accountability	Ⓐ = Alternative School		
88 Alternative/At Risk	271 Migrant Education	295 Network System	Ⓒ = Charter School	New Schools are shaded	
89 Multi-Cultural Curriculum	273 Teacher Mentor	296 Title II Programs	Ⓜ = Magnet School	New Superintendents and Principals are bold	
90 Social Work	274 Before/After Sch	297 Webmaster	Ⓨ = Year-Round School	Personnel with email addresses are underscored	

Suffolk County

Market Data Retrieval

Southold Jr Sr High Sch	7-12	456	20%	631/765-5081
420 Oaklawn Ave, Southold 11971		50		Fax 631/765-1387
William Galati				

● **Springs Union Free School Dist** PID: 00775956   631/324-0144
48 School St, East Hampton 11937   Fax 631/324-0269

Schools: 1 \ **Teachers:** 71 \ **Students:** 750 \ **Special Ed Students:** 93 \ **LEP Students:** 127 \ **Ethnic:** Asian 1%, Hispanic 59%, Caucasian 39% \ **Exp:** $464 (High) \ **Poverty:** 14% \ **Title I:** $199,923 \ **Special Education:** $933,000 \ **Open-Close:** 09/09 - 06/30 \ **DTBP:** $2,698 (High)

Debra Winter 1		Michael Henery 2	
Daniel Newman 3*		Marion Flaherty 5	
Whitney Reidlinger 6*		Joseph Colavito 7*	
Eric Casale 9,93,288,294*		Cherese Allan 11,59,83,88,90,271,296,298	
William Hallman 16*		Margaret Garsetti 35,57*	
Barbara Dayton 67		Stacy Schmidt 69	
John Gibbons 73,286*		Danielle Hamilton 277*	
Sean Gibbins 295			

Public Schs..Principal	Grd	Prgm	Enr/#Cls	SN	
ⓨ Springs Sch	PK-8	M	750	7%	631/324-0144
48 School St, East Hampton 11937			32		
Eric Casale					

● **Three Village Central Sch Dist** PID: 00775970   631/730-4000
100 Suffolk Ave, Stony Brook 11790   Fax 631/474-7784

Schools: 9 \ **Teachers:** 504 \ **Students:** 6,400 \ **Special Ed Students:** 953 \ **LEP Students:** 64 \ **College-Bound:** 97% \ **Ethnic:** Asian 11%, African American 1%, Hispanic 7%, Caucasian 81% \ **Exp:** $380 (High) \ **Poverty:** 2% \ **Title I:** $172,445 \ **Special Education:** $6,224,000 \ **Open-Close:** 09/08 - 06/25 \ **DTBP:** $324 (High)

Cheryl Pedisich 1		Jeffrey Carlson 2,11,15	
James Ohagan 3		Jean Ecker 4	
Kathy Cassella 5		Kevin Finnerty 6,35	
Kevin Scanlon 8,15,74,273,288		Dr Nathalie Lilavois 9	
Alan Baum 10,68		Dr Gary Dabrusky 15,68	
Anthony Pollera 23		Catherine Taldone 30,83,88,93,274,298	
Dr Paul Gold 39		Dawn Mason 58,79*	
Inger Germano 67		Kerrin Welch-Pollera 73,286	
Jack Blaum 91			

Public Schs..Principal	Grd	Prgm	Enr/#Cls	SN	
Arrowhead Elem Sch	PK-6		574	12%	631/730-4100
62 Arrowhead Ln, East Setauket 11733			44		Fax 631/730-4104
Marisa Redden					
Minnesauke Elem Sch	PK-6		585	9%	631/730-4200
21 High Gate Dr, Setauket 11733			37		Fax 631/730-4204
Brian Biscari					
Nassakeag Elem Sch	PK-6		472	4%	631/730-4400
490 Pond Path, Setauket 11733			40		Fax 631/730-4403
Heather Levine					
Paul J Gelinas Jr High Sch	7-9	V	739	9%	631/730-4700
25 Mud Rd, Setauket 11733			75		Fax 631/730-4707
Corinne Keane					
Robert C Murphy Jr High Sch	7-9	V	714	13%	631/730-4800
351 Oxhead Rd, Stony Brook 11790					Fax 631/730-4804
Brian Biscari					
Setauket Elem Sch	PK-6		584	7%	631/730-4600
134 Main St, Setauket 11733					Fax 631/730-4604
Karen Mizell					

Ⓐ Three Village Academy	9-12	V	40		631/730-5051
100 Suffolk Ave, Stony Brook 11790					Fax 631/730-4087
Gustave Hueber					
Ward Melville Sr High Sch	10-12	GV	1,688	11%	631/730-4900
380 Old Town Rd, East Setauket 11733			100		Fax 631/730-4901
William Bernhard					
William Sidney Mount Elem Sch	PK-6		479	11%	631/730-4300
50 Dean Ln, Stony Brook 11790			39		Fax 631/730-4309
Roseanne DiBella					

● **Tuckahoe Common School Dist** PID: 00776077   631/283-3550
468 Magee St, Southampton 11968   Fax 631/283-3469

Schools: 1 \ **Teachers:** 39 \ **Students:** 285 \ **Special Ed Students:** 46 \ **LEP Students:** 67 \ **Ethnic:** Asian 2%, African American 3%, Hispanic 66%, Caucasian 29% \ **Exp:** $643 (High) \ **Poverty:** 7% \ **Title I:** $46,818 \ **Special Education:** $374,000 \ **Open-Close:** 09/08 - 06/25 \ **DTBP:** $172 (High)

Leonard Skuggevik 1		Carl Fraser 2,11,16,285,296,298	
Mitch Sobczyk 3,91		Matt Doris 4*	
Joseph Pallas 6,35*		Wendy Meyer 7	
Doreen Buckley 9,57,59,79,752*		Bonnie Downs 12	
Christian Pena 13,73,295		Sean Hattrick 67	
Angela Parisi 97		Maryann Mujumuci 274*	
Jessica Ovanessian 286		Arlette Sicari 288*	

Public Schs..Principal	Grd	Prgm	Enr/#Cls	SN	
Tuckahoe Common Sch	PK-8	T	285	66%	631/283-3550
468 Magee St, Southampton 11968			25		Fax 631/283-3552
Arlette Sicari					

● **Wainscott Common School Dist** PID: 00776091   631/537-1080
47 Main St, Wainscott 11975   Fax 631/537-6977

Schools: 1 \ **Teachers:** 3 \ **Students:** 30 \ **Special Ed Students:** 17 \ **LEP Students:** 12 \ **Ethnic:** Asian 4%, Hispanic 58%, Caucasian 38% \ **Exp:** $598 (High) \ **Poverty:** 35% \ **Title I:** $73,961 \ **Special Education:** $63,000 \ **Open-Close:** 09/09 - 06/25 \ **DTBP:** $137 (High)

Deborah Haab 1,11,73,288		Christine Schnell 2	
Norma Bushman 15		Mary Johnsen 59	
David Eagan 67			

Public Schs..Principal	Grd	Prgm	Enr/#Cls	SN	
Wainscott Common Sch	K-3	T	30	12%	631/537-1080
47 Main St, Wainscott 11975			2		
Deborah Haab					

● **West Babylon Union Free SD** PID: 00776118   631/376-7000
10 Farmingdale Rd, West Babylon 11704   Fax 631/376-7019

Schools: 7 \ **Teachers:** 333 \ **Students:** 4,000 \ **Special Ed Students:** 815 \ **LEP Students:** 181 \ **College-Bound:** 81% \ **Ethnic:** Asian 4%, African American 9%, Hispanic 27%, Caucasian 61% \ **Exp:** $219 (Med) \ **Poverty:** 7% \ **Title I:** $377,656 \ **Special Education:** $7,716,000 \ **Open-Close:** 09/02 - 06/25 \ **DTBP:** $292 (High) \ 🇫 🇹

Yiendhy Farrelly 1		Michele Psarakis 2,3,15	
Raymond Graziano 3		Jeannette Srabizio 4*	
Anthony Reid 5		Louis Howard 6*	
Anthony Spinelli 7,35,83*		Scott Payne 8,15	
Michael Mack 11,58,79,90,296,298		Shawn Hanley 15,68,74,288	
Dr Alice Robinson 16,82*		Katharine Reilly-Johnson 26,95*	
Donna McGrath 30*		Gina Curcio 36	

1 Superintendent	8 Curric/Instruct K-12	19 Chief Financial Officer	29 Family/Consumer Science	39 Social Studies K-12	49 English/Lang Arts Elem	59 Special Education Elem	69 Academic Assessment
2 Bus/Finance/Purchasing	9 Curric/Instruct Elem	20 Art K-12	30 Adult Education	40 Social Studies Elem	50 English/Lang Arts Sec	60 Special Education Sec	70 Research/Development
3 Buildings And Grounds	10 Curric/Instruct Sec	21 Art Elem	31 Career/Sch-to-Work El	41 Social Studies Sec	51 Reading K-12	61 Foreign/World Lang K-12	71 Public Information
4 Food Service	11 Federal Program	22 Art Sec	32 Career/Sch-to-Work Elem	42 Science K-12	52 Reading Elem	62 Foreign/World Lang Elem	72 Summer School
5 Transportation	12 Title I	23 Music K-12	33 Career/Sch-to-Work Sec	43 Science Elem	53 Reading Sec	63 Foreign/World Lang Sec	73 Instructional Tech
6 Athletic	13 Title V	24 Music Elem	34 Early Childhood Ed	44 Science Sec	54 Remedial Reading K-12	64 Religious Education K-12	74 Inservice Training
7 Health Services	14 Asst Superintendent	25 Music Sec	35 Health/Phys Education	45 Math K-12	55 Remedial Reading Elem	65 Religious Education Elem	75 Marketing/Distributive
	15 Instructional Media Svcs	26 Business Education	36 Guidance Services K-12	46 Math Elem	56 Remedial Reading Sec	66 Religious Education Sec	76 Info Systems
	16 Chief Operations Officer	27 Career & Tech Ed	37 Guidance Services Elem	47 Math Sec	57 Bilingual/ELL	67 School Board President	77 Psychological Assess
	18 Chief Academic Officer	28 Technology Education	38 Guidance Services Sec	48 English/Lang Arts K-12	58 Special Education K-12	68 Teacher Personnel	78 Affirmative Action

New York School Directory — Suffolk County

Harry Theo 42,47*	Theresa Chaplin 45,277
Lynette Jabour 48,51,54*	Jennifer Hoffman 57,69,81*
Lucy Campasano 67	Stephanie Nocerino 73,76,286*
Jaime Lemmo 90*	Edwin Salas 91

Public Schs..Principal	Grd	Prgm	Enr/#Cls	SN	
Forest Ave Elem Sch 200 Forest Ave, West Babylon 11704 Patricia Acocella	K-5	T	274 20	44%	631/376-7300 Fax 631/376-7309
John F Kennedy Elem Sch 175 Brookvale Ave, West Babylon 11704 Denisha Van Liew	K-5		361 23	26%	631/376-7800 Fax 631/376-7809
Santapogue Elem Sch 1130 Herzel Blvd, West Babylon 11704 Jennifer Carere	K-5		340 26	29%	631/376-7401 Fax 631/376-7409
South Bay Elem Sch 160 Great East Neck Rd, West Babylon 11704 Christina Cotter	K-5		276 14	37%	631/376-7500 Fax 631/376-7509
Tooker Ave Elem Sch 855 Tooker Ave, West Babylon 11704 Charles Germano	K-5	T	289 20	43%	631/376-7600 Fax 631/376-7609
West Babylon Jr High Sch 200 Old Farmingdale Rd, West Babylon 11704 Daniel McKeon	6-8	T	896 50	44%	631/376-7200 Fax 631/376-7299
West Babylon Sr High Sch 500 Great East Neck Rd, West Babylon 11704 Dr Ellice Vassallo	9-12	AGT	1,268 100	42%	631/376-7100 Fax 631/376-7119

• **West Islip School Dist** PID: 00776209 631/893-3200
100 Sherman Ave, West Islip 11795 Fax 631/893-3212

Schools: 7 \ **Teachers:** 358 \ **Students:** 3,720 \ **Special Ed Students:** 878 \ **LEP Students:** 14 \ **College-Bound:** 91% \ **Ethnic:** Asian 2%, Hispanic 12%, Caucasian 86% \ **Exp:** $441 (High) \ **Poverty:** 5% \ **Title I:** $204,567 \ **Special Education:** $7,215,000 \ **Open-Close:** 09/04 - 06/25 \ **DTBP:** $339 (High)

Bernadette Burns 1	Elisa Pellati 2,11,15
James Bosse 3	Christine Kearney 4
Tim Horan 6,7,35,83,85	Dawn Morrison 8,12,15,288
Karen Appollo 16,48,51,54	Reanna Fulton 16,73,82,95,286
Eric Albinder 20,23	James Grover 26,29,45
Debbie Langone 28,42	Kevin Murphy 30
James Gilmartin 39	Jeanne Dowling 58,77,79,81,275
Steven Gellar 67	Brian Taylor 68,285
Amit Pathak 76,295	Mary Hock 84
Byron McRay 91*	Michelle Walsh 275

Public Schs..Principal	Grd	Prgm	Enr/#Cls	SN	
Bayview Elem Sch 165 Snedecor Ave, West Islip 11795 John Mullins	PK-5		405 22	11%	631/504-5600 Fax 631/893-3335
Beach Street Middle Sch 17 Beach St, West Islip 11795 Andrew O'Farrell	6-8		485 45	15%	631/930-1600 Fax 631/893-3318
Manetuck Elem Sch 800 Van Buren Ave, West Islip 11795 Vanessa Williams	PK-5		477 35	15%	631/504-5640 Fax 631/893-3356
Oquenock Elem Sch 425 Spruce Ave, West Islip 11795 Jack Maniscalco	PK-5		409 18	18%	631/893-3360 Fax 631/893-3367
Paul J Bellew Elem Sch 25 Higbie Ln, West Islip 11795 Rhonda Pratt	PK-5		455 20	11%	631/504-5680 Fax 631/893-3346
Udall Road Middle Sch 900 Udall Rd, West Islip 11795 Daniel Marquardt	6-8		494 90	17%	631/930-1650 Fax 631/893-3301
West Islip Senior High Sch 1 Lions Path, West Islip 11795 Dr Anthony Bridgeman	9-12	AGV	1,380 50	15%	631/504-5800 Fax 631/893-3270

• **Westhampton Beach School Dist** PID: 00776338 631/288-3800
340 Mill Rd, W Hampton Bch 11978 Fax 631/288-6509

Schools: 3 \ **Teachers:** 182 \ **Students:** 1,819 \ **Special Ed Students:** 281 \ **LEP Students:** 128 \ **College-Bound:** 87% \ **Ethnic:** Asian 2%, African American 2%, Hispanic 27%, Caucasian 70% \ **Exp:** $373 (High) \ **Poverty:** 8% \ **Title I:** $87,256 \ **Special Education:** $835,000 \ **Open-Close:** 09/08 - 06/25 \ **DTBP:** $161 (High) \ [f] [t]

Michael Radday 1,11	Kathleen O'Hara 2,4,15
Mary Ann Milton 2	Anthony Verga 3
Kathleen Masterson 6,35*	William Fisher 8,15,68
Susan Kearns 11,74*	Dr Rob Finn 38,69,76*
Matthew Ramsay 44,47,73*	Mary Ann Ambrosini 58,79,83,85,88,286
Suzanne Mensch 67	

Public Schs..Principal	Grd	Prgm	Enr/#Cls	SN	
Westhampton Beach Elem Sch 379 Mill Rd, W Hampton Bch 11978 Lisa Slover	K-5	T	383 24	47%	631/288-3800 Fax 631/288-7867
Westhampton Beach High Sch 49 Lilac Rd, W Hampton Bch 11978 Christopher Herr	9-12		1,008	26%	631/288-3800 Fax 631/288-3915
Westhampton Beach Middle Sch 340 Mill Rd, W Hampton Bch 11978 Charisse Miller	6-8		428 46	30%	631/288-3800 Fax 631/288-5496

• **William Floyd School Dist** PID: 00776376 631/874-1100
240 Mastic Beach Rd, Mastic Beach 11951 Fax 631/281-3047

Schools: 8 \ **Teachers:** 614 \ **Students:** 8,700 \ **Special Ed Students:** 1,510 \ **LEP Students:** 544 \ **College-Bound:** 69% \ **Ethnic:** Asian 3%, African American 15%, Hispanic 37%, Caucasian 45% \ **Exp:** $205 (Med) \ **Poverty:** 15% \ **Title I:** $2,269,551 \ **Special Education:** $28,901,000 \ **Open-Close:** 09/02 - 06/24 \ **DTBP:** $228 (High) \ [f] [t]

Kevin Coster 1	David Beggins 2,4,5,15,91
Michelle Romanosky 2	Dawn Ducoing 4
Laura Ruhle 5	Mark Mensch 6,35
Stacey Scalise 9	Kathleen Keane 10,15,71
Janet Gilmore 15,68,78	Craig Clasen 39*
Malasia Walker 58,77*	Robert Vecchio 67
Michael Stam 68	John DeBenedetto 72,88*
Robert Lavigna 73,76,95	Al Peterson 79
Mary Koehler 298	

Public Schs..Principal	Grd	Prgm	Enr/#Cls	SN	
John S Hobart Elem Sch 230 Van Buren St, Shirley 11967 James Westcott	K-5	T	846 44	71%	631/874-1296 Fax 631/874-1618
Moriches Elem Sch 16 Louis Ave, Moriches 11955 Deirdre Redding	K-5	T	869 41	66%	631/874-1398 Fax 631/874-1890
Nathaniel Woodhull Elem Sch 6 Francis Landau Pl, Shirley 11967 Monica Corona	K-5	T	662 23	57%	631/874-1302 Fax 631/874-1804
Tangier Smith Elem Sch 336 Blanco Dr, Mastic Beach 11951 Toni Komorowski	K-5	T	761 52	68%	631/874-1342 Fax 631/874-1416
William Floyd Elem Sch 111 Lexington Rd, Shirley 11967 Keith Fasciana	K-5	T	699 38	60%	631/874-1257 Fax 631/874-1637

79 Student Personnel	91 Safety/Security	275 Response To Intervention	298 Grant Writer/Ptnrships
80 Driver Ed/Safety	92 Magnet School	277 Remedial Math K-12	750 Chief Innovation Officer
81 Gifted/Talented	93 Parental Involvement	280 Literacy Coach	751 Chief of Staff
82 Video Services	95 Tech Prep Program	285 STEM	752 Social Emotional Learning
83 Substance Abuse Prev	97 Chief Information Officer	286 Digital Learning	
84 Erate	98 Chief Technology Officer	288 Common Core Standards	
85 AIDS Education	270 Character Education	294 Accountability	
88 Alternative/At Risk	271 Migrant Education	295 Network System	
89 Multi-Cultural Curriculum	273 Teacher Mentor	296 Title II Programs	
90 Social Work	274 Before/After Sch	297 Webmaster	

School Programs
A = Alternative Program
G = Adult Classes
M = Magnet Program
T = Title I Schoolwide
V = Career & Tech Ed Programs

Other School Types
Ⓐ = Alternative School
Ⓒ = Charter School
Ⓜ = Magnet School
Ⓨ = Year-Round School

Social Media
[f] = Facebook
[t] = Twitter

New Schools are shaded
New Superintendents and Principals are bold
Personnel with email addresses are underscored

Suffolk County

Market Data Retrieval

School	Grd	Prgm	Enr/#Cls	SN	Phone
William Floyd High Sch 240 Mastic Beach Rd, Mastic Beach 11951 Philip Scotto	9-12	AGV	2,767 261	59%	631/874-1120 Fax 631/874-1540
William Floyd Middle Sch 630 Moriches Middle Island Rd, Moriches 11955 Matthew Sanders	6-8	T	1,124	60%	631/874-5505 Fax 631/878-7690
William Paca Middle Sch 338 Blanco Dr, Mastic Beach 11951 Michele Gode	6-8	TV	1,063 80	68%	631/874-1414 Fax 631/874-1561

• **Wyandanch Union Free Sch Dist** PID: 00776429   631/870-0401
  1445 Straight Path, Wyandanch 11798   Fax 631/491-8539

Schools: 4 \ **Teachers:** 209 \ **Students:** 2,811 \ **Special Ed Students:** 529 \ **LEP Students:** 853 \ **Ethnic:** African American 43%, Hispanic 56%, Caucasian 1% \ **Exp:** $300 (High) \ **Poverty:** 21% \ **Title I:** $769,099 \ **Special Education:** $8,196,000 \ **Open-Close:** 09/08 - 06/25 \ **DTBP:** $148 (High)

Gina Talbert ... 1		Montgomery Granger ... 3	
Danielle Teicher ... 4		Izett Thomas ... 11,285,296,298	
Carl Baldini ... 15,58,79		Kester Hodge ... 15,68	
Sharon Wilson ... 16,73,95,295		Christine Jordan ... 42,45	
James Crawford ... 67		Steve Berger ... 69	
David Holliday ... 83,88		Cruz Pearsall ... 91	

Public Schs..Principal	Grd	Prgm	Enr/#Cls	SN	Phone
La Francis Hardiman Elem Sch 792 Mount Ave, Wyandanch 11798 Shamika Simpson	PK-2	T	787	57%	631/870-0580 Fax 631/491-8572
Martin Luther King Jr Elem Sch 792 Mount Ave, Wyandanch 11798 Monique Habersham	3-5	T	601 53	79%	631/870-0580 Fax 631/491-8572
Milton L Olive Middle Sch 140 Garden City Ave, Wyandanch 11798 Dr Darlene White	6-8	T	615 57	79%	631/870-0525 Fax 631/491-8570
Wyandanch Memorial High Sch 54 S 32nd St, Wyandanch 11798 Paul Sibblies	9-12	TV	808 60	77%	631/870-0450 Fax 631/491-8525

SUFFOLK CATHOLIC SCHOOLS

• **Diocese of Rockville Ed Office** PID: 00739512
Listing includes only schools located in this county. See District Index for location of Diocesan Offices.

Catholic Schs..Principal	Grd	Prgm	Enr/#Cls	SN	Phone
Holy Angels Regional Sch 1 Division St, Patchogue 11772 Michael Connell	PK-8		225 18		631/475-0422 Fax 631/475-2036
O L Queen of Apostles Reg Sch 2 Saint Johns Pl, CTR Moriches 11934 John Sureau	PK-8		200 15		631/878-1033 Fax 631/878-1059
Our Lady of Providence Reg Sch 82 Carleton Ave, Central Islip 11722 Sharon Swift	PK-8		300 21		631/234-6324 Fax 631/234-6360
Our Lady of the Hamptons Sch 160 N Main St, Southampton 11968 Sr Kathryn Schlueter	PK-8		309 9		631/283-9140 Fax 631/287-3958
SS Cyril & Methodius Sch 105 Half Hollow Rd, Deer Park 11729 Sr Susan Snyder	PK-8		205 14		631/667-4044 Fax 631/667-0093
SS Philip & James Sch 359 Clinton Ave, Saint James 11780 Diane Anderson	PK-8		200 13		631/584-7896 Fax 631/584-3258
St Anthony High Sch 275 Wolf Hill Rd, Huntingtn Sta 11747 Br David Migliorino	9-12		2,240 76		631/271-2020 Fax 631/547-6820
St John the Baptist High Sch 1170 Montauk Hwy, West Islip 11795 Biagio Arpino	9-12		1,725 30		631/587-8000 Fax 631/587-8996
St Martin of Tours Sch 30 Union Ave, Amityville 11701 Mr Parisi	PK-8		400		631/264-7166 Fax 631/264-0136
St Mary Sch 16 Harrison Ave, East Islip 11730 Laura McMahon	PK-8		472 18		631/581-3423 Fax 631/581-7509
St Patrick Sch 284 E Main St, Smithtown 11787 Barbara Pellerito	PK-8		460 20		631/724-0285 Fax 631/265-4841
St Patrick Sch 360 Main St, Huntington 11743 Sr Maureen McDade	PK-8		577 30		631/385-3322 Fax 631/673-4609
St Patrick Sch 9 N Clinton Ave, Bay Shore 11706 Roseann Petruccio	PK-8		526 18		631/665-0569 Fax 631/968-6007
Trinity Regional Sch 1025 5th Ave, E Northport 11731 Patricia Ayers	PK-8		400 23		631/261-5130 Fax 631/266-5345

SUFFOLK PRIVATE SCHOOLS

Private Schs..Principal	Grd	Prgm	Enr/#Cls	SN	Phone
Alternatives for Children 14 Research Way, East Setauket 11733 Dr Marie Ficano	Spec		160 14		631/331-6400 Fax 631/331-6865
Ascent Sch 819 Grand Blvd Ste 2, Deer Park 11729 Dr Nancy Sharnow	Spec		24 4		631/254-6100 Fax 631/254-6008
Bay Shore Christian Sch 211 Bay Shore Rd, Bay Shore 11706 John Johnson	PK-6		150 7		631/665-5241 Fax 631/665-1066
Bethesda SDA Elem Sch 76 Parkway Ave, Amityville 11701 Celestine Creighton	PK-9		48 9		631/842-3321 Fax 631/842-1623
Building Blocks Dev Pre-School 29 Pinewood Dr, Commack 11725 Donna Sharbino	PK-PK		350		631/499-1237 Fax 631/499-1074
Children's Ctr UCP Sch-Suffolk 9 Smiths Ln, Commack 11725 Ingrid Trouve	Spec		86		631/543-2338 Fax 631/543-5981
Cleary School for the Deaf 301 Smithtown Blvd, Nesconset 11767 Kathleen Kerzner	Spec	G	80 11		631/588-0530 Fax 631/588-0016
Copiague Christian Academy 2675 Great Neck Rd, Copiague 11726 Eugene Pagliarulo	PK-2		40 4		631/842-5993 Fax 631/841-1672
Daytop Village Sec Sch 2075 New York Ave, Huntingtn Sta 11746 Khia Fulton	7-12		25		631/351-7112 Fax 631/351-0862
Developmental Disability Inst 99 Hollywood Dr, Smithtown 11787 Mary Hoffman	Spec	G	104		631/366-2900 Fax 631/366-2997
Emanuel Lutheran Sch 179 E Main St, Patchogue 11772 Denise Norman	PK-8		150 14		631/758-2250 Fax 631/758-2418

1 Superintendent	8 Curric/Instruct K-12	19 Chief Financial Officer	29 Family/Consumer Science	39 Social Studies K-12	49 English/Lang Arts Elem	59 Special Education Elem	69 Academic Assessment
2 Bus/Finance/Purchasing	9 Curric/Instruct Elem	20 Art K-12	30 Adult Education	40 Social Studies Elem	50 English/Lang Arts Sec	60 Special Education Sec	70 Research/Development
3 Buildings And Grounds	10 Curric/Instruct Sec	21 Art Elem	31 Career/Sch-to-Work K-12	41 Social Studies Sec	51 Reading K-12	61 Foreign/World Lang K-12	71 Public Information
4 Food Service	11 Federal Program	22 Art Sec	32 Career/Sch-to-Work Elem	42 Science K-12	52 Reading Elem	62 Foreign/World Lang Elem	72 Summer School
5 Transportation	12 Title I	23 Music K-12	33 Career/Sch-to-Work Sec	43 Science Elem	53 Reading Sec	63 Foreign/World Lang Sec	73 Instructional Tech
6 Athletic	13 Title V	24 Music Elem	34 Early Childhood Ed	44 Science Sec	54 Remedial Reading K-12	64 Religious Education K-12	74 Inservice Training
7 Health Services	14 Asst Superintendent	25 Music Sec	35 Health/Phys Education	45 Math K-12	55 Remedial Reading Elem	65 Religious Education Elem	75 Marketing/Distributive
	15 Instructional Media Svcs	26 Business Education	36 Guidance Services K-12	46 Math Elem	56 Remedial Reading Sec	66 Religious Education Sec	76 Info Systems
	16 Chief Operations Officer	27 Career & Tech Ed	37 Guidance Services Elem	47 Math Sec	57 Bilingual/ELL	67 School Board President	77 Psychological Assess
	18 Chief Academic Officer	28 Technology Education	38 Guidance Services Sec	48 English/Lang Arts K-12	58 Special Education K-12	68 Teacher Personnel	78 Affirmative Action

New York School Directory — Suffolk County

School	Grades	Enroll	Phone
Gersh Academy Hauppauge 358 Hoffman Ln, Hauppauge 11788 Diana Devivio	Spec	25	631/232-3855
Gersh Academy-West Hills 21 Sweet Hollow Rd, Huntington 11743 Kim Doxey-Davila	Spec	41	631/385-3342
Harbor Country Day Sch 17 Three Sisters Rd, Saint James 11780 Dorothy Woo \ Nicole Fotis	PK-8	100 22	631/584-5555 Fax 631/862-7664
Hayground Sch 151 Mitchells Ln, Bridgehampton 11932 Marcella Langendal	PK-8	44 4	631/537-7068 Fax 631/537-5195
Heritage Christian Academy 1380 5th Ave, Bay Shore 11706 Sonya Williams	PK-5	51 4	631/968-5358 Fax 631/968-5555
Huntington Montessori Sch 165 Pidgeon Hill Rd Ste 2, S Huntington 11746 Phyllis LaFauci	PK-6	102	631/385-3388 Fax 631/385-8517
Ivy League Sch 211 Brooksite Dr, Smithtown 11787 Ismael Colon	PK-8	300 16	631/265-4177 Fax 631/265-4698
Kid Esteem of Montessori Schoo 354 Veterans Memorial Hwy, Commack 11725 Marianne Chasen	PK-5	100 4	631/321-6675 Fax 631/226-8249
Knox Sch 541 Long Beach Rd, Saint James 11780 Kristen Baker	6-12	140 12	631/686-1600 Fax 631/686-1650
Laurel Hill Sch 201 Old Town Rd, East Setauket 11733 Robert Stark	PK-8	350	631/751-1154 Fax 631/751-2421
Leeway Sch 335 Johnson Ave, Sayville 11782 Linda Imbesi	PK-PK	100 10	631/589-8060 Fax 631/589-0908
Leonard E Burket Christian Sch 34 Oak St, CTR Moriches 11934 Dominic Scibetta	PK-12	70	631/878-1727 Fax 631/878-8968
Long Island Baptist Academy 125 Long Island Ave, Holtsville 11742 John Graft	1-12	40	631/447-2552
Long Island School for Gifted 165 Pidgeon Hill Rd Ste 1, Huntingtn Sta 11746 Dr Patricia Geyer	PK-9	256 22	631/423-3557 Fax 631/423-4368
Love of Learning Mont Sch 105 Prospect Rd, Centerport 11721 Denise Brazeau	PK-6	80 6	631/754-4109 Fax 631/754-4110
Madonna Heights Sch 151 Burrs Ln, Dix Hills 11746 Carmen Pinto	Spec	40 12	631/643-8800 Fax 631/491-4440
Maimonides Day Sch 360 Nicolls Rd, East Setauket 11733 Rivkie Grossbaum	PK-7	26 4	631/585-0521 Fax 631/585-0570
Maryhaven Center of Hope 450 Myrtle Ave, Prt Jefferson 11777 Ingrid Jeannis-Desire	Spec	105	631/474-3400 Fax 631/474-4181
Mdq Academy 1725 Brentwood Rd, Brentwood 11717 Sr Atia Pasha	PK-12	400	631/665-5036
New Interdisciplinary Sch 430 Sills Rd, Yaphank 11980 Dr Jay Silverstein	Spec	40 17	631/924-5583 Fax 631/924-5687
Nssa 80 Hauppauge Rd, Commack 11725 Debra Kennedy	Spec	25 5	631/462-0386 Fax 631/462-4201
Our Savior New American Sch 140 Mark Tree Rd, Centereach 11720 Dolores Reade	PK-12	300	631/588-2757 Fax 631/588-2617
Peconic Community Sch 269 Main Rd, Aquebogue 11931 Kathryn Quigley	PK-6	60	631/779-2934
Raynor Country Day Sch 4 Mill Pond Path, Speonk 11972 Kerry Coonan	PK-6	150 9	631/288-4658 Fax 631/288-4654
Ross Lower Sch 18 Goodfriend Dr, East Hampton 11937 Jeanette Tyndall	PK-6	130 12	631/907-5000
Ross Upper Sch 18 Goodfriend Dr, East Hampton 11937 Bill O'Hearn	7-12	400	631/907-5000 Fax 631/907-5565
Saul and Elaine Seiff Ctr 45 Crossway E, Bohemia 11716 Andrea Nickdow	Spec G	125	631/218-4949 Fax 631/567-3640
Smithtown Christian Sch 1 Higbie Dr Ste 5, Smithtown 11787 Tracy Berner \ Dr Heather Lee	PK-12	476 28	631/265-3334 Fax 631/265-1079
South Bay Jr Academy 150 Fire Island Ave, Babylon 11702 Maria Thomas	PK-8	70 3	631/321-0857 Fax 631/321-0821
Southampton Montessori Sch 135 Saint Andrews Rd, Southampton 11968 Nicole Tinker	PK-3	50	631/283-2223
St Pius V Sch 18 Old East Neck Rd, Melville 11747 Sr Mary Agnes	1-12	140	631/351-0116 Fax 631/351-0118
The Bridges Academy 339 Snedecor Ave, West Islip 11795 Stephen Rubenacker	PK-8	260	631/358-5035 Fax 631/677-3900
The School House 106 Vernon Valley Rd, E Northport 11731 Mimosa Jones-Tunney	K-6	100	631/261-9000
The Stony Brook Sch 11 Cedar St, Stony Brook 11790 Joshua Crane	7-12	350 26	631/751-1800 Fax 631/751-4211
Upper Room Christian Sch 722 Deer Park Rd, Dix Hills 11746 Dr Gregory Eck	K-12 GV	200 12	631/242-5359 Fax 631/492-2976
Victory Christian Academy 1343 Montauk Hwy, E Patchogue 11772 Barbara Seaton	PK-12	80 10	631/654-9284 Fax 631/654-9297
West Hills Montessori Sch 21 Sweet Hollow Rd, Huntington 11743 Kevin Gersh	PK-6	82 6	631/385-3342 Fax 631/427-6332
West Sayville Christian Sch 37 Rollstone Ave, West Sayville 11796 Karen Warren	K-8	65 9	631/589-2180 Fax 631/589-2143
Winston Preparatory School-Li 30 Deforest Rd, Dix Hills 11746 Keith Oncale	3-12	401	631/779-2400

SUFFOLK REGIONAL CENTERS

• **Eastern Suffolk BOCES** PID: 00776560   631/289-2200
201 Sunrise Hwy, Patchogue 11772   Fax 631/289-2381

David Wicks 1	Collen Lipponer 2
Dr Julie Davis Lutz 3,17	Keith Anderson 3
Susan Maddi 4,5,70	Dr Peggie Staib 8,15
Dr R Terri McSweeney 15,68	Ryan Ruf 15
Leah Arnold 27,30,31	Gina Reilly 58
Lisa Israel 67	Grant Nelsen 73

---

79 Student Personnel
80 Driver Ed/Safety
81 Gifted/Talented
82 Video Services
83 Substance Abuse Prev
84 Erate
85 AIDS Education
88 Alternative/At Risk
89 Multi-Cultural Curriculum
90 Social Work
91 Safety/Security
92 Magnet School
93 Parental Involvement
95 Tech Prep Program
97 Chief Infomation Officer
98 Chief Technology Officer
270 Character Education
271 Migrant Education
273 Teacher Mentor
274 Before/After Sch
275 Response To Intervention
277 Remedial Math K-12
280 Literacy Coach
285 STEM
286 Digital Learning
288 Common Core Standards
294 Accountability
295 Network System
296 Title II Programs
297 Webmaster
298 Grant Writer/Ptnrships
750 Chief Innovation Officer
751 Chief of Staff
752 Social Emotional Learning

School Programs
A = Alternative Program
G = Adult Classes
M = Magnet Program
T = Title I Schoolwide
V = Career & Tech Ed Programs

Other School Types
Ⓐ = Alternative School
Ⓒ = Charter School
Ⓜ = Magnet School
Ⓨ = Year-Round School

Social Media
▌ = Facebook
▌ = Twitter

New Schools are shaded
New Superintendents and Principals are bold
Personnel with email addresses are underscored

Sullivan County

Market Data Retrieval

- **Western Suffolk BOCES** PID: 00776522 — 631/549-4900
  507 Deer Park Rd, Huntingtn Sta 11746 — Fax 631/623-4996

Angelique Johnson-Dingle	1	Warren Taylor	2,19
Michael Flynn	3,17	Sara Kardaz	16
Nancy Kelsey	27,31	Nancy Wilson	58
Salvatore Marinello	67	Dr Hugh Gigante	68
Nancy Fischetti	71	Renee Allen	74

SULLIVAN COUNTY

SULLIVAN COUNTY SCHOOLS

County Schs..Principal	Grd	Prgm	Enr/#Cls	SN	
Sullivan Co BOCES Special Ed 52 Ferndale Loomis Rd, Liberty 12754 Adam Riehl	Spec	AG	300 29	37%	845/295-4111 Fax 845/292-7910
Sullivan Co Career & Tech Ctr 52 Ferndale Loomis Rd, Liberty 12754 Scott Palermo	Voc	A	450 20		845/295-4152 Fax 845/295-0513

SULLIVAN PUBLIC SCHOOLS

- **Eldred Central School Dist** PID: 00776730 — 845/456-1100
  600 State Route 55, Eldred 12732 — Fax 845/557-3672

Schools: 2 \ **Teachers:** 40 \ **Students:** 525 \ **Special Ed Students:** 74 \ **LEP Students:** 3 \ **College-Bound:** 85% \ **Ethnic:** Hispanic 9%, Caucasian 90% \ **Exp:** $204 (Med) \ **Poverty:** 17% \ **Title I:** $222,715 \ **Special Education:** $315,000 \ **Open-Close:** 09/10 - 06/25 \ **DTBP:** $387 (High)

John Morgano	1,11	Caleb Russell	2
Jim Dorcas	3*	Jill Decker	4*
Mellissa Muller	5	Gerald Gaff	6,83,85
Tina Rodriguez	16,73*	Kim Gueren	36*
Faith Mursch	55	Scott Hallock	67
Zita Kurtzman	270	Marikate Oset	273*

Public Schs..Principal	Grd	Prgm	Enr/#Cls	SN	
Eldred Jr Sr High Sch 600 State Route 55, Eldred 12732 Virginia Keegan	7-12	T	223 29	42%	845/456-1100
George Ross MacKenzie Elem Sch 1045 Proctor Rd, Glen Spey 12737 David Krebs	PK-6	T	259 30	44%	845/456-1100 Fax 845/856-8579

- **Fallsburg Central School Dist** PID: 00776754 — 845/434-5884
  115 Brickman Rd, Fallsburg 12733 — Fax 845/434-0418

Schools: 2 \ **Teachers:** 128 \ **Students:** 1,440 \ **Special Ed Students:** 261 \ **LEP Students:** 235 \ **College-Bound:** 85% \ **Ethnic:** Asian 1%, African American 11%, Hispanic 55%, Native American: 1%, Caucasian 32% \ **Exp:** $398 (High) \ **Poverty:** 31% \ **Title I:** $1,260,933 \ **Special Education:** $803,000 \ **Open-Close:** 09/09 - 06/25 \ **DTBP:** $364 (High) \ ▣

Dr Ivan Katz	1	Daniel Grecco	2,5,71,91,97
David Burke	3	Dara Smith	4
Suzanne Lendzian	6	Dr Matthew Evans	8,11,15,69,288,296
Joe Lezner	38	Leighanne Russell	58,79,88
Debra Barbiani	67	Debra Tingley	73
Dawn Adams	83	Aleta Lymon	93
Deborah Jacobson	274*		

Public Schs..Principal	Grd	Prgm	Enr/#Cls	SN	
Benjamin Cosor Elem Sch 15 Old Falls Rd, Fallsburg 12733 Mary Kate Stinehour	PK-6	T	792 40	73%	845/434-6800 Fax 845/434-0871
Fallsburg Junior Senior HS 115 Brickman Rd, Fallsburg 12733 Dawne Adams	7-12	ATV	648 30	61%	845/434-6800 Fax 845/434-0168

- **Liberty Central School Dist** PID: 00776807 — 845/292-6171
  115 Buckley St, Liberty 12754 — Fax 845/292-1164

Schools: 3 \ **Teachers:** 151 \ **Students:** 1,700 \ **Special Ed Students:** 257 \ **LEP Students:** 135 \ **College-Bound:** 76% \ **Ethnic:** Asian 1%, African American 8%, Hispanic 44%, Caucasian 47% \ **Exp:** $306 (High) \ **Poverty:** 20% \ **Title I:** $514,805 \ **Special Education:** $4,776,000 \ **Open-Close:** 09/08 - 06/25

Dr Augustine Tornatore	1,11	Georgia Gonzalez	2,97
Albert Demarmels	3	Dara Smith	4
Peter Bianco	6,83,85	Rebecca Rielly	7
Dr Patrick Sullivan	17,91,285,298,752	Penny Medina	57,271*
Charlotte Mennona	58	John Nichols	67
Theresa DeLaney	68	Terry Harcleroad	73
Sheila Wormuth	77		

Public Schs..Principal	Grd	Prgm	Enr/#Cls	SN	
Liberty Elem Sch 201 N Main St, Liberty 12754 Jacqueline Harris	PK-4	T	708 34	76%	845/292-5400 Fax 845/295-9201
Liberty High Sch 125 Buckley St, Liberty 12754 Derek Adams	9-12		490 52	63%	845/292-5400 Fax 845/292-7262
Liberty Middle Sch 145 Buckley St, Liberty 12754 Andy Cameron	5-8		575 41	70%	845/292-5400 Fax 845/292-5691

- **Livingston Manor Ctl Sch Dist** PID: 00776833 — 845/439-4400
  19 School St, Livingstn MNR 12758 — Fax 845/439-4717

Schools: 2 \ **Teachers:** 49 \ **Students:** 432 \ **Special Ed Students:** 88 \ **LEP Students:** 3 \ **College-Bound:** 78% \ **Ethnic:** Asian 2%, African American 6%, Hispanic 10%, Caucasian 81% \ **Exp:** $519 (High) \ **Poverty:** 21% \ **Title I:** $237,356 \ **Special Education:** $228,000 \ **Open-Close:** 09/04 - 06/25 \ **DTBP:** $344 (High)

John Evans	1	Timothy MaGuire	2
Arthur Hoag	3*	Stephen Rogers	4*
Adam Larson	6*	Christopher Hubert	8,16,73*
Lauren Marrero	11,57,58,296*	Chris Towsley	38,69,88
Elliott Madison	67	Danielle Dalcero	83,85
Jamie Dymond	273*		

Public Schs..Principal	Grd	Prgm	Enr/#Cls	SN	
Livingston Manor Elem Sch 19 School St, Livingstn MNR 12758 **Christopher Hubert**	PK-6	TV	238 50	51%	845/439-4400
Livingston Mid High Sch 19 School St, Livingstn MNR 12758 Shirlee Davis	7-12		194		845/439-4400

1 Superintendent	8 Curric/Instruct K-12	19 Chief Financial Officer
2 Bus/Finance/Purchasing	9 Curric/Instruct Elem	20 Art K-12
3 Buildings And Grounds	10 Curric/Instruct Sec	21 Art Elem
4 Food Service	11 Federal Program	22 Art Sec
5 Transportation	12 Title I	23 Music K-12
6 Athletic	13 Title V	24 Music Elem
7 Health Services	15 Asst Superintendent	25 Music Sec
	16 Instructional Media Svcs	26 Business Education
	17 Chief Operations Officer	27 Career & Tech Ed
	18 Chief Academic Officer	28 Technology Education
29 Family/Consumer Science	39 Social Studies K-12	49 English/Lang Arts Elem
30 Adult Education	40 Social Studies Elem	50 English/Lang Arts Sec
31 Career/Sch-to-Work K-12	41 Social Studies Sec	51 Reading K-12
32 Career/Sch-to-Work Elem	42 Science K-12	52 Reading Elem
33 Career/Sch-to-Work Sec	43 Science Elem	53 Reading Sec
34 Early Childhood Ed	44 Science Sec	54 Remedial Reading K-12
35 Health/Phys Education	45 Math K-12	55 Remedial Reading Elem
36 Guidance Services K-12	46 Math Elem	56 Remedial Reading Sec
37 Guidance Services Elem	47 Math Sec	57 Bilingual/ELL
38 Guidance Services Sec	48 English/Lang Arts K-12	58 Special Education K-12
59 Special Education Elem	69 Academic Assessment
60 Special Education Sec	70 Research/Development
61 Foreign/World Lang K-12	71 Public Information
62 Foreign/World Lang Elem	72 Summer School
63 Foreign/World Lang Sec	73 Instructional Tech
64 Religious Education K-12	74 Inservice Training
65 Religious Education Elem	75 Marketing/Distributive
66 Religious Education Sec	76 Info Systems
67 School Board President	77 Psychological Assess
68 Teacher Personnel	78 Affirmative Action

NY—236

New York School Directory — Sullivan County

- **Monticello Central School Dist** PID: 00776857 845/794-7700
  60 Jefferson St Ste 3, Monticello 12701 Fax 845/794-7710

Schools: 5 \ **Teachers:** 259 \ **Students:** 2,785 \ **Special Ed Students:** 738 \ **LEP Students:** 106 \ **Ethnic:** Asian 2%, African American 19%, Hispanic 33%, Caucasian 46% \ **Exp:** $401 (High) \ **Poverty:** 23% \ **Title I:** $1,508,497 \ **Special Education:** $7,039,000 \ **Open-Close:** 09/14 - 06/25 \ **DTBP:** $224 (High) \ f

Dr Matthew Evans 1	Lisa Failla 2,15,68
Stephen Lewis 3,91	Dawn Parsons 4
Robin Sklar 5	Kurt Boddenhagen 6,35
Jacqueline Jara-Cole 7	Dr Linda Oehler-Marx 8,15
Sandy Wagner 16,73,74	Sheryl Manz 36*
Jennifer Gorr 58	Tanya Duryea 58,79,271
Lori Orestano-James 67	Courtney Bonfante 71
Dana Taylor 83,88*	

Public Schs..Principal	Grd	Prgm	Enr/#Cls	SN	
Emma C Chase Elem Sch 28 Pennsylvania Ave, Wurtsboro 12790 William Frandino	K-5	T	230 17 f	52%	845/888-2471 Fax 845/888-2029
George L Cooke Elem Sch 69 Richardson Ave, Monticello 12701 Christopher Palmer	K-5	T	565 33 f	74%	845/794-8830 Fax 845/794-8854
Kenneth L Rutherford Elem Sch 26 Patricia Pl, Monticello 12701 Michelle Knowlton	K-5	T	457 28 f	76%	845/794-4240 Fax 845/794-5137
Monticello High Sch 39 Breakey Ave, Monticello 12701 Stephen Wilder	9-12	ATV	861 45	63%	845/794-8840 Fax 845/794-8133
Robert J Kaiser Middle Sch 45 Breakey Ave, Monticello 12701 Nicholas Millas	6-8	TV	672 40	66%	845/796-3058 Fax 845/796-3099

- **Roscoe Central School Dist** PID: 00776948 607/498-4126
  6 Academy St, Roscoe 12776 Fax 607/498-6015

Schools: 1 \ **Teachers:** 29 \ **Students:** 257 \ **Special Ed Students:** 38 \ **Ethnic:** African American 1%, Hispanic 12%, Native American: 1%, Caucasian 85% \ **Exp:** $139 (Low) \ **Poverty:** 14% \ **Title I:** $56,319 \ **Special Education:** $442,000 \ **Open-Close:** 09/07 - 06/25 \ **DTBP:** $352 (High) \ f

John Evans 1	Tim MaGuire 2
Ryan Vogler 3	Joe Papp 4*
Frederick Ahart 6	Janice Phillips 9,11,16,73,273,288,296*
Kelly Hendrickson 36*	Robin Francisco 58*
Gary Dahlman 67	Gabrielle Westfall 83
Steve Livsey 295*	

Public Schs..Principal	Grd	Prgm	Enr/#Cls	SN	
Roscoe Central Sch 6 Academy St, Roscoe 12776 Janice Phillips	PK-12	T	257 45	40%	607/498-4126 Fax 607/498-5609

- **Sullivan West Central SD** PID: 00776780 845/482-4610
  33 Schoolhouse Rd, Jeffersonvlle 12748 Fax 845/482-3022

Schools: 2 \ **Teachers:** 97 \ **Students:** 1,068 \ **Special Ed Students:** 173 \ **LEP Students:** 11 \ **College-Bound:** 74% \ **Ethnic:** Asian 1%, African American 1%, Hispanic 10%, Caucasian 88% \ **Exp:** $259 (Med) \ **Poverty:** 16% \ **Title I:** $382,707 \ **Special Education:** $1,732,000 \ **Open-Close:** 09/04 - 06/25 \ **DTBP:** $395 (High)

Stephen Walker 1	Lorraine Poston 2,15
Nick Tranchina 3	Dawn Priebe 5
David Franskevicz 6*	Dr Kathleen Bressler 15,58,79
Rose Joyce-Turner 67	Elizabeth Huggler 73,98

Public Schs..Principal	Grd	Prgm	Enr/#Cls	SN	
Sullivan West Elem Sch 33 Schoolhouse Hill Rd, Jeffersonvlle 12748 Rod McLaughlin	PK-6	T	582 50	37%	845/482-4610 Fax 845/482-9883
Sullivan West High Sch 6604 State Route 52, Lk Huntington 12752 Mark Plescia	7-12	V	486	37%	845/932-8401 Fax 845/932-8425

- **Tri-Valley Central School Dist** PID: 00776962 845/985-2296
  34 Moore Hill Rd, Grahamsville 12740 Fax 845/985-0310

Schools: 2 \ **Teachers:** 100 \ **Students:** 975 \ **Special Ed Students:** 167 \ **LEP Students:** 3 \ **College-Bound:** 70% \ **Ethnic:** Asian 1%, African American 2%, Hispanic 11%, Caucasian 86% \ **Exp:** $312 (High) \ **Poverty:** 21% \ **Title I:** $390,893 \ **Special Education:** $2,050,000 \ **Open-Close:** 09/14 - 06/22 \ **DTBP:** $363 (High)

Michael Williams 1	Robert Whitaker 2,4,5,84,274
Jesse Bell 3	Lori Schmidtz 5
Jason Closs 6	Debra Kelley 8,11,15,74,288,298
Jennifer Williams 9	David Pulley 10*
Danielle Cornish 58,79,752	Keri Poley 67
Aaron Butler 73,286	

Public Schs..Principal	Grd	Prgm	Enr/#Cls	SN	
Tri-Valley Elem Sch 34 Moore Hill Rd, Grahamsville 12740 Jennifer Williams	PK-6	T	519 21	51%	845/985-2296 Fax 845/985-0046
Tri-Valley High Sch 34 Moore Hill Rd, Grahamsville 12740 David Pulley	7-12	AGT	463	42%	845/985-2296 Fax 845/985-7261

SULLIVAN PRIVATE SCHOOLS

Private Schs..Principal	Grd	Prgm	Enr/#Cls	SN	
Bais Yisroel Sch-Girls 213 Gibber Rd, Kiamesha Lake 12751 Eliezer Meth	K-7		200		845/794-9915
Center for Discovery Ben Mosche Road, Harris 12742 Patrick Dollard	Spec		290		845/794-1400 Fax 845/707-8927
Hebrew Day School-Sullivan Co 4718 Route 42, Kiamesha Lake 12751 Menachem Fruchter	PK-8		50 12		845/794-7890 Fax 845/794-0859
Homestead Sch 428 Hollow Rd, Glen Spey 12737 Peter Comstock	PK-8		200 7		845/856-6359
Talmud Torah Imrei Burech-Boys PO Box 406, Kiamesha Lake 12751 Eliezer Meth	K-7		195		845/794-9915
Yeshiva Gedolah Zichron Moshe 84 Laurel Park Road, S Fallsburg 12779 Esther Gorelick	PK-8	G	272		845/434-5240 Fax 845/434-1009

79 Student Personnel	91 Safety/Security	275 Response To Intervention	298 Grant Writer/Ptnrships
80 Driver Ed/Safety	92 Magnet School	277 Remedial Math K-12	750 Chief Innovation Officer
81 Gifted/Talented	93 Parental Involvement	280 Literacy Coach	751 Chief of Staff
82 Video Services	95 Tech Prep Program	285 STEM	752 Social Emotional Learning
83 Substance Abuse Prev	97 Chief Infomation Officer	286 Digital Learning	
84 Erate	98 Chief Technology Officer	288 Common Core Standards	**Other School Types**
85 AIDS Education	270 Character Education	294 Accountability	Ⓐ = Alternative School
88 Alternative/At Risk	271 Migrant Education	295 Network System	Ⓒ = Charter School
89 Multi-Cultural Curriculum	273 Teacher Mentor	296 Title II Programs	Ⓜ = Magnet School
90 Social Work	274 Before/After Sch	297 Webmaster	Ⓨ = Year-Round School

School Programs
A = Alternative Program
G = Adult Classes
M = Magnet Program
T = Title I Schoolwide
V = Career & Tech Ed Programs

Social Media
f = Facebook
t = Twitter

New Schools are shaded
New Superintendents and Principals are bold
Personnel with email addresses are underscored

Tioga County

Market Data Retrieval

SULLIVAN REGIONAL CENTERS

• **Sullivan BOCES** PID: 00776998
6 Wierk Ave, Liberty 12754
845/295-4000
Fax 845/292-8694

Dr Robert DuFour 1	Keith Menges 2,3,73,76
Steven Lewis 3	Donna Flynn Brown 8,15,30,58,88
Susan Schmidt 15	Lynn Miller 16
Scott Palermo 27,31	Linda Berkowitz 67
Jennifer DeFrank 68	Donna Hemmer 71
Dr Dola Deloff 74	Linda Blanton 88

TIOGA COUNTY

TIOGA COUNTY SCHOOLS

County Schs..Principal	Grd	Prgm	Enr/#Cls	SN	
Ⓐ Tioga Learning Center 471 Pennsylvania Ave, Apalachin 13732 Maria Kessler	7-12		200		607/748-8261 Fax 607/748-8262

TIOGA PUBLIC SCHOOLS

• **Candor Central School Dist** PID: 00777021
1 Academy St, Candor 13743
607/659-5010
Fax 607/659-7112

Schools: 2 \ **Teachers:** 77 \ **Students:** 750 \ **Special Ed Students:** 124 \ **LEP Students:** 3 \ **College-Bound:** 73% \ **Ethnic:** Asian 1%, African American 1%, Hispanic 3%, Caucasian 95% \ **Exp:** $309 (High) \ **Poverty:** 15% \ **Title I:** $196,542 \ **Special Education:** $1,374,000 \ **Open-Close:** 09/09 - 06/23 \ **DTBP:** $359 (High)

Jeff Kisloski 1	Sydney Wade 2,298
Laverne Smith 3	Brian Lanphere 4*
Holly Carling 5	Peter Ahart 6
Kim Nichols 8	Angela Holmes 11,58
Beth Gance-Virkler 36*	Jason Banks 36*
Ray Parmarter 67	Matt Gelder 73
Mike Williams 76,295*	John Benjamin 83*
Denise Ahart 273,280*	

Public Schs..Principal	Grd	Prgm	Enr/#Cls	SN	
Candor Elem Sch 2 Academy St, Candor 13743 Kathryn Volpicelli	PK-6	T	415 45	57%	607/659-3935 Fax 607/659-4688
Candor Jr Sr High Sch 1 Academy St, Candor 13743 Wayne Aman	7-12	AGTV	341 40	51%	607/659-5020 Fax 607/659-4692

• **Newark Valley Central Sch Dist** PID: 00777057
68 Wilson Creek Rd, Newark Valley 13811
607/642-3221
Fax 607/642-8821

Schools: 3 \ **Teachers:** 100 \ **Students:** 1,060 \ **Special Ed Students:** 167 \ **College-Bound:** 63% \ **Ethnic:** Hispanic 2%, Caucasian 97% \ **Exp:** $203 (Med) \ **Poverty:** 14% \ **Title I:** $253,221 \ **Special Education:** $2,147,000 \ **Open-Close:** 09/04 - 06/25 \ **DTBP:** $375 (High)

Ryan Dougherty 1	Ji Katchuk 2,11,296,298
Gary Hoskins 3	Lorraine Trotman 4*
Randy Zukowski 5	Scott Wandell 6*
Jennifer Hoover 7	Valerie Murtha 8,76
Robert Rodgers 34*	Erica Delessandro 36,69
Lisa Pomeroy 36*	Jami Fabrizio 58*
Randal Kerr 67	Greg Asfoury 73,286,288
Morgan Crandell 752	

Public Schs..Principal	Grd	Prgm	Enr/#Cls	SN	
Nathan T Hall Elem Sch 86 Whig St, Newark Valley 13811 Robert Rodgers	PK-3	T	338 19	54%	607/642-3340 Fax 607/642-5004
Newark Valley High Sch 68 Wilson Creek Rd, Newark Valley 13811 Gregory Asfoury	8-12	V	443 80	44%	607/642-8351 Fax 607/642-5292
Newark Valley Middle Sch 88 Whig St, Newark Valley 13811 Todd Schaffer	4-7		331 42	53%	607/642-5524 Fax 607/642-8175

• **Owego Apalachin Ctl Sch Dist** PID: 00777112
5 Sheldon Guile Blvd, Owego 13827
607/687-6224
Fax 607/687-6313

Schools: 4 \ **Teachers:** 158 \ **Students:** 2,005 \ **Special Ed Students:** 391 \ **LEP Students:** 5 \ **College-Bound:** 80% \ **Ethnic:** African American 1%, Hispanic 2%, Caucasian 97% \ **Exp:** $182 (Low) \ **Poverty:** 13% \ **Title I:** $422,923 \ **Special Education:** $3,539,000 \ **Open-Close:** 09/04 - 06/22 \ **DTBP:** $162 (High)

Corey Green 1	Randy Pryor 2
Ron Bieber 3	Mark Bordeau 4
Anthony Quaranta 5	Andre Buchsbaum 6*
Robert Farrell 8,11,15,97,288	Jill Bennedum 16,58,68,79,271,275
Heather Kotula 26,31,36*	Gene Cvik 67
Phil Schofield 69	Luke McEvoy 71
Eric Kochis 73,295	Jennifer Potter 90,93

Public Schs..Principal	Grd	Prgm	Enr/#Cls	SN	
Apalachin Elem Sch 405 Pennsylvania Ave, Apalachin 13732 Thomas Beatty	PK-5		442 25	35%	607/687-6289 Fax 607/625-5811
Owego Apalachin Middle Sch 3 Sheldon Guile Blvd, Owego 13827 Heath Georgia	6-8		466 53	46%	607/687-7302 Fax 607/687-6593
Owego Elem Sch 2 Sheldon Guile Blvd, Owego 13827 Ken Francisco	PK-5	T	498 26	49%	607/687-7303 Fax 607/687-6268
Owego Free Academy 1 Sheldon Guile Blvd, Owego 13827 Heath Georgia	9-12		599	41%	607/687-7301 Fax 607/687-6247

• **Spencer Van Etten Central SD** PID: 00777186
16 Dartts Xrd, Spencer 14883
607/589-7100
Fax 607/589-3010

Schools: 3 \ **Teachers:** 85 \ **Students:** 985 \ **Special Ed Students:** 152 \ **LEP Students:** 3 \ **College-Bound:** 66% \ **Ethnic:** Asian 1%, African American 1%, Hispanic 1%, Caucasian 96% \ **Exp:** $298 (Med) \ **Poverty:** 14% \ **Title I:** $223,119 \ **Special Education:** $1,626,000 \ **Open-Close:** 09/10 - 06/23 \ **DTBP:** $49 (Low)

Diahnne Hesler 1	Debra Eichholtz 2
Lance Cundy 3,91*	Jerry Carr 4*
Timothy Wilson 5	Rebecca Saggiomo 6
Christina Lampila 8,11,58,83,88,273,296,298	Britany Elsey 16,82*
Maritza Pena 57	Don Johnson 67
Jennifer Swayze 71	Darla Thomas 73,95,286*
Jack Wiiki 97	

NY-238

1 Superintendent	8 Curric/Instruct K-12	19 Chief Financial Officer	29 Family/Consumer Science	39 Social Studies K-12	49 English/Lang Arts Elem	59 Special Education Elem	69 Academic Assessment
2 Bus/Finance/Purchasing	9 Curric/Instruct Elem	20 Art K-12	30 Adult Education	40 Social Studies Elem	50 English/Lang Arts Sec	60 Special Education Sec	70 Research/Development
3 Buildings And Grounds	10 Curric/Instruct Sec	21 Art Elem	31 Career/Sch-to-Work K-12	41 Social Studies Sec	51 Reading K-12	61 Foreign/World Lang K-12	71 Public Information
4 Food Service	11 Federal Program	22 Art Sec	32 Career/Sch-to-Work Elem	42 Science K-12	52 Reading Elem	62 Foreign/World Lang Elem	72 Summer School
5 Transportation	12 Title I	23 Music K-12	33 Career/Sch-to-Work Sec	43 Science Elem	53 Reading Sec	63 Foreign/World Lang Sec	73 Instructional Tech
6 Athletic	13 Title V	24 Music Elem	34 Early Childhood Ed	44 Science Sec	54 Remedial Reading K-12	64 Religious Education K-12	74 Inservice Training
7 Health Services	15 Asst Superintendent	25 Music Sec	35 Health/Phys Education	45 Math K-12	55 Remedial Reading Elem	65 Religious Education Elem	75 Marketing/Distributive
	16 Instructional Media Svcs	26 Business Education	36 Guidance Services K-12	46 Math Elem	56 Remedial Reading Sec	66 Religious Education Sec	76 Info Systems
	17 Chief Operations Officer	27 Career & Tech Ed	37 Guidance Services Elem	47 Math Sec	57 Bilingual/ELL	67 School Board President	77 Psychological Assess
	18 Chief Academic Officer	28 Technology Education	38 Guidance Services Sec	48 English/Lang Arts K-12	58 Special Education K-12	68 Teacher Personnel	78 Affirmative Action

New York School Directory — Tompkins County

Public Schs..Principal	Grd	Prgm	Enr/#Cls	SN
Spencer Van Etten Elem Sch 7 Langford St, Van Etten 14889 Matt Stroup	PK-4	T	366 23	50% 607/589-7110 Fax 607/589-3017
Spencer Van Etten High Sch 16 Dartts Xrd, Spencer 14883 Melissa Jewell	9-12	V	290 25	54% 607/589-7140 Fax 607/589-3011
Spencer Van Etten Middle Sch 1 Center St, Spencer 14883 Brandon Foley	5-8		245 30	57% 607/589-7120 Fax 607/589-3020

- **Tioga Central School Dist** PID: 00777227 607/687-8000
  27 5th Ave, Tioga Center 13845 Fax 607/687-8007

Schools: 3 \ **Teachers:** 82 \ **Students:** 950 \ **Special Ed Students:** 121 \ **College-Bound:** 65% \ **Ethnic:** Hispanic 1%, Caucasian 98% \ **Exp:** $239 (Med) \ **Poverty:** 16% \ **Title I:** $270,710 \ **Special Education:** $937,000 \ **Open-Close:** 09/04 - 06/25 \ **DTBP:** $149 (High)

Dr David Hamilton 1
David Keene 3*
David VanDusen 5
Kathleen Keene 8,11,91,286,288*
Meredith Meister 58,79
Nicholas Aiello 73
Kendra Seaver 2
Mark Bordeau 4
Jim Houseknecht 6
Leanne Schneider 27,30,36*
Cathi Root 67
Joshua Roe 298*

Public Schs..Principal	Grd	Prgm	Enr/#Cls	SN
Tioga Central High Sch 27 5th Ave, Tioga Center 13845 Joshua Roe	9-12	AV	262 28	54% 607/687-8001 Fax 607/687-8010
Tioga Elem Sch 41 5th Ave, Tioga Center 13845 **Michelle Bombard**	PK-4	T	368 17	57% 607/687-8002 Fax 607/687-6945
Tioga Middle Sch 27 5th Ave, Tioga Center 13845 Will Cook	5-8	AT	289 22	71% 607/687-8004 Fax 607/687-6910

- **Waverly Ctl School Dist** PID: 00777277 607/565-2841
  15 Frederick St, Waverly 14892 Fax 607/565-4997

Schools: 4 \ **Teachers:** 115 \ **Students:** 1,700 \ **Special Ed Students:** 253 \ **LEP Students:** 3 \ **Ethnic:** Asian 1%, African American 1%, Hispanic 1%, Caucasian 98% \ **Exp:** $286 (Med) \ **Poverty:** 16% \ **Title I:** $409,443 \ **Special Education:** $2,155,000 \ **Open-Close:** 09/04 - 06/25 \ **DTBP:** $160 (High)

Eric Knolles 1
David Mastrantuono 3
Richard McIntosh 5,6
Elizabeth MacIntosh 8,11,280,288,296,298
Toni Risboskin 27*
Parvin Mensch 67
Jack Wiiki 97
Kathy Rote 2
Tina Finch 4
Rebecca Rorick 7*
Cheryl Wood-Walter 16*
Jeffrey DeAngelo 57,58
Kyle Ackland 73,295*
Cindy Schafer 274

Public Schs..Principal	Grd	Prgm	Enr/#Cls	SN
Elm Street Elem Sch 145 Elm St, Waverly 14892 John Cheresnowsky	2-4	T	323 21	54% 607/565-8186 Fax 607/948-0072
Lincoln Street Elem Sch 45 Lincoln St, Waverly 14892 Colleen Hall	PK-1	T	264 15	39% 607/565-8176 Fax 607/948-0073
Waverly High Sch 1 Frederick St, Waverly 14892 Ashlee Hunt	9-12	V	449 50	39% 607/565-8101 Fax 607/565-3718
Waverly Middle Sch 1 Frederick St, Waverly 14892 Paul Vesci	5-8	T	460	54% 607/565-3410 Fax 607/565-3718

TIOGA PRIVATE SCHOOLS

Private Schs..Principal	Grd	Prgm	Enr/#Cls	SN
North Spencer Christian Acad 721 Ithaca Rd, Spencer 14883 Ed Brown	PK-12		80 10	607/589-6366 Fax 607/589-4455

TOMPKINS COUNTY

TOMPKINS COUNTY SCHOOLS

County Schs..Principal	Grd	Prgm	Enr/#Cls	SN
Darwin Smith Sch 555 Warren Rd, Ithaca 14850 David Barr	Spec	G	215 21	607/257-1551 Fax 607/257-2958
T S T BOCES Voc Tech Center 555 Warren Rd, Ithaca 14850 Jeffrey Podolak	Voc		465	607/257-1555 Fax 607/266-0498
ⓐ T S T Community Sch 555 Warren Rd, Ithaca 14850 Maxine Parker	6-12	V	90 17	27% 607/273-9015 Fax 607/275-9702

TOMPKINS PUBLIC SCHOOLS

- **Dryden Central School Dist** PID: 00777332 607/844-5361
  118 Freeville Rd, Dryden 13053 Fax 607/844-4733

Schools: 5 \ **Teachers:** 153 \ **Students:** 1,500 \ **Special Ed Students:** 335 \ **LEP Students:** 11 \ **College-Bound:** 73% \ **Ethnic:** Asian 1%, African American 2%, Hispanic 5%, Caucasian 92% \ **Exp:** $282 (Med) \ **Poverty:** 15% \ **Title I:** $510,875 \ **Special Education:** $3,599,000 \ **Open-Close:** 09/08 - 06/24 \ **DTBP:** $376 (High)

Joshua Bacidalupi 1,83
Kenneth Smith 3
Lora Cavanagh 5
Janet Roscoe-Strebel 12,58,77
Marjie Malape 67
Lora Champlain 69
Mary Wright 280
Jennifer Case 2,17,19
Darlene Serbaniewicz 4
Cheryl Covell 8,12,57,288,298
Todd Kwiatkowski 35
Jordan Kashuba 68
Patti MacCheyne 73

Public Schs..Principal	Grd	Prgm	Enr/#Cls	SN
Cassavant Elem Sch 32 School St, Mc Lean 13102 Audrey Ryan	K-3	T	92 6	57% 607/844-8694 Fax 607/838-8907
Dryden Elem Sch 36 Union St, Dryden 13053 Dawn Wenzel	PK-5	T	523 34	52% 607/844-8694 Fax 607/844-4641
Dryden High Sch 118 Freeville Rd, Dryden 13053 Kyle Colunio	9-12		424 60	42% 607/844-8694 Fax 607/844-8541

---

79 Student Personnel
80 Driver Ed/Safety
81 Gifted/Talented
82 Video Services
83 Substance Abuse Prev
84 Erate
85 AIDS Education
88 Alternative/At Risk
89 Multi-Cultural Curriculum
90 Social Work
91 Safety/Security
92 Magnet School
93 Parental Involvement
95 Tech Prep Program
97 Chief Information Officer
98 Chief Technology Officer
270 Character Education
271 Migrant Education
273 Teacher Mentor
274 Before/After Sch
275 Response To Intervention
277 Remedial Math K-12
280 Literacy Coach
285 STEM
286 Digital Learning
288 Common Core Standards
294 Accountability
295 Network System
296 Title II Programs
297 Webmaster
298 Grant Writer/Ptnrships
750 Chief Innovation Officer
751 Chief of Staff
752 Social Emotional Learning

School Programs
A = Alternative Program
G = Adult Classes
M = Magnet Program
T = Title I Schoolwide
V = Career & Tech Ed Programs

Other School Types
Ⓐ = Alternative School
Ⓒ = Charter School
Ⓜ = Magnet School
Ⓨ = Year-Round School

Social Media
= Facebook
= Twitter

New Schools are shaded
New Superintendents and Principals are bold
Personnel with email addresses are underscored

Tompkins County

Dryden Middle Sch 118 Freeville Rd, Dryden 13053 Lora Champlain	6-8	T	291	45%	607/844-8694 Fax 607/844-5174
Freeville Elem Sch 43 Main St, Freeville 13068 Audrey Ryan	K-3	T	80 6	50%	607/844-8694 Fax 607/844-3826

• **George Junior Republic UFSD** PID: 00777382   607/844-6365
24 McDonald Rd, Freeville 13068   Fax 607/844-3410

Schools: 1 \ **Teachers:** 37 \ **Students:** 186 \ **Special Ed Students:** 81 \ **Ethnic:** African American 24%, Hispanic 6%, Native American: 1%, Caucasian 70% \ **Exp:** $956 (High) \ **Open-Close:** 09/04 - 06/29 \ **DTBP:** $1,067 (High)

Sonya Apker 1
Stacy Bradley 6*
Tom Watts 15
Ashley Morehouse 38,83
Alex Perkins 73,274*
Larry Lipfert 3
Christina Sanford 10
Ron Trumino 33
Robert Newman 67
Mary Converse 77*

Public Schs..Principal	Grd	Prgm	Enr/#Cls	SN	
ⓥ George Junior Republic Sch 24 McDonald Rd, Freeville 13068 Francisco Paler-Large	7-12	MTV	186 33	77%	607/844-6365

• **Groton Central School Dist** PID: 00777409   607/898-5301
400 Peru Rd, Groton 13073   Fax 607/898-4647

Schools: 2 \ **Teachers:** 73 \ **Students:** 852 \ **Special Ed Students:** 136 \ **LEP Students:** 4 \ **College-Bound:** 67% \ **Ethnic:** African American 2%, Hispanic 3%, Caucasian 95% \ **Exp:** $383 (High) \ **Poverty:** 16% \ **Title I:** $250,063 \ **Special Education:** $1,957,000 \ **Open-Close:** 09/04 - 06/24 \ **DTBP:** $402 (High)

Margo Martin 1,11
Jim Sedorus 5
Sophia Darling 67
Nick Darling 3
Billie Downs 6*

Public Schs..Principal	Grd	Prgm	Enr/#Cls	SN	
Groton Elem Sch 516 Elm St, Groton 13073 Kent Maslin	PK-5	T	433 25	39%	607/898-5853 Fax 607/898-5896
Groton Jr Sr High Sch 400 Peru Rd, Groton 13073 Tammy Farrell	6-12	V	419 20	45%	607/898-5803 Fax 607/898-5824

• **Ithaca City School Dist** PID: 00777435   607/274-2101
400 Lake St, Ithaca 14850   Fax 607/274-2271

Schools: 12 \ **Teachers:** 464 \ **Students:** 5,103 \ **Special Ed Students:** 892 \ **LEP Students:** 190 \ **College-Bound:** 82% \ **Ethnic:** Asian 11%, African American 9%, Hispanic 8%, Caucasian 71% \ **Exp:** $255 (Med) \ **Poverty:** 10% \ **Title I:** $803,030 \ **Special Education:** $7,093,000 \ **Open-Close:** 09/04 - 06/25 \ **DTBP:** $217 (High) \ 🇫 🇹

Dr Luvelle Brown 1
Paul Alexander 3,91
Elizabeth Berner 5
Kari Burke 7
Lily Talcott 15*
Dapheny Shululu 20,23
Robert Ainslie 67
Zachary Lind 76,97
Amanda Verba 2,17
Beth Kuse 4
Samantha Little 6*
Laura Evans 8
Mary Grover 18,69*
Sheila McEnery 58
Robert Vankeuren 68

Public Schs..Principal	Grd	Prgm	Enr/#Cls	SN	
Belle Sherman Elem Sch 501 Mitchell St, Ithaca 14850 Daniel Brieman	PK-5	T	363 20	39%	607/274-2206 Fax 607/272-4059 🇹
Beverly J Martin Elem Sch 302 W Buffalo St, Ithaca 14850 Susan Eschbach	PK-5	T	308 19	61%	607/274-2209 Fax 607/274-2196
Boynton Middle Sch 1601 N Cayuga St, Ithaca 14850 Jeffrey Tomasik	6-8		546	35%	607/274-2241 Fax 607/274-2357
Caroline Elem Sch 2439 Slaterville Rd, Slatervle SPG 14881 Kristin Herman	PK-5		307 17	38%	607/539-7155 Fax 607/539-6966
Cayuga Heights Elem Sch 110 E Upland Rd, Ithaca 14850 Brad Pollack	K-5		344 18	37%	607/257-8557 Fax 607/257-8142
DeWitt Middle Sch 560 Warren Rd, Ithaca 14850 Mac Knight	6-8		501 60	37%	607/257-3222 Fax 607/266-3502
Enfield Elem Sch 20 Enfield Main Rd, Ithaca 14850 Keith Harrington	PK-5	T	175 16	57%	607/274-2221 Fax 607/274-6810
Fall Creek Elem Sch 202 King St, Ithaca 14850 Caitlin Bram	PK-5		218 13	32%	607/274-2214 Fax 607/274-2339
Ithaca High Sch 1401 N Cayuga St, Ithaca 14850 Jason Trumble	9-12	AV	1,354	29%	607/274-2143 Fax 607/277-3061 🇹
ⓐ Lehman Alternative Cmty Sch 111 Chestnut St, Ithaca 14850 Deborah Ptak	6-12		284 20	38%	607/274-2183 Fax 607/274-2351
Northeast Elem Sch 425 Winthrop Dr, Ithaca 14850 Elizabeth Coyle	K-5		418 25	32%	607/257-2121 Fax 607/257-8154
South Hill Elem Sch 520 Hudson St, Ithaca 14850 Perry Gorgen	PK-5		385 18	22%	607/274-2129 Fax 607/274-2379

• **Lansing Central School Dist** PID: 00777617   607/533-3020
284 Ridge Rd, Lansing 14882   Fax 607/533-3602

Schools: 3 \ **Teachers:** 112 \ **Students:** 1,187 \ **Special Ed Students:** 165 \ **LEP Students:** 14 \ **College-Bound:** 78% \ **Ethnic:** Asian 4%, African American 1%, Hispanic 3%, Caucasian 91% \ **Exp:** $210 (Med) \ **Poverty:** 6% \ **Title I:** $145,932 \ **Special Education:** $1,342,000 \ **Open-Close:** 09/04 - 06/25 \ **DTBP:** $365 (High)

Chris Pettograsso 1
Glenn Fenner 3
Roger Dedrick 5
Coleen Ledley 8,69,71,74,280,288
Christine Lacobucci 67
Ronald Frost 274*
Kathryn Heath 2
Sandi Swearingen 4
Matt Loveless 6
Colleen Valletta 11,58
Mike Lockwood 73

Public Schs..Principal	Grd	Prgm	Enr/#Cls	SN	
Lansing High Sch 300 Ridge Rd, Lansing 14882 Patrick Hornbrook	9-12	AV	345 60	22%	607/533-3020 Fax 607/533-4612
Lansing Middle Sch 6 Ludlowville Rd, Lansing 14882 Christine Rebera	5-8	AV	392 100	28%	607/533-3020 Fax 607/533-3530
Raymond C Buckley Elem Sch 284 Ridge Rd, Lansing 14882 Lorri Whiteman	K-4	AV	450 25	26%	607/533-4183 Fax 607/533-4684

1	Superintendent	8	Curric/Instruct K-12	19	Chief Financial Officer	29	Family/Consumer Science	
2	Bus/Finance/Purchasing	9	Curric/Instruct Elem	20	Art K-12	30	Adult Education	
3	Buildings And Grounds	10	Curric/Instruct Sec	21	Art Elem	31	Career/Sch-to-Work K-12	
4	Food Service	11	Federal Program	22	Art Sec	32	Career/Sch-to-Work Elem	
5	Transportation	12	Title I	23	Music K-12	33	Career/Sch-to-Work Sec	
6	Athletic	13	Title V	24	Music Elem	34	Early Childhood Ed	
7	Health Services	15	Asst Superintendent	25	Music Sec	35	Health/Phys Education	
		16	Instructional Media Svcs	26	Business Education	36	Guidance Services K-12	
		17	Chief Operations Officer	27	Career & Tech Ed	37	Guidance Services Elem	
		18	Chief Academic Officer	28	Technology Education	38	Guidance Services Sec	

39	Social Studies K-12	49	English/Lang Arts Elem	59	Special Education Elem	69	Academic Assessment
40	Social Studies Elem	50	English/Lang Arts Sec	60	Special Education Sec	70	Research/Development
41	Social Studies Sec	51	Reading K-12	61	Foreign/World Lang K-12	71	Public Information
42	Science K-12	52	Reading Elem	62	Foreign/World Lang Elem	72	Summer School
43	Science Elem	53	Reading Sec	63	Foreign/World Lang Sec	73	Instructional Tech
44	Science Sec	54	Remedial Reading K-12	64	Religious Education K-12	74	Inservice Training
45	Math K-12	55	Remedial Reading Elem	65	Religious Education Elem	75	Marketing/Distributive
46	Math Elem	56	Remedial Reading Sec	66	Religious Education Sec	76	Info Systems
47	Math Sec	57	Bilingual/ELL	67	School Board President	77	Psychological Assess
48	English/Lang Arts K-12	58	Special Education K-12	68	Teacher Personnel	78	Affirmative Action

New York School Directory

Ulster County

• **Newfield Central School Dist** PID: 00777655   607/564-9955
247 Main St, Newfield 14867   Fax 607/564-0055

Schools: 3 \ **Teachers:** 82 \ **Students:** 780 \ **Special Ed Students:** 182 \ **College-Bound:** 84% \ **Ethnic:** African American 6%, Hispanic 4%, Native American: 1%, Caucasian 90% \ **Exp:** $255 (Med) \ **Poverty:** 14% \ **Title I:** $231,090 \ **Special Education:** $1,811,000 \ **Open-Close:** 09/03 - 06/25 \ **DTBP:** $359 (High)

Dr Cheryl Thomas 1	Debra Eichholtz 2
Richard Labbe 2	Steve Yaple 3*
Robin Wood 4*	Chuck Brockner 5
Jeff Augustine 6*	Alison Grunder 7,83*
Tammy Wilcox 7,83*	Mark Jasinski 8
Victoria Volpicelli 11*	Cheryl Jackson 12,58
Jeremy Tenwolde 67	Cathy Griggs 73,74
Kittie Hollander 274*	

Public Schs..Principal	Grd	Prgm	Enr/#Cls	SN		
Newfield Elem Sch 247 Main St, Newfield 14867 Victoria Volpicelli	PK-5	T	387 30	60%	607/564-9955 Fax 607/330-9001	
Newfield Middle Sch 247 Main St, Newfield 14867 Eric Hartz	6-8		176 17	68%	607/564-9955 Fax 607/564-3403	
Newfield Senior High Sch 247 Main St, Newfield 14867 Patrick Mahunik	9-12		217 15	56%	607/564-9955 Fax 607/564-3624	

• **Trumansburg Central SD** PID: 00777681   607/387-7551
100 Whig St, Trumansburg 14886   Fax 607/387-2807

Schools: 3 \ **Teachers:** 105 \ **Students:** 1,043 \ **Special Ed Students:** 216 \ **LEP Students:** 3 \ **College-Bound:** 78% \ **Ethnic:** Asian 1%, African American 2%, Hispanic 5%, Caucasian 92% \ **Exp:** $373 (High) \ **Poverty:** 11% \ **Title I:** $204,540 \ **Special Education:** $2,404,000 \ **Open-Close:** 09/09 - 06/25 \ **DTBP:** $402 (High) \ 🆃

Kimberly Bell 1	Matthew Fotarty 2
Tim Denmake 3,5	Rose Astron 4
Jason Hodge 6*	Angela Gemignami 8,11,57,58,69,298
Joshua Hunkele 16,28,82,295*	Scott Sherwood 67
Pam Rapoza 79	Lisa Collins 274

Public Schs..Principal	Grd	Prgm	Enr/#Cls	SN	
Charles O Dickerson High Sch 100 Whig St, Trumansburg 14886 Jon Koeng	9-12	V	300 60	33%	607/387-7551 Fax 607/387-2843
Russell I Doig Middle Sch 100 Whig St, Trumansburg 14886 Megan Conaway	5-8		314 40	35%	607/387-7551 Fax 607/387-2888
Trumansburg Elem Sch 100 Whig St, Trumansburg 14886 Jeanie Wiggins	PK-4		429 30	39%	607/387-7551 Fax 607/387-2820

TOMPKINS PRIVATE SCHOOLS

Private Schs..Principal	Grd	Prgm	Enr/#Cls	SN	
Cascadilla Sch 116 Summit Ave, Ithaca 14850 Patricia Kendall	9-12	GV	50 8		607/272-3110 Fax 607/272-0747
Covenant Love Community Sch 1768 Dryden Rd, Freeville 13068 Pam Bateman	PK-8		45 8		607/347-4413 Fax 607/347-4466 🅵
E A Clune Mont School-Ithaca 120 King Rd E, Ithaca 14850 Laura Gottfried	PK-8		194 12		607/277-7335 Fax 607/277-0251 🅵
Franziska Racker Center 3226 Wilkins Rd, Ithaca 14850 Gretchen Jacobs	Spec		100 5		607/272-5891 Fax 607/272-0188
Ithaca Waldorf Sch 20 Nelson Rd, Ithaca 14850 Dr Emily Butler	PK-8		75		607/256-2020 Fax 607/273-5182

TOMPKINS REGIONAL CENTERS

• **Tompkins-Seneca-Tioga BOCES** PID: 00777722   607/257-1551
555 Warren Rd, Ithaca 14850   Fax 607/697-8273

Dr Jeffrey Matteson 1	Tina Hollenbeck 2
David Pitcher 3,5,7,91	Dr Barry Derfel 8,15,16
David Parsons 15	Mary Kay Welgoss 16
Cindy Walter 27,31	Dr Nicole Eschler 30,72
David Barr 58,88	Kathy Zahler 67
Donna Donahue 68	Dan Parker 73
Beth Dryer 74	

ULSTER COUNTY

ULSTER COUNTY SCHOOLS

County Schs..Principal	Grd	Prgm	Enr/#Cls	SN	
Ⓐ Ulster BOCES Phoenix Acad 1372 Old Post Rd, Ulster Park 12487 Peter Harris	7-12		401		845/339-8722
Ulster BOCES Special Educ Ctr 319 Broadway, Port Ewen 12466 Dr Carleen Meers	Spec		140		845/339-8707
Ulster Career & Tech Center Route 9W, Port Ewen 12466 Dean Lucera	Voc	AG	1,000 25		845/331-6680 Fax 845/331-4655

ULSTER PUBLIC SCHOOLS

• **Ellenville Central School Dist** PID: 00777760   845/647-0200
28 Maple Ave, Ellenville 12428   Fax 845/647-0105

Schools: 3 \ **Teachers:** 129 \ **Students:** 1,500 \ **Special Ed Students:** 357 \ **LEP Students:** 88 \ **Ethnic:** Asian 2%, African American 12%, Hispanic 37%, Native American: 1%, Caucasian 48% \ **Exp:** $274 (Med) \ **Poverty:** 21% \ **Title I:** $587,117 \ **Special Education:** $3,449,000 \ **Open-Close:** 09/07 - 06/22

Lisa Wiles 1,11,73	Sue Schwall 2
Vince Napoli 2,15	Kelly White 8,12,288
Dr James Fogarty 58	Philip Mattracion 67
Edwin Aponte 76,286	

---

79 Student Personnel 80 Driver Ed/Safety 81 Gifted/Talented 82 Video Services 83 Substance Abuse Prev 84 Erate 85 AIDS Education 88 Alternative/At Risk 89 Multi-Cultural Curriculum 90 Social Work	91 Safety/Security 92 Magnet School 93 Parental Involvement 95 Tech Prep Program 97 Chief Infomation Officer 98 Chief Technology Officer 270 Character Education 271 Migrant Education 273 Teacher Mentor 274 Before/After Sch	275 Response To Intervention 277 Remedial Math K-12 280 Literacy Coach 285 STEM 286 Digital Learning 288 Common Core Standards 294 Accountability 295 Network System 296 Title II Programs 297 Webmaster	298 Grant Writer/Ptnrships 750 Chief Innovation Officer 751 Chief of Staff 752 Social Emotional Learning **Other School Types** Ⓐ = Alternative School Ⓒ = Charter School Ⓜ = Magnet School Ⓨ = Year-Round School	**School Programs** A = Alternative Program G = Adult Classes M = Magnet Program T = Title I Schoolwide V = Career & Tech Ed Programs New Schools are shaded New Superintendents and Principals are bold Personnel with email addresses are underscored

Social Media
🅵 = Facebook
🆃 = Twitter

NY–241

Ulster County

Public Schs..Principal	Grd	Prgm	Enr/#Cls	SN	
Ellenville Elem Sch 28 Maple Ave, Ellenville 12428 Nicole Ey	PK-5	T	677 36	65%	845/647-0131 Fax 845/647-7090
Ellenville High Sch 28 Maple Ave, Ellenville 12428 Carl Pabon	9-12	AGTV	478 40	63%	845/647-0123 Fax 845/647-5972
Ellenville Middle Sch 28 Maple Ave, Ellenville 12428 Andre Spinelli	6-8	T	408 30	71%	845/647-0126 Fax 845/647-0230

- **Highland Ctl School Dist** PID: 00777796 845/691-1000
  320 Pancake Hollow Rd, Highland 12528 Fax 845/691-1039

Schools: 3 \ Teachers: 137 \ Students: 1,667 \ Special Ed Students: 284 \ LEP Students: 20 \ Ethnic: Asian 4%, African American 7%, Hispanic 16%, Caucasian 73% \ Exp: $277 (Med) \ Poverty: 11% \ Title I: $315,276 \ Special Education: $3,374,000 \ Open-Close: 09/08 - 06/24 \ DTBP: $171 (High) \

Tom Bongiovi 1
Peter Miller 3
Cathy Mekulik 5
Joel Freer 9*
Sarah Dudley-Lemek 15*
Christian Candia 37*
Nancy Jensen 38*
Lissa Jilek 2
Maria McCarthy 4*
Frank Alfonso 6,35,85
Patrick Boyd 11,34,57,58,79,88,271
Carol Potash 30,73,295
Carly Jacobsen 38
Alan Barone 67

Public Schs..Principal	Grd	Prgm	Enr/#Cls	SN	
Highland Elem Sch 16 Lockhart Ln, Highland 12528 Joel Freer	K-5	T	735 37	37%	845/691-1070 Fax 845/691-1073
Highland High Sch 320 Pancake Hollow Rd, Highland 12528 William Zimmer	9-12	V	518 50	37%	845/691-1020 Fax 845/691-1038
Highland Middle Sch 71 Main St, Highland 12528 Dan Seyler-Wetzel	6-8		414	39%	845/691-1080 Fax 845/691-1083

- **Kingston City School Dist** PID: 00777837 845/339-3000
  21 Wynkoop Pl, Kingston 12401 Fax 845/339-9279

Schools: 10 \ Teachers: 537 \ Students: 6,800 \ Special Ed Students: 1,653 \ LEP Students: 445 \ College-Bound: 78% \ Ethnic: Asian 3%, African American 14%, Hispanic 25%, Caucasian 58% \ Exp: $198 (Low) \ Poverty: 17% \ Title I: $2,097,402 \ Special Education: $19,699,000 \ Open-Close: 09/04 - 06/24

Dr Paul Padalino 1
Thomas Clapper 3
Judy Falcon 5
John Voerg 8,11,15,36,58,79,90,298
Mary Beth Bonville 10
James Shaughnessy 67
Leshawn Parker 91*
Allen Olson 2,15
Ed Carelli 4
Rick Silverstein 6,35*
Dr Stacia Felicello 9
Beth Lewis-Jackson 58
Gary Tomczk 71,73,76,97

Public Schs..Principal	Grd	Prgm	Enr/#Cls	SN	
Chambers Elem Sch 945 Morton Blvd, Kingston 12401 Katherine Petrie	K-4	T	365 19	58%	845/336-5995 Fax 845/336-5616
Edson Elem Sch 116 Merilina Ave, Kingston 12401 Brian Martin	K-4		412 20	57%	845/338-6990 Fax 845/331-9034
Edward R Crosby Elem Sch 767 Neighborhood Rd, Lake Katrine 12449 Kathleen Sickles	K-4		313 21	55%	845/382-2633 Fax 845/382-2668
Ernest C Myer Elem Sch 121 Schoolhouse Rd, Hurley 12443 Erin Nelson	K-4		224 20	36%	845/331-6905 Fax 845/331-1520
George Washington Elem Sch 67 Wall St, Kingston 12401 Wanda Lobianco	PK-4	T	507 20	65%	845/338-1978 Fax 845/338-3041
J Watson Bailey Middle Sch 118 Merilina Ave, Kingston 12401 Debra Fitzgerald	5-8		1,101 60	59%	845/943-3940 Fax 845/338-6312
John F Kennedy Elem Sch 107 Gross St, Kingston 12401 Melissa Jamieson	K-4	T	349 14	75%	845/943-3100 Fax 845/943-2477
Kingston Senior High Sch 403 Broadway, Kingston 12401 Vincent Decicco	9-12	AGV	1,947 110	53%	845/331-1970 Fax 845/331-1628
M Clifford Miller Mid Sch 65 Fording Place Rd, Lake Katrine 12449 Andrew Sheber	5-8	T	875	70%	845/943-3941 Fax 845/382-6069
Robert Graves Elem Sch 345 Mountain View Ave, Port Ewen 12466 Dr Erinn Parese	K-4		361	44%	845/943-3915 Fax 845/338-3049

- **Marlboro Central School Dist** PID: 00778037 845/236-5802
  21 Milton Tpke Ste 100, Milton 12547 Fax 845/795-5904

Schools: 3 \ Teachers: 153 \ Students: 1,893 \ Special Ed Students: 382 \ LEP Students: 60 \ College-Bound: 65% \ Ethnic: Asian 2%, African American 8%, Hispanic 23%, Caucasian 67% \ Exp: $260 (Med) \ Poverty: 8% \ Title I: $239,955 \ Special Education: $814,000 \ Open-Close: 09/08 - 06/25 \ DTBP: $162 (High)

Michael Brooks 1
Larry Cavazza 3
Johnnah O'Donnell 6*
Michael Bakatsias 15,16,68,73,76,79,295
Megan Febbie 58
Kathleen Harden 83*
Rosanne Mele 2,5,11,15,91,296
Frederick Callo 4
Robin Hecht 8,15,69,285,286,288,298
Marcy Scaturro 38*
Frank Milazzo 67

Public Schs..Principal	Grd	Prgm	Enr/#Cls	SN	
Marlboro Elem Sch 1380 Route 9W, Marlboro 12542 Patricia Walsh	K-5	T	839	41%	845/236-1636 Fax 845/236-1639
Marlboro High Sch 50 Cross Rd, Marlboro 12542 Ryan Lawler	9-12	AGV	589 51	35%	845/236-8000 Fax 845/236-2638
Marlboro Middle Sch 1375 Route 9W, Marlboro 12542 Debra Clinton	6-8		465 35	39%	845/236-5840 Fax 845/236-3634

- **New Paltz Ctl School Dist** PID: 00778099 845/256-4020
  196 Main St, New Paltz 12561 Fax 845/256-4025

Schools: 4 \ Teachers: 181 \ Students: 2,035 \ Special Ed Students: 394 \ LEP Students: 48 \ Ethnic: Asian 3%, African American 4%, Hispanic 13%, Caucasian 79% \ Exp: $220 (Med) \ Poverty: 7% \ Title I: $242,876 \ Special Education: $3,096,000 \ Open-Close: 09/02 - 06/25 \ DTBP: $181 (High)

Angela Urbina Medina 1
Guy Gardner 3
Maureen Ryan 5
Michele Martoni 8,11,15,288,296
Kathleen Coughlin 60
Keith Baisley 73
Debra Kosinski 2
Michael Robinson 4*
Gregory Warren 6,35
Kathleen Clark 59
Glenn Lapolt 67

1	Superintendent	8	Curric/Instruct K-12	19	Chief Financial Officer	29	Family/Consumer Science	39	Social Studies K-12	49	English/Lang Arts Elem	59	Special Education Elem	69	Academic Assessment
2	Bus/Finance/Purchasing	9	Curric/Instruct Elem	20	Art K-12	30	Adult Education	40	Social Studies Elem	50	English/Lang Arts Sec	60	Special Education Sec	70	Research/Development
3	Buildings And Grounds	10	Curric/Instruct Sec	21	Art Elem	31	Career/Sch-to-Work K-12	41	Social Studies Sec	51	Reading K-12	61	Foreign/World Lang K-12	71	Public Information
4	Food Service	11	Federal Program	22	Art Sec	32	Career/Sch-to-Work Elem	42	Science K-12	52	Reading Elem	62	Foreign/World Lang Elem	72	Summer School
5	Transportation	12	Title I	23	Music K-12	33	Career/Sch-to-Work Sec	43	Science Elem	53	Reading Sec	63	Foreign/World Lang Sec	73	Instructional Tech
6	Athletic	13	Title V	24	Music Elem	34	Early Childhood Ed	44	Science Sec	54	Remedial Reading K-12	64	Religious Education K-12	74	Inservice Training
7	Health Services	15	Asst Superintendent	25	Music Sec	35	Health/Phys Education	45	Math K-12	55	Remedial Reading Elem	65	Religious Education Elem	75	Marketing/Distributive
		16	Instructional Media Svcs	26	Business Education	36	Guidance Services K-12	46	Math Elem	56	Remedial Reading Sec	66	Religious Education Sec	76	Info Systems
		17	Chief Operations Officer	27	Career & Tech Ed	37	Guidance Services Elem	47	Math Sec	57	Bilingual/ELL	67	School Board President	77	Psychological Assess
		18	Chief Academic Officer	28	Technology Education	38	Guidance Services Sec	48	English/Lang Arts K-12	58	Special Education K-12	68	Teacher Personnel	78	Affirmative Action

New York School Directory — Ulster County

Public Schs..Principal	Grd	Prgm	Enr/#Cls	SN	
Duzine Elem Sch 31 Sunset Ridge, New Paltz 12561 Ross Hogan	K-2	T	365 24	26%	845/256-4350 Fax 845/256-4359
Lenape Elem Sch 1 Eugene L Brown Dr, New Paltz 12561 Sean Inglee	3-5	T	426 25	24%	845/256-4300 Fax 845/256-4309
New Paltz High Sch 130 S Putt Corners Rd, New Paltz 12561 Mario Fernandez	9-12	AV	751 35	24%	845/256-4100 Fax 845/256-4109
New Paltz Middle Sch 196 Main St, New Paltz 12561 Ann Sheldon	6-8	T	493 22	26%	845/256-4200 Fax 845/256-4209 t

● **Onteora Central School Dist** PID: 00778142 — 845/657-6383
4166 State Route 28, Boiceville 12412 — Fax 845/657-8742

Schools: 4 \ Teachers: 129 \ Students: 1,200 \ Special Ed Students: 281 \ LEP Students: 42 \ College-Bound: 82% \ Ethnic: Asian 2%, African American 2%, Hispanic 13%, Caucasian 83% \ Exp: $750 (High) \ Poverty: 23% \ Title I: $699,201 \ Special Education: $2,650,000 \ Open-Close: 09/08 - 06/25 \ DTBP: $445 (High) \ f

Victoria McLaren 1
Monica LaClair 2,15
Christine Downs 4
Kimberly Pilla 6*
Cindy Bishop 12,57,58,79,83,88,275,296
Laurie Osmond 67
Debra D'Aprile 2
Kyle Harjes 3,91
Nicole Sommer 5
Dr Jodi DeLucia 8,11,15,54,69,277,288,298
Sarah Turck 27,38*
John Reimer 73

Public Schs..Principal	Grd	Prgm	Enr/#Cls	SN	
Bennett Elem Sch 4166 State Route 28, Boiceville 12412 Gabriel Buono	4-6	T	255 22	46%	845/657-2354 Fax 845/657-8504
Onteora Middle Senior High Sch 4166 State Route 28, Boiceville 12412 Jennifer O'Connor \ Lance Edelman	7-12	T	639 70	43%	845/657-2373 Fax 845/657-8430
Phoenicia Elem Sch School Lane, Phoenicia 12464 Linda Sella	K-3	T	140 14	61%	845/688-5580 Fax 845/688-2324
Woodstock Elem Sch 8 W Hurley Rd, Woodstock 12498 Scott Richards	K-3	T	168 14	42%	845/679-2316 Fax 845/679-1207

● **Rondout Valley Ctl Sch Dist** PID: 00778207 — 845/687-2400
122 Kyserike Rd, Accord 12404 — Fax 845/687-9577

Schools: 5 \ Teachers: 184 \ Students: 1,975 \ Special Ed Students: 406 \ LEP Students: 15 \ Ethnic: Asian 2%, African American 4%, Hispanic 8%, Native American: 1%, Caucasian 86% \ Exp: $263 (Med) \ Poverty: 14% \ Title I: $503,994 \ Special Education: $3,809,000 \ Open-Close: 09/08 - 06/24 \ DTBP: $367 (High) \ f t

Dr Joseph Morgan 1
Michael Shore 3,91
Dr Hans Sebeald 6
Megan Braren 58,79
Cynthia Farrell 73
Debra Rosinski 2
Chris Vandamm 4*
Lisa Pacht 8,11,15,69,288
Dawn Vankleeck 67

Public Schs..Principal	Grd	Prgm	Enr/#Cls	SN	
Kerhonkson Elem Sch 30 Academy St, Kerhonkson 12446 Jacqueline Van Nosdall	PK-3	T	258 18	61%	845/626-2451 Fax 845/626-5767 f t
Marbletown Elem Sch 12 Pine Bush Rd, Stone Ridge 12484 Andrew Davenport	PK-3	T	301 16	41%	845/687-0284 Fax 845/687-7691 f
Rondout Valley High Sch 122 Kyserike Rd, Accord 12404 Jessica Torok	9-12	ATV	648 50	45%	845/687-2400 Fax 845/687-4840 f t
Rondout Valley Interm Sch 122 Kyserike Rd, Accord 12404 Lee Cutler	4-6	T	429	53%	845/687-2400 Fax 845/687-8980
Rondout Valley Jr High Sch 122 Kyserike Rd, Accord 12404 Charles Tadduni	7-8	T	277	45%	845/687-2400 Fax 845/687-4937 f t

● **Saugerties Central School Dist** PID: 00778295 — 845/246-1043
310 Washington Avenue Ext, Saugerties 12477 — Fax 845/246-8364

Schools: 6 \ Teachers: 200 \ Students: 2,500 \ Special Ed Students: 583 \ LEP Students: 44 \ College-Bound: 76% \ Ethnic: Asian 2%, African American 2%, Hispanic 14%, Caucasian 82% \ Exp: $286 (Med) \ Poverty: 12% \ Title I: $500,360 \ Special Education: $5,418,000 \ Open-Close: 09/08 - 06/24 \ DTBP: $323 (High)

Kirk Reinhardt 1,83
Sheila Melville 4
Darlene Westinghousa 8,69
Eileen Madden 36*
Robert Thomman 67
Carol Petramale 3,5
Dominic Zarrella 6*
Tom Averill 27,88,89*
Kristina Paez 38*
Gina Kinery 90

Public Schs..Principal	Grd	Prgm	Enr/#Cls	SN	
Cahill Elem Sch 134 Main St, Saugerties 12477 Dawn Scannapieco	K-6	T	273 22	54%	845/247-6800 Fax 845/246-4302
Grant E Morse Elem Sch 70 Harry Wells Rd, Saugerties 12477 Donald Dieckmann	K-6	T	321 30	38%	845/247-6960 Fax 845/246-4184
Mt Marion Elem Sch 744 Glasco Tpke, Saugerties 12477 Carole Kelder	K-6	T	310 26	54%	845/247-6920 Fax 845/246-4103
Riccardi Elem Sch 70 Plenty St, Glasco 12432 Susan Osterhoudt	K-6	T	344 23	33%	845/247-6500 Fax 845/246-2582
Saugerties Junior High Sch 310 Washington Avenue Ext, Saugerties 12477 Tom Averill	7-8	T	403 50	47%	845/247-6561 Fax 845/246-4322
Saugerties Senior High Sch 310 Washington Avenue Ext, Saugerties 12477 Tom Averill	9-12	ATV	798 45	42%	845/247-6650 Fax 845/246-4312

● **Wallkill Central School Dist** PID: 00778362 — 845/895-7100
19 Main St, Wallkill 12589 — Fax 845/895-3630

Schools: 5 \ Teachers: 239 \ Students: 2,831 \ Special Ed Students: 445 \ LEP Students: 49 \ College-Bound: 78% \ Ethnic: Asian 1%, African American 7%, Hispanic 24%, Caucasian 68% \ Exp: $330 (High) \ Poverty: 11% \ Title I: $520,811 \ Special Education: $6,809,000 \ Open-Close: 09/08 - 06/24 \ DTBP: $313 (High)

Kevin Castle 1
Amy Bishopp 4
Brian Masopust 6
Nichole Parete 11
Yvonne Herrington 15
Anthony White 34,57,58,69,88,270
Tom Thomas 73,295
Elizabeth Werlau 81*
Brian Devincenzi 2,15,71,79,97
Devin Venzi 5
Ursula Petricek 7
Gary Callahan 12
Kirsten Rolon 23
Joseph Locicero 67
Alex Danon 76
Sandi Hecht 83

---

79 Student Personnel	91 Safety/Security	275 Response To Intervention	298 Grant Writer/Ptnrships	**School Programs**	**Social Media**		
80 Driver Ed/Safety	92 Magnet School	277 Remedial Math K-12	750 Chief Innovation Officer	A = Alternative Program	f = Facebook		
81 Gifted/Talented	93 Parental Involvement	280 Literacy Coach	751 Chief of Staff	G = Adult Classes			
82 Video Services	95 Tech Prep Program	285 STEM	752 Social Emotional Learning	M = Magnet Program	t = Twitter		
83 Substance Abuse Prev	97 Chief Infomation Officer	286 Digital Learning		T = Title I Schoolwide			
84 Erate	98 Chief Technology Officer	288 Common Core Standards	**Other School Types**	V = Career & Tech Ed Programs			
85 AIDS Education	270 Character Education	294 Accountability	Ⓐ = Alternative School				
88 Alternative/At Risk	271 Migrant Education	295 Network System	Ⓒ = Charter School	New Schools are shaded			
89 Multi-Cultural Curriculum	273 Teacher Mentor	296 Title II Programs	Ⓜ = Magnet School	New Superintendents and Principals are bold			
90 Social Work	274 Before/After Sch	297 Webmaster	Ⓨ = Year-Round School	Personnel with email addresses are underscored			

Warren County

Market Data Retrieval

Public Schs..Principal	Grd	Prgm	Enr/#Cls	SN	
John G Borden Middle Sch 109 Bona Ventura Ave, Wallkill 12589 Marjorie Anderson	7-8		478 30	34%	845/895-7175 Fax 845/895-8036
Leptondale Elem Sch 48 Mill St, Wallkill 12589 Scott Brown	K-6		471 26	26%	845/895-7200 Fax 845/564-8098
Ostrander Elem Sch 137 Viola St, Wallkill 12589 Natalie Harjes	K-6		470 36	30%	845/895-7225 Fax 845/895-8043
Plattekill Elem Sch 1270 Route 32, Plattekill 12568 Monica Hasbrouck	K-6	T	427 40	50%	845/895-7250 Fax 845/564-5103
Wallkill Senior High Sch 90 Robinson St, Wallkill 12589 Joseph Salamone	9-12	A	985 40	34%	845/895-7150 Fax 845/895-8003

ULSTER CATHOLIC SCHOOLS

- **Archdiocese of New York Ed Off** PID: 00754976
  Listing includes only schools located in this county. See District Index for location of Diocesan Offices.

Catholic Schs..Principal	Grd	Prgm	Enr/#Cls	SN	
Kingston Catholic Sch 159 Broadway, Kingston 12401 Jill Albert	PK-8		160 15		845/339-4390 Fax 845/339-7994

ULSTER PRIVATE SCHOOLS

Private Schs..Principal	Grd	Prgm	Enr/#Cls	SN	
Center for Septrum Services 70 Kukuk Ln, Kingston 12401 Jamey Wolff	Spec		146		845/336-2616 Fax 845/336-4153
Community Rehab Center 250 Tuytenbridge Rd, Lake Katrine 12449 Ashley Quesnell	Spec	G	84 10		845/336-7235 Fax 845/336-5919
Good Shepherd Christian Sch 83 E Chester St, Kingston 12401 Heather Flagsvol	PK-8		50 7		845/339-4488 Fax 845/331-5206
Grove Street Academy 26 Grove St, Kingston 12401 Christina Fabbie	Spec	V	35 12		845/331-1448 Fax 845/340-0502
High Meadow Sch 3643 Main St, Stone Ridge 12484 Susan Paynter	PK-8		140 8		845/687-4855 Fax 845/687-5151
Hudson Valley Sudbury Sch 84 Zena Rd, Kingston 12401 Matthew Gioia	PK-12		77		845/679-1002 Fax 845/679-3874
John A Coleman Catholic HS 430 Hurley Ave, Hurley 12443 Ellen Anderson	9-12		200 18		845/338-2750 Fax 845/338-0250
Mount Academy 1001 Broadway, Esopus 12429 Paul Button	9-12		200		845/384-8080 Fax 845/384-8081
Mountain Laurel Waldorf Sch 16 S Chestnut St, New Paltz 12561 Judith Jaeckel	PK-8		155		845/255-0033 Fax 845/255-0597
NYSARC-Brookside Sch 11 Tan House Brook Rd, Cottekill 12419 Marcene Johnson	Spec		160 10		845/687-7250 Fax 845/687-0902

Wawarsing Christian Academy 7227 Route 209, Wawarsing 12489 Ron Mahany	PK-12		55 10		845/647-3810 Fax 845/210-7100
Woodstock Day Sch 1430 Glasco Tpke, Saugerties 12477 Kara Stern	PK-12		200 18		845/246-3744 Fax 845/246-0053

ULSTER REGIONAL CENTERS

- **Ulster BOCES** PID: 00778427 845/255-1400
  175 State Route 32 N, New Paltz 12561 Fax 845/255-1287

Dr Charles Khoury 1	Allison Dodd 2,15,68
Lori Wightman 2	Victor DeStefano 3
Maria McCarthy 4	Gwendolyn Roraback 8,69,70,73,74
Jonah Schenker 15,69,70,73,74	Amy Storenski 27
Mary Jalloh 30	Gail Hutchins 67
Evelyn LaFontaine 68	Holly Brooker 71
Eugene Knudsen 73,76	Janice Ianelli 298

WARREN COUNTY

WARREN COUNTY SCHOOLS

County Schs..Principal	Grd	Prgm	Enr/#Cls	SN	
Sanford St Teaching & Lrng Ctr 10 Sanford St, Glens Falls 12801 Julie Franklin	Spec		42		518/761-6964 Fax 518/761-0804

WARREN PUBLIC SCHOOLS

- **Bolton Central School Dist** PID: 00778465 518/644-2400
  26 Horicon Ave, Bolton Lndg 12814 Fax 518/644-2124

> **Schools:** 1 \ **Teachers:** 30 \ **Students:** 200 \ **Special Ed Students:** 19 \ **College-Bound:** 80% \ **Ethnic:** Asian 2%, African American 6%, Hispanic 3%, Caucasian 90% \ **Exp:** $962 (High) \ **Poverty:** 4% \ **Title I:** $9,299 \ **Special Education:** $138,000 \ **Open-Close:** 09/10 - 06/25 \ **DTBP:** $397 (High)

Michael Graney 1	Kathleen Dennin 2,19
Charles Morel 3*	Margaret Maranville 4*
Patrick Ross 5	Margaret Lawrence 6,83,85*
Chad Shippee 8,19*	Denise Jorgensen 16*
Molly Gordan 18,19,58	Denise Clark 36*
Nicole Willams 44*	Leona Denne 57*
Francisco Roca 63*	Kathleen Pfau 67
Jennifer Carlson 73*	

Public Schs..Principal	Grd	Prgm	Enr/#Cls	SN	
Bolton Central Sch 26 Horicon Ave, Bolton Lndg 12814 Chad Shippee	PK-12		200 30	30%	518/644-2400 Fax 518/644-5125

1 Superintendent	8 Curric/Instruct K-12	19 Chief Financial Officer	29 Family/Consumer Science	39 Social Studies K-12	49 English/Lang Arts Elem	59 Special Education Elem	69 Academic Assessment
2 Bus/Finance/Purchasing	9 Curric/Instruct Elem	20 Art K-12	30 Adult Education	40 Social Studies Elem	50 English/Lang Arts Sec	60 Special Education Sec	70 Research/Development
3 Buildings And Grounds	10 Curric/Instruct Sec	21 Art Elem	31 Career/Sch-to-Work K-12	41 Social Studies Sec	51 Reading K-12	61 Foreign/World Lang K-12	71 Public Information
4 Food Service	11 Federal Program	22 Art Sec	32 Career/Sch-to-Work Elem	42 Science K-12	52 Reading Elem	62 Foreign/World Lang Elem	72 Summer School
5 Transportation	12 Title I	23 Music K-12	33 Career/Sch-to-Work Sec	43 Science Elem	53 Reading Sec	63 Foreign/World Lang Sec	73 Instructional Tech
6 Athletic	13 Title V	24 Music Elem	34 Early Childhood Ed	44 Science Sec	54 Remedial Reading K-12	64 Religious Education K-12	74 Inservice Training
7 Health Services	15 Asst Superintendent	25 Music Sec	35 Health/Phys Education	45 Math K-12	55 Remedial Reading Elem	65 Religious Education Elem	75 Marketing/Distributive
	16 Instructional Media Svcs	26 Business Education	36 Guidance Services K-12	46 Math Elem	56 Remedial Reading Sec	66 Religious Education Sec	76 Info Systems
	17 Chief Operations Officer	27 Career & Tech Ed	37 Guidance Services Elem	47 Math Sec	57 Bilingual/ELL	67 School Board President	77 Psychological Assess
	18 Chief Academic Officer	28 Technology Education	38 Guidance Services Sec	48 English/Lang Arts K-12	58 Special Education K-12	68 Teacher Personnel	78 Affirmative Action

New York School Directory — Warren County

- **Glens Falls City School Dist** PID: 00778520   518/792-1212
  15 Quade St, Glens Falls 12801   Fax 518/792-1538

Schools: 5 \ **Teachers:** 161 \ **Students:** 2,058 \ **Special Ed Students:** 410 \ **LEP Students:** 3 \ **College-Bound:** 79% \ **Ethnic:** Asian 1%, African American 2%, Hispanic 5%, Caucasian 91% \ **Exp:** $319 (High) \ **Poverty:** 15% \ **Title I:** $462,268 \ **Special Education:** $4,206,000 \ **Open-Close:** 09/07 - 06/22 \ **DTBP:** $214 (High)

Paul Jenkins 1	Robert Yusko 2,78,91
Kenneth Chester 3,5	Larry Young 4*
Arthur Corlew 6,35,83*	Kathleen Callaghan 7*
Trent Clay 8,11,57,69,273,288,296,298	Michele Hogan 16,82*
Allison Wolfstich 31*	John Woodell-Freire 36*
Rebecca Van Der Klish 58,88*	Timothy Graham 67
Skye Heritage 71	Paul Streicher 73,286
Michelle Aleva 77*	

Public Schs..Principal	Grd	Prgm	Enr/#Cls	SN	
Big Cross Elem Sch 15 Big Cross St, Glens Falls 12801 Deborah Hall	K-4	T	260 15		518/792-2619 Fax 518/792-2668
Glens Falls High Sch 10 Quade St, Glens Falls 12801 Tammy Silvernell	9-12	V	639 45		518/792-6564 Fax 518/792-1442
Glens Falls Middle Sch 20 Quade St, Glens Falls 12801 Kristy Moore	5-8	TV	609		518/793-3418 Fax 518/793-4888
Jackson Heights Elem Sch 24 Jackson Ave, Glens Falls 12801 Carrie Mauro	PK-4	T	271 12		518/793-1071 Fax 518/798-6501
Kensington Road Elem Sch 43 Kensington Rd, Glens Falls 12801 Jennifer Hayes	K-4		279 12		518/793-5151 Fax 518/793-5404

- **Glens Falls Common Sch Dist** PID: 00778441   518/792-3231
  120 Lawrence St, Glens Falls 12801   Fax 518/792-2557

Schools: 1 \ **Teachers:** 16 \ **Students:** 155 \ **Special Ed Students:** 43 \ **Ethnic:** Asian 1%, African American 3%, Hispanic 8%, Native American: 1%, Caucasian 88% \ **Exp:** $164 (Low) \ **Poverty:** 22% \ **Title I:** $167,983 \ **Special Education:** $535,000 \ **Open-Close:** 09/08 - 06/25 \ **DTBP:** $223 (High)

Brian George 1,11,83,288	Judy Hemingway 2,73
Jeanne Kozloski 59*	Peter Accardi 67
Michelle Villanueva 88	

Public Schs..Principal	Grd	Prgm	Enr/#Cls	SN	
Abraham Wing Elem Sch 120 Lawrence St, Glens Falls 12801 John Godfrey	K-6	T	155 23	74%	518/792-3231

- **Hadley-Luzerne Ctl Sch Dist** PID: 00778609   518/696-2378
  2700 Hyland Dr C, Lake Luzerne 12846   Fax 518/696-5884

Schools: 2 \ **Teachers:** 71 \ **Students:** 665 \ **Special Ed Students:** 124 \ **LEP Students:** 3 \ **College-Bound:** 71% \ **Ethnic:** Asian 1%, Hispanic 3%, Caucasian 96% \ **Exp:** $276 (Med) \ **Poverty:** 13% \ **Title I:** $178,817 \ **Special Education:** $1,796,000 \ **Open-Close:** 09/04 - 06/25

Beecher Baker 1	Michelle Taylor 2
Brian Gereau 3	Jaclyn Adler 4
Rick McFarlane 5	Gary Wilson 6*
Jennifer Sheerer 57	Robert Mark 58*
Eddie Moulton 67	Lenny Locke 73,76

Scot Carpenter 98

Public Schs..Principal	Grd	Prgm	Enr/#Cls	SN	
Hadley-Luzerne Jr Sr High Sch 273 Lake Ave, Lake Luzerne 12846 Burgess Ovitt	7-12	AGTV	315 23	49%	518/696-2112 Fax 518/696-2356
Stuart M Townsend Elem Sch 27 Hyland Dr, Lake Luzerne 12846 Jon Baker	PK-6	AT	350 15	54%	518/696-2378 Fax 518/696-2485

- **Johnsburg Central School Dist** PID: 00778661   518/251-2921
  165 Main St, North Creek 12853   Fax 518/251-2562

Schools: 1 \ **Teachers:** 35 \ **Students:** 333 \ **Special Ed Students:** 50 \ **College-Bound:** 60% \ **Ethnic:** African American 2%, Hispanic 1%, Caucasian 97% \ **Exp:** $328 (High) \ **Poverty:** 13% \ **Title I:** $118,544 \ **Special Education:** $534,000 \ **Open-Close:** 09/08 - 06/25 \ **DTBP:** $355 (High)

Michael Markwica 1	Lawrence Ringer 2*
Frank Morehouse 3	Karen Moore 4*
Fred Morse 5	Ryan Carpenter 6
Heather Flanagan . 7,8,69,73,83,270,271,273*	Patty Ordway 11,296,298*
Eric Gelber 16*	Jane Kokoletsos 30,36*
Amanda Durkee 57,58*	Rachel Degroat 67
David Pede 285	

Public Schs..Principal	Grd	Prgm	Enr/#Cls	SN	
Johnsburg Central Sch 165 Main St, North Creek 12853 Heather Olesheski	PK-12	AGTV	333 50	42%	518/251-2921

- **Lake George Central Sch Dist** PID: 00778685   518/668-5456
  381 Canada St, Lake George 12845   Fax 518/668-2285

Schools: 2 \ **Teachers:** 91 \ **Students:** 721 \ **Special Ed Students:** 93 \ **LEP Students:** 4 \ **College-Bound:** 85% \ **Ethnic:** Asian 3%, African American 1%, Hispanic 2%, Caucasian 93% \ **Exp:** $384 (High) \ **Poverty:** 8% \ **Title I:** $161,401 \ **Special Education:** $914,000 \ **Open-Close:** 09/08 - 06/25 \ **DTBP:** $359 (High)

Lynne Rutnik 1	Kate DuBois 2
Richard Clothier 3	Jeffrey DeStefanis 4
Andy Raymond 5	Kyle Manny 6*
Bonnie Hart 8*	Sarah Olson 16*
Rosemarie Sandora-Earl 27,83,88*	Karen Breslin 31*
Bernadette Bechard 57,58	Tricia Biles 67
Megan Coker 73	Matthew Hull 76
Andrea Daley 280*	

Public Schs..Principal	Grd	Prgm	Enr/#Cls	SN	
Lake George Elem Sch 69 Sun Valley Dr, Lake George 12845 James Conway	K-6		310 35	25%	518/668-5714 Fax 518/668-5876
Lake George Jr Sr High Sch 381 Canada St, Lake George 12845 Francis Cocozza	7-12	A	411 35	23%	518/668-5452

79	Student Personnel	91	Safety/Security	275	Response To Intervention	298	Grant Writer/Ptnrships	**School Programs**	**Social Media**
80	Driver Ed/Safety	92	Magnet School	277	Remedial Math K-12	750	Chief Innovation Officer	A = Alternative Program	
81	Gifted/Talented	93	Parental Involvement	280	Literacy Coach	751	Chief of Staff	G = Adult Classes	= Facebook
82	Video Services	95	Tech Prep Program	285	STEM	752	Social Emotional Learning	M = Magnet Program	
83	Substance Abuse Prev	97	Chief Infomation Officer	286	Digital Learning			T = Title I Schoolwide	= Twitter
84	Erate	98	Chief Technology Officer	288	Common Core Standards	**Other School Types**		V = Career & Tech Ed Programs	
85	AIDS Education	270	Accountability	294	Character Education	Ⓐ = Alternative School			
88	Alternative/At Risk	271	Migrant Education	295	Network System	Ⓒ = Charter School		New Schools are shaded	
89	Multi-Cultural Curriculum	273	Teacher Mentor	296	Title II Programs	Ⓜ = Magnet School		New Superintendents and Principals are bold	
90	Social Work	274	Before/After Sch	297	Webmaster	Ⓨ = Year-Round School		Personnel with email addresses are underscored	

NY-245

Washington County

Market Data Retrieval

- **North Warren Central Sch Dist** PID: 00778489   518/494-3015
  6110 State Route 8, Chestertown 12817   Fax 518/494-2929

  Schools: 1 \ **Teachers:** 58 \ **Students:** 508 \ **Special Ed Students:** 59 \ **LEP Students:** 10 \ **College-Bound:** 70% \ **Ethnic:** Asian 1%, African American 1%, Hispanic 4%, Caucasian 94% \ **Exp:** $259 (Med) \ **Poverty:** 17% \ **Title I:** $148,431 \ **Special Education:** $538,000 \ **Open-Close:** 09/08 - 06/25 \ **DTBP:** $366 (High)

Michele French 1	Mary Lou Carstensen 2
Brian Sabattis 3*	David Scroggins 4
Robert Hill 5	Lynn Lewis 6,35
Shelley Dupis 8,11,296*	Mike Pherio 27,31,36,83,88
Caleb Martin 57,69,270,288,294*	John Maday 67
Vivienne Frederick 73,76,295*	Lori Korniak 273

Public Schs..Principal	Grd	Prgm	Enr/#Cls	SN	
North Warren Central Sch 6110 State Route 8, Chestertown 12817 Caleb Martin \ Theresa Middleton	PK-12	TV	508 63	53%	518/494-3015

- **Queensbury Union Free Sch Dist** PID: 00778714   518/824-5699
  429 Aviation Rd, Queensbury 12804   Fax 518/793-4476

  Schools: 4 \ **Teachers:** 248 \ **Students:** 3,200 \ **Special Ed Students:** 532 \ **LEP Students:** 12 \ **College-Bound:** 78% \ **Ethnic:** Asian 1%, African American 1%, Hispanic 2%, Caucasian 95% \ **Exp:** $192 (Low) \ **Poverty:** 12% \ **Title I:** $583,526 \ **Special Education:** $3,797,000 \ **Open-Close:** 09/08 - 06/24 \ **DTBP:** $324 (High) \ 📘 🅃

Kyle Gannon 1	Scott Whittemore 2,15
Rob Chapman 3	Josh Hodge 4
Cheri Martindale 5	Richard Keys 6,7,35,83,85,88
Denise Troelstra ...8,11,15,18,275,288,296,298	Kristine Bennett-Barnes 11,57,58,77,79
John Luthringer 16,73,76,286,295	Janelle Sipowitz 27,31,36
Daniel Mannix 67	Amy Georgeadis 68
William Oreilly 91	Maria Muldner 280

Public Schs..Principal	Grd	Prgm	Enr/#Cls	SN	
Queensbury Elem Sch 431 Aviation Rd, Queensbury 12804 Jessica Rossetti	K-3		880 48	37%	518/824-1600 Fax 518/824-1680
Queensbury High Sch 409 Aviation Rd, Queensbury 12804 Damian Switzer	9-12	AV	1,092 56	27%	518/824-4600 Fax 518/824-4680
Queensbury Middle Sch 455 Aviation Rd, Queensbury 12804 Michael Brannigan	6-8		716 40	34%	518/824-3600 Fax 518/824-3682 📘🅃
William H Barton Interm Sch 425 Aviation Rd, Queensbury 12804 Gwynne Cosh	4-5		470 25	42%	518/824-2600 Fax 518/824-2681

- **Warrensburg Central Sch Dist** PID: 00778752   518/623-2861
  103 Schroon River Rd, Warrensburg 12885   Fax 518/623-2436

  Schools: 2 \ **Teachers:** 75 \ **Students:** 687 \ **Special Ed Students:** 161 \ **LEP Students:** 4 \ **College-Bound:** 70% \ **Ethnic:** Hispanic 2%, Caucasian 98% \ **Exp:** $258 (Med) \ **Poverty:** 17% \ **Title I:** $219,642 \ **Special Education:** $2,527,000 \ **Open-Close:** 09/04 - 06/25 \ **DTBP:** $163 (High) \ 📘 🅃

John Goralski 1,11,288	Cynthia Turcotte 2,19
Jonathan Parker 3	Alicia Taylor 4
Dan Bruce 5	Scott Smith 6*
Amy Langworthy 8*	Bonnie Trapasso-Roth 31*
Sarah Landers 36,69,88*	Stephanie Gibson 57,58,79,275,296*

Douglas West 67
Laura Uhly 83,85*

Louis Fisher 73,76,286*

Public Schs..Principal	Grd	Prgm	Enr/#Cls	SN	
Warrensburg Elem Sch 1 James St, Warrensburg 12885 Amy Langworthy	PK-6	T	365 28	59%	518/623-9747 Fax 518/623-3779
Warrensburg Jr Sr High Sch 103 Schroon River Rd, Warrensburg 12885 Doug Duell	7-12		322 55	50%	518/623-2861 Fax 518/623-5089

WARREN CATHOLIC SCHOOLS

- **Diocese of Albany Ed Office** PID: 00715059
  Listing includes only schools located in this county. See District Index for location of Diocesan Offices.

Catholic Schs..Principal	Grd	Prgm	Enr/#Cls	SN	
SS Mary-Alphonsus Reg Cath Sch 10-12 Church St, Glens Falls 12801 Patricia Balmer	PK-8		273 27		518/792-3178 Fax 518/792-6056 📘

WARREN PRIVATE SCHOOLS

Private Schs..Principal	Grd	Prgm	Enr/#Cls	SN	
Prospect UCP Family Center 133 Aviation Rd, Queensbury 12804 Sally Yilicetti	Spec		125 8		518/798-0170 Fax 518/798-0533

WASHINGTON COUNTY

WASHINGTON COUNTY SCHOOLS

County Schs..Principal	Grd	Prgm	Enr/#Cls	SN	
Southern Adirondack Ed Center 1051 Dix Ave, Hudson Falls 12839 Richard Horn	Voc	AG	600 30		518/746-3400 Fax 518/746-3409

WASHINGTON PUBLIC SCHOOLS

- **Argyle Central School Dist** PID: 00778788   518/638-8243
  5023 State Route 40, Argyle 12809   Fax 518/638-6373

  Schools: 2 \ **Teachers:** 49 \ **Students:** 480 \ **Special Ed Students:** 81 \ **College-Bound:** 34% \ **Ethnic:** Asian 1%, Hispanic 3%, Caucasian 96% \ **Exp:** $344 (High) \ **Poverty:** 12% \ **Title I:** $106,780 \ **Special Education:** $1,266,000 \ **Open-Close:** 09/04 - 06/25 \ **DTBP:** $373 (High)

Mike Healey 1,11	Rachel Schwendinger 2
Robert Ellis 3*	Meaghan Wilkins 4*
Jack Sherwin 6,83*	Dawn Wood 8*
Donna Smyth 16*	Erin Bray 58,79

1 Superintendent	8 Curric/Instruct K-12	19 Chief Financial Officer	29 Family/Consumer Science	39 Social Studies K-12	49 English/Lang Arts Elem	59 Special Education Elem	69 Academic Assessment
2 Bus/Finance/Purchasing	9 Curric/Instruct Elem	20 Art K-12	30 Adult Education	40 Social Studies Elem	50 English/Lang Arts Sec	60 Special Education Sec	70 Research/Development
3 Buildings And Grounds	10 Curric/Instruct Sec	21 Art Elem	31 Career/Sch-to-Work K-12	41 Social Studies Sec	51 Reading K-12	61 Foreign/World Lang K-12	71 Public Information
4 Food Service	11 Federal Program	22 Art Sec	32 Career/Sch-to-Work Elem	42 Science K-12	52 Reading Elem	62 Foreign/World Lang Elem	72 Summer School
5 Transportation	12 Title I	23 Music K-12	33 Career/Sch-to-Work Sec	43 Science Elem	53 Reading Sec	63 Foreign/World Lang Sec	73 Instructional Tech
6 Athletic	13 Title V	24 Music Elem	34 Early Childhood Ed	44 Science Sec	54 Remedial Reading K-12	64 Religious Education K-12	74 Inservice Training
7 Health Services	14 Asst Superintendent	25 Music Sec	35 Health/Phys Education	45 Math K-12	55 Remedial Reading Elem	65 Religious Education Elem	75 Marketing/Distributive
	15 Instructional Media Svcs	26 Business Education	36 Guidance Services K-12	46 Math Elem	56 Remedial Reading Sec	66 Religious Education Sec	76 Info Systems
	16 Chief Operations Officer	27 Career & Tech Ed	37 Guidance Services Elem	47 Math Sec	57 Bilingual/ELL	67 School Board President	77 Psychological Assess
	18 Chief Academic Officer	28 Technology Education	38 Guidance Services Sec	48 English/Lang Arts K-12	58 Special Education K-12	68 Teacher Personnel	78 Affirmative Action

New York School Directory — Washington County

Pamela Ellis 67

Public Schs..Principal	Grd	Prgm	Enr/#Cls	SN	
Argyle Elem Sch 5023 State Route 40, Argyle 12809 Dawn Wood	PK-6	A	263 50	39%	518/638-8243 Fax 518/638-6075
Argyle Jr Sr High Sch 5023 State Route 40, Argyle 12809 Susan Passaro	7-12		217	38%	518/638-8243

- **Cambridge Central School Dist** PID: 00778805   518/677-2653
  58 S Park St, Cambridge 12816   Fax 518/677-3889

Schools: 1 \ **Teachers:** 81 \ **Students:** 844 \ **Special Ed Students:** 133 \ **LEP Students:** 4 \ **Ethnic:** Asian 2%, African American 2%, Hispanic 1%, Caucasian 94% \ **Exp:** $319 (High) \ **Poverty:** 12% \ **Title I:** $152,698 \ **Special Education:** $1,756,000 \ **Open-Close:** 09/08 - 06/25 \ **DTBP:** $349 (High)

Dr Douglas Silvernell 1   Anthony Cammarata 2
Amy Braun .... 4*   Randi Sica 5
Deborah Lauver .... 6*   Colleen Lester 11,288,296,298*
Terese Brennan .... 16*   Aydin O'Hearn 31,36,88*
Ralph Harrington .... 58*   Neil Gifford 67
Chris Eatman 71,97   Stephen Butz 73*
Bianca Bates .... 280*   Deb Brownell 286

Public Schs..Principal	Grd	Prgm	Enr/#Cls	SN	
Cambridge Central Sch 24 S Park St, Cambridge 12816 Colleen Lester \ Caroline Goss	PK-12	V	844	28%	518/677-8527 Fax 518/677-3246

- **Fort Ann Central School Dist** PID: 00778831   518/639-5594
  1 Catherine St, Fort Ann 12827   Fax 518/639-8911

Schools: 2 \ **Teachers:** 46 \ **Students:** 500 \ **Special Ed Students:** 81 \ **LEP Students:** 4 \ **Ethnic:** Asian 1%, Hispanic 5%, Caucasian 94% \ **Exp:** $356 (High) \ **Poverty:** 11% \ **Title I:** $80,439 \ **Special Education:** $113,000 \ **Open-Close:** 09/08 - 06/25 \ **DTBP:** $329 (High)

Kevin Froats 1   Alexander Bodensiek 2
Craig Masten 3   Mary Howerton 4*
Jason Humiston .... 6*   Lisa Pearl 7*
Michelle Discenza .... 8,11,57,270,271*   Michelle Discenza 8,11,57,270,271
Leann Hamm .... 16*   Meghan Theis 51,55*
Lori Johnson .... 58*   James Seeley 67
Kristin Casey .... 77*   Diane Quick 97
Justin Hoskins .... 286,288*   Ted Wood 295

Public Schs..Principal	Grd	Prgm	Enr/#Cls	SN	
Fort Ann Elem Sch 1 Catherine St, Fort Ann 12827 Michelle Discenza	PK-5	TV	235 45	41%	518/639-5594
Fort Ann Jr Sr High Sch 1 Catherine St, Fort Ann 12827 Justin Hoskins	6-12	T	217	41%	518/639-5594

- **Ft Edward Union Free Sch Dist** PID: 00778855   518/747-4529
  220 Broadway, Fort Edward 12828   Fax 518/747-6543

Schools: 2 \ **Teachers:** 47 \ **Students:** 450 \ **Special Ed Students:** 97 \ **College-Bound:** 67% \ **Ethnic:** African American 1%, Hispanic 5%, Caucasian 94% \ **Exp:** $189 (Low) \ **Poverty:** 20% \ **Title I:** $165,647 \ **Special Education:** $1,476,000 \ **Open-Close:** 09/09 - 06/25 \ **DTBP:** $179 (High) \ 🇫 🇹

Daniel Ward 1,11,83   Michelle Taylor 2
Craig Masten 3   Jeanna Sartell 4
Lorenda Huntington .... 6*   Debbie Lebarron 37
Joanna Scotch .... 38,69*   Stephanie Iuliucci 51,54,274*
Karen Jones .... 58,285*   Thomas Roche 67
Jocelyn Nolan 77

Public Schs..Principal	Grd	Prgm	Enr/#Cls	SN	
Ft Edward Elem Sch 220 Broadway, Fort Edward 12828 Karen Jones	PK-5		283 15		518/747-4594 Fax 518/747-4529
Ft Edward Middle High Sch 220 Broadway, Fort Edward 12828 Samuel Ratti	6-12	AGTV	260 24	45%	518/747-4529 Fax 518/747-6247

- **Granville Central School Dist** PID: 00778881   518/642-1051
  58 Quaker St, Granville 12832   Fax 518/642-2491

Schools: 3 \ **Teachers:** 107 \ **Students:** 1,200 \ **Special Ed Students:** 220 \ **LEP Students:** 3 \ **College-Bound:** 67% \ **Ethnic:** African American 1%, Hispanic 1%, Caucasian 97% \ **Exp:** $310 (High) \ **Poverty:** 17% \ **Title I:** $337,726 \ **Special Education:** $3,350,000 \ **Open-Close:** 09/08 - 06/25 \ **DTBP:** $169 (High) \ 🇹

Thomas McGurl 1   Katherine Somich 2
Daniell Daigle 3   Joanne Warner 4
Tyler Kelly 5   Brooke Hover 7
Lisa Meade 8   Paul Morcone 11,57,271,296,298
Ann Marie Clark 13,58   Carrie Gresens 16
Audrey Hicks 67   Jereme Randles 73
Jennifer Powell .... 83*   Ann O'Brien 273*

Public Schs..Principal	Grd	Prgm	Enr/#Cls	SN	
Granville Elem Sch 61 Quaker St, Granville 12832 Cara Talmadge	4-6	T	223 40	59%	518/642-9357 Fax 518/642-0771
Granville Jr Sr High Sch 58 Quaker St, Granville 12832 Lisa Meade	7-12	T	511 28	46%	518/642-1051 Fax 518/642-4544
Mary J Tanner Elem Sch Route 22, MDL Granville 12849 Paul Morcone	PK-3	T	338	50%	518/642-9460 Fax 518/642-9594

- **Greenwich Central School Dist** PID: 00778922   518/692-9542
  10 Gray Ave, Greenwich 12834   Fax 518/692-9547

Schools: 2 \ **Teachers:** 91 \ **Students:** 943 \ **Special Ed Students:** 165 \ **LEP Students:** 6 \ **College-Bound:** 83% \ **Ethnic:** Asian 1%, African American 1%, Hispanic 2%, Caucasian 96% \ **Exp:** $239 (Med) \ **Poverty:** 7% \ **Title I:** $110,905 \ **Special Education:** $1,731,000 \ **Open-Close:** 09/08 - 06/25 \ **DTBP:** $399 (High)

Mark Fish 1   Troy Tyler 2
Ron Nicholson .... 3*   Erica Sloan 4
Trevor LeBlanc 5   Kevin Collins 6,7,83,85*
Susan Bishop 11,58,79   Katrina Williams 16
Dana Finney .... 33,38*   Richard Zwirn 38*

---

79 Student Personnel	91 Safety/Security	275 Response To Intervention	298 Grant Writer/Ptnrships	**School Programs**	**Social Media**		
80 Driver Ed/Safety	92 Magnet School	277 Remedial Math K-12	750 Chief Innovation Officer	A = Alternative Program	🇫 = Facebook		
81 Gifted/Talented	93 Parental Involvement	280 Literacy Coach	751 Chief of Staff	G = Adult Classes			
82 Video Services	95 Tech Prep Program	285 STEM	752 Social Emotional Learning	M = Magnet Program	🇹 = Twitter		
83 Substance Abuse Prev	97 Chief Infomation Officer	286 Digital Learning	**Other School Types**	T = Title I Schoolwide			
84 Erate	98 Chief Technology Officer	288 Common Core Standards	Ⓐ = Alternative School	V = Career & Tech Ed Programs			
85 AIDS Education	270 Character Education	294 Accountability	Ⓒ = Charter School				
88 Alternative/At Risk	271 Migrant Education	295 Network System	Ⓜ = Magnet School	New Schools are shaded			
89 Multi-Cultural Curriculum	273 Teacher Mentor	296 Title II Programs	Ⓨ = Year-Round School	New Superintendents and Principals are bold			
90 Social Work	274 Before/After Sch	297 Webmaster		Personnel with email addresses are underscored			

NY—247

Washington County

Market Data Retrieval

James Nolan 67   Lisa Williams 77

Public Schs..Principal	Grd	Prgm	Enr/#Cls	SN		
Greenwich Elem Sch 10 Gray Ave, Greenwich 12834 Jennie Mueller	K-6		458	33%	518/692-9542 Fax 518/692-7658	
Greenwich Jr Sr High Sch 10 Gray Ave, Greenwich 12834 George Niesz	7-12	V	485 30	26%	518/692-9542 Fax 518/692-8503	

● Hartford Central School Dist PID: 00778960   518/632-5222
4704 State Rte 149, Hartford 12838   Fax 518/632-5231

Schools: 1 \ **Teachers:** 48 \ **Students:** 413 \ **Special Ed Students:** 96 \ **LEP Students:** 3 \ **College-Bound:** 85% \ **Ethnic:** Asian 1%, African American 1%, Hispanic 1%, Caucasian 96% \ **Exp:** $175 (Low) \ **Poverty:** 17% \ **Title I:** $144,309 \ **Special Education:** $950,000 \ **Open-Close:** 09/08 - 06/25 \ **DTBP:** $392 (High)

Andrew Cook 1,11   Joanne Searles 2
Kevin Lovely 3   Melanie Howe 4*
Mike Rogers 5   Andrew Capone 6*
Bethellen Mannex .... 9,12,58*   Shelley DuPuis 10*
Monica Pollack .... 16*   Trisha Shaw 37*
Wendy Harrington 38   Brian Getty 67
Alyssa Arlen 83,85*

Public Schs..Principal	Grd	Prgm	Enr/#Cls	SN	
Hartford Central Sch 4704 State Rte 149, Hartford 12838 Shelley DuPuis	PK-12	T	413 35	46%	518/632-5222 Fax 518/632-5148

● Hudson Falls Central Sch Dist PID: 00778984   518/747-2121
80 E La Barge St, Hudson Falls 12839   Fax 518/681-4147

Schools: 5 \ **Teachers:** 179 \ **Students:** 2,400 \ **Special Ed Students:** 518 \ **LEP Students:** 9 \ **Ethnic:** Asian 1%, African American 1%, Hispanic 3%, Caucasian 95% \ **Exp:** $239 (Med) \ **Poverty:** 15% \ **Title I:** $515,678 \ **Special Education:** $4,160,000 \ **Open-Close:** 09/09 - 06/25 \ **DTBP:** $161 (High)

Dr John Hunter 1   Kevin Polunci 2,68
David McKeighan 3   James Murray 4
Thomas Murphy 5   Vincent Medici 6,35*
Jodie Boucher 7   Michael DeCaprio 8,11,15,288,294,296,298,752
Aubree Kammler 16,82   Justine Miles 58
Benjamin Bishop 67   Sue Bishop 72
Christine MacPherson .... 73,76,285,295*   Jessica Gunning 273*

Public Schs..Principal	Grd	Prgm	Enr/#Cls	SN	
Hudson Falls High Sch 80 E La Barge St, Hudson Falls 12839 James Bennefield	9-12	AV	693 70	37%	518/681-4206 Fax 518/746-9033
Hudson Falls Intermediate Sch 139 Maple St, Hudson Falls 12839 Michael McTague	4-5	T	344 15	44%	518/681-4400 Fax 518/747-2774
Hudson Falls Middle Sch 131 Notre Dame St, Hudson Falls 12839 Jordan Tezanos	6-8	T	531 50	46%	518/681-4300 Fax 518/746-2790
Hudson Falls Primary Sch 47 Vaughn Rd, Hudson Falls 12839 April Struwing	K-3	T	518 29	45%	518/681-4450 Fax 518/747-3502
Margaret Murphy Kdgn Center 2 Clark St, Hudson Falls 12839 Michael McTague	PK-K	T	264 16	38%	518/681-4500 Fax 518/747-3853

● Putnam Central School Dist PID: 00779067   518/547-8266
126 County Rt 2, Putnam Sta 12861   Fax 518/547-9567

Schools: 1 \ **Teachers:** 8 \ **Students:** 35 \ **Ethnic:** Hispanic 3%, Caucasian 97% \ **Exp:** $529 (High) \ **Poverty:** 24% \ **Title I:** $38,253 \ **Special Education:** $20,000 \ **Open-Close:** 09/08 - 06/25 \ **DTBP:** $275 (High)

Matthew Boucher 1,11,73,83   Jaime Odell 2
James Forbes .... 3*   Jenny Smith 4*
John Remington .... 57,59*   Charles Bain 67
Kim Brown 297

Public Schs..Principal	Grd	Prgm	Enr/#Cls	SN	
Putnam Central Sch 126 County Rt 2, Putnam Sta 12861 Matthew Boucher	PK-6	T	35 6	61%	518/547-8266

● Salem Central School Dist PID: 00779081   518/854-7855
41 E Broadway, Salem 12865   Fax 518/854-3957

Schools: 1 \ **Teachers:** 53 \ **Students:** 550 \ **Special Ed Students:** 99 \ **LEP Students:** 6 \ **College-Bound:** 64% \ **Ethnic:** African American 2%, Hispanic 4%, Caucasian 94% \ **Exp:** $208 (Med) \ **Poverty:** 13% \ **Title I:** $114,934 \ **Special Education:** $952,000 \ **Open-Close:** 09/09 - 06/25 \ **DTBP:** $414 (High)

David Glover 1   Karen MacGregor 2,12,298
Scott Cameron 5   Don Zarzycki 6,38*
Lisa Hansen .... 58,77*   Anne Dunigan 67
Randy North 297*

Public Schs..Principal	Grd	Prgm	Enr/#Cls	SN	
Salem Central Sch 41 E Broadway, Salem 12865 Julie Adams \ Karen Vieira	PK-12	T	550 58	49%	518/854-7855

● Whitehall Central School Dist PID: 00779108   518/499-1772
87 Buckley Rd, Whitehall 12887   Fax 518/499-1759

Schools: 2 \ **Teachers:** 74 \ **Students:** 719 \ **Special Ed Students:** 145 \ **LEP Students:** 3 \ **College-Bound:** 75% \ **Ethnic:** Hispanic 2%, Caucasian 97% \ **Exp:** $354 (High) \ **Poverty:** 20% \ **Title I:** $278,152 \ **Special Education:** $1,777,000 \ **Open-Close:** 09/04 - 06/25 \ **DTBP:** $383 (High)

Patrick Dee 1   Kate DuBois 2
Thomas Foryan 3   Deborah Mackey 4
Sue Ryder 5   Keith Redmond 6*
Mrs Hoagland 8   Brianne Hazelton ... 11,58,77,79,83,90,275
Kathi Ripley 16   Michael Bennett 16,73,295*
Roxanne Waters 67

Public Schs..Principal	Grd	Prgm	Enr/#Cls	SN	
Whitehall Elem Sch 99 Buckley Rd, Whitehall 12887 Judy Gould	PK-5	T	346 36	63%	518/499-0330 Fax 518/499-1752
Whitehall Jr Sr High Sch 87 Buckley Rd, Whitehall 12887 B Jeff Keller	6-12	T	373 25	59%	518/499-1770 Fax 518/499-1760

1	Superintendent	8	Curric/Instruct K-12	19	Chief Financial Officer	29	Family/Consumer Science	39	Social Studies K-12	49	English/Lang Arts Elem	59	Special Education Elem	69	Academic Assessment
2	Bus/Finance/Purchasing	9	Curric/Instruct Elem	20	Art K-12	30	Adult Education	40	Social Studies Elem	50	English/Lang Arts Sec	60	Special Education Sec	70	Research/Development
3	Buildings And Grounds	10	Curric/Instruct Sec	21	Art Elem	31	Career/Sch-to-Work K-12	41	Social Studies Sec	51	Reading K-12	61	Foreign/World Lang K-12	71	Public Information
4	Food Service	11	Federal Program	22	Art Sec	32	Career/Sch-to-Work Elem	42	Science K-12	52	Reading Elem	62	Foreign/World Lang Elem	72	Summer School
5	Transportation	12	Title I	23	Music K-12	33	Career/Sch-to-Work Sec	43	Science Elem	53	Reading Sec	63	Foreign/World Lang Sec	73	Instructional Tech
6	Athletic	13	Title V	24	Music Elem	34	Early Childhood Ed	44	Science Sec	54	Remedial Reading K-12	64	Religious Education K-12	74	Inservice Training
7	Health Services	15	Asst Superintendent	25	Music Sec	35	Health/Phys Education	45	Math K-12	55	Remedial Reading Elem	65	Religious Education Elem	75	Marketing/Distributive
		16	Instructional Media Svcs	26	Business Education	36	Guidance Services K-12	46	Math Elem	56	Remedial Reading Sec	66	Religious Education Sec	76	Info Systems
		17	Chief Operations Officer	27	Career & Tech Ed	37	Guidance Services Elem	47	Math Sec	57	Bilingual/ELL	67	School Board President	77	Psychological Assess
		18	Chief Academic Officer	28	Technology Education	38	Guidance Services Sec	48	English/Lang Arts K-12	58	Special Education K-12	68	Teacher Personnel	78	Affirmative Action

New York School Directory — Wayne County

WASHINGTON PRIVATE SCHOOLS

Private Schs..Principal	Grd	Prgm	Enr/#Cls	SN
Kingsbury SDA Sch 3991 State Route 4, Hudson Falls 12839 Alicia Biek	1-8		8 3	518/747-4424
Truthville Christian Academy County Rt 12, N Granville 12854 Linda Rathbun	K-12		25 6	518/642-2517

WASHINGTON REGIONAL CENTERS

- **WSWHE BOCES** PID: 00779134   518/746-3310
  1153 Burgoyne Ave Ste 2, Fort Edward 12828   Fax 518/746-3319

James Dexter 1   Ronald Black 2,19
Mike Nelson 3   Lance Freiberger 5
Nancy Destfano 8,15,27,58,88,275   Anthony Muller 15,69
Donna Wisenburn 15,68   Catherine Jones 69
Maribeth Macica 71   David Ashdown 73
Lisa Palmer 74   Turina Parker 79

WAYNE COUNTY

WAYNE COUNTY SCHOOLS

County Schs..Principal	Grd	Prgm	Enr/#Cls	SN
Wayne Educational Center 4440 Ridge Rd, Williamson 14589 Jessica Schoonerman	Spec		90 19	315/589-2400 Fax 315/589-2670
Wayne Technical & Career Ctr 4440 Ridge Rd, Williamson 14589 Andy McVey	Voc		400 20	315/589-2600 Fax 315/589-5158

WAYNE PUBLIC SCHOOLS

- **Clyde-Savannah Central SD** PID: 00779160   315/902-3000
  215 Glasgow St, Clyde 14433   Fax 315/923-2560

Schools: 3 \ Teachers: 77 \ Students: 784 \ Special Ed Students: 152 \ LEP Students: 7 \ Ethnic: African American 5%, Hispanic 5%, Caucasian 90% \ Exp: $538 (High) \ Poverty: 18% \ Title I: $272,869 \ Special Education: $2,321,000 \ Open-Close: 09/03 - 06/25 \ DTBP: $330 (High)

Michael Hayden 1   Susan Gray 2,3,15,19,288
Jeff Mochaen 3   Donna Riviello 4
Scott Convers 5   Larry Lang 6*
Jay Roscup 11,296,298   Christopher Nicol 58,69,77,79
Richard Drahms 67   Jennifer Kelly 73*
Nora Haldeman 76   Erin Church 285

Public Schs..Principal	Grd	Prgm	Enr/#Cls	SN
Clyde-Savannah Elem Sch 212 E Dezeng St, Clyde 14433 Kathryn Lumb	PK-5	T	403 24	54% 315/902-3100 Fax 315/923-2415
Ⓨ Clyde-Savannah High Sch 215 Glasgow St, Clyde 14433 Craig Pawlak	9-12	MT	214 42	47% 315/902-3050 Fax 315/923-7906
Clyde-Savannah Middle Sch 215 Glasgow St, Clyde 14433 Jennifer Kelly	6-8	T	167	53% 315/902-3200

- **Gananda Central School Dist** PID: 02205490   315/986-3521
  1500 Dayspring Rdg, Walworth 14568   Fax 315/986-2003

Schools: 3 \ Teachers: 96 \ Students: 960 \ Special Ed Students: 122 \ LEP Students: 12 \ College-Bound: 82% \ Ethnic: Asian 2%, African American 2%, Hispanic 7%, Caucasian 89% \ Exp: $242 (Med) \ Poverty: 4% \ Title I: $49,909 \ Special Education: $1,205,000 \ Open-Close: 09/03 - 06/25 \ 📘

Dr Shawn Van Scoy 1   Natalie Melnik 2
Lori Brown ....3,4*   Scott Remillard 5
John Tichacek ....6*   Kelly Vanlaeken 8,11,273,288,296
Theresa Grevell ....16,73,295*   Melissa Phelps 58*
William Buchko 67

Public Schs..Principal	Grd	Prgm	Enr/#Cls	SN
Gananda Middle Sch 1500 Dayspring Rdg, Walworth 14568 Elliott Butt	6-8		214 25	28% 315/986-3521 Fax 315/986-1927
Richard Mann Elem Sch 1366 Waterford Rd, Walworth 14568 Kimberly Ernstberger	PK-5		488 30	31% 315/986-3521 Fax 315/986-3506
Ruben A Cirillo High Sch 3195 Wiedrick Rd, Walworth 14568 Matt Mahoney	9-12		284 30	25% 315/986-3521 Fax 315/986-1761

- **Lyons Central School Dist** PID: 00779201   315/946-2200
  10 Clyde Rd, Lyons 14489   Fax 315/946-2205

Schools: 2 \ Teachers: 79 \ Students: 920 \ Special Ed Students: 180 \ LEP Students: 5 \ College-Bound: 77% \ Ethnic: Asian 1%, African American 12%, Hispanic 6%, Caucasian 82% \ Exp: $358 (High) \ Poverty: 18% \ Title I: $335,268 \ Special Education: $3,224,000 \ Open-Close: 09/08 - 06/25 \ DTBP: $148 (High)

Donald Putman 1   Michael Pangallo 2,5,15
Jeff Coons ....3,91*   Jennifer Tyler 4
Renae Lawson 4   Steve Veeder 5,6,7,35*
Jennifer Devinney 8,73   Erin Long 9,34*
Leibarid Alenanian 10   Lisa Tyler 27,31,36,83,85,88*
Margaret Blask 57,58,77,275,277,296   Martha Bailey 67

Public Schs..Principal	Grd	Prgm	Enr/#Cls	SN
Lyons Elem Sch 98 William St, Lyons 14489 Erin Long	PK-6	T	499 24	60% 315/946-2240 Fax 315/946-2254
Lyons Jr Sr High Sch 10 Clyde Rd, Lyons 14489 Libarid Alexanian	7-12	TV	374 50	49% 315/946-2220 Fax 315/946-2221

---

79 Student Personnel
80 Driver Ed/Safety
81 Gifted/Talented
82 Video Services
83 Substance Abuse Prev
84 Erate
85 AIDS Education
88 Alternative/At Risk
89 Multi-Cultural Curriculum
90 Social Work
91 Safety/Security
92 Magnet School
93 Parental Involvement
95 Tech Prep Program
97 Chief Information Officer
98 Chief Technology Officer
270 Character Education
271 Migrant Education
273 Teacher Mentor
274 Before/After Sch
275 Response To Intervention
277 Remedial Math K-12
280 Literacy Coach
285 STEM
286 Digital Learning
288 Common Core Standards
294 Accountability
295 Network System
296 Title II Programs
297 Webmaster
298 Grant Writer/Ptnrships
750 Chief Innovation Officer
751 Chief of Staff
752 Social Emotional Learning

School Programs
A = Alternative Program
G = Adult Classes
M = Magnet Program
T = Title I Schoolwide
V = Career & Tech Ed Programs

Other School Types
Ⓐ = Alternative School
Ⓒ = Charter School
Ⓜ = Magnet School
Ⓨ = Year-Round School

Social Media
📘 = Facebook
🐦 = Twitter

New Schools are shaded
New Superintendents and Principals are bold
Personnel with email addresses are underscored

NY–249

Wayne County

Market Data Retrieval

• Marion Central School Dist   PID: 00779237
4034 Warner Rd, Marion 14505

315/926-2300
Fax 315/926-5797

Schools: 2 \ **Teachers:** 72 \ **Students:** 687 \ **Special Ed Students:** 131 \ **LEP Students:** 9 \ **College-Bound:** 67% \ **Ethnic:** African American 1%, Hispanic 10%, Caucasian 89% \ **Exp:** $313 (High) \ **Poverty:** 10% \ **Title I:** $125,476 \ **Special Education:** $2,311,000 \ **Open-Close:** 09/08 - 06/24 \ **DTBP:** $366 (High)

Donald Bavis 1	Richard Walker 2
Thomas Nortier 3,91	Warren Bushart 4*
Lori Delyser 6*	Dr Ellen Lloyd 9,12
Kristin Miller 11,57,58,88,275,285,288	Lisa Garigen 16
Karen Livingston 38,69*	Rob Marshall 67
David Wise 70,73	

Public Schs..Principal	Grd	Prgm	Enr/#Cls	SN	
Marion Elem Sch 3863 N Main St, Marion 14505 Ellen Lloyd	PK-6	T	382 29	47%	315/926-4256 Fax 315/926-3115
Marion Jr Sr High Sch 4034 Warner Rd, Marion 14505 Nicholas Ganster	7-12	V	305 40	43%	315/926-4228 Fax 315/926-3114

• Newark Central School Dist   PID: 00779263
100 E Miller St, Newark 14513

315/332-3230
Fax 315/332-3517

Schools: 5 \ **Teachers:** 189 \ **Students:** 2,091 \ **Special Ed Students:** 333 \ **LEP Students:** 27 \ **College-Bound:** 68% \ **Ethnic:** African American 9%, Hispanic 16%, Caucasian 74% \ **Exp:** $272 (Med) \ **Poverty:** 16% \ **Title I:** $647,186 \ **Special Education:** $5,553,000 \ **Open-Close:** 09/08 - 06/24 \ **DTBP:** $167 (High)

Matthew Cook 1	Edwar Gnau 2,12,15
Micheal Steve 3*	Warren Bushart 4*
Sheila Dittmer 5	Chris Corey 6,35,83,88*
Ingar Rothpearl 7*	Krista Lewis 8,15,57,69,285,294
Mark Miller 11,298	Jackie Miller 16*
Debora Barry 30*	Monica Stadler 58,78,79
Russell Harris 67	Susan Carr 68
Jamie Sonneville 73	Kyle Bliek 82
Julia Rodriguez 93	Jamie Fonneville 295*

Public Schs..Principal	Grd	Prgm	Enr/#Cls	SN	
Lincoln Elem Sch 1014 N Main St, Newark 14513 John Ginter	PK-2	T	221 12	53%	315/332-3342 Fax 315/332-3604
Newark High Sch 625 Peirson Ave, Newark 14513 Thomas Roote	9-12	AGTV	622 50	46%	315/332-3240 Fax 315/332-3567
Newark Middle Sch 701 Peirson Ave, Newark 14513 Teresa Prinzi	6-8	AT	473 60	58%	315/332-3290 Fax 315/332-3584
Norman R Kelley Interm Sch 316 W Miller St, Newark 14513 Jeff Hamelinck	3-5	T	469 22	67%	315/332-3326 Fax 315/332-3624
Perkins Elem Sch 439 W Maple Ave, Newark 14513 Rhonda Underhill	PK-2	T	306 18	54%	315/332-3315 Fax 315/332-3614

• North Rose Wolcott Central SD   PID: 00779330
11631 Salter Colvin Rd, Wolcott 14590

315/594-3141
Fax 315/594-2352

Schools: 3 \ **Teachers:** 128 \ **Students:** 1,155 \ **Special Ed Students:** 183 \ **LEP Students:** 23 \ **College-Bound:** 46% \ **Ethnic:** African American 1%, Hispanic 9%, Caucasian 90% \ **Exp:** $278 (Med) \ **Poverty:** 15% \ **Title I:** $344,106 \ **Special Education:** $2,793,000 \ **Open-Close:** 09/08 - 06/25 \ **DTBP:** $375 (High)

Michael Pullins 1	Robert Magin 2,3,15
Donna Riviello 4	Jeremy Barnes 5
Robyn Roberts-Grant 6,35*	Megan Paliotti 8,15,16,70,79,274
Brigedtte Barr 11	Kellie Marciano 57,58,68
Lucinda Collier 67	Lisa Brower 73

Public Schs..Principal	Grd	Prgm	Enr/#Cls	SN	
North Rose Elem Sch 10456 Salter Rd, North Rose 14516 Melissa Pietricola	PK-4	T	420 21	65%	315/587-4005 Fax 315/587-2432
North Rose Wolcott High Sch 11631 Salter Colvin Rd, Wolcott 14590 Brian Read	9-12	AV	367 35	56%	315/594-3100 Fax 315/594-6235
North Rose Wolcott MS 5957 New Hartford St, Wolcott 14590 Mark Mathews	5-8	TV	368 40	65%	315/594-3115 Fax 315/594-3120

• Palmyra-Macedon Central SD   PID: 00779380
127 Cuyler St, Palmyra 14522

315/597-3400
Fax 315/597-3898

Schools: 4 \ **Teachers:** 173 \ **Students:** 1,861 \ **Special Ed Students:** 268 \ **LEP Students:** 7 \ **College-Bound:** 79% \ **Ethnic:** African American 1%, Hispanic 3%, Caucasian 95% \ **Exp:** $314 (High) \ **Poverty:** 12% \ **Title I:** $323,121 \ **Special Education:** $3,387,000 \ **Open-Close:** 09/08 - 06/24 \ **DTBP:** $167 (High)

Dr Robert Ike 1,11	Jim Sapienza 2
H James Carlett 3	Warren Bushart 4
Scott Banner 5	Tom Schmandt 6,35,85
Deborah Matzan 7*	Brian Brooks 8,288,298
Michael Yates 16*	Colleen Moquin 42
Joan Karnisky 58,83	Sharon Lang 67
Kenneth Azzarello 68,79	Dr Steven Sanzo 72*
Chip Dolce 73,286,295	

Public Schs..Principal	Grd	Prgm	Enr/#Cls	SN	
Palmyra-Macedon High Sch 151 Hyde Pkwy, Palmyra 14522 Andrew Wahl	9-12		568 75	36%	315/597-3420 Fax 315/597-3438
Palmyra-Macedon Interm Sch 4 West St, MacEdon 14502 Christopher Barnard	3-5	T	353 25	46%	315/597-3400 Fax 315/986-8223
Palmyra-Macedon Middle Sch 163 Hyde Pkwy, Palmyra 14522 Darcy Smith	6-8	T	470 70	40%	315/597-3400 Fax 315/597-3460
Palmyra-Macedon Primary Sch 120 Canandaigua St, Palmyra 14522 Brian Brooks	PK-2	T	470 26	41%	315/597-3475 Fax 315/597-6903

1 Superintendent	8 Curric/Instruct K-12	19 Chief Financial Officer	29 Family/Consumer Science	39 Social Studies K-12	49 English/Lang Arts Elem	59 Special Education Elem	69 Academic Assessment
2 Bus/Finance/Purchasing	9 Curric/Instruct Elem	20 Art K-12	30 Adult Education	40 Social Studies Elem	50 English/Lang Arts Sec	60 Special Education Sec	70 Research/Development
3 Buildings And Grounds	10 Curric/Instruct Sec	21 Art Elem	31 Career/Sch-to-Work K-12	41 Social Studies Sec	51 Reading K-12	61 Foreign/World Lang K-12	71 Public Information
4 Food Service	11 Federal Program	22 Art Sec	32 Career/Sch-to-Work Elem	42 Science K-12	52 Reading Elem	62 Foreign/World Lang Elem	72 Summer School
5 Transportation	12 Title I	23 Music K-12	33 Career/Sch-to-Work Sec	43 Science Elem	53 Reading Sec	63 Foreign/World Lang Sec	73 Instructional Tech
6 Athletic	13 Title V	24 Music Elem	34 Early Childhood Ed	44 Science Sec	54 Remedial Reading K-12	64 Religious Education K-12	74 Inservice Training
7 Health Services	15 Asst Superintendent	25 Music Sec	35 Health/Phys Education	45 Math K-12	55 Remedial Reading Elem	65 Religious Education Elem	75 Marketing/Distributive
	16 Instructional Media Svcs	26 Business Education	36 Guidance Services K-12	46 Math Elem	56 Remedial Reading Sec	66 Religious Education Sec	76 Info Systems
	17 Chief Operations Officer	27 Career & Tech Ed	37 Guidance Services Elem	47 Math Sec	57 Bilingual/ELL	67 School Board President	77 Psychological Assess
	18 Chief Academic Officer	28 Technology Education	38 Guidance Services Sec	48 English/Lang Arts K-12	58 Special Education K-12	68 Teacher Personnel	78 Affirmative Action

New York School Directory — Wayne County

Red Creek Central School Dist PID: 00779433
6624 South St, Red Creek 13143
315/754-2010
Fax 315/754-8169

Schools: 3 \ **Teachers:** 90 \ **Students:** 870 \ **Special Ed Students:** 185 \ **LEP Students:** 3 \ **College-Bound:** 56% \ **Ethnic:** Asian 1%, African American 1%, Hispanic 2%, Caucasian 96% \ **Exp:** $254 (Med) \ **Poverty:** 19% \ **Title I:** $268,352 \ **Special Education:** $2,185,000 \ **Open-Close:** 09/08 - 06/25 \ **DTBP:** $378 (High)

Brian Corey 1	Pat Davenport 3
Pam Gallant 4*	David Gasbarro 5
Mark Blankenberg 6	Cindy Hay 8,285,288,296,298,752
Dennis Taylor 9*	Julia Herbst 11,58,271*
William McDonald 15	Merrilee Witherell 16*
Kyle Meddaugh 67	Erik Robbins 73,286,295*
Kristin Arnonee 77	

Public Schs..Principal	Grd	Prgm	Enr/#Cls	SN	
Margaret W Cuyler Elem Sch 6624 South St, Red Creek 13143 Dennis Taylor	PK-5	T	410 23	52%	315/754-2100 Fax 315/754-2192
Red Creek High Sch 6574 South St, Red Creek 13143 Patrick Chierichella	9-12	T	226 35	49%	315/754-2040 Fax 315/754-2068
Red Creek Middle Sch 6608 South St, Red Creek 13143 Matthew VanOrman	6-8	T	188	52%	315/754-2070 Fax 315/754-2077

Sodus Central School Dist PID: 00779483
6375 Robinson Rd, Sodus 14551
315/483-2331
Fax 315/483-4755

Schools: 3 \ **Teachers:** 114 \ **Students:** 1,050 \ **Special Ed Students:** 179 \ **LEP Students:** 71 \ **Ethnic:** African American 11%, Hispanic 24%, Caucasian 65% \ **Exp:** $286 (Med) \ **Poverty:** 21% \ **Title I:** $527,812 \ **Special Education:** $2,721,000 \ **Open-Close:** 09/04 - 06/22 \ **DTBP:** $170 (High)

Nelson Kise 1,11	Steven Moore 2
Steve Spinelli 3,91	Scott Mongeon 4
Sheila Dittmeir 5	Heather Uetz 8,15,285,288
Joe Keeney 58,79	Laura Alampi 67
Karen Rawden 73,297*	Matt Wilbur 73
Jay Roscop 296	

Public Schs..Principal	Grd	Prgm	Enr/#Cls	SN	
Sodus Elem Sch Route 88, Sodus 14551 Michael Sereno	PK-3	T	377 13	73%	315/483-5282 Fax 315/483-5292
Sodus Intermediate Sch 54 Mill St, Sodus 14551 Gene Hoskins	4-6	ATV	221 25	71%	315/483-2331 Fax 315/483-5291
Sodus Jr Sr High Sch 54 Mill St, Sodus 14551 Arkee Allen	7-12	TV	438 45	65%	315/483-5280 Fax 315/483-6168

Wayne Central School Dist PID: 00779524
6200 Ontario Ctr Rd, Ontario CTR 14520
315/524-1000
Fax 315/524-1049

Schools: 4 \ **Teachers:** 201 \ **Students:** 2,180 \ **Special Ed Students:** 333 \ **LEP Students:** 11 \ **College-Bound:** 73% \ **Ethnic:** Asian 1%, African American 1%, Hispanic 3%, Caucasian 95% \ **Exp:** $222 (Med) \ **Poverty:** 6% \ **Title I:** $215,414 \ **Special Education:** $2,403,000 \ **Open-Close:** 09/02 - 06/24 \ **DTBP:** $226 (High) \ f

Dr Joseph Siracuse 1	Dr Daniel Driffill 2,15
Robert Fussa 3,91	Veronique Wilson 4
Fred Prince 5	Anthony Carusone 6,35*
Michelle Schiek 7,27,34,58,78,79,83,88	Holly Armitage 15,68
Karen Palmer 36*	Jennifer Schoene 67
Barbara Heald 73,95	

Public Schs..Principal	Grd	Prgm	Enr/#Cls	SN	
James A Beneway High Sch 6200 Ontario Center Road, Ontario CTR 14520 Michael Pullen	9-12	AV	697 60		315/524-1050 Fax 315/524-1079 f
Thomas C Armstrong Middle Sch 6076 Ontario Center Rd, Ontario CTR 14520 James Herendeen	5-8	A	693 75		315/524-1080 Fax 315/524-1119
Wayne Central Elem Sch 1784 Ridge Road, Ontario CTR 14520 Donna Rizzo	3-4	A	303 20	38%	315/524-1130 Fax 315/524-1149
Wayne Central Primary Sch 1730 Ridge Road, Ontario CTR 14520 Pamela Tatro	K-2	AT	443 23	33%	315/524-1150 Fax 315/524-1169

Williamson Central School Dist PID: 00779598
4184 Miller St, Williamson 14589
315/589-9661
Fax 315/589-7611

Schools: 3 \ **Teachers:** 100 \ **Students:** 1,106 \ **Special Ed Students:** 171 \ **LEP Students:** 14 \ **Ethnic:** Asian 1%, African American 4%, Hispanic 11%, Caucasian 85% \ **Exp:** $201 (Med) \ **Poverty:** 10% \ **Title I:** $178,936 \ **Special Education:** $2,226,000 \ **Open-Close:** 09/09 - 06/25 \ **DTBP:** $402 (High) \ f

Mary Grace Mazzullo 1	Gary Barno 2,11,19
Jimmy Nikolevski 3	Brenda Patrzalek 4*
Charles O'Neil 5	James Newby 6,35,85*
Rachel Liberatore 7,58,79*	Manuela Mitchell 57*
Jamie Sonneville 67	Timothy Tyler 73*
Ingrid Wander 90*	

Public Schs..Principal	Grd	Prgm	Enr/#Cls	SN	
Williamson Elem Sch 6036 Highland Ave, Williamson 14589 Ellen Saxby	PK-4	T	420 25	48%	315/589-9668 Fax 315/589-8315 f
Williamson High Sch 5891 State Route 21, Williamson 14589 Kathryn Avery	9-12	AGV	316 32	44%	315/589-9621 Fax 315/589-8310
Williamson Middle Sch 4184 Miller St, Williamson 14589 John Fulmer	5-8	T	303 40	48%	315/589-9665 Fax 315/589-8314

WAYNE PRIVATE SCHOOLS

Private Schs..Principal	Grd	Prgm	Enr/#Cls	SN	
Clyde Mennonite Parochial Sch 1851 River Rd, Clyde 14433 Curtis Horning	1-8		43 2		315/923-7242
East Palmyra Christian Sch 2023 E Palmyra Port Gibson Rd, Palmyra 14522 Reid Robbins	PK-12		52 9		315/597-4400 Fax 315/597-9717
Roosevelt Childrens Center 848 Peirson Ave, Newark 14513 Lynne Ward	Spec		200 15		315/331-2086 Fax 315/331-3215

---

79 Student Personnel	91 Safety/Security	275 Response To Intervention	298 Grant Writer/Ptnrships
80 Driver Ed/Safety	92 Magnet School	277 Remedial Math K-12	750 Chief Innovation Officer
81 Gifted/Talented	93 Parental Involvement	280 Literacy Coach	751 Chief of Staff
82 Video Services	95 Tech Prep Program	285 STEM	752 Social Emotional Learning
83 Substance Abuse Prev	97 Chief Information Officer	286 Digital Learning	
84 Erate	98 Chief Technology Officer	288 Common Core Standards	
85 AIDS Education	270 Character Education	294 Accountability	
88 Alternative/At Risk	271 Migrant Education	295 Network System	
89 Multi-Cultural Curriculum	273 Teacher Mentor	296 Title II Programs	
90 Social Work	274 Before/After Sch	297 Webmaster	

School Programs
A = Alternative Program
G = Adult Classes
M = Magnet Program
T = Title I Schoolwide
V = Career & Tech Ed Programs

Other School Types
Ⓐ = Alternative School
Ⓒ = Charter School
Ⓜ = Magnet School
Ⓨ = Year-Round School

Social Media
f = Facebook
t = Twitter

New Schools are shaded
New Superintendents and Principals are bold
Personnel with email addresses are underscored

Westchester County

Market Data Retrieval

WAYNE REGIONAL CENTERS

- **Wayne-Finger Lakes BOCES** PID: 00764024 — 315/332-7400
  131 Drumlin Ct, Newark 14513 — Fax 315/332-7325

Scott Bischoping	1	Keith Henry	2,11,15
Erin Fairben	8,27,30,31,58	Marla Iverson	15
Kate Hammill	16	Dr O Sahler	67
Quinn Smith	68	Shannon Marshall	71
Kelli Eckdahl	73	Jessica Sheridan	74

WESTCHESTER COUNTY

WESTCHESTER COUNTY SCHOOLS

County Schs..Principal	Grd	Prgm	Enr/#Cls	SN	
Pines Bridge Sch 200 Boces Dr, Yorktown Hts 10598 Csilla Mate	Spec		130 10		914/248-2250 Fax 914/248-3801
ⓐ Regional Alter HS-Fox Meadow 845 Fox Meadow Rd, Yorktown Hts 10598 Dr Nicole Murphy	7-12		65		914/248-3640 Fax 914/248-3659
Rye Lake Campus 1606 Old Orchard St, White Plains 10604 Scott Kaufmann	Spec		100 25		914/948-7271 Fax 914/948-7598
Southern Westchester BOCES Voc 65 Grasslands Rd, Valhalla 10595 Jim Matera	Voc	AG	560 20	12%	914/761-3400 Fax 914/761-8099
Tech Center at Yorktown 200 Boces Dr, Yorktown Hts 10598 James Bellucci	Voc	G	1,100 42		914/248-2452 Fax 914/248-2472
Walden Learning Center 200 Boces Dr, Yorktown Hts 10598 Michael Sowul	Spec		125		914/248-2270 Fax 914/245-2427

WESTCHESTER PUBLIC SCHOOLS

- **Ardsley Union Free School Dist** PID: 00779639 — 914/295-5500
  500 Farm Rd, Ardsley 10502 — Fax 914/295-5976

  > Schools: 3 \ Teachers: 192 \ Students: 2,326 \ Special Ed Students: 308
  > \ LEP Students: 39 \ College-Bound: 95% \ Ethnic: Asian 21%,
  > African American 4%, Hispanic 14%, Caucasian 61% \ Exp: $374 (High)
  > \ Poverty: 3% \ Title I: $61,708 \ Special Education: $1,771,000 \
  > Open-Close: 09/08 - 06/24 \ DTBP: $165 (High)

Dr Ryan Schoenfeld	1	Cheri Rosenblatt	2,3,15
Joseph Urbanowicz	3,5	Lesley Lowe	4
Victor Granuzzo	5	Michael Ramponi	6*
Duncan Wilson	8,15	Jeanne Farruggio	58
Matthew Bonney	67	Leonora Perini	68
Sabrina Rich	73*	Layne Hudes	288

Public Schs..Principal	Grd	Prgm	Enr/#Cls	SN	
Ardsley High Sch 300 Farm Rd, Ardsley 10502 Danielle Trippodo	9-12	V	702 40	8%	914/295-5800 Fax 914/295-5977
Ardsley Middle Sch 700 Ashford Ave, Ardsley 10502 Stuart Horlacher	5-8	V	739 60	9%	914/295-5600 Fax 914/295-5677
Concord Road Elem Sch 2 Concord Rd, Ardsley 10502 Jennifer Darling	K-4		885 40	6%	914/231-0800 Fax 914/231-0876

- **Bedford Central School Dist** PID: 00780781 — 914/241-6000
  632 S Bedford Rd, Bedford 10506 — Fax 914/241-6176

  > Schools: 8 \ Teachers: 363 \ Students: 4,100 \ Special Ed Students: 650
  > \ LEP Students: 590 \ College-Bound: 93% \ Ethnic: Asian 4%,
  > African American 3%, Hispanic 37%, Caucasian 56% \ Exp: $272 (Med)
  > \ Poverty: 7% \ Title I: $543,269 \ Special Education: $2,985,000 \
  > Open-Close: 09/08 - 06/25 \ DTBP: $322 (High) \ 🇪

Dr Joel Adelberg	1,288	Angelo Rubbo	2,5,15,71
Robert Gimigliano	3,91	Chrisopher Coughlin	6,7,35
Dr Ed Escobar	11,58,83,286,296,298	Stacey Haynsworth	15*
Steve Marcisz	36*	Adrienne Viscardi	57,271
Colette Dow	67	David Gee	73,76,295

Public Schs..Principal	Grd	Prgm	Enr/#Cls	SN	
Bedford Hills Elem Sch 123 Babbitt Rd, Bedford Hills 10507 Zbynek Gold	K-5		327 17	35%	914/666-2708 Fax 914/864-3492
Bedford Village Elem Sch 45 Court Rd, Bedford 10506 Regina Smith	K-5		274 23	3%	914/234-4178 Fax 914/864-3493
Fox Lane High Sch 632 S Bedford Rd, Bedford 10506 Brett Miller	9-12	AV	1,395 50	30%	914/241-6085 Fax 914/241-6064
Fox Lane Middle Sch 632 S Bedford Rd, Bedford 10506 Susan Ostrofsky	6-8		919 50	32%	914/241-6143 Fax 914/241-6129
ⓐ Hillside Alternative Sch 12 Green St Ste 2, Mount Kisco 10549 Greg Fedorczak	9-12		50		914/666-3257
Mt Kisco Elem Sch 47 W Hyatt Ave, Mount Kisco 10549 Inas Morsi	K-5	T	477	50%	914/666-2677 Fax 914/864-3494
Pound Ridge Elem Sch 7 Pound Ridge Rd, Pound Ridge 10576 Amy Fishkin	K-5		241 21	7%	914/764-8133 Fax 914/864-3495
West Patent Elem Sch 80 W Patent Rd, Bedford Hills 10507 Judy Brewster	K-5		268	20%	914/666-2190 Fax 914/864-3496

- **Blind Brook-Rye Union Free SD** PID: 00781656 — 914/937-3600
  390 N Ridge St, Rye Brook 10573 — Fax 914/937-5871

  > Schools: 3 \ Teachers: 122 \ Students: 1,364 \ Special Ed Students: 166
  > \ LEP Students: 17 \ College-Bound: 97% \ Ethnic: Asian 6%, African
  > American 1%, Hispanic 8%, Caucasian 85% \ Exp: $310 (High) \ Poverty: 2%
  > \ Title I: $33,478 \ Special Education: $419,000 \ Open-Close: 09/08 -
  > 06/25 \ DTBP: $154 (High)

Patrick Brimstein	1	Jonathan Ross	2,3,15
Douglas Goldman	6,35*	Marnita Brown	16
Jennifer Vasquez	28	Harry Burg	58,79
Ashley Welde	67	Charles Von Hollen	73,295
Robin Willig	285*		

---

1 Superintendent	8 Curric/Instruct K-12	19 Chief Financial Officer	29 Family/Consumer Science	39 Social Studies K-12	49 English/Lang Arts Elem	59 Special Education Elem	69 Academic Assessment
2 Bus/Finance/Purchasing	9 Curric/Instruct Elem	20 Art K-12	30 Adult Education	40 Social Studies Elem	50 English/Lang Arts Sec	60 Special Education Sec	70 Research/Development
3 Buildings And Grounds	10 Curric/Instruct Sec	21 Art Elem	31 Career/Sch-to-Work K-12	41 Social Studies Sec	51 Reading K-12	61 Foreign/World Lang K-12	71 Public Information
4 Food Service	11 Federal Program	22 Art Sec	32 Career/Sch-to-Work Elem	42 Science K-12	52 Reading Elem	62 Foreign/World Lang Elem	72 Summer School
5 Transportation	12 Title I	23 Music K-12	33 Career/Sch-to-Work Sec	43 Science Elem	53 Reading Sec	63 Foreign/World Lang Sec	73 Instructional Tech
6 Athletic	13 Title V	24 Music Elem	34 Early Childhood Ed	44 Science Sec	54 Remedial Reading K-12	64 Religious Education K-12	74 Inservice Training
7 Health Services	15 Asst Superintendent	25 Music Sec	35 Health/Phys Education	45 Math K-12	55 Remedial Reading Elem	65 Religious Education Elem	75 Marketing/Distributive
	16 Instructional Media Svcs	26 Business Education	36 Guidance Services K-12	46 Math Elem	56 Remedial Reading Sec	66 Religious Education Sec	76 Info Systems
	17 Chief Operations Officer	27 Career & Tech Ed	37 Guidance Services Elem	47 Math Sec	57 Bilingual/ELL	67 School Board President	77 Psychological Assess
	18 Chief Academic Officer	28 Technology Education	38 Guidance Services Sec	48 English/Lang Arts K-12	58 Special Education K-12	68 Teacher Personnel	78 Affirmative Action

New York School Directory — Westchester County

Public Schs..Principal	Grd	Prgm	Enr/#Cls	SN	
Blind Brook High Sch 840 King St, Rye Brook 10573 Derek Schuelein	9-12	T	463 30	1%	914/937-3600 Fax 914/937-4509
Blind Brook Middle Sch 840 King St, Rye Brook 10573 Patricia Lambert	6-8	T	301	2%	914/937-3600 Fax 914/937-4509
Bruno M Ponterio Ridge St ES 390 N Ridge St, Rye Brook 10573 Tracy Taylor	K-5	T	600 40	2%	914/937-3600 Fax 914/937-1265

● Briarcliff Manor Union Free SD PID: 00779689
45 Ingham Rd, Briarcliff 10510
914/941-8880 Fax 914/941-2177

Schools: 3 \ **Teachers:** 134 \ **Students:** 1,347 \ **Special Ed Students:** 139 \ **LEP Students:** 15 \ **College-Bound:** 100% \ **Ethnic:** Asian 17%, African American 3%, Hispanic 9%, Caucasian 72% \ **Exp:** $323 (High) \ **Poverty:** 1% \ **Special Education:** $1,010,000 \ **Open-Close:** 09/08 - 06/25 \ **DTBP:** $165 (High)

Dr James Kaishian 1
George Hula 3
Dr Debra Serio-Vaughan 12,58,77,78,79
Erica Beasley 73,76,286,295,750
Anthony Commardo 2,5,15,17
Chris Drosopoulos 6*
Michael Haberman 67

Public Schs..Principal	Grd	Prgm	Enr/#Cls	SN	
Briarcliff High Sch 444 Pleasantville Rd, Briarcliff 10510 Deborah French	9-12	T	559 35	5%	914/769-6299 Fax 914/432-8217
Briarcliff Middle Sch 444 Pleasantville Rd, Briarcliff 10510 Susan Howard	6-8	T	317 36	1%	914/769-6343 Fax 914/432-8208
Todd Elem Sch 45 Ingham Rd, Briarcliff 10510 Colleen O'Neill-Mangan	K-5	T	471 59	2%	914/941-8300 Fax 914/941-0125

● Bronxville Union Free SD PID: 00779720
177 Pondfield Rd, Bronxville 10708
914/395-0500 Fax 914/337-7109

Schools: 3 \ **Teachers:** 135 \ **Students:** 1,640 \ **Special Ed Students:** 150 \ **LEP Students:** 7 \ **College-Bound:** 97% \ **Ethnic:** Asian 7%, Hispanic 6%, Caucasian 86% \ **Exp:** $308 (High) \ **Poverty:** 3% \ **Title I:** $46,493 \ **Special Education:** $963,000 \ **Open-Close:** 09/04 - 06/25 \ **DTBP:** $157 (High)

Dr Roy Montesano 1
Mike Lee 3
Dr Mara Koetke 8,12,288,298
Dr Rachel Kelly 11,57,58,68,79,83,296
Arleen Thomas 67
Dr Denise Lutter 74*
Marcellus Lessane 91*
L Daniel Carlin 2,15
Karen Peterson 6
Daniel Carlin 11
Anne Abbatecola 36*
Brad Ashley 73
Jennifer Forsberg 82,286,295

Public Schs..Principal	Grd	Prgm	Enr/#Cls	SN	
Bronxville Elem Sch 177 Pondfield Rd, Bronxville 10708 Patricia Murray	K-5	T	700	1%	914/395-0500 Fax 914/337-6827
Bronxville High Sch 177 Pondfield Rd, Bronxville 10708 Ann Meyer	9-12	T	550	4%	914/395-0500 Fax 914/337-1904
Bronxville Middle Sch 177 Pondfield Rd, Bronxville 10708 Dr Thomas Wilson	6-8	T	397 22	2%	914/395-0500 Fax 914/771-6223

● Byram Hills Central Sch Dist PID: 00779756
10 Tripp Ln Ste 1, Armonk 10504
914/273-4082 Fax 914/273-2516

Schools: 4 \ **Teachers:** 215 \ **Students:** 2,300 \ **Special Ed Students:** 397 \ **LEP Students:** 9 \ **College-Bound:** 99% \ **Ethnic:** Asian 7%, African American 1%, Hispanic 6%, Caucasian 86% \ **Exp:** $373 (High) \ **Poverty:** 2% \ **Title I:** $61,708 \ **Special Education:** $1,700,000 \ **Open-Close:** 09/01 - 06/25 \ **DTBP:** $313 (High)

Dr Jen Lamia 1
Steve Thompson 3
Gina Cunningham 5,91
Robert Castagna 6,83*
Dr Tim Kaltenecker 8,15,288
Deepak Marwah 20,23
Michael McGrath 36*
Dr Andrew Taylor 73,74,76,286,295*
Kelly Seibert 2,15
Melinda Hamilton 4*
Phil Peterson 5
Jill Boyton 7,58
Jill Boynton 11,34,57,79,81*
Rob Castanga 35
Ira Schulman 67

Public Schs..Principal	Grd	Prgm	Enr/#Cls	SN	
Byram Hills High Sch 12 Tripp Ln, Armonk 10504 Christopher Walsh	9-12	T	730	4%	914/273-9200 Fax 914/273-2067
Coman Hill Sch 558 Bedford Rd, Armonk 10504 Mary Crupi	K-2	T	460 28	4%	914/273-4183 Fax 914/273-3257
H C Crittenden Middle Sch 10 MacDonald Ave, Armonk 10504 Kim Lapple	6-8	T	562 30	4%	914/273-4250 Fax 914/273-4618
Wampus Sch 41 Wampus Ave, Armonk 10504 Peggy McInerney	3-5	T	542 30	5%	914/273-4190 Fax 914/273-3608

● Chappaqua Central School Dist PID: 00779811
66 Roaring Brook Rd, Chappaqua 10514
914/238-7200 Fax 914/238-7218

Schools: 6 \ **Teachers:** 319 \ **Students:** 3,900 \ **Special Ed Students:** 401 \ **LEP Students:** 51 \ **College-Bound:** 99% \ **Ethnic:** Asian 14%, African American 1%, Hispanic 6%, Caucasian 79% \ **Exp:** $391 (High) \ **Poverty:** 1% \ **Special Education:** $3,379,000 \ **Open-Close:** 09/02 - 06/25 \ **DTBP:** $312 (High)

Dr Christine Ackerman 1,11
Joseph Gramando 3,91
Jason Semo 6,35,85*
Ellen Doherty 12,57,58,81,83,88,90
Maura Marcon 30*
Rosemary Matthews 58
David Hayes 71
Steven Vazquez 295
John Chow 2,15
Deidre McManus 4
Dr Adam Pease 8,13,15,288,296
Tony Sinanis 15,68
Josh Block 47,70,73,76,285,286,295*
Victoria Tipp 67
Jamie Edellman 280

Public Schs..Principal	Grd	Prgm	Enr/#Cls	SN	
Douglas G Grafflin Elem Sch 650 King St, Chappaqua 10514 Carol Bartlik	K-4		424 30	8%	914/238-7204 Fax 914/238-5285
Horace Greeley High Sch 70 Roaring Brook Rd, Chappaqua 10514 Andrew Corsilia	9-12	AGV	1,228 40	5%	914/238-7201 Fax 914/238-6073
Roaring Brook Elem Sch 530 Quaker Rd, Chappaqua 10514 Doreen O'Leary	K-4		408 34	2%	914/238-7205
Robert E Bell Middle Sch 50 Senter St, Chappaqua 10514 Martin Fitzgerald	5-8	V	617 71	5%	914/238-7202 Fax 914/238-2085
Seven Bridges Middle Sch 222 Seven Bridges Rd, Chappaqua 10514 Joseph Mazza	5-8		559 49	3%	914/238-7203 Fax 914/666-7306

---

79 Student Personnel
80 Driver Ed/Safety
81 Gifted/Talented
82 Video Services
83 Substance Abuse Prev
84 Erate
85 AIDS Education
88 Alternative/At Risk
89 Multi-Cultural Curriculum
90 Social Work
91 Safety/Security
92 Magnet School
93 Parental Involvement
95 Tech Prep Program
97 Chief Infomation Officer
98 Chief Technology Officer
270 Character Education
271 Migrant Education
273 Teacher Mentor
274 Before/After Sch
275 Response To Intervention
277 Remedial Math K-12
280 Literacy Coach
285 STEM
286 Digital Learning
288 Common Core Standards
294 Accountability
295 Network System
296 Title II Programs
297 Webmaster
298 Grant Writer/Ptnrships
750 Chief Innovation Officer
751 Chief of Staff
752 Social Emotional Learning

Other School Types
Ⓐ = Alternative School
Ⓒ = Charter School
Ⓜ = Magnet School
Ⓨ = Year-Round School

School Programs
A = Alternative Program
G = Adult Classes
M = Magnet Program
T = Title I Schoolwide
V = Career & Tech Ed Programs

Social Media
= Facebook
= Twitter

New Schools are shaded
New Superintendents and Principals are bold
Personnel with email addresses are underscored

Westchester County

Market Data Retrieval

West Orchard Elem Sch	K-4	390	2%	914/238-7206
25 Granite Rd., Chappaqua 10514		25		Fax 914/238-6885
James Skoog				

● Croton-Harmon Union Free SD PID: 00779897
10 Gerstein St, Croton Hdsn 10520
914/271-4713
Fax 914/827-3185

Schools: 3 \ **Teachers:** 135 \ **Students:** 1,568 \ **Special Ed Students:** 230 \ **LEP Students:** 43 \ **Ethnic:** Asian 7%, African American 2%, Hispanic 18%, Caucasian 73% \ **Exp:** $427 (High) \ **Poverty:** 2% \ **Title I:** $77,362 \ **Special Education:** $1,095,000 \ **Open-Close:** 09/02 - 06/25 \ **DTBP:** $162 (High)

Dr Deborah O'Connell	1	Denise Harrington	2,4,15,19
Paul Gibbons	3,91*	Rochell O'Mara	5
Michael Gulino	6,35	John Griffiths	8,15,288
Denise Cuomo	11	Pam Morrison	16*
Karen Gatto	57,58,77,79,88,280,298,752	Sarah Carrier	67
Deborah August	73,97,98		

Public Schs..Principal	Grd	Prgm	Enr/#Cls	SN		
Carrie E Tompkins Elem Sch	K-4	T	571	7%	914/271-5184	
8 Gerstein St, Croton Hdsn 10520			40		Fax 914/271-5337	
Kelly Maloney						
Croton-Harmon High Sch	9-12	T	493	13%	914/271-2147	
36 Old Post Rd S, Croton Hdsn 10520			30		Fax 914/271-6643	
Laura Dubak						
Pierre Van Cortlandt Mid Sch	5-8	T	520	10%	914/271-2191	
3 Glen Pl, Croton Hdsn 10520			25		Fax 914/271-6618	
Michael Plotkin						

● Dobbs Ferry Union Free SD PID: 00779938
505 Broadway, Dobbs Ferry 10522
914/693-1500
Fax 914/693-1787

Schools: 3 \ **Teachers:** 145 \ **Students:** 1,500 \ **Special Ed Students:** 224 \ **LEP Students:** 33 \ **College-Bound:** 91% \ **Ethnic:** Asian 8%, African American 4%, Hispanic 20%, Caucasian 69% \ **Exp:** $401 (High) \ **Poverty:** 3% \ **Title I:** $215,414 \ **Special Education:** $658,000 \ **Open-Close:** 09/08 - 06/25 \ **DTBP:** $154 (High)

Dr Lisa Brady	1	Ron Clamser	2,3,4,15,295
David Robertson	3	Andrew Klaich	6,35
Douglas Berry	8,15,69,298	Jean Gismervik	11,34,58,88,275
Marion Halberg	57*	Louis Schwartz	67
Liz Hausman	71	Diane Newell	73,97,286*
Terance Huyter	73,286*		

Public Schs..Principal	Grd	Prgm	Enr/#Cls	SN		
Dobbs Ferry High Sch	9-12		470	15%	914/693-7645	
505 Broadway, Dobbs Ferry 10522			35		Fax 914/693-5227	
John Falino						
Dobbs Ferry Middle Sch	6-8	T	326	17%	914/693-7640	
505 Broadway, Dobbs Ferry 10522			22		Fax 914/693-5299	
Patrick Mussolini						
Springhurst Elem Sch	K-5		721	14%	914/693-1503	
175 Walgrove Ave, Dobbs Ferry 10522			33		Fax 914/693-3188	
Julia Drake						

● Eastchester Union Free SD PID: 00779976
580 White Plains Rd, Eastchester 10709
914/793-6130
Fax 914/793-9006

Schools: 5 \ **Teachers:** 250 \ **Students:** 3,140 \ **Special Ed Students:** 486 \ **LEP Students:** 164 \ **College-Bound:** 90% \ **Ethnic:** Asian 15%, African American 2%, Hispanic 13%, Caucasian 71% \ **Exp:** $252 (Med) \ **Poverty:** 3% \ **Title I:** $79,460 \ **Special Education:** $1,920,000 \ **Open-Close:** 09/08 - 06/25 \ **DTBP:** $296 (High) \ f t

Dr Robert Glass	1	Lisa Sanfilippo	2,15
Edward Kear	3	Nicole Dolce	5
Jason Karol	6*	Scott Wynne	8,15*
Dr Noreen Urso	11,15,68,79,83,88,275	Ripalda Arena	12
Bill Blum	16,73,295	Kristen Shearer	36
Erin McGee	58	Dr Cheryl Smith	67
Helene Litwak	274	Jerrod Blair	285

Public Schs..Principal	Grd	Prgm	Enr/#Cls	SN		
Anne Hutchinson Elem Sch	2-5		440	2%	914/793-6130	
60 Mill Rd, Eastchester 10709			22		Fax 914/961-7367	
Annette Keane						
Eastchester High Sch	9-12	TV	991	1%	914/793-6103	
2 Stewart Pl, Eastchester 10709			40			
Dr Jeffery Capuano						
Eastchester Middle Sch	6-8		786	1%	914/793-6130	
560 White Plains Rd, Eastchester 10709					Fax 914/793-1699	
Josh Elder						
Greenvale Elem Sch	2-5		559	1%	914/793-6130	
1 Gabriel Resicgno Dr, Scarsdale 10583			24		Fax 914/725-6899	
Darrell Stinchcomb						
Waverly Sch	K-1		475	1%	914/793-6130	
45 Hall Ave, Eastchester 10709			24		Fax 914/779-0237	
Mari Doyle						

● Edgemont Union Free Sch Dist PID: 00780066
300 White Oak Ln, Scarsdale 10583
914/472-7768
Fax 914/472-6846

Schools: 3 \ **Teachers:** 162 \ **Students:** 2,050 \ **Special Ed Students:** 251 \ **LEP Students:** 42 \ **College-Bound:** 100% \ **Ethnic:** Asian 37%, African American 2%, Hispanic 10%, Caucasian 51% \ **Exp:** $366 (High) \ **Poverty:** 3% \ **Title I:** $52,588 \ **Special Education:** $1,540,000 \ **Open-Close:** 09/09 - 06/24 \ f

Dr Victoria Kniewel	1	Michael Curtin	2,8,16
John McCabe	3	Susan Shirken	15
Alce Clarke	67	Paul Garofano	73
Joseph Schippa	79	Brent Kammerer	97

Public Schs..Principal	Grd	Prgm	Enr/#Cls	SN		
Edgemont Jr Sr High Sch	7-12		985		914/725-1500	
200 White Oak Ln, Scarsdale 10583			60		Fax 914/725-1506	
Kyle Hosier						
Greenville Elem Sch	K-6		548	1%	914/472-7760	
100 Glendale Rd, Scarsdale 10583			26		Fax 914/472-7785	
Jennifer Allen						
Seely Place Elem Sch	K-6		517		914/472-8040	
51 Seely Pl, Scarsdale 10583			24		Fax 914/472-3512	
Eve Feuerstein						

1	Superintendent	8	Curric/Instruct K-12	19	Chief Financial Officer	29	Family/Consumer Science	39	Social Studies K-12	49	English/Lang Arts Elem	59	Special Education Elem	69	Academic Assessment
2	Bus/Finance/Purchasing	9	Curric/Instruct Elem	20	Art K-12	30	Adult Education	40	Social Studies Elem	50	English/Lang Arts Sec	60	Special Education Sec	70	Research/Development
3	Buildings And Grounds	10	Curric/Instruct Sec	21	Art Elem	31	Career/Sch-to-Work K-12	41	Social Studies Sec	51	Reading K-12	61	Foreign/World Lang K-12	71	Public Information
4	Food Service	11	Federal Program	22	Art Sec	32	Career/Sch-to-Work Elem	42	Science K-12	52	Reading Elem	62	Foreign/World Lang Elem	72	Summer School
5	Transportation	12	Title I	23	Music K-12	33	Career/Sch-to-Work Sec	43	Science Elem	53	Reading Sec	63	Foreign/World Lang Sec	73	Instructional Tech
6	Athletic	13	Title V	24	Music Elem	34	Early Childhood Ed	44	Science Sec	54	Remedial Reading K-12	64	Religious Education K-12	74	Inservice Training
7	Health Services	15	Asst Superintendent	25	Music Sec	35	Health/Phys Education	45	Math K-12	55	Remedial Reading Elem	65	Religious Education Elem	75	Marketing/Distributive
		16	Instructional Media Svcs	26	Business Education	36	Guidance Services K-12	46	Math Elem	56	Remedial Reading Sec	66	Religious Education Sec	76	Info Systems
		17	Chief Operations Officer	27	Career & Tech Ed	37	Guidance Services Elem	47	Math Sec	57	Bilingual/ELL	67	School Board President	77	Psychological Assess
		18	Chief Academic Officer	28	Technology Education	38	Guidance Services Sec	48	English/Lang Arts K-12	58	Special Education K-12	68	Teacher Personnel	78	Affirmative Action

New York School Directory — Westchester County

- **Elmsford Union Free SD** PID: 00780107 914/592-8440
  98 S Goodwin Ave, Elmsford 10523 Fax 914/592-2181

  Schools: 3 \ **Teachers:** 94 \ **Students:** 1,002 \ **Special Ed Students:** 194 \ **LEP Students:** 147 \ **College-Bound:** 72% \ **Ethnic:** Asian 11%, African American 21%, Hispanic 59%, Caucasian 9% \ **Exp:** $375 (High) \ **Poverty:** 8% \ **Title I:** $163,922 \ **Special Education:** $837,000 \ **Open-Close:** 09/08 - 06/25 \ f t

Marc Baiocco	1	Linda Carlin	2,3,15
Robert Pollok	6*	Jo-Anne Dobbins	8,58,79
Laura Wygant	12*	Lisa Watson	16*
Nick Campbell	24	Erica Carrasquillo	57*
Veronica Cronin	57*	Candice Wood	67
Jeffrey Olender	68,73*		

Public Schs..Principal	Grd	Prgm	Enr/#Cls	SN	
Alexander Hamilton High Sch 98 S Goodwin Ave, Elmsford 10523 Joseph Engelhardt	7-12	TV	453 30		914/592-7311 Fax 914/592-2881 t
Alice E Grady Elem Sch 45 S Goodwin Ave, Elmsford 10523 Dr Andrea Hamilton	2-6	T	341 30		914/592-8962 Fax 914/592-5439 t
Carl L Dixson Primary Sch 22 S Hillside Ave, Elmsford 10523 Jeffrey Olender	PK-1		208 10		914/592-2092 Fax 914/592-2163

- **Greenburgh 11 Union Free SD** PID: 00780042 914/693-8500
  1 Echo Hl Bldg 36, Dobbs Ferry 10522 Fax 914/693-4029

  Schools: 2 \ **Teachers:** 29 \ **Students:** 85 \ **Special Ed Students:** 64 \ **LEP Students:** 5 \ **College-Bound:** 67% \ **Ethnic:** African American 34%, Hispanic 60%, Native American: 1%, Caucasian 5% \ **Exp:** $2,241 (High) \ **Open-Close:** 09/04 - 06/25 \ **DTBP:** $159 (High)

Anthony Danquah	1	Marsha Maddox	2
Emmanuel Glasu	11	Lisa Tane	67

Public Schs..Principal	Grd	Prgm	Enr/#Cls	SN	
ⓨ Greenburgh 11 Elem Middle Sch 175 Walgrove Ave, Dobbs Ferry 10522 Elton Thompson	Spec	MT	19 11	56%	914/693-8500
ⓨ Greenburgh 11 High Sch 175 Walgrove Ave, Dobbs Ferry 10522 Elton Thompson	Spec	MTV	68	96%	914/693-8500 Fax 914/674-0640

- **Greenburgh Central School Dist** PID: 00780183 914/761-6000
  475 W Hartsdale Ave, Hartsdale 10530 Fax 914/761-2354

  Schools: 5 \ **Teachers:** 156 \ **Students:** 1,903 \ **Special Ed Students:** 351 \ **LEP Students:** 121 \ **College-Bound:** 91% \ **Ethnic:** Asian 7%, African American 38%, Hispanic 42%, Caucasian 12% \ **Exp:** $501 (High) \ **Poverty:** 7% \ **Title I:** $278,487 \ **Special Education:** $2,547,000 \ **Open-Close:** 09/08 - 06/25 \ **DTBP:** $167 (High)

Dr Tahira Chase	1,83	Mary O'Neil	2,15
Michael Falcone	3	Gary O'Grady	4
Frank Gunn	5	Michael McCoy	6
Shelly Yapchanyk	7	Dr Ronald Valenti	8,15,68
Catherine Addor	20,23	Brendan Gallivan	57,61
Antoinette Darden-Cintron	67	Carlos Ramirez	71,97,286
Diego Rendon	73	Teri Kincade	79
Todd Mensch	285	Laser Alert	295
Dr Teresa Taylor-William	752		

Public Schs..Principal	Grd	Prgm	Enr/#Cls	SN	
Greenburgh Ctl 7 Ecp 475 W Hartsdale Ave, Hartsdale 10530 Dawn Male	PK-PK	T	135 7	45%	914/949-2745 Fax 914/949-1548
Highview Elem Sch 200 N Central Ave Bldg 1, Hartsdale 10530 Gary Mastrangelo	2-3	T	238 14	58%	914/946-6946 Fax 914/946-0397
Lee F Jackson Elem Sch 2 Saratoga Rd, White Plains 10607 Patricia Simone	K-1	T	257 19	50%	914/948-2992 Fax 914/681-9038
Richard J Bailey Sch 33 Hillside Ave S, White Plains 10607 Shqype Rraci	4-6	T	368 30	65%	914/948-8107 Fax 914/948-2934
Woodlands Middle High Sch 475 W Hartsdale Ave, Hartsdale 10530 Matthew Smith	7-12	T	740 30	60%	914/761-6052 Fax 914/761-6951

- **Greenburgh-Graham UFSD** PID: 00780169 914/478-1106
  1 S Broadway, Hastings HDSN 10706 Fax 914/478-0904

  Schools: 2 \ **Teachers:** 49 \ **Students:** 286 \ **Ethnic:** African American 69%, Hispanic 25%, Caucasian 6% \ **Exp:** $997 (High) \ **Open-Close:** 08/31 - 06/25 \ **DTBP:** $159 (High)

Oliver Levy	1	Edward Davis	2,3,15,91
Andrea Byrne	8*	Dr Andrea Loscalzo	58,79
Jess Dannhauser	67	Vicky Wilkins	68*
Bea Gavish	69	Surendra Kumar	73,82*

Public Schs..Principal	Grd	Prgm	Enr/#Cls	SN	
ⓨ Martin Luther King Jr High Sch 1 S Broadway, Hastings HDSN 10706 Shakira Petit	Spec	MT	94 30	87%	914/478-1161 Fax 914/478-2521
ⓨ Vincent Ziccolella Elem MS 1 S Broadway, Hastings HDSN 10706 Donald Griggs	Spec	MT	198 15		914/478-8004 Fax 914/613-0050

- **Greenburgh-North Castle SD** PID: 00781931 914/231-8620
  71 Broadway, Dobbs Ferry 10522 Fax 914/693-2829

  Schools: 4 \ **Teachers:** 67 \ **Students:** 309 \ **Special Ed Students:** 24 \ **College-Bound:** 100% \ **Ethnic:** Asian 2%, African American 33%, Hispanic 38%, Caucasian 26% \ **Exp:** $588 (High) \ **Open-Close:** 09/04 - 06/25 \ **DTBP:** $132 (High) \ f t

Dr Carolyn McGuffog	1,11	John Marino	2
Dr Robert Hedrickson	67	Denise Rivera	70*
Dr Robin Levine	79		

Public Schs..Principal	Grd	Prgm	Enr/#Cls	SN	
ⓨ Dr Kenneth B Clark Academy 914/798-7200 71 Broadway, Dobbs Ferry 10522 Dr David Fine	Spec	AGMTV	83	29%	Fax 914/520-5282
ⓨ Greenburgh Academy 108 Shonnard Pl, Yonkers 10703 Mike Voron	Spec	AGMV	134 17	5%	914/476-1938
ⓨ Kaplan Career Academy 623 Blooming Grove Tpke, New Windsor 12553 Jay Posephney	Spec	AMTV	75	38%	845/522-8460 Fax 845/522-8456
ⓨ Reach Academy 914/686-8159 45 Gainsborg Ave E, West Harrison 10604 Paul Pizzutello	Spec	AGMTV	17	31%	Fax 914/948-3924

---

79 Student Personnel	91 Safety/Security	275 Response To Intervention	298 Grant Writer/Ptnrships	**School Programs**	**Social Media**	
80 Driver Ed/Safety	92 Magnet School	277 Remedial Math K-12	750 Chief Innovation Officer	A = Alternative Program		
81 Gifted/Talented	93 Parental Involvement	280 Literacy Coach	751 Chief of Staff	G = Adult Classes	f = Facebook	
82 Video Services	95 Tech Prep Program	285 STEM	752 Social Emotional Learning	M = Magnet Program		
83 Substance Abuse Prev	97 Chief Information Officer	286 Digital Learning		T = Title I Schoolwide	t = Twitter	
84 Erate	98 Chief Technology Officer	288 Common Core Standards	**Other School Types**	V = Career & Tech Ed Programs		
85 AIDS Education	270 Character Education	294 Accountability	Ⓐ = Alternative School			
88 Alternative/At Risk	271 Migrant Education	295 Network System	Ⓒ = Charter School	New Schools are shaded		
89 Multi-Cultural Curriculum	273 Teacher Mentor	296 Title II Programs	Ⓜ = Magnet School	New Superintendents and Principals are bold		
90 Social Work	274 Before/After Sch	297 Webmaster	Ⓨ = Year-Round School	Personnel with email addresses are underscored		

Westchester County

Market Data Retrieval

• Harrison Central School Dist PID: 00780274   914/835-3300
50 Union Ave, Harrison 10528   Fax 914/835-3356

Schools: 6 \ **Teachers:** 335 \ **Students:** 3,600 \ **Special Ed Students:** 519 \ **LEP Students:** 337 \ **College-Bound:** 88% \ **Ethnic:** Asian 13%, African American 2%, Hispanic 19%, Caucasian 66% \ **Exp:** $282 (Med) \ **Poverty:** 5% \ **Title I:** $416,746 \ **Special Education:** $2,366,000 \ **Open-Close:** 09/08 - 06/25 \ **DTBP:** $308 (High)

Louis Wool	1	Robert Salierno	2,4,5,15
Lenny Purcell	3,91	Geraldine Barbagallo	5
Christopher Galano	6,35	Michael Greenfield	8,11,15,16,95
Brian Seligman	12,73,76*	Dr Brian Ladewig	15,68,79
Lynn Fusco	20,23	Kelly Malczewski	36
Marlene Colonna	39	Joan O'Keeffe	42
Veronica D'Andrea	45	Jaimie Kanter	48
Marina Moran	57,61	Julie Snider	59,90*
Kelly Mangan	67	Helen Oliva	286

Public Schs..Principal	Grd	Prgm	Enr/#Cls	SN	
Harrison Avenue Elem Sch 480 Harrison Ave, Harrison 10528 Valerie Hymes	K-5		576 25	10%	914/630-3192 Fax 914/835-4311
Harrison High Sch 255 Union Ave, Harrison 10528 Kimberly Beukema	9-12		1,061	22%	914/630-3095 Fax 914/835-5471
Louis M Klein Middle Sch 50 Union Ave, Harrison 10528 Scott Fried	6-8		847 65	21%	914/630-3033 Fax 914/630-3324
Parsons Memorial Elem Sch 200 Halstead Ave, Harrison 10528 Mark Woodward	K-5		477 25	22%	914/630-3222 Fax 914/835-4657
Purchase Elem Sch 2995 Purchase St, Purchase 10577 Adam Gutterman	K-5		302 22	9%	914/630-3172 Fax 914/946-0286
Samuel J Preston Elem Sch 50 Taylor Ave, West Harrison 10604 Dennis Kortright	K-5		359 19	31%	914/630-3152 Fax 914/761-7166

• Hastings on Hudson Union FR SD PID: 00780365   914/478-2900
27 Farragut Ave, Hastings HDSN 10706   Fax 914/478-3293

Schools: 3 \ **Teachers:** 156 \ **Students:** 1,654 \ **Special Ed Students:** 244 \ **LEP Students:** 24 \ **College-Bound:** 98% \ **Ethnic:** Asian 6%, African American 2%, Hispanic 15%, Caucasian 77% \ **Exp:** $286 (Med) \ **Poverty:** 2% \ **Title I:** $49,874 \ **Special Education:** $770,000 \ **Open-Close:** 09/02 - 06/24 \ **DTBP:** $166 (High)

Dr Valerie Piedmonte	1	Maureen Caraballo	2,73
Joseph Martorana	3*	Victor Granuzzo	5
Jesse Merchant	6*	Joanne Cipollina	7*
Melissa Szymanski	8,15	Patrick Theodule	16
Jeanette Kocur	36*	Laura Sullivan	58*
Lauren Berman	67	Lynn Walker	68,79
Jeanine Genauer	71		

Public Schs..Principal	Grd	Prgm	Enr/#Cls	SN	
Farragut Middle Sch 27 Farragut Ave, Hastings HDSN 10706 Gail Kipper	5-8	T	510 26	5%	914/478-6230 Fax 914/478-6314
Hastings High Sch 1 Mount Hope Blvd, Hastings HDSN 10706 Lou Adipietro	9-12	AT	520	7%	914/478-6250 Fax 914/478-7842
Hillside Elem Sch 120 Lefurgy Ave, Hastings HDSN 10706 Amy Cazes	K-4	T	624 29	1%	914/478-6270 Fax 914/478-6279

• Hawthorne Cedar Knolls UFSD PID: 00780406   914/749-2917
226 Linda Ave, Hawthorne 10532   Fax 914/749-2920

Schools: 4 \ **Teachers:** 33 \ **Students:** 400 \ **Special Ed Students:** 88 \ **College-Bound:** 57% \ **Ethnic:** Asian 1%, African American 46%, Hispanic 42%, Caucasian 11% \ **Exp:** $552 (High) \ **Open-Close:** 09/07 - 06/25 \ **DTBP:** $153 (High)

Mark Silverstein	1	Lou Petty	3
Dr Chris Casey	8,11,15,298	Daniel Leffell	67
Ann Izzo	76	Ellen Bergman	79

Public Schs..Principal	Grd	Prgm	Enr/#Cls	SN	
ⓨ Geller House Sch 77 Chicago Ave, Staten Island 10305 Vikki Palmer	Spec	MT	22	86%	718/442-7828 Fax 718/273-3239
ⓨ Hawthorne Little Sch 226 Linda Ave, Hawthorne 10532 Raymond Raefski	Spec	MT	69	24%	914/749-2964 Fax 914/749-2967
ⓨ Hawthorne Sr Jr High Sch 226 Linda Ave, Hawthorne 10532 Eric Ford	Spec	MT	42 6	51%	914/749-2930 Fax 914/749-2935
ⓨ Linden Hill Sch 226 Linda Ave, Hawthorne 10532 Robert Worden	Spec	MT	102 25	67%	914/749-2975 Fax 914/749-2952

• Hendrick Hudson Ctl Sch Dist PID: 00780420   914/257-5112
61 Trolley Rd, Montrose 10548   Fax 914/257-5101

Schools: 5 \ **Teachers:** 223 \ **Students:** 2,122 \ **Special Ed Students:** 352 \ **LEP Students:** 63 \ **College-Bound:** 89% \ **Ethnic:** Asian 4%, African American 6%, Hispanic 30%, Caucasian 60% \ **Exp:** $316 (High) \ **Poverty:** 5% \ **Title I:** $200,417 \ **Special Education:** $2,485,000 \ **Open-Close:** 09/08 - 06/24 \ **DTBP:** $312 (High) \ 🅕

Joseph Hochreiter	1	Enrique Catalan	2,15
Anthony Merlini	3	Claire Carey	4
Elizabeth Gilleo	5	Thomas Baker	6,35*
Dr Margaret Ruller	8,11,31,57,273,288,296,298	Lisa Schuchman	34,58,79,83
Carol Abraham	67	Laura Neier	73
Laura Mattioli	274		

Public Schs..Principal	Grd	Prgm	Enr/#Cls	SN	
Blue Mountain Middle Sch 7 Furnace Woods Rd, Cortlandt MNR 10567 John Owens	6-8	T	520 50	30%	914/257-5700 Fax 914/257-5701
Buchanan-Verplank Elem Sch 160 Westchester Ave, Buchanan 10511 Joshua Cohen	K-5	T	319 18	48%	914/257-5400 Fax 914/257-5401
Frank G Lindsey Elem Sch 57 Trolley Rd, Montrose 10548 Donna Torrisi	K-5	T	412 30	25%	914/257-5500 Fax 914/257-5501
Furnace Woods Elem Sch 239 Watch Hill Rd, Cortlandt MNR 10567 Cynthia Kramer	K-5	T	223 18	13%	914/257-5600 Fax 914/257-5601
Hendrick Hudson High Sch 2166 Albany Post Rd, Montrose 10548 James Mackin	9-12	ATV	794 85	24%	914/257-5800 Fax 914/257-5801

---

1 Superintendent	8 Curric/Instruct K-12	19 Chief Financial Officer	29 Family/Consumer Science	39 Social Studies K-12	49 English/Lang Arts Elem	59 Special Education Elem	69 Academic Assessment
2 Bus/Finance/Purchasing	9 Curric/Instruct Elem	20 Art K-12	30 Adult Education	40 Social Studies Elem	50 English/Lang Arts Sec	60 Special Education Sec	70 Research/Development
3 Buildings And Grounds	10 Curric/Instruct Sec	21 Art Elem	31 Career/Sch-to-Work K-12	41 Social Studies Sec	51 Reading K-12	61 Foreign/World Lang K-12	71 Public Information
4 Food Service	11 Federal Program	22 Art Sec	32 Career/Sch-to-Work Elem	42 Science K-12	52 Reading Elem	62 Foreign/World Lang Elem	72 Summer School
5 Transportation	12 Title I	23 Music K-12	33 Career/Sch-to-Work Sec	43 Science Elem	53 Reading Sec	63 Foreign/World Lang Sec	73 Instructional Tech
6 Athletic	13 Title V	24 Music Elem	34 Early Childhood Ed	44 Science Sec	54 Remedial Reading K-12	64 Religious Education K-12	74 Inservice Training
7 Health Services	15 Asst Superintendent	25 Music Sec	35 Health/Phys Education	45 Math K-12	55 Remedial Reading Elem	65 Religious Education Elem	75 Marketing/Distributive
	16 Instructional Media Svcs	26 Business Education	36 Guidance Services K-12	46 Math Elem	56 Remedial Reading Sec	66 Religious Education Sec	76 Info Systems
	17 Chief Operations Officer	27 Career & Tech Ed	37 Guidance Services Elem	47 Math Sec	57 Bilingual/ELL	67 School Board President	77 Psychological Assess
	18 Chief Academic Officer	28 Technology Education	38 Guidance Services Sec	48 English/Lang Arts K-12	58 Special Education K-12	68 Teacher Personnel	78 Affirmative Action

New York School Directory — Westchester County

● **Irvington Union Free Sch Dist** PID: 00780494 914/591-8500
6 Dows Ln, Irvington 10533 Fax 914/591-3064

Schools: 4 \ **Teachers:** 169 \ **Students:** 1,781 \ **Special Ed Students:** 269 \ **LEP Students:** 30 \ **College-Bound:** 94% \ **Ethnic:** Asian 12%, African American 5%, Hispanic 10%, Caucasian 73% \ **Exp:** $463 (High) \ **Poverty:** 4% \ **Title I:** $76,924 \ **Special Education:** $1,491,000 \ **Open-Close:** 09/08 - 06/24 \ **DTBP:** $161 (High) \ 📘 🐦

Dr Kristopher Harrison 1	Carol Stein 2,3,15
Gary Knowles 3	David Alberts 4*
Vic Granuzzo 5	Dr Raina Kor 8,15,68,288
Gail Krieger 11,57,58,79	Brian Friedman 67
Jason Strumwasser 73	

Public Schs..Principal	Grd	Prgm	Enr/#Cls	SN	
Dows Lane Elem Sch 6 Dows Ln, Irvington 10533 Andrea Kantor	K-3		520 26	5%	914/591-6012 Fax 914/591-6863
Irvington High Sch 40 N Broadway, Irvington 10533 Juliet Mizimakoski	9-12		546 60	10%	914/591-8648 Fax 914/591-6714
Irvington Middle Sch 40 N Broadway, Irvington 10533 David Sottile	6-8		445 25	8%	914/269-5312 Fax 914/591-8535
Main St Elem Sch 101 Main St, Irvington 10533 Joyce Chapnick	4-5		270	9%	914/591-1961 Fax 914/591-3099

● **Katonah-Lewisboro Sch Dist** PID: 00780535 914/763-7000
60 N Salem Rd, South Salem 10590 Fax 914/763-7035

Schools: 5 \ **Teachers:** 257 \ **Students:** 2,917 \ **Special Ed Students:** 542 \ **LEP Students:** 39 \ **College-Bound:** 95% \ **Ethnic:** Asian 3%, African American 1%, Hispanic 11%, Caucasian 85% \ **Exp:** $469 (High) \ **Poverty:** 2% \ **Title I:** $86,223 \ **Special Education:** $3,758,000 \ **Open-Close:** 09/09 - 06/25 \ **DTBP:** $319 (High)

Andrew Selesnick 1	Danelle Placella 2,4
David Quatrocchi 2,15	Paul Christensen 3,91
Nora Mavrommatis 5	Christian McCarthy 6,7,35,80*
Mary Ford 8,11,57,69,83,280,285,288	Marisa Merlino 36*
Catherine McNulty 58,77,79	Marjorie Schiff 67
Maureen Jones 71,97	Christopher Nelson 73

Public Schs..Principal	Grd	Prgm	Enr/#Cls	SN	
Increase Miller Elem Sch 186 Waccabuc Rd Route 138, Goldens BRG 10526 Kerry Ford	K-5		454 21	6%	914/763-7100 Fax 914/763-7173
John Jay High Sch 60 N Salem Rd, Cross River 10518 Steven Siciliano	9-12	V	1,041 80	6%	914/763-7201 Fax 914/763-7494
John Jay Middle Sch 40 N Salem Rd, Cross River 10518 Jeffrey Swiatowicz	6-8	V	667	7%	914/763-7500 Fax 914/763-7665
Katonah Elem Sch 106 Huntville Rd, Katonah 10536 Cristy Harris	K-5		415 22	8%	914/763-7700 Fax 914/763-7789
Meadow Pond Elem Sch 185 Smith Ridge Rd, South Salem 10590 Carolann Castellano	K-5		340 22	4%	914/763-7900 Fax 914/763-7986

● **Lakeland Central School Dist** PID: 00780602 914/245-1700
1086 E Main St, Shrub Oak 10588 Fax 914/245-1589

Schools: 8 \ **Teachers:** 468 \ **Students:** 5,845 \ **Special Ed Students:** 931 \ **LEP Students:** 87 \ **College-Bound:** 94% \ **Ethnic:** Asian 5%, African American 6%, Hispanic 22%, Caucasian 67% \ **Exp:** $225 (Med) \ **Poverty:** 4% \ **Title I:** $224,010 \ **Special Education:** $8,967,000 \ **Open-Close:** 09/01 - 06/25 \ **DTBP:** $323 (High)

Brendan Lyons 1	Binoy Alunkal 2
Steve Calabrese 3	Joann Ricapito 4*
Paul Cavaluzzi 5	Daniel Belfi 6*
Jean Miccio 8,11,15,288,298	Mary Ellen Herzog 15,57,58,79,83,88,271
Dr Tammy Cosgrove 15,68,273	Dwayne Hoffman 16,73
James Van Develde 30,71,80,91	Frank Accetta 36*
Patricia Viggiano 42*	Christopher Ruggiero 45*
Theresa Wilkowski 48*	Michael Daly 67
Maryellen Rafferty 88*	Rebecca Carcova 297*

Public Schs..Principal	Grd	Prgm	Enr/#Cls	SN	
Benjamin Franklin Elem Sch 3477 Kamhi Dr, Yorktown Hts 10598 Ken Craft	K-5		519 35	15%	914/245-7444 Fax 914/245-7668
George Washington Elem Sch 3634 Lexington Ave, Mohegan Lake 10547 Tracy Norman	K-5		408 35	25%	914/528-2021 Fax 914/528-2134
Lakeland Copper Beech Mid Sch 3401 Old Yorktown Rd, Yorktown Hts 10598 Frank Ruolo	6-8	T	1,324 43	24%	914/245-1885 Fax 914/245-1259
Lakeland High Sch 1349 E Main St, Shrub Oak 10588 Chris Cummings	9-12		993 100	21%	914/528-0600 Fax 914/528-0521
Lincoln-Titus Elem Sch 10 Lincoln Ave, Crompond 10517 Elizabeth McGowan	PK-5		402 30	13%	914/528-2519 Fax 914/528-1471
Thomas Jefferson Elem Sch 3636 Gomer St, Yorktown Hts 10598 Alfonse Davino	K-5		431 24	7%	914/245-4802 Fax 914/245-0511
Van Cortlandtville Elem Sch 3100 E Main St, Mohegan Lake 10547 Jacqueline Woodruff	K-5	T	582 35	26%	914/528-1354 Fax 914/528-1376
Walter Panas High Sch 300 Croton Ave, Cortlandt MNR 10567 Joseph Spero	9-12		904	25%	914/739-2823 Fax 914/739-3545

● **Mamaroneck Union Free Sch Dist** PID: 00780717 914/220-3000
1000 W Boston Post Rd, Mamaroneck 10543 Fax 914/220-3010

Schools: 6 \ **Teachers:** 431 \ **Students:** 5,230 \ **Special Ed Students:** 845 \ **LEP Students:** 253 \ **College-Bound:** 95% \ **Ethnic:** Asian 4%, African American 3%, Hispanic 22%, Caucasian 71% \ **Exp:** $304 (High) \ **Poverty:** 4% \ **Title I:** $221,474 \ **Special Education:** $4,233,000 \ **Open-Close:** 09/08 - 06/25 \ **DTBP:** $313 (High) \ 📘

Dr Robert Shaps 1	Lauren Leone 2
Sylvia Wallach 2,15	Steve Brugge 3,91
Jeff Tirums 4	Bari Suman 6,35*
Dr Nora Mazzone 7,15,79	Annie Ward 8,15,288
Claire Reinhard 11,69,70,76,294	Jeremy Barker 15,68
Kristina Pantginis 16*	Dina Madden 23
Judith Ravina 57	Alexandra Casabona 58
Jennifer Monaco 58	Rinna Beder 67
Debbie Manetta 71	Adish Ramratton 73
Helene Fremder 83*	Dina Reynoso 90*

---

79 Student Personnel	91 Safety/Security	275 Response To Intervention	298 Grant Writer/Ptnrships	**School Programs**
80 Driver Ed/Safety	92 Magnet School	277 Remedial Math K-12	750 Chief Innovation Officer	A = Alternative Program
81 Gifted/Talented	93 Parental Involvement	280 Literacy Coach	751 Chief of Staff	G = Adult Classes
82 Video Services	95 Tech Prep Program	285 STEM	752 Social Emotional Learning	M = Magnet Program
83 Substance Abuse Prev	97 Chief Infomation Officer	286 Digital Learning		T = Title I Schoolwide
84 Erate	98 Chief Technology Officer	288 Common Core Standards	**Other School Types**	V = Career & Tech Ed Programs
85 AIDS Education	270 Accountability	294 Accountability	Ⓐ = Alternative School	
88 Alternative/At Risk	271 Migrant Education	295 Network System	Ⓒ = Charter School	
89 Multi-Cultural Curriculum	273 Teacher Mentor	296 Title II Programs	Ⓜ = Magnet School	
90 Social Work	274 Before/After Sch	297 Webmaster	Ⓨ = Year-Round School	

Social Media
📘 = Facebook
🐦 = Twitter

New Schools are shaded
New Superintendents and Principals are bold
Personnel with email addresses are underscored

Westchester County

Market Data Retrieval

Public Schs..Principal	Grd	Prgm	Enr/#Cls	SN	
Central Elem Sch 1100 Palmer Ave, Larchmont 10538 Joanne Hindley	PK-5		514 26	15%	914/220-3401 Fax 914/220-3415
Chatsworth Avenue Sch 34 Chatsworth Ave, Larchmont 10538 Katie Andersen	K-5		689 33	4%	914/220-3500 Fax 914/220-3515
Hommocks Middle Sch 130 Hommocks Rd, Larchmont 10538 Emilia Capellan	6-8		1,296 90	18%	914/220-3300 Fax 914/220-3315
Mamaroneck Avenue Elem Sch 850 Mamaroneck Ave, Mamaroneck 10543 Neill Alleva	K-5	T	712 35	47%	914/220-3600 Fax 914/220-3615
Mamaroneck High Sch 1000 W Boston Post Rd, Mamaroneck 10543 Clain Elizabeth	9-12	G	1,661	18%	914/220-3100 Fax 914/220-3115
Murray Avenue Elem Sch 250 Murray Ave, Larchmont 10538 Colleen Melnyk	K-5		745 33	1%	914/220-3700 Fax 914/220-3715

- **Mount Vernon City School Dist** PID: 00780860 914/665-5000
  165 N Columbus Ave, Mount Vernon 10553 Fax 914/665-6077

Schools: 16 \ **Teachers:** 648 \ **Students:** 8,000 \ **Special Ed Students:** 1,591 \ **LEP Students:** 652 \ **College-Bound:** 87% \ **Ethnic:** Asian 1%, African American 69%, Hispanic 24%, Caucasian 5% \ **Exp:** $395 (High) \ **Poverty:** 15% \ **Title I:** $2,979,195 \ **Special Education:** $17,155,000 \ **Open-Close:** 09/08 - 06/25 \ **DTBP:** $298 (High)

Dr Kenneth Hamilton 1
Shaji Zacharia 2
Robert Cimmino 6*
Dr Waveline Bennett-Conroy 11,15,70,294
Dr Jeff Gorman 15,69
Marci Tiggs 15,68
Evelyn Collins 22,25,81*
Gale White-Wallace 34,280
Dr Marguerita Circello 57
Frank Gallo 280
Ken Silver 2,3,4,15
Michael Pelliccio 3,91
Dr Claytisha Walden 8,15
Denise Kurpiewski 15,68
Dr K Veronica Smith 15,36,79
Joseph McGrath 16,73,286,295
Sherry Ward 27*
Dr Satish Jagnandan 42,45,277,285
Darcy Miller 67

Public Schs..Principal	Grd	Prgm	Enr/#Cls	SN	
Benjamin Turner Middle Sch 624 S 3rd Ave, Mount Vernon 10550 Rodney McBride	6-8	TV	359 30	86%	914/665-5150 Fax 914/665-5152
Cecil Parker Elem Sch 461 S 6th Ave, Mount Vernon 10550 Natalie Dweck	PK-7	T	339 25	81%	914/665-5040 Fax 914/665-5353
Columbus Elem Sch 455 N High St, Mount Vernon 10550 Colleen Seivright	PK-7	T	530 25	81%	914/358-2700 Fax 914/665-0481
Edward Williams Elem Sch 9 Union Ln, Mount Vernon 10553 Crystal Smalls	PK-6	T	470 26	84%	914/665-5070 Fax 914/665-5237
Graham Elem Sch 421 E 5th St, Mount Vernon 10553 Natasha Gregor	PK-8	T	446 25	75%	914/358-2803 Fax 914/665-1230
Grimes Elem Sch 58 S 10th Ave, Mount Vernon 10550 Erik Van Gunten	K-7	T	450 29	79%	914/665-5020 Fax 914/665-5016
Hamilton Elem Sch 20 Oak St, Mount Vernon 10550 **Jennifer Wesolowski**	K-6	T	413 24	87%	914/665-5050 Fax 914/665-5052
Ⓜ Holmes Magnet Elem Sch 195 N Columbus Ave, Mount Vernon 10553 Danielle Davis-Marrow	PK-8	T	382 15	71%	914/665-5110 Fax 914/665-5116
Lincoln Elem Sch 170 E Lincoln Ave, Mount Vernon 10552 Rebecca Jones	K-8	T	675 38	75%	914/665-5039 Fax 914/665-5378
Mount Vernon High Sch 100 California Rd, Mount Vernon 10552 Ronald Gonzalez	9-12	GTV	1,417 200	75%	914/665-5300 Fax 914/665-5281
Mount Vernon Steam Academy 350 Gramatan Ave, Mount Vernon 10552 Sharon Bradley	8-10	T	491	85%	914/665-5120
Nellie Thornton High Sch 121 S 6th Ave, Mount Vernon 10550 Evelyn Collins	6-12	T	531	76%	914/358-2740 Fax 914/358-2792
Ⓐ Nelson Mandela-Zollicoffer HS 250 Gramatan Ave, Mount Vernon 10550 Ralph Burts	9-12		80 12		914/358-2720 Fax 914/665-5086
Pennington Elem Sch 20 Fairway St, Mount Vernon 10552 Daniel Brady	PK-6	T	383 17	47%	914/665-5105 Fax 914/665-5107
Rebecca Turner Elem Sch 625 S 4th Ave, Mount Vernon 10550 Jamal Doggett	PK-5	T	290 40	77%	914/665-5100 Fax 914/665-5096
Traphagen Elem Sch 72 Lexington Ave, Mount Vernon 10552 Carol Quinones	PK-6	T	429 22	56%	914/665-5060 Fax 914/665-5062

- **Mt Pleasant Cottage UFSD** PID: 01854737 914/769-0456
  1075 Broadway, Pleasantville 10570 Fax 914/769-7331

Schools: 2 \ **Teachers:** 34 \ **Students:** 215 \ **Special Ed Students:** 125 \ **LEP Students:** 3 \ **College-Bound:** 69% \ **Ethnic:** African American 61%, Hispanic 31%, Caucasian 8% \ **Exp:** $849 (High) \ **Open-Close:** 09/04 - 06/25 \ **DTBP:** $161 (High)

Stephen Beovich 1
David Rader 5
Rita Golden 67
Angelo Rubbo 2,15
Millicent Lee 36,79

Public Schs..Principal	Grd	Prgm	Enr/#Cls	SN	
⑨ Edenwald Sch 1075 Broadway, Pleasantville 10570 Christine Leamon	Spec	MT	82	97%	914/769-0456 Fax 914/747-9279
⑨ Mt Pleasant Cottage Sch 1075 Broadway, Pleasantville 10570 Jessica Harris	Spec	MT	133 33	91%	914/769-0456 Fax 914/747-5596

- **Mt Pleasant Ctl School Dist** PID: 00781034 914/769-5500
  825 Westlake Dr, Thornwood 10594 Fax 914/769-3733

Schools: 4 \ **Teachers:** 182 \ **Students:** 2,000 \ **Special Ed Students:** 343 \ **LEP Students:** 55 \ **College-Bound:** 97% \ **Ethnic:** Asian 5%, African American 1%, Hispanic 14%, Caucasian 81% \ **Exp:** $266 (Med) \ **Poverty:** 3% \ **Title I:** $64,244 \ **Special Education:** $1,374,000 \ **Open-Close:** 09/03 - 06/24 \ **DTBP:** $168 (High)

Dr Kurtis Kotes 1
Stefanie Flynn 2,11
Donna Pirro 6*
Traci Holtz 58,79
Alyson Walsh 71*
Dr Nasrin Rouzati 286,295
Andrew Lennon 2,5
Eric Strack 3
Adam Bronstein 8
Colleen Neglia 67
Vineetha Joy 73

Public Schs..Principal	Grd	Prgm	Enr/#Cls	SN	
Columbus Elem Sch 580 Columbus Ave, Thornwood 10594 Mike Cunzio	3-5		450 23	8%	914/769-8538 Fax 914/769-8512

1 Superintendent	8 Curric/Instruct K-12	19 Chief Financial Officer	29 Family/Consumer Science	39 Social Studies K-12	49 English/Lang Arts Elem	59 Special Education Elem	69 Academic Assessment
2 Bus/Finance/Purchasing	9 Curric/Instruct Elem	20 Art K-12	30 Adult Education	40 Social Studies Elem	50 English/Lang Arts Sec	60 Special Education Sec	70 Research/Development
3 Buildings And Grounds	10 Curric/Instruct Sec	21 Art Elem	31 Career/Sch-to-Work K-12	41 Social Studies Sec	51 Reading K-12	61 Foreign/World Lang K-12	71 Public Information
4 Food Service	11 Federal Program	22 Art Sec	32 Career/Sch-to-Work Elem	42 Science K-12	52 Reading Elem	62 Foreign/World Lang Elem	72 Summer School
5 Transportation	12 Title I	23 Music K-12	33 Career/Sch-to-Work Sec	43 Science Elem	53 Reading Sec	63 Foreign/World Lang Sec	73 Instructional Tech
6 Athletic	13 Title V	24 Music Elem	34 Early Childhood Ed	44 Science Sec	54 Remedial Reading K-12	64 Religious Education K-12	74 Inservice Training
7 Health Services	15 Asst Superintendent	25 Music Sec	35 Health/Phys Education	45 Math K-12	55 Remedial Reading Elem	65 Religious Education Elem	75 Marketing/Distributive
	16 Instructional Media Svcs	26 Business Education	36 Guidance Services K-12	46 Math Elem	56 Remedial Reading Sec	66 Religious Education Sec	76 Info Systems
	17 Chief Operations Officer	27 Career & Tech Ed	37 Guidance Services Elem	47 Math Sec	57 Bilingual/ELL	67 School Board President	77 Psychological Assess
	18 Chief Academic Officer	28 Technology Education	38 Guidance Services Sec	48 English/Lang Arts K-12	58 Special Education K-12	68 Teacher Personnel	78 Affirmative Action

New York School Directory — Westchester County

Hawthorne Elem Sch 225 Memorial Dr, Hawthorne 10532 Anne Stern	K-2		475 23	5%	914/769-8536 Fax 914/769-8527
Westlake High Sch 825 Westlake Dr, Thornwood 10594 Keith Schenker	9-12		561 100	6%	914/769-8311 Fax 914/769-0596
Westlake Middle Sch 825 Westlake Dr, Thornwood 10594 Anthony Mungioli	6-8		423 40	8%	914/769-8540 Fax 914/769-8550

● **Mt Pleasant-Blythedale UFSD** PID: 01854749 914/347-1800
  95 Bradhurst Ave, Valhalla 10595 Fax 914/347-2307

Schools: 1 \ **Teachers:** 20 \ **Students:** 134 \ **Special Ed Students:** 106 \ **College-Bound:** 100% \ **Ethnic:** Asian 5%, African American 25%, Hispanic 38%, Caucasian 31% \ **Exp:** $400 (High) \ **Open-Close:** 09/04 - 06/25 \ **DTBP:** $137 (High) \ [f]

Dr Emily Hersh 1,11,73   Peter Rittmaster 67

Public Schs..Principal	Grd	Prgm	Enr/#Cls	SN	
ⓨ Mt Pleasant-Blythdale Sch 95 Bradhurst Ave, Valhalla 10595 Griselda Reyes	Spec	MT	134 18	2%	914/347-1800

● **New Rochelle City School Dist** PID: 00781096 914/576-4300
  515 North Ave, New Rochelle 10801 Fax 914/632-4144

Schools: 10 \ **Teachers:** 732 \ **Students:** 11,000 \ **Special Ed Students:** 1,771 \ **LEP Students:** 1,286 \ **Ethnic:** Asian 5%, African American 21%, Hispanic 48%, Caucasian 26% \ **Exp:** $171 (Low) \ **Poverty:** 10% \ **Title I:** $2,029,968 \ **Special Education:** $10,776,000 \ **Open-Close:** 09/09 - 06/25 \ **DTBP:** $221 (High)

Dr Laura Feijoo 1   Gregory Kerm 2,15
Carl Thurnau 3   Dr Brooke Balchan 7,85
Dr Alex Marrero 8,18,57,69,273   Tiara Reyes-Vega 8,57
Dr Anthony Bongo 15,77,79,90,271,275   Ryan Reed 15,68
Francis Curley 36   Dara Joseph 58
Rachel Relkin 67   Debra Fishman 73
Bruce Daniele 91*

Public Schs..Principal	Grd	Prgm	Enr/#Cls	SN	
Albert Leonard Middle Sch 25 Gerada Ln, New Rochelle 10804 John Barnes	6-8		1,169 50	29%	914/576-4339 Fax 914/576-4784
Ⓜ Columbus Elem Sch 275 Washington Ave, New Rochelle 10801 Michael Galland	K-5	T	806 50	78%	914/576-4401 Fax 914/576-4628
Ⓜ Daniel Webster Magnet Sch 95 Glenmore Dr, New Rochelle 10801 Melissa Passarelli	K-5		486 26	24%	914/576-4460 Fax 914/576-4479
George M Davis Elem Sch 80 Iselin Dr, New Rochelle 10804 Anthony Bambrola	K-5		719 40	27%	914/576-4420 Fax 914/576-4225
Henry Barnard Early Chldhd Ctr 129 Barnard Rd, New Rochelle 10801 Dr Nicolas Cracco	PK-2	T	481 26	41%	914/576-4386 Fax 914/576-4625
Isaac E Young Middle Sch 270 Centre Ave, New Rochelle 10805 Dr Anthony Bongo	6-8		1,069	62%	914/576-4360 Fax 914/632-2738
Jefferson Elem Sch 131 Weyman Ave, New Rochelle 10805 Kimmerly Nieves	K-5	T	528 34	67%	914/576-4430 Fax 914/576-4631
New Rochelle High Sch 265 Clove Rd, New Rochelle 10801 Joseph Starvaggi	9-12	AGTV	3,385 128	44%	914/576-4500 Fax 914/576-4284
Trinity Elem Sch 180 Pelham Rd, New Rochelle 10805 Michael Hilderbrand	K-5	T	821 37	57%	914/576-4440 Fax 914/576-4266
William B Ward Elem Sch 311 Broadfield Rd, New Rochelle 10804 Franco Miele	K-5		1,039 70	26%	914/576-4450 Fax 914/576-4263

● **New York Alt High Sch SD 79** PID: 00740626
  (Part of New York City Dept of Ed in New York County)

Public Schs..Principal	Grd	Prgm	Enr/#Cls	SN
Ⓐ Passages Acad-Dobbs Ferry 1 Echo Hills Dr, Dobbs Ferry 10522 Brendan Daly	9-12		401	

● **North Salem Central Sch Dist** PID: 00781242 914/669-5414
  230 June Rd, North Salem 10560 Fax 914/669-8753

Schools: 2 \ **Teachers:** 116 \ **Students:** 1,046 \ **Special Ed Students:** 163 \ **LEP Students:** 27 \ **College-Bound:** 95% \ **Ethnic:** Asian 3%, African American 1%, African American 17%, Caucasian 78% \ **Exp:** $375 (High) \ **Poverty:** 5% \ **Title I:** $105,219 \ **Special Education:** $1,000,000 \ **Open-Close:** 09/07 - 06/25 \ **DTBP:** $359 (High)

Dr Kenneth Freeston 1   Barbara Briganti 2,15
Dr Joannes Sieverding 3,5,73,91   Denise Kiernan 6,35
Dr Julio Vazquez 8,68,69,273   Dr Adam Vanderstuyf 11,36,58,79,83,85,88,298
Deborah D'Agostino 67   Michelle Sands 81*
Elizabeth Lofran 270

Public Schs..Principal	Grd	Prgm	Enr/#Cls	SN	
North Salem Middle High Sch 230 June Rd, North Salem 10560 Vincent Digrandi	6-12		620 27	12%	914/669-5414 Fax 914/669-5663
Pequenakonck Elem Sch 173 June Rd, North Salem 10560 Mary Johnson	K-5	T	426 29	14%	914/669-5317 Fax 914/669-4326

● **Ossining Union Free Sch Dist** PID: 00781292 914/941-7700
  400 Executive Blvd, Ossining 10562 Fax 914/941-7291

Schools: 6 \ **Teachers:** 383 \ **Students:** 5,100 \ **Special Ed Students:** 734 \ **LEP Students:** 506 \ **College-Bound:** 87% \ **Ethnic:** Asian 4%, African American 10%, Hispanic 63%, Caucasian 22% \ **Exp:** $205 (Med) \ **Poverty:** 8% \ **Title I:** $665,094 \ **Special Education:** $3,976,000 \ **Open-Close:** 09/03 - 06/25 \ **DTBP:** $341 (High) \ [f] [t]

Raymond Sanchez 1   Alita Zuber 2,4,15
Ken Waldron 3   James Minihan 5,91
Jim Dennett .... 6,35*   Dianne Thomas 7
Elizabeth Smith 8   Carrieann Sipos 9,296
Dr Brian Alm 10   Nancy Arroyo 11,52,57,298
Joan Garone 12,68   Bradley Morrison 20,23
Mirla Puello 34,48,52,57,77,280   Alexandra Greenberg 45
Maureen Boozang-Hill 58,79   Lisa Rudley 67
Kelly Douai 73   Mike Hanna 73,295
Phyllis Arduino 76

Public Schs..Principal	Grd	Prgm	Enr/#Cls	SN	
Anne M Dorner Middle Sch 100 Van Cortlandt Ave, Ossining 10562 Kate Mathews	6-8	V	1,077 40	60%	914/762-5740 Fax 914/762-5246 [f][t]

---

79 Student Personnel	91 Safety/Security	275 Response To Intervention	298 Grant Writer/Ptnrships	**School Programs**	**Social Media**
80 Driver Ed/Safety	92 Magnet School	277 Remedial Math K-12	750 Chief Innovation Officer	A = Alternative Program	
81 Gifted/Talented	93 Parental Involvement	280 Literacy Coach	751 Chief of Staff	G = Adult Classes	[f] = Facebook
82 Video Services	95 Tech Prep Program	285 STEM	752 Social Emotional Learning	M = Magnet Program	
83 Substance Abuse Prev	97 Chief Infomation Officer	286 Digital Learning		T = Title I Schoolwide	[t] = Twitter
84 Erate	98 Chief Technology Officer	288 Common Core Standards	**Other School Types**	V = Career & Tech Ed Programs	
85 AIDS Education	270 Character Education	294 Accountability	Ⓐ = Alternative School		
88 Alternative/At Risk	271 Migrant Education	295 Network System	Ⓒ = Charter School	New Schools are shaded	
89 Multi-Cultural Curriculum	273 Teacher Mentor	296 Title II Programs	Ⓜ = Magnet School	New Superintendents and Principals are bold	
90 Social Work	274 Before/After Sch	297 Webmaster	Ⓨ = Year-Round School	Personnel with email addresses are underscored	

NY–259

Westchester County

Market Data Retrieval

Brookside Primary Sch 30 Ryder Rd, Ossining 10562 Dr Ann Dealy	1-2	T	692 27	59%	914/762-5780 Fax 914/941-4674
Claremont Elem Sch 2 Claremont Rd, Ossining 10562 Ferzeen Shamsi	3-4		723 25	63%	914/762-5830 Fax 914/941-4964
Ossining High Sch 29 S Highland Ave, Ossining 10562 Stephen Hancock	9-12		1,560 60	52%	914/762-5760 Fax 914/762-4011
Park Early Childhood Center 22 Edward St, Ossining 10562 Cynthia Bardwell	PK-K	T	597 23	40%	914/762-5850
Roosevelt Elem Sch 190 Croton Ave, Ossining 10562 Michelle Grier	5-5		376	59%	914/762-2682 Fax 914/941-5341

- **Peekskill City School Dist** PID: 00781369 914/737-3300
  1031 Elm St, Peekskill 10566 Fax 914/737-3912

Schools: 6 \ **Teachers:** 228 \ **Students:** 3,400 \ **Special Ed Students:** 651 \ **LEP Students:** 773 \ **Ethnic:** Asian 1%, African American 20%, Hispanic 71%, Caucasian 8% \ **Exp:** $296 (Med) \ **Poverty:** 15% \ **Title I:** $921,472 \ **Special Education:** $7,139,000 \ **Open-Close:** 09/03 - 06/25 \ **DTBP:** $322 (High) \

Dr David Mauricio 1
Carmine Crisci 3
Andrew Weisman 4*
Dr Mary Foster 9,15
Joseph Mosey 11,15,68,69,270,280
Madeline Sanchez 57,61,280
Laura Belfiore 71
Sadika Clarke 79
Dr Anchala Sobrin 285
Robin Zimmerman 2,15
Andrew Weisman 4
Austin Goldberg 6,7,35
Daniel Callahan 10,15
Ellen Gerace 12,58,88,275
Allen Jenkins 67
Janice Reid 73,97,295
David Santiago 91*

Public Schs..Principal	Grd	Prgm	Enr/#Cls	SN	
Hillcrest Elem Sch 4 Horton Dr, Peekskill 10566 Randy Lichtenwalner	4-5	T	504 30	61%	914/739-2284 Fax 914/737-9053
Oakside Elem Sch 200 Decatur Ave, Peekskill 10566 Staci Woodly	2-3	T	521 25	68%	914/737-1591 Fax 914/737-1530
Peekskill High Sch 1072 Elm St, Peekskill 10566 Rodney Arthur	9-12	T	1,027 45	57%	914/737-0201 Fax 914/737-2550
Peekskill Middle Sch 212 Ringgold St, Peekskill 10566 Jamal Lewis	6-8	T	715 35	63%	914/737-4542 Fax 914/737-3253
Uriah Hill Elem Sch 980 Pemart Ave, Peekskill 10566 Carmen Vargas	PK-PK		164	53%	914/739-0682 Fax 914/739-8795
Woodside Elem Sch 612 Depew St, Peekskill 10566 Rebecca Rodriguez	K-1	T	550 21	63%	914/739-0093 Fax 914/737-9039

- **Pelham Union Free School Dist** PID: 00781436 914/738-3434
  18 Franklin Pl, Pelham 10803 Fax 914/738-7223

Schools: 6 \ **Teachers:** 225 \ **Students:** 2,800 \ **Special Ed Students:** 324 \ **LEP Students:** 26 \ **College-Bound:** 94% \ **Ethnic:** Asian 6%, African American 6%, Hispanic 17%, Caucasian 72% \ **Exp:** $221 (Med) \ **Poverty:** 3% \ **Title I:** $91,295 \ **Special Education:** $1,725,000 \ **Open-Close:** 09/08 - 06/25 \ **DTBP:** $310 (High) \

Dr Cheryl Champ 1,11
John Condon 3
James Hricay 2,5,15
Karla Grimaldi 4
Christian Hodge 6,35
Julia Chung 11,15,58,79,275,752
Dr Thomas Callahan 42,45,277
Greg Lau 60
Alex Wolff 71
Andrea Pellicane 83,285
Dr Steven Garcia 8,11,15,68,69,288,296
Eugene Farrell 36*
Dr Maria Thompson 54
Jessica DeDomenico 67
John Sebelos 73,286,295
Ralph DeMasi 91

Public Schs..Principal	Grd	Prgm	Enr/#Cls	SN	
Colonial Elem Sch 315 Highbrook Ave, Pelham 10803 Tonya Wilson	K-5		335	3%	914/738-2680 Fax 914/738-8187
Hutchinson Elem Sch 301 Third Ave, Pelham 10803 Trisha Fitzgerald	K-5	T	362 15	26%	914/738-3640 Fax 914/738-8198
Pelham Memorial High Sch 575 Colonial Ave, Pelham 10803 Jeannine Clark	9-12		907 56	11%	914/738-8110 Fax 914/738-8122
Pelham Middle Sch 28 Franklin Pl, Pelham 10803 Lynn Sabia	6-8		701	9%	914/738-8190 Fax 914/738-8132
Prospect Hill Elem Sch 1000 Washington Ave, Pelham 10803 Jeannine Carr	K-5		311 20	3%	914/738-6690 Fax 914/738-8258
Siwanoy Elem Sch 489 Siwanoy Pl, Pelham 10803 Susan Gilbert	K-5		297 17	3%	914/738-7650 Fax 914/738-8199

- **Pleasantville Union Free SD** PID: 00781503 914/741-1400
  60 Romer Ave, Pleasantville 10570 Fax 914/741-1499

Schools: 3 \ **Teachers:** 141 \ **Students:** 1,700 \ **Special Ed Students:** 290 \ **LEP Students:** 43 \ **College-Bound:** 92% \ **Ethnic:** Asian 6%, African American 2%, Hispanic 12%, Caucasian 80% \ **Exp:** $280 (Med) \ **Poverty:** 1% \ **Title I:** $360,215 \ **Special Education:** $1,953,000 \ **Open-Close:** 09/08 - 06/25 \ **DTBP:** $166 (High) \

Mary Fox-Alter 1,11
Steve Chamberlain 3
Dr Cameron Fadjo 8,15,73
Angela Vella 67
Timothy Whipple 2,15
John Bauerlein 6,35
Daniel Lorio 34,58
Julie Schwartz 71

Public Schs..Principal	Grd	Prgm	Enr/#Cls	SN	
Bedford Road Sch 289 Bedford Rd, Pleasantville 10570 Peggy Galotti	K-4		567	11%	914/741-1440 Fax 914/741-1468
Pleasantville High Sch 60 Romer Ave, Pleasantville 10570 Joe Palumbo	9-12		598 30	16%	914/741-1420 Fax 914/741-1407
Pleasantville Middle Sch 40 Romer Ave, Pleasantville 10570 Donald Marra	5-8		530 36	12%	914/741-1450 Fax 914/741-1476

- **Pocantico Hills Ctl Sch Dist** PID: 00781553 914/631-2440
  599 Bedford Rd, Sleepy Hollow 10591 Fax 914/631-3280

Schools: 1 \ **Teachers:** 37 \ **Students:** 308 \ **Special Ed Students:** 33 \ **LEP Students:** 8 \ **Ethnic:** Asian 14%, African American 14%, Hispanic 29%, Caucasian 43% \ **Exp:** $998 (High) \ **Poverty:** 9% \ **Title I:** $62,715 \ **Special Education:** $465,000 \ **Open-Close:** 09/03 - 06/25 \ **DTBP:** $162 (High)

Richard Calkins 1
Donald Booth 3
Jane Anastasi 5
Adam Brown 9,11,69,73,76,288*
Alferd Pacille 67
Lisa Raymond 2,15
Kassie Arcate 4
Emma Goodman 5
Joy Scantlebury 57*
Dawn Horecky 274

1 Superintendent	8 Curric/Instruct K-12	19 Chief Financial Officer	29 Family/Consumer Science	39 Social Studies K-12	49 English/Lang Arts Elem	59 Special Education Elem	69 Academic Assessment
2 Bus/Finance/Purchasing	9 Curric/Instruct Elem	20 Art K-12	30 Adult Education	40 Social Studies Elem	50 English/Lang Arts Sec	60 Special Education Sec	70 Research/Development
3 Buildings And Grounds	10 Curric/Instruct Sec	21 Art Elem	31 Career/Sch-to-Work K-12	41 Social Studies Sec	51 Reading K-12	61 Foreign/World Lang K-12	71 Public Information
4 Food Service	11 Federal Program	22 Art Sec	32 Career/Sch-to-Work Elem	42 Science K-12	52 Reading Elem	62 Foreign/World Lang Elem	72 Summer School
5 Transportation	12 Title I	23 Music K-12	33 Career/Sch-to-Work Sec	43 Science Elem	53 Reading Sec	63 Foreign/World Lang Sec	73 Instructional Tech
6 Athletic	13 Title V	24 Music Elem	34 Early Childhood Ed	44 Science Sec	54 Remedial Reading K-12	64 Religious Education K-12	74 Inservice Training
7 Health Services	15 Asst Superintendent	25 Music Sec	35 Health/Phys Education	45 Math K-12	55 Remedial Reading Elem	65 Religious Education Elem	75 Marketing/Distributive
	16 Instructional Media Svcs	26 Business Education	36 Guidance Services K-12	46 Math Elem	56 Remedial Reading Sec	66 Religious Education Sec	76 Info Systems
	17 Chief Operations Officer	27 Career & Tech Ed	37 Guidance Services Elem	47 Math Sec	57 Bilingual/ELL	67 School Board President	77 Psychological Assess
	18 Chief Academic Officer	28 Technology Education	38 Guidance Services Sec	48 English/Lang Arts K-12	58 Special Education K-12	68 Teacher Personnel	78 Affirmative Action

New York School Directory — Westchester County

Marianne Heslin 296

Public Schs..Principal	Grd	Prgm	Enr/#Cls	SN	
Pocantico Hills Central Sch 599 Bedford Rd, Sleepy Hollow 10591 Adam Brown	PK-8		308 21	20%	914/631-2440

● **Port Chester Rye Union Free SD** PID: 00781577   914/934-7900
113 Bowman Ave, Port Chester 10573   Fax 914/934-0727

Schools: 6 \ **Teachers:** 333 \ **Students:** 5,000 \ **Special Ed Students:** 727 \ **LEP Students:** 1,445 \ **College-Bound:** 85% \ **Ethnic:** Asian 2%, African American 4%, Hispanic 81%, Caucasian 14% \ **Exp:** $205 (Med) \ **Poverty:** 15% \ **Title I:** $1,164,202 \ **Special Education:** $4,488,000 \ **Open-Close:** 09/02 - 06/25 \ **DTBP:** $292 (High)

Dr Edward Kliszus 1		Philip Silano 2,4,5,15	
Ray Renda 3,91		James Ryan 6,7,35	
Dr Colleen Carroll 8,69		Dr Mitchell Combs 11,15,68,296,298	
Felipe Orozco 57		Tatiana Memoli 58	
Sherry George 84			

Public Schs..Principal	Grd	Prgm	Enr/#Cls	SN	
Ⓜ John F Kennedy Magnet Sch 40 Olivia St, Port Chester 10573 Judy Diaz	1-5	T	680	89%	914/934-7990 Fax 914/939-6625
King Street Elem Sch 697 King St, Port Chester 10573 Samuel Ortiz	K-5	T	407 20	52%	914/934-7996 Fax 914/939-9351
Park Avenue Elem Sch 75 Park Ave, Port Chester 10573 Rosa Taylor	K-5	T	453 21	63%	914/934-7895 Fax 914/939-9243
Port Chester High Sch 1 Tamarack Rd, Port Chester 10573 Dr Mitchell Combs	9-12	T	1,618 65	70%	914/934-7950 Fax 914/934-2998
Port Chester Middle Sch 113 Bowman Ave, Port Chester 10573 Patrick Swift	6-8	T	1,079 55	76%	914/934-7930 Fax 914/934-7886
Thomas A Edison Elem Sch 132 Rectory St, Port Chester 10573 Ivan Tolentino	K-5	T	416 40	87%	914/934-7981 Fax 914/934-7879

● **Rye City School Dist** PID: 00781682   914/967-6100
555 Theodore Fremd Ave Ste 101, Rye 10580   Fax 914/967-6957

Schools: 6 \ **Teachers:** 268 \ **Students:** 3,510 \ **Special Ed Students:** 364 \ **LEP Students:** 115 \ **Ethnic:** Asian 8%, African American 1%, Hispanic 7%, Caucasian 83% \ **Exp:** $516 (High) \ **Poverty:** 2% \ **Title I:** $69,316 \ **Special Education:** $2,096,000 \ **Open-Close:** 09/08 - 06/25 \ **DTBP:** $316 (High)

Dr Eric Byrne 1	Gabriella O'Connor 2,5,15
Gerald Abbey 3	Stacy Falcone 4
Michael Arias 6,35*	Tracey Barnett 7
Sheryl Goffman 8,11,15,288,296	Elaine Cuglietto 15,68
Dr Erin Vredenburgh 58,79	Jennifer Fall 58*
Jennifer Boyle 67	Kerri Winderman 69
Sarah Derman 71	Kaitlyn Sassone 73,97
Julie Heller 280	

Public Schs..Principal	Grd	Prgm	Enr/#Cls	SN	
Midland Elem Sch 312 Midland Ave, Rye 10580 Jim Boylan	K-5		540 29	1%	914/967-6100 Fax 914/921-6848
Milton Elem Sch 12 Hewlett St, Rye 10580 Dr Joanne Nardone	K-5		375 18		914/967-6100 Fax 914/921-2796
Osborn Elem Sch 10 Osborn Rd, Rye 10580 Angela Garcia	K-5		519 30	3%	914/967-6100 Fax 917/921-3842
Rye High Sch 1 Parsons St, Rye 10580 Patricia Taylor	9-12	AT	1,032 60	2%	914/967-6100 Fax 914/967-4380
Rye Middle Sch 3 Parsons St, Rye 10580 Dr Ann Edwards	6-8	T	768 45	3%	914/967-6100 Fax 914/921-6189
Ⓐ Rye School of Leadership 324 Midland Ave, Rye 10580 Jennifer Fall	9-12		25 3		914/760-1462 Fax 914/921-2414

● **Rye Neck Union Free Sch Dist** PID: 00781735   914/777-5200
310 Hornidge Rd, Mamaroneck 10543   Fax 914/777-5201

Schools: 4 \ **Teachers:** 126 \ **Students:** 1,525 \ **Special Ed Students:** 188 \ **LEP Students:** 66 \ **College-Bound:** 90% \ **Ethnic:** Asian 8%, African American 3%, Hispanic 22%, Caucasian 66% \ **Exp:** $218 (Med) \ **Poverty:** 4% \ **Title I:** $65,090 \ **Special Education:** $837,000 \ **Open-Close:** 09/08 - 06/24 \ **DTBP:** $161 (High) \ 📘 🅣

Dr Barbara Ferraro 1	Carolyn Mahar 2,5
Christine Torregrossa 4	Joe Ceglia 6
Tina Wilson 10,69,83,88*	Diane Santangelo 11,58,298*
Linda Costelloe 16*	Corinne Ryan 33,36,79*
Jean Aggarwala 57	Jennifer Rubin 67
Steve Bavaro 73	Ernie Ricketts 91*
Laurel Ryan 93	

Public Schs..Principal	Grd	Prgm	Enr/#Cls	SN	
Daniel Warren Elem Sch 1310 Harrison Ave, Mamaroneck 10543 Tara Goldberg	K-2	T	325 17	12%	914/777-4200 Fax 914/777-4201
F E Bellows Elem Sch 200 Carroll Ave, Mamaroneck 10543 Michael Scarantino	3-5	T	368 20	14%	914/777-4602 Fax 914/777-4601
Rye Neck High Sch 300 Hornidge Rd, Mamaroneck 10543 Tina Wilson	9-12	T	470 50	15%	914/777-4800 Fax 914/777-4801
Rye Neck Middle Sch 300 Hornidge Rd, Mamaroneck 10543 Eric Lutinski	6-8	T	409 18	16%	914/777-4702 Fax 914/777-4701

● **Scarsdale Union Free Sch Dist** PID: 00781802   914/721-2410
2 Brewster Rd, Scarsdale 10583   Fax 914/722-2822

Schools: 7 \ **Teachers:** 400 \ **Students:** 4,771 \ **Special Ed Students:** 505 \ **LEP Students:** 74 \ **College-Bound:** 98% \ **Ethnic:** Asian 22%, African American 1%, Hispanic 7%, Caucasian 70% \ **Exp:** $358 (High) \ **Poverty:** 2% \ **Title I:** $80,305 \ **Special Education:** $2,763,000 \ **Open-Close:** 09/08 - 06/25 \ **DTBP:** $309 (High)

Dr Thomas Hagerman 1	Stuart Mattey 2,3,4,5,15,88,91,275
John Trenholm 3	Gerson Katuemutima 5
Raymond Pappalardi 6,35*	Raymond Tappalardi 7
Edgar McIntosh 8,15	Andrew Patrick 15,68
Jerry Crisci 16,73,295	Micahel Basso 16,82
Adgar MacAntash 51,54,57,294,296	Eric Rauschenbach 58,79,83*
Pamela Fuehrer 67	Rachel Moseley 71,76,97,750
Victoria Presser 71	Anne Marie Nee 74,273,285
Wayne Ricketts 76	

---

79 Student Personnel	91 Safety/Security	275 Response To Intervention	298 Grant Writer/Ptnrships	**School Programs**	**Social Media**
80 Driver Ed/Safety	92 Magnet School	277 Remedial Math K-12	750 Chief Innovation Officer	A = Alternative Program	📘 = Facebook
81 Gifted/Talented	93 Parental Involvement	280 Literacy Coach	751 Chief of Staff	G = Adult Classes	🅣 = Twitter
82 Video Services	95 Tech Prep Program	285 STEM	752 Social Emotional Learning	M = Magnet Program	
83 Substance Abuse Prev	97 Chief Infomation Officer	286 Digital Learning		T = Title I Schoolwide	
84 Erate	98 Chief Technology Officer	288 Common Core Standards	**Other School Types**	V = Career & Tech Ed Programs	
85 AIDS Education	270 Accountability	294 Accountability	Ⓐ = Alternative School		
88 Alternative/At Risk	271 Migrant Education	295 Network System	Ⓒ = Charter School	New Schools are shaded	
89 Multi-Cultural Curriculum	273 Teacher Mentor	296 Title II Programs	Ⓜ = Magnet School	New Superintendents and Principals are bold	
90 Social Work	274 Before/After Sch	297 Webmaster	Ⓨ = Year-Round School	Personnel with email addresses are underscored	

Westchester County

Market Data Retrieval

Public Schs..Principal	Grd	Prgm	Enr/#Cls	SN
Edgewood Elem Sch 1 Roosevelt Pl, Scarsdale 10583 Tashia Brown	K-5		372 23	914/721-2700 Fax 914/721-2717
Fox Meadow Elem Sch 59 Brewster Rd, Scarsdale 10583 Melissa Feinberg	K-5		474 25	914/721-2720 Fax 914/721-2730
Greenacres Elem Sch 41 Huntington Rd, Scarsdale 10583 Sharon Hill	K-5		337 22	914/721-2740 Fax 914/721-2755
Heathcote Elem Sch 26 Palmer Ave, Scarsdale 10583 Maria Stile	K-5		376 35	914/721-2760 Fax 914/721-2777
Quaker Ridge Elem Sch 125 Weaver St, Scarsdale 10583 Felix Gil	K-5		508 26	914/721-2780 Fax 914/721-2784
Scarsdale Middle Sch 134 Mamaroneck Rd, Scarsdale 10583 Meghan Troy	6-8	V	1,154 105	914/721-2600 Fax 914/721-2655
Scarsdale Senior High Sch 1057 Post Rd, Scarsdale 10583 Kenneth Bonamo	9-12	AV	1,524 75	914/721-2500 Fax 914/722-2800

● **Somers Central School Dist** PID: 00781888 914/277-2400
250 Route 202, Somers 10589 Fax 914/277-2409

Schools: 4 \ **Teachers:** 251 \ **Students:** 2,866 \ **Special Ed Students:** 547 \ **LEP Students:** 36 \ **College-Bound:** 95% \ **Ethnic:** Asian 4%, African American 1%, Hispanic 10%, Caucasian 86% \ **Exp:** $234 (Med) \ **Poverty:** 2% \ **Title I:** $62,554 \ **Special Education:** $2,882,000 \ **Open-Close:** 09/08 - 06/25 \ **DTBP:** $313 (High) \ f

Dr Raymond Blanch .... 1 Kenneth Crowley 2,15
Robert Klick .... 3 Norma Zeller 4*
Joseph Bernardi .... 5,91 Roman Catalino 6,35*
Julie Gherardi .... 8,273,280,285,288 Stacey Elconin 11,34,57,58,79,275
Philip Kavanaugh .... 36,69,83,88 Lindsay Portney 67
Matthew Carr .... 71 Kimelyz Blau 73,76,295
Theresa Reda 90*

Public Schs..Principal	Grd	Prgm	Enr/#Cls	SN
Primrose Elem Sch 110 Primrose St, Lincolndale 10540 Katie Winter	K-2		517 37	6% 914/248-8888 Fax 914/248-5384
Somers High Sch 120 Primrose St, Lincolndale 10540 Mark Bayer	9-12	A	1,097 65	10% 914/248-8585 Fax 914/248-8186
Somers Intermediate Sch 240 Route 202, Somers 10589 Elizabeth Turner	3-5		553 36	11% 914/277-4344 Fax 914/277-3168
Somers Middle Sch 250 Route 202, Somers 10589 Jeffrey Getman	6-8		699 40	9% 914/277-3399 Fax 914/277-2236

● **Tarrytown Union Free Sch Dist** PID: 00781955 914/631-9404
200 N Broadway, Sleepy Hollow 10591 Fax 914/332-6283

Schools: 5 \ **Teachers:** 229 \ **Students:** 2,900 \ **Special Ed Students:** 374 \ **LEP Students:** 436 \ **Ethnic:** Asian 3%, African American 3%, Hispanic 62%, Caucasian 32% \ **Exp:** $369 (High) \ **Poverty:** 9% \ **Title I:** $407,987 \ **Special Education:** $2,681,000 \ **Open-Close:** 09/10 - 06/25 \ **DTBP:** $306 (High)

Christopher Borsari .... 1 Joy Myke 2
Anthony Deman .... 3 Maria Filippelli 4
Cyryl Hughes .... 5 Micheal Arias 6

Gail Duffy .... 8,11,68,69,91,273,288,296 Scott Dorn 15,58,79,752
Gail Persad .... 20* David Ziegler 36*
John Paine .... 67 Jean O'Brien 76*
Joe DeRose .... 295 Tina Kelly 298

Public Schs..Principal	Grd	Prgm	Enr/#Cls	SN
John Paulding Primary Sch 154 N Broadway, Tarrytown 10591 Maureen Barnett	PK-K	T	250 13	44% 914/631-5526 Fax 914/332-4265
Sleepy Hollow High Sch 210 N Broadway, Sleepy Hollow 10591 Dr Tracy Smith	9-12		850 70	53% 914/631-8838 Fax 914/332-6219
Sleepy Hollow Middle Sch 210 N Broadway, Sleepy Hollow 10591 Joshua Whitham	6-8		607	60% 914/332-6275 Fax 914/332-6546
W L Morse Elem Sch 30 Pocantico St, Sleepy Hollow 10591 Torrance Walley	1-2	T	397 18	56% 914/631-4144 Fax 914/332-4267
Washington Irving Sch 103 S Broadway, Tarrytown 10591 Thomas Holland	3-5		603 28	56% 914/631-4442 Fax 914/332-4077

● **Tuckahoe Union Free SD** PID: 00782026 914/337-6600
65 Siwanoy Blvd, Eastchester 10709 Fax 914/337-5735

Schools: 3 \ **Teachers:** 94 \ **Students:** 1,100 \ **Special Ed Students:** 163 \ **LEP Students:** 59 \ **College-Bound:** 88% \ **Ethnic:** Asian 8%, African American 9%, Hispanic 15%, Caucasian 68% \ **Exp:** $336 (High) \ **Poverty:** 4% \ **Title I:** $43,111 \ **Special Education:** $949,000 \ **Open-Close:** 09/03 - 06/25 \ **DTBP:** $138 (High)

Amy Goodman .... 1 Lee Lew 2,11,15
Christine Torregrossa .... 4 Paul Tobin 6
Ellen McDonnell .... 8,79* Evelyn Johnson 16*
Joseph Spatolo .... 58 Peter Casson 67
Michael Olivieri 73

Public Schs..Principal	Grd	Prgm	Enr/#Cls	SN
Tuckahoe High Sch 65 Siwanoy Blvd, Eastchester 10709 Dr Bart Linehan	9-12		306 30	25% 914/337-5376 Fax 914/337-5168
Tuckahoe Middle Sch 65 Siwanoy Blvd, Eastchester 10709 Gregory Stiefle	6-8		274 33	14% 914/337-5376 Fax 914/337-5236
William E Cottle Elem Sch 2 Siwanoy Blvd, Eastchester 10709 John Morash	K-5		600 32	16% 914/337-5376 Fax 914/337-5334

● **Valhalla Union Free Sch Dist** PID: 00782052 914/683-5040
316 Columbus Ave, Valhalla 10595 Fax 914/683-5075

Schools: 3 \ **Teachers:** 130 \ **Students:** 1,420 \ **Special Ed Students:** 237 \ **LEP Students:** 64 \ **College-Bound:** 95% \ **Ethnic:** Asian 7%, African American 7%, Hispanic 27%, Caucasian 58% \ **Exp:** $470 (High) \ **Poverty:** 3% \ **Title I:** $63,334 \ **Special Education:** $1,174,000 \ **Open-Close:** 09/08 - 06/25 \ **DTBP:** $167 (High) \ f t

Christina Howe .... 1,11,83 Kevin McLeod 2,15,19
Peter Kelly .... 3 Jaime Block 6*
Elizabeth Kimiecik .... 8,15,73 Genieve Holder 12,58
Jon Hirsch .... 27 Haidee Anaya 34,295*
Meghan Jacobsen .... 36 Laverne Clark 67

---

1 Superintendent	8 Curric/Instruct K-12	19 Chief Financial Officer	29 Family/Consumer Science	39 Social Studies K-12	49 English/Lang Arts Elem	59 Special Education Elem	69 Academic Assessment
2 Bus/Finance/Purchasing	9 Curric/Instruct Elem	20 Art K-12	30 Adult Education	40 Social Studies Elem	50 English/Lang Arts Sec	60 Special Education Sec	70 Research/Development
3 Buildings And Grounds	10 Curric/Instruct Sec	21 Art Elem	31 Career/Sch-to-Work K-12	41 Social Studies Sec	51 Reading K-12	61 Foreign/World Lang K-12	71 Public Information
4 Food Service	11 Federal Program	22 Art Sec	32 Career/Sch-to-Work Elem	42 Science K-12	52 Reading Elem	62 Foreign/World Lang Elem	72 Summer School
5 Transportation	12 Title I	23 Music K-12	33 Career/Sch-to-Work Sec	43 Science Elem	53 Reading Sec	63 Foreign/World Lang Sec	73 Instructional Tech
6 Athletic	13 Title V	24 Music Elem	34 Early Childhood Ed	44 Science Sec	54 Remedial Reading K-12	64 Religious Education K-12	74 Inservice Training
7 Health Services	15 Asst Superintendent	25 Music Sec	35 Health/Phys Education	45 Math K-12	55 Remedial Reading Elem	65 Religious Education Elem	75 Marketing/Distributive
	16 Instructional Media Svcs	26 Business Education	36 Guidance Services K-12	46 Math Elem	56 Remedial Reading Sec	66 Religious Education Sec	76 Info Systems
	17 Chief Operations Officer	27 Career & Tech Ed	37 Guidance Services Elem	47 Math Sec	57 Bilingual/ELL	67 School Board President	77 Psychological Assess
	18 Chief Academic Officer	28 Technology Education	38 Guidance Services Sec	48 English/Lang Arts K-12	58 Special Education K-12	68 Teacher Personnel	78 Affirmative Action

New York School Directory — Westchester County

Public Schs..Principal	Grd	Prgm	Enr/#Cls	SN	
Kensico Elem Sch 320 Columbus Ave, Valhalla 10595 Matthew Curran	3-5		314 18	21%	914/683-5030 Fax 914/683-5304
Valhalla Middle High Sch 300 Columbus Ave, Valhalla 10595 Jason Schrammel \ Jon Hirsch	6-12	T	766	19%	914/683-5000 Fax 914/683-5003 f t
Virginia Road Elem Sch 86 Virginia Rd, White Plains 10603 Haidee Anaya	K-2		307 19	14%	914/683-5035 Fax 914/683-5291

• White Plains City School Dist PID: 00782105

5 Homeside Ln, White Plains 10605
914/422-2000 Fax 914/422-2382

Schools: 9 \ **Teachers:** 464 \ **Students:** 7,000 \ **Special Ed Students:** 1,319 \ **LEP Students:** 1,160 \ **College-Bound:** 89% \ **Ethnic:** Asian 4%, African American 13%, Hispanic 60%, Caucasian 23% \ **Exp:** $424 (High) \ **Poverty:** 11% \ **Title I:** $1,345,684 \ **Special Education:** $6,946,000 \ **Open-Close:** 09/09 - 06/25 \ **DTBP:** $223 (High) \ f t

Dr Joseph Ricca 1	Dr Ann Vaccaro-Teich 2,5,15,91
Frank Stefanelli 3	Edward Marra 4
Sergio Alfonso 5	Mathew Cameron 6
Maggie Racioppo 7,35,85	Dr Debbie Hand .. 8,12,69,89,270,271,280,285
Ron Velez 11,76,295	Deborah Augarten 15,58,79
Scott Pepper 15,68	Gary West 23*
Sara Hall 36,77*	Richard Dillon 39*
Margaret Doty 42*	Lisa Panaro 57,61*
Susan Le Cointe 58	Susan Dorsett 58
Rosemarie Eller 67	Dr J Manning Campbell 68
Michele Schoenfeld 71	Rocco Varuolo 73,95,286
Susan Murphy 83*	Paul Bratcher 88
Tina Kelly 298	

Public Schs..Principal	Grd	Prgm	Enr/#Cls	SN	
Church Street Elem Sch 295 Church St, White Plains 10603 Myra Castillo	K-5	T	640 45	56%	914/422-2401 Fax 914/422-2409 f t
Eastview Middle Sch 350 Main St, White Plains 10601 Daisy Rodriguez	6-6		550 45		914/422-2223 Fax 914/422-2222 f t
George Washington Elem Sch 100 Orchard St, White Plains 10604 Laura Mungin	K-5	T	648 43	61%	914/422-2380 Fax 914/422-2108
Highlands Middle Sch 128 Grandview Ave, White Plains 10605 Ernest Spatafore	7-8	T	1,044 80	61%	914/422-2092 Fax 914/422-2273
Mamaroneck Avenue Elem Sch 7 Nosband Ave, White Plains 10605 Eileen McGuire	K-5	T	645 35	47%	914/422-2286 Fax 914/422-2109 f t
Post Road Elem Sch 175 W Post Rd, White Plains 10606 Jesimae Ossorio	K-5	T	634 40	62%	914/422-2320 Fax 914/422-2097
Ridgeway Elem Sch 225 Ridgeway, White Plains 10605 Jessica Torres	K-5	T	635 35	42%	914/422-2081 Fax 914/422-2366
Rochambeau Alt High Sch 228 Fisher Ave, White Plains 10606 Pual Bratcher	9-12		140 15		914/422-2420 Fax 914/422-2340
White Plains High Sch 550 North St, White Plains 10605 Ellen Doherty	9-12	V	2,239 85	58%	914/422-2182 Fax 914/422-2196

• Yonkers Public School Dist PID: 00782234

1 Larkin Ctr, Yonkers 10701
914/376-8000 Fax 914/376-8584

Schools: 40 \ **Teachers:** 1,523 \ **Students:** 27,000 \ **Special Ed Students:** 4,977 \ **LEP Students:** 3,328 \ **College-Bound:** 89% \ **Ethnic:** Asian 5%, African American 18%, Hispanic 60%, Caucasian 16% \ **Exp:** $108 (Low) \ **Poverty:** 16% \ **Title I:** $10,098,260 \ **Special Education:** $48,865,000 \ **Open-Close:** 09/08 - 06/25 \ **DTBP:** $226 (High) \ f t

Dr Edwin Quezada 1	Thomas Collich 2
John Carr 3	Paul Carney 3
James Rose 6,35	Rosanne Collins-Judon 8,15
Elaine Shine 11	Dr Andrea Coddett 15
Dr Luis Rodriguez 15,58	Susan Naber 27,30,31,95*
Jade Sharpe 36	Steve Lopez 67
James Anderson 69	Rachel Cole 69,70,79,294
Chris Carvalho 73,84,295	Brian Schulder 91
Tanya Long 298	

Public Schs..Principal	Grd	Prgm	Enr/#Cls	SN	
Caesar Chavez Sch 20 Cedar Pl, Yonkers 10705 Magdaline DeLany	PK-8	T	630 21	68%	914/376-8969 Fax 914/376-8972
Casimir Pulaski Sch 150 Kings Cross, Scarsdale 10583 Christine Montero	PK-8	T	575 24	23%	914/376-8575 Fax 914/722-7697
Cross Hill Academy 160 Bolmer Ave, Yonkers 10703 Gail Joyner-White	PK-8	T	707 40	58%	914/376-8300 Fax 914/376-8499
Ⓜ Enrico Fermi Sch Perf Arts 27 Poplar St, Yonkers 10701 Mark Ametrano	PK-8	T	984 50	73%	914/376-8460 Fax 914/376-8468 f t
Eugenio Maria De Hostos Sch 75 Morris St, Yonkers 10705 Elda Perez-Mejia	PK-8	T	605 20	72%	914/376-8430 Fax 914/376-8432
Family School 32 1 Montclair Pl, Yonkers 10710 Dr Miriam Digneo	PK-8	T	613 25	52%	914/376-8595 Fax 914/376-8597
Gorton High Sch 100 Shonnard Pl, Yonkers 10703 William Shaggura	9-12	TV	1,022 60	63%	914/376-8350 Fax 914/376-8377
Kahlil Gibran Sch 18 Rosedale Rd, Yonkers 10710 Dianne White	PK-8	T	525 19	43%	914/376-8580 Fax 914/376-8583
Ⓜ Lincoln High Sch 375 Kneeland Ave, Yonkers 10704 Ian Sherman	9-12	TV	1,182 100	61%	914/376-8400 Fax 914/376-8414
Ⓜ Martin Luther King Jr Sch 135 Locust Hill Ave, Yonkers 10701 Natalie Davy	PK-8	T	515	68%	914/376-8470 Fax 914/376-8472
Montessori School 27 132 Valentine Ln, Yonkers 10705 Moira Gleeson	PK-6	T	370	45%	914/376-8455 Fax 914/376-8457
Montessori School 31 7 Ravenswood Rd, Yonkers 10710 Dr Sharon Banks-Williams	PK-6	T	379 20	44%	914/376-8623 Fax 914/376-8626
Museum School 25 579 Warburton Ave, Yonkers 10701 Joann DiMaria	PK-6	T	315 25	60%	914/376-8450 Fax 914/376-8452 f t
Paideia School 15 175 Westchester Ave, Yonkers 10707 Jane Wermuth	PK-8	T	579 24	20%	914/376-8645 Fax 914/376-8630
Ⓜ Paideia School 24 50 Colin St, Yonkers 10701 Kim Davis	PK-6	T	416 16	53%	914/376-8640 Fax 914/376-8642

---

79 Student Personnel	91 Safety/Security	275 Response To Intervention	298 Grant Writer/Ptnrships	**School Programs**
80 Driver Ed/Safety	92 Magnet School	277 Remedial Math K-12	750 Chief Innovation Officer	A = Alternative Program
81 Gifted/Talented	93 Parental Involvement	280 Literacy Coach	751 Chief of Staff	G = Adult Classes
82 Video Services	95 Tech Prep Program	285 STEM	752 Social Emotional Learning	M = Magnet Program
83 Substance Abuse Prev	97 Chief Infomation Officer	286 Digital Learning		T = Title I Schoolwide
84 Erate	98 Chief Technology Officer	288 Common Core Standards	**Other School Types**	V = Career & Tech Ed Programs
85 AIDS Education	270 Character Education	294 Accountability	Ⓐ = Alternative School	
88 Alternative/At Risk	271 Migrant Education	295 Network System	Ⓒ = Charter School	**Social Media**
89 Multi-Cultural Curriculum	273 Teacher Mentor	296 Title II Programs	Ⓜ = Magnet School	f = Facebook
90 Social Work	274 Before/After Sch	297 Webmaster	Ⓨ = Year-Round School	t = Twitter

New Schools are shaded
New Superintendents and Principals are bold
Personnel with email addresses are underscored

Westchester County

Market Data Retrieval

School	Grd	Prgm	Enr/#Cls	SN	Phone
Palisade Preparatory Sch 201 Palisade Ave, Yonkers 10703 Michelle Yazurlo	7-12	T	802 12	59%	914/376-8177 Fax 914/376-8484
Patricia A DiChiaro Elem Sch 373 Bronxville Rd, Yonkers 10708 Patricia Langan	PK-8	T	547 20	21%	914/376-8565 Fax 914/376-8567
Pearls Hawthorne Sch 350 Hawthorne Ave, Yonkers 10705 Marwan Sayegh	PK-8	T	918 48	19%	914/376-8250 Fax 914/376-8257
Riverside High Sch 565 Warburton Ave, Yonkers 10701 Dr Don Solimene	9-12	T	975 35	62%	914/376-8425 Fax 914/376-8475
Robert C Dodson Sch 105 Avondale Rd, Yonkers 10710 Isabel Hernandez	PK-8	T	830 46	66%	914/376-8159 Fax 914/337-5207
Roosevelt HS Early Clg Studies 631 Tuckahoe Rd, Yonkers 10710 Edward De Chent	9-12	T	1,007	57%	914/376-8118 Fax 914/793-4971
Rosemarie Ann Siragusa Sch 14 60 Crescent Pl, Yonkers 10704 Anthony Cioffi	PK-6	T	512 24	52%	914/376-8570 Fax 914/776-7041
Saunders Trade & Tech High Sch 183 Palmer Rd, Yonkers 10701 Steven Mazzola	Voc	GT	1,135 60	46%	914/376-8150 Fax 914/376-8154
Scholastic Acad-Academic Excel 77 Park Hill Ave, Yonkers 10701 Dr Valencia Brown-Wyatt	PK-8	T	527	73%	914/376-8420 Fax 914/376-8423
School 5 118 Lockwood Ave, Yonkers 10701 Dr Geraldine Pisacreta	PK-8	T	609 24	49%	914/376-8320 Fax 914/376-8322
School 9 53 Fairview St, Yonkers 10703 Robert Vicuna	PK-6	T	335 18	68%	914/376-8325 Fax 914/376-8327
School 13 195 McLean Ave, Yonkers 10705 Brian Gray	PK-8	T	587 30	70%	914/376-8335 Fax 914/377-0850
School 16 759 N Broadway, Yonkers 10701 Cynthia Eisner	PK-8	T	659 17	56%	914/376-8340 Fax 914/376-8342
School 17 745 Midland Ave, Yonkers 10704 Brian Curtis	PK-6	T	460 19	59%	914/376-8345 Fax 914/376-8347
School 21 100 Lee Ave, Yonkers 10705 Leslie Powell-Grant	PK-6	T	426 20	51%	914/376-8435 Fax 914/375-3907
School 22 1408 Nepperhan Ave, Yonkers 10703 Leslie Dildy	PK-6	T	428 21	53%	914/376-8440 Fax 914/376-8442
School 23 56 Van Cortlandt Pk Ave, Yonkers 10701 Michael Walpole	PK-8	T	577 24	68%	914/376-8445 Fax 914/376-8448
School 30 30 Nevada Pl, Yonkers 10708 Michael Shapiro	PK-8	T	576 22	27%	914/376-8590 Fax 914/376-8592
Thomas Cornell Academy 15 Saint Marys St, Yonkers 10701 Dr Edward Beglane	PK-6	T	375	65%	914/376-8315 Fax 914/968-5790
Vive School Pathways-Success 75 Riverdale Ave, Yonkers 10701 Susan Naber	Adult	V	600 13		914/376-8600 Fax 914/376-8605
Westchester Hills School 29 47 Croydon Rd, Yonkers 10710 Steven Murphy	PK-8	T	647 30	53%	914/376-8585 Fax 914/961-1287
William Boyce Thompson Sch 1061 N Broadway, Yonkers 10701 Taren Washington	PK-8	T	497 22	61%	914/376-8563 Fax 914/376-8578
Yonkers Early Childhood Acad 160 Bolmer Ave, Yonkers 10703 Dr Fred Hernandez	PK-2	T	391	47%	914/376-8500 Fax 914/376-8499
Yonkers Middle High Sch 150 Rockland Ave, Yonkers 10705 Jade Sharp	6-12	TV	1,198	39%	914/376-8191 Fax 914/376-8245
Yonkers Montessori Academy 160 Woodlawn Ave, Yonkers 10704 Dr Eileen Rivera	PK-12	T	1,259	39%	914/376-8540 Fax 914/376-8552

• **Yorktown Central School Dist** PID: 00782703   914/243-8000
2725 Crompond Rd, Yorktown Hts 10598   Fax 914/243-8003

Schools: 5 \ **Teachers:** 285 \ **Students:** 3,400 \ **Special Ed Students:** 602 \ **LEP Students:** 74 \ **Ethnic:** Asian 7%, African American 3%, Hispanic 15%, Caucasian 74% \ **Exp:** $330 (High) \ **Poverty:** 3% \ **Title I:** $122,571 \ **Special Education:** $3,866,000 \ **Open-Close:** 09/08 - 06/24 \ **DTBP:** $325 (High)

Dr Ron Hattar 1
Dennis Verboys 3
Laura Tolosi 7
Pamela Chesser 48
Jackie Carbone 67
David Leis 69,76
Amanda Burns 297
Thomas Cole 2,3,5,15,91
Barrett Robert 6
Lisa O'Shea 8,11,15,286,298
Michael Rosen 58,79
Shela McGuinness 68
Jennifer Forsberg 73,295

Public Schs..Principal	Grd	Prgm	Enr/#Cls	SN	Phone
Brookside Elem Sch 2285 Broad St, Yorktown Hts 10598 Deirde Amerling	K-3		474 25	12%	914/243-8130 Fax 914/243-0017
Crompond Elem Sch 2901 Manor St, Yorktown Hts 10598 Lori Roberts	4-5		517 25	11%	914/243-8140 Fax 914/243-0018
Mildred E Strang Middle Sch 2701 Crompond Rd, Yorktown Hts 10598 Marie Horowitz	6-8		809 56	10%	914/243-8100 Fax 914/243-0016
Mohansic Elem Sch 704 Locksley Rd, Yorktown Hts 10598 Susan Berry	K-3		484 33	6%	914/243-8160 Fax 914/243-0019
Yorktown High Sch 2727 Crompond Rd, Yorktown Hts 10598 Joseph DeGennaro	9-12	A	1,116 90	12%	914/243-8050 Fax 914/245-0546

WESTCHESTER CATHOLIC SCHOOLS

• **Archdiocese of New York Ed Off** PID: 00754976
Listing includes only schools located in this county. See District Index for location of Diocesan Offices.

Catholic Schs..Principal	Grd	Prgm	Enr/#Cls	SN	Phone
Annunciation School-Crestwood 465 Westchester Ave, Tuckahoe 10707 Rose Ragone	PK-8		553 20		914/337-8760 Fax 914/337-8878
Archbishop Stepinac High Sch 950 Mamaroneck Ave, White Plains 10605 Paul Carty	9-12		800 25		914/946-4800 Fax 914/684-2591
Corpus Christi Holy Rosary Sch 135 S Regent St, Port Chester 10573 Deirdre McDermott	PK-8		200 11		914/937-4407 Fax 914/937-6904
Immaculate Conception Sch 53 Winter Hill Rd, Tuckahoe 10707 Maureen Harten	PK-8		250 20		914/961-3785 Fax 914/961-6054

---

1 Superintendent	8 Curric/Instruct K-12	19 Chief Financial Officer	29 Family/Consumer Science	39 Social Studies K-12	49 English/Lang Arts Elem	59 Special Education Elem	69 Academic Assessment
2 Bus/Finance/Purchasing	9 Curric/Instruct Elem	20 Art K-12	30 Adult Education	40 Social Studies Elem	50 English/Lang Arts Sec	60 Special Education Sec	70 Research/Development
3 Buildings And Grounds	10 Curric/Instruct Sec	21 Art Elem	31 Career/Sch-to-Work K-12	41 Social Studies Sec	51 Reading K-12	61 Foreign/World Lang K-12	71 Public Information
4 Food Service	11 Federal Program	22 Art Sec	32 Career/Sch-to-Work Elem	42 Science K-12	52 Reading Elem	62 Foreign/World Lang Elem	72 Summer School
5 Transportation	12 Title I	23 Music K-12	33 Career/Sch-to-Work Sec	43 Science Elem	53 Reading Sec	63 Foreign/World Lang Sec	73 Instructional Tech
6 Athletic	13 Title V	24 Music Elem	34 Early Childhood Ed	44 Science Sec	54 Remedial Reading K-12	64 Religious Education K-12	74 Inservice Training
7 Health Services	15 Asst Superintendent	25 Music Sec	35 Health/Phys Education	45 Math K-12	55 Remedial Reading Elem	65 Religious Education Elem	75 Marketing/Distributive
	16 Instructional Media Svcs	26 Business Education	36 Guidance Services K-12	46 Math Elem	56 Remedial Reading Sec	66 Religious Education Sec	76 Info Systems
	17 Chief Operations Officer	27 Career & Tech Ed	37 Guidance Services Elem	47 Math Sec	57 Bilingual/ELL	67 School Board President	77 Psychological Assess
	18 Chief Academic Officer	28 Technology Education	38 Guidance Services Sec	48 English/Lang Arts K-12	58 Special Education K-12	68 Teacher Personnel	78 Affirmative Action

New York School Directory — Westchester County

School	Grd	Enr/#Cls	Phone
Immaculate Heart of Mary Sch 201 Boulevard, Scarsdale 10583 Tracy Keelin	PK-8	293 15	914/723-5608 Fax 914/723-8004
Iona Prep Lower Sch 173 Stratton Rd, New Rochelle 10804 Joseph Blanco	PK-8	190 18	914/633-7744 Fax 914/235-6338
Iona Preparatory Sch 255 Wilmot Rd, New Rochelle 10804 Kieran Daly	9-12	740	914/632-0714 Fax 914/632-9760
Kennedy Catholic High Sch 54 Route 138, Somers 10589 Mark Vaillancourt	9-12	700 30	914/232-5061 Fax 914/232-3416
Maria Regina High Sch 500 W Hartsdale Ave, Hartsdale 10530 Rosemarie Decker	9-12	550 33	914/761-3300 Fax 914/761-0860
Our Lady of Mt Carmel Sch 59 E Main St, Elmsford 10523 Sr Mary Stephen	PK-8	218 10	914/592-7575 Fax 914/345-1591
Our Lady of Sorrows Sch 888 Mamaroneck Ave, White Plains 10605 Sr Marie Cecile	K-8	220 9	914/761-0124 Fax 914/761-0176
Our Lady of Victory Sch 38 N 5th Ave, Mount Vernon 10550 Helena Castilla	PK-8	360 16	914/667-4063 Fax 914/665-3135
Resurrection Sch 116 Milton Rd, Rye 10580 Gina Marie Fonte	PK-8	610 27	914/967-1218 Fax 914/925-3511
Sacred Heart Elem Sch 34 Convent Ave, Yonkers 10703 Tracy Strub	PK-8	305 11	914/963-5318 Fax 914/709-0250
Sacred Heart High Sch 34 Convent Ave, Yonkers 10703 Frances Acosta	9-12	330	914/965-3114 Fax 914/965-4510
Sacred Heart Sch 59 Wilson St, Hartsdale 10530 Christopher Siegfried	PK-8	215 15	914/946-7242 Fax 914/946-7323
Salesian High Sch 148 E Main St, New Rochelle 10801 Devin Chisolm	9-12	516 25	914/632-0248 Fax 914/632-1362
School of the Holy Child 2225 Westchester Ave, Rye 10580 Melissa Dan	5-12	350	914/967-5622 Fax 914/967-6476
SS John & Paul Sch 280 Weaver St, Larchmont 10538 Fatima Gianni	PK-8	373 20	914/834-6332 Fax 914/834-8242
St Anthony Sch 1395 Nepperhan Ave, Yonkers 10703 George Eacobacci	PK-8	260 14	914/476-8489 Fax 914/965-7939
St Augustine Sch 381 N Highland Ave, Ossining 10562 Sr Mary Donoghue	PK-8	440 18	914/941-3849 Fax 914/941-4342
St Columbanus Sch 122 Oregon Rd, Cortlandt MNR 10567 Carole Arbolino	PK-8	170	914/739-1200 Fax 914/739-1109
St Eugene Sch 707 Tuckahoe Rd, Yonkers 10710 Joan Fox	PK-8	210 19	914/779-2956 Fax 914/779-7668
St John the Baptist Sch 670 Yonkers Ave, Yonkers 10704 Sr Mary Alice Reamer	PK-8	310 10	914/965-2356 Fax 914/375-1115
St Joseph Sch 30 Meadow Ave, Bronxville 10708 Margaret Kazan	K-8	210 13	914/337-0261 Fax 914/395-1192
St Patrick's Sch 117 Moseman Rd, Yorktown Hts 10598 Rebecca Steck	PK-8	150 18	914/962-2211 Fax 914/243-4814
St Peter Sch 204 Hawthorne Ave, Yonkers 10705 Sheila Alagia	PK-8	260 10	914/963-2314 Fax 914/966-8822
The Ursuline Sch 1354 North Ave, New Rochelle 10804 Rosemary Beirne	6-12	825 50	914/636-3950 Fax 914/636-3949
Transfiguration Sch 40 Prospect Ave, Tarrytown 10591 Margaret Kazan	PK-8	200 10	914/631-3737 Fax 914/631-6640

WESTCHESTER PRIVATE SCHOOLS

Private Schs..Principal	Grd	Prgm	Enr/#Cls	SN
Andalusia Sch 380 Walnut St, Yonkers 10701 Br Abdelnasser Nofal	PK-12		288	914/964-5600 Fax 914/964-5603
Cardinal McCloskey Sch 155 N Highland Ave, Ossining 10562 Jennifer Fedele	4-12		42 3	914/762-5302 Fax 914/762-7844
Cerebral Palsy of Westchester 1186 King St, Rye Brook 10573 Michael Musante	Spec	G	100 5	914/937-3800 Fax 914/937-0967
Clear View Sch 480 Albany Post Rd, Briarcliff 10510 Jackie Hastings	Spec		120 14	914/941-9513 Fax 914/941-2339
Devereux Millwood Learning Ctr 27 Radio Circle Dr, Mount Kisco 10549 Dr Cindy Alterson	Spec		48	914/941-1991 Fax 914/941-2852
E F Academy New York 582 Columbus Ave, Thornwood 10594 Dr Brian Mahoney	9-12		450	914/597-7241 Fax 914/597-7260
Elizabth Seton Chldrn Sch-WP 317 North St, White Plains 10605 Jennifer Geskie	Spec		140	914/597-4071 Fax 914/470-0449
Emmanuel Childrens Mission Sch 32 S 5th Ave, Mount Vernon 10550 Sonya Brown	K-4		210	914/664-1810 Fax 914/668-5332
Flexschool-Bronxville 171 White Plains Rd, Bronxville 10708 Lynne Henwood	8-12		15	914/704-3334
Four Winds Learning Center 800 Cross River Rd, Katonah 10536 Catherine Zacotinsky	Spec		170 9	914/763-8151 Fax 914/763-6407
French American Sch of NY-Elem 111 Larchmont Ave, Larchmont 10538 Charles Grenon	1-3		325	914/250-0469
French American Sch of NY-Sec 145 New St, Mamaroneck 10543 Mark Rosenbrum	6-12		380 19	914/250-0451 Fax 914/698-8696
Fusion Academy-Westchester 1 N Bordway Ste 210, White Plains 10601 Taurean Kennedy	5-12		60	914/285-9036 Fax 914/285-9147
German Int'l School New York 50 Partridge Rd, White Plains 10605 Dr Simone Bruemmer \ Lars Hierath	K-12		375 26	914/948-6513 Fax 914/948-6529
Hackley Sch 293 Benedict Ave, Tarrytown 10591 Lisa Oberstein \ Cyndy Jean \ Andy King	K-12		850	914/631-0128 Fax 914/631-9240
Hawthorne Country Day Sch 5 Bradhurst Ave, Hawthorne 10532 Tina Covington	Spec		190 30	914/592-8526 Fax 914/592-3227
Hudson Country Mont Sch 340 Quaker Ridge Rd, New Rochelle 10804 Neeru Bhambree	PK-8		220	914/636-6202 Fax 914/636-5139

79 Student Personnel
80 Driver Ed/Safety
81 Gifted/Talented
82 Video Services
83 Substance Abuse Prev
84 Erate
85 AIDS Education
88 Alternative/At Risk
89 Multi-Cultural Curriculum
90 Social Work
91 Safety/Security
92 Magnet School
93 Parental Involvement
95 Tech Prep Program
97 Chief Infomation Officer
98 Chief Technology Officer
270 Character Education
271 Migrant Education
273 Teacher Mentor
274 Before/After Sch
275 Response To Intervention
277 Remedial Math K-12
280 Literacy Coach
285 STEM
286 Digital Learning
288 Common Core Standards
294 Accountability
295 Network System
296 Title II Programs
297 Webmaster
298 Grant Writer/Ptnrships
750 Chief Innovation Officer
751 Chief of Staff
752 Social Emotional Learning

Other School Types
Ⓐ = Alternative School
Ⓒ = Charter School
Ⓜ = Magnet School
Ⓨ = Year-Round School

School Programs
A = Alternative Program
G = Adult Classes
M = Magnet Program
T = Title I Schoolwide
V = Career & Tech Ed Programs

New Schools are shaded
New Superintendents and Principals are bold
Personnel with email addresses are underscored

Social Media
= Facebook
= Twitter

Westchester County

Market Data Retrieval

School	Grades		Enrollment	Phone
Hudson View Christian Academy 170 Hudson Ter, Yonkers 10701 Mark Benedict	K-12		54 4	914/968-7047 Fax 914/423-8865
Ives School-Lincoln Hall Route 202, Lincolndale 10540 Ronald Linchner	7-12	AV	175 30	914/248-7474 Fax 914/248-5673
John A Coleman Sch-Yonkers 300 Corporate Blvd S, Yonkers 10701 Sharon Herl	Spec		140 10	914/294-6100 Fax 914/294-6179
John Cardinal O'Connor Sch 16 N Broadway Ste 1, Irvington 10533 Kristen O'Leary	Spec		51	914/591-9330 Fax 914/231-7688
Karafin Sch 40 Radio Circle Dr, Mount Kisco 10549 Dr Bart Donow	Spec		84 22	914/666-9211 Fax 914/666-9868
Keio Academy of New York 3 College Rd, Purchase 10577 Fumiko Kikuchi	9-12		345 25	914/694-4825 Fax 914/694-4830
Kodomono Kuni Sch 252 Soundview Ave, White Plains 10606 Kuniko Hayatsu	PK-1		100 6	914/949-0067 Fax 914/949-0247
Leake & Watts Chldrns Home Sch 463 Hawthorne Ave, Yonkers 10705 Roland Lewis \ Maria Baker	Spec		300	914/375-8700 Fax 914/375-8907
Masters Sch 49 Clinton Ave, Dobbs Ferry 10522 Tasha Elsbach \ Nikki Willis	5-12		800 35	914/479-6400 Fax 914/693-0290
Milestone Sch 70 Broad St W, Mount Vernon 10552 Angela Freeman	PK-4		122 9	914/667-3478 Fax 914/667-2259
Montessori Children's Room 67 Old Route 22, Armonk 10504 Marina Anandappa	PK-1		147	914/273-3291
Montfort Academy 125 E Birch St, Mount Vernon 10552 David Petrillo	9-12		40	914/699-7090
Mt Tom Day Sch 48 Mount Tom Rd, New Rochelle 10805 Erin Dutton	PK-1		120 6	914/636-8130 Fax 914/576-3270
New York School for the Deaf 555 Knollwood Rd, White Plains 10603 Jennifer Labriola-Megee	Spec		160	914/949-7310 Fax 914/949-8768
Oakview Prep Sch 29 Chestnut St, Yonkers 10701 J Eric Imbert	PK-8		250	914/423-7369 Fax 914/423-0813
Orchard Sch 1156 N Broadway, Yonkers 10701 Vivian CO	Spec	V	150 19	914/965-3700 Fax 914/965-3883
Rippowam Cisqua Sch-Lower 325 W Patent Rd, Mount Kisco 10549 Colm MacMahon	PK-4		309	914/244-1200 Fax 914/234-4140
Rippowam Cisqua Sch-Upper 439 Cantitoe St, Bedford 10506 Matt Hall	5-9		230	914/244-1250 Fax 914/244-1245
Rye Country Day Sch 3 Cedar St, Rye 10580 Barbara Shea \ Jonathan Leef	PK-12		890 50	914/967-1417 Fax 914/967-1418
Sail School-Ferncliff Manor 1154 Saw Mill River Rd, Yonkers 10710 Matthew Rubensteine	Spec		60	914/968-4854 Fax 914/968-4857
Solomon Schechter Sch 30 Dellwood Rd, White Plains 10605 Ilanit Hoory	K-5	G	500 35	914/948-3111 Fax 914/948-4356
Soundview Preparatory Sch 370 Underhill Ave, Yorktown Hts 10598 Dr Ken Cotrone	6-12		70 20	914/962-2780 Fax 914/302-2769
St Mark's Lutheran Sch 7 Saint Marks Pl, Yonkers 10704 Debra Masiello	PK-8		133 9	914/237-4944 Fax 914/237-4480
Stein Yeshiva of Lincoln Park 287 Central Park Ave, Yonkers 10704 Joseph Cherns	PK-8	G	125 11	914/965-7082 Fax 914/965-1902
Talmud Torah Bais Yechiel Sch Pines Bridge Road, Mount Kisco 10549 Reuven Lefkowitz	K-12		320 12	718/387-0422 Fax 718/387-9400
The Chapel Sch 172 White Plains Rd, Bronxville 10708 Michael Schultz	PK-8	G	370 24	914/337-3202 Fax 914/771-9711
The Harvey Sch 260 Jay St, Katonah 10536 Dr Brendan Byrne \ Philip Lazzaro	6-12		350	914/232-3161 Fax 914/232-2986
The Leffell Sch 555 W Hartsdale Ave, Hartsdale 10530 Amy Holtzer \ Eric Bassin	6-12		275 20	914/948-8333 Fax 914/948-7979
Thornton-Donovan Sch 100 Overlook Cir, New Rochelle 10804 Douglas Fleming	K-12		170	914/632-8836 Fax 914/576-7936
Westchester Area Sch 456 Webster Ave, New Rochelle 10801 Nadine Spencer Elysee	PK-8		104 11	914/235-5799 Fax 914/235-4332
Westchester Day Sch 856 Orienta Ave, Mamaroneck 10543 Ahuva Halberstam \ Amy Ament	PK-8		450 20	914/698-8900 Fax 914/777-2145
Westchester Excptnl Chldrn's 520 Route 22, North Salem 10560 Linda Zinn	Spec		75 12	914/277-5533 Fax 914/277-7219
Westchester Hebrew High Sch 856 Orienta Ave, Mamaroneck 10543 Jeffrey Beer	9-12		175 22	914/698-0806 Fax 914/698-1330
Westchester Sch for Spec Child 45 Park Ave, Yonkers 10703 Corinne Safarowic	Spec		70 27	914/693-2504 Fax 914/965-7059
Westchester Sch for Spec Chldn 45 Park Ave, Yonkers 10703 Jay Tabasco	Spec		256 22	914/376-4300 Fax 914/965-7059
Westchester Torah Academy 295 Soundview Ave, White Plains 10606 Deganit Ronen	1-4		401	914/712-6497
Windward Sch-Westchester Lower 13 Windward Ave, White Plains 10605 Jamie Williamson	Spec		560	914/949-6968 Fax 914/949-8220
Windward Sch-Westchester Mid 40 W Red Oak Ln, White Plains 10604 Dr John Russell	Spec		540	914/949-6968 Fax 914/696-0950
Yeshiva Farm Settlement Sch Pines Bridge Rd, Mount Kisco 10549 David Herzog	K-12	V	300	914/666-2087 Fax 914/666-5448
Yeshiva Kehilath Yaakov Sch 340 Illington Rd, Ossining 10562 Shimshon Katz	11-12		90	718/963-1212 Fax 718/387-8586

WESTCHESTER REGIONAL CENTERS

• **Putnam-Northern Wstchstr BOCES** PID: 00782818   914/245-2700
  200 Boces Dr, Yorktown Hts 10598   Fax 914/248-2308

Dr James Ryan 1,11	Todd Currie 2,15
Katharina Cerreta 3,5,91	Fred Ende 8,74
John McCarthy 15	Dr Lynn Allen 15
Joseph Mannozzi 16	Catherine Balestrieri 27
Dr Andrew Ecker 36	Shelley Fleischmann 58

---

1 Superintendent	8 Curric/Instruct K-12	19 Chief Financial Officer	29 Family/Consumer Science	39 Social Studies K-12	49 English/Lang Arts Elem	59 Special Education Elem	69 Academic Assessment
2 Bus/Finance/Purchasing	9 Curric/Instruct Elem	20 Art K-12	30 Adult Education	40 Social Studies Elem	50 English/Lang Arts Sec	60 Special Education Sec	70 Research/Development
3 Buildings And Grounds	10 Curric/Instruct Sec	21 Art Elem	31 Career/Sch-to-Work K-12	41 Social Studies Sec	51 Reading K-12	61 Foreign/World Lang K-12	71 Public Information
4 Food Service	11 Federal Program	22 Art Sec	32 Career/Sch-to-Work Elem	42 Science K-12	52 Reading Elem	62 Foreign/World Lang Elem	72 Summer School
5 Transportation	12 Title I	23 Music K-12	33 Career/Sch-to-Work Sec	43 Science Elem	53 Reading Sec	63 Foreign/World Lang Sec	73 Instructional Tech
6 Athletic	13 Title V	24 Music Elem	34 Early Childhood Ed	44 Science Sec	54 Remedial Reading K-12	64 Religious Education K-12	74 Inservice Training
7 Health Services	15 Asst Superintendent	25 Music Sec	35 Health/Phys Education	45 Math K-12	55 Remedial Reading Elem	65 Religious Education Elem	75 Marketing/Distributive
	16 Instructional Media Svcs	26 Business Education	36 Guidance Services K-12	46 Math Elem	56 Remedial Reading Sec	66 Religious Education Sec	76 Info Systems
	17 Chief Operations Officer	27 Career & Tech Ed	37 Guidance Services Elem	47 Math Sec	57 Bilingual/ELL	67 School Board President	77 Psychological Assess
	18 Chief Academic Officer	28 Technology Education	38 Guidance Services Sec	48 English/Lang Arts K-12	58 Special Education K-12	68 Teacher Personnel	78 Affirmative Action

New York School Directory — Wyoming County

Richard Kreps 67
Ellen Lane 71
Michael Skerritt 68,74
Jamie Molina 73,76

- **Southern Westchester BOCES** PID: 00782789   914/937-3820
  17 Berkley Dr, Rye Brook 10573   Fax 914/937-8768

Dr Harold Coles 1
Jackie O'Donnell 3,15,17
James Grotto 15,27,30,58
Catherine Draper 67
Brian Howard 71
Stephen Tibbetts 2,5,15
Thomas Briggs 3
Frank Alvarez 58
Suzanne Doherty 68
Victor Piniero 73,76,295

WYOMING COUNTY

WYOMING PUBLIC SCHOOLS

- **Attica Central School Dist** PID: 00783056   585/591-0400
  3338 E Main Street Rd, Attica 14011   Fax 585/591-2681

Schools: 3 \ **Teachers:** 115 \ **Students:** 1,150 \ **Special Ed Students:** 199 \ **LEP Students:** 3 \ **College-Bound:** 75% \ **Ethnic:** Hispanic 2%, Caucasian 97% \ **Exp:** $282 (Med) \ **Poverty:** 8% \ **Title I:** $180,331 \ **Special Education:** $2,567,000 \ **Open-Close:** 09/09 - 06/25 \ **DTBP:** $550 (High)

Bryce Thompson 1
David Barber 3,15
Eric Romesser 6
Melanie Loranty 16
Susan Cusmano 31*
Paul Clark 35,36,69*
Douglas Ewert 73,98*
Kelly Beitz 88,270*
Megan Matuszak 2,19
Ralph Marvin 5
Matt Steerjake 8,288
Melanie Loranty 16*
Debra Lacey 34,58*
Brian Fugle 67
Mary Richards 77

Public Schs..Principal	Grd	Prgm	Enr/#Cls	SN	
Attica Elem Sch 31 Prospect St, Attica 14011 Kelly Beitz	K-4		417 23	37%	585/591-0400 Fax 585/591-4497
Attica Middle Sch 3338 E Main Street Rd, Attica 14011 Paul Clark	5-8		347 40	37%	585/591-0400 Fax 585/591-4496
Attica Senior High Sch 3338 E Main Street Rd, Attica 14011 Josh Audsley	9-12	GV	414 70	29%	585/591-0400 Fax 585/591-4987

- **Letchworth Central School Dist** PID: 00783109   585/493-5450
  5550 School Rd, Gainesville 14066   Fax 585/493-2762

Schools: 3 \ **Teachers:** 99 \ **Students:** 936 \ **Special Ed Students:** 144 \ **LEP Students:** 3 \ **Ethnic:** Asian 1%, African American 1%, Hispanic 2%, Caucasian 97% \ **Exp:** $385 (High) \ **Poverty:** 12% \ **Title I:** $187,580 \ **Special Education:** $2,272,000 \ **Open-Close:** 09/04 - 06/25 \ **DTBP:** $419 (High)

Todd Campbell 1,11
Todd Brant 3
Wayne Gloff 5
Julie Pernesky 8,12,57,69,74,288,296,298
Daniel Woitaszek 27,38*
Raelyn Helman 58,79*
Jeff Nevinger 73,295*
John Novak 2,13,88,91
Karen Almeter 4*
Mark Sanderson 6*
Amelia White 16,82*
Sue Murphy 35,83,85*
Pete Broughton 67

Public Schs..Principal	Grd	Prgm	Enr/#Cls	SN	
Letchworth Central High Sch 5550 School Rd, Gainesville 14066 Paul Rogers	9-12	V	276 26	38%	585/493-2571
Letchworth Middle Sch 5550 School Rd, Gainesville 14066 Amy Leone	5-8	T	281 17	43%	585/493-2592
Lockwood Elem Sch 5550 School Rd, Gainesville 14066 William Bean	PK-4	T	379 23	47%	585/493-2581 Fax 585/493-2756

- **Perry Central School Dist** PID: 00783161   585/237-0270
  33 Watkins Ave, Perry 14530   Fax 585/237-6172

Schools: 2 \ **Teachers:** 87 \ **Students:** 806 \ **Special Ed Students:** 128 \ **LEP Students:** 9 \ **College-Bound:** 51% \ **Ethnic:** Asian 1%, African American 1%, Hispanic 5%, Caucasian 93% \ **Exp:** $248 (Med) \ **Poverty:** 12% \ **Title I:** $171,732 \ **Special Education:** $1,487,000 \ **Open-Close:** 09/04 - 06/25 \ **DTBP:** $361 (High)

Daryl McLaughlin 1
Reed Pettys 2,5,71,275
Laurie Cutcliff 4*
Robin Kwiecien 7*
Dan Schular 11,57,58,79,285,296*
Amy Ellis 36
Mark Eberstein 73,76*
Rebecca Belkota 273*
Mary Kreutter 2
David Wolfanger 3,91
Jeremy Ohlson 6*
Lauren Combo 8
Amy Vongunden 35*
Nathan Paddock 67
Jeffery Gerhart 90
Maura Gelsinan 298

Public Schs..Principal	Grd	Prgm	Enr/#Cls	SN	
Perry Elem Sch 50 Olin Ave, Perry 14530 Maura Gilsinan	PK-6	T	437 65	45%	585/237-0270 Fax 585/237-3483
Perry Junior Senior High Sch 33 Watkins Ave, Perry 14530 Rebecca Belkota	7-12	AV	369 40	45%	585/237-0270 Fax 585/237-6350

- **Warsaw Central School Dist** PID: 00783197   585/786-8000
  153 W Buffalo St, Warsaw 14569   Fax 585/786-8008

Schools: 2 \ **Teachers:** 91 \ **Students:** 800 \ **Special Ed Students:** 112 \ **LEP Students:** 7 \ **Ethnic:** Asian 1%, African American 1%, Hispanic 3%, Caucasian 95% \ **Exp:** $250 (Med) \ **Poverty:** 11% \ **Title I:** $192,867 \ **Special Education:** $2,247,000 \ **Open-Close:** 09/09 - 06/24 \ **DTBP:** $351 (High)

Matthew Wilkens 1
Edward Papke 3
Rodney Harris 6
Timothy Suleski 27*
Christine Adniolfe 36
Jeremy DeWitt 73*
Kari Grisewood 2
Alexandria Bergio 4
Kimberly Monhanon 8
Richard Ellis 34,58
Dean Robb 67

Public Schs..Principal	Grd	Prgm	Enr/#Cls	SN	
Warsaw Central Mid High Sch 81 W Court St, Warsaw 14569 Kimberly D'Amico \ Amy Burnham	6-12	V	449 50	45%	585/786-8000 Fax 585/786-3193
Warsaw Elem Sch 153 W Buffalo St, Warsaw 14569 Tom Lyons	PK-5	T	423 25	50%	585/786-8000 Fax 585/786-2537

---

79 Student Personnel
80 Driver Ed/Safety
81 Gifted/Talented
82 Video Services
83 Substance Abuse Prev
84 Erate
85 AIDS Education
88 Alternative/At Risk
89 Multi-Cultural Curriculum
90 Social Work
91 Safety/Security
92 Magnet School
93 Parental Involvement
95 Tech Prep Program
97 Chief Information Officer
98 Chief Technology Officer
270 Character Education
271 Migrant Education
273 Teacher Mentor
274 Before/After Sch
275 Response To Intervention
277 Remedial Math K-12
280 Literacy Coach
285 STEM
286 Digital Learning
288 Common Core Standards
294 Accountability
295 Network System
296 Title II Programs
297 Webmaster
298 Grant Writer/Ptnrships
750 Chief Innovation Officer
751 Chief of Staff
752 Social Emotional Learning

Other School Types
Ⓐ = Alternative School
Ⓒ = Charter School
Ⓜ = Magnet School
Ⓨ = Year-Round School

School Programs
A = Alternative Program
G = Adult Classes
M = Magnet Program
T = Title I Schoolwide
V = Career & Tech Ed Programs

Social Media
 = Facebook
 = Twitter

New Schools are shaded
New Superintendents and Principals are bold
Personnel with email addresses are underscored

Yates County

Market Data Retrieval

- **Wyoming Central School Dist** PID: 00783226   585/495-6222
  1225 State Route 19, Wyoming 14591   Fax 585/495-6351

Schools: 1 \ **Teachers:** 16 \ **Students:** 130 \ **Special Ed Students:** 16 \ **Ethnic:** African American 1%, Hispanic 1%, Native American: 2%, Caucasian 97% \ **Exp:** $242 (Med) \ **Poverty:** 9% \ **Title I:** $32,721 \ **Special Education:** $424,000 \ **Open-Close:** 09/08 - 06/24

Kathleen Schueffleir	1,11	Joelle Stroud		2
Vern Baker	3*	Adam Richley		5
Peter Terbuska	6,35*	Maria Herman		7*
Marie May	16,288*	Kim Alfes		20*
Emily Herman	59,69,79,83,88*	Barry True		67
Julie Larson	73,297*			

Public Schs..Principal	Grd	Prgm	Enr/#Cls	SN	
Wyoming Central Sch	K-8	T	130	41%	585/495-6222
1225 State Route 19, Wyoming 14591			26		Fax 585/495-6341
Kathleen Schuessler					

WYOMING PRIVATE SCHOOLS

Private Schs..Principal	Grd	Prgm	Enr/#Cls	SN	
Castile Christian Academy	K-12		15		585/493-2528
26 Beechwood Ave, Castile 14427			4		
Joanne Burdick					
Gilead School of Discipleship	K-12		145		585/330-4113
181 Main St S, Perry 14530					
Justin Perry					

YATES COUNTY

YATES COUNTY SCHOOLS

County Schs..Principal	Grd	Prgm	Enr/#Cls	SN	
Finger Lakes Secondary Sch	Spec		86		585/554-6492
4120 Baldwin Rd, Rushville 14544			20		Fax 585/554-4219
Dan Healy					

YATES PUBLIC SCHOOLS

- **Dundee Ctl School Dist** PID: 00783240   607/243-5533
  55 Water St, Dundee 14837   Fax 607/243-7912

Schools: 2 \ **Teachers:** 67 \ **Students:** 700 \ **Special Ed Students:** 146 \ **College-Bound:** 54% \ **Ethnic:** Hispanic 4%, Caucasian 96% \ **Exp:** $313 (High) \ **Poverty:** 22% \ **Title I:** $501,728 \ **Special Education:** $1,319,000 \ **Open-Close:** 09/08 - 06/23 \ **DTBP:** $370 (High)

Kelly Houck	1	Melissa Lawson		2
Andrew Schuck	3	Ann Overhiser		4
Rob Cole	4	Stephanie Cleveland		5
Scott Shepardson	6	Agnes Woodard		7,85
Kevin McNally	37	Robert Neu		67
Jeffery Bailey	73,295*	Stephanie Betts		83*
Laurie Halbert	285*			

Public Schs..Principal	Grd	Prgm	Enr/#Cls	SN	
Dundee Elem Sch	PK-6	T	373	60%	607/243-5535
55 Water St, Dundee 14837			21		
Laurie Halbert					
Dundee Jr Sr High Sch	7-12	TV	283	55%	607/243-7912
55 Water St, Dundee 14837					
Chris Arnold					

- **Penn Yan Ctl School Dist** PID: 00783276   315/536-3371
  1 School Dr, Penn Yan 14527   Fax 315/536-0068

Schools: 3 \ **Teachers:** 149 \ **Students:** 1,338 \ **Special Ed Students:** 221 \ **LEP Students:** 11 \ **College-Bound:** 66% \ **Ethnic:** Asian 1%, Hispanic 4%, Caucasian 95% \ **Exp:** $317 (High) \ **Poverty:** 18% \ **Title I:** $681,645 \ **Special Education:** $1,594,000 \ **Open-Close:** 09/08 - 06/25 \ **DTBP:** $369 (High)

Howard Dennis	1	Cathy Milliman		2,3,15
Kim Fitzgerald	2	Dana Burton		4
David Mulberger	5	Tobin Tansey		6
Gregory Baker	8,15,74	Stacey Barden		11,58,77,79,271
Tom Lightfoote	16,73	Scott Bluett		36,83*
Tara Alegre	38*	Christine Hallings		51*
Lisa Garvey	57*	David Willson		67
Rebecca Perrault	76,298			

Public Schs..Principal	Grd	Prgm	Enr/#Cls	SN	
Penn Yan Academy High Sch	9-12	TV	405	56%	315/536-4408
305 Court St, Penn Yan 14527			30		Fax 315/536-0341
David Pullen					
Penn Yan Elem Sch	PK-5	T	630	57%	315/536-3346
3 School Dr, Penn Yan 14527			60		Fax 315/536-4354
Edward Foote					
Penn Yan Middle Sch	6-8	TV	303	47%	315/536-3366
515 Liberty St, Penn Yan 14527			50		Fax 315/279-1242
Kelley Johnson					

YATES CATHOLIC SCHOOLS

- **Diocese of Rochester Ed Office** PID: 00733623
  Listing includes only schools located in this county. See District Index for location of Diocesan Offices.

Catholic Schs..Principal	Grd	Prgm	Enr/#Cls	SN	
St Michael Sch	PK-5		82		315/536-6112
214 Keuka St, Penn Yan 14527			6		
Debra Marvin					

YATES PRIVATE SCHOOLS

Private Schs..Principal	Grd	Prgm	Enr/#Cls	SN	
Crystal Valley Christian Sch	1-12		18		607/243-7209
2420 State Route 230, Dundee 14837			2		
Dwight Troyer					
Emmanuel Baptist Academy	K-12		40		315/536-8278
332 Main St, Penn Yan 14527			6		Fax 315/536-3413
Ron Woudenburg					
Townline Sch	1-8		26		315/536-0051
1240 Townline Rd, Penn Yan 14527			1		
Ellen Shirk					

1 Superintendent	20 Art K-12	40 Social Studies Elem	60 Special Education Sec
2 Bus/Finance/Purchasing	21 Art Elem	41 Social Studies Sec	61 Foreign/World Lang K-12
3 Buildings And Grounds	22 Art Sec	42 Science K-12	62 Foreign/World Lang Elem
4 Food Service	23 Music K-12	43 Science Elem	63 Foreign/World Lang Sec
5 Transportation	24 Music Elem	44 Science Sec	64 Religious Education K-12
6 Athletic	25 Music Sec	45 Math K-12	65 Religious Education Elem
7 Health Services	26 Business Education	46 Math Elem	66 Religious Education Sec
8 Curric/Instruct K-12	27 Career & Tech Ed	47 Math Sec	67 School Board President
9 Curric/Instruct Elem	28 Technology Education	48 English/Lang Arts K-12	68 Teacher Personnel
10 Curric/Instruct Sec	29 Family/Consumer Science	49 English/Lang Arts Elem	69 Academic Assessment
11 Federal Program	30 Adult Education	50 English/Lang Arts Sec	70 Research/Development
12 Title I	31 Career/Sch-to-Work K-12	51 Reading K-12	71 Public Information
13 Title V	32 Career/Sch-to-Work Elem	52 Reading Elem	72 Summer School
14 Instructional Media Svcs	33 Career/Sch-to-Work Sec	53 Reading Sec	73 Instructional Tech
15 Asst Superintendent	34 Early Childhood Ed	54 Remedial Reading K-12	74 Inservice Training
16 Instructional Media Svcs	35 Health/Phys Education	55 Remedial Reading Elem	75 Marketing/Distributive
17 Chief Operations Officer	36 Guidance Services K-12	56 Remedial Reading Sec	76 Info Systems
18 Chief Academic Officer	37 Guidance Services Elem	57 Bilingual/ELL	77 Psychological Assess
19 Chief Financial Officer	38 Guidance Services Sec	58 Special Education K-12	78 Affirmative Action
	39 Social Studies K-12	59 Special Education Elem	

New York School Directory

DISTRICT INDEX

SCHOOL DISTRICT	NO. OF SCHOOLS	ENROLL-MENT	COUNTY	PAGE
PUBLIC SCHOOL DISTRICTS				
Addison Central School Dist	3	1,100	Steuben	213
Adirondack Central Sch Dist	4	1,200	Oneida	150
Afton Central School Dist	1	522	Chenango	41
Akron Central School Dist	3	1,500	Erie	56
Albany City School Dist	19	9,024	Albany	9
Albion Central School Dist	3	1,860	Orleans	169
Alden Central School Dist	4	1,581	Erie	56
Alexander Ctl School Dist	2	788	Genesee	73
Alexandria Central School Dist	1	492	Jefferson	79
Alfred Almond Ctl School Dist	1	600	Allegany	13
Allegany-Limestone Ctl SD	2	1,156	Cattaraugus	31
Altmar-Parish-Williamstown SD	2	1,500	Oswego	170
Amagansett Union Free Sch Dist	1	79	Suffolk	216
Amherst Central School Dist	4	2,990	Erie	56
Amityville Union Free Sch Dist	5	3,100	Suffolk	216
Andes Central School Dist	1	73	Delaware	48
Andover Central School Dist	1	300	Allegany	13
Ardsley Union Free School Dist	3	2,326	Westchester	252
Argyle Central School Dist	2	480	Washington	246
Arkport Central School Dist	1	475	Steuben	213
Arlington Central School Dist	11	7,000	Dutchess	51
Attica Central School Dist	3	1,150	Wyoming	267
Auburn Enlarged City Sch Dist	7	4,200	Cayuga	34
Ausable Valley Ctl Sch Dist	3	1,151	Clinton	43
Averill Park Central Sch Dist	5	2,665	Rensselaer	189
Avoca Central School Dist	1	440	Steuben	213
Avon Central School Dist	3	1,006	Livingston	102
Babylon Union Free Sch Dist	3	1,554	Suffolk	216
Bainbridge Guilford CSD	3	850	Chenango	41
Baldwin Union Free School Dist	7	5,450	Nassau	116
Baldwinsville Central Sch Dist	8	5,500	Onondaga	154
Ballston Spa Ctl School Dist	6	4,200	Saratoga	200
Barker Central School Dist	2	750	Niagara	146
Batavia City School Dist	4	2,374	Genesee	73
Bath Central School Dist	3	1,500	Steuben	213
Bay Shore Union Free Sch Dist	7	6,000	Suffolk	217
Bayport- Blue Point USD	5	2,080	Suffolk	217
Beacon City School Dist	6	3,200	Dutchess	51
Beaver River Central Sch Dist	1	875	Lewis	101
Bedford Central School Dist	8	4,100	Westchester	252
Beekmantown Ctl School Dist	4	2,000	Clinton	43
Belfast Central School Dist	1	343	Allegany	14
Belleville Henderson Sch Dist	1	450	Jefferson	79
Bellmore Union Free Sch Dist	3	1,100	Nassau	117
Bellmore-Merrick Ctl High SD	5	5,273	Nassau	117
Bemus Point Ctl School Dist	2	715	Chautauqua	36
Berkshire Union Free Sch Dist	2	40	Columbia	45
Berlin Central School Dist	2	800	Rensselaer	189
Berne-Knox-Westerlo Central SD	2	751	Albany	10
Bethlehem Central School Dist	7	4,400	Albany	10
Bethpage Union Free Sch Dist	5	2,946	Nassau	117
Binghamton City School Dist	10	5,500	Broome	27
Blind Brook-Rye Union Free SD	3	1,364	Westchester	252
Bloomfield Central SD	2	850	Ontario	161
Bolivar-Richburg Ctrl Sch Dist	3	850	Allegany	14
Bolton Central School Dist	1	200	Warren	244
Boquet Valley Central Sch Dist	2	202	Essex	67
Bradford Central Sch Dist	1	265	Schuyler	207
Brasher Falls School Dist	3	1,000	St Lawrence	209
Brentwood Union Free Sch Dist	17	20,000	Suffolk	217
Brewster Central School Dist	4	3,066	Putnam	175
Briarcliff Manor Union Free SD	3	1,347	Westchester	253
Bridgehampton Union Free SD	1	227	Suffolk	218
Brighton Central School Dist	4	3,518	Monroe	106
Broadalbin-Perth Ctl Sch Dist	2	1,800	Fulton	71
Brockport Ctl School Dist	5	3,562	Monroe	106
Brocton Central School Dist	1	540	Chautauqua	36
Bronxville Union Free SD	3	1,640	Westchester	253
Brookfield Central School Dist	1	240	Madison	104
Brookhaven Comsewogue Unif SD	6	3,702	Suffolk	218

SCHOOL DISTRICT	NO. OF SCHOOLS	ENROLL-MENT	COUNTY	PAGE
Brunswick Central School Dist	2	1,200	Rensselaer	190
Brushton Moira Ctl Sch Dist	1	800	Franklin	69
Buffalo Public Schools	68	33,428	Erie	56
Burnt Hills Ballston Lake SD	5	3,000	Saratoga	200
Byram Hills Central Sch Dist	4	2,300	Westchester	253
Byron-Bergen Ctl School Dist	2	864	Genesee	73
Cairo-Durham Ctl School Dist	3	1,275	Greene	75
Caledonia-Mumford Ctl Sch Dist	3	815	Livingston	102
Cambridge Central School Dist	1	844	Washington	247
Camden Central School Dist	4	2,000	Oneida	150
Campbell-Savona Ctl Sch Dist	2	829	Steuben	213
Canajoharie Ctl School Dist	3	855	Montgomery	115
Canandaigua City School Dist	3	3,500	Ontario	161
Canaseraga Central Sch Dist	1	272	Allegany	14
Canastota Central School Dist	4	1,275	Madison	104
Candor Central School Dist	2	750	Tioga	238
Canisteo-Greenwood Central SD	2	1,000	Steuben	214
Canton Central School Dist	3	1,000	St Lawrence	209
Carle Place Union Free SD	3	1,360	Nassau	117
Carmel Central School Dist	5	3,973	Putnam	175
Carthage Central School Dist	5	3,200	Jefferson	80
Cassadaga Valley Ctl Sch Dist	2	851	Chautauqua	36
Cato Meridian Central Sch Dist	3	922	Cayuga	34
Catskill Central School Dist	3	1,385	Greene	75
Cattaraugus-Little Vly Ctl SD	3	975	Cattaraugus	31
Cazenovia Ctl School Dist	3	1,360	Madison	104
Center Moriches Union Free SD	3	1,400	Suffolk	218
Central Islip Union Free SD	8	7,400	Suffolk	218
Central Square Central SD	6	3,800	Oswego	170
Central Valley School Dist	4	2,201	Herkimer	77
Chappaqua Central School Dist	6	3,900	Westchester	253
Charlotte Valley Ctl Sch Dist	1	300	Delaware	49
Chateaugay Central School Dist	2	503	Franklin	69
Chatham Central School Dist	3	1,100	Columbia	46
Chautauqua Lake Central SD	1	950	Chautauqua	36
Chazy Central Rural Sch Dist	1	455	Clinton	44
Cheektowaga Central SD	3	2,249	Erie	58
Cheektowaga Maryvale UFSD	4	2,183	Erie	58
Cheektowaga-Sloan UFSD	4	1,279	Erie	59
Chenango Forks Central SD	3	1,404	Broome	28
Chenango Valley Ctl Sch Dist	4	1,719	Broome	28
Cherry Valley-Springfield SD	1	449	Otsego	172
Chester Union Free School Dist	2	986	Orange	163
Chittenango Central SD	4	1,904	Madison	104
Churchville Chili Ctl Sch Dist	6	3,900	Monroe	107
Cincinnatus Ctl School Dist	2	530	Cortland	47
Clarence Central School Dist	6	4,600	Erie	59
Clarkstown Central School Dist	13	7,907	Rockland	195
Cleveland Hill Union Free SD	3	1,284	Erie	59
Clifton-Fine Central Sch Dist	1	295	St Lawrence	209
Clinton Central School Dist	3	1,258	Oneida	150
Clyde-Savannah Central SD	3	784	Wayne	249
Clymer Central School Dist	1	444	Chautauqua	37
Cobleskill Richmondville SD	4	1,700	Schoharie	206
Cohoes City School Dist	5	2,000	Albany	10
Cold Spring Harbor Central SD	4	1,650	Suffolk	219
Colton Pierrepont School Dist	1	368	St Lawrence	209
Commack Union Free School Dist	8	5,889	Suffolk	219
Community School Dist 1			New York	135
Community School Dist 2			New York	135
Community School Dist 3			New York	138
Community School Dist 4			New York	139
Community School Dist 5			New York	140
Community School Dist 6			New York	141
Community School Dist 7			Bronx	16
Community School Dist 8			Bronx	17
Community School Dist 9			Bronx	18
Community School Dist 10			Bronx	20
Community School Dist 11			Bronx	22
Community School Dist 12			Bronx	23
Community School Dist 13			Kings	82
Community School Dist 14			Kings	83

DISTRICT INDEX

SCHOOL DISTRICT	NO. OF SCHOOLS	ENROLLMENT	COUNTY	PAGE
Community School Dist 15			Kings	84
Community School Dist 16			Kings	85
Community School Dist 17			Kings	86
Community School Dist 18			Kings	87
Community School Dist 19			Kings	88
Community School Dist 20			Kings	89
Community School Dist 21			Kings	90
Community School Dist 22			Kings	91
Community School Dist 23			Kings	92
Community School Dist 24			Queens	176
Community School Dist 25			Queens	178
Community School Dist 26			Queens	179
Community School Dist 27			Queens	180
Community School Dist 28			Queens	181
Community School Dist 29			Queens	183
Community School Dist 30			Queens	184
Community School Dist 31			Richmond	192
Community School Dist 32			Kings	93
Connetquot Central School Dist	11	5,653	Suffolk	219
Cooperstown Ctl School Dist	2	818	Otsego	173
Copenhagen Central SD	1	460	Lewis	101
Copiague Union Free Sch Dist	6	4,864	Suffolk	220
Corinth Central School Dist	3	1,139	Saratoga	200
Corning-Painted Post Area SD	9	4,500	Steuben	214
Cornwall Central School Dist	5	3,122	Orange	163
Cortland Enlarged City SD	4	2,100	Cortland	47
Coxsackie-Athens Central SD	4	1,400	Greene	75
Croton-Harmon Union Free SD	3	1,568	Westchester	254
Crown Point Central Sch Dist	1	306	Essex	67
Cuba-Rushford Central Sch Dist	2	818	Allegany	14
Dansville Ctl School Dist	3	1,300	Livingston	102
De Ruyter Central School Dist	2	360	Madison	105
Deer Park Union Free Sch Dist	5	4,015	Suffolk	220
Delaware Academy Ctrl SD Delhi	2	797	Delaware	49
Depew Union Free School Dist	3	1,785	Erie	59
Deposit Central School Dist	2	482	Broome	28
Dist 75 City Wide Programs			New York	142
Dobbs Ferry Union Free SD	3	1,500	Westchester	254
Dolgeville Central School Dist	2	900	Herkimer	77
Dover Union Free School Dist	4	1,352	Dutchess	52
Downsville Central Sch Dist	1	240	Delaware	49
Dryden Central School Dist	5	1,500	Tompkins	239
Duanesburg Central Sch Dist	2	770	Schenectady	203
Dundee Ctl School Dist	2	700	Yates	268
Dunkirk City School Dist	6	2,300	Chautauqua	37
East Aurora Union Free SD	3	1,760	Erie	60
East Greenbush Central SD	7	5,042	Rensselaer	190
East Hampton Union Free SD	3	1,781	Suffolk	220
East Irondequoit Ctl Sch Dist	6	3,000	Monroe	107
East Islip Union Free SD	6	3,782	Suffolk	220
East Meadow Union Free SD	9	7,100	Nassau	118
East Moriches Union Free SD	2	750	Suffolk	221
East Quogue Union Free SD	1	390	Suffolk	221
East Ramapo Central Sch Dist	14	8,843	Rockland	196
East Rochester Union Free SD	2	1,007	Monroe	107
East Rockaway Union Free SD	3	1,200	Nassau	118
East Syracuse Minoa Ctl SD	7	3,600	Onondaga	154
East Williston Union Free SD	3	1,722	Nassau	118
Eastchester Union Free SD	5	3,140	Westchester	254
Eastport-South Manor Ctrl SD	6	3,294	Suffolk	221
Eden Central School Dist	3	1,538	Erie	60
Edgemont Union Free Sch Dist	3	2,050	Westchester	254
Edinburg Common School Dist	1	65	Saratoga	200
Edmeston Ctl School Dist	1	390	Otsego	173
Edwards-Knox Central Sch Dist	1	537	St Lawrence	210
Elba Central School Dist	1	403	Genesee	73
Eldred Central School Dist	2	525	Sullivan	236
Ellenville Central School Dist	3	1,500	Ulster	241
Ellicottville Central Sch Dist	1	600	Cattaraugus	31
Elmira City School Dist	11	6,000	Chemung	40
Elmira Heights Ctl Sch Dist	3	1,100	Chemung	40
Elmont Union Free School Dist	6	3,500	Nassau	118
Elmsford Union Free SD	3	1,002	Westchester	255
Elwood Union Free School Dist	4	2,049	Suffolk	221
Evans-Brant Central Sch Dist	5	2,260	Erie	60
Fabius Pompey Central SD	2	611	Onondaga	155
Fairport Ctl School Dist	8	5,900	Monroe	108
Falconer Central School Dist	3	1,200	Chautauqua	37
Fallsburg Central School Dist	2	1,440	Sullivan	236
Farmingdale Union Free SD	6	5,900	Nassau	119
Fayetteville-Manlius Ctl SD	6	4,259	Onondaga	155
Fillmore Central School Dist	1	680	Allegany	14
Fire Island Union Free SD	1	32	Suffolk	222
Fishers Island Union Free SD	1	65	Suffolk	222
Floral Park Bellerose Sch Dist	2	1,479	Nassau	119
Florida Union Free Sch Dist	2	807	Orange	164
Fonda Fultonville Central SD	1	1,340	Montgomery	115
Forestville Central Sch Dist	2	457	Chautauqua	37
Fort Ann Central School Dist	2	500	Washington	247
Frankfort-Schuyler Ctl SD	2	893	Herkimer	77
Franklin Central School Dist	1	262	Delaware	49
Franklin Square Union Free SD	3	1,940	Nassau	119
Franklinville Ctl School Dist	2	700	Cattaraugus	31
Fredonia Central School Dist	4	1,500	Chautauqua	37
Freeport Public School Dist	8	6,885	Nassau	119
Frewsburg Central School Dist	2	805	Chautauqua	38
Friendship Central Sch Dist	1	350	Allegany	15
Frontier Ctl School Dist	6	4,760	Erie	60
Ft Edward Union Free Sch Dist	2	450	Washington	247
Ft Plain Central School Dist	2	750	Montgomery	115
Fulton City School Dist	6	3,500	Oswego	170
Galway Central School Dist	2	837	Saratoga	201
Gananda Central School Dist	3	960	Wayne	249
Garden City School Dist	7	3,800	Nassau	120
Garrison Union Free Sch Dist	1	207	Putnam	175
Gates Chili Central Sch Dist	6	4,000	Monroe	108
General Brown Ctl School Dist	3	1,600	Jefferson	80
Genesee Valley Ctl School Dist	1	536	Allegany	15
Geneseo Central Sch Dist	1	853	Livingston	102
Geneva City School Dist	4	2,078	Ontario	161
George Junior Republic UFSD	1	186	Tompkins	240
Germantown Central School Dist	1	550	Columbia	46
Gilbertsville-Mt Upton SD	1	350	Otsego	173
Gilboa-Conesville Central SD	1	312	Schoharie	206
Glen Cove City School Dist	6	3,200	Nassau	120
Glens Falls City School Dist	5	2,058	Warren	245
Glens Falls Common Sch Dist	1	155	Warren	245
Gloversville Enlarged Sch Dist	6	2,521	Fulton	71
Goshen Central School Dist	4	2,935	Orange	164
Gouverneur Ctl School Dist	3	1,515	St Lawrence	210
Gowanda Central School Dist	3	1,063	Cattaraugus	32
Grand Island Central Sch Dist	5	2,905	Erie	61
Granville Central School Dist	3	1,200	Washington	247
Great Neck Public Schools	12	6,700	Nassau	120
Greater Amsterdam School Dist	6	3,690	Montgomery	115
Greater Johnstown Sch Dist	5	1,700	Fulton	71
Greece Central School Dist	17	10,700	Monroe	108
Green Island Union Free SD	1	262	Albany	10
Greenburgh 11 Union Free SD	2	85	Westchester	255
Greenburgh Central School Dist	5	1,903	Westchester	255
Greenburgh-Graham UFSD	2	286	Westchester	255
Greenburgh-North Castle SD	4	309	Westchester	255
Greene Ctl School Dist	4	954	Chenango	42
Greenport Union Free Sch Dist	1	627	Suffolk	222
Greenville Central School Dist	3	1,100	Greene	75
Greenwich Central School Dist	2	943	Washington	247
Greenwood Lake Union Free SD	2	500	Orange	164
Groton Central School Dist	2	852	Tompkins	240
Guilderland Central Sch Dist	7	5,000	Albany	10
Hadley-Luzerne Ctl Sch Dist	2	665	Warren	245
Haldane Central School Dist	1	794	Putnam	175
Half Hollow Hills Central SD	9	8,017	Suffolk	222
Hamburg Central School Dist	6	3,550	Erie	61
Hamilton Central Sch Dist	1	588	Madison	105

New York School Directory

DISTRICT INDEX

SCHOOL DISTRICT	NO. OF SCHOOLS	ENROLL-MENT	COUNTY	PAGE
Hammond Central School Distict	1	257	St Lawrence	210
Hammondsport Ctl School Dist	2	450	Steuben	214
Hampton Bays Union Free SD	3	2,060	Suffolk	222
Hancock Central School Dist	2	316	Delaware	49
Hannibal Central School Dist	3	1,310	Oswego	171
Harborfields Ctl School Dist	4	2,965	Suffolk	223
Harpursville Central Sch Dist	2	677	Broome	28
Harrison Central School Dist	6	3,600	Westchester	256
Harrisville Central Sch Dist	1	359	Lewis	101
Hartford Central School Dist	1	413	Washington	248
Hastings on Hudson Union FR SD	3	1,654	Westchester	256
Hauppauge Union Free Sch Dist	5	3,200	Suffolk	223
Hawthorne Cedar Knolls UFSD	4	400	Westchester	256
Hempstead Union Free SD	10	7,355	Nassau	121
Hendrick Hudson Ctl Sch Dist	5	2,122	Westchester	256
Herkimer Ctl School Dist	2	1,112	Herkimer	77
Hermon-DeKalb Central Sch Dist	1	430	St Lawrence	210
Herricks Union Free Sch Dist	5	3,950	Nassau	121
Heuvelton Central School Dist	1	580	St Lawrence	210
Hewlett Woodmere Union Free SD	5	3,000	Nassau	121
Hicksville Union Free Sch Dist	9	5,000	Nassau	122
Highland Ctl School Dist	3	1,667	Ulster	242
Highland Falls-Ft Montgmry SD	3	1,000	Orange	164
Hilton Central School Dist	5	4,482	Monroe	109
Hinsdale Central School Dist	1	404	Cattaraugus	32
Holland Central School Dist	3	800	Erie	61
Holland Patent Ctl School Dist	4	1,316	Oneida	150
Holley Central School Dist	2	1,200	Orleans	169
Homer Central School Dist	4	1,700	Cortland	47
Honeoye Central School Dist	1	251	Ontario	161
Honeoye Falls Lima Sch Dist	4	2,122	Monroe	109
Hoosic Valley Central Sch Dist	2	931	Rensselaer	190
Hoosick Falls Central Sch Dist	2	1,200	Rensselaer	190
Hornell City School Dist	4	1,700	Steuben	214
Horseheads Ctl School Dist	7	4,245	Chemung	40
Hudson City School Dist	4	1,652	Columbia	46
Hudson Falls Central Sch Dist	5	2,400	Washington	248
Hunter Tannersville Ctl SD	2	355	Greene	76
Huntington Union Free Sch Dist	8	4,545	Suffolk	223
Hyde Park Central School Dist	6	3,500	Dutchess	52
Ichabod Crane Central Schools	3	1,683	Columbia	46
Indian Lake Ctl School Dist	1	112	Hamilton	76
Indian River Ctl School Dist	8	3,900	Jefferson	80
Iroquois Central School Dist	5	2,127	Erie	61
Irvington Union Free Sch Dist	4	1,781	Westchester	257
Island Park Union Free SD	2	743	Nassau	122
Island Trees Union Free SD	4	2,236	Nassau	122
Islip Union Free School Dist	5	2,726	Suffolk	223
Ithaca City School Dist	12	5,103	Tompkins	240
Jamestown City School Dist	9	5,000	Chautauqua	38
Jamesville-DeWitt Central SD	5	2,694	Onondaga	155
Jasper Troupsburg Central SD	2	450	Steuben	214
Jefferson Central Sch Dist	1	195	Schoharie	206
Jericho Union Free School Dist	5	3,155	Nassau	122
Johnsburg Central School Dist	1	333	Warren	245
Johnson City Central Sch Dist	5	2,443	Broome	28
Jordan Elbridge Ctl Sch Dist	3	1,300	Onondaga	155
Katonah-Lewisboro Sch Dist	5	2,917	Westchester	257
Keene Central School Dist	1	170	Essex	67
Kendall Central School Dist	2	710	Orleans	169
Kenmore-Tonawanda UF Sch Dist	9	7,000	Erie	62
Keshequa Central School Dist	3	617	Livingston	103
Kings Park Ctl School Dist	5	2,888	Suffolk	224
Kingston City School Dist	10	6,800	Ulster	242
Kiryas Joel Union Free SD	1	167	Orange	164
La Fargeville Central School Dist	1	539	Jefferson	80
La Fayette Central School Dist	4	825	Onondaga	156
Lackawanna City School Dist	4	1,946	Erie	62
Lake George Central Sch Dist	2	721	Warren	245
Lake Placid Ctl School Dist	2	650	Essex	67
Lake Pleasant Central Sch Dist	1	80	Hamilton	76
Lakeland Central School Dist	8	5,845	Westchester	257
Lancaster Central Sch Dist	7	5,630	Erie	62
Lansing Central School Dist	3	1,187	Tompkins	240
Lansingburgh Central Sch Dist	4	2,335	Rensselaer	190
Laurens Central School Dist	1	300	Otsego	173
Lawrence Union Free Sch Dist	5	2,600	Nassau	123
Le Roy Central School Dist	2	1,350	Genesee	73
Letchworth Central School Dist	3	936	Wyoming	267
Levittown Union Free Sch Dist	11	7,215	Nassau	123
Lewiston Porter Ctl Sch Dist	4	2,187	Niagara	146
Liberty Central School Dist	3	1,700	Sullivan	236
Lindenhurst Union Free SD	8	5,694	Suffolk	224
Lisbon Central School Dist	1	587	St Lawrence	210
Little Falls City School Dist	3	1,116	Herkimer	78
Little Flower Union Free SD	1	96	Suffolk	224
Liverpool Ctl School Dist	14	7,000	Onondaga	156
Livingston Manor Ctl School Dist	2	432	Sullivan	236
Livonia Ctl School Dist	2	1,500	Livingston	103
Lockport City School Dist	9	5,100	Niagara	147
Locust Valley Ctl School Dist	6	2,000	Nassau	123
Long Beach City School Dist	7	3,800	Nassau	124
Long Lake Central School Dist	1	65	Hamilton	76
Longwood Central School Dist	7	9,150	Suffolk	224
Lowville Acad-Central Sch Dist	1	1,350	Lewis	101
Lyme Central School Dist	1	349	Jefferson	81
Lynbrook Union Free Sch Dist	7	2,809	Nassau	124
Lyncourt Union Free Sch Dist	1	450	Onondaga	156
Lyndonville Central School Dist	2	700	Orleans	169
Lyons Central School Dist	2	920	Wayne	249
Madison Central School Dist	1	450	Madison	105
Madrid-Waddington Central SD	1	647	St Lawrence	211
Mahopac Ctl School Dist	5	3,968	Putnam	176
Maine Endwell Ctl School Dist	4	2,492	Broome	29
Malone Central School Dist	5	2,289	Franklin	69
Malverne Union Free Sch Dist	4	1,725	Nassau	124
Mamaroneck Union Free Sch Dist	6	5,230	Westchester	257
Manchester-Shortsville Ctl SD	3	800	Ontario	162
Manhasset Union Free Sch Dist	4	3,250	Nassau	124
Marathon Ctl School Dist	2	689	Cortland	48
Marcellus Central School Dist	3	1,507	Onondaga	157
Marcus Whitman Central SD	3	1,227	Ontario	162
Margaretville Central Sch Dist	1	370	Delaware	49
Marion Central School Dist	2	687	Wayne	250
Marlboro Central School Dist	3	1,893	Ulster	242
Massapequa Union Free SD 23	9	8,000	Nassau	125
Massena Central School Dist	5	2,500	St Lawrence	211
Mattituck-Cutchogue UFSD	2	1,100	Suffolk	225
Mayfield Ctl School Dist	2	876	Fulton	72
McGraw Central School Dist	2	570	Cortland	48
Mechanicville City Sch Dist	2	1,345	Saratoga	201
Medina Central School Dist	3	1,475	Orleans	169
Menands Union Free Sch Dist	1	305	Albany	11
Merrick Union Free School Dist	3	1,490	Nassau	125
Mexico Central School Dist	5	2,055	Oswego	171
Middle Country Ctl Sch Dist	14	9,860	Suffolk	225
Middleburgh Ctl School Dist	2	750	Schoharie	206
Middletown Enlarged City SD	6	7,312	Orange	165
Milford Central School Dist	1	361	Otsego	173
Millbrook Ctl School Dist	4	875	Dutchess	52
Miller Place Union Free SD	4	2,489	Suffolk	225
Mineola Union Free Sch Dist	5	2,927	Nassau	125
Minerva Central School Dist	1	110	Essex	68
Minisink Valley Central SD	5	3,493	Orange	165
Mohonasen Central Sch Dist	4	2,799	Schenectady	203
Monroe Woodbury Central SD	7	6,900	Orange	165
Montauk Union Free School Dist	1	320	Suffolk	226
Monticello Central School Dist	5	2,785	Sullivan	237
Moravia Central School Dist	2	907	Cayuga	34
Moriah Central School Dist	1	780	Essex	68
Morris Central School Dist	1	322	Otsego	173
Morristown Ctl School Dist	1	333	St Lawrence	211
Morrisville Eaton Central SD	2	621	Madison	105
Mount Markham Central Sch Dist	3	1,100	Herkimer	78

School Year 2020-2021   800-333-8802   **NY-Q3**

DISTRICT INDEX

Market Data Retrieval

SCHOOL DISTRICT	NO. OF SCHOOLS	ENROLL-MENT	COUNTY	PAGE
Mount Vernon City School Dist	16	8,000	Westchester	258
Mt Morris Central School Dist	1	500	Livingston	103
Mt Pleasant Cottage UFSD	2	215	Westchester	258
Mt Pleasant Ctl School Dist	4	2,000	Westchester	258
Mt Pleasant-Blythedale UFSD	1	134	Westchester	259
Mt Sinai Union Free SD	3	2,100	Suffolk	226
Nanuet Union Free School Dist	5	2,220	Rockland	196
Naples Central School Dist	2	600	Ontario	162
New Hartford Central Sch Dist	5	2,553	Oneida	151
New Hyde-Garden City Park UFSD	4	1,785	Nassau	126
New Lebanon Ctl School Dist	2	428	Columbia	46
New Paltz Ctl School Dist	4	2,035	Ulster	242
New Rochelle City School Dist	10	11,000	Westchester	259
New Suffolk Common School Dist	1	13	Suffolk	226
New York Alt High Sch SD 79			New York	142
New York City Dept of Ed	1,680	1,150,000	New York	134
New York Mills Union Free SD	1	550	Oneida	151
Newark Central School Dist	5	2,091	Wayne	250
Newark Valley Central Sch Dist	3	1,060	Tioga	238
Newburgh Enlarged City SD	13	11,562	Orange	165
Newcomb Central School Dist	1	405	Essex	68
Newfane Central School Dist	4	1,511	Niagara	147
Newfield Central School Dist	3	780	Tompkins	241
Niagara Falls City Sch Dist	12	7,100	Niagara	147
Niagara-Wheatfield Ctl SD	6	3,650	Niagara	148
Niskayuna Central School Dist	8	4,240	Schenectady	204
North Babylon Union Free SD	7	4,491	Suffolk	226
North Bellmore Union Free SD	5	2,031	Nassau	126
North Collins Ctl Sch Dist	2	620	Erie	63
North Colonie Central SD	8	5,800	Albany	11
North Greenbush Common SD	1	13	Rensselaer	191
North Merrick Union Free SD	3	1,177	Nassau	126
North Rockland Central SD	8	8,000	Rockland	197
North Rose Wolcott Central SD	3	1,155	Wayne	250
North Salem Central Sch Dist	2	1,046	Westchester	259
North Shore Central SD	5	2,548	Nassau	126
North Syracuse Ctl Sch Dist	11	8,400	Onondaga	157
North Tonawanda City Sch Dist	6	3,400	Niagara	148
North Warren Central Sch Dist	1	508	Warren	246
Northeastern Clinton Ctl SD	4	1,200	Clinton	44
Northern Adirondack Ctl SD	2	805	Clinton	44
Northport-East Northport UFSD	9	5,141	Suffolk	227
Northville Central School Dist	1	500	Fulton	72
Norwich City School Dist	4	2,000	Chenango	42
Norwood-Norfolk Ctl SD	3	987	St Lawrence	211
Nyack Union Free School Dist	5	3,000	Rockland	197
O E S J Central School Dist	2	719	Fulton	72
Oakfield Alabama Ctl SD	2	800	Genesee	74
Oceanside Union Free Sch Dist	10	5,400	Nassau	127
Odessa Montour Ctl Sch Dist	3	733	Schuyler	207
Ogdensburg City School Dist	3	1,535	St Lawrence	211
Olean City School Dist	4	2,075	Cattaraugus	32
Oneida City School Dist	6	2,000	Madison	105
Oneonta City School Dist	5	1,736	Otsego	174
Onondaga Central School Dist	3	830	Onondaga	157
Onteora Central School Dist	4	1,200	Ulster	243
Orchard Park Central Sch Dist	6	5,010	Erie	63
Oriskany Ctl School Dist	2	587	Oneida	151
Ossining Union Free Sch Dist	6	5,100	Westchester	259
Oswego City School Dist	7	3,669	Oswego	171
Otselic Valley Central SD	1	300	Chenango	42
Owego Apalachin Ctl Sch Dist	4	2,005	Tioga	238
Owen D Young Central Sch Dist	1	182	Herkimer	78
Oxford Academy Central SD	3	750	Chenango	42
Oyster Bay East Norwich Ctl SD	3	1,565	Nassau	127
Oysterponds Union Free SD	1	104	Suffolk	227
Palmyra-Macedon Central SD	4	1,861	Wayne	250
Panama Central School Dist	1	450	Chautauqua	38
Parishville Hopkinton Sch Dist	1	420	St Lawrence	212
Patchogue-Medford Unified SD	11	7,503	Suffolk	227
Pavilion Ctl School Dist	2	680	Genesee	74
Pawling Ctl School Dist	3	1,100	Dutchess	52
Pearl River School Dist	5	2,360	Rockland	197
Peekskill City School Dist	6	3,400	Westchester	260
Pelham Union Free School Dist	6	2,800	Westchester	260
Pembroke Ctl School Dist	3	1,000	Genesee	74
Penfield Central School Dist	6	4,600	Monroe	109
Penn Yan Ctl School Dist	3	1,338	Yates	268
Perry Central School Dist	2	806	Wyoming	267
Peru Central School Dist	2	1,857	Clinton	44
Phelps-Clifton Springs Ctl SD	4	1,549	Ontario	162
Phoenix Central School Dist	3	1,684	Oswego	171
Pine Bush Central School Dist	8	5,000	Orange	166
Pine Plains Ctl School Dist	3	905	Dutchess	53
Pine Valley Central Sch Dist	2	550	Chautauqua	38
Pittsford Central Sch Dist	9	6,000	Monroe	110
Plainedge Union Free Sch Dist	5	2,825	Nassau	127
Plainview-Old Bethpage Ctl SD	7	5,000	Nassau	127
Plattsburgh City School Dist	5	1,852	Clinton	44
Pleasantville Union Free SD	3	1,700	Westchester	260
Pocantico Hills Ctl Sch Dist	1	308	Westchester	260
Poland Central School Dist	1	523	Herkimer	78
Port Byron Ctl School Dist	2	800	Cayuga	35
Port Chester Rye Union Free SD	6	5,000	Westchester	261
Port Jefferson Union Free SD 6	3	1,048	Suffolk	227
Port Jervis City School Dist	4	2,332	Orange	166
Port Washington Union Free SD	7	5,000	Nassau	128
Portville Central School Dist	1	1,030	Cattaraugus	32
Potsdam Central School Dist	3	1,200	St Lawrence	212
Poughkeepsie City School Dist	8	4,420	Dutchess	53
Prattsburgh Central Sch Dist	1	388	Steuben	215
Pulaski Central School Dist	2	971	Oswego	172
Putnam Central School Dist	1	35	Washington	248
Putnam Valley Ctl School Dist	3	1,587	Putnam	176
Queensbury Union Free Sch Dist	4	3,200	Warren	246
Quogue Union Free School Dist	1	130	Suffolk	228
Randolph Acad Union Free SD	2	200	Cattaraugus	32
Randolph Central School Dist	2	903	Cattaraugus	33
Ravena Coeymans Selkirk Ctl SD	4	1,839	Albany	11
Red Creek Central School Dist	3	870	Wayne	251
Red Hook Central School Dist	4	1,750	Dutchess	53
Remsen Central School Dist	2	400	Oneida	151
Remsenburg-Speonk UFSD	1	132	Suffolk	228
Rensselaer City School Dist	2	1,060	Rensselaer	191
Rhinebeck Central School Dist	3	1,000	Dutchess	53
Richfield Springs Central SD	1	450	Otsego	174
Ripley Central School Dist	1	165	Chautauqua	39
Riverhead Central School Dist	7	5,600	Suffolk	228
Rochester City School Dist	57	28,000	Monroe	110
Rockville Ctr Union Free SD	7	3,500	Nassau	128
Rocky Point Union Free SD	4	2,947	Suffolk	228
Rome City School Dist	10	5,300	Oneida	151
Romulus Ctl School Dist	1	420	Seneca	208
Rondout Valley Ctl Sch Dist	5	1,975	Ulster	243
Roosevelt Union Free Sch Dist	5	3,511	Nassau	128
Roscoe Central School Dist	1	257	Sullivan	237
Roslyn School Dist	5	3,150	Nassau	129
Roxbury Central School Dist	1	260	Delaware	50
Royalton Hartland Central SD	3	1,271	Niagara	148
Rush Henrietta Central SD	9	5,300	Monroe	112
Rye City School Dist	6	3,510	Westchester	261
Rye Neck Union Free Sch Dist	4	1,525	Westchester	261
Sachem Central School Dist	15	13,500	Suffolk	229
Sackets Harbor Ctl School Dist	1	418	Jefferson	81
Sag Harbor Union Free Sch Dist	2	953	Suffolk	229
Sagaponack Common School Dist	1	16	Suffolk	229
Salamanca City Central SD	3	1,400	Cattaraugus	33
Salem Central School Dist	1	550	Washington	248
Salmon River Central Sch Dist	4	1,800	Franklin	70
Sandy Creek Central Sch Dist	1	800	Oswego	172
Saranac Central School Dist	4	1,400	Clinton	45
Saranac Lake Central Sch Dist	4	1,280	Franklin	70
Saratoga Springs City Sch Dist	8	6,375	Saratoga	201
Saugerties Central School Dist	6	2,500	Ulster	243

New York School Directory — DISTRICT INDEX

SCHOOL DISTRICT	NO. OF SCHOOLS	ENROLLMENT	COUNTY	PAGE
Sauquoit Valley Central SD	3	900	Oneida	152
Sayville Union Free Sch Dist	5	2,823	Suffolk	229
Scarsdale Union Free Sch Dist	7	4,771	Westchester	261
Schalmont Central School Dist	3	1,798	Schenectady	204
Schenectady City School Dist	17	9,921	Schenectady	204
Schenevus Ctl School Dist	1	350	Otsego	174
Schodack Central School Dist	2	900	Rensselaer	191
Schoharie Central SD	2	875	Schoharie	206
Schroon Lake Ctl School Dist	1	230	Essex	68
Schuylerville Central Sch Dist	3	1,500	Saratoga	201
Scio Central School Dist	1	300	Allegany	15
Scotia Glenville Ctl Sch Dist	6	2,600	Schenectady	205
Seaford Union Free SD	4	2,249	Nassau	129
Seneca Falls Central Sch Dist	4	1,173	Seneca	208
Sewanhaka Ctl High Sch Dist	5	8,145	Nassau	129
Sharon Springs Ctl SD	1	226	Schoharie	207
Shelter Island Union Free SD	1	202	Suffolk	230
Shenendehowa Central Sch Dist	12	9,499	Saratoga	202
Sherburne Earlville Central SD	3	1,267	Chenango	42
Sherman Central School Dist	1	434	Chautauqua	39
Shoreham-Wading River Ctl SD	4	2,000	Suffolk	230
Sidney Central School Dist	3	1,090	Delaware	50
Silver Creek Central Sch Dist	3	1,212	Chautauqua	39
Skaneateles Central Sch Dist	4	1,200	Onondaga	157
Smithtown Central Sch Dist	12	8,946	Suffolk	230
Sodus Central School Dist	3	1,050	Wayne	251
Solvay Union Free Sch Dist	3	1,500	Onondaga	158
Somers Central School Dist	4	2,866	Westchester	262
South Colonie Central Sch Dist	8	4,700	Albany	12
South Country Central Sch Dist	7	4,400	Suffolk	231
South Glens Falls Ctl Sch Dist	6	3,000	Saratoga	202
South Huntington Union Free SD	7	5,900	Suffolk	231
South Jefferson Central SD	4	1,894	Jefferson	81
South Kortright Ctl SD	1	350	Delaware	50
South Lewis Central Sch Dist	4	1,028	Lewis	101
South Orangetown Central SD	4	2,911	Rockland	197
South Seneca Ctl Sch Dist	2	700	Seneca	208
Southampton Union Free SD	3	1,575	Suffolk	231
Southern Cayuga Central SD	2	683	Cayuga	35
Southold Union Free Sch Dist	2	750	Suffolk	231
Southwestern Central Sch Dist	3	1,400	Chautauqua	39
Spackenkill Union Free SD	4	1,500	Dutchess	54
Spencer Van Etten Central SD	3	985	Tioga	238
Spencerport Central Sch Dist	6	3,700	Monroe	112
Springs Union Free School Dist	1	750	Suffolk	232
Springville Griffith Inst CSD	4	1,700	Erie	63
St Regis Falls Ctl Sch Dist	1	268	Franklin	70
Stamford Central School Dist	1	270	Delaware	50
Starpoint Central School Dist	4	2,931	Niagara	149
Stillwater Central Sch Dist	3	1,035	Saratoga	202
Stockbridge Valley Central SD	1	460	Madison	106
Suffern Central School Dist	7	4,283	Rockland	198
Sullivan West Central SD	2	1,068	Sullivan	237
Susquehanna Valley Central SD	4	1,412	Broome	29
Sweet Home Central Sch Dist	6	3,300	Erie	63
Syosset Central School Dist	10	6,500	Nassau	129
Syracuse City School Dist	37	21,116	Onondaga	158
Taconic Hills Central Sch Dist	2	1,241	Columbia	47
Tarrytown Union Free Sch Dist	5	2,900	Westchester	262
Thousand Islands Central SD	4	867	Jefferson	81
Three Village Central Sch Dist	9	6,400	Suffolk	232
Ticonderoga Central Sch Dist	2	735	Essex	68
Tioga Central School Dist	3	950	Tioga	239
Tonawanda City School Dist	4	2,000	Erie	64
Town of Webb Union Free SD	1	270	Herkimer	78
Tri-Valley Central School Dist	2	975	Sullivan	237
Troy City School Dsitrict	7	4,090	Rensselaer	191
Trumansburg Central SD	3	1,043	Tompkins	241
Tuckahoe Common School Dist	1	285	Suffolk	232
Tuckahoe Union Free SD	3	1,100	Westchester	262
Tully Central School Dist	2	770	Onondaga	159
Tupper Lake Ctl School Dist	2	749	Franklin	70
Tuxedo Union Free Sch Dist	2	225	Orange	166
Unadilla Valley Ctl Sch Dist	2	850	Chenango	43
Unatego Unadilla Central SD	3	716	Otsego	174
Union Springs Ctl School Dist	3	823	Cayuga	35
Union-Endicott Ctl Sch Dist	7	4,000	Broome	29
Uniondale Union Free Sch Dist	9	6,970	Nassau	130
Utica City School Dist	13	10,000	Oneida	152
Valhalla Union Free Sch Dist	3	1,420	Westchester	262
Valley Central School Dist	7	4,200	Orange	167
Valley Stream Ctl High SD	4	4,600	Nassau	130
Valley Stream Union Free SD 13	4	1,964	Nassau	130
Valley Stream Union Free SD 24	3	1,093	Nassau	131
Valley Stream Union Free SD 30	3	1,450	Nassau	131
Vernon-Verona-Sherrill CSD	5	1,900	Oneida	152
Vestal Ctl School Dist	7	3,397	Broome	29
Victor Central School Dist	5	4,450	Ontario	162
Voorheesville Central Sch Dist	3	1,175	Albany	12
Wainscott Common School Dist	1	30	Suffolk	232
Wallkill Central School Dist	5	2,831	Ulster	243
Walton Central School Dist	3	900	Delaware	50
Wantagh Union Free Sch Dist 23	5	2,770	Nassau	131
Wappingers Central Sch Dist	15	10,616	Dutchess	54
Warrensburg Central Sch Dist	2	687	Warren	246
Warsaw Central School Dist	2	800	Wyoming	267
Warwick Valley Central SD	4	3,569	Orange	167
Washingtonville Central SD	5	3,793	Orange	167
Waterford Halfmoon School Dist	2	800	Saratoga	203
Waterloo Central School Dist	4	1,538	Seneca	208
Watertown City School Dist	8	3,800	Jefferson	81
Waterville Central Sch Dist	2	742	Oneida	153
Watervliet City School Dist	2	1,297	Albany	12
Watkins Glen Central Sch Dist	2	1,040	Schuyler	207
Waverly Ctl School Dist	4	1,700	Tioga	239
Wayland-Cohocton Central SD	4	1,246	Steuben	215
Wayne Central School Dist	4	2,180	Wayne	251
Webster Central School Dist	11	8,331	Monroe	112
Webutuck Ctl School Dist	3	649	Dutchess	54
Weedsport Ctl School Dist	2	800	Cayuga	35
Wells Central School Dist	1	135	Hamilton	77
Wellsville Central Sch Dist	2	1,118	Allegany	15
West Babylon Union Free SD	7	4,000	Suffolk	232
West Canada Valley Ctl SD	2	650	Herkimer	79
West Genesee Ctl School Dist	7	4,600	Onondaga	159
West Hempstead School Dist	5	2,300	Nassau	131
West Irondequoit Ctl SD	10	3,600	Monroe	113
West Islip School Dist	7	3,720	Suffolk	233
West Point School Dist	2	629	Orange	167
West Seneca Central Sch Dist	9	6,100	Erie	64
West Valley Ctl Sch Dist	1	230	Cattaraugus	33
Westbury Union Free Sch Dist	6	5,000	Nassau	132
Westfield Central School Dist	1	700	Chautauqua	39
Westhampton Beach School Dist	3	1,819	Suffolk	233
Westhill Central School Dist	4	1,700	Onondaga	159
Westmoreland Central Sch Dist	3	853	Oneida	153
Wheatland Chili Ctl Sch Dist	2	637	Monroe	113
Wheelerville Union Free SD	1	130	Fulton	72
White Plains City School Dist	9	7,000	Westchester	263
Whitehall Central School Dist	2	719	Washington	248
Whitesboro Ctl School Dist	7	3,135	Oneida	153
Whitesville Central Sch Dist	1	200	Allegany	15
Whitney Point Central Sch Dist	3	1,359	Broome	30
William Floyd School Dist	8	8,700	Suffolk	233
Williamson Central School Dist	3	1,106	Wayne	251
Williamsville Ctl School Dist	13	9,900	Erie	64
Willsboro Central Sch Dist	1	243	Essex	68
Wilson Central School Dist	2	1,060	Niagara	149
Windham Ashland Jewett Ctl SD	1	310	Greene	76
Windsor Central School Dist	5	1,700	Broome	30
Worcester Ctl School Dist	1	350	Otsego	174
Wyandanch Union Free Sch Dist	4	2,811	Suffolk	234
Wynantskill Union Free SD	1	400	Rensselaer	191
Wyoming Central School Dist	1	130	Wyoming	268

DISTRICT INDEX

SCHOOL DISTRICT	NO. OF SCHOOLS	ENROLL-MENT	COUNTY	PAGE
Yonkers Public School Dist	40	27,000	Westchester	263
York Central School Dist	2	780	Livingston	103
Yorkshire-Pioneer Ctl Sch Dist	4	2,700	Cattaraugus	33
Yorktown Central School Dist	5	3,400	Westchester	264

CATHOLIC DIOCESE

SCHOOL DISTRICT	NO. OF SCHOOLS	ENROLL-MENT	COUNTY	PAGE
Archdiocese of New York Ed Off	147	62,605	New York	142
Diocese of Albany Ed Office	21	5,553	Albany	12
Diocese of Brooklyn Ed Office	91	44,500	Kings	94
Diocese of Buffalo Ed Office	49	15,000	Erie	65
Diocese of Ogdensburg Ed Off	9	1,293	St Lawrence	212
Diocese of Rochester Ed Office	16	2,800	Monroe	113
Diocese of Rockville Ed Office	44	32,000	Nassau	132
Diocese of Syracuse Ed Office	22	5,100	Onondaga	160

REGIONAL CENTERS

SCHOOL DISTRICT	COUNTY	PAGE
Broome-Tioga BOCES	Broome	31
Capital Region BOCES	Albany	13
Cattaraugus-Allegany BOCES	Cattaraugus	34
Cayuga-Onondaga BOCES	Cayuga	36
Champlain Valley Ed Services	Clinton	45
Ctr for Instruct Tech Innov	Oswego	172
Dcmo BOCES Chenango	Chenango	43
Dutchess Co BOCES	Dutchess	55
Eastern Suffolk BOCES	Suffolk	235
Erie 1 BOCES	Erie	67
Erie 2 Chautauqua-Catta BOCES	Erie	67
Franklin-Essex-Hamilton BOCES	Franklin	71
Genesee Valley BOCES	Genesee	74
Greater Southern Tier BOCES	Steuben	215
Hamilton-Fulton-Montgmry BOCES	Fulton	72
Herkimer BOCES	Herkimer	79
Jefferson Lewis BOCES	Jefferson	82
Madison-Oneida BOCES	Oneida	154
Monroe 1 BOCES	Monroe	115
Monroe 2 Orleans BOCES	Monroe	115
Nassau BOCES	Nassau	134
Onc BOCES	Delaware	51
Oneida-Herkimer-Mad BOCES	Oneida	154
Onondaga-Cortland-Madson BOCES	Onondaga	160
Orange-Ulster BOCES	Orange	168
Orleans-Niagara BOCES	Orleans	170
Putnam-Northern Wstchstr BOCES	Westchester	266
Questar III BOCES	Rensselaer	192
Rockland BOCES	Rockland	199
Southern Westchester BOCES	Westchester	267
Southtown Teachers Center	Erie	67
St Lawrence-Lewis BOCES	St Lawrence	212
Sullivan BOCES	Sullivan	238
Tompkins-Seneca-Tioga BOCES	Tompkins	241
Ulster BOCES	Ulster	244
Wayne-Finger Lakes BOCES	Wayne	252
Western Suffolk BOCES	Suffolk	236
WSWHE BOCES	Washington	249

New York School Directory

COUNTY INDEX

COUNTY District/City	NO. OF SCHOOLS	ENROLL-MENT	PAGE
ALBANY			
Albany City School Dist/Albany	19	9,024	9
Berne-Knox-Westerlo Central SD/Berne	2	751	10
Bethlehem Central School Dist/Delmar	7	4,400	10
Capital Region BOCES/Albany			13
Cohoes City School Dist/Cohoes	5	2,000	10
Diocese of Albany Ed Office/Albany	21	5,553	12
Green Island Union Free SD/Green Island	1	262	10
Guilderland Central Sch Dist/GuildrInd CTR	7	5,000	10
Menands Union Free Sch Dist/Menands	1	305	11
North Colonie Central SD/Latham	8	5,800	11
Ravena Coeymans Selkirk Ctl SD/Ravena	4	1,839	11
South Colonie Central Sch Dist/Albany	8	4,700	12
Voorheesville Central Sch Dist/Voorheesville	3	1,175	12
Watervliet City School Dist/Watervliet	2	1,297	12
ALLEGANY			
Alfred Almond Ctl School Dist/Almond	1	600	13
Andover Central School Dist/Andover	1	300	13
Belfast Central School Dist/Belfast	1	343	14
Bolivar-Richburg Ctrl Sch Dist/Bolivar	3	850	14
Canaseraga Central Sch Dist/Canaseraga	1	272	14
Cuba-Rushford Central Sch Dist/Cuba	2	818	14
Fillmore Central School Dist/Fillmore	1	680	14
Friendship Central Sch Dist/Friendship	1	350	15
Genesee Valley Ctl School Dist/Belmont	1	536	15
Scio Central School Dist/Scio	1	300	15
Wellsville Central Sch Dist/Wellsville	2	1,118	15
Whitesville Central School Dist/Whitesville	1	200	15
BRONX			
Community School Dist 7/Bronx			16
Community School Dist 8/Bronx			17
Community School Dist 9/Bronx			18
Community School Dist 10/Bronx			20
Community School Dist 11/Bronx			22
Community School Dist 12/Bronx			23
BROOME			
Binghamton City School Dist/Binghamton	10	5,500	27
Broome-Tioga BOCES/Binghamton			31
Chenango Forks Central SD/Binghamton	3	1,404	28
Chenango Valley Ctl Sch Dist/Binghamton	4	1,719	28
Deposit Central School Dist/Deposit	2	482	28
Harpursville Central Sch Dist/Harpursville	2	677	28
Johnson City Central Sch Dist/Johnson City	5	2,443	28
Maine Endwell Ctl School Dist/Endwell	4	2,492	29
Susquehanna Valley Central SD/Conklin	4	1,412	29
Union-Endicott Ctl Sch Dist/Endicott	7	4,000	29
Vestal Ctl School Dist/Vestal	7	3,397	29
Whitney Point Central Sch Dist/Whitney Point	3	1,359	30
Windsor Central School Dist/Windsor	5	1,700	30
CATTARAUGUS			
Allegany-Limestone Ctl SD/Allegany	2	1,156	31
Cattaraugus-Allegany BOCES/Olean			34
Cattaraugus-Little Vly Ctl SD/Cattaraugus	3	975	31
Ellicottville Central Sch Dist/Ellicottville	1	600	31
Franklinville Ctl School Dist/Franklinville	2	700	31
Gowanda Central School Dist/Gowanda	3	1,063	32
Hinsdale Central School Dist/Hinsdale	1	404	32
Olean City School Dist/Olean	4	2,075	32
Portville Central School Dist/Portville	1	1,030	32
Randolph Acad Union Free SD/Randolph	2	200	32
Randolph Central School Dist/Randolph	2	903	33
Salamanca City Central SD/Salamanca	3	1,400	33
West Valley Ctl Sch Dist/West Valley	1	230	33
Yorkshire-Pioneer Ctl Sch Dist/Yorkshire	4	2,700	33
CAYUGA			
Auburn Enlarged City Sch Dist/Auburn	7	4,200	34
Cato Meridian Central Sch Dist/Cato	3	922	34
Cayuga-Onondaga BOCES/Auburn			36
Moravia Central School Dist/Moravia	2	907	34
Port Byron Ctl School Dist/Port Byron	2	800	35
Southern Cayuga Central SD/Aurora	2	683	35
Union Springs Ctl School Dist/Union Springs	3	823	35
Weedsport Ctl School Dist/Weedsport	2	800	35
CHAUTAUQUA			
Bemus Point Ctl School Dist/Bemus Point	2	715	36
Brocton Central School Dist/Brocton	1	540	36
Cassadaga Valley Ctl Sch Dist/Sinclairville	2	851	36
Chautauqua Lake Central SD/Mayville	1	950	36
Clymer Central School Dist/Clymer	1	444	37
Dunkirk City School Dist/Dunkirk	6	2,300	37
Falconer Central School Dist/Falconer	3	1,200	37
Forestville Central Sch Dist/Forestville	2	457	37
Fredonia Central School Dist/Fredonia	4	1,500	37
Frewsburg Central School Dist/Frewsburg	2	805	38
Jamestown City School Dist/Jamestown	9	5,000	38
Panama Central School Dist/Panama	1	450	38
Pine Valley Central Sch Dist/South Dayton	2	550	38
Ripley Central School Dist/Ripley	1	165	39
Sherman Central School Dist/Sherman	1	434	39
Silver Creek Central Sch Dist/Silver Creek	3	1,212	39
Southwestern Central Sch Dist/Jamestown	3	1,400	39
Westfield Central School Dist/Westfield	1	700	39
CHEMUNG			
Elmira City School Dist/Elmira	11	6,000	40
Elmira Heights Ctl Sch Dist/Elmira Hgts	3	1,100	40
Horseheads Ctl School Dist/Horseheads	7	4,245	40
CHENANGO			
Afton Central School Dist/Afton	1	522	41
Bainbridge Guilford CSD/Bainbridge	3	850	41
Dcmo BOCES Chenango/Norwich			43
Greene Ctl School Dist/Greene	4	954	42
Norwich City School Dist/Norwich	4	2,000	42
Otselic Valley Central SD/South Otselic	1	300	42
Oxford Academy Central SD/Oxford	3	750	42
Sherburne Earlville Central SD/Sherburne	3	1,267	42
Unadilla Valley Ctl Sch Dist/New Berlin	2	850	43
CLINTON			
Ausable Valley Ctl Sch Dist/Clintonville	3	1,151	43
Beekmantown Ctl School Dist/West Chazy	4	2,000	43
Champlain Valley Ed Services/Plattsburgh			45
Chazy Central Rural Sch Dist/Chazy	1	455	44
Northeastern Clinton Ctl SD/Champlain	4	1,200	44
Northern Adirondack Ctl SD/Ellenburg Dep	2	805	44
Peru Central School Dist/Peru	2	1,857	44
Plattsburgh City School Dist/Plattsburgh	5	1,852	44
Saranac Central School Dist/Dannemora	4	1,400	45
COLUMBIA			
Berkshire Union Free Sch Dist/Canaan	2	40	45
Chatham Central School Dist/Chatham	3	1,100	46
Germantown Central School Dist/Germantown	1	550	46
Hudson City School Dist/Hudson	4	1,652	46
Ichabod Crane Central Schools/Valatie	3	1,683	46
New Lebanon Ctl School Dist/New Lebanon	2	428	46
Taconic Hills Central Sch Dist/Craryville	2	1,241	47
CORTLAND			
Cincinnatus Ctl School Dist/Cincinnatus	2	530	47
Cortland Enlarged City SD/Cortland	4	2,100	47
Homer Central School Dist/Homer	4	1,700	47
Marathon Ctl School Dist/Marathon	2	689	48
McGraw Central School Dist/Mc Graw	2	570	48
DELAWARE			
Andes Central School Dist/Andes	1	73	48
Charlotte Valley Ctl Sch Dist/Davenport	1	300	49
Delaware Academy Ctrl SD Delhi/Delhi	2	797	49
Downsville Central Sch Dist/Downsville	1	240	49
Franklin Central School Dist/Franklin	1	262	49
Hancock Central School Dist/Hancock	2	316	49
Margaretville Central Sch Dist/Margaretville	1	370	49
Onc BOCES/Grand Gorge			51
Roxbury Central School Dist/Roxbury	1	260	50
Sidney Central School Dist/Sidney	3	1,090	50
South Kortright Ctl SD/S Kortright	1	350	50
Stamford Central School Dist/Stamford	1	270	50
Walton Central School Dist/Walton	3	900	50
DUTCHESS			
Arlington Central School Dist/Lagrangeville	11	7,000	51
Beacon City School Dist/Beacon	6	3,200	51
Dover Union Free School Dist/Dover Plains	4	1,352	52
Dutchess Co BOCES/Poughkeepsie			55
Hyde Park Central School Dist/Hyde Park	6	3,500	52
Millbrook Ctl School Dist/Millbrook	4	875	52
Pawling Ctl School Dist/Pawling	3	1,100	52
Pine Plains Ctl School Dist/Pine Plains	3	905	53
Poughkeepsie City School Dist/Poughkeepsie	8	4,420	53
Red Hook Central School Dist/Red Hook	4	1,750	53
Rhinebeck Central School Dist/Rhinebeck	3	1,000	53
Spackenkill Union Free SD/Poughkeepsie	4	1,500	54
Wappingers Central Sch Dist/Hopewell Jct	15	10,616	54
Webutuck Ctl School Dist/Amenia	3	649	54

School Year 2020-2021

COUNTY INDEX

Market Data Retrieval

COUNTY District/City	NO. OF SCHOOLS	ENROLL- MENT	PAGE
ERIE			
Akron Central School Dist/Akron	3	1,500	56
Alden Central School Dist/Alden	4	1,581	56
Amherst Central School Dist/Amherst	4	2,990	56
Buffalo Public Schools/Buffalo	68	33,428	56
Cheektowaga Central SD/Cheektowaga	3	2,249	58
Cheektowaga Maryvale UFSD/Cheektowaga	4	2,183	58
Cheektowaga-Sloan UFSD/Sloan	4	1,279	59
Clarence Central School Dist/Clarence	6	4,600	59
Cleveland Hill Union Free SD/Cheektowaga	3	1,284	59
Depew Union Free School Dist/Depew	3	1,785	59
Diocese of Buffalo Ed Office/Buffalo	49	15,000	65
East Aurora Union Free SD/East Aurora	3	1,760	60
Eden Central School Dist/Eden	3	1,538	60
Erie 1 BOCES/West Seneca			67
Erie 2 Chautauqua-Catta BOCES/Angola			67
Evans-Brant Central Sch Dist/Angola	5	2,260	60
Frontier Ctl School Dist/Hamburg	6	4,760	60
Grand Island Central Sch Dist/Grand Island	5	2,905	61
Hamburg Central School Dist/Hamburg	6	3,550	61
Holland Central School Dist/Holland	3	800	61
Iroquois Central School Dist/Elma	5	2,127	61
Kenmore-Tonawanda UF Sch Dist/Buffalo	9	7,000	62
Lackawanna City School Dist/Lackawanna	4	1,946	62
Lancaster Central Sch Dist/Lancaster	7	5,630	62
North Collins Ctl Sch Dist/North Collins	2	620	63
Orchard Park Central Sch Dist/West Seneca	6	5,010	63
Southtown Teachers Center/Hamburg			67
Springville Griffith Inst CSD/Springville	4	1,700	63
Sweet Home Central Sch Dist/Amherst	6	3,300	63
Tonawanda City School Dist/Tonawanda	4	2,000	64
West Seneca Central Sch Dist/West Seneca	9	6,100	64
Williamsville Ctl School Dist/East Amherst	13	9,900	64
ESSEX			
Boquet Valley Central Sch Dist/Westport	2	202	67
Crown Point Central Sch Dist/Crown Point	1	306	67
Keene Central School Dist/Keene Valley	1	170	67
Lake Placid Ctl School Dist/Lake Placid	2	650	67
Minerva Central School Dist/Olmstedville	1	110	68
Moriah Central School Dist/Port Henry	1	780	68
Newcomb Central School Dist/Newcomb	1	405	68
Schroon Lake Ctl School Dist/Schroon Lake	1	230	68
Ticonderoga Central Sch Dist/Ticonderoga	2	735	68
Willsboro Central Sch Dist/Willsboro	1	243	68
FRANKLIN			
Brushton Moira Ctl Sch Dist/Brushton	1	800	69
Chateaugay Central School Dist/Chateaugay	2	503	69
Franklin-Essex-Hamilton BOCES/Malone			71
Malone Central School Dist/Malone	5	2,289	69
Salmon River Central Sch Dist/Ft Covington	4	1,800	70
Saranac Lake Central Sch Dist/Saranac Lake	4	1,280	70
St Regis Falls Ctl Sch Dist/St Regis FLS	1	268	70
Tupper Lake Ctl School Dist/Tupper Lake	2	749	70
FULTON			
Broadalbin-Perth Ctl Sch Dist/Broadalbin	2	1,800	71
Gloversville Enlarged Sch Dist/Gloversville	6	2,521	71
Greater Johnstown Sch Dist/Johnstown	5	1,700	71
Hamilton-Fulton-Montgmry BOCES/Johnstown			72
Mayfield Ctl School Dist/Mayfield	2	876	72
Northville Central School Dist/Northville	1	500	72
O E S J Central School Dist/St Johnsville	2	719	72
Wheelerville Union Free SD/Caroga Lake	1	130	72
GENESEE			
Alexander Ctl School Dist/Alexander	2	788	73
Batavia City School Dist/Batavia	4	2,374	73
Byron-Bergen Ctl School Dist/Bergen	2	864	73
Elba Central School Dist/Elba	1	403	73
Genesee Valley BOCES/Le Roy			74
Le Roy Central School Dist/Le Roy	2	1,350	73
Oakfield Alabama Ctl SD/Oakfield	2	800	74
Pavilion Ctl School Dist/Pavilion	2	680	74
Pembroke Ctl School Dist/Corfu	3	1,000	74
GREENE			
Cairo-Durham Ctl School Dist/Cairo	3	1,275	75
Catskill Central School Dist/Catskill	3	1,385	75
Coxsackie-Athens Central SD/Coxsackie	4	1,400	75
Greenville Central School Dist/Greenville	3	1,100	75
Hunter Tannersville Ctl SD/Tannersville	2	355	76
Windham Ashland Jewett Ctl SD/Windham	1	310	76
HAMILTON			

COUNTY District/City	NO. OF SCHOOLS	ENROLL- MENT	PAGE
Indian Lake Ctl School Dist/Indian Lake	1	112	76
Lake Pleasant Central Sch Dist/Speculator	1	80	76
Long Lake Central School Dist/Long Lake	1	65	76
Wells Central School Dist/Wells	1	135	77
HERKIMER			
Central Valley School Dist/Ilion	4	2,201	77
Dolgeville Central School Dist/Dolgeville	2	900	77
Frankfort-Schuyler Ctl SD/Frankfort	2	893	77
Herkimer BOCES/Herkimer			79
Herkimer Ctl School Dist/Herkimer	2	1,112	77
Little Falls City School Dist/Little Falls	3	1,116	78
Mount Markham Central Sch Dist/West Winfield	3	1,100	78
Owen D Young Central Sch Dist/Van Hornesvle	1	182	78
Poland Central School Dist/Poland	1	523	78
Town of Webb Union Free SD/Old Forge	1	270	78
West Canada Valley Ctl SD/Newport	2	650	79
JEFFERSON			
Alexandria Central School Dist/Alex Bay	1	492	79
Belleville Henderson Sch Dist/Adams	1	450	79
Carthage Central School Dist/Carthage	5	3,200	80
General Brown Ctl School Dist/Dexter	3	1,600	80
Indian River Ctl School Dist/Philadelphia	8	3,900	80
Jefferson Lewis BOCES/Watertown			82
La Fargeville Central Sch Dist/La Fargeville	1	539	80
Lyme Central School Dist/Chaumont	1	349	81
Sackets Harbor Ctl School Dist/Sackets HBR	1	418	81
South Jefferson Central SD/Adams Center	4	1,894	81
Thousand Islands Central SD/Clayton	4	867	81
Watertown City School Dist/Watertown	8	3,800	81
KINGS			
Community School Dist 13/Brooklyn			82
Community School Dist 14/Brooklyn			83
Community School Dist 15/Brooklyn			84
Community School Dist 16/Brooklyn			85
Community School Dist 17/Brooklyn			86
Community School Dist 18/Brooklyn			87
Community School Dist 19/Brooklyn			88
Community School Dist 20/Brooklyn			89
Community School Dist 21/Brooklyn			90
Community School Dist 22/Brooklyn			91
Community School Dist 23/Brooklyn			92
Community School Dist 32/Brooklyn			93
Diocese of Brooklyn Ed Office/Brooklyn	91	44,500	94
LEWIS			
Beaver River Central Sch Dist/Beaver Falls	1	875	101
Copenhagen Central SD/Copenhagen	1	460	101
Harrisville Central Sch Dist/Harrisville	1	359	101
Lowville Acad-Central Sch Dist/Lowville	1	1,350	101
South Lewis Central Sch Dist/Turin	4	1,028	101
LIVINGSTON			
Avon Central School Dist/Avon	3	1,006	102
Caledonia-Mumford Ctl Sch Dist/Caledonia	3	815	102
Dansville Ctl School Dist/Dansville	3	1,300	102
Geneseo Central Sch Dist/Geneseo	1	853	102
Keshequa Central School Dist/Nunda	3	617	103
Livonia Ctl School Dist/Livonia	2	1,500	103
Mt Morris Central School Dist/Mount Morris	1	500	103
York Central School Dist/Retsof	2	780	103
MADISON			
Brookfield Central School Dist/Brookfield	1	240	104
Canastota Central School Dist/Canastota	4	1,275	104
Cazenovia Ctl School Dist/Cazenovia	3	1,360	104
Chittenango Central SD/Chittenango	4	1,904	104
De Ruyter Central School Dist/De Ruyter	2	360	105
Hamilton Central Sch Dist/Hamilton	1	588	105
Madison Central School Dist/Madison	1	450	105
Morrisville Eaton Central SD/Morrisville	2	621	105
Oneida City School Dist/Oneida	6	2,000	105
Stockbridge Valley Central SD/Munnsville	1	460	106
MONROE			
Brighton Central School Dist/Rochester	4	3,518	106
Brockport Ctl School Dist/Brockport	5	3,562	106
Churchville Chili Ctl Sch Dist/Churchville	6	3,900	107
Diocese of Rochester Ed Office/Rochester	16	2,800	113
East Irondequoit Ctl Sch Dist/Rochester	6	3,000	107
East Rochester Union Free SD/E Rochester	2	1,007	107
Fairport Ctl School Dist/Fairport	8	5,900	108
Gates Chili Central Sch Dist/Rochester	6	4,000	108
Greece Central School Dist/Rochester	17	10,700	108
Hilton Central School Dist/Hilton	5	4,482	109

New York School Directory

COUNTY INDEX

COUNTY District/City	NO. OF SCHOOLS	ENROLLMENT	PAGE
Honeoye Falls Lima Sch Dist/Honeoye Falls	4	2,122	109
Monroe 1 BOCES/Fairport			115
Monroe 2 Orleans BOCES/Spencerport			115
Penfield Central School Dist/Rochester	6	4,600	109
Pittsford Central Sch Dist/Pittsford	9	6,000	110
Rochester City School Dist/Rochester	57	28,000	110
Rush Henrietta Central SD/Henrietta	9	5,300	112
Spencerport Central Sch Dist/Spencerport	6	3,700	112
Webster Central School Dist/Webster	11	8,331	112
West Irondequoit Ctl SD/Rochester	10	3,600	113
Wheatland Chili Ctl Sch Dist/Scottsville	2	637	113

MONTGOMERY
Canajoharie Ctl School Dist/Canajoharie	3	855	115
Fonda Fultonville Central SD/Fonda	1	1,340	115
Ft Plain Central School Dist/Fort Plain	2	750	115
Greater Amsterdam School Dist/Amsterdam	6	3,690	115

NASSAU
Baldwin Union Free School Dist/Baldwin	7	5,450	116
Bellmore Union Free Sch Dist/Bellmore	3	1,100	117
Bellmore-Merrick Ctl High SD/North Merrick	5	5,273	117
Bethpage Union Free Sch Dist/Bethpage	5	2,946	117
Carle Place Union Free SD/Carle Place	3	1,360	117
Diocese of Rockville Ed Office/Hicksville	44	32,000	132
East Meadow Union Free SD/Westbury	9	7,100	118
East Rockaway Union Free SD/East Rockaway	3	1,200	118
East Williston Union Free SD/Old Westbury	3	1,722	118
Elmont Union Free School Dist/Elmont	6	3,500	118
Farmingdale Union Free SD/Farmingdale	6	5,900	119
Floral Park Bellerose Sch Dist/Floral Park	2	1,479	119
Franklin Square Union Free SD/Franklin Sq	3	1,940	119
Freeport Public School Dist/Freeport	8	6,885	119
Garden City School Dist/Garden City	7	3,800	120
Glen Cove City School Dist/Glen Cove	6	3,200	120
Great Neck Public Schools/Great Neck	12	6,700	120
Hempstead Union Free SD/Hempstead	10	7,355	121
Herricks Union Free Sch Dist/New Hyde Park	5	3,950	121
Hewlett Woodmere Union Free SD/Woodmere	5	3,000	121
Hicksville Union Free Sch Dist/Hicksville	9	5,000	122
Island Park Union Free SD/Island Park	2	743	122
Island Trees Union Free SD/Levittown	4	2,236	122
Jericho Union Free School Dist/Jericho	5	3,155	122
Lawrence Union Free School Dist/Lawrence	5	2,600	123
Levittown Union Free Sch Dist/Levittown	11	7,215	123
Locust Valley Ctl School Dist/Locust Valley	6	2,000	123
Long Beach City School Dist/Lido Beach	7	3,800	124
Lynbrook Union Free Sch Dist/Lynbrook	7	2,809	124
Malverne Union Free Sch Dist/Malverne	4	1,725	124
Manhasset Union Free Sch Dist/Manhasset	4	3,250	124
Massapequa Union Free SD 23/Massapequa	9	8,000	125
Merrick Union Free School Dist/Merrick	3	1,490	125
Mineola Union Free Sch Dist/Mineola	5	2,927	125
Nassau BOCES/Garden City			134
New Hyde-Garden City Park UFSD/New Hyde Park	4	1,785	126
North Bellmore Union Free SD/Bellmore	5	2,031	126
North Merrick Union Free SD/Merrick	3	1,177	126
North Shore Central SD/Sea Cliff	5	2,548	126
Oceanside Union Free Sch Dist/Oceanside	10	5,400	127
Oyster Bay East Norwich Ctl SD/Oyster Bay	3	1,565	127
Plainedge Union Free Sch Dist/N Massapequa	5	2,825	127
Plainview-Old Bethpage Ctl SD/Plainview	7	5,000	127
Port Washington Union Free SD/Prt Washingtn	7	5,000	128
Rockville Ctr Union Free SD/Rockville CTR	7	3,500	128
Roosevelt Union Free Sch Dist/Roosevelt	5	3,511	128
Roslyn School Dist/Roslyn	5	3,150	129
Seaford Union Free SD/Seaford	4	2,249	129
Sewanhaka Ctl High Sch Dist/Floral Park	5	8,145	129
Syosset Central School Dist/Syosset	10	6,500	129
Uniondale Union Free Sch Dist/Uniondale	9	6,970	130
Valley Stream Ctl High SD/Valley Stream	4	4,600	130
Valley Stream Union Free SD 13/Valley Stream	4	1,964	130
Valley Stream Union Free SD 24/Valley Stream	3	1,093	131
Valley Stream Union Free SD 30/Valley Stream	3	1,450	131
Wantagh Union Free Sch Dist 23/Wantagh	5	2,770	131
West Hempstead School Dist/W Hempstead	5	2,300	131
Westbury Union Free Sch Dist/Old Westbury	6	5,000	132

NEW YORK
Archdiocese of New York Ed Off/New York	147	62,605	142
Community School Dist 1/New York			135
Community School Dist 2/New York			135
Community School Dist 3/New York			138
Community School Dist 4/New York			139
Community School Dist 5/New York			140
Community School Dist 6/New York			141
Dist 75 City Wide Programs/New York			142
New York Alt High Sch SD 79/New York			142
New York City Dept of Ed/New York	1,680	1,150,000	134

NIAGARA
Barker Central School Dist/Barker	2	750	146
Lewiston Porter Ctl Sch Dist/Youngstown	4	2,187	146
Lockport City School Dist/Lockport	9	5,100	147
Newfane Central School Dist/Burt	4	1,511	147
Niagara Falls City Sch Dist/Niagara Falls	12	7,100	147
Niagara-Wheatfield Ctl SD/Niagara Falls	6	3,650	148
North Tonawanda City Sch Dist/N Tonawanda	6	3,400	148
Royalton Hartland Central SD/Middleport	3	1,271	148
Starpoint Central School Dist/Lockport	4	2,931	149
Wilson Central School Dist/Wilson	2	1,060	149

ONEIDA
Adirondack Central Sch Dist/Boonville	4	1,200	150
Camden Central School Dist/Camden	4	2,000	150
Clinton Central School Dist/Clinton	3	1,258	150
Holland Patent Ctl School Dist/Holland Patnt	4	1,316	150
Madison-Oneida BOCES/Verona			154
New Hartford Central Sch Dist/New Hartford	5	2,553	151
New York Mills Union Free SD/New York Mls	1	550	151
Oneida-Herkimer-Mad BOCES/New Hartford			154
Oriskany Ctl School Dist/Oriskany	2	587	151
Remsen Central School Dist/Remsen	2	400	151
Rome City School Dist/Rome	10	5,300	151
Sauquoit Valley Central SD/Sauquoit	3	900	152
Utica City School Dist/Utica	13	10,000	152
Vernon-Verona-Sherrill CSD/Verona	5	1,900	152
Waterville Central Sch Dist/Waterville	2	742	153
Westmoreland Central Sch Dist/Westmoreland	3	853	153
Whitesboro Ctl School Dist/Whitesboro	7	3,135	153

ONONDAGA
Baldwinsville Central Sch Dist/Baldwinsville	8	5,500	154
Diocese of Syracuse Ed Office/Syracuse	22	5,100	160
East Syracuse Minoa Ctl SD/East Syracuse	7	3,600	154
Fabius Pompey Central SD/Fabius	2	611	155
Fayetteville-Manlius Ctl SD/Manlius	6	4,259	155
Jamesville-DeWitt Central SD/Fayetteville	5	2,694	155
Jordan Elbridge Ctl Sch Dist/Jordan	3	1,300	155
La Fayette Central School Dist/La Fayette	4	825	156
Liverpool Ctl School Dist/Liverpool	14	7,000	156
Lyncourt Union Free Sch Dist/Syracuse	1	450	156
Marcellus Central School Dist/Marcellus	3	1,507	157
North Syracuse Ctl Sch Dist/N Syracuse	11	8,400	157
Onondaga Central School Dist/Nedrow	3	830	157
Onondaga-Cortland-Madson BOCES/Syracuse			160
Skaneateles Central Sch Dist/Skaneateles	4	1,200	157
Solvay Union Free Sch Dist/Syracuse	3	1,500	158
Syracuse City School Dist/Syracuse	37	21,116	158
Tully Central School Dist/Tully	2	770	159
West Genesee Ctl School Dist/Camillus	7	4,600	159
Westhill Central School Dist/Syracuse	4	1,700	159

ONTARIO
Bloomfield Central SD/Bloomfield	2	850	161
Canandaigua City School Dist/Canandaigua	3	3,500	161
Geneva City School Dist/Geneva	4	2,078	161
Honeoye Central School Dist/Honeoye	1	251	161
Manchester-Shortsville Ctl SD/Shortsville	3	800	162
Marcus Whitman Central SD/Rushville	3	1,227	162
Naples Central School Dist/Naples	2	600	162
Phelps-Clifton Springs Ctl SD/Clifton Spgs	4	1,549	162
Victor Central School Dist/Victor	5	4,450	162

ORANGE
Chester Union Free School Dist/Chester	2	986	163
Cornwall Central School Dist/Cornwall HDSN	5	3,122	163
Florida Union Free Sch Dist/Florida	2	807	164
Goshen Central School Dist/Goshen	4	2,935	164
Greenwood Lake Union Free SD/Monroe	2	500	164
Highland Falls-Ft Montgmry SD/Highland FLS	3	1,000	164
Kiryas Joel Union Free SD/Monroe	1	167	164
Middletown Enlarged City SD/Middletown	6	7,312	165
Minisink Valley Central SD/Slate Hill	5	3,493	165
Monroe Woodbury Central SD/Central Vly	7	6,900	165
Newburgh Enlarged City SD/Newburgh	13	11,562	165
Orange-Ulster BOCES/Goshen			168
Pine Bush Central School Dist/Pine Bush	8	5,000	166
Port Jervis City School Dist/Port Jervis	4	2,332	166
Tuxedo Union Free Sch Dist/Tuxedo Park	2	225	166
Valley Central School Dist/Montgomery	7	4,200	167

COUNTY INDEX

Market Data Retrieval

COUNTY District/City	NO. OF SCHOOLS	ENROLL- MENT	PAGE
Warwick Valley Central SD/Warwick	4	3,569	167
Washingtonville Central SD/Washingtonvle	5	3,793	167
West Point School Dist/West Point	2	629	167
ORLEANS			
Albion Central School Dist/Albion	3	1,860	169
Holley Central School Dist/Holley	2	1,200	169
Kendall Central School Dist/Kendall	2	710	169
Lyndonville Central Sch Dist/Lyndonville	2	700	169
Medina Central School Dist/Medina	3	1,475	169
Orleans-Niagara BOCES/Medina			170
OSWEGO			
Altmar-Parish-Williamstown SD/Parish	2	1,500	170
Central Square Central Sch/Central Sq	6	3,800	170
Ctr for Instruct Tech Innov/Mexico			172
Fulton City School Dist/Fulton	6	3,500	170
Hannibal Central School Dist/Hannibal	3	1,310	171
Mexico Central School Dist/Mexico	5	2,055	171
Oswego City School Dist/Oswego	7	3,669	171
Phoenix Central School Dist/Phoenix	3	1,684	171
Pulaski Central School Dist/Pulaski	2	971	172
Sandy Creek Central Sch Dist/Sandy Creek	1	800	172
OTSEGO			
Cherry Valley-Springfield SD/Cherry Valley	1	449	172
Cooperstown Ctl School Dist/Cooperstown	2	818	173
Edmeston Ctl School Dist/Edmeston	1	390	173
Gilbertsville-Mt Upton SD/Gilbertsville	1	350	173
Laurens Central School Dist/Laurens	1	300	173
Milford Central School Dist/Milford	1	361	173
Morris Central School Dist/Morris	1	322	173
Oneonta City School Dist/Oneonta	5	1,736	174
Richfield Springs Central SD/Richfld Spgs	1	450	174
Schenevus Ctl School Dist/Schenevus	1	350	174
Unatego Unadilla Central SD/Otego	3	716	174
Worcester Ctl School Dist/Worcester	1	350	174
PUTNAM			
Brewster Central School Dist/Brewster	4	3,066	175
Carmel Central School Dist/Patterson	5	3,973	175
Garrison Union Free Sch Dist/Garrison	1	207	175
Haldane Central School Dist/Cold Spring	1	794	175
Mahopac Ctl School Dist/Mahopac	5	3,968	176
Putnam Valley Ctl School Dist/Putnam Valley	3	1,587	176
QUEENS			
Community School Dist 24/Corona			176
Community School Dist 25/Flushing			178
Community School Dist 26/Bayside			179
Community School Dist 27/Ozone Park			180
Community School Dist 28/Jamaica			181
Community School Dist 29/Queens Vlg			183
Community School Dist 30/Long Is City			184
RENSSELAER			
Averill Park Central Sch Dist/Averill Park	5	2,665	189
Berlin Central School Dist/Cherry Plain	2	800	189
Brunswick Central School Dist/Troy	2	1,200	190
East Greenbush Central SD/E Greenbush	7	5,042	190
Hoosic Valley Central Sch Dist/Schaghticoke	2	931	190
Hoosick Falls Central Sch Dist/Hoosick Falls	2	1,200	190
Lansingburgh Central Sch Dist/Troy	4	2,335	190
North Greenbush Common SD/Troy	1	13	191
Questar III BOCES/Castleton			192
Rensselaer City School Dist/Rensselaer	2	1,060	191
Schodack Central School Dist/Castleton	2	900	191
Troy City School Dsitrict/Troy	7	4,090	191
Wynantskill Union Free SD/Troy	1	400	191
RICHMOND			
Community School Dist 31/Staten Island			192
ROCKLAND			
Clarkstown Central School Dist/New City	13	7,907	195
East Ramapo Central Sch Dist/Spring Valley	14	8,843	196
Nanuet Union Free School Dist/Nanuet	5	2,220	196
North Rockland Central SD/Garnerville	8	8,000	197
Nyack Union Free School Dist/Nyack	5	3,000	197
Pearl River School Dist/Pearl River	5	2,360	197
Rockland BOCES/West Nyack			199
South Orangetown Central SD/Blauvelt	4	2,911	197
Suffern Central School Dist/Hillburn	7	4,283	198
SARATOGA			
Ballston Spa Ctl School Dist/Ballston Spa	6	4,200	200
Burnt Hills Ballston Lake SD/Burnt Hills	5	3,000	200

COUNTY District/City	NO. OF SCHOOLS	ENROLL- MENT	PAGE
Corinth Central School Dist/Corinth	3	1,139	200
Edinburg Common School Dist/Northville	1	65	200
Galway Central School Dist/Galway	2	837	201
Mechanicville City Sch Dist/Mechanicville	2	1,345	201
Saratoga Springs City Sch Dist/Saratoga Spgs	8	6,375	201
Schuylerville Central Sch Dist/Schuylerville	3	1,500	201
Shenendehowa Central Sch Dist/Clifton Park	12	9,499	202
South Glens Falls Ctl Sch Dist/S Glens Falls	6	3,000	202
Stillwater Central Sch Dist/Stillwater	3	1,035	202
Waterford Halfmoon School Dist/Waterford	2	800	203
SCHENECTADY			
Duanesburg Central Sch Dist/Delanson	2	770	203
Mohonasen Central Sch Dist/Schenectady	4	2,799	203
Niskayuna Central School Dist/Niskayuna	8	4,240	204
Schalmont Central School Dist/Schenectady	3	1,798	204
Schenectady City School Dist/Schenectady	17	9,921	204
Scotia Glenville Ctl Sch Dist/Scotia	6	2,600	205
SCHOHARIE			
Cobleskill Richmondville SD/Cobleskill	4	1,700	206
Gilboa-Conesville Central SD/Gilboa	1	312	206
Jefferson Central Sch Dist/Jefferson	1	195	206
Middleburgh Ctl School Dist/Middleburgh	2	750	206
Schoharie Central SD/Schoharie	2	875	206
Sharon Springs Ctl SD/Sharon Spgs	1	226	207
SCHUYLER			
Bradford Central Sch Dist/Bradford	1	265	207
Odessa Montour Ctl Sch Dist/Odessa	3	733	207
Watkins Glen Central Sch Dist/Watkins Glen	2	1,040	207
SENECA			
Romulus Ctl School Dist/Romulus	1	420	208
Seneca Falls Central Sch Dist/Seneca Falls	4	1,173	208
South Seneca Ctl Sch Dist/Ovid	2	700	208
Waterloo Central School Dist/Waterloo	4	1,538	208
ST LAWRENCE			
Brasher Falls School Dist/Brasher Falls	3	1,000	209
Canton Central School Dist/Canton	3	1,000	209
Clifton-Fine Central Sch Dist/Star Lake	1	295	209
Colton Pierrepont School Dist/Colton	1	368	209
Diocese of Ogdensburg Ed Off/Ogdensburg	9	1,293	212
Edwards-Knox Central Sch Dist/Hermon	1	537	210
Gouverneur Ctl School Dist/Gouverneur	3	1,515	210
Hammond Central School Distict/Hammond	1	257	210
Hermon-DeKalb Central Sch Dist/De Kalb Jct	1	430	210
Heuvelton Central School Dist/Heuvelton	1	580	210
Lisbon Central School Dist/Lisbon	1	587	210
Madrid-Waddington Central SD/Madrid	1	647	211
Massena Central School Dist/Massena	5	2,500	211
Morristown Ctl School Dist/Morristown	1	333	211
Norwood-Norfolk Ctl SD/Norwood	3	987	211
Ogdensburg City School Dist/Ogdensburg	3	1,535	211
Parishville Hopkinton Sch Dist/Parishville	1	420	212
Potsdam Central School Dist/Potsdam	3	1,200	212
St Lawrence-Lewis BOCES/Canton			212
STEUBEN			
Addison Central School Dist/Addison	3	1,100	213
Arkport Central School Dist/Arkport	1	475	213
Avoca Central School Dist/Avoca	1	440	213
Bath Central School Dist/Bath	3	1,500	213
Campbell-Savona Ctl Sch Dist/Campbell	2	829	213
Canisteo-Greenwood Central SD/Canisteo	2	1,000	214
Corning-Painted Post Area SD/Painted Post	9	4,500	214
Greater Southern Tier BOCES/Painted Post			215
Hammondsport Ctl School Dist/Hammondsport	2	450	214
Hornell City School Dist/Hornell	4	1,700	214
Jasper Troupsburg Central SD/Jasper	2	450	214
Prattsburgh Central Sch Dist/Prattsburgh	1	388	215
Wayland-Cohocton Central SD/Wayland	4	1,246	215
SUFFOLK			
Amagansett Union Free Sch Dist/Amagansett	1	79	216
Amityville Union Free Sch Dist/Amityville	5	3,100	216
Babylon Union Free Sch Dist/Babylon	3	1,554	216
Bay Shore Union Free Sch Dist/Bay Shore	7	6,000	217
Bayport- Blue Point USD/Bayport	5	2,080	217
Brentwood Union Free Sch Dist/Brentwood	17	20,000	217
Bridgehampton Union Free SD/Bridgehampton	1	227	218
Brookhaven Comsewogue Unif SD/Port Jeff Sta	6	3,702	218
Center Moriches Union Free SD/CTR Moriches	3	1,400	218
Central Islip Union Free SD/Central Islip	8	7,400	218
Cold Spring Harbor Central SD/Cold SPG HBR	4	1,650	219
Commack Union Free School Dist/E Northport	8	5,889	219

New York School Directory

COUNTY INDEX

COUNTY District/City	NO. OF SCHOOLS	ENROLL-MENT	PAGE
Connetquot Central School Dist/Bohemia	11	5,653	219
Copiague Union Free Sch Dist/Copiague	6	4,864	220
Deer Park Union Free Sch Dist/Deer Park	5	4,015	220
East Hampton Union Free SD/East Hampton	3	1,781	220
East Islip Union Free SD/Islip Terrace	6	3,782	220
East Moriches Union Free SD/East Moriches	2	750	221
East Quogue Union Free SD/East Quogue	1	390	221
Eastern Suffolk BOCES/Patchogue			235
Eastport-South Manor Ctrl SD/Manorville	6	3,294	221
Elwood Union Free School Dist/Greenlawn	4	2,049	221
Fire Island Union Free SD/Ocean Beach	1	32	222
Fishers Island Union Free SD/Fishers Isle	1	65	222
Greenport Union Free Sch Dist/Greenport	1	627	222
Half Hollow Hills Central SD/Dix Hills	9	8,017	222
Hampton Bays Union Free SD/Hampton Bays	3	2,060	222
Harborfields Ctl School Dist/Greenlawn	4	2,965	223
Hauppauge Union Free Sch Dist/Hauppauge	5	3,200	223
Huntington Union Free Sch Dist/Huntingtn Sta	8	4,545	223
Islip Union Free School Dist/Islip	5	2,726	223
Kings Park Ctl School Dist/Kings Park	5	2,888	224
Lindenhurst Union Free SD/Lindenhurst	8	5,694	224
Little Flower Union Free SD/Wading River	1	96	224
Longwood Central School Dist/Middle Island	7	9,150	224
Mattituck-Cutchogue UFSD/Cutchogue	2	1,100	225
Middle Country Ctl Sch Dist/Centereach	14	9,860	225
Miller Place Union Free SD/Miller Place	4	2,489	225
Montauk Union Free School Dist/Montauk	1	320	226
Mt Sinai Union Free SD/Mount Sinai	3	2,100	226
New Suffolk Common School Dist/New Suffolk	1	13	226
North Babylon Union Free SD/North Babylon	7	4,491	226
Northport-East Northport UFSD/Northport	9	5,141	227
Oysterponds Union Free SD/Orient	1	104	227
Patchogue-Medford Unified SD/Patchogue	11	7,503	227
Port Jefferson Union Free SD 6/Prt Jefferson	3	1,048	227
Quogue Union Free School Dist/Quogue	1	130	228
Remsenburg-Speonk UFSD/Remsenburg	1	132	228
Riverhead Central School Dist/Riverhead	7	5,600	228
Rocky Point Union Free SD/Rocky Point	4	2,947	228
Sachem Central Sch Dist/Lk Ronkonkoma	15	13,500	229
Sag Harbor Union Free Sch Dist/Sag Harbor	2	953	229
Sagaponack Common School Dist/Sagaponack	1	16	229
Sayville Union Free Sch Dist/Sayville	5	2,823	229
Shelter Island Union Free SD/Shelter Is	1	202	230
Shoreham-Wading River Ctl SD/Shoreham	4	2,000	230
Smithtown Central Sch Dist/Smithtown	12	8,946	230
South Country Central Sch Dist/Patchogue	7	4,400	231
South Huntington Union Free SD/Huntingtn Sta	7	5,900	231
Southampton Union Free SD/Southampton	3	1,575	231
Southold Union Free Sch Dist/Southold	2	750	231
Springs Union Free School Dist/East Hampton	1	750	232
Three Village Central Sch Dist/Stony Brook	9	6,400	232
Tuckahoe Common School Dist/Southampton	1	285	232
Wainscott Common School Dist/Wainscott	1	30	232
West Babylon Union Free SD/West Babylon	7	4,000	232
West Islip School Dist/West Islip	7	3,720	233
Western Suffolk BOCES/Huntingtn Sta			236
Westhampton Beach School Dist/W Hampton Bch	3	1,819	233
William Floyd School Dist/Mastic Beach	8	8,700	233
Wyandanch Union Free Sch Dist/Wyandanch	4	2,811	234

SULLIVAN

Eldred Central School Dist/Eldred	2	525	236
Fallsburg Central School Dist/Fallsburg	2	1,440	236
Liberty Central School Dist/Liberty	3	1,700	236
Livingston Manor Ctl Sch Dist/Livingstn MNR	2	432	236
Monticello Central School Dist/Monticello	5	2,785	237
Roscoe Central School Dist/Roscoe	1	257	237
Sullivan BOCES/Liberty			238
Sullivan West Central SD/Jeffersonvlle	2	1,068	237
Tri-Valley Central School Dist/Grahamsville	2	975	237

TIOGA

Candor Central School Dist/Candor	2	750	238
Newark Valley Central Sch Dist/Newark Valley	3	1,060	238
Owego Apalachin Ctl Sch Dist/Owego	4	2,005	238
Spencer Van Etten Central SD/Spencer	3	985	238
Tioga Central School Dist/Tioga Center	3	950	239
Waverly Ctl School Dist/Waverly	4	1,700	239

TOMPKINS

Dryden Central School Dist/Dryden	5	1,500	239
George Junior Republic UFSD/Freeville	1	186	240
Groton Central School Dist/Groton	2	852	240
Ithaca City School Dist/Ithaca	12	5,103	240
Lansing Central School Dist/Lansing	3	1,187	240
Newfield Central School Dist/Newfield	3	780	241
Tompkins-Seneca-Tioga BOCES/Ithaca			241
Trumansburg Central SD/Trumansburg	3	1,043	241

ULSTER

Ellenville Central School Dist/Ellenville	3	1,500	241
Highland Ctl School Dist/Highland	3	1,667	242
Kingston City School Dist/Kingston	10	6,800	242
Marlboro Central School Dist/Milton	3	1,893	242
New Paltz Ctl School Dist/New Paltz	4	2,035	242
Onteora Central School Dist/Boiceville	4	1,200	243
Rondout Valley Ctl Sch Dist/Accord	5	1,975	243
Saugerties Central School Dist/Saugerties	6	2,500	243
Ulster BOCES/New Paltz			244
Wallkill Central School Dist/Wallkill	5	2,831	243

WARREN

Bolton Central School Dist/Bolton Lndg	1	200	244
Glens Falls City School Dist/Glens Falls	5	2,058	245
Glens Falls Common Sch Dist/Glens Falls	1	155	245
Hadley-Luzerne Ctl Sch Dist/Lake Luzerne	2	665	245
Johnsburg Central School Dist/North Creek	1	333	245
Lake George Central Sch Dist/Lake George	2	721	245
North Warren Central Sch Dist/Chestertown	1	508	246
Queensbury Union Free Sch Dist/Queensbury	4	3,200	246
Warrensburg Central Sch Dist/Warrensburg	2	687	246

WASHINGTON

Argyle Central School Dist/Argyle	2	480	246
Cambridge Central School Dist/Cambridge	1	844	247
Fort Ann Central School Dist/Fort Ann	2	500	247
Ft Edward Union Free Sch Dist/Fort Edward	2	450	247
Granville Central School Dist/Granville	3	1,200	247
Greenwich Central School Dist/Greenwich	2	943	247
Hartford Central School Dist/Hartford	1	413	248
Hudson Falls Central Sch Dist/Hudson Falls	5	2,400	248
Putnam Central School Dist/Putnam Sta	1	35	248
Salem Central School Dist/Salem	1	550	248
Whitehall Central School Dist/Whitehall	2	719	248
WSWHE BOCES/Fort Edward			249

WAYNE

Clyde-Savannah Central SD/Clyde	3	784	249
Gananda Central School Dist/Walworth	3	960	249
Lyons Central School Dist/Lyons	2	920	249
Marion Central School Dist/Marion	2	687	250
Newark Central School Dist/Newark	5	2,091	250
North Rose Wolcott Central SD/Wolcott	3	1,155	250
Palmyra-Macedon Central SD/Palmyra	4	1,861	250
Red Creek Central School Dist/Red Creek	3	870	251
Sodus Central School Dist/Sodus	3	1,050	251
Wayne Central School Dist/Ontario CTR	4	2,180	251
Wayne-Finger Lakes BOCES/Newark			252
Williamson Central School Dist/Williamson	3	1,106	251

WESTCHESTER

Ardsley Union Free School Dist/Ardsley	3	2,326	252
Bedford Central School Dist/Bedford	8	4,100	252
Blind Brook-Rye Union Free SD/Rye Brook	3	1,364	252
Briarcliff Manor Union Free SD/Briarcliff	3	1,347	253
Bronxville Union Free SD/Bronxville	3	1,640	253
Byram Hills Central Sch Dist/Armonk	4	2,300	253
Chappaqua Central School Dist/Chappaqua	6	3,900	253
Croton-Harmon Union Free SD/Croton Hdsn	3	1,568	254
Dobbs Ferry Union Free SD/Dobbs Ferry	3	1,500	254
Eastchester Union Free SD/Eastchester	5	3,140	254
Edgemont Union Free Sch Dist/Scarsdale	3	2,050	254
Elmsford Union Free SD/Elmsford	3	1,002	255
Greenburgh 11 Union Free SD/Dobbs Ferry	2	85	255
Greenburgh Central School Dist/Hartsdale	5	1,903	255
Greenburgh-Graham UFSD/Hastings HDSN	2	286	255
Greenburgh-North Castle SD/Dobbs Ferry	4	309	255
Harrison Central School Dist/Harrison	6	3,600	256
Hastings on Hudson Union FR SD/Hastings HDSN	3	1,654	256
Hawthorne Cedar Knolls UFSD/Hawthorne	4	400	256
Hendrick Hudson Ctl Sch Dist/Montrose	5	2,122	256
Irvington Union Free Sch Dist/Irvington	4	1,781	257
Katonah-Lewisboro Sch Dist/South Salem	5	2,917	257
Lakeland Central School Dist/Shrub Oak	8	5,845	257
Mamaroneck Union Free Sch Dist/Mamaroneck	6	5,230	257
Mount Vernon City School Dist/Mount Vernon	16	8,000	258
Mt Pleasant Cottage UFSD/Pleasantville	2	215	258
Mt Pleasant Ctl School Dist/Thornwood	4	2,000	258
Mt Pleasant-Blythedale UFSD/Valhalla	1	134	259
New Rochelle City School Dist/New Rochelle	10	11,000	259
North Salem Central Sch Dist/North Salem	2	1,046	259

School Year 2020-2021   800-333-8802   NY-R5

COUNTY INDEX

Market Data Retrieval

COUNTY District/City	NO. OF SCHOOLS	ENROLL-MENT	PAGE
Ossining Union Free Sch Dist/Ossining	6	5,100	259
Peekskill City School Dist/Peekskill	6	3,400	260
Pelham Union Free School Dist/Pelham	6	2,800	260
Pleasantville Union Free SD/Pleasantville	3	1,700	260
Pocantico Hills Ctl Sch Dist/Sleepy Hollow	1	308	260
Port Chester Rye Union Free SD/Port Chester	6	5,000	261
Putnam-Northern Wstchstr BOCES/Yorktown Hts			266
Rye City School Dist/Rye	6	3,510	261
Rye Neck Union Free Sch Dist/Mamaroneck	4	1,525	261
Scarsdale Union Free Sch Dist/Scarsdale	7	4,771	261
Somers Central School Dist/Somers	4	2,866	262
Southern Westchester BOCES/Rye Brook			267
Tarrytown Union Free Sch Dist/Sleepy Hollow	5	2,900	262
Tuckahoe Union Free SD/Eastchester	3	1,100	262
Valhalla Union Free Sch Dist/Valhalla	3	1,420	262
White Plains City School Dist/White Plains	9	7,000	263
Yonkers Public School Dist/Yonkers	40	27,000	263
Yorktown Central School Dist/Yorktown Hts	5	3,400	264
WYOMING			
Attica Central School Dist/Attica	3	1,150	267
Letchworth Central School Dist/Gainesville	3	936	267
Perry Central School Dist/Perry	2	806	267
Warsaw Central School Dist/Warsaw	2	800	267
Wyoming Central School Dist/Wyoming	1	130	268
YATES			
Dundee Ctl School Dist/Dundee	2	700	268
Penn Yan Ctl School Dist/Penn Yan	3	1,338	268

New York School Directory

DISTRICT PERSONNEL INDEX

NAME/District	JOB FUNCTIONS	PAGE
A		
Aanensen, Aanen/Duanesburg Central Sch Dist	3	203
Abate, Meghan/Rochester City School Dist	68	110
Abbatecola, Anne/Bronxville Union Free SD	36	253
Abbatiello, Tony/Cayuga-Onondaga BOCES	73,286	36
Abbey, Gerald/Rye City School Dist	3	261
Abbey, Timothy/Dunkirk City School Dist	3,5	37
Abbott, John/East Irondequoit Ctl Sch Dist	2,15	107
Abbott, Paul/Jamestown City School Dist	67	38
Abbruzzese, Chris/Richfield Springs Central SD	4	174
Abdoo, Christopher/Burnt Hills Ballston Lake SD	2,15,91	200
Abenes, Wayne/Brentwood Union Free Sch Dist	36,93	217
Abitabile, Antonio, Dr/Lansingburgh Central Sch Dist	1	190
Abraham, Carol/Hendrick Hudson Ctl Sch Dist	67	256
Abraham, Jocyln/Nyack Union Free School Dist	271	197
Abrams, Marty/Herricks Union Free Sch Dist	3	121
Abrams, Randy/Bath Central School Dist	6	213
Abrams, Rudy/Dover Union Free School Dist	3	52
Abrams, Sarah/Brookfield Central School Dist	6	104
Abruzzo, Lynette/Garden City School Dist	7,57,58,69,77,79,81,85	120
Acanfora, Liza/Kenmore-Tonawanda UF Sch Dist	30	62
Accardi, Peter/Glens Falls Common Sch Dist	67	245
Accetta, Frank/Lakeland Central School Dist	36	257
Accordo, Catherine/Rochester City School Dist	58	110
Acee, John/Westmoreland Central Sch Dist	67	153
Acker, Kathleen/Huntington Union Free Sch Dist	2,15	223
Ackerman, Christine, Dr/Chappaqua Central School Dist	1,11	253
Ackerman, Hollie/Oneida City School Dist	4	105
Ackerman, Holly/Vernon-Verona-Sherrill CSD	4	152
Ackerman, Mike/Cuba-Rushford Central Sch Dist	38	14
Ackland, Kyle/Waverly Ctl School Dist	73,295	239
Adamczak, Kyle/Avon Central School Dist	71	102
Adams, David/Rochester City School Dist	2	110
Adams, Dawn/Fallsburg Central School Dist	83	236
Adams, Jennifer/Middleburgh Ctl School Dist	7	206
Adams, Julie/Hoosic Valley Central Sch Dist	10	190
Adams, Kathy/Fulton City School Dist	58,79	170
Adams, Kaweeda/Albany City School Dist	1	9
Adams, Lucinda/Campbell-Savona Ctl Sch Dist	73	213
Adams, Lynda, Dr/Connetquot Central School Dist	1	219
Adams, Matthew/Holland Central School Dist	6	61
Adams, Robert/Alexander Ctl School Dist	6	73
Adams, Ryan/Salmon River Central Sch Dist	3	70
Adams, Steve/Madrid-Waddington Central SD	4	211
Adcock, Alan/Massapequa Union Free SD 23	2,15	125
Adcroft, Sean/Manhasset Union Free Sch Dist	16,73,82	124
Addor, Catherine/Greenburgh Central School Dist	20,23	255
Addor, Forrest/Orange-Ulster BOCES	73,76	168
Adelberg, Joel, Dr/Bedford Central School Dist	1,288	252
Adelson, Michael/Montauk Union Free School Dist	752	226
Adey, Michael/Westmoreland Central Sch Dist	6	153
Adler, Jaclyn/Hadley-Luzerne Ctl Sch Dist	4	245
Adniolfe, Christine/Warsaw Central School Dist	36	267
Agett, Brent/Falconer Central School Dist	2	37
Aggarwala, Jean/Rye Neck Union Free Sch Dist	57	261
Agosto, Michele/Buffalo Public Schools	20	57
Agrusa, Regina/Sewanhaka Ctl High Sch Dist	11,38,77,79,90,93,296,298	129
Aguiar, Angela/Whitesboro Ctl School Dist	4	153
Aguilar, Rolando/Chester Union Free School Dist	6	163
Ahart, Denise/Candor Central School Dist	273,280	238
Ahart, Frederick/Roscoe Central School Dist	6	237
Ahart, Peter/Candor Central School Dist	6	238
Ahearn, Jeffrey/Vestal Ctl School Dist	1	29
Ahl, Ryan/Menands Union Free Sch Dist	7	11
Ahles, Wendy/Rome City School Dist	76	151
Ahmad, Azhar/East Ramapo Central Sch Dist	73,76,286	196
Aiello, Nicholas/Tioga Central School Dist	73	239
Aierstok, Dave/Rhinebeck Central School Dist	7	53
Aikins, Jane/Alexandria Central School Dist	67	79
Ainslie, Robert/Ithaca City School Dist	67	240
Aires, Collene/Parishville Hopkinton Sch Dist	2	212
Aitken, Patricia/Manhasset Union Free Sch Dist	67	124
Akin, Wayne/Hoosic Valley Central Sch Dist	5	190
Akoma, Ahunna, Dr/Hempstead Union Free SD	15,73	121

NAME/District	JOB FUNCTIONS	PAGE
Alagna, Michelle/Central Square Central SD	58	170
Alaimo, Louis/Brighton Central School Dist	2,15,68	106
Alampi, Laura/Sodus Central School Dist	67	251
Albanese, Michele/Utica City School Dist	2,5	152
Albano, Phyllis/Bethlehem Central School Dist	2	10
Albers, Amy, Dr/Rockland BOCES	15,79	199
Alberti, Michele/Rochester City School Dist	70	110
Alberts, David/Irvington Union Free Sch Dist	4	257
Albi, Barbara/Depew Union Free School Dist	4	59
Albinder, Eric/West Islip School Dist	20,23	233
Albrecht, Jamie/Camden Central School Dist	67	150
Alderman, Ami, Dr/Lancaster Central Sch Dist	30	62
Aldous, Leta/Mayfield Ctl School Dist	5	72
Alegre, Tara/Penn Yan Ctl School Dist	38	268
Alenanian, Leibarid/Lyons Central School Dist	10	249
Alert, Laser/Greenburgh Central School Dist	295	255
Aleva, Michelle/Glens Falls City School Dist	77	245
Alexander, Lisa/Whitesboro Ctl School Dist	45	153
Alexander, Mark/Akron Central School Dist	5	56
Alexander, Nicole/Half Hollow Hills Central SD	26,73	222
Alexander, Paul/Ithaca City School Dist	3,91	240
Alfes, Kim/Wyoming Central School Dist	20	268
Alfonso, Frank/Highland Ctl School Dist	6,35,85	242
Alfonso, Sergio/White Plains City School Dist	5	263
Alford, Linda/Edwards-Knox Central Sch Dist	38,69	210
Alger, Maureen/De Ruyter Central School Dist	38,69,79	105
Ali, Lindsay/Honeoye Falls Lima Sch Dist	7,34,36,58,79,83,271,275	109
Ali, Muhammad/Chester Union Free School Dist	6	163
Aliasso, Stacey/Lockport City School Dist	58	147
Alicea, Jaime/Syracuse City School Dist	1	158
Alioto, Paul, Dr/Dansville Ctl School Dist	1	102
Alizadeh, Theresa/Grand Island Central Sch Dist	5	61
Allam, Ashraf/Little Falls City School Dist	2,73	78
Allan, Cherese/Springs Union Free School Dist	11,59,83,88,90,271,296,298	232
Allard, Nancy/Huntington Union Free Sch Dist	12	223
Allen Waite, Tracy/Saranac Central School Dist	67	45
Allen, Cory/Spencerport Central Sch Dist	71,73,97	112
Allen, Dustin/Bolivar-Richburg Ctrl Sch Dist	6	14
Allen, John/Belleville Henderson Sch Dist	67	79
Allen, John/Connetquot Central School Dist	15	219
Allen, Kathryn/Madison-Oneida BOCES	27,31	154
Allen, Larry/Marcellus Central Sch Dist	3	157
Allen, Lynn, Dr/Putnam-Northern Wstchstr BOCES	15	266
Allen, Melissa/Saratoga Springs City Sch Dist	38	201
Allen, Penny/Edwards-Knox Central Sch Dist	67,83	210
Allen, Renee/Western Suffolk BOCES	74	236
Allen, Robin/Port Washington Union Free SD	5	128
Allen, Sarah/Lake Placid Ctl School Dist	58	67
Allen, Stephanie/Port Washington Union Free SD	58,79	128
Allen, Thomas/Elmira City School Dist	297	40
Allentuck, Cindy/East Hampton Union Free SD	11,58,77,79,285	220
Allian, Cathie, Dr/Berlin Central School Dist	10	189
Alm, Brian, Dr/Ossining Union Free Sch Dist	10	259
Almasi, Lisa/Jamestown City School Dist	17	38
Almasi, Lisa/Lackawanna City School Dist	2	62
Almeida, Kourtney/Randolph Central School Dist	11,58	33
Almeter, Karen/Letchworth Central School Dist	4	267
Almy, Derek/Elmira City School Dist	34,36,57,79,88,90,274	40
Alperti, Ryan/Wantagh Union Free Sch Dist 23	12	131
Alterio, Danielle/Royalton Hartland Central SD	91	148
Althoff, Charles/Shoreham-Wading River Ctl SD	58,88	230
Altruda, Jeanette, Dr/Copiague Union Free Sch Dist	8	220
Altschul, Ilene/Community School District 3	1	138
Alunkal, Binoy/Lakeland Central School Dist	2	257
Alvarez, Frank/Southern Westchester BOCES	58	267
Alvarez, Rafael/Community School District 7	1	16
Alvarado, Shannon/Monroe 2 Orleans BOCES	81	115
Amarosa, Cj/New Hartford Central Sch Dist	73	151
Amato, Christopher/Riverhead Central School Dist	294	228
Ambert, Jennifer/Community School District 27	1	180
Ambrose, Amy/Richfield Springs Central SD	37	174
Ambrosini, Mary Ann/Westhampton Beach School Dist	58,79,83,85,88,286	233
Amen, James/Manhasset Union Free Sch Dist	6,7,35,83,85	124
Ames, Timothy/Kenmore-Tonawanda UF Sch Dist	3,91	62
Amesti, Anthony/Lindenhurst Union Free SD	6,35	224
Amitrano, Ralph/Mineola Union Free Sch Dist	6,35	125

School Year 2020-2021   800-333-8802

DISTRICT PERSONNEL INDEX

Market Data Retrieval

NAME/District	JOB FUNCTIONS	PAGE
Amo, Shelley/Hermon-DeKalb Central Sch Dist	6	210
Amodeo, Daniel/West Valley Ctl Sch Dist	8	33
Amon-Harris, Rahesha/Community School District 16	1	85
Amoroso, Salvatore/Webster Central School Dist	5	112
Anastasi, Jane/Pocantico Hills Ctl Sch Dist	5	260
Anastasia, Steven/Olean City School Dist	6	32
Anaya, Haidee/Valhalla Union Free Sch Dist	34,295	262
Anderalli, Janine/Morrisville Eaton Central SD	38	105
Anderson, Abigail/Schenectady City School Dist	76	204
Anderson, Bethany/Elba Central School Dist	285	73
Anderson, Bob/Gowanda Central School Dist	1	32
Anderson, James/Yonkers Public School Dist	69	263
Anderson, Jay/Galway Central School Dist	67	201
Anderson, Keith/Eastern Suffolk BOCES	3	235
Anderson, Linda/Germantown Central School Dist	5	46
Anderson, Michael/Rockville Ctr Union Free SD	73,286,295	128
Anderson, Michelle/Oriskany Ctl School Dist	67	151
Anderson, Molly/Westfield Central School Dist	8,13	39
Anderson, Richard/Morristown Ctl School Dist	4	211
Anderson, Rick/Lisbon Central School Dist	4	210
Anderson, Sarajean/East Islip Union Free SD	39,48	220
Anderson, Tasha/Mohonasen Central Sch Dist	295	204
Anderson, Travis/Rush Henrietta Central SD	71	112
Anderson, William/Massapequa Union Free SD 23	12,57,69	125
Andrea, Laureen/Remsenburg-Speonk UFSD	16,82	228
Andrejcak, Stephanie/Burnt Hills Ballston Lake SD	31	200
Andreotti, Angelo/Shoreham-Wading River Ctl SD	3,91	230
Andrew, Krazmien/Lancaster Central Sch Dist	10	62
Andrews, Jason, Dr/Windsor Central School Dist	1	30
Andrews, John/Starpoint Central School Dist	2	149
Andrews, Steve/Norwich City School Dist	73,295	42
Andrews, Todd/Copiague Union Free Sch Dist	15,68	220
Andriaccio, Kristen/Smithtown Central Sch Dist	298	230
Andryshak, Tom/Florida Union Free Sch Dist	3	164
Angelo, Kelly/Island Park Union Free SD	5	122
Anisansel, Josh/Farmingdale Union Free SD	48,51,54	119
Annino, Eileen/Plainview-Old Bethpage Ctl SD	280	127
Annunziata, Karen/Sewanhaka Ctl High Sch Dist	16	129
Anselme, Nerlande/Rush Henrietta Central SD	13,15,77,79,90,294	112
Anson, Mark/East Irondequoit Ctl Sch Dist	8,15	107
Ansons, Aldis/Monroe Woodbury Central SD	4	165
Anstett, Jeff/Newfane Central School Dist	73	147
Anthony, Larry/Rhinebeck Central School Dist	4	53
Anthony, Lawrence/Pine Plains Ctl School Dist	4	53
Anthony, Lawrence/Red Hook Central School Dist	4	53
Antkowiak, Jane/Yorkshire-Pioneer Ctl Sch Dist	97,295	33
Antoine, Gerard/Valley Stream Union Free SD 13	2,15,68	130
Antonacci, Joanne/Monroe 2 Orleans BOCES	1	115
Anzalone, Anthony/Levittown Union Free Sch Dist	297	123
Anzalone, Sandra/Eden Central School Dist	1,11	60
Apicella, James/Susquehanna Valley Central SD	23	29
Apker, Sonia/Homer Central School Dist	67	48
Apker, Sonya/George Junior Republic UFSD	1	240
Aponte, Edwin/Ellenville Central School Dist	76,286	241
Apostol, G Michael/Hoosic Valley Central Sch Dist	1	190
Appiarias, Maureen, Dr/Garden City School Dist	11,15,68,298	120
Appleton, Debbie/Brighton Central School Dist	88	106
Appollo, Karen/West Islip School Dist	16,48,51,54	233
Aranov, Ari/Kendall Central School Dist	31,38,77,90	169
Araoz, Lee/East Rockaway Union Free SD	73	118
Arcate, Kassie/Pocantico Hills Ctl Sch Dist	4	260
Arcelus, Julie/Fishers Island Union Free SD	36,69,275	222
Arcuri, Glen/Shoreham-Wading River Ctl SD	2,4,15	230
Arduino, Phyllis/Ossining Union Free Sch Dist	76	259
Arena, Ripalda/Eastchester Union Free SD	12	254
Arena, Susan/Depew Union Free School Dist	2	59
Argenio, Megan/Cornwall Central School Dist	8,11,15,69,88,285,288,295	163

NAME/District	JOB FUNCTIONS	PAGE
Argento, Joseph/Penfield Central School Dist	4	109
Argo, Joseph/Buffalo Public Schools	79	57
Arias, Michael/Rye City School Dist	6,35	261
Arias, Micheal/Tarrytown Union Free Sch Dist	6	262
Arini, Justin/Cold Spring Harbor Central SD	36	219
Arini, Justin/Cold Spring Harbor Central SD	36	219
Arlen, Alyssa/Hartford Central School Dist	83,85	248
Arlin, Eric/Bellmore-Merrick Ctl High SD	60,77,79,275,280	117
Armbrewster, Sonja/Le Roy Central School Dist	77	73
Armezzani, Gregg/Maine Endwell Ctl School Dist	67	29
Arminio, Kathy/Monroe 2 Orleans BOCES	43	115
Armitage, Holly/Wayne Central School Dist	15,68	251
Armstrong, Colleen/Webster Central School Dist	11,36,58,77,79	112
Armstrong, John/Lancaster Central Sch Dist	58	62
Armstrong, Peter/Newcomb Central School Dist	67	68
Armstrong, Regina/Hempstead Union Free SD	1	121
Arno, Matthew/Northeastern Clinton Ctl SD	3	44
Arnold, Anissa/Herricks Union Free Sch Dist	23	121
Arnold, Leah/Eastern Suffolk BOCES	27,30,31	235
Arnonee, Kristin/Red Creek Central School Dist	77	251
Arpino, Biagio/Diocese of Rockville Ed Office	15,68	132
Arroyo, Nancy/Ossining Union Free Sch Dist	11,52,57,298	259
Arthurs, William/Bemus Point Ctl School Dist	16,73,76,286,295	36
Arthurton, Ryan/Honeoye Central School Dist	73	161
Asfoury, Greg/Newark Valley Central Sch Dist	73,286,288	238
Ashdown, David/WSWHE BOCES	73	249
Ashley, Brad/Bronxville Union Free SD	73	253
Ashley, Craig/Madrid-Waddington Central SD	5	211
Ashton, Elizabeth/Honeoye Central School Dist	1	161
Astron, Rose/Trumansburg Central SD	4	241
Atlas, Stacey/Middletown Enlarged City SD	273	165
Atwater, Randall/Barker Central School Dist	67	146
Atwell, Allison/Mt Morris Central School Dist	31,36,69	103
Atwell, Tyler/Boquet Valley Central Sch Dist	5	67
Aubel, Michael/Maine Endwell Ctl School Dist	5	29
Auclair, Sean/Tupper Lake Ctl School Dist	5	70
Audi, Lori/Wynantskill Union Free SD	4	191
Auerfeld, Edna/Greenwood Lake Union Free SD	16,286	164
Aufiero, Kathleen/Huntington Union Free Sch Dist	47	223
Augarten, Deborah/White Plains City School Dist	15,58,79	263
Augello, Michael/Elba Central School Dist	67	73
Augugliaro, Mary/Smithtown Central Sch Dist	5	230
August, Deborah/Croton-Harmon Union Free SD	73,97,98	254
Augusta, John/Mahopac Ctl School Dist	6	176
Augustine, Jeff/Newfield Central School Dist	6	241
Ausfeld, Mel/Cobleskill Richmondville SD	11,79,270	206
Austin, Adrienne/New York City Dept of Ed	15,71,298	134
Austin, Angela, Dr/Bridgehampton Union Free SD	57,79	218
Austin, Christine/Port Jefferson Union Free SD 6	18,298	228
Austin, Heather/Syracuse City School Dist	295	158
Austin, Hilary/Elmira City School Dist	1	40
Austin, James/Lyncourt Union Free Sch Dist	1	156
Austin, Paul/Cuba-Rushford Central SD	16	14
Auyugliaro, Tami/Lancaster Central Sch Dist	4	62
Averill, Tom/Saugerties Central School Dist	27,88,89	243
Aversa, Sonja/Syracuse City School Dist	294	158
Avery, Jennifer, Dr/Onc BOCES	15	51
Aviles, Luis/Bethlehem Central School Dist	57	10
Axelson, Bruce/Lackawanna City School Dist	98	62
Aylor, Chelsey/Fillmore Central School Dist	8,11,273,288,296,752	14
Ayotte, Diane/Hammond Central School Distict	6,11	210
Ayres, Brian/Greene Ctl School Dist	6,11,57,270,271	42
Azzarello, Kenneth/Palmyra-Macedon Central SD	68,79	250

B

Babbie, Michele/Sauquoit Valley Central SD	16	152
Babcock, Leon/Keshequa Central School Dist	5	103

---

1 Superintendent
2 Bus/Finance/Purchasing
3 Buildings And Grounds
4 Food Service
5 Transportation
6 Athletic
7 Health Services
8 Curric/Instruct K-12
9 Curric/Instruct Elem
10 Curric/Instruct Sec
11 Federal Program
12 Title I
13 Title V
15 Asst Superintendent
16 Instructional Media Svcs
17 Chief Operations Officer
18 Chief Academic Officer
19 Chief Financial Officer
20 Art K-12
21 Art Elem
22 Art Sec
23 Music K-12
24 Music Elem
25 Music Sec
26 Business Education
27 Career & Tech Ed
28 Technology Education
29 Family/Consumer Science
30 Adult Education
31 Career/Sch-to-Work K-12
32 Career/Sch-to-Work Elem
33 Career/Sch-to-Work Sec
34 Early Childhood Ed
35 Health/Phys Education
36 Guidance Services K-12
37 Guidance Services Elem
38 Guidance Services Sec
39 Social Studies K-12
40 Social Studies Elem
41 Social Studies Sec
42 Science K-12
43 Science Elem
44 Science Sec
45 Math K-12
46 Math Elem
47 Math Sec
48 English/Lang Arts K-12
49 English/Lang Arts Elem
50 English/Lang Arts Sec
51 Reading K-12
52 Reading Elem
53 Reading Sec
54 Remedial Reading K-12
55 Remedial Reading Elem
56 Remedial Reading Sec
57 Bilingual/ELL
58 Special Education K-12
59 Special Education Elem
60 Special Education Sec
61 Foreign/World Lang K-12
62 Foreign/World Lang Elem
63 Foreign/World Lang Sec
64 Religious Education K-12
65 Religious Education Elem
66 Religious Education Sec
67 School Board President
68 Teacher Personnel
69 Academic Assessment
70 Research/Development
71 Public Information
72 Summer School
73 Instructional Tech
74 Inservice Training
75 Marketing/Distributive
76 Info Systems
77 Psychological Assess
78 Affirmative Action
79 Student Personnel
80 Driver Ed/Safety
81 Gifted/Talented
82 Video Services
83 Substance Abuse Prev
84 Erate
85 AIDS Education
88 Alternative/At Risk
89 Multi-Cultural Curriculum
90 Social Work
91 Safety/Security
92 Magnet School
93 Parental Involvement
95 Tech Prep Program
97 Chief Information Officer
98 Chief Technology Officer
270 Character Education
271 Migrant Education
273 Teacher Mentor
274 Before/After Sch
275 Response To Intervention
277 Remedial Math K-12
280 Literacy Coach
285 STEM
286 Digital Learning
288 Common Core Standards
294 Accountability
295 Network System
296 Title II Programs
297 Webmaster
298 Grant Writer/Ptnrships
750 Chief Innovation Officer
751 Chief of Staff
752 Social Emotional Learning

New York School Directory

DISTRICT PERSONNEL INDEX

NAME/District	JOB FUNCTIONS	PAGE
Baber, Adam/Fishers Island Union Free SD	6,35,83	222
Babino, Angelica/Smithtown Central Sch Dist	45	230
Babino, Connie/Afton Central School Dist	4	41
Bacidalupi, Joshua/Dryden Central School Dist	1,83	239
Backe, Denelle/Oakfield Alabama Ctl SD	58	74
Backer, Allen/Allegany-Limestone Ctl SD	3	31
Backus, Tim/South Colonie Central Sch Dist	8,11,16,57,270,288,296,298	12
Badanes, David/Northport Northport UFSD	67	227
Badger, Rosemary/Greene Ctl School Dist	4	42
Baez, Asheena/Baldwin Union Free School Dist	9	116
Baez, Karina/Roslyn School Dist	9,15	129
Bahgat, Louann/Clymer Central School Dist	2,11	37
Bahn, Michelle/Arlington Central School Dist	58	51
Baier, Jeff/Downsville Central Sch Dist	6	49
Bailer, Thomas/Phoenix Central School Dist	33	171
Bailey, Brian/Ravena Coeymans Selkirk Ctl SD	1,11	11
Bailey, Jeffery/Dundee Ctl School Dist	73,295	268
Bailey, Jessica/Rush Henrietta Central SD	58	112
Bailey, Julia/Canton Central School Dist	16	209
Bailey, Katherin/Sidney Central School Dist	11,280,285,286,288,298	50
Bailey, Margaret/Syracuse City School Dist	69	158
Bailey, Martha/Lyons Central School Dist	67	249
Bailey, Nancy/Syracuse City School Dist	7	158
Bailey, Patrick/Hoosick Falls Central Sch Dist	12	190
Bailey, Steve/Tully Central School Dist	5	159
Bailey, Suzanne/Manchester-Shortsville Ctl SD	73,295	162
Bain, Charles/Putnam Central School Dist	67	248
Bainbridge, Anna/Fire Island Union Free SD	6,35	222
Baio, Michael/Sayville Union Free Sch Dist	30	229
Baiocco, Marc/Elmsford Union Free SD	1	255
Baird, Eric/North Rockland Central SD	15,68	197
Baisley, Keith/New Paltz Ctl School Dist	73	242
Baize, Penny/Royalton Hartland Central SD	16	148
Bajohr, Randy/Camden Central School Dist	3,91	150
Bakatsias, Michael/Marlboro Central School Dist	15,16,68,73,76,79,295	242
Baker, Andrew/Bethlehem Central School Dist	48	10
Baker, Beecher/Hadley-Luzerne Ctl Sch Dist	1	245
Baker, Christine/Greece Central School Dist	58	108
Baker, Deborah, Dr/Brighton Central School Dist	8,11,57,81,286,288	106
Baker, Gregory/Penn Yan Ctl School Dist	8,15,74	268
Baker, Jarrod/Fonda Fultonville Central SD	73	115
Baker, Jeffrey/Questar III BOCES	71,97	192
Baker, Katarzyna/Morris Central School Dist	7,83,85	174
Baker, Kent/Albany City School Dist	15,69,76,294	9
Baker, Melissa/Greater Johnstown Sch Dist	2	71
Baker, Paul/Hoosick Falls Central Sch Dist	3	190
Baker, Thomas/Hendrick Hudson Ctl Sch Dist	6,35	256
Baker, Vern/Wyoming Central School Dist	3	268
Balchan, Brooke, Dr/New Rochelle City School Dist	7,85	259
Balcout, Deb/West Genesee Ctl School Dist	7	159
Balden, Darren/Edmeston Ctl School Dist	3	173
Baldini, Carl/Wyandanch Union Free Sch Dist	15,58,79	234
Baldwin, Annette/Southtown Teachers Center	1	67
Baldwin, Erin/Bolivar-Richburg Ctrl Sch Dist	67	14
Baldwin, Lori/Rochester City School Dist	91	110
Baldwin, Sue, Dr/Buffalo Public Schools	35	57
Balen, Marie, Dr/Williamsville Ctl School Dist	8,15,31,34,69,288	64
Balestrieri, Catherine/Putnam-Northern Wstchstr BOCES	27	266
Balfour, Mark/Webster Central School Dist	4	112
Balilo, Helen/West Point School Dist	1	167
Ball, Karen/Plainview-Old Bethpage Ctl SD	4	127
Ball, Mitchell/Gates Chili Central School Dist	2,15	108
Ballard, Genevieve/Onc BOCES	76	51
Ballard, Jay/Geneseo Central Sch Dist	5	103
Ballerstein, Nancy/Fonda Fultonville Central SD	7	115
Balsamo, Louis/Bay Shore Union Free Sch Dist	36	217
Baltar, Yuvelin/Farmingdale Union Free SD	9	119
Balzan, Dan/Malverne Union Free Sch Dist	3,5,11,15,79,271	124
Banaszak, Mary/Victor Central School Dist	27,36,69,88	162
Bandlow, Lorie, Dr/Brewster Central School Dist	1	175
Banek, John/New Hartford Central Sch Dist	6,35,91	151
Banker, Brett/Kenmore-Tonawanda UF Sch Dist	6,35	62
Banks, Jason/Candor Central School Dist	36	238
Banner, Craig/Greece Central School Dist	5	108
Banner, Scott/Palmyra-Macedon Central SD	5	250
Bannerman, Brigette/Andover Central School Dist	29,35,85	14

NAME/District	JOB FUNCTIONS	PAGE
Bannerman, Jacob/Andover Central School Dist	6,31,271	14
Bannon, Kathleen, Dr/Copiague Union Free Sch Dist	1,11	220
Banzer, Robert/Northport-East Northport UFSD	1	227
Barbagallo, Geraldine/Harrison Central School Dist	5	256
Barber, Casey/Cattaraugus-Little Vly Ctl SD	36,57	31
Barber, David/Attica Central School Dist	3,15	267
Barber, Kevin/Port Byron Ctl School Dist	38	35
Barber, Patty/Phoenix Central School Dist	4	171
Barbiani, Debra/Fallsburg Central School Dist	67	236
Barbour, Tamara Anne/Pawling Ctl School Dist	6	52
Bard, Alan/Mount Markham Central Sch Dist	273	78
Barden, Stacey/Penn Yan Ctl School Dist	11,58,77,79,271	268
Bardin, Casey/North Colonie Central SD	11,36,57,58,85,270,294	11
Bardin, Robert/Greater Amsterdam School Dist	4	115
Barduhn, Casey/Westhill Central School Dist	1	159
Baretta, Joseph/Clinton Central School Dist	2,5,11,15,298	150
Bargstedt, Laurie/Hamilton-Fulton-Montgmry BOCES	30	72
Barile, Domenic/Niagara-Wheatfield Ctl SD	4	148
Barker, Barbara/Fonda Fultonville Central SD	28	115
Barker, Gerald/Geneva City School Dist	4	161
Barker, Jennifer/Hamburg Central School Dist	79,90	61
Barker, Jeremy/Mamaroneck Union Free Sch Dist	15,68	257
Barker, Leonard/Saranac Lake Central Sch Dist	5	70
Barker, Scott/Pittsford Central Sch Dist	6	110
Barkley, Kaitlyn/Brocton Central School Dist	2,11,76,286,296	36
Barlow, Justin/Holland Patent Ctl School Dist	6	150
Barnes, Cassandra/Orleans-Niagara BOCES	57	170
Barnes, Jeff/Evans-Brant Central Sch Dist	73,76,98	60
Barnes, Jeremy/North Rose Wolcott Central SD	5	250
Barnes, Roxann/Beekmantown Ctl School Dist	4	43
Barnes, Sandra/Hancock Central School Dist	16	49
Barnett, Tracey/Rye City School Dist	7	261
Barney, Francis/Parishville Hopkinton Sch Dist	3,5	212
Barno, Gary/Williamson Central School Dist	2,11,19	251
Barnum, Jessica/Fabius Pompey Central SD	36	155
Barnum, Jessica/Hamilton Central Sch Dist	36	105
Barone, Alan/Highland Ctl School Dist	67	242
Baroody, David/Plattsburgh City School Dist	2,15	44
Barr, Brigedtte/North Rose Wolcott Central SD	11	250
Barr, David/Tompkins-Seneca-Tioga BOCES	58,88	241
Barra, Rose/Shenendehowa Central Sch Dist	7,29	202
Barrett, Alex/Beaver River Central Sch Dist	36	101
Barrett, Margaret/Lancaster Central Sch Dist	90	62
Barros, Michelle/Wells Central School Dist	11,58,296	77
Barrow, Melissa/East Ramapo Central Sch Dist	57,61	196
Barrs, Charles/Schuylerville Central Sch Dist	5	201
Barry, Debora/Newark Central School Dist	30	250
Barry, Jean/Laurens Central School Dist	274	173
Barry, John/Remsenburg-Speonk UFSD	67	228
Barry, Mike/Schenectady City School Dist	3	204
Barry, Penny/Lyndonville Central Sch Dist	77	169
Barse, Dominic/Malone Central School Dist	5	69
Barse, John/Morristown Ctl School Dist	3,5	211
Barshay, David/Hauppauge Union Free Sch Dist	67	223
Barsottelli, Sheri/Depew Union Free School Dist	280	60
Barstys, Ron/Orleans-Niagara BOCES	58	170
Bartalo, Brian/Holley Central School Dist	1	169
Bartels, Robert/Rockville Ctr Union Free SD	2,15,68,78,271	128
Barth, David/East Rockaway Union Free SD	6	118
Barthelmess, Greg/Schuylerville Central Sch Dist	11,27,36,57,58,69,79,88	201
Barthokmbu, Dave/Pulaski Central School Dist	4	172
Bartholomew, David/Altmar-Parish-Williamstown SD	4	170
Bartholomew, David/Central Square Central SD	4	170
Bartholomew, Joseph/Ft Plain Central School Dist	67	115
Bartholomew, Paul/Hancock Central School Dist	3	49
Bartlett Prati, Jen/Romulus Ctl School Dist	11,286,288,296	208
Bartlett, Bill/Delaware Academy Ctrl SD Delhi	3	49
Bartlett, Dannell/Wheelerville Union Free SD	4	72
Bartlett, Russ/Tupper Lake Ctl School Dist	1	70
Barton, Shane/Schoharie Central SD	6	206
Bascom, Rebecca/Clifton-Fine Central Sch Dist	11,73	209
Bashaw, Michael/Thousand Islands Central SD	1	81
Bass, Garner/Farmingdale Union Free SD	39,89	119
Bass, Mimi/Valley Stream Union Free SD 13	90	130
Bassette, Jon/Lowville Acad-Central Sch Dist	295	101
Basso, Micahel/Scarsdale Union Free Sch Dist	16,82	261

School Year 2020-2021   800-333-8802

DISTRICT PERSONNEL INDEX

Market Data Retrieval

NAME/District	JOB FUNCTIONS	PAGE
Bastian, Mike/Honeoye Central School Dist	2	161
Basting, Donna/Dover Union Free School Dist	8,15,68,69	52
Bateman, Christopher/Hudson City School Dist	4	46
Bateman, Eric/Canandaigua City School Dist	16,82	161
Bates-Wilkins, Janet/North Shore Central SD	11	126
Bates, Bianca/Cambridge Central School Dist	280	247
Bates, Brian/Sherman Central School Dist	67	39
Bates, Eileen/Holland Patent Ctl School Dist	81	150
Bates, Susan/Sherman Central School Dist	4	39
Bateson, Michael/Pulaski Central School Dist	8,11,31,36,57	172
Batewell, Patricia/Monroe Woodbury Central SD	5	165
Batson, Robert/Poland Central School Dist	67	78
Battista, Lauren/Quogue Union Free School Dist	67	228
Batzel, Tim/Alexander Ctl School Dist	2,3	73
Batzing, Jennifer/Corning-Painted Post Area SD	12,58	214
Baudo, Kelly/Buffalo Public Schools	8,15,16,69	56
Bauer, Barbara/Jericho Union Free School Dist	8,15,69,74,81,83,85,273	122
Bauerlein, John/Pleasantville Union Free SD	6,35	260
Baum, Alan/Three Village Central Sch Dist	10,68	232
Baumann, Michael/Newfane Central School Dist	1	147
Baumgarden, Doug/Depew Union Free School Dist	5	59
Baumgartner, Judy/Alden Central School Dist	83,90	56
Baumgartner, Krystyna/Bay Shore Union Free Sch Dist	71	217
Bavaro, Steve/Rye Neck Union Free Sch Dist	73	261
Bavis, Donald/Marion Central School Dist	1	250
Bavis, Terri/Waterloo Central School Dist	1	208
Baxter, Rachel/Brasher Falls School Dist	38,83	209
Bay, Kory/Prattsburgh Central Sch Dist	1	215
Bayer, Chris/Newburgh Enlarged City SD	15,36,39,58,79	165
Baylor, Kevin/Southern Cayuga Central SD	3	35
Bayne, Roseann/Ctr for Instruct Tech Innov	8,15	172
Beach, Brian/Chateaugay Central School Dist	3	69
Beadle, Bill/Unadilla Valley Ctl Sch Dist	3	43
Beal, Jessica/Albion Central School Dist	58	169
Beale, Noelle, Dr/Archdiocese of New York Ed Off	15	142
Beall, Greg/Andes Central School Dist	2	48
Beall, Greg/Schenevus Ctl School Dist	2	174
Beamer, Jackie/Hancock Central School Dist	79	49
Bean, Linda/Fishers Island Union Free SD	73,286,295	222
Beaney, Tammy/Holley Central School Dist	5	169
Beardsley, Jeff/Pittsford Central Sch Dist	3,91	110
Beardsley, Priscilla/Fillmore Central School Dist	4	14
Beardsley, Steven/York Central School Dist	67	103
Bearup, Greg/South Colonie Central Sch Dist	43,46,277	12
Beasley, Erica/Briarcliff Manor Union Free SD	73,76,286,295,750	253
Beattie, Penny/Salamanca City Central SD	68,74	33
Beattie, Scott/Windsor Central School Dist	8,11,16,73,83,275,288,296	30
Beauregard, Steven/Hunter Tannersville Ctl SD	73	76
Bechard, Bernadette/Lake George Central Sch Dist	57,58	245
Bechdol, Karen/Albany City School Dist	8	9
Bechtel, Matt/Vestal Ctl School Dist	2	29
Beck, Jason/Schalmont Central School Dist	85	204
Beck, Kathleen/Schenectady City School Dist	20,23	204
Beck, Megan/Guilderland Central School Dist	4	11
Becker, Cherie/Monroe 1 BOCES	7,57,58,79	115
Becker, Debbie/Evans-Brant Central Sch Dist	4	60
Becker, Josh/Fayetteville-Manlius Ctl SD	295	155
Becker, Julianne/Orchard Park Central Sch Dist	71	63
Beckerink, Todd/Falconer Central School Dist	67	37
Beckley, Patrick/Garrison Union Free Sch Dist	6	175
Beder, Rinna/Mamaroneck Union Free Sch Dist	67	257
Bednarek, Peter/Scotia Glenville Ctl Sch Dist	8	205
Bednarski, Tim/North Syracuse Ctl Sch Dist	6,35,85	157
Beecher, Heidi/Canisteo-Greenwood Central SD	5	214
Beedon, Kristi/Hamilton-Fulton-Montgmry BOCES	16	72
Beehler, Mark/Elba Central School Dist	6	73
Beehler, Mark, Dr/Salamanca City Central SD	7,8,11,15,91,285,288	33

NAME/District	JOB FUNCTIONS	PAGE
Beeler, Don/Monroe Woodbury Central SD	67	165
Beers, Darryl/Franklin Central School Dist	6	49
Beggins, David/William Floyd School Dist	2,4,5,15,91	233
Beggs, Amber/Northeastern Clinton Ctl SD	30	44
Begnoche, Collin/Schenevus Ctl School Dist	98	174
Behnke, Jeff/Wappingers Central Sch Dist	30	54
Behr, Katie/Jericho Union Free School Dist	20,23	122
Behr, Tammy/Sharon Springs Ctl SD	35	207
Beichner, Joyce/Cassadaga Valley Ctl Sch Dist	16	36
Beisler, Paul/Onc BOCES	67	51
Beitz, Kelly/Attica Central School Dist	88,270	267
Bekermus, Barbara/Sag Harbor Union Free Sch Dist	11,58	229
Bel, Marisa, Dr/Oyster Bay East Norwich Ctl SD	57	127
Belden, Nicole/Newcomb Central School Dist	34	68
Beleckas, Gerard, Dr/Lynbrook Union Free Sch Dist	11,15,69	124
Belfi, Daniel/Lakeland Central School Dist	6	257
Belfield, Jeremie/La Fayette Central School Dist	1	156
Belfiore, Laura/Peekskill City School Dist	71	260
Belknap, Brian/Edmeston Ctl School Dist	4	173
Belkota, Rebecca/Perry Central School Dist	273	267
Bell, Christine/Saranac Lake Central Sch Dist	38	70
Bell, David/Hicksville Union Free Sch Dist	3	122
Bell, Eric/Champlain Valley Ed Services	2,15,68	45
Bell, Jesse/Tri-Valley Central School Dist	3	237
Bell, Kathleen/Holland Central School Dist	36,69	61
Bell, Kimberly/Trumansburg Central SD	1	241
Bell, Richard/Downsville Central School Dist	67	49
Bell, Susan/Wilson Central School Dist	4	149
Bellair, Brian/Whitesboro Ctl School Dist	1	153
Bellarosa, Michael/Valley Central School Dist	15,68	167
Bellavia, Carol/Honeoye Falls Lima Sch Dist	67	109
Belle-Isle, Michael/Amherst Central School Dist	15,58,68,71,79	56
Bellew, Joseph/Lake Placid Ctl School Dist	295	67
Bellino, Lydia, Dr/Cold Spring Harbor Central SD	8,15,296	219
Belmont, William/Lynbrook Union Free Sch Dist	67	124
Belmonte, John/Sayville Union Free Sch Dist	2,3,15,71,91	229
Belt, Seth/Brasher Falls School Dist	67	209
Belton-Cottman, Sharon/Buffalo Public Schools	67	57
Belz, Lisa/East Islip Union Free SD	11,58,79,88	220
Bemis, Lynne/Clymer Central School Dist	11,298	37
Benamati, Mikal/Stillwater Central Sch Dist	77	202
Benante, Phillip, Dr/Haldane Central School Dist	1	175
Bender, Cole/Dutchess Co BOCES	3,5	55
Benedict, Alice Ann/Batavia City School Dist	67	73
Benedict, Eric/Cincinnatus Ctl School Dist	3	47
Benedict, Jill/Evans-Brant Central Sch Dist	11,57,58	60
Bengel, Jennifer/Warwick Valley Central SD	2	167
Benjamin-Legg, Andrea/Hunter Tannersville Ctl SD	67	76
Benjamin, John/Candor Central School Dist	83	238
Benjamin, Polly/Duanesburg Central Sch Dist	273	203
Bennardo, David, Dr/South Huntington Union Free SD	1	231
Bennedum, Jill/Owego Apalachin Ctl Sch Dist	16,58,68,79,271,275	238
Benner, Jonathan/Thousand Islands Central SD	16,73,74,76,275,285,295	81
Bennet, Debra/Elmont Union Free School Dist	35	118
Bennett-Barnes, Kristine/Queensbury Union Free Sch Dist	11,57,58,77,79	246
Bennett-Conroy, Waveline, Dr/Mount Vernon City School Dist	11,15,70,294	258
Bennett, Amy/Oysterponds Union Free SD	73	227
Bennett, Eric/Saranac Lake Central Sch Dist	6	70
Bennett, Janet/Frewsburg Central School Dist	4	38
Bennett, Jefffrey/Roxbury Central School Dist	1	50
Bennett, Kathy/Indian Lake Ctl School Dist	4	76
Bennett, Lisa/Union-Endicott Ctl School Dist	5	29
Bennett, Michael/Schodack Central School Dist	8,11,57,58,77,280,288,296	191
Bennett, Michael/Whitehall Central School Dist	16,73,295	248
Bennett, Ricky/Webster Central School Dist	295	112
Bennett, Roger/St Lawrence-Lewis BOCES	67	212
Bennett, William/Copiague Union Free Sch Dist	6	220

#	Function	#	Function	#	Function	#	Function	#	Function	#	Function
1	Superintendent	16	Instructional Media Svcs	30	Adult Education	44	Science Sec	58	Special Education K-12	72	Summer School
2	Bus/Finance/Purchasing	17	Chief Operations Officer	31	Career/Sch-to-Work K-12	45	Math K-12	59	Special Education Elem	73	Instructional Tech
3	Buildings And Grounds	18	Chief Academic Officer	32	Career/Sch-to-Work Elem	46	Math Elem	60	Special Education Sec	74	Inservice Training
4	Food Service	19	Chief Financial Officer	33	Career/Sch-to-Work Sec	47	Math Sec	61	Foreign/World Lang K-12	75	Marketing/Distributive
5	Transportation	20	Art K-12	34	Early Childhood Ed	48	English/Lang Arts K-12	62	Foreign/World Lang Elem	76	Info Systems
6	Athletic	21	Art Elem	35	Health/Phys Education	49	English/Lang Arts Elem	63	Foreign/World Lang Sec	77	Psychological Assess
7	Health Services	22	Art Sec	36	Guidance Services K-12	50	English/Lang Arts Sec	64	Religious Education K-12	79	Affirmative Action
8	Curric/Instruct K-12	23	Music K-12	37	Guidance Services Elem	51	Reading K-12	65	Religious Education Elem	79	Student Personnel
9	Curric/Instruct Elem	24	Music Elem	38	Guidance Services Sec	52	Reading Elem	66	Religious Education Sec	80	Driver Ed/Safety
10	Curric/Instruct Sec	25	Music Sec	39	Social Studies K-12	53	Reading Sec	67	School Board President	81	Gifted/Talented
11	Federal Program	26	Business Education	40	Social Studies Elem	54	Remedial Reading K-12	68	Teacher Personnel	82	Video Services
12	Title I	27	Career & Tech Ed	41	Social Studies Sec	55	Remedial Reading Elem	69	Academic Assessment	83	Substance Abuse Prev
13	Title V	28	Technology Education	42	Science K-12	56	Remedial Reading Sec	70	Research/Development	84	Erate
15	Asst Superintendent	29	Family/Consumer Science	43	Science Elem	57	Bilingual/ELL	71	Public Information	85	AIDS Education

#	Function	#	Function
88	Alternative/At Risk	277	Remedial Math K-12
89	Multi-Cultural Curriculum	280	Literacy Coach
90	Social Work	285	STEM
91	Safety/Security	286	Digital Learning
92	Magnet School	288	Common Core Standards
93	Parental Involvement	294	Accountability
95	Tech Prep Program	295	Network System
97	Chief Information Officer	296	Title II Programs
98	Chief Technology Officer	297	Webmaster
270	Character Education	298	Grant Writer/Ptnrships
271	Migrant Education	750	Chief Innovation Officer
273	Teacher Mentor	751	Chief of Staff
274	Before/After Sch	752	Social Emotional Learning
275	Response To Intervention		

New York School Directory

DISTRICT PERSONNEL INDEX

NAME/District	JOB FUNCTIONS	PAGE
Bens, Phillip/Cassadaga Valley Ctl Sch Dist	73,286	36
Benson, Mark/New Hartford Central Sch Dist	80	151
Bentley, Brian/Greater Southern Tier BOCES	3	215
Bentley, Elizabeth/Greece Central School Dist	15,68	108
Bentley, Monica/North Greenbush Common SD	7	191
Beovich, Stephen/Mt Pleasant Cottage UFSD	1	258
Berardo, Dean/Brewster Central School Dist	6,83	175
Beres, Diane/West Seneca Central Sch Dist	67	64
Berez-Kelly, Lydia/Holland Patent Ctl School Dist	67	150
Bergen, Karyn/O E S J Central School Dist	7	72
Berger, Steve/Wyandanch Union Free Sch Dist	69	234
Bergin, Michael/Eastport-South Manor Ctrl SD	3	221
Bergin, Michael/Eastport-South Manor Ctrl SD	3	221
Bergio, Alexandria/Warsaw Central School Dist	4	267
Bergler, Melissa/Evans-Brant Central Sch Dist	8,15,17,285,288,296,298,751	60
Bergman, Ellen/Hawthorne Cedar Knolls UFSD	79	256
Berkoski, Kate/Sag Harbor Union Free Sch Dist	54	229
Berkowitz, Barbara/Great Neck Public Schools	67	120
Berkowitz, Dovid, Dr/East Ramapo Central Sch Dist	77	196
Berkowitz, Linda/Sullivan BOCES	67	238
Berlin, Cheryl/Hammondsport Ctl School Dist	2	214
Berlin, Marla/Ctr for Instruct Tech Innov	27,31	172
Berman, Lauren/Hastings on Hudson Union FR SD	67	256
Berman, Maureen, Dr/Lynbrook Union Free Sch Dist	5,15,79	124
Bernardi, Joseph/Somers Central School Dist	5,91	262
Berner, Angela/Huntington Union Free Sch Dist	48	223
Berner, Elizabeth/Ithaca City School Dist	5	240
Bernstein, Debbie/Plainview-Old Bethpage Ctl SD	67	127
Bernstein, Vicki/New York City Dept of Ed	68	134
Bernys, Minser/Frontier Ctl School Dist	79	60
Berry, Bonnie/Champlain Valley Ed Services	58	45
Berry, Bonnie/Peru Central School Dist	67	44
Berry, Douglas/Dobbs Ferry Union Free SD	8,15,69,298	254
Berry, Ethan/Deposit Central School Dist	2	28
Berry, Ethan/Susquehanna Valley Central SD	2	29
Berry, Jennifer/Hoosick Falls Central Sch Dist	37	190
Berry, Matt/Peru Central School Dist	6,7,35,83	44
Berry, Stephanie/Union Springs Ctl School Dist	16,82	35
Berson, Robert/Sherburne Earlville Central SD	1,11	42
Bertram, David/Cooperstown Ctl School Dist	6	173
Bertram, David/Mohonasen Central School Dist	6,7,35	203
Bertram, Karen/Cato Meridian Central Sch Dist	285	34
Bertrand, Katie/Monroe 1 BOCES	16	115
Bertrand, Peter/Massena Central School Dist	4	211
Berube, Aaron/Cato Meridian Central Sch Dist	16,73,295	34
Besant, Daryl/Evans-Brant Central Sch Dist	6	60
Besenfelder, Eric/Coxsackie-Athens Central SD	3	75
Bessey, Robert/Newcomb Central School Dist	5	68
Best, Robert/Potsdam Central School Dist	16,73	212
Beswick, Helene/Le Roy Central School Dist	49,52	73
Bett, Allan/Holland Central School Dist	35	61
Betters, Cynthia/Cornwall Central School Dist	273	163
Bettinelli, Donna/Bay Shore Union Free Sch Dist	42,285	217
Betts, Stephanie/Dundee Ctl School Dist	83	268
Betz, Danielle/East Meadow Union Free SD	77,79	118
Beutel, Gary/Sachem Central School Dist	6,7,35	229
Bianco, Peter/Liberty Central School Dist	6,83,85	236
Bichler, Cindy/Cuba-Rushford Central Sch Dist	7,83	14
Bickel, Paul/East Greenbush Central SD	3	190
Bickelhaupt, Lenny/Hammond Central School Distict	3,5	210
Bickford, John/Caledonia-Mumford Ctl Sch Dist	67	102
Bieber, Ron/Owego Apalachin Ctl School Dist	3	238
Bierker, Tamara/Clarkstown Central School Dist	67	195
Biernacki, Christine/Huntington Union Free Sch Dist	67	223
Biery, Denise/Hyde Park Central School Dist	67	52
Bigelow, Andrew/Heuvelton Central School Dist	73,295	210
Biggane, Tabatha/Fonda Fultonville Central SD	2,12	115
Biles, Tricia/Lake George Central Sch Dist	67	245
Billotte, Jennifer/Wayland-Cohocton Central SD	27,36,69,75	215
Bills, David/West Genesee Ctl School Dist	1	159
Bilodeau, Greg/Cincinnatus Ctl School Dist	4	47
Bilodeau, Troy/Cincinnatus Ctl School Dist	2,12	47
Bilodeau, Troy/McGraw Central School Dist	2	48
Bilski, Rebecca/Hauppauge Union Free Sch Dist	58,79	223
Binaxas, Patti/Evans-Brant Central Sch Dist	7,83	60
Bindigni, Jamie/Byron-Bergen Ctl School Dist	5	73
Bingle, Amy/Lowville Acad-Central Sch Dist	81	101
Bingle, Steve/Lowville Acad-Central Sch Dist	73	101
Binion, Joseph/Madrid-Waddington Central SD	10,12	211
Binkin, Linda/North Shore Central SD	36	126
Binkley, April/Falconer Central School Dist	16	37
Birch, Jodi/Mechanicville City Sch Dist	2	201
Bird, Thomas/Williamsville Ctl School Dist	28,29,42,285	64
Birmingham, John/Moravia Central School Dist	1	34
Birmingham, Michael/Dansville Ctl School Dist	295	102
Bisaillon, Clara/Scotia Glenville Ctl Sch Dist	5	205
Bischoping, Scott/Wayne-Finger Lakes BOCES	1	252
Bishop, Amy/Cornwall Central School Dist	4	163
Bishop, Benjamin/Hudson Falls Central Sch Dist	67	248
Bishop, Cindy/Onteora Central School Dist	12,57,58,79,83,88,275,296	243
Bishop, Dan/Canaseraga Central Sch Dist	36	14
Bishop, John/Ft Plain Central School Dist	1,11	115
Bishop, Nicole/Andes Central School Dist	36,69,286	48
Bishop, Sue/Hudson Falls Central Sch Dist	72	248
Bishop, Susan/Greenwich Central School Dist	11,58,79	247
Bishopp, Amy/Wallkill Central School Dist	4	243
Bissetta, Shawn/Canastota Central School Dist	1	104
Bitely, Julie/Victor Central School Dist	58	162
Bittar, Elizabeth/North Tonawanda City Sch Dist	60	148
Bivins, Heather/Sharon Springs Ctl SD	16,82	207
Bizzarro, Deana/Germantown Central School Dist	2	46
Bjork, Anthony/Ogdensburg City School Dist	6	211
Black, Jeffery, Dr/Naples Central School Dist	2,15,19	162
Black, Jeffrey/Prattsburgh Central Sch Dist	11	215
Black, Ronald/WSWHE BOCES	2,19	249
Blackman, Kathryn/Broome-Tioga BOCES	2	31
Blaine, Connie/Boquet Valley Central Sch Dist	73	67
Blair, Derrek/Rochester City School Dist	2	110
Blair, Jerrod/Eastchester Union Free SD	285	254
Blair, Paul, Dr/Skaneateles Central Sch Dist	70,73,286,295	157
Blake, Daniel/Milford Central School Dist	16,73,82,295	173
Blake, Peter/Rome City School Dist	1	151
Blake, Robert/Le Roy Central School Dist	8,11,16,73,74,285,286	73
Blamble, Karissa/Seneca Falls Central Sch Dist	58,79	208
Blanch, Raymond, Dr/Somers Central School Dist	1	262
Blanchard, David/Schoharie Central SD	1	206
Blanchfield, Terrence/Berne-Knox-Westerlo Central SD	2	10
Blank, Bruce/Andover Central School Dist	295	14
Blank, Lisa/Watertown City School Dist	285	81
Blankenberg, Daniel/Marcus Whitman Central SD	3	162
Blankenberg, Mark/Red Creek Central School Dist	6	251
Blanton, Linda/Sullivan BOCES	88	238
Blask, Eric/Webster Central School Dist	26,45	112
Blask, Margaret/Lyons Central School Dist	57,58,77,275,277,296	249
Blau, Kimelyz/Somers Central School Dist	73,76,295	262
Blaum, Jack/Three Village Central Sch Dist	91	232
Blecha, Mark/Franklinville Ctl School Dist	6	31
Blevins, Tim/Frontier Ctl School Dist	5	60
Bliek, Kyle/Newark Central School Dist	82	250
Blish, Harry/Elmira Heights Ctl Sch Dist	67	40
Bliss, Patrick/Frankfort-Schuyler Ctl SD	295	77
Bliss, Steven/Unadilla Valley Ctl Sch Dist	12,73	43
Bliven, Tracie/Alfred Almond Ctl School Dist	1	13
Block, Jaime/Valhalla Union Free Sch Dist	6	262
Block, Josh/Chappaqua Central School Dist	47,70,73,76,285,286,295	253
Blommer, Jesse/Berne-Knox-Westerlo Central SD	73,295,297	10
Bloom, Jared, Dr/Franklin Square Union Free SD	1	119
Bloom, Roger/Westbury Union Free Sch Dist	15,68	132
Blossey, Jennifer/La Fayette Central School Dist	11	156
Bluett, Scott/Penn Yan Ctl School Dist	36,83	268
Blum, Bill/Eastchester Union Free SD	16,73,295	254
Blum, Jim/Dansville Ctl School Dist	73,295	102
Blum, Lynne/Dansville Ctl School Dist	16	102
Bo Wright, Laurence/Rush Henrietta Central SD	1	112
Boak, Jack/Oneida-Herkimer-Mad BOCES	3,17	154
Boardman, William/South Colonie Central Sch Dist	58	12
Bobbett, Cristy/Tully Central School Dist	58	159
Bobseine, Michael/Fredonia Central School Dist	67	38
Boccanfuso, Kimberly/Lindenhurst Union Free SD	48	224
Boces, Boces/Nanuet Union Free School Dist	295	196
Boces, Sue/Willsboro Central Sch Dist	298	68
Bochniak, Aaron/Schenectady City School Dist	11,294	204

School Year 2020-2021 800-333-8802

DISTRICT PERSONNEL INDEX
Market Data Retrieval

NAME/District	JOB FUNCTIONS	PAGE
Bockmier, Alicia/Allegany-Limestone Ctl SD	58	31
Boddenhagen, Kurt/Monticello Central School Dist	6,35	237
Bodensiek, Alexander/Fort Ann Central School Dist	2	247
Bodnar, Michael/Schuylerville Central Sch Dist	67	201
Bodnar, Peter/Arlington Central School Dist	67	51
Boehm, Ellen/Port Jefferson Union Free SD 6	67	228
Boehm, Nicky/Burnt Hills Ballston Lake SD	4	200
Boffey, David/Frontier Ctl School Dist	3	60
Bogart, Craig/Colton Pierrepont School Dist	6	209
Bogart, Jill/Allegany-Limestone Ctl SD	38,270	31
Bogert, Keith/North Colonie Central SD	44,285	11
Bogler, Ryan/Downsville Central Sch Dist	3	49
Bohen, Eileen/Buffalo Public Schools	79	57
Bohlke, Timothy/Tuxedo Union Free Sch Dist	1	166
Bohringer, Kerri/Wappingers Central Sch Dist	57	54
Boise, Leisa/Plattsburgh City School Dist	67	44
Bokman, Susan/Bolivar-Richburg Ctrl Sch Dist	58	14
Boldt, Dana/Honeoye Falls Lima Sch Dist	4	109
Boliver, Eliza/Beaver River Central Sch Dist	58,77,88	101
Boller, Liz/Middletown Enlarged City SD	11,48,51,54,280,296,298	165
Bollettieri, Mara, Dr/Bellmore-Merrick Ctl High SD	15,68,273	117
Bolton-Wales, Diane/Questar III BOCES	27	192
Bombardiere, Dina/Garden City School Dist	16,82,83,88,90	120
Bonacorsi, Janna/East Rockaway Union Free SD	36	118
Bonadonna, Louis/Connetquot Central School Dist	58	219
Bonaker, Robert/Schoharie Central SD	2,73,82	206
Bonasia, Rose Mary/Merrick Union Free School Dist	76,286	125
Bond, Bruce/Pearl River School Dist	67	197
Bond, Joseph/Bay Shore Union Free Sch Dist	1	217
Bond, Joseph/Valley Central School Dist	67	167
Bonfante, Courtney/Monticello Central School Dist	71	237
Bongermino, Jenna/North Colonie Central SD	68	11
Bongino, Michael/Cold Spring Harbor Central SD	6	219
Bongiovi, Tom/Highland Ctl School Dist	1	242
Bongo, Anthony, Dr/New Rochelle City School Dist	15,77,79,90,271,275	259
Bonk, Dwight/Wappingers Central Sch Dist	15,68,273	54
Bonk, Stephanie/O E S J Central School Dist	79	72
Bonneville, Margaret/Pine Plains Ctl School Dist	2	53
Bonnewell, Michael/Albion Central School Dist	1,83	169
Bonney, Dacey/Burnt Hills Ballston Lake SD	30	200
Bonney, Matthew/Ardsley Union Free School Dist	67	252
Bonnville, Donna/Hunter Tannersville Ctl SD	77	76
Bonsick, Corin/Downsville Central Sch Dist	58,77	49
Bonville, Mary Beth/Kingston City School Dist	10	242
Bonzkowski, Greg/Gilbertsville-Mt Upton SD	6,85	173
Booan, Joe/Onc BOCES	8,15,27,30,58	51
Booth, Donald/Pocantico Hills Ctl Sch Dist	3	260
Boothby, Amy/Ichabod Crane Central Schools	30	46
Boothe, Stephen/Silver Creek Central Sch Dist	67	39
Boozang-Hill, Maureen/Ossining Union Free Sch Dist	58,79	259
Borchardt, Rick/Chenango Forks Central SD	91	28
Borda, Rose, Dr/Hicksville Union Free Sch Dist	31,39	122
Bordeau, Mark/Binghamton City School Dist	4	27
Bordeau, Mark/Broome-Tioga BOCES	4	31
Bordeau, Mark/Chenango Forks Central SD	4	28
Bordeau, Mark/Chenango Valley Ctl Sch Dist	4	28
Bordeau, Mark/Owego Apalachin Ctl Sch Dist	4	238
Bordeau, Mark/Susquehanna Valley Central SD	4	29
Bordeau, Mark/Tioga Central School Dist	4	239
Bordeau, Mark/Vestal Ctl School Dist	4	29
Bordeau, Mark/Whitney Point Central School Dist	4	30
Boresky, Kaitlyn/Archdiocese of New York Ed Off	295	142
Borsari, Christopher/Tarrytown Union Free Sch Dist	1	262
Borza, Colleen/Weedsport Ctl School Dist	67	35
Bosarge, Jessica/Moriah Central School Dist	36	68
Bosco, Giulio/Churchville Chili Ctl Sch Dist	8,11,15,16,74,88,273,274	107
Boshnack, Dana, Dr/Northport-East Northport UFSD	8	227
Bosinski, Bill/Orchard Park Central Sch Dist	3,91	63
Bosinski, Laura/Amherst Central School Dist	2,13	56
Bosse, James/West Islip School Dist	3	233
Bossert, Kenneth, Dr/Elwood Union Free School Dist	1	221
Bostelman, Cindy/Afton Central School Dist	6	41
Bostelman, Matt/Afton Central School Dist	295	41
Bott, Christopher/Diocese of Albany Ed Office	15	12
Botticelli, Anne/Buffalo Public Schools	8,18,74,273	56
Bouchard, Jay/Northern Adirondack Ctl SD	3	44
Boucher, Jodie/Hudson Falls Central Sch Dist	7	248
Boucher, Matthew/Putnam Central School Dist	1,11,73,83	248
Boucher, Steve/Rhinebeck Central School Dist	6	53
Boulais, Jeff/Salmon River Central Sch Dist	73,295	70
Boutet, Kate/Ellicottville Central School Dist	35,83	31
Bova, Jennifer/Lindenhurst Union Free SD	74	224
Bovard, Adele/Syosset Central School Dist	8,15,78	129
Bove, Julianna/Community School District 22	1	91
Bovino, Rosmarie, Dr/Island Park Union Free SD	1	122
Bowen, Christian/Valley Stream Ctl High SD	10,11,57,69,74,273,288,298	130
Bower, Daniel/Tupper Lake Ctl School Dist	2	70
Bower, Jennifer/Newfane Central School Dist	58,79	147
Bower, Kyle/Hammondsport Ctl School Dist	1	214
Bowerman, Christina/Spencerport Central Sch Dist	30	112
Bowers, Diana/Norwich City School Dist	1,11	42
Bowers, Teresa/Liverpool Ctl School Dist	59	156
Bowles, Daniel/North Syracuse Ctl Sch Dist	1	157
Bowman, Daniel/Canandaigua City School Dist	73	161
Boyd, Brady/Central Valley School Dist	3	77
Boyd, Janet/Hermon-DeKalb Central Sch Dist	2	210
Boyd, Patrick/Highland Ctl School Dist	11,34,57,58,79,88,271	242
Boyer, Katie/Hammondsport Ctl School Dist	58,77	214
Boyer, Vanessa/West Canada Valley Ctl SD	752	79
Boylan, Alana/West Canada Valley Ctl SD	73,76,295	79
Boyle, Jennifer/Rye City School Dist	67	261
Boynton, Jill/Byram Hills Central Sch Dist	11,34,57,79,81	253
Boynton, Steven/Schenectady City School Dist	6	204
Boyton, Jill/Byram Hills Central Sch Dist	7,58	253
Brace, Tammy/Bloomfield Central SD	5	161
Bradish, Julie/Mexico Central School Dist	5	171
Bradley, Lynn/Afton Central School Dist	5	41
Bradley, Michelle/Lockport City School Dist	1	147
Bradley, Stacy/George Junior Republic UFSD	6	240
Bradshaw, Jennifer/Smithtown Central Sch Dist	8,15,288	230
Bradstreet, Nancy/Penfield Central School Dist	71	109
Bradt, Jefferey/Niskayuna Central School Dist	4	204
Bradt, Linda/Middletown Enlarged City SD	57,61,271	165
Bradtke, Jessica/Weedsport Ctl School Dist	38	35
Brady, Anne/Rochester City School Dist	68	110
Brady, George/South Orangetown Central SD	73,295	197
Brady, Lisa, Dr/Dobbs Ferry Union Free SD	1	254
Brady, Patrick/Massena Central School Dist	1	211
Brady, Sheila/Greenville Central School Dist	273	75
Bragen, Cathy/Rome City School Dist	11,36,58,77,81,274	151
Braico, Joseph/Plainview-Old Bethpage Ctl SD	6,35,83	127
Bramley, Cindy/Andes Central School Dist	83	48
Bramoff, Eric/Sag Harbor Union Free Sch Dist	6	229
Bramski, Lynn/Cobleskill Richmondville SD	58	206
Branagan, Maureen/Rocky Point Union Free SD	4	228
Brand, Sean/Southampton Union Free SD	273	231
Brandell, Kim/Chazy Central Rural Sch Dist	57	44
Brandell, Thomas/Northeastern Clinton Ctl SD	8	44
Brandy, Woody/Buffalo Public Schools	39	57
Branius, Jen/Lake Pleasant Central Sch Dist	58,88,273	76
Brannock, Shari/Crown Point Central Sch Dist	1,11	67
Branscombe, Peter, Dr/Sayville Union Free Sch Dist	68	229
Brant, Todd/Letchworth Central School Dist	3	267
Brantaer, Michelle/Marcellus Central School Dist	1,11	157

---

1 Superintendent	16 Instructional Media Svcs	30 Adult Education	44 Science Sec	58 Special Education K-12	72 Summer School	88 Alternative/At Risk	277 Remedial Math K-12
2 Bus/Finance/Purchasing	17 Chief Operations Officer	31 Career/Sch-to-Work K-12	45 Math K-12	59 Special Education Elem	73 Instructional Tech	89 Multi-Cultural Curriculum	280 Literacy Coach
3 Buildings And Grounds	18 Chief Academic Officer	32 Career/Sch-to-Work Elem	46 Math Elem	60 Special Education Sec	74 Inservice Training	90 Social Work	285 STEM
4 Food Service	19 Chief Financial Officer	33 Career/Sch-to-Work Sec	47 Math Sec	61 Foreign/World Lang K-12	75 Marketing/Distributive	91 Safety/Security	286 Digital Learning
5 Transportation	20 Art K-12	34 Early Childhood Ed	48 English/Lang Arts K-12	62 Foreign/World Lang Elem	76 Info Systems	92 Magnet School	288 Common Core Standards
6 Athletic	21 Art Elem	35 Health/Phys Education	49 English/Lang Arts Elem	63 Foreign/World Lang Sec	77 Psychological Assess	93 Parental Involvement	294 Accountability
7 Health Services	22 Art Sec	36 Guidance Services K-12	50 English/Lang Arts Sec	64 Religious Education K-12	78 Affirmative Action	95 Tech Prep Program	295 Network System
8 Curric/Instruct K-12	23 Music K-12	37 Guidance Services Elem	51 Reading K-12	65 Religious Education Elem	79 Student Personnel	97 Chief Information Officer	296 Title II Programs
9 Curric/Instruct Elem	24 Music Elem	38 Guidance Services Sec	52 Reading Elem	66 Religious Education Sec	80 Driver Ed/Safety	98 Chief Technology Officer	297 Webmaster
10 Curric/Instruct Sec	25 Music Sec	39 Social Studies K-12	53 Reading Sec	67 School Board President	81 Gifted/Talented	270 Character Education	298 Grant Writer/Ptnrships
11 Federal Program	26 Business Education	40 Social Studies Elem	54 Remedial Reading K-12	68 Teacher Personnel	82 Video Services	271 Migrant Education	750 Chief Innovation Officer
12 Title I	27 Career & Tech Ed	41 Social Studies Sec	55 Remedial Reading Elem	69 Academic Assessment	83 Substance Abuse Prev	273 Teacher Mentor	751 Chief of Staff
13 Title V	28 Technology Education	42 Science K-12	56 Remedial Reading Sec	70 Research/Development	84 Erate	274 Before/After Sch	752 Social Emotional Learning
15 Asst Superintendent	29 Family/Consumer Science	43 Science Elem	57 Bilingual/ELL	71 Public Information	85 AIDS Education	275 Response To Intervention	

New York School Directory
DISTRICT PERSONNEL INDEX

NAME/District	JOB FUNCTIONS	PAGE
Brantley, John/Chatham Central School Dist	6	46
Braren, Megan/Rondout Valley Ctl Sch Dist	58,79	243
Brase, Robert/Oceanside Union Free Sch Dist	20,23	127
Brashear, Morgan/Morris Central School Dist	16,82	174
Bratcher, Paul/White Plains City School Dist	88	263
Braun, Amy/Cambridge Central School Dist	4	247
Brauner, Genevieve/Oneida City School Dist	73,91	105
Braunscheidel, Maureen/Starpoint Central School Dist	8,15,73	149
Bray, Erin/Argyle Central School Dist	58,79	246
Breakstone, Jay/Bellmore Union Free Sch Dist	67	117
Breda, Constance/Edinburg Common School Dist	4	201
Breen, Taryn/Schenectady City School Dist	2	204
Breese, David/Hoosick Falls Central Sch Dist	73	190
Breidenbach, Ruth/Freeport Public School Dist	71	119
Breidenstein, Robert/Salamanca City Central SD	1	33
Breitseller, Thomas/Highland Falls-Ft Montgmry SD	16,31,36,270,271	164
Bremer, Kathleen/Waterloo Central School Dist	90	208
Brennan, Amy/South Country Central Sch Dist	9	231
Brennan, Erin/Chester Union Free School Dist	2,4,5	163
Brennan, James/West Irondequoit Ctl SD	2,5,15,19,294	113
Brennan, Lisa/Silver Creek Central Sch Dist	16,76	39
Brennan, Michael/Ichabod Crane Central Schools	2,11	46
Brennan, Terese/Cambridge Central School Dist	16	247
Brennan, William/East Meadow Union Free SD	72	118
Brennan, William/Farmingdale Union Free SD	15,70,73,76,295,297	119
Bresett, Christin/Watkins Glen Central Sch Dist	88	207
Bresett, Julie/Madrid-Waddington Central SD	2	211
Breslin, Karen/Lake George Central Sch Dist	31	245
Breslin, Rachel/Syracuse City School Dist	11	158
Bresnahan, Barbara/Alexandria Central School Dist	85	79
Bressler, Kathleen, Dr/Sullivan West Central SD	15,58,79	237
Bressler, Tricia/Keshequa Central School Dist	76	103
Brewer, Christopher/Rome City School Dist	8,15,296	151
Brewer, Hillary, Dr/Saratoga Springs City Sch Dist	68,78,273	201
Brewer, Samantha/Berlin Central School Dist	58,81	189
Brezezski, Randy/Bath Central School Dist	11,71,286,288,296	213
Bricco, Bryan/Penfield Central School Dist	23	109
Briganti, Barbara/North Salem Central Sch Dist	2,15	259
Briggs, Leann/Barker Central School Dist	81	146
Briggs, Mary/Wayland-Cohocton Central SD	2	215
Briggs, Nelson/South Country Central Sch Dist	15,68	231
Briggs, Thomas/Southern Westchester BOCES	3	267
Brigham, Walter/Shelter Island Union Free SD	73	230
Bright, Donna/Stamford Central School Dist	2	50
Bright, Marice/Brushton Moira Ctl Sch Dist	67	69
Brimstein, Patrick/Blind Brook-Rye Union Free SD	1	252
Brincka, Michelle/Webster Central School Dist	7	112
Brindisi, Stacey/Greece Central School Dist	79	108
Brindley, Thomas/Oneonta City School Dist	1	174
Briner, Donna/Corinth Central School Dist	7	200
Brisky, Elizabeth/Franklinville Ctl School Dist	16	31
Brissette, Paul/Central Square Central SD	3	170
Bristol, Aimee/Prattsburgh Central Sch Dist	36	215
Bristol, Christine/Gouverneur Ctl School Dist	4	210
Bristol, Christine/Harrisville Central Sch Dist	4	101
Bristol, Mary/Cobleskill Richmondville SD	26	206
Broas, Ron/Wappingers Central Sch Dist	3	54
Brocher, Charles/Valley Stream Union Free SD 24	3,91	131
Brock, John/New York State Dept Education	16	1
Brockbank, Trish/Brentwood Union Free Sch Dist	39,48	217
Brockley, Susan/New York State Dept Education	45	1
Brockner, Amy/Pine Bush Central School Dist	8,13,15,288	166
Brockner, Chuck/Newfield Central School Dist	5	241
Brockway, Brian/Genesee Valley Ctl School Dist	6	15
Brody, Mark, Dr/Canajoharie Ctl School Dist	67	115
Brogan, Amelia/Cold Spring Harbor Central SD	67	219
Brogan, Kerry/Jordan Elbridge Ctl Sch Dist	83,85	156
Brohm, Karen/West Hempstead School Dist	67	131
Bromley, Michael/Batavia City School Dist	6,7,35	73
Bromm, Andrew/Islip Union Free School Dist	4	224
Bronchetti, Patrick/Massena Central School Dist	67	211
Bronson, Dawn/Willsboro Central Sch Dist	35,85	68
Bronstein, Adam/Mt Pleasant Ctl School Dist	8	258
Brook, Carolyn/Coxsackie-Athens Central SD	16	75
Brooke, Melinda/Rocky Point Union Free SD	16,20,39,48,57	228
Brooker, Holly/Ulster BOCES	71	244
Brooker, Jennifer/West Irondequoit Ctl SD	42,74,273,285	113
Brooks, Brian/Palmyra-Macedon Central SD	8,288,298	250
Brooks, Mark/Broadalbin-Perth Ctl Sch Dist	83,85,88	71
Brooks, Michael/Marlboro Central School Dist	1	242
Brophy, Jim/Cherry Valley-Springfield SD	12	173
Brosdal, Gordon/Mt Sinai Union Free SD	1	226
Broughton, Pete/Letchworth Central School Dist	67	267
Brouillette, Melanie/Madison Central School Dist	2,19,97	105
Brouwer, Rudy/Crown Point Central Sch Dist	76	67
Brovetto, Russell/Jefferson Central Sch Dist	5	206
Brower, Donna/Hunter Tannersville Ctl SD	4	76
Brower, Lisa/North Rose Wolcott Central SD	73	250
Brower, Rudy/Willsboro Central Sch Dist	76,295	68
Brown, Adam/Pocantico Hills Ctl Sch Dist	9,11,69,73,76,288	260
Brown, Alfred, Dr/Arlington Central School Dist	15,288,296	51
Brown, Allison/Roslyn School Dist	1,83	129
Brown, Andy/Vernon-Verona-Sherrill CSD	8,15,69	152
Brown, Annmarie/Weedsport Ctl School Dist	7	35
Brown, Anthony/Syracuse City School Dist	91	158
Brown, Christine/Northville Central School Dist	12	72
Brown, Christopher/Central Islip Union Free SD	5,15,68,69	218
Brown, Christopher, Dr/Marcus Whitman Central SD	1,83	162
Brown, Dan/Tupper Lake Ctl School Dist	6	70
Brown, Dana/Arlington Central School Dist	8,39,48,57,280	51
Brown, Darren/Buffalo Public Schools	15,751	56
Brown, David, Dr/De Ruyter Central School Dist	1	105
Brown, Jason/Carthage Central School Dist	6,30	80
Brown, Jay/Indian River Ctl School Dist	6,35,83,85	80
Brown, Jeanette/Wells Central School Dist	45	77
Brown, Jennifer/Northeastern Clinton Ctl SD	2	44
Brown, Karen/Monroe 2 Orleans BOCES	68	115
Brown, Kari, Dr/Catskill Central School Dist	8,11,58	75
Brown, Kim/Manchester-Shortsville Ctl SD	2	162
Brown, Kim/Norwood-Norfolk Ctl SD	7	211
Brown, Kim/Port Byron Ctl School Dist	6	35
Brown, Kim/Putnam Central School Dist	297	248
Brown, Lori/Gananda Central School Dist	3,4	249
Brown, Luvelle, Dr/Ithaca City School Dist	1	240
Brown, Marnita/Blind Brook-Rye Union Free SD	16	252
Brown, Martha/Wells Central School Dist	2	77
Brown, Paul/Lansingburgh Central Sch Dist	295	190
Brown, Paul/Tuxedo Union Free Sch Dist	73	167
Brown, Robin/Erie 2 Chautauqua-Catta BOCES	16	67
Brown, Sarah/Cairo-Durham Ctl School Dist	7	75
Brown, Sheila/Marcus Whitman Central SD	67	162
Brown, Susan/Germantown Central School Dist	1,73,288	46
Brown, Terry/Pine Valley Central Sch Dist	4	38
Brown, Theresa/Newburgh Enlarged City SD	20,23,294	165
Brown, Theresa/Northville Central School Dist	16	72
Brown, Will/Andover Central School Dist	39	14
Brownell, Deb/Cambridge Central School Dist	286	247
Brownell, James/Wayland-Cohocton Central SD	6	215
Brubaker, Gloria/Watkins Glen Central Sch Dist	67	207
Brubaker, Natalie/Susquehanna Valley Central SD	8,11,15,34,69,273,274,288	29
Brucato, John/Kenmore-Tonawanda UF Sch Dist	2,15	62
Bruce, Amanda/Brushton Moira Ctl Sch Dist	31,69	69
Bruce, Dan/Warrensburg Central Sch Dist	5	246
Bruce, Michael/Wheelerville Union Free SD	67	72
Bruce, Patricia/Lancaster Central Sch Dist	295	62
Brucz, Mary/Cheektowaga-Sloan UFSD	4	59
Bruder, Frederick/Manhasset Union Free Sch Dist	3,91	124
Brudvig, Christine/Northern Adirondack Ctl SD	37	44
Bruening, Joseph/Gowanda Central School Dist	6,35	32
Brugge, Steve/Mamaroneck Union Free Sch Dist	3,91	257
Brunco, Michelle/Falconer Central School Dist	7,85	37
Brundage, Dan/Kendall Central School Dist	3,91	169
Bruni, James/Seneca Falls Central Sch Dist	2,19,73,97,295,296	208
Bruno, Allison/South Huntington Union Free SD	8,11,83,285,288,296	231
Bruno, Sean/Brockport Ctl School Dist	1	106
Bruskowski, Michael/Roslyn School Dist	6	129
Bryan, Janet/Longwood Central School Dist	2,3,15	224
Bryan, Nancy/Cornwall Central School Dist	67	163
Bryant, Willard/Marcellus Central School Dist	35	157
Bryniarski, Michael/Lancaster Central Sch Dist	3,91	62
Buatsi, Olivia/North Shore Central SD	2,68	126
Bubniak, Mark/Averill Park Central Sch Dist	6,35	189

DISTRICT PERSONNEL INDEX

Market Data Retrieval

NAME/District	JOB FUNCTIONS	PAGE
Bucciarelli, Lavon/West Irondequoit Ctl SD	31	113
Bucciferro, David/Scotia Glenville Ctl Sch Dist	67	205
Buchko, William/Gananda Central School Dist	67	249
Buchsbaum, Andre/Owego Apalachin Ctl Sch Dist	6	238
Buckley, Cathy/Beekmantown Ctl School Dist	67	43
Buckley, Doreen/Tuckahoe Common School Dist	9,57,59,79,752	232
Buckley, Michael/Diocese of Albany Ed Office	67	12
Buckley, Russell/Lockport City School Dist	88	147
Buczek, Chris/Pine Valley Central Sch Dist	6	38
Buczkowski, Leslie/Niagara-Wheatfield Ctl SD	5	148
Buddendeck, Pamela/East Syracuse Minoa Ctl SD	7,34	154
Budelmann, Scott/Madison-Oneida BOCES	3,4,5,15,16,68	154
Budgar, Tricia/Geneva City School Dist	6	161
Budhai, Eudes/Westbury Union Free Sch Dist	1	132
Bueller, Paul/Boquet Valley Central Sch Dist	6	67
Bufano, Joseph/Onondaga-Cortland-Madison BOCES	68	160
Bufkins, Marlene/Southold Union Free Sch Dist	69	231
Bughan, Caitlyn/Campbell-Savona Ctl Sch Dist	6	213
Buhrmaster, James/Taconic Hills Central Sch Dist	88	47
Buhse, Sheila/South Huntington Union Free SD	4	231
Buisch, Kelly/Avoca Central School Dist	12,58,77	213
Bull, Jennifer/Waterford Halfmoon School Dist	11,58	203
Bull, Sarah/Keshequa Central School Dist	36	103
Bullard, Rhonda/Oswego City School Dist	6,35	171
Bullock, Kerri/Broome-Tioga BOCES	74	31
Bult, Timothy/Minisink Valley Central SD	6,35	165
Bump, Gregory/Mt Morris Central School Dist	1	103
Bunce, Liz/Dcmo BOCES Chenango	68	43
Bunn, Thomas/Auburn Enlarged City Sch Dist	73,95,295	34
Buono, Michael/East Greenbush Central SD	67	190
Buono, Michael/Questar III BOCES	68	192
Burak, Melissa, Dr/Lynbrook Union Free Sch Dist	1	124
Burch, Kerri/Questar III BOCES	16	192
Burch, Robin/Voorheesville Central Sch Dist	2	12
Burd, Kevin/Holland Central School Dist	91	61
Burdick, Bryan/Alfred Almond Ctl School Dist	5	13
Burdick, Lynn/Averill Park Central Sch Dist	73,295,297	189
Burg, Harry/Blind Brook-Rye Union Free SD	58,79	252
Burger, Jinelle/North Collins Ctl Sch Dist	79	63
Burger, Laurie/Erie 2 Chautauqua-Catta BOCES	68	67
Burger, Louise/Connetquot Central School Dist	45	219
Burgess, Sandy/Diocese of Syracuse Ed Office	2	160
Burgess, Sarah/Campbell-Savona Ctl Sch Dist	5	213
Burgio, Patricia/Lancaster Central Sch Dist	71	62
Burhans, Ashley/Millbrook Ctl School Dist	2	52
Burka, Karen/Pawling Ctl School Dist	67	52
Burke, Christine/Berkshire Union Free Sch Dist	2,3,15	45
Burke, David/Fallsburg Central School Dist	3	236
Burke, Doreen/Brookhaven Comsewogue Unif SD	4	218
Burke, Eric/Madrid-Waddington Central SD	1,11	211
Burke, Jack/South Country Central Sch Dist	285	231
Burke, James/Prattsburgh Central Sch Dist	6	215
Burke, Jason/Cooperstown Ctl School Dist	295	173
Burke, Jeri/Westhill Central School Dist	5	159
Burke, Joelle/Cheektowaga Maryvale UFSD	58,79	59
Burke, Kari/Ithaca City School Dist	7	240
Burke, Michelle/Madrid-Waddington Central SD	73,295	211
Burke, Ronald/Canton Central School Dist	1	209
Burke, Tanya/Portville Central School Dist	11,58,296	32
Burm, Victoria/Seneca Falls Central Sch Dist	7	208
Burmingham, Julie/South Lewis Central Sch Dist	38	101
Burnell, Thomas/Rhinebeck Central School Dist	15,79	53
Burnett, Bonnie/Fredonia Central School Dist	57	37
Burnett, Kathy/Bemus Point Ctl School Dist	6	36
Burnett, Renee/Baldwinsville Central School Dist	10,280,285	154
Burnham, Debra/Seneca Falls Central Sch Dist	5	208
Burns, Amanda/Yorktown Central School Dist	297	264
Burns, Bernadette/West Islip School Dist	1	233
Burns, Michael/West Genesee Ctl School Dist	6,35	159
Burns, Richard/East Hampton Union Free SD	1	220
Burns, Sean/Island Trees Union Free SD	6,35	122
Burns, Thomas/St Lawrence-Lewis BOCES	1	212
Burns, Timothy/Manchester-Shortsville Ctl SD	2	162
Burr, Rick/Indian River Ctl School Dist	5	80
Burrow, Brian/Putnam Valley Ctl School Dist	6,35	176
Burrows, Denise/Andover Central School Dist	54	14
Burton, Bonnie/Copiague Union Free Sch Dist	69	220
Burton, Bryan/Norwich City School Dist	2,15,67	42
Burton, Dana/Penn Yan Ctl School Dist	4	268
Burton, Daniel/Syracuse City School Dist	294	158
Burton, Terry/Schoharie Central SD	67	206
Buscemi, Jennifer/Merrick Union Free School Dist	2,5,15	125
Buscemi, Jennifer/Sag Harbor Union Free Sch Dist	11	229
Busch, Kathy/Alexander Ctl School Dist	79	73
Bush, Carol/Elba Central School Dist	8,11,69,83,88,273,296,298	73
Bush, Eric/Schoharie Central SD	4	206
Bush, Gretchen/West Irondequoit Ctl SD	36	113
Bush, Hathy/Alexander Ctl School Dist	58	73
Bush, Jill/Shenendehowa Central Sch Dist	15	202
Bush, Maren/Ellicottville Central Sch Dist	8,11,58,69,296,298	31
Bush, Nancy/Averill Park Central Sch Dist	30	189
Bush, Nellie, Dr/Greater Amsterdam School Dist	67	115
Bush, Patricia/Gouverneur Ctl School Dist	31,36,69	210
Bush, Ray/Newcomb Central School Dist	3,91	68
Bush, Sue/Lowville Acad-Central Sch Dist	83,85	101
Bush, Tina/Lisbon Central School Dist	9,58	210
Bush, Wendy/Ticonderoga Central School Dist	7	68
Bushart, Warren/Marion Central School Dist	4	250
Bushart, Warren/Newark Central School Dist	4	250
Bushart, Warren/Palmyra-Macedon Central SD	4	250
Bushman, Norma/Wainscott Common School Dist	15	232
Bushman, Willam, Dr/Valley Stream Ctl High SD	60,77,83,90	130
Bussick, Ernie/Cheektowaga Maryvale UFSD	73,98,295,297	59
Bustamante, Karen/Babylon Union Free Sch Dist	5	216
Butchko, Erica/Cato Meridian Central Sch Dist	68	34
Butera, Vincent, Dr/Manhasset Union Free Sch Dist	1	124
Butler, Aaron/Tri-Valley Central School Dist	73,286	237
Butler, Barbara/North Babylon Union Free SD	15,68	226
Butler, Barbra/Valley Central School Dist	58	167
Butler, Cheryl/Charlotte Valley Ctl Sch Dist	6	49
Butler, Cliff/Johnson City Central Sch Dist	73,295	28
Butler, Daniel/Hauppauge Union Free Sch Dist	6,29,35	223
Butler, Donald/Panama Central School Dist	67	38
Butler, James/Southwestern Central Sch Dist	67	39
Butler, Joe/Fillmore Central School Dist	2	14
Butler, Kristin/Cooperstown Ctl School Dist	8,11,285,288,298	173
Butler, Wendy, Dr/Belfast Central School Dist	1	14
Butler, Wendy, Dr/Belfast Central School Dist	8	14
Button, Tina/Keshequa Central School Dist	11,73,76,286,295	103
Butz, Stephen/Cambridge Central School Dist	73	247
Buyck, Allen/Broome-Tioga BOCES	1,11	31
Buza, Mark/Johnson City Central School Dist	42	28
Buzzetti, Katie/Horseheads Ctl School Dist	2	40
Bykowicz, Stephen/Hamburg Central School Dist	3	61
Byrne, Andrea/Greenburgh-Graham UFSD	8	255
Byrne, Ann/Nanuet Union Free School Dist	67	196
Byrne, Christine/Sewanhaka Ctl High Sch Dist	2	129
Byrne, Christopher/Phoenix Central School Dist	1	171
Byrne, Eric, Dr/Rye City School Dist	1	261
Byrne, Jenn/Pine Bush Central School Dist	2	166
Byrne, Paul/Cato Meridian Central Sch Dist	67	34
Byrnes, Jane/Buffalo Public Schools	51	57
Byrnes, Michael/Cazenovia Ctl School Dist	6	104
Byrnes, Michael/Eastport-South Manor Ctrl SD	67	221

---

1 Superintendent
2 Bus/Finance/Purchasing
3 Buildings And Grounds
4 Food Service
5 Transportation
6 Athletic
7 Health Services
8 Curric/Instruct K-12
9 Curric/Instruct Elem
10 Curric/Instruct Sec
11 Federal Program
12 Title I
13 Title V
15 Asst Superintendent
16 Instructional Media Svcs
17 Chief Operations Officer
18 Chief Academic Officer
19 Chief Financial Officer
20 Art K-12
21 Art Elem
22 Art Sec
23 Music K-12
24 Music Elem
25 Music Sec
26 Business Education
27 Career & Tech Ed
28 Technology Education
29 Family/Consumer Science
30 Adult Education
31 Career/Sch-to-Work K-12
32 Career/Sch-to-Work Elem
33 Career/Sch-to-Work Sec
34 Early Childhood Ed
35 Health/Phys Education
36 Guidance Services K-12
37 Guidance Services Elem
38 Guidance Services Sec
39 Social Studies K-12
40 Social Studies Elem
41 Social Studies Sec
42 Science K-12
43 Science Elem
44 Science Sec
45 Math K-12
46 Math Elem
47 Math Sec
48 English/Lang Arts K-12
49 English/Lang Arts Elem
50 English/Lang Arts Sec
51 Reading K-12
52 Reading Elem
53 Reading Sec
54 Remedial Reading K-12
55 Remedial Reading Elem
56 Remedial Reading Sec
57 Bilingual/ELL
58 Special Education K-12
59 Special Education Elem
60 Special Education Sec
61 Foreign/World Lang K-12
62 Foreign/World Lang Elem
63 Foreign/World Lang Sec
64 Religious Education K-12
65 Religious Education Elem
66 Religious Education Sec
67 School Board President
68 Teacher Personnel
69 Academic Assessment
70 Research/Development
71 Public Information
72 Summer School
73 Instructional Tech
74 Inservice Training
75 Marketing/Distributive
76 Info Systems
77 Psychological Assess
78 Affirmative Action
79 Student Personnel
80 Driver Ed/Safety
81 Gifted/Talented
82 Video Services
83 Substance Abuse Prev
84 Erate
85 AIDS Education
88 Alternative/At Risk
89 Multi-Cultural Curriculum
90 Social Work
91 Safety/Security
92 Magnet School
93 Parental Involvement
95 Tech Prep Program
97 Chief Infomation Officer
98 Chief Technology Officer
270 Character Education
271 Migrant Education
273 Teacher Mentor
274 Before/After Sch
275 Response To Intervention
277 Remedial Math K-12
280 Literacy Coach
285 STEM
286 Digital Learning
288 Common Core Standards
294 Accountability
295 Network Services
296 Title II Programs
297 Webmaster
298 Grant Writer/Ptnrships
750 Chief Innovation Officer
751 Chief of Staff
752 Social Emotional Learning

NY-T8

New York School Directory

DISTRICT PERSONNEL INDEX

NAME/District	JOB FUNCTIONS	PAGE
Bystrak, Matthew/West Seneca Central Sch Dist	1	64

C

NAME/District	JOB FUNCTIONS	PAGE
Caballero, Eric/Bellmore-Merrick Ctl High SD	35,80	117
Cabbell, Audrey/Nyack Union Free School Dist	57	197
Cacioppo, John/Le Roy Central School Dist	295	73
Cadle, Herbert/Buffalo Public Schools	68	57
Cady, Tammy/Cato Meridian Central Sch Dist	5	34
Caezza, Tracey/Afton Central School Dist	11,58,275,288	41
Caffrey, Patrick/Hauppauge Union Free Sch Dist	91	223
Cahill, Jody/Port Jefferson Union Free SD 6	58,78	228
Cahill, Patrick/Monroe Woodbury Central SD	2,15	165
Cain, Kelly/Odessa Montour Ctl Sch Dist	3	207
Cala, Elena/Buffalo Public Schools	71	57
Calabese-Gray, Teri/Champlain Valley Ed Services	8,15	45
Calabrese, Steve/Lakeland Central School Dist	3	257
Calahan, Sarah/East Rochester Union Free SD	2,8,11,57	107
Calarco, Matt/Hicksville Union Free Sch Dist	6,35,80,83	122
Calderon, Matt/Pembroke Ctl School Dist	1	74
Caldwell, Amanda/Liverpool Ctl School Dist	8,288	156
Caldwell, Roger/Byron-Bergen Ctl School Dist	3,91	73
Caldwell, William/Ripley Central School Dist	1	39
Caldwell, William/Ripley Central School Dist	11,288	39
Caleb, Terry/Alfred Almond Ctl School Dist	295	13
Caleo, Nadia/Utica City School Dist	74	152
Calice, Tim/Greene Ctl School Dist	285	42
Calice, Timothy/Greene Ctl School Dist	1	42
Caliendo, Anne Marie/Half Hollow Hills Central SD	2,3,15	222
Calkins, Richard/Pocantico Hills Ctl Sch Dist	1	260
Calladine, Michelle/Andover Central School Dist	67	14
Callaghan, Kathleen/Glens Falls City School Dist	7	245
Callahan, Christine/Newfane Central School Dist	51	147
Callahan, Daniel/Peekskill City School Dist	10,15	260
Callahan, Gary/Wallkill Central School Dist	12	243
Callahan, Mary/Port Washington Union Free SD	2,4,15	128
Callahan, Thomas, Dr/Pelham Union Free School Dist	42,45,277	260
Calleja, Joseph/Worcester Ctl School Dist	4	174
Calleja, Vinny/Schenevus Ctl School Dist	4	174
Callo, Frederick/Marlboro Central School Dist	4	242
Callon, Kathy/East Irondequoit Ctl Sch Dist	5	107
Calmes, Maureen/Byron-Bergen Ctl School Dist	83,88	73
Calosso, Patricia/Wantagh Union Free Sch Dist 23	26,61	131
Calvin, Mathis, Dr/Oswego City School Dist	1	171
Cameron, Bill/Corning-Painted Post Area SD	71	214
Cameron, Mathew/White Plains City School Dist	6	263
Cameron, Scott/Salem Central School Dist	5	248
Camhi, Shari, Dr/Baldwin Union Free School Dist	1	116
Cammarata, Anthony/Cambridge Central School Dist	2	247
Cammarata, Anthony/Hoosic Valley Central Sch Dist	2	190
Cammarata, Craig/East Meadow Union Free SD	3,91	118
Cammarata, Sandra/Lancaster Central Sch Dist	58	62
Cammer, Rick/Jefferson Central Sch Dist	6,35	206
Camp, Elizabeth/Greece Central School Dist	68	108
Campanella, Terry/South Orangetown Central SD	30	197
Campasano, Lucy/West Babylon Union Free SD	67	233
Campbell, Amy/Peru Central School Dist	8	44
Campbell, David/Watertown City School Dist	16,73,76,295	81
Campbell, Denise/Cold Spring Harbor Central SD	15,58,90,288	219
Campbell, J Manning, Dr/White Plains City School Dist	68	263
Campbell, Jennifer/Rush Henrietta Central SD	58	112
Campbell, Laurie/Hudson City School Dist	280	46
Campbell, Leah/Walton Central School Dist	2	50
Campbell, Lori/Half Hollow Hills Central SD	57,61	222
Campbell, Nick/Elmsford Union Free SD	24	255
Campbell, Sara/New Suffolk Common School Dist	9,69,286,752	226
Campbell, Todd/Letchworth Central School Dist	1,11	267
Campese, Jordan/Pine Valley Central Sch Dist	8,30,73,295	38
Campisi, Robert/Mahopac Ctl School Dist	4	176
Campolieta, Christopher/Baldwinsville Central Sch Dist	6,35,85	154
Campos, Christopher/Southold Union Free Sch Dist	4,5	231
Canallatos, Katrina/Ft Plain Central School Dist	58	115
Canario, Jose/Geneva City School Dist	67	161
Cancemi, Vincent/Niagara Falls City Sch Dist	67	147
Candia, Christian/Highland Ctl School Dist	37	242
Canfield, James/Troy City School Dsitrict	36,88	191
Cangemi, Joseph/West Hempstead School Dist	285	131
Cangero, Nick/Middle Country Ctl Sch Dist	31	225
Cangero, Robert/South Huntington Union Free SD	273	231
Cannan, Patricia/Frontier Ctl School Dist	36	60
Cannetti, Lori/Patchogue-Medford Unified SD	8,11,15,288	227
Cannioto, Jeanette/Rush Henrietta Central SD	48,54,57,280	112
Cannon, Marissa/East Greenbush Central SD	68,74,91	190
Cannone, Edward, Dr/Garden City School Dist	8,11,34,74,270,285,288,296	120
Cansenary, Diane/East Williston Union Free SD	2,15	118
Canzone-Ball, Kerri, Dr/Albany City School Dist	79	9
Capel-Eden, Kristin/Sachem Central School Dist	15,68,74	229
Capezzuto, Joseph/Rochester City School Dist	79	110
Caplan, Lori, Dr/Watervliet City School Dist	1	12
Capone, Andrew/Hartford Central School Dist	6	248
Capone, Marcia/Niagara Falls City Sch Dist	69,71,97,288	147
Capone, Michele/Carthage Central School Dist	58,79	80
Capozzi, John/Sewanhaka Ctl High Sch Dist	15,68	129
Capozzi, Karen/Berlin Central School Dist	2,5,71,97	189
Cappelletti, Chris/Cuba-Rushford Central Sch Dist	6,35,85	14
Cappelletti, Jennifer/Scio Central School Dist	1,11	15
Cappiello, Flo/Wayland-Cohocton Central SD	16,73,82	215
Capron, Bruce, Dr/Honeoye Falls Lima Sch Dist	2,3,12,15	109
Capsis, Doric/Westbury Union Free Sch Dist	6,35	132
Capuana, Michael/Erie 1 BOCES	27	67
Caputo, Christopher/Malverne Union Free Sch Dist	2,15	124
Caputo, Lisa/Massapequa Union Free SD 23	42	125
Caputo, Paul/Ichabod Crane Central Schools	73	46
Caputo, Paul/Webutuck Ctl School Dist	73	54
Caraballo, Maureen/Hastings on Hudson Union FR SD	2,73	256
Carambia, Salvatore/Freeport Public School Dist	15	119
Carambia, Salvatore/North Babylon Union Free SD	2	226
Caravana, Vincent/Lindenhurst Union Free SD	8,11,15,69,70,72,81	224
Carberry, Ryan/Barker Central School Dist	6,35	146
Carbon, Sharifa/Hudson City School Dist	2	46
Carbone, Jackie/Yorktown Central School Dist	67	264
Carbone, Sal/Diocese of Albany Ed Office	91	12
Carbone, Terry Ann/Brockport Ctl School Dist	67	106
Carbone, Ursula/Nanuet Union Free School Dist	16,71,73,76,97	196
Carcova, Rebecca/Lakeland Central School Dist	297	257
Card, Colleen/Miller Place Union Free SD	2	226
Card, Deb/Binghamton City School Dist	57,79	27
Card, Kenneth, Dr/East Meadow Union Free SD	1	118
Card, Kristin/Averill Park Central Sch Dist	69,294	189
Cardamone, Denise/Tully Central School Dist	67	159
Cardamone, Tony/Baldwinsville Central Sch Dist	9	154
Carder, Samuel/North Merrick Union Free SD	3	126
Cardettino, Paul/Coxsackie-Athens Central SD	73,295	75
Cardone, Cheryl/Grand Island Central Sch Dist	7,13,57,58,79,90	61
Cardone, Peter/Glen Cove City School Dist	6,35,83,85	120
Cardwell, Michelle, Dr/Wappingers Central Sch Dist	8,15,274	54
Carella-Dean, Catherine/Patchogue-Medford Unified SD	79	227
Carella, Richard/Niagara Falls City Sch Dist	8,74	147
Carella, Robert/Suffern Central School Dist	295	198
Carelli, Ed/Kingston City School Dist	4	242
Carey, Brian/Schodack Central School Dist	2	191
Carey, Claire/Hendrick Hudson Ctl Sch Dist	4	256
Carey, Debra/Kenmore-Tonawanda UF Sch Dist	7	62
Carey, Denise/Oxford Academy Central SD	5	42
Carey, Jodi/Oxford Academy Central SD	38	42
Carfora, Anthony/Nassau BOCES	8,73,76	134
Carinci, Anneliese/Rome City School Dist	73,76	151
Carlett, H James/Palmyra-Macedon Central SD	3	250
Carlie, Kelly/Elba Central School Dist	37	73
Carlin, Daniel/Bronxville Union Free SD	11	253
Carlin, David/Iroquois Central School Dist	3	61
Carlin, L Daniel/Bronxville Union Free SD	2,15	253
Carlin, Linda/Elmsford Union Free SD	2,3,15	255
Carlin, Theresa/Schenevus Ctl School Dist	1	174
Carling, Holly/Candor Central School Dist	5	238
Carll, Robbin/Livonia Ctl School Dist	3,16,73,76	103
Carlozzo, Paul/Central Islip Union Free SD	4	218
Carlson, David/Clarkstown Central School Dist	15,58,79	195
Carlson, Dennis/Hammondsport Ctl School Dist	67	214
Carlson, Jeffrey/Three Village Central Sch Dist	2,11,15	232
Carlson, Jennifer/Bolton Central School Dist	73	244
Carlson, Lisa/Sherman Central School Dist	16,82	39
Carlson, Micheal/Hampton Bays Union Free SD	8,15,69,270,288	222

School Year 2020-2021   800-333-8802   NY-T9

DISTRICT PERSONNEL INDEX

Market Data Retrieval

NAME/District	JOB FUNCTIONS	PAGE
Carlton, Jennifer/Springville Griffith Inst CSD	2	63
Carman, Rebecca/Shenendehowa Central Sch Dist	70	202
Carmello, John/Troy City School Dsitrict	1	191
Carney, Jessica/East Islip Union Free SD	67	220
Carney, Kathy/Central Valley School Dist	8,288	77
Carney, Kathy/Stockbridge Valley Central SD	4	106
Carney, Michael/Broadalbin-Perth Ctl Sch Dist	3,5,91	71
Carney, Paul/Yonkers Public School Dist	3	263
Carnright, Andrew/Orange-Ulster BOCES	30	168
Caroleo, Daniel/North Babylon Union Free SD	67	226
Carpenter, Elizabeth/Pittsford Central Sch Dist	68	110
Carpenter, Julie/Baldwinsville Central Sch Dist	7	154
Carpenter, Kevin/Roslyn School Dist	3,91	129
Carpenter, Larry/Sackets Harbor Ctl School Dist	5	81
Carpenter, Ryan/Johnsburg Central School Dist	6	245
Carpenter, Scot/Galway Central School Dist	73	201
Carpenter, Scot/Hadley-Luzerne Ctl Sch Dist	98	245
Carpenter, Scott/South Lewis Central Sch Dist	73,76,286	101
Carr, Annie/Niagara Falls City Sch Dist	5	147
Carr, Eric/Cooperstown Ctl School Dist	31,36,69,88	173
Carr, Jennifer/Milford Central School Dist	31	173
Carr, Jerry/Spencer Van Etten Central SD	4	238
Carr, John/Yonkers Public School Dist	3	263
Carr, Joyce/Elmira City School Dist	58,77	40
Carr, Marian/Fabius Pompey Central SD	4	155
Carr, Matthew/Somers Central School Dist	71	262
Carr, Shelly/Harrisville Central Sch Dist	36	101
Carr, Susan/Newark Central School Dist	68	250
Carragher, Lynn/Brockport Ctl School Dist	8,36	106
Carranza, Richard/New York City Dept of Ed	1	134
Carrasquillo, Erica/Elmsford Union Free SD	57	255
Carrasquillo, Russell/Clarkstown Central School Dist	3	195
Carrese, Jacquelin/Niskayuna Central School Dist	285	204
Carrier, Sarah/Croton-Harmon Union Free SD	67	254
Carrington, David/Charlotte Valley Ctl Sch Dist	2,3,5	49
Carrion, Jose/Wappingers Central Sch Dist	1	54
Carroll, Colleen, Dr/Port Chester Rye Union Free SD	8,69	261
Carroll, Daniel/Fulton City School Dist	79	170
Carroll, Maureen/Cazenovia Ctl School Dist	35	104
Carroll, Robert/Arlington Central School Dist	76	51
Carroll, Teresa/Clarkstown Central School Dist	84	195
Carson, Kerry/South Country Central Sch Dist	58,79,81	231
Carstensen, Mary Lou/North Warren Central Sch Dist	2	246
Carte, Rob/Voorheesville Central Sch Dist	73	12
Carter, Jason/Goshen Central School Dist	8,11,15,68,73,288	164
Carter, Linda/Vernon-Verona-Sherrill CSD	23	152
Carter, Lisa/Northern Adirondack Ctl SD	4	44
Carter, Lisa-Marie/Oswego City School Dist	58	171
Carter, Michael/Barker Central School Dist	79,83,285	146
Carter, Timothy/Wilson Central School Dist	1,11	149
Cartisano, Marianne, Dr/Miller Place Union Free SD	1	226
Cartisano, Ralph, Dr/Kings Park Ctl School Dist	8,13,15,69,88	224
Carusone, Anthony/Wayne Central School Dist	6,35	251
Carusone, Beth/Schenectady City School Dist	2	204
Carvalho, Chris/Yonkers Public School Dist	73,84,295	263
Carvelli, Suzanne/Madison-Oneida BOCES	67	154
Cary, Mark/Scotia Glenville Ctl Sch Dist	3,91	205
Casab, Clifford/Holland Patent Ctl School Dist	4	150
Casabona, Alexandra/Mamaroneck Union Free Sch Dist	58	257
Casale, Eric/Springs Union Free School Dist	9,93,288,294	232
Casali, Susan/Brookhaven Comsewogue Unif SD	2,91,274	218
Casamento, David/East Meadow Union Free SD	8,15,34,74,89,271,273	118
Casamento, Jane/Willsboro Central Sch Dist	4	68
Casamento, Jessica/Vernon-Verona-Sherrill CSD	77	152
Casarella, Joe/North Rockland Central SD	6	197
Casavant, Kevin/Syracuse City School Dist	58	158
Case, Barbara/General Brown Ctl School Dist	1	80
Case, Jennifer/Dryden Central School Dist	2,17,19	239
Case, Ryan/Greenport Union Free Sch Dist	73,286	222
Case, Ryan/Southold Union Free Sch Dist	73,76,285,295	231
Casey, Chris, Dr/Hawthorne Cedar Knolls UFSD	8,11,15,298	256
Casey, Erin/Parishville Hopkinton Sch Dist	55	212
Casey, Kristin/Fort Ann Central School Dist	77	247
Casey, Marybeth/New York State Dept Education	8	1
Casey, Tammy/Lake Placid Ctl School Dist	10,88	67
Cash, Kriner, Dr/Buffalo Public Schools	1	56
Cashel, Robin/Sandy Creek Central Sch Dist	5	172
Cashman, Janice/Gilboa-Conesville Central SD	58	206
Casilio, Mary Jo/Niagara-Wheatfield Ctl SD	8,73,74	148
Casper, Annette/Westhill Central School Dist	297	160
Casper, Susan/Berne-Knox-Westerlo Central SD	58	10
Cass, Andrea/Hamilton Central Sch Dist	4	105
Cassale, Anthony/Schalmont Central School Dist	73	204
Cassamassa, Maria/Riverhead Central School Dist	48,280	228
Cassata, Tom/Red Hook Central School Dist	6,7,35	53
Cassel, Cathleen/Archdiocese of New York Ed Off	15	142
Cassella, Kathy/Three Village Central Sch Dist	5	232
Casseri, Paul/Lewiston Porter Ctl Sch Dist	1	146
Cassidy, Donald/Farmingdale Union Free SD	58	119
Casson, Peter/Tuckahoe Union Free SD	67	262
Castagna, Robert/Byram Hills Central Sch Dist	6,83	253
Castanga, Rob/Byram Hills Central Sch Dist	35	253
Castellani, Raymond/Webutuck Ctl School Dist	1	54
Castellucci, Louis/Johnson City Central Sch Dist	5	28
Castelluzzo, Matt/Sewanhaka Ctl High Sch Dist	3	129
Castillo, Catalina, Dr/Freeport Public School Dist	11,76,92,298	119
Castillo, Diane/Margaretville Central Sch Dist	90	50
Castine, Dana/Florida Union Free Sch Dist	73,76,285,295	164
Castle, Katie/Coxsackie-Athens Central SD	27,34,58,77	75
Castle, Kevin/Wallkill Central School Dist	1	243
Castricone, Amy/Albion Central School Dist	79	169
Castrio, Christopher/Corinth Central School Dist	37	200
Castro, Maria/Longwood Central School Dist	8,15	225
Castro, Rich/Great Neck Public Schools	91	120
Catalan, Enrique/Hendrick Hudson Ctl Sch Dist	2,15	256
Catalano, Kim/Wappingers Central Sch Dist	5,91	54
Catalano, Ronald/Erie 2 Chautauqua-Catta BOCES	67	67
Cataldo, John/North Collins Ctl Sch Dist	9,12,97	63
Catalino, Roman/Somers Central School Dist	6,35	262
Catania, Joseph/Washingtonville Central SD	76,295	167
Catania, Roger, Dr/Lake Placid Ctl School Dist	1	67
Cates-Williams, Sharon/New York State Dept Education	15,69,70	1
Catlin, Rob/Mt Sinai Union Free SD	274	226
Cauley, Patrick/Hamburg Central School Dist	6,35	61
Caulfield, Michelle/Corning-Painted Post Area SD	1	214
Cavallero, Alfredo/Great Neck Public Schools	3	120
Cavalucci, Christine/Archdiocese of New York Ed Off	83	142
Cavaluzzi, Paul/Lakeland Central School Dist	5	257
Cavanagh, Lora/Dryden Central School Dist	5	239
Cavanaugh, Amanda/Watervliet City School Dist	67	12
Cavassa, Peter/Bethpage Union Free Sch Dist	3	117
Cavazza, Larry/Marlboro Central School Dist	3	242
Cavellier, Scott/Homer Central School Dist	3	48
Cavlieri, Aileen/Lindenhurst Union Free SD	8,73	224
Cedeira, Denise/Highland Falls-Ft Montgmry SD	15	164
Cedrone, Anthony/Wantagh Union Free Sch Dist 23	2,4,15,90,91	131
Ceglia, Joe/Rye Neck Union Free Sch Dist	6	261
Celano, Fino, Dr/Herricks Union Free Sch Dist	1	121
Celej, Kate/Clarence Central School Dist	8	59
Celentano, Alison/Commack Union Free School Dist	42	219
Celotti, Tara/Crown Point Central Sch Dist	83	67
Cemaro, Carmella/East Ramapo Central Sch Dist	4	196
Cenci, Brandy/Rensselaer City School Dist	36	191
Ceng, Tarkan/Jefferson Central Sch Dist	1,11	206

#	Function	#	Function	#	Function	#	Function	#	Function	#	Function
1	Superintendent	16	Instructional Media Svcs	30	Adult Education	44	Science Sec	58	Special Education K-12	72	Summer School
2	Bus/Finance/Purchasing	17	Chief Operations Officer	31	Career/Sch-to-Work K-12	45	Math K-12	59	Special Education Elem	73	Instructional Tech
3	Buildings And Grounds	18	Chief Academic Officer	32	Career/Sch-to-Work Elem	46	Math Elem	60	Special Education Sec	74	Inservice Training
4	Food Service	19	Chief Financial Officer	33	Career/Sch-to-Work Sec	47	Math Sec	61	Foreign/World Lang K-12	75	Marketing/Distributive
5	Transportation	20	Art K-12	34	Early Childhood Ed	48	English/Lang Arts K-12	62	Foreign/World Lang Elem	76	Info Systems
6	Athletic	21	Art Elem	35	Health/Phys Education	49	English/Lang Arts Elem	63	Foreign/World Lang Sec	77	Psychological Assess
7	Health Services	22	Art Sec	36	Guidance Services K-12	50	English/Lang Arts Sec	64	Religious Education K-12	78	Affirmative Action
8	Curric/Instruct K-12	23	Music K-12	37	Guidance Services Elem	51	Reading K-12	65	Religious Education Elem	79	Student Personnel
9	Curric/Instruct Elem	24	Music Elem	38	Guidance Services Sec	52	Reading Elem	66	Religious Education Sec	80	Driver Ed/Safety
10	Curric/Instruct Sec	25	Music Sec	39	Social Studies K-12	53	Reading Sec	67	School Board President	81	Gifted/Talented
11	Federal Program	26	Business Education	40	Social Studies Elem	54	Remedial Reading K-12	68	Teacher Personnel	82	Video Services
12	Title I	27	Career & Tech Ed	41	Social Studies Sec	55	Remedial Reading Elem	69	Academic Assessment	83	Substance Abuse Prev
13	Title V	28	Technology Education	42	Science K-12	56	Remedial Reading Sec	70	Research/Development	84	Erate
15	Asst Superintendent	29	Family/Consumer Science	43	Science Elem	57	Bilingual/ELL	71	Public Information	85	AIDS Education

#	Function	#	Function	#	Function
88	Alternative/At Risk	277	Remedial Math K-12		
89	Multi-Cultural Curriculum	280	Literacy Coach		
90	Social Work	285	STEM		
91	Safety/Security	286	Digital Learning		
92	Magnet School	288	Common Core Standards		
93	Parental Involvement	294	Accountability		
96	Tech Prep Program	295	Network System		
97	Chief Information Officer	296	Title II Programs		
98	Chief Technology Officer	297	Webmaster		
270	Character Education	298	Grant Writer/Ptnrships		
271	Migrant Education	750	Chief Innovation Officer		
273	Teacher Mentor	751	Chief of Staff		
274	Before/After Sch	752	Social Emotional Learning		
275	Response To Intervention				

New York School Directory

DISTRICT PERSONNEL INDEX

NAME/District	JOB FUNCTIONS	PAGE
Centamore, Joseph, Dr/South Huntington Union Free SD	11,15,69,73,76,286,298	231
Centore, Jenny/Fabius Pompey Central SD	51,54	155
Centrella, Jane/Franklin Square Union Free SD	68	119
Cepero, Shirley/Port Washington Union Free SD	57	128
Cerasaro, Paul/Johnson City Central Sch Dist	4	28
Cercone, Gretchen/Starpoint Central School Dist	68	149
Cerreta, Katharina/Putnam-Northern Wstchstr BOCES	3,5,91	266
Cerrone, Dawn/Garden City School Dist	6,35	120
Ceruti, Christine/Carle Place Union Free SD	6	117
Ceruti, Theresa/Deer Park Union Free Sch Dist	77	220
Cervoli, Jonthan/West Seneca Central Sch Dist	78,93	64
Cervone, Joseph/Sachem Central School Dist	5	229
Cervoni, Jonathan/West Seneca Central Sch Dist	15	64
Cesta, Michelle/Morrisville Eaton Central SD	38	105
Cetinkaya, Deniz/Frontier Ctl School Dist	76	60
Chadzutko, Thomas, Dr/Diocese of Brooklyn Ed Office	1	94
Chafee, Chuck/Waterville Central Sch Dist	1	153
Chaffee, Michael/Andover Central School Dist	16,28,73,286,297	14
Chakar, Robert, Dr/Andes Central School Dist	1,288	48
Chakar, Robert, Dr/Margaretville Central Sch Dist	1	49
Chamberlain, Annette/South Colonie Central Sch Dist	4	12
Chamberlain, Christina/Indian River Ctl School Dist	8	80
Chamberlain, Christina/Oswego City School Dist	7	171
Chamberlain, Steve/Pleasantville Union Free SD	3	260
Chamberlin, Samuel/Beaver River Central Sch Dist	67	101
Chambers, Joann/Potsdam Central School Dist	1,11	212
Champ, Cheryl, Dr/Pelham Union Free School Dist	1,11	260
Champine, Foster/Morristown Ctl School Dist	73	211
Champlain, Lora/Dryden Central School Dist	69	239
Champney, Stephanie/Whitney Point Central Sch Dist	67	30
Chan, Carry/Community School District 1	1	135
Chan, Grace, Dr/Lindenhurst Union Free SD	2,15	224
Chan, Michael, Dr/Rochester City School Dist	8,42	110
Chandler, Jayson/Scio Central School Dist	5	15
Chandler, Melanie/Watkins Glen Central Sch Dist	73,295	207
Chang, June/Rockville Ctr Union Free SD	1	128
Chanowski, Tom/Millbrook Ctl School Dist	33	52
Chapin, Darlene/West Genesee Ctl School Dist	58	159
Chaplin, Theresa/West Babylon Union Free SD	45,277	233
Chapman, Carolyn/Canandaigua City School Dist	71	161
Chapman, Joseph/Whitesville Central Sch Dist	5	15
Chapman, Lynette/Thousand Islands Central SD	4	81
Chapman, Richard/Liverpool Ctl School Dist	9,57,285	156
Chapman, Rob/Queensbury Union Free Sch Dist	3	246
Chapple, Ashley/Albany City School Dist	35,83,85	9
Charleston, Sabrina/Ogdensburg City School Dist	5	211
Chartrand, Rick/Harrisville Central Sch Dist	3	101
Chase, Cortney/Pembroke Ctl School Dist	23	74
Chase, Jeff/Pine Valley Central Sch Dist	67	38
Chase, Jolene/Milford Central School Dist	7,85	173
Chase, Lester/Gilboa-Conesville Central SD	3,91	206
Chase, Lynn/Onc BOCES	2,3,4	51
Chase, Tahira, Dr/Greenburgh Central School Dist	1,83	255
Chatterton, Steven/Greece Central School Dist	91	108
Chauncey, Sarah/Rockland BOCES	73	199
Chauvin, James/Beekmantown Ctl School Dist	5	43
Chaves, Suzanne/Freeport Public School Dist	57	119
Chavez, Monica/Glen Cove City School Dist	57	120
Cheasty, Susan/Royalton Hartland Central SD	5	148
Chef, David/Depew Union Free School Dist	67	59
Chefalo, Marla/Gates Chili Central Sch Dist	30	108
Chehovich, Jesse/Auburn Enlarged City Sch Dist	295	34
Cheladyn, Amber/Allegany-Limestone Ctl SD	16	31
Chen, Linda/New York City Dept of Ed	18	134
Chen, Lionel, Dr/Jericho Union Free School Dist	27,61	122
Cheney-Bovee, Jill/Corinth Central School Dist	11,15,58,275	200
Cheng, Candice/Brentwood Union Free Sch Dist	76	217
Cheng, Jerry/Brentwood Union Free Sch Dist	97	217
Chesser, Pamela/Yorktown Central School Dist	48	264
Chester, Kenneth/Glens Falls City School Dist	3,5	245
Chevrier, Jason/Schodack Central School Dist	1	191
Chiapperino, Amy/Nanuet Union Free School Dist	61	196
Chichester, Terri/South Kortright Ctl SD	67	50
Chieffo, J/Sewanhaka Ctl High Sch Dist	27,95	129
Chiera, Jacquelyn/Diocese of Albany Ed Office	83	12
Chiesa, Laurel/Fayetteville-Manlius Ctl SD	73	155

NAME/District	JOB FUNCTIONS	PAGE
Childress, Jennifer/New York State Dept Education	20,23	1
Childs, Donald/Pavilion Ctl School Dist	2,11,296,298	74
Chimera, Matthew/Kenmore-Tonawanda UF Sch Dist	67	62
China, Richard/Holland Patent Ctl School Dist	23	150
Chitester, Chad/Frewsburg Central School Dist	67	38
Chittenden, Susan/Wells Central School Dist	48,273	77
Chlebicki, Robert/North Shore Central SD	8,273	126
Chow, John/Chappaqua Central School Dist	2,15	253
Chowske, Rebecca/Manhasset Union Free Sch Dist	48	124
Christ, Scott/Holland Central School Dist	3	61
Christensen, Julie/Kendall Central School Dist	1,11	169
Christensen, Lucas/Chatham Central School Dist	298	46
Christensen, Marissa/Milford Central School Dist	2	173
Christensen, William, Dr/Sidney Central School Dist	1	50
Christensian, Paul/Katonah-Lewisboro Sch Dist	3,91	257
Christiansen, Eric/Albion Central School Dist	77	169
Christine, Natoli/Rhinebeck Central School Dist	2	53
Christman, Elisha/Lake Pleasant Central Sch Dist	2,84	76
Christman, Mariann/Schuylerville Central Sch Dist	2	201
Christman, Mark/East Irondequoit Ctl Sch Dist	76,294	107
Christopher, Kathryn/Williamsville Ctl School Dist	4	64
Christopherson, Karen/Jamestown City School Dist	2	38
Chudy, Michael/Chatham Central School Dist	2	46
Chumney, Donalda/Community School District 2	1	135
Chung, Alissa/Jefferson Central Sch Dist	36	206
Chung, Julia/Pelham Union Free School Dist	11,15,58,79,275,752	260
Church, Erin/Clyde-Savannah Central SD	285	249
Church, James/Questar III BOCES	27,31,70	192
Churchill, Tracey/Greenville Central School Dist	4	75
Churnetski, Julie/Spencerport Central Sch Dist	5	112
Ciaccio, Thomas/Fonda Fultonville Central SD	1	115
Ciaci, Maureen/Lindenhurst Union Free SD	5	224
Ciappetta, Nicholas/South Huntington Union Free SD	67	231
Ciccarelli, Debra/Patchogue-Medford Unified SD	60	227
Ciereck, Chris/Onondaga Central School Dist	38	157
Cieri, Matt/Westmoreland Central Sch Dist	73,76,295	153
Ciesla, Sue/Franklinville Ctl School Dist	67	31
Cietek, Kathy/Menands Union Free Sch Dist	2	11
Cifonelli, Melanie/Syracuse City School Dist	45	158
Cihocki, Sharon/Adirondack Central Sch Dist	2,296	150
Cima, John/Pembroke Ctl School Dist	67	74
Cimato, Sabatino/Buffalo Public Schools	15	57
Cimato, Sabatino/Kenmore-Tonawanda UF Sch Dist	1	62
Cimbricz, Sandra/Gowanda Central School Dist	8	32
Ciminiello, Nicole/Patchogue-Medford Unified SD	2	227
Cimmerer, Allison/Honeoye Falls Lima Sch Dist	9	109
Cimmerer, Jeff/Pittsford Central Sch Dist	71,97	110
Cimmino, Robert/Mount Vernon City School Dist	6	258
Cincotta, Robert/Hempstead Union Free SD	6,58	121
Cinelli, Mary/Pearl River School Dist	5	197
Cioffi, Sarah/Shenendehowa Central Sch Dist	57,61	202
Cipolla, Michael/Westfield Central School Dist	1,11,288	39
Cipollina, Joanne/Hastings on Hudson Union FR SD	7	256
Cipriani, Michael/Oyster Bay East Norwich Ctl SD	2,15	127
Circello, Marguerita, Dr/Mount Vernon City School Dist	57	258
Cirillo, David/West Genesee Ctl School Dist	68	159
Cirone, Adrienne/Remsenburg-Speonk UFSD	11,296,752	228
Ciuffo, Ben/Jericho Union Free School Dist	15,68	122
Ciulis, James/Kenmore-Tonawanda UF Sch Dist	5	62
Ciulla, Ross/Fairport Ctl School Dist	3	108
Ciurczak, David/Starpoint Central School Dist	3,91	149
Clairmont, William/Bethlehem Central School Dist	45	10
Clamser, Ron/Dobbs Ferry Union Free SD	2,3,4,15,295	254
Clancy, Christopher/Canastota Central School Dist	15,59,73	104
Clancy, Richard/Fabius Pompey Central SD	3	155
Clapper, Christopher/Alexandria Central School Dist	1	79
Clapper, Thomas/Kingston City School Dist	3	242
Clar, Lisa/Rush Henrietta Central SD	45,277	112
Clare, Robert/Wilson Central School Dist	3	149
Clareen, Spence/Stamford Central School Dist	5	50
Clark, Ann Marie/Granville Central School Dist	13,58	247
Clark, Barrie/Alfred Almond Ctl School Dist	55	13
Clark, Brenda, Dr/Smithtown Central Sch Dist	59	230
Clark, Cindy/Canastota Central School Dist	5	104
Clark, Cora/Lake Placid Ctl School Dist	7	67
Clark, Craig/Hamilton-Fulton-Montgmry BOCES	71	72

School Year 2020-2021   800-333-8802   NY-T11

DISTRICT PERSONNEL INDEX

Market Data Retrieval

NAME/District	JOB FUNCTIONS	PAGE
Clark, Denise/Bolton Central School Dist	36	244
Clark, James/Hempstead Union Free SD	10,15,288	121
Clark, Jamie/Le Roy Central School Dist	6	73
Clark, Jason/Chittenango Central SD	8,11,15,74	104
Clark, Karen/Sidney Central School Dist	16	50
Clark, Kathleen/Hudson City School Dist	274	46
Clark, Kathleen/New Paltz Ctl School Dist	59	242
Clark, Laverne/Valhalla Union Free Sch Dist	67	262
Clark, Martha/Elmira Heights Ctl Sch Dist	2	40
Clark, Mary/Addison Central School Dist	83	213
Clark, Michelle/Odessa Montour Ctl Sch Dist	5	207
Clark, Michelle/Watkins Glen Central Sch Dist	5	207
Clark, Neil/O E S J Central School Dist	67	72
Clark, Patrick/Vestal Ctl School Dist	57	29
Clark, Paul/Attica Central School Dist	35,36,69	267
Clark, Scott/Carmel Central School Dist	73	175
Clark, Susan/Webster Central School Dist	26,45	112
Clark, Tina/Lake Placid Ctl School Dist	83	67
Clark, Tony/Long Lake Central School Dist	3	76
Clark, William/Galway Central School Dist	5	201
Clarke, Alce/Edgemont Union Free Sch Dist	67	254
Clarke, Dale/Copenhagen Central SD	3	101
Clarke, Jill/Evans-Brant Central Sch Dist	280	60
Clarke, Sadika/Peekskill City School Dist	79	260
Clarke, Stacy/South Seneca Ctl Sch Dist	11,58	208
Clasen, Craig/William Floyd School Dist	39	233
Clay, Trent/Glens Falls City School Dist	8,11,57,69,273,288,296,298	245
Clayson, Nancy/Hinsdale Central School Dist	16,73,82	32
Cleary, Seth/Canandaigua City School Dist	5	161
Clemens, Candace/Cattaraugus-Allegany BOCES	67	34
Clemensen, Lars/Hampton Bays Union Free SD	1	222
Clements, Richard/East Aurora Union Free SD	73,295	60
Clester, Kristopher/North Tonawanda City Sch Dist	71,97	148
Cleveland, Adam/Whitesboro Ctl School Dist	73,76,295	153
Cleveland, Michelle/Delaware Academy Ctrl SD Delhi	38	49
Cleveland, Stephanie/Dundee Ctl School Dist	5	268
Climenhaga, Therijo/Cherry Valley-Springfield SD	1	173
Climtzak, Timothy/Cheektowaga Maryvale UFSD	6,35,85	59
Cline, Melanie/Brasher Falls School Dist	4	209
Clingerman, Jeremy/Seneca Falls Central Sch Dist	1,11,83	208
Clisson, Darrell/Liverpool Ctl School Dist	3	156
Cloidt, Christina/Newburgh Enlarged City SD	81	166
Clonan, Mike/East Syracuse Minoa Ctl SD	6	154
Closs, Jason/Tri-Valley Central School Dist	6	237
Clothier, Richard/Lake George Central Sch Dist	3	245
Clouden, Mary/Frontier Ctl School Dist	2	60
CO, Allissa/Gilboa-Conesville Central SD	7	206
Coakley, Kathryn/Highland Falls-Ft Montgmry SD	4	164
Coates, Ameigh/York Central School Dist	79	103
Coates, David/Middletown Enlarged City SD	6,35	165
Coats, Christa/Bradford Central Sch Dist	270,274	207
Cobb, Joan/Whitesville Central Sch Dist	7	15
Coburn, Jesse/Heuvelton Central School Dist	1	210
Cocca, Sandra/Sweet Home Central Sch Dist	4	63
Coddett, Andrea, Dr/Yonkers Public Sch Dist	15	263
Coder, Deborah/Lockport City School Dist	2,15,91	147
Cody, John/Carmel Central School Dist	67	175
Coffey, Dave/Norwood-Norfolk Ctl SD	73	211
Coffey, David/New York State Dept Education	48	1
Coffey, Kevin/Carle Place Union Free SD	2,11,15,296	117
Coffey, Kevin/Mattituck-Cutchogue UFSD	2,68	225
Coffin, Laura/Lake Placid Ctl School Dist	11,69	67
Coffin, Sean/Brentwood Union Free Sch Dist	7,77,90	217
Coffin, Steven/Parishville Hopkinton Sch Dist	6,10,31,74,83,275	212
Coghlin, Mike/Horseheads Ctl School Dist	3	40
Cogliano, Michael, Dr/Washingtonville Central SD	15,57,58,79	167
Cohen, Amy/Lynbrook Union Free Sch Dist	30	124

NAME/District	JOB FUNCTIONS	PAGE
Cohen, Brian/Skaneateles Central Sch Dist	8,27,44,47,285,288	157
Cohen, Harmon/Oysterponds Union Free SD	59	227
Cohen, Howard/Florida Union Free Sch Dist	2,5,91	164
Cohen, Jaime/Buffalo Public Schools	11	56
Cohen, Joey, Dr/Patchogue-Medford Unified SD	15,68	227
Cohen, Stefan/Rochester City School Dist	74	110
Coker, Megan/Lake George Central Sch Dist	73	245
Cokley, Jerel/East Hampton Union Free SD	2,3,11	220
Colabufo, Thomas/Central Square Central SD	1	170
Colavito, Joseph/Springs Union Free School Dist	7	232
Colbert, Keturah/New York State Dept Education	69,88	1
Colby-Rooney, Danielle, Dr/Kings Park Ctl School Dist	12,34,79,298	224
Cole, Carrie/East Aurora Union Free SD	37,270	60
Cole, John/Sweet Home Central Sch Dist	58,79	63
Cole, Matthew/Livonia Ctl School Dist	1,11	103
Cole, Rachel/Yonkers Public School Dist	69,70,79,294	263
Cole, Rob/Dundee Ctl School Dist	4	268
Cole, Rob/Odessa Montour Ctl Sch Dist	4	207
Cole, Rob/Watkins Glen Central Sch Dist	4	207
Cole, Thomas/Yorktown Central School Dist	2,3,5,15,91	264
Coleman, Joan/Whitesville Central Sch Dist	4	15
Coleman, Mark/Orange-Ulster BOCES	3	168
Coleman, Tammy/Valley Central School Dist	34	167
Colerick, Jenna/Buffalo Public Schools	57	57
Coles, Harold, Dr/Southern Westchester BOCES	1	267
Coletti, Rosemarie/Hicksville Union Free Sch Dist	15,68	122
Colfer, Sean/Lansingburgh Central Sch Dist	6,7,35	190
Colicchio, Katryn/Greece Central School Dist	10,15,79,294	108
Collesano, Ann/Buffalo Public Schools	36	57
Collette, Brenda/Brushton Moira Ctl Sch Dist	83	69
Colletti, Thomas/Elwood Union Free School Dist	68	221
Collica, Lauren/Pawling Ctl School Dist	4	52
Collich, Thomas/Yonkers Public School Dist	2	263
Collier, Lucinda/North Rose Wolcott Central SD	67	250
Collier, Stephen/East Williston Union Free SD	50	118
Colligan, Elizabeth/Portville Central School Dist	6,35	32
Colling, Maryellen/Clarence Central School Dist	57,58,271	59
Collins-Judon, Rosanne/Yonkers Public School Dist	8,15	263
Collins, Bridget/Montauk Union Free School Dist	12,69,270,286,288,298	226
Collins, Brigid/Montauk Union Free School Dist	298	226
Collins, David/Burnt Hills Ballston Lake SD	8,11,15,69,285	200
Collins, Evelyn/Mount Vernon City School Dist	22,25,81	258
Collins, Jane/Belleville Henderson Sch Dist	1	79
Collins, Kay/Odessa Montour Ctl Sch Dist	68	207
Collins, Kevin/Greenwich Central School Dist	6,7,83,85	247
Collins, Kristin/West Seneca Central Sch Dist	58	64
Collins, Lisa/Trumansburg Central SD	274	241
Collins, Maggie/Broome-Tioga BOCES	58	31
Collins, Randy/Clifton-Fine Central Sch Dist	4	209
Collins, Ryan/Gloversville Enlarged Sch Dist	58,77,79,93	71
Collins, Theresa/Babylon Union Free Sch Dist	48	216
Collins, William/Montauk Union Free School Dist	6,35,83,85	226
Collins, William, Dr/Parishville Hopkinton Sch Dist	1	212
Collopy, Lisa/Rockland BOCES	74	199
Colomaio, Anthony/Bath Central School Dist	3,91	213
Colon-Collins, Lisette/New York State Dept Education	57,61	1
Colon, Kevin/Smithtown Central Sch Dist	36	230
Colon, Rosemarie/Buffalo Public Schools	57	57
Colonna, Marlene/Harrison Central School Dist	39	256
Colucci, Kathleen/East Syracuse Minoa Ctl SD	58	154
Colucci, Peter/Weedsport Ctl School Dist	2,15	35
Columbia, Stephanie/Longwood Central School Dist	7	225
Colvin, Julie/East Rochester Union Free SD	7	107
Colvin, Whitney/Brunswick Central School Dist	3,5	190
Combo, Lauren/Perry Central School Dist	8	267
Combs, Mitchell, Dr/Port Chester Rye Union Free SD	11,15,68,296,298	261
Comis, Scott, Dr/Valley Stream Union Free SD 24	12,83,85	131

1	Superintendent	16	Instructional Media Svcs	30	Adult Education	44	Science Sec	58	Special Education K-12
2	Bus/Finance/Purchasing	17	Chief Operations Officer	31	Career/Sch-to-Work K-12	45	Math K-12	59	Special Education Elem
3	Buildings And Grounds	18	Chief Academic Officer	32	Career/Sch-to-Work Elem	46	Math Elem	60	Special Education Sec
4	Food Service	19	Chief Financial Officer	33	Career/Sch-to-Work Sec	47	Math Sec	61	Foreign/World Lang K-12
5	Transportation	20	Art K-12	34	Early Childhood Ed	48	English/Lang Arts K-12	62	Foreign/World Lang Elem
6	Athletic	21	Art Elem	35	Health/Phys Education	49	English/Lang Arts Elem	63	Foreign/World Lang Sec
7	Health Services	22	Art Sec	36	Guidance Services K-12	50	English/Lang Arts Sec	64	Religious Education K-12
8	Curric/Instruct K-12	23	Music K-12	37	Guidance Services Elem	51	Reading K-12	65	Religious Education Elem
9	Curric/Instruct Elem	24	Music Elem	38	Guidance Services Sec	52	Reading Elem	66	Religious Education Sec
10	Curric/Instruct Sec	25	Music Sec	39	Social Studies K-12	53	Reading Sec	67	School Board President
11	Federal Program	26	Business Education	40	Social Studies Elem	54	Remedial Reading K-12	68	Teacher Personnel
12	Title I	27	Career & Tech Ed	41	Social Studies Sec	55	Remedial Reading Elem	69	Academic Assessment
13	Title V	28	Technology Education	42	Science K-12	56	Remedial Reading Sec	70	Research/Development
15	Asst Superintendent	29	Family/Consumer Science	43	Science Elem	57	Bilingual/ELL	71	Public Information

72	Summer School	88	Alternative/At Risk	277	Remedial Math K-12
73	Instructional Tech	89	Multi-Cultural Curriculum	280	Literacy Coach
74	Inservice Training	90	Social Work	285	STEM
75	Marketing/Distributive	91	Safety/Security	286	Digital Learning
76	Info Systems	92	Magnet School	288	Common Core Standards
77	Psychological Assess	93	Parental Involvement	294	Accountability
78	Affirmative Action	95	Tech Prep Program	295	Network System
79	Student Personnel	97	Chief Infomation Officer	296	Title II Programs
80	Driver Ed/Safety	98	Chief Technology Officer	297	Webmaster
81	Gifted/Talented	270	Character Education	298	Grant Writer/Ptnrships
82	Video Services	271	Migrant Education	750	Chief Innovation Officer
83	Substance Abuse Prev	273	Teacher Mentor	751	Chief of Staff
84	Erate	274	Before/After Sch	752	Social Emotional Learning
85	AIDS Education	275	Response To Intervention		

NY-T12

New York School Directory

DISTRICT PERSONNEL INDEX

NAME/District	JOB FUNCTIONS	PAGE
Commardo, Anthony/Briarcliff Manor Union Free SD	2,5,15,17	253
Compani, Erin/Broadalbin-Perth Ctl Sch Dist	77	71
Compo, Jason/Watertown City School Dist	3,91	81
Compo, Mary/Lowville Acad-Central Sch Dist	58	101
Composto, Philip, Dr/Community School District 30	1	184
Conbeer, Wayne/Canajoharie Ctl School Dist	5	115
Condello, Dawn/Beacon City School Dist	11,58,79,81,85,88,90	51
Condie, Tracy/Alfred Almond Ctl School Dist	2	13
Condon, John/Pelham Union Free School Dist	3	260
Condon, Sandra/Clarkstown Central School Dist	34	195
Conforti, Judith/Garden City School Dist	16	120
Congden, Stanley/Canastota Central School Dist	6	104
Conger, Kim/Jericho Union Free School Dist	58,79,298	122
Coniglio, Debbi/Sweet Home Central Sch Dist	23	63
Conklin, Amanda/Edmeston Ctl School Dist	31	173
Conklin, Bert/Horseheads Ctl School Dist	6,35	40
Conklin, Brad/Valley Central School Dist	2	167
Conklin, Kady/West Canada Valley Ctl SD	31,36,270	79
Conley, Daniel/Hammondsport Ctl School Dist	6	214
Conley, Melanie/Orleans-Niagara BOCES	2	170
Conley, Paul/Webster Central School Dist	82	112
Connell, Scott/Copenhagen Central SD	1,11	101
Connell, Todd/Levittown Union Free Sch Dist	16,73	123
Conner, Ruth/Buffalo Public Schools	4	56
Conners, Elizabeth/Fulton City School Dist	8,11,54,57,69,88,285,288	170
Connolly, Dan/Orleans-Niagara BOCES	3	170
Connor, Daniel/Goshen Central School Dist	1	164
Connor, Kristen/Bethlehem Central School Dist	36	10
Connors, Chris/Herricks Union Free Sch Dist	73	121
Connors, Danielle/Sharon Springs Ctl SD	57	207
Conover, Andrea/Duanesburg Central Sch Dist	9,34,58,69,275,288	203
Conrad, Maria/Buffalo Public Schools	88	57
Conrow, Todd/Waterloo Central School Dist	76	208
Conroy, Karen/Voorheesville Central Sch Dist	8,11,69,288,296	12
Conroy, Karen/Voorheesville Central Sch Dist	11,83,286	12
Conroy, Lori/Buffalo Public Schools	91	57
Consolo, Lisa/Babylon Union Free Sch Dist	58	216
Conte, Angeline/Cherry Valley-Springfield SD	38	173
Conte, Lisa, Dr/Valley Stream Union Free SD 24	9,15,57,280,288	131
Contento, Joseph/Niagara Falls City Sch Dist	6	147
Conti, John/West Irondequoit Ctl SD	3,91	113
Conti, Matthew/North Syracuse Ctl Sch Dist	5	157
Convers, Scott/Clyde-Savannah Central SD	5	249
Converse, Mary/George Junior Republic UFSD	77	240
Converse, Rob/Unadilla Valley Ctl Sch Dist	11	43
Conway, Jennifer/Kenmore-Tonawanda UF Sch Dist	57	62
Conyers, Donald/New York City Dept of Ed	15	134
Cook, Amanda/Batavia City School Dist	9	73
Cook, Andrew/Hartford Central School Dist	1,11	248
Cook, Christopher/Galway Central School Dist	3	201
Cook, Danielle/Panama Central School Dist	83,85,90	38
Cook, David/Maine Endwell Ctl School Dist	6	29
Cook, Denise/Deposit Central School Dist	1	28
Cook, Diana/Middle Country Ctl Sch Dist	20,23,270	225
Cook, Laurie/North Syracuse Ctl Sch Dist	71,97	157
Cook, Matthew/Newark Central School Dist	1	250
Cook, Matthew/North Tonawanda City Sch Dist	6	148
Cook, Ronel, Dr/Catskill Central School Dist	1	75
Cook, Ruthie/Greater Johnstown Sch Dist	15	71
Coolican, Colleen/Odessa Montour Ctl Sch Dist	36	207
Coon, Jen/Rochester City School Dist	286	110
Coon, Katie/Gates Chili Central Sch Dist	8,23	108
Coon, Kelly/Charlotte Valley Ctl Sch Dist	58	49
Coons, Jeff/Lyons Central School Dist	3,91	249
Cooper, Ron/La Fayette Central School Dist	3,5	156
Cooper, Scott/Westfield Central School Dist	27,31,36,69,83	39
Cooper, William/Gloversville Enlarged Sch Dist	73,76,295,297	71
Copani, Louis/Syracuse City School Dist	4	158
Copleston, Leslie/Coxsackie-Athens Central SD	2,15	75
Coppola, Jamie/Altmar-Parish-Williamstown SD	6	170
Coppotelli, Michael/Archdiocese of New York Ed Off	15,79	142
Coram, Michael/Akron Central School Dist	3	56
Corasanti, Lisa/Waterville Central Sch Dist	83	153
Corbin, Bradley/Tully Central School Dist	2	159
Corbin, Chantal/Fabius Pompey Central SD	9,34,58,73,270	155
Corcoran, Dana/Syracuse City School Dist	28,42	158
Corcoran, Kim/Greene Ctl School Dist	4	42
Corcoran, Kim/Sherburne Earlville Central SD	4	42
Corcoran, Kim/Sidney Central School Dist	4	50
Corcoran, Kim/Unatego Unadilla Central SD	4	174
Corcoran, Kim/Walton Central School Dist	4	50
Corder, Lynn/Portville Central School Dist	12	32
Cordero, Andrea/Frankfort-Schuyler Ctl SD	36	77
Cordts, Sarah/Broadalbin-Perth Ctl Sch Dist	16	71
Coreless, Rosemarie/North Bellmore Union Free SD	67	126
Corey, Brian/Red Creek Central School Dist	1	251
Corey, Brian/Waterloo Central School Dist	4	208
Corey, Chris/Newark Central School Dist	6,35,83,88	250
Corey, Molly, Dr/Batavia City School Dist	8,11,57,280,285,288,296,298	73
Coriale, Eric/Oneida City School Dist	7	105
Corlen, Michael/Hoosic Valley Central Sch Dist	4	190
Corlew, Arthur/Glens Falls City School Dist	6,35,83	245
Cornell, Michael/Hamburg Central School Dist	1,11	61
Cornish, Danielle/Tri-Valley Central School Dist	58,79,752	237
Cornish, Robert/Jasper Troupsburg Central SD	5	215
Cornwell, Christian/Friendship Central Sch Dist	11,273	15
Corona, Karen/Schenectady City School Dist	71	204
Coronado, Eric/Pearl River School Dist	73	197
Corr, D Joseph/North Colonie Central SD	1	11
Corsaro, Dennis/Cleveland Hill Union Free SD	2	59
Corsey, Michelle/Berlin Central School Dist	7	189
Corso, Karen/Berne-Knox-Westerlo Central SD	36	10
Cory, Susan/Holley Central School Dist	10,12,69,79	169
Coryat, Eileen/Onc BOCES	16	51
Coryell, Julia/Hudson City School Dist	57	46
Cosgrove, Tammy, Dr/Lakeland Central School Dist	15,68,273	257
Cossey, Laurie/Ticonderoga Central Sch Dist	2,5,12	68
Cossu, Frank/Middleburgh Ctl School Dist	73,76	206
Costa, Russell/Seaford Union Free SD	3	129
Costello-Roth, Linda/Huntington Union Free Sch Dist	60	223
Costello, Jack/Red Hook Central School Dist	11,58,79,271	53
Costello, Jeff/Barker Central School Dist	82	146
Costello, Steve/Levittown Union Free Sch Dist	39	123
Costelloe, Linda/Rye Neck Union Free Sch Dist	16	261
Coster, Kevin/William Floyd School Dist	1	233
Cotter, William/Madison Central School Dist	4	105
Cotto, Carlos/Rochester City School Dist	6,35,85	110
Coughlin, Chrisopher/Bedford Central School Dist	6,7,35	252
Coughlin, Ellen Rose, Sr/Diocese of Ogdensburg Ed Off	1	212
Coughlin, Kathleen/New Paltz Ctl School Dist	60	242
Coughlin, Mary/Fayetteville-Manlius Ctl SD	8,15,27,54,69,277,288,294	155
Cousins, Albert/Rhinebeck Central School Dist	1	53
Court, Bob/Bethlehem Central School Dist	3,15	10
Courtney, Dan/Holley Central School Dist	6	169
Couse, Fred/Pine Plains Ctl School Dist	67	53
Covell, Cheryl/Dryden Central School Dist	8,12,57,288,298	239
Covell, Erin/Massena Central School Dist	83,88	211
Covell, Nicole/Phoenix Central School Dist	73,76,275,286,295	172
Covell, Scott/Monroe 1 BOCES	2,3,15	115
Covert, Marybeth/East Aurora Union Free SD	67	60
Covey, Flora/South Glens Falls Ctl Sch Dist	71,76,97	202
Covey, Reid/South Lewis Central Sch Dist	295	101
Cowen, Charles/Oneida-Herkimer-Mad BOCES	2,3,5,7,15,68,91	154
Cowherd, Karen/Cazenovia Ctl School Dist	5	104
Cox, Jordan/Commack Union Free School Dist	8,34,77	219
Cox, Martin/Clarkstown Central School Dist	1	195
Cox, Michael/Mt Morris Central School Dist	2,11	103
Cox, Ryan/Patchogue-Medford Unified SD	6,7,35	227
Cox, Tim/Cattaraugus-Allegany BOCES	8,15,16,74	34
Coykendall, Karen/Churchville Chili Ctl Sch Dist	58	107
Coyle, Brendon/Franklin Central School Dist	36,57,271,752	49
Coyne, Kim, Dr/North Babylon Union Free SD	20,23	226
Coyne, Kimberly/West Genesee Ctl School Dist	67	159
Coyne, Patricia/Newburgh Enlarged City SD	5	165
Cozzetto, Robert/Lindenhurst Union Free SD	3,91	224
Craddock, Robin/Buffalo Public Schools	5	56
Craddock, Susan/Miller Place Union Free SD	15	226
Craft, Brian/North Colonie Central SD	3,91	11
Craig, Jeffery/Cortland Enlarged City SD	8,12	47
Craig, John/Kings Park Ctl School Dist	3,68	224
Cramer, Michelle/West Irondequoit Ctl SD	15	113
Crandall, Brian/Herkimer Ctl School Dist	67	77

School Year 2020-2021   800-333-8802   NY-T13

DISTRICT PERSONNEL INDEX

Market Data Retrieval

NAME/District	JOB FUNCTIONS	PAGE
Crandall, Kristen/Wappingers Central Sch Dist	2,15	54
Crandall, Michelle/Schroon Lake Ctl School Dist	11,58,271,275,294,296,298	68
Crandall, Todd/Silver Creek Central Sch Dist	1	39
Crandell, Morgan/Newark Valley Central Sch Dist	752	238
Crankshaw, William, Dr/Cooperstown Ctl School Dist	1	173
Cranmer, James/Island Trees Union Free SD	85	122
Crast, Laurie/Sandy Creek Central Sch Dist	7,85	172
Crast, Theresa/Sandy Creek Central Sch Dist	16	172
Crawford, James/Wyandanch Union Free Sch Dist	67	234
Crawford, Jason/Jamesville-DeWitt Central SD	3,91	155
Creeden, Amy/Middletown Enlarged City SD	8,15	165
Creedon, Daniel/Greenport Union Free Sch Dist	67	222
Creedon, Dennis, Dr/Mahopac Ctl School Dist	288	176
Crenshaw, Karen/Floral Park Bellerose Sch Dist	4	119
Creter, Frank/Levittown Union Free Sch Dist	27,286	123
Crewell, Amy/Schoharie Central SD	5	206
Cring, Michael/Arlington Central School Dist	6,35	51
Crino, Mark/Hinsdale Central School Dist	6	32
Crisafulli, David/Oswego City School Dist	3	171
Crisci, Carmine/Peekskill City School Dist	3	260
Crisci, Jerry/Scarsdale Union Free Sch Dist	16,73,295	261
Criscione, Cristine, Dr/Sayville Union Free Sch Dist	8,15	229
Criscone, Nicholas/Mayfield Ctl School Dist	11	72
Criser-Eighmy, Jennifer/Hyde Park Central School Dist	50,280	52
Crist, William/Diocese of Syracuse Ed Office	1	160
Cristil, Kimberly/West Irondequoit Ctl SD	39	113
Cristman, Barbara/Central Valley School Dist	4	77
Crnkovich, Lisa/Elba Central School Dist	4	73
Crocetti, Robert/East Irondequoit Ctl Sch Dist	6	107
Croft, Sean, Dr/Starpoint Central School Dist	1,11	149
Cronin, Veronica/Elmsford Union Free SD	57	255
Crook, Tom/Canisteo-Greenwood Central SD	1	214
Cross-Baker, Tracey/Boquet Valley Central Sch Dist	31,69	67
Cross, Brian/Moriah Central School Dist	6	68
Cross, Darcey/Clinton Central School Dist	35	150
Cross, Joanna/Potsdam Central School Dist	298	212
Cross, Lisa/Kenmore-Tonawanda UF Sch Dist	10	62
Crossett, Kelley/West Canada Valley Ctl SD	2	79
Crotty, Ann/New York State Dept Education	42	1
Crouse, Kari/Elmira City School Dist	4	40
Croutch, Charlena/Roosevelt Union Free Sch Dist	67	128
Crowe, Debbie/Highland Falls-Ft Montgmry SD	6,85	164
Crowley, Kenneth/Somers Central School Dist	2,15	262
Cruikshank, James/Norwood-Norfolk Ctl SD	1	211
Cruikshank, Kathleen/Harrisville Central School Dist	58	101
Crumb, Matthew/Hamilton Central Sch Dist	2,11	105
Crump, Al/Fulton City School Dist	3,5,91	170
Cruz, Gladys, Dr/Questar III BOCES	1	192
Cruz, Miguel/Brentwood Union Free Sch Dist	3	217
Cucci, Audrey/Frankfort-Schuyler Ctl SD	45	77
Cuddy-Miller, Karen/Grand Island Central Sch Dist	8,12,15,296	61
Cuddy, Laurie/Hinsdale Central School Dist	8,69,88,270,273,274	32
Cuglietto, Elaine/Rye City School Dist	15,68	261
Culella-Sun, Mary/Seaford Union Free SD	11,58,88	129
Culhane, Terry/Riverhead Central School Dist	91	228
Cullen, Adele/Middle Country Ctl Sch Dist	60	225
Cullen, Emily/Skaneateles Central Sch Dist	4	157
Culnan, Chris/Shenendehowa Central Sch Dist	6,35	202
Culot, Brian, Dr/South Orangetown Central SD	8,11,57,69,83,280,288,298	197
Cummings, Brian/Jericho Union Free School Dist	42	122
Cummings, Emery/Hammondsport Ctl School Dist	5	214
Cummings, James/Deer Park Union Free School Dist	1	220
Cummings, Kelly/Sayville Union Free Sch Dist	81	229
Cummings, Kristen/Farmingdale Union Free SD	42	119
Cundy, Lance/Spencer Van Etten Central SD	3,91	238
Cunneely, Daniel/Floral Park Bellerose Sch Dist	73,76,295	119
Cunningham, Blaine/Webster Central School Dist	3	112
Cunningham, Gina/Byram Hills Central Sch Dist	5,91	253
Cunningham, John/Fayetteville-Manlius Ctl SD	5	155
Cunningham, Richard/Plainview-Old Bethpage Ctl SD	2,11,15	127
Cunningham, Thomas/Hyde Park Central School Dist	6,7,35	52
Cuomo, Denise/Croton-Harmon Union Free SD	11	254
Cupples, Cerri/Rochester City School Dist	2	110
Curcio, Gina/West Babylon Union Free SD	36	232
Curiale, Gina/Longwood Central School Dist	6,35	225
Curley, Francis/New Rochelle City School Dist	36	259
Curningnenser, Ed/East Williston Union Free SD	73	118
Curran, Melissa/East Hampton Union Free SD	4	220
Curran, Sarah/Caledonia-Mumford Ctl Sch Dist	38	102
Currey, Julianna/Troy City School Dsitrict	11,296,298	191
Currie-Hall, Marianne/Lockport City School Dist	8	147
Currie, Steven/Oneonta City School Dist	295	174
Currie, Todd/Putnam-Northern Wstchstr BOCES	2,15	266
Curry, Penny/Wantagh Union Free Sch Dist 23	16,27,28,73,76,286,295,297	131
Curry, Trent/Clifton-Fine Central Sch Dist	35	209
Curtain, Tom/Geneseo Central Sch Dist	3	103
Curtin, Michael/Edgemont Union Free Sch Dist	2,8,16	254
Curtin, Rachel/Chautauqua Lake Central SD	1	36
Curtis, Robert/Gloversville Enlarged Sch Dist	67	71
Curtis, Ryan/Remsenburg-Speonk UFSD	73,295	228
Curtis, Susan/Brockport Ctl School Dist	9	106
Cushman, Jeanine/Greece Central School Dist	2	108
Cusmano, Karen/Elba Central School Dist	6	73
Cusmano, Susan/Attica Central School Dist	31	267
Cutcliff, Laurie/Perry Central School Dist	4	267
Cutcliffe, Laurie/York Central School Dist	4	103
Cuthbertson, Greg/Poland Central School Dist	8,58,275,296	78
Cutting, Deborah/Fillmore Central School Dist	275	14
Cutting, Lisa/Saratoga Springs City Sch Dist	8,11,15	201
Cvik, Gene/Owego Apalachin Ctl School Dist	67	238
Czaja, Kevin/Lyndonville Central School Dist	3	169
Czarny, Jason/Onondaga Central School Dist	6	157
Czemerynski, Lynn/Orchard Park Central Sch Dist	7,79	63
Czerkies, Karen/Oneonta City School Dist	2	174
Czub, Joseph/Burnt Hills Ballston Lake SD	5	200

D

NAME/District	JOB FUNCTIONS	PAGE
D Ulise, Vincent/Levittown Union Free Sch Dist	23	123
D'Abate, Rosa, Dr/Williamsville Ctl School Dist	79	64
D'Agostino, Carol/Kendall Central School Dist	10	169
D'Agostino, Deborah/North Salem Central Sch Dist	67	259
D'Agostino, Roberta/Churchville Chili Ctl Sch Dist	4	107
D'Ambrese, Christopher/Rockland BOCES	30	199
D'Amico, Daniel/Babylon Union Free Sch Dist	8,11,15,294	216
D'Andrea, Veronica/Harrison Central School Dist	45	256
D'Angelo, John/Williamsville Ctl School Dist	58	64
D'Angelo, Joseph/Cheektowaga Maryvale UFSD	1	59
D'Aprile, Debra/Onteora Central School Dist	2	243
D'Elia, Vito, Dr/South Huntington Union Free SD	2,15,78,79	231
D'Maato, Joseph/Depew Union Free School Dist	36,73,79,83,88	59
Dabrusky, Gary, Dr/Three Village Central Sch Dist	15,68	232
Dacek, Joanne, Dr/Bellmore Union Free Sch Dist	11,19,83,98,286,288,296,298	117
Dack, Todd/South Jefferson Central SD	67	81
Dade, Terry/Cornwall Central School Dist	1,83	163
Dahlman, Gary/Roscoe Central School Dist	67	237
Daigle, Daniell/Granville Central School Dist	3	247
Daigler, Darcy/Amherst Central School Dist	5,30	56
Dailey, Christopher/Gates Chili Central Sch Dist	1	108
Dailey, Craig/Liverpool Ctl School Dist	67	156
Dailey, Douglas/Akron Central School Dist	73	56
Dailey, Jim/Niagara-Wheatfield Ctl SD	8,73	148
Daily, Darryl/New York State Dept Education	35	1
Dalbo, Jonathon/West Seneca Central Sch Dist	39,71,73,76,97	64

#		#		#		#		#		#	
1	Superintendent	16	Instructional Media Svcs	30	Adult Education	44	Science Sec	58	Special Education K-12	72	Summer School
2	Bus/Finance/Purchasing	17	Chief Operations Officer	31	Career/Sch-to-Work K-12	45	Math K-12	59	Special Education Elem	73	Instructional Tech
3	Buildings And Grounds	18	Chief Academic Officer	32	Career/Sch-to-Work Elem	46	Math Elem	60	Special Education Sec	74	Inservice Training
4	Food Service	19	Chief Financial Officer	33	Career/Sch-to-Work Sec	47	Math Sec	61	Foreign/World Lang K-12	75	Marketing/Distributive
5	Transportation	20	Art K-12	34	Early Childhood Ed	48	English/Lang Arts K-12	62	Foreign/World Lang Elem	76	Info Systems
6	Athletic	21	Art Elem	35	Health/Phys Education	49	English/Lang Arts Elem	63	Foreign/World Lang Sec	77	Psychological Assess
7	Health Services	22	Art Sec	36	Guidance Services K-12	50	English/Lang Arts Sec	64	Religious Education K-12	78	Affirmative Action
8	Curric/Instruct K-12	23	Music K-12	37	Guidance Services Elem	51	Reading K-12	65	Religious Education Elem	79	Student Personnel
9	Curric/Instruct Elem	24	Music Elem	38	Guidance Services Sec	52	Reading Elem	66	Religious Education Sec	80	Driver Ed/Safety
10	Curric/Instruct Sec	25	Music Sec	39	Social Studies K-12	53	Reading Sec	67	School Board President	81	Gifted/Talented
11	Federal Program	26	Business Education	40	Social Studies Elem	54	Remedial Reading K-12	68	Teacher Personnel	82	Video Services
12	Title I	27	Career & Tech Ed	41	Social Studies Sec	55	Remedial Reading Elem	69	Academic Assessment	83	Substance Abuse Prev
13	Title V	28	Technology Education	42	Science K-12	56	Remedial Reading Sec	70	Research/Development	84	Erate
15	Asst Superintendent	29	Family/Consumer Science	43	Science Elem	57	Bilingual/ELL	71	Public Information	85	AIDS Education

#		#	
88	Alternative/At Risk	277	Remedial Math K-12
89	Multi-Cultural Curriculum	280	Literacy Coach
90	Social Work	285	STEM
91	Safety/Security	286	Digital Learning
92	Magnet School	288	Common Core Standards
93	Parental Involvement	294	Accountability
95	Tech Prep Program	295	Network System
96	Title II Programs	296	Title II Programs
97	Chief Information Officer	297	Webmaster
98	Chief Technology Officer	298	Grant Writer/Ptnrships
270	Character Education	750	Chief Innovation Officer
271	Migrant Education	751	Chief of Staff
273	Teacher Mentor	752	Social Emotional Learning
274	Before/After Sch		
275	Response To Intervention		

NY-T14

New York School Directory

DISTRICT PERSONNEL INDEX

NAME/District	JOB FUNCTIONS	PAGE
Dalcero, Danielle/Livingston Manor Ctl Sch Dist	83,85	236
Dale, Kristine/Horseheads Ctl School Dist	67	40
Dale, Ned/Elba Central School Dist	1	73
Daley, Andrea/Lake George Central Sch Dist	280	245
Daley, Cindy/La Fayette Central School Dist	2	156
Daley, Madeline/Saratoga Springs City Sch Dist	85	201
Daley, Mary Jane/Archdiocese of New York Ed Off	15	142
Daley, Maryann/Huntington Union Free Sch Dist	81	223
Daley, Matthew/Madrid-Waddington Central SD	9,34,52,55,57	211
Dalrymple, Rebecca/South Jefferson Central SD	5	81
Dalton, Cheryl/Saratoga Springs City Sch Dist	5	201
Dalton, Mark/Malone Central School Dist	16,73	69
Daly, Elizabeth/Cairo-Durham Ctl School Dist	67	75
Daly, James/East Rockaway Union Free SD	3	118
Daly, Jen/Haldane Central School Dist	67	176
Daly, Michael/Lakeland Central School Dist	67	257
Daly, Peter/Babylon Union Free Sch Dist	2,15,91	216
Damato, Anthony/Beacon City School Dist	3	51
Damato, Trish/Middle Country Ctl Sch Dist	273	225
Dambro, Louis/Mount Markham Central Sch Dist	2,71,91	78
Damiani, Nicholas/Peru Central School Dist	73	44
Damico, David/Dunkirk City School Dist	67	37
Dana, Stephanie/Penfield Central School Dist	38	109
Daneshvar, Sean/Poughkeepsie City School Dist	16,73	53
Daniel, David/Susquehanna Valley Central SD	31,88	29
Daniel, Kim/Pavilion Ctl School Dist	83,85,90	74
Daniele, Bruce/New Rochelle City School Dist	91	259
Daniels, Gary/Syracuse City School Dist	295	158
Daniels, Kelli/Buffalo Public Schools	79	57
Dankwerth, Shannon/Brunswick Central School Dist	71	190
Dannhauser, Jess/Greenburgh-Graham UFSD	67	255
Danon, Alex/Wallkill Central School Dist	76	243
Danquah, Anthony/Greenburgh 11 Union Free SD	1	255
Dansen, Patricia/Le Roy Central School Dist	7	73
Dantuono, Mark/Northport-East Northport UFSD	6,35	227
Dantuono, Mark/Northport-East Northport UFSD	6,35	227
Danturno, Shannon/Northport-East Northport UFSD	36,79	227
Danzger, Elise/Lawrence Union Free Sch Dist	7,36,58,77,79	123
Dapenta, Lauren/North Rockland Central SD	30	197
Dapice, Joseph/Mount Markham Central Sch Dist	1	78
Darcangelis, Laura/Liverpool Ctl School Dist	5	156
Darden-Cintron, Antoinette/Greenburgh Central School Dist	67	255
Darigo, Kevin/Lansingburgh Central Sch Dist	4	190
Daring, Orande/Orange-Ulster BOCES	27,31	168
Dark, James/West Genesee Ctl School Dist	5	159
Darling, Deb/Hancock Central School Dist	8,288	49
Darling, Justin/Rensselaer City School Dist	295	191
Darling, Nick/Groton Central School Dist	3	240
Darling, Sophia/Groton Central School Dist	67	240
Darmento, Ralph, Br/Diocese of Brooklyn Ed Office	15	95
Darrisaw-Akil, Monique, Dr/Brentwood Union Free Sch Dist	10,15	217
Darrow, Molly/Chenango Valley Ctl Sch Dist	71	28
Darstein, Michele/Hamburg Central School Dist	71	61
DaSilva, Marcus/Southampton Union Free SD	3	231
Dauey, Tim/Jefferson Lewis BOCES	73	82
Daum, Ann/Union Springs Ctl School Dist	67	35
Dauria, Marissa/Sweet Home Central Sch Dist	6	63
Davenport, Carrie/Pine Valley Central Sch Dist	58	38
Davenport, Pat/Red Creek Central School Dist	3	251
Davern, William/West Genesee Ctl School Dist	20,25,27	159
Davey, Andrew/Chatham Central School Dist	3	46
Davey, Mark, Dr/Champlain Valley Ed Services	1	45
Davidson, Anthony/Locust Valley Ctl School Dist	8,15	123
Davidson, Dan/Bolivar-Richburg Ctrl Sch Dist	73	14
Davidson, Melissa/Cherry Valley-Springfield SD	4	173
Davie, Lori/Roxbury Central School Dist	4	50
Davies, Carole/Arlington Central School Dist	58	51
Davies, Michael/South Glens Falls Ctl Sch Dist	16,82	202
Davis Lutz, Julie, Dr/Eastern Suffolk BOCES	3,17	235
Davis, Alan/Roxbury Central School Dist	3	50
Davis, Allison/Niagara-Wheatfield Ctl SD	2	148
Davis, Anthony/Syracuse City School Dist	10,15,27	158
Davis, Barry/Lyme Central School Dist	6	81
Davis, Beth/Berne-Knox-Westerlo Central SD	16,82	10
Davis, Edward/Greenburgh-Graham UFSD	2,3,15,91	255
Davis, Jennifer/Oxford Academy Central SD	73,97,295	42
Davis, Kerry/Hornell City School Dist	67	214
Davis, Mike/Pulaski Central School Dist	73,295	172
Davis, Patrick/Archdiocese of New York Ed Off	73	142
Davis, Rebecca/Wynantskill Union Free SD	59	192
Davis, Ryan/Phelps-Clifton Springs Ctl SD	67	162
Davis, Shannon/Hornell City School Dist	3,91	214
Davis, Sharon/Warwick Valley Central SD	67	167
Davis, Shawna/Stamford Central School Dist	8,11,15,57,69,273,288	50
Davis, Steven/Utica City School Dist	73,76,295	152
Davis, Terry/New Hyde-Garden City Park UFSD	35,85	126
Davis, Timothy/Oxford Academy Central SD	6	42
Davison, Betsy/Homer Central School Dist	16,82	48
Davison, Emily/Rhinebeck Central School Dist	58	53
Davison, Meghan/Jefferson Lewis BOCES	16	82
Dawkins, Tim/South Glens Falls Ctl Sch Dist	8,15	202
Day, Anthony/Sweet Home Central Sch Dist	1	63
Dayton, Barbara/Springs Union Free School Dist	67	232
Daza, Yvonne/Malverne Union Free Sch Dist	26,57,61	124
De Angelo, Sal, Dr/Chatham Central School Dist	1	46
De Jong, Jason/Gates Chili Central Sch Dist	79,83	108
De La Cruz, Kristy, Dr/Community School District 4	1	139
De Maria, Alison/Lindenhurst Union Free SD	71	224
De Pena-Elder, Roxana/Diocese of Brooklyn Ed Office	15	95
Dean, Danielle/Mt Morris Central School Dist	59,288	103
Dean, Harold/Little Flower Union Free SD	1	224
Dean, Marcus, Dr/Fillmore Central School Dist	67	14
Dean, Matthew/Lyncourt Union Free Sch Dist	73	156
Dean, Matthew/Solvay Union Free Sch Dist	73	158
DeAngelo, James/Rome City School Dist	8,12,57,288	151
DeAngelo, Jeffrey/Waverly Ctl School Dist	57,58	239
Dearing, Brent/Hunter Tannersville Ctl SD	6	76
Dease, Andrew/Hyde Park Central School Dist	59	52
DeBarbieri, Joseph/Baldwinsville Central Sch Dist	8,11,36,74,273,288,296	154
Debari, Dena/Island Park Union Free SD	4	122
Debartolo, Fernando/Elmont Union Free School Dist	73,76,91	118
Debell, Bettina/Geneseo Central Sch Dist	81	103
DeBenedetto, John/William Floyd School Dist	72,88	233
DeBiase, Danielle/Altmar-Parish-Williamstown SD	2	170
Debold, Joseph/Cornwall Central School Dist	36,270	163
Decanio, Camille/Huntington Union Free Sch Dist	27	223
DeCaprio, Michael/Hudson Falls Central Sch Dist	8,11,15,288,294,296,298,752	248
DeCarlo, Lori/Randolph Acad Union Free SD	1,11,288	32
DeCato, Patricia/Pine Plains Ctl School Dist	78	53
DeChant, George/Indian Lake Ctl School Dist	16	76
Decker, Amy/Alfred Almond Ctl School Dist	69,83	13
Decker, Jessica/Whitesboro Ctl School Dist	23	153
Decker, Jill/Eldred Central School Dist	4	236
Decker, Lisa/Madison-Oneida BOCES	2	154
Decker, Timothy/Jamesville-DeWitt Central SD	2,5	155
Decker, Troy/Indian River Ctl School Dist	8,15	80
DeDomenico, Jessica/Pelham Union Free School Dist	67	260
DeDominicis, Nikki/Hudson City School Dist	5	46
Dedominick, Cynthia/Lansingburgh Central Sch Dist	11	190
Dedrick, Roger/Lansing Central School Dist	5	240
Dee, Patrick/Whitehall Central School Dist	1	248
Deegan, Michael/Archdiocese of New York Ed Off	1	142
Deen, Catharine/Penfield Central School Dist	67	109
Deering, Kevin/Erie 2 Chautauqua-Catta BOCES	3	67
Defayette, Aime/Ausable Valley Ctl Sch Dist	27,58,77	43
DeFazio, Ann/Weedsport Ctl School Dist	11,58,76,296,298	35
Defeciani, Kelly/Shenendehowa Central Sch Dist	71	202
Defendini, Paul/Farmingdale Union Free SD	1	119
DeFilippo, Kaitlyn/Horseheads Ctl School Dist	68	40
Defrancisco, Robert/South Glens Falls Ctl Sch Dist	4	202
DeFrank, Jennifer/Sullivan BOCES	68	238
Defreest, Kathleen/Spackenkill Union Free SD	31	54
Degrace, Adam/Remsen Central School Dist	3,5	151
DeGraff, Jason/Batavia City School Dist	3,91	73
Degroat, Kristyn/Laurens Central School Dist	2	173
Degroat, Rachel/Johnsburg Central School Dist	67	245
Deguire, Andy/Wynantskill Union Free SD	3	191
Dehn, Charlene/Manchester-Shortsville Ctl SD	1	162
Dejak, Kerrie/North Bellmore Union Free SD	77	126
DeJoseph, Michael/Babylon Union Free Sch Dist	6	216
Delahunt, Terry/Genesee Valley Ctl School Dist	298	15
Deland, Sharon/Patchogue-Medford Unified SD	16,40,49,51	227

School Year 2020-2021   800-333-8802   NY-T15

DISTRICT PERSONNEL INDEX

Market Data Retrieval

NAME/District	JOB FUNCTIONS	PAGE
DeLaney, Lindsey/Orleans-Niagara BOCES	16	170
DeLaney, Theresa/Liberty Central School Dist	68	236
Delano, Dan/Watkins Glen Central Sch Dist	3	207
Delargy, Charles/Rocky Point Union Free SD	6,7,35,83	228
Delcamp, Jason/Brocton Central School Dist	1	36
DelConte, Heather/Oswego City School Dist	67	171
Deleel, Samantha/Edwards-Knox Central Sch Dist	37,270	210
DeLeo, Frank/Hewlett Woodmere Union Free SD	91	121
Delessandro, Erica/Newark Valley Central Sch Dist	36,69	238
Delia, Jeff/Homer Central School Dist	5	48
Delisle, Cindy/Brasher Falls School Dist	271	209
Delisle, Richard/Baldwinsville Central Sch Dist	16,73,76,295	154
Dell'Oso, Vincent/Starpoint Central School Dist	6,35	149
Della Penna, Mary/Byron-Bergen Ctl School Dist	4	73
Della Penna, Matt/Genesee Valley BOCES	3,91	74
DellaPenna, Mary/Oakfield Alabama Ctl SD	4	74
Dellarocco, Denise/Taconic Hills Central Sch Dist	52,55	47
Dellenbaugh, Holly/Bethlehem Central School Dist	67	10
Delloso, Vinnie/West Seneca Central Sch Dist	6	64
Dellova, Jennifer/Washingtonville Central SD	67	167
Delmoro, Richard/Middletown Enlarged City SD	1	165
Deloff, Dola, Dr/Sullivan BOCES	74	238
Delorme, Jeff/Corning-Painted Post Area SD	15	214
Delornze, Jason/Penfield Central School Dist	73,295	109
Delrossa, Mike/Geneva City School Dist	5	161
Delsignore, Frank/Albany City School Dist	285	9
DeLuca, Deborah, Dr/Rocky Point Union Free SD	13,88,275,277,285,294,296	228
DeLuca, Diane/Sewanhaka Ctl High Sch Dist	57	129
DeLuca, Jeffrey/Poland Central School Dist	5	78
DeLucia, Jodi, Dr/Onteora Central School Dist	8,11,15,54,69,277,288,298	243
Delutri, Joseph/Hicksville Union Free Sch Dist	5	122
Delyser, Lori/Marion Central School Dist	6	250
Demagistris, Michael/Gloversville Enlarged Sch Dist	6,35,80	71
Deman, Anthony/Tarrytown Union Free Sch Dist	3	262
DeMarco, Christopher/Grand Island Central Sch Dist	35	61
DeMarco, Jennifer/Troy City School Dsitrict	275	191
DeMarco, Jennifer/Troy City School Dsitrict	275	191
Demarmels, Albert/Liberty Central School Dist	3	236
DeMartino, Joe/Springville Griffith Inst CSD	6,35	63
DeMasi, Ralph/Pelham Union Free School Dist	91	260
Demass, Christine/Skaneateles Central Sch Dist	2,15	157
Demento, Kirsten/Watervliet City School Dist	8,69,76,273,286,288,298	12
Demers, Sherry/Ballston Spa Ctl School Dist	5	200
Demonte, Elizabeth/South Huntington Union Free SD	71	231
Demster, Timothy/Andover Central School Dist	42	14
Denaker, Steven/Avoca Central School Dist	10,27	213
Denardo, Betty/Greater Southern Tier BOCES	74	215
Dender, Cheryl/Plainview-Old Bethpage Ctl SD	274	127
Denee, Tanya/Wayland-Cohocton Central SD	93	215
Dengler, Brian/Albany City School Dist	3	9
Dengler, Krislynn, Dr/South Kortright Ctl SD	1,11	50
Dengler, Mike/South Kortright Ctl SD	3	50
DeNicola, Thomas/Amityville Union Free Sch Dist	15,73	216
Dening, Dale/Remsen Central School Dist	6	151
Denis, Susan/Sag Harbor Union Free Sch Dist	7,83,85	229
DeNisco, Irene/Lindenhurst Union Free SD	12	224
Denmake, Tim/Trumansburg Central SD	3,5	241
Denne, Leona/Bolton Central School Dist	57	244
Dennett, Danielle/Laurens Central School Dist	38,83,88	173
Dennett, Jim/Ossining Union Free Sch Dist	6,35	259
Dennin, Kathleen/Bolton Central School Dist	2,19	244
Dennis, Heather/Hyde Park Central School Dist	58	52
Dennis, Howard/Penn Yan Ctl School Dist	1	268
Dennis, Robert/Medina Central School Dist	5	169
Dennison, David/Monroe 1 BOCES	73,76	115
Dennison, Jacqueline/Gates Chili Central Sch Dist	7	108
Denniston, Bill/Kings Park Ctl School Dist	6	224
Denny, Carol/Gowanda Central School Dist	30	32
Dent, Ramona/Carthage Central School Dist	73,76,295	80
Denton, Vaughn/Longwood Central School Dist	15,79	225
DePaola, Lisa/Plainedge Union Free Sch Dist	8,15,274	127
DePriest, Shar/Starpoint Central School Dist	5	149
DePue, Joann/Springville Griffith Inst CSD	11,69,73,76	63
DePue, Laura/Fredonia Central School Dist	31	37
Derfel, Barry, Dr/Tompkins-Seneca-Tioga BOCES	8,15,16	241
DeRienzo, Lisa/Half Hollow Hills Central SD	49,52	222
Derman, Sarah/Rye City School Dist	71	261
DeRosa, Jill, Dr/Oceanside Union Free Sch Dist	15,68,79	127
DeRosa, Michael/Bridgehampton Union Free SD	6	218
DeRose, Joe/Tarrytown Union Free Sch Dist	295	262
Derouchie, Vicky/Norwood-Norfolk Ctl SD	57	211
Derr, James/Hammondsport Ctl School Dist	38	214
Des Rosiers, Dennis/Fairport Ctl School Dist	58	108
Desa, Tina, Dr/Arlington Central School Dist	11,15,79,83	51
DeSantis, Dean/Syracuse City School Dist	3,17	158
DeSantis, Emily/New York State Dept Education	71	1
DeSesa, Brian/Sag Harbor Union Free Sch Dist	67	229
Desiato, Donna, Dr/East Syracuse Minoa Ctl SD	1	154
Desiderio, Tricia/Mattituck-Cutchogue UFSD	57,58,79	225
DeSimone, Tina/Medina Central School Dist	36,90	169
Desire, Charmise/Uniondale Union Free Sch Dist	67	130
Desmond, Thomas/Huntington Union Free Sch Dist	3	223
Desormoux, Michelle/Heuvelton Central School Dist	51,54	210
DeStefanis, Jeffrey/Lake George Central Sch Dist	4	245
DeStefano, Victor/Ulster BOCES	3	244
Destfano, Nancy/WSWHE BOCES	8,15,27,58,88,275	249
Detommaso, John/Bellmore-Merrick Ctl High SD	1	117
Detor, Kristi/East Meadow Union Free SD	6,7,30,35,83,85	118
Detraglia, Jay/Hamilton-Fulton-Montgmry BOCES	27	72
Dettelis, Phillip/New York State Dept Education	28	1
Dettenrider, Nicole/Wheelerville Union Free SD	1,11,73,288	72
Deuel, Michael/Whitesboro Ctl School Dist	6,35	153
Devarakonda, Madhavi/Rochester City School Dist	68	110
Devincenzi, Brian/Wallkill Central School Dist	2,15,71,79,97	243
DeVincenzo, Matt/Brookhaven Comsewogue Unif SD	6	218
Devinney, Jennifer/Lyons Central School Dist	8,73	249
DeVita, Nate/Westhill Central School Dist	295	160
DeVito, Michael/Long Beach City School Dist	2,3,15,17	124
Devitt, Tom/Fairport Ctl School Dist	16,73,82,295	108
DeVivo, Marianne, Dr/Freeport Public School Dist	8,15,288	119
DeVoe, Bill/Berne-Knox-Westerlo Central SD	71	10
DeVoe, William/Schalmont Central School Dist	71	204
Dew, Lisa/Saranac Central School Dist	84	45
Dewey, Perry/Dcmo BOCES Chenango	1	43
Dewey, Terry/Greater Johnstown Sch Dist	58,79	71
DeWitt, Jeremy/Warsaw Central School Dist	73	267
Dexter, James/WSWHE BOCES	1	249
Dezali, Brent/Schroon Lake Ctl School Dist	5	68
Di Carlo, Anthony/Mahopac Ctl School Dist	1	176
Di Pasqua, Franco/West Seneca Central Sch Dist	11,42,45,89	64
Diamico, Albert/Buffalo Public Schools	5	56
Diamond, Michele/Berne-Knox-Westerlo Central SD	11,88,273	10
DiBartolo, Joseph/Hewlett Woodmere Union Free SD	5	121
DiBartolomeo, Joan/Clarence Central School Dist	4	59
Dibble, Michelle/Milford Central School Dist	11,69	173
Dibianco, Jennifer/Central Square Central SD	79,275	170
Dibianco, Jennifer/Liverpool Ctl School Dist	11,79,88	156
Dibiasi, Andrew/Onondaga-Cortland-Madson BOCES	15	160
Dicaprio, Colleen/Greater Amsterdam School Dist	2	115
DiCapua, Dana/Garden City School Dist	2,15,16,91	120
Dicietro, T J/East Rockaway Union Free SD	69,270	118
Dickerson, Holly/Buffalo Public Schools	7	56
Dickson, Kristine/Fonda Fultonville Central SD	11,58,271,296,298	115
Dickson, Myrtle/Uniondale Union Free Sch Dist	15,68	130

1 Superintendent	16 Instructional Media Svcs	30 Adult Education	44 Science Sec	58 Special Education K-12	72 Summer School	88 Alternative/At Risk	277 Remedial Math K-12
2 Bus/Finance/Purchasing	17 Chief Operations Officer	31 Career/Sch-to-Work K-12	45 Math K-12	59 Special Education Elem	73 Instructional Tech	89 Multi-Cultural Curriculum	280 Literacy Coach
3 Buildings And Grounds	18 Chief Academic Officer	32 Career/Sch-to-Work Elem	46 Math Elem	60 Special Education Sec	74 Inservice Training	90 Social Work	285 STEM
4 Food Service	19 Chief Financial Officer	33 Career/Sch-to-Work Sec	47 Math Sec	61 Foreign/World Lang K-12	75 Marketing/Distributive	91 Safety/Security	286 Digital Learning
5 Transportation	20 Art K-12	34 Early Childhood Ed	48 English/Lang Arts K-12	62 Foreign/World Lang Elem	76 Info Systems	92 Magnet School	288 Common Core Standards
6 Athletic	21 Art Elem	35 Health/Phys Education	49 English/Lang Arts Elem	63 Foreign/World Lang Sec	77 Psychological Assess	93 Parental Involvement	294 Accountability
7 Health Services	22 Art Sec	36 Guidance Services K-12	50 English/Lang Arts Sec	64 Religious Education K-12	78 Affirmative Action	96 Tech Prep Program	295 Network System
8 Curric/Instruct K-12	23 Music K-12	37 Guidance Services Elem	51 Reading K-12	65 Religious Education Elem	79 Student Personnel	97 Chief Information Officer	296 Title II Programs
9 Curric/Instruct Elem	24 Music Elem	38 Guidance Services Sec	52 Reading Elem	66 Religious Education Sec	80 Driver Ed/Safety	98 Chief Technology Officer	297 Webmaster
10 Curric/Instruct Sec	25 Music Sec	39 Social Studies K-12	53 Reading Sec	67 School Board President	81 Gifted/Talented	270 Character Education	298 Grant Writer/Ptnrships
11 Federal Program	26 Business Education	40 Social Studies Elem	54 Remedial Reading K-12	68 Teacher Personnel	82 Video Services	271 Migrant Education	750 Chief Innovation Officer
12 Title I	27 Career & Tech Ed	41 Social Studies Sec	55 Remedial Reading Elem	69 Academic Assessment	83 Substance Abuse Prev	273 Teacher Mentor	751 Chief of Staff
13 Title V	28 Technology Education	42 Science K-12	56 Remedial Reading Sec	70 Research/Development	84 Erate	274 Before/After Sch	752 Social Emotional Learning
15 Asst Superintendent	29 Family/Consumer Science	43 Science Elem	57 Bilingual/ELL	71 Public Information	85 AIDS Education	275 Response To Intervention	

NY-T16

New York School Directory

DISTRICT PERSONNEL INDEX

NAME/District	JOB FUNCTIONS	PAGE
Dickson, Robert/Monroe 1 BOCES	67	115
Dicosimo, Elizabeth/Chenango Valley Ctl Sch Dist	15,288	28
Dicosimo, Elizabeth/Mexico Central School Dist	15,68	171
DiDiego, Krista/Garrison Union Free Sch Dist	37	175
DiDio, Christine/Valley Stream Union Free SD 13	21,24	130
DiDio, Michael/Fire Island Union Free SD	5	222
Didonna, Jane/Germantown Central School Dist	270	46
Dieck, Susan/Carmel Central School Dist	71,298	175
Dieffenbacher, Mary/Town of Webb Union Free SD	8,12,57,58,69,77,271	78
DiFabio, Carolann/Auburn Enlarged City Sch Dist	5	34
Diflorio, Robert/Syracuse City School Dist	9	158
Diflorio, Valerie/North Syracuse Ctl Sch Dist	58,77,79,90,275	157
Difrisco, John/Carle Place Union Free SD	67	117
Difulvio, Chris/Onondaga-Cortland-Madson BOCES	15,16,69,70,74	160
Diggins, Dan/Burnt Hills Ballston Lake SD	3,91	200
DiGirolamo, Marie/Niskayuna Central School Dist	8,11,15,18,57,288,296	204
DiGregorio, Patricia/Southold Union Free Sch Dist	68	231
DiGrigoli, Todd/Ichabod Crane Central Schools	4	46
Digsby, Alan/Gilbertsville-Mt Upton SD	3	173
DiLalla, Jerilee/Brockport Ctl School Dist	15,68	106
DiLaura, Alexandra/Medina Central School Dist	58	169
Dilbone, James/Mohonasen Central Sch Dist	16,73	203
Dilello, Brendan/Rensselaer City School Dist	37	191
DiLeo, David/Babylon Union Free Sch Dist	73,95,295	216
Dill, Tony/New Suffolk Common School Dist	67	226
Dillon, Christopher/Levittown Union Free Sch Dist	2,15	123
Dillon, Richard/White Plains City School Dist	39	263
Dillon, Robert, Dr/Nassau BOCES	1	134
Dimaio, Melinda/Hyde Park Central School Dist	20,23	52
Dimango, Andera/Valley Stream Union Free SD 13	16,73,295	130
Dimango, Danielle/Community School District 25	1	178
Dimattina, Joseph/Florida Union Free Sch Dist	6	164
Dimgba, Marguerite/Greece Central School Dist	74	108
Dimola, Isabel/Community School District 21	1	90
DiNapoli, Andrew/Baldwin Union Free School Dist	8	116
Dineen, Philip/Islip Union Free School Dist	67	224
Dinio, Anne/Haldane Central School Dist	2,4	175
Dinneen, Lisa/Fayetteville-Manlius Ctl SD	11,15,16,57,58,79,275	155
Dioguardi, Joseph/Addison Central School Dist	1	213
Dioguardi, Kristin/Rush Henrietta Central SD	68	112
DiPace, Anthony/Sharon Springs Ctl SD	2	207
DiPasquale, Charles/Genesee Valley BOCES	30	74
Dipassio, Joseph/Lyndonville Central Sch Dist	2,11,19,296	169
Dippold, John/Solvay Union Free Sch Dist	6	158
Dirolf, Issac/Saranac Central School Dist	4	45
Discenza, Michelle/Fort Ann Central School Dist	8,11,57,270,271	247
Discenza, Michelle/Fort Ann Central School Dist	8,11,57,270,271	247
Disotto, Daniel/Wynantskill Union Free SD	6	191
DiStefano, Mary/Coxsackie-Athens Central SD	4	75
Ditanna, Dave/Randolph Acad Union Free SD	2	32
Dittmeir, Sheila/Sodus Central School Dist	5	251
Dittmer, Sheila/Newark Central School Dist	5	250
Diveris, Michelle/East Quogue Union Free SD	12,296	221
Diveronica, Jeffery/West Irondequoit Ctl SD	71	113
DiVirgilio, Jane/North Tonawanda City Sch Dist	28,73,76,295	148
DiVita, Amy/Liverpool Ctl School Dist	58,275	156
Dixon, Brenda/Berlin Central School Dist	270	189
Dixon, Chris/Lancaster Central Sch Dist	35	62
Dixon, Marianne/Buffalo Public Schools	70	57
Dixon, Sonya/Newburgh Enlarged City SD	11,296,298	165
Dlugos, Amy/Prattsburgh Central Sch Dist	67	215
Dobbertin, Cheryl/East Irondequoit Ctl Sch Dist	10	107
Dobbertin, Timothy/Monroe 2 Orleans BOCES	8,15,34	115
Dobbins, Jo-Anne/Elmsford Union Free SD	8,58,79	255
Dobek, Jeremy/Dunkirk City School Dist	73	37
Dobies, Patrice/East Meadow Union Free SD	58,77,79	118
Dobmeier, Maryann/Indian River Ctl School Dist	1	80
Dobroff, Larry/Hempstead Union Free SD	2,15	121
Docteur, Jessica/Cayuga-Onondaga BOCES	15,74	36
Docteur, Nichole/Caledonia-Mumford Ctl Sch Dist	16	102
Dodd, Allison/Ulster BOCES	2,15,68	244
Dodds, John/Taconic Hills Central Sch Dist	73	47
Dodge, Brent/New York Mills Union Free SD	11,35,296	151
Dodge, Michael/Fillmore Central School Dist	1,83	14
Dodge, Tricia/Canisteo-Greenwood Central SD	58	214
Dodson, Brigid/Albany City School Dist	34	9

NAME/District	JOB FUNCTIONS	PAGE
Doe, David/Morristown Ctl School Dist	8,88,294	211
Doelger, Brian/Shelter Island Union Free SD	1	230
Doell, Andrew/Bloomfield Central SD	1	161
Doherty, Carol/Fishers Island Union Free SD	5	222
Doherty, Ellen/Chappaqua Central School Dist	12,57,58,81,83,88,90	253
Doherty, Gerri/Mattituck-Cutchogue UFSD	73,76,295	225
Doherty, Natalie/Putnam Valley Ctl School Dist	12,15	176
Doherty, Suzanne/Southern Westchester BOCES	68	267
Doig, Roland/Susquehanna Valley Central SD	1	29
Dolan, John/East Islip Union Free SD	1	220
Dolce, Chip/Palmyra-Macedon Central SD	73,286,295	250
Dolce, Larry/Brocton Central School Dist	3,91	36
Dolce, Nicole/Clarkstown Central School Dist	5	195
Dolce, Nicole/Eastchester Union Free SD	5	254
Dolly, O Jeanne/Indian River Ctl School Dist	7	80
Dolson, Kasey/Liverpool Ctl School Dist	8,69	156
Domagala, Deborah/South Lewis Central Sch Dist	8,88,288,298	101
Dombkowski, Richard/Buffalo Public Schools	11	56
Dombrowski, Lynn/Iroquois Central School Dist	4	61
Domermuth, Keith/Berne-Knox-Westerlo Central SD	3	10
Dominguez, Nelson/Farmingdale Union Free SD	3,91	119
Dona Rummo, Christopher/Plainview-Old Bethpage Ctl SD	15	127
Donaghy, Tim/Haldane Central School Dist	273	176
Donahue, Donna/Tompkins-Seneca-Tioga BOCES	68	241
Donahue, Elizabeth/Chenango Valley Ctl Sch Dist	2,11	28
Donahue, Karen/Diocese of Ogdensburg Ed Off	8,11,15	212
Donahue, Maureen/Southwestern Central Sch Dist	1	39
Donahue, Michael/Coxsackie-Athens Central SD	67	75
Donahue, Sheila/Syracuse City School Dist	36	158
Donaleski, Matthew/Camden Central School Dist	23	150
Donleavy, Debra/Middletown Enlarged City SD	4	165
Donlon-Yates, Julie, Dr/Genesee Valley BOCES	8,15,70	74
Donnelly, Marie/Hewlett Woodmere Union Free SD	2,15	121
Donnelly, Marie/Seaford Union Free SD	2,5,15	129
Donnelly, Rebecca/Cassadaga Valley Ctl Sch Dist	58	36
Donnelly, Scott/Bloomfield Central SD	2,19,34,68	161
Donnelly, Sharon/Harborfields Ctl School Dist	2,4,5,15	223
Donner, Jessi/Tonawanda City School Dist	73	64
Donohue, Brian/Honeoye Falls Lima Sch Dist	6,35	109
Donovan, Brita/Galway Central School Dist	1	201
Donovan, James/Middle Country Ctl Sch Dist	15,68	225
Donovan, Mike/Wayland-Cohocton Central SD	3,91	215
Donovan, Pamela/Longwood Central School Dist	71	225
Doody, Brett/Phoenix Central School Dist	55,270,274	172
Dopp, Edward/North Colonie Central SD	30	11
Dorcas, Jim/Eldred Central School Dist	3	236
Dorfman, Susan/Farmingdale Union Free SD	60	119
Dorgan, Kate/Averill Park Central Sch Dist	58	189
Doris, Matt/Tuckahoe Common School Dist	4	232
Dorn, Scott/Tarrytown Union Free Sch Dist	15,58,79,752	262
Dornburg, Dana/Town of Webb Union Free SD	36,79,273	78
Doroshenko, Nichole/Morrisville Eaton Central SD	67	105
Dorr, Kate/New Hartford Central Sch Dist	4	151
Dorr, Maria/Amagansett Union Free Sch Dist	11,57,88,274,285,288,298	216
Dorrance, Robert/Ravena Coeymans Selkirk Ctl SD	6,35,85	11
Dorritie, William/Laurens Central School Dist	1,288	173
Dorsett, Susan/White Plains City School Dist	58	263
Dorsey, James/Minerva Central School Dist	8,27,36,58	68
Doscher, Danielle/Bridgehampton Union Free SD	36,69	218
Dossena, Salvatore, Dr/Merrick Union Free School Dist	7,59,79	125
Doster, Wendy/Cheektowaga Central SD	4	58
Doty, Margaret/White Plains City School Dist	42	263
Douai, Kelly/Ossining Union Free Sch Dist	73	259
Doucette, Jamie/Fishers Island Union Free Sch Dist	67	222
Dougal, Dwayne/York Central School Dist	5	103
Dougherty, Edmund/West Canada Valley Ctl SD	6,58,83,286,296	79
Dougherty, Linda/Archdiocese of New York Ed Off	15	142
Dougherty, Maria/Spencerport Central Sch Dist	58	112
Dougherty, Marianna/Clarkstown Central School Dist	77	195
Dougherty, Ryan/Newark Valley Central Sch Dist	1	238
Dougherty, Terrance/Hancock Central School Dist	1	49
Doughty, Gary/Berkshire Union Free Sch Dist	83	45
Douglas, Michael/Willsboro Central Sch Dist	6	68
Douglas, Thomas, Dr/Horseheads Ctl School Dist	1	40
Dove, Jennifer/Binghamton City School Dist	8,48	27
Dow, Colette/Bedford Central School Dist	67	252

DISTRICT PERSONNEL INDEX

Market Data Retrieval

NAME/District	JOB FUNCTIONS	PAGE
Dow, Stephanie/La Fayette Central School Dist	67	156
Dowling, Jeanne/West Islip School Dist	58,77,79,81,275	233
Down, Tracey/Town of Webb Union Free SD	16	78
Downes, David/Spackenkill Union Free SD	3,91	54
Downs, Billie/Groton Central School Dist	6	240
Downs, Bonnie/Tuckahoe Common School Dist	12	232
Downs, Christine/Onteora Central School Dist	4	243
Downs, Laurie/Riverhead Central School Dist	67	228
Dowsland, William/Hamilton Central Sch Dist	1	105
Doyle, Dan/Ichabod Crane Central Schools	5	46
Doyle, Jared/Newcomb Central School Dist	26	68
Doyle, Natalie/Bayport- Blue Point USD	58	217
Dragone, Anthony/Southold Union Free Sch Dist	3,91	231
Dragone, Joseph/Roslyn School Dist	2	129
Dragone, Joseph, Dr/Capital Region BOCES	15	13
Drahms, Richard/Clyde-Savannah Central SD	67	249
Drahos, Michael/Otselic Valley Central SD	1,11	42
Drake, Benjamin/Jamestown City School Dist	6,35	38
Drake, Nelson/Spencerport Central Sch Dist	3	112
Dramm, Cecily/Saranac Lake Central Sch Dist	85	70
Drancsak, James/Central Square Central SD	6,7,35,85	170
Draper, Catherine/Southern Westchester BOCES	67	267
Drechsler, Scott/Penfield Central School Dist	2,15,34,58	109
Dreher, Ashli/Grand Island Central Sch Dist	67	61
Dreiss, Joanne/Diocese of Brooklyn Ed Office	15,34	94
Drescher, Elena/Marcellus Central School Dist	73,286	157
Dresher, Wayne/Cheektowaga-Sloan UFSD	8,18	59
Drexel, Charles, Dr/Little Flower Union Free SD	67	224
Driadel, David/Rome City School Dist	2	151
Driffill, Dan/Penfield Central School Dist	2	109
Driffill, Daniel, Dr/Wayne Central School Dist	2,15	251
Driscoll, Pam/Schuylerville Central Sch Dist	7	201
Drosopoulos, Chris/Briarcliff Manor Union Free SD	6	253
Drossel, Karen/Cairo-Durham Ctl School Dist	83	75
Drumm, Pam/Addison Central School Dist	4	213
Drumm, Pam/Bradford Central Sch Dist	4	207
Drumm, Pam/Campbell-Savona Ctl Sch Dist	4	213
Drumnond, Crory/Ichabod Crane Central Schools	285	46
Dryer, Beth/Tompkins-Seneca-Tioga BOCES	74	241
Dubner, David/Rockville Ctr Union Free SD	67	128
DuBois, Erin/Greenville Central School Dist	15,68,296,298	75
DuBois, Kate/Lake George Central Sch Dist	2	245
DuBois, Kate/Whitehall Central School Dist	2	248
Dubrava, Vanessa/Maine Endwell Ctl School Dist	12,34,58,79,275	29
DuCharme, James/Schuylerville Central Sch Dist	273	201
DuCharme, Leanne/Canandaigua City School Dist	38	161
Ducoing, Dawn/William Floyd School Dist	4	233
Dudden, Tammy/Skaneateles Central Sch Dist	16,82	157
Dudek, Kristen/Salamanca City Central SD	58,77,79,298	33
Dudek, Mary Jo, Dr/Iroquois Central School Dist	8,11,15	61
Dudley-Lemek, Sarah/Highland Ctl School Dist	15	242
Duell, Nicole/Fonda Fultonville Central SD	34	115
Duffy, Christine/Eastport-South Manor Ctrl SD	31,36	221
Duffy, Gail/Tarrytown Union Free Sch Dist	8,11,68,69,91,273,288,296	262
Duffy, Robert/Oswego City School Dist	57,77,79,83,88,90,271	171
Duffy, Susan/Chazy Central Rural Sch Dist	51	44
DuFour, Robert, Dr/Sullivan BOCES	2	238
Duggan, Colleen/Frontier Ctl School Dist	8,11,15,69,77,285,288,298	60
Duke, Megan/Andover Central School Dist	58,77,78,93	14
Dullea, Rebecca/Brasher Falls School Dist	16	209
Dullea, Susan/Carmel Central School Dist	6,35	175
Dumas, Michelle/Gilboa-Conesville Central SD	11,298	206
Dumhan, Jeff/Whitney Point Central Sch Dist	3,91	30
Dunbar, Michelle/Wellsville Central Sch Dist	2	15
Dunbar, Tonda/Schenectady City School Dist	8,57,288	204
Dungate, Tim/Connetquot Central School Dist	3	219
Dungee, Sharon/Central Islip Union Free SD	1	218

NAME/District	JOB FUNCTIONS	PAGE
Dunham, Denise/Dansville Ctl School Dist	58	102
Dunham, Stephen/West Genesee Ctl School Dist	10	159
Dunham, Timothy/Akron Central School Dist	58,77	56
Dunigan, Anne/Salem Central School Dist	67	248
Dunkel, Lorraine/Elwood Union Free School Dist	2,15,84,91	221
Dunkle-King, Rebecca/Lowville Acad-Central Sch Dist	1,11	101
Dunlap, Sean/Baldwinsville Central Sch Dist	91	154
Dunlop, Tammy/Berlin Central School Dist	73	189
Dunn, Brian/Canajoharie Ctl School Dist	6	115
Dunn, Brian/Mayfield Ctl School Dist	6	72
Dunn, Brian/Middleburgh Ctl School Dist	1	206
Dunn, David/Poughkeepsie City School Dist	4	53
Dunn, Jennifer/Town of Webb Union Free SD	2	78
Dunn, Lisa/Copiague Union Free Sch Dist	30	220
Dunn, Michael/Elmira City School Dist	3	40
Dunne, James/Otselic Valley Central SD	295	42
Dunne, James/Otselic Valley Central SD	295	42
Dunne, Regina/Smithtown Central Sch Dist	4	230
Dunning, Michael/Shelter Island Union Free SD	3	230
Dunst, Ian/Half Hollow Hills Central SD	45	222
Dupis, Shelley/North Warren Central Sch Dist	8,11,296	246
DuPrey, Heather/Northeastern Clinton Ctl SD	34,37	44
DuPuis, Anthony/Dolgeville Central School Dist	4	77
DuPuis, Shelley/Hartford Central School Dist	10	248
Duquette, Jared/Peru Central School Dist	295	44
Durdon, Christopher/Windsor Central School Dist	3,5,6,35	30
Durham, Melissa/Keene Central School Dist	2	67
Durham, Rick/Plattsburgh City School Dist	285	44
Durkalski, Arlene/Riverhead Central School Dist	68	228
Durkee, Amanda/Johnsburg Central School Dist	57,58	245
Durr, Kevin/Alexandria Central School Dist	38,57	79
Durrett, Albert/North Collins Ctl Sch Dist	5	63
Duryea, Tanya/Monticello Central School Dist	58,79,271	237
Duschen, Teffenie/Canisteo-Greenwood Central SD	12,73,288	214
Dusinberre, Brett/Alfred Almond Ctl School Dist	6	13
Duso, Francesca/Willsboro Central Sch Dist	57	68
Dussing, Jon/Westhill Central School Dist	295	160
Dustin, Joseph/Bemus Point Ctl School Dist	5	36
Dutcher, Andrew/Cayuga-Onondaga BOCES	16	36
Dutton, Laura/Poland Central School Dist	1,11,57	78
DuVall, Lee/Tully Central School Dist	73	159
Duwe, Allison/Springville Griffith Inst CSD	67	63
Dworsal, William/West Hempstead School Dist	3	131
Dwyer, Kate/Chateaugay Central School Dist	11,288,296	69
Dwyer, Susan/Oceanside Union Free Sch Dist	73	127
Dyba, Arlene/Tuxedo Union Free Sch Dist	76	167
Dyke, Elizabeth, Dr/Poughkeepsie City School Dist	76	53
Dykes, Nadine/Brighton Central School Dist	82	106
Dyment, Wendy/Westfield Central School Dist	67	39
Dymond, Jamie/Livingston Manor Ctl Sch Dist	273	236
Dyno, Nicholas, Dr/Southampton Union Free SD	1	231
Dyroff, Matt/Mt Sinai Union Free SD	36	226
Dzadur, Elena/Niagara-Wheatfield Ctl SD	57	148
Dzembo, Tiffany/Green Island Union Free SD	12	10
Dziebra, Carrie/Gowanda Central School Dist	57	32
Dzierzanowski, Chris/Hinsdale Central School Dist	11	32
Dzikowski, Denise/Dutchess Co BOCES	58	55
Dziubinski, Michelle/Frewsburg Central School Dist	77	38

E

NAME/District	JOB FUNCTIONS	PAGE
Eadie, Susan/Avon Central School Dist	2	102
Eagan, David/Wainscott Common School Dist	67	232
Eagan, James/Fishers Island Union Free SD	2	222
Eagen, Timothy, Dr/Kings Park Ctl School Dist	1	224
Easter, Ann/Indian River Ctl School Dist	4	80
Eastman, Bobbie Jo/Solvay Union Free Sch Dist	5	158
Eatman, Chris/Cambridge Central School Dist	71,97	247

1 Superintendent
2 Bus/Finance/Purchasing
3 Buildings And Grounds
4 Food Service
5 Transportation
6 Athletic
7 Health Services
8 Curric/Instruct K-12
9 Curric/Instruct Elem
10 Curric/Instruct Sec
11 Federal Program
12 Title I
13 Title V
15 Asst Superintendent
16 Instructional Media Svcs
17 Chief Operations Officer
18 Chief Academic Officer
19 Chief Financial Officer
20 Art K-12
21 Art Elem
22 Art Sec
23 Music K-12
24 Music Elem
25 Music Sec
26 Business Education
27 Career & Tech Ed
28 Technology Education
29 Family/Consumer Science
30 Adult Education
31 Career/Sch-to-Work K-12
32 Career/Sch-to-Work Elem
33 Career/Sch-to-Work Sec
34 Early Childhood Ed
35 Health/Phys Education
36 Guidance Services K-12
37 Guidance Services Elem
38 Guidance Services Sec
39 Social Studies K-12
40 Social Studies Elem
41 Social Studies Sec
42 Science K-12
43 Science Elem
44 Science Sec
45 Math K-12
46 Math Elem
47 Math Sec
48 English/Lang Arts K-12
49 English/Lang Arts Elem
50 English/Lang Arts Sec
51 Reading K-12
52 Reading Elem
53 Reading Sec
54 Remedial Reading K-12
55 Remedial Reading Elem
56 Remedial Reading Sec
57 Bilingual/ELL
58 Special Education K-12
59 Special Education Elem
60 Special Education Sec
61 Foreign/World Lang K-12
62 Foreign/World Lang Elem
63 Foreign/World Lang Sec
64 Religious Education K-12
65 Religious Education Elem
66 Religious Education Sec
67 School Board President
68 Teacher Personnel
69 Academic Assessment
70 Research/Development
71 Public Information
72 Summer School
73 Instructional Tech
74 Inservice Training
75 Marketing/Distributive
76 Info Systems
77 Psychological Assess
78 Tech Prep Program
79 Student Personnel
80 Driver Ed/Safety
81 Gifted/Talented
82 Video Services
83 Substance Abuse Prev
84 Erate
85 AIDS Education
88 Alternative/At Risk
89 Multi-Cultural Curriculum
90 Social Work
91 Safety/Security
92 Magnet School
93 Parental Involvement
95 Tech Prep Program
97 Chief Information Officer
98 Chief Technology Officer
270 Character Education
271 Migrant Education
273 Teacher Mentor
274 Before/After Sch
275 Response To Intervention
277 Remedial Math K-12
280 Literacy Coach
285 STEM
286 Digital Learning
288 Common Core Standards
294 Accountability
295 Network System
296 Title II Programs
297 Webmaster
298 Grant Writer/Ptnrships
750 Chief Innovation Officer
751 Chief of Staff
752 Social Emotional Learning

NY-T18

New York School Directory

DISTRICT PERSONNEL INDEX

NAME/District	JOB FUNCTIONS	PAGE
Eaton, Chelsea/Le Roy Central School Dist	11,55,57,58,79,271	73
Eaton, Elisa/Johnson City Central Sch Dist	58,271	28
Eaves, Lacey/Otselic Valley Central SD	8,13,58	42
Eberle, Kevin, Dr/Buffalo Public Schools	3	56
Eberstein, Mark/Perry Central School Dist	73,76	267
Eccleston, Larry/Corning-Painted Post Area SD	5	214
Eccleston, Robin/Broome-Tioga BOCES	68	31
Eckdahl, Kelli/Wayne-Finger Lakes BOCES	73	252
Ecker, Andrew, Dr/Putnam-Northern Wstchstr BOCES	36	266
Ecker, Jean/Three Village Central Sch Dist	4	232
Ecker, Roxanne/Amagansett Union Free Sch Dist	2	216
Ecker, Vincenza/Gloversville Enlarged Sch Dist	4	71
Ecklund, Christina/Avon Central School Dist	8,74	102
Eckstein, Jason/Freeport Public School Dist	73	119
Eckwahl, Emily/Sherman Central School Dist	35,83	39
Eddy, Tammy/Ellicottville Central Sch Dist	38	31
Edellman, Jamie/Chappaqua Central School Dist	280	253
Edelson, Barry/Roslyn School Dist	30,71,297,298	129
Edgar, Heidi/South Jefferson Central SD	31,83	81
Edger, Erin/Odessa Montour Ctl Sch Dist	71	207
Edgerton, Amy/Tonawanda City School Dist	36,58,79,88,752	64
Edmondson, Cathy/Albany City School Dist	71	9
Edmondson, Shannon/Johnson City Central Sch Dist	67	28
Edsall, Rebecca/Marathon Ctl School Dist	67	48
Edson, Larry/East Greenbush Central SD	2,15	190
Edward, Maltbie/North Rockland Central SD	76	197
Edwards, Bob/Phoenix Central School Dist	11,16,57,68,288,294,296	171
Edwards, Danelle/Colton Pierrepont School Dist	57	209
Edwards, Jack/Pine Plains Ctl School Dist	31,88	53
Edwards, Jacquline/New York Mills Union Free SD	67	151
Edwards, Kevin/Niagara Falls City Sch Dist	4,79	147
Edwards, Mark/Hilton Central School Dist	3	109
Edwards, Mickey/Byron-Bergen Ctl School Dist	1	73
Edwards, Peter/Colton Pierrepont School Dist	73	209
Edwards, Robert/Cortland Enlarged City SD	1	47
Edwards, Sarah/Buffalo Public Schools	73	57
Edwards, Tammi/South Glens Falls Ctl Sch Dist	2	202
Egan, Dennis/Franklin-Essex-Hamilton BOCES	67	71
Eger, Stacey/Watertown City School Dist	8,286,288,296	81
Eggleston, Sarah/Arkport Central School Dist	36	213
Ehelers, Susan/Holland Central School Dist	5	61
Ehlenfield, Robert/Sweet Home Central Sch Dist	73,76,82	63
Ehrensbeck, Judy/Town of Webb Union Free SD	51	78
Eichholtz, Debra/Newfield Central School Dist	2	241
Eichholtz, Debra/Spencer Van Etten Central SD	2	238
Eichner, Nancy/Rochester City School Dist	69	110
Eighmey, Rex/Pavilion Ctl School Dist	3	74
Eirind, Brendon/Tuxedo Union Free Sch Dist	3	167
Eisele, Marylynn/Levittown Union Free Sch Dist	76	123
Eiser, Allissa/Bethlehem Central School Dist	4	10
Eisse, Michael/Chittenango Central SD	1	104
Elble, Nathan/Berne-Knox-Westerlo Central SD	67	10
Elconin, Stacey/Somers Central School Dist	11,34,57,58,79,275	262
Elder, William/South Glens Falls Ctl Sch Dist	67	202
Elefante, Angela, Dr/Utica City School Dist	16,71,82	152
Elefante, Marc/New Hartford Central Sch Dist	3	151
Elias, Jackie/Onondaga Central School Dist	58	157
Ellen, Marylou/Remsen Central School Dist	67	151
Eller, Rosemarie/White Plains City School Dist	67	263
Ellesen, Nancy/Goshen Central School Dist	7,83	164
Ellett, Debra/Hoosic Valley Central Sch Dist	7,85	190
Ellinghaus, Susan/Bellmore-Merrick Ctl High SD	88	117
Elliott, Donna/Deer Park Union Free Sch Dist	67	220
Elliott, Greg/Canaseraga Central Sch Dist	4	14
Elliott, Greg/Prattsburgh Central Sch Dist	4	215
Elliott, Kristin/Victor Central School Dist	67	162
Ellis, Amy/Perry Central School Dist	36	267
Ellis, Clarence/Community School District 17	1	86
Ellis, Debra/New York Mills Union Free SD	36,90	151
Ellis, Jim/Avon Central School Dist	73	102
Ellis, Kevin/Hamilton Central Sch Dist	8,79	105
Ellis, Michelle/Edinburg Common School Dist	1,73	201
Ellis, Pamela/Argyle Central School Dist	67	247
Ellis, Richard/Warsaw Central School Dist	34,58	267
Ellis, Robert/Argyle Central School Dist	3	246
Ellison, Fortune/Plattsburgh City School Dist	58	44

NAME/District	JOB FUNCTIONS	PAGE
Ellison, Katheryn/Bradford Central Sch Dist	8,11,74,288,296	207
Ellison, Ken/Pavilion Ctl School Dist	1	74
Ells, Christopher/Fulton City School Dist	6,7,35,83	170
Ells, Mary/Grand Island Central Sch Dist	23	61
Ellsworth, Bruce/Northville Central School Dist	2	72
Elsasser, Kerry/Corning-Painted Post Area SD	15	214
Elser, Kathy/Olean City School Dist	2,5	32
Elsey, Britany/Spencer Van Etten Central SD	16,82	238
Emeka, Anjeanette/Saratoga Springs City Sch Dist	67	201
Emery, James/Mexico Central School Dist	67	171
Emery, Tammy/Whitesville Central Sch Dist	1	15
Emery, Timothy/Geneva City School Dist	3	161
Emory, Cory/Sherman Central School Dist	6	39
Emrich, George/Watertown City School Dist	6	81
Ende, Fred/Putnam-Northern Wstchstr BOCES	8,74	266
Endes, Russell, Dr/Bay Shore Union Free Sch Dist	58,79,90	217
Engel, Glori/Freeport Public School Dist	48	119
Englehardt, Charles/Ravena Coeymans Selkirk Ctl SD	8,12,15,285,288	11
Englehardt, Fred/Ravena Coeymans Selkirk Ctl SD	83	11
Englert, Andy/Avon Central School Dist	6	102
English, George/Gates Chili Central Sch Dist	3	108
English, Robert/North Collins Ctl Sch Dist	31,36,88,95,270	63
English, Steven/Waterville Central Sch Dist	73	153
English, Terry/Falconer Central School Dist	91	37
Enigk, Matthew/Liverpool Ctl School Dist	2	156
Ennis, Josh/Hilton Central School Dist	295	109
Eppich, Alesia/Jefferson Central Sch Dist	4	206
Eppolito, Deb/Kenmore-Tonawanda UF Sch Dist	73,286,295	62
Eppolito, Debra/Orchard Park Central Sch Dist	76	63
Eppolito, Deby/Orchard Park Central Sch Dist	16,73,82,270	63
Epstein, Arnold/Long Beach City School Dist	6,7,35,83	124
Epstein, Steven/Uniondale Union Free Sch Dist	2,4,5,15	130
Epstien, Nora/Floral Park Bellerose Sch Dist	7,83,85	119
Erdmann, Jeffery/Whitesville Central Sch Dist	67	15
Eric, Baird/North Rockland Central SD	15,68	197
Erickson, Kevin/Cuba-Rushford Central Sch Dist	8,11,51,57,69,270	14
Erickson, Robert, Dr/Iroquois Central School Dist	7	61
Ernest, Julie/Averill Park Central Sch Dist	30	189
Ernst, Brian/Farmingdale Union Free SD	2	119
Ervay, Melinda/Weedsport Ctl School Dist	8,69	35
Erwin, Daniel/Patchogue-Medford Unified SD	4	227
Erwin, Matthew/Cazenovia Ctl School Dist	3,91	104
Eschbach, Glen/North Babylon Union Free SD	1	226
Eschler, Nicole, Dr/Tompkins-Seneca-Tioga BOCES	30,72	241
Escobar, Ed, Dr/Bedford Central School Dist	11,58,83,286,296,298	252
Escobar, Edward/Mineola Union Free Sch Dist	68	125
Eskew, Carol/North Bellmore Union Free SD	15,59	126
Espina, Daniel/Sewanhaka Ctl High Sch Dist	73	129
Espinosa, Dolores/Plainview-Old Bethpage Ctl SD	58,88,752	127
Esposito, Peter/Shoreham-Wading River Ctl SD	73,95,295	230
Estabrooks, Paul/Caledonia-Mumford Ctl Sch Dist	11,57,58,88,271	102
Estrada, Lisa/Hicksville Union Free Sch Dist	57	122
Estremera, Jeff/Wappingers Central Sch Dist	3	54
Ethington, Marirose/Pavilion Ctl School Dist	67	74
Etri, John/Newburgh Enlarged City SD	27	165
Etter, Jack/Gilboa-Conesville Central SD	288	206
Etter, John/Gilboa-Conesville Central SD	1,83	206
Eulau, Eric/Monroe Woodbury Central SD	58	165
Evangelist, Jason/Holland Patent Ctl School Dist	1	150
Evans, Amy/Syracuse City School Dist	58	158
Evans, David/Cleveland Hill Union Free SD	15	59
Evans, Holly/Pittsford Central Sch Dist	2	110
Evans, John/Downsville Central Sch Dist	1	49
Evans, John/Livingston Manor Ctl Sch Dist	1	236
Evans, John/Roscoe Central School Dist	1	237
Evans, Laura/Ithaca City School Dist	8	240
Evans, Matthew, Dr/Fallsburg Central School Dist	8,11,15,69,288,296	236
Evans, Matthew, Dr/Monticello Central School Dist	1	237
Evans, Melissa/Syracuse City School Dist	79	158
Evans, Michael/Edinburg Common School Dist	67	201
Evans, Tawn/Canton Central School Dist	5	209
Evelyn, Constance/Valley Stream Union Free SD 13	1	130
Evener, Jeffrey/Auburn Enlarged City Sch Dist	15,68	34
Everhart, Darren/Victor Central School Dist	5	162
Everly, Rich/Addison Central School Dist	2,298	213
Ewert, Douglas/Attica Central School Dist	73,98	267

School Year 2020-2021   800-333-8802   NY-T19

DISTRICT PERSONNEL INDEX

Market Data Retrieval

NAME/District	JOB FUNCTIONS	PAGE
Eysaman, Heather/Kendall Central School Dist	8,270,273,274	169
Ezman, Jordan/Clinton Central School Dist	295	150

F

NAME/District	JOB FUNCTIONS	PAGE
Fabian, Courtney/Center Moriches Union Free SD	298	218
Fabiano, Michael/Floral Park Bellerose Sch Dist	2,15	119
Fabiatos, Cathy/Holland Central School Dist	1	61
Fabrizio, Jami/Newark Valley Central Sch Dist	58	238
Facchini, Tracy/Sauquoit Valley Central SD	58	152
Facci, Mary/New York Mills Union Free SD	10,58	151
Faccilonga, Darren/Baldwin Union Free School Dist	73	116
Facin, Ken/Hoosick Falls Central Sch Dist	1,11	190
Factor, Aaron/Rocky Point Union Free SD	8	228
Fadale, Brianne/Clymer Central School Dist	58	37
Fadale, Thomas/Friendship Central Sch Dist	8,12,79,88,296,298	15
Fadjo, Cameron, Dr/Pleasantville Union Free SD	8,15,73	260
Fagan, Jacqueline/Central Islip Union Free SD	79	218
Fahey, Brennan/Owen D Young Central Sch Dist	1	78
Fahey, Brennan/Owen D Young Central Sch Dist	12,288	78
Fahey, Sean/West Genesee Ctl School Dist	294	159
Fahy, Karen/Rochester City School Dist	48,280	110
Fahy, Kelley/Churchville Chili Ctl Sch Dist	27,31,95	107
Failla, Lisa/Monticello Central School Dist	2,15,68	237
Fairben, Erin/Wayne-Finger Lakes BOCES	8,27,30,31,58	252
Fairbrother, Bryan/Morrisville Eaton Central SD	58,76,275	105
Fairchild, Chris/Manchester-Shortsville Ctl SD	5	162
Falchi, Steven/Utica City School Dist	8,288	152
Falcon, Judy/Kingston City School Dist	5	242
Falcone, Debbie/Schalmont Central School Dist	71,97	204
Falcone, Michael/Greenburgh Central School Dist	3	255
Falcone, Stacy/Rye City School Dist	4	261
Fale, Edward/Hewlett Woodmere Union Free SD	68	121
Fall, Jennifer/Rye City School Dist	58	261
Fallacaro, Marisa/Eden Central School Dist	6	60
Faller, Mary/Sachem Central School Dist	29	229
Fallon, Kerry/Long Beach City School Dist	36	124
Falls, Mike/Homer Central School Dist	2,11,15,296	48
Falore, Jennifer/West Seneca Central Sch Dist	71	64
Falsioni, Sandra/Lackawanna City School Dist	273	62
Falvo, Andrea/Rome City School Dist	20,23,45,285	151
Falvo, Elaine/Oneida-Herkimer-Mad BOCES	67	154
Falvo, Tracy/Burnt Hills Ballston Lake SD	76,97	200
Falzarano, Annamaria/Greece Central School Dist	57,61	108
Famularo, Joseph, Dr/Bellmore Union Free Sch Dist	1	117
Fancher, Bret/Tupper Lake Ctl School Dist	286	70
Fancher, Carl/Gilboa-Conesville Central SD	5	206
Fanelli, Patrick/Kenmore-Tonawanda UF Sch Dist	71	62
Fannon, PJ/Le Roy Central School Dist	3,91	73
Fanton, Kim/Andover Central School Dist	274	14
Faraci, Thomas/Roxbury Central School Dist	6	50
Farber, Mary/Chittenango Central SD	58,79	104
Farber, Susan, Dr/Levittown Union Free Sch Dist	58,79	123
Farfaglia, Paul/North Syracuse Ctl Sch Dist	67	157
Fargo, Thomas/Highland Falls-Ft Montgmry SD	3,5,91	164
Faricatore, Allen/East Quogue Union Free SD	4	221
Faris, Jessica/Windsor Central School Dist	4	30
Farkas, Evan/Amityville Union Free Sch Dist	6,35	216
Farleo, Robert/Williamsville Ctl School Dist	3	64
Farley, Daniel/Amherst Central School Dist	71,97	56
Farmer, Lyndon/St Regis Falls Ctl Sch Dist	67	70
Farr, Jamie/Canandaigua City School Dist	1	161
Farr, Joseph/West Seneca Central Sch Dist	3	64
Farrand, Patrick/Lisbon Central School Dist	1	210
Farrar, Taweeton, Dr/Akron Central School Dist	8,11,71,97	56
Farrell, Brenna/West Irondequoit Ctl SD	48	113
Farrell, Brian/Starpoint Central School Dist	58,78,79,83,88,271,275	149
Farrell, Cynthia/Rondout Valley Ctl Sch Dist	73	243
Farrell, Eugene/Pelham Union Free School Dist	36	260
Farrell, Robert/Owego Apalachin Ctl Sch Dist	8,11,15,97,288	238
Farrell, Timothy/Minerva Central School Dist	1	68
Farrell, Tina/Massapequa Union Free SD 23	48,280	125
Farrelly, Yiendhy/West Babylon Union Free SD	1	232
Farruggio, Jeanne/Ardsley Union Free School Dist	58	252
Farscai, Daniel/Liverpool Ctl School Dist	73,76	156
Farwell, Robert/Orchard Park Central Sch Dist	30	63
Fasano, Thomas, Dr/Massapequa Union Free SD 23	8,15	125
Fasolino, Greg/East Islip Union Free SD	71	220
Fasolino, Maria/Buffalo Public Schools	11	56
Fauci, Kim/Brentwood Union Free Sch Dist	58	217
Faulkner, Deadra/Westbury Union Free Sch Dist	36	132
Faulkner, Donna/Kendall Central School Dist	4	169
Faulkner, Kyle/Sandy Creek Central Sch Dist	1	172
Favro, Joshua/Lake Placid Ctl School Dist	5	67
Fay, Ryan/Quogue Union Free School Dist	6,35,85	228
Feathers, Paul/Lewiston Porter Ctl Sch Dist	3	146
Febbie, Megan/Marlboro Central School Dist	58	242
Febbie, Meghan/Mahopac Ctl School Dist	58	176
Febres, Julian/Clarkstown Central School Dist	3	195
Febrizio, Felica/Oyster Bay East Norwich Ctl SD	71	127
Fecura, Linda/Wynantskill Union Free SD	16	192
Feder, Jeremy/Lawrence Union Free Sch Dist	2,3,5,15	123
Fedorspiel, Elizabeth/Indian Lake Ctl School Dist	2	76
Feeley, Amy/Hornell City School Dist	57,58,79,275	214
Feeley, Michelle/New Suffolk Common School Dist	71	226
Feeney, Patty/Fabius Pompey Central SD	7	155
Fegley, Sue/Romulus Ctl School Dist	73	208
Feiden, Tamerlane/Minerva Central School Dist	35,83,88,270	68
Feijoo, Laura, Dr/New Rochelle City School Dist	1	259
Feinman, Eileen/Wayland-Cohocton Central SD	38	215
Feinman, Eileen/Wayland-Cohocton Central SD	1	215
Feit, Lorayne/Carle Place Union Free SD	16	117
Feldman, Laura/Eden Central School Dist	2,5	60
Feldmann, Donald/Sweet Home Central Sch Dist	7,71	63
Feldmeyer, Judy/Lancaster Central Sch Dist	5	62
Felice, Regina/Vestal Ctl School Dist	71	29
Felice, Ronald/Victor Central School Dist	80	162
Felicello, Kris, Dr/North Rockland Central SD	1	197
Felicello, Stacia, Dr/Kingston City School Dist	9	242
Feliciano, Robert/Brentwood Union Free Sch Dist	67	217
Feliz, Sara/Newburgh Enlarged City SD	8,15	165
Felt, Cheryl/Franklin-Essex-Hamilton BOCES	8,15	71
Felton, Giles/Chatham Central School Dist	73,295	46
Feneilius, Mary/Merrick Union Free School Dist	274	125
Fenick, Elaine/Port Washington Union Free SD	68	128
Fenlong, Bluejay/Canton Central School Dist	4	209
Fenlong, Bluejay/Norwood-Norfolk Ctl SD	4	211
Fenlong, David/Gouverneur Ctl School Dist	67	210
Fenner, Glenn/Lansing Central School Dist	3	240
Fenner, Karen/Westhill Central School Dist	16	160
Fenter, Robert/Cold Spring Harbor Central SD	1	219
Fernandez, Frances/Amityville Union Free Sch Dist	20	216
Fernandez, Richard/North Rockland Central SD	67	197
Fernandez, Ruby/New York City Dept of Ed	78	134
Ferone, Laura/Floral Park Bellerose Sch Dist	67	119
Ferrante, Robert/Island Park Union Free SD	81	122
Ferrara, Anthony/Seneca Falls Central Sch Dist	6	208
Ferrara, Thomas/Syracuse City School Dist	3	158
Ferraro, Barbara, Dr/Rye Neck Union Free Sch Dist	1	261
Ferraro, Loretta/Fire Island Union Free SD	1,11,73	222
Ferraro, Michael/Utica City School Dist	3	152
Ferreira, Janet/Middletown Enlarged City SD	294	165
Ferrera, Denise/Middle Country Ctl Sch Dist	298	225
Ferretti, Craig/Camden Central School Dist	11	150
Ferris, Christina/Arkport Central School Dist	16,82	213

#		#		#		#		#		#	
1	Superintendent	16	Instructional Media Svcs	30	Adult Education	44	Science Sec	58	Special Education K-12	72	Summer School
2	Bus/Finance/Purchasing	17	Chief Operations Officer	31	Career/Sch-to-Work K-12	45	Math K-12	59	Special Education Elem	73	Instructional Tech
3	Buildings And Grounds	18	Chief Academic Officer	32	Career/Sch-to-Work Elem	46	Math Elem	60	Special Education Sec	74	Inservice Training
4	Food Service	19	Chief Financial Officer	33	Career/Sch-to-Work Sec	47	Math Sec	61	Foreign/World Lang K-12	75	Marketing/Distributive
5	Transportation	20	Art K-12	34	Early Childhood Ed	48	English/Lang Arts K-12	62	Foreign/World Lang Elem	76	Info Systems
6	Athletic	21	Art Elem	35	Health/Phys Education	49	English/Lang Arts Elem	63	Foreign/World Lang Sec	77	Psychological Assess
7	Health Services	22	Art Sec	36	Guidance Services K-12	50	English/Lang Arts Sec	64	Religious Education K-12	78	Affirmative Action
8	Curric/Instruct K-12	23	Music K-12	37	Guidance Services Elem	51	Reading K-12	65	Religious Education Elem	79	Student Personnel
9	Curric/Instruct Elem	24	Music Elem	38	Guidance Services Sec	52	Reading Elem	66	Religious Education Sec	80	Driver Ed/Safety
10	Curric/Instruct Sec	25	Music Sec	39	Social Studies K-12	53	Reading Sec	67	School Board President	81	Gifted/Talented
11	Federal Program	26	Business Education	40	Social Studies Elem	54	Remedial Reading K-12	68	Teacher Personnel	82	Video Services
12	Title I	27	Career & Tech Ed	41	Social Studies Sec	55	Remedial Reading Elem	69	Academic Assessment	83	Substance Abuse Prev
13	Title V	28	Technology Education	42	Science K-12	56	Remedial Reading Sec	70	Research/Development	84	Erate
15	Asst Superintendent	29	Family/Consumer Science	43	Science Elem	57	Bilingual/ELL	71	Public Information	85	AIDS Education

#		#	
88	Alternative/At Risk	277	Remedial Math K-12
89	Multi-Cultural Curriculum	280	Literacy Coach
90	Social Work	285	STEM
91	Safety/Security	286	Digital Learning
92	Magnet School	288	Common Core Standards
93	Parental Involvement	294	Accountability
95	Tech Prep Program	295	Network System
97	Chief Information Officer	296	Title II Programs
98	Chief Technology Officer	297	Webmaster
270	Character Education	298	Grant Writer/Ptnrships
271	Migrant Education	750	Chief Innovation Officer
273	Teacher Mentor	751	Chief of Staff
274	Before/After Sch	752	Social Emotional Learning
275	Response To Intervention		

NY-T20

New York School Directory
DISTRICT PERSONNEL INDEX

NAME/District	JOB FUNCTIONS	PAGE
Ferris, Mark, Dr/Wantagh Union Free Sch Dist	238,11,83,285,288,294,296,298	131
Ferro, Kristen/Fredonia Central School Dist	54,58	37
Ferro, William/Jericho Union Free School Dist	67	122
Ferry, Chris/Greenwood Lake Union Free SD	6	164
Ferry, Debra/Half Hollow Hills Central SD	6	222
Fersch, Ed/Roxbury Central School Dist	67	50
Fetcie, Thomas/Hermon-DeKalb Central Sch Dist	4	210
Fetzner, Lynne/Lyndonville Central Sch Dist	5	169
Feuchter, Ann/Bolivar-Richburg Ctrl Sch Dist	5	14
Feudi, Carol/East Islip Union Free SD	68	220
Feyerabend, Michelle/Chenango Valley Ctl Sch Dist	15	28
Feyl-Crane, Heidi/Syracuse City School Dist	285	158
Fial, Carol/Cattaraugus-Allegany BOCES	15,58	34
Fial, Leo/Erie 2 Chautauqua-Catta BOCES	27	67
Fibble, Alexis/Suffern Central School Dist	12	198
Ficetti, Jason/North Bellmore Union Free SD	70,71,73,97,295,750	126
Fidurko, Andrea/Hinsdale Central School Dist	58	32
Field, Maggie/Watkins Glen Central Sch Dist	16,82	207
Field, Nicole/Catskill Central School Dist	273	75
Fierro, Anthony/Nassau BOCES	3	134
Figarella, Jill/Putnam Valley Ctl School Dist	2	176
Filarecki, Lori/Lansingburgh Central Sch Dist	273	190
Filieau, Dave/Green Island Union Free SD	3,91	10
Filippelli, Maria/Tarrytown Union Free Sch Dist	4	262
Filli, Jaime/Caledonia-Mumford Ctl Sch Dist	73,295	102
Filosa, Keith/Sayville Union Free Sch Dist	4	229
Filus, Kelly/Carthage Central School Dist	4	80
Finch, Paul/Arlington Central School Dist	15,68	51
Finch, Robert/Salamanca City Central SD	5	33
Finch, Tina/Waverly Ctl School Dist	4	239
Finder, Richard/Lindenhurst Union Free SD	39	224
Fine, Pamela/Elwood Union Free School Dist	275,280	221
Finelli, Joanne/Bellmore-Merrick Ctl High SD	4	117
Finkenbinder, Lisa/Albany City School Dist	4	9
Finkle, Jennifer/Andes Central School Dist	11,274,296,298	48
Finlay, Michele/Islip Union Free School Dist	71,97	224
Finn, Christine, Dr/Carle Place Union Free SD	1	117
Finn, Janelle/Cheektowaga-Sloan UFSD	8,12,74,285,294	59
Finn, Josh/Homer Central School Dist	73,98,295	48
Finn, Patricia/Community School District 27	34	180
Finn, Rob, Dr/Westhampton Beach School Dist	38,69,76	233
Finnerty, Kelly/Canton Central School Dist	11,34,58	209
Finnerty, Kevin/Three Village Central Sch Dist	6,35	232
Finnerty, Thomas/Cazenovia Ctl School Dist	2,15	104
Finney, Dana/Greenwich Central School Dist	33,38	247
Finney, Ryan/Bath Central School Dist	295	213
Finnigan, Trisha/Batavia City School Dist	36,58,77,79,88,90	73
Finster, Robert/Harrisville Central Sch Dist	1	101
Finter, Karen/West Irondequoit Ctl SD	10,11,73,88	113
Finton, Jeffrey/Mahopac Ctl School Dist	58	176
Finton, Shelly/South Glens Falls Ctl Sch Dist	280	202
Fiola, Elizabeth/Seaford Union Free SD	4	129
Fiore, Doug/Clinton Central School Dist	6	150
Fiorentino, Andrew/Windsor Central School Dist	2,15	30
Fiorentino, Chris/Dutchess Co BOCES	8,69,74,81	55
Fiorentino, Chris/Newburgh Enlarged City SD	45	166
Fiorino, Frank/Middle Country Ctl Sch Dist	3,91	225
Fiorino, Joseph/Bellmore Union Free Sch Dist	3,5	117
Firkins, Scott/West Seneca Central School Dist	76	64
Fischer, Chris/Newcomb Central School Dist	1	68
Fischer, Joan/Heuvelton Central School Dist	16,274	210
Fischetti, Nancy/Western Suffolk BOCES	71	236
Fisgus, John/Oakfield Alabama Ctl SD	1	74
Fish, Danie'L/McGraw Central School Dist	16,82	48
Fish, John/Greene Ctl School Dist	67	42
Fish, Mark/Greenwich Central School Dist	1	247
Fishbough, Sandra/Mechanicville City Sch Dist	4	201
Fisher, Adam/Wantagh Union Free Sch Dist 23	67	131
Fisher, Chris/Moravia Central School Dist	11,57,58,83,88,271,298	35
Fisher, Gretchen/Bloomfield Central SD	38	161
Fisher, James/Carle Place Union Free SD	16,57	117
Fisher, Kevin/Olean City School Dist	4	32
Fisher, Kim/Cuba-Rushford Central Sch Dist	58	14
Fisher, Louis/Warrensburg Central Sch Dist	73,76,286	246
Fisher, Sara/Ripley Central School Dist	7,83	39
Fisher, Scott/Johnson City Central Sch Dist	3	28
Fisher, Scott/Sag Harbor Union Free Sch Dist	73,295	229
Fisher, Sherri/South Colonie Central Sch Dist	3,30	12
Fisher, William/Westhampton Beach School Dist	8,15,68	233
Fisher, William/Worcester Ctl School Dist	67	174
Fishman, Catherine/Mineola Union Free Sch Dist	79	125
Fishman, Debra/New Rochelle City School Dist	73	259
Fisk, Betsy/Elmira City School Dist	294	40
Fiske, Evelyn/Massena Central School Dist	12,69,288,298	211
Fitch, Matthew/Canandaigua City School Dist	2,15	161
Fitch, Stephen/Mount Markham Central Sch Dist	5	78
Fitz, James/Fire Island Union Free SD	3	222
Fitzgerald, Cynthia/Islip Union Free School Dist	15,68	224
Fitzgerald, Donna/Troy City School Dsitrict	58,79	191
Fitzgerald, Jennifer/Forestville Central Sch Dist	2	37
Fitzgerald, Kim/Penn Yan Ctl School Dist	2	268
Fitzgerald, Margaret/Arlington Central School Dist	58	51
Fitzgerald, Nick/Canajoharie Ctl School Dist	1	115
Fitzgerald, Shannon/Northville Central School Dist	97	72
Fitzgibbon, Maggie/Genesee Valley BOCES	71	75
Fitzpatrick, Paul/Rome City School Dist	67	151
Fitzpatrick, Shelley/Sandy Creek Central Sch Dist	2,11	172
Fitzsimmons, Sarah/Highland Falls-Ft Montgmry SD	83,88,90	164
Flaherty, Dave/Randolph Central School Dist	3	33
Flaherty, Joseph/Minisink Valley Central SD	67	165
Flaherty, Marion/Springs Union Free School Dist	5	232
Flaherty, Michael/Moriah Central School Dist	67	68
Flaitz, Patrick/Arkport Central School Dist	67	213
Flaitz, Patrick/Hornell City School Dist	2	214
Flanagan, Elizabeth/Bridgehampton Union Free SD	7	218
Flanagan, Heather/Johnsburg Central School Dist	7,8,69,73,83,270,271,273	245
Flanagan, Steven/Southold Union Free Sch Dist	6	231
Flanders, Cathy/South Seneca Ctl Sch Dist	35	208
Flannigan, Catherine/Plainedge Union Free Sch Dist	67	127
Flansburg, Joseph/Bloomfield Central SD	3,91	161
Flatley, David/Hewlett Woodmere Union Free SD	15	121
Flattery, Alicia/Moriah Central School Dist	4	68
Fleck, Vincent/West Hempstead School Dist	28,73	131
Fleet, Brian/Prattsburgh Central Sch Dist	58	215
Fleischman, Joseph/Naples Central School Dist	3	162
Fleischman, Michael/Gilboa-Conesville Central SD	67	206
Fleischmann, Brian/Randolph Acad Union Free SD	73,76,295	32
Fleischman, Shelley/Putnam-Northern Wstchstr BOCES	58	266
Fleming, Kenneth/Hoosick Falls Central Sch Dist	4	190
Fleming, Tracy/Ctr for Instruct Tech Innov	76	172
Flint, Alicia/Milford Central School Dist	35,83	173
Flitton, Elizabeth/Holland Central School Dist	4	61
Flood, David/Rush Henrietta Central SD	3,5	112
Flood, Neil/Webster Central School Dist	3,91	112
Flood, Susan/West Irondequoit Ctl SD	7,11,34,58,79,81,88,298	113
Flores, Sherley/Rochester City School Dist	57	110
Florian, Katie/Oneida-Herkimer-Mad BOCES	68	154
Flowers, Cindy/Geneseo Central Sch Dist	1	102
Flowers, Melissa/Whitesville Central Sch Dist	97	15
Flusser, Matthew/Wappingers Central Sch Dist	4	54
Flynn Brown, Donna/Sullivan BOCES	8,15,30,58,88	238
Flynn, Aaron/Mayfield Ctl School Dist	67	72
Flynn, Don/Connetquot Central School Dist	91	219
Flynn, Kari/Brushton Moira Ctl Sch Dist	36	69
Flynn, Michael/Western Suffolk BOCES	3,17	236
Flynn, Stefanie/Mt Pleasant Ctl School Dist	2,11	258
Flynn, Thomas/Hamburg Central School Dist	67	61
Foederer, Richard/Baldwinsville Central Sch Dist	3	154
Foeller, Brian/Le Roy Central School Dist	2,78,298	73
Fogarazzo, Christian/Half Hollow Hills Central SD	42,285	222
Fogarty, James, Dr/Ellenville Central School Dist	58	241
Fogerty, Patrick/Jericho Union Free School Dist	73,295	122
Foley, John/Schenectady City School Dist	67	204
Foley, Patricia/Seaford Union Free SD	57	129
Foley, Susan/Corinth Central School Dist	2,11,19,91,294	200
Follette, Patricia/Whitney Point Central Sch Dist	1	30
Folsom, Denise/Canton Central School Dist	2	209
Fonda, Kathleen/Clinton Central School Dist	58	150
Fonneville, Jamie/Newark Central School Dist	295	250
Fontana, Cheryl/Bellmore-Merrick Ctl High SD	22,25,30	117
Fontana, Dominick/Deer Park Union Free Sch Dist	6	220
Fontana, Kim/Pawling Ctl School Dist	1	52

DISTRICT PERSONNEL INDEX

Market Data Retrieval

NAME/District	JOB FUNCTIONS	PAGE
Fontanez, Daniel/Rochester City School Dist	58	110
Forbes, James/Putnam Central School Dist	3	248
Forbes, John/Fredonia Central School Dist	2,19	37
Ford-Johnston, Cynthia/Ticonderoga Central Sch Dist	1	68
Ford, Brian/Green Island Union Free SD	6	10
Ford, Christian/Willsboro Central Sch Dist	8,27,36	68
Ford, Leslie, Dr/Northville Central School Dist	1,11	72
Ford, Mary/Katonah-Lewisboro Sch Dist	8,11,57,69,83,280,285,288	257
Ford, Sheree/Willsboro Central Sch Dist	51,54	68
Fordyce, Annette/Northville Central School Dist	7	72
Forester, Jill/Morris Central School Dist	4	174
Forget, Christopher/Fire Island Union Free SD	295	222
Forgit, Ed/Newburgh Enlarged City SD	15	165
Forman, Guy/Westbury Union Free Sch Dist	3	132
Forman, Murray/Lawrence Union Free Sch Dist	67	123
Forrester, Ken/Geneseo Central Sch Dist	2,11	102
Forsberg, Jennifer/Bronxville Union Free SD	82,286,295	253
Forsberg, Jennifer/Yorktown Central School Dist	73,295	264
Forsgren, Peter/Fairport Ctl School Dist	67	108
Forster, Linda/Clarence Central School Dist	5	59
Forte, Christopher/Sackets Harbor Ctl School Dist	73	81
Fortunato, Mary/Niagara-Wheatfield Ctl SD	30	148
Foryan, Thomas/Whitehall Central School Dist	3	248
Fosella, Danielle/Schroon Lake Ctl School Dist	2	68
Foster, Brian/Bainbridge Guilford CSD	285	41
Foster, Chris/Questar III BOCES	30	192
Foster, David/Wellsville Central Sch Dist	1	15
Foster, James/East Hampton Union Free SD	67	220
Foster, Mary, Dr/Peekskill City School Dist	9,15	260
Foster, Megan/Hermon-DeKalb Central Sch Dist	5,57,296	210
Foster, Nicole/Salmon River Central Sch Dist	4	70
Fotarty, Matthew/Trumansburg Central SD	2	241
Foti, Christien/New York City Dept of Ed	58	134
Foti, Mark/Hoosic Valley Central School Dist	11	190
Fottrell, Kevin/New Lebanon Ctl School Dist	2	46
Foulds, Stanley/Norwich City School Dist	3,91	42
Fountain, Tony/Wellsville Central Sch Dist	16,297	15
Foust, Tracy/Rensselaer City School Dist	97	191
Fowler, Donna/Schenectady City School Dist	58	204
Fowler, Jacquie/Cheektowaga-Sloan UFSD	57,58	59
Fowler, Loretta/Chateaugay Central School Dist	1	69
Fowler, Timothy/South Colonie Central Sch Dist	7,34	12
Fowler, Todd/Bloomfield Central SD	4	161
Fowler, Todd/Canandaigua City School Dist	4	161
Fox-Alter, Mary/Pleasantville Union Free SD	1,11	260
Fox, Bradley/Mexico Central School Dist	295	171
Fox, Corrine/Victor Central School Dist	7	162
Fox, Dave/Holland Central School Dist	73	61
Fox, Denise/Cortland Enlarged City SD	73,76	47
Fox, Diane/Saranac Lake Central Sch Dist	1	70
Fox, Kathy/Herkimer BOCES	8,27,31	79
Fox, Mary/Warwick Valley Central SD	31,36	167
Fox, Meredith/Nanuet Union Free School Dist	11,15,286,288,296,298	196
Fox, Shawna/Holland Patent Ctl School Dist	58	150
Foy, Love Karima/Half Hollow Hills Central SD	50,53,288	222
Foye, Wendy/Adirondack Central Sch Dist	12,60	150
Fragola, Jennifer/Liverpool Ctl School Dist	60	156
Frahm, Matthew/Naples Central School Dist	1	162
Fraleigh, Tracy/Cobleskill Richmondville SD	2	206
Frame, James/Greater Southern Tier BOCES	1	215
Frame, Mike/Randolph Central School Dist	73	33
Frament, Bridget/Diocese of Albany Ed Office	68	12
France, Kayla/Hunter Tannersville Ctl SD	2	76
France, Roxanne, Dr/Nassau BOCES	8,15	134
Franceschi, Susan/Manchester-Shortsville Ctl SD	6	162
Franchanni, James, Dr/Averill Park Central Sch Dist	1	189
Franchi, John/Bethpage Union Free Sch Dist	6,35	117
Franchini, Paul/Voorheesville Central Sch Dist	4	12
Francisco, Chad/Central Valley School Dist	5	77
Francisco, Robin/Roscoe Central School Dist	58	237
Frangella, Elizabeth, Dr/Diocese of Brooklyn Ed Office	8,15	94
Frank, Ann/Diocese of Rochester Ed Office	11,69,74	113
Frank, Bryon/Smithtown Central Sch Dist	39	230
Frank, Erica/Southold Union Free Sch Dist	2	231
Frank, Joe/West Canada Valley Ctl SD	273	79
Frank, Michael/New Hyde-Garden City Park UFSD	2,15	126
Frank, Tina/Indian River Ctl School Dist	16,82	80
Frankel, Tracy/Syosset Central School Dist	67	129
Franskevicz, David/Sullivan West Central SD	6	237
Franz, Nathan/Syracuse City School Dist	8,15	158
Fraser, Carl/Tuckahoe Common School Dist	2,11,16,285,296,298	232
Fraser, Cynthia/Brasher Falls School Dist	2	209
Fraser, Ryan/York Central School Dist	73	103
Fratto, Francisco/Herricks Union Free Sch Dist	57,63	121
Frawley, Colleen/Jordan Elbridge Ctl Sch Dist	58	155
Frazer, Sue/Minerva Central School Dist	7,85	68
Frazier, Michele/Franklin-Essex-Hamilton BOCES	297	71
Frederick, Vivienne/North Warren Central Sch Dist	73,76,295	246
Fredericks, Eileen/Carle Place Union Free SD	8,69,288,298	117
Fredrickson, Kelly/Manhasset Union Free Sch Dist	5	124
Free, Michael/Marcellus Central School Dist	6,35	157
Freedman, Ari/Honeoye Falls Lima Sch Dist	30	109
Freeman, Brian/Webster Central School Dist	2,15	112
Freeman, Kate/Bellmore-Merrick Ctl High SD	2,15,294	117
Freeman, Suzanne/Avon Central School Dist	16	102
Freeman, Todd/Cincinnatus Ctl School Dist	1	47
Freer, Joel/Highland Ctl School Dist	9	242
Frees, James/Chester Union Free School Dist	3	163
Freeston, Kenneth, Dr/North Salem Central Sch Dist	1	259
Freglette, James/Erie 1 BOCES	2,76	67
Frego, Artie/Norwood-Norfolk Ctl SD	67	211
Freiberger, Lance/WSWHE BOCES	5	249
Freitag, Lisa/Thousand Islands Central SD	37,58,69,83,288	81
Fremder, Helene/Mamaroneck Union Free Sch Dist	83	257
French, Carrie/Norwood-Norfolk Ctl SD	37	211
French, Lauren/Gouverneur Ctl School Dist	1	210
French, Lisa/Spackenkill Union Free SD	4	54
French, Michele/North Warren Central Sch Dist	1	246
Frey, Susan/Depew Union Free School Dist	8,11,15,68,69,288,296,298	59
Freyer, Glen/Brewster Central School Dist	3,88	175
Fried, Brian/Millbrook Ctl School Dist	2,15,298	52
Friedel, Jennifer/New Hartford Central Sch Dist	7,85	151
Friedermann, Maryanne/Rockville Ctr Union Free SD	4,5	128
Friedman, Beth/North Merrick Union Free SD	9,11,15,68,69	126
Friedman, Brian/Irvington Union Free Sch Dist	67	257
Friedman, Daniel/Hicksville Union Free Sch Dist	11,73	122
Friedman, Josh/East Meadow Union Free SD	6	118
Friedman, Michele/Champlain Valley Ed Services	27,31	45
Friel, Patrick/Commack Union Free School Dist	6,35,83	219
Friends, Marc/Olean City School Dist	295	32
Fries, Chad/Friendship Central Sch Dist	3,5	15
Friesen, Jason/North Babylon Union Free SD	6,7,83	226
Frisbee, Melissa/Downsville Central Sch Dist	83	49
Froass, Sherri/Vernon-Verona-Sherrill CSD	71	152
Froats, Kevin/Fort Ann Central School Dist	1	247
Froio, Dee/Hannibal Central School Dist	8,288	171
Froio, James/Jordan Elbridge Ctl Sch Dist	1	155
Frost, Judy/Watervliet City School Dist	71	12
Frost, Ronald/Lansing Central School Dist	274	240
Frye, Lynn/Fayetteville-Manlius Ctl SD	2	155
Frymire, Donna/Amherst Central School Dist	73	56
Fucci, Tom/Wantagh Union Free Sch Dist 23	3,5	131
Fuchs, Michael/Clarence Central School Dist	67	59
Fudin, Shirah/Menands Union Free Sch Dist	7	11

---

1 Superintendent
2 Bus/Finance/Purchasing
3 Buildings And Grounds
4 Food Service
5 Transportation
6 Athletic
7 Health Services
8 Curric/Instruct K-12
9 Curric/Instruct Elem
10 Curric/Instruct Sec
11 Federal Program
12 Title I
13 Title V
15 Asst Superintendent
16 Instructional Media Svcs
17 Chief Operations Officer
18 Chief Academic Officer
19 Chief Financial Officer
20 Art K-12
21 Art Elem
22 Art Sec
23 Music K-12
24 Music Elem
25 Music Sec
26 Business Education
27 Career & Tech Ed
28 Technology Education
29 Family/Consumer Science
30 Adult Education
31 Career/Sch-to-Work K-12
32 Career/Sch-to-Work Elem
33 Career/Sch-to-Work Sec
34 Early Childhood Ed
35 Health/Phys Education
36 Guidance Services K-12
37 Guidance Services Elem
38 Guidance Services Sec
39 Social Studies K-12
40 Social Studies Elem
41 Social Studies Sec
42 Science K-12
43 Science Elem
44 Science Sec
45 Math K-12
46 Math Elem
47 Math Sec
48 English/Lang Arts K-12
49 English/Lang Arts Elem
50 English/Lang Arts Sec
51 Reading K-12
52 Reading Elem
53 Reading Sec
54 Remedial Reading K-12
55 Remedial Reading Elem
56 Remedial Reading Sec
57 Bilingual/ELL
58 Special Education K-12
59 Special Education Elem
60 Special Education Sec
61 Foreign/World Lang K-12
62 Foreign/World Lang Elem
63 Foreign/World Lang Sec
64 Religious Education K-12
65 Religious Education Elem
66 Religious Education Sec
67 School Board President
68 Teacher Personnel
69 Academic Assessment
70 Research/Development
71 Public Information
72 Summer School
73 Instructional Tech
74 Inservice Training
75 Marketing/Distributive
76 Info Systems
77 Psychological Assess
78 Affirmative Action
79 Student Personnel
80 Driver Ed/Safety
81 Gifted/Talented
82 Video Services
83 Substance Abuse Prev
84 Erate
85 AIDS Education
88 Alternative/At Risk
89 Multi-Cultural Curriculum
90 Social Work
91 Safety/Security
92 Magnet School
93 Parental Involvement
94 Accountability
95 Tech Prep Program
96 Title III Programs
97 Chief Information Officer
98 Chief Technology Officer
270 Character Education
271 Migrant Education
273 Teacher Mentor
274 Before/After Sch
275 Response To Intervention
277 Remedial Math K-12
280 Literacy Coach
285 STEM
286 Digital Learning
288 Common Core Standards
294 Accountability
295 Network System
296 Title II Programs
297 Webmaster
298 Grant Writer/Ptnrships
750 Chief Innovation Officer
751 Chief of Staff
752 Social Emotional Learning

New York School Directory

DISTRICT PERSONNEL INDEX

NAME/District	JOB FUNCTIONS	PAGE
Fuehrer, Pamela/Scarsdale Union Free Sch Dist	67	261
Fuerch, Julie/Barker Central School Dist	4	146
Fuerch, Julie/Royalton Hartland Central SD	4	148
Fuest, Norbert/Genesee Valley BOCES	67	74
Fugle, Brian/Attica Central School Dist	67	267
Fuller, Caleb/Edwards-Knox Central Sch Dist	71,97	210
Fuller, Deborah/Scio Central School Dist	7	15
Fuller, Kimberly/Morristown Ctl School Dist	2	211
Fuller, Kyle/Bainbridge Guilford CSD	5	41
Fullerton, April/Parishville Hopkinton Sch Dist	752	212
Fullerton, Dan/West Irondequoit Ctl SD	16,27,76,97,286,295,297	113
Fulton, Reanna/West Islip School Dist	16,73,82,95,286	233
Fulton, Terry, Dr/Amityville Union Free Sch Dist	67	216
Fulton, Theodore, Dr/Bayport- Blue Point USD	8,12,15	217
Funck, Ryan/Hunter Tannersville Ctl SD	10,83	76
Furcht, Colette/Riverhead Central School Dist	5	228
Furcht, Mary/Baldwin Union Free School Dist	71	116
Furletti, David/York Central School Dist	1,11	103
Furlong, Meredith/Altmar-Parish-Williamstown SD	11,58	170
Furlong, Michelle/Brunswick Central School Dist	73	190
Furlong, William/Fayetteville-Manlius Ctl SD	2,5,7,15,31,83,85,88	155
Furman, Gary, Dr/Edmeston Ctl School Dist	1,11	173
Furnia, Maryjo/Canton Central School Dist	294	209
Fursman, Daniel/Pittsford Central Sch Dist	3	110
Fusco, Lynn/Cattaraugus-Allegany BOCES	1	34
Fusco, Lynn/Harrison Central School Dist	20,23	256
Fusco, Lynn, Dr/Erie 1 BOCES	1	67
Fusco, Nicholas/East Williston Union Free SD	3	118
Fussa, Robert/Wayne Central School Dist	3,91	251
Fyvie, Thomas/Scotia Glenville Ctl Sch Dist	36	205

G

NAME/District	JOB FUNCTIONS	PAGE
Gabree-Huba, Michelle/Shenendehowa Central Sch Dist	43	202
Gabri, Meghan/Madrid-Waddington Central SD	16,82	211
Gaff, Gerald/Eldred Central School Dist	6,83,85	236
Gaffney, Jennifer/Sackets Harbor Ctl School Dist	1,11,288	81
Gaffney, Lynn/Jefferson Lewis BOCES	74	82
Gaffney, Scott/New Hartford Central Sch Dist	5	151
Gaffney, Timothy/Oriskany Ctl School Dist	1	151
Gagan, Shaun/Belleville Henderson Sch Dist	36	79
Gaglioti, Lisa/Mohonasen Central Sch Dist	67	204
Gagnon, Kimberly/Mohonasen Central Sch Dist	4	203
Gaiss, Tara/Northport-East Northport UFSD	51	227
Gajewski, Janet/Depew Union Free School Dist	58	59
Gajewski, Mike/Forestville Central Sch Dist	5	37
Galano, Christopher/Harrison Central School Dist	6,35	256
Galano, Pat/Garden City School Dist	73	120
Galante, Thomas/Elmont Union Free School Dist	2	118
Galante, Victoria/Glen Cove City School Dist	2,15	120
Galbraith, Carol/Brunswick Central School Dist	274	190
Galenski, Andrea/Cheektowaga-Sloan UFSD	1	59
Galente, Dawn/Arlington Central School Dist	42,45,285	51
Gallagher, Jennifer, Dr/Long Beach City School Dist	1	124
Gallagher, John/Longwood Central School Dist	20,23	225
Gallagher, Julie/Maine Endwell Ctl School Dist	8,15,294	29
Gallagher, Lindsey/Madison Central School Dist	7	105
Gallagher, Maura/Franklin Square Union Free SD	9,15,69,74,273,285,288,294	119
Gallagher, Richard/Bay Shore Union Free Sch Dist	5	217
Gallagher, Tammy/Hammond Central School Distict	2	210
Gallaher, Patricia/Dcmo BOCES Chenango	58,275	43
Gallant, Pam/Red Creek Central School Dist	4	251
Gallassio, Vincenza/Community School District 31	1	192
Gallegos, Alba/Hewlett Woodmere Union Free SD	57	121
Gallivan, Brendan/Greenburgh Central School Dist	57,61	255
Gallo, Frank/Mount Vernon City School Dist	280	258
Gallo, Julia/Half Hollow Hills Central SD	90	222
Gallo, Michelle/Baldwin Union Free School Dist	15,68	116
Galluzzo, Charles, Dr/Evans-Brant Central Sch Dist	1	60
Galton, Todd/Keshequa Central School Dist	67	103
Galusha, Nancy/Seneca Falls Central Sch Dist	16	208
Galvan, Concetta/Central Square Central SD	8,11,15,68,296,298	170
Galvin, Sue/Lackawanna City School Dist	58	62
Gamble, Kevin/Heuvelton Central School Dist	3	210
Gamello, Joann/Diocese of Albany Ed Office	2	12
Gance-Virkler, Beth/Candor Central School Dist	36	238
Gander, Ryan/Wheelerville Union Free SD	6	72

NAME/District	JOB FUNCTIONS	PAGE
Gandolfo, Gina/West Hempstead School Dist	5	131
Gannon, Josh/Vestal Ctl School Dist	6,35	29
Gannon, Kyle/Queensbury Union Free Sch Dist	1	246
Ganoug, Dina/South Seneca Ctl Sch Dist	7	208
Garassi, Bernard/Fredonia Central School Dist	27	37
Garbarino, David/Binghamton City School Dist	6,7,35,85	27
Garcia, Carlos/Rochester City School Dist	71	110
Garcia, Elliot/Millbrook Ctl School Dist	73	52
Garcia, John/Ticonderoga Central Sch Dist	3	68
Garcia, Patricia, Dr/Geneva City School Dist	1	161
Garcia, Steven, Dr/Pelham Union Free School Dist	8,11,15,68,69,288,296	260
Garcia, Wilfredo/Buffalo Public Schools	57	57
Gardineer, Erin/Northville Central School Dist	58	72
Gardiner, Scott/Greenville Central School Dist	73	75
Gardiner, Vicki/Chateaugay Central School Dist	73	69
Gardner, Guy/New Paltz Ctl School Dist	3	242
Gardner, Jen/Hunter Tannersville Ctl SD	58	76
Gardner, Jennifer/Hammond Central School Distict	67	210
Gardner, Justin/Willsboro Central Sch Dist	1,11,83	68
Gardner, Michael/Town of Webb Union Free SD	3,5	78
Gardner, Sandra/Taconic Hills Central Sch Dist	8,12,69,74,286,288,296,298	47
Gardner, Sharon/Hempstead Union Free SD	4	121
Garigen, Lisa/Marion Central School Dist	16	250
Garland, Bob/Troy City School Dsitrict	3,91	191
Garling, Debra/Monroe Woodbury Central SD	81	165
Garman, Connie/Saranac Central School Dist	8,58	45
Garman, Connie/Saranac Central School Dist	8,58	45
Garner, James/Broadalbin-Perth Ctl Sch Dist	4	71
Garner, Rebecca/South Lewis Central Sch Dist	77	101
Garnsey, Kenny/Thousand Islands Central SD	3	81
Garofalo, Lisa/North Syracuse Ctl Sch Dist	58	157
Garofano, Paul/Edgemont Union Free Sch Dist	73	254
Garone, Joan/Ossining Union Free Sch Dist	12,68	259
Garrand, Rob/Northeastern Clinton Ctl SD	1	44
Garrett, Renee/Forestville Central Sch Dist	1	37
Garsan, Susan/Bay Shore Union Free Sch Dist	67	217
Garsetti, Margaret/Springs Union Free School Dist	35,57	232
Garuccio, Larry/Auburn Enlarged City Sch Dist	3,91	34
Garverick, John/Connetquot Central School Dist	5	219
Garvey, Lisa/Penn Yan Ctl School Dist	57	268
Gasbarro, David/Red Creek Central School Dist	5	251
Gassar, Charles/Riverhead Central School Dist	36	228
Gately, Danielle/East Williston Union Free SD	8,288	118
Gates, Andrew/Mexico Central School Dist	6,27,31,83	171
Gates, Scott/Syracuse City School Dist	3	158
Gathen, Shawn/Schoharie Central SD	3	206
Gatto, Karen/Croton-Harmon Union Free SD	57,58,77,79,88,280,298,752	254
Gattus, Michael/Levittown Union Free School Dist	274	123
Gaven, Matthew/Mineola Union Free Sch Dist	8,15,58,73,74,81	125
Gavish, Bea/Greenburgh-Graham UFSD	69	255
Gay, Pierre/Longwood Central School Dist	73,76	225
Gaylord, Karen/Holley Central School Dist	2,71,97	169
Gayne, Julie/Sackets Harbor Ctl School Dist	2	81
Gear, Judy/Whitesville Central Sch Dist	77	15
Gebo, Mike/Lyme Central School Dist	73,295	81
Gee, David/Bedford Central School Dist	73,76,295	252
Geelan, Karen, Dr/Greater Johnstown Sch Dist	1	71
Geidel, Barbara/Walton Central School Dist	16	50
Geidel, Henry/Niskayuna Central School Dist	73,286	204
Geiger, Karl/Long Lake Central School Dist	4	76
Geist, Adam/Hilton Central School Dist	15	109
Geitner, Geri/Fulton City School Dist	11,36,79,275	170
Gelber, Eric/Johnsburg Central School Dist	16	245
Gelder, Matt/Candor Central School Dist	73	238
Gelfer, Kelly/East Meadow Union Free SD	20,23	118
Gellar, Steven/West Islip School Dist	67	233
Gellman, Robert/Washingtonville Central SD	4	167
Gelsinan, Maura/Perry Central School Dist	298	267
Gelz, Karin/Oakfield Alabama Ctl SD	77	74
Gemignami, Angela/Trumansburg Central SD	8,11,57,58,69,298	241
Genauer, Jeanine/Hastings on Hudson Union FR SD	71	256
Genden-Sage, Arlene, Dr/Island Trees Union Free SD	15,58,69	122
Gendrue, Michael/Barker Central School Dist	36,88	146
Gennett, Stephen/Broadalbin-Perth Ctl Sch Dist	73,286,295	71
Genter, Jeff/Sherburne Earlville Central SD	3	42
Gentile, Sarah/Syracuse City School Dist	20,23	158

DISTRICT PERSONNEL INDEX

Market Data Retrieval

NAME/District	JOB FUNCTIONS	PAGE
Genton, Von/Longwood Central School Dist	30	225
Genzel, Karen/McGraw Central School Dist	9,12,58,69	48
George, Brian/Glens Falls Common Sch Dist	1,11,83,288	245
George, Jenna/Albion Central School Dist	37	169
George, Joanne/East Aurora Union Free SD	2,5	60
George, Maureen/Cheektowaga Central SD	8,57,288	58
George, Rodney/Avon Central School Dist	67	102
George, Sherry/Port Chester Rye Union Free SD	84	261
Georgeadis, Amy/Queensbury Union Free Sch Dist	68	246
Georgi, Bonnie/Cherry Valley-Springfield SD	58,77	173
Gerace, Deborah/Phoenix Central School Dist	5	171
Gerace, Ellen/Peekskill City School Dist	12,58,88,275	260
Gerace, Ross/Keshequa Central School Dist	275	103
Gerarde, Beth/Gowanda Central School Dist	36,83,90	32
Gerber, Jennifer/Galway Central School Dist	35	201
Gerchman, Iraina/Central Square Central SD	3,295	170
Gere-Penna, Mary/Geneva City School Dist	2	161
Gereau, Brian/Hadley-Luzerne Ctl Sch Dist	3	245
Gergis, Sam, Dr/South Country Central Sch Dist	2,15	231
Gerhart, Jeffery/Perry Central School Dist	90	267
Geringswald, Eric/Half Hollow Hills Central SD	67	222
Germano, Inger/Three Village Central Sch Dist	67	232
Germer, Rex/Town of Webb Union Free SD	1,11,73	78
Gerold, Roberta, Dr/Middle Country Ctl Sch Dist	1	225
Gerome, Timothy/Lisbon Central School Dist	3	210
Geroux, Greg/Florida Union Free Sch Dist	36,79,88,752	164
Gerson, Barbara/Commack Union Free School Dist	45	219
Gerst, Pam/Greene Ctl School Dist	7,85	42
Gertis, Bradley/Friendship Central Sch Dist	6	15
Gesing, Amanda/Jamestown City School Dist	298	38
Gesner, Rena/Suffern Central School Dist	2	198
Getty, Brian/Hartford Central School Dist	67	248
Gherardi, Julie/Somers Central School Dist	8,273,280,285,288	262
Giacoia, Lisa/Bay Shore Union Free Sch Dist	15,68	217
Giaculli, Sarah/Corinth Central School Dist	82	200
Giametta, John/Beacon City School Dist	6,7,35	51
Giancoli, William/Horseheads Ctl School Dist	73,295	40
Giangreco, Elizabeth/Cheektowaga Maryvale UFSD	8,11,57,88,288,296,298,750	59
Giani, Joseph, Dr/South Country Central Sch Dist	1	231
Giannicchi, Tony/Allegany-Limestone Ctl SD	1	31
Giannopollous, Maria/Great Neck Public Schools	72	120
Giansante, Amanda/Avon Central School Dist	36	102
Giaquinto, Andrew/Scotia Glenville Ctl Sch Dist	2	205
Giardina, Michael/Minisink Valley Central SD	15,68	165
Giarrizzo, Joseph/Niagara Falls City Sch Dist	2	147
Giarrizzo, Peter, Dr/North Shore Central SD	1	126
Gibbins, Sean/Springs Union Free School Dist	295	232
Gibbone, Michael/Levittown Union Free Sch Dist	295	123
Gibbons, John/Carthage Central School Dist	5	80
Gibbons, John/Springs Union Free School Dist	73,286	232
Gibbons, Patricia/Lyme Central School Dist	8,11,58,69,273,288,298	81
Gibbons, Paul/Croton-Harmon Union Free SD	3,91	254
Giboo, Amy/Belfast Central School Dist	35	14
Gibson, Stephanie/Warrensburg Central Sch Dist	57,58,79,275,296	246
Gidding, Josh/Chateaugay Central School Dist	35,85	69
Gierasch, Jill/Mattituck-Cutchogue UFSD	1	225
Giese, Barbara/Hewlett Woodmere Union Free SD	12,71,296,298	121
Gifford, Don/Wells Central School Dist	73,295	77
Gifford, Lindsey/Laurens Central School Dist	58,69,288,752	173
Gifford, Neil/Cambridge Central School Dist	67	247
Gifford, Tucker/Broadalbin-Perth Ctl Sch Dist	6,35	71
Gigante, Hugh, Dr/Western Suffolk BOCES	68	236
Giglio Blanco, Daniel/Half Hollow Hills Central SD	34	222
Giglio, Brad/Canaseraga Central Sch Dist	3	14
Giglio, Tom/Albany City School Dist	57,89,271	9
Gilberg, William/Mineola Union Free Sch Dist	5	125
Gilbert, Shannon/Canaseraga Central Sch Dist	7,8,11,69,74,288,294	14
Gilbert, Stephanie/Heuvelton Central School Dist	77	210
Gilbertson, Karen/Walton Central School Dist	38	50
Gilbo, Erin/Moriah Central School Dist	295	68
Gildemeister, Carlos/Cuba-Rushford Central Sch Dist	1	14
Giles, Carol/Fishers Island Union Free SD	29	222
Gilet, Tracey/Jericho Union Free School Dist	4	122
Gilevski, Joshua/Cassadaga Valley Ctl Sch Dist	11,31,34	36
Gilfus, Joseph/Thousand Islands Central SD	27,30,88	81
Gilhuley, Steven/Malverne Union Free Sch Dist	8,15	124
Gill, Anthony/Horseheads Ctl School Dist	15	40
Gill, Chris/Campbell-Savona Ctl Sch Dist	8,69,273	213
Gill, Dave/Chenango Valley Ctl Sch Dist	1	28
Gill, Lottie/Gowanda Central School Dist	88	32
Gill, Michael/Elmira Heights Ctl Sch Dist	1	40
Gilleo, Elizabeth/Hendrick Hudson Ctl Sch Dist	5	256
Giller, Margaret/Mechanicville City Sch Dist	71,97	201
Gillespie, Micheal/Pine Bush Central School Dist	6,35	166
Gillette, Brigitte/Copenhagen Central SD	31,36,69,83,85,88,270	101
Gillette, John/Herkimer BOCES	295	79
Gillette, Shannon/Union-Endicott Ctl Sch Dist	73,76,98,286	29
Gillie, Andrew/Hermon-DeKalb Central Sch Dist	58,77	210
Gillooley, Larry/Niskayuna Central School Dist	35	204
Gillooley, Terry/Middleburgh Ctl School Dist	2	206
Gilman, Judy/Massena Central School Dist	7	211
Gilmartin, James/West Islip School Dist	39	233
Gilmore, Janet/William Floyd School Dist	15,68,78	233
Gilmore, Paul/Northern Adirondack Ctl SD	67	44
Gilmore, Rodney, Dr/Hempstead Union Free SD	15,68	121
Gilmour, Jessica/Millbrook Ctl School Dist	83,85	52
Gimigliano, Robert/Bedford Central School Dist	3,91	252
Ginestre, Michael/Sherman Central School Dist	1	39
Giodinao, Carlo/South Huntington Union Free SD	3,91	231
Giopulos, Dean/Wellsville Central Sch Dist	6,35	15
Giordano, Daniel/Lindenhurst Union Free SD	1	224
Giordano, Paul/Commack Union Free School Dist	16,73,76	219
Giosi, Ken/Bridgehampton Union Free SD	12,58	218
Giovinazzi, Lizzette/Wappingers Central Sch Dist	41,50	54
Gipe, Michele/East Syracuse Minoa Ctl SD	8	154
Girard, Kari/Schenectady City School Dist	77,83	204
Giroux, James/Saranac Central School Dist	3	45
Giroux, Peter/Burnt Hills Ballston Lake SD	23	200
Girton, John/Franklin Central School Dist	76,286,294,295	49
Giruzzi, Michael/Hilton Central School Dist	6,35	109
Gismervik, Jean/Dobbs Ferry Union Free SD	11,34,58,88,275	254
Gitlen, Brad/East Ramapo Central Sch Dist	6,35	196
Giunta, Danielle/Community School District 26	1	179
Glascott, Edgar/Newburgh Enlarged City SD	6	165
Glass, Robert, Dr/Eastchester Union Free SD	1	254
Glassman, Julie/Edmeston Ctl School Dist	6	173
Glasu, Emmanuel/Greenburgh 11 Union Free SD	11	255
Glavin, Teresa/Milford Central School Dist	8,275,285	173
Gleason, Cassandra/Stockbridge Valley Central SD	36,69,88	106
Gleason, Charles/Syosset Central School Dist	83	129
Gleason, David/Rockland BOCES	2,15	199
Gleason, Peter/Oneida City School Dist	58,77	105
Gleason, Phil/Belleville Henderson Sch Dist	5	79
Glinski, Sheila/Malone Central School Dist	7,83	69
Gloff, Wayne/Letchworth Central School Dist	5	267
Gloss, Wendy/Orchard Park Central Sch Dist	58	63
Glover, David/Salem Central School Dist	1	248
Glurich, Ben/North Tonawanda City Sch Dist	4	148
Gnau, Edwar/Newark Central School Dist	2,12,15	250
Godkin, Jason/Phoenix Central School Dist	3,91	171
Godshall, Barbara, Dr/Lewiston Porter Ctl Sch Dist	57,58,77,88,271,298	146
Godshall, Clark, Dr/Orleans-Niagara BOCES	1	170
Godzich, Norine/Cheektowaga-Sloan UFSD	5	59
Goebel, Kristina/Duanesburg Central Sch Dist	31,36,83	203

#		#		#		#		#		#	
1	Superintendent	16	Instructional Media Svcs	30	Adult Education	44	Science Sec	58	Special Education K-12	72	Summer School
2	Bus/Finance/Purchasing	17	Chief Operations Officer	31	Career/Sch-to-Work K-12	45	Math K-12	59	Special Education Elem	73	Instructional Tech
3	Buildings And Grounds	18	Chief Academic Officer	32	Career/Sch-to-Work Elem	46	Math Elem	60	Special Education Sec	74	Inservice Training
4	Food Service	19	Chief Financial Officer	33	Career/Sch-to-Work Sec	47	Math Sec	61	Foreign/World Lang K-12	75	Marketing/Distributive
5	Transportation	20	Art K-12	34	Early Childhood Ed	48	English/Lang Arts K-12	62	Foreign/World Lang Elem	76	Info Systems
6	Athletic	21	Art Elem	35	Health/Phys Education	49	English/Lang Arts Elem	63	Foreign/World Lang Sec	77	Psychological Assess
7	Health Services	22	Art Sec	36	Guidance Services K-12	50	English/Lang Arts Sec	64	Religious Education K-12	78	Affirmative Action
8	Curric/Instruct K-12	23	Music K-12	37	Guidance Services Elem	51	Reading K-12	65	Religious Education Elem	79	Student Personnel
9	Curric/Instruct Elem	24	Music Elem	38	Guidance Services Sec	52	Reading Elem	66	Religious Education Sec	80	Driver Ed/Safety
10	Curric/Instruct Sec	25	Music Sec	39	Social Studies K-12	53	Reading Sec	67	School Board President	81	Gifted/Talented
11	Federal Program	26	Business Education	40	Social Studies Elem	54	Remedial Reading K-12	68	Teacher Personnel	82	Video Services
12	Title I	27	Career & Tech Ed	41	Social Studies Sec	55	Remedial Reading Elem	69	Academic Assessment	83	Substance Abuse Prev
13	Title V	28	Technology Education	42	Science K-12	56	Remedial Reading Sec	70	Research/Development	84	Erate
15	Asst Superintendent	29	Family/Consumer Science	43	Science Elem	57	Bilingual/ELL	71	Public Information	85	AIDS Education

88	Alternative/At Risk	277	Remedial Math K-12
89	Multi-Cultural Curriculum	280	Literacy Coach
90	Social Work	285	STEM
91	Safety/Security	286	Digital Learning
92	Magnet School	288	Common Core Standards
93	Parental Involvement	294	Accountability
95	Tech Prep Program	295	Network System
97	Chief Infomation Officer	296	Title II Programs
98	Chief Technology Officer	297	Webmaster
270	Character Education	298	Grant Writer/Ptnrships
271	Migrant Education	750	Chief Innovation Officer
273	Teacher Mentor	751	Chief of Staff
274	Before/After Sch	752	Social Emotional Learning
275	Response To Intervention		

New York School Directory
DISTRICT PERSONNEL INDEX

NAME/District	JOB FUNCTIONS	PAGE
Goetze, Dana/Long Lake Central School Dist	6,35	76
Goff, Suzanne/Gates Chili Central Sch Dist	74	108
Goffman, Sheryl/Rye City School Dist	8,11,15,288,296	261
Gold, Paul, Dr/Three Village Central Sch Dist	39	232
Goldbeck, Michael/Pine Plains Ctl School Dist	2,15	53
Goldberg, Austin/Peekskill City School Dist	6,7,35	260
Goldberg, Lisa/North Syracuse Ctl Sch Dist	36,93,270,752	157
Goldberg, Michael/Farmingdale Union Free SD	67	119
Goldberg, Michael/Roosevelt Union Free Sch Dist	2,15,19	128
Goldberg, Steven/Babylon Union Free Sch Dist	274	216
Golden, Rita/Mt Pleasant Cottage UFSD	67	258
Goldman, Douglas/Blind Brook-Rye Union Free SD	6,35	252
Goldmark, Karin/New York City Dept of Ed	15	134
Goldspiel, Michael/Roslyn School Dist	15	129
Goldstein, Lori/Patchogue-Medford Unified SD	59	227
Gomez, Eric/East Quogue Union Free SD	3	221
Gomez, Evelyn/Geneva City School Dist	57	161
Gondek, Allison/Silver Creek Central Sch Dist	27,36	39
Gonyea, Jennifer/Bethlehem Central School Dist	42	10
Gonyeau, Christine/Schroon Lake Ctl School Dist	280	68
Gonyo, Joseph/Minerva Central School Dist	5	68
Gonzales, Timothy/Worcester Ctl School Dist	1,11	174
Gonzalez, Gabrielle/Windham Ashland Jewett Ctl SD	85	76
Gonzalez, Georgia/Liberty Central School Dist	2,97	236
Gonzalez, Xiomara/Roosevelt Union Free Sch Dist	57,61	128
Goodfellow, Chad/Questar III BOCES	73,76	192
Goodman, Amy/Tuckahoe Union Free SD	1	262
Goodman, Barbara/Akron Central School Dist	4	56
Goodman, Emma/Pocantico Hills Ctl Sch Dist	6	260
Goodman, Patrick/Vernon-Verona-Sherrill CSD	58	152
Goodrow, Joseph/Cheektowaga-Sloan UFSD	3	59
Goodson, John/Jamesville-DeWitt Central SD	6,7,35	155
Goodway, Joe/Pine Valley Central Sch Dist	5	38
Goodwin, Karen/Fishers Island Union Free SD	1,11,288	222
Goodwin, Kathy/Saratoga Springs City Sch Dist	76	201
Goodwin, Peter/East Greenbush Central SD	73,76,286,295	190
Goodwin, Peter/Schenectady City School Dist	16,95,295	204
Goolden, Katherine/Norwich City School Dist	57,58,270,298	42
Gooshaw, James/South Colonie Central Sch Dist	3	12
Goossen, Doreen/East Irondequoit Ctl Sch Dist	36,88	107
Goralski, John/Warrensburg Central Sch Dist	1,11,288	246
Gordan, Molly/Bolton Central School Dist	18,19,58	244
Gordon, Doreen/Hauppauge Union Free Sch Dist	26,39	223
Gordon, Jeffrey/Fayetteville-Manlius Ctl SD	11,15,68	155
Gordon, Michael/Lawrence Union Free Sch Dist	6,35,85	123
Gordon, Michael/Little Flower Union Free SD	58	224
Gorham, Ronald/South Glens Falls Ctl Sch Dist	3,91	202
Gorley, Cindy/Honeoye Falls Lima Sch Dist	73,76,95,286,295,297	109
Gorman, Jeff, Dr/Mount Vernon City School Dist	15,69	258
Gorman, Sue/Schenectady City School Dist	34	204
Gorr, Jennifer/Monticello Central School Dist	58	237
Gorski, Sheila/Community School District 32	1	93
Gorton, John/Franklin Central School Dist	73,76,752	49
Gorton, Michael/Geneva City School Dist	38	161
Gosh, Michelle/Brewster Central School Dist	8,15,69	175
Goskoski, Tom/Marathon Ctl School Dist	2	48
Goss, Philomena/Lowville Acad-Central Sch Dist	9	101
Goss, Rob/Lowville Acad-Central Sch Dist	6	101
Gosselin, Kim/Chazy Central Rural Sch Dist	7,69	44
Gotham, Jaime/Edwards-Knox Central Sch Dist	93	210
Gottesman, Rebecca/Malverne Union Free Sch Dist	36	124
Gounaris, James/Great Neck Public Schools	4	120
Gow, Cindy/Springville Griffith Inst CSD	298,752	63
Gowan, William/Phelps-Clifton Springs Ctl SD	73,76,295	162
Goyer, James/Wynantskill Union Free SD	5	191
Gracy, Timothy/Oneonta City School Dist	11,58	174
Gradoski, Carol-Anne/Brentwood Union Free Sch Dist	4	217
Grady, Aaron/Fonda Fultonville Central SD	83	115
Graf, Michael/Cattaraugus-Allegany BOCES	73	34
Graff, Marc/Medina Central School Dist	2,15,68	169
Graham, Brian/Islip Union Free School Dist	3	224
Graham, Brian, Dr/Grand Island Central Sch Dist	1	61
Graham, Dawn/New York State Dept Education	81	1
Graham, Jackson/Chautauqua Lake Central SD	2,71	36
Graham, Keith/Riverhead Central School Dist	4	228
Graham, Kenneth, Dr/Locust Valley Ctl School Dist	1	123
Graham, Scott/Bainbridge Guilford CSD	286	41
Graham, Timothy/Glens Falls City School Dist	67	245
Graham, Tom/Lynbrook Union Free Sch Dist	6	124
Graham, Vincenza/Smithtown Central Sch Dist	57,63	230
Gramando, Joseph/Chappaqua Central School Dist	3,91	253
Grambs, Fred/Wayland-Cohocton Central SD	76	215
Grandjean, Mindy/Belleville Henderson Sch Dist	4	79
Grandjean, Nicole/Copenhagen Central SD	4	101
Graney, Michael/Bolton Central School Dist	1	244
Granger, Montgomery/Wyandanch Union Free Sch Dist	3	234
Granieri, Ray/Niagara Falls City Sch Dist	76	147
Grannell, Francine/Skaneateles Central Sch Dist	8,48	157
Grant, Cyril/Berlin Central School Dist	3	189
Grant, Daniel/Lackawanna City School Dist	15	62
Grant, James/Akron Central School Dist	67	56
Grant, Kristin/Edwards-Knox Central Sch Dist	73	210
Grant, Laura/North Rockland Central SD	16	197
Grant, Michelle/Sag Harbor Union Free Sch Dist	37	229
Granuzzo, Vic/Irvington Union Free Sch Dist	5	257
Granuzzo, Victor/Ardsley Union Free School Dist	5	252
Granuzzo, Victor/Hastings on Hudson Union FR SD	5	256
Gratto, Stephen/Schroon Lake Ctl School Dist	1	68
Grau, Bill/Oneonta City School Dist	67	174
Graupman, Kathleen/Greece Central School Dist	1	108
Gravelin, Jody/Sidney Central School Dist	36	50
Gravell, Allen/Salmon River Central Sch Dist	58	70
Graves, Cynthia/Copenhagen Central SD	23	101
Gravlin, David/Potsdam Central School Dist	4	212
Gray-Tinnesz, Christine, Dr/Orchard Park Central Sch Dist	67	63
Gray, Chris/Sharon Springs Ctl SD	5	207
Gray, Maureen/Waterville Central Sch Dist	8	153
Gray, Richard/Frontier Ctl School Dist	6,7,35	60
Gray, Robert/Waterville Central Sch Dist	36,69,72,81,88	153
Gray, Susan/Clyde-Savannah Central SD	2,3,15,19,288	249
Gray, Terry/Frewsburg Central School Dist	6	38
Graziano, Raymond/West Babylon Union Free SD	3	232
Grecco, Daniel/Fallsburg Central School Dist	2,5,71,91,97	236
Greco, Joseph, Dr/Saratoga Springs City Sch Dist	2	201
Greco, Karen/Williamsville Ctl School Dist	39,57,61	64
Green, Amy/Lowville Acad-Central Sch Dist	5	101
Green, Corey/Owego Apalachin Ctl School Dist	1	238
Green, Dan/Sackets Harbor Ctl School Dist	6	81
Green, Dave/East Rochester Union Free SD	3,5	107
Green, Gary/Pawling Ctl School Dist	3	52
Green, Heidi/Fayetteville-Manlius Ctl SD	36	155
Green, Jean/Jasper Troupsburg Central SD	6	215
Green, Jessica/Honeoye Central School Dist	68	161
Green, Kerri/Sidney Central School Dist	67	50
Green, Lisa/Auburn Enlarged City Sch Dist	2	34
Green, Mariann/South Lewis Central Sch Dist	38	101
Green, Maura/Middleburgh Ctl School Dist	31,36,57,58,79,88	206
Green, Patterson/Sharon Springs Ctl SD	1	207
Green, Rebecca/Pine Plains Ctl School Dist	79	53
Green, Sean/South Seneca Ctl Sch Dist	38,83	208
Green, Todd/Beaver River Central School Dist	1,11	101
Green, Vicent/Massapequa Union Free SD 23	20,23	125
Greenberg, Alexandra/Ossining Union Free Sch Dist	45	259
Greenberg, Heather/Greenwood Lake Union Free SD	77	164
Greene, Heather/Geneseo Central Sch Dist	16,82	103
Greene, Joanne/Keshequa Central School Dist	2	103
Greenfield, Michael/Harrison Central School Dist	8,11,15,16,95	256
Greenman, Vicky/Richfield Springs Central SD	16	174
Greenway, Rhonda/Rensselaer City School Dist	5	191
Greenway, Rhonda/Schodack Central School Dist	5	191
Greer, Thomas/Fulton City School Dist	68	170
Gregg, Timothy/Hempstead Union Free SD	3	121
Gregor, Mary Ann/Nanuet Union Free School Dist	4	196
Gregory, Barbara/Penfield Central School Dist	78	109
Gregory, Gary/Roosevelt Union Free Sch Dist	6,35	128
Gregory, Greta/Allegany-Limestone Ctl SD	10,37	31
Gregory, Jeff/Guilderland Central Sch Dist	30	11
Gregory, Laurie/Holland Central School Dist	8,76,288	61
Gregory, Lorre/Milford Central School Dist	298	173
Gregory, Melissa/Duanesburg Central Sch Dist	285	203
Gregory, Ronald/Vernon-Verona-Sherrill CSD	3,91	152
Gregory, Winsome, Dr/Nyack Union Free School Dist	8,12,15,68,69,288	197

DISTRICT PERSONNEL INDEX

Market Data Retrieval

NAME/District	JOB FUNCTIONS	PAGE
Greig, Linda/Pembroke Ctl School Dist	2	74
Greiner, Michael/Diocese of Brooklyn Ed Office	73,76	95
Greklek, David/Lansingburgh Central Sch Dist	5	190
Grenier, Kathy/Adirondack Central Sch Dist	33,38	150
Grenier, Randy/Geneva City School Dist	6	161
Grennan, Kyle/Greenville Central School Dist	295	75
Gresens, Carrie/Granville Central School Dist	16	247
Grevell, Theresa/Gananda Central School Dist	16,73,295	249
Grey, Christopher/Sharon Springs Ctl SD	73	207
Grey, Dan/Schroon Lake Ctl School Dist	3,91	68
Gribbin, Matthew/Smithtown Central Sch Dist	67	230
Gridley, Stacey/Afton Central School Dist	73	41
Grieco, Christopher/Sandy Creek Central Sch Dist	73	172
Griep, Matthew/South Glens Falls Ctl Sch Dist	6,7,35,85	202
Griffin, Christine/Medina Central School Dist	2	169
Griffin, Janet/Cortland Enlarged City SD	67	47
Griffin, Jay/Indian Lake Ctl School Dist	3,5	76
Griffin, Jerry/Malone Central School Dist	1	69
Griffin, Robbin/Fulton City School Dist	67	170
Griffin, Todd/Sherburne Earlville Central SD	2,15,16,73,286	42
Griffith, Elizabeth/Portville Central School Dist	37	32
Griffith, Holly/Bemus Point Ctl School Dist	2	36
Griffith, Johnathan/Herkimer BOCES	74	79
Griffiths, John/Croton-Harmon Union Free SD	8,15,288	254
Griffiths, Kerry/Amagansett Union Free Sch Dist	3,5	216
Griggs, Cathy/Newfield Central School Dist	73,74	241
Grimaldi, Karla/Pelham Union Free School Dist	4	260
Grimes, Karen/Waterford Halfmoon School Dist	77	203
Grimes, Todd/Wheatland Chili Ctl Sch Dist	6	113
Grimm, Garrett/General Brown Ctl School Dist	3,5,17,91	80
Grimm, Jeanie/Canandaigua City School Dist	67	161
Grimm, Pamela/Edmeston Ctl School Dist	8,58	173
Grimm, Stephen, Dr/Clinton Central School Dist	1	150
Grinnell, Cindy/Moriah Central School Dist	273	68
Grisewood, Kari/Warsaw Central School Dist	2	267
Grishman, Henry/Jericho Union Free School Dist	1,11	122
Grodski, Carolynn/Island Trees Union Free SD	4	122
Groduina, Claire/Berne-Knox-Westerlo Central SD	4	10
Groe, Suzanne/Sachem Central School Dist	63	229
Groff, Chad/Canaseraga Central Sch Dist	1	14
Groff, Donald/Greater Johnstown Sch Dist	295	71
Groff, Rosanne/New York State Dept Education	3	1
Groff, Russell/Copenhagen Central SD	5	101
Grogan, Jack/Albany City School Dist	91	9
Grogan, Melissa/Stockbridge Valley Central SD	3,16,72	106
Grome, Phillip/Onondaga-Cortland-Madson BOCES	27,31,88	160
Grose, Krista/Webster Central School Dist	71	112
Gross, Rebecca/Avon Central School Dist	5	102
Gross, Stan/Richfield Springs Central SD	5	174
Grossane, James, Dr/Sewanhaka Ctl High Sch Dist	1	129
Grossman, Harry/East Ramapo Central Sch Dist	67	196
Groth, Anja/Rocky Point Union Free SD	8,11,69,280,298	228
Groth, Daniel/Genesee Valley BOCES	2,19	74
Grotto, James/Southern Westchester BOCES	15,27,30,58	267
Group, Martha/Vernon-Verona-Sherrill CSD	1,11	152
Group, Robert/Oneida City School Dist	67	105
Grover, James/West Islip School Dist	26,29,45	233
Grover, Mary/Ithaca City School Dist	18,69	240
Grow, Mary/East Irondequoit Ctl Sch Dist	1,11,57	107
Gruber, Liz/Fredonia Central School Dist	16,28	37
Grund, Rosanna/Onondaga-Cortland-Madson BOCES	58,77	160
Grunder, Alison/Newfield Central School Dist	7,83	241
Gruner, Jane/Farmingdale Union Free SD	34	119
Grupka, Patricia/Lewiston Porter Ctl Sch Dist	2,5,15,68	146
Grusenmeyer, Philip/Hicksville Union Free Sch Dist	20	122
Gryczka, David/Chittenango Central SD	6	104
Gryczka, David/Chittenango Central SD	6	104

NAME/District	JOB FUNCTIONS	PAGE
Grymala, John/Royalton Hartland Central SD	6	148
Grymes, Heather/Nanuet Union Free School Dist	273	196
Guardino, Joseph/South Colonie Central Sch Dist	6,35	12
Guarino, Steven/Brentwood Union Free Sch Dist	20,23	217
Guarnieri, Emily/Diocese of Rockville Ed Office	73	132
Guay, Kevin/Lockport City School Dist	3	147
Guccia, Joseph/Johnson City Central Sch Dist	8,15,294	28
Guccione, Andrew/Suffern Central School Dist	6,35	198
Guenthner, Daniel/Dolgeville Central School Dist	27,36,69	77
Guercin, Elizabeth/Herricks Union Free Sch Dist	8,15,78,285,288	121
Guercio, William/Solvay Union Free Sch Dist	31,36	158
Gueren, Kim/Eldred Central School Dist	36	236
Guererri, Kristine/Manchester-Shortsville Ctl SD	8,11,58,69,273,275,288,296	162
Guernsey, Linda/Adirondack Central Sch Dist	288	150
Guerra, Jacquelin/Garden City School Dist	273	120
Guerrette, Karen/Jordan Elbridge Ctl Sch Dist	67	155
Gugel, Paul/Ctr for Instruct Tech Innov	271	172
Gugino, Joseph/Oxford Academy Central SD	2,7,11,71	42
Gugino, Nicole/Depew Union Free School Dist	71	60
Gugino, Shawna/West Valley Ctl Sch Dist	58	33
Guglielmo, Paul/South Orangetown Central SD	5	197
Gugliotta, Bruce/Chateaugay Central School Dist	33,38,69	69
Guidotti, Carl/Holland Central School Dist	10,11,83,85,88	61
Guilford, Ann/Scio Central School Dist	54	15
Guiliano, Susan/Hicksville Union Free Sch Dist	8,69	122
Guillen, Richard/Arlington Central School Dist	23	51
Guillon, Tom/Maine Endwell Ctl School Dist	18,73,76,288,295	29
Gulino, Michael/Croton-Harmon Union Free SD	6,35	254
Gulisane, John/Taconic Hills Central Sch Dist	274	47
Gullo, Tony/York Central School Dist	3	103
Gulluscio, Todd/Shelter Island Union Free SD	6,35,83	230
Gumina, Carmen/Webster Central School Dist	1	112
Gunn, Frank/Greenburgh Central School Dist	5	255
Gunn, Thomas/Oswego City School Dist	5	171
Gunning, Jessica/Hudson Falls Central Sch Dist	273	248
Gunnison, Tia/Crown Point Central Sch Dist	58	67
Gunther, Richard/Westhill Central School Dist	4	159
Guntlow, Suzanne/Ichabod Crane Central Schools	1	46
Gurdineer, Erin/Edinburg Common School Dist	59	201
Gurley, Kate/Burnt Hills Ballston Lake SD	48,51,54,68,74,275	200
Gurowski, Tammy/Webster Central School Dist	67	112
Guryn, Deborah/Mattituck-Cutchogue UFSD	11,58,72,296,298	225
Gustafsson, Paul/Floral Park Bellerose Sch Dist	3	119
Gyoerkoe, Tracy/Jefferson Lewis BOCES	30,31	82
Gyr, Chris/Genesee Valley Ctl School Dist	285	15

H

NAME/District	JOB FUNCTIONS	PAGE
Haab, Deborah/Wainscott Common School Dist	1,11,73,288	232
Haanraadts, Diana/Massapequa Union Free SD 23	9,288	125
Haberman, Michael/Briarcliff Manor Union Free SD	67	253
Habib, Mary/Syracuse City School Dist	2	158
Hack, David/Orchard Park Central Sch Dist	6	63
Hacker, Shane/East Syracuse Minoa Ctl SD	8,12,57,69,88,288	154
Hacker, Tracy/Averill Park Central Sch Dist	77	189
Hackett, Donna/Pembroke Ctl School Dist	5	74
Haddad, Ann/South Country Central Sch Dist	90	231
Haddad, Bill/Canastota Central School Dist	67	104
Hadden, Kristi/Roxbury Central School Dist	274	50
Hadden, Sarah/Greenwood Lake Union Free SD	1	164
Hadjioannou, Charalambos/Questar III BOCES	2,15	192
Hadley-Bell, Margo/Washingtonville Central SD	34,58	167
Hadley, Sally/Cattaraugus-Little Vly Ctl SD	2	31
Hadock, Mary/Lansingburgh Central School Dist	273	190
Hafele, Matthew/Unatego Unadilla Central SD	6	174
Hafer, Liz/Lisbon Central School Dist	9,58	210
Hagan, Greg/Cairo-Durham Ctl School Dist	6	75
Hagan, Molly/Cazenovia Ctl School Dist	27,57,83,88	104

---

1 Superintendent	16 Instructional Media Svcs	30 Adult Education	44 Science Sec	58 Special Education K-12	72 Summer School	88 Alternative/At Risk	277 Remedial Math K-12
2 Bus/Finance/Purchasing	17 Chief Operations Officer	31 Career/Sch-to-Work K-12	45 Math K-12	59 Special Education Elem	73 Instructional Tech	89 Multi-Cultural Curriculum	280 Literacy Coach
3 Buildings And Grounds	18 Chief Academic Officer	32 Career/Sch-to-Work Elem	46 Math Elem	60 Special Education Sec	74 Inservice Training	90 Social Work	285 STEM
4 Food Service	19 Chief Financial Officer	33 Career/Sch-to-Work Sec	47 Math Sec	61 Foreign/World Lang K-12	75 Marketing/Distributive	91 Safety/Security	286 Digital Learning
5 Transportation	20 Art K-12	34 Early Childhood Ed	48 English/Lang Arts K-12	62 Foreign/World Lang Elem	76 Info Systems	92 Magnet School	288 Common Core Standards
6 Athletic	21 Art Elem	35 Health/Phys Education	49 English/Lang Arts Elem	63 Foreign/World Lang Sec	77 Psychological Assess	93 Parental Involvement	294 Accountability
7 Health Services	22 Art Sec	36 Guidance Services K-12	50 English/Lang Arts Sec	64 Religious Education K-12	78 Affirmative Action	95 Tech Prep Program	295 Network System
8 Curric/Instruct K-12	23 Music K-12	37 Guidance Services Elem	51 Reading K-12	65 Religious Education Elem	79 Student Personnel	97 Chief Infomation Officer	296 Title II Programs
9 Curric/Instruct Elem	24 Music Elem	38 Guidance Services Sec	52 Reading Elem	66 Religious Education Sec	80 Driver Ed/Safety	98 Chief Technology Officer	297 Webmaster
10 Curric/Instruct Sec	25 Music Sec	39 Social Studies K-12	53 Reading Sec	67 School Board President	81 Gifted/Talented	270 Character Education	298 Grant Writer/Ptnrships
11 Federal Program	26 Business Education	40 Social Studies Elem	54 Remedial Reading K-12	68 Teacher Personnel	82 Video Services	271 Migrant Education	750 Chief Innovation Officer
12 Title I	27 Career & Tech Ed	41 Social Studies Sec	55 Remedial Reading Elem	69 Academic Assessment	83 Substance Abuse Prev	273 Teacher Mentor	751 Chief of Staff
13 Title V	28 Technology Education	42 Science K-12	56 Remedial Reading Sec	70 Research/Development	84 Erate	274 Before/After Sch	752 Social Emotional Learning
15 Asst Superintendent	29 Family/Consumer Science	43 Science Elem	57 Bilingual/ELL	71 Public Information	85 AIDS Education	275 Response To Intervention	

New York School Directory

DISTRICT PERSONNEL INDEX

NAME/District	JOB FUNCTIONS	PAGE
Hagash, Bradly/Lewiston Porter Ctl Sch Dist	35	146
Hagenbuch, Kathy/Campbell-Savona Ctl Sch Dist	1,11	213
Hager, Karin/Ellicottville Central Sch Dist	7,85	31
Hagerman, Thomas, Dr/Scarsdale Union Free Sch Dist	1	261
Hagert, Ellen/Stamford Central School Dist	67	50
Hagerty, Erica/Oneida City School Dist	31,36	105
Hagmann, Rebecca/Sherburne Earlville Central SD	37	42
Hagreen, Todd/Brockport Ctl School Dist	6,35	106
Hahn, Michael/Jericho Union Free School Dist	3	122
Haier, Joe/Orchard Park Central Sch Dist	5	63
Haight, Eric/Franklin Central School Dist	35,83,85	49
Haining, Bill/Mattituck-Cutchogue UFSD	295	225
Haitz, Nancy/Batavia City School Dist	7,85	73
Halberg, Laural/Duanesburg Central Sch Dist	77	203
Halberg, Marion/Dobbs Ferry Union Free SD	57	254
Halbert, Laurie/Dundee Ctl School Dist	285	268
Haldeman, Nora/Clyde-Savannah Central SD	76	249
Haley, Eric/Worcester Ctl School Dist	5	174
Haley, Raymond/Salamanca City Central SD	91	33
Halgash, Brad/Lewiston Porter Ctl School Dist	6	146
Hall, Emily/Bainbridge Guilford CSD	67	41
Hall, Jacob/Naples Central School Dist	67	162
Hall, Jennifer/Galway Central School Dist	58,79	201
Hall, John/North Shore Central SD	3,91	126
Hall, Michelle/North Shore Central SD	5	126
Hall, Sara/White Plains City School Dist	36,77	263
Hall, Shakia/Herricks Union Free Sch Dist	4	121
Hallahan, Carol/Brasher Falls School Dist	7,85	209
Hallberg, Dan/Frewsburg Central School Dist	3	38
Hallenbeck, Ryan/Union-Endicott Ctl Sch Dist	6,35,85	29
Hallenbeck, William/Hudson City School Dist	91	46
Halliday, Antoinette/Sherburne Earlville Central SD	271,274,275	42
Hallings, Christine/Penn Yan Ctl School Dist	51	268
Hallman, William/Springs Union Free School Dist	16	232
Hallock, Scott/Eldred Central School Dist	67	236
Halpern, Jehuda/Kiryas Joel Union Free SD	9,59,83,288	164
Halpin, Robert/Odessa Montour Ctl Sch Dist	67	207
Halpin, Sandy/New Hartford Central Sch Dist	30,74	151
Halsey, Benjamin/Yorkshire-Pioneer Ctl Sch Dist	1	33
Hameister, Kristina/Little Falls City School Dist	67	78
Hamill, Christine/North Greenbush Common SD	1,11,83,288	191
Hamilton, Danielle/Springs Union Free School Dist	277	232
Hamilton, David, Dr/Tioga Central School Dist	1	239
Hamilton, Gregory/Syosset Central School Dist	3,91	129
Hamilton, Kaitlin/Amagansett Union Free Sch Dist	90,270	216
Hamilton, Kenneth, Dr/Mount Vernon City School Dist	1	258
Hamilton, Melinda/Byram Hills Central Sch Dist	4	253
Hamm, Leann/Fort Ann Central School Dist	16	247
Hammill, Kate/Wayne-Finger Lakes BOCES	16	252
Hammond, Adam/Spackenkill Union Free SD	36	54
Hammond, Annette/Gilbertsville-Mt Upton SD	69,273,288	173
Hammond, Annette/Gilbertsville-Mt Upton SD	1	173
Hamp, Wade/North Bellmore Union Free SD	295	126
Hance, Sharon/Alden Central School Dist	8,34,58,74,79,273,288	56
Hancock, Cathy/Brewster Central School Dist	4	175
Hancy, Richard/Kendall Central School Dist	73,295	169
Hand, Debbie, Dr/White Plains City School Dist	8,12,69,89,270,271,280,285	263
Hand, Kristina/Morris Central School Dist	2	173
Hand, Timothy/Genesee Valley Ctl School Dist	67	15
Handin, Kenneth/Scotia Glenville Ctl School Dist	7,58,79,90	205
Handler, Martin, Dr/Pine Plains Ctl School Dist	1	53
Hanernan, Stephen/Dover Union Free School Dist	73,295	52
Haney, Peg/Pembroke Ctl School Dist	273	74
Hanley, Shawn/West Babylon Union Free SD	15,68,74,288	232
Hanlon, Lisa/Holland Central School Dist	38	61
Hanlon, Neil/Berkshire Union Free Sch Dist	35,85	45
Hanlon, Robert/Mayfield Ctl School Dist	71	72
Hanlon, Robert/Scotia Glenville Ctl School Dist	16,71	205
Hanna, Mike/Ossining Union Free Sch Dist	73,295	259
Hannan, Maureen/Diocese of Rockville Ed Office	2	132
Hannan, Richard/Byron-Bergen Ctl School Dist	6	73
Hannaoui, Denise/Connetquot Central School Dist	61	219
Hannon, Mary/Bethpage Union Free Sch Dist	49,280	117
Hanrahan, Dawn/Elmira Heights Ctl Sch Dist	8,12,57,58	40
Hans, Jason, Dr/Windsor Central School Dist	54,57,58	30
Hans, Philip/Malone Central School Dist	67	70

NAME/District	JOB FUNCTIONS	PAGE
Hansen, Bryan/West Valley Ctl Sch Dist	16,73,82	33
Hansen, Christian/Brockport Ctl School Dist	3	106
Hansen, Craig/Questar III BOCES	3,7,91	192
Hansen, Katie/Unadilla Valley Ctl School Dist	68	43
Hansen, Lisa/Salem Central School Dist	58,77	248
Hansen, Meridyth/Hauppauge Union Free Sch Dist	45	223
Hantzidiamants, Patricia, Dr/Bethpage Union Free Sch Dist	15,79	117
Hao, Winona/New York State Dept Education	34	1
Harcleroad, Terry/Liberty Central School Dist	73	236
Harden, Briana/Fonda Fultonville Central SD	274	115
Harden, Kathleen/Marlboro Central School Dist	83	242
Hardenstine, Penny/Duanesburg Central Sch Dist	6,8	203
Hardes, Claudia/Syosset Central School Dist	5	129
Harding, Christine/Williamsville Ctl School Dist	7	64
Harding, Steve/Longwood Central School Dist	91	225
Hardman, Dave/Cuba-Rushford Central Sch Dist	3	14
Hardwick, Andrew/Hempstead Union Free SD	91	121
Hardy, Amber/Scio Central School Dist	31,36	15
Hardy, Betsy/Fillmore Central School Dist	73,98,295	14
Hares, Nancy/Weedsport Ctl School Dist	5	35
Harjes, Kyle/Onteora Central School Dist	3,91	243
Hark, Frank/Brentwood Union Free Sch Dist	2	217
Harley, Debra/East Meadow Union Free SD	42,45	118
Harlin, Richard/Pine Plains Ctl School Dist	73,286	53
Harling, Kathy/Albion Central School Dist	67	169
Harmer, Bryan/Madrid-Waddington Central SD	6	211
Harmon, Joseph/Churchville Chili Ctl Sch Dist	295	107
Harmon, Katie/Westhill Central School Dist	73	160
Harmon, Randy/Bolivar-Richburg Ctrl Sch Dist	3	14
Harmon, Todd/Wilson Central School Dist	3	149
Harper, Al/Elmont Union Free School Dist	1	118
Harper, Christopher/Mayfield Ctl School Dist	1	72
Harper, Fay/Remsen Central School Dist	58,752	151
Harper, Jesse/Arkport Central School Dist	1,288	213
Harper, Stanley, Dr/Salmon River Central Sch Dist	1	70
Harrigan, Patrick, Dr/Half Hollow Hills Central SD	1	222
Harriger, Nancy/McGraw Central School Dist	35,85	48
Harriman, Maureen/Tupper Lake Ctl School Dist	45	70
Harrington, Bob/West Valley Ctl Sch Dist	5	33
Harrington, Brent, Dr/Brewster Central School Dist	68	175
Harrington, David/Indian Lake Ctl School Dist	67	76
Harrington, Denise/Croton-Harmon Union Free SD	2,4,15,19	254
Harrington, Michael/Bellmore-Merrick Ctl High SD	10,11,15,57,71,296,298	117
Harrington, Phyllis, Dr/Oceanside Union Free Sch Dist	1	127
Harrington, Ralph/Cambridge Central School Dist	58	247
Harrington, Scott/Bethpage Union Free Sch Dist	2,3,4,15	117
Harrington, Stephanie/Andover Central School Dist	280,285	14
Harrington, Wendy/Hartford Central School Dist	38	248
Harris Maxwell, Katie/Romulus Ctl School Dist	752	208
Harris, Christopher/Edwards-Knox Central Sch Dist	3	210
Harris, Chritopher, Dr/Genesee Valley BOCES	16	74
Harris, Jennifer/Syracuse City School Dist	8	158
Harris, Karen/Brentwood Union Free Sch Dist	5	217
Harris, Rachel/Greater Johnstown Sch Dist	76	71
Harris, Robert/Buffalo Public Schools	27	57
Harris, Rodney/Warsaw Central School Dist	6	267
Harris, Ruby, Dr/Grand Island Central Sch Dist	2,15	61
Harris, Russell/Newark Central School Dist	67	250
Harris, Timothy/Saratoga Springs City Sch Dist	88	201
Harrison, Jennifer, Dr/Middle Country Ctl Sch Dist	58,77,88	225
Harrison, Kristopher, Dr/Irvington Union Free Sch Dist	1	257
Harrison, Linda/North Colonie Central SD	67	11
Harrison, Melissa/Andover Central School Dist	23	14
Harrison, Stephen/East Islip Union Free SD	2,4,5,15,84	220
Harstone, Joshua/Watertown City School Dist	2,298	81
Hart, Andy/Le Roy Central School Dist	5	73
Hart, Bonnie/Lake George Central Sch Dist	8	245
Hart, Brian/Skaneateles Central Sch Dist	77	157
Hart, James/North Tonawanda City Sch Dist	3	148
Hart, Kathy/Farmingdale Union Free SD	76	119
Hart, Laura/Potsdam Central School Dist	2	212
Hart, Tom/Pavilion Ctl School Dist	5	74
Harter, James/Charlotte Valley Ctl Sch Dist	1,11,73	49
Hartford, Barbara/West Irondequoit Ctl SD	45,277	113
Hartman, Lisa/Brighton Central School Dist	68	106
Hartman, Steven/Commack Union Free School Dist	67	219

DISTRICT PERSONNEL INDEX

Market Data Retrieval

NAME/District	JOB FUNCTIONS	PAGE
Hartmann, Christopher/Plattsburgh City School Dist	6,7	44
Hartswick, Perry/Millbrook Ctl School Dist	67	52
Hartwell, Brian, Dr/Cayuga-Onondaga BOCES	1	36
Harvey, Bill/Honeoye Falls Lima Sch Dist	5	109
Harvey, Cora/South Jefferson Central SD	2	81
Harvey, Donald/Milford Central School Dist	3,5,91	173
Harvey, Emily/Panama Central School Dist	8,11,58,69,74,273,275	38
Harvey, John/Broome-Tioga BOCES	2,3,17	31
Hasbrouck, Brett/Spackenkill Union Free SD	295	54
Hash, Daniel/Greenville Central School Dist	275	75
Haskell, Hilary/Corinth Central School Dist	6,35	200
Hassall, Erin/Spencerport Central Sch Dist	93	112
Hasseler, Terrence/Caledonia-Mumford Ctl Sch Dist	2	102
Hasselsterom, Erica/Marcus Whitman Central SD	8,69	162
Hassett, David/Eden Central School Dist	38	60
Hassinger, Robert/Westbury Union Free Sch Dist	30	132
Hassler, Eric, Dr/Monroe Woodbury Central SD	8,15	165
Hasty, Melissa/Albany City School Dist	34	9
Hatchell, David/South Jefferson Central SD	3	81
Hatgistavrou, Cathy/Sagaponack Common School Dist	67	229
Hathaway, Dean, Dr/De Ruyter Central School Dist	67	105
Hattar, Ron, Dr/Yorktown Central School Dist	1	264
Hatten, Jeffery/Tonawanda City School Dist	3,91	64
Hattrick, Sean/Tuckahoe Common School Dist	67	232
Hauber, Cathy, Dr/Monroe 1 BOCES	8,15	115
Hauck, Fred/Jefferson Lewis BOCES	7,91	82
Haug, Cathryn/Carthage Central School Dist	68	80
Haugh, James/East Rochester Union Free SD	1	107
Haugh, James/Victor Central School Dist	15,68,78	162
Hauryski, Tom/Campbell-Savona Ctl Sch Dist	67	213
Hauser, Robert/Bridgehampton Union Free SD	1	218
Hausman, Diane/Montauk Union Free School Dist	67	226
Hausman, Liz/Dobbs Ferry Union Free SD	71	254
Havens, Terry/Richfield Springs Central SD	35,85	174
Haver, Greg/Poland Central School Dist	6,35	78
Hawker, Susan/Cato Meridian Central Sch Dist	73	34
Hawkins, David/New Lebanon Ctl School Dist	73	46
Hawkins, Maryann/Westmoreland Central Sch Dist	2	153
Haws, Nancy/De Ruyter Central School Dist	295	105
Hawse, Kelly/Frankfort-Schuyler Ctl SD	39	77
Hawthorne, Marjorie/Oneida City School Dist	23	105
Hay, Cindy/Red Creek Central School Dist	8,285,288,296,298,752	251
Haycock, Alynda/Sackets Harbor Ctl School Dist	11,88,280,296	81
Hayden, Jennifer/Waterloo Central School Dist	8,11,15,31,57,69,271,288	208
Hayden, Michael/Clyde-Savannah Central SD	1	249
Hayers, Colleen/Clifton-Fine Central Sch Dist	2	209
Hayes, Amy/Northern Adirondack Ctl SD	27,36,69,83	44
Hayes, David/Chappaqua Central School Dist	71	253
Hayes, Donna/Fonda Fultonville Central SD	5	115
Hayes, E Anne/South Country Central Sch Dist	67	231
Hayes, Frank/Margaretville Central Sch Dist	57	50
Hayes, Gloria/Fredonia Central School Dist	7,83,85	37
Hayes, Murphee/Whitney Point Central Sch Dist	6,7,83,88	30
Hayes, Timothy/Cooperstown Ctl School Dist	67	173
Hayes, Timothy/Massena Central School Dist	6,35	211
Haynia, Jennifer/Middle Country Ctl School Dist	73	225
Haynsworth, Stacey/Bedford Central School Dist	15	252
Hayter, Elizabeth/Dutchess Co BOCES	27,30,31	55
Hazel, Jeffery/Niagara-Wheatfield Ctl SD	76	148
Hazelton, Brianne/Whitehall Central School Dist	11,58,77,79,83,90,275	248
Head, Coleen/Bainbridge Guilford CSD	58	41
Head, Mike/Whitesboro Ctl School Dist	67	153
Headwell, Katy/Shenendehowa Central Sch Dist	4	202
Heady, Holly/Millbrook Ctl School Dist	4	52
Heagerty, Maria/Medina Central School Dist	4	169
Heald, Barbara/Wayne Central School Dist	73,95	251
Healey, Mike/Argyle Central School Dist	1,11	246

NAME/District	JOB FUNCTIONS	PAGE
Healy, Christine/East Ramapo Central Sch Dist	7	196
Healy, Kevin/Westmoreland Central Sch Dist	8,79	153
Healy, Robert/Stockbridge Valley Central SD	273	106
Healy, Vincent/East Rockaway Union Free SD	11,57,58,79,85,88,271	118
Heaney, Teresa/Belfast Central School Dist	36	14
Hearney, Timothy, Dr/Bayport- Blue Point USD	1	217
Heath, Kathryn/Lansing Central School Dist	2	240
Heaton, Kevin/Nyack Union Free School Dist	3	197
Hebert, Pamela/Jefferson Lewis BOCES	68	82
Hecht, Mona/East Rockaway Union Free SD	8,15,288	118
Hecht, Robin/Marlboro Central School Dist	8,15,69,285,286,288,298	242
Hecht, Sandi/Wallkill Central School Dist	83	243
Hecht, William/Orange-Ulster BOCES	1	168
Heck, Jill/Royalton Hartland Central SD	8,12,73,285,286,288,296,298	148
Heckelman, Paul/Massapequa Union Free SD 23	4	125
Heckler, Phil/Hicksville Union Free Sch Dist	67	122
Hedrickson, Robert, Dr/Greenburgh-North Castle SD	67	255
Heed, Diane/Brockport Ctl School Dist	68	106
Heed, Janet/Diocese of Brooklyn Ed Office	15	94
Heenan, Michele/Dunkirk City School Dist	58	37
Heff, Jessica/Belfast Central School Dist	58	14
Heffner, Aaron/Averill Park Central Sch Dist	3,91	189
Heggarty, Thomas/Lockport City School Dist	4	147
Hehl, Jessica/Solvay Union Free Sch Dist	8,11,15,288,296,298	158
Hehr, David/Cleveland Hill Union Free SD	3	59
Heid, Keith/Watervliet City School Dist	2	12
Heiden, Laurel/Greece Central School Dist	71	108
Heidenreich, Bill, Dr/Valley Stream Ctl High SD	1	130
Heiligenthaler, Carol/Barker Central School Dist	2,5	146
Heimroth, Megan/Rensselaer City School Dist	2,19	191
Heise, Tracie/Kendall Central School Dist	298	169
Heiser, Jerry/Webutuck Ctl School Dist	5	54
Heiser, Julia/Clymer Central School Dist	285	37
Heiser, Travis/O E S J Central School Dist	6	72
Heitmann, Lance/South Seneca Ctl Sch Dist	3,5	208
Helft, John/Hoosick Falls Central Sch Dist	67	190
Helgeland, Stephanie/Avoca Central School Dist	9	213
Heller, Julie/Rye City School Dist	280	261
Heller, Renee/Schalmont Central School Dist	4	204
Hellmer, Jordan/Norwood-Norfolk Ctl SD	38	211
Helman, Raelyn/Letchworth Central School Dist	58,79	267
Helmbold, Matthew/Gates Chili Central Sch Dist	5	108
Helmer, Michele/Silver Creek Central Sch Dist	8,12,74,288	39
Helmer, Sean/Silver Creek Central School Dist	6	39
Helms, Daniel/Smithtown Central Sch Dist	15,58,79	230
Helou-Care, Yasmin/Rockland BOCES	15,68	199
Hemingway, Judy/Glens Falls Common Sch Dist	2,73	245
Hemmer, Donna/Sullivan BOCES	71	238
Henaey, Judith/Nanuet Union Free School Dist	58,79	196
Hence, Jerry/Marathon Ctl School Dist	16,73,286,295	48
Henchen, Kevin/Fairport Ctl School Dist	74	108
Hender, Christopher/Huntington Union Free Sch Dist	68	223
Hendershot, Heather/Goshen Central School Dist	34,57,58,79,88,271	164
Henderson, Becky/Corning-Painted Post Area SD	58	214
Henderson, David/Victor Central School Dist	73,295	162
Henderson, John/Greece Central School Dist	91	108
Hendricken, John/Carle Place Union Free SD	3	117
Hendrickson, Kelly/Roscoe Central School Dist	36	237
Henery, Michael/Springs Union Free School Dist	2	232
Henesey, Michael/Syracuse City School Dist	71	158
Hengen, Jennifer/Webutuck Ctl School Dist	59	54
Henner, Daniel/Liverpool Ctl School Dist	15	156
Hennessy, Theresa/Franklin Square Union Free SD	2,3,15	119
Hennigan, Chris/Cazenovia Ctl School Dist	16,73,76,295	104
Henrie, Greg/Fulton City School Dist	5	170
Henry-Montante, Anne/Buffalo Public Schools	69	57
Henry, Deanna/La Fargeville Central Sch Dist	16	80

1	Superintendent	16	Instructional Media Svcs	30	Adult Education	44	Science Sec	58	Special Education K-12	72	Summer School
2	Bus/Finance/Purchasing	17	Chief Operations Officer	31	Career/Sch-to-Work K-12	45	Math K-12	59	Special Education Elem	73	Instructional Tech
3	Buildings And Grounds	18	Chief Academic Officer	32	Career/Sch-to-Work Elem	46	Math Elem	60	Special Education Sec	74	Inservice Training
4	Food Service	19	Chief Financial Officer	33	Career/Sch-to-Work Sec	47	Math Sec	61	Foreign/World Lang K-12	75	Marketing/Distributive
5	Transportation	20	Art K-12	34	Early Childhood Ed	48	English/Lang Arts K-12	62	Foreign/World Lang Elem	76	Info Systems
6	Athletic	21	Art Elem	35	Health/Phys Education	49	English/Lang Arts Elem	63	Foreign/World Lang Sec	77	Psychological Assess
7	Health Services	22	Art Sec	36	Guidance Services K-12	50	English/Lang Arts Sec	64	Religious Education K-12	78	Affirmative Action
8	Curric/Instruct K-12	23	Music K-12	37	Guidance Services Elem	51	Reading K-12	65	Religious Education Elem	79	Student Personnel
9	Curric/Instruct Elem	24	Music Elem	38	Guidance Services Sec	52	Reading Elem	66	Religious Education Sec	80	Driver Ed/Safety
10	Curric/Instruct Sec	25	Music Sec	39	Social Studies K-12	53	Reading Sec	67	School Board President	81	Gifted/Talented
11	Federal Program	26	Business Education	40	Social Studies Elem	54	Remedial Reading K-12	68	Teacher Personnel	82	Video Services
12	Title I	27	Career & Tech Ed	41	Social Studies Sec	55	Remedial Reading Elem	69	Academic Assessment	83	Substance Abuse Prev
13	Title V	28	Technology Education	42	Science K-12	56	Remedial Reading Sec	70	Research/Development	84	Erate
15	Asst Superintendent	29	Family/Consumer Science	43	Science Elem	57	Bilingual/ELL	71	Public Information	85	AIDS Education

88	Alternative/At Risk	277	Remedial Math K-12
89	Multi-Cultural Curriculum	280	Literacy Coach
90	Social Work	285	STEM
91	Safety/Security	286	Digital Learning
92	Magnet School	288	Common Core Standards
93	Parental Involvement	294	Accountability
95	Tech Prep Program	295	Network System
97	Chief Infomation Officer	296	Title II Programs
98	Chief Technology Officer	297	Webmaster
270	Character Education	298	Grant Writer/Ptnrships
271	Migrant Education	750	Chief Innovation Officer
273	Teacher Mentor	751	Chief of Staff
274	Before/After Sch	752	Social Emotional Learning
275	Response To Intervention		

NY-T28

New York School Directory

DISTRICT PERSONNEL INDEX

NAME/District	JOB FUNCTIONS	PAGE
Henry, John/Cobleskill Richmondville SD	6,7,42,83,85	206
Henry, Karen/Solvay Union Free Sch Dist	2,7	158
Henry, Keith/Wayne-Finger Lakes BOCES	2,11,15	252
Henry, Maureen/Valley Stream Ctl High SD	88,270	130
Henry, Todd/East Syracuse Minoa Ctl SD	5	154
Hensel, Renee/Churchville Chili Ctl Sch Dist	5,16,88,273,274	107
Henslin, Mimi/Pawling Ctl School Dist	2,15	52
Herbert, Rhonda/Allegany-Limestone Ctl SD	4	31
Herbs, Tim/Averill Park Central Sch Dist	9,270	189
Herbst, Julia/Red Creek Central School Dist	11,58,271	251
Heritage, Skye/Glens Falls City School Dist	71	245
Herman, Emily/Wyoming Central School Dist	59,69,79,83,88	268
Herman, Maria/Wyoming Central School Dist	7	268
Hermanet, Robert/South Seneca Ctl Sch Dist	286	208
Hernandez, Allison/Glen Cove City School Dist	58	120
Hernandez, Richard/Clarkstown Central School Dist	73,286	195
Heroth, Adam/O E S J Central School Dist	1	72
Heroth, Rachel/Greater Johnstown Sch Dist	73	71
Herrera, Zolita/Archdiocese of New York Ed Off	15	142
Herrick, Kathleen/Pittsford Central Sch Dist	5	110
Herrick, Louise/Yorkshire-Pioneer Ctl Sch Dist	47	33
Herrick, Raymond/Tully Central School Dist	91	159
Herrington, Yvonne/Wallkill Central School Dist	15	243
Herrling, Lindsay/Southern Cayuga Central SD	58	35
Hersh, Emily, Dr/Mt Pleasant-Blythedale UFSD	1,11,73	259
Hershey, Alysha/Arlington Central School Dist	58	51
Hertzog, Scott/Sidney Central School Dist	57	50
Herzog, Mary Ellen/Lakeland Central School Dist	15,57,58,79,83,88,271	257
Hesler, Diahnne/Spencer Van Etten Central SD	1	238
Heslin, Marianne/Pocantico Hills Ctl Sch Dist	296	261
Hess, Chad/Poland Central School Dist	2,3,11,78,294	78
Hess, David/Depew Union Free School Dist	3,91	59
Heubel, Janet/Pawling Ctl School Dist	2	52
Heuer, Meredith/Beacon City School Dist	67	51
Hewett, Carrie/Unatego Unadilla Central SD	274	174
Heyn, Matthew/Fabius Pompey Central SD	83,85,88	155
Heyward, Brian/Shoreham-Wading River Ctl SD	15	230
Hibbard, Kimberly/Sauquoit Valley Central SD	2,11	152
Hickey, Joseph, Dr/Great Neck Public Schools	58,79	120
Hicks, Audrey/Granville Central School Dist	67	247
Hicks, Geoffrey/Clarence Central School Dist	1	59
Hicks, John/Pine Bush Central School Dist	16,73,82,95,295	166
Hicks, Mark/Arlington Central School Dist	4	51
Hickson, Brian/Cheektowaga Central SD	6	58
Higgins, Benjamin/Springville Griffith Inst CSD	297	63
Higgins, Michelle/Lyndonville Central Sch Dist	4	169
Hilburger, Mark/Hilton Central School Dist	67	109
Hildebrandt, Robert/Charlotte Valley Ctl Sch Dist	36,69	49
Hilgendorff, Todd/Greenville Central School Dist	8,69,288	75
Hilker, Tim/Saratoga Springs City Sch Dist	2,15	201
Hill, Brenda/Roxbury Central School Dist	73,295	50
Hill, Christopher/Oneida-Herkimer-Mad BOCES	8,27,30,31,58,72,88,271	154
Hill, Donna/Tonawanda City School Dist	2,5	64
Hill, Erin/Cohoes City School Dist	58	10
Hill, John/Questar III BOCES	67	192
Hill, Johnetta, Dr/Hempstead Union Free SD	6	121
Hill, Johnetta, Dr/Hempstead Union Free SD	6,58	121
Hill, Maria/Pittsford Central Sch Dist	58	110
Hill, Orissa/Holley Central School Dist	7	169
Hill, Robert/North Warren Central Sch Dist	5	246
Hill, Ryan/Livonia Ctl School Dist	295	103
Hiller, Michael/North Tonawanda City Sch Dist	58	148
Hillis, John/Oxford Academy Central SD	1	42
Hillman, Barbara/Otselic Valley Central SD	4	42
Hillman, John/Elmira City School Dist	8	40
Hilt, Stephanie/Geneseo Central Sch Dist	2	103
Hilton, Greg/Rocky Point Union Free SD	5	228
Hilts, Joe/Schalmont Central School Dist	5	204
Himme, Bill/Cobleskill Richmondville SD	3,5	206
Hine, Dawn/Quogue Union Free School Dist	16,82	228
Hines, Robert/Riverhead Central School Dist	16,73,76,84,286,295	228
Hinkley, Jo/Roxbury Central School Dist	270	50
Hinkley, Karen/Roxbury Central School Dist	83,85,88	50
Hinkley, Mary/Roxbury Central School Dist	58	50
Hinman, Shana/Harpursville Central Sch Dist	7	28
Hinsdale, Brynne/Panama Central School Dist	73,76,295	38
Hipwell, Mary Alice/Mechanicville City Sch Dist	58	201
Hirsch-Schena, Mary/Olean City School Dist	67	32
Hirsch, Jon/Valhalla Union Free Sch Dist	27	262
Hirschey, Johnathan/Brasher Falls School Dist	12,73,295	209
Hitchcock, Jake/Westfield Central School Dist	6,35,38,88	39
Hitchcock, Michelle/Cooperstown Ctl School Dist	16	173
Hlad, Mike/Lowville Acad-Central Sch Dist	3	101
Hladun, Matthew/Averill Park Central Sch Dist	8,11,18,83,285,286,288,296	189
Hlavenka, Susan/Island Trees Union Free SD	2,15	122
Hoag, Arthur/Livingston Manor Ctl School Dist	3	236
Hoag, Jeff/Hoosic Valley Central Sch Dist	16,73,286	190
Hoagland, Mrs/Whitehall Central School Dist	8	248
Hochheiser, Claire/Hicksville Union Free Sch Dist	58,79	122
Hochman, Donna/Lindenhurst Union Free SD	67	224
Hochreiter, Joseph/Hendrick Hudson Ctl Sch Dist	1	256
Hock, Lori/Monroe Woodbury Central SD	6,35,83,85	165
Hock, Mary/West Islip School Dist	84	233
Hodge, Christian/Pelham Union Free School Dist	6,35	260
Hodge, Christian/Poughkeepsie City School Dist	6,35	53
Hodge, Jason/Trumansburg Central SD	6	241
Hodge, Josh/Queensbury Union Free Sch Dist	4	246
Hodge, Kester/Wyandanch Union Free Sch Dist	15,68	234
Hodge, Mark/Oxford Academy Central SD	3	42
Hodosky, Joseph/Bay Shore Union Free Sch Dist	3,91	217
Hoelscher, Kim/Buffalo Public Schools	15,58	57
Hoff, Cindy/Northern Adirondack Ctl SD	58,69,77	44
Hoffman, Brian/Schenectady City School Dist	3	204
Hoffman, David/Westmoreland Central Sch Dist	77	153
Hoffman, Debbie/Alden Central School Dist	5	56
Hoffman, Debra/Rocky Point Union Free SD	2	228
Hoffman, Dwayne/Lakeland Central School Dist	16,73	257
Hoffman, Edward/North Rockland Central SD	73	197
Hoffman, Jackie/Chatham Central School Dist	270	46
Hoffman, Jennifer/West Babylon Union Free SD	57,69,81	233
Hoffman, Lee/Depew Union Free School Dist	71,97	60
Hoffman, Lisa/Central Valley School Dist	79,271	77
Hoffman, Racheal/Lowville Acad-Central Sch Dist	4	101
Hoffman, Terri/Taconic Hills Central Sch Dist	70	47
Hogan, David/Chenango Forks Central SD	6,35	28
Hogan, Michele/Glens Falls City School Dist	16,82	245
Hogan, Tom/Locust Valley Ctl School Dist	20	123
Hohenforst, Lorraine, Dr/Hamilton-Fulton-Montgmry BOCES	15	72
Holbert, Kevin/Ausable Valley Ctl Sch Dist	6,35	43
Holbrook, Julie/Boquet Valley Central Sch Dist	4	67
Holbrook, Julie/Keene Central School Dist	4	67
Holbrook, Julie/Schroon Lake Ctl School Dist	4	68
Holden, Joy/Margaretville Central Sch Dist	58,77	50
Holden, Maryann/Dansville Ctl School Dist	67	102
Holder, Genieve/Valhalla Union Free Sch Dist	12,58	262
Holdorf, John/Edmeston Ctl School Dist	67	173
Holesko, Patrick/North Tonawanda City Sch Dist	8	148
Hollander, Kittie/Newfield Central School Dist	274	241
Hollenbeck, Tina/Tompkins-Seneca-Tioga BOCES	2	241
Holliday, David/Wyandanch Union Free Sch Dist	83,88	234
Holloran, David/Gloversville Enlarged Sch Dist	1	71
Hollowood, Karen/New York State Dept Education	7	1
Holly, Merritt/Le Roy Central School Dist	1	73
Holmes, Angela/Candor Central School Dist	11,58	238
Holmes, Barbara/Stockbridge Valley Central SD	51,54	106
Holmes, Timothy/Warwick Valley Central SD	2,11,15	167
Holody, Rebecca/Niagara Falls City Sch Dist	2	147
Holt, Cheryl/Oneonta City School Dist	30	174
Holt, John/Geneseo Central Sch Dist	73,76,295	103
Holt, Ruth/Pine Bush Central School Dist	30	166
Holton, Karen/Vernon-Verona-Sherrill CSD	27,31,36	152
Holtz, Traci/Mt Pleasant Ctl School Dist	58,79	258
Holub, William/Garden City School Dist	67	120
Holyk, Ray/Port Jervis City School Dist	6,7,35,85	166
Homer, Christopher/Cold Spring Harbor Central SD	83,88	219
Honan, Jakob/West Irondequoit Ctl SD	16,82	113
Honeyman, Catherine/Plainedge Union Free Sch Dist	8,15	127
Hongo, Scott/Dolgeville Central School Dist	67	77
Honsinger, Sandra/Berlin Central School Dist	35,85	189
Hooker, Margaret/Livonia Ctl School Dist	31,36	103
Hooley, Richard, Dr/Dutchess Co BOCES	1	55
Hooper, Robin/Rochester City School Dist	34	110

School Year 2020-2021 800-333-8802 NY-T29

DISTRICT PERSONNEL INDEX

Market Data Retrieval

NAME/District	JOB FUNCTIONS	PAGE
Hooper, Rod/Edwards-Knox Central Sch Dist	286	210
Hoops, James/Huntington Union Free Sch Dist	71	223
Hoose, Richard/Mayfield Ctl School Dist	3	72
Hoot, Rochelle/Brunswick Central School Dist	58	190
Hoot, Scott/North Colonie Central SD	15	11
Hoover, Amanda/Walton Central School Dist	11,57,296	50
Hoover, Jennifer/Newark Valley Central Sch Dist	7	238
Hoover, Travis/La Fargeville Central School Dist	1	80
Hopcia, Jill/Alden Central School Dist	67	56
Hopeck, Joan/Stillwater Central Sch Dist	4	202
Hopkins, Brandy/Greenport Union Free Sch Dist	88	222
Hopper, Theresa/Rensselaer City School Dist	4	191
Hopps, Luci/Unatego Unadilla Central SD	4	174
Horan, Tim/West Islip School Dist	6,7,35,83,85	233
Hordines, Beth/Highland Falls-Ft Montgmry SD	11,57,59,69	164
Horecky, Dawn/Pocantico Hills Ctl Sch Dist	274	260
Horese, Kevin/Bainbridge Guilford CSD	6,35,296	41
Horn, Leah/Haldane Central School Dist	76	176
Horschel, Jennifer/Eden Central School Dist	67	60
Horsley, Barbara/Farmingdale Union Free SD	11,92,93,271,273,274,296	119
Horton, Pamela/Harpursville Central Sch Dist	9,12	28
Hoskins, Gary/Newark Valley Central Sch Dist	3	238
Hoskins, Justin/Fort Ann Central School Dist	286,288	247
Hotaling, Adam/Troy City School Dsitrict	2,15	191
Hotaling, Josh/Ausable Valley Ctl Sch Dist	2	43
Houck, Kelly/Dundee Ctl School Dist	1	268
Houde, Garth/Ausable Valley Ctl Sch Dist	16,82	43
Houlihan, Kerry/Coxsackie-Athens Central SD	8,11,15,69,74,296,298	75
Houseknecht, Jim/Tioga Central School Dist	6	239
Hovenden, Jenny/Copenhagen Central SD	20	101
Hover, Brooke/Granville Central School Dist	7	247
Howard, Brian/Southern Westchester BOCES	71	267
Howard, Cybil/Taconic Hills Central Sch Dist	2,11	47
Howard, Donna/Franklinville Ctl School Dist	2,12,17,19,298	31
Howard, Kathleen/Webutuck Ctl School Dist	6	54
Howard, Ken/Afton Central School Dist	2	41
Howard, Louis/West Babylon Union Free SD	6	232
Howard, Neil, Dr/Taconic Hills Central Sch Dist	1	47
Howard, Robert/Northport-East Northport UFSD	2,15	227
Howard, Teri/Chatham Central School Dist	30	46
Howe, Christina/Valhalla Union Free Sch Dist	1,11,83	262
Howe, Heather/Middleburgh Ctl School Dist	270	206
Howe, Melanie/Hartford Central School Dist	4	248
Howe, William/Addison Central School Dist	8,11,286	213
Howell, David/Rensselaer City School Dist	73	191
Howell, Jennifer/Hinsdale Central School Dist	67	32
Howell, Lisa/Jasper Troupsburg Central SD	16	215
Howerton, Mary/Fort Ann Central School Dist	4	247
Howland, Elizabeth/Walton Central School Dist	37	50
Hoyt, Kathleen/Marathon Ctl School Dist	8,298	48
Hricay, James/Pelham Union Free School Dist	2,5,15	260
Hrvatin, Ingrid/South Country Central Sch Dist	36	231
Hsu, Wenwei/Port Byron Ctl School Dist	73,76,295	35
Hubbard, Eric/Marcellus Central School Dist	70,285	157
Hubbard, James/Potsdam Central School Dist	67	212
Hubbard, Megan/Avoca Central School Dist	67	213
Hubbell, Matthew/Mohonasen Central Sch Dist	285	204
Huber, Jodi/Brocton Central School Dist	285	36
Huber, Katherine, Dr/Alexander Ctl School Dist	1,11	73
Huber, Mary Ann/East Aurora Union Free SD	38	60
Hubert, Christopher/Livingston Manor Ctl Sch Dist	8,16,73	236
Hudes, Layne/Ardsley Union Free School Dist	288	252
Hudson, Christopher/East Quogue Union Free SD	67	221
Hudson, Philene/Ft Plain Central School Dist	2	115
Huetter, Sue/Garrison Union Free Sch Dist	2	175
Huff, Sharon, Dr/Cattaraugus-Little Vly Ctl SD	1	31
Hugg, Megan/Churchville Chili Ctl Sch Dist	286	107
Huggler, Elizabeth/Sullivan West Central SD	73,98	237
Hughes, Andrea/Mahopac Ctl School Dist	8,15	176
Hughes, Cyryl/Tarrytown Union Free Sch Dist	5	262
Hughes, Ellen/Waterloo Central School Dist	67	208
Hughes, Karen/Herricks Union Free Sch Dist	11,42	121
Hughes, Kimberly/Schenectady City School Dist	68	204
Hughes, Lura/Edwards-Knox Central Sch Dist	12,288	210
Hughes, Mary/Watertown City School Dist	4	81
Hughes, Richard, Dr/Frontier Ctl School Dist	1	60
Hughes, Robert/Tully Central School Dist	1	159
Hula, George/Briarcliff Manor Union Free SD	3	253
Hulihan, Tim/Stillwater Central Sch Dist	12,298	202
Hull, Matthew/Lake George Central Sch Dist	76	245
Hull, Maureen, Dr/Elwood Union Free School Dist	8,288,298	221
Hull, Sue/Susquehanna Valley Central SD	5	29
Hulla, Maribel/Community School District 10	1	20
Hulse, Michael/Andover Central School Dist	3,5	14
Hume, Michael/Buffalo Public Schools	73,76	57
Humiston, Jason/Fort Ann Central School Dist	6	247
Humphrey, James/Central Valley School Dist	2,5	77
Humphrey, Karen/Liverpool Ctl School Dist	68,294	156
Huneau, Jeff/Cohoes City School Dist	6	10
Huneke, Elizabeth/Delaware Academy Ctrl SD Delhi	67	49
Hungerford, Meg/Walton Central School Dist	2,298	50
Hunkele, Joshua/Trumansburg Central SD	16,28,82,295	241
Hunkins, Jonathan/Massena Central School Dist	25	211
Hunt, Ami/Keshequa Central School Dist	9,69,273,280,288	103
Hunt, Chad/Naples Central School Dist	5,6	162
Hunt, Jennifer/Hancock Central School Dist	7	49
Hunt, Scott/Holland Central School Dist	27	61
Hunt, Shawne/Ellicottville Central Sch Dist	73,76,274,295	31
Hunt, Tom/Schenevus Ctl School Dist	3,5,73,91	174
Hunter, John, Dr/Hudson Falls Central Sch Dist	1	248
Huntington, Joanne/Newfane Central School Dist	4	147
Huntington, Lorenda/Ft Edward Union Free Sch Dist	6	247
Huntington, Maria/Capital Region BOCES	30	13
Huot, Glenn/Stamford Central School Dist	1	50
Hurley, Sean/Northport-East Northport UFSD	39	227
Hurst, David/Bethlehem Central School Dist	8,15,280,288,296,298	10
Hurteau, John/Holland Patent Ctl School Dist	73	150
Huselstein, Mark/Olean City School Dist	3,91	32
Hussar, Na'Lisa/York Central School Dist	38,83,88	103
Husser, Tom/Hoosick Falls Central Sch Dist	6	190
Husson, Candice/Minerva Central School Dist	6	68
Hutchins, Gail/Ulster BOCES	67	244
Hutton, Kevin/Spencerport Central Sch Dist	67	112
Huyter, Terance/Dobbs Ferry Union Free SD	73,286	254
Hybicki, Linda/Cheektowaga-Sloan UFSD	2	59
Hyde, Allen/New Hartford Central Sch Dist	8,11,15,57,270,273,275,288	151
Hyde, Andrew/Berkshire Union Free Sch Dist	38	45
Hyde, Jackson/Lowville Acad-Central Sch Dist	16	101
Hyman, Tom/Brighton Central School Dist	5	106
Hynes, Erin/Sachem Central School Dist	8,15,280	229
Hynes, Michael, Dr/Port Washington Union Free SD	1,288	128

I

NAME/District	JOB FUNCTIONS	PAGE
Ianelli, Janice/Ulster BOCES	298	244
Ianello, Dorothy/Gilbertsville-Mt Upton SD	2,11	173
Iannelli, Michael/Morris Central School Dist	6	174
Ianni, Francesco, Dr/Harborfields Ctl School Dist	1,11	223
Iconis, Lucille/Massapequa Union Free SD 23	1	125
Ifedigbo, Obi/East Ramapo Central Sch Dist	3,91	196
Ike, Robert, Dr/Palmyra-Macedon Central SD	1,11	250
Illg, Kiel/Lackawanna City School Dist	6,15,68	62
Illig, Pamela/Ellicottville Central Sch Dist	16	31
Imperato, Lynn/Washingtonville Central SD	68	167
Indriolo, Toni/Randolph Central School Dist	11,31,83,88	33

#		#		#		#		#		#	
1	Superintendent	16	Instructional Media Svcs	30	Adult Education	44	Science Sec	58	Special Education K-12	72	Summer School	88	Alternative/At Risk	277	Remedial Math K-12
2	Bus/Finance/Purchasing	17	Chief Operations Officer	31	Career/Sch-to-Work K-12	45	Math K-12	59	Special Education Elem	73	Instructional Tech	89	Multi-Cultural Curriculum	280	Literacy Coach
3	Buildings And Grounds	18	Chief Academic Officer	32	Career/Sch-to-Work Elem	46	Math Elem	60	Special Education Sec	74	Inservice Training	90	Social Work	285	STEM
4	Food Service	19	Chief Financial Officer	33	Career/Sch-to-Work Sec	47	Math Sec	61	Foreign/World Lang K-12	75	Marketing/Distributive	91	Safety/Security	286	Digital Learning
5	Transportation	20	Art K-12	34	Early Childhood Ed	48	English/Lang Arts K-12	62	Foreign/World Lang Elem	76	Info Systems	92	Magnet School	288	Common Core Standards
6	Athletic	21	Art Elem	35	Health/Phys Education	49	English/Lang Arts Elem	63	Foreign/World Lang Sec	77	Psychological Assess	93	Parental Involvement	294	Accountability
7	Health Services	22	Art Sec	36	Guidance Services K-12	50	English/Lang Arts Sec	64	Religious Education K-12	78	Affirmative Action	94	Tech Prep Program	295	Network System
8	Curric/Instruct K-12	23	Music K-12	37	Guidance Services Elem	51	Reading K-12	65	Religious Education Elem	79	Student Personnel	97	Chief Infomation Officer	296	Title II Programs
9	Curric/Instruct Elem	24	Music Elem	38	Guidance Services Sec	52	Reading Elem	66	Religious Education Sec	80	Driver Ed/Safety	98	Chief Technology Officer	297	Webmaster
10	Curric/Instruct Sec	25	Music Sec	39	Social Studies K-12	53	Reading Sec	67	School Board President	81	Gifted/Talented	270	Character Education	298	Grant Writer/Ptnrships
11	Federal Program	26	Business Education	40	Social Studies Elem	54	Remedial Reading K-12	68	Teacher Personnel	82	Video Services	271	Migrant Education	750	Chief Innovation Officer
12	Title I	27	Career & Tech Ed	41	Social Studies Sec	55	Remedial Reading Elem	69	Academic Assessment	83	Substance Abuse Prev	273	Teacher Mentor	751	Chief of Staff
13	Title V	28	Technology Education	42	Science K-12	56	Remedial Reading Sec	70	Research/Development	84	Erate	274	Before/After Sch	752	Social Emotional Learning
15	Asst Superintendent	29	Family/Consumer Science	43	Science Elem	57	Bilingual/ELL	71	Public Information	85	AIDS Education	275	Response To Intervention		

New York School Directory

DISTRICT PERSONNEL INDEX

NAME/District	JOB FUNCTIONS	PAGE
Infantino, Russel/Dover Union Free School Dist	67	52
Inflesey, Alex/Northern Adirondack Ctl SD	73,295	44
Inforna, Micheal/Commack Union Free School Dist	15	219
Ingham, Kelly/Gilbertsville-Mt Upton SD	7	173
Ingles, Angela/Addison Central School Dist	16	213
Ingolia, Raina/Center Moriches Union Free SD	3,8,11,15,76,288	218
Ingram, Mary/Skaneateles Central Sch Dist	38	157
Innaco, Joseph/Bellmore-Merrick Ctl High SD	16,69,73,95,295	117
Insognia, Nick/Bethlehem Central School Dist	3,15	10
Intintoli, Deanna/Garden City School Dist	4	120
Inzana, David/Hilton Central School Dist	91	109
Ireland, Maureen/Waterville Central Sch Dist	4	153
Irizarry, Michael/Yorkshire-Pioneer Ctl Sch Dist	8,11,48,57,69,72,73,288	33
Irizary, Michael/Yorkshire-Pioneer Ctl Sch Dist	73	33
Irvin, Andy/Carmel Central School Dist	1	175
Irving, Patrick/Gates Chili Central Sch Dist	6,35	108
Irwin, Diane/Ballston Spa Ctl School Dist	42	200
Isoldi, Theresa/Suffern Central School Dist	2	198
Israel, Lisa/Eastern Suffolk BOCES	67	235
Israel, Michael, Dr/Glen Cove City School Dist	8,15,73,288	120
Iuliucci, Stephanie/Ft Edward Union Free Sch Dist	51,54,274	247
Ivan, Tamara/Chenango Valley Ctl Sch Dist	8,69	28
Iverson, Marla/Wayne-Finger Lakes BOCES	15	252
Iwouha, Ogechi/East Ramapo Central Sch Dist	15,74	196
Izzo, Ann/Hawthorne Cedar Knolls UFSD	76	256
Izzo, Beth/Elwood Union Free School Dist	71	221
Izzo, Karen/Northville Central School Dist	31,36	72

J

NAME/District	JOB FUNCTIONS	PAGE
Jabour, Lynette/West Babylon Union Free SD	48,51,54	233
Jackowski, Devin/Germantown Central School Dist	36,69	46
Jackson, Ann/Ravena Coeymans Selkirk Ctl SD	58	11
Jackson, Cheryl/Newfield Central School Dist	12,58	241
Jackson, Daniel/Randolph Central School Dist	67	33
Jackson, Howard/Syracuse City School Dist	11,298	158
Jackson, Jessica/Wheatland Chili Ctl Sch Dist	2	113
Jackson, John/Walton Central School Dist	3	50
Jackson, Laura/Sharon Springs Ctl SD	67	207
Jacob, Michael/Hamilton-Fulton-Montgmry BOCES	58	72
Jacob, Sheena/Glen Cove City School Dist	39	120
Jacobellis, Ryan/Riverhead Central School Dist	3	228
Jacobs, Erica/Andover Central School Dist	20	14
Jacobs, Jade/Rockville Ctr Union Free SD	16	128
Jacobs, Monique/Duanesburg Central Sch Dist	297	203
Jacobs, Sue/West Irondequoit Ctl SD	20	113
Jacobsen, Carly/Highland Ctl School Dist	38	242
Jacobsen, Meghan/Valhalla Union Free Sch Dist	36	262
Jacobsen, Michelle/Hamilton Central Sch Dist	67	105
Jacobson, Deborah/Fallsburg Central School Dist	274	236
Jaffe-Bennek, Gail/Red Hook Central School Dist	30	53
Jagnandan, Satish, Dr/Mount Vernon City School Dist	42,45,277,285	258
Jaime, Michael/Elmont Union Free School Dist	67	118
Jaime, Michael/Sewanhaka Ctl High Sch Dist	67	129
Jalal, Janine/Gowanda Central School Dist	11,58,298	32
Jalloh, Mary/Ulster BOCES	30	244
James, Danielle/Sandy Creek Central Sch Dist	36	172
James, Deb/Marathon Ctl School Dist	36,69,288	48
James, Donald, Dr/Commack Union Free School Dist	1	219
James, Todd/Marathon Ctl School Dist	6,31	48
James, Vernon/Saranac Lake Central Sch Dist	3	70
Jankeloff, Lois/Herricks Union Free Sch Dist	79,88,298	121
Jankowski, Carol/Dover Union Free School Dist	4	52
Jantson, Chris/Voorheesville Central Sch Dist	20,23	12
Janus, Daryl/Cleveland Hill Union Free SD	8,69	59
Jaquish, Glenn/Worcester Ctl School Dist	3	174
Jaquith, Jennifer/Hinsdale Central School Dist	2	32
Jara-Cole, Jacqueline/Monticello Central School Dist	7	237
Jareo, Dina/Lyme Central School Dist	5	81
Jareo, Dina/Thousand Islands Central SD	5	81
Jaronczyk, Joe/Plainedge Union Free Sch Dist	3,91	127
Jasinski, Mark/Newfield Central School Dist	8	241
Jay, Phillip/Gates Chili Central Sch Dist	16,295	108
Jean, Bobbie/Ticonderoga Central Sch Dist	4	68
Jeff, Platt/Portville Central School Dist	3	32
Jefferson, Jonathan, Dr/Uniondale Union Free Sch Dist	6,35,83,85	130
Jeffries, John/Phoenix Central School Dist	6,35	171

NAME/District	JOB FUNCTIONS	PAGE
Jeffs, Sybil/Suffern Central School Dist	60	198
Jehring, Jan/Florida Union Free Sch Dist	1	164
Jemiola, Larrilee/Southampton Union Free SD	294	231
Jenkins, Allen/Peekskill City School Dist	67	260
Jenkins, Kelvin/Uniondale Union Free Sch Dist	20,23	130
Jenkins, Lynne/Corinth Central School Dist	27,36	200
Jenkins, Paul/Glens Falls City School Dist	1	245
Jenkins, Thomas/Greece Central School Dist	295	108
Jenne, Larry/St Lawrence-Lewis BOCES	27,31	212
Jennings, Kelli/Patchogue-Medford Unified SD	67	227
Jennings, Peter/South Seneca Ctl Sch Dist	67	208
Jennings, Tom/Pulaski Central School Dist	1	172
Jenny, Timmothy/Remsen Central School Dist	1,11	151
Jensen, Kristi/Ballston Spa Ctl School Dist	58	200
Jensen, Linda/Mt Sinai Union Free SD	2,5	226
Jensen, Nancy/Highland Ctl School Dist	38	242
Jensen, Patrick/Southern Cayuga Central SD	1	35
Jensen, Samantha/Monroe 1 BOCES	3	115
Jensen, Stephen/Rhinebeck Central School Dist	71,73,98,295	53
Jermaine, Ryan/Lake Pleasant Central Sch Dist	3	76
Jerome, Amy/Hamilton Central Sch Dist	16	105
Jerosz, Adam/Fayetteville-Manlius Ctl SD	4	155
Jerreld, Randy/Mohonasen Central Sch Dist	5	203
Jesman, Kurt/Wappingers Central Sch Dist	6,35	54
Jessup, Peggy/Sherburne Earlville Central SD	7	42
Jester, Jen/Charlotte Valley Ctl Sch Dist	274	49
Jewell, Mary/Duanesburg Central Sch Dist	4	203
Jilek, Lissa/Highland Ctl School Dist	2	242
Jimenez, Marguerite/Deer Park Union Free Sch Dist	2,4,15	220
Jiuffidra, Jo/Syosset Central School Dist	274	129
Joannon, Stephanie/Port Washington Union Free SD	6,35	128
Jock, Darrin/Brushton Moira Ctl Sch Dist	5	69
Jock, Natascha/Salmon River Central Sch Dist	2	70
Jockers, Ken/Mt Sinai Union Free SD	76,295	226
Johannessen, Jennifer/Sackets Harbor Ctl School Dist	7	81
Johanson, Jill/Huntington Union Free Sch Dist	285	223
John, Sunil/Half Hollow Hills Central SD	76,84	222
Johnsen, Mary/Wainscott Common School Dist	59	232
Johnsen, Tim/Rochester City School Dist	73	110
Johnson-Dingle, Angelique/Western Suffolk BOCES	1	236
Johnson, Aaron, Dr/West Irondequoit Ctl SD	1	113
Johnson, Alex/Middleburgh Ctl School Dist	50	206
Johnson, Beth/Margaretville Central Sch Dist	73	50
Johnson, Beth/West Seneca Central Sch Dist	68	64
Johnson, Bonnie/Franklin Central School Dist	11,58,69,74,273	49
Johnson, Bonnie/Onc BOCES	74	51
Johnson, C Douglas/Greater Southern Tier BOCES	68	215
Johnson, Camille/Auburn Enlarged City Sch Dist	15,69,77,79,271	34
Johnson, Cynthia/Randolph Acad Union Free SD	7,8,12,85,298	32
Johnson, David/Harpursville Central Sch Dist	3	28
Johnson, Deborah/Catskill Central School Dist	67	75
Johnson, Diane/Garden City School Dist	36	120
Johnson, Don/Spencer Van Etten Central SD	67	238
Johnson, Evelyn/Tuckahoe Union Free SD	16	262
Johnson, Jatha/Keene Central School Dist	31,69,81,83,85,88	67
Johnson, Jenna/Le Roy Central School Dist	16	73
Johnson, Joanna/Mount Markham Central Sch Dist	2	78
Johnson, Lamont/Hempstead Union Free SD	67	121
Johnson, Lori/Fort Ann Central School Dist	58	247
Johnson, Maria/Roxbury Central School Dist	16	50
Johnson, Megan/Scotia Glenville Ctl Sch Dist	42	205
Johnson, Nora/Port Washington Union Free SD	67	128
Johnson, Norm/Springville Griffith Inst CSD	82	63
Johnson, Ronald/Ogdensburg City School Dist	67	211
Johnson, Rosemary/Manhasset Union Free Sch Dist	2,15	124
Johnson, Scott/Sweet Home Central Sch Dist	67	63
Johnson, Shawn/Eden Central School Dist	58,79	60
Johnson, Taryn, Dr/Sewanhaka Ctl High Sch Dist	10,15	129
Johnston, Andrew/Clarence Central School Dist	16	59
Johnston, Joann/North Tonawanda City Sch Dist	68,288	148
Johnston, Kathleen/Bethlehem Central School Dist	58	10
Johnston, Kerrie/Sidney Central School Dist	8,15	50
Johnston, Reagan/Guilderland Central Sch Dist	6	11
Jones, Amanda/Rome City School District	36	151
Jones, Amy/Bolivar-Richburg Ctrl Sch Dist	77	14
Jones, Brian/Holland Central School Dist	67	61

School Year 2020-2021   800-333-8802   NY-T31

DISTRICT PERSONNEL INDEX

Market Data Retrieval

NAME/District	JOB FUNCTIONS	PAGE
Jones, Catherine/WSWHE BOCES	69	249
Jones, Donna/Patchogue-Medford Unified SD	1	227
Jones, Douglas/Sauquoit Valley Central SD	6	152
Jones, Jennifer/De Ruyter Central School Dist	16,82	105
Jones, Julie/Brookfield Central School Dist	7	104
Jones, Karen/Camden Central School Dist	2	150
Jones, Karen/Ft Edward Union Free Sch Dist	58,285	247
Jones, Karen/Voorheesville Central Sch Dist	34,58,79,752	12
Jones, Kelly/Wantagh Union Free Sch Dist 23	23	131
Jones, Kevin/Oriskany Ctl School Dist	6	151
Jones, Mark/Capital Region BOCES	2,3,15,17,68	13
Jones, Maureen/Katonah-Lewisboro Sch Dist	71,97	257
Jones, Nathan/Hunter Tannersville Ctl SD	1,11,288	76
Jones, Patricia/Onondaga Central School Dist	2	157
Jones, Richard/Phelps-Clifton Springs Ctl SD	36	162
Jones, Scott/Pulaski Central School Dist	83,85	172
Jones, Verdel/Plainedge Union Free Sch Dist	36	127
Jordan, Brent/Hamburg Central School Dist	71,73,76,97	61
Jordan, Christine/Wyandanch Union Free Sch Dist	42,45	234
Jordan, Eric/Brighton Central School Dist	73	106
Jordan, Karen/Cortland Enlarged City SD	57	47
Jordan, Karen/Monroe Woodbury Central SD	58	165
Jordan, Oneeka/Archdiocese of New York Ed Off	76	142
Jordan, Robert/Massena Central School Dist	36	211
Jorgensen, Denise/Bolton Central School Dist	16	244
Jorgensen, Mallory/Morris Central School Dist	5	174
Jorgensen, Michael/Port Byron Ctl School Dist	8	35
Jory, Thomas/Jefferson Central Sch Dist	73,286,295	206
Joseph, Dara/New Rochelle City School Dist	58	259
Joseph, Sylvi/Cohoes City School Dist	73,98	10
Joslin, Wanda/Beaver River Central Sch Dist	6,35	101
Joy, Jessie/Jamestown City School Dist	69,71,97,294	38
Joy, Vineetha/Mt Pleasant Ctl School Dist	73	258
Joyce-Turner, Rose/Sullivan West Central SD	67	237
Joyce, Eric/Catskill Central School Dist	6	75
Joyce, Jennifer/Andover Central School Dist	2,11,71,275,296,298	14
Joyner, Eric/Wayland-Cohocton Central SD	57	215
Judeikis, Mary/Greenville Central School Dist	5	75
Judge, Andrea/Lindenhurst Union Free SD	36	224
Jurewicz, Cindy/Bethlehem Central School Dist	5	10

K

NAME/District	JOB FUNCTIONS	PAGE
Kaden, Fred/Seaford Union Free SD	16,73,76,286,295	129
Kafka, Aviva/Hyde Park Central School Dist	8,11,57,74,83,88,91,285	52
Kahn, Bruce/Roslyn School Dist	67	129
Kahn, Bruce/Seaford Union Free SD	67	129
Kahn, Judy/Saratoga Springs City Sch Dist	91	201
Kaishian, James, Dr/Briarcliff Manor Union Free SD	1	253
Kakascik, Tina/Cornwall Central School Dist	73,76,286	163
Kalem, Kim/Greene Ctl School Dist	73,76	42
Kalem, Kimberly/Otselic Valley Central SD	73,286	42
Kallich, Sylvia/Uniondale Union Free Sch Dist	7	130
Kalman, Nicole/Chateaugay Central School Dist	9,11,58	69
Kaltenecker, Tim, Dr/Byram Hills Central Sch Dist	8,15,288	253
Kalvana, Amanda/Commack Union Free School Dist	5,80	219
Kamberg, Mark/East Williston Union Free SD	67	118
Kamensky, Josh/Kiryas Joel Union Free SD	11,15,84,298	164
Kaminski, Aaron/Whitney Point Central Sch Dist	11,58	30
Kamlet, Steven/Long Beach City School Dist	4	124
Kammerer, Brent/Edgemont Union Free Sch Dist	97	254
Kammler, Aubree/Guilderland Central Sch Dist	71	11
Kammler, Aubree/Hudson Falls Central Sch Dist	16,82	248
Kanarek, Nathan/South Kortright Ctl SD	2,19	50
Kanarvogel, Mary/Shelter Island Union Free SD	7	230
Kanas, Elaine, Dr/East Williston Union Free SD	1	118
Kandefer, Gale/Depew Union Free School Dist	7	59
Kane, Brenda/Burnt Hills Ballston Lake SD	2	200

NAME/District	JOB FUNCTIONS	PAGE
Kane, Carrie/Syracuse City School Dist	4	158
Kane, Karen/Schuylerville Central Sch Dist	71,97	201
Kane, Rebecca/York Central School Dist	91	103
Kane, Taryn/North Colonie Central SD	71	11
Kanellopoulos, Helen, Dr/Freeport Public School Dist	58,79	119
Kaney, Colleen/Hamburg Central School Dist	8,15,36,58,79,83,275,288	61
Kanter, Jaimie/Harrison Central School Dist	48	256
Kaplan, Melanie/Baldwin Union Free School Dist	30	116
Kaplan, Nancy/Merrick Union Free School Dist	67	125
Kaplan, Pam/Locust Valley Ctl School Dist	71	123
Kaplan, Scott/North Collins Ctl Sch Dist	16,273	63
Kaplan, Stuart/Oceanside Union Free Sch Dist	67	127
Karam, Alfred/Shenendehowa Central Sch Dist	5	202
Karam, Bruce/Utica City School Dist	1	152
Karas, Joseph/Schalmont Central School Dist	2	204
Karbowski, John/Northville Central School Dist	6	72
Karcher, Shannon/Rochester City School Dist	88	110
Karcz, Jim/Pulaski Central School Dist	6	172
Kardash, Joseph/Rensselaer City School Dist	1	191
Kardaz, Sara/Western Suffolk BOCES	16	236
Karis, Bridget/West Hempstead School Dist	7,58,79,83	131
Karker, Charlie/Ft Plain Central School Dist	6	115
Karker, Justin/Cairo-Durham Ctl School Dist	27,31,36	75
Karl, Jim/Sidney Central School Dist	6	50
Karlsson, Victor/Brewster Central School Dist	2,3,11,15	175
Karlund, Erik/Brentwood Union Free Sch Dist	3	217
Karn, Jessica/Schenectady City School Dist	58	204
Karnisky, Joan/Palmyra-Macedon Central SD	58,83	250
Karol, Jason/Eastchester Union Free SD	6	254
Karp, Jill, Dr/Merrick Union Free School Dist	9,11,15,69,74,288,296,298	125
Karpik, Paul/Alden Central School Dist	2,3	56
Karstedt, Lucinda/Eden Central School Dist	71,73,97	60
Karwiel, Christopher/Green Island Union Free SD	2	10
Kashuba, Jordan/Dryden Central School Dist	68	239
Kasson, Cliff/Vestal Ctl School Dist	15,19	29
Katchuk, Ji/Newark Valley Central Sch Dist	2,11,296,298	238
Katuemutima, Gerson/Scarsdale Union Free Sch Dist	5	261
Katuna, Ed/Middle Country Ctl Sch Dist	295	225
Katz, Ivan, Dr/Fallsburg Central School Dist	1	236
Katz, Neil/Smithtown Central Sch Dist	15,68	230
Katz, Steven/New York State Dept Education	69	1
Kauhn, Lori/Rocky Point Union Free SD	30,80	228
Kauter, Chris/Bay Shore Union Free Sch Dist	286	217
Kavanagh, Amanda/Hewlett Woodmere Union Free SD	73,286	121
Kavanaugh, Nancy/Longwood Central School Dist	2	224
Kavanaugh, Philip/Somers Central School Dist	36,69,83,88	262
Kaye, Elliot/North Shore Central SD	73,95	126
Kazlo, Joseph/Moriah Central School Dist	3,5	68
Kazmark, Jennifer/Union-Endicott Ctl Sch Dist	15,68	29
Keane, Jennifer/Wantagh Union Free Sch Dist 23	6,35	131
Keane, Kathleen/William Floyd School Dist	10,15,71	233
Keane, Kevin/Cherry Valley-Springfield SD	6	173
Kear, Edward/Eastchester Union Free SD	3	254
Kearney, Bret/Lindenhurst Union Free SD	7,15,58,79,90	224
Kearney, Christine/West Islip School Dist	4	233
Kearney, Steve, Dr/Farmingdale Union Free SD	77	119
Kearns, Susan/Westhampton Beach School Dist	11,74	233
Keating, Danielle/Malone Central School Dist	48	70
Keating, Ryan/Alexander Ctl School Dist	8,285,288	73
Keddell, Donald/Greater Southern Tier BOCES	67	215
Keefer, Nicole/Bradford Central Sch Dist	58	207
Keegan, Don/North Syracuse Ctl Sch Dist	2,3,5,17,19,73,91,98	157
Keeler, George/Hudson City School Dist	3	46
Keen, Sarah/Schuylerville Central Sch Dist	4	201
Keenan, Joseph/Carmel Central School Dist	71,97,285,295	175
Keene, David/Tioga Central School Dist	3	239
Keene, Kathleen/Tioga Central School Dist	8,11,91,286,288	239

---

1 Superintendent
2 Bus/Finance/Purchasing
3 Buildings And Grounds
4 Food Service
5 Transportation
6 Athletic
7 Health Services
8 Curric/Instruct K-12
9 Curric/Instruct Elem
10 Curric/Instruct Sec
11 Federal Program
12 Title I
13 Title V
15 Asst Superintendent
16 Instructional Media Svcs
17 Chief Operations Officer
18 Chief Academic Officer
19 Chief Financial Officer
20 Art K-12
21 Art Elem
22 Art Sec
23 Music K-12
24 Music Elem
25 Music Sec
26 Business Education
27 Career & Tech Ed
28 Technology Education
29 Family/Consumer Science
30 Adult Education
31 Career/Sch-to-Work K-12
32 Career/Sch-to-Work Elem
33 Career/Sch-to-Work Sec
34 Early Childhood Ed
35 Health/Phys Education
36 Guidance Services K-12
37 Guidance Services Elem
38 Guidance Services Sec
39 Social Studies K-12
40 Social Studies Elem
41 Social Studies Sec
42 Science K-12
43 Science Elem
44 Science Sec
45 Math K-12
46 Math Elem
47 Math Sec
48 English/Lang Arts K-12
49 English/Lang Arts Elem
50 English/Lang Arts Sec
51 Reading K-12
52 Reading Elem
53 Reading Sec
54 Remedial Reading K-12
55 Remedial Reading Elem
56 Remedial Reading Sec
57 Bilingual/ELL
58 Special Education K-12
59 Special Education Elem
60 Special Education Sec
61 Foreign/World Lang K-12
62 Foreign/World Lang Elem
63 Foreign/World Lang Sec
64 Religious Education K-12
65 Religious Education Elem
66 Religious Education Sec
67 School Board President
68 Teacher Personnel
69 Academic Assessment
70 Research/Development
71 Public Information
72 Summer School
73 Instructional Tech
74 Inservice Training
75 Marketing/Distributive
76 Info Systems
77 Psychological Assess
78 Affirmative Action
79 Student Personnel
80 Driver Ed/Safety
81 Gifted/Talented
82 Video Services
83 Substance Abuse Prev
84 Erate
85 AIDS Education
88 Alternative/At Risk
89 Multi-Cultural Curriculum
90 Social Work
91 Safety/Security
92 Magnet School
93 Parental Involvement
95 Tech Prep Program
97 Chief Information Officer
98 Chief Technology Officer
270 Character Education
271 Migrant Education
273 Teacher Mentor
274 Before/After Sch
275 Response To Intervention
277 Remedial Math K-12
280 Literacy Coach
285 STEM
286 Digital Learning
288 Common Core Standards
294 Accountability
295 Network System
296 Title II Programs
297 Webmaster
298 Grant Writer/Ptnrships
750 Chief Innovation Officer
751 Chief of Staff
752 Social Emotional Learning

New York School Directory

DISTRICT PERSONNEL INDEX

NAME/District	JOB FUNCTIONS	PAGE
Keeney, Joe/Sodus Central School Dist	58,79	251
Kehl, Eric/Southold Union Free Sch Dist	82	231
Kehoe, Judith/Bethlehem Central School Dist	2,19	10
Keil, Karl/Camden Central School Dist	15	150
Keingstein, Kristi/Commack Union Free School Dist	58	219
Keith, Thomas/Spackenkill Union Free SD	67	54
Kelahan, Gregory/Watkins Glen Central Sch Dist	1,11	207
Kelder, Tina/Margaretville Central Sch Dist	16,27	49
Keley, Michael/Beacon City School Dist	73	51
Kellam, Genevieve/Dutchess Co BOCES	71,298	55
Kellar, Randy/Sackets Harbor Ctl School Dist	3	81
Kelleher, Bill/East Rochester Union Free SD	36,83,85	107
Kelleher, Keri/Lynbrook Union Free Sch Dist	58	124
Kellenbenz, Tammi/Germantown Central School Dist	67	46
Keller, Richard/Cheektowaga-Sloan UFSD	16,23	59
Kelley, Debra/Tri-Valley Central School Dist	8,11,15,74,288,298	237
Kelley, Marcia/East Syracuse Minoa Ctl SD	71	154
Kelley, Michelle/Broadalbin-Perth Ctl Sch Dist	71,298	71
Kelley, William/Fillmore Central School Dist	36	14
Kellner, Paul/North Collins Ctl Sch Dist	6	63
Kelly - Gorman, Eileen/Elwood Union Free School Dist	11,57,58,88,296	221
Kelly, Beth/Germantown Central School Dist	4	46
Kelly, Jacquelyn/Ogdensburg City School Dist	8,15,58	211
Kelly, Jeff/Canton Central School Dist	16,73,82,295	209
Kelly, Jennifer/Clyde-Savannah Central SD	73	249
Kelly, Jeremiah/La Fayette Central School Dist	6	156
Kelly, Kaine/Randolph Central School Dist	1	33
Kelly, Katie/Bay Shore Union Free Sch Dist	83,88,275	217
Kelly, Mary, Dr/Amityville Union Free Sch Dist	1	216
Kelly, Michael/Bethpage Union Free Sch Dist	67	117
Kelly, Michael/Little Falls City School Dist	3	78
Kelly, Peter/Valhalla Union Free Sch Dist	3	262
Kelly, Rachel, Dr/Bronxville Union Free SD	11,57,58,68,79,83,296	253
Kelly, Sara/Geneseo Central Sch Dist	57	103
Kelly, Sharon/Schroon Lake Ctl School Dist	7	68
Kelly, Tina/Tarrytown Union Free Sch Dist	298	262
Kelly, Tina/White Plains City School Dist	298	263
Kelly, Tracy/Chatham Central School Dist	90	46
Kelly, Tyler/Granville Central School Dist	5	247
Kelsey, Nancy/Western Suffolk BOCES	27,31	236
Kelsey, Valerie/Capital Region BOCES	27,31	13
Kelsie, Tyrone/Floral Park Bellerose Sch Dist	5	119
Kemp, Beth/Brushton Moira Ctl Sch Dist	16,82	69
Kempney, Keith/Sauquoit Valley Central SD	73	152
Kempster, Michael/Silver Creek Central Sch Dist	73,295	39
Kendall-Jakus, Kristin/Iroquois Central School Dist	69,77,79	61
Kendall, Jean, Dr/Manhasset Union Free Sch Dist	15,68	124
Kendall, Kevin/Ogdensburg City School Dist	1,11	211
Kennedy, Donna, Dr/Indian River Ctl School Dist	78	80
Kennedy, Elizabeth/Brewster Central School Dist	58,79	175
Kennedy, Mark/Westmoreland Central Sch Dist	2	153
Kennedy, Matthew/North Tonawanda City Sch Dist	67	148
Kennedy, Robert/La Fayette Central School Dist	4	156
Kennedy, Robert/Tully Central School Dist	4	159
Kenney, Darrin/Pittsford Central Sch Dist	2,15	110
Kenny, Paul/Dover Union Free School Dist	6	52
Kenny, Thomas/Bethpage Union Free Sch Dist	38,88	117
Kent, Christal/Waterloo Central School Dist	6,35	208
Kent, Phill/New Suffolk Common School Dist	1,11	226
Kent, Tracy/Berlin Central School Dist	9,11	189
Kenyon, James/Worcester Ctl School Dist	6	174
Keough, Deborah/North Colonie Central SD	23	11
Kerm, Gregory/New Rochelle City School Dist	2,15	259
Kern, Greg/Newburgh Enlarged City SD	2,15	165
Kern, Matthew/Suffern Central School Dist	67	198
Kern, Sarah/Suffern Central School Dist	38	198
Kerr, Jeannine/Peru Central School Dist	4	44
Kerr, Randal/Newark Valley Central Sch Dist	67	238
Kerrane, Jennifer/New Hyde-Garden City Park UFSD	67	126
Kerrick, Melissa/Saratoga Springs City Sch Dist	68,74	201
Kersh, Allison/Nanuet Union Free School Dist	83,88	196
Kershner, Sherri/Onondaga-Cortland-Madson BOCES	2	160
Kersting, Terry/Greater Johnstown Sch Dist	5	71
Kesel, Brian/West Genesee Ctl School Dist	8,15,18,83,270,288	159
Kester, Corinna/Dunkirk City School Dist	2,11,70,274	37
Ketcham, Diana/Half Hollow Hills Central SD	9,15	222

NAME/District	JOB FUNCTIONS	PAGE
Keys, Richard/Queensbury Union Free Sch Dist	6,7,35,83,85,88	246
Keyser, Sue/Rome City School Dist	73,76	151
Khan, Natasha/Herricks Union Free Sch Dist	38	121
Khoury, Charles, Dr/Ulster BOCES	1	244
Kiang, Angela/Sagaponack Common School Dist	286	229
Kidd, Bill/Middle Country Ctl Sch Dist	4	225
Kiembock, Regan/Southampton Union Free SD	4	231
Kiernan, Denise/North Salem Central Sch Dist	6,35	259
Kiernan, Katrina/Washingtonville Central SD	42,45	167
Kies, Leonard/Bethlehem Central School Dist	6	10
Kight, Ernest/Freeport Public School Dist	67	119
Kikpole, Jamie/Cairo-Durham Ctl School Dist	73,295	75
Kilburn, Kay/Yorkshire-Pioneer Ctl Sch Dist	83	33
Kilby, Aimee/Ellicottville Central Sch Dist	2	31
Kilcourse, David/Baldwinsville Central Sch Dist	68,79	154
Kilcullen, Eileen/Malone Central School Dist	6,35,85	69
Kiley-Rendon, Patrick/Long Beach City School Dist	73	124
Kilian, Fritz/Fairport Ctl School Dist	6,35	108
Kilmer, Gina/Port Byron Ctl School Dist	4	35
Kilmer, Joseph/Corning-Painted Post Area SD	4	214
Kilmer, Joseph/Horseheads Ctl School Dist	4	40
Kilmer, Walt/Webutuck Ctl School Dist	3	54
Kilpatrick, Kelly/Andes Central School Dist	67	48
Kimiecik, Elizabeth/Valhalla Union Free Sch Dist	8,15,73	262
Kinball, Laura/Connetquot Central School Dist	9	219
Kincade, Teri/Greenburgh Central School Dist	79	255
Kinery, Gina/Saugerties Central School Dist	90	243
King, Bonnie/Wappingers Central Sch Dist	20,23,61	54
King, Dan/New York State Dept Education	39	1
King, Darlene/Saratoga Springs City Sch Dist	7,57,58,79	201
King, Douglas/Royalton Hartland Central SD	11,58,77,271	148
King, Irvin/Clymer Central School Dist	83,85,88	37
King, Larry/Cleveland Hill Union Free SD	73	59
King, Pamela/New Hartford Central Sch Dist	67	151
Kingsbury, Jeffrey/Lyndonville Central Sch Dist	38,69	169
Kingsley, Kevin/Potsdam Central School Dist	5	212
Kingston, Deena/Naples Central School Dist	4	162
Kinnard, Paige/Allegany-Limestone Ctl SD	8,12,57,69,296	31
Kinne, Pamela/Solvay Union Free Sch Dist	4	158
Kinney, Mike/Stillwater Central Sch Dist	6	202
Kinney, Richard/Canaseraga Central Sch Dist	67	14
Kinsley, Gerald/Hauppauge Union Free Sch Dist	5	223
Kipfer, Caroline/Bayport- Blue Point USD	73,286	217
Kirby, Jennifer/Great Neck Public Schools	68	120
Kirchoff, Brianne/Alexandria Central School Dist	2	79
Kirk, Andrew/Whitesboro Ctl School Dist	5	153
Kirkhus, Debra/Pawling Ctl School Dist	11,69,273,288,294,295,296,298	52
Kirkwood, Pam/Cattaraugus-Allegany BOCES	68	34
Kise, Nelson/Sodus Central School Dist	1,11	251
Kiskiel, Deb/Vernon-Verona-Sherrill CSD	42	152
Kisloski, Jeff/Candor Central School Dist	1	238
Kissinger, Lisa/Shenendehowa Central Sch Dist	41	202
Kittelberger, Wayne/Rochester City School Dist	5	110
Klafehn, Matthew/New Lebanon Ctl School Dist	10	46
Klaich, Andrew/Dobbs Ferry Union Free SD	6,35	254
Klar, Tina/New Hartford Central Sch Dist	81	151
Klein, Beth/Andover Central School Dist	7	14
Klein, John/Greece Central School Dist	23	108
Klein, Kattie/Port Washington Union Free SD	36,57,88,271	128
Klein, Kitty/Huntington Union Free Sch Dist	36,69	223
Klein, Phyllis/Willsboro Central Sch Dist	67	68
Kleinberg, Rachel/Montauk Union Free School Dist	16,82	226
Klenk, Jeff/Cobleskill Richmondville SD	72	206
Klenotiz, Mike/Oneida City School Dist	5	105
Klick, Robert/Somers Central School Dist	3	262
Klievoneit, Linda/Horseheads Ctl School Dist	2	40
Klime, Linda/Lansingburgh Central Sch Dist	2,73,91	190
Klimek, Nicole/Rochester City School Dist	295	110
Kline, Kristina/Johnson City Central Sch Dist	57	28
Kline, Mary/Herkimer BOCES	30,34,57,271	79
Kline, Maureen/Susquehanna Valley Central SD	58	29
Kline, Melany/Parishville Hopkinton Sch Dist	4	212
Klips, Gina/Elba Central School Dist	31	73
Kliszus, Edward, Dr/Port Chester Rye Union Free SD	1	261
Klubek, James/Gowanda Central School Dist	288	32
Kluth, Rachael, Dr/Brockport Ctl School Dist	10	106

DISTRICT PERSONNEL INDEX

Market Data Retrieval

NAME/District	JOB FUNCTIONS	PAGE
Knaak, Randy/Albion Central School Dist	6	169
Knaggs, Bronson/Schalmont Central School Dist	7,8,288	204
Knapp, Cristina/Fabius Pompey Central SD	79	155
Knapp, Lauren/Scio Central School Dist	67	15
Knapp, Monique/Campbell-Savona Ctl Sch Dist	35	213
Knapp, Stephanie/Canandaigua City School Dist	11,31,57,58	161
Knierim, Eric/Minerva Central School Dist	51,54	68
Kniewel, Victoria, Dr/Edgemont Union Free Sch Dist	1	254
Knight, James/Northern Adirondack Ctl SD	1	44
Knight, Lianne/Colton Pierrepont School Dist	12,58,77,79,296,298	209
Knisell, Kim/Hyde Park Central School Dist	42,45	52
Knolles, Eric/Waverly Ctl School Dist	1	239
Knott, Yvonne/Massapequa Union Free SD 23	76	125
Knowles, Gary/Irvington Union Free Sch Dist	3	257
Knowles, Lisa/Guilderland Central School Dist	11,58,77,88,90	11
Knowlton, Robyn/Gouverneur Ctl School Dist	58,77	210
Knudsen, Eugene/Ulster BOCES	73,76	244
Knuth, Eric/Altmar-Parish-Williamstown SD	1	170
Knuth, Eric/Skaneateles Central Sch Dist	1	157
Koch, Jeremy/Miller Place Union Free SD	79	226
Kochan, Jan/Poland Central School Dist	37	78
Kochis, Eric/Owego Apalachin Ctl Sch Dist	73,295	238
Kocur, Jeanette/Hastings on Hudson Union FR SD	36	256
Koczyals, Robert/Depew Union Free School Dist	6	59
Koehler, Chris/Canisteo-Greenwood Central SD	6	214
Koehler, Mary/William Floyd School Dist	298	233
Koehring, Joseph/Long Lake Central School Dist	57	76
Koelbel, Fred/Port Jefferson Union Free SD 6	3,5	228
Koelbl, Lynn/Alden Central School Dist	30	56
Koetke, Mara, Dr/Bronxville Union Free SD	8,12,288,298	253
Kohl, Angela/New Suffolk Common School Dist	2	226
Kohler, Joe/Hammondsport Ctl School Dist	12	214
Kohlstaedt, Nicole/Elba Central School Dist	58	73
Kokanovich, Mark/Brighton Central School Dist	67	106
Kokoletsos, Jane/Johnsburg Central School Dist	30,36	245
Kolakowski, Kevin/Mechanicville City Sch Dist	10,27,31,83,88	201
Kolar, Keith/Sayville Union Free Sch Dist	67	229
Kolceski, Michelle/Auburn Enlarged City Sch Dist	8	34
Kolczynski, Zoe/Marcus Whitman Central SD	2,12,296	162
Kollar, Richard/Longwood Central School Dist	15,68,80,83	225
Kolod, Deb/East Syracuse Minoa Ctl SD	67	154
Kolstee, Amanda/Panama Central School Dist	2,4,5,7	38
Komanecky, Stephen/Camden Central School Dist	6	150
Kondrick, Karen/Ripley Central School Dist	16,82	39
Koneckni, Alicia/Deer Park Union Free Sch Dist	15	220
Kopp, Thomas/Keshequa Central School Dist	1	103
Kor, Raina, Dr/Irvington Union Free Sch Dist	8,15,68,288	257
Korba, Terri/Schenevus Ctl School Dist	36	174
Koretzki, Paul/Shoreham-Wading River Ctl SD	30	230
Korniak, Lori/North Warren Central Sch Dist	273	246
Korokeyi, Audrey/Rochester City School Dist	35	110
Kortbus, Kate/Red Hook Central School Dist	67	53
Kosicki, Brenna/Frankfort-Schuyler Ctl SD	27,57,58,271	77
Kosinski, Debra/New Paltz Ctl School Dist	2	242
Kosiorek, Casey, Dr/Hilton Central School Dist	1	109
Koss, Emelin/Chazy Central Rural Sch Dist	2	44
Koster, Alicia/South Orangetown Central SD	2	197
Kotes, Kurtis, Dr/Mt Pleasant Ctl School Dist	1	258
Kotula, Heather/Owego Apalachin Ctl Sch Dist	26,31,36	238
Kowalski-Kelly, Janice/Cleveland Hill Union Free SD	16	59
Kowalski, Leonard/Lackawanna City School Dist	67	62
Kowalsky, Laurie/Oyster Bay East Norwich Ctl SD	67	127
Kozak, Jeremy/West Canada Valley Ctl SD	8,74,85,92,288	79
Kozin, Carol/Lowville Acad-Central Sch Dist	31	101
Kozloski, Jeanne/Glens Falls Common Sch Dist	59	245
Kozlowski, Debra/Holland Central School Dist	16	61
Kozlowsky, Jeanne/Deer Park Union Free Sch Dist	10	220

NAME/District	JOB FUNCTIONS	PAGE
Krajewski, Patricia/Gowanda Central School Dist	38	32
Krall, Kathleen/Archdiocese of New York Ed Off	15,70	142
Kramer, Mariah/Barker Central School Dist	8,57,58,280,288,296,298	146
Kramer, Michael/Adirondack Central Sch Dist	67	150
Kramer, Ricki, Dr/Kiryas Joel Union Free SD	12,85,88	164
Krammer, Ellen/Farmingdale Union Free SD	34	119
Kraus, Donna/Oceanside Union Free Sch Dist	71	127
Krause, Keith/Jasper Troupsburg Central SD	67	215
Kravatz, Matthew/Monroe Woodbury Central SD	15,68,74	165
Krecisz, Aliscia/Grand Island Central Sch Dist	51	61
Krempler, Jeanette/Sagaponack Common School Dist	76	229
Krenrich, Theodore/Sandy Creek Central Sch Dist	42	172
Krenzer, Aubrey/York Central School Dist	8	103
Kreps, Marvin/Rhinebeck Central School Dist	8,11	53
Kreps, Richard/Putnam-Northern Wstchstr BOCES	67	267
Kressler, Debra/Cincinnatus Ctl School Dist	67	47
Kreutter, Mary/Perry Central School Dist	2	267
Krieger, Gail/Irvington Union Free Sch Dist	11,57,58,79	257
Kriegstein, Helene/Jericho Union Free School Dist	45,277	122
Kring, Lawrence, Dr/Morristown Ctl School Dist	67	211
Krivoshey, Matt, Dr/South Huntington Union Free SD	58	231
Kriwox, Dennis/La Fargeville Central School Dist	3	80
Kroemer, Michael/Cornwall Central School Dist	6	163
Krokowski, Andrew/South Lewis Central Sch Dist	5	101
Krouskoff, John/Newburgh Enlarged City SD	73,76,98,295	166
Krueger, Lisa, Dr/Orchard Park Central Sch Dist	8,15	63
Kruger, Stephen/Geneva City School Dist	15	161
Kruzynski, Mark/Medina Central School Dist	1,11	169
Kryzak, Jen/Wheelerville Union Free SD	76,97,98	72
Kubera, Colleen/Fredonia Central School Dist	4	37
Kuhl, Nicky/Beaver River Central Sch Dist	30	101
Kuhl, Patricia/Chenango Forks Central SD	58,77	28
Kuhn, Deedee/Wayland-Cohocton Central SD	30	215
Kuhnel, Lisa/Bradford Central Sch Dist	2,19	207
Kuhnel, Lisa/Odessa Montour Ctl Sch Dist	2,19	207
Kukenberger, Amy/Cooperstown Ctl School Dist	2,11	173
Kukenberger, Joseph/Cooperstown Ctl School Dist	5	173
Kulpa, Keith/Westmoreland Central Sch Dist	36	153
Kumar, Surendra/Greenburgh-Graham UFSD	73,82	255
Kuncham, Kishore, Dr/Freeport Public School Dist	1	119
Kunz, Nancy/Catskill Central School Dist	16,82	75
Kupiec, Elizabeth/Cato Meridian Central Sch Dist	11,58,79,296,298	34
Kupris, Paul/Brookfield Central School Dist	3,91	104
Kurner, Johnathan/Greenville Central School Dist	27,28	75
Kurpiewski, Denise/Mount Vernon City School Dist	15,68	258
Kurst, Debra/Sherburne Earlville Central SD	67	42
Kurtz, Robert/Hempstead Union Free SD	39,74	121
Kurtzman, Zita/Eldred Central School Dist	270	236
Kurz, Mary/Lyndonville Central Sch Dist	7	169
Kuse, Beth/Ithaca City School Dist	4	240
Kuss, Nichole/Clarence Central School Dist	2	59
Kuss, Theresa/Syracuse City School Dist	5	158
Kutzscher, Kevin/Capital Region BOCES	67	13
Kuzan, Edward/Buffalo Public Schools	70,294	57
Kwiatek, Robin/Grand Island Central Sch Dist	73,76	61
Kwiatkowski, Cynthia/Wheatland Chili Ctl Sch Dist	3	113
Kwiatkowski, Matthew/Pittsford Central Sch Dist	73	110
Kwiatkowski, Todd/Dryden Central School Dist	35	239
Kwiecien, Robin/Perry Central School Dist	7	267
Kyer, Lisa/Lansingburgh Central Sch Dist	68	190
Kysor, Stefanena/Gowanda Central School Dist	30	32
Kyvelos, Effie, Dr/East Meadow Union Free SD	60	118

L

L'Hommedieu, David/Saratoga Springs City Sch Dist	15,295	201
Laba, Dennis/Monroe 2 Orleans BOCES	67	115
Labare, John/Uniondale Union Free Sch Dist	3,91	130

1	Superintendent	16	Instructional Media Svcs	30	Adult Education	44	Science Sec	58	Special Education K-12
2	Bus/Finance/Purchasing	17	Chief Operations Officer	31	Career/Sch-to-Work K-12	45	Math K-12	59	Special Education Elem
3	Buildings And Grounds	18	Chief Academic Officer	32	Career/Sch-to-Work Elem	46	Math Elem	60	Special Education Sec
4	Food Service	19	Chief Financial Officer	33	Career/Sch-to-Work Sec	47	Math Sec	61	Foreign/World Lang K-12
5	Transportation	20	Art K-12	34	Early Childhood Ed	48	English/Lang Arts K-12	62	Foreign/World Lang Elem
6	Athletic	21	Art Elem	35	Health/Phys Education	49	English/Lang Arts Elem	63	Foreign/World Lang Sec
7	Health Services	22	Art Sec	36	Guidance Services K-12	50	English/Lang Arts Sec	64	Religious Education K-12
8	Curric/Instruct K-12	23	Music K-12	37	Guidance Services Elem	51	Reading K-12	65	Religious Education Elem
9	Curric/Instruct Elem	24	Music Elem	38	Guidance Services Sec	52	Reading Elem	66	Religious Education Sec
10	Curric/Instruct Sec	25	Music Sec	39	Social Studies K-12	53	Reading Sec	67	School Board President
11	Federal Program	26	Business Education	40	Social Studies Elem	54	Remedial Reading K-12	68	Teacher Personnel
12	Title I	27	Career & Tech Ed	41	Social Studies Sec	55	Remedial Reading Elem	69	Academic Assessment
13	Title V	28	Technology Education	42	Science K-12	56	Remedial Reading Sec	70	Research/Development
15	Asst Superintendent	29	Family/Consumer Science	43	Science Elem	57	Bilingual/ELL	71	Public Information

72	Summer School	88	Alternative/At Risk	277	Remedial Math K-12
73	Instructional Tech	89	Multi-Cultural Curriculum	280	Literacy Coach
74	Inservice Training	90	Social Work	285	STEM
75	Marketing/Distributive	91	Safety/Security	286	Digital Learning
76	Info Systems	92	Magnet School	288	Common Core Standards
77	Psychological Assess	94	Parental Involvement	294	Accountability
78	Affirmative Action	95	Tech Prep Program	295	Network System
79	Student Personnel	97	Chief Infomation Officer	296	Title II Programs
80	Driver Ed/Safety	98	Chief Technology Officer	297	Webmaster
81	Gifted/Talented	270	Character Education	298	Grant Writer/Ptnrships
82	Video Services	271	Migrant Education	750	Chief Innovation Officer
83	Substance Abuse Prev	273	Teacher Mentor	751	Chief of Staff
84	Erate	274	Before/After Sch	752	Social Emotional Learning
85	AIDS Education	275	Response To Intervention		

New York School Directory

DISTRICT PERSONNEL INDEX

NAME/District	JOB FUNCTIONS	PAGE
LaBarr, Patricia/Watertown City School Dist	1,11,57	81
LaBarre, Lucas/Shenendehowa Central Sch Dist	38	202
Labbe, Richard/Newfield Central School Dist	2	241
LaBelle-Matott, Nadine/Northeastern Clinton Ctl SD	4	44
LaBelle, Jamie/Plainedge Union Free Sch Dist	6,35,85	127
Labenne, Jeff/Genesee Valley Ctl School Dist	16,73,295	15
Labombard, Emily/Moriah Central School Dist	57	68
Labrake, Matthew/West Valley Ctl Sch Dist	69	33
Lacek, Gail/Pittsford Central Sch Dist	58	110
Lacey, Debra/Attica Central School Dist	34,58	267
Lachenauer, Mariette/Westhill Central School Dist	58	160
Lackey, Tonya/Boquet Valley Central Sch Dist	285	67
Lackner, John/Northport-East Northport UFSD	3	227
LaClair, Matt/Schodack Central School Dist	3,91	191
LaClair, Monica/Onteora Central School Dist	2,15	243
Lacobucci, Christine/Lansing Central School Dist	67	240
LaCorte, Michele/Schenectady City School Dist	76	204
LaCrosse, Joanne/New York State Dept Education	58	1
Ladd, Maureen/Central Square Central SD	2,91	170
Ladd, Tom/Averill Park Central Sch Dist	277	189
Ladewig, Brian, Dr/Harrison Central School Dist	15,68,79	256
Ladouce, Sheila/Union Springs Ctl School Dist	59	35
Lafage, Todd/Lyme Central School Dist	3	81
Lafever, Michael, Dr/Diocese of Buffalo Ed Office	1	65
LaFleche, Jennifer/Mechanicville City Sch Dist	36,57,72,77	201
LaFontaine, Evelyn/Ulster BOCES	68	244
LaForgia, Michael/Diocese of Brooklyn Ed Office	15	95
LaFountain, Mark/Ctr for Instruct Tech Innov	15,68	172
LaFountain, Richard/Harborfields Ctl School Dist	3,91	223
LaFountain, Terry/Broadalbin-Perth Ctl Sch Dist	8,11,285,288,296	71
Lagase, Jeff/Frankfort-Schuyler Ctl SD	6	77
Lagase, Michele/Utica City School Dist	11,298	152
LaGrou, Tom/Avon Central School Dist	3	102
Lahey, Steve/Long Beach City School Dist	3	124
Lahue, Paul/Marcus Whitman Central SD	6	162
Lair, Robin/Mayfield Ctl School Dist	36	72
Lajeunesse, Yvonne/Mechanicville City Sch Dist	7,85	201
Lajewski, Cara/Seneca Falls Central Sch Dist	67	208
Lake, Mike, Dr/Half Hollow Hills Central SD	70	222
Lakeman, Audra/Barker Central School Dist	38	146
LaLonde, Craig/St Lawrence-Lewis BOCES	73	212
LaLonde, Dan/Herkimer BOCES	67	79
Lamacchia, Karrie/Baldwinsville Central Sch Dist	58,752	154
Lamadrid, Dan/South Orangetown Central SD	67	197
LaMarca, Joe/Hilton Central School Dist	5	109
LaMarca, Rosemarie/Herricks Union Free Sch Dist	273	121
Lamare, Bob/Tupper Lake Ctl School Dist	4	70
Lamash, Laura, Dr/Vestal Ctl School Dist	8,15	29
Lamb, Beth/Stockbridge Valley Central SD	2,11,91,271,296	106
Lamb, Laura/Cooperstown Ctl School Dist	58	173
Lamb, Matthew/Oakfield Alabama Ctl SD	67	74
Lambdin, Thomas/Skaneateles Central Sch Dist	67	157
Lambert, Gary/Beekmantown Ctl School Dist	16,73,286	43
Lambert, Sonya/Chazy Central Rural Sch Dist	273	44
Lambert, Susan/Massena Central School Dist	58,79,271	211
Lambert, Timothy/New Lebanon Ctl School Dist	67	46
Lambiaso, Julie/Unatego Unadilla Central SD	10,69,273	174
Lamelza, Joseph, Dr/Syosset Central School Dist	15,58,79	129
LaMendola, Suzanne/Guilderland Central Sch Dist	9,273	11
Lamerand, Lorine/Washingtonville Central SD	2,11,15,97	167
Lamia, Jen, Dr/Byram Hills Central Sch Dist	1	253
Lamm, Doreen/Patchogue-Medford Unified SD	2	227
LaMonica, Steve/Webster Central School Dist	6,35	112
Lamoreaux, Jeffery/Maine Endwell Ctl School Dist	2,11,15,68	29
Lamorte, Steven/Rochester City School Dist	39	110
Lampila, Christina/Spencer Van Etten Central SD	8,11,58,83,88,273,296,298	238
Lana, Allison/Wayland-Cohocton Central SD	273	215
Lancto, Karen/Duanesburg Central Sch Dist	68	203
Land, Erin/Webster Central School Dist	59	112
Land, Joanna/Valley Stream Union Free SD 13	24	130
Landahl, Matthew, Dr/Beacon City School Dist	1	51
Lander, Justin/Glen Cove City School Dist	73	120
Lander, Justin/Great Neck Public Schools	16,73,76,286	120
Landers, Sarah/Warrensburg Central Sch Dist	36,69,88	246
Landi, Nina/Sag Harbor Union Free Sch Dist	273	229
Lando, Stephen, Dr/Great Neck Public Schools	10,15	120

NAME/District	JOB FUNCTIONS	PAGE
Landor, Laura, Dr/Hauppauge Union Free Sch Dist	20,23	223
Landro, John/Tuxedo Union Free Sch Dist	6	167
Landry, Annette/Berne-Knox-Westerlo Central SD	8	10
Landversicht, Kenneth/Greenville Central School Dist	36	75
Landy, Julie/Ctr for Instruct Tech Innov	58,88	172
Lane, Ellen/Putnam-Northern Wstchstr BOCES	71	267
Lane, John-Henry/Mount Markham Central Sch Dist	73,295	78
Lane, Tina/Watertown City School Dist	15,68,79	81
Lanesey, Andrew/Wynantskill Union Free SD	67	192
Lang-Shapiro, Julia/Long Beach City School Dist	22,25	124
Lang, Andrea/Union Springs Ctl School Dist	5	35
Lang, Andy/Royalton Hartland Central SD	2	148
Lang, Diane, Dr/Orange-Ulster BOCES	74	168
Lang, Don/North Shore Central SD	6,35,85	126
Lang, Larry/Clyde-Savannah Central SD	6	249
Lang, Sharon/Palmyra-Macedon Central SD	67	250
Langey, Carrie/Moriah Central School Dist	11,58,83,296,298	68
Langlotz, Keith/Williamsville Ctl School Dist	3,91	64
Lango, Danielle/Hamburg Central School Dist	34	61
Langone, Debbie/West Islip School Dist	28,42	233
Langworthy, Amy/Warrensburg Central Sch Dist	8	246
Lanoue, Anne/Averill Park Central Sch Dist	7	189
Lanoue, Paula/Hoosic Valley Central Sch Dist	6	190
Lanphere, Brian/Candor Central School Dist	4	238
Lans, Daniella/Ballston Spa Ctl School Dist	60	200
Lansing, Anne/Utica City School Dist	91	152
Lanzoni, Marco/Spackenkill Union Free SD	6,7,35,83	54
LaPage, Todd/Brushton Moira Ctl Sch Dist	58,88	69
LaPage, Todd/Brushton Moira Ctl Sch Dist	1	69
LaPaglia, Fran/Central Valley School Dist	9,11,68	77
LaPolla, Luis/Utica City School Dist	67	152
Lapolt, Glenn/New Paltz Ctl School Dist	67	242
Lapp, Marjorie/Kendall Central School Dist	7	169
Lapp, Thomas/Indian River Ctl School Dist	67	80
Laquay, Bruce/O E S J Central School Dist	5	72
Laquay, Lisa/Cattaraugus-Little Vly Ctl SD	16,82	31
Laramie, Tina/Vernon-Verona-Sherrill CSD	16	152
Laregina, Kim/New Hyde-Garden City Park UFSD	9	126
Larkin, Lucas/Lansingburgh Central Sch Dist	76	190
Larkin, Stephanie/Middle Country Ctl Sch Dist	71	225
Larnerd, Karen/Johnson City Central Sch Dist	61	28
LaRocca, Judith/Valley Stream Union Free SD 13	9,15,285,288	130
LaRoche, Laura/Greenwood Lake Union Free SD	7	164
LaRosa, Kelly/Eden Central School Dist	8,288	60
LaRose, Leslie/Jefferson Lewis BOCES	8,15	82
Larrow, William/Moriah Central School Dist	1,288	68
Larsen, Julie/Rockland BOCES	58	199
Larsen, Kristin/Fairport Ctl School Dist	27,42,45	108
Larson, Adam/Livingston Manor Ctl Sch Dist	6	236
Larson, Julie/Geneva City School Dist	73,76,295	161
Larson, Julie/Wyoming Central School Dist	73,297	268
LaSala, Carol/Gouverneur Ctl School Dist	2,78	210
LaSalle, Carolyn/Herkimer Ctl School Dist	38	77
Lasch, Debroah/Port Jervis City School Dist	67	166
Lasche, Jeffery/Lowville Acad-Central Sch Dist	35	101
Lasher, Kim/East Irondequoit Ctl Sch Dist	67	107
Laskey, Jane/Webster Central School Dist	30	112
Lasson, Dallah/Waterloo Central School Dist	5	208
Lastowski, Walter/Hewlett Woodmere Union Free SD	20,23	121
Lathers, Emily/Greece Central School Dist	58	108
Lathrop, Deanna/Lyme Central School Dist	67	81
Latimer, Sarah/Chenango Valley Ctl Sch Dist	73,286	28
Latore, Danielle/Gates Chili Central Sch Dist	59	108
Latten, Darlene/Homer Central School Dist	38	48
Lattin, Sara/Elmira City School Dist	67	40
Lau, Greg/Pelham Union Free School Dist	60	260
Laube, Timothy/Eastport-South Manor Ctrl SD	2,15	221
Lauchert, Mary Lou/Clinton Central School Dist	67	150
Lauer, Greg/Fredonia Central School Dist	6	37
Lauf, Douglas/Fairport Ctl School Dist	15,68,78	108
Laurenau, Justin/Kendall Central School Dist	35,83,85	169
Laurenzano, Jacqueline/Nanuet Union Free School Dist	38	196
Lauria, Laurie/Manhasset Union Free Sch Dist	57	124
Lauritobahgat, Luann/Ripley Central School Dist	2,11	39
Laurrie, Mark/Niagara Falls City Sch Dist	1,11	147
Lautato, Michelle/Brookhaven Comsewogue Unif SD	68	218

School Year 2020-2021   800-333-8802   NY-T35

DISTRICT PERSONNEL INDEX

Market Data Retrieval

NAME/District	JOB FUNCTIONS	PAGE
Lauver, Deborah/Cambridge Central School Dist	6	247
Lauzon, Emily/Salmon River Central Sch Dist	67	70
Lavallee, Melissa/Keene Central School Dist	11,51,54	67
LaVelle, Caroline/Bethpage Union Free Sch Dist	12,15,68	117
Lavere, James/Herkimer Ctl School Dist	73	78
Lavere, Jim/Richfield Springs Central SD	73,295	174
Lavere, Ron/Cheektowaga Central SD	73,76	58
Lavery, James/Valley Stream Ctl High SD	67	130
Lavigna, Robert/William Floyd School Dist	73,76,95	233
Lavigne, Missie/Brushton Moira Ctl Sch Dist	6	69
Lavine, Alex/Garrison Union Free Sch Dist	9,270	175
Laviolette, Janet/Fire Island Union Free SD	7,83,85	222
LaVoie, Jennifer/Madison Central School Dist	67	105
Law, Cathy/Scio Central School Dist	71	15
Law, Elizabeth/Minisink Valley Central SD	79	165
Lawless, Anne/Highland Falls-Ft Montgmry SD	67	164
Lawlor, Denise/Malverne Union Free Sch Dist	68	124
Lawrence, Chad/Malone Central School Dist	3,91	69
Lawrence, Jeffery/Moravia Central School Dist	2,91	34
Lawrence, Margaret/Bolton Central School Dist	6,83,85	244
Lawrence, Peter/Fairport Ctl School Dist	5	108
Lawson, Marion/Hampton Bays Union Free SD	68	222
Lawson, Melissa/Dundee Ctl School Dist	2	268
Lawson, Renae/Lyons Central School Dist	4	249
Lawton, Eric/West Valley Ctl Sch Dist	1	33
Lawton, Kevin/Cairo-Durham Ctl School Dist	3,91	75
Laytham, Janet/Dcmo BOCES Chenango	8,16,74	43
Lazarony, Ann/Berlin Central School Dist	31,36,69,83	189
Lazarski, Caitlin/Newburgh Enlarged City SD	4	165
Lazzaro, Cheryl/Williamsville Ctl School Dist	58	64
Le Cointe, Susan/White Plains City School Dist	58	263
Le Vaillant, Guy, Dr/Plainedge Union Free Sch Dist	15,68,286	127
Leach, Brian/Stockbridge Valley Central SD	5	106
Leach, David, Dr/Warwick Valley Central SD	1	167
Leahey, Christopher/North Syracuse Ctl Sch Dist	8,18,34,51,54,57,271,274	157
Leahy, David/Honeoye Falls Lima Sch Dist	68	109
Leahy, Noreen, Dr/Rockville Ctr Union Free SD	15,54,58,76,83	128
Leandro, Cindy/Warwick Valley Central SD	15,91	167
Leatherbarrow, Teresa/Williamsville Ctl School Dist	67	64
Leavitt, Ruth/Dolgeville Central School Dist	288	77
Lebarron, Debbie/Ft Edward Union Free Sch Dist	37	247
LeBeau, Nicole/Heuvelton Central School Dist	8	210
Leber, Lisa/Marathon Ctl School Dist	5	48
LeBlanc, Christopher/Vernon-Verona-Sherrill CSD	20	152
LeBlanc, Susan/Madison-Oneida BOCES	16	154
LeBlanc, Trevor/Greenwich Central School Dist	5	247
LeBrun, Jay/Plattsburgh City School Dist	1	44
LeClair, Julie/Northern Adirondack Ctl SD	5	44
LeClaire, Daniel/Burnt Hills Ballston Lake SD	80,88,286	200
Leddy, Dan/Smithtown Central Sch Dist	3	230
Ledley, Coleen/Lansing Central School Dist	8,69,71,74,280,288	240
Lee, Jung/Franklin Square Union Free SD	11,73,296,298	119
Lee, Matthew/Clinton Central School Dist	10	150
Lee, Maureen/Springville Griffith Inst CSD	2	63
Lee, Michael/Madison Central School Dist	6,27,31,36,77,79,88	105
Lee, Michael/Putnam Valley Ctl School Dist	71,97	176
Lee, Mike/Bronxville Union Free SD	3	253
Lee, Millicent/Mt Pleasant Cottage UFSD	36,79	258
Lee, Steven/Kings Park Ctl School Dist	5	224
Leef, Danielle/Southampton Union Free SD	2	231
Leeyaw, Jerome/Frewsburg Central School Dist	2,19	38
LeFevre, Matt/Peru Central School Dist	3	44
Leffell, Daniel/Hawthorne Cedar Knolls UFSD	67	256
Leffler, Eileen/Albany City School Dist	298	9
Legato, Debra/Mahopac Ctl School Dist	15,68	176
Leh, Deborah, Dr/Wheatland Chili Ctl Sch Dist	11	113
Lehman, Bradley/Keshequa Central School Dist	6	103

NAME/District	JOB FUNCTIONS	PAGE
Lehman, Brenda/Marcus Whitman Central SD	73,295	162
Lehmann, Jay/Stockbridge Valley Central SD	6,35,83,85	106
Lehr, Greg/Oxford Academy Central SD	83,88	42
Leibeck, Jennifer/Willsboro Central Sch Dist	58	68
Leichner, Charles/Cassadaga Valley Ctl Sch Dist	1	36
Leid, Kim/Fredonia Central School Dist	4	37
Leins, Christopher/Marathon Ctl School Dist	58	48
Leis, David/Yorktown Central School Dist	69,76	264
Leister, Sean/Port Jefferson Union Free SD 6	2,11,15,76	228
LeJeune, Gazella/Webutuck Ctl School Dist	2	54
Lelemer, Cathy/Clifton-Fine Central Sch Dist	752	209
Lemk, Daniel/Jamestown City School Dist	5	38
Lemmo, Jaime/West Babylon Union Free SD	90	233
Lendzian, Suzanne/Fallsburg Central School Dist	6	236
Lennon, Andrew/Mt Pleasant Ctl School Dist	2,5	258
Lennon, Barbara/Franklin Central School Dist	16,82	49
Lentivech, Douglas/New York State Dept Education	15,31	1
Lentsch, Brenda/Commack Union Free School Dist	71,297	219
Lentsch, Brenda/Commack Union Free School Dist	297	219
Lenz, Deana/Goshen Central School Dist	36	164
Lenz, Jospeh/Port Jervis City School Dist	2,15	166
Leo, Robert/West Genesee Ctl School Dist	73,285	159
Leon, Carmen/Archdiocese of New York Ed Off	10	142
Leon, Jason/Lake Placid Ctl School Dist	73	67
Leonard, Ronald/Southern Cayuga Central SD	5	35
Leonardi, Paul/Chittenango Central SD	73,295	104
Leonas, Kevin/Middletown Enlarged City SD	295	165
Leone, Lauren/Mamaroneck Union Free Sch Dist	2	257
Leone, Michael/Pittsford Central Sch Dist	12,15,68	110
Leone, Tracy/Waterville Central Sch Dist	2,3,11,298	153
Lerner, Scott/Washingtonville Central SD	36,285	167
Leroy, Jacqueline/Syracuse City School Dist	57,61	158
Lesinski, Jennifer/East Rochester Union Free SD	67	107
Lesio, Catherine/Webster Central School Dist	58	112
Lesko, Ron/Albany City School Dist	71	9
Leslie, Robert/Syracuse City School Dist	27,31	158
Lessane, Marcellus/Bronxville Union Free SD	91	253
Lesser, Karen, Dr/Middle Country Ctl Sch Dist	67	225
Lester, Colleen/Cambridge Central School Dist	11,288,296,298	247
Lester, Monica/South Glens Falls Ctl Sch Dist	71	202
Leto, Mary/Albion Central School Dist	8,11,16,69,74,271,296,298	169
Leuer, Gerhard/Medina Central School Dist	3	169
Leupold, Jim/Schenectady City School Dist	76	204
Leuthauser, Ellen/Clinton Central School Dist	9	150
Levatino, Keith, Dr/Little Falls City School Dist	1	78
Levett, Lisa/Kendall Central School Dist	67	169
Levey, Philip/Greece Central School Dist	4	108
Levigne, Katherine/Brasher Falls School Dist	58	209
Levine, Melissa/Merrick Union Free School Dist	16,82	125
Levine, Robin, Dr/Greenburgh-North Castle SD	79	255
Levitt, Tessa/Whitesville Central Sch Dist	8,288	15
Levy, Kim/New Hyde-Garden City Park UFSD	59,79	126
Levy, Laurie/Rockville Ctr Union Free SD	31,38	128
Levy, Oliver/Greenburgh-Graham UFSD	1	255
Lew, Lee/Tuckahoe Union Free SD	2,11,15	262
Lewandowski, Janice/West Seneca Central Sch Dist	2,295	64
Lewis Gursslin, Christina/Fairport Ctl School Dist	71	108
Lewis-Hoover, Heather/Mount Markham Central Sch Dist	37	78
Lewis-Jackson, Beth/Kingston City School Dist	58	242
Lewis, David/Bradford Central Sch Dist	5	207
Lewis, Doug/Addison Central School Dist	5	213
Lewis, Gail/Frontier Ctl School Dist	79	60
Lewis, Kathie/Hamilton-Fulton-Montgmry BOCES	2,19	72
Lewis, Keith/Lackawanna City School Dist	1	62
Lewis, Kimberly/Schenectady City School Dist	2	204
Lewis, Krista/Newark Central School Dist	8,15,57,69,285,294	250
Lewis, Lora/Malverne Union Free Sch Dist	67	124

1 Superintendent	16 Instructional Media Svcs	30 Adult Education	44 Science Sec	58 Special Education K-12	72 Summer School	88 Alternative/At Risk	277 Remedial Math K-12
2 Bus/Finance/Purchasing	17 Chief Operations Officer	31 Career/Sch-to-Work K-12	45 Math K-12	59 Special Education Elem	73 Instructional Tech	89 Multi-Cultural Curriculum	280 Literacy Coach
3 Buildings And Grounds	18 Chief Academic Officer	32 Career/Sch-to-Work Elem	46 Math Elem	60 Special Education Sec	74 Inservice Training	90 Social Work	285 STEM
4 Food Service	19 Chief Financial Officer	33 Career/Sch-to-Work Sec	47 Math Sec	61 Foreign/World Lang K-12	75 Marketing/Distributive	91 Safety/Security	286 Digital Learning
5 Transportation	20 Art K-12	34 Early Childhood Ed	48 English/Lang Arts K-12	62 Foreign/World Lang Elem	76 Info Systems	92 Magnet School	288 Common Core Standards
6 Athletic	21 Art Elem	35 Health/Phys Education	49 English/Lang Arts Elem	63 Foreign/World Lang Sec	77 Psychological Assess	93 Parental Involvement	294 Accountability
7 Health Services	22 Art Sec	36 Guidance Services K-12	50 English/Lang Arts Sec	64 Religious Education K-12	78 Affirmative Action	96 Tech Prep Program	295 Network System
8 Curric/Instruct K-12	23 Music K-12	37 Guidance Services Elem	51 Reading K-12	65 Religious Education Elem	79 Student Personnel	97 Chief Innovation Officer	296 Title II Programs
9 Curric/Instruct Elem	24 Music Elem	38 Guidance Services Sec	52 Reading Elem	66 Religious Education Sec	80 Driver Ed/Safety	98 Chief Technology Officer	297 Webmaster
10 Curric/Instruct Sec	25 Music Sec	39 Social Studies K-12	53 Reading Sec	67 School Board President	81 Gifted/Talented	270 Character Education	298 Grant Writer/Ptnrships
11 Federal Program	26 Business Education	40 Social Studies Elem	54 Remedial Reading K-12	68 Teacher Personnel	82 Video Services	271 Migrant Education	750 Chief Innovation Officer
12 Title I	27 Career & Tech Ed	41 Social Studies Sec	55 Remedial Reading Elem	69 Academic Assessment	83 Substance Abuse Prev	273 Teacher Mentor	751 Chief of Staff
13 Title V	28 Technology Education	42 Science K-12	56 Remedial Reading Sec	70 Research/Development	84 Erate	274 Before/After Sch	752 Social Emotional Learning
15 Asst Superintendent	29 Family/Consumer Science	43 Science Elem	57 Bilingual/ELL	71 Public Information	85 AIDS Education	275 Response To Intervention	

NY-T36

New York School Directory

DISTRICT PERSONNEL INDEX

NAME/District	JOB FUNCTIONS	PAGE
Lewis, Loran, Dr/Malverne Union Free Sch Dist	1	124
Lewis, Lynn/North Warren Central Sch Dist	6,35	246
Lewis, Michael/Shoreham-Wading River Ctl SD	67	230
Lewis, Michael, Dr/Kenmore-Tonawanda UF Sch Dist	58,79	62
Lewis, Sara/Mohonasen Central Sch Dist	58,275	204
Lewis, Stephen/Monticello Central School Dist	3,91	237
Lewis, Steven/Sullivan BOCES	3	238
Lewis, Theodore/Lyndonville Central Sch Dist	67	169
Lewis, Tyra/Rochester City School Dist	275	110
Lewis, Veronica/Odessa Montour Ctl Sch Dist	8,11,58,271,298	207
Lewner, Jennifer/Valley Stream Union Free SD 30	15,28,752	131
Leyva, Alex/Cuba-Rushford Central Sch Dist	4	14
Lezner, Joe/Fallsburg Central School Dist	38	236
Liberatore, Rachel/Williamson Central School Dist	7,58,79	251
Liberman, Ari/Liverpool Ctl School Dist	6,35	156
Libertini, Kimberly/Cold Spring Harbor Central SD	285	219
Libka, Tom/Millbrook Ctl School Dist	9,57	52
Libritz, John/O E S J Central School Dist	73	72
Librock, Matthew/East Aurora Union Free SD	6,35	60
Licalzi, Kira/South Kortright Ctl SD	29,83,85	50
Licardi, James/Pine Bush Central School Dist	3	166
Licastri, Christine/Sewanhaka Ctl High Sch Dist	26,28	129
Licker, Brook/Middle Country Ctl Sch Dist	10,11	225
Licopoli, Lorenzo/Arlington Central School Dist	1	51
Lictus, Bert/Panama Central School Dist	1	38
Liddell, Josh/Chautauqua Lake Central SD	6	36
Liddle, Shawn/Albion Central School Dist	2,5,15,91	169
Lidestri, Brenda/Binghamton City School Dist	27,42,45	27
Liebentritt, Kathleen/Manchester-Shortsville Ctl SD	16	162
Lieberman, Ari/Liverpool Ctl School Dist	6,7,35,83	156
Lien, Rosa, Dr/Central Islip Union Free SD	57	218
Liendecker, Andrew/South Lewis Central Sch Dist	67	101
Lierow, Ann/Greenwood Lake Union Free SD	2,15	164
Liess, Paul/York Central School Dist	2,12,36	103
Lightfoote, Tom/Penn Yan Ctl School Dist	16,73	268
Liguori, Kim/Long Beach City School Dist	59	124
Liisi, Todd/Homer Central School Dist	6,35	48
Lilavois, Nathalie, Dr/Three Village Central Sch Dist	9	232
Lilla, Darlene, Dr/Half Hollow Hills Central SD	20,23	222
Lilleck, David/Orchard Park Central Sch Dist	15,68,78,79	63
Lilley, Jordon/Cortland Enlarged City SD	5	47
Lima, David/Union Springs Ctl School Dist	73	35
Limone, Michael/Carle Place Union Free SD	20,23,27,75	117
Linck, Kevin/Fabius Pompey Central SD	10,27,57	155
Lincoln, Amy/Cattaraugus-Little Vly Ctl SD	12,298	31
Lincoln, Tim/Waterloo Central School Dist	28	208
Lind, Zachary/Ithaca City School Dist	76,97	240
Lindeman, Dan/Watervliet City School Dist	73	12
Lindeman, Nicole/Albany City School Dist	16,73	9
Linderman, Nichelle/Scio Central School Dist	2	15
Lineberger, Amy/Gowanda Central School Dist	4	32
Lingenfelter, Robert/Belfast Central School Dist	2,11	14
Linger, Matthew, Dr/Lindenhurst Union Free SD	42	224
Linton, Robert/Greece Central School Dist	3	108
Lipani, Joseph/East Hampton Union Free SD	5	220
Lipczynski, Martin/Frontier Ctl School Dist	3,91	60
Lipfert, Larry/George Junior Republic UFSD	3	240
Lippert, Jay/Fire Island Union Free SD	67	222
Lippitt, Nicole/Milford Central School Dist	58	173
Lippold, Brian/Brockport Ctl School Dist	295	106
Lipponer, Collen/Eastern Suffolk BOCES	2	235
Lipshie, Seth/Miller Place Union Free SD	15	226
Lipson, Melissa/Nanuet Union Free School Dist	37	196
Lipuma, Robert, Dr/Lockport City School Dist	16,69,71,73,97,295	147
Lisa, Angelo/Bethpage Union Free Sch Dist	91	117
Lisa, Angelo/Copiague Union Free Sch Dist	3	220
Lisack, Debbie/Florida Union Free Sch Dist	274	164
Lisi, Dominic/Fulton City School Dist	16,73	170
Lisi, Mario/Binghamton City School Dist	3,91	27
Lissow, Jamie/Spencerport Central Sch Dist	15,68	112
List, Debi/Byron-Bergen Ctl School Dist	67	73
Little, Samantha/Ithaca City School Dist	6	240
Little, Susan/Andes Central School Dist	8	48
Littlefield, Catherine/South Lewis Central Sch Dist	58,88	101
Litwak, Helene/Eastchester Union Free SD	274	254
Litzman, Marianne/Hicksville Union Free Sch Dist	1	122
Lively, Michael/Jefferson Lewis BOCES	58	82
Livingston, Karen/Marion Central School Dist	38,69	250
Livingston, Karen/Poland Central School Dist	273	78
Livsey, Steve/Roscoe Central School Dist	295	237
Ljiljanich, Daniel/Niagara-Wheatfield Ctl SD	1	148
Ljungberg, Christine/Holland Central School Dist	2	61
Ljungberg, Larry/Hinsdale Central School Dist	1	32
Lloyd, Celestine/Elmont Union Free School Dist	4	118
Lloyd, Ellen, Dr/Marion Central School Dist	9,12	250
Lloyd, Joseph/South Orangetown Central SD	68	197
Lloyd, Rebecca/Middletown Enlarged City SD	68	165
Lloyd, William, Dr/Uniondale Union Free Sch Dist	1	130
Llyod, Micheal/Hampton Bays Union Free SD	295	222
Lobb, Erica/Frewsburg Central School Dist	51,54,273,280	38
Loccisano, Mario/Troy City School Dsitrict	5	191
Locey, Karen/Brasher Falls School Dist	11	209
Locicero, Joseph/Wallkill Central School Dist	67	243
Locke, Laurie/Le Roy Central School Dist	4	73
Locke, Lenny/Hadley-Luzerne Ctl Sch Dist	73,76	245
Lockman, Rachel/Manchester-Shortsville Ctl SD	4	162
Lockwood, Mike/Lansing Central School Dist	73	240
Lockwood, Nancy/Greenville Central School Dist	16	75
Lodico, Guy/Plainview-Old Bethpage Ctl SD	73	127
Loechner, Dawn/Pine Bush Central School Dist	2	166
Loeschner, Richard/Brentwood Union Free Sch Dist	1	217
Loewy, Ellen/Oyster Bay East Norwich Ctl SD	58	127
Lofran, Elizabeth/North Salem Central Sch Dist	270	259
Lofrese, Christine/Smithtown Central Sch Dist	26,28	230
Loftus, Rachel/Chester Union Free School Dist	58	163
Logan King, Laurel/Mohonasen Central Sch Dist	8,11,15,286,296	203
Logan-King, Laurel/Ballston Spa Ctl School Dist	8,11,30,57,69,79,83,90	200
Logel, Brian/Clarence Central School Dist	3	59
Logiudice, Betsy/West Irondequoit Ctl SD	4	113
Lohman, Lance/Longwood Central School Dist	9,12,34,54	225
Loiselle, Rock/Middleburgh Ctl School Dist	5	206
Loker, Patricia/Unatego Unadilla Central SD	2	174
Lolkema, Daren/Wappingers Central Sch Dist	15,76	54
Lombardi, John/Phelps-Clifton Springs Ctl SD	6,35	162
Lombardo, Katherine/Sagaponack Common School Dist	16,73	229
Lonergan, Michael, Dr/Longwood Central School Dist	1	224
Long, David/West Irondequoit Ctl SD	67	113
Long, Deborah/Hudson City School Dist	2	46
Long, Erin/Lyons Central School Dist	9,34	249
Long, Joe/Little Falls City School Dist	11	78
Long, Maureen, Dr/Menands Union Free Sch Dist	1	11
Long, Robert/East Quogue Union Free SD	9,11,16,69,83,270,288	221
Long, Robert/East Quogue Union Free SD	1	221
Long, Sarah/Colton Pierrepont School Dist	7	209
Long, Sarah/Syracuse City School Dist	58	158
Long, Tanya/Yonkers Public School Dist	298	263
Longacker, Genine/Indian Lake Ctl School Dist	8,13,36,69,88	76
Longing, Lorraine/Nyack Union Free School Dist	36,752	197
Lonneville, Jeremy/Livonia Ctl School Dist	2,68	103
Lontrato, Shari/Schalmont Central School Dist	11,58,79,275	204
Loomis, Michael/Chatham Central School Dist	31	46
Loomis, Tanya/Addison Central School Dist	58,77,85,88	213
Loomis, William/Norwich City School Dist	5	42
Loper, Wayne, Dr/Valley Stream Ctl High SD	2,3,4,5,11,15,78	130
Lopes, Christine/Uniondale Union Free Sch Dist	298	130
Lopez, Jason/Roslyn School Dist	73,286	129
Lopez, Miguelina/North Rockland Central SD	9,11,57	197
Lopez, Steve/Yonkers Public School Dist	67	263
LoPresti, Michael/Greenwood Lake Union Free SD	73,76,295	164
Loranty, Melanie/Attica Central School Dist	16	267
Loranty, Melanie/Attica Central School Dist	16	267
Lorch, Jean/Shenendehowa Central Sch Dist	44	202
Lore, Lisa/Frankfort-Schuyler Ctl SD	48	77
Loretz, Joseph/Vestal Ctl School Dist	3	29
Lorio, Daniel/Pleasantville Union Free SD	34,58	260
Loscalzo, Andrea, Dr/Greenburgh-Graham UFSD	58,79	255
Losee, Scott/Menands Union Free Sch Dist	3	11
Losie, Christine/Charlotte Valley Ctl Sch Dist	83	49
Lotter, Joanne/Fredonia Central School Dist	35	37
Loughan, Kim/Peru Central School Dist	36	44
Loughlin, Keri/Center Moriches Union Free SD	2	218
Louis, Poletta/Worcester Ctl School Dist	36,83,85,88,271	174

School Year 2020-2021   800-333-8802   NY-T37

DISTRICT PERSONNEL INDEX

Market Data Retrieval

NAME/District	JOB FUNCTIONS	PAGE
Louissaint, Ketler/District 75 City Wide Programs	1	142
Love, Jeannie/Wantagh Union Free Sch Dist 23	58	131
Love, Theodore/Homer Central School Dist	8,27,31,285,288	48
Lovelass, Melissa/Ballston Spa Ctl School Dist	2	200
Loveless, Fred/Jefferson Central Sch Dist	3	206
Loveless, Matt/Lansing Central School Dist	6	240
Lovell, Todd/Ellicottville Central Sch Dist	5	31
Lovely, Kevin/Hartford Central School Dist	3	248
Lovely, Melissa/Parishville Hopkinton Sch Dist	73,76,295	212
Lovett, James/South Colonie Central Sch Dist	73,286	12
Lovett, Janett/Hempstead Union Free SD	57	121
Lovrich, Deborah, Dr/Long Beach City School Dist	285	124
Lowe, Lesley/Ardsley Union Free School Dist	4	252
Lowe, Sheila/Honeoye Central School Dist	4	161
Lowe, Teri/Alexandria Central School Dist	81	79
Lowe, Teri/Alexandria Central School Dist	6	79
Lowell, Melissa/Oriskany Ctl School Dist	58	151
Lowin, John/Hammondsport Ctl School Dist	285	214
Lown, Hayley/Oakfield Alabama Ctl SD	16	74
Lozier, Arthur/Corinth Central School Dist	67	200
Lubberts, Paul/Bloomfield Central SD	35,83,85	161
Lubrano, Anthony/Hicksville Union Free Sch Dist	15	122
Lucas, Robert/North Tonawanda City Sch Dist	63	148
Lucchesi, Lisa/Bethpage Union Free Sch Dist	58	117
Luce, Jon/Allegany-Limestone Ctl SD	6	31
Luce, Lawrence/Hampton Bays Union Free SD	2,15	222
Luce, Robert/Brighton Central School Dist	3	106
Luckert, Lauren/Northville Central School Dist	73,98,295	72
Luckette, Phillip/Jamesville-DeWitt Central SD	73,95,295	155
Luckman, James/Barker Central School Dist	73,76,286,295	146
Luckman, Maevonne/Albion Central School Dist	4	169
Ludlam, Robert/Brushton Moira Ctl Sch Dist	73	69
Ludmar, Dave/North Shore Central SD	67	126
Luettger, Ramona/Cincinnatus Ctl School Dist	58	47
Lufrano, Robin/Bellmore Union Free Sch Dist	2,15,73,76,295	117
Luft, Jeremy, Dr/Putnam Valley Ctl School Dist	1	176
Luka, Denise/Franklin-Essex-Hamilton BOCES	58	71
Lukas, Jessica/Patchogue-Medford Unified SD	15,58	227
Lukasik, Frank/East Meadow Union Free SD	11,48,51,280	118
Lukaszewizc, Matthew/Valley Stream Union Free SD 13	3	130
Luke, Jason/Susquehanna Valley Central SD	71,73,76,95,97	29
Luke, Richard/Clymer Central School Dist	3	37
Lumia, John/Wappingers Central Sch Dist	67	54
Luna, Jean/Cold Spring Harbor Central SD	5	219
Lunden, Stephen, Dr/Cheektowaga Maryvale UFSD	2,15,68,71,78,97	59
Lundgren, Megan/Chautauqua Lake Central SD	12,58,296	36
Lupinski, Amy/Minerva Central School Dist	91	68
Lupinskie, Lorraine/Half Hollow Hills Central SD	39	222
Lupisella, Robert/Avon Central School Dist	9	102
Lustig, Susie/Harborfields Ctl School Dist	67	223
Luthart, Gordon/Medina Central School Dist	35,83,85	169
Luther, Amanda/Portville Central School Dist	38	32
Luther, Chris/Greece Central School Dist	3	108
Luther, Delos/Pawling Ctl School Dist	5	52
Luther, Eric/Harrisville Central Sch Dist	6	101
Luther, Scott/Copenhagen Central SD	2,12,58	101
Luthringer, John/Queensbury Union Free Sch Dist	16,73,76,286,295	246
Lutter, Denise, Dr/Bronxville Union Free SD	74	253
Lutz, Mathew/Wynantskill Union Free SD	73	192
Lux, Kara/Marcellus Central School Dist	58,298	157
Luxon, Allison/Le Roy Central School Dist	7	73
Luxon, Joshua/Oakfield Alabama Ctl SD	5	74
Lybolt, Kim/Hudson City School Dist	7,58,77,90	46
Lymon, Aleta/Fallsburg Central School Dist	93	236
Lynch, Chris/Stillwater Central Sch Dist	73	202
Lynch, Kate/Miller Place Union Free SD	16,82	226
Lynch, Kathleen/Shelter Island Union Free SD	67	230

NAME/District	JOB FUNCTIONS	PAGE
Lynch, Louise/Goshen Central School Dist	2,15	164
Lynch, Mary/Falconer Central School Dist	4	37
Lynch, Melanie/De Ruyter Central School Dist	37,83,88	105
Lynch, Mike/Broome-Tioga BOCES	7,91	31
Lynch, Paul, Dr/Lynbrook Union Free Sch Dist	2,15,76	124
Lynch, Susan/Cayuga-Onondaga BOCES	58	36
Lynch, Thomas/Seaford Union Free SD	285	129
Lynch, Timothy/Baldwinsville Central Sch Dist	2	154
Lynn, Laurie/Plainview-Old Bethpage Ctl SD	36	127
Lyon, Heather, Dr/Lewiston Porter Ctl Sch Dist	8,16,73,79,83,273,288,294	146
Lyon, Michelle/Moravia Central School Dist	67	35
Lyons-Lawrence, Stephanie/Seneca Falls Central Sch Dist	4	208
Lyons, Brendan/Lakeland Central School Dist	1	257
Lyons, Diane/Rhinebeck Central School Dist	67	53
Lyons, Freida/Unadilla Valley Ctl Sch Dist	58	43
Lysack, Marlene/Florida Union Free Sch Dist	7	164
Lytle, Anne/Newburgh Enlarged City SD	76,97	166

M

NAME/District	JOB FUNCTIONS	PAGE
Maassmann, Janet/Greenville Central School Dist	2,26	75
Mabbett, Lisa/Weedsport Ctl School Dist	285	35
Mable, Julie/Delaware Academy Ctrl SD Delhi	9	49
Mac Dermott, Neil/Lynbrook Union Free Sch Dist	12	124
MacAluso, Jonathan/Connetquot Central School Dist	36	219
MacAntash, Adgar/Scarsdale Union Free Sch Dist	51,54,57,294,296	261
MacBain, Bruce/Moravia Central School Dist	10,69	35
MacCheyne, Patti/Dryden Central School Dist	73	239
MacChiole, Kristen/Erie 1 BOCES	58	67
MacDonald, Kevin/Genesee Valley BOCES	1	74
MacDonald, Michael/Dcmo BOCES Chenango	15,58,79	43
MacGowan, Andrew/Rochester City School Dist	34	110
MacGregor, Karen/Salem Central School Dist	2,12,298	248
Mach, Jason/Malverne Union Free Sch Dist	16,41,50	124
Macias, Leo/Nyack Union Free School Dist	58,79,91	197
Macica, Maribeth/WSWHE BOCES	71	249
MacIntosh, Elizabeth/Waverly Ctl School Dist	8,11,280,288,296,298	239
MacIntyre, Dana/Geneseo Central Sch Dist	7,83,85	103
Mack, Michael/West Babylon Union Free SD	11,58,79,90,296,298	232
Macken, Sharon, Dr/Kings Park Ctl School Dist	73	224
Macken, Sharon, Dr/Kings Park Ctl School Dist	76	224
MacKenzie, Jean/Canandaigua City School Dist	275	161
MacKenzie, William/York Central School Dist	31	103
Mackey, Deborah/Whitehall Central School Dist	4	248
Mackey, Gerald/Oneonta City School Dist	6	174
Mackey, Robert/Unadilla Valley Ctl Sch Dist	1	43
Mackey, Ron/Beacon City School Dist	5	51
Mackey, Stacey/Cohoes City School Dist	2	10
Macko, Patricia/Greenville Central School Dist	67	75
Mackowiak, Cynthia/Dunkirk City School Dist	2	37
MacMillan, Mark/Rush Henrietta Central SD	2,39	112
MacPherson, Christine/Hudson Falls Central Sch Dist	73,76,285,295	248
Macri, Frank/Voorheesville Central Sch Dist	1	12
Macswan, John/Cleveland Hill Union Free SD	1	59
Maday, John/North Warren Central School Dist	67	246
Madden, Dina/Mamaroneck Union Free Sch Dist	23	257
Madden, Eileen/Saugerties Central School Dist	36	243
Maddi, Susan/Eastern Suffolk BOCES	4,5,70	235
Maddox, Marsha/Greenburgh 11 Union Free SD	2	255
Maderer, Julie/Elba Central School Dist	54	73
Madison, Elliott/Livingston Manor Ctl School Dist	67	236
Madsen, William/Eastport-South Manor Ctrl SD	6	221
Maeder, Edel/Greece Central School Dist	42	108
Magara, Karen/Salamanca City Central SD	2,4,5,15	33
Magej, Hannah/Fabius Pompey Central SD	77	155
Maggiacomo, Dina/Herricks Union Free Sch Dist	15,68	121
Magill, Elizabeth/Averill Park Central Sch Dist	273	189

1	Superintendent	16	Instructional Media Svcs	30	Adult Education	44	Science Sec	58	Special Education K-12	72	Summer School
2	Bus/Finance/Purchasing	17	Chief Operations Officer	31	Career/Sch-to-Work K-12	45	Math K-12	59	Special Education Elem	73	Instructional Tech
3	Buildings And Grounds	18	Chief Academic Officer	32	Career/Sch-to-Work Elem	46	Math Elem	60	Special Education Sec	74	Inservice Training
4	Food Service	19	Chief Financial Officer	33	Career/Sch-to-Work Sec	47	Math Sec	61	Foreign/World Lang K-12	75	Marketing/Distributive
5	Transportation	20	Art K-12	34	Early Childhood Ed	48	English/Lang Arts K-12	62	Foreign/World Lang Elem	76	Info Systems
6	Athletic	21	Art Elem	35	Health/Phys Education	49	English/Lang Arts Elem	63	Foreign/World Lang Sec	77	Psychological Assess
7	Health Services	22	Art Sec	36	Guidance Services K-12	50	English/Lang Arts Sec	64	Religious Education K-12	78	Affirmative Action
8	Curric/Instruct K-12	23	Music K-12	37	Guidance Services Elem	51	Reading K-12	65	Religious Education Elem	79	Student Personnel
9	Curric/Instruct Elem	24	Music Elem	38	Guidance Services Sec	52	Reading Elem	66	Religious Education Sec	80	Driver Ed/Safety
10	Curric/Instruct Sec	25	Music Sec	39	Social Studies K-12	53	Reading Sec	67	School Board President	81	Gifted/Talented
11	Federal Program	26	Business Education	40	Social Studies Elem	54	Remedial Reading K-12	68	Teacher Personnel	82	Video Services
12	Title I	27	Career & Tech Ed	41	Social Studies Sec	55	Remedial Reading Elem	69	Academic Assessment	83	Substance Abuse Prev
13	Title V	28	Technology Education	42	Science K-12	56	Remedial Reading Sec	70	Research/Development	84	Erate
15	Asst Superintendent	29	Family/Consumer Science	43	Science Elem	57	Bilingual/ELL	71	Public Information	85	AIDS Education

88	Alternative/At Risk	277	Remedial Math K-12
89	Multi-Cultural Curriculum	280	Literacy Coach
90	Social Work	285	STEM
91	Safety/Security	286	Digital Learning
92	Magnet School	288	Common Core Standards
93	Parental Involvement	294	Accountability
95	Tech Prep Program	295	Network System
97	Chief Information Officer	296	Title II Programs
98	Chief Technology Officer	297	Webmaster
270	Character Education	298	Grant Writer/Ptnrships
271	Migrant Education	750	Chief Innovation Officer
273	Teacher Mentor	751	Chief of Staff
274	Before/After Sch	752	Social Emotional Learning
275	Response To Intervention		

NY-T38

New York School Directory
DISTRICT PERSONNEL INDEX

NAME/District	JOB FUNCTIONS	PAGE
Magin, Robert/North Rose Wolcott Central SD	2,3,15	250
Magoulis, Lynn/West Genesee Ctl School Dist	30	159
Magouney, Stephen/Belleville Henderson Sch Dist	2	79
MaGuire, Tim/Roscoe Central School Dist	2	237
MaGuire, Timothy/Downsville Central Sch Dist	2,11	49
MaGuire, Timothy/Livingston Manor Ctl Sch Dist	2	236
Mahan, Peter/Greenville Central School Dist	9,11,34	75
Mahar, Carolyn/Rye Neck Union Free Sch Dist	2,5	261
Mahar, Jen/Olean City School Dist	11,51	32
Mahardy, Scott/Chittenango Central SD	2,15	104
Mahoney, Christina/Schenectady City School Dist	68,74,78	204
Mahoney, Katie/Lyncourt Union Free Sch Dist	12,59	156
Mahoney, Kelly/Millbrook Ctl School Dist	31,271	52
Mahoney, Maggie/Onondaga Central School Dist	67	157
Mahoney, Stepehen/Genesee Valley BOCES	68	75
Mahunik, Peter/Fabius Pompey Central SD	2,5,11,91	155
Maier, Kathleen/Nanuet Union Free School Dist	71	196
Mains, Tim/Pine Bush Central School Dist	1,11	166
Maisano, Christie/Pembroke Ctl School Dist	16,73,82,295	74
Maisano, Joe/Plainedge Union Free Sch Dist	83,88	127
Majewski, Matt/Oneida City School Dist	295	105
Makowiec, Joni/Hammondsport Ctl School Dist	8	214
Makowiec, Michael/Addison Central School Dist	6	213
Makras, Jill/Sayville Union Free Sch Dist	73	229
Malape, Marjie/Dryden Central School Dist	67	239
Malave, Joseph/Montauk Union Free School Dist	285	226
Malczewski, Kelly/Harrison Central School Dist	36	256
Maldonado, Audrey/Cherry Valley-Springfield SD	16	173
Maleski, David/Sherman Central School Dist	5	39
Malette, Michael/Brushton Moira Ctl Sch Dist	3	69
Malinowitzer, Israel/East Islip Union Free SD	27,31,36	220
Malloy, Bill/Clarkstown Central School Dist	11	195
Malone, Brad/Rush Henrietta Central SD	16,76,295	112
Malone, Christopher/Valley Stream Union Free SD 30	3	131
Malone, Richard/Oysterponds Union Free SD	1,288	227
Maloney, Angelina, Dr/Brunswick Central School Dist	1	190
Maloney, Dennis/Sayville Union Free Sch Dist	6,35	229
Maloney, James/Cheektowaga Maryvale UFSD	15	59
Maloney, James/South Colonie Central Sch Dist	3	12
Maloney, Steven, Dr/Bay Shore Union Free Sch Dist	8,11,15,69,270,288,296	217
Maltbie, Ed/North Rockland Central SD	76	197
Mambretti, Mark/East Aurora Union Free SD	8,11,68,69,97,285,298,750	60
Mamo, Michael/East Irondequoit Ctl Sch Dist	3,91	107
Manarel, David/Ichabod Crane Central Schools	57	46
Manchester, Meachele/Elmira City School Dist	11	40
Mancuso, Gene/Honeoye Falls Lima Sch Dist	1	109
Mancuso, Lawrence/Monroe 1 BOCES	68	115
Mancuso, Richard/Clarence Central School Dist	2,4,91	59
Mandel, Mary/New Hartford Central Sch Dist	2,15,68	151
Mandelaro, Doug/Diocese of Rochester Ed Office	71	113
Manderville, Craig/Sauquoit Valley Central SD	5	152
Maneen, Brian/Adirondack Central School Dist	5	150
Manetta, Debbie/Mamaroneck Union Free Sch Dist	71	257
Manfreda, Rebecca/Byron-Bergen Ctl School Dist	8	73
Manfredi, Kim/Sandy Creek Central Sch Dist	58	172
Mangan, Kelly/Harrison Central School Dist	67	256
Mangan, Robert/Belfast Central School Dist	73,76,286	14
Mangieri, Louis/South Huntington Union Free SD	295	231
Mankowich, John/Jericho Union Free School Dist	6,35	122
Manley, Jennifer/Elba Central School Dist	7	73
Manley, Sharon/Wayland-Cohocton Central SD	273,280	215
Mann, Linda/North Bellmore Union Free SD	273	126
Mannex, Bethellen/Hartford Central School Dist	9,12,58	248
Manning, J Francis, Dr/Onondaga-Cortland-Madison BOCES	1	160
Manning, Rory, Dr/Harborfields Ctl School Dist	8,73	223
Manning, Timothy/Liverpool Ctl School Dist	15,68	156
Mannino, Rosemary/Pine Bush Central School Dist	58	166
Mannino, Veddo/Plainedge Union Free Sch Dist	23	127
Mannion, Joanne/Plainview-Old Bethpage Ctl SD	8,15,57,69,70	127
Mannix, Daniel/Beekmantown Ctl School Dist	1	43
Mannix, Daniel/Queensbury Union Free Sch Dist	67	246
Mannozzi, Joseph/Putnam-Northern Wstchstr BOCES	16	266
Manny, Kyle/Lake George Central Sch Dist	6	245
Manny, Maura/Saratoga Springs City Sch Dist	71	201
Mansfield, Michael/Dunkirk City School Dist	1	37
Mansir, Debbie/East Hampton Union Free SD	30	220
Manuel, Victor/Jericho Union Free School Dist	2,15	122
Manwaring, Beth/Elmira City School Dist	71	40
Many, Scott/Haldane Central School Dist	83,90	176
Manz, Sheryl/Monticello Central School Dist	36	237
Manzella, Anne/North Colonie Central SD	20	11
Manzella, Carolyn/Stillwater Central Sch Dist	58,79	202
Manzi, Monica/Connetquot Central School Dist	15,58	219
Manzo, Paul/East Islip Union Free SD	8,15,57,68,69,294,298	220
Marangiello, Daniel/Northeastern Clinton Ctl SD	11,58	44
Maranville, Margaret/Bolton Central School Dist	4	244
Marble, Marjorie/Webster Central School Dist	58	112
Marble, Tammy/Canaseraga Central Sch Dist	5	14
Marchbanks, Annette/Liverpool Ctl School Dist	4	156
Marchese, Cathryn/Lyncourt Union Free Sch Dist	2,5,11	156
Marchese, Don/Lancaster Central Sch Dist	38	62
Marchioli, Karen/Lancaster Central Sch Dist	9	62
Marchionda, Tracy/Geneva City School Dist	70	161
Marciano, Kellie/North Rose Wolcott Central SD	57,58,68	250
Marcinelli, Lindsay/Forestville Central Sch Dist	9	37
Marcisz, Steve/Bedford Central School Dist	36	252
Marcon, Maura/Chappaqua Central School Dist	30	253
Marconi, Karen/Middletown Enlarged City SD	58	165
Margata, Marco/Tuxedo Union Free Sch Dist	285	167
Marguccio, Melissa/Cheektowaga Maryvale UFSD	61	59
Margulis, Mike/Carle Place Union Free SD	5	117
Mariani, Nancy/Lancaster Central Sch Dist	20	62
Mariano, Thomas/Greece Central School Dist	71,73,286	108
Marinaccil, Cindy/Pembroke Ctl School Dist	11,34,58,77,79,93	74
Marinello, Salvatore/Western Suffolk BOCES	67	236
Marino, Christopher/North Shore Central SD	34,58,90	126
Marino, Cynthia/Milford Central School Dist	4	173
Marino, Don/Catskill Central School Dist	76,295	75
Marino, John/Chenango Valley Ctl Sch Dist	4	28
Marino, John/Greenburgh-North Castle SD	2	255
Marino, Ralph, Dr/Hewlett Woodmere Union Free SD	1,11	121
Mark, Michael/Nyack Union Free School Dist	67	197
Mark, Robert/Hadley-Luzerne Ctl Sch Dist	58	245
Markhum, Corey/Westfield Central School Dist	10,57,270	39
Markwica, Kathryn/Newcomb Central School Dist	8,31,36,69	68
Markwica, Michael/Johnsburg Central School Dist	1	245
Marolf, Carolyn/Beaver River Central Sch Dist	61	101
Marotta, Steven/Ichabod Crane Central Schools	3,91	46
Marquette, Elizabeth/Albion Central School Dist	273	169
Marra, Edward/White Plains City School Dist	4	263
Marreck, John/Cold Spring Harbor Central SD	3	219
Marrero, Alex/East Ramapo Central Sch Dist	15	196
Marrero, Alex, Dr/New Rochelle City School Dist	8,18,57,69,273	259
Marrero, Lauren/Livingston Manor Ctl Sch Dist	11,57,58,296	236
Marris, Timothy/Syracuse City School Dist	295	158
Marrone, Michelle/Patchogue-Medford Unified SD	57,61	227
Marsden, Margaret/Broadalbin-Perth Ctl Sch Dist	273	71
Marsh, Barbara/Cornwall Central School Dist	77	163
Marshall, Ann/Cleveland Hill Union Free SD	16	59
Marshall, Christopher/Gouverneur Ctl School Dist	6,35	210
Marshall, Christopher/Victor Central School Dist	3,91	162
Marshall, Don/Burnt Hills Ballston Lake SD	67	200
Marshall, John/Bradford Central Sch Dist	1,11,57	207
Marshall, Rob/Marion Central School Dist	67	250
Marshall, Shannon/Wayne-Finger Lakes BOCES	71	252
Marshall, Tracy/Phelps-Clifton Springs Ctl SD	2	162
Martin, Andrew/Central Square Central SD	67	170
Martin, Andrew/Heuvelton Central School Dist	67	210
Martin, Beth/Gouverneur Ctl School Dist	7,83	210
Martin, Bruce/Red Hook Central School Dist	2,298	53
Martin, Caleb/North Warren Central Sch Dist	57,69,270,288,294	246
Martin, Christopher/Mount Markham Central Sch Dist	77	78
Martin, David/Eden Central School Dist	3	60
Martin, Doreen/Scio Central School Dist	3,6,35,83	15
Martin, Edwin/Ballston Spa Ctl School Dist	3,91	200
Martin, Jeff/Chittenango Central SD	3	104
Martin, Joann/Tuxedo Union Free Sch Dist	5	167
Martin, Margo/Groton Central School Dist	1,11	240
Martin, Molly/Sherman Central School Dist	286	39
Martin, Robert/Cortland Enlarged City SD	3	47
Martin, Shirley, Dr/Roosevelt Union Free Sch Dist	15,68	128
Martin, Terri, Dr/Windham Ashland Jewett Ctl SD	67	76

DISTRICT PERSONNEL INDEX

Market Data Retrieval

NAME/District	JOB FUNCTIONS	PAGE
Martin, Tony/Chateaugay Central School Dist	67	69
Martindale, Cheri/Queensbury Union Free Sch Dist	5	246
Martineau, Michelle/Ausable Valley Ctl Sch Dist	4	43
Martinez, Ana/Southampton Union Free SD	57	231
Martinez, Anjelieeque/South Colonie Central Sch Dist	2	12
Martinez, Jaime/Westbury Union Free Sch Dist	30	132
Martinez, Paul/Rocky Point Union Free SD	3	228
Martini, Meredyth/Malverne Union Free Sch Dist	58	124
Martoni, Michele/New Paltz Ctl School Dist	8,11,15,288,296	242
Martorana, Barbara/Monroe 2 Orleans BOCES	58,77	115
Martorana, Joseph/Hastings on Hudson Union FR SD	3	256
Martzloff, Scott, Dr/Williamsville Ctl School Dist	1,11	64
Marvel, Rose/Farmingdale Union Free SD	20	119
Marvin, Ralph/Attica Central School Dist	5	267
Marwah, Deepak/Byram Hills Central Sch Dist	20,23	253
Marzec, Charles/Jamestown City School Dist	73,76,286,295	38
Marzec, Lindsay/Frewsburg Central School Dist	48	38
Mascarenhas, Joseph/Arlington Central School Dist	3	51
Masera, Ron/Center Moriches Union Free SD	1	218
Masline, Jeff/Menands Union Free Sch Dist	67	11
Mason, Dawn/Three Village Central Sch Dist	58,79	232
Masopust, Brian/Wallkill Central School Dist	6	243
Massaro, Maria/Niagara Falls City Sch Dist	68	147
Massetti, Bonnie/Longwood Central School Dist	2	224
Massie, Scott/Hilton Central School Dist	15,68,78	109
Masten, Craig/Fort Ann Central School Dist	3	247
Masten, Craig/Ft Edward Union Free Sch Dist	3	247
Masterson, Kathleen/Westhampton Beach School Dist	6,35	233
Masterson, Valerie/Stillwater Central Sch Dist	67	202
Mastin, Jonathan/Bloomfield Central SD	6,31,35	161
Mastrantuono, David/Waverly Ctl School Dist	3	239
Mastropieto, Matt/Deposit Central School Dist	6	28
Mathers, Mary/Northport-East Northport UFSD	30	227
Mathias, Gail/Ballston Spa Ctl School Dist	71	200
Mathieson, Constance/Margaretville Central Sch Dist	4	49
Mato, Lisa/Longwood Central School Dist	11,69	225
Matteson, Diane/Onc BOCES	68	51
Matteson, Jeffrey, Dr/Tompkins-Seneca-Tioga BOCES	1	241
Mattey, Stuart/Scarsdale Union Free Sch Dist	2,3,4,5,15,88,91,275	261
Matthews, Andy/Mt Sinai Union Free SD	285	226
Matthews, Kimberly/Schenevus Ctl School Dist	8,11,58	174
Matthews, Roberta/Herkimer BOCES	58,88	79
Matthews, Rosemary/Chappaqua Central School Dist	58	253
Mattice, John/Windham Ashland Jewett Ctl SD	3	76
Mattice, Michelle/Windham Ashland Jewett Ctl SD	2,12	76
Mattice, Shannon/Gouverneur Ctl School Dist	71,73,76,97,295	210
Mattimore, Cassidy/Norwood-Norfolk Ctl SD	58	211
Mattioli, Laura/Hendrick Hudson Ctl Sch Dist	274	256
Mattison, Mark/Altmar-Parish-Williamstown SD	67	170
Mattracion, Philip/Ellenville Central School Dist	67	241
Maturo, Stehanie/Ctr for Instruct Tech Innov	73	172
Maturski, Thomas/Williamsville Ctl School Dist	2,15,76,298	64
Matuszak, Megan/Attica Central School Dist	2,19	267
Matzak, Maryanne/Copiague Union Free Sch Dist	4	220
Matzan, Deborah/Palmyra-Macedon Central SD	7	250
Matzek, Zach/Dansville Ctl School Dist	27,38	102
Mauricio, David, Dr/Peekskill City School Dist	1	260
Mauro, Anthony/Southold Union Free Sch Dist	1	231
Maury, Brett/Gilboa-Conesville Central SD	73	206
Mautone, Lawrence/Suffern Central School Dist	15,68	198
Mavretish, Sarah/Cato Meridian Central Sch Dist	69	34
Mavrommatis, Nora/Katonah-Lewisboro Sch Dist	5	257
Maxim, Danielle/Harpursville Central Sch Dist	5	28
Maxwell, Celine/Cornwall Central School Dist	2	163
Maxwell, George/Center Moriches Union Free SD	67	218
May, Gary/Canajoharie Ctl School Dist	3	115
May, Judy/Friendship Central Sch Dist	1	15

NAME/District	JOB FUNCTIONS	PAGE
May, Marie/Wyoming Central School Dist	16,288	268
Mayberry, Daniel/Keene Central School Dist	1,288	67
Maycock, Robin/Randolph Central School Dist	6	33
Mayewksi, Carol/Nyack Union Free School Dist	2	197
Maynard, Linda/Bainbridge Guilford CSD	70,71,97,294,750	41
Mayo, Joe/Mohonasen Central Sch Dist	3	203
Mayo, Thomas/Troy City School Dsitrict	67	191
Mays, Dean/Scotia Glenville Ctl Sch Dist	76	205
Mayton, David/Cherry Valley-Springfield SD	3,5	173
Mazourek, Katherine/Unatego Unadilla Central SD	58	174
Mazza, Andrea/Frankfort-Schuyler Ctl SD	85	77
Mazza, Lynn/East Williston Union Free SD	11,58,79	118
Mazza, Steve/Lindenhurst Union Free SD	16,73	224
Mazzaferro, Jeane-Marie/Riverhead Central School Dist	7,58,79,83,85,88,90,274	228
Mazzaferro, Jeanne-Marie/Southampton Union Free SD	58	231
Mazzaferro, Pam/Onondaga-Cortland-Madison BOCES	73,76,295	160
Mazzie, Frank/Patchogue-Medford Unified SD	2	227
Mazzilia, Joseph/Carle Place Union Free SD	275,285	117
Mazzone, Nora, Dr/Mamaroneck Union Free Sch Dist	7,15,79	257
Mazzotte, Joanne/Crown Point Central Sch Dist	8,36,57,69,73,270	67
Mazzuca, Frank/Nanuet Union Free School Dist	6,7,77	196
Mazzullo, Mary Grace/Williamson Central School Dist	1	251
McAfee, Timothy/Northern Adirondack Ctl SD	38	44
McAffee, Danielle/Saranac Central School Dist	2	45
McAlpin, Daniel/Bloomfield Central SD	10,27,81,273	161
McAney, Lara/Windham Ashland Jewett Ctl SD	8,11,69,288	76
McArdle, Tim/Le Roy Central School Dist	10,33,69,88	73
McAuliff, Michael/Marcellus Central School Dist	67	157
McAulisse, Robert/Chazy Central Rural Sch Dist	9,12,13,270,275,296	44
McBride-Heppes, Deborah/Orange-Ulster BOCES	2,4,15	168
McBride, Diane/Rush Henrietta Central SD	67	112
McBride, Effie/Greater Amsterdam School Dist	48	115
McBryde, Thomas/Community School District 19	1	88
McCabe, John/Brighton Central School Dist	91	106
McCabe, John/Edgemont Union Free Sch Dist	3	254
McCabe, Patrick/Akron Central School Dist	1	56
McCabe, Sean/Greece Central School Dist	67	108
McCaffrey, Angela/Lackawanna City School Dist	8,11	62
McCahill, Kevin/Nanuet Union Free School Dist	1	196
McCall, Tom/McGraw Central School Dist	3,5,91	48
McCann, Dave/Ellicottville Central Sch Dist	6	31
McCann, Robert/Romulus Ctl School Dist	67	208
McCarthy, Christian/Katonah-Lewisboro Sch Dist	6,7,35,80	257
McCarthy, Georgia/Huntington Union Free Sch Dist	6,35	223
McCarthy, James/Ogdensburg City School Dist	3,91	211
McCarthy, Jennifer/Longwood Central School Dist	60	225
McCarthy, John/Putnam-Northern Wstchstr BOCES	15	266
McCarthy, Lisa/Spencerport Central Sch Dist	9,74,273	112
McCarthy, Maria/Highland Ctl School Dist	4	242
McCarthy, Maria/Ulster BOCES	4	244
McCarthy, Michael/Liverpool Ctl School Dist	91	156
McCarthy, Suzanne/Albany City School Dist	7	9
McCarthy, Terrance/Webster Central School Dist	48	112
McCarthy, Tim, Dr/Hauppauge Union Free Sch Dist	57,61,73	223
McCarthy, Traci/Arkport Central School Dist	4	213
McCarthy, Tracie/Hornell City School Dist	4	214
McCarty, Russ/Fayetteville-Manlius Ctl SD	3,91	155
McCarville, Carol/Genesee Valley Ctl School Dist	8,12,58,69,288	15
McCaul, James/Clifton-Fine Central Sch Dist	6	209
McCaw, Jordan/Massapequa Union Free SD 23	13,58,79,88	125
McCheyne, Liz/South Seneca Ctl Sch Dist	16,82	208
McClain, Michael/Canandaigua City School Dist	3	161
McCloskey, Amy/Southwestern Central Sch Dist	58,79	39
McClure, Don/Tully Central School Dist	6	159
McConnely, Dan/Duanesburg Central Sch Dist	5	203
McCool, Melinda/McGraw Central School Dist	1,11	48
McCorkell, Maureen/Farmingdale Union Free SD	4	119

1 Superintendent	16 Instructional Media Svcs	30 Adult Education	44 Science Sec	58 Special Education K-12	72 Summer School	88 Alternative/At Risk	277 Remedial Math K-12
2 Bus/Finance/Purchasing	17 Chief Operations Officer	31 Career/Sch-to-Work K-12	45 Math K-12	59 Special Education Elem	73 Instructional Tech	89 Multi-Cultural Curriculum	280 Literacy Coach
3 Buildings And Grounds	18 Chief Academic Officer	32 Career/Sch-to-Work Elem	46 Math Elem	60 Special Education Sec	74 Inservice Training	90 Social Work	285 STEM
4 Food Service	19 Chief Financial Officer	33 Career/Sch-to-Work Sec	47 Math Sec	61 Foreign/World Lang K-12	75 Marketing/Distributive	91 Safety/Security	286 Digital Learning
5 Transportation	20 Art K-12	34 Early Childhood Ed	48 English/Lang Arts K-12	62 Foreign/World Lang Elem	76 Info Systems	92 Magnet School	288 Common Core Standards
6 Athletic	21 Art Elem	35 Health/Phys Education	49 English/Lang Arts Elem	63 Foreign/World Lang Sec	77 Psychological Assess	93 Parental Involvement	294 Accountability
7 Health Services	22 Art Sec	36 Guidance Services K-12	50 English/Lang Arts Sec	64 Religious Education K-12	78 Affirmative Action	95 Tech Prep Program	295 Network System
8 Curric/Instruct K-12	23 Music K-12	37 Guidance Services Elem	51 Reading K-12	65 Religious Education Elem	79 Student Personnel	97 Chief Infomation Officer	296 Title II Programs
9 Curric/Instruct Elem	24 Music Elem	38 Guidance Services Sec	52 Reading Elem	66 Religious Education Sec	80 Driver Ed/Safety	98 Chief Technology Officer	297 Webmaster
10 Curric/Instruct Sec	25 Music Sec	39 Social Studies K-12	53 Reading Sec	67 School Board President	81 Gifted/Talented	270 Character Education	298 Grant Writer/Ptnrships
11 Federal Program	26 Business Education	40 Social Studies Elem	54 Remedial Reading K-12	68 Teacher Personnel	82 Video Services	271 Migrant Education	750 Chief Innovation Officer
12 Title I	27 Career & Tech Ed	41 Social Studies Sec	55 Remedial Reading Elem	69 Academic Assessment	83 Substance Abuse Prev	273 Teacher Mentor	751 Chief of Staff
13 Title V	28 Technology Education	42 Science K-12	56 Remedial Reading Sec	70 Research/Development	84 Erate	274 Before/After Sch	752 Social Emotional Learning
15 Asst Superintendent	29 Family/Consumer Science	43 Science Elem	57 Bilingual/ELL	71 Public Information	85 AIDS Education	275 Response To Intervention	

New York School Directory

DISTRICT PERSONNEL INDEX

NAME/District	JOB FUNCTIONS	PAGE
McCormack, Amy/Sandy Creek Central Sch Dist	8,12,51,54,69	172
McCormack, Artie/Pearl River School Dist	6,35	197
McCormack, T J/Archdiocese of New York Ed Off	71	142
McCowan, Denise/Cheektowaga-Sloan UFSD	67	59
McCoy, Beth/Huntington Union Free Sch Dist	8,15,30	223
McCoy, Bryan/Maine Endwell Ctl School Dist	4	29
McCoy, Michael/Greenburgh Central School Dist	6	255
McCrann, William/Island Park Union Free SD	73	122
McCreadle, Teresa/Schalmont Central School Dist	295	204
McCue, Patrick/Rush Henrietta Central SD	15,68	112
McCutcheon, Paul/Ripley Central School Dist	67	39
McDaid, Thomas/North Merrick Union Free SD	2,15	126
McDarby, Kathy/Elmira City School Dist	71	40
McDermith, Ken/Shenendehowa Central Sch Dist	73,76,295	202
McDermott, Bernard/Chenango Forks Central SD	2,3,5	28
McDonald, John/Elwood Union Free School Dist	3	221
McDonald, Mathew/Baldwinsville Central Sch Dist	1	154
McDonald, Michael/Walton Central School Dist	1	50
McDonald, Reginald/Malone Central School Dist	11,58,79,88,271,275,280,298	69
McDonald, Scott/Cobleskill Richmondville SD	8	206
McDonald, Toni, Dr/Levittown Union Free Sch Dist	1	123
McDonald, William/Red Creek Central School Dist	15	251
McDonell, Ellen/Arlington Central School Dist	16,73,295	51
McDonnell, Ellen/Tuckahoe Union Free SD	8,79	262
McDonough, Joanne/Suffern Central School Dist	59	198
McDonough, Joseph/Canton Central School Dist	9	209
McDonough, Shawn/Horseheads Ctl School Dist	71,97	40
McDowell, Michelle/Jamestown City School Dist	8,12,18	38
McElheron, Dennis/North Babylon Union Free SD	58	226
McElroy, Jason/Monroe Woodbury Central SD	72	165
McEnery, Sheila/Ithaca City School Dist	58	240
McEnroe, Katy/Webutuck Ctl School Dist	8,11,79,273	54
McEntee, Shannon/Sachem Central School Dist	6,35	229
McEvoy, Luke/Owego Apalachin Ctl Sch Dist	71	238
McFarland, Katie/Canandaigua City School Dist	74	161
McFarland, Kyle/Northville Central School Dist	10,57,69	72
McFarlane, Erika/Schenectady City School Dist	8,30	204
McFarlane, Rick/Hadley-Luzerne Ctl Sch Dist	5	245
McGarrity, Matthew/Orchard Park Central Sch Dist	1	63
McGarry, Margaret/Binghamton City School Dist	20,23,61	27
McGarry, Nicole/Livonia Ctl School Dist	58	103
McGee, Erin/Eastchester Union Free SD	58	254
McGinley, Christopher, Dr/Williamsville Ctl School Dist	45	64
McGlynn, Daniel/Gilboa-Conesville Central SD	6	206
McGourty, Meghan/Warwick Valley Central SD	58,79	167
McGovern, Dennis/Babylon Union Free Sch Dist	88	216
McGowan, Bruce/Unadilla Valley Ctl Sch Dist	288	43
McGowan, Kevin, Dr/Brighton Central School Dist	1	106
McGowan, Susan/Geneva City School Dist	37,90	161
McGrane, Trish/Northport-East Northport UFSD	5	227
McGrath, Donna/West Babylon Union Free SD	30	232
McGrath, Joseph/Mount Vernon City School Dist	16,73,286,295	258
McGrath, Megan/Edwards-Knox Central Sch Dist	13,16	210
McGrath, Michael/Byram Hills Central Sch Dist	36	253
McGrath, Molly/East Greenbush Central SD	7,34,58,79	190
McGrath, Patrick/Burnt Hills Ballston Lake SD	1	200
McGrath, Penelope/Longwood Central School Dist	67	225
McGrath, Terisa/Manhasset Union Free Sch Dist	27,35,42	124
McGraw, John/Greene Ctl School Dist	295	42
McGraw, Sarah/Albany City School Dist	285	9
McGreevy, Colleen/Quogue Union Free School Dist	73,295	228
McGuffog, Carolyn, Dr/Greenburgh-North Castle SD	1,11	255
McGuinness, Shela/Yorktown Central School Dist	68	264
McGuire, Theresa/Harborfields Ctl School Dist	58,79	223
McGuire, Wayne/Cattaraugus-Little Vly Ctl SD	3	31
McGuirre, Sara/Montauk Union Free School Dist	88,275	226
McGurl, Thomas/Granville Central School Dist	1	247
McHugh, James/East Greenbush Central SD	8,11,57,77,275,285,288,296	190
McHugh, Kathy/Saranac Lake Central Sch Dist	76	70
McIntosh, Edgar/Scarsdale Union Free Sch Dist	8,15	261
McIntosh, Lori/Madrid-Waddington Central SD	2	211
McIntosh, Richard/Waverly Ctl School Dist	5,6	239
McIntyre, Mike/Whitesville Central Sch Dist	3	15
McIntyre, Robert/South Country Central Sch Dist	6,7,35	231
McKane, Shawn/Sherman Central School Dist	270,275	39
McKee, Sarah/Barker Central School Dist	7	146
McKeighan, David/Hudson Falls Central Sch Dist	3	248
McKenna, Helina/North Bellmore Union Free SD	4	126
McKenna, John, Dr/Williamsville Ctl School Dist	15,68	64
McKenna, Lori/Albany City School Dist	10,15	9
McKenna, Matt/Niagara-Wheatfield Ctl SD	6,7	148
McKenna, Theresa/Canisteo-Greenwood Central SD	2	214
McKenney, Rebecca/La Fayette Central School Dist	36	156
McKeon, Daniel/East Moriches Union Free SD	1	221
McKibben, Richard/Pine Plains Ctl School Dist	3	53
McKinley, Cristy/Scio Central School Dist	8,69,285	15
McKinley, Nancy/Colton Pierrepont School Dist	273	209
McKinna, Theresa/Bath Central School Dist	2	213
McKotch, Tami/Frewsburg Central School Dist	37,58,79,83,90	38
McLaren, Victoria/Onteora Central School Dist	1	243
McLaughlin, Cletus/Little Falls City School Dist	2,5	78
McLaughlin, Daryl/Perry Central School Dist	1	267
McLaughlin, Irene/Northport-East Northport UFSD	15,68	227
McLaughlin, Joseph/Harpursville Central Sch Dist	2	28
McLaughlin, Kira/Sag Harbor Union Free Sch Dist	16	229
McLaughlin, Patrick/Potsdam Central School Dist	3	212
McLean-Randall, Davina/Rochester City School Dist	34,58	110
McLean, Cindy/Colton Pierrepont School Dist	67	209
McLean, Kenneth/Island Trees Union Free SD	3,91	122
McLeod, Kevin/Valhalla Union Free Sch Dist	2,15,19	262
McLoughlin, Elizabeth/Locust Valley Ctl School Dist	4	123
McLymore, Michael/Newburgh Enlarged City SD	15,68,88	165
McMahon, Jennifer/Livonia Ctl School Dist	9,296	103
McMahon, Shauna/Cattaraugus-Little Vly Ctl SD	58	31
McMann, Francine/Middle Country Ctl Sch Dist	8,15,51,274	225
McManus, Dana/West Seneca Central Sch Dist	57	64
McManus, Deidre/Chappaqua Central School Dist	4	253
McMaster, Joan/Diocese of Brooklyn Ed Office	15,68	94
McMullen, Teresa/Le Roy Central School Dist	2	73
McNair, Lorraine/Moravia Central School Dist	295	35
McNair, Tom/Broome-Tioga BOCES	27	31
McNally, Kevin/Dundee Ctl School Dist	37	268
McNamara, Daniel/Arlington Central School Dist	5	51
McNamara, Eugene/Rochester City School Dist	58	110
McNamara, John/Wantagh Union Free Sch Dist 23	1	131
McNamara, Tillie/North Bellmore Union Free SD	9,74,280	126
McNamara, Timothy/Afton Central School Dist	1,11	41
McNay, Tom/Schodack Central School Dist	4	191
McNeely, Renee/Whitesville Central Sch Dist	11,58,69,294,298	15
McNiff, Alan/Penfield Central School Dist	3,91	109
McNulty, Catherine/Katonah-Lewisboro Sch Dist	58,77,79	257
McPartland, Nicholas/Saratoga Springs City Sch Dist	6	201
McQuay, William/Burnt Hills Ballston Lake SD	45	200
McQueer, Douglas/Hammond Central School Districte	1	210
McRay, Byron/West Islip School Dist	91	233
McSweeney, R Terri, Dr/Eastern Suffolk BOCES	15,68	235
McTygue, Sharon/Burnt Hills Ballston Lake SD	12,34,58,90,271	200
McVea, Nateasha/East Ramapo Central Sch Dist	8,15	196
McVea, Nateseha/Roosevelt Union Free Sch Dist	8,15,288	128
Meacham, Brandi/Pine Valley Central Sch Dist	11,58	38
Mead, Jennifer/Waterford Halfmoon School Dist	7,35,85	203
Mead, Michael/Jasper Troupsburg Central SD	1,11	215
Meade, Lisa/Granville Central School Dist	8	247
Meaker, Patricia/Mexico Central School Dist	36	171
Meal, Kimberlyann/Lyndonville Central Sch Dist	57	169
Meaney, Debra/Brookhaven Comsewogue Unif SD	5	218
Means, Ashley/Brocton Central School Dist	17	36
Meddaugh, Kyle/Red Creek Central School Dist	67	251
Medici, Vincent/Hudson Falls Central Sch Dist	6,35	248
Medin, Elaine/Central Islip Union Free SD	30	218
Medina, Penny/Liberty Central School Dist	57,271	236
Mednick, Kristen/East Rockaway Union Free SD	83,90	118
Medvit, Nadine/Adirondack Central Sch Dist	32,36,69	150
Meehan, Shannon/Kings Park Ctl School Dist	2	224
Megan, Jason/Schuylerville Central Sch Dist	73	201
Meher, Cathy/Gloversville Enlarged Sch Dist	2	71
Mehlenbacher, Jennifer/Geneseo Central Sch Dist	67	103
Mehlenbacher, Linda/Diocese of Rochester Ed Office	65	113
Mehr, Patrick/Garden City School Dist	3	120
Meier, Gretchen/Pine Bush Central School Dist	67	166
Meinster, Alan/Shoreham-Wading River Ctl SD	8,16,27,54,69,277,288,298	230
Meister, Meredith/Tioga Central School Dist	58,79	239

DISTRICT PERSONNEL INDEX

Market Data Retrieval

NAME/District	JOB FUNCTIONS	PAGE
Mekulik, Cathy/Highland Ctl School Dist	5	242
Mele, Rosanne/Marlboro Central School Dist	2,5,11,15,91,296	242
Melfi, Michelle/Half Hollow Hills Central SD	60	222
Melia, Robert/Shenendehowa Central Sch Dist	15	202
Meliambro, Toni/Locust Valley Ctl School Dist	2,15,68	123
Melikian, Rita, Dr/Garden City School Dist	73,286	120
Melnick, Matthew/East Meadow Union Free SD	67	118
Melnik, Natalie/Gananda Central School Dist	2	249
Meloni, Ryan/Port Washington Union Free SD	73,76,95,286,297	128
Melore, Peter/Connetquot Central School Dist	6,35	219
Melore, Peter/Connetquot Central School Dist	6	219
Melville, Sheila/Saugerties Central School Dist	4	243
Memoli, Tatiana/Port Chester Rye Union Free SD	58	261
Menapace, Tracey/Jamesville-DeWitt Central SD	58,79	155
Mendola, Pietro/Buffalo Public Schools	57,61	57
Mendolera, Melissa/Elmira City School Dist	2	40
Mendonis, Demetrios/East Meadow Union Free SD	39	118
Mendrek, Steve/Jordan Elbridge Ctl Sch Dist	73,295	156
Menegio, Greg/East Moriches Union Free SD	67	221
Menges, Keith/Sullivan BOCES	2,3,73,76	238
Mennona, Charlotte/Liberty Central School Dist	58	236
Menoutis, Gloria/Nyack Union Free School Dist	11	197
Mensch, Mark/William Floyd School Dist	6,35	233
Mensch, Parvin/Waverly Ctl School Dist	67	239
Mensch, Suzanne/Westhampton Beach School Dist	67	233
Mensch, Todd/Greenburgh Central School Dist	285	255
Mentz, Christopher/Bay Shore Union Free Sch Dist	26,45	217
Menz, Suzanne/Rochester City School Dist	2	110
Mercado, Joseph/Middle Country Ctl Sch Dist	6,35,83,85	225
Mercado, Rose Ann/Nanuet Union Free School Dist	274	196
Mercer, Tim/Albion Central School Dist	3	169
Merchant, Brian/Ballston Spa Ctl School Dist	16,295	200
Merchant, Jesse/Hastings on Hudson Union FR SD	6	256
Meredith, Diane/Unadilla Valley Ctl School Dist	8,271	43
Merenghi, Peggy/Levittown Union Free Sch Dist	67	123
Mergen, Izzet, Dr/Northport-East Northport UFSD	20,23	227
Merihew, Teresa/Cincinnatus Ctl School Dist	35	47
Merkal, Robert/West Seneca Central Sch Dist	26,27,31,75	64
Merlini, Anthony/Hendrick Hudson Ctl School Dist	3	256
Merlino, Marisa/Katonah-Lewisboro Sch Dist	36	257
Mero, Philip/Boquet Valley Central Sch Dist	67	67
Merrick, Tatiana/Buffalo Public Schools	8	56
Merrill, Nels/Syracuse City School Dist	2	158
Merrill, Stacy/Romulus Ctl School Dist	16	208
Merritt, Nate/Brighton Central School Dist	6,35,85	106
Merritt, Norah/Dutchess Co BOCES	68	55
Meserole, Caroleigh/Saranac Lake Central Sch Dist	73,295	70
Mesidor, Veronsky/West Hempstead School Dist	16,48	131
Mesika, Sonia/Brewster Central School Dist	67	175
Mesires, Maria/Watertown City School Dist	67	81
Mesite, Allie/Fishers Island Union Free SD	16,58	222
Mesite, Allie/Fishers Island Union Free SD	16,58	222
Messenger, Ann/Hancock Central School Dist	6	49
Messer, Margaret/Niagara-Wheatfield Ctl SD	5	148
Messina, Michael/Malverne Union Free Sch Dist	20,23,29	124
Messineo, Scott/Stillwater Central Sch Dist	2	202
Messinger, Brian/Sewanhaka Ctl High Sch Dist	73	129
Messler, Kerri/Schenectady City School Dist	16,48,51,54	204
Messura, Carol/Le Roy Central School Dist	9,34,69,72,88,270	73
Metcalf, Nate/Altmar-Parish-Williamstown SD	5	170
Mettler, Karen/O E S J Central School Dist	2	72
Metz, Debbie/Iroquois Central School Dist	30	61
Metz, Tamara/Indian River Ctl School Dist	11,36,58,69,271,294	80
Meyer, Joshua/Boquet Valley Central Sch Dist	1	67
Meyer, Laura/Quogue Union Free School Dist	57	228
Meyer, Maria/Westbury Union Free Sch Dist	8,11,69	132
Meyer, Michele/Caledonia-Mumford Ctl Sch Dist	8	102
Meyer, Sharon/Floral Park Bellerose Sch Dist	9	119
Meyer, Wendy/Tuckahoe Common School Dist	7	232
Meyers, Bob/Wellsville Central Sch Dist	4	15
Meyers, Sally/North Syracuse Ctl Sch Dist	286,297	157
Mezza, Robert/Rome City School Dist	3,15	151
Miano, Diane/Jordan Elbridge Ctl Sch Dist	5	155
Miaski, Kristen/Troy City School Dsitrict	68	191
Miccio, Jean/Lakeland Central School Dist	8,11,15,288,298	257
Micek, David/Falconer Central School Dist	3	37
Michael, Christopher, Dr/Hauppauge Union Free Sch Dist	16,48,51	223
Michael, Senno/North Rockland Central SD	2,15	197
Michalak, Paula/Silver Creek Central Sch Dist	286	39
Michalec, Jennifer/Evans-Brant Central Sch Dist	67	60
Michel, Robert/Clarence Central School Dist	68,78,79	59
Michele, John/Babylon Union Free Sch Dist	45	216
Mierlak, Barbara/Locust Valley Ctl School Dist	16	123
Miga, Christina/West Irondequoit Ctl SD	9,12,51,54,69,296	113
Mighells, Paula/Genesee Valley Ctl School Dist	8,12,58,83,288	15
Migliori, Rocco/Westmoreland Central Sch Dist	1	153
Mignella, Anthony/Baldwin Union Free School Dist	8,12,15	116
Mikols, Jeff/Rochester City School Dist	45,286	110
Miktuk, Kevin/Panama Central School Dist	3	38
Milano, Christopher/Levittown Union Free Sch Dist	3,91	123
Milano, Ryan/Middle Country Ctl Sch Dist	45	225
Milazzo, Frank/Marlboro Central School Dist	67	242
Milburn, Karen/Rush Henrietta Central SD	76	112
Milburn, Patricia/Orange-Ulster BOCES	5	168
Mildon, Valrie/Moriah Central School Dist	2	68
Mileham, Kristina/Rochester City School Dist	58,73	110
Miles, Deborah/Fairport Ctl School Dist	7,11,36,77,79,85,270	108
Miles, Justine/Hudson Falls Central Sch Dist	58	248
Miletich, John/Malone Central School Dist	44	69
Milgate, Daniel/Spencerport Central Sch Dist	1	112
Milioto, Carmen/Buffalo Public Schools	79	57
Militello, Gail/Williamsville Ctl School Dist	48,51,54,280	64
Milkowich, Kelly/General Brown Ctl School Dist	67	80
Millar, Pam/Alden Central School Dist	2	56
Millen, Nancy/Margaretville Central School Dist	37	49
Miller, Allen/North Babylon Union Free SD	5	226
Miller, Christine/Delaware Academy Ctrl SD Delhi	4	49
Miller, Christopher/Syracuse City School Dist	68	158
Miller, Cynthia/Mount Markham Central Sch Dist	67	78
Miller, Daniel/Corinth Central School Dist	3	200
Miller, Darcy/Mount Vernon City School Dist	67	258
Miller, Dawn/Sauquoit Valley Central SD	67	152
Miller, Donald/Phelps-Clifton Springs Ctl SD	3	162
Miller, Ed/Sachem Central School Dist	3	229
Miller, Elizabeth/Rochester City School Dist	15	110
Miller, Jackie/Newark Central School Dist	16	250
Miller, Jennifer/Amagansett Union Free Sch Dist	16,73,76,82,295	216
Miller, Joe/Bradford Central Sch Dist	67	207
Miller, John/Hilton Central School Dist	73,286	109
Miller, Joshua/Elmira City School Dist	73,76,295	40
Miller, Karen/Bradford Central Sch Dist	7,83,85	207
Miller, Kristin/Marion Central School Dist	11,57,58,88,275,285,288	250
Miller, Kristy/Alexander Ctl School Dist	16	73
Miller, Lorraine/Morris Central School Dist	37	174
Miller, Lynn/Sullivan BOCES	16	238
Miller, Mark/Newark Central School Dist	11,298	250
Miller, Melanie/Vernon-Verona-Sherrill CSD	48	152
Miller, Melinda/Colton Pierrepont School Dist	16	209
Miller, Michael/Bayport- Blue Point USD	67	217
Miller, Michael/Bridgehampton Union Free SD	35	218
Miller, Michael/Indian Lake Ctl School Dist	73,76,295	76
Miller, Michelle/Alfred Almond Ctl School Dist	4	13
Miller, Michelle/Canisteo-Greenwood Central SD	4	214
Miller, Monica/Glen Cove City School Dist	67	120

#		#		#		#		#		#	
1	Superintendent	16	Instructional Media Svcs	30	Adult Education	44	Science Sec	58	Special Education K-12	72	Summer School
2	Bus/Finance/Purchasing	17	Chief Operations Officer	31	Career/Sch-to-Work K-12	45	Math K-12	59	Special Education Elem	73	Instructional Tech
3	Buildings And Grounds	18	Chief Academic Officer	32	Career/Sch-to-Work Elem	46	Math Elem	60	Special Education Sec	74	Inservice Training
4	Food Service	19	Chief Financial Officer	33	Career/Sch-to-Work Sec	47	Math Sec	61	Foreign/World Lang K-12	75	Marketing/Distributive
5	Transportation	20	Art K-12	34	Early Childhood Ed	48	English/Lang Arts K-12	62	Foreign/World Lang Elem	76	Info Systems
6	Athletic	21	Art Elem	35	Health/Phys Education	49	English/Lang Arts Elem	63	Foreign/World Lang Sec	77	Psychological Assess
7	Health Services	22	Art Sec	36	Guidance Services K-12	50	English/Lang Arts Sec	64	Religious Education K-12	78	Affirmative Action
8	Curric/Instruct K-12	23	Music K-12	37	Guidance Services Elem	51	Reading K-12	65	Religious Education Elem	79	Student Personnel
9	Curric/Instruct Elem	24	Music Elem	38	Guidance Services Sec	52	Reading Elem	66	Religious Education Sec	80	Driver Ed/Safety
10	Curric/Instruct Sec	25	Music Sec	39	Social Studies K-12	53	Reading Sec	67	School Board President	81	Gifted/Talented
11	Federal Program	26	Business Education	40	Social Studies Elem	54	Remedial Reading K-12	68	Teacher Personnel	82	Video Services
12	Title I	27	Career & Tech Ed	41	Social Studies Sec	55	Remedial Reading Elem	69	Academic Assessment	83	Substance Abuse Prev
13	Title V	28	Technology Education	42	Science K-12	56	Remedial Reading Sec	70	Research/Development	84	Erate
15	Asst Superintendent	29	Family/Consumer Science	43	Science Elem	57	Bilingual/ELL	71	Public Information	85	AIDS Education

#		#	
88	Alternative/At Risk	277	Remedial Math K-12
89	Multi-Cultural Curriculum	280	Literacy Coach
90	Social Work	285	STEM
91	Safety/Security	286	Digital Learning
92	Magnet School	288	Common Core Standards
93	Parental Involvement	294	Accountability
95	Tech Prep Program	295	Network System
97	Chief Information Officer	296	Title II Programs
98	Chief Technology Officer	297	Webmaster
270	Character Education	298	Grant Writer/Ptnrships
271	Migrant Education	750	Chief Innovation Officer
273	Teacher Mentor	751	Chief of Staff
274	Before/After Sch	752	Social Emotional Learning
275	Response To Intervention		

New York School Directory

DISTRICT PERSONNEL INDEX

NAME/District	JOB FUNCTIONS	PAGE
Miller, Nanci/Bainbridge Guilford CSD	38,288	41
Miller, Nicole/York Central School Dist	16	103
Miller, Peter/Highland Ctl School Dist	3	242
Miller, Ray/Monroe 2 Orleans BOCES	16,73	115
Miller, Robert/Ellicottville Central Sch Dist	1	31
Miller, Robert/Herkimer Ctl School Dist	1	77
Miller, Robert/Salamanca City Central SD	73,76,286,295	33
Miller, Roxeanne/Jordan Elbridge Ctl Sch Dist	2	155
Miller, Sandy/Windham Ashland Jewett Ctl SD	58	76
Miller, Sarah/Union-Endicott Ctl Sch Dist	10	29
Miller, Shawn/Salmon River Central Sch Dist	6	70
Miller, Stephine/Geneseo Central Sch Dist	18,58	103
Miller, Sue/Albion Central School Dist	71	169
Miller, William/Valley Central School Dist	6,35	167
Miller, Zachary/De Ruyter Central School Dist	73	105
Milligan, Dornzella/Nyack Union Free School Dist	83	197
Milliman, Cathy/Penn Yan Ctl School Dist	2,3,15	268
Mills, Deahbra/Port Jervis City School Dist	4	166
Mills, Eleanore/Valley Central School Dist	4	167
Mills, Matthew/Keene Central School Dist	6	67
Milton, Mary Ann/Westhampton Beach School Dist	2	233
Mims, Marissa/Fayetteville-Manlius Ctl SD	67	155
Mineo, Carole/Newburgh Enlarged City SD	67	166
Miner, Gary/Spencerport Central Sch Dist	4	112
Miner, Kristie/Whitney Point Central Sch Dist	280	30
Mingo, Marian/Diocese of Rockville Ed Office	15	132
Mingot, Jean/Southampton Union Free SD	2,15,298	231
Minihan, James/Ossining Union Free Sch Dist	5,91	259
Minnekine, Matt/Cattaraugus-Little Vly Ctl SD	6,35	31
Miriello, Jeff/Cairo-Durham Ctl School Dist	2	75
Mishanie, Arlene/Lynbrook Union Free Sch Dist	7,58,88	124
Mishook, Michael/Bath Central School Dist	67	213
Miskell, Stephen/Jasper Troupsburg Central SD	2	215
Misteretta, Chris/West Hempstead School Dist	6,29,35,80	131
Mistretta, Jenette/Putnam Valley Ctl School Dist	8	176
Mistretta, Margeret/Dansville Ctl School Dist	68	102
Mistretta, Mike/Dansville Ctl School Dist	3,5,91	102
Mitchell, Anne/Portville Central School Dist	8,273	32
Mitchell, Beverly/Community School District 29	1	183
Mitchell, Brian/Ogdensburg City School Dist	4	211
Mitchell, Cherrie/Skaneateles Central Sch Dist	5	157
Mitchell, Jack/Valley Stream Union Free SD 24	2,4,5,11,294,298	131
Mitchell, Jason/Canastota Central School Dist	8,11,15,271,296	104
Mitchell, Jason/Madison Central School Dist	1,11,83	105
Mitchell, Laura/Garrison Union Free Sch Dist	1,11,288	175
Mitchell, Laura/Millbrook Ctl School Dist	1	52
Mitchell, Laurie/Lynbrook Union Free Sch Dist	31	124
Mitchell, Manuela/Williamson Central School Dist	57	251
Mitchell, Michael/Boquet Valley Central Sch Dist	3	67
Mitchell, Rosey/Cornwall Central School Dist	30	175
Mitchell, Tara/Burnt Hills Ballston Lake SD	71	200
Mitras, Lisa/Norwood-Norfolk Ctl SD	2,11	211
Mittleman, Dean/Connetquot Central School Dist	8,11,15,16,285	219
Mocarski, Barbara/Erie 1 BOCES	73	67
Mochaen, Jeff/Clyde-Savannah Central SD	3	249
Mochan, Jeffery/Waterloo Central School Dist	3,91	208
Mochrie, Jeffrey/Cheektowaga-Sloan UFSD	93,273,274	59
Moe, Khinsoe/Utica City School Dist	57,79	152
Moesch, Trish/Cazenovia Ctl School Dist	85	104
Moffa, Carolyn/Pearl River School Dist	34,36,58,79,83,85,90	197
Mohawk-Jensen, Mary/Gowanda Central School Dist	88	32
Mohr, Christopher/Valley Central School Dist	73	167
Molina, Jamie/Putnam-Northern Wstchstr BOCES	73,76	267
Molisani, Robert/Caledonia-Mumford Ctl Sch Dist	1	102
Molle, Wendy/Schoharie Central SD	16	206
Molloy, Gregory/Morrisville Eaton Central SD	1	105
Molnar, Philip, Dr/Carle Place Union Free SD	58,79,83,88	117
Moloney, Michele/Spackenkill Union Free SD	2	54
Moloughney, Maureen/Farmingdale Union Free SD	36	119
Molyneux, Raymond/Greece Central School Dist	295	108
Momberger, Lisa/Albany City School Dist	34	9
Monaco, Jennifer/Mamaroneck Union Free Sch Dist	58	257
Monaghan, Cindy/Voorheesville Central Sch Dist	67	12
Monahan, Brian/Minisink Valley Central SD	1	165
Monastero, Joseph/Cold Spring Harbor Central SD	16,73	219
Mondore, Scott/Richfield Springs Central SD	67	174
Monell, Sherri/Waterloo Central School Dist	7,58,79	208
Monforte, Valerie/Huntington Union Free Sch Dist	59	223
Mongeon, Scott/Sodus Central School Dist	4	251
Mongon, Michael/Mahopac Ctl School Dist	67	176
Monhanon, Kimberly/Warsaw Central School Dist	8	267
Monica, Pam/Alexandria Central School Dist	58	79
Monico, Ed/Bainbridge Guilford CSD	11,73,76	41
Monnat, Franklyn/Beaver River Central Sch Dist	5	101
Monnat, Gil/Lowville Acad-Central Sch Dist	27,36,69	101
Monpesano, James, Dr/Nyack Union Free School Dist	1,11	197
Monroe, Jody/Bethlehem Central School Dist	1,11	10
Montague, Melissa/New York State Dept Education	8	1
Montemaro, Joe/Webster Central School Dist	73	112
Montesano, Roy, Dr/Bronxville Union Free SD	1	253
Montgomery, Josh/Jordan Elbridge Ctl Sch Dist	295	156
Montoro, Anthony/North Tonawanda City Sch Dist	2,15,91	148
Moody, Cynthia/Saranac Lake Central Sch Dist	2	70
Moody, David/Dansville Ctl School Dist	6	102
Moon, Timothy/Syracuse City School Dist	294	158
Mooney, John/Rensselaer City School Dist	67	191
Moore, Chris/Homer Central School Dist	51,54,58,69,77	48
Moore, Colby/Hornell City School Dist	97	214
Moore, Karen/Germantown Central School Dist	52	46
Moore, Karen/Johnsburg Central School Dist	4	245
Moore, Kelley/Gouverneur Ctl School Dist	5	210
Moore, Let/Riverhead Central School Dist	5	228
Moore, Molly/Southwestern Central Sch Dist	8,11,69,73,77,79,288,295	39
Moore, Rick/Olean City School Dist	1	32
Moore, Ron/Skaneateles Central Sch Dist	3	157
Moore, Sandy/Edinburg Common School Dist	2,19,298	201
Moore, Steven/Sodus Central School Dist	2	251
Moore, Tanya/Oneida City School Dist	2	105
Moore, Thomas/Byron-Bergen Ctl School Dist	73	73
Moore, Thomas/Edinburg Common School Dist	16,73,295	201
Moore, Wendy/Morris Central School Dist	67	174
Moot, Douglas/Whitesville Central Sch Dist	2,73,76,295	15
Moquin, Colleen/Palmyra-Macedon Central SD	42	250
Morales-Hanley, Glenda/Edwards-Knox Central Sch Dist	2	210
Morales, Della/Albion Central School Dist	16	169
Morales, Karen/Monroe Woodbury Central SD	12	165
Morales, Karin/Monroe Woodbury Central SD	11,57	165
Morales, Marguerite/Mahopac Ctl School Dist	15	176
Moran, Joann/Ravena Coeymans Selkirk Ctl SD	2	11
Moran, John/East Quogue Union Free SD	5,91	221
Moran, John/Hampton Bays Union Free SD	5	222
Moran, Judy/Webutuck Ctl School Dist	67	54
Moran, Kevin/New York City Dept of Ed	3,5	134
Moran, Marina/Harrison Central School Dist	57,61	256
Moran, Sheila/Webutuck Ctl School Dist	4	54
Moran, Walter/Cornwall Central School Dist	3	163
Morasco, Nicole/Oakfield Alabama Ctl SD	2,17	74
Morbidi, Julio/Sherburne Earlville Central SD	5	42
Morck, Kathy/Galway Central School Dist	38	201
Morcone, Paul/Granville Central School Dist	11,57,271,296,298	247
Morehouse, Ashley/George Junior Republic UFSD	38,83	240
Morehouse, Frank/Johnsburg Central School Dist	3	245
Morehouse, Kelly/Scio Central School Dist	58,752	15
Morel, Charles/Bolton Central School Dist	3	244
Moreno, Anthony/Medina Central School Dist	73	170
Morgan, Joseph, Dr/Rondout Valley Ctl Sch Dist	1	243
Morgan, Kisha/Rochester City School Dist	58	110
Morgan, Lisa/Frankfort-Schuyler Ctl SD	67	77
Morgan, Sharon/Central Islip Union Free SD	2	218
Morgan, Stacey, Dr/Central Islip Union Free SD	11,296,298	218
Morgani, Jenice/East Meadow Union Free SD	57	118
Morgano, John/Eldred Central School Dist	1,11	236
Morganstein, Lea/Chester Union Free School Dist	79,752	163
Morgia, Kylie/Alexandria Central School Dist	273,288	79
Moriarty, Nicole/Mineola Union Free Sch Dist	57	125
Moritz, Kimberly/Springville Griffith Inst CSD	1	63
Morley, Lauren/Lisbon Central School Dist	28,57,88	211
Moroff, Judy/Huntington Union Free Sch Dist	57,61	223
Morotti, Joseph/Little Falls City School Dist	81	78
Morrell, Fatima, Dr/Buffalo Public Schools	8,15,69,271,288	56
Morrell, Thomas/Elmira City School Dist	6,35	40
Morrill, Jill/Hermon-DeKalb Central Sch Dist	7,83	210

School Year 2020-2021   800-333-8802   NY-T43

DISTRICT PERSONNEL INDEX

Market Data Retrieval

NAME/District	JOB FUNCTIONS	PAGE
Morris, Debra/Oxford Academy Central SD	4	42
Morris, Genelle, Dr/Buffalo Public Schools	71,97,294	57
Morris, Jay/Cuba-Rushford Central Sch Dist	16,73,295	14
Morris, Jennifer/New Lebanon Ctl School Dist	12	46
Morris, Jon/Andover Central School Dist	8,68,74,79,90,273,288	14
Morris, Kathy/Friendship Central Sch Dist	7,83	15
Morris, Mary/Cheektowaga Central SD	1	58
Morris, Patricia/Stillwater Central Sch Dist	1,83	202
Morris, Phyllis/New York State Dept Education	2,19	1
Morris, Rose/Floral Park Bellerose Sch Dist	68	119
Morris, Scott/Oneida-Herkimer-Mad BOCES	16,295	154
Morrison, Bradley/Ossining Union Free Sch Dist	20,23	259
Morrison, Cammy/Lyme Central School Dist	1	81
Morrison, Dawn/West Islip School Dist	8,12,15,288	233
Morrison, Jennifer, Dr/New Hyde-Garden City Park UFSD	1	126
Morrison, Jim/Chautauqua Lake Central SD	5	36
Morrison, Kyle/Buffalo Public Schools	58	57
Morrison, Mindy/Wells Central School Dist	5	77
Morrison, Pam/Croton-Harmon Union Free SD	16	254
Morrissey, Douglas/Cairo-Durham Ctl School Dist	11,34,58,79,88,270,296	75
Morrissey, Martha/New York State Dept Education	7,85	1
Morrow, Janet/Barker Central School Dist	16	146
Morrow, Rita/Dansville Ctl School Dist	4	102
Morse, Cassandra/South Jefferson Central SD	4	81
Morse, Fred/Johnsburg Central School Dist	5	245
Morse, Julia/Lisbon Central School Dist	8,31,36,69	210
Mortiz Booth, Bryna/Pine Valley Central Sch Dist	1	38
Morton, Ben/Tonawanda City School Dist	6	64
Morton, Geoffery/Rome City School Dist	68,79	151
Morton, Jessica/South Kortright Ctl SD	27,38	50
Morton, Richard/Salamanca City Central SD	6	33
Mosciatello, Andrea/Rocky Point Union Free SD	58	228
Mosco, Kristen/Haldane Central School Dist	38	176
Moseley, Rachel/Scarsdale Union Free Sch Dist	71,76,97,750	261
Moses, Patrick/Kenmore-Tonawanda UF Sch Dist	11,68	62
Mosey, Joseph/Peekskill City School Dist	11,15,68,69,270,280	260
Mosher, Allan/Wellsville Central Sch Dist	67	15
Mosher, Elizabeth/Little Falls City School Dist	29	78
Mosher, Jan/Harrisville Central Sch Dist	67	101
Moshier, Kendra/Alexandria Central School Dist	90	79
Moss, Thomas, Dr/Hicksville Union Free Sch Dist	16,48,51	122
Mossman, Marion/Milford Central School Dist	67	173
Mott, Heather/South Seneca Ctl Sch Dist	6	208
Motto, Margrett/Sag Harbor Union Free Sch Dist	38	229
Moughan, Tom/Rochester City School Dist	295	110
Moulton, Eddie/Hadley-Luzerne Ctl Sch Dist	67	245
Mouthrop, Rachel/Lisbon Central School Dist	16	210
Moxley, Joanne/Bainbridge Guilford CSD	57,83,88	41
Moyse, Matt/Charlotte Valley Ctl Sch Dist	67	49
Mroz, Alicia/Utica City School Dist	34	152
Mucica, Chris/Williamsville Ctl Sch Dist	6,35	64
Mueller, Joseph/Whitesboro Ctl School Dist	11,15,91,296,298	153
Muffo, Tracy/Moravia Central School Dist	10	35
Muhlnickel, Alan/Goshen Central School Dist	4	164
Muhlnickel, Alan/Greenwood Lake Union Free SD	4	164
Muirhead, Bill/Catskill Central School Dist	4,5	75
Mujumuci, Maryann/Tuckahoe Common School Dist	274	232
Mulberger, David/Penn Yan Ctl School Dist	5	268
Mulcahy, Juli, Dr/Floral Park Bellerose Sch Dist	7,9,15,59,74	119
Muldner, Maria/Queensbury Union Free Sch Dist	280	246
Mulford, Lori, Dr/Spackenkill Union Free SD	8,11,58,73,273,288,294,295	54
Mulhall, Lisa, Dr/Oyster Bay East Norwich Ctl SD	8,11,15,288,298	127
Mulieri, Vincent, Dr/Plainview-Old Bethpage Ctl SD	15,68,79	127
Mulkearn, Ed/Clymer Central School Dist	67	37
Mull, Carleen/Seneca Falls Central Sch Dist	12,275	208
Mullen, Amanda/Prattsburgh Central Sch Dist	16,82	215
Mullen, Tracy/Starpoint Central School Dist	2	149

NAME/District	JOB FUNCTIONS	PAGE
Muller, Anthony/WSWHE BOCES	15,69	249
Muller, Mellissa/Eldred Central School Dist	5	236
Muller, Stephanie/Elmont Union Free School Dist	7,59,77,79,88	118
Mullikin, Kim/Campbell-Savona Ctl Sch Dist	7	213
Mullins, James/Broome-Tioga BOCES	8,15	31
Mullins, Karry/Binghamton City School Dist	2,5,11,15	27
Mullins, Timothy/Bayport-Blue Point USD	6,35	217
Multer, Colleen/Rensselaer City School Dist	27,58,76	191
Mulvaney, Todd/Moravia Central School Dist	6	34
Mummenthey, Carl/Cobleskill Richmondville SD	1	206
Mundell, Timothy/Berne-Knox-Westerlo Central SD	1	10
Munn, Dale/Colton Pierrepont School Dist	2,11,19	209
Munson, Margaret/Greater Southern Tier BOCES	2,15	215
Muntz, Jill/Jamestown City School Dist	7,83	38
Murabito, Anthony/Mexico Central School Dist	273	171
Murdock, Bruce/Schroon Lake Ctl School Dist	67	68
Murphy, Amber/Madrid-Waddington Central SD	7	211
Murphy, Amy/Wynantskill Union Free SD	83	192
Murphy, Anita/Capital Region BOCES	1	13
Murphy, Bradley/Deer Park Union Free Sch Dist	20,23	220
Murphy, Bridget/Plainedge Union Free Sch Dist	58	127
Murphy, Charles, Dr/Island Trees Union Free SD	1	122
Murphy, David/Garden City School Dist	5	120
Murphy, Dennis/Babylon Union Free Sch Dist	31,36	216
Murphy, Donald, Dr/Hauppauge Union Free Sch Dist	8,11,15,73,295,752	223
Murphy, Edward, Dr/North Merrick Union Free SD	59	126
Murphy, Jay/Deer Park Union Free Sch Dist	16,73,76,286	220
Murphy, Joanna/Hyde Park Central School Dist	60	52
Murphy, Julia/Westfield Central School Dist	2,3,4,5	39
Murphy, Kevin/West Islip School Dist	30	233
Murphy, Kristen/Avon Central School Dist	2,294	102
Murphy, Matthew/Cooperstown Ctl School Dist	3	173
Murphy, Mike/Forestville Central Sch Dist	73	37
Murphy, Patrick/Half Hollow Hills Central SD	29,35,80,83,85	222
Murphy, Rachel/Syracuse City School Dist	4	158
Murphy, Sheila/Lockport City School Dist	79	147
Murphy, Sue/Letchworth Central School Dist	35,83,85	267
Murphy, Susan/White Plains City School Dist	83	263
Murphy, Thomas/Hudson Falls Central Sch Dist	5	248
Murphy, Thomas/Longwood Central School Dist	4	224
Murphy, Thomas/Stillwater Central Sch Dist	5	202
Murraw, Lynn/Copenhagen Central SD	67	101
Murray, Anthony, Dr/Freeport Public School Dist	45	119
Murray, Barbara/Chatham Central School Dist	4	46
Murray, James/Hudson Falls Central Sch Dist	4	248
Murray, Kim/Morris Central School Dist	11,58,296,298	174
Murray, Kim/Unadilla Valley Ctl Sch Dist	8,296	43
Murray, Lisa/Chittenango Central SD	88	104
Murray, Michael/Churchville Chili Ctl Sch Dist	6,35,85	107
Murray, Susan/West Genesee Ctl School Dist	34,58,77	159
Murry, James/Madrid-Waddington Central SD	3	211
Mursch, Faith/Eldred Central School Dist	55	236
Mursch, Kimberly/Waterville Central Sch Dist	6,35	153
Murtha, Eileen/Archdiocese of New York Ed Off	58	142
Murtha, Valerie/Newark Valley Central Sch Dist	8,76	238
Musa, Joseph/Hannibal Central School Dist	11,58,79	171
Muscarella, Brett/Jamestown City School Dist	58	38
Muscarella, Michael/Kenmore-Tonawanda UF Sch Dist	9	62
Mushtare, John/Laurens Central School Dist	76	173
Musich, Diana/Pearl River School Dist	15,30,68,71,80	197
Musshafen, James/Wheatland Chili Ctl Sch Dist	67	113
Musso, Stephen/Skaneateles Central Sch Dist	6,7,35	157
Mustafa, Osama/Gloversville Enlarged Sch Dist	71	71
Muzio, Frank/Wantagh Union Free Sch Dist 23	29,36	131
Myatt, Brad/Vernon-Verona-Sherrill CSD	39	152
Myers-Small, Lesli/Rochester City School Dist	1	110
Myers, Cindy/Massena Central School Dist	2	211

1 Superintendent	16 Instructional Media Svcs	30 Adult Education	44 Science Sec	58 Special Education K-12	72 Summer School	88 Alternative/At Risk	277 Remedial Math K-12
2 Bus/Finance/Purchasing	17 Chief Operations Officer	31 Career/Sch-to-Work K-12	45 Math K-12	59 Special Education Elem	73 Instructional Tech	89 Multi-Cultural Curriculum	280 Literacy Coach
3 Buildings And Grounds	18 Chief Academic Officer	32 Career/Sch-to-Work Elem	46 Math Elem	60 Special Education Sec	74 Inservice Training	90 Social Work	285 STEM
4 Food Service	19 Chief Financial Officer	33 Career/Sch-to-Work Sec	47 Math Sec	61 Foreign/World Lang K-12	75 Marketing/Distributive	91 Safety/Security	286 Digital Learning
5 Transportation	20 Art K-12	34 Early Childhood Ed	48 English/Lang Arts K-12	62 Foreign/World Lang Elem	76 Info Systems	92 Magnet School	288 Common Core Standards
6 Athletic	21 Art Elem	35 Health/Phys Education	49 English/Lang Arts Elem	63 Foreign/World Lang Sec	77 Psychological Assess	93 Parental Involvement	294 Accountability
7 Health Services	22 Art Sec	36 Guidance Services K-12	50 English/Lang Arts Sec	64 Religious Education K-12	78 Affirmative Action	95 Tech Prep Program	295 Network System
8 Curric/Instruct K-12	23 Music K-12	37 Guidance Services Elem	51 Reading K-12	65 Religious Education Elem	79 Student Personnel	97 Chief Infomation Officer	296 Title II Programs
9 Curric/Instruct Elem	24 Music Elem	38 Guidance Services Sec	52 Reading Elem	66 Religious Education Sec	80 Driver Ed/Safety	98 Chief Technology Officer	297 Webmaster
10 Curric/Instruct Sec	25 Music Sec	39 Social Studies K-12	53 Reading Sec	67 School Board President	81 Gifted/Talented	270 Character Education	298 Grant Writer/Ptnrships
11 Federal Program	26 Business Education	40 Social Studies Elem	54 Remedial Reading K-12	68 Teacher Personnel	82 Video Services	271 Migrant Education	750 Chief Innovation Officer
12 Title I	27 Career & Tech Ed	41 Social Studies Sec	55 Remedial Reading Elem	69 Academic Assessment	83 Substance Abuse Prev	273 Teacher Mentor	751 Chief of Staff
13 Title V	28 Technology Education	42 Science K-12	56 Remedial Reading Sec	70 Research/Development	84 Erate	274 Before/After Sch	752 Social Emotional Learning
15 Asst Superintendent	29 Family/Consumer Science	43 Science Elem	57 Bilingual/ELL	71 Public Information	85 AIDS Education	275 Response To Intervention	

NY-T44

New York School Directory

DISTRICT PERSONNEL INDEX

NAME/District	JOB FUNCTIONS	PAGE
Myers, John/North Colonie Central SD	5	11
Myers, Laura/Panama Central School Dist	83,85,90	38
Myers, Linda/Union-Endicott Ctl Sch Dist	71	29
Myers, Lisa/Middle Country Ctl Sch Dist	5	225
Myers, Mary/Randolph Acad Union Free SD	67	32
Myers, Randolph/Beaver River Central Sch Dist	2	101
Myke, Joy/Tarrytown Union Free Sch Dist	2	262
Mylod, Michelle/Shenendehowa Central Sch Dist	12,58,79	202

N

NAME/District	JOB FUNCTIONS	PAGE
Naber, Susan/Yonkers Public School Dist	27,30,31,95	263
Nabinger, Melissa/General Brown Ctl School Dist	57,58,77,88,271	80
Naccarato, Joanne/East Meadow Union Free SD	69,73	118
Naccarato, Ryan/Coxsackie-Athens Central SD	6	75
Nagel, Eric/Iroquois Central School Dist	5	61
Nages, Cheryl/Unatego Unadilla Central SD	23	174
Nagle, Angela/Ballston Spa Ctl School Dist	59	200
Nagler, Michael, Dr/Mineola Union Free Sch Dist	1	125
Nahorney, Daniel/Baldwinsville Central Sch Dist	298	154
Nakoski, Pamela/Bloomfield Central SD	67	161
Nakutavicus, Erik/Locust Valley Ctl School Dist	3	123
Nalli, Rocco/Baldwinsville Central Sch Dist	34,57,58,69,77,90,271	154
Nally, Diane/Kings Park Ctl School Dist	67	224
Naples, Bailey/Berkshire Union Free Sch Dist	88	45
Napoli, Vince/Ellenville Central School Dist	2,15	241
Napolitano, Christine/Mineola Union Free Sch Dist	67	125
Napolitano, Guy/Remsenburg-Speonk UFSD	6	228
Napper, Laura/Boquet Valley Central School Dist	57	67
Nardelli, Raymond/Bethlehem Central School Dist	73,76,295	10
Nardone, Frank/Churchville Chili Ctl Sch Dist	2,15	107
Nardone, Jeremy/Hilton Central School Dist	2	109
Nash-Graham, Elena/Brewster Central School Dist	2	175
Nash, Denise/Jericho Union Free School Dist	71	122
Nashir, Nadia/Buffalo Public Schools	15,57	57
Natale, Joseph/Voorheesville Central Sch Dist	2,3,15	12
Natale, Joseph, Dr/O E S J Central School Dist	11	72
Natali, Michele, Dr/Long Beach City School Dist	15,68,74	124
Ndembera, Rachel/Middle Country Ctl Sch Dist	42	225
Neal, Nicole/Churchville Chili Ctl Sch Dist	34,36,77,79,81,270	107
Neal, Rhonda/Rochester City School Dist	27	110
Neaton, Jennifer/Potsdam Central School Dist	12,58	212
Nebins, Megan/Long Lake Central School Dist	31,58	76
Neckers, Scott/Clymer Central School Dist	6	37
Nee, Anne Marie/Scarsdale Union Free Sch Dist	74,273,285	261
Nee, James/Colton Pierrepont School Dist	1,288	209
Neenan, Brian/Webster Central School Dist	8,15	112
Neglia, Colleen/Mt Pleasant Ctl School Dist	67	258
Neiderer, Norbert/Plattsburgh City School Dist	3,5	44
Neier, Laura/Hendrick Hudson Ctl Sch Dist	73	256
Nelan, Robert/Pearl River School Dist	3,91	197
Nelsen, Grant/Eastern Suffolk BOCES	73	235
Nelson, Annette/Gowanda Central School Dist	5	32
Nelson, Christopher/Katonah-Lewisboro Sch Dist	73	257
Nelson, Christopher/Sewanhaka Ctl High Sch Dist	71,76	129
Nelson, Crystal/Genesee Valley BOCES	73,76	75
Nelson, Dana/Baldwinsville Central Sch Dist	5	154
Nelson, David/Falconer Central School Dist	6	37
Nelson, Guy/Brentwood Union Free Sch Dist	73,76,295	217
Nelson, Kenneth/Rush Henrietta Central SD	3	112
Nelson, Laura/Mount Markham Central Sch Dist	11,34,51,58,271,296,298	78
Nelson, Matthew/Ichabod Crane Central Schools	67	46
Nelson, Mike/WSWHE BOCES	3	249
Nephew, Jason/North Syracuse Ctl Sch Dist	15,68,78,273	157
Nephew, Mark/Gowanda Central School Dist	67	32
Neratto, Laura/Brocton Central School Dist	83	36
Nesbitt, Jim/Duanesburg Central Sch Dist	91	203
Nestico, James/Kenmore-Tonawanda UF Sch Dist	5	62
Netzband, Elizabeth/Waterville Central Sch Dist	270	153
Neu, Mark/Cuba-Rushford Central Sch Dist	67	14
Neu, Robert/Dundee Ctl School Dist	67	268
Neu, Sheri/Bath Central School Dist	35	213
Neugebauer, Donald/Fabius Pompey Central SD	67	155
Neuschwender, Mathew/Montauk Union Free School Dist	2	226
Neveldine, Thomas/East Syracuse Minoa Ctl SD	15	154
Nevers, Jim/General Brown Ctl School Dist	4	80
Nevinger, Jeff/Letchworth Central School Dist	73,295	267

NAME/District	JOB FUNCTIONS	PAGE
Nevinsm, Megan/Indian Lake Ctl School Dist	58	76
New, Benjamin/Cazenovia Ctl School Dist	8,58,275,296,298	104
Newby, James/Williamson Central School Dist	6,35,85	251
Newcomer, Laurie/Saratoga Springs City Sch Dist	77	201
Newell, Diane/Dobbs Ferry Union Free SD	73,97,286	254
Newman, Daniel/Springs Union Free School Dist	3	232
Newman, Jodi/Deposit Central School Dist	5	28
Newman, Jodi/Hancock Central School Dist	5	49
Newman, Kelly/Great Neck Public Schools	12,15,32	120
Newman, Laura/Commack Union Free School Dist	2,4,5,11,15,76,80,91	219
Newman, Robert/George Junior Republic UFSD	67	240
Newman, Shelly/North Shore Central SD	71	126
Nicchitta, Thomas/Webster Central School Dist	68	112
Nicholas, Suzanne/Saranac Lake Central Sch Dist	11,57,58,79,83,88,275	70
Nichols, Christine/Edmeston Ctl School Dist	69,273,288	173
Nichols, Jeff/Sag Harbor Union Free Sch Dist	1	229
Nichols, Jen/Madrid-Waddington Central SD	77	211
Nichols, John/Liberty Central School Dist	67	236
Nichols, Kathy/Fulton City School Dist	2	170
Nichols, Kim/Candor Central School Dist	8	238
Nicholson, Harold/Minisink Valley Central SD	5	165
Nicholson, Ron/Greenwich Central School Dist	3	247
Nickson, Michael/Burnt Hills Ballston Lake SD	68	200
Nicol, Christopher/Clyde-Savannah Central SD	58,69,77,79	249
Nicolette, Sarah/Herkimer BOCES	7	79
Nicolosi, Darlene/Nyack Union Free School Dist	73,76	197
Nicometo, Carol/Oakfield Alabama Ctl SD	83	74
Niedermeier, James, Dr/Duanesburg Central Sch Dist	1	203
Nielsen, Jackie/Kendall Central School Dist	286	169
Nienstadt, Paul/Washingtonville Central SD	3,15,91	167
Nikolevski, Jimmy/Williamson Central School Dist	3	251
Nilsen, Audrey/Brookhaven Comsewogue Unif SD	34,58,77,79,83,88,90	218
Ninestine, Ed/Romulus Ctl School Dist	2	208
Nisbit, Michael/Canisteo-Greenwood Central SD	67	214
Nixon, Patrick/Gowanda Central School Dist	3	32
Niznik, Ed/Adirondack Central Sch Dist	1	150
Nobiling, Bonnie/Oneonta City School Dist	16,73,76,297	174
Noble, Tracey/Fayetteville-Manlius Ctl SD	68	155
Nocera-Collins, Melissa/Yorkshire-Pioneer Ctl Sch Dist	67	33
Nocerino, Stephanie/West Babylon Union Free SD	73,76,286	233
Nocero, Heather/Cassadaga Valley Ctl Sch Dist	38,69,83,88	36
Noeth, Mark/East Greenbush Central SD	5	190
Noetzel, John/South Colonie Central Sch Dist	71	12
Nohle, Laurie/General Brown Ctl School Dist	6	80
Nolan, Brian/Canandaigua City School Dist	15,68,78	161
Nolan, Brian/Cohoes City School Dist	4	10
Nolan, Brian/Locust Valley Ctl School Dist	67	123
Nolan, James/Greenwich Central School Dist	67	248
Nolan, James/Odessa Montour Ctl Sch Dist	73,295	207
Nolan, Jocelyn/Ft Edward Union Free Sch Dist	77	247
Nolan, John/Franklin Central School Dist	5	49
Nolan, John/Smithtown Central Sch Dist	73,76,286	230
Nolan, Stephen/Greater Amsterdam School Dist	6,35	115
Nole, Robert/New Hartford Central Sch Dist	1	151
Nolett, De/Corinth Central School Dist	295	200
Nolin, Matthew/Cohoes City School Dist	67	10
Nolte, Gregg/Bethlehem Central School Dist	3	10
Noon, George/Newfane Central School Dist	3	147
Noonan, Claire/Victor Central School Dist	280	162
Noonan, Daniel/Beekmantown Ctl School Dist	3	43
Noonan, Paul/Patchogue-Medford Unified SD	3	227
Nooney, Clifford/Guilderland Central Sch Dist	3,91	11
Norasethaporn, Nicole/Genesee Valley Ctl School Dist	16	15
Norberg, Jillian/Afton Central School Dist	36	41
Norcross, Brian/Chazy Central Rural Sch Dist	6	44
Norris, Laura/Margaretville Central Sch Dist	8,11,69	49
North, Randy/Salem Central School Dist	297	248
Northway, Kathy/Southtown Teachers Center	15	67
Nortier, Thomas/Marion Central School Dist	3,91	250
Norton, Adam/Hilton Central School Dist	3	109
Norton, Brian/Farmingdale Union Free SD	10	119
Norton, Donna/North Syracuse Ctl Sch Dist	23,39,61,69,76,88,294	157
Norton, Nancy/Haldane Central School Dist	4	175
Norton, Raquel/Gilbertsville-Mt Upton SD	16	173
Notar, Donna/Schalmont Central School Dist	30	204
Nothel, James/Valley Stream Ctl High SD	3,91	130

School Year 2020-2021   800-333-8802   NY-T45

DISTRICT PERSONNEL INDEX

Market Data Retrieval

NAME/District	JOB FUNCTIONS	PAGE
Nothnagle, Aneli/Rochester City School Dist	68	110
Nothnagoe, Tammy/Caledonia-Mumford Ctl Sch Dist	9,69	102
Novak, Danielle/West Canada Valley Ctl SD	16,82	79
Novak, John/Letchworth Central School Dist	2,13,88,91	267
Nowacki, Peter/Windsor Central School Dist	67	30
Nowak, Anne/Sweet Home Central Sch Dist	36,83,90,93	63
Nowalk, Carolyn/Cincinnatus Ctl School Dist	68	47
Nowicki, Melissa/Bradford Central Sch Dist	61	207
Nowicki, Nancy/Holland Patent Ctl School Dist	8,11,15,16,69,296	150
Nowicki, Zigmund/Cornwall Central School Dist	68	163
Noyd, Heather/Windsor Central School Dist	31	30
Nugent, Kimberly/Averill Park Central Sch Dist	68	189
Nugent, Theodore/Coxsackie-Athens Central SD	5	75
Nunweiler, James/Gowanda Central School Dist	3	32
Nunziata, Janice/North Shore Central SD	7	126
Nunziata, Nancy/Long Beach City School Dist	5	124
Nuwer, Mike/Pembroke Ctl School Dist	3,91	74
Nyberg, Zachary/Lindenhurst Union Free SD	2	224
Nyc Chevrier, Carrie/Niskayuna Central School Dist	2,15	204

O

NAME/District	JOB FUNCTIONS	PAGE
O Connor, Teresa/Andover Central School Dist	90,752	14
O'Beirne, James/Merrick Union Free School Dist	3	125
O'Boyle, Shelly/Frewsburg Central School Dist	1	38
O'Brien, Amy/Chenango Forks Central SD	67	28
O'Brien, Ann/Granville Central School Dist	273	247
O'Brien, Ann/West Valley Ctl Sch Dist	2	33
O'Brien, Catherine/Rockland BOCES	7,15,27	199
O'Brien, Donna/Weedsport Ctl School Dist	4	35
O'Brien, Elizabeth/Babylon Union Free Sch Dist	67	216
O'Brien, Jean/Tarrytown Union Free Sch Dist	76	262
O'Brien, Jpseph/Community School District 20	1	89
O'Brien, Kevin/Sewanhaka Ctl High Sch Dist	2,3,15	129
O'Brien, Kimberly/De Ruyter Central School Dist	8	105
O'Brien, Kyle/O E S J Central School Dist	58	72
O'Brien, Nancy/Minerva Central School Dist	2	68
O'Brien, Neil/Port Byron Ctl School Dist	1	35
O'Brien, Patrick/Iroquois Central School Dist	30,83,88,270	61
O'Brien, Roni/Watervliet City School Dist	5	12
O'Brien, Scott, Dr/Rocky Point Union Free SD	1	228
O'Brien, Sean/Deer Park Union Free Sch Dist	58	220
O'Brien, Timothy/Oxford Academy Central SD	67	42
O'Callaghan, Kate/Islip Union Free School Dist	58,79	224
O'Connell, Deborah, Dr/Croton-Harmon Union Free SD	1	254
O'Connell, Greg/Stamford Central School Dist	6,35,85	50
O'Connell, Mary Anne/Westmoreland Central Sch Dist	58	153
O'Connell, Melanie/Lake Pleasant Central School Dist	4	76
O'Connell, Michael/Hicksville Union Free Sch Dist	42	122
O'Connell, Susan/North Greenbush Common SD	67	191
O'Connor, Charlene/Plattsburgh City School Dist	4	44
O'Connor, Danielle/Erie 2 Chautauqua-Catta BOCES	8,15	67
O'Connor, Gabriella/Rye City School Dist	2,5,15	261
O'Connor, John, Dr/Erie 2 Chautauqua-Catta BOCES	2,15	67
O'Connor, Kieran/East Syracuse Minoa Ctl SD	73,286,298	154
O'Connor, Paul/Otselic Valley Central SD	67	42
O'Connor, Shaun/Weedsport Ctl School Dist	1	35
O'Connor, Stacy/Brentwood Union Free Sch Dist	2,15	217
O'Connor, Tim/Spencerport Central Sch Dist	76,79,298	112
O'Day, Patricia/Southold Union Free Sch Dist	7	231
O'Doherty, Marie/Sachem Central School Dist	43	229
O'Donnell, Jackie/Southern Westchester BOCES	3,15,17	267
O'Donnell, Johnnah/Marlboro Central School Dist	6	242
O'Donnell, Timothy/Massapequa Union Free SD 23	3	125
O'Farrell, John/Half Hollow Hills Central SD	10,11,15,298	222
O'Geary, Melissa/Oceanside Union Free Sch Dist	69	127
O'Grady, Gary/Greenburgh Central School Dist	4	255
O'Hagan, Jaclyn/South Country Central Sch Dist	48	231
O'Hagan, Mary Jo/Baldwin Union Free School Dist	67	116
O'Hara, Kathleen/Westhampton Beach School Dist	2,4,15	233
O'Hara, Laurie/South Country Central Sch Dist	8	231
O'Hearn, Aydin/Cambridge Central School Dist	31,36,88	247
O'Hern, Jessica/Niagara-Wheatfield Ctl SD	58	148
O'Keefe, John/Sachem Central School Dist	2,15	229
O'Keeffe, Joan/Harrison Central School Dist	42	256
O'Leary, Bill/La Fayette Central School Dist	36	156
O'Leary, Dan/East Rochester Union Free SD	31,77	107
O'Mara, Rochell/Croton-Harmon Union Free SD	5	254
O'Meara, Mary, Dr/Plainview-Old Bethpage Ctl SD	1	127
O'Neil, Charles/Williamson Central School Dist	5	251
O'Neil, Jane/Odessa Montour Ctl Sch Dist	7,83,85	207
O'Neil, Mary/Greenburgh Central School Dist	2,15	255
O'Neill, Joseph/Duanesburg Central Sch Dist	73,76,286,295	203
O'Reilly, John/Margaretville Central Sch Dist	3	49
O'Reilly, Kevin/Brentwood Union Free Sch Dist	6,35,85	217
O'Rourke, Aileen/East Islip Union Free SD	58,79	220
O'Rourke, David, Dr/Erie 2 Chautauqua-Catta BOCES	1	67
O'Shea, Jane/Schenectady City School Dist	52,280	204
O'Shea, Lisa/Yorktown Central School Dist	8,11,15,286,298	264
O'Shea, Peggy/Cohoes City School Dist	8,11,57,83,88,273,288,298	10
Oag, Jeanne/Cassadaga Valley Ctl Sch Dist	67	36
Oaks, C Brian/South Lewis Central Sch Dist	6,7,35,83	101
Oates, Lindsy/New York City Dept of Ed	2	134
Oberst, Philip/East Irondequoit Ctl Sch Dist	15,68,74,78	107
Obrian, Genene/Schuylerville Central School Dist	31	201
Obrien, Matthew/Goshen Central School Dist	6	164
Ocque, Karen/La Fayette Central School Dist	58,79	156
Oddi, Perry/Evans-Brant Central Sch Dist	5	60
Oddo, Maria/Amherst Central School Dist	57	56
Odell, Clifford/Valley Stream Ctl High SD	15,68	130
Odell, Georgia/Downsville Central Sch Dist	7	49
Odell, Jaime/Putnam Central School Dist	2	248
Odom, Pamela/Syracuse City School Dist	10	158
Odonell, John/Schalmont Central School Dist	3	204
Odonell, Nicki/Morristown Ctl School Dist	58	211
Oehlbeck, Jared/Sherman Central School Dist	3	39
Oehlbeck, Kimberly/Sherman Central School Dist	2,296	39
Oehler-Marx, Linda, Dr/Monticello Central School Dist	8,15	237
Ofrias, Paulette/Southold Union Free Sch Dist	67	231
Ogilvie, Tracey/Amherst Central School Dist	4	56
Ogrady, Linda/West Seneca Central Sch Dist	5	64
Ogundipe, Idowu/Island Park Union Free SD	2	122
Ohagan, James/Three Village Central Sch Dist	3	232
Ohara, Dennis, Dr/Hauppauge Union Free Sch Dist	1	223
Ohlson, Jeremy/Perry Central School Dist	6	267
Olazagasti, Rafael/St Lawrence-Lewis BOCES	68	212
Oldenburg, Timothy, Dr/Tonawanda City School Dist	1	64
Oldfield, Edward/Romulus Ctl School Dist	3,91	208
Oldham, Micah/Ripley Central School Dist	12,59,69,73,286	39
Olds, Garrett/Central Valley School Dist	6,10	77
Olender, Jeffrey/Elmsford Union Free SD	68,73	255
Oleynek, Steve/Chatham Central School Dist	5,8	46
Oligny, Debra/Chatham Central School Dist	57	46
Olin, Troy/Gates Chili Central Sch Dist	73	108
Oliva, Christine/Tuxedo Union Free Sch Dist	36	167
Oliva, Helen/Harrison Central School Dist	286	256
Oliver, Angela/Clifton-Fine Central Sch Dist	71,97	209
Oliver, Beverly/La Fayette Central School Dist	274	156
Oliver, David/Auburn Enlarged City Sch Dist	270	34
Oliver, Gary/Vernon-Verona-Sherrill CSD	35,85	152
Oliver, Megan/Delaware Academy Ctrl SD Delhi	16	49
Oliveri, Carolyn/Wilson Central School Dist	2	149
Olivieri, Michael/Tuckahoe Union Free SD	73	262
Olkey, Angela/Greater Southern Tier BOCES	285	215
Olles, Lea/Albion Central School Dist	5	169

#		#		#		#		#		#	
1	Superintendent	16	Instructional Media Svcs	30	Adult Education	44	Science Sec	58	Special Education K-12	72	Summer School
2	Bus/Finance/Purchasing	17	Chief Operations Officer	31	Career/Sch-to-Work K-12	45	Math K-12	59	Special Education Elem	73	Instructional Tech
3	Buildings And Grounds	18	Chief Academic Officer	32	Career/Sch-to-Work Elem	46	Math Elem	60	Special Education Sec	74	Inservice Training
4	Food Service	19	Chief Financial Officer	33	Career/Sch-to-Work Sec	47	Math Sec	61	Foreign/World Lang K-12	75	Marketing/Distributive
5	Transportation	20	Art K-12	34	Early Childhood Ed	48	English/Lang Arts K-12	62	Foreign/World Lang Elem	76	Info Systems
6	Athletic	21	Art Elem	35	Health/Phys Education	49	English/Lang Arts Elem	63	Foreign/World Lang Sec	77	Psychological Assess
7	Health Services	22	Art Sec	36	Guidance Services K-12	50	English/Lang Arts Sec	64	Religious Education K-12	78	Affirmative Action
8	Curric/Instruct K-12	23	Music K-12	37	Guidance Services Elem	51	Reading K-12	65	Religious Education Elem	79	Student Personnel
9	Curric/Instruct Elem	24	Music Elem	38	Guidance Services Sec	52	Reading Elem	66	Religious Education Sec	80	Driver Ed/Safety
10	Curric/Instruct Sec	25	Music Sec	39	Social Studies K-12	53	Reading Sec	67	School Board President	81	Gifted/Talented
11	Federal Program	26	Business Education	40	Social Studies Elem	54	Remedial Reading K-12	68	Teacher Personnel	82	Video Services
12	Title I	27	Career & Tech Ed	41	Social Studies Sec	55	Remedial Reading Elem	69	Academic Assessment	83	Substance Abuse Prev
13	Title V	28	Technology Education	42	Science K-12	56	Remedial Reading Sec	70	Research/Development	84	Erate
15	Asst Superintendent	29	Family/Consumer Science	43	Science Elem	57	Bilingual/ELL	71	Public Information	85	AIDS Education

#		#	
88	Alternative/At Risk	277	Remedial Math K-12
89	Multi-Cultural Curriculum	280	Literacy Coach
90	Social Work	285	STEM
91	Safety/Security	286	Digital Learning
92	Magnet School	288	Common Core Standards
93	Parental Involvement	294	Accountability
95	Tech Prep Program	295	Network System
97	Chief Information Officer	296	Title II Programs
98	Chief Technology Officer	297	Webmaster
270	Character Education	298	Grant Writer/Ptnrships
271	Migrant Education	750	Chief Innovation Officer
273	Teacher Mentor	751	Chief of Staff
274	Before/After Sch	752	Social Emotional Learning
275	Response To Intervention		

New York School Directory — DISTRICT PERSONNEL INDEX

NAME/District	JOB FUNCTIONS	PAGE
Olsen, Jennifer/Farmingdale Union Free SD	16,81	119
Olson, Allen/Kingston City School Dist	2,15	242
Olson, Beth/Clymer Central School Dist	1	37
Olson, Sarah/Lake George Central Sch Dist	16	245
Olson, Steve/Southwestern Central Sch Dist	3	39
Omans, Christina/Canastota Central School Dist	4	104
Omans, Tena/Camden Central School Dist	4	150
Omeis, Lisa, Dr/Lindenhurst Union Free SD	15,79	224
Ondus, Paula/Gowanda Central School Dist	26	32
Oneil, Christopher/Whitesboro Ctl School Dist	12,38	153
Onorato, Mark/Valley Stream Union Free SD 24	16,73,286,295	131
Onufrey, Michael/Sewanhaka Ctl High Sch Dist	5	129
Onze, Jeffrey/East Rochester Union Free SD	6,7	107
Opera, Anthony/McGraw Central School Dist	67	48
Ordway, Patty/Johnsburg Central School Dist	11,296,298	245
Oreilly, Lisa/Westhill Central School Dist	67	160
Oreilly, William/Queensbury Union Free Sch Dist	91	246
Orestano-James, Lori/Monticello Central School Dist	67	237
Orilio, Ryan/Herkimer Ctl School Dist	73	78
Oris, Caryl, Dr/Sewanhaka Ctl High Sch Dist	77	129
Orlando, Kristina/Baldwin Union Free School Dist	5	116
Orman, Bob/Livonia Ctl School Dist	5	103
Orman, Ed/York Central School Dist	6,35	103
Ormandy, Gerard/Downsville Central Sch Dist	5	49
Ormiston, William/Washingtonville Central SD	41,50	167
Orologio, Lori/Churchville Chili Ctl Sch Dist	1	107
Orozco, Felipe/Port Chester Rye Union Free SD	57	261
Orr, James/Webutuck Ctl School Dist	57,271	54
Orr, Kristine/South Glens Falls Ctl Sch Dist	1,11	202
Orr, Scout/Binghamton City School Dist	42	27
Orser, Cassandra/Beacon City School Dist	34	51
Ortiz-Rivera, Wanda/Brentwood Union Free Sch Dist	15,57	217
Ortiz, Derek/Bath Central School Dist	5	213
Ortiz, Mayra/Rochester City School Dist	57	110
Ortiz, Michele/Levittown Union Free School Dist	8,69	123
Orvis, Greg/Lyme Central School Dist	4	81
Osadciw, Christine/East Irondequoit Ctl Sch Dist	73,97,286	107
Osborne-Coy, Jennifer/Erie 2 Chautauqua-Catta BOCES	71	67
Osborne, Matt/Unadilla Valley Ctl Sch Dist	6	43
Osborne, Scott/Chazy Central Rural Sch Dist	1	44
Oset, Marikate/Eldred Central School Dist	273	236
Osgood, Mary/Bemus Point Ctl School Dist	88	36
Oshea, Jane/Walton Central School Dist	8,286,288	50
Osmond, Laurie/Onteora Central School Dist	67	243
Ostempowski, Mark/Cheektowaga-Sloan UFSD	6	59
Ostrander, Erin/Genesee Valley Ctl School Dist	2	15
Ostroff, Janna/Oyster Bay East Norwich Ctl SD	73,285	127
Ostrowski, Lisa/North Colonie Central SD	4	11
Osur, Lisa/Holley Central School Dist	16	169
Ottaway, Heidi/Cassadaga Valley Ctl Sch Dist	4	36
Ottman, William/Webster Central School Dist	27,42,73,285	112
Otto, Ron/Caledonia-Mumford Ctl Sch Dist	5	102
Otty, Carrie/Hudson City School Dist	67	46
Ouimet, Micheal/Averill Park Central Sch Dist	15,76,78	189
Outtrim, Richard/Greenville Central School Dist	3	75
Ouwendijk, Eva/Valley Stream Ctl High SD	16,82	130
Ovanessian, Jessica/Tuckahoe Common School Dist	286	232
Overbaugh, Paul/New York State Dept Education	5	1
Overhiser, Ann/Dundee Ctl School Dist	4	268
Overhiser, Ann/Odessa Montour Ctl School Dist	4	207
Overholt, Kristin/Clarence Central School Dist	8,11,15,27,31,273,296,298	59
Owen, Chad/Royalton Hartland Central SD	67	148
Owen, John/Moravia Central School Dist	73,76	35
Owens, Cecelie/Buffalo Public Schools	6,15,35	56
Owens, Robin/Portville Central School Dist	2	32
Owens, Tiffany/Horseheads Ctl School Dist	285	40
Oyer, Michael/Avoca Central School Dist	3	213
Oyoung, Sarah/South Jefferson Central SD	58,79	81
Ozog, Rosanne/Poland Central School Dist	7,83	78

P

NAME/District	JOB FUNCTIONS	PAGE
Pacatte, Kelly/Middleburgh Ctl School Dist	38	206
Pacatte, Ryan/Avon Central School Dist	1	102
Paccia, James/Tully Central School Dist	16,82	159
Pacella, Michael/Pine Bush Central School Dist	2,5,15	166
Pacer, Jeff/West Seneca Central Sch Dist	16,82	64
Pacholk, Eugene/Mattituck-Cutchogue UFSD	3	225
Pacht, Lisa/Rondout Valley Ctl Sch Dist	8,11,15,69,288	243
Paci, Valter/East Ramapo Central School Dist	2,15	196
Pacille, Alferd/Pocantico Hills Ctl Sch Dist	67	260
Pacos, Daniel/Evans-Brant Central Sch Dist	2,12,15,91	60
Padalino, Paul, Dr/Kingston City School Dist	1	242
Padden, Rita/Farmingdale Union Free SD	23,61	119
Paddock, Nathan/Perry Central School Dist	67	267
Padilla, Maddie/Bay Shore Union Free Sch Dist	39	217
Padilla, Roberto, Dr/Newburgh Enlarged City SD	1	165
Padrone, Nancy/Babylon Union Free Sch Dist	4	216
Paez, Kristina/Saugerties Central School Dist	38	243
Pagano, Karen/Beacon City School Dist	4	51
Pagano, Mark/Hampton Bays Union Free SD	11,15,58,296	222
Paige, Chris/Canandaigua City School Dist	58	161
Pain, Jeremy/Gilbertsville-Mt Upton SD	67	173
Paine, John/Tarrytown Union Free Sch Dist	67	262
Paine, Valerie, Dr/Greece Central School Dist	9,11,15	108
Painter, Melanie/Bethlehem Central School Dist	20	10
Paladino, Michael/Rush Henrietta Central SD	91	112
Palermo, Lori/Hilton Central School Dist	5	109
Palermo, Melissa/Oysterponds Union Free SD	2	227
Palermo, Scott/Sullivan BOCES	27,31	238
Palios, Mark/Middle Country Ctl School Dist	36	225
Paliotti, Megan/North Rose Wolcott Central SD	8,15,16,70,79,274	250
Palkovic, Matthew/Chazy Central Rural Sch Dist	73	44
Palladino, Kathie/Phoenix Central School Dist	36,58,79,271	172
Pallas, Joseph/Tuckahoe Common School Dist	6,35	232
Pallischeck, Anne/Onc BOCES	73	51
Pallotta, Joseph/Lynbrook Union Free Sch Dist	20,23	124
Palma, Dominick, Dr/Merrick Union Free School Dist	1	125
Palmateer, Jake/Schoharie Central SD	71,297	206
Palmer, Ann/Brentwood Union Free Sch Dist	9,15	217
Palmer, Brian/Greece Central School Dist	295	108
Palmer, Joe/New York Mills Union Free SD	6	151
Palmer, Joseph/Schenectady City School Dist	294	204
Palmer, Karen/Wayne Central School Dist	36	251
Palmer, Kate/Alfred Almond Ctl School Dist	58	13
Palmer, Leola/Roosevelt Union Free Sch Dist	5	128
Palmer, Lisa/WSWHE BOCES	74	249
Palmer, Melissa/Vernon-Verona-Sherrill CSD	67	152
Palmer, Paul/Greece Central School Dist	2	108
Palmer, Thomas, Dr/Peru Central School Dist	1	44
Palmer, Vicki/Fonda Fultonville Central SD	4	115
Palmer, Yvonne/Poughkeepsie City School Dist	79	53
Palmetier, Maryann/Afton Central School Dist	67	41
Palmieri, Jim/Germantown Central School Dist	3	46
Palmore, Hellse/Elmont Union Free School Dist	34,59,79	118
Palonetti, Steve/Archdiocese of New York Ed Off	4	142
Palotti, Jeremy/Hornell City School Dist	1	214
Paluseo, Emily/Bellmore-Merrick Ctl High SD	60,79	117
Pampel, Lynne/Newburgh Enlarged City SD	79	166
Pamper, Barb/Dansville Ctl School Dist	10,73,286	102
Panariello, Robert/Bay Shore Union Free Sch Dist	6,35	217
Panaro, Lisa/White Plains City School Dist	57,61	263
Pane, Jamie/Whitney Point Central Sch Dist	73,98	30
Panebianco, Cathy/Jamestown City School Dist	71	38
Panebianco, John/Jamestown City School Dist	68	38
Panella, Anthony/Amherst Central School Dist	1	56
Pangallo, Michael/Lyons Central School Dist	2,5,15	249
Panico, Eileen/Connetquot Central School Dist	67	219
Panoni, Andrea/Stockbridge Valley Central SD	295,752	106
Pantaleone, Nicholas/Port Jervis City School Dist	8,15,288,296	166
Pantginis, Kristina/Mamaroneck Union Free Sch Dist	16	257
Panton, Nicole/Greater Johnstown Sch Dist	8,71,74	71
Panzer, Adam/Wappingers Central Sch Dist	27,44,47	54
Paolini, Kristen/Spencerport Central Sch Dist	8	112
Paolino, Shaun/Lansingburgh Central Sch Dist	57,58	190
Papa, Joe/Garden City School Dist	72	120
Papalia, Lisa/North Shore Central SD	4	126
Papke, Edward/Warsaw Central School Dist	3	267
Papp, Joe/Roscoe Central School Dist	4	237
Pappalardi, Raymond/Scarsdale Union Free Sch Dist	6,35	261
Paragi, Cristi/Herkimer Ctl School Dist	6	77
Parahus, Kim/Hewlett Woodmere Union Free SD	3	121

School Year 2020-2021   800-333-8802   NY-T47

DISTRICT PERSONNEL INDEX

Market Data Retrieval

NAME/District	JOB FUNCTIONS	PAGE
Parchesky, Brian/Berkshire Union Free Sch Dist	67	45
Pardee, Katie/Andes Central School Dist	6	48
Parent, Danae/Frontier Ctl School Dist	274	60
Parente, Carmella/Schenectady City School Dist	29,39,61	204
Parete, Nichole/Wallkill Central School Dist	11	243
Paris, Brian/Alexander Ctl School Dist	67	73
Parisi, Angela/Tuckahoe Common School Dist	97	232
Parker-Smith, Jennifer/Moravia Central School Dist	4	34
Parker, Christopher/Jasper Troupsburg Central SD	88	215
Parker, Dan/Tompkins-Seneca-Tioga BOCES	73	241
Parker, Jonathan/Warrensburg Central Sch Dist	3	246
Parker, Leshawn/Kingston City School Dist	91	242
Parker, Lisa/Hinsdale Central School Dist	4	32
Parker, Steve/Sauquoit Valley Central SD	3	152
Parker, Teresia/Minisink Valley Central SD	74	165
Parker, Timothy/Lockport City School Dist	3	147
Parker, Turina/WSWHE BOCES	79	249
Parliament, Jennifer/Beekmantown Ctl School Dist	2	43
Parliament, Nicole/La Fargeville Central Sch Dist	2	80
Parmalee, Matt/Hinsdale Central School Dist	3	32
Parmarter, Ray/Candor Central School Dist	67	238
Parmenter, Stacy/Fillmore Central School Dist	7	14
Parobeck, Michael/General Brown Ctl School Dist	71,73,76,97,295,297	80
Parow, Jeffrey/Mount Markham Central Sch Dist	38	78
Parra, Elizabeth/Brocton Central School Dist	12	36
Parslow, Joseph/Lake Pleasant Central Sch Dist	35	76
Parslow, Sharon/Wells Central School Dist	8,31,69,88,270,285	77
Parsons, David/Tompkins-Seneca-Tioga BOCES	15	241
Parsons, Dawn/Monticello Central School Dist	4	237
Parsons, Jan/Frewsburg Central School Dist	57,61	38
Parsons, Lisa/South Jefferson Central SD	8,15	81
Partridge, James/Hunter Tannersville Ctl SD	3	76
Parulski, Roger/Dansville Ctl School Dist	2	102
Pascale, Kathleen/Webutuck Ctl School Dist	6	54
Pascarella, Christina, Dr/Byron-Bergen Ctl School Dist	77	73
Pascuale, Matt/Webutuck Ctl School Dist	6,35	54
Pascucci, Monica/Portville Central School Dist	69,83,85,88	32
Pascuzzi, Andrea/Spencerport Central Sch Dist	12,58,77	112
Paser, Patricia/Schenectady City School Dist	15	204
Paske, Jeffrey/Johnson City Central School Dist	6,7	28
Passai, Gaurav/Manhasset Union Free Sch Dist	8,88	124
Passamonte, Mark/Shoreham-Wading River Ctl SD	6,35	230
Passeggiata, Michelle/Copiague Union Free Sch Dist	57	220
Passero, Mary/Herricks Union Free Sch Dist	20	121
Passi, Gaurav, Dr/Manhasset Union Free Sch Dist	8,15,18	124
Passiglia, Judi/Mattituck-Cutchogue UFSD	5	225
Pastuf, Amy/St Lawrence-Lewis BOCES	2	212
Patchen, Georgia/Valley Central School Dist	58	167
Pate, Miatheresa/Community School District 23	1	92
Pate, Tammy, Dr/Community School District 28	1	181
Patel, Kaushika/Rockland BOCES	295	199
Patenaude, Caitlyn/Lake Placid Ctl School Dist	16,82	67
Paternostro, Peter/Amityville Union Free Sch Dist	58,79	216
Pathak, Amit/West Islip School Dist	76,295	233
Patnode, Steven/Chazy Central Rural Sch Dist	16,82	44
Patrick, Andrew/Scarsdale Union Free Sch Dist	15,68	261
Patrick, Joanne/Sackets Harbor Ctl School Dist	4	81
Patrone, Nick/Olean City School Dist	298	32
Patrzalek, Brenda/Williamson Central School Dist	4	251
Patsch, Lucas/Highland Falls-Ft Montgmry SD	273	164
Patsos, Christina/Remsenburg-Speonk UFSD	73,76	228
Patt, David/Rush Henrietta Central SD	58	112
Patterson, Ian/Peru Central School Dist	16,82	44
Patti, Danielle/Frewsburg Central School Dist	8,11,15,288	38
Patton, Michael, Dr/Saratoga Springs City Sch Dist	1	201
Paul, Rooney/North Rockland Central SD	3	197
Pauley, Rebecca/Mohonasen Central Sch Dist	36	204
Paulsen, Barbara/Troy City School Dsitrict	76	191
Pavek, Eugenia/Orange-Ulster BOCES	67	168
Pavlick, Angela/Campbell-Savona Ctl Sch Dist	57,58,77,79,270,271,275	213
Pavlock, Mike/Scio Central School Dist	73	15
Pavlovich, Michael/Sidney Central School Dist	2	50
Pavlus, Paul/Wheelerville Union Free SD	5	72
Pawlaczyk, Alrlene/Medina Central School Dist	67	169
Pawloski, Tina/Whitesboro Ctl School Dist	57,58	153
Payne, Brianne/Canaseraga Central Sch Dist	16	14
Payne, Chrisatine/Syosset Central School Dist	73,76	129
Payne, Christopher/Panama Central School Dist	6	38
Payne, Pat/Carmel Central School Dist	5	175
Payne, Scott/West Babylon Union Free SD	8,15	232
Pazzaglia, Mirella/Dolgeville Central School Dist	38,79	77
Peake, Mary Joe/Phelps-Clifton Springs Ctl SD	68	162
Pearl, Lisa/Fort Ann Central School Dist	7	247
Pearsall, Cruz/Wyandanch Union Free Sch Dist	91	234
Pearsall, Wade/Friendship Central Sch Dist	36,69,83,88	15
Pearson, Marijo, Dr/Monroe 2 Orleans BOCES	8,15,74	115
Pease, Adam/Mahopac Ctl School Dist	11,85,298	176
Pease, Adam, Dr/Chappaqua Central School Dist	8,13,15,288,296	253
Pease, Marcia/Rochester City School Dist	58	110
Peavey, Colleen/Brookfield Central School Dist	16,73,76,295	104
Peavey, Emily/Wellsville Central Sch Dist	11,91	15
Peck, Benjamin/Saratoga Springs City Sch Dist	73	201
Peck, Erin/Prattsburgh Central Sch Dist	8	215
Peck, Lloyd, Dr/Chenango Forks Central SD	1	28
Peck, Mike/Vernon-Verona-Sherrill CSD	5	152
Peconie, Anthony/Scotia Glenville Ctl Sch Dist	60,72	205
Pecor, Carrie/Rochester City School Dist	70	110
Pecora, Adele, Dr/Seaford Union Free SD	1	129
Pede, David/Johnsburg Central School Dist	285	245
Pedersen, Ann, Dr/Lawrence Union Free Sch Dist	1	123
Pedisich, Cheryl/Three Village Central Sch Dist	1	232
Peiffer, James/Penfield Central School Dist	8,15	109
Pekar, Andrea/Amityville Union Free Sch Dist	8,12,15,296,298	216
Pelan, Micheal/Malverne Union Free Sch Dist	6,35	124
Pelech, Stanley/Farmingdale Union Free SD	27	119
Pellam, Heather/Beaver River Central Sch Dist	4	101
Pellati, Elisa/West Islip School Dist	2,11,15	233
Pellerin, Heidi/Northeastern Clinton Ctl SD	83	44
Pellettieri, Christopher/Rockville Ctr Union Free SD	8,11,69,74,275,277,288,298	128
Pellicane, Andrea/Pelham Union Free School Dist	83,285	260
Pelliccio, Michael/Mount Vernon City School Dist	3,91	258
Pelton, Jim/South Jefferson Central SD	88,273	81
Pelton, Paul/West Genesee Ctl School Dist	2,4,11,15,298	159
Pena, Christian/Tuckahoe Common School Dist	13,73,295	232
Pena, Maritza/Spencer Van Etten Central SD	57	238
Pendergast, Lawrence/New York City Dept of Ed	8,74	134
Penhollow, Stephen/Falconer Central School Dist	1,11,73	37
Penna, Lisa/Elba Central School Dist	2	73
Penrose, Brian/Long Lake Central School Dist	67	76
Pepe, Chris/Hoosic Valley Central Sch Dist	67	190
Pepey, Michele/East Moriches Union Free SD	59,296,298	221
Pepper, Scott/White Plains City School Dist	15,68	263
Perdomo, Emma/Freeport Public School Dist	36	119
Perez-Pherett, Abel/Rochester City School Dist	57,61	110
Perez, Angel/Hempstead Union Free SD	16,20,23	121
Perez, Jason/Cleveland Hill Union Free SD	6	59
Perez, Javier/Saranac Central School Dist	1	45
Perez, Ralph/Washingtonville Central SD	5	167
Perini, Leonora/Ardsley Union Free School Dist	68	252
Perkins, Alex/George Junior Republic UFSD	73,274	240
Perkins, Susan/St Regis Falls Ctl Sch Dist	2	70
Perkowski, Lisa/Port Jervis City School Dist	16	166
Perkowski, Melissa/Honeoye Central School Dist	8	161
Perna, J Philip/Montauk Union Free School Dist	11,88	226

#		#		#		#		#		#	
1	Superintendent	16	Instructional Media Svcs	30	Adult Education	44	Science Sec	58	Special Education K-12	72	Summer School
2	Bus/Finance/Purchasing	17	Chief Operations Officer	31	Career/Sch-to-Work K-12	45	Math K-12	59	Special Education Elem	73	Instructional Tech
3	Buildings And Grounds	18	Chief Academic Officer	32	Career/Sch-to-Work Elem	46	Math Elem	60	Special Education Sec	74	Inservice Training
4	Food Service	19	Chief Financial Officer	33	Career/Sch-to-Work Sec	47	Math Sec	61	Foreign/World Lang K-12	75	Marketing/Distributive
5	Transportation	20	Art K-12	34	Early Childhood Ed	48	English/Lang Arts K-12	62	Foreign/World Lang Elem	76	Info Systems
6	Athletic	21	Art Elem	35	Health/Phys Education	49	English/Lang Arts Elem	63	Foreign/World Lang Sec	77	Psychological Assess
7	Health Services	22	Art Sec	36	Guidance Services K-12	50	English/Lang Arts Sec	64	Religious Education K-12	78	Affirmative Action
8	Curric/Instruct K-12	23	Music K-12	37	Guidance Services Elem	51	Reading K-12	65	Religious Education Elem	79	Student Personnel
9	Curric/Instruct Elem	24	Music Elem	38	Guidance Services Sec	52	Reading Elem	66	Religious Education Sec	80	Driver Ed/Safety
10	Curric/Instruct Sec	25	Music Sec	39	Social Studies K-12	53	Reading Sec	67	School Board President	81	Gifted/Talented
11	Federal Program	26	Business Education	40	Social Studies Elem	54	Remedial Reading K-12	68	Teacher Personnel	82	Video Services
12	Title I	27	Career & Tech Ed	41	Social Studies Sec	55	Remedial Reading Elem	69	Academic Assessment	83	Substance Abuse Prev
13	Title V	28	Technology Education	42	Science K-12	56	Remedial Reading Sec	70	Research/Development	84	Erate
15	Asst Superintendent	29	Family/Consumer Science	43	Science Elem	57	Bilingual/ELL	71	Public Information	85	AIDS Education

#		#	
88	Alternative/At Risk	277	Remedial Math K-12
89	Multi-Cultural Curriculum	280	Literacy Coach
90	Social Work	285	STEM
91	Safety/Security	286	Digital Learning
92	Magnet School	288	Common Core Standards
93	Parental Involvement	294	Accountability
95	Tech Prep Program	295	Network System
97	Chief Innovation Officer	296	Title II Programs
98	Chief Technology Officer	297	Webmaster
270	Character Education	298	Grant Writer/Ptnrships
271	Migrant Education	750	Chief Innovation Officer
273	Teacher Mentor	751	Chief of Staff
274	Before/After Sch	752	Social Emotional Learning
275	Response To Intervention		

NY-T48

New York School Directory — DISTRICT PERSONNEL INDEX

NAME/District	JOB FUNCTIONS	PAGE
Perna, J Philip/Montauk Union Free School Dist	1,11	226
Pernesky, Julie/Letchworth Central School Dist	8,12,57,69,74,288,296,298	267
Pero, Michael/Pittsford Central Sch Dist	1,11	110
Perrault, Rebecca/Penn Yan Ctl School Dist	76,298	268
Perrello, Mary/Greece Central School Dist	7	108
Perrotto, Michaela/Gates Chili Central Sch Dist	12,15,68	108
Perry, Amy/Alfred Almond Ctl School Dist	16,82	13
Perry, Benjamin/Saranac Central School Dist	5	45
Perry, Brad/Sherburne Earlville Central SD	6	42
Perry, David/Liverpool Ctl School Dist	20,25	156
Perry, David, Dr/South Colonie Central Sch Dist	1	12
Perry, Linda/Corning-Painted Post Area SD	8,11,73,285,286,288	214
Perry, Linda/Greater Southern Tier BOCES	69,70	215
Perry, Matthew/Alexander Ctl School Dist	73,286,295	73
Persad, Gail/Tarrytown Union Free Sch Dist	20	262
Persico, Carmelina/West Seneca Central Sch Dist	8,15	64
Persons, Velvette/Clymer Central School Dist	280	37
Pesiri, Christina/Island Trees Union Free SD	16	122
Peters Haduke, Jeff/Madison Central School Dist	5	105
Peters, Amy/Lake Pleasant Central Sch Dist	280	76
Peters, Kisun/Dunkirk City School Dist	34,752	37
Petersen, Mark/Cassadaga Valley Ctl Sch Dist	6,35	36
Peterson, Al/William Floyd School Dist	79	233
Peterson, Karen/Bronxville Union Free SD	6	253
Peterson, Kristen/Amagansett Union Free Sch Dist	67	216
Peterson, Laura/Hewlett Woodmere Union Free SD	58	121
Peterson, Laura/Valley Stream Union Free SD 24	58,77,79,88,270,275	131
Peterson, Mark/Berne-Knox-Westerlo Central SD	296	10
Peterson, Nicole/Middle Country Ctl School Dist	30	225
Peterson, Pamela/Newburgh Enlarged City SD	93	166
Peterson, Phil/Byram Hills Central Sch Dist	5	253
Peterson, Scott/Falconer Central School Dist	5	37
Petix, Elsa/Mahopac Ctl School Dist	30	176
Petlin, Joel/Kiryas Joel Union Free SD	1	164
Petramale, Carol/Saugerties Central School Dist	3,5	243
Petrassi, Amy/Greenwood Lake Union Free SD	11,59,79	164
Petrell, Peggy/Orchard Park Central Sch Dist	4	63
Petrell, William/Delaware Academy Ctrl SD Delhi	58	49
Petrella, Maria/Rochester City School Dist	58	110
Petricek, Ursula/Wallkill Central School Dist	7	243
Petrie, Ron/Miller Place Union Free SD	6,58,85	226
Petrilak, Denis/Chester Union Free School Dist	1	163
Petrin, Matthew/Albany City School Dist	68	9
Petro-Durgen, Charlene/Boquet Valley Central Sch Dist	2	67
Petrosillo, Susan/Jamesville-DeWitt Central SD	67	155
Petrus, Jeff/Orchard Park Central Sch Dist	2,15	63
Pettenski, Jeffrey/Gates Chili Central Sch Dist	67	108
Pettifer, Suzanne/Greece Central School Dist	51,275	108
Pettit, Erica/Belleville Henderson Sch Dist	58	79
Pettograsso, Chris/Lansing Central School Dist	1	240
Petty, Lou/Hawthorne Cedar Knolls UFSD	3	256
Pettys, Reed/Perry Central School Dist	2,5,71,275	267
Pezzementi, Vincent/Salamanca City Central SD	71	33
Pfaffe, Linda/Hicksville Union Free Sch Dist	26,45	122
Pfau, Kathleen/Bolton Central School Dist	67	244
Pfeifer, Cindy/Honeoye Falls Lima Sch Dist	2	109
Pfister, Tom/Frankfort-Schuyler Ctl SD	4	77
Pfisterer, Thomas/Herkimer Ctl School Dist	4	77
Pfisterer, Tom/Oneida-Herkimer-Mad BOCES	4	154
Pfisterer, Tom/Westmoreland Central Sch Dist	4	153
Pfleegor, Matthew/Avoca Central School Dist	73	213
Phaneuf, Joseph/Town of Webb Union Free SD	67	78
Phelan, Diane/Diocese of Brooklyn Ed Office	15,69,77,79	94
Phelan, Patrick/Niagara-Wheatfield Ctl SD	68	148
Phelps, Melissa/Gananda Central School Dist	58	249
Pherio, Mike/North Warren Central Sch Dist	27,31,36,83,88	246
Philips, Bryan/Pulaski Central School Dist	5	172
Philips, Lawrence/Central Islip Union Free SD	6,7	218
Phillips, Barbara/Windsor Central School Dist	76,294	30
Phillips, Brian/Valley Stream Union Free SD 30	2,5,15	131
Phillips, Chelsea/Chatham Central School Dist	16	46
Phillips, Dale/Sackets Harbor Ctl School Dist	67	81
Phillips, Darren/Southampton Union Free SD	6,83,85	231
Phillips, Eric/North Colonie Central SD	27,95	11
Phillips, Erin/Central Square Central SD	9	170
Phillips, Jamie/Lancaster Central Sch Dist	2,15	62
Phillips, Janice/Gates Chili Central Sch Dist	4	108
Phillips, Janice/Roscoe Central School Dist	9,11,16,73,273,288,296	237
Phillips, Jeffery/Brockport Ctl School Dist	91	106
Phillips, Joseph/Cato Meridian Central Sch Dist	3	34
Phillips, Kim/Hilton Central School Dist	5	109
Phillips, Rebecca/Harrisville Central Sch Dist	2	101
Phillips, Shane/Lyndonville Central Sch Dist	85	169
Phillips, Shelly/Cheektowaga Maryvale UFSD	72	59
Philo, Heather/Lake Pleasant Central Sch Dist	1,11,288	76
Philpott, Kristin/Hoosick Falls Central Sch Dist	58	190
Phinney, Shawn/Allegany-Limestone Ctl SD	5	31
Piacente, Ken/Iroquois Central School Dist	16,73,82,295	61
Piacentini, Dominic/Rush Henrietta Central SD	74	112
Piatti, Thomas/Richfield Springs Central SD	1	174
Piazza, Paul/Haldane Central School Dist	91	176
Picardo, Nick/Kendall Central School Dist	6,58	169
Piccirillo, Alex/Sachem Central School Dist	67	229
Pickard, D/Rochester City School Dist	20,23	110
Pickering, Cindy/Chateaugay Central School Dist	16,82	69
Picolla, James/Herkimer BOCES	3,15,91	79
Picunas, Angela/Thousand Islands Central SD	2,11,271	81
Pidala, Caroline/Millbrook Ctl School Dist	8,11,38,58,79,288,296	52
Piedici, Katherine/Naples Central School Dist	58,79	162
Piedmonte, Valerie, Dr/Hastings on Hudson Union FR SD	1	256
Piejko, Mary Beth/Holland Patent Ctl School Dist	31,271	150
Pierce, Earl/Alfred Almond Ctl School Dist	67	13
Pierce, John/Central Square Central SD	5	170
Pierce, Paul/Middleburgh Ctl School Dist	6	206
Pierce, William/Corning-Painted Post Area SD	3	214
Pierre, Kimberlee, Dr/Uniondale Union Free Sch Dist	11,69,77,81,296	130
Pietrantoni, Christy/South Kortright Ctl SD	4	50
Pietrantonio, Chris/Schenectady City School Dist	73	204
Pietrowski, Tim/Royalton Hartland Central SD	3	148
Pignataro, Victor/Greenwood Lake Union Free SD	297	164
Pike, Cory/Owen D Young Central Sch Dist	6,69	78
Pilc, Cindy/Pavilion Ctl School Dist	73,286	74
Pilla, Kimberly/Onteora Central School Dist	6	243
Pilla, William/South Orangetown Central SD	6,35	197
Pillitteri, Frank/East Islip Union Free SD	45,285	220
Pillittier, Kerri/Bethpage Union Free Sch Dist	30	117
Pillittieri, Carl/Jamestown City School Dist	3,5,91	38
Pinckney, John/Cornwall Central School Dist	7,91	163
Pincoski, Richard/Salamanca City Central SD	3	33
Pine, Doug/Gowanda Central School Dist	73,76,95,286	32
Piniero, Victor/Southern Westchester BOCES	73,76,295	267
Pinker, Myra/Frontier Ctl School Dist	15,68	60
Pino, Ruth/Saranac Lake Central Sch Dist	4	70
Piotrowski, Bryan/Massapequa Union Free SD 23	11,73,91,286,298	125
Piper, Amy/Fredonia Central School Dist	275	38
Piper, Meghan/Liverpool Ctl School Dist	71	156
Piropato, John/Massapequa Union Free SD 23	6,7,35,83,85	125
Pirozzolo, Jeffrey/Auburn Enlarged City Sch Dist	1	34
Pirozzolo, Susan/Horseheads Ctl School Dist	71	40
Pirozzolo, Tracey/Port Byron Ctl School Dist	36	35
Pirro, Donna/Mt Pleasant Ctl School Dist	6	258
Pirro, Jacqueline/Hauppauge Union Free Sch Dist	2,3,15	223
Pisani, Rebecca/Holland Patent Ctl School Dist	74,273	150
Piscatelli, Gail/East Ramapo Central Sch Dist	71,97	196
Pisegna, Jennifer/Westhill Central School Dist	88	160
Piskin, Gina/Bellmore-Merrick Ctl High SD	67	117
Pitcher, Danielle/Arlington Central School Dist	73	51
Pitcher, David/Tompkins-Seneca-Tioga BOCES	3,5,7,91	241
Piteo, Dawn/Roslyn School Dist	4	129
Pizzo, Patrick/East Meadow Union Free SD	2,5,15	118
Pizzuto, Alicia/North Syracuse Ctl Sch Dist	8,45,277	157
Place, Mark/Milford Central School Dist	1	173
Placella, Danelle/Katonah-Lewisboro Sch Dist	2,4	257
Placito, Jen/Spencerport Central Sch Dist	6,7,35	112
Plasse, Carrie/Oswego City School Dist	9,11,34,294,296,298	171
Platt, Roger, Dr/New York City Dept of Ed	7	134
Pliss, Mike/South Seneca Ctl Sch Dist	73	208
Ploetz, Erich/Ellicottville Central Sch Dist	270	31
Plotze, Tim/West Valley Ctl Sch Dist	67	33
Plows, James/Brookfield Central School Dist	1,83	104
Pluta, Terry/Cheektowaga Maryvale UFSD	4	59
Pochintesta, Marco/Pearl River School Dist	1	197

DISTRICT PERSONNEL INDEX

Market Data Retrieval

NAME/District	JOB FUNCTIONS	PAGE
Pochkar, Gary/Worcester Ctl School Dist	2	174
Pockett, Michael/Ticonderoga Central Sch Dist	73	68
Pockett, Mike/Schroon Lake Ctl School Dist	73	68
Podkulski, Davis/Frontier Ctl School Dist	67	60
Podvesker, Lori/New York City Dept of Ed	67	134
Poirier, Danielle/Guilderland Central Sch Dist	5	11
Poirier, Rhonda/Malone Central School Dist	2	69
Poirier, Rosalyn/Malone Central School Dist	36	69
Polachak, Harry/Kiryas Joel Union Free SD	67	164
Polakiewicz, Jerome/East Aurora Union Free SD	11,27,57,58,79,83,88,275	60
Poland, Karen, Dr/Monroe 2 Orleans BOCES	27,31	115
Polansky, James/Huntington Union Free Sch Dist	1	223
Polchinski, Lina/Greenwood Lake Union Free SD	9	164
Poledro, Mallory/Sewanhaka Ctl High Sch Dist	60	129
Poley, Keri/Tri-Valley Central School Dist	67	237
Polikowski, Sandra/Greater Amsterdam School Dist	57,69,73,277,280,286,294,295	115
Polino, Robert/Cleveland Hill Union Free SD	67	59
Polit, Virginia/Hicksville Union Free Sch Dist	4	122
Polizzi, Christoph/Nanuet Union Free School Dist	9,70,285	196
Polizzi, Dave/Elmont Union Free School Dist	3	118
Polka, Kathy/Royalton Hartland Central SD	2	148
Pollack, Monica/Hartford Central School Dist	16	248
Pollaro, Robert/North Colonie Central SD	41	11
Pollera, Anthony/Three Village Central Sch Dist	23	232
Pollitt, Janet/North Bellmore Union Free SD	9,11,15,57,69,296,298	126
Pollok, Robert/Elmsford Union Free SD	6	255
Polney, Carole/Connetquot Central School Dist	16,28,73,76,84,286	219
Polowy, Jen/Silver Creek Central School Dist	4	39
Polunci, Kevin/Hudson Falls Central Sch Dist	2,68	248
Polychronakos, Jennifer, Dr/Brookhaven Comsewogue Unif SD	8,12	218
Pomeroy, Lisa/Newark Valley Central Sch Dist	36	238
Pomerville, Patrick/Waterford Halfmoon School Dist	1	203
Poniktera, Richard/South Lewis Central Sch Dist	3	101
Poole, Gerard/Shoreham-Wading River Ctl SD	1	230
Poore, David/Altmar-Parish-Williamstown SD	3	170
Popkin, James/Great Neck Public Schools	5	120
Popkin, Stacey/Bethpage Union Free Sch Dist	5	117
Popky, Stephanie/Brookhaven Comsewogue Unif SD	3	218
Popp, Barbara/Avon Central School Dist	4	102
Popp, Barbara/Mt Morris Central School Dist	4	103
Popp, Jeffrey/Red Hook Central School Dist	5	53
Poppe, Christina/Connetquot Central School Dist	48	219
Poprilo, Andre/Baldwin Union Free School Dist	20,23	116
Poprilo, April/South Huntington Union Free SD	7	231
Porcella, Frank/Greece Central School Dist	295	108
Porras, Robert/Greenwood Lake Union Free SD	3,91	164
Porrazzo, Peter/Plainedge Union Free Sch Dist	2,15	127
Porter, Douglas/Ravena Coeymans Selkirk Ctl SD	4	11
Porter, Randy/South Kortright Ctl SD	5	50
Porter, Rose/Holley Central School Dist	7	169
Porter, Shane/Boquet Valley Central Sch Dist	73	67
Porter, William/Canton Central School Dist	6	209
Portney, Lindsay/Somers Central School Dist	67	262
Posluszny, Stanley/Greater Amsterdam School Dist	3,5,91	115
Post, Chris/Madison Central School Dist	3	105
Posterli, Tina/Long Beach City School Dist	67	124
Poston, Lorraine/Sullivan West Central SD	2,15	237
Potash, Carol/Highland Ctl School Dist	30,73,295	242
Potrzeba, Jennifer/Franklin Central School Dist	69,77	49
Potrzeba, Luke/Delaware Academy Ctrl SD Delhi	73,76,286,295	49
Potter, Alyssa/Andover Central School Dist	11,27,36,69,88,271,294	14
Potter, Andrew/Franklinville Ctl School Dist	16,73,76,286,295,752	31
Potter, Bruce/Mechanicville City Sch Dist	1	201
Potter, Chad/Fillmore Central School Dist	5	14
Potter, Dave/Dcmo BOCES Chenango	285	43
Potter, David/Walton Central School Dist	73	50
Potter, Elizabeth/Whitesville Central Sch Dist	36,79,83,88,275	15

NAME/District	JOB FUNCTIONS	PAGE
Potter, Jennifer/Owego Apalachin Ctl Sch Dist	90,93	238
Potter, Mark, Dr/Liverpool Ctl School Dist	1	156
Potter, Rick/Hamilton-Fulton-Montgmry BOCES	88	72
Potter, Thomas/Cattaraugus-Allegany BOCES	2	34
Potts, Anne/Voorheesville Central Sch Dist	5	12
Poulton, Tracy, Dr/Longwood Central School Dist	8,39	225
Pound, Angelina/Gates Chili Central Sch Dist	79,93	108
Pound, Scott/Silver Creek Central Sch Dist	3	39
Poupore, Patricia/Brunswick Central School Dist	38,273	190
Powell, Chelsea/Phoenix Central School Dist	16	171
Powell, Jennifer/Granville Central School Dist	83	247
Powell, John/Great Neck Public Schools	2,11,15	120
Powers, Frederick/Bethlehem Central School Dist	35,85	10
Powers, Jarrett/Union Springs Ctl School Dist	1	35
Powers, Kimberly/Whitesboro Ctl School Dist	2	153
Powers, Lesley/East Irondequoit Ctl Sch Dist	79	107
Poyer, Candice/Sherburne Earlville Central SD	83	42
Poyer, Jessica/Oneida City School Dist	8,11,57,69,83,275,298	105
Poyser, Desmond/Roosevelt Union Free Sch Dist	73,76,286	128
Prahl, Matthew/Smithtown Central Sch Dist	60	230
Pramataris, Peter/Mt Sinai Union Free SD	8	226
Pratt, Heather/Bainbridge Guilford CSD	61	41
Pratt, January/Greene Ctl School Dist	8,273	42
Pratt, Michael/Mechanicville City Sch Dist	5	201
Pray, Randy/Ausable Valley Ctl School Dist	3	43
Pray, Robyn/Ausable Valley Ctl Sch Dist	67	43
Preiss, Don/Port Jervis City School Dist	3	166
Preiss, Robert/Clarkstown Central School Dist	4	195
Premo, Douglas/South Lewis Central Sch Dist	1	101
Premo, Jennifer/Carthage Central School Dist	1	80
Premo, Mark/Averill Park Central Sch Dist	5	189
Prendergast, Teresa, Dr/Great Neck Public Schools	1	120
Presher, Laurel/East Irondequoit Ctl Sch Dist	4	107
Presher, Susan/Batavia City School Dist	4	73
Press, Joel/West Hempstead School Dist	2,4,5,15,17,91	131
Presser, Victoria/Scarsdale Union Free Sch Dist	71	261
Presson, David/Duanesburg Central Sch Dist	90	203
Prestia, Lyn/Pine Bush Central School Dist	4	166
Prestipino, April/Hudson City School Dist	8,11,288,296	46
Preston, Bradley/Clinton Central School Dist	3,91	150
Preston, Josie/Belfast Central School Dist	67	14
Preston, Josie/Genesee Valley Ctl School Dist	31,38,88	15
Preston, Justin/Walton Central School Dist	6,69	50
Preston, Richard, Dr/Lake Placid Ctl School Dist	67	67
Preston, Tracie/Cattaraugus-Allegany BOCES	15,27,30	34
Price, Dean/Deposit Central School Dist	67	28
Price, Marianna/Harborfields Ctl School Dist	5	223
Price, Robin/Onondaga Central School Dist	1,83	157
Price, Tracy/Ticonderoga Central Sch Dist	11,58,271,275	68
Priebe, Dawn/Sullivan West Central SD	5	237
Prill, Christopher/Dover Union Free School Dist	2,5	52
Primeau, Michelle/Dolgeville Central School Dist	11,58,88	77
Primiano, Thomas/Merrick Union Free School Dist	2	125
Prince, Doug/Fredonia Central School Dist	71,73,76,82,97,98,295	38
Prince, Fred/Wayne Central School Dist	5	251
Prince, Lauren/Millbrook Ctl School Dist	38	52
Prince, Todd/Greece Central School Dist	91	108
Prinz, Lori/Byron-Bergen Ctl School Dist	2,11,296	73
Prior, Noah/Indian River Ctl School Dist	3	80
Pristash, Ellen/Onondaga Central School Dist	16	157
Pritchard, Catherine/Yorkshire-Pioneer Ctl Sch Dist	4	33
Pritchard, Geoffrey/Buffalo Public Schools	2,19	56
Pritchard, Robert, Dr/South Orangetown Central SD	1	197
Priuitera, Peter/Mt Morris Central School Dist	67	103
Proctor, Adriana/Montauk Union Free School Dist	57,271	226
Proctor, Tracey/Wayland-Cohocton Central SD	5	215
Proscia, Judy/Northport-East Northport UFSD	73	227

1 Superintendent
2 Bus/Finance/Purchasing
3 Buildings And Grounds
4 Food Service
5 Transportation
6 Athletic
7 Health Services
8 Curric/Instruct K-12
9 Curric/Instruct Elem
10 Curric/Instruct Sec
11 Federal Program
12 Title I
13 Title V
15 Asst Superintendent
16 Instructional Media Svcs
17 Chief Operations Officer
18 Chief Academic Officer
19 Chief Financial Officer
20 Art K-12
21 Art Elem
22 Art Sec
23 Music K-12
24 Music Elem
25 Music Sec
26 Business Education
27 Career & Tech Ed
28 Technology Education
29 Family/Consumer Science
30 Adult Education
31 Career/Sch-to-Work K-12
32 Career/Sch-to-Work Elem
33 Career/Sch-to-Work Sec
34 Early Childhood Ed
35 Health/Phys Education
36 Guidance Services K-12
37 Guidance Services Elem
38 Guidance Services Sec
39 Social Studies K-12
40 Social Studies Elem
41 Social Studies Sec
42 Science K-12
43 Science Elem
44 Science Sec
45 Math K-12
46 Math Elem
47 Math Sec
48 English/Lang Arts K-12
49 English/Lang Arts Elem
50 English/Lang Arts Sec
51 Reading K-12
52 Reading Elem
53 Reading Sec
54 Remedial Reading K-12
55 Remedial Reading Elem
56 Remedial Reading Sec
57 Bilingual/ELL
58 Special Education K-12
59 Special Education Elem
60 Special Education Sec
61 Foreign/World Lang K-12
62 Foreign/World Lang Elem
63 Foreign/World Lang Sec
64 Religious Education K-12
65 Religious Education Elem
66 Religious Education Sec
67 School Board President
68 Teacher Personnel
69 Academic Assessment
70 Research/Development
71 Public Information
72 Summer School
73 Instructional Tech
74 Inservice Training
75 Marketing/Distributive
76 Info Systems
77 Psychological Assess
78 Affirmative Action
79 Student Personnel
80 Driver Ed/Safety
81 Gifted/Talented
82 Video Services
83 Substance Abuse Prev
84 Erate
85 AIDS Education
88 Alternative/At Risk
89 Multi-Cultural Curriculum
90 Social Work
91 Safety/Security
92 Magnet School
93 Parental Involvement
95 Tech Prep Program
97 Chief Information Officer
98 Chief Technology Officer
270 Character Education
271 Migrant Education
273 Teacher Mentor
274 Before/After Sch
275 Response To Intervention
277 Remedial Math K-12
280 Literacy Coach
285 STEM
286 Digital Learning
288 Common Core Standards
294 Accountability
295 Network System
296 Title II Programs
297 Webmaster
298 Grant Writer/Ptnrships
750 Chief Innovation Officer
751 Chief of Staff
752 Social Emotional Learning

NY-T50

New York School Directory

DISTRICT PERSONNEL INDEX

NAME/District	JOB FUNCTIONS	PAGE
Proudman, Danielle/Gilboa-Conesville Central SD	4	206
Provenzano, Brett/Fairport Ctl School Dist	1	108
Providente, Matthew/Central Islip Union Free SD	3	218
Provvido, Diane/Oceanside Union Free Sch Dist	8,15,70	127
Pruden, Edward/Wells Central School Dist	42	77
Prudente, James/Islip Union Free School Dist	73,286,295	224
Prue, Scott/Saranac Lake Central Sch Dist	91	70
Pryor, Randy/Owego Apalachin Ctl Sch Dist	2	238
Psarakis, Michele/West Babylon Union Free SD	2,3,15	232
Ptaszynski, Scott/Sachem Central School Dist	3	229
Pucci, Jason/Goshen Central School Dist	67	164
Pucilowski, Kristin/Patchogue-Medford Unified SD	58	227
Pudney, Christina/Germantown Central School Dist	6	46
Puello, Mirla/Ossining Union Free Sch Dist	34,48,52,57,77,280	259
Pugh, Mara/Elwood Union Free School Dist	4	221
Puglisi, Veronica/Victor Central School Dist	79	162
Puleo, Amanda/Churchville Chili Ctl Sch Dist	71,82	107
Pulizzi, Nicholas/Camden Central School Dist	58,79	150
Pulley, David/Tri-Valley Central School Dist	10	237
Pullins, Michael/North Rose Wolcott Central SD	1	250
Pullows Tetuan, Monica/South Country Central Sch Dist	57,61	231
Pulvino, Brian/Fulton City School Dist	1	170
Puntschenko, Michael/Syracuse City School Dist	58	158
Purcell, Julieann/Southampton Union Free SD	16,286	231
Purcell, Lenny/Harrison Central School Dist	3,91	256
Purinton, Julie/West Canada Valley Ctl SD	52,54,280	79
Purinton, Julie/West Canada Valley Ctl SD	275	79
Pursel, Ann/Pavilion Ctl School Dist	285	74
Pusateri, Denise/Jamestown City School Dist	45	38
Pustulka, Joseph/Webster Central School Dist	3,5	112
Pustullca, Joseph/Webster Central School Dist	17	112
Putcher, Katherine/Brocton Central School Dist	36	36
Putman, Donald/Lyons Central School Dist	1	249
Putman, Katrina/Ogdensburg City School Dist	69	211
Putnam, Tom/Penfield Central School Dist	1	109
Putrino, Mark/Chenango Forks Central SD	2	28
Puylara, Christopher/Romulus Ctl School Dist	8	208
Pylman, Elisha/Long Lake Central School Dist	8,11,36,69	76

Q

NAME/District	JOB FUNCTIONS	PAGE
Quanbeck, Melinda/Cayuga-Onondaga BOCES	67	36
Quaranta, Anthony/Owego Apalachin Ctl Sch Dist	5	238
Quartironi, Peter/Monroe Woodbury Central SD	3	165
Quatrocchi, David/Katonah-Lewisboro Sch Dist	2,15	257
Quayle, Garrett/Whitesboro Ctl School Dist	295	153
Quezada, Edwin, Dr/Yonkers Public School Dist	1	263
Quick, Diane/Fort Ann Central School Dist	97	247
Quick, Josh/Harpursville Central Sch Dist	6,58	28
Quick, Krista/Webster Central School Dist	58	112
Quick, Lynda/Wheatland Chili Ctl Sch Dist	1	113
Quicker, Jeanine/Bay Shore Union Free Sch Dist	4	217
Quinlan, Kendra/Heuvelton Central School Dist	31,36,69,271,294	210
Quinn, Barbara/Washingtonville Central SD	8,15,296,298	167
Quinn, Jennifer/Brookhaven Comsewogue Unif SD	1	218
Quinn, Jennifer, Dr/Brookhaven Comsewogue Unif SD	15,73	218
Quinn, Kimberly/Plattsburgh City School Dist	83,85	44
Quinn, Patrick/Chautauqua Lake Central SD	3	36
Quinn, Sheryl/Keene Central School Dist	67	67
Quinones, Blanca/Community School District 30	11	184
Quinones, Christopher/Pawling Ctl School Dist	73	52

R

NAME/District	JOB FUNCTIONS	PAGE
Rabey, Jeffrey, Dr/Depew Union Free School Dist	1	59
Rabidoux, Carolyn/Brighton Central School Dist	7,58,79,83,85	106
Rabinowitz, Cheryl/Catskill Central School Dist	73	75
Race, Christine/Sidney Central School Dist	27	50
Race, Eric/Johnson City Central Sch Dist	2,7,15,71,91	28
Race, Ethan/New Lebanon Ctl School Dist	295	46
Racine, Amy/Chazy Central Rural Sch Dist	8,31,36	44
Racioppo, Maggie/White Plains City School Dist	7,35,85	263
Radbwitz, Brian/Schodack Central School Dist	71	191
Radcliff, Deborah/Auburn Enlarged City Sch Dist	8	34
Radday, Michael/Westhampton Beach School Dist	1,11	233
Radell, Caren/Auburn Enlarged City Sch Dist	7	34
Rader, David/Mt Pleasant Cottage UFSD	5	258
Radice, Deborah/Williamsville Ctl School Dist	73,295	64
Radice, Lorane/Long Beach City School Dist	9	124
Radin-Snaith, Anneke/Naples Central School Dist	73	162
Radley, Jessica/Dolgeville Central School Dist	2,19	77
Radley, Kelly/Batavia City School Dist	273	73
Rafferty, Maryellen/Lakeland Central School Dist	88	257
Rafferty, Stephen/De Ruyter Central School Dist	60	105
Rafferty, Todd/Union Springs Ctl School Dist	3	35
Rago, Stephanie/Greece Central School Dist	83	108
Ragusa, Michael/Millbrook Ctl School Dist	3	52
Raicovi, Vincent, Dr/Middle Country Ctl Sch Dist	73,76,286	225
Rakowski, Kenneth/Weedsport Ctl School Dist	77	35
Rallo, Jack/South Orangetown Central SD	3	197
Ralph, Ann/West Seneca Central Sch Dist	4	64
Ralph, William/Lake Pleasant Central Sch Dist	5	76
Ramin, John/Ctr for Instruct Tech Innov	8	172
Ramirez, Carlos/Greenburgh Central School Dist	71,97,286	255
Ramirez, Ed/Baldwin Union Free School Dist	6,7,35,83,270	116
Ramirez, Joan/Long Beach City School Dist	2	124
Ramirez, Manuel/Community School District 6	1	141
Ramirez, Ursulina/New York City Dept of Ed	3,17,68	134
Rammelt, Jennifer/Brocton Central School Dist	7	36
Rampado, Mark/Amherst Central School Dist	3	56
Rampersant, Mark/New York City Dept of Ed	91	134
Ramponi, Michael/Ardsley Union Free School Dist	6	252
Ramratton, Adish/Mamaroneck Union Free Sch Dist	73	257
Ramsay, Matthew/Westhampton Beach School Dist	44,47,73	233
Ramsey, Greg/Skaneateles Central Sch Dist	295	157
Ranaudo, Christian/Minisink Valley Central SD	8,11,15,69	165
Ranca, Matthew/Schalmont Central School Dist	6	204
Rancy, Pierre/Uniondale Union Free Sch Dist	57	130
Randall-Nevel, Heather/Carthage Central School Dist	42	80
Randazo, Vincent/Island Park Union Free SD	15	122
Randazzo, Kevin/Freeport Public School Dist	3	119
Randazzo, Russ/Baldwin Union Free School Dist	3	116
Randhare, Kristin/Monroe Woodbury Central SD	79	165
Randle, Andrea/Lisbon Central School Dist	67	211
Randles, Jereme/Granville Central School Dist	73	247
Rann, Robin/Northport-East Northport UFSD	45	227
Rapoza, Pam/Trumansburg Central SD	79	241
Rapp, Mitchell/Charlotte Valley Ctl Sch Dist	11,296	49
Rashford, Gregory/Lansingburgh Central Sch Dist	38,83,88	190
Rastello, Dalimar/Patchogue-Medford Unified SD	49,57,62	227
Rath, Melisa/Kendall Central School Dist	77	169
Rathbun, Melissa/Cooperstown Ctl School Dist	4	173
Rattle, Nadine/Cheektowaga Maryvale UFSD	5	59
Rauschenbach, Eric/Scarsdale Union Free Sch Dist	58,79,83	261
Ravina, Judith/Mamaroneck Union Free Sch Dist	57	257
Rawady, Erin/Whitesville Central Sch Dist	6	15
Rawden, Karen/Sodus Central School Dist	73,297	251
Ray, Felix/West Canada Valley Ctl SD	5	79
Ray, Tam/Auburn Enlarged City Sch Dist	6,35,83	34
Ray, Teresa/Salamanca City Central SD	67	33
Raymond, Andy/Lake George Central Sch Dist	5	245
Raymond, Lisa/Pocantico Hills Ctl Sch Dist	2,15	260
Raymond, Posillipo/North Rockland Central SD	4	197
Raynor, Ashley/Westfield Central School Dist	275	39
Raynor, Maureen/Harborfields Ctl School Dist	68	223
Rayome, Suzanne/Burnt Hills Ballston Lake SD	57,61,82	200
Reakes, Michele/Cincinnatus Ctl School Dist	16	47
Reale, Heidi/Frewsburg Central School Dist	73,297	38
Reardon, Barbara/West Irondequoit Ctl SD	30,274	113
Reardon, Derek/Hudson City School Dist	6	46
Reardon, Thomas/Schalmont Central School Dist	1	204
Reaves, Barbary/Stockbridge Valley Central SD	67	106
Reda, Theresa/Somers Central School Dist	90	262
Redband, Tom/Batavia City School Dist	31	73
Reddick, Paulette/Brockport Ctl School Dist	58	106
Reddock, Gina/Long Beach City School Dist	30	124
Redeker, Jonathan/Goshen Central School Dist	73	164
Redman, John/Florida Union Free Sch Dist	67	164
Redman, Ken/Fillmore Central School Dist	3	14
Redman, Kurt/Schenectady City School Dist	42,45	204
Redmond, David/Dolgeville Central School Dist	3	77
Redmond, Keith/Whitehall Central School Dist	6	248
Redmond, Timothy/Brasher Falls School Dist	3,5	209
Reeb, Andrew/Elba Central School Dist	5	73

DISTRICT PERSONNEL INDEX

Market Data Retrieval

NAME/District	JOB FUNCTIONS	PAGE
Reed, Ellen/Fairport Ctl School Dist	48	108
Reed, Fredrick/Andes Central School Dist	5	48
Reed, Iris/East Aurora Union Free SD	4	60
Reed, Jamie/Remsenburg-Speonk UFSD	2,71	228
Reed, Michael/Caledonia-Mumford Ctl Sch Dist	6,7,85	102
Reed, Michelle, Dr/Cairo-Durham Ctl School Dist	8	75
Reed, Ryan/New Rochelle City School Dist	15,68	259
Reese, Wendy/Churchville Chili Ctl Sch Dist	30	107
Reeves, Dajuana/Levittown Union Free Sch Dist	5	123
Reeves, Joan/Baldwinsville Central Sch Dist	67	154
Reff, Melissa/Little Falls City School Dist	2	78
Regina, Karen/Taconic Hills Central Sch Dist	295	47
Reh, Scott/Mt Sinai Union Free SD	3,6	226
Rehack, Jaqueline/North Bellmore Union Free SD	2,5,15,71	126
Rehm, Chris/Lyncourt Union Free Sch Dist	6	156
Rehman, Dan/West Hempstead School Dist	1,11,57	131
Reichhart, Jill/Brockport Ctl School Dist	2	106
Reid, Anthony/West Babylon Union Free SD	5	232
Reid, Brooke/Parishville Hopkinton Sch Dist	8,11,58,270,298	212
Reid, Fatimat/Rochester City School Dist	15,751	110
Reid, Irastina/Syracuse City School Dist	58	158
Reid, Janice/Peekskill City School Dist	73,97,295	260
Reid, Mark/Salamanca City Central SD	38	33
Reid, Stacie/Uniondale Union Free Sch Dist	36	130
Reidlinger, Whitney/Springs Union Free School Dist	6	232
Reigles, Billie/Bainbridge Guilford CSD	4	41
Reilly-Johnson, Katharine/West Babylon Union Free SD	26,95	232
Reilly, Anne/Remsen Central School Dist	16	151
Reilly, Dina/West Hempstead School Dist	8,15,18,296,298,752	131
Reilly, Ellen/Hicksville Union Free Sch Dist	2	122
Reilly, Gina/Eastern Suffolk BOCES	58	235
Reilly, Lindsay/Sag Harbor Union Free Sch Dist	271	229
Reilly, Matthew/Cazenovia Ctl School Dist	1,11	104
Reilly, Sean/Andover Central School Dist	45	14
Reimer, Jacob/Barker Central School Dist	1,11	146
Reimer, John/Onteora Central School Dist	73	243
Reina, Robert/Frankfort-Schuyler Ctl SD	1,11	77
Reinhard, Claire/Mamaroneck Union Free Sch Dist	11,69,70,76,294	257
Reinhardt, Kirk/Saugerties Central School Dist	1,83	243
Reinisch, Paul/Troy City School Dsitrict	6,7,35,78	191
Reisen, Jaime/Edmeston Ctl School Dist	54	173
Reiser, Doug/Minisink Valley Central SD	73,76	165
Reiss, Amity/Port Washington Union Free SD	76	128
Reister, Leeanne/Pittsford Central Sch Dist	2	110
Reiter, Deborah/New York State Dept Education	27	1
Reither, Tracy/Margaretville Central Sch Dist	6,35	49
Relkin, Rachel/New Rochelle City School Dist	67	259
Rella, Beth, Dr/Freeport Public School Dist	2	119
Rella, Beth, Dr/Middle Country Ctl School Dist	2,15,19	225
Remillard, Scott/Gananda Central School Dist	5	249
Remington, Anne/Alexandria Central School Dist	4	79
Remington, John/Putnam Central School Dist	57,59	248
Remsburger, Michael/Pine Plains Ctl School Dist	3	53
Renahan, David/Deer Park Union Free Sch Dist	59	220
Renda, Jack/Sachem Central School Dist	9,16,27,73,81,295	229
Renda, Ray/Port Chester Rye Union Free SD	3,91	261
Rendon, Diego/Greenburgh Central School Dist	73	255
Rendon, Juliette/Sag Harbor Union Free Sch Dist	57	229
Renna, Kayla/Cornwall Central School Dist	5	163
Renner, Jeff/Susquehanna Valley Central SD	20	29
Renner, Lynne/Homer Central School Dist	80	48
Renwick, Kelly/Franklin Central School Dist	2,11,296,298	49
Reome, Joey/Brasher Falls School Dist	6	209
Repard, Amy/Bloomfield Central SD	297	161
Repass, Cheryl, Dr/Churchville Chili Ctl Sch Dist	67	107
Resavage, Michele/Fairport Ctl School Dist	4	108
Resnikoff, Nadia/Middle Country Ctl Sch Dist	74,78	225
Restivo, Jenna/South Country Central Sch Dist	77	231
Restivo, Stephen/East Islip Union Free SD	6,7,78	220
Retallack, Lisa/Nyack Union Free School Dist	71	197
Retzlaff, Michael/Bolivar-Richburg Ctrl Sch Dist	1,11	14
Reukauf, Cheryl/Lancaster Central Sch Dist	68	62
Reveiz, Elizabeth/East Hampton Union Free SD	57	220
Reville, Edward/Ravena Coeymans Selkirk Ctl SD	67	11
Rey, Janiel/Erie 2 Chautauqua-Catta BOCES	30	67
Reyda, Joseph/Fredonia Central School Dist	8,11,69,74,271,296,298	37
Reyes-Vega, Tiara/New Rochelle City School Dist	8,57	259
Reyes, Peter/Jamesville-DeWitt Central SD	8	155
Reynolds, Elaine/Schenectady City School Dist	4	204
Reynolds, Eric/Huntington Union Free Sch Dist	20,23	223
Reynolds, Lauren/Hamilton Central School Dist	6	105
Reynolds, Mary/Deer Park Union Free Sch Dist	11,68,296,298	220
Reynolds, Michelle/Chateaugay Central School Dist	6	69
Reynolds, Ramona/Buffalo Public Schools	93	57
Reynolds, Theresa/Orange-Ulster BOCES	8,15,298	168
Reynolds, Thomas/Sharon Springs Ctl SD	97,295	207
Reynolds, Troy/Malone Central School Dist	4	69
Reynoso, Dina/Mamaroneck Union Free Sch Dist	90	257
Rezek, John/Island Trees Union Free SD	73	122
Rhebergen, Annette/Southwestern Central Sch Dist	2	39
Rhinehart, Robert/Downsville Central Sch Dist	8,11,88,90,270	49
Rhoades, Ben/Downsville Central Sch Dist	16,82	49
Rhoades, Cindi/Franklinville Ctl School Dist	27,36,69	31
Rhode, Brian/Averill Park Central Sch Dist	280	189
Rhodes, Corey/Clymer Central School Dist	27,31,36	37
Rhodes, Michael/Harpursville Central Sch Dist	67	28
Rhone, Lynn/Dolgeville Central School Dist	1	77
Rhow, Kathleen/Phelps-Clifton Springs Ctl SD	5	162
Rianna, Maria, Dr/Glen Cove City School Dist	1	120
Ribera, Jacqueline/Bay Shore Union Free Sch Dist	34	217
Ricapito, Joann/Lakeland Central School Dist	4	257
Ricca, Joseph, Dr/White Plains City School Dist	1	263
Ricci, Marsha/Waterford Halfmoon School Dist	67	203
Rice, Donna/Marcellus Central School Dist	4	157
Rice, Grace/Jefferson Lewis BOCES	67	82
Rice, Joan/Hancock Central School Dist	36	49
Rice, John/North Syracuse Ctl Sch Dist	16,20,28,29,31,42,73,285	157
Rice, Nicole/Cincinnatus Ctl School Dist	73	47
Rice, Scott/Pawling Ctl School Dist	58,79	52
Rich, Anne/Hamburg Central School Dist	4	61
Rich, Diana/Huntington Union Free Sch Dist	58	223
Rich, Jeremy/Central Valley School Dist	1	77
Rich, Michael/Island Trees Union Free SD	67	122
Rich, Sabrina/Ardsley Union Free School Dist	73	252
Richards, Brian/Depew Union Free School Dist	73,295	60
Richards, Carlyle/Westbury Union Free Sch Dist	83,88	132
Richards, Dave/Wheelerville Union Free SD	3	72
Richards, Dave/Wheelerville Union Free SD	17	72
Richards, David, Dr/Unatego Unadilla Central SD	1	174
Richards, Jeff/Kenmore-Tonawanda UF Sch Dist	15,68	62
Richards, Kimberly/Ogdensburg City School Dist	58	211
Richards, Mary/Attica Central School Dist	77	267
Richardson, Carolyn/Caledonia-Mumford Ctl Sch Dist	26,31	102
Richardson, Collene/Riverhead Central School Dist	80	228
Richardson, Jason/Chautauqua Lake Central SD	38,88	36
Richardson, Joel/Waterford Halfmoon School Dist	69	203
Richardson, Kathleen/Greece Central School Dist	27	108
Richardson, Mary/Longwood Central School Dist	298	225
Richardson, Ronald/Liverpool Ctl School Dist	295	156
Richert, Katlyn/Elba Central School Dist	57	73
Riches, Michelle/Brushton Moira Ctl Sch Dist	4	69
Richley, Adam/Wyoming Central School Dist	5	268
Richmond, Carol/Andover Central School Dist	4	14
Richmond, Marcella/Olean City School Dist	58,88	32

#		#		#		#		#		#	
1	Superintendent	16	Instructional Media Svcs	30	Adult Education	44	Science Sec	58	Special Education K-12	72	Summer School
2	Bus/Finance/Purchasing	17	Chief Operations Officer	31	Career/Sch-to-Work K-12	45	Math K-12	59	Special Education Elem	73	Instructional Tech
3	Buildings And Grounds	18	Chief Academic Officer	32	Career/Sch-to-Work Elem	46	Math Elem	60	Special Education Sec	74	Inservice Training
4	Food Service	19	Chief Financial Officer	33	Career/Sch-to-Work Sec	47	Math Sec	61	Foreign/World Lang K-12	75	Marketing/Distributive
5	Transportation	20	Art K-12	34	Early Childhood Ed	48	English/Lang Arts K-12	62	Foreign/World Lang Elem	76	Info Systems
6	Athletic	21	Art Elem	35	Health/Phys Education	49	English/Lang Arts Elem	63	Foreign/World Lang Sec	77	Psychological Assess
7	Health Services	22	Art Sec	36	Guidance Services K-12	50	English/Lang Arts Sec	64	Religious Education K-12	78	Affirmative Action
8	Curric/Instruct K-12	23	Music K-12	37	Guidance Services Elem	51	Reading K-12	65	Religious Education Elem	79	Student Personnel
9	Curric/Instruct Elem	24	Music Elem	38	Guidance Services Sec	52	Reading Elem	66	Religious Education Sec	80	Driver Ed/Safety
10	Curric/Instruct Sec	25	Music Sec	39	Social Studies K-12	53	Reading Sec	67	School Board President	81	Gifted/Talented
11	Federal Program	26	Business Education	40	Social Studies Elem	54	Remedial Reading K-12	68	Teacher Personnel	82	Video Services
12	Title I	27	Career & Tech Ed	41	Social Studies Sec	55	Remedial Reading Elem	69	Academic Assessment	83	Substance Abuse Prev
13	Title V	28	Technology Education	42	Science K-12	56	Remedial Reading Sec	70	Research/Development	84	Erate
15	Asst Superintendent	29	Family/Consumer Science	43	Science Elem	57	Bilingual/ELL	71	Public Information	85	AIDS Education

#		#		#	
88	Alternative/At Risk	277	Remedial Math K-12		
89	Multi-Cultural Curriculum	280	Literacy Coach		
90	Social Work	285	STEM		
91	Safety/Security	286	Digital Learning		
92	Magnet School	288	Common Core Standards		
93	Parental Involvement	294	Accountability		
95	Tech Prep Program	295	Network System		
97	Chief Information Officer	296	Title II Programs		
98	Chief Technology Officer	297	Webmaster		
270	Character Education	298	Grant Writer/Ptnrships		
271	Migrant Education	750	Chief Innovation Officer		
273	Teacher Mentor	751	Chief of Staff		
274	Before/After Sch	752	Social Emotional Learning		
275	Response To Intervention				

New York School Directory

DISTRICT PERSONNEL INDEX

NAME/District	JOB FUNCTIONS	PAGE
Richroath, James/Patchogue-Medford Unified SD	76,295	227
Ricker, Christine/Monroe Woodbury Central SD	7,77,79,90	165
Ricketts, Ernie/Rye Neck Union Free Sch Dist	91	261
Ricketts, Wayne/Scarsdale Union Free Sch Dist	76	261
Rickman, Wayne/Brockport Ctl School Dist	295	106
Ridder, Stella/Taconic Hills Central Sch Dist	58,79	47
Riddle, Matt/Schroon Lake Ctl School Dist	273	68
Riddleberger, Pamela/Union-Endicott Ctl Sch Dist	2,12,15	29
Riddleberger, Toby/Union-Endicott Ctl Sch Dist	3,91	29
Riddock, Thomas/Franklinville Ctl School Dist	9,81	31
Ridegiato, Michael/Brocton Central School Dist	67	36
Rideout, James/Bainbridge Guilford CSD	3	41
Rideout, Janice/Bainbridge Guilford CSD	2	41
Ridgeway, Andy/Sandy Creek Central Sch Dist	3	172
Rielly, Rebecca/Liberty Central School Dist	7	236
Rifkin, Debbie/Levittown Union Free Sch Dist	15,68	123
Riggi, Peter/Schuylerville Central Sch Dist	3	201
Riggi, Sue/Le Roy Central School Dist	76	73
Riggins, Jacob/Keene Central School Dist	3,5	67
Riley, Catina/Averill Park Central Sch Dist	2	189
Riley, James/Goshen Central School Dist	3,91	164
Riley, John/Archdiocese of New York Ed Off	15	142
Riley, Judy/Cortland Enlarged City SD	11,31,34,75,77,79,83,298	47
Rinaldo, Ed/Madison-Oneida BOCES	74	154
Rinaldo, Ginger/Sherburne Earlville Central SD	8,58	42
Rinaldo, Kathleen/Madison-Oneida BOCES	30	154
Rinchiera, Lillian/Suffern Central School Dist	76,97	198
Ringel, Lisa/Chester Union Free School Dist	88	163
Ringer, Lawrence/Johnsburg Central School Dist	2	245
Ringuette, Daniel/Gilboa-Conesville Central SD	31,36,57,81,88	206
Riordan, Evie/Tonawanda City School Dist	4	64
Riordan, Jodee/Lewiston Porter Ctl Sch Dist	67	146
Riordan, Kim/Friendship Central Sch Dist	58	15
Ripley, Joan/Farmingdale Union Free SD	8,12,15,16,69,74	119
Ripley, Kathi/Whitehall Central School Dist	16	248
Risboskin, Toni/Waverly Ctl School Dist	27	239
Risener, Jeffrey/Oceanside Union Free Sch Dist	6	127
Risley, Bruce/Dolgeville Central School Dist	35,83,85	77
Rissetto, Rachel/Hudson City School Dist	68	46
Ristano, James/Port Washington Union Free SD	3,91	128
Ristau, Tim/Jamesville-DeWitt Central SD	79	155
Ristoff, Thomas/Syracuse City School Dist	91	158
Ritchie, William/Friendship Central Sch Dist	67	15
Ritter, Ann/Uniondale Union Free Sch Dist	16,73	130
Rittmaster, Peter/Mt Pleasant-Blythedale UFSD	67	259
Rivas, Michelle/Pawling Ctl School Dist	57	52
Rivenburg, Jeff/Duanesburg Central Sch Dist	2,11	203
Rivera, Denise/Greenburgh-North Castle SD	70	255
Rivera, Seema/Guilderland Central Sch Dist	67	11
Rivers, Melissa/Alfred Almond Ctl School Dist	11,273	13
Rivers, Nichelle, Dr/Roosevelt Union Free Sch Dist	11,296,298	128
Rivers, Sandra/Lowville Acad-Central Sch Dist	2	101
Riviello, Donna/Clyde-Savannah Central SD	4	249
Riviello, Donna/North Rose Wolcott Central SD	4	250
Rizzieri, Rich/Wayland-Cohocton Central SD	67	215
Rizzo, Bethany/Connetquot Central School Dist	285	219
Rizzo, Frank/Alden Central School Dist	16,71,73,97	56
Rizzo, Nicholas/Clarence Central School Dist	36	59
Rizzo, Patrica/Dover Union Free School Dist	11,58,271,273	52
Roa, Lourdos/Monroe 2 Orleans BOCES	57	115
Roach, Chuck/Weedsport Ctl School Dist	3,5,73	35
Roach, Judith/Falconer Central School Dist	8,12,273	37
Robb, Dean/Warsaw Central School Dist	67	267
Robbins, Angela/Carthage Central School Dist	83,85	80
Robbins, Erik/Red Creek Central School Dist	73,286,295	251
Robbins, Marge/Union Springs Ctl School Dist	2,15	35
Robbins, Mike/Waterford Halfmoon School Dist	6	203
Robbins, Shayne/Thousand Islands Central SD	6	81
Roberge, William/West Genesee Ctl School Dist	16,73,286	159
Robert, Angela/Salmon River Central Sch Dist	8,11,15,285,286,298	70
Robert, Barrett/Yorktown Central School Dist	6	264
Roberts-Grant, Robyn/North Rose Wolcott Central SD	6,35	250
Roberts, Ben/Freeport Public School Dist	15,68	119
Roberts, Christopher/Holland Patent Ctl School Dist	5	150
Roberts, Joan/Pawling Ctl School Dist	28,76	52
Roberts, Jodi/Webster Central School Dist	752	112

NAME/District	JOB FUNCTIONS	PAGE
Roberts, Kenneth/Brocton Central School Dist	5	36
Roberts, Kevin/Remsen Central School Dist	3,5	151
Roberts, Lucinda/Remsen Central School Dist	2	151
Roberts, Rebecca/Dcmo BOCES Chenango	73	43
Roberts, Thomas/Sweet Home Central Sch Dist	12,298	63
Robertson, David/Dobbs Ferry Union Free SD	3	254
Robertson, Keith/Buffalo Public Schools	2,15,298	56
Robinette, Marybeth/Huntington Union Free Sch Dist	46,69,73	223
Robinson, Alice, Dr/West Babylon Union Free SD	16,82	232
Robinson, Jacqueline/Southampton Union Free SD	67	231
Robinson, L Oliver, Dr/Shenendehowa Central Sch Dist	1	202
Robinson, Lashawn/New York City Dept of Ed	15,79,91,752	134
Robinson, Michael/Heuvelton Central School Dist	2	210
Robinson, Michael/New Paltz Ctl School Dist	4	242
Robinson, Mike/Lisbon Central School Dist	2,11	210
Robinson, Mr/Baldwin Union Free School Dist	2,15	116
Robinson, Richard/Walton Central School Dist	76,295	50
Robinson, Scott/Rochester City School Dist	48	110
Robson, Terri/East Irondequoit Ctl Sch Dist	9,46,49,52,280	107
Roca, Francisco/Bolton Central School Dist	63	244
Roche, Michael/Belfast Central School Dist	288	14
Roche, Michael/Belfast Central School Dist	12	14
Roche, Thomas/Ft Edward Union Free Sch Dist	67	247
Rockenstyre, Kimberly/Questar III BOCES	58	192
Rockett, Tiona/Syracuse City School Dist	11,298	158
Rockew, Connie/Oakfield Alabama Ctl SD	8,12	74
Rockey, Mary, Dr/Westfield Central School Dist	9,12,58,271,752	39
Rockhill, Jamian/Scotia Glenville Ctl Sch Dist	6	205
Rockwell, Cuyle/Central Valley School Dist	71	77
Rockwin, George/Connetquot Central School Dist	20,23	219
Roda, David/Minisink Valley Central SD	3	165
Roddenbery, Mike/Manchester-Shortsville Ctl SD	3	162
Roddy, Jack/Brunswick Central School Dist	67	190
Rodems, James/Baldwinsville Central Sch Dist	2,15,19	154
Rodger, Dawn/Poughkeepsie City School Dist	5	53
Rodgers, Jamie/Pine Valley Central Sch Dist	2	38
Rodgers, Michael/Amagansett Union Free Sch Dist	6	216
Rodgers, Michael/Plainview-Old Bethpage Ctl SD	23	127
Rodgers, Robert/Newark Valley Central Sch Dist	34	238
Rodia, Pat/Carmel Central School Dist	4	175
Rodridez, Susan/Valley Stream Union Free SD 30	9,16,73,74,76,295	131
Rodriguez, Alex/Rome City School Dist	3	151
Rodriguez, Elsie/Monroe Woodbury Central SD	1	165
Rodriguez, Julia/Newark Central School Dist	93	250
Rodriguez, Kim, Dr/Southampton Union Free SD	38,88	231
Rodriguez, Lisa/Brentwood Union Free Sch Dist	30,72	217
Rodriguez, Luis, Dr/Yonkers Public School Dist	15,58	263
Rodriguez, Tia/Binghamton City School Dist	58	27
Rodriguez, Tina/Eldred Central School Dist	16,73	236
Rodriquez, Jodie/Herkimer BOCES	2,15	79
Roe, Joshua/Tioga Central School Dist	298	239
Roehr, Judith/Hudson City School Dist	16	46
Roelle, Robert, Dr/Pearl River School Dist	8,11,57,76,88,286,288,298	197
Roemer, Elizabeth/Island Trees Union Free SD	8,15,74,280,296	122
Roeske, Lynne/Andover Central School Dist	76	14
Rogers, Christopher/Hamilton Central Sch Dist	73	105
Rogers, Faron/Bradford Central Sch Dist	3,91	207
Rogers, Jeff/Barker Central School Dist	37	146
Rogers, Mary/Farmingdale Union Free SD	68	119
Rogers, Matt/Ausable Valley Ctl Sch Dist	36,69	43
Rogers, Mike/Hartford Central School Dist	5	248
Rogers, Patricia/Bay Shore Union Free Sch Dist	61	217
Rogers, Patricia/Bay Shore Union Free Sch Dist	57	217
Rogers, Patricia/Shoreham-Wading River Ctl SD	5	230
Rogers, Stephen/Livingston Manor Ctl Sch Dist	4	236
Rogers, Thomas, Dr/Syosset Central School Dist	1	129
Rogers, Tina/Randolph Acad Union Free SD	68	32
Rohloff, Lisa/Silver Creek Central Sch Dist	2,11,68	39
Rohring, Michelle/Marcus Whitman Central SD	7	162
Rokhvadze, Mary/Laurens Central School Dist	16	173
Roland, Kristen/Ctr for Instruct Tech Innov	69	172
Roland, Marykay/Johnson City Central Sch Dist	1	28
Roland, Steve/Monroe 2 Orleans BOCES	2	115
Roll, Kim/Kenmore-Tonawanda UF Sch Dist	4	62
Roller, Michael/Webster Central School Dist	20,23	112
Rolon, Kirsten/Wallkill Central School Dist	23	243

DISTRICT PERSONNEL INDEX

Market Data Retrieval

NAME/District	JOB FUNCTIONS	PAGE
Romain, Julie/Buffalo Public Schools	48,54	57
Roman, Dana/Lansingburgh Central Sch Dist	71	190
Roman, Pedro, Dr/Newburgh Enlarged City SD	68	166
Romanelli, Paul, Dr/Long Beach City School Dist	8,15	124
Romano, Alfred/Newburgh Enlarged City SD	42	166
Romano, Dan/Mineola Union Free Sch Dist	3	125
Romano, Nancy/Garrison Union Free Sch Dist	73,295	175
Romanosky, Michelle/William Floyd School Dist	2	233
Romans, Steven/Fredonia Central School Dist	36,79	37
Romeo, Ann/Little Flower Union Free SD	2,15	224
Romeo, Pamela/Mahopac Ctl School Dist	5	176
Romesser, Eric/Attica Central School Dist	6	267
Ronai, Margaret/Connetquot Central School Dist	26,39	219
Ronan, Kelly/Le Roy Central School Dist	83	73
Roof, Brenda/Webster Central School Dist	76	112
Rooker, Corey/Port Byron Ctl School Dist	3,5	35
Rooney, Sandra/Lyme Central School Dist	2	81
Root, Cathi/Tioga Central School Dist	67	239
Root, Coleen/Mexico Central School Dist	8,11,57,280,285,286,288,296	171
Root, Colleen/Mexico Central School Dist	15,76	171
Root, Ravo, Dr/Camden Central School Dist	1	150
Roraback, Gwendolyn/Ulster BOCES	8,69,70,73,74	244
Rorick, Rebecca/Waverly Ctl School Dist	7	239
Rosa-Farleigh, Patti/New York State Dept Education	58	1
Rosa, Betty/New York State Dept Education	67	1
Rosado, Jacqueline/Community School District 12	1	23
Rosales, Gretchen/Elba Central School Dist	12	73
Rosario, Leticia/Community School District 9	1	18
Roscoe-Strebel, Janet/Dryden Central School Dist	12,58,77	239
Roscop, Jay/Sodus Central School Dist	296	251
Roscup, Jay/Clyde-Savannah Central SD	11,296,298	249
Rose, Daniel/North Babylon Union Free SD	73,79,295	226
Rose, David, Dr/Oceanside Union Free Sch Dist	57,61	127
Rose, James/Yonkers Public School Dist	6,35	263
Rose, Jessica/Bolivar-Richburg Ctrl Sch Dist	8	14
Rosebrittan, Carmen/Albion Central School Dist	57	169
Rosen, Michael/Yorktown Central School Dist	58,79	264
Rosen, Nomi/Baldwin Union Free School Dist	74	116
Rosenbaum, Alison/Saranac Central School Dist	38	45
Rosenberg, Ashley/Deer Park Union Free Sch Dist	57	220
Rosenblatt, Cheri/Ardsley Union Free School Dist	2,3,15	252
Rosenthal, Michelle/Hewlett Woodmere Union Free SD	4	121
Roseto, Carol/Rockville Ctr Union Free SD	6,7,35	128
Rosetti, Tori/Franklinville Ctl School Dist	7	31
Rosinski, Debra/Rondout Valley Ctl School Dist	2	243
Rosner, Kenneth/Elmont Union Free School Dist	9,11,69,72,74,273	118
Rosno, Jason/Campbell-Savona Ctl School Dist	2,15,78	213
Ross, Jonathan/Blind Brook-Rye Union Free SD	2,3,15	252
Ross, Kimberly/Green Island Union Free SD	1,11,288	10
Ross, Patrick/Bolton Central School Dist	5	244
Ross, Teresa/Central Square Central SD	77,79,81,275	170
Ross, Tom/Cohoes City School Dist	91	10
Rossbach, Kelsey/Southern Cayuga Central SD	67	35
Rosselli, Frank/Shenendehowa Central Sch Dist	20,23	202
Rosser, Eric, Dr/Buffalo Public Schools	15,79,83,85	56
Rosser, Eric, Dr/Poughkeepsie City School Dist	1	53
Rosslee, Julie/Wantagh Union Free Sch Dist 23	48,57	131
Rosweiler, Sonja/Edmeston Ctl School Dist	2	173
Rote, Kathy/Waverly Ctl School Dist	2	239
Rotella, Bryan/Niagara Falls City Sch Dist	58	147
Rotello, Michael/Bay Shore Union Free Sch Dist	20,23	217
Roth, Gregg/O E S J Central School Dist	76,286,295	72
Roth, Jeffrey/Wilson Central School Dist	6,57,69	149
Roth, Jon/Grand Island Central Sch Dist	6,85	61
Roth, Sheila/Mexico Central School Dist	2	171
Rothpearl, Ingar/Newark Central School Dist	7	250
Rottcamp, Jason/Riverhead Central School Dist	20,23	228

NAME/District	JOB FUNCTIONS	PAGE
Rotundo, Amy/Lyncourt Union Free Sch Dist	76	156
Rotz, Marty/Romulus Ctl School Dist	1	208
Rounds, Tara/Haldane Central School Dist	79	176
Rountos, Muriel/East Moriches Union Free SD	9,12	221
Rouse, Katherine/Town of Webb Union Free SD	4	78
Rouse, Laura/Vernon-Verona-Sherrill CSD	8,57	152
Rousell, Heather/Colton Pierrepont School Dist	36	209
Rouzati, Nasrin, Dr/Mt Pleasant Ctl School Dist	286,295	258
Rovito, Eileen/Mayfield Ctl School Dist	35	72
Rovitolli, David/East Rochester Union Free SD	73,88,286	107
Rowan, Tim/Bemus Point Ctl School Dist	3	36
Rowe, Doreen/Dcmo BOCES Chenango	2,15	43
Rowland, Christopher/Lyme Central School Dist	36,88	81
Rowledge, Allen/Massena Central School Dist	5	211
Rowles, Jack/Seneca Falls Central Sch Dist	3,91	208
Rowley, James/Oneida City School Dist	2,15,79	105
Royer-Loiselle, Natalie/Schroon Lake Ctl School Dist	57	68
Rozanski, Scott/Batavia City School Dist	2,5	73
Rozbicki, Joe/Starpoint Central School Dist	295	149
Rozler, James/Grand Island Central Sch Dist	3,91	61
Rozzi, Linda/Babylon Union Free Sch Dist	1	216
Rubbo, Angelo/Bedford Central School Dist	2,5,15,71	252
Rubbo, Angelo/Mt Pleasant Cottage UFSD	2,15	258
Ruberti, Christopher/Mohonasen Central Sch Dist	2,15,19	203
Ruberti, Richard/Greater Amsterdam School Dist	1	115
Rubin, Jennifer/Rye Neck Union Free Sch Dist	67	261
Rubitski, Mark/Greene Ctl School Dist	2,13	42
Ruch, Terrence/Southold Union Free Sch Dist	10	231
Ruddy, Joseph/Clifton-Fine Central Sch Dist	58	209
Ruddy, Patrick/Cazenovia Ctl School Dist	79	104
Rudley, Lisa/Ossining Union Free Sch Dist	67	259
Rudnicki, Scott/Franklinville Ctl School Dist	18,58,76,98,288,296,750,751	31
Rudy, Earl/Phoenix Central School Dist	67	172
Ruf, Christopher/Chenango Valley Ctl Sch Dist	16	28
Ruf, Ryan/Eastern Suffolk BOCES	15	235
Ruffell, Tanner/Town of Webb Union Free SD	6,35,83,85	78
Ruffo, Sandra/Broome-Tioga BOCES	67	31
Rufo, Jeanine/Putnam Valley Ctl School Dist	67	176
Rufo, Patricia, Dr/Syosset Central School Dist	2,12,15,288	129
Rugg, Ann/Springville Griffith Inst CSD	5	63
Ruggeri, Lori/Greece Central School Dist	58	108
Ruggiero, Christopher/Lakeland Central School Dist	45	257
Ruhle, Laura/William Floyd School Dist	5	233
Ruiz, Lisa/East Rockaway Union Free SD	1	118
Ruiz, Raymond/Patchogue-Medford Unified SD	31	227
Ruland, Lisa/Gilbertsville-Mt Upton SD	37,270	173
Ruller, Margaret, Dr/Hendrick Hudson Ctl Sch Dist	8,11,31,57,273,288,296,298	256
Rullo, Michael/Harpursville Central Sch Dist	1	28
Rumovicz, Kristin/Unadilla Valley Ctl Sch Dist	67	43
Rumsey, Joseph/Bath Central School Dist	1,11,83	213
Runbincin, Leslie/Carle Place Union Free SD	61	117
Rundle, Randy/Westmoreland Central Sch Dist	3	153
Rung, Lori/Canaseraga Central Sch Dist	58	14
Runner, Donna, Dr/Gouverneur Ctl School Dist	8,11,288,296,298	210
Rupp, Bill/Heuvelton Central School Dist	5	210
Rusinski, Nancy/Alden Central School Dist	8,11,88	56
Russ, Brian/East Aurora Union Free SD	1	60
Russell, Bonnie/West Genesee Ctl School Dist	71	159
Russell, Caleb/Eldred Central School Dist	2	236
Russell, Dawn/Monroe Woodbury Central SD	5	165
Russell, Douglas/Sidney Central School Dist	5	50
Russell, Kathleen/Edmeston Ctl School Dist	83,85,88	173
Russell, Leighanne/Fallsburg Central School Dist	58,79,83	236
Russell, Mark/Ticonderoga Central Sch Dist	67	68
Russell, Megan/Franklinville Ctl School Dist	13,77,83,88,270	31
Russell, Melinda/Broome-Tioga BOCES	31	31
Russell, Tonya/Geneva City School Dist	79	161

1 Superintendent	16 Instructional Media Svcs	30 Adult Education	44 Science Sec	58 Special Education K-12	72 Summer School	88 Alternative/At Risk	277 Remedial Math K-12
2 Bus/Finance/Purchasing	17 Chief Operations Officer	31 Career/Sch-to-Work K-12	45 Math K-12	59 Special Education Elem	73 Instructional Tech	89 Multi-Cultural Curriculum	280 Literacy Coach
3 Buildings And Grounds	18 Chief Academic Officer	32 Career/Sch-to-Work Elem	46 Math Elem	60 Special Education Sec	74 Inservice Training	90 Social Work	285 STEM
4 Food Service	19 Chief Financial Officer	33 Career/Sch-to-Work Sec	47 Math Sec	61 Foreign/World Lang K-12	75 Marketing/Distributive	91 Safety/Security	286 Digital Learning
5 Transportation	20 Art K-12	34 Early Childhood Ed	48 English/Lang Arts K-12	62 Foreign/World Lang Elem	76 Info Systems	92 Magnet School	288 Common Core Standards
6 Athletic	21 Art Elem	35 Health/Phys Education	49 English/Lang Arts Elem	63 Foreign/World Lang Sec	77 Psychological Assess	93 Parental Involvement	294 Accountability
7 Health Services	22 Art Sec	36 Guidance Services K-12	50 English/Lang Arts Sec	64 Religious Education K-12	78 Affirmative Action	95 Tech Prep Program	295 Network System
8 Curric/Instruct K-12	23 Music K-12	37 Guidance Services Elem	51 Reading K-12	65 Religious Education Elem	79 Student Personnel	97 Chief Information Officer	296 Title II Programs
9 Curric/Instruct Elem	24 Music Elem	38 Guidance Services Sec	52 Reading Elem	66 Religious Education Sec	80 Driver Ed/Safety	98 Chief Technology Officer	297 Webmaster
10 Curric/Instruct Sec	25 Music Sec	39 Social Studies K-12	53 Reading Sec	67 School Board President	81 Gifted/Talented	270 Character Education	298 Grant Writer/Ptnrships
11 Federal Program	26 Business Education	40 Social Studies Elem	54 Remedial Reading K-12	68 Teacher Personnel	82 Video Services	271 Migrant Education	750 Chief Innovation Officer
12 Title I	27 Career & Tech Ed	41 Social Studies Sec	55 Remedial Reading Elem	69 Academic Assessment	83 Substance Abuse Prev	273 Teacher Mentor	751 Chief of Staff
13 Title V	28 Technology Education	42 Science K-12	56 Remedial Reading Sec	70 Research/Development	84 Erate	274 Before/After Sch	752 Social Emotional Learning
15 Asst Superintendent	29 Family/Consumer Science	43 Science Elem	57 Bilingual/ELL	71 Public Information	85 AIDS Education	275 Response To Intervention	

NY-T54

New York School Directory

DISTRICT PERSONNEL INDEX

NAME/District	JOB FUNCTIONS	PAGE
Russell, Vicki/Crown Point Central Sch Dist	2	67
Russem, Jacob/Island Park Union Free SD	59,69	122
Russo, Anthony/East Meadow Union Free SD	15,68	118
Russo, Charles, Dr/East Moriches Union Free SD	84	221
Russo, David/Whitesboro Ctl School Dist	8,15,16,74,273,288,294	153
Russo, Jill/Nanuet Union Free School Dist	5	196
Russo, Katherine/Locust Valley Ctl School Dist	5	123
Russo, Patricia/Smithtown Central Sch Dist	30	230
Russo, Peter/Long Beach City School Dist	60	124
Russo, Richard/North Bellmore Union Free SD	3	126
Russo, William/Buffalo Public Schools	73	57
Rust, Cathie/Wells Central School Dist	67	77
Rust, Dennis/Long Lake Central School Dist	73	76
Rutherford, Louise/Camden Central School Dist	8,15	150
Rutkoske, Lisa/Herricks Union Free Sch Dist	2,15	121
Rutlugde, Jeff/Bradford Central Sch Dist	6	207
Rutnik, Lynne/Lake George Central Sch Dist	1	245
Rux, Danika/Community School District 5	1	140
Ryan, Andrea/Green Island Union Free SD	67	10
Ryan, Angela/Buffalo Public Schools	297	57
Ryan, Corinne/Rye Neck Union Free Sch Dist	33,36,79	261
Ryan, Deb/Kendall Central School Dist	2,19	169
Ryan, James/Port Chester Rye Union Free SD	6,7,35	261
Ryan, James, Dr/Putnam-Northern Wstchstr BOCES	1,11	266
Ryan, John/Longwood Central School Dist	5	224
Ryan, John/Victor Central School Dist	83,90	162
Ryan, Kathy/Albany City School Dist	6	9
Ryan, Laurel/Rye Neck Union Free Sch Dist	93	261
Ryan, Lisa/Monroe 1 BOCES	2,3,15	115
Ryan, Lori/Manchester-Shortsville Ctl SD	36	162
Ryan, Maureen/New Paltz Ctl School Dist	5	242
Ryan, Megan/North Merrick Union Free SD	67	126
Ryan, Michelle, Dr/Monroe 1 BOCES	15,69,294	115
Ryan, Michelle, Dr/Monroe 2 Orleans BOCES	15,69,294	115
Ryan, Paul, Dr/Port Byron Ctl School Dist	67	35
Ryan, Robert/Kendall Central School Dist	5	169
Ryan, Sean/Whitesboro Ctl School Dist	42	153
Ryan, Tim/Bainbridge Guilford CSD	1	41
Ryan, Timothy/Fabius Pompey Central SD	1	155
Rychcik, Greer, Dr/Hyde Park Central School Dist	1	52
Rycroft, Victor/Canton Central School Dist	67	209
Rydell, Mike/Port Jervis City School Dist	1,11,57,83	166
Ryder, Denise/Jericho Union Free School Dist	16,82	122
Ryder, Sue/Whitehall Central School Dist	5	248
Ryfun, Naomi/Altmar-Parish-Williamstown SD	8,15,76	170
Rylott, Jennifer/Shelter Island Union Free SD	8,288	230
Ryvicker, Jeffrey/Quogue Union Free School Dist	1	228

S

NAME/District	JOB FUNCTIONS	PAGE
Sabattis, Brian/North Warren Central Sch Dist	3	246
Sabo, Steven/Niagara-Wheatfield Ctl SD	67	148
Saboda, Jennifer/Erie 2 Chautauqua-Catta BOCES	58,77,275	67
Sackett, Tara/Walton Central School Dist	58	50
Sacks, Brian/Riverhead Central School Dist	6,35,80	228
Sacks, Ron/Sachem Central School Dist	2,84	229
Sadia, Dan/Roosevelt Union Free Sch Dist	3	128
Sadowski, Colleen/Rochester City School Dist	16,82	110
Sage, Coleen/Newcomb Central School Dist	2	68
Sage, Michael/Lancaster Central Sch Dist	67	62
Saggiomo, Rebecca/Spencer Van Etten Central SD	6	238
Saglibene, Stacy/Greater Southern Tier BOCES	58,77	215
Sahler, O, Dr/Wayne-Finger Lakes BOCES	67	252
Saidens, Michael/Locust Valley Ctl School Dist	58,79	123
Saitta, James/Lynbrook Union Free SD	3	124
Saks, Damian/Corning-Painted Post Area SD	6	214
Salamino, Lawrence/Lyncourt Union Free Sch Dist	67	156
Salas, Edwin/West Babylon Union Free SD	91	233
Salasny, Jeff/Windsor Central School Dist	27,72,88	30
Sales, Brian/Copiague Union Free Sch Dist	67	220
Salierno, Robert/Harrison Central School Dist	2,4,5,15	256
Salina, Edward, Dr/Plainedge Union Free Sch Dist	1	127
Salisbury, Al/Oriskany Ctl School Dist	5	151
Salisbury, James/Unatego Unadilla Central SD	67	174
Salisbury, Kevin/Southwestern Central Srch Dist	6	39
Salls, Todd/Union Springs Ctl School Dist	6	35
Saltzberg, Jonathan/Spencerport Central Sch Dist	3	112
Salum, Christopher/Haldane Central School Dist	6,7,35	175
Salvato, Steven/Warwick Valley Central SD	3	167
Salvo, Tracy/Burnt Hills Ballston Lake SD	16,73	200
Salzman, Daniel/Jericho Union Free School Dist	48,51	122
Sambets, Frank/Chester Union Free School Dist	67	163
Sammarco, Cono/Niagara-Wheatfield Ctl SD	3	148
Sampino, Janine/Rockville Ctr Union Free SD	8	128
Sample, Heidi/Northeastern Clinton Ctl SD	9,12	44
Samuels, Kamar/Community School District 13	1	82
Samuels, Teresa/North Rockland Central SD	5,91	197
Sanborn, William/Churchville Chili Ctl Sch Dist	91	107
Sanchez-Medina, Mirza/New York City Dept of Ed	57	134
Sanchez, Carlos/Brentwood Union Free Sch Dist	91	217
Sanchez, Jason/Central Valley School Dist	67	77
Sanchez, Jason/Onc BOCES	58	51
Sanchez, Madeline/Peekskill City School Dist	57,61,280	260
Sanchez, Mandi/Gouverneur Ctl School Dist	57	210
Sanchez, Raymond/Ossining Union Free Sch Dist	1	259
Sanchez, Stephanie/Holley Central School Dist	58	169
Sandak, Brian/Port Jefferson Union Free SD 6	73,84	228
Sandell, Rosanna/Lockport City School Dist	11,70,298	147
Sander, David/Cobleskill Richmondville SD	73	206
Sanders, Emily/Hoosick Falls Central Sch Dist	2,84	190
Sanders, Gail/Harborfields Ctl School Dist	4	223
Sanders, Karryann/Worcester Ctl School Dist	57	174
Sanders, Mathew/North Collins Ctl Sch Dist	3	63
Sanders, Neil/Guilderland Central Sch Dist	2,15	10
Sanders, Pam/Port Washington Union Free SD	4	128
Sanderson, Mark/Letchworth Central School Dist	6	267
Sanderson, Scott/Canton Central School Dist	3	209
Sandford, Darla/Mayfield Ctl School Dist	4	72
Sandora-Earl, Rosemarie/Lake George Central Sch Dist	27,83,88	245
Sands, Michelle/North Salem Central School Dist	81	259
Sandstrom, Tina/Jamestown City School Dist	11,34,271	38
Sandusky, Patricia/La Fayette Central School Dist	295	156
Sanfilippo, Lisa/Eastchester Union Free SD	2,15	254
Sanford-Krug, Phyllis/East Greenbush Central SD	4	190
Sanford, Christina/George Junior Republic UFSD	10	240
Sanford, Holly/Catskill Central School Dist	2	75
Sanford, Sally/Gates Chili Central Sch Dist	2	108
Sangiacomo, Jennifer/Cohoes City School Dist	73	10
Sansone, Carla/Washingtonville Central SD	273	167
Sansoucie, Stacy/East Rochester Union Free SD	2	107
Santabarbara, Angelo/Schalmont Central School Dist	67	204
Santandrea, Amy/Berne-Knox-Westerlo Central SD	5	10
Santangelo, Diane/Rye Neck Union Free Sch Dist	11,58,298	261
Santiago, David/Peekskill City School Dist	91	260
Santiago, Jorge/Westbury Union Free Sch Dist	58	132
Santillo, Frank/Island Park Union Free SD	3	122
Santo, Gail/Connetquot Central School Dist	57,79,83,88	219
Santomassino, Mark/New York Mills Union Free SD	3	151
Santomassino, Mark/Oriskany Ctl School Dist	3	151
Santora, Sarah/Caledonia-Mumford Ctl Sch Dist	30	102
Santoro, Gregory/Skaneateles Central Sch Dist	72	157
Santoro, William/Bethpage Union Free Sch Dist	295	117
Sanzo, Steven, Dr/Palmyra-Macedon Central SD	72	250
Sapia, Jolynn/Half Hollow Hills Central SD	26,73	222
Sapienza, Jim/Palmyra-Macedon Central SD	2	250
Sapienza, Joseph/Voorheesville Central Sch Dist	35	12
Sapp, Randolph/Peru Central School Dist	2,11	44
Sarkees, Deborah/Sweet Home Central Sch Dist	2	63
Sarner, Eric/New York Mills Union Free SD	73,295	151
Sartell, Jeanna/Ft Edward Union Free Sch Dist	4	247
Sass, Emily/Niagara-Wheatfield Ctl SD	58	148
Sassi, Lisa, Dr/Monroe Woodbury Central SD	7	165
Sassone, Kaitlyn/Rye City School Dist	73,97	261
Saterlee, Mike/Greater Johnstown Sch Dist	6,35,85	71
Sattora, James/Pavilion Ctl School Dist	6	74
Sattora, Kelly/Geneseo Central Sch Dist	12	103
Saucke, Kristina/Naples Central School Dist	8,11	162
Sauer, Lisa/Pavilion Ctl School Dist	7	74
Saunders, Andrea/Haldane Central School Dist	51,54	176
Saunders, Dave/Wellsville Central Sch Dist	5	15
Saunders, Megan/Bolivar-Richburg Ctrl Sch Dist	2	14
Saunders, Patricia/Corinth Central School Dist	56	200
Sautner, Jeffrey/Commack Union Free School Dist	39	219

DISTRICT PERSONNEL INDEX

Market Data Retrieval

NAME/District	JOB FUNCTIONS	PAGE
Savage, Anne/Albany City School Dist	67	9
Savage, Paul/Ausable Valley Ctl Sch Dist	1	43
Savasta, Anthony/Windham Ashland Jewett Ctl SD	73,295	76
Savella, Mark/North Babylon Union Free SD	4	226
Savin, Nicholas/Onc BOCES	1,11	51
Savino, Alicia/Niagara Falls City Sch Dist	68	147
Savino, Lori-Ann/Jericho Union Free School Dist	5	122
Savory, Michelle/Broome-Tioga BOCES	70,74	31
Sawmiller, Patricia/Syracuse City School Dist	8	158
Sawyer, Patti/Hoosic Valley Central Sch Dist	58	190
Saxton, Joshua/Westmoreland Central Sch Dist	10	153
Saxton, Stephen/Avoca Central School Dist	1,11	213
Scaduto, Elizabeth/Riverhead Central School Dist	57	228
Scagel, Timm/Hammond Central School Distict	77	210
Scalise, Joseph/Burnt Hills Ballston Lake SD	6,7,35	200
Scalise, Stacey/William Floyd School Dist	9	233
Scalisi, John/Rockville Ctr Union Free SD	3,91	128
Scally, Bonnie/Half Hollow Hills Central SD	4	222
Scammell, Terry/Sagaponack Common School Dist	9,11,69,271,275	229
Scanlon, Kevin/Three Village Central Sch Dist	8,15,74,273,288	232
Scantlebury, Joy/Pocantico Hills Ctl Sch Dist	57	260
Scanzuso, Anthony/Williamsville Ctl School Dist	15,58,77,275	64
Scappatore, Robert/Little Flower Union Free SD	8,73	224
Scarpinato, Joseph/Longwood Central School Dist	76	225
Scarunio, Nicole/Tuxedo Union Free Sch Dist	77,79	167
Scatorro, Micheal/East Williston Union Free SD	6,35,85	118
Scaturro, Marcy/Marlboro Central School Dist	38	242
Schading, Rachael/Canandaigua City School Dist	58	161
Schafer, Cindy/Waverly Ctl School Dist	274	239
Schafer, Jill/Adirondack Central Sch Dist	73	150
Schafer, Robert/Town of Webb Union Free SD	73,295	78
Schaffer, Leah/Canajoharie Ctl School Dist	2	115
Schaming, Mark/New York State Dept Education	15,89	1
Schanck, Daniel/South Seneca Ctl School Dist	77	208
Schaub, Karen/Moravia Central School Dist	285	35
Schaus, Amanda/Wilson Central School Dist	12,58	149
Scheemaker, Erin/Vernon-Verona-Sherrill CSD	68,79	152
Scheibling, Barbara/Florida Union Free School Dist	31	164
Scheid, Charles/Greenport Union Free Sch Dist	2	222
Scheid, Charles/Southold Union Free Sch Dist	2,15,84	231
Scheiten, Crista/Buffalo Public Schools	79	57
Schelmidine, John/Sandy Creek Central Sch Dist	67	172
Schenker, Jonah/Ulster BOCES	15,69,70,73,74	244
Schenone, Eric/Corinth Central School Dist	8,288	200
Schick, Craig/Hamilton Central Sch Dist	3	105
Schiedo, Michael/Mexico Central School Dist	1	171
Schiek, Michelle/Wayne Central School Dist	7,27,34,58,78,79,83,88	251
Schiff, Marjorie/Katonah-Lewisboro Sch Dist	67	257
Schifley, Sue/Allegany-Limestone Ctl SD	67	31
Schilling, Jill/Lindenhurst Union Free SD	57,61	224
Schimitt, James/Newfane Central School Dist	67	147
Schimpf, Nicole/Valley Stream Union Free SD 30	59	131
Schippa, Joseph/Edgemont Union Free Sch Dist	79	254
Schiumo, Chris/West Valley Ctl Sch Dist	6	33
Schlenke, Liz/Sharon Springs Ctl SD	31,36,83,88	207
Schloicka, Steve/Poughkeepsie City School Dist	2,3,15	53
Schlossberg, Howard/Niskayuna Central School Dist	67	204
Schloth, Robert/Oceanside Union Free Sch Dist	3	127
Schmandt, Tim/Rochester City School Dist	2	110
Schmandt, Tom/Palmyra-Macedon Central SD	6,35,85	250
Schmettan, Jessica/Port Jefferson Union Free SD 6	1	228
Schmidt, Laura/Averill Park Central Sch Dist	57	189
Schmidt, Nicole/Red Hook Central School Dist	31,36,69,83	53
Schmidt, Stacy/Springs Union Free School Dist	69	232
Schmidt, Susan/Sullivan BOCES	15	238
Schmidt, Theresa/Sewanhaka Ctl High Sch Dist	6,35,80,83,85	129
Schmidtz, Lori/Tri-Valley Central School Dist	5	237

NAME/District	JOB FUNCTIONS	PAGE
Schmieder, Edward/Sayville Union Free Sch Dist	48	229
Schmitt, Brian/Genesee Valley Ctl School Dist	1,11	15
Schmitt, Mary/Delaware Academy Ctrl SD Delhi	7	49
Schmitt, Michael/Rochester City School Dist	3,17	110
Schmitt, Patricia/Northport-East Northport UFSD	48	227
Schneeberger, Thomas/Lowville Acad-Central Sch Dist	67	101
Schneider, David/Bethpage Union Free Sch Dist	1	117
Schneider, James/Belfast Central School Dist	5	14
Schneider, James/Belfast Central School Dist	3	14
Schneider, Leanne/Tioga Central School Dist	27,30,36	239
Schneider, Sam/Riverhead Central School Dist	2,15,68	228
Schneider, Sue/Wheelerville Union Free SD	7	72
Schnell, Christine/Sag Harbor Union Free Sch Dist	2	229
Schnell, Christine/Wainscott Common School Dist	2	232
Schneller, Sara/Schenectady City School Dist	70,294	204
Schoene, Jennifer/Wayne Central School Dist	67	251
Schoenfeld, Michele/White Plains City School Dist	71	263
Schoenfeld, Ryan, Dr/Ardsley Union Free School Dist	1	252
Schofield, Phil/Owego Apalachin Ctl Sch Dist	69	238
Scholl, David/Cato Meridian Central Sch Dist	6,7	34
Schon, Kim/West Irondequoit Ctl SD	6,35	113
Schongar, Robert/Lansingburgh Central Sch Dist	3	190
Schoonmaker, Gail/Hancock Central School Dist	82	49
Schorer, Rebecca/Wayland-Cohocton Central SD	4	215
Schorr, Rebecca/Livonia Ctl School Dist	4	103
Schouten, Art/Wappingers Central Sch Dist	16,73	54
Schowe, Bonnie/Unadilla Valley Ctl Sch Dist	4,295	43
Schrader, Rebecca/Bradford Central School Dist	81	207
Schrage, Matt/Canandaigua City School Dist	8,12,15,288,296	161
Schramm, Richard/Commack Union Free School Dist	3	219
Schreiber, Shea/Alexander Ctl School Dist	5	73
Schretzmayer, Cathy/Miller Place Union Free SD	4	226
Schroeder, Antonietta/Menands Union Free Sch Dist	9,59,88,270,273	11
Schroeder, Lisa/Lockport City School Dist	7,15,68	147
Schrom, Bill/Ravena Coeymans Selkirk Ctl SD	3,73,91,295	11
Schubmehal, David/Avoca Central School Dist	5	213
Schuchman, Lisa/Hendrick Hudson Ctl Sch Dist	34,58,79,83	256
Schuchman, Matthew/Clarkstown Central School Dist	285	195
Schuck, Andrew/Dundee Ctl School Dist	3	268
Schue, Janice/Jordan Elbridge Ctl Sch Dist	8,11,15,31,57,69,273,288	155
Schueffleir, Kathleen/Wyoming Central School Dist	1,11	268
Schular, Dan/Perry Central School Dist	11,57,58,79,285,296	267
Schulder, Brian/Yonkers Public School Dist	91	263
Schuler, Bart/Newfane Central School Dist	2,5,11	147
Schulman, Ira/Byram Hills Central Sch Dist	67	253
Schultz, Brian/West Seneca Central Sch Dist	2,70	64
Schultz, Carey/Delaware Academy Ctrl SD Delhi	2,11,296	49
Schultz, Edie/Cobleskill Richmondville SD	31,36,83	206
Schultz, Eric/Nassau BOCES	67	134
Schultz, Michael/Brocton Central School Dist	73,98,295	36
Schulz, Sara/Jefferson Central Sch Dist	67	206
Schunke, Derek/Franklinville Ctl School Dist	273	31
Schuster, Judy/Rochester City School Dist	2,298	110
Schutt, Karissa/Geneva City School Dist	34	161
Schwabrow, Jennifer/Canajoharie Ctl School Dist	8,58	115
Schwall, Sue/Ellenville Central School Dist	2	241
Schwanekamp, Danielle/Buffalo Public Schools	298	57
Schwanse, Herb/Cairo-Durham Ctl School Dist	5	75
Schwanz, James/Buffalo Public Schools	23	57
Schwartz, Barbara/Roslyn School Dist	11,58,79	129
Schwartz, Gary/Carthage Central School Dist	67	80
Schwartz, Ira/New York State Dept Education	12,15,70,271,294	1
Schwartz, Julie/Pleasantville Union Free SD	71	260
Schwartz, Louis/Dobbs Ferry Union Free SD	67	254
Schwegler, Douglas/East Ramapo Central Sch Dist	5	196
Schweizer, Samantha/Mayfield Ctl School Dist	2	72
Schweizer, Samantha/Troy City School Dsitrict	2	191

1 Superintendent	16 Instructional Media Svcs	30 Adult Education	44 Science Sec	58 Special Education K-12	72 Summer School	88 Alternative/At Risk	277 Remedial Math K-12
2 Bus/Finance/Purchasing	17 Chief Operations Officer	31 Career/Sch-to-Work K-12	45 Math K-12	59 Special Education Elem	73 Instructional Tech	89 Multi-Cultural Curriculum	280 Literacy Coach
3 Buildings And Grounds	18 Chief Academic Officer	32 Career/Sch-to-Work Elem	46 Math Elem	60 Special Education Sec	74 Inservice Training	90 Social Work	285 STEM
4 Food Service	19 Chief Financial Officer	33 Career/Sch-to-Work Sec	47 Math Sec	61 Foreign/World Lang K-12	75 Marketing/Distributive	91 Safety/Security	286 Digital Learning
5 Transportation	20 Art K-12	34 Early Childhood Ed	48 English/Lang Arts K-12	62 Foreign/World Lang Elem	76 Info Systems	92 Magnet School	288 Common Core Standards
6 Athletic	21 Art Elem	35 Health/Phys Education	49 English/Lang Arts Elem	63 Foreign/World Lang Sec	77 Psychological Assess	93 Parental Involvement	294 Accountability
7 Health Services	22 Art Sec	36 Guidance Services K-12	50 English/Lang Arts Sec	64 Religious Education K-12	78 Affirmative Action	95 Tech Prep Program	295 Network System
8 Curric/Instruct K-12	23 Music K-12	37 Guidance Services Elem	51 Reading K-12	65 Religious Education Elem	79 Student Personnel	97 Chief Information Officer	296 Title II Programs
9 Curric/Instruct Elem	24 Music Elem	38 Guidance Services Sec	52 Reading Elem	66 Religious Education Sec	80 Driver Ed/Safety	98 Chief Technology Officer	297 Webmaster
10 Curric/Instruct Sec	25 Music Sec	39 Social Studies K-12	53 Reading Sec	67 School Board President	81 Gifted/Talented	270 Character Education	298 Grant Writer/Ptnrships
11 Federal Program	26 Business Education	40 Social Studies Elem	54 Remedial Reading K-12	68 Teacher Personnel	82 Video Services	271 Migrant Education	750 Chief Innovation Officer
12 Title I	27 Career & Tech Ed	41 Social Studies Sec	55 Remedial Reading Elem	69 Academic Assessment	83 Substance Abuse Prev	273 Teacher Mentor	751 Chief of Staff
13 Title V	28 Technology Education	42 Science K-12	56 Remedial Reading Sec	70 Research/Development	84 Erate	274 Before/After Sch	752 Social Emotional Learning
15 Asst Superintendent	29 Family/Consumer Science	43 Science Elem	57 Bilingual/ELL	71 Public Information	85 AIDS Education	275 Response To Intervention	

NY-T56

New York School Directory

DISTRICT PERSONNEL INDEX

NAME/District	JOB FUNCTIONS	PAGE
Schwendinger, Rachel/Argyle Central School Dist	2	246
Schwendinger, Rachel/Waterford Halfmoon School Dist	2,5	203
Schwetz, Patricia/Nassau BOCES	58	134
Scialbone, Peter/Sauquoit Valley Central SD	38	152
Scialdone, Peter/Sauquoit Valley Central SD	38	152
Scimeca, Russell/Sharon Springs Ctl SD	11,58,271,296	207
Scism, Grace/Hilton Central School Dist	71,297	109
Scofield, Douglas/Iroquois Central School Dist	1	61
Scotch, Joanna/Ft Edward Union Free Sch Dist	38,69	247
Scott, Alissa/Mohonasen Central Sch Dist	71,76	204
Scott, Kimberly/Parishville Hopkinton Sch Dist	16,82	212
Scott, Robert/Pine Plains Ctl School Dist	6	53
Scott, Thomas/Middletown Enlarged City SD	3,91	165
Scott, Warren/Franklinville Ctl School Dist	8,11	31
Scrio, Jacqueline/Connetquot Central School Dist	2,15	219
Scrio, Jacqueline/East Rockaway Union Free SD	2,3,15	118
Scriven, Julie/North Colonie Central SD	73	11
Scro, Anthony/Port Byron Ctl School Dist	2	35
Scroger, Vickie/Holley Central School Dist	4	169
Scroggins, David/North Warren Central School Dist	4	246
Scudder, Melissa/Parishville Hopkinton Sch Dist	33,36,69,88,271,296	212
Scudiero, Theresa/Long Beach City School Dist	10,16,41,50,53,57	124
Scullion, Mary/Tonawanda City School Dist	8,11,69,74,275,280,285,288	64
Sculnick, Mary/East Ramapo Central Sch Dist	15,68	196
Scutt, Brenda/De Ruyter Central School Dist	4	105
Seaman, Linda/New York State Dept Education	72,83,91	1
Seamans, Howard/Moravia Central School Dist	9,34,51,54,273	35
Searles, Joanne/Hartford Central School Dist	2	248
Sears, Deann/Skaneateles Central Sch Dist	6	157
Sears, Jennifer/Frewsburg Central School Dist	23	38
Sears, Kate/Remsenburg-Speonk UFSD	57	228
Sears, Michael/Cuba-Rushford Central Sch Dist	5	14
Seaver, Kendra/Tioga Central School Dist	2	239
Sebeald, Hans, Dr/Rondout Valley Ctl Sch Dist	6	243
Sebeck, Susan/Gilbertsville-Mt Upton SD	4	173
Sebelos, John/Pelham Union Free School Dist	73,286,295	260
Sebor, Lauren/Bridgehampton Union Free SD	83,88	218
Seckner, Karl/Phoenix Central School Dist	2,15	171
Sedorus, Jim/Groton Central School Dist	5	240
Seelbach, Donna/Red Hook Central School Dist	16,73,82,295	53
Seeley, James/Fort Ann Central School Dist	67	247
Segal, Carolyn/Cheektowaga-Sloan UFSD	69,91,295	59
Segal, Peter/North Shore Central SD	88	126
Segara, Emerson/Port Jervis City School Dist	73	166
Seguin, William/Massena Central School Dist	91	211
Seibert, Erica/Hornell City School Dist	8,11	214
Seibert, Kelly/Byram Hills Central Sch Dist	2,15	253
Seiders, Amy/Silver Creek Central Sch Dist	83,85,88	39
Seiflein, Dave/Springville Griffith Inst CSD	3	63
Seifried, Fred/Owen D Young Central Sch Dist	2,11,296	78
Seigers, Mark/Gilbertsville-Mt Upton SD	285	173
Seiler, Keren/Bainbridge Guilford CSD	37	41
Seinfeld, Laura, Dr/Oyster Bay East Norwich Ctl SD	1	127
Selby, Kathleen/Hamburg Central School Dist	2	61
Selesnick, Andrew/Katonah-Lewisboro Sch Dist	1	257
Seligman, Brian/Harrison Central School Dist	12,73,76	256
Sellers, Dottie/Ballston Spa Ctl School Dist	67	200
Sells-Ash, Lisa/Valley Stream Union Free SD 13	15,57,78	130
Selser, Susan/Greenwood Lake Union Free SD	67	164
Semel, Ellen, Dr/Islip Union Free School Dist	1	224
Semeraro, Brenda/Cato Meridian Central Sch Dist	2,11,83,88,91	34
Semler, Suzanne/Sewanhaka Ctl High Sch Dist	4	129
Semo, Jason/Chappaqua Central School Dist	6,35,85	253
Seniuk, Cynthia, Dr/North Merrick Union Free SD	1	126
Senn, Lisa/Remsenburg-Speonk UFSD	4	228
Senn, Ron/Remsenburg-Speonk UFSD	3	228
Senus, Barbara/North Collins Ctl Sch Dist	7	63
Serbaniewicz, Darlene/Dryden Central School Dist	4	239
Serio-Vaughan, Debra, Dr/Briarcliff Manor Union Free SD	12,58,77,78,79	253
Serra, Christopher, Dr/Clarkstown Central School Dist	6,35	195
Serratore, Marianne/Valley Central School Dist	8,15	167
Serro, Karen/Valley Stream Union Free SD 24	90	131
Sesso, Gloria/Patchogue-Medford Unified SD	41	227
Seus, William/Sayville Union Free Sch Dist	16,73,76,82,295	229
Severance, Lin, Dr/Guilderland Central Sch Dist	15,68,78	11

NAME/District	JOB FUNCTIONS	PAGE
Severtson, Sally/Whitesville Central Sch Dist	16	15
Sewell, Everton/Rochester City School Dist	2,19	110
Sexton, Joann/Whitney Point Central Sch Dist	8,57,270,285,288,296,298	30
Seymour, Edith/Hermon-DeKalb Central Sch Dist	11,69,73,76	210
Seymour, Nicole/Franklin Central School Dist	7	49
Seymour, Timothy/St Regis Falls Ctl Sch Dist	1	70
Sgarlata, John/Weedsport Ctl School Dist	83	35
Shafer, Kristy/Wayland-Cohocton Central SD	285	215
Shafer, Stephen/Franklin-Essex-Hamilton BOCES	1,11	71
Shaffer, Stacie/Phoenix Central School Dist	9,285	171
Shaibi, Finune/Clarence Central School Dist	8,97	59
Shaji, Neena/Clarkstown Central School Dist	69	195
Shalna, Delores/Norwich City School Dist	4	42
Shambo, Peter/Penfield Central School Dist	6	109
Shampoe, Carrie/Clymer Central School Dist	57,63	37
Shanahan, Daniel, Dr/East Ramapo Central Sch Dist	11,15,296,298	196
Shanahan, David/Elwood Union Free School Dist	6,35,83	221
Shanahan, Lynn, Dr/Amherst Central School Dist	8,15,73	56
Shanahan, Patrick/Cayuga-Onondaga BOCES	68	36
Shands, Mary/Schalmont Central School Dist	16	204
Shaner, Linda/Andover Central School Dist	26	14
Shannon, Cassie/Glen Cove City School Dist	45	120
Shannon, Monica/Fairport Ctl School Dist	2	108
Shaps, Robert, Dr/Mamaroneck Union Free Sch Dist	1	257
Sharlette, Bernie/Oneida City School Dist	3	105
Sharlow, Jean/Marcellus Central School Dist	8,15,69,76	157
Sharlow, Paula/Rush Henrietta Central SD	11,296	112
Sharma, Anuraag/New York City Dept of Ed	73,76	134
Sharp, Edie/New York City Dept of Ed	70,751	134
Sharp, Mike/Schroon Lake Ctl School Dist	35,85	68
Sharpe, Jade/Yonkers Public School Dist	36	263
Sharpsteen, Dale/Moravia Central School Dist	3	34
Sharrock, Duane/Dutchess Co BOCES	88	55
Sharrott, Joanne/Connetquot Central School Dist	2	219
Shatraw, Adam/East Syracuse Minoa Ctl SD	23	154
Shaughnessy, James/Kingston City School Dist	67	242
Shaw, Trisha/Hartford Central School Dist	37	248
Shawhan, Joanne, Dr/New York State Dept Education	16	1
Shea, Barbara/Buffalo Public Schools	51,280	57
Shearer, Jennifer/Chautauqua Lake Central SD	4	36
Shearer, Kristen/Eastchester Union Free SD	36	254
Shearer, Kristen/Schenectady City School Dist	79	204
Sheboy, Frank, Dr/Highland Falls-Ft Montgmry SD	1	164
Shedlock, Nancy/Hornell City School Dist	83	214
Sheehan, Brian/Elmira City School Dist	68	40
Sheehan, Ellen/Solvay Union Free Sch Dist	58	158
Sheeley, James/Pulaski Central School Dist	3	172
Sheerer, Jennifer/Hadley-Luzerne Ctl Sch Dist	57	245
Sheevers, Erin/Troy City School Dsitrict	73,285,286	191
Sheffield, Diane/Lyncourt Union Free Sch Dist	52,55	156
Sheilds, Christopher, Dr/Port Washington Union Free SD	15	128
Sheilds, Maryanne/Manhasset Union Free Sch Dist	11	124
Sheinin, Debra/Hewlett Woodmere Union Free SD	67	121
Sheldon, Elliot/Hyde Park Central School Dist	3	52
Sheldon, Kevin/Arlington Central School Dist	2,15	51
Sheldon, Margaret/Keene Central School Dist	16	67
Sheldon, Matthew/Morris Central School Dist	1	173
Sheldon, Perry/Red Hook Central School Dist	3,91	53
Shelmidine, Joanne/Westmoreland Central Sch Dist	8,12,79	153
Shelmidine, Joanne, Dr/New York Mills Union Free SD	1	151
Shelmidine, John/Ctr for Instruct Tech Innov	67	172
Shepard, Leah/Honeoye Falls Lima Sch Dist	71	109
Shepardson, Donald/West Canada Valley Ctl SD	11	79
Shepardson, Donald/West Canada Valley Ctl SD	1	79
Shepardson, Scott/Dundee Ctl School Dist	6	268
Sheperd, Michael/Ctr for Instruct Tech Innov	15	172
Sheppard, Joseph/Auburn Enlarged City Sch Dist	67	34
Sheppard, Kacey/Frankfort-Schuyler Ctl SD	2,11,73	77
Sher, Karen/Nyack Union Free School Dist	5	197
Sheridan, Danielle, Dr/Deer Park Union Free Sch Dist	9,12,288	220
Sheridan, Jessica/Wayne-Finger Lakes BOCES	74	252
Sheridan, Karen/Copiague Union Free Sch Dist	7,15,36,58,79,88,90	220
Sherlock, Susan/Clarkstown Central School Dist	7	195
Sherman, Daniel/Questar III BOCES	71	192
Sherman, John/Erie 1 BOCES	67	67
Sherman, John/Holley Central School Dist	3	169

School Year 2020-2021   800-333-8802   NY-T57

DISTRICT PERSONNEL INDEX

Market Data Retrieval

NAME/District	JOB FUNCTIONS	PAGE
Sherman, Michael/Edinburg Common School Dist	3,5	201
Sherman, Ryan/Schuylerville Central Sch Dist	1,83	201
Sherrard, Adam/Port Jefferson Union Free SD 6	6	228
Sherwin, Jack/Argyle Central School Dist	6,83	246
Sherwin, Kathleen/Shenendehowa Central Sch Dist	48,280	202
Sherwood, Melissa/Cato Meridian Central Sch Dist	4	34
Sherwood, Sandra/Herkimer BOCES	1	79
Sherwood, Scott/Trumansburg Central SD	67	241
Shevlin, Charles/Randolph Central School Dist	2,5	33
Shimmel, Michael/Sherman Central School Dist	73,295	39
Shine, Elaine/Yonkers Public School Dist	11	263
Shine, Shannon/Mohonasen Central Sch Dist	1	203
Shipley, Cynthia/Scotia Glenville Ctl Sch Dist	30	205
Shipman, Leeann/Marcus Whitman Central SD	5	162
Shippee, Chad/Bolton Central School Dist	8,19	244
Shirken, Susan/Edgemont Union Free Sch Dist	15	254
Shoob, David/Roslyn School Dist	5	129
Shore, Michael/Rondout Valley Ctl Sch Dist	3,91	243
Short, Noelle/Long Lake Central School Dist	1,288	76
Shover, Jason/Lansingburgh Central Sch Dist	67	190
Showah, Anthony/Haldane Central School Dist	11,58,69,295,296	175
Shue, Sue/Frankfort-Schuyler Ctl SD	16	77
Shululu, Dapheny/Ithaca City School Dist	20,23	240
Siano Enders, Camille/Duanesburg Central Sch Dist	67	203
Siano, Patricia/Corinth Central School Dist	63	200
Sica, Randi/Cambridge Central School Dist	5	247
Sicari, Arlette/Tuckahoe Common School Dist	288	232
Sicignano, Carol/Patchogue-Medford Unified SD	5	227
Sickles, Matthew/Phelps-Clifton Springs Ctl SD	1	162
Siddon, Jeremy/Wells Central School Dist	6,288	77
Siddon, Toni/Madrid-Waddington Central SD	31,36,58,69,88,271,752	211
Sidebottom, Holly/Honeoye Falls Lima Sch Dist	10,31	109
Sidoti, Mark/Oceanside Union Free Sch Dist	16	127
Siebels, Shelly/Indian River Ctl School Dist	295	80
Siegel, Kayria/Middle Country Ctl Sch Dist	9,48,54	225
Sieverding, Joannes, Dr/North Salem Central Sch Dist	3,5,73,91	259
Sigeti, Maria/Brocton Central School Dist	35	36
Sigillo, Joseph/Nyack Union Free School Dist	6,7	197
Signorelli, Jo Ann/North Bellmore Union Free SD	83,85,88,270	126
Sikora, Arielle/Washingtonville Central SD	77	167
Silano, Philip/Port Chester Rye Union Free SD	2,4,5,15	261
Silky, Daniel/Otselic Valley Central SD	2,298	42
Silvanic, John/Chenango Forks Central SD	3	28
Silvaroli, Jo/Niagara Falls City Sch Dist	7	147
Silvaroli, Nicholas/Yorkshire-Pioneer Ctl Sch Dist	2,5,15	33
Silver, Ken/Mount Vernon City School Dist	2,3,4,15	258
Silvera, Don/Broome-Tioga BOCES	71	31
Silvernail, Lee/Schroon Lake Ctl School Dist	6	68
Silvernell, Douglas, Dr/Cambridge Central School Dist	1	247
Silverstein, Mark/Hawthorne Cedar Knolls UFSD	1	256
Silverstein, Rick/Kingston City School Dist	6,35	242
Silvis, Robin/Holley Central School Dist	67	169
Simchik, Lorna/Hamilton Central Sch Dist	5	105
Simmons, Craig/Chatham Central School Dist	67	46
Simmons, Dane/Panama Central School Dist	31,36,78,90,270	38
Simmons, Harold/Gouverneur Ctl School Dist	3	210
Simmons, James/Canandaigua City School Dist	6	161
Simms, Ed/South Colonie Central Sch Dist	67	12
Simon, Brian/Chatham Central School Dist	11,58,88,275	46
Simon, Thomas/Portville Central School Dist	1,11	32
Simoni, Joseph/Carmel Central School Dist	58,79	175
Simonitti, Lisa, Dr/Southold Union Free Sch Dist	11,36,57,58,79,275,296,298	231
Simons, Jeffrey/East Greenbush Central SD	1	190
Simonson, Charla/Broadalbin-Perth Ctl Sch Dist	69,79	71
Simpkins, Jon/Bellmore-Merrick Ctl High SD	3	117
Simpson, Edward/Utica City School Dist	58	152
Simpson, Jackie/Avon Central School Dist	79,298	102
Simpson, Jacquiline/Avon Central School Dist	8,11,57,58,296	102
Simpson, Maurita/Half Hollow Hills Central SD	5	222
Sinanis, Tony/Chappaqua Central School Dist	15,68	253
Sincavage, Thomas/Wells Central School Dist	1	77
Sincerbox, Michelle/Bath Central School Dist	58	213
Singer, Jonathan/Middle Country Ctl Sch Dist	57,285,288	225
Singleton, Demian, Dr/Guilderland Central Sch Dist	8,11,57,69,275,285,286,288	11
Sinha, Kusum, Dr/Garden City School Dist	1	120
Sinicropi, Erica/Port Byron Ctl School Dist	58,77	35
Sinsebox, Jennifer/Wheatland Chili Ctl Sch Dist	8,288	113
Sinski, Elizabeth/Wellsville Central Sch Dist	9	15
Sipes, Jessica/Buffalo Public Schools	34	57
Sipos, Carrieann/Ossining Union Free Sch Dist	9,296	259
Sipowitz, Janelle/Queensbury Union Free Sch Dist	27,31,36	246
Sira, John/Northville Central School Dist	67	72
Siracuse, Joseph, Dr/Wayne Central School Dist	1	251
Sirianni, Brian/Ballston Spa Ctl School Dist	2,4,15	200
Sirico, Gregory/Warwick Valley Central SD	6	167
Skahen, Katherine/East Syracuse Minoa Ctl SD	2	154
Skarzynski, Vikki/Ichabod Crane Central Schools	12,298	46
Skeals, Kathleen/North Colonie Central SD	10,69,288	11
Skelton, Jacqueline/Port Byron Ctl School Dist	35,83	35
Skerritt, Michael/Putnam-Northern Wstchstr BOCES	68,74	267
Skiff, Aimee/Duanesburg Central Sch Dist	11,298	203
Skillen, Kimberly/North Babylon Union Free SD	8,15,288	226
Sklar, Robin/Monticello Central School Dist	5	237
Skokrwatson, Deb/Springville Griffith Inst CSD	83	63
Skop, Anita/Community School District 15	1	84
Skuggevik, Leonard/Tuckahoe Common School Dist	1	232
Slack, Aaron/Lyndonville Central Sch Dist	10	169
Slack, Suzanne/Syracuse City School Dist	2,19	158
Slate, Penny/Hammond Central School Distict	16,73,295	210
Slate, Sue/Keshequa Central School Dist	4	103
Slate, Susan/Pavilion Ctl School Dist	4	74
Slater, Melissa/Chenango Forks Central SD	16	28
Slater, Scott/South Jefferson Central SD	1,11,57	81
Slavinski, Kathryn/Andover Central School Dist	10,30,34,48,51	14
Sledziewski, Nancy/Cheektowaga Maryvale UFSD	60	59
Sleight, Steve/Hornell City School Dist	5	214
Slentz, Kenneth/Ballston Spa Ctl School Dist	1	200
Slesinski, Christopher/Florida Union Free Sch Dist	2	164
Slesinsky, Karen/Harpursville Central Sch Dist	27,35,36,69,88	28
Sloan, Erica/Greenwich Central School Dist	4	247
Sloan, Gregory/Jericho Union Free School Dist	31,36	122
Sloan, Mathew/Middleburgh Ctl School Dist	8	206
Sloand, Bill/West Valley Ctl Sch Dist	3	33
Sluga, Ryan/Frewsburg Central School Dist	5	38
Slugg, Susan/West Irondequoit Ctl SD	77	113
Small, Marlon/Greenport Union Free Sch Dist	1,11	222
Small, Marlon/South Country Central Sch Dist	8,15,294	231
Smalline, Jeremy/Greece Central School Dist	70,79	108
Smardz, Paul/Clymer Central School Dist	16	37
Smarrelli, Jen/Westhill Central School Dist	6	159
Smiegal, Cynthia/Clinton Central School Dist	7,83	150
Smith Auer, Lisa/Schodack Central School Dist	30	191
Smith-Gravanda, Shirley/Rush Henrietta Central SD	5	112
Smith, Aaron/Honeoye Falls Lima Sch Dist	3	109
Smith, Amber/Fonda Fultonville Central SD	16	115
Smith, Andrea/Marcus Whitman Central SD	57,58,79,752	162
Smith, Anthony/Brockport Ctl School Dist	73	106
Smith, Barb/Gowanda Central School Dist	2	32
Smith, Beth/Margaretville Central Sch Dist	5	49
Smith, Brian/East Irondequoit Ctl Sch Dist	16,82	107
Smith, Carrie/Brookfield Central School Dist	8,11,68,74,271,288,294	104
Smith, Cheryl, Dr/Eastchester Union Free SD	67	254
Smith, Chris/Sharon Springs Ctl SD	6	207
Smith, Christian/Greater Amsterdam School Dist	13,58,78,79,275	115

1 Superintendent	16 Instructional Media Svcs	30 Adult Education	44 Science Sec	58 Special Education K-12	72 Summer School	88 Alternative/At Risk	277 Remedial Math K-12
2 Bus/Finance/Purchasing	17 Chief Operations Officer	31 Career/Sch-to-Work K-12	45 Math K-12	59 Special Education Elem	73 Instructional Tech	89 Multi-Cultural Curriculum	280 Literacy Coach
3 Buildings And Grounds	18 Chief Academic Officer	32 Career/Sch-to-Work Elem	46 Math Elem	60 Special Education Sec	74 Inservice Training	90 Social Work	285 STEM
4 Food Service	19 Chief Financial Officer	33 Career/Sch-to-Work Sec	47 Math Sec	61 Foreign/World Lang K-12	75 Marketing/Distributive	91 Safety/Security	286 Digital Learning
5 Transportation	20 Art K-12	34 Early Childhood Ed	48 English/Lang Arts K-12	62 Foreign/World Lang Elem	76 Info Systems	92 Magnet School	288 Common Core Standards
6 Athletic	21 Art Elem	35 Health/Phys Education	49 English/Lang Arts Elem	63 Foreign/World Lang Sec	77 Psychological Assess	93 Parental Involvement	294 Accountability
7 Health Services	22 Art Sec	36 Guidance Services K-12	50 English/Lang Arts Sec	64 Religious Education K-12	78 Affirmative Action	95 Tech Prep Program	295 Network System
8 Curric/Instruct K-12	23 Music K-12	37 Guidance Services Elem	51 Reading K-12	65 Religious Education Elem	79 Student Personnel	97 Chief Infomation Officer	296 Title II Programs
9 Curric/Instruct Elem	24 Music Elem	38 Guidance Services Sec	52 Reading Elem	66 Religious Education Sec	80 Driver Ed/Safety	98 Chief Technology Officer	297 Webmaster
10 Curric/Instruct Sec	25 Music Sec	39 Social Studies K-12	53 Reading Sec	67 School Board President	81 Gifted/Talented	270 Character Education	298 Grant Writer/Ptnrships
11 Federal Program	26 Business Education	40 Social Studies Elem	54 Remedial Reading K-12	68 Teacher Personnel	82 Video Services	271 Migrant Education	750 Chief Innovation Officer
12 Title I	27 Career & Tech Ed	41 Social Studies Sec	55 Remedial Reading Elem	69 Academic Assessment	83 Substance Abuse Prev	273 Teacher Mentor	751 Chief of Staff
13 Title V	28 Technology Education	42 Science K-12	56 Remedial Reading Sec	70 Research/Development	84 Erate	274 Before/After Sch	752 Social Emotional Learning
15 Asst Superintendent	29 Family/Consumer Science	43 Science Elem	57 Bilingual/ELL	71 Public Information	85 AIDS Education	275 Response To Intervention	

New York School Directory

DISTRICT PERSONNEL INDEX

NAME/District	JOB FUNCTIONS	PAGE
Smith, Christopher/Bath Central School Dist	73,84	213
Smith, Claire/Arkport Central School Dist	8,11,54,57,83,296,298	213
Smith, Dara/Fallsburg Central School Dist	4	236
Smith, Dara/Liberty Central School Dist	4	236
Smith, Elizabeth/Ossining Union Free Sch Dist	8	259
Smith, Erik/Holland Central School Dist	79	61
Smith, Gerilyn, Dr/East Meadow Union Free SD	36	118
Smith, Gillian/New York City Dept of Ed	36	134
Smith, Heidi/Adirondack Central Sch Dist	88,270,271	150
Smith, James/Addison Central School Dist	3,91	213
Smith, Janice/Batavia City School Dist	79	73
Smith, Jason/Lyndonville Central Sch Dist	1	169
Smith, Jeff/Johnson City Central Sch Dist	39	28
Smith, Jeffery/Jamestown City School Dist	4	38
Smith, Jeffrey/Churchville Chili Ctl Sch Dist	20,23	107
Smith, Jennifer/Andover Central School Dist	81	14
Smith, Jenny/Putnam Central School Dist	4	248
Smith, Joanne/Hancock Central School Dist	4	49
Smith, K Veronica, Dr/Mount Vernon City School Dist	15,36,79	258
Smith, Kathleen/Union Springs Ctl School Dist	4	35
Smith, Kathy/Morris Central School Dist	8,11,69,270,271,273	174
Smith, Keena/Greece Central School Dist	76	108
Smith, Kelly/Berne-Knox-Westerlo Central SD	85	10
Smith, Kelly/Lansingburgh Central Sch Dist	8,12	190
Smith, Kenneth/Dryden Central School Dist	3	239
Smith, Kenneth/Holland Patent Ctl School Dist	3	150
Smith, Kevin/New York State Dept Education	15,30,88	1
Smith, Laverne/Candor Central School Dist	3	238
Smith, Linda/Fredonia Central School Dist	29	37
Smith, Lisa/General Brown Ctl School Dist	2,8,11,15,19,285,296	80
Smith, Mary/Brewster Central School Dist	5	175
Smith, Michael/East Ramapo Central Sch Dist	20,23	196
Smith, Nicholas/Taconic Hills Central Sch Dist	3	47
Smith, Patrick/Grand Island Central Sch Dist	4	61
Smith, Patrick/Smithtown Central Sch Dist	6,35,83	230
Smith, Paul/Cortland Enlarged City SD	91	47
Smith, Peter/Jamesville-DeWitt Central SD	1,11,83	155
Smith, Quinn/Wayne-Finger Lakes BOCES	68	252
Smith, Rich/Gowanda Central School Dist	3	32
Smith, Rick/Greene Ctl School Dist	6	42
Smith, Ronald/Hermon-DeKalb Central Sch Dist	67	210
Smith, Scott/Warrensburg Central Sch Dist	6	246
Smith, Sharon/Lyndonville Central Sch Dist	8,36,58,88,97	169
Smith, Sheri/De Ruyter Central School Dist	6	105
Smith, Steve/Westhill Central School Dist	2,15	159
Smith, Steven/Central Valley School Dist	73	77
Smith, Tina, Dr/Oceanside Union Free Sch Dist	58	127
Smith, Todd/Greece Central School Dist	45,275	108
Smith, Tom/Boquet Valley Central School Dist	6	67
Smith, Trica/Arkport Central School Dist	7,85	213
Smith, Vincent/Jordan Elbridge Ctl Sch Dist	3	155
Smith, Warren/Onondaga Central School Dist	8,11,57,69,271	157
Smithers, Patricia/Ogdensburg City School Dist	2	211
Smithson, Steve/Owen D Young Central Sch Dist	73	78
Smoulcey, Pamela/New Hartford Central Sch Dist	58,69,77,79,90	151
Smyth, Donna/Argyle Central School Dist	16	246
Snavely, Christina/Bath Central School Dist	57	213
Snell, Laura/Smithtown Central Sch Dist	42	230
Snide, David/Indian Lake Ctl School Dist	11,288,296	76
Snide, David/Indian Lake Ctl School Dist	1,11,288	76
Snide, Victoria/Long Lake Central School Dist	2,5	76
Snider, Julie/Harrison Central School Dist	59,90	256
Snieszko, Tracy/Manchester-Shortsville Ctl SD	31	162
Snizek, Jackie/Clinton Central School Dist	36,88	150
Snow, Cathy/Champlain Valley Ed Services	30	45
Snow, Christine/Hicksville Union Free Sch Dist	58,79	122
Snow, Cynthia/Waterville Central Sch Dist	5	153
Snow, Ed/Camden Central School Dist	5	150
Snow, Zachary/Rome City School Dist	16	151
Snyder, Gene/Alfred Almond Ctl School Dist	3,91	13
Snyder, Heather/Southern Cayuga Central SD	285	35
Snyder, Keith/Levittown Union Free Sch Dist	6,7,35,83	123
Snyder, Linda/Chenango Forks Central SD	71	28
Snyder, Lindsey/West Irondequoit Ctl SD	83	113
Snyder, Richard/Bayport- Blue Point USD	2,3,15	217
Snyder, Scott/Susquehanna Valley Central SD	83	29
Snyder, Wayne/Andes Central School Dist	3,91	48
Soanes, Karen/Bloomfield Central SD	73	161
Sobczyk, Mitch/Tuckahoe Common School Dist	3,91	232
Sobrin, Anchala, Dr/Peekskill City School Dist	285	260
Socola, Mark/Marcus Whitman Central SD	2	162
Socola, Mark/Waterloo Central School Dist	2	208
Sodeman, John/Gates Chili Central Sch Dist	91	108
Soderberg, Uris/Sherman Central School Dist	77	39
Sohal, Dharminder/Patchogue-Medford Unified SD	285	227
Sojewicz, Katie/Syracuse City School Dist	67	158
Solan, Kevin/McGraw Central School Dist	73	48
Soler, Anabell/Batavia City School Dist	1	73
Solomon, Megan/Friendship Central Sch Dist	4	15
Soluri, Katie/Sandy Creek Central Sch Dist	45	172
Soman, Sheldon/Orleans-Niagara BOCES	295	170
Somerville, Kristine/Watkins Glen Central Sch Dist	8,15,34,58,69,74,288	207
Somich, Katherine/Granville Central School Dist	2	247
Sommer, Nicole/Onteora Central School Dist	5	243
Sonders, Jessica/Ft Plain Central School Dist	68	115
Sonnacchio, Anthony/Marcellus Central School Dist	2	157
Sonneville, Jamie/Newark Central School Dist	73	250
Sonneville, Jamie/Williamson Central School Dist	67	251
Soper, Alicia/Owen D Young Central Sch Dist	31,58,752	78
Sorbera, Michael/Spencerport Central Sch Dist	58	112
Sorochin, Jennifer/Hornell City School Dist	285	214
Sortisio, Jeff/Fredonia Central School Dist	1	37
Sosenko, Lori/Depew Union Free School Dist	71	60
Sotland, Harvey/Cornwall Central School Dist	2,5,15	163
Sotland, Harvey/Mahopac Ctl School Dist	2,15	176
Soto, Ricardo/Center Moriches Union Free SD	15,68,73,79,296	218
Soto, Taren/North Rockland Central SD	58	197
Sottile, Kathleen/Floral Park Bellerose Sch Dist	1	119
Soucier, Jan/Victor Central School Dist	273	162
Southard, James/De Ruyter Central School Dist	2,11	105
Southwell, Joel/Pulaski Central School Dist	67	172
Southwick, Matt/Tupper Lake Ctl School Dist	10,11,58,79,88,273,296	70
Southwick, Matthew/Clifton-Fine Central Sch Dist	1	209
Southwick, Stephen/Northeastern Clinton Ctl SD	67	44
Southwick, Traci/Clifton-Fine Central Sch Dist	31,36,69,83,274	209
Spacht, John/Southwestern Central Sch Dist	5	39
Spada, Alex/South Glens Falls Ctl School Dist	73,295	202
Spagnolo, Frank/Kenmore-Tonawanda UF Sch Dist	76,294	62
Spagnolo, Tracy/West Seneca Central Sch Dist	79	64
Spagnuolo, Mario/Nanuet Union Free School Dist	2,15	196
Spangenburg, Lawrence/Andover Central School Dist	1	14
Sparacio, John/Islip Union Free School Dist	35	224
Sparks, Erica/Bradford Central Sch Dist	36,271	207
Spasiano, Michelle/Bemus Point Ctl School Dist	1	36
Spasiano, Michelle/Cattaraugus-Allegany BOCES	17	34
Spatolo, Joseph/Tuckahoe Union Free SD	58	262
Spaulding, Debrah/Boquet Valley Central Sch Dist	5	67
Spawton, Karen/Rochester City School Dist	34,58	110
Speers, Jennifer/Manchester-Shortsville Ctl SD	67	162
Spellburg, Jessica/South Glens Falls Ctl Sch Dist	58	202
Spence, Ed/Chester Union Free School Dist	8,16,73,76,286	163
Spence, Michael/Bethpage Union Free Sch Dist	8,15	117
Spera, David/Half Hollow Hills Central SD	91	222
Spielberg, David/Farmingdale Union Free SD	72	119
Spillman, Karen/Hilton Central School Dist	70	109
Spinelli, Anthony/West Babylon Union Free SD	7,35,83	232
Spinelli, Steve/Sodus Central School Dist	3,91	251
Spinks, Matthew/Valley Stream Union Free SD 13	24	130
Spittal, David/Putnam Valley Ctl School Dist	3,5	176
Sporyz, Barbara/Hamburg Central School Dist	15,91	61
Spota, Jennifer/Hampton Bays Union Free SD	16	222
Sprague, Mary/Webster Central School Dist	68	112
Sprague, Wendy/Roxbury Central School Dist	2,298	50
Spreckels, Michael/Seaford Union Free SD	6	129
Spretty, Joseph/Waterford Halfmoon School Dist	73	203
Spring, Constance/Friendship Central Sch Dist	2,11	15
Spring, Jennifer, Dr/Cohoes City School Dist	1	10
Spring, Laurence/Schenectady City School Dist	1	204
Springer, Kevin/De Ruyter Central School Dist	3,5	105
Springer, Kevin/Hampton Bays Union Free SD	67	222
Spulnick, Nicole/Waterford Halfmoon School Dist	273	203
Squier, Randall/Coxsackie-Athens Central SD	1	75

DISTRICT PERSONNEL INDEX

Market Data Retrieval

NAME/District	JOB FUNCTIONS	PAGE
Squillante, Frank/Monroe Woodbury Central SD	91	165
Squires, Kelly/Cheektowaga Maryvale UFSD	27,31,36,83,88	59
Squires, Kelly/Horseheads Ctl School Dist	7,11,34,57,58,88,90,296	40
Squires, Nancy/Oswego City School Dist	2	171
Srabizio, Jeannette/West Babylon Union Free SD	4	232
St Croix, Amy/Alexandria Central School Dist	12	79
St Croix, Amy/Alexandria Central School Dist	8,11,296,298	79
St Pierre, Mitch/Crown Point Central Sch Dist	67	67
St Pierre, Pierre/Tupper Lake Ctl School Dist	3,91	70
Stack, Joseph/Dolgeville Central School Dist	5	77
Stadler, Monica/East Rochester Union Free SD	13,58,79,752	107
Stadler, Monica/Newark Central School Dist	58,78,79	250
Stadtmiller, Dan/Jordan Elbridge Ctl Sch Dist	6,35	155
Stager, Tony/Horseheads Ctl School Dist	91	40
Stahl, Kim/Stamford Central School Dist	58	50
Stahl, Stacey/Moriah Central School Dist	12	68
Staib, John/Chateaugay Central School Dist	295	69
Staib, Peggie, Dr/Eastern Suffolk BOCES	8,15	235
Stalker, Sarah/Medina Central School Dist	7	169
Stalteri, April/O E S J Central School Dist	36,88	72
Stalteri, Michael/Frankfort-Schuyler Ctl SD	10,69,88,273	77
Stam, Michael/William Floyd School Dist	68	233
Stamboly, Lisa/New York Mills Union Free SD	2	151
Stamboly, Mike/Rome City School Dist	6,7,35,83,85	151
Stamoulacatos, Nicholas/Syracuse City School Dist	39	158
Standhart, Pamela/Middleburgh Ctl School Dist	67	206
Stang, Maria/Cattaraugus-Little Vly Ctl SD	5	31
Stangev, Doris/Mt Sinai Union Free SD	58	226
Stanton, Jennifer/Mexico Central School Dist	58,79	171
Stanton, Stephen/Waterville Central Sch Dist	67	153
Stapleton, James/Cohoes City School Dist	3	10
Stapleton, Rochelle/East Islip Union Free SD	74,273	220
Starbird, Sarah/Pulaski Central School Dist	2	172
Stark, Eric/Carmel Central School Dist	2,15	175
Stark, Julie/Gates Chili Central Sch Dist	60	108
Starke, Nancy/Chittenango Central SD	30	104
Starks, Jacklin/Madison-Oneida BOCES	1	154
Starks, Jacklin/Oneida-Herkimer-Mad BOCES	1	154
Starkweather, Kathy/Oakfield Alabama Ctl SD	85	74
Starr, Ken/Vestal Ctl School Dist	5	29
Starzee, Helene/Shelter Island Union Free SD	4	230
Staszak, Heather/Rensselaer City School Dist	90	191
Stath, William/Rensselaer City School Dist	6	191
Staulters, Candy/Ballston Spa Ctl School Dist	2	200
Stawicki, Eli/Jefferson Lewis BOCES	73,76	82
Stazzone, Raymond/Syracuse City School Dist	76	158
Stead, Gerald/West Valley Ctl Sch Dist	27	33
Stearns, Susan/Marcellus Central School Dist	5	157
Steel, John/Niagara-Wheatfield Ctl SD	73	148
Steele, David/Heuvelton Central School Dist	6	210
Steenberg, Donna/Brushton Moira Ctl Sch Dist	12	69
Steenberge, Jamie/Saranac Central School Dist	76	45
Steerjake, Matt/Attica Central School Dist	8,288	267
Stefanelli, Frank/White Plains City School Dist	3	263
Steger, Amy/Amherst Central School Dist	34	56
Steimel, Joeph/Eastport-South Manor Ctrl SD	1	221
Steimle, Jennifer/Saratoga Springs City Sch Dist	12,48,51,81,288	201
Steimle, Paul/Amherst Central School Dist	67	56
Stein, Carol/Irvington Union Free Sch Dist	2,3,15	257
Stein, Mark/Dutchess Co BOCES	286	55
Stein, Matt/North Colonie Central SD	6	11
Steinberg, Linda/Hyde Park Central School Dist	2,15	52
Steindam, Mara/Manhasset Union Free Sch Dist	31,39	124
Steiner, Dale/Arkport Central School Dist	6	213
Steinfeld, Sheldon/Central Islip Union Free SD	58,77	218
Steinhart, Stephanie/Brunswick Central School Dist	2,15	190
Steinmetz, Joseph/Orleans-Niagara BOCES	8,27,30,31,73,74	170
Stellato, Louis/Patchogue-Medford Unified SD	285	227
Steller, Joe/Hoosick Falls Central Sch Dist	5	190
Stem, Carol/Gates Chili Central Sch Dist	11	108
Stempel, Cora/Dutchess Co BOCES	15	55
Stenta, Tony/Sidney Central School Dist	8	50
Stephens, Mary/Amityville Union Free Sch Dist	48,57,61	216
Stephenson, Deanna/Shenendehowa Central Sch Dist	67	202
Stephney, Irene/Peru Central School Dist	12,58,79,298	44
Sterett, James/Goshen Central School Dist	76,286,295	164
Sternin, Heather/Tonawanda City School Dist	19,67	64
Steve, Micheal/Newark Central School Dist	3	250
Stevens, Cara/Canastota Central School Dist	2	104
Stevens, Donald/Watervliet City School Dist	15	12
Stevens, Matthew/Fairport Ctl School Dist	2,15,91	108
Stevens, Michael/Sandy Creek Central Sch Dist	6,35	172
Stevenson, Amy/Potsdam Central School Dist	57	212
Stevenson, Audrey/Indian River Ctl School Dist	2	80
Stevenson, Melanie/Greece Central School Dist	58	108
Stevenson, Thomas/Oysterponds Union Free SD	67	227
Stever, John/Frankfort-Schuyler Ctl SD	3,91	77
Steves, Tanya/Poland Central School Dist	4	78
Stewart, Bart/East Moriches Union Free SD	3	221
Stewart, Glen/Freeport Public School Dist	79	119
Stewart, Robert/Brasher Falls School Dist	1	209
Stewart, Russell/Smithtown Central Sch Dist	1	230
Stewart, Tim/Ichabod Crane Central Schools	6	46
Stewart, Tom/Rush Henrietta Central SD	6,35	112
Stiglmeier, Jessica/Cheektowaga-Sloan UFSD	88,90,275	59
Stile, Theresa/Waterville Central Sch Dist	16,82	153
Stillan-Dowman, Roberta/Heuvelton Central School Dist	12	210
Stillin-Dowman, Roberta/Malone Central School Dist	12	69
Stillin-Dowman, Roberta/Morristown Ctl School Dist	12	211
Stillman, Christopher/Sidney Central School Dist	3,91	50
Stimmel, John, Dr/Sayville Union Free Sch Dist	1	229
Stirling, Nicholas, Dr/Valley Stream Union Free SD 30	1	131
Stockbridge, Ashley/Fonda Fultonville Central SD	35,74	115
Stocker, Cynthia/Stockbridge Valley Central SD	1	106
Stockman, Kevin/Minerva Central School Dist	57	68
Stockmeyer, Eric/Buffalo Public Schools	73	57
Stockslader, Christine/Lancaster Central Sch Dist	16,82	62
Stoddard, Lynda/Sherburne Earlville Central SD	85	42
Stoddard, Selma/Nassau BOCES	68	134
Stolfelano, Stephen/Wells Central School Dist	286	77
Stoll, Ben/Cattaraugus-Little Vly Ctl SD	67	31
Stoltman, Adam/Alden Central School Dist	1	56
Stomieroski, Jake/Questar III BOCES	88	192
Stone Martin, Sharon/Minerva Central School Dist	16	68
Stone, Greg/North Syracuse Ctl Sch Dist	9,37	157
Stone, Jason/Laurens Central School Dist	5	173
Stone, Rebecca/Marathon Ctl School Dist	1,11	48
Stone, Steven/Northeastern Clinton Ctl SD	5	44
Stone, Todd/Northeastern Clinton Ctl SD	73,295	44
Stoorvogel, Maryann/Pine Plains Ctl School Dist	12,58,83,88,298	53
Stopinski, Hank/Royalton Hartland Central SD	1	148
Storch, David/Northport-East Northport UFSD	42	227
Storenski, Amy/Ulster BOCES	27	244
Storey, Carol/Haldane Central School Dist	37,93	175
Storey, Scott/Belleville Henderson Sch Dist	8,11,288	79
Storie, Trisha/Hammond Central School Distict	8,36,57,58,69,88,271	210
Storm, Carrie/New Hartford Central Sch Dist	16	151
Stormer, Erika/Sherman Central School Dist	12,51,54,280	39
Storms, Scott/Peru Central School Dist	74	44
Storsberg, Kevin/Whitesboro Ctl School Dist	3	153
Stoutenburg, Brian/Stamford Central School Dist	3	50
Stowell, Gregory, Dr/Mahopac Ctl School Dist	15,79	176
Stowelthouse, Theresa/Camden Central School Dist	83	150
Strack, Eric/Mt Pleasant Ctl School Dist	3	258

1 Superintendent	16 Instructional Media Svcs	30 Adult Education	44 Science Sec	58 Special Education K-12	72 Summer School	88 Alternative/At Risk	277 Remedial Math K-12
2 Bus/Finance/Purchasing	17 Chief Operations Officer	31 Career/Sch-to-Work K-12	45 Math K-12	59 Special Education Elem	73 Instructional Tech	89 Multi-Cultural Curriculum	280 Literacy Coach
3 Buildings And Grounds	18 Chief Academic Officer	32 Career/Sch-to-Work Elem	46 Math Elem	60 Special Education Sec	74 Inservice Training	90 Social Work	285 STEM
4 Food Service	19 Chief Financial Officer	33 Career/Sch-to-Work Sec	47 Math Sec	61 Foreign/World Lang K-12	75 Marketing/Distributive	91 Safety/Security	286 Digital Learning
5 Transportation	20 Art K-12	34 Early Childhood Ed	48 English/Lang Arts K-12	62 Foreign/World Lang Elem	76 Info Systems	92 Magnet School	288 Common Core Standards
6 Athletic	21 Art Elem	35 Health/Phys Education	49 English/Lang Arts Elem	63 Foreign/World Lang Sec	77 Psychological Assess	93 Parental Involvement	294 Accountability
7 Health Services	22 Art Sec	36 Guidance Services K-12	50 English/Lang Arts Sec	64 Religious Education K-12	78 Affirmative Action	96 Tech Prep Program	295 Network System
8 Curric/Instruct K-12	23 Music K-12	37 Guidance Services Elem	51 Reading K-12	65 Religious Education Elem	79 Student Personnel	97 Chief Infomation Officer	296 Title II Programs
9 Curric/Instruct Elem	24 Music Elem	38 Guidance Services Sec	52 Reading Elem	66 Religious Education Sec	80 Driver Ed/Safety	98 Chief Technology Officer	297 Webmaster
10 Curric/Instruct Sec	25 Music Sec	39 Social Studies K-12	53 Reading Sec	67 School Board President	81 Gifted/Talented	270 Character Education	298 Grant Writer/Ptnrships
11 Federal Program	26 Business Education	40 Social Studies Elem	54 Remedial Reading K-12	68 Teacher Personnel	82 Video Services	271 Migrant Education	750 Chief Innovation Officer
12 Title I	27 Career & Tech Ed	41 Social Studies Sec	55 Remedial Reading Elem	69 Academic Assessment	83 Substance Abuse Prev	273 Teacher Mentor	751 Chief of Staff
13 Title V	28 Technology Education	42 Science K-12	56 Remedial Reading Sec	70 Research/Development	84 Erate	274 Before/After Sch	752 Social Emotional Learning
15 Asst Superintendent	29 Family/Consumer Science	43 Science Elem	57 Bilingual/ELL	71 Public Information	85 AIDS Education	275 Response To Intervention	

NY-T60

New York School Directory

DISTRICT PERSONNEL INDEX

NAME/District	JOB FUNCTIONS	PAGE
Strack, Shawn/Northern Adirondack Ctl SD	16,48	44
Strader, Paul/Smithtown Central Sch Dist	8	230
Strait, Bradley/Broadalbin-Perth Ctl Sch Dist	58,275	71
Strait, Lisa/South Lewis Central Sch Dist	4	101
Strand, Allison/Half Hollow Hills Central SD	27,31,58,69,88,273	222
Straney, Bethany/Dolgeville Central School Dist	7	77
Strassburg, Fred/South Glens Falls Ctl Sch Dist	5	202
Strasser, Edward/North Tonawanda City Sch Dist	5	148
Stratton, Mark, Dr/Corinth Central School Dist	1	200
Straub, Kevin/Allegany-Limestone Ctl SD	73,295	31
Straus, Aaron/Salamanca City Central SD	30	33
Strawser, Ronda/Campbell-Savona Ctl Sch Dist	83,88	213
Streb, Laurie/Monroe 2 Orleans BOCES	298	115
Strege, Shawn/Webster Central School Dist	6,35	112
Streib, Rebecca/East Syracuse Minoa Ctl SD	68,294	154
Streicher, Paul/Glens Falls City School Dist	73,286	245
Strick, Robert/Susquehanna Valley Central SD	67	29
Striffolino, John/Seaford Union Free SD	8,15,69,273,285,288,298	129
Strock, Tracy/Carthage Central School Dist	2,11	80
Stroka, Kerri/Orange-Ulster BOCES	58,88	168
Strompf, Pam/Taconic Hills Central Sch Dist	4	47
Strother, Stuart/Clymer Central School Dist	73,286,295	37
Stroud, Joelle/Wyoming Central School Dist	2	268
Stroud, Matthew/Alexander Ctl School Dist	9,12,34	73
Struckle, Cindy/Laurens Central School Dist	67	173
Strumwasser, Jason/Irvington Union Free Sch Dist	73	257
Stuart, Amy/Cobleskill Richmondville SD	4	206
Stuart, Michon/Vestal Ctl School Dist	67	29
Stucchio, James/Cold Spring Harbor Central SD	2,11,15	219
Stuck, Kathy/Romulus Ctl School Dist	58	208
Stuckey, Mark/Patchogue-Medford Unified SD	20,23	227
Stuetzel, Helen/Gloversville Enlarged Sch Dist	280	71
Stuitje, Gerald/Sweet Home Central Sch Dist	2,3	63
Stumbo, Keith/Honeoye Central School Dist	67	161
Sturges, Mark/Keene Central School Dist	13,73,91,295	67
Sturdivant, Emily/South Seneca Ctl Sch Dist	274	208
Sturz, Don, Dr/Valley Stream Union Free SD 24	1	131
Styles, Melissa/Bridgehampton Union Free SD	2,15	218
Suber, Julie/Stockbridge Valley Central SD	57,72,270,274,288	106
Sucharzewski, Allison/Willsboro Central Sch Dist	2	68
Sucharzewski, John/Willsboro Central Sch Dist	3,5	68
Sucy, Nancy/Churchville Chili Ctl Sch Dist	2	107
Sugar, Scott/Fayetteville-Manlius Ctl SD	6	155
Sugarman, Anna/Shenendehowa Central Sch Dist	74	202
Suhr, Eric/New York State Dept Education	26,27,31,75	1
Suhr, Kristine/Wells Central School Dist	16,82	77
Sukdolak, Todd/Lockport City School Dist	6,35,85	147
Sukdollak, Gretchen/Cheektowaga Central SD	58	58
Suleski, Timothy/Warsaw Central School Dist	27	267
Sullivan, Amy/New Hyde-Garden City Park UFSD	11	126
Sullivan, Catherine/Niagara Falls City Sch Dist	34,48,275	147
Sullivan, Denise/Remsenburg-Speonk UFSD	1,83	228
Sullivan, Gregory/Mahopac Ctl School Dist	15	176
Sullivan, Jane/Iroquois Central School Dist	67	61
Sullivan, Joanne/Mahopac Ctl School Dist	8,15	176
Sullivan, Laura/Hastings on Hudson Union FR SD	58	256
Sullivan, Margaret/Saratoga Springs City Sch Dist	4	201
Sullivan, Matt/Fonda Fultonville Central SD	67	115
Sullivan, Maureen/Clarkstown Central School Dist	2,91	195
Sullivan, Meagan/Port Jervis City School Dist	58	166
Sullivan, Mike/Marcus Whitman Central SD	8,18,27,31,36	162
Sullivan, Patrick/Rome City School Dist	73,76,295	151
Sullivan, Patrick, Dr/Liberty Central School Dist	17,91,285,298,752	236
Sullivan, Rosalee/Vestal Ctl School Dist	58	29
Sullivan, Susan/Rocky Point Union Free SD	67	228
Sullivan, Tracy/Sandy Creek Central Sch Dist	4	172
Sullivan, Tracy/Williamsville Ctl School Dist	2	64
Suman, Bari/Mamaroneck Union Free Sch Dist	6,35	257
Summers, Kitty, Dr/Red Hook Central School Dist	8,15,57,68,74,288	53
Summers, Tonianne/Massapequa Union Free SD 23	45	125
Sunderland, Kurt/Richfield Springs Central SD	2	174
Sunkes, David/Ballston Spa Ctl School Dist	6	200
Sunser-King, Kristin/Solvay Union Free Sch Dist	67	158
Surash, Barbara, Dr/Hilton Central School Dist	8,11,15,69,286,288	109
Surears, Stanley/Franklin Central School Dist	67	49
Suriano, Christopher/New York State Dept Education	15,58	1
Susino, Jamie/Jordan Elbridge Ctl Sch Dist	38	155
Sutherland, Tammy/Greenville Central School Dist	1	75
Sutphen, Bob/Ticonderoga Central Sch Dist	6	68
Suttmeier, Maria/Hudson City School Dist	1	46
Svendsen, James/New Hyde-Garden City Park UFSD	9,12,16,73,82,295	126
Svendsen, John/New York State Dept Education	45	1
Svenson, Derek/Chautauqua Lake Central SD	73	36
Svenson, Lori/Sherman Central School Dist	36,88	39
Swain, Karen/Scotia Glenville Ctl Sch Dist	8,11,15,288	205
Swalbach, Tracie/Churchville Chili Ctl Sch Dist	83	107
Swan, Martha/Newcomb Central School Dist	57	68
Swan, Tara/Falconer Central School Dist	38,83	37
Swann, Kristin/Victor Central School Dist	8,11,15,57,79,288,298	162
Swanson, Barry/Bemus Point Ctl School Dist	67	36
Swanson, Heather/Geneva City School Dist	71	161
Swart, Veronica/Mayfield Ctl School Dist	57	72
Swarthout, Jil/Phelps-Clifton Springs Ctl SD	4	162
Swartwout, Ed/Susquehanna Valley Central SD	6	29
Swartz, Jeffrey/O E S J Central School Dist	3	72
Swartz, Susan/Scotia Glenville Ctl Sch Dist	1	205
Swayze, Jennifer/Spencer Van Etten Central SD	71	238
Swearingen, Sandi/Lansing Central School Dist	4	240
Swearingen, Wendy/Orleans-Niagara BOCES	67	170
Sweed, Wayne/Mt Morris Central School Dist	6,16,60,73,271	103
Sweeney, Heidi, Dr/Oswego City School Dist	10,68	171
Sweeney, Mary/Lansingburgh Central Sch Dist	71	190
Sweeney, Mike/Westmoreland Central Sch Dist	5	153
Sweeney, Robert/Mt Sinai Union Free SD	67	226
Sweet, Erik/New York State Dept Education	48	1
Sweetman, Marcy/Cassadaga Valley Ctl Sch Dist	8,12,285,288	36
Swenning, John/Brookhaven Comsewogue Unif SD	67	218
Swenson, Erik/Thousand Islands Central SD	67	81
Swiatek, Christopher/Franklinville Ctl School Dist	1	31
Swiatek, Paul/Rush Henrietta Central SD	83	112
Swick, John/Town of Webb Union Free SD	288	78
Swierczek, Sandra/Cortland Enlarged City SD	68	47
Swift, John/Lake Pleasant Central Sch Dist	6,73,76	76
Swift, Wendi/Homer Central School Dist	4	48
Swift, Wendy/Chittenango Central SD	4	104
Swift, Wendy/McGraw Central School Dist	4	48
Swift, Wendy/North Syracuse Ctl School Dist	4	157
Swinson, David/Webster Central School Dist	15,68	112
Swinton, John/Crown Point Central Sch Dist	6	67
Swords, Michael/Cheektowaga Maryvale UFSD	30	59
Sykes, Amy/Edwards-Knox Central Sch Dist	10,274	210
Sykut, Jaime/Oswego City School Dist	73,76,286,295	171
Sylak, Amy/Hunter Tannersville Ctl SD	5	76
Sylvester, Kaitlin/Hamburg Central School Dist	8	61
Sylvester, Tammy/Diocese of Rochester Ed Office	68	113
Syzdek, Steve/Broadalbin-Perth Ctl Sch Dist	67	71
Szczepanski, Steve/Edwards-Knox Central Sch Dist	85	210
Szymanski, Melissa/Hastings on Hudson Union FR SD	8,15	256
Szymendera, Paul/Sweet Home Central Sch Dist	273	63

T

NAME/District	JOB FUNCTIONS	PAGE
Tabor, Robert/Cherry Valley-Springfield SD	67	173
Tabor, Robin/Mount Markham Central Sch Dist	16,82	78
Tahoe, Shannon/New York State Dept Education	1	1
Talada, Matthew/Greater Southern Tier BOCES	27	215
Talbert, Gina/Wyandanch Union Free Sch Dist	1	234
Talcott, Lily/Ithaca City School Dist	15	240
Taldone, Catherine/Three Village Central Sch Dist	30,83,88,93,274,298	232
Tallarine, Lauren/Manhasset Union Free Sch Dist	45	124
Tallon, Christopher/Greater Johnstown Sch Dist	67	71
Tallon, Stacey/Pavilion Ctl School Dist	11,51,57,58,275	74
Tamarazio, Andrea/Niagara-Wheatfield Ctl SD	73	148
Tamarazio, Andrea/Tonawanda City School Dist	76	64
Tambasco, Regina/Miller Place Union Free SD	5	226
Tamberino, Philip/Fire Island Union Free SD	78	222
Tambroni, Mike/North Tonawanda City Sch Dist	7,11,36,79,83,90,275	148
Tamburino, Tonya/Oriskany Ctl School Dist	16,82	151
Tamol, Andrew/Frontier Ctl School Dist	28	60
Tandoi, Debra/Fairport Ctl School Dist	3	108
Tane, Lisa/Greenburgh 11 Union Free SD	67	255
Tangorra, Cosimo, Dr/Niskayuna Central School Dist	1	204
Tangorra, Julie/Waterville Central Sch Dist	58	153

School Year 2020-2021   800-333-8802   NY-T61

DISTRICT PERSONNEL INDEX

Market Data Retrieval

NAME/District	JOB FUNCTIONS	PAGE
Tannamore, Can/Westfield Central School Dist	73	39
Tannenbaum, Marcy/Hicksville Union Free Sch Dist	2,15	122
Tanner, Clara/Gilbertsville-Mt Upton SD	31,83	173
Tanner, Vevlet/Binghamton City School Dist	58,77,90	27
Tansey, Tobin/Penn Yan Ctl School Dist	6	268
Tanski, Alan/Sherman Central School Dist	28,95	39
Tappalardi, Raymond/Scarsdale Union Free Sch Dist	7	261
Tasber, Norene/Harpursville Central Sch Dist	4	28
Tasendos, Jorden/Schuylerville Central Sch Dist	8,74	201
Tasman, Joseph/Hauppauge Union Free Sch Dist	15,68	223
Tastor, Ryan/Sackets Harbor Ctl School Dist	31,36,83,270	81
Tata, Amy/Rochester City School Dist	58	110
Tate, Robyn/Buffalo Public Schools	45,58	57
Taub, Madelene/Community School District 24	1	176
Tauzel, James/Diocese of Rochester Ed Office	1	113
Tavernia, Polly/Beekmantown Ctl School Dist	11,58,72	43
Taylor-William, Teresa, Dr/Greenburgh Central School Dist	752	255
Taylor, Alicia/Warrensburg Central Sch Dist	4	246
Taylor, Andrew, Dr/Byram Hills Central Sch Dist	73,74,76,286,295	253
Taylor, Barbara/Schroon Lake Ctl School Dist	274	68
Taylor, Brian/West Islip School Dist	68,285	233
Taylor, Christine/Windsor Central School Dist	36,69,79	30
Taylor, Courtney/Sherman Central School Dist	58,298	39
Taylor, Dana/Monticello Central School Dist	83,88	237
Taylor, Dennis/Red Creek Central School Dist	9	251
Taylor, Doreen/Andover Central School Dist	277	14
Taylor, Jessica/Seneca Falls Central Sch Dist	38	208
Taylor, Kathryn/Bloomfield Central SD	8,12,51,54,69,288	161
Taylor, Kim/Coxsackie-Athens Central SD	16	75
Taylor, Michelle/Ft Edward Union Free Sch Dist	2	247
Taylor, Michelle/Hadley-Luzerne Ctl Sch Dist	2	245
Taylor, Pamela, Dr/Franklin Square Union Free SD	59	119
Taylor, Rhonda/Uniondale Union Free Sch Dist	8,15,88,270,273	130
Taylor, Scott/North Collins Ctl Sch Dist	1,11	63
Taylor, Warren/Western Suffolk BOCES	2,19	236
Tebo, Ginger/St Lawrence-Lewis BOCES	16	212
Teicher, Danielle/Wyandanch Union Free Sch Dist	4	234
Tejedor, Andrea/Highland Falls-Ft Montgmry SD	10,11,15,73,286	164
Tejedor, Andrea/Highland Falls-Ft Montgmry SD	71	164
Telfer, Joanne/Morris Central School Dist	57	174
Tellone, Carolyn/Plainview-Old Bethpage Ctl SD	16	127
Ten Dyke, Elizabeth, Dr/Poughkeepsie City School Dist	8,11,15,294	53
Ten Eyck, Jill/Roxbury Central School Dist	8,273	50
Tencza, Joyce/Utica City School Dist	68	152
Tenney, Vernon/Canandaigua City School Dist	752	161
Tenwolde, Jeremy/Newfield Central School Dist	67	241
Tepoel, Alexandra/Victor Central School Dist	4	162
Terbuska, Peter/Wyoming Central School Dist	6,35	268
Terranova, Tim, Dr/Victor Central School Dist	1	162
Terry, Karen/Franklin Central School Dist	4	49
Terwilliger, Michelle/Addison Central School Dist	67	213
Teseo, Robert/East Williston Union Free SD	45	118
Tesik, Karen/South Orangetown Central SD	58,79,88,275	197
Tessier, Greg/Massena Central School Dist	3	211
Testa, Dick/Union-Endicott Ctl School Dist	67	29
Testa, Johonna/Miller Place Union Free SD	67	226
Testa, Marie/North Bellmore Union Free SD	1	126
Tevendale, Lisa/Corinth Central School Dist	4	200
Tewinkle, Tracy/Clymer Central School Dist	5	37
Tham, Jeff/Bradford Central Sch Dist	73,76,286,295	207
Tharp, Linda/Owen D Young Central Sch Dist	67	78
Theis, Meghan/Fort Ann Central School Dist	51,55	247
Theo, Harry/West Babylon Union Free SD	42,47	233
Theodorou, Carla/Nassau BOCES	27,30,31	134
Theodule, Patrick/Hastings on Hudson Union FR SD	16	256
Thesier, Jeremy/Carthage Central School Dist	3	80
Thibault, Andrew/Greece Central School Dist	295	108
Thiel, William/Frontier Ctl School Dist	2	60
Thode, Jeremy/Center Moriches Union Free SD	6,35	218
Thom, Greg/Morris Central School Dist	73,76,286	174
Thomas-McCoy, Lauriel/Deposit Central School Dist	58	28
Thomas, Amy/Pittsford Central Sch Dist	67	110
Thomas, Arleen/Bronxville Union Free SD	67	253
Thomas, Brenda/Mexico Central School Dist	4	171
Thomas, Charles/Rensselaer City School Dist	3	191
Thomas, Cheryl, Dr/Newfield Central School Dist	1	241
Thomas, Darla/Spencer Van Etten Central SD	73,95,286	238
Thomas, Dianne/Ossining Union Free Sch Dist	7	259
Thomas, Izett/Wyandanch Union Free Sch Dist	11,285,296,298	234
Thomas, James, Dr/Newburgh Enlarged City SD	7	165
Thomas, Rae Ann/South Jefferson Central SD	73	81
Thomas, Randy/Vernon-Verona-Sherrill CSD	6	152
Thomas, Tom/Wallkill Central School Dist	73,295	243
Thomman, Robert/Saugerties Central School Dist	67	243
Thompson, Amy/Galway Central School Dist	4	201
Thompson, Andrew/Rome City School Dist	5	151
Thompson, Bryce/Attica Central School Dist	1	267
Thompson, Edith/Malone Central School Dist	20	69
Thompson, Jeremy/Clifton-Fine Central Sch Dist	67	209
Thompson, Lorraine/North Greenbush Common SD	59	191
Thompson, Maria, Dr/Pelham Union Free School Dist	54	260
Thompson, Steve/Byram Hills Central Sch Dist	3	253
Thompson, Susan/Hempstead Union Free SD	27,30,88	121
Thompson, Tasha/Carthage Central School Dist	82	80
Thompson, Tonya/Binghamton City School Dist	1	27
Thompson, Traci/Jamestown City School Dist	42	38
Thompsonmiller, Erin/Binghamton City School Dist	70,73	27
Thon, David/Binghamton City School Dist	68,273	27
Thornsland, Mica/Charlotte Valley Ctl Sch Dist	4	49
Thorp, Connie/Chittenango Central SD	5	104
Thorsland, Mica/Onc BOCES	4	51
Threehouse, Matt/Olean City School Dist	27,38	32
Thurnau, Carl/New Rochelle City School Dist	3	259
Tibbetts, Stephen/Southern Westchester BOCES	2,5,15	267
Tice, Craig, Dr/Fayetteville-Manlius Ctl SD	1	155
Tice, Stacey/Oneida City School Dist	6	105
Tichacek, John/Gananda Central School Dist	6	249
Ticknor, Sue/Chenango Valley Ctl Sch Dist	5	28
Tidd, Rod/Alexandria Central School Dist	5,82	79
Tiecher, Danielle/Northport-East Northport UFSD	4	227
Tieder, Sheldon/Rhinebeck Central School Dist	3	53
Tierney, Marlene/Mechanicville City Sch Dist	67	201
Tierney, Michael/Dover Union Free School Dist	1,11	52
Tiger, Gerri/Cold Spring Harbor Central SD	4	219
Tiger, Lisa/Florida Union Free Sch Dist	8,11,58,83,286,288,296,298	164
Tiggs, Marci/Mount Vernon City School Dist	15,68	258
Tilley, Wayne/Unadilla Valley Ctl Sch Dist	2,5,7,91	43
Tillinghast, Skip/Yorkshire-Pioneer Ctl Sch Dist	71,297	33
Timm, Brian/Pine Plains Ctl School Dist	8	53
Timo, Deena/Mt Sinai Union Free SD	8,11,16,69,73,77,288	226
Tingley, Debra/Fallsburg Central School Dist	73	236
Tinklepaugh, Jay/Solvay Union Free Sch Dist	1	158
Tipp, Victoria/Chappaqua Central School Dist	67	253
Tirums, Jeff/Mamaroneck Union Free Sch Dist	4	257
Titolo, John/Bethpage Union Free Sch Dist	47	117
Titus, Nick/Yorkshire-Pioneer Ctl Sch Dist	3	33
Tobia, Erika/Community School District 8	1	17
Tobin, Andrew/Smithtown Central Sch Dist	2,3,15	230
Tobin, Paul/Tuckahoe Union Free SD	6	262
Todd, Christoper/Ctr for Instruct Tech Innov	1,11	172
Todd, Donna/Little Falls City School Dist	4	78
Todd, Stephen/Jefferson Lewis BOCES	1,11	82
Toia-Kramer, Denise/Clinton Central School Dist	57	150
Tokarczyk, Kaitlyn/Cheektowaga Central SD	2,7	58

1 Superintendent
2 Bus/Finance/Purchasing
3 Buildings And Grounds
4 Food Service
5 Transportation
6 Athletic
7 Health Services
8 Curric/Instruct K-12
9 Curric/Instruct Elem
10 Curric/Instruct Sec
11 Federal Program
12 Title I
13 Title V
15 Asst Superintendent
16 Instructional Media Svcs
17 Chief Operations Officer
18 Chief Academic Officer
19 Chief Financial Officer
20 Art K-12
21 Art Elem
22 Art Sec
23 Music K-12
24 Music Elem
25 Music Sec
26 Business Education
27 Career & Tech Ed
28 Technology Education
29 Family/Consumer Science
30 Adult Education
31 Career/Sch-to-Work K-12
32 Career/Sch-to-Work Elem
33 Career/Sch-to-Work Sec
34 Early Childhood Ed
35 Health/Phys Education
36 Guidance Services K-12
37 Guidance Services Elem
38 Guidance Services Sec
39 Social Studies K-12
40 Social Studies Elem
41 Social Studies Sec
42 Science K-12
43 Science Elem
44 Science Sec
45 Math K-12
46 Math Elem
47 Math Sec
48 English/Lang Arts K-12
49 English/Lang Arts Elem
50 English/Lang Arts Sec
51 Reading K-12
52 Reading Elem
53 Reading Sec
54 Remedial Reading K-12
55 Remedial Reading Elem
56 Remedial Reading Sec
57 Bilingual/ELL
58 Special Education K-12
59 Special Education Elem
60 Special Education Sec
61 Foreign/World Lang K-12
62 Foreign/World Lang Elem
63 Foreign/World Lang Sec
64 Religious Education K-12
65 Religious Education Elem
66 Religious Education Sec
67 School Board President
68 Teacher Personnel
69 Academic Assessment
70 Research/Development
71 Public Information
72 Summer School
73 Instructional Tech
74 Inservice Training
75 Marketing/Distributive
76 Info Systems
77 Psychological Assess
78 Affirmative Action
79 Student Personnel
80 Driver Ed/Safety
81 Gifted/Talented
82 Video Services
83 Substance Abuse Prev
84 Erate
85 AIDS Education
88 Alternative/At Risk
89 Multi-Cultural Curriculum
90 Social Work
91 Safety/Security
92 Magnet School
93 Parental Involvement
95 Tech Prep Program
97 Chief Information Officer
98 Chief Technology Officer
270 Character Education
271 Migrant Education
273 Teacher Mentor
274 Before/After Sch
275 Response To Intervention
277 Remedial Math K-12
280 Literacy Coach
285 STEM
286 Digital Learning
288 Common Core Standards
294 Accountability
295 Network System
296 Title II Programs
297 Webmaster
298 Grant Writer/Ptnrships
750 Chief Innovation Officer
751 Chief of Staff
752 Social Emotional Learning

NY-T62

New York School Directory

DISTRICT PERSONNEL INDEX

NAME/District	JOB FUNCTIONS	PAGE
Tol, John/Morris Central School Dist	3	174
Tolan, Leslie/Island Trees Union Free SD	68	122
Toleson, Mitchell/Port Byron Ctl School Dist	2,15	35
Tolosi, Laura/Yorktown Central School Dist	7	264
Tomandi, Doug/Cayuga-Onondaga BOCES	2	36
Tomasello, Debbie/South Country Central Sch Dist	4	231
Tomasetti, Cara/Webutuck Ctl School Dist	88	54
Tomczk, Gary/Kingston City School Dist	71,73,76,97	242
Tomeo, James/Elwood Union Free School Dist	67	221
Tomizawa, Julisa/Beacon City School Dist	79	51
Tomlinson, Stephen/Broadalbin-Perth Ctl Sch Dist	1	71
Tomm, Brad/Chenango Valley Ctl Sch Dist	69,79	28
Tona, Christine/Riverhead Central School Dist	1,11,288	228
Tooley, Bart/Little Falls City School Dist	6,12,15,58	78
Toomer, Matthew/Mayfield Ctl School Dist	73,295	72
Toomey, Rosemary/Moriah Central School Dist	7	68
Torchia, Bonnie/Taconic Hills Central Sch Dist	67	47
Tormey, Sarah/Garrison Union Free Sch Dist	67	175
Tornatore, Augustine, Dr/Liberty Central School Dist	1,11	236
Torreano, Beth/New Hyde-Garden City Park UFSD	274	126
Torregrossa, Christine/Rye Neck Union Free Sch Dist	4	261
Torregrossa, Christine/Tuckahoe Union Free SD	4	262
Torres, Geraldo/Rush Henrietta Central SD	4	112
Torres, Robert/Bay Shore Union Free Sch Dist	79	217
Torrey, Mike/Portville Central School Dist	73,295	32
Toscano, Toby/Spencerport Central Sch Dist	91	112
Tote, Andrea/Schenectady City School Dist	79	204
Toto, Stephen/Franklin Square Union Free SD	67	119
Tousignant, Brian/Northern Adirondack Ctl SD	2	44
Towers, John/Levittown Union Free Sch Dist	45	123
Towne, Denise/Albany City School Dist	5	9
Towne, Kristin/Hammond Central School Districst	280,285,288,296,298	210
Townsend, Dawn/Stamford Central School Dist	4	50
Townsend, Joseph/Center Moriches Union Free SD	91	218
Townsend, Katherine/Springville Griffith Inst CSD	58,79	63
Towsley, Chris/Livingston Manor Ctl Sch Dist	38,69,88	236
Tracy, Bristie/South Glens Falls Ctl Sch Dist	7	202
Tranchina, Nick/Sullivan West Central SD	3	237
Tranchino, Gene/Elwood Union Free School Dist	5,16,73,76,286,295	221
Trank, Rebecca/Elmira City School Dist	58	40
Trapani, Brian/Massapequa Union Free SD 23	39	125
Trapani, Jon/Lindenhurst Union Free SD	20,23	224
Trapasso-Roth, Bonnie/Warrensburg Central Sch Dist	31	246
Trask, Brian/Unatego Unadilla Central SD	3,5,73	174
Trautwein, Anita/Alden Central School Dist	4	56
Traynor, Michele/Jefferson Lewis BOCES	2,15	82
Treadwell, George/Hyde Park Central School Dist	5	52
Trelfa, Michael/South Huntington Union Free SD	5	231
Treloar, James/Brewster Central School Dist	28,73,76,286,295	175
Tremblay, Sarah/Keene Central School Dist	57	67
Tremper, Alex/Pine Bush Central School Dist	91	166
Trender, William/La Fargeville Central Sch Dist	73,76,286	80
Trenholm, John/Scarsdale Union Free Sch Dist	3	261
Trentowski, Kevin/Oyster Bay East Norwich Ctl SD	7,35	127
Treptow, Norman/Salmon River Central School Dist	5	70
Tretter, Cynthia/Akron Central School Dist	2	56
Trevisani, Rebecca/Vernon-Verona-Sherrill CSD	51,54	152
Triassi, Nicole/Cornwall Central School Dist	11,58,79,90,271	163
Tricarico, Chris/New York City Dept of Ed	4	134
Triebe, Britney/Margaretville Central Sch Dist	38	49
Trimble, Linda/Richfield Springs Central SD	58	174
Tripp, Faith/West Hempstead School Dist	280	131
Troelstra, Denise/Queensbury Union Free Sch Dist	8,11,15,18,275,288,296,298	246
Troiano, Robert/Westbury Union Free Sch Dist	67	132
Tromblee, Michael/Mahopac Ctl School Dist	8,15	176
Trombley, Joey/Chazy Central Rural Sch Dist	67	44
Trombley, Nicholas/Northeastern Clinton Ctl SD	6	44
Trombley, Rebecca/Northern Adirondack Ctl SD	11,273,296,298	44
Tromer, Annmarie/Pearl River School Dist	2,15	197
Tronetti, Linda/Whitesville Central Sch Dist	54,57,280	15
Trotman, Lorraine/Newark Valley Central Sch Dist	4	238
Trotta, Robert/Frankfort-Schuyler Ctl SD	42	77
Troutman, Paula/Gowanda Central School Dist	296	32
True, Barry/Wyoming Central School Dist	67	268
Trumbull, Myra/O E S J Central School Dist	4	72
Trumino, Ron/George Junior Republic UFSD	33	240

NAME/District	JOB FUNCTIONS	PAGE
Tryon, Bruce/Cobleskill Richmondville SD	67	206
Tsaveras, Joseph/Greenport Union Free Sch Dist	58,69	222
Tstorner, Ashley/Valley Stream Union Free SD 30	2	131
Tuber, Beth/Margaretville Central Sch Dist	2	49
Tucker, Christine/Owen D Young Central Sch Dist	8	78
Tucker, Danae/Minerva Central School Dist	67	68
Tullo, Gayle/Glen Cove City School Dist	295	120
Tumilowicz, Megan/Unadilla Valley Ctl Sch Dist	273	43
Tunis, Susan/Buffalo Public Schools	34	57
Tunison, Jan/Scotia Glenville Ctl Sch Dist	73,286	205
Tunny, Peter/South Colonie Central Sch Dist	5	12
Tuohy, Eileen/Sagaponack Common School Dist	2,12,296	229
Turcio, Karen/Arlington Central School Dist	30	51
Turcio, Karen/Arlington Central School Dist	30	51
Turck, Sarah/Onteora Central School Dist	27,38	243
Turck, Thomas/Homer Central School Dist	1	48
Turcotte, Cynthia/Warrensburg Central Sch Dist	2,19	246
Turcotte, Martin/Minerva Central School Dist	3	68
Turek, Bruce/Bethlehem Central School Dist	71,97	10
Turgeon, Tom/Indian River Ctl School Dist	73	80
Turnbull, Bonnie/Wheelerville Union Free SD	2	72
Turnbull, Madison/North Collins Ctl Sch Dist	67	63
Turnbull, Rich/Norwich City School Dist	6	42
Turner, Ann/Oneida-Herkimer-Mad BOCES	74	154
Turner, Danielle/Locust Valley Ctl School Dist	6,7,35	123
Turner, Heather/Fabius Pompey Central SD	16,82	155
Turner, Jessica/Wappingers Central Sch Dist	9	54
Turner, Kari/Silver Creek Central Sch Dist	5	39
Turner, Kathleen/Warwick Valley Central SD	16,82	167
Turner, Ruth/Rochester City School Dist	752	110
Turner, Seth/Amagansett Union Free Sch Dist	1	216
Turpin, Teresa/Buffalo Public Schools	2	56
Tuttle, Michael/Middletown Enlarged City SD	2,5,15,73,76	165
Tuttle, Michael/Schodack Central School Dist	67	191
Tvorttnaos, Anastasia, Dr/Carle Place Union Free SD	16,73,286,297	117
Twardy, Mike/Garrison Union Free Sch Dist	3,5	175
Tweed, Joseph/Archdiocese of New York Ed Off	15	142
Tweed, Michael/Glen Cove City School Dist	79	120
Two-Axe, Jennifer/Ichabod Crane Central Schools	16,82	46
Tyler, Jennifer/Lyons Central School Dist	4	249
Tyler, Lee/Oakfield Alabama Ctl SD	2	74
Tyler, Lisa/Lyons Central School Dist	27,31,36,83,85,88	249
Tyler, Timothy/Williamson Central School Dist	73	251
Tyler, Troy/Greenwich Central School Dist	2	247
Tymann, Robert/East Hampton Union Free SD	8,34,69,72,85,270,273,288	220
Tymchynyuk, Viktor/Glen Cove City School Dist	3,91	120
Tyner-Doyle, Paula/New York State Dept Education	4	1
Tyner, Andrew/Hannibal Central School Dist	82	171
Tyx, Jim/Alexander Ctl School Dist	4	73
Tyx, Jim/Pembroke Ctl School Dist	4	74

U

NAME/District	JOB FUNCTIONS	PAGE
Uaplou, Bob/Andes Central School Dist	16,58,73	48
Uetz, Heather/Sodus Central School Dist	8,15,285,288	251
Ugine, Erin/Gates Chili Central Sch Dist	34	108
Uhly, Laura/Warrensburg Central Sch Dist	83,85	246
Ukleya, Mari/Onondaga-Cortland-Madson BOCES	30	160
Ulinger, Melanie/Brocton Central School Dist	8,58,275,288,294	36
Ulrich, Colleen/Mayfield Ctl School Dist	58	72
Uopta, Joann/Sherman Central School Dist	7	39
Urbanek, David/West Seneca Central Sch Dist	91	64
Urbanowicz, Joseph/Ardsley Union Free School Dist	3,5	252
Urbina Medina, Angela/New Paltz Ctl School Dist	1	242
Urraro, Kelly/Copiague Union Free Sch Dist	73	220
Urso, Noreen, Dr/Eastchester Union Free SD	11,15,68,79,83,88,275	254

V

NAME/District	JOB FUNCTIONS	PAGE
Vacca, Holly/Schenectady City School Dist	7	204
Vacca, Patricia/Madison-Oneida BOCES	8,15	154
Vaccaro-Teich, Ann, Dr/White Plains City School Dist	2,5,15,91	263
Vachris, Susan/Scotia Glenville Ctl Sch Dist	39,48	205
Vadala, Jessica/De Ruyter Central School Dist	7	105
Vagres, Shannon/Saranac Central School Dist	8,58	45
Vakkas, Sarah/Greater Southern Tier BOCES	8,15	215
Val, Pierre/Guilderland Central Sch Dist	73,295	11
Valachovic, Al/Schenectady City School Dist	5	204

DISTRICT PERSONNEL INDEX

Market Data Retrieval

NAME/District	JOB FUNCTIONS	PAGE
Valente, Jenny/De Ruyter Central School Dist	9,59	105
Valente, John/Harborfields Ctl School Dist	6,7,35	223
Valente, Sharon/Bellmore-Merrick Ctl High SD	76	117
Valenti, Anthony/Clarkstown Central School Dist	3	195
Valenti, Joseph/Churchville Chili Ctl Sch Dist	3	107
Valenti, Ronald, Dr/Greenburgh Central School Dist	8,15,68	255
Valentine, Babette/Auburn Enlarged City Sch Dist	59	34
Vallance, Jean/Yorkshire-Pioneer Ctl Sch Dist	58	33
Vallely, Michael, Dr/Lancaster Central Sch Dist	1	62
Vallentin, Lillian/Archdiocese of New York Ed Off	76	142
Vallese, Donna/Syracuse City School Dist	294	158
Valletta, Colleen/Lansing Central School Dist	11,58	240
Valley, Eric/Medina Central School Dist	6	169
Vallone, Jim/East Irondequoit Ctl Sch Dist	79	107
Valovic, Michael/Mayfield Ctl School Dist	27	72
Van Avery, Paul/Ft Plain Central School Dist	3	115
Van Cott, Alan/Sagaponack Common School Dist	1	229
Van Cott, Christopher/Oceanside Union Free Sch Dist	2,15	127
Van Der Klish, Rebecca/Glens Falls City School Dist	58,88	245
Van Dermeid, Nicole/East Rochester Union Free SD	4	107
Van Develde, James/Lakeland Central School Dist	30,71,80,91	257
Van Etten, Mary/Wellsville Central Sch Dist	58,79	15
Van Eyken, Michele/Roosevelt Union Free Sch Dist	9	128
Van Fleet, Brook/Greenville Central School Dist	12,57,58,77,79	75
Van Fossen, Jason/Maine Endwell Ctl School Dist	1	29
Van Horn, Paul/Spencerport Central Sch Dist	295	112
Van Scoy, Shawn, Dr/Gananda Central School Dist	1	249
Van Slyke, Deb/Clinton Central School Dist	8,31,69,286,288	150
Van Slyke, Tyler/Montauk Union Free School Dist	73,76	226
Van Valkenberg, Krystal/Mt Morris Central School Dist	58	103
Van Wicklin, Robert/Ellicottville Central Sch Dist	67	31
Van Wie, Christina/O E S J Central School Dist	8	72
Vanacore, Mark/Albion Central School Dist	73,295	169
Vanaerman, Joanna/West Canada Valley Ctl SD	4	79
Vanbalkeburg, Adam/Andes Central School Dist	35	48
Vanbeveren, Kevin/Solvay Union Free Sch Dist	3,91	158
Vandamm, Chris/Rondout Valley Ctl Sch Dist	4	243
Vandekker, Jessica/Garrison Union Free Sch Dist	83,88,90	175
Vandenhandel, Derek/Churchville Chili Ctl Sch Dist	28,73,76	107
Vanderlee, Cynthia/Canandaigua City School Dist	83	161
Vandermeid, Nicole/Brighton Central School Dist	4	106
Vanderstuyf, Adam, Dr/North Salem Central Sch Dist	11,36,58,79,83,85,88,298	259
Vandervelt, Alice/Brentwood Union Free Sch Dist	68,273	217
Vanderwater, Glen/Rochester City School Dist	73,98	110
Vanderzyden, Sue/Randolph Acad Union Free SD	58	32
Vandeusen, Nathan/Diocese of Albany Ed Office	73	12
Vandreason, Mary Kay/Utica City School Dist	4	152
Vandresser, Todd/Madison-Oneida BOCES	3	154
VanDusen, David/Tioga Central School Dist	5	239
Vang, Scott/Addison Central School Dist	73	213
Vangellow, Paulette/Pittsford Central School Dist	4	110
Vangiesen, Sandy/Auburn Enlarged City Sch Dist	2	34
VanHouten, Richard/Elmira Heights Ctl Sch Dist	5	40
Vanier, Jenifer/Malone Central School Dist	23	69
Vankeuren, Robert/Ithaca City School Dist	68	240
Vankleeck, Dawn/Rondout Valley Ctl Sch Dist	67	243
Vanlaeken, Kelly/Gananda Central School Dist	8,11,273,288,296	249
VanSickle, James/Keshequa Central School Dist	3	103
Vanvalkenberg, Robert/South Kortright Ctl SD	6	50
Vanyo, Michael/Berkshire Union Free Sch Dist	1,11	45
VanZandt, Donna/Brunswick Central School Dist	6	190
VanZandt, Stan/Carthage Central School Dist	91	80
Vanzile, David/Pine Valley Central Sch Dist	3	38
Varay, James/Archdiocese of New York Ed Off	295	142
Varieur, Kathy/North Rockland Central SD	7	197
Varullo, Rocco/Westbury Union Free Sch Dist	73,76	132
Varuolo, Rocco/White Plains City School Dist	73,95,286	263
Vasile-Cozzo, Joseph/East Hampton Union Free SD	6,35,83,85	220
Vasquez, Jennifer/Blind Brook-Rye Union Free SD	28	252
Vasylevskyy, Dennis/East Syracuse Minoa Ctl SD	16,295	154
Vaughan, Cristine/Community School District 11	1	22
Vaughn Brogan, Patricia/Pittsford Central Sch Dist	79	110
Vaughn, Staci/Morristown Ctl School Dist	1,11,288	211
Vazquez, Julio, Dr/North Salem Central Sch Dist	8,68,69,273	259
Vazquez, Steven/Chappaqua Central School Dist	295	253
Vecchio, Deborah/Shelter Island Union Free SD	2	230
Vecchio, Robert/William Floyd School Dist	67	233
Veeder, Steve/Lyons Central School Dist	5,6,7,35	249
Velasquez, Yvonne/Sagaponack Common School Dist	57	229
Veley, Craig/Geneseo Central Sch Dist	6	103
Velez, Anibal/Newburgh Enlarged City SD	3	165
Velez, Ron/White Plains City School Dist	11,76,295	263
Vella, Angela/Pleasantville Union Free SD	67	260
Vella, Craig/Malverne Union Free Sch Dist	73	124
Venettozzi, Cheryl/Holland Patent Ctl School Dist	2,15	150
Venezia, Drew/Salamanca City Central SD	4	33
Venzi, Devin/Wallkill Central School Dist	5	243
Verba, Amanda/Ithaca City School Dist	2,17	240
Verboys, Dennis/Yorktown Central School Dist	3	264
Vereline, Joseph/North Babylon Union Free SD	91	226
Verga, Anthony/Westhampton Beach School Dist	3	233
Verky, Jodie/Seneca Falls Central Sch Dist	8,273,288	208
Verral, Stephen, Dr/Saratoga Springs City Sch Dist	3	201
Versinger, Michael/Bay Shore Union Free Sch Dist	73,76,295,297	217
Verspoor, Gregg/Delaware Academy Ctrl SD Delhi	5	49
Vetter, Carrie/Iroquois Central School Dist	6	61
Vetter, Norma/Greece Central School Dist	8	108
Vevone, Jeremy/Auburn Enlarged City Sch Dist	295	34
Vicente, Milagros/Valley Stream Union Free SD 13	67	130
Vick, Monae/Elmont Union Free School Dist	5	118
Vidulich, Diane/Chenango Valley Ctl Sch Dist	77,88	28
Viebrock, Richard/Taconic Hills Central Sch Dist	5	47
Viegas, David/Hewlett Woodmere Union Free SD	6,35,85	121
Viesta, Maria/Diocese of Brooklyn Ed Office	15	95
Viggiano, Colleen/Onondaga-Cortland-Madson BOCES	15,27,58,79,88	160
Viggiano, Nicole/Greece Central School Dist	30,274	108
Viggiano, Patricia/Lakeland Central School Dist	42	257
Vile, Kimberly/Cortland Enlarged City SD	2	47
Vile, Kimberly/Southern Cayuga Central SD	2	35
Villante, Michelle/Sherburne Earlville Central SD	91	42
Villanueva, Michelle/Glens Falls Common Sch Dist	88	245
Villanyi, Rudy/Nanuet Union Free School Dist	3,91	196
Villez, Janine/Longwood Central School Dist	59	225
Vincent, Stacy/Franklin-Essex-Hamilton BOCES	2	71
Vinski, Edward, Dr/Sagaponack Common School Dist	752	229
Viola, Cynthia/Waterford Halfmoon School Dist	53,56	203
Violetti, Courtney/Suffern Central School Dist	60	198
Violino, Graham/Williamsville Ctl School Dist	5	64
Virgadamo, Tom/Haldane Central School Dist	273	176
Virgiglio, Giovanni/Diocese of Albany Ed Office	1	12
Virgilio, Vita/Huntington Union Free Sch Dist	5	223
Virkler, Joseph/Beaver River Central Sch Dist	73	101
Virsinger, Maureen/Bay Shore Union Free Sch Dist	2,15	217
Viscardi, Adrienne/Bedford Central School Dist	57,271	252
Vita, William/Jordan Elbridge Ctl Sch Dist	4	155
Viteritti, Frank/Archdiocese of New York Ed Off	15,68	142
Vito, Larry/Churchville Chili Ctl Sch Dist	7,11,15,68,294	107
Vito, Mary/Wheatland Chili Ctl Sch Dist	57,58	113
Vizzo, Vincent/Diocese of Rockville Ed Office	15	132
Vobis, Jack/Island Park Union Free SD	67	122
Voerg, John/Kingston City School Dist	8,11,15,36,58,79,90,298	242
Vogelsang, Eric/Syracuse City School Dist	76	158
Vogler, Ryan/Roscoe Central School Dist	3	237
Voight, Phillip/Central Islip Union Free SD	76,98	218

1 Superintendent	16 Instructional Media Svcs	30 Adult Education	44 Science Sec	58 Special Education K-12	72 Summer School	88 Alternative/At Risk	277 Remedial Math K-12
2 Bus/Finance/Purchasing	17 Chief Operations Officer	31 Career/Sch-to-Work K-12	45 Math K-12	59 Special Education Elem	73 Instructional Tech	89 Multi-Cultural Curriculum	280 Literacy Coach
3 Buildings And Grounds	18 Chief Academic Officer	32 Career/Sch-to-Work Elem	46 Math Elem	60 Special Education Sec	74 Inservice Training	90 Social Work	285 STEM
4 Food Service	19 Chief Financial Officer	33 Career/Sch-to-Work Sec	47 Math Sec	61 Foreign/World Lang K-12	75 Marketing/Distributive	91 Safety/Security	286 Digital Learning
5 Transportation	20 Art K-12	34 Early Childhood Ed	48 English/Lang Arts K-12	62 Foreign/World Lang Elem	76 Info Systems	92 Magnet School	288 Common Core Standards
6 Athletic	21 Art Elem	35 Health/Phys Education	49 English/Lang Arts Elem	63 Foreign/World Lang Sec	77 Psychological Assess	93 Parental Involvement	294 Accountability
7 Health Services	22 Art Sec	36 Guidance Services K-12	50 English/Lang Arts Sec	64 Religious Education K-12	78 Affirmative Action	95 Tech Prep Program	295 Network System
8 Curric/Instruct K-12	23 Music K-12	37 Guidance Services Elem	51 Reading K-12	65 Religious Education Elem	79 Student Personnel	97 Chief Information Officer	296 Title II Programs
9 Curric/Instruct Elem	24 Music Elem	38 Guidance Services Sec	52 Reading Elem	66 Religious Education Sec	80 Driver Ed/Safety	98 Chief Technology Officer	297 Webmaster
10 Curric/Instruct Sec	25 Music Sec	39 Social Studies K-12	53 Reading Sec	67 School Board President	81 Gifted/Talented	270 Character Education	298 Grant Writer/Ptnrships
11 Federal Program	26 Business Education	40 Social Studies Elem	54 Remedial Reading K-12	68 Teacher Personnel	82 Video Services	271 Migrant Education	750 Chief Innovation Officer
12 Title I	27 Career & Tech Ed	41 Social Studies Sec	55 Remedial Reading Elem	69 Academic Assessment	83 Substance Abuse Prev	273 Teacher Mentor	751 Chief of Staff
13 Title V	28 Technology Education	42 Science K-12	56 Remedial Reading Sec	70 Research/Development	84 Erate	274 Before/After Sch	752 Social Emotional Learning
15 Asst Superintendent	29 Family/Consumer Science	43 Science Elem	57 Bilingual/ELL	71 Public Information	85 AIDS Education	275 Response To Intervention	

New York School Directory — DISTRICT PERSONNEL INDEX

NAME/District	JOB FUNCTIONS	PAGE
Voloshin, Gregory, Dr/Goshen Central School Dist	68	164
Volpe, Thomas/Bellmore-Merrick Ctl High SD	5,91	117
Volpicelli, Victoria/Newfield Central School Dist	11	241
Volz, Kelly/Cuba-Rushford Central Sch Dist	38	14
Von Hollen, Charles/Blind Brook-Rye Union Free SD	73,295	252
Von-Eschen, Tracey/Sayville Union Free Sch Dist	58	229
Vona, Bruce/Cheektowaga Central SD	3,5	58
Vonbargen, Eric/Wantagh Union Free Sch Dist 23	74	131
Vondel, Mary/Chateaugay Central School Dist	271	69
Vongunden, Amy/Perry Central School Dist	35	267
Vonwurmb, Liz, Dr/Clarkstown Central School Dist	8,16,20,23	195
Voorhees, Bruce/Stamford Central School Dist	16,73,82	50
Voorhees, Eric/Gilbertsville-Mt Upton SD	73,74,76,295	173
Vredenburgh, Erin, Dr/Rye City School Dist	58,79	261
Vulpis, Dominick/East Rockaway Union Free SD	67	118
Vultaggio, Pat/Elmont Union Free School Dist	16,82	118
Vyas, Bhargav/Monroe Woodbury Central SD	15,73,295	165

W

NAME/District	JOB FUNCTIONS	PAGE
Wachter, Kerry/Massapequa Union Free SD 23	67	125
Wade, Lisa/Syracuse City School Dist	68	158
Wade, Marylisa/Syracuse City School Dist	78,93	158
Wade, Sydney/Candor Central School Dist	2,298	238
Wager, Rebecca/Wayland-Cohocton Central SD	8,288,296	215
Wagner, David/Peru Central School Dist	5	44
Wagner, James/Gloversville Enlarged Sch Dist	8,11,15,298	71
Wagner, Janine/Yorkshire-Pioneer Ctl Sch Dist	11,68	33
Wagner, Norman/Central Islip Union Free SD	67	218
Wagner, Sandy/Monticello Central School Dist	16,73,74	237
Wagner, Sue/Peru Central School Dist	2	44
Wagoner, Patty/Alexandria Central School Dist	37	79
Wagstaff, Jadawn/Buffalo Public Schools	45	57
Wahl, Laurence/Webster Central School Dist	16,48	112
Waite-Ambra, Jennifer/Dcmo BOCES Chenango	27,30,31,88	43
Wald, Daniel/Hauppauge Union Free Sch Dist	76	223
Walden, Claytisha, Dr/Mount Vernon City School Dist	8,15	258
Walden, Kenneth/Levittown Union Free Sch Dist	30	123
Waldron-Oneill, Ellen/Southold Union Free Sch Dist	9	231
Waldron, Ken/Ossining Union Free Sch Dist	3	259
Wales, William/Niskayuna Central School Dist	45	204
Waligory-Lee, Jennifer/Clinton Central School Dist	12,70,273	150
Walker, Charles/Laurens Central School Dist	73,295	173
Walker, Drew/Hampton Bays Union Free SD	6,35	222
Walker, Lisa/Long Lake Central School Dist	2	76
Walker, Lynn/Hastings on Hudson Union FR SD	68,79	256
Walker, Malasia/William Floyd School Dist	58,77	233
Walker, Mary/Hamilton Central Sch Dist	11,58,77	105
Walker, Patricia/Unatego Unadilla Central SD	4	174
Walker, Richard/Marion Central School Dist	2	250
Walker, Rob/Richfield Springs Central SD	3	174
Walker, Robert/Herkimer Ctl School Dist	3	77
Walker, Scott/Owen D Young Central Sch Dist	295	78
Walker, Stephen/Sullivan West Central SD	1	237
Walker, Tamar/East Ramapo Central Sch Dist	15,58	196
Walker, Todd/Greater Johnstown Sch Dist	286	71
Walker, Wayne/Brookfield Central School Dist	5	104
Wall, Mary/New York City Dept of Ed	751	134
Wallach, Merryl/Vestal Ctl School Dist	83,88	29
Wallach, Sylvia/Mamaroneck Union Free Sch Dist	2,15	257
Wallack, Josh/New York City Dept of Ed	15,34	134
Walling, Diane/Morris Central School Dist	51,280	174
Walsh, Alyson/Mt Pleasant Ctl School Dist	71	258
Walsh, Joanne/Archdiocese of New York Ed Off	15,34	142
Walsh, Kathleen, Dr/Diocese of Rockville Ed Office	1	132
Walsh, Michelle/West Islip School Dist	275	233
Walter, Cindy/Tompkins-Seneca-Tioga BOCES	27,31	241
Walter, Patricia/McGraw Central School Dist	38	48
Walters, James/Greene Ctl School Dist	10,72	42
Walvbauer, Nicole/Shoreham-Wading River Ctl SD	57	230
Walz, Susan/Fairport Ctl School Dist	58	108
Wandell, Scott/Newark Valley Central Sch Dist	6	238
Wander, Ingrid/Williamson Central School Dist	90	251
Wankmuller, Robert, Dr/Hauppauge Union Free Sch Dist	42,73	223
Ward, Andrew/Plainview-Old Bethpage Ctl SD	3	127
Ward, Annie/Mamaroneck Union Free Sch Dist	8,15,288	257
Ward, Daniel/Ft Edward Union Free Sch Dist	1,11,83	247
Ward, Jon/North Syracuse Ctl Sch Dist	3	157
Ward, Melanie/Pittsford Central Sch Dist	8,15,288	110
Ward, Sherry/Mount Vernon City School Dist	27	258
Ward, Stacy/Canajoharie Ctl School Dist	11	115
Ward, Terry, Dr/Cato Meridian Central Sch Dist	1	34
Wardell, Cathleen/Corinth Central School Dist	5	200
Wardell, Mary Jo/Windsor Central School Dist	31	30
Warden, Janet/Carmel Central School Dist	8,11,15,57,273,274,288	175
Warden, Janet/Red Hook Central School Dist	1	53
Warner, Ashly/Falconer Central School Dist	69,77	37
Warner, Doris/Margaretville Central Sch Dist	67	50
Warner, Joanne/Granville Central School Dist	4	247
Warner, Michelle/Ichabod Crane Central Schools	7	46
Warner, Peg/Ichabod Crane Central Schools	58,88	46
Warner, Zachary/New York State Dept Education	69	1
Warren, Gregory/New Paltz Ctl School Dist	6,35	242
Warren, Jamie/Buffalo Public Schools	15,68	57
Warren, Kateri/Bloomfield Central SD	16,36,58,76,79,88	161
Warren, Kevin/Babylon Union Free Sch Dist	3	216
Warsaw, Dennis/Miller Place Union Free SD	3	226
Warwick, Kelly/Chenango Valley Ctl Sch Dist	67	28
Warwick, Terry/Fulton City School Dist	4	170
Wasecka, Joe/Chenango Forks Central SD	73	28
Washington, Larry, Dr/Washingtonville Central SD	1	167
Wasielewski, Karen/Frankfort-Schuyler Ctl SD	5	77
Waskie-Laura, Nicole/Broome-Tioga BOCES	16	31
Waskowitz, Lindsay/Carle Place Union Free SD	83	117
Waskowitz, Nancy/Carle Place Union Free SD	4	117
Wasserman, Greg/Roslyn School Dist	27,31,36,85	129
Waters, Jack/Mineola Union Free Sch Dist	2,15	125
Waters, Mark/Ellicottville Central Sch Dist	3	31
Waters, Roxanne/Whitehall Central School Dist	67	248
Waters, Yvonne/Germantown Central School Dist	58,79	46
Watkins, Amy/Wappingers Central Sch Dist	71	54
Watkins, Cindy/Syracuse City School Dist	34	158
Watkis, Shelita/Lindenhurst Union Free SD	57,61,89	224
Watrous, Janice/Poland Central School Dist	31,36,270,271	78
Watrous, Susan/Clymer Central School Dist	4	37
Watson, Brandon/Amherst Central School Dist	295,297	56
Watson, Donna, Dr/Troy City School Dsitrict	8,15,288	191
Watson, Felisha, Dr/Poughkeepsie City School Dist	67	53
Watson, John/Wantagh Union Free Sch Dist 23	45	131
Watson, Laura/Portville Central School Dist	4	32
Watson, Laura/Springville Griffith Inst CSD	4	63
Watson, Lisa/Elmsford Union Free SD	16	255
Watson, Mike/Allegany-Limestone Ctl SD	2,5,11,68	31
Watt, Laura/Cassadaga Valley Ctl Sch Dist	2	36
Watts, Donna/Rush Henrietta Central SD	20,23	112
Watts, Tom/George Junior Republic UFSD	15	240
Wawrzynski, Melissa/Pavilion Ctl School Dist	38,69	74
Waye, Milton/Brockport Ctl School Dist	5	106
Wayman, Nancy/Pittsford Central Sch Dist	71	110
Weakfall, Nichole/Potsdam Central School Dist	8,76,83,88,286,288,296,752	212
Weatherell, Diane/Cuba-Rushford Central Sch Dist	2	14
Weaver, Andrew/Lake Pleasant Central Sch Dist	67	76
Weaver, Drew/Pine Plains Ctl School Dist	5	53
Weaver, James/Madison-Oneida BOCES	58,88	154
Weaver, Joshua/Berlin Central School Dist	6	189
Weaver, William/Genesee Valley Ctl School Dist	5	15
Webb, Amy/Chautauqua Lake Central SD	67	36
Weber, Jeremy/Pine Plains Ctl School Dist	35	53
Weber, Lisa, Dr/Suffern Central School Dist	1	198
Weber, Paul/Massapequa Union Free SD 23	77	125
Webster, Angela/Taconic Hills Central Sch Dist	6	47
Webster, Gordon/South Colonie Central Sch Dist	3	12
Webster, Kelly/Watervliet City School Dist	88,270	12
Webster, Kevin/South Seneca Ctl Sch Dist	37	208
Webster, Paul/Corning-Painted Post Area SD	2	214
Weddell, Ashlee/Edinburg Common School Dist	7	201
Weed, Georgia/Addison Central School Dist	9	213
Weeks, Lisa/Oneonta City School Dist	12	174
Weeks, Vanessa/Arlington Central School Dist	58	51
Weglarski, Margaret/Kenmore-Tonawanda UF Sch Dist	2	62
Wegrzyn, Donna/New York Mills Union Free SD	85	151
Weidner, William/Yorkshire-Pioneer Ctl Sch Dist	6,7	33
Weimer, Duane/Victor Central School Dist	6,35	162

DISTRICT PERSONNEL INDEX

Market Data Retrieval

NAME/District	JOB FUNCTIONS	PAGE
Weimer, James/Buffalo Public Schools	15,17	56
Weinberd, Richard/Cattaraugus-Little Vly Ctl SD	73,295	31
Weinberger, Kathleen/Kings Park Ctl School Dist	4	224
Weiner, Thomas/Central Islip Union Free SD	91	218
Weinhofer, Steven/Middleburgh Ctl School Dist	3	206
Weinlein, Russell/Burnt Hills Ballston Lake SD	36	200
Weinstein, Jason/Windsor Central School Dist	71	30
Weir, Barbara/Miller Place Union Free SD	73,84,295	226
Weise, John/Carmel Central School Dist	3	175
Weisman, Andrew/Peekskill City School Dist	4	260
Weisman, Andrew/Peekskill City School Dist	4	260
Weiss, Linda/Eastport-South Manor Ctrl SD	15,78,273	221
Weisse, Steven/Kings Park Ctl School Dist	73,91	224
Weissman, Debbie/Warwick Valley Central SD	5	167
Welch-Chestaro, Eileen/Brentwood Union Free Sch Dist	42,45	217
Welch-Pollera, Kerrin/Three Village Central Sch Dist	73,286	232
Welch, Marguirte/Wells Central School Dist	4	77
Welch, Melanie/Frankfort-Schuyler Ctl SD	9,11,51,54	77
Welde, Ashley/Blind Brook-Rye Union Free SD	67	252
Weldon, Maryann/Heuvelton Central School Dist	7,35,83,85	210
Welgoss, Mary Kay/Tompkins-Seneca-Tioga BOCES	16	241
Wells, Jennifer/South Colonie Central Sch Dist	40,49,52,280	12
Wells, Jennifer/Syracuse City School Dist	68	158
Wells, Karen/Goshen Central School Dist	5	164
Wells, Lynne, Dr/Capital Region BOCES	8,15	13
Welsh, Jaycee/La Fargeville Central Sch Dist	11,58,270,288	80
Wenke, Dan/Portville Central School Dist	67	32
Wenke, Mary Lee/Olean City School Dist	38	32
Wercberger, Shaye/Kiryas Joel Union Free SD	2	164
Werlau, Elizabeth/Wallkill Central School Dist	81	243
Werner, Margaret/Bolivar-Richburg Ctrl Sch Dist	16,82	14
Wert, Rick/Hyde Park Central School Dist	73,76,95,286,295	52
Weselak, Robert/Sweet Home Central Sch Dist	5	63
Wesley, Sherre, Dr/Dutchess Co BOCES	2,15	55
West, Anne/Fillmore Central School Dist	58	14
West, Barry/Chazy Central Rural Sch Dist	3,5	44
West, Cheryl/East Syracuse Minoa Ctl SD	83,275,752	154
West, Douglas/Warrensburg Central School Dist	67	246
West, Gary/White Plains City School Dist	23	263
West, Steve/Shenendehowa Central Sch Dist	91	202
West, Steven/Laurens Central School Dist	6	173
Westergard, Charles/East Hampton Union Free SD	16,73,286,295	220
Western, Marie/Lowville Acad-Central Sch Dist	8,288,296,298	101
Westervelt, Jason/Watkins Glen Central Sch Dist	35,83,85	207
Westervelt, Wafa, Dr/Port Washington Union Free SD	8,11,15,34,69,81,83	128
Westfall, Diane/West Valley Ctl Sch Dist	298	33
Westfall, Gabrielle/Roscoe Central School Dist	83	237
Westinghousa, Darlene/Saugerties Central School Dist	8,69	243
Westler, Kelly/Holland Central School Dist	9	61
Weston, Jill/Solvay Union Free Sch Dist	280	158
Westover, Jenifer/Moravia Central School Dist	16	35
Wetherbee, Michael/Cairo-Durham Ctl School Dist	1	75
Wetmore-Chase, Kathleen/Shenendehowa Central Sch Dist	2,15	202
Wetmore, Eric/Brunswick Central School Dist	295	190
Wetzel, David/South Colonie Central Sch Dist	88	12
Wexell, Dale, Dr/Corning-Painted Post Area SD	67	214
Weydig, Paul/Uniondale Union Free Sch Dist	5	130
Whalen, Brian/Binghamton City School Dist	67	27
Whalen, Sandra/Vernon-Verona-Sherrill CSD	11,76,97	152
Whaley, Catherine/Middletown Enlarged City SD	45	165
Whaley, Ernest/Caledonia-Mumford Ctl Sch Dist	3	102
Wheaton, Barbara/Mattituck-Cutchogue UFSD	67	225
Wheaton, Jeffrey/Amherst Central School Dist	6,35	56
Wheeler, Charles/Broome-Tioga BOCES	88	31
Wheeler, Kerstin/Fairport Ctl School Dist	8,15	108
Wheeler, Kimberly/Valley Stream Union Free SD 24	67	131
Wheelock, Ronald/Sauquoit Valley Central SD	1,83	152
Whipple, Jason/Frontier Ctl School Dist	4	60
Whipple, Jennifer/Skaneateles Central Sch Dist	8,12,58	157
Whipple, Patrick, Dr/Genesee Valley BOCES	74	75
Whipple, Timothy/Pleasantville Union Free SD	2,15	260
Whitacre, Bernie/Brookfield Central School Dist	67	104
Whitaker, Kevin/Geneva City School Dist	8,11,15,70,294	161
Whitaker, Kevin, Dr/Jamestown City School Dist	1	38
Whitaker, Robert/Tri-Valley Central School Dist	2,4,5,84,274	237
Whitbeck, Thrisha/Cairo-Durham Ctl School Dist	294	75
Whitcomb, Laura/Hilton Central School Dist	58,79	109
Whitcomb, Leslie/New Lebanon Ctl School Dist	1,288	46
White-Wallace, Gale/Mount Vernon City School Dist	34,280	258
White, Alvin/Huntington Union Free Sch Dist	3	223
White, Amelia/Letchworth Central School Dist	16,82	267
White, Anthony/Wallkill Central School Dist	34,57,58,69,88,270	243
White, Aurora/Saranac Lake Central Sch Dist	67	70
White, Brian/Willsboro Central Sch Dist	73	68
White, Daniel/Monroe 1 BOCES	1	115
White, Debra/South Kortright Ctl SD	274	50
White, Georganne/Huntington Union Free Sch Dist	16	223
White, Jeffery/Copiague Union Free Sch Dist	2,5,15	220
White, Kelly/Ellenville Central School Dist	8,12,288	241
White, Kelly/Kenmore-Tonawanda UF Sch Dist	8,15,69,79,288	62
White, Kristen/Rocky Point Union Free SD	79	228
White, Mark/Hermon-DeKalb Central Sch Dist	1	210
White, Michael/Saranac Central School Dist	11,271,273	45
White, Rob/Edwards-Knox Central Sch Dist	6	210
White, Ronald/Bridgehampton Union Free SD	67	218
White, Sean/Miller Place Union Free SD	36	226
White, Sherry/Edwards-Knox Central Sch Dist	58	210
White, Van Henri/Rochester City School Dist	67	110
Whited, Darryl/Watervliet City School Dist	4	12
Whiteford, Nichole/Byron-Bergen Ctl School Dist	77	73
Whitfield, Serena/Long Beach City School Dist	58	124
Whiting, Jackie/Le Roy Central School Dist	67	73
Whitman, Sayde/Corinth Central School Dist	38	200
Whitman, Tammy/Berlin Central School Dist	4	189
Whitmore, Christopher/Rome City School Dist	4	151
Whitmore, Jane/Tupper Lake Ctl School Dist	67	70
Whitney-Rivera, Kelly/Valley Stream Ctl High SD	38,71,97	130
Whitney, Shannon/Watertown City School Dist	58,77	81
Whitt, Terry/Hancock Central School Dist	67	49
Whittaker, Tara/Chenango Valley Ctl Sch Dist	34,58	28
Whittel, Charles/Livonia Ctl School Dist	9	103
Whittemore, Scott/Queensbury Union Free Sch Dist	2,15	246
Wickham, Denise/Greenville Central School Dist	6,35	75
Wickham, Kurt/Pine Bush Central School Dist	5	166
Wicks, Brandi/Auburn Enlarged City Sch Dist	60	34
Wicks, David/Eastern Suffolk BOCES	1	235
Wicks, Douglas/East Aurora Union Free SD	3,91	60
Wideman, Wayne/Ctr for Instruct Tech Innov	3	172
Widen, Julie/Falconer Central School Dist	34,58	37
Widman, Laurie/Oriskany Ctl School Dist	2,11,298	151
Widmann, Christopher/Wantagh Union Free Sch Dist 23	39	131
Widmer, James/Nassau BOCES	2,15	134
Wiederman, Joe/New Suffolk Common School Dist	73	226
Wiegert, Mark/North Colonie Central SD	3	11
Wieland, Heather/Camden Central School Dist	73	150
Wightman, Lori/Ulster BOCES	2	244
Wiiki, Jack/Spencer Van Etten Central SD	97	238
Wiiki, Jack/Waverly Ctl School Dist	97	239
Wiktorko, John/Windham Ashland Jewett Ctl SD	1	76
Wilber, Lisa/Owen D Young Central Sch Dist	16	78
Wilbur, Matt/Sodus Central School Dist	73	251
Wilcox, Heather/Gilbertsville-Mt Upton SD	58,274	173
Wilcox, Peter/Horseheads Ctl School Dist	5	40
Wilcox, Peter/Middletown Enlarged City SD	3,15	165

1 Superintendent	16 Instructional Media Svcs	30 Adult Education	44 Science Sec	58 Special Education K-12	72 Summer School
2 Bus/Finance/Purchasing	17 Chief Operations Officer	31 Career/Sch-to-Work K-12	45 Math K-12	59 Special Education Elem	73 Instructional Tech
3 Buildings And Grounds	18 Chief Academic Officer	32 Career/Sch-to-Work Elem	46 Math Elem	60 Special Education Sec	74 Inservice Training
4 Food Service	19 Chief Financial Officer	33 Career/Sch-to-Work Sec	47 Math Sec	61 Foreign/World Lang K-12	75 Marketing/Distributive
5 Transportation	20 Art K-12	34 Early Childhood Ed	48 English/Lang Arts K-12	62 Foreign/World Lang Elem	76 Info Systems
6 Athletic	21 Art Elem	35 Health/Phys Education	49 English/Lang Arts Elem	63 Foreign/World Lang Sec	77 Psychological Assess
7 Health Services	22 Art Sec	36 Guidance Services K-12	50 English/Lang Arts Sec	64 Religious Education K-12	78 Affirmative Action
8 Curric/Instruct K-12	23 Music K-12	37 Guidance Services Elem	51 Reading K-12	65 Religious Education Elem	79 Student Personnel
9 Curric/Instruct Elem	24 Music Elem	38 Guidance Services Sec	52 Reading Elem	66 Religious Education Sec	80 Driver Ed/Safety
10 Curric/Instruct Sec	25 Music Sec	39 Social Studies K-12	53 Reading Sec	67 School Board President	81 Gifted/Talented
11 Federal Program	26 Business Education	40 Social Studies Elem	54 Remedial Reading K-12	68 Teacher Personnel	82 Video Services
12 Title I	27 Career & Tech Ed	41 Social Studies Sec	55 Remedial Reading Elem	69 Academic Assessment	83 Substance Abuse Prev
13 Title V	28 Technology Education	42 Science K-12	56 Remedial Reading Sec	70 Research/Development	84 Erate
15 Asst Superintendent	29 Family/Consumer Science	43 Science Elem	57 Bilingual/ELL	71 Public Information	85 AIDS Education
88 Alternative/At Risk	277 Remedial Math K-12				
89 Multi-Cultural Curriculum	280 Literacy Coach				
90 Social Work	285 STEM				
91 Safety/Security	286 Digital Learning				
92 Magnet School	288 Common Core Standards				
93 Parental Involvement	294 Accountability				
95 Tech Prep Program	295 Network System				
97 Chief Information Officer	296 Title II Programs				
98 Chief Technology Officer	297 Webmaster				
270 Character Education	298 Grant Writer/Ptnrships				
271 Migrant Education	750 Chief Innovation Officer				
273 Teacher Mentor	751 Chief of Staff				
274 Before/After Sch	752 Social Emotional Learning				
275 Response To Intervention					

NY-T66

New York School Directory

DISTRICT PERSONNEL INDEX

NAME/District	JOB FUNCTIONS	PAGE
Wilcox, Tammy/Newfield Central School Dist	7,83	241
Wilcox, Timothy/Fabius Pompey Central SD	6	155
Wild, Brian/Lancaster Central Sch Dist	6	62
Wiles, Lisa/Ellenville Central School Dist	1,11,73	241
Wiles, Marie, Dr/Guilderland Central Sch Dist	1	10
Wiley, Ben/Plainview-Old Bethpage Ctl SD	20,286	127
Wiley, Jay/South Jefferson Central SD	6	81
Wilford, Fred/Sagaponack Common School Dist	3	229
Wilfore, Theda/Chazy Central Rural Sch Dist	11,58,88	44
Wilhelm, Jason/Lyndonville Central Sch Dist	73	169
Wilk, Steve/Minerva Central School Dist	77	68
Wilk, Steven/Newcomb Central School Dist	58	68
Wilken, Paul/Sag Harbor Union Free Sch Dist	3	229
Wilkens, Matthew/Warsaw Central School Dist	1	267
Wilkes, Donna/Duanesburg Central Sch Dist	16	203
Wilkins, Beverly/Community School District 18	1	87
Wilkins, Kim, Dr/New York State Dept Education	8,15	1
Wilkins, Meaghan/Argyle Central School Dist	4	246
Wilkins, Vicky/Greenburgh-Graham UFSD	68	255
Wilkowski, Theresa/Lakeland Central School Dist	48	257
Willabay, John/Poughkeepsie City School Dist	3	53
Willams, Nicole/Bolton Central School Dist	44	244
Williams, Barbara/Amherst Central School Dist	2	56
Williams, Christopher/Oriskany Ctl School Dist	31,36,69	151
Williams, Gary/Sidney Central School Dist	58	50
Williams, Jennifer/Tri-Valley Central School Dist	9	237
Williams, John/Middletown Enlarged City SD	67	165
Williams, Joseph/Farmingdale Union Free SD	5	119
Williams, Karen/Syracuse City School Dist	58	158
Williams, Katrina/Greenwich Central School Dist	16	247
Williams, Keith/Mount Markham Central Sch Dist	3	78
Williams, Lisa/Greenwich Central School Dist	77	248
Williams, Michael/Tri-Valley Central School Dist	1	237
Williams, Mike/Candor Central School Dist	76,295	238
Williams, Monique/Syracuse City School Dist	15,751	158
Williams, Rebecca/Diocese of Rochester Ed Office	2	113
Williams, Renee/Honeoye Falls Lima Sch Dist	8,11,15,16,74,288,296,298	109
Williams, Ronda/Walton Central School Dist	67	50
Williams, Scott/Vernon-Verona-Sherrill CSD	45	152
Williams, Stuart/Ballston Spa Ctl School Dist	71	200
Williams, Tara/Chenango Valley Ctl Sch Dist	58	28
Williams, Tom/Deposit Central School Dist	3	28
Williams, Tracy/Walton Central School Dist	5	50
Williams, Vicky/Ellicottville Central Sch Dist	4	31
Williams, Wayne/Monroe Woodbury Central SD	36	165
Willig, Robin/Blind Brook-Rye Union Free SD	285	252
Willis, Joseph/Morrisville Eaton Central SD	73,295	105
Willsky, Hope/Berkshire Union Free Sch Dist	298	45
Willson, David/Penn Yan Ctl School Dist	67	268
Willson, John/Arlington Central School Dist	3,91	51
Wilson- Bush, Tina/Madrid-Waddington Central SD	67	211
Wilson-Turner, Cecily/Albany City School Dist	9,15	9
Wilson, Bob/Campbell-Savona Ctl Sch Dist	3,91	213
Wilson, Charlene/Prattsburgh Central Sch Dist	5	215
Wilson, Dina/Rush Henrietta Central SD	8,15,69,80,288	112
Wilson, Djuana/Hempstead Union Free SD	15,58	121
Wilson, Duncan/Ardsley Union Free School Dist	8,15	252
Wilson, Eric/Fonda Fultonville Central SD	6	115
Wilson, Gary/Hadley-Luzerne Ctl School Dist	6	245
Wilson, John/Evans-Brant Central Sch Dist	3	60
Wilson, Kathleen/Chazy Central Rural Sch Dist	54	44
Wilson, Kelly/Gouverneur Ctl School Dist	16	210
Wilson, Margaret/Syracuse City School Dist	9,15	158
Wilson, Mark/Potsdam Central School Dist	6	212
Wilson, Nancy/Western Suffolk BOCES	58	236
Wilson, Rene/Richfield Springs Central SD	11,69	174
Wilson, Renee/Cheektowaga Central SD	67	58
Wilson, Sharon/Wyandanch Union Free Sch Dist	16,73,95,295	234
Wilson, Sheryl/La Fargeville Central Sch Dist	67	80
Wilson, Stephanie/Greater Southern Tier BOCES	16	215
Wilson, Steve/Nyack Union Free School Dist	4	197
Wilson, Susan/Rocky Point Union Free SD	8,16,34,73,76,273,295	228
Wilson, Timothy/Spencer Van Etten Central SD	5	238
Wilson, Tina/Rye Neck Union Free Sch Dist	10,69,83,88	261
Wilson, Veronique/Wayne Central School Dist	4	251
Wilson, Wayne/Sachem Central School Dist	91	229

NAME/District	JOB FUNCTIONS	PAGE
Winas, Carol/Wantagh Union Free Sch Dist 23	42	131
Winch, Todd/Levittown Union Free Sch Dist	8,15	123
Winchell, Cindy/Scio Central School Dist	4	15
Winchell, Dave/Fredonia Central School Dist	3	37
Winchip, Ryan/Pembroke Ctl School Dist	6	74
Winderman, Kerri/Rye City School Dist	69	261
Windus, Amy/Cattaraugus-Allegany BOCES	16	34
Wineks, Carla/Forestville Central Sch Dist	58	37
Wing, Ted/Franklinville Ctl School Dist	5	31
Winick, Sheri/Plainview-Old Bethpage Ctl SD	81	127
Winkley, Darrin/Brockport Ctl School Dist	2,15	106
Winnicki, Alicja/Community School District 14	1	83
Winslow, Milly/Newcomb Central School Dist	6	68
Winter, Debra/Springs Union Free School Dist	1	232
Winters, Danielle/Moravia Central School Dist	5	34
Winters, Lisa/Union Springs Ctl School Dist	30	35
Wisbeski, Catherine/South Orangetown Central SD	4	197
Wise, Angela/Pine Bush Central School Dist	68,76	166
Wise, Coleen/Averill Park Central Sch Dist	4	189
Wise, David/Marion Central School Dist	70,73	250
Wise, Elizabeth/Morrisville Eaton Central SD	16	105
Wisenburn, Donna/WSWHE BOCES	15,68	249
Wisniewski, John/Onondaga-Cortland-Madison BOCES	3	160
Wisnowski, Madelynn/Lyncourt Union Free Sch Dist	2	156
Wissiak, Ryan/Horseheads Ctl School Dist	285	40
Wist, Denise/Cherry Valley-Springfield SD	2	173
Witherell, Merrilee/Red Creek Central School Dist	16	251
Witherow, Patrick/Minisink Valley Central SD	2,15	165
Witkiewicz, Rob/Boquet Valley Central Sch Dist	8,11,58,69,88,273,294	67
Witmore, Andrew/Rush Henrietta Central SD	2,3,15	112
Witriol, Moses/Kiryas Joel Union Free SD	91	164
Witt, Kevin/Middletown Enlarged City SD	71	165
Witter, Heather/Fulton City School Dist	34,280	170
Witter, Susan/Churchville Chili Ctl Sch Dist	8,57,69,74,275,280,285,288	107
Wittkowski, Ed/Westhill Central School Dist	3	159
Wixson, Mark/Vernon-Verona-Sherrill CSD	2,15,19,34,83,271,295	152
Woellhof, Eric/East Islip Union Free SD	3,91	220
Woitaszek, Daniel/Letchworth Central School Dist	27,38	267
Wojcik, Brandon/North Collins Ctl Sch Dist	10	63
Wojnowski, Sandra/Miller Place Union Free SD	10,12,58,296	226
Wolcott, Katherine/Wayland-Cohocton Central SD	11,34,58	215
Wolf, Jim/Charlotte Valley Ctl Sch Dist	35	49
Wolf, Robert/Whitney Point Central Sch Dist	5	30
Wolf, Scott/Sweet Home Central Sch Dist	8,285	63
Wolf, Steven/Guilderland Central Sch Dist	72	11
Wolfanger, David/Perry Central School Dist	3,91	267
Wolfe, Aaron/Olean City School Dist	68,74	32
Wolfe, Nicole/Union-Endicott Ctl Sch Dist	1	29
Wolfe, Patricia/Albany City School Dist	76	9
Wolff, Alex/Pelham Union Free School Dist	71	260
Wolff, Michele/South Seneca Ctl Sch Dist	273	208
Wolff, Rita/Williamsville Ctl School Dist	71	64
Wolford, Todd/Lyndonville Central Sch Dist	16,73,82	169
Wolfstich, Allison/Glens Falls City School Dist	31	245
Wolski, John/Iroquois Central School Dist	2	61
Wolter, Peter/Southampton Union Free SD	73,76,295	231
Wolzmuth, Robin/Camden Central School Dist	7	150
Wommack, Kathy/Pavilion Ctl School Dist	8	74
Wong, Trecia/Lindenhurst Union Free SD	45	224
Wood-Walter, Cheryl/Waverly Ctl School Dist	16	239
Wood, Brett/Franklin Central School Dist	3	49
Wood, Bridget/Buffalo Public Schools	4	56
Wood, Candice/Elmsford Union Free SD	67	255
Wood, Christopher/Odessa Montour Ctl Sch Dist	1	207
Wood, Cindy/Florida Union Free Sch Dist	4	164
Wood, Cory/Gouverneur Ctl School Dist	88,270	210
Wood, Dana/Lake Placid Ctl School Dist	2,3	67
Wood, David/Greater Johnstown Sch Dist	3	71
Wood, Dawn/Argyle Central School Dist	8	246
Wood, Elizabeth, Dr/Shenendehowa Central Sch Dist	8,11,15,40,69,78,286,288	202
Wood, Erika/Brockport Ctl School Dist	68	106
Wood, Jacob/Whitesville Central Sch Dist	285	15
Wood, James/Albion Central School Dist	68	169
Wood, Micheal/Mexico Central School Dist	3	171
Wood, Richard/Spencerport Central Sch Dist	2,15	112
Wood, Robin/Newfield Central School Dist	4	241

DISTRICT PERSONNEL INDEX

Market Data Retrieval

NAME/District	JOB FUNCTIONS	PAGE
Wood, Tammy/Phelps-Clifton Springs Ctl SD	7,11,58,81,273,296	162
Wood, Ted/Fort Ann Central School Dist	295	247
Woodard, Agnes/Dundee Ctl School Dist	7,85	268
Woodard, Steve/Cayuga-Onondaga BOCES	27,30,31,88	36
Woodard, Zachary/Whitney Point Central Sch Dist	2	30
Woodbury, Jeffrey, Dr/Half Hollow Hills Central SD	15	222
Woodcock, Darcy/Westhill Central School Dist	8,15,69,274	160
Woodell-Freire, John/Glens Falls City School Dist	36	245
Woodhead, Kristen/Bolivar-Richburg Ctrl School Dist	2	14
Woodin, Kyle/West Valley Ctl Sch Dist	83,85,88	33
Woodruff, David, Dr/Livonia Ctl School Dist	67	103
Woods, Elizabeth/Pittsford Central Sch Dist	58	110
Woods, Erin/Edwards-Knox Central Sch Dist	1,11	210
Woodward, Carol/Forestville Central Sch Dist	67	37
Woodward, Joelle/Cassadaga Valley Ctl Sch Dist	2,298	36
Woodward, Rex/Chateaugay Central Sch Dist	5	69
Woodworth, Csobanka/Olean City School Dist	28,73,295	32
Woodworth, Jan, Dr/Cazenovia Ctl School Dist	67	104
Woody, Jennifer/Onondaga Central School Dist	2,3,5,11,296	157
Wool, Louis/Harrison Central School Dist	1	256
Wooldrige, Michael/Hammondsport Ctl School Dist	73,286	214
Woolsey, Robert/Deer Park Union Free Sch Dist	3,91	220
Woolston, Carla/Marcus Whitman Central SD	4	162
Wormuth, Gregory/Mattituck-Cutchogue UFSD	6,7,35,83	225
Wormuth, Sheila/Liberty Central School Dist	77	236
Wortham, Deborah, Dr/East Ramapo Central Sch Dist	1	196
Wortham, Deborah, Dr/Roosevelt Union Free Sch Dist	1	128
Wottawa, Robert/East Islip Union Free SD	20,23	220
Woughter, Robert/Keene Central School Dist	58	67
Woytila, Gregory/North Tonawanda City Sch Dist	1	148
Wren, Robert/Cato Meridian Central Sch Dist	9	34
Wright, Ann/Onondaga-Cortland-Madson BOCES	67	160
Wright, Brian/Baldwinsville Central Sch Dist	4	154
Wright, Carly/Randolph Central School Dist	16	33
Wright, Casandra/Buffalo Public Schools	15,27	56
Wright, Doreen/Spackenkill Union Free SD	5	54
Wright, Erik/Beacon City School Dist	8,15,69	51
Wright, Jennifer/Beaver River Central Sch Dist	16	101
Wright, Jim, Dr/South Huntington Union Free SD	6	231
Wright, Joy/Brunswick Central School Dist	4	190
Wright, Kathryn/Albany City School Dist	20,23	9
Wright, Katie/Waterloo Central School Dist	36	208
Wright, Keyana/Massapequa Union Free SD 23	5	125
Wright, Kristy/Wells Central School Dist	7	77
Wright, Mary/Dryden Central School Dist	280	239
Wright, Matthew/Schoharie Central SD	8,58,79	206
Wright, Stephanie/West Seneca Central Sch Dist	30,274	64
Wright, Steven/Cheektowaga Central SD	15,16	58
Wrobbel, Kristin/Phelps-Clifton Springs Ctl SD	83,88	162
Wrobel, Maria/Arlington Central School Dist	58	51
Wuest, Colleen/Madison-Oneida BOCES	34	154
Wurtz, Kevin/Fire Island Union Free SD	2	222
Wygant, Laura/Elmsford Union Free SD	12	255
Wylke, Dawn/Lockport City School Dist	58	147
Wyllie- Dacon, Ingrid/Valley Stream Union Free SD 30	67	131
Wyner, Roberta/Starpoint Central School Dist	76	149
Wynn, Dionne, Dr/Roosevelt Union Free Sch Dist	58,79	128
Wynne, Scott/Eastchester Union Free SD	8,15	254
Wysocki, Jerome/Cheektowaga-Sloan UFSD	36	59

X

NAME/District	JOB FUNCTIONS	PAGE
Xanthis, John/Valley Central School Dist	1	167

Y

NAME/District	JOB FUNCTIONS	PAGE
Yagaloff, Jeffrey/Plainview-Old Bethpage Ctl SD	50	127
Yager, Jordan/Oakfield Alabama Ctl SD	3	74
Yale, Janice/Bethpage Union Free Sch Dist	44	117
Yando, Allison/Delaware Academy Ctrl SD Delhi	83	49
Yanni, Janelle/Watervliet City School Dist	12,58,79	12
Yantz, Theresa/Gilbertsville-Mt Upton SD	77	173
Yap, James/Warwick Valley Central SD	8,15,73	167
Yapchanyk, Shelly/Greenburgh Central School Dist	7	255
Yaple, Steve/Newfield Central School Dist	3	241
Yates, David/East Irondequoit Ctl Sch Dist	71	107
Yates, Jeannine/Galway Central School Dist	2	201
Yates, Michael/Palmyra-Macedon Central SD	16	250
Yavoski, Marc/Locust Valley Ctl School Dist	23	123
Yee, Randy/Bellmore Union Free Sch Dist	71	117
Yehl, Rick/Manchester-Shortsville Ctl SD	85	162
Yerkie, Dawn/Mount Markham Central Sch Dist	83	78
Yette, Barry/South Lewis Central Sch Dist	2,11,296	101
Yoder, David/Batavia City School Dist	73	73
Yodis, Mary/Wynantskill Union Free SD	9,71,88,270,273	192
Yohe, Carrie/Bemus Point Ctl School Dist	11,58,298	36
Yohe, Carrie/Bemus Point Ctl School Dist	8,57,74	36
Yost, Jennifer/Averill Park Central Sch Dist	16	189
Young, Caroline/Gowanda Central School Dist	88	32
Young, David/Portville Central School Dist	5	32
Young, John/East Syracuse Minoa Ctl SD	3,91	154
Young, Karen/Lockport City School Dist	67	147
Young, Larry/Glens Falls City School Dist	4	245
Young, Peter/Newfane Central School Dist	8,12,69,73	147
Young, Rich/Marathon Ctl School Dist	3,91	48
Young, Sherrisee/Baldwin Union Free School Dist	13,58,79,88,90	116
Young, Stephen, Dr/Berlin Central School Dist	1	189
Younger, Martha/Buffalo Public Schools	36	57
Yox, Jim/Schodack Central School Dist	73,76,295	191
Yusko, Mark/Elmira City School Dist	5	40
Yusko, Robert/Glens Falls City School Dist	2,78,91	245

Z

NAME/District	JOB FUNCTIONS	PAGE
Zacharia, Shaji/Mount Vernon City School Dist	2	258
Zacher, Sharon/Holley Central School Dist	15	169
Zaczek, Joe/Gilbertsville-Mt Upton SD	5	173
Zaczek, Linda/Dcmo BOCES Chenango	67	43
Zaffuts, Michael/Greece Central School Dist	15	108
Zahler, Kathy/Tompkins-Seneca-Tioga BOCES	67	241
Zajac, Rhonda/Syracuse City School Dist	48,54	158
Zakian, Glen/Farmingdale Union Free SD	15,68	119
Zales, Carrie/Plattsburgh City School Dist	8,15	44
Zaleski, Karen/Clinton Central School Dist	16,73	150
Zambito, Chantal/Gates Chili Central Sch Dist	69,76	108
Zamiarski, Mona/Brighton Central School Dist	30	106
Zanetti, Henry/Herricks Union Free Sch Dist	67	121
Zanfardino, Michael/Patchogue-Medford Unified SD	36,69,73	227
Zanghi, Thomas/Cassadaga Valley Ctl Sch Dist	3,5	36
Zanrucha, Laura/Afton Central School Dist	285,298	41
Zappia, John/Victor Central School Dist	2,15	162
Zarcone, Laura/South Orangetown Central SD	2	197
Zarrella, Dominic/Saugerties Central School Dist	6	243
Zaryski, Frances/Jamesville-DeWitt Central SD	4	155
Zaryski, Francis/Cortland Enlarged City SD	4	47
Zarzycki, Don/Salem Central School Dist	6,38	248
Zastrow, Melissa/Westfield Central School Dist	16,82	39
Zautner, Steven/North Colonie Central SD	2	11
Zawatson, David/Great Neck Public Schools	6	120
Zdanowski, Daniel/Rush Henrietta Central SD	7,27,42,73,285	112
Zdenek, Lisa/Sachem Central School Dist	4	229
Zdrogewski, Robert/Oakfield Alabama Ctl SD	73	74
Zehner, Sean/La Fayette Central School Dist	73	156
Zehr, Adam/Copenhagen Central SD	73,295	101
Zehr, Barbara/Carthage Central School Dist	8,57,69,88,275,280,288,296	80
Zehr, Barbara/Indian River Ctl School Dist	57	80
Zehr, Mary-Margaret/Oneida City School Dist	1	105

---

1 Superintendent	16 Instructional Media Svcs	30 Adult Education	44 Science Sec	58 Special Education K-12	72 Summer School	88 Alternative/At Risk	277 Remedial Math K-12
2 Bus/Finance/Purchasing	17 Chief Operations Officer	31 Career/Sch-to-Work K-12	45 Math K-12	59 Special Education Elem	73 Instructional Tech	89 Multi-Cultural Curriculum	280 Literacy Coach
3 Buildings And Grounds	18 Chief Academic Officer	32 Career/Sch-to-Work Elem	46 Math Elem	60 Special Education Sec	74 Inservice Training	90 Social Work	285 STEM
4 Food Service	19 Chief Financial Officer	33 Career/Sch-to-Work Sec	47 Math Sec	61 Foreign/World Lang K-12	75 Marketing/Distributive	91 Safety/Security	286 Digital Learning
5 Transportation	20 Art K-12	34 Early Childhood Ed	48 English/Lang Arts K-12	62 Foreign/World Lang Elem	76 Info Systems	92 Magnet School	288 Common Core Standards
6 Athletic	21 Art Elem	35 Health/Phys Education	49 English/Lang Arts Elem	63 Foreign/World Lang Sec	77 Psychological Assess	93 Parental Involvement	294 Accountability
7 Health Services	22 Art Sec	36 Guidance Services K-12	50 English/Lang Arts Sec	64 Religious Education K-12	78 Affirmative Action	95 Tech Prep Program	295 Network System
8 Curric/Instruct K-12	23 Music K-12	37 Guidance Services Elem	51 Reading K-12	65 Religious Education Elem	79 Student Personnel	97 Chief Information Officer	296 Title II Programs
9 Curric/Instruct Elem	24 Music Elem	38 Guidance Services Sec	52 Reading Elem	66 Religious Education Sec	80 Driver Ed/Safety	98 Chief Technology Officer	297 Webmaster
10 Curric/Instruct Sec	25 Music Sec	39 Social Studies K-12	53 Reading Sec	67 School Board President	81 Gifted/Talented	270 Character Education	298 Grant Writer/Ptnrships
11 Federal Program	26 Business Education	40 Social Studies Elem	54 Remedial Reading K-12	68 Teacher Personnel	82 Video Services	271 Migrant Education	750 Chief Innovation Officer
12 Title I	27 Career & Tech Ed	41 Social Studies Sec	55 Remedial Reading Elem	69 Academic Assessment	83 Substance Abuse Prev	273 Teacher Mentor	751 Chief of Staff
13 Title V	28 Technology Education	42 Science K-12	56 Remedial Reading Sec	70 Research/Development	84 Erate	274 Before/After Sch	752 Social Emotional Learning
15 Asst Superintendent	29 Family/Consumer Science	43 Science Elem	57 Bilingual/ELL	71 Public Information	85 AIDS Education	275 Response To Intervention	

New York School Directory

DISTRICT PERSONNEL INDEX

NAME/District	JOB FUNCTIONS	PAGE
Zeliff, James/Lyndonville Central Sch Dist	6	169
Zelik, Judah/Kiryas Joel Union Free SD	73	164
Zeller, Norma/Somers Central School Dist	4	262
Zellweger, Timothy/Parishville Hopkinton Sch Dist	67	212
Zenoski-Bartle, Kelli/Genesee Valley Ctl School Dist	4	15
Zervas, Jim/East Rockaway Union Free SD	285	118
Zeterberg, Michael/Islip Union Free School Dist	2,5,15	224
Ziegelbauer, Dorothy/Tuxedo Union Free Sch Dist	67	167
Ziegler, David/Tarrytown Union Free Sch Dist	36	262
Zielinski, Lisa/Depew Union Free School Dist	16,82	59
Zielinski, Stephen/South Seneca Ctl Sch Dist	1	208
Ziemba, Kevin/Tuxedo Union Free Sch Dist	2,4,11,296	166
Ziesel, Lori/Archdiocese of New York Ed Off	751	142
Zigler, Michelle/Lancaster Central Sch Dist	73,294	62
Zilkowski, Daniel/Dolgeville Central School Dist	6	77
Zilliox, Brad/Franklin Central School Dist	1	49
Zimbrich, Hanna/La Fargeville Central Sch Dist	38	80
Zimmer, Brian/Webster Central School Dist	69,73	112
Zimmer, Geoffery/Chittenango Central SD	67	104
Zimmerman, Bob/Plainview-Old Bethpage Ctl SD	71	127
Zimmerman, Kelly/Delaware Academy Ctrl SD Delhi	1	49
Zimmerman, Michael/Starpoint Central School Dist	67	149
Zimmerman, Robin/Peekskill City School Dist	2,15	260
Zingaro, Brandon/Mt Morris Central School Dist	3,295	103
Zink, Julie/Greece Central School Dist	68	108
Zinkievich, Winsome/Worcester Ctl School Dist	58	174
Zinkiewich, Ty/Spencerport Central Sch Dist	8,11,57,83,285,286,288,296	112
Ziobrowski, Kenneth/Questar III BOCES	2	192
Ziobrowski, Scott/Hilton Central School Dist	4	109
Zipp, Richard/Wappingers Central Sch Dist	15,58,79	54
Ziskin, David, Dr/Hamilton-Fulton-Montgmry BOCES	1	72
Zito, Lisa/Half Hollow Hills Central SD	59	222
Zito, Nicole/Kings Park Ctl School Dist	58	224
Zittel, Katie/Evans-Brant Central Sch Dist	20,286	60
Zlock, George/Chenango Valley Ctl Sch Dist	3	28
Zolnowski, Brian/North Collins Ctl Sch Dist	71,73,295	63
Zsebehazy, Ann/Buffalo Public Schools	76,294	57
Zuar, Brian, Dr/Rockville Ctr Union Free SD	23	128
Zuba, Jason/Cheektowaga-Sloan UFSD	73,74	59
Zuber, Alita/Ossining Union Free Sch Dist	2,4,15	259
Zuber, Andrew/South Jefferson Central SD	295	81
Zublionis, Natasha/Brookhaven Comsewogue Unif SD	295,296	218
Zuccaro, Micheal/Quogue Union Free School Dist	2	228
Zuckerman, Naomi/South Seneca Ctl Sch Dist	2,4,83,88,91	208
Zugelder, Steve/West Irondequoit Ctl SD	23	113
Zugibe, Peggy/Rockland BOCES	67	199
Zukowski, Randy/Newark Valley Central Sch Dist	5	238
Zumbolo, Marco/Broadalbin-Perth Ctl Sch Dist	2	71
Zumpano, Francesca/Holland Patent Ctl School Dist	2	150
Zuppo, Deb/Yorkshire-Pioneer Ctl Sch Dist	49	33
Zuroski, Kathryn/Genesee Valley BOCES	58	74
Zwack, Frank/Berlin Central School Dist	67	189
Zwack, Pete/Scotia Glenville Ctl Sch Dist	3	205
Zweig, Jessica/Averill Park Central Sch Dist	67	189
Zweig, Robert/New York Alt High Sch SD 79	1	142
Zwirn, Richard/Greenwich Central School Dist	38	247
Zwycewicz, Richard/East Islip Union Free SD	73	220

New York School Directory

PRINCIPAL INDEX

NAME/School	PAGE

A

Abai, Wintanna/Success Acad CS Flatbush ES [245]	7
Abbe, Zachary/Herkimer Jr Sr High Sch	78
Abbey, Michael/Emolior Academy	24
Abbott, David/Bell Academy	178
Abboud, Joseph/Yeshiva Shaarei Torah-Boys	100
Abdo, Amy/Manlius Pebble Hill Sch	160
Abdulmateen, N/Northeast College Prep HS	111
Abraham, Marck/PS 305 McKinley High Sch	58
Abramovitz, Asher/Kinneret Day Sch	26
Abreu, Hilduara/PS 192 Jacob H Schiff	141
Abreu, Ysidro/MS 319 Maria Teresa	141
Abtan, Celia/Yeshiva Ohel Torah	100
Accardi, Ignazio/Flushing High Sch	178
Acevedo Suarez, Sonia/PS 170	20
Ackerman, Allison/Michael F Stokes Elem Sch	122
Ackerman, Esther/Rabbi Jacob Joseph-Girls	195
Ackles, Wayne/West Genesee High Sch	159
Acocella, Patricia/Forest Ave Elem Sch	233
Acosta, Frances/Sacred Heart High Sch	265
Adam, Anna, Dr/St Anthony St Paul Sch	198
Adamek, Rebekah/Girls Prep Lower East Side ES [244]	4
Adams, Brooke/Colden Elem Sch	63
Adams, Dawne/Fallsburg Junior Senior HS	236
Adams, Derek/Liberty High Sch	236
Adams, Jaime/Floral Park Bellerose Elem Sch	119
Adams, Julie/Salem Central Sch	248
Adams, Megan/NYC Lab MS for Coll Studies	137
Adams, Thomas/Hamburg Middle Sch	61
Addison-Harris, Lucresha/Valley Cottage Elem Sch	197
Addison, Barry/Alpha Sch	96
Addo, Bernard/MS 661 Vista Academy	89
Ade, Jennifer/PS 46 Edgar Allan Poe	21
Adelman, Shlomo/Hanc High Sch	133
Adelstein, Rachel/Fort Montgomery Elem Sch	164
Adipietro, Lou/Hastings High Sch	256
Adler, Patricia/Spruce Elem Sch	148
Adsuar-Pizzi, Manuela/Queen of All Saints Cath Acad	95
Afriyie, Osei/Frederick Douglass Academy II	138
Agard, Victoria/IS 381	92
Agarwal, Rishabh/Success Acad CS Bed Stuy 1 [245]	7
Agnes, Mary, Sr/St Pius V Sch	235
Agosta, Joseph/Walter G O'Connell Copiague HS	220
Agostinoni, Ron/Shenendehowa High Sch	202
Agramonte, Fernando/Westbury Middle Sch	132
Aguilar, Angela/Cherry Lane Elem Sch	198
Aguirre, Claudia/PS 149 Sojourner Truth	139
Ahearn, Teri/JHS 14 Shell Bank	92
Ahmed, Iffat/Crescent Sch	133
Aiken, Mary Jo/St Mary Sch-Swormville	66
Ainley, Amanda/New World Preparatory CS	6
Aiuvalasit, Sharon/Urban Dove Team CS II	8
Akano, Abigail/Sacred Heart Sch	26
Akel, Samuel/George Washington Campus YABC	141
Akey, Harold/Adirondack Christian Sch	69
Alagia, Sheila/St Peter Sch	265
Alaimo, Lynn/St Gregory the Great Sch	186
Alaimo, Sal/Eastport South Manor Jr Sr HS	221
Albano, Beth/PS 53 Barbara Esselborn Sch	193
Albert, Jill/Kingston Catholic Sch	244
Alberti, Lisa/Trevor Day School-West	146
Albertini, Yasmine/PS 276 Louis Marshall	88
Albetta, Daniel/Bronx Theatre High Sch	20
Albrecht, Vincent/St Edward the Confessor Sch	132
Aldea-Pollack, Iris/PS 360	22
Aldrich, Margaret/Harris Hill Elem Sch	59
Alesi, Marilyn/PS 129 Patricia A Larkin	178
Alexander, Alison/PS 18 Edward Bush	84
Alexander, Angela/Pomona Middle Sch	196
Alexander, Denise/Bronx Charter Sch for Children	16
Alexander, Edwin/Lorge Sch	144
Alexander, Kuricheses/Steam at Dr King Elem Sch	159
Alexander, Michael/School for Human Rights	87

NAME/School	PAGE
Alexanian, Libarid/Lyons Jr Sr High Sch	249
Alexis, Sanatha/Cultural Acad Arts & Sciences	87
Alfano, Keri/Harry S Truman High Sch	22
Alfeo, Danielle/St Peter Catholic Academy	95
Alhasel, Abdelhakeem/AL Noor Sch	96
Alicandro, Agatha/PS 127 McKinley Park	90
Allanbrook, Anna/Brooklyn New Sch at PS 146	84
Allen, Arkee/Sodus Jr Sr High Sch	251
Allen, Jennifer/Greenville Elem Sch	254
Allen, Katrina/JT Roberts Prek-8 Sch	158
Allen, Lisa/Ellis B Hyde Elem Sch	102
Allen, Michael/New Beginnings Sch	111
Allen, Michelle/Icahn Charter School 4	4
Alleva, Neill/Mamaroneck Avenue Elem Sch	258
Alleyne, Tessa/PS 91 the Albany Ave Sch	87
Allian, Cathie, Dr/Berlin Middle High Sch	189
Almedina, Veronica/Amber Charter Sch Kingsbridge	1
Almonaitis, Patricia/Lawrence Universal Pre-K	123
Alovisetti, Robert/Queens Lutheran Sch	188
Altabe, Richard/Halb Elementary	133
Alterson, Cindy, Dr/Devereux Millwood Learning Ctr	265
Altman, Ailene/JHS 88 Peter Rouget	84
Altman, Chad/Munsey Park Elem Sch	125
Altobello, Jay/Canastota Jr Sr High Sch	104
Alvara, Martin/PS 134 George F Bristow	24
Alvarez-Rooney, Angelina/Oak Grove Elem Sch	54
Alvarez, Carlos/Lewis J Bennett Sch Innov Tech	57
Alvey, Jack/Donald P Sutherland Elem Sch	190
Amador, Carmen/IS 303 Herbert Eisenberg Sch	91
Aman, Wayne/Candor Jr Sr High Sch	238
Amato, Anna/PS 110 the Monitor	84
Amato, Jann/Notre Dame Academy High Sch	194
Amato, Laura/Grundy Avenue Elem Sch	229
Amato, Michelle/PS 527 East Side Sch-Soc Acton	137
Amato, Rosa/PS 372 the Children's Sch	94
Ambrosio, Rosalie/Willow Road Elem Sch	131
Ament, Amy/Westchester Day Sch	266
Amerling, Deirde/Brookside Elem Sch	264
Amesbury, Brian/Canandaigua Prim Elem Sch	161
Ametrano, Mark/Enrico Fermi Sch Perf Arts	263
Aminov, Mrs/Jewish Institue of Queens	188
Amodeo, Daniel/West Valley Central Sch	33
Amodeo, David/New Scotland Elem Sch	9
Amodeo, Jean/Emily Howland Elem Sch	35
Amon, Carrie/School In the Square PCS	7
Amore, Jean/Sacred Heart Academy	132
Amott, Jill/PS 250 George Lindsay	84
Amster, Robert/Plainedge High Sch	127
Anaman, Donna/PS 87 Bronx	23
Anandappa, Marina/Montessori Children's Room	266
Anaya, Haidee/Virginia Road Elem Sch	263
Anaya, Rene/Lower East Side Prep High Sch	135
Ancona, Jessica/Liverpool Elem Sch	156
Anders, William/Craig Elem Sch	204
Andersen, Katie/Chatsworth Avenue Sch	258
Andersen, Theresa/St Rose of Lima Catholic Acad	187
Anderson, Charles/Prep Academy for Writers	183
Anderson, Christina/Westbury Friends Sch	134
Anderson, Diane/SS Philip & James Sch	234
Anderson, Ellen/John A Coleman Catholic HS	244
Anderson, James/Campbell-Savona Elem Sch	213
Anderson, James/Fdny High School Fire & Safety	88
Anderson, Kathryn/PS 889	92
Anderson, Marjorie/John G Borden Middle Sch	244
Anderson, Nadia/Mott Hall Bridges Academy	93
Anderson, Robert, Dr/Gowanda High Sch	32
Anderson, Susan/Emerson Dillon Middle Sch	172
Andino-Flohr, Amy/Academy of Public Relations	16
Andreano, Jeffrey/Olean Senior High Sch	32
Andreassi, Anthony/Regis High Sch	143
Andrews, Martha/Bronx Cmty Charter Sch	20
Andrews, Scott, Dr/Roslyn High Sch	129
Andrias, Eve/Rodeph Sholom Elem Sch	145
Andriello, Ellen/Elmwood Elem Sch	196

PRINCIPAL INDEX

NAME/School	PAGE
Andriello, Maggie/C V Starr Intermediate Sch	175
Andruszkiewicz, John/James Wilson Young Middle Sch	217
Anest, Christophe/PS 5 Ellen Lurie	141
Anesta, Leslei/Harmony Heights Sch	133
Angeles, Noah/York Early College Academy	183
Angelis, Genie/Dover High Sch	52
Angrisani, Alison/MS 593 South Bronx Int'l MS	19
Angueira, Alexander/Shanker Sch Visual Perf Arts	185
Annello, Brian/JHS 67 Louis Pasteur Sch	179
Annio, Ursula/PS 748 Sch Global Scholars	90
Ansari, Faifal/Darul Ullom AL Madania Sch	66
Anspach, Jami/Lee Road Elem Sch	123
Antoine, Louise/PS 40 George W Carver	86
Antolina, Elizabeth/Brocton Central Sch	36
Antonetti, Kandie/Edmund O'Neal MS of Excellence	9
Antonetti, Louis/Sachem High School East	229
Antonini, Victoria/Sunset Park High Sch	85
Antonio, Maysa/St Joseph High Sch	95
Anzalone, Christopher/Concord High Sch	192
Anzalone, Dina/Ogden Elem Sch	121
Apfel, Alexandra/Brilla College Prep Elem CS	2
Aprea, Anna/PS 122 Mamie Fay	185
Aquino, Leslie/School for Excellence	20
Arberman, Ruth/Sterling Sch	99
Arbolino, Ariana/PS 100 Isaac Clason	18
Arbolino, Carole/St Columbanus Sch	265
Archer, Brian/Sargent Elem Sch	51
Archer, Celeste/Woods Road Elem Sch	226
Arcuri, Laura/Riverhead Charter Sch	6
Arcuri, Lisa/PS 5 Huguenot	193
Arfman, Melanie/Deasy Elem Sch	120
Arietta, Rudy/Tappan Zee High Sch	198
Arket, Richard/Draper Middle Sch	204
Arles, Debra/St Joseph School for the Deaf	27
Arlt, Christine/Central Valley Elem Sch	165
Armano, Victoria/Academy of Finance Enterprise	176
Armbrust, Karen/Deposit Middle High Sch	28
Armstrong, Anthony/JHS 74 Nathaniel Hawthorne	179
Armstrong, Jason/Lemoyne Elem Sch	158
Armstrong, Jason/Montessori at Lemoyne	159
Armstrong, Rebecca/Stanley G Falk Sch	66
Arnold, Chris/Dundee Jr Sr High Sch	268
Arnold, Jamie/Eden II Sch-Autistic Chldrn	195
Aronson, Marnl/Success Acad CS Bed Sty MS [245]	7
Arpino, Biagio/St John the Baptist High Sch	234
Arpino, Leona/Maria Regina Elem Sch	132
Arquiett, Mark/Hamilton Central Sch	105
Arrastia, Lisa/Brooklyn Friends Sch	97
Arroyo, Jenna/Sheridan Hill Elem Sch	59
Arsenault, Christian/Fishers Island Sch	222
Arte, Gregory/Brooklyn Jesuit Prep Sch	95
Arthur, John/Canandaigua Middle Sch	161
Arthur, Rodney/Peekskill High Sch	260
Arvizzigno, Frank/St Lawrence Sch	114
Arzuaga, Joe/Downtown Brooklyn YABC	82
Arzuaga, Joey/George Westinghouse Cte HS	82
Ascona, Bernardo/Union Sq Acad-Hlth Sciences	138
Asfoury, Gregory/Newark Valley High Sch	238
Ashe, Carol/Poughkeepsie SDA Elem Sch	55
Ashley, Jordan/Randall Middle Sch	47
Ashton, Elizabeth/Naples Jr Sr High Sch	162
Ashton, Kirk/Northwood Elem Sch	109
Ashton, Libby/Success Acad CS Crown Heights [245]	7
Askew, Raevan/PS 354 J L Green STEM Inst	182
Aspetti, Stephen/Birch Lane Elem Sch	125
Asquith, Lori/MacArthur Elem Sch	27
Asselta, Carmen/PS 34 Oliver H Perry	84
Asterita, Ewa/Manhattan Sch Career Develop	142
Athy, Michael/Bayside High Sch	179
Attanas, John/Greek American Institute	26
Attleson, Eric/Chenango Valley Middle Sch	28
Aubel, Teresa/Theatre Street Sch	188
Aubrey, Patricia/Chippewa Elem Sch	229
Audsley, Josh/Attica Senior High Sch	267
Auer, Andrew/Lewiston Porter Middle Sch	147
Augello, Peg/Our Lady of Victory Sch	132
Augustin, Gus/Rockland Children Psy Center	7
Ault-Baker, Cheryl/PS 81 Thaddeus Stevens	86
Autera, Vincent/Freshman Center	217
Avakians, Laura/PS 94 David D Porter	179
Avellino, Grenardo/East Syracuse Minoa Central HS	155
Avena, John/Wisdom Lane Middle Sch	123
Averill, Tom/Saugerties Junior High Sch	243
Averill, Tom/Saugerties Senior High Sch	243
Averin, Alex/Faith Christian Academy	55
Avery, Kathryn/Williamson High Sch	251
Avery, Melessa/PS 273 Wortman	89
Avila, Nicole/PS Q811	185
Avin, C/Academy Charter ES-Uniondale	1
Avione, Maureen/Schalmont High Sch	204
Awosogba, Patrick, Dr/Sci & Tech Acad-A Mott Hall	20
Axelson, Bruce/Lackawanna High Sch	62
Aybar, Jessica/St Athanasius Sch	26
Ayers, Andrew/University Prep Charter HS	8
Ayers, Patricia/Trinity Regional Sch	234
Ayetiwa, Kayode/Humanities & Arts High Sch	183
Aylor, Chelsey/Fillmore Central Sch	14
Ayres, Brian/Greene Central Interm Sch	42

B

NAME/School	PAGE
Babbie, Shannon/McConnellsville Elem Sch	150
Baber, Adam/McQuaid Jesuit High Sch	114
Bacalles, Kelley/Beecher Elem Sch	40
Bacarella, Rosalia/PS 199 Frederick Wachtel	91
Bachellor, Hadassa/PS 33 Bilingual Center	57
Backon, Mia/Democracy Prep Harlem ES [235]	3
Badette, Jocelyn/William Maxwell Career Tech HS	89
Badia, George/Pan American International HS	177
Baehr, James/Spry Middle Sch	113
Baez, Asheena/Lenox Elem Sch	116
Bagwell, Maryalice/St Benedict Sch	65
Bahl, Amit/Urban Dove Team Charter Sch	8
Bai-Rossi, Frank/Midlakes High Sch	162
Bai-Rossi, Frank/Midlakes Middle Sch	162
Bailer, Thomas/John C Birdlebough High Sch	172
Bailey, Anne-Marie/Ridge Road Elem Sch	41
Bailey, Beryl/PS 195 William Haberle	183
Bailey, Isora/NYC Ischool	137
Bailey, Jacqueline/PS 9 Ryer Ave Elem Sch	21
Bailey, Janeice/PS 93 William H Prescott	83
Bailey, Karen/PS 153 Adam Clayton Powell	141
Bailey, Michelle/Davis Elem Sch	70
Bailey, Nicole/Learning Tree STEM-Arts Sch	188
Bailey, Novella/MS 250 West Side Collaborative	138
Bailey, Robert/Broadway Academy	40
Bailey, Susanne/Oakdale-Bohemia Middle Sch	220
Bain-Lucey, Susan/Alfred Almond Sch	13
Bainbridge, Jenny/St John the Baptist Sch-Knmore	65
Baines, Lisa/Career Collegiate Institute	57
Bajana, Alice/Bronx High School of Business	18
Baker, Ann Marie/PS 177 the Marlboro Sch	91
Baker, Curtis/Southeast Christian Academy	114
Baker, Derek/Sweet Home Middle Sch	64
Baker, Greg/Geneva High Sch	161
Baker, Jon/Stuart M Townsend Elem Sch	245
Baker, Kristen/Knox Sch	235
Baker, L/PS 160 Walt Disney	23
Baker, Marcy/Jamesville Elem Sch	155
Baker, Maria/Leake & Watts Chldrns Home Sch	266
Balbuena, Patricia/PS 161 Pedro Albizu Campos	140
Baldassarre, Italo/Henry J Kalfas Magnet Sch	147
Baldi, John/Vincent Smith Sch	134
Baldino, Joseph/Adlai E Stevenson School 29	110
Baldwin, Bart/St Luke's Sch	145
Baldwin, Shelley/Glencliff Elem Sch	204
Ballan, Bruce/Maple Avenue Middle Sch	201
Ballou, Laura/Klem Road North Elem Sch	113
Balmer, Patricia/SS Mary-Alphonsus Reg Cath Sch	246

New York School Directory

PRINCIPAL INDEX

NAME/School	PAGE
Balsamo, Mark/Park Road Elem Sch	110
Baly, Julia/Bronx Career & College Prep HS	24
Bambrick, Georgia/Achievement First Aspire ES [128]	1
Bambrola, Anthony/George M Davis Elem Sch	259
Banas, Rachel/West Buffalo Charter Sch	8
Bandelian, Marc/Southtowns Catholic Sch	65
Banhazl, Allison/Waverly Park Elem Sch	124
Banks-Williams, Sharon, Dr/Montessori School 31	263
Banks, Jeffrey/PS 72 Lorraine Elem Sch	57
Banks, John/Origins High Sch	92
Banucci-Smith, Katherine/Special Music Sch	139
Bar-Horin, Bluma/Yaldeinu Sch	99
Barakat, Michael/Bronx HS Law-Community Service	20
Baran, Rhonda/Pine City Elem Sch	40
Baratta, Pasquale/PS 92 Harry T Stewart Sr	184
Baratz, Shimshan/Yeshiva Bais Meir	99
Barbato, Gabriel/Eagle Point Elem Sch	9
Barbella, John/IS 347 School of Humanties	93
Barber, Frank/High School Lrng Ctr-CCC	214
Barber, Julie/Albany High Sch	9
Barber, Julie/North Albany Middle Sch	9
Barber, Sam/Ed Smith PK-8 Sch	158
Barbera, Lena/PS 20 Clinton Hill	83
Barbetta, Anthony/Robert F Kennedy Cmty High Sch	179
Bardwell, Cynthia/Park Early Childhood Center	260
Barge, Allen/Edward R Murrow High Sch	91
Barker, Jill/Howard L Goff Middle Sch	190
Barkley, Ben/Salmon River Elem Sch	70
Barlow, Deborah/V E Wightman Primary Sch	213
Barnard, Christopher/Palmyra-Macedon Interm Sch	250
Barnes, John/Albert Leonard Middle Sch	259
Barnetsky, Boruch/Bnos Yisroel School-Girls	97
Barnett, Maureen/John Paulding Primary Sch	262
Barnhart, Jayson/Oak Street Elem Sch	45
Baron-Meyer, Monica/Salmon River High Sch	70
Baron, Dov/Lubavitcher Yeshiva High Sch	98
Barone, Matthew/IS 27 Anning S Prall	192
Barr, Brett/Cobleskill-Richmondville HS	206
Barr, Brooke/Children's Lab Sch	177
Barr, David/Darwin Smith Sch	239
Barr, Fran/St Louis Sch	114
Barr, Matthew/Finger Lakes Tech & Career Ctr	161
Barrera, Freddy/PS 3 D'Youville Porter Campus	57
Barrera, Hilde/Union Springs Academy	36
Barrett, Ellen/JHS 144 Michelangelo Sch	23
Barron, Amy/St Mel Sch	187
Barron, James/John F Kennedy YABC	21
Barry-Grant, Relda/PS 251 Queens	184
Barry, Kevin/Harmony Christian Sch	168
Barry, Mary/Immaculate Conception Sch	143
Barter, Hope/Energy Tech High Sch	184
Barthelmas, Gregg/Schuylerville Elem Sch	201
Bartlett, Russell/Tupper Lake Middle High Sch	70
Bartlik, Carol/Douglas G Grafflin Elem Sch	253
Bartolillo, Marie/St Francis DeSales School-Deaf	99
Barton, Carlina/PS 38 Roberto Clemente	139
Barton, Michelle/Paddy Hill Elem Sch	109
Barton, Teresa, Sr/Villa Maria Academy	26
Bascom, Rebecca/Clifton-Fine Central Sch	209
Bashir, Darlene/Clara Muhammad Sch	97
Basile, Benjamin/Mott Hall Community Sch	17
Basile, Mary/St Clare Catholic Academy	186
Basile, Roseann/Achievement First Crown Hghts [128]	86
Baskin, Walter/Valleyview Elem Sch	174
Bassell, William/Academy of American Studies	184
Bassin, Eric/The Leffell Sch	266
Bastian, Dorald/New Millennium Bus Academy	19
Basu, Sita/PS 59 Community Sch of Tech	21
Bateman, Pam/Covenant Love Community Sch	241
Bates, Sarah/Poly Prep Country Day Sch-Uppr	98
Batista, Roxanne/Garden of Lrng & Discovery PK	19
Battaglino, Kristine/West Middle Sch	27
Batty, Mark/Gloversville Middle Sch	71
Bauer, Al/Woodmere Middle Sch	122

NAME/School	PAGE
Bauer, Luke/Urban Assembly Maker Academy	138
Baughman, Kate/KIPP AII Middle Sch [242]	5
Baxter, Jayme/Valley Central High Sch	167
Baxter, Kate/Coney Island Prep Public CS	3
Baxter, Robert/Health Sciences Charter Sch	4
Baybachayev, Daniel/Midrash L'Man Achai High Sch	188
Bayer, Mark/Somers High Sch	262
Beach, Rina/Lawrence Elem Sch	123
Beale, Annette/PS 277Q the Riverview Sch	185
Bean, William/Lockwood Elem Sch	267
Beard, Lorie/Long Beach Middle Sch	124
Beattie, Kathaleen/Carthage High Sch	80
Beatty, Thomas/Apalachin Elem Sch	238
Beaulieu, Renee/Hamilton Elem Sch	204
Beauvoir-Soto, Sandra/Bronx Arts & Science CS [231]	2
Becker, Cheri/Monroe 1 Special Education Ctr	106
Becker, Jean Marie/De La Salle Sch	133
Becker, Stephanie/Our Lady Queen of Angels Sch	143
Beckles, Stephen/PS 28 Mt Hope Sch	19
Beckman, Mandana/PS/IS 217 Roosevelt Island	137
Beckwith, Kathleen/Soule Road Middle Sch	156
Bedette, Daniel/Newfane High Sch	147
Bediako, Adwoa/Brooklyn East Collegiate CS [246]	2
Bednarek, Peter/Scotia Glenville High Sch	205
Bednarski, Mark/Onondaga Hill Middle Sch	160
Beebe, Ajeia/St Philip Neri Sch	26
Beecher, Kristina/PS 3 Bedford Village	83
Beekman, Lori/Bellerose Elem Sch	227
Beer, Jeffrey/Westchester Hebrew High Sch	266
Beglane, Edward, Dr/Thomas Cornell Academy	264
Beglin, Sheila/W O Schaefer Elem Sch	198
Begum, Rozina/Wellspring Sch	189
Beirne, Mary Ellen/IS 25 Adrien Block	178
Beirne, Rosemary/The Ursuline Sch	265
Beitz, Kelly/Attica Elem Sch	267
Bekisz, Hester/Genesis Sch	133
Belden, Mary/John F Hughes Elem Sch	152
Belferder, Tiffany/Fusion Academy-Long Island	133
Belizaire, Carmel/James Monroe Ed Campus YABC	24
Belkota, Rebecca/Perry Junior Senior High Sch	267
Bell, Aimee/St Mary's School for the Deaf	66
Bell, Clinton/Lincoln School 22	111
Bell, Gary/Royalton Hartland High Sch	148
Bell, Mr/Excellence Boys Charter Sch [246]	3
Bell, Tom/Centereach High Sch	225
Bellafatto, Barbara/PS 36 J C Drumgoole	193
Bellai, Marianne/Van Corlaer Elem Sch	205
Belle, Letta/La Cima Elem Charter Sch	5
Bellizzi, Joseph, Br/Chaminade High Sch	132
Bellon, James/Cornerstone Acad-Soc Action ES	22
Bellone, Mary/Incarnation Sch	186
Bellone, Mary/Mary Queen of Heaven Sch	95
Bellovin, Audrey/Hemlock Sch	120
Bellucci, James/Tech Center at Yorktown	252
Belton, Renee/PS 200 James McCune Smith	140
Bemis, Catherine/St Agnes Elem Sch	69
Ben-Zvi, Julie/Hebrew Acad for Spec Children	97
Benadi, Kelly/Richard P Connor Elem Sch	198
Bender, Keith/Joy Fellowship Christian Acad	26
Bender, Maria/IS 281 Joseph B Cavallaro	91
Bender, Robert/PS 011 William T Harris	137
Benedict, Mark/Hudson View Christian Academy	266
Benevento, Paulette/PS R373	194
Benfer, Nancy/Bishop Dunn Memorial Sch	168
Benitez, Carlos/Jill Chaifetz Transfer HS	16
Benjamin, Alexandra/Immaculate Conception Sch	25
Benn, Teneika/PS 938	89
Bennefield, James/Hudson Falls High Sch	248
Bennett, Amanda/Niagara Academy	146
Bennett, Andrew/Selden Middle Sch	225
Bennett, Jeffrey/Mont Pleasant Middle Sch	205
Bennett, Karen/Keshequa Middle High Sch	103
Bennett, Leslie/Armor Elem Sch	61
Bennett, Mark/A A Kingston Middle Sch	212

School Year 2020-2021 · 800-333-8802 · NY-U3

PRINCIPAL INDEX

Market Data Retrieval

NAME/School	PAGE
Bennett, Mark/Potsdam High Sch	212
Benson, Heather/PS 14 Fairview	177
Benson, Kelly/John F Kennedy Interm Sch	220
Benson, Mark/New Hartford Sr High Sch	151
Benton, Kris/Addison Jr Sr High Sch	213
Benton, Scott/Wilson Middle High Sch	149
Benz, Paul/Schroeder High Sch	113
Berg, Kinzel/Yeshiva Tiferes Yisroel	100
Berger, Christopher/Smith Clove Elem Sch	165
Berger, Miriam/Bais Yaakov D'Khal Adas Yereim	96
Berger, Seth/PS 229 Emmanuel Kaplan	178
Bergeson, Angela/Ideal School of Manhattan	144
Bergin, Katie/Marymount School-New York	145
Bergman, Julie/Hancock Elem Sch	49
Bergman, Julie/Hancock Jr Sr High Sch	49
Beriman, Kristin/C R Weeks Elem Sch	30
Berkowitz, Alan/Magen David Yeshivah	98
Berkowitz, David/PS 153 Maspeth	177
Berkowitz, Mark/New Explorations Sci-Tech-Math	135
Berkshire, Matthew/Paige Elem Sch	205
Berlin, Marla/Technical Career Center	170
Berman, Justin/IS 187 Christa McAuliffe Sch	90
Berman, Kristin, Dr/Quad Preparatory Sch	145
Bermas, Dana/Chatterton Sch	125
Bermingham, Julia/Big Tree Elem Sch	60
Bernard, Mark/East Islip High Sch	221
Berndt, Deborah/Birchwood Elem Sch	204
Berner, Lenore/MS 51 William Alexander	84
Berner, Tracy/Smithtown Christian Sch	235
Bernero, Theresa/St Joseph School-Yorkville	143
Bernhard, William/Ward Melville Sr High Sch	232
Bernieri, Jean/Visitation Academy	95
Bernstein, Ephraim/Joseph S Gruss Yeshiva	98
Bero, Danielle/Northside Charter High Sch	6
Berry, Matt/Peru Jr/Sr High Sch	44
Berry, Monica/PS 87 William Sherman	139
Berry, Susan/Mohansic Elem Sch	264
Bertrand, Kerdy/PS IS 109 Glenwood Academy	92
Besch, Jeremy/Park School-Buffalo	66
Best, James/Dalton Sch	144
Best, Jim/Dalton Lower Sch	144
Bethany, Naudia/Icahn Charter School 7	5
Bethea, Mahaliel/Eagle Academy Young Men-Harlem	140
Betters, Sandra/Our Lady of Mercy Academy	132
Beukema, Kimberly/Harrison High Sch	256
Beyda, Joseph/Joel Braverman High Sch	98
Bezio, Matthew/Beekmantown High Sch	43
Bhambree, Neeru/Hudson Country Mont Sch	265
Bialasik, James/Springville Griffith Inst HS	63
Biamonte, Kristina/Deauville Gardens West ES	220
Bianco, Wade/Notre Dame High Sch	74
Biek, Alicia/Kingsbury SDA Sch	249
Biele, Vincent/Otisville Elem Sch	165
Biernat, Joseph/Leaders of Tomorrow	23
Bierwiler, Brennen/Center Street Elem Sch	121
Bifalco, Toni/Clinton Avenue Elem Sch	218
Bigham, Amanda/Loudonville Christian Sch	13
Bigio, Gabriel/Yeshiva Shaari Torah Sch	100
Billet, Rookie/Shulamith School for Girls	134
Billings, Robert/Our Lady of Refuge Sch	26
Bilotti, Nicholas/Connetquot Elem Sch	221
Bini, Beth, Dr/Westmere Elem Sch	11
Biniaris, Vasilios/Q300 Citywide Gifted Talented	185
Binion, Joseph/Madrid-Waddington Central Sch	211
Biondi, Michael/Allen Creek Elem Sch	110
Bird, Amy/Fairley Elem Sch	171
Bird, Clifford/Abram Lansing Elem Sch	10
Birgeles, Joseph/Goddard HS of Comm Arts & Tech	180
Biscari, Brian/Minnesauke Elem Sch	232
Biscari, Brian/Robert C Murphy Jr High Sch	232
Bish, Mary/Kinry Road Elem Sch	54
Bishop, Alissa/Success Acad CS Cobble Hill [245]	7
Bishop, John/Poestenkill Elem Sch	189
Bissaillon, Gary/John D George Elem Sch	153
Biviano, Carla/Harrison Avenue Elem Sch	202
Bivona, Theresa/St Clare of Assisi Sch	26
Blackman, Sandra/James Monroe High Sch	111
Blake, Eric, Dr/Science Tech & Research HS	87
Blake, Lisa/Pembroke Primary Sch	74
Blake, Verna/New Covenant Christian Sch	27
Blanco, Joseph/Iona Prep Lower Sch	265
Blank, Daryl/High Sch of Fashion Industries	136
Blatt, Karen/Flushing Christian Sch	187
Blatter, Amanda/PS 204 Morris Heights Sch	20
Bleiberg, Nicholas/Voyages Preparatory Sch	178
Blesofsky, Dina/Chabad Acad of Arts & Sciences	187
Blesy, Mark/Cantalician Center for Lrng	66
Blige, Iris/Fordham High School of Arts	20
Blissett, Chantandre/Acad Environmental Leadership	93
Block, Chaim/Yeshiva Toras Emes Kamenitz	100
Blocker, Marlene/East Upper Sch	111
Bloomberg, Jill/Park Slope Collegiate Sch	85
Bloomgarden, James/North Side Sch	118
Blossey, Jennifer/C Grant Grimshaw Sch	156
Blough, Brian/South Bronx Early Clg Acad CS	7
Boardman, Keith/South High Sch	65
Boatfield, Mary/UCP Happiness House Sch	163
Bobowski, Trisha/Kingsborough Elem Sch	71
Boccaccio, Robert/Edge Academy	55
Boccaccio, Robert/Northtowns Academy	56
Bock, Patricia/Riverside Elem Sch	128
Bodenheimer, Chaim/Bais Mikroh Boys Sch	198
Bodensteiner, Craig/Plank Road North Elem Sch	113
Boettcher, Martin/Vanderbilt Elem Sch	222
Bohen, William, Dr/Maple East Elem Sch	65
Bohkle, Timothy/George F Baker High Sch	167
Bohrer, Eileen/Solomon Schechter Sch	134
Boice, Tom/Marathon Christian Academy	48
Boily, Elizabeth/Pine Brook Elem Sch	109
Bolan, Edward/Bishop Loughlin Memorial HS	95
Bold, Carrie/Cuba-Rushford Middle High Sch	14
Bolen, James/Cold Spring Harbor Jr Sr HS	219
Boletsis, Siv/Manhattan Acad-Arts & Lang	136
Bolognino, Marisa/PS 264 Bay Ridge ES-the Arts	90
Bolton, Florence/Bronx Excellence 1 [236]	2
Bomani, Tabari/Nelson Mandela High Sch	86
Bombard, Michelle/Tioga Elem Sch	239
Bonacio, Jill/Pashley Elem Sch	200
Bonacquist, Heidi/Slingerlands Elem Sch	10
Bonadonna, Emily/Canandaigua Prim Elem Sch	161
Bonagura, Randee/Wantagh Elem Sch	131
Bonamo, Kenneth/Scarsdale Senior High Sch	262
Bonanno, Kevin/H B Thompson Middle Sch	130
Bonds, Crystal/HS Math Science & Engr at Ccny	140
Bongo, Anthony, Dr/Isaac E Young Middle Sch	259
Bonici, Miriam/Divine Wisdom Acad-Douglaston	186
Bonilla, Robert/PS 217 Col David Marcus Sch	92
Bonner, Nancy/Highview Elem Sch	196
Bonnet, Jennifer/PS 150 Tribeca Learning Center	137
Borenstein, Ellen/International CS of New York	5
Borgen, Jacqueline/Ashar Sch	198
Borgese, Loren/Denton Avenue Elem Sch	121
Boritz, Eslie/Commack High Sch	219
Bornkamp, Kathleen/PS 97 Bronx	23
Borrero, Carlos/HS for Community Leadership	182
Borum, George/Henry Johnson Charter Sch	4
Bostwick, Michael/Horseheads Intermediate Sch	41
Botfeld, Lynn/Learners & Leaders	177
Bottari, Gregory/Barnum Woods Elem Sch	118
Bottcher, Jaime/Southampton Elem Sch	231
Bottino, Nicholas/Canajoharie High Sch	115
Bouchard, Sueellen/John F Kennedy Elem Sch	211
Boucher, Matthew/Putnam Central Sch	248
Bourcy, Todd/Chestnut Hill Elem Sch	156
Bourgoine, Kevin/Academy at Maple Avenue	36
Bove, Antonella/PS 215 Morris H Weiss	91

New York School Directory

PRINCIPAL INDEX

NAME/School	PAGE
Bowden, Brent/Brewerton Elem Sch	170
Bowden, Karen/Manor Plains High Sch	216
Bowell, David/Amer Sign Lang-Eng Lwr Sch 47	135
Bowen, Andrew/Country Parkway Elem Sch	64
Bowen, Nikki/Excellence Girls CS Elem Acad [246]	3
Bowen, Nikki/Leadership Prep Ocean Hill Mid	5
Bowen, Rod/Explore Charter Sch [237]	3
Bowles, Kevin/PS 532 New Bridges	87
Bowman, Alice/Plainview Old Bethpage Mid Sch	128
Bowman, Chad/Mekeel Christian Academy	205
Bowman, Jamaal/Cornerstone Acad-Soc Action MS	22
Boyanowski, Ronald/Thomas Edison High Sch	40
Boyce, Alicia/Charles F Johnson Elem Sch	29
Boyce, Sarah/Massena High Sch	211
Boyd, Brian/Mill Road Intermediate Sch	53
Boyd, Everett/Renaissance Charter Sch 2	6
Boyd, Kourtney/PS 157 Benjamin Franklin Acad	84
Boyda, David/Dunkirk Elem School 5	37
Boylan, Jim/Midland Elem Sch	261
Boyle, John/Crispell Middle Sch	166
Boyle, John/IS 34 Tottenville	192
Boyle, Richard/Mater Dei Academy	160
Brabant, Peter/Altamont Elem Sch	11
Bracamonte, Micaela/The Lang Sch	146
Bracey, Daniel/Clinton V Bush Elem Sch	38
Bracey, Natasha/PS 277	17
Bracht, Kevin/Walnut Street Elem Sch	130
Bracy, Mark/Red Jacket High Sch	162
Bradley, Brian/Renaissance School of the Arts	140
Bradley, Jeanne/PS 94M the Spectrum Sch	142
Bradley, Luci/Saddle Rock Elem Sch	121
Bradley, Matthew/East Woods Sch	133
Bradley, Roger/Washington Irving YABC	138
Bradley, Rosemary, Dr/Jamestown High Sch	38
Bradley, Sharon/Mount Vernon Steam Academy	258
Brady, Daniel/Pennington Elem Sch	258
Brady, Monica/IS 303 Ldrshp & Cmty Svc Acad	19
Brady, Robyn/Winchester Elem Sch	64
Bragan, Kathy/Gansevoort Elem Sch	151
Bragg, Benjamin/Catskill High Sch	75
Bram, Caitlin/Fall Creek Elem Sch	240
Branch, Ryan/Community Voices Middle Sch	183
Brand, Debbie/James I O'Neill High Sch	164
Brand, Jeannine/Syracuse Academy of Science CS	8
Brandefine, Natalie/The Titus Sch	146
Brandell, Thomas/Northeastern Clinton Mid Sch	44
Branker, Alison/PS 40 Samuel Huntington	182
Brannigan, Michael/Queensbury Middle Sch	246
Brashwell, Clyde/Washington Rose Elem Sch	129
Braswell, Tara/St Simon Stock Sch	26
Bratcher, Pual/Rochambeau Alt High Sch	263
Brathwaite, Earl/IS 313 Sch of Leadership Dev	19
Braun, Gary/Southtown Academy	56
Brazeau, Denise/Love of Learning Mont Sch	235
Breed, Tamara/New Sch	160
Breedy, Alison/Urban Assembly Academy Gov/Law	138
Breen, Dorothea/Immaculate Conception Academy	186
Breen, Kristen/Epic High School-North	180
Breen, Patrick/Suffern High Sch	198
Breheny, Brian/Pakanasink Elem Sch	166
Breivogel, Carolyn/Wantagh High Sch	131
Brenneman, Mark/Montgomery C Smith Elem Sch	46
Brenord, Dudrige/Ben Franklin HS Finance & It	183
Breslin, Stacy/W T Clarke Middle Sch	118
Brewster, Judy/West Patent Elem Sch	252
Bribnza, Stephanie/Good Shepherd Lutheran Sch	133
Bricker, Elizabeth/St William the Abbot Sch	133
Bridgeman, Anthony, Dr/West Islip Senior High Sch	233
Bridges, Bobby/Achievement First Bushwick MS [128]	1
Bridges, Coretta/Sch Without Walls Commenc Acad	111
Brieman, Daniel/Belle Sherman Elem Sch	240
Brienza, Victoria/Success Acad CS Fort Greene [245]	7
Briggs, Robert/Soule Road Elem Sch	156
Brillante, Debra/Bishop Grimes Jr Sr High Sch	160
Brillante, Kyle/Highbridge Green Sch	19
Brilliant, Jackie/Notre Dame High Sch	143
Brinker, Jay/West Seneca West Sr High Sch	64
Briscoe-Perez, Ciria/Vails Gate High Tech Magnet ES	166
Brito, Patricia, Sr/St Frances De Chantal Sch	26
Britton, Christine/PS 384	185
Broadwell, Stephen/Willsboro Central Sch	68
Brockett, Kara/Dream Charter Sch	3
Brockhausen, Christy/The Gateway Sch	146
Brockner, Amy/Circleville Elem Sch	166
Broder, Hillel, Dr/Halb Drs Yeshiva HS for Boys	133
Brodie, Candice, Dr/Lindenhurst Senior High Sch	224
Bromberg, Hillary/Camp Avenue Elem Sch	126
Bronfeld, Stanley/Mesivta Tifereth Jerusalem	145
Brookman, Heather/Fusion Academy-Park Avenue	144
Brooks, Brian/Palmyra-Macedon Primary Sch	250
Brooks, Chante/South Middle Sch	166
Brooks, Mark/Broadalbin-Perth Jr Sr HS	71
Broughton, Brandon/Fred W Hill Elem Sch	107
Brower, Jilda/Montessori Sch of Finger Lakes	35
Brown-Wyatt, Valencia, Dr/Scholastic Acad-Academic Excel	264
Brown, Adam/Pocantico Hills Central Sch	261
Brown, Andrew/Judith S Kaye High Sch	142
Brown, Carlton/Gardiner Manor Sch	217
Brown, Daniel/Kent Primary Sch	175
Brown, Ed/North Spencer Christian Acad	239
Brown, Elisa/PS 249 the Caton	87
Brown, Fritzy/Queens Transition Center	185
Brown, Isaiah/Capital Prep Bronx CS	3
Brown, James/PS 297 Abraham Stockton	84
Brown, Jeff/Columbia Christian Academy	47
Brown, Lisa/Saratoga Independent Sch	203
Brown, Lorrie/PS 68 Port Richmond Vis Lrng	194
Brown, Marlon/St Joseph's Parish Day Sch	188
Brown, Matthew/East Aurora Middle Sch	60
Brown, Michael/Tonawanda Middle-High Sch	64
Brown, Mrs/Giffen Memorial Elem Sch	9
Brown, Pat/Belle H Waterman Elem Sch	157
Brown, Richard/Jackson Main Elem Sch	121
Brown, Scott/Leptondale Elem Sch	244
Brown, Shawn/EBC HS Pub Service Bushwick	93
Brown, Sonya/Emmanuel Childrens Mission Sch	265
Brown, Tammy/PS 398 Walter Weaver	87
Brown, Tashia/Edgewood Elem Sch	262
Brown, Teresa/Thomas O'Brien Acad-Sci & Tech	9
Browne, Graham/Forte Prep Academy	4
Brownell, Colleen/Canisteo-Greenwood Elem Sch	214
Bruce, Bradley/Clayton Ave Elem Sch	30
Bruce, Janice/JHS 291 Roland Hayes	94
Bruemmer, Simone, Dr/German Int'l School New York	265
Brugge, Danica/John G Dinkelmeyer Elem Sch	126
Brull, M/Bnos Yaakov Girls Center	97
Brumfield, Latrina/Frazer K-8 Sch	158
Bruna, Annita/Churchill Center & Sch	144
Brunger, Lynnette/Heritage Middle Sch	166
Brunjes, Debbie/Hudson Valley Career Academies	163
Brunner, Alexander/Brooklyn Brownstone Sch	85
Bruno, Bryan/California Ave Elem Sch	130
Bruno, Danielle/Elmwood Village CS-Days Park	3
Brunson, Tim/Burnt Hills Ballston Lake HS	200
Brunswick, Jan/St Luke Sch	187
Bryan, William/Most Holy Rosary Sch	160
Bryansmith, Juliana/Coney Island Prep Public CS	3
Bryant-Bell, Juanita/Grand Avenue Elem Sch	130
Bryant, Claude/Lyceum Kennedy Sch	145
Bryant, Kevin/A-Tech High Sch	83
Bryant, Marquita/PS 64 Frederick Law Olmsted	57
Bryant, Tanya/PS 309 George E Wibecan Prep	86
Buccello, Joseph/Deauville Gardens East ES	220
Bucco, Ann/Anthony Alfano Elem Sch	218
Buchanan, Amy/Dutch Broadway Elem Sch	118
Buckheit, Joanne/Michael J Petrides Sch	193
Buckley, Gerard/St Mary's High Sch	132
Buckley, Russell/Lockport High School West	147
Buckshaw, Lisa/Gates Chili Middle Sch	108

PRINCIPAL INDEX

NAME/School	PAGE
Buczkowski, Thomas/Silver Creek High Sch	39
Budd, Deirdre/PS 178M Prof Juan Bosch	141
Buddendeck, Pamela/Park Hill Pre-School	155
Buddington, Winton/Bay Trail Middle Sch	109
Bueno, Vivian/PS 73X Bronx	19
Buffa, John/PS 84 Steinway	184
Buhrmaster, James/Taconic Hills Central High Sch	47
Bull, Jacqueline/William Street Sch	63
Bull, Matthew/Amber Charter Sch East Harlem	1
Bullard, Patricia/PS 221 North Hills Sch	180
Bullis, Scott/School 5 North Oceanside Road	127
Bulter, David/Caledonia-Mumford Elem Sch	102
Buon, Lisa/Balmville Elem Sch	166
Buono, Gabriel/Bennett Elem Sch	243
Burakov, Ana/High School Arts & Business	177
Burch, Alison/Moriah Central Sch	68
Burch, Kate/Harvest Collegiate High Sch	136
Burdick, Joanne/Castile Christian Academy	268
Burdick, Nora/Immaculate Conception Sch	15
Burg, Melissa/Queens Technical High Sch	178
Burgess, Gregory/North Tonawanda Middle Sch	148
Burget, Michelle/South Woods Middle Sch	130
Burgos, Sandra/Astor Collegiate Academy	22
Burgos, Zoranlly/Brilla Caritas Elem Sch	2
Burke, Kelly/St Stephen of Hungary Sch	143
Burke, Richard/Dr R Izquierdo Health & Sci CS	24
Burke, Sheena/Jackson Annex Sch	121
Burke, Thomas/Seaford Harbor Elem Sch	129
Burkhardt, Thomas/Maine Endwell Senior High Sch	29
Burnett, Deborah/Frederick Douglass Acad VI HS	180
Burnham, Amy/Warsaw Central Mid High Sch	267
Burns, Casey/Unity Preparatory CS- Brooklyn	8
Burns, Edward/Holy Cross High Sch	186
Burns, John/Acadia Middle Sch	202
Burns, Kevin/Expeditionary Learning Mid Sch	158
Burns, Michael/Chatham Middle Sch	46
Burns, Patrick/JHS 217 Robert A Van Wyck	182
Burns, Russel/Valley Central Middle Sch	167
Burnside, Robert/MS 663 Sch of the Future-Bklyn	89
Burts, Ralph/Nelson Mandela-Zollicoffer HS	258
Burzynski, C/Elwood-John Glenn High Sch	221
Bush, Carol/Elba Central Sch	73
Bush, Dana/Dorothy Nolan Elem Sch	201
Bush, Kathleen/Briarwood Sch	113
Bush, Kathleen/Colebrook Sch	113
Bush, Maren/Ellicottville Sch	31
Bush, Nellie/Fonda Fultonville Central Sch	115
Bussu, Yael/Yeshivat Shaare Torah Girls ES	100
Butler, Barbra/Alternative Learning Center	167
Butler, Emily, Dr/Ithaca Waldorf Sch	241
Butler, Kristin/Cooperstown Junior-Senior High	173
Butman, Shireen/Silverstein Hebrew Academy	134
Butt, Elliott/Gananda Middle Sch	249
Button, Adam/Cohocton Elem Sch	215
Button, Adam/Wayland Elem Sch	215
Button, Paul/Mount Academy	244
Buzas, Laura/Ravena Coeymans Selkirk MS	11
Bye, Bridgit Clair/Pan American Int'l HS-Monroe	24
Bynum, Marlon/Transit Tech Career High Sch	89
Byrne, Brendan, Dr/The Harvey Sch	266

C

NAME/School	PAGE
Caban, Janette/PS 94 Henry Longfellow	85
Caban, Michael/Amherst Christian Academy	66
Cabarcas, Berena/International Cmty High Sch	16
Cabello, Irina/PS 97 the Highlawn Sch	91
Cabello, Steven/Millbrook Middle Sch	52
Cabral, Rafael/IS 206 Ann Mersereau	21
Cabrall-Njenga, Desiree/East Harlem Scholars Acad CS 2	3
Cabrall-Njenga, Desree/East Harlem Scholars Acad CS	3
Cabrejos, Fiorella/Fordham Leadership Academy	20
Caceres, Sergio/PS/IS 218 Hernandez Dual Lang	20
Cadotte, Bayan/PS 186 Dr Irving Gladstone	90
Caesar, Lisette/Mosaic Prep Academy	139
Caesar, Wynette/Brooklyn Urban Garden CS	2
Caezza, Tracey/Afton Central Sch	41
Cafararo, Kevin/Cortland Jr Sr High Sch	47
Cahill, Heather/St Dominic Sch	199
Cahill, Laura/South Avenue Elem Sch	51
Cahill, Maria/St Pius Tenth Sch	114
Caiazza, David/Leo Bernabi Elem Sch	112
Caifa, Kevin/PS 346 Abe Stark	89
Cain, Sandra/North Elem Sch	81
Calacone, Kevin/Schoharie High Sch	207
Calandra, Michael/Mill Middle Sch	65
Calderaro, Lisa/Fjc Southeast Elem Sch	217
Calderon, Eduardo/PS 16 Wakefield Sch	23
Caldwell, Caitlin/Sapphire Elem Sch	165
Cali, Maria/Children's Home of Wyoming	30
Calibar, Genie/PS 19 Marino P Jeantet	177
Callahan, Laura/Long Island Lutheran Sch	133
Callan, Helen/Pawling High Sch	52
Callan, John/Brentwood High Sch	217
Callender, Maria/Raven's Sch	98
Calnon, Nicole/Chateaugay Elem Sch	69
Cambridge, Janique/New Visions CHS Humanities III [243]	6
Cameron, Andy/Liberty Middle Sch	236
Cameron, Darlene/PS 63 the Star Academy	135
Cameron, James/Commack Road Elem Sch	224
Cameron, Jermaine/Eagle Acad Young Men-Staten IS	192
Cameron, Maxine/PS 13 Roberto Clemente	89
Cammarata, Philip/Persell Middle Sch	38
Campailla, Giuseppe/Our Lady of Hope Sch	186
Campbell, Gene/The Browning Sch	145
Campbell, Maureen/PS 183 Dr Richard R Green	181
Campbell, Monique/School of Integrated Learning	87
Campolieta, Judy/Liverpool HS 9th Grade Annex	156
Camt, Dennis/New Windsor Sch	166
Canale, Joseph/CSI HS-International Studies	192
Cancredi, Brett/Anna S Kuhl Elem Sch	166
Canestrari, Alaine/Hugh R Jones Elem Sch	152
Cangelosi, Karla/Great Neck Road Elem Sch	220
Canino, Matthew/Montgomery Elem Sch	167
Cannon, Paul/PS 140 Eagle Sch	18
Canny, Michael/William C Munn Elem Sch	112
Capellan, Carlos/KIPP NYC College Prep High Sch [242]	5
Capellan, Emilia/Hommocks Middle Sch	258
Capetanakis, Jaynemarie/PS 69 Vincent D Grippo Sch	90
Capone, Neal/Faith Heritage Sch	160
Capri, Deborah/Enders Road Elem Sch	155
Caprio, Joseph/Akron Middle Sch	56
Capuano, Jeffery, Dr/Eastchester High Sch	254
Capuano, Marisa/East Rochester Elem Sch	107
Caputo, James/Harlem Renaissance High Sch	140
Caraballo, Liza/PS 120 Carlos Tapia	84
Caraccio, Michael/Skaneateles Middle Sch	158
Caraisco, Janet/PS 188 Kingsbury	180
Carberry, Marianne/St Christopher Sch	132
Carde, Awilda/PS 28 Wright Brothers	141
Cardona, Elizabeth/PS 310 Marble Hill	21
Careddu, Laurie/PS 18 Winchester	179
Carere, Jennifer/Santapogue Elem Sch	233
Carew, Judith/St Raymond High Sch for Boys	26
Carey, Aaron/Barringer Road Elem Sch	77
Carleton, Fred/Fusion Academy-Upper West Side	144
Carlos, Jumel/Frederick Douglass Academy III	19
Carlson, Christine/Lincoln Avenue Elem Sch	230
Carlson, Kristy/Gail N Chapman Elem Sch	33
Carman, Heather/C J Hooker Middle Sch	164
Carman, Patricia/Nassau BOCES-Jerusalem ES	116
Carnabuci, Frank/Birch Wathen Lenox Sch	144
Carney, Patricia/PS 340 Sixth Ave Elem Sch	137
Carney, Shaun/Clinton Middle Sch	150
Carnhan, Jennifer/Peterboro St Elem Sch	104
Carnicelli, Luke/Southern Cayuga Jr Sr HS	35
Carollo, Philip/PS 56 Louis DeSario Sch	194

New York School Directory

PRINCIPAL INDEX

NAME/School	PAGE
Carpenter, Michele/Sayville Elementary	216
Carpenter, Renee/Dogwood Elem Sch	230
Carr-Gay, Marcella/MS 898 Brooklyn Green Sch	86
Carr, Jeannine/Prospect Hill Elem Sch	260
Carrasquillo, Brenda/Icahn Charter School 2	4
Carriero, Brittany/Pierson Middle High Sch	229
Carrillo, Holger/Enterprise Bus & Tech HS	83
Carroll, Regina, Dr/Lexington School for Deaf	188
Carroll, Scott/Hornell High Sch	214
Carroll, Stephanie/PS 307 Daniel Hale Williams	83
Carson, Arlise/Front Street Sch	121
Carson, Emily/Harlem Hebrew Language Acad CS [240]	4
Cartagena, Betty/Academy for New Americans	184
Cartagena, Jason/Icahn Charter School 6	5
Cartagena, Lynette/PS 19 the Curtis Sch	193
Carter, George/PS 79 Francis Lewis	178
Carter, Loran/G L Priess Primary Sch	60
Carter, Michael/Barker Jr Sr High Sch	146
Carter, Michael/Pratt Elem Sch	146
Carter, Ron/Passages Acad-South Ozone Park	185
Cartolano, Gina, Dr/Great Neck South Middle Sch	120
Carton, Nick/Neighborhood Charter Sch Bronx	6
Carty, Paul/Archbishop Stepinac High Sch	264
Carty, Thomas/PS 49 Dorothy Bonawit Kole	177
Carulli, Lee/Bolivar Road Elem Sch	104
Casab, Kristin/General Wm Floyd Elem Sch	150
Casado, Hilary/PS 3 Charrette Sch	137
Casale, Andrew/Mineola Middle Sch	125
Casale, Eric/Springs Sch	232
Casale, Michael/IS 73 Frank Sansivieri	177
Casertano, Drew/Millbrook Sch	55
Casey, Dan/Broadalbin-Perth Elem Sch	71
Cassano, Maria, Sr/St Jean Baptiste High Sch	143
Cassant, Sandy/Doane Stuart Sch	192
Cassidy, Debra/PS 24 Andrew Jackson	178
Casswell, Edward/Center Moriches High Sch	218
Castanza, Tim/Bridge Prep Charter Sch	1
Castellane, William, Dr/Sloatsburg Elem Sch	198
Castellani, Warren/Our Saviour Lutheran Sch	188
Castellano, Aracelis/PS 165 Robert E Simon	139
Castellano, Carolann/Meadow Pond Elem Sch	257
Castellano, Kerry/PS 70 Max Schoenfeld Sch	19
Castello, Marisa/PS 176 Cambria Heights	183
Castelluccio, Maria/Leman Manhattan Prep Sch	144
Castiello, Beth-Ann/School 3 Oaks Sch	127
Castilla, Helena/Our Lady of Victory Sch	265
Castillo, Frances/PS 83 Luis Munoz Rivera	139
Castillo, Lucia/PS 42 Claremont	19
Castillo, Myra/Church Street Elem Sch	263
Castillo, Nelsie/Bronx Bridges High Sch	17
Castillo, Zoranlly/Brilla College Prep CS-Veritas	2
Castine, Patricia/Reinhard Early Childhood Ctr	117
Castrataro, James/Monsignor McClancy Memorial HS	186
Castro, Laura/University Neighborhood MS	135
Castronovo, Johanna/PS 105 the Blythebourne	90
Catalano, Celeste/Sacred Heart Elem Sch	195
Cataldo, John/North Collins Elem Sch	63
Catandella, Lisa/Oak Park Elem Sch	218
Catania, Patricia/PS-IS 224	17
Catanzaro, Karen/PS 54 Charles W Leng	194
Catapano, Carrie/West End Day Sch	146
Catapano, Deanna/Unqua Elem Sch	125
Catapano, Janice/Promise Christian Academy	188
Catapano, Michael, Dr/Half Hollow Hills High Sch W	222
Catavero, Joe/New York Inst for Special Ed	27
Cathey, Marcy/Chemung Valley Montessori Sch	41
Catitulo-Saide, Valerie/Jefferson Primary Sch	223
Catlett, Lauren/Troy Prep Charter Sch [246]	8
Catlin, Rob/Mt Sinai Elem Sch	226
Causey, Elizabeth/The Spence Sch	146
Cavagnaro, Larry/Academy of Chrn Leadership	47
Cavanagh, Michael/Medina High Sch	170
Cavaretta, Amy/Marilla Primary Sch	62
Cazer, Bonnie/Middlesex Valley Primary Sch	162
Cazes, Amy/Hillside Elem Sch	256

NAME/School	PAGE
Cecchini, Marianna/PS 17 Early Childhood Center	57
Cecile, Marie, Sr/Our Lady of Sorrows Sch	265
Ceffalia, Beth/PS 132 Conselyea	84
Celestine, Cynthia, Dr/PS 26 Jesse Owens	86
Celmer, Marylou/Blessed Sacrament Sch	95
Celotti, Tara/Crown Point Central Sch	67
Centeno, Evelyn/Family Life Acad Charter Sch I	4
Centner, Chris/Camden High Sch	150
Centola, James/Cosgrove Middle Sch	112
Cercone, Gretchen/John F Kennedy Middle Sch	59
Cervola, Thomas/Gilboa-Conesville Central Sch	206
Cervoni, Jeffrey/Eden Middle High Sch	60
Cesar, Janette/Tag Young Scholars	140
Cesene, Ty/Bronx Arena High Sch	17
Chadwick, Gary/Fulmar Road Elem Sch	176
Chakar, Robert/Andes Central Sch	49
Chamberlain, Davis/Shaker Junior High Sch	11
Chamberlin, Brian/Harding Avenue Elem Sch	224
Chambers, Lorenzo/PS 279 Herman Schreiber	88
Chambers, Robert/Park Avenue Sch	132
Champlain, Lora/Dryden Middle Sch	240
Chan, Priscilla/Brooklyn Sch-Collab Studies	84
Chanales, E/Yeshiva Derech Hatorah ES	100
Chandler, Craig/Mohonasen High Sch	204
Chaney, Ana/Little Red Schlhse-Irwin HS	144
Chang, Ann/PS 85 Judge Charles Vallone	184
Chant, Benedict/Poughkeepsie Day Sch	55
Chapman, Danielle/Madison Elem Sch	211
Chapman, Eric/St David's Sch	145
Chapnick, Joyce/Main St Elem Sch	257
Charland, Daniel/Frontier Central High Sch	61
Charlebois, Daniel/Immaculate Heart Ctl ES	82
Charlebois, Daniel/Immaculate Heart Ctl Jr/Sr HS	82
Charles, Jacqueline/MS 35 Stephen Decatur	86
Charles, Jeanette/SS Catherine & Therese Acad	95
Charles, Pamela/Cbi Tech-Gateway	195
Chasen, Marianne/Kid Esteem of Montessori Schoo	235
Chatain, Jennifer/Stephen & Harriet Myers MS	9
Chau, Kristy/Kennedy Child Study Center	144
Chaucer, Kathleen/Milton Terrace North Elem Sch	200
Chavez, Christine/PS 45 John Tyler	193
Chavez, Evelyn/Bronx Manhattan SDA Sch	26
Check, Jennifer/Victor Primary Sch	163
Chekima, Sohaib, Dr/An Nur Islamic Sch	205
Chen, Anne/A MacArthur Barr 5-6 Academy	196
Chenaille, Rebekah, Dr/Caledonia-Mumford Senior HS	102
Cheng, Alan/HS 560-City as Sch	136
Cheresnowsky, John/Elm Street Elem Sch	239
Cherns, Joseph/Stein Yeshiva of Lincoln Park	266
Cheslow, Samantha/Success Acad CS Bronx 4 [245]	7
Chesney, Taleema/Storefront Acad Harlem CS	7
Chetirko, Jeffrey/Urban Assembly NY Harbor Sch	138
Cheung, Pagee/Math Engineering & Sci Academy	5
Chierichella, Patrick/Red Creek High Sch	251
Chille-Zafuto, Maria/Maple Avenue Elem Sch	148
Chilson, David/Theodore Roosevelt Elem Sch	27
Chiluiza, Karla/Global Learning Collaborative	138
Chin, Jason/PS 7 Louis Simeone	177
Chiodo, Melissa/Mae E Reynolds Elem Sch	154
Chislett, Leslie/Metropolitan High Sch	24
Chism, Harvey/South Bronx Cmty Charter HS	7
Chisolm, Devin/Salesian High Sch	265
Chiu, Chia-Chee/Fieldston Middle Upper Sch	26
Chmielewski, Rebecca/Grapeville Christian Sch	76
Chmielewski, Tina/Lakeshore Road Elem Sch	157
Chory, Cynthia/PS/IS 187 Hudson Cliffs	142
Chrem, Elisa/Imagine Academy	98
Chrisman, Crystal/Dolgeville Elem Middle Sch	77
Christensen, Carl/Churchville Chili Middle Sch	107
Christie, Claudette/World Acad Total Cmty Hlth HS	89
Christopher, Jon/South Jefferson Middle Sch	81
Chung, Ingrid/Urban Assembly Math & Science	20
Chunn, Shante/PS 723X	25
Churba, Yosef/Yeshivat Magen Abraham	100

PRINCIPAL INDEX

NAME/School	PAGE
Cianfrani, Chad/Oakwood Friends Sch	55
Ciarametaro, Maria/Bowling Green Elem Sch	118
Ciarlo, Aimee/Finn Academy-Elmira Chtr Sch	4
Ciccarelli, Anthony/Birchwood Intermediate Sch	231
Ciccone, Stephanie/Crestwood Children's Center	114
Cieloszczyk, Christina/St Stanislaus Kostka Cath Acad	95
Ciliotta-Young, Madeleine/Urban Assem Sch-Green Careers	139
Ciliotta, Andrea/Brooklyn Studio Secondary Sch	91
Cimino, Maria/Nottingham High Sch	159
Cimmerer, Allison/Lima Primary Sch	109
Cineus, Omotayo/Catherine & Count Basie MS 72	181
Cintron, David/PS 214	24
Cioffi, Anthony/Rosemarie Ann Siragusa Sch 14	264
Cioffi, Maria/Matilida Avenue School PS 483	23
Ciranni, Pam/Minerva Deland Sch	108
Cirone, Al/Babylon Jr Sr High Sch	216
Citrano, Kerianne/PS 194 Countee Cullen	140
Ciuffo, Anthony/Wantagh Middle Sch	131
Ciulla, Robert/JHS 201 Dyker Heights	90
Clacken, Mrs/New Visions CHS Math & Sci II [243]	6
Clagnaz, Paul/St Brigid-Our Lady of Hope Sch	132
Clahar, Ron/Pat Kam Sch	134
Clancy, Mary/Cooke Center Academy	142
Clare, Katherine/Nord Anglia Int'l Sch-New York	145
Clark, Alison/Stratford Road Elem Sch	128
Clark, Claudine/Bailey Avenue Elem Sch	45
Clark, James/Teenage Parenting Program	116
Clark, Janet/John S Burke Catholic High Sch	168
Clark, Jason/St Paul's Lutheran Sch	74
Clark, Jeannette/Onondaga Road Elem Sch	159
Clark, Jeannine/Pelham Memorial High Sch	260
Clark, Jill/A J Schmidt Elem Sch	60
Clark, John/Henry H Wells Middle Sch	175
Clark, Karen/Bridges Alt Junior High Sch	154
Clark, Matthew/North Country Rd Middle Sch	226
Clark, Paul/Attica Middle Sch	267
Clark, Robert/Fairport High Sch	108
Clark, Sean/Kreamer Street Elem Sch	231
Clark, Shawn/Jefferson Road Elem Sch	110
Clarke-Raysor, Ann/Bronx CS Better Learning II	2
Clarke-Raysor, Anne/Bronx Charter Sch Better Lrng	2
Clarke, Charleton/Bronx Excellence 3 Elementary [236]	2
Clarke, Debra/Urban Scholars Cmty Sch	25
Clarke, Maria/Children's Workshop Sch	135
Claudio, Josette/PS 109 Sedgwick	19
Claus, Michael/Phyllilsuster Birch Sch	188
Clause, Michael/Phyllis L Susser Sch	188
Clayman, Andrew/Health Opportunities High Sch	16
Clayton, Heather/Mendon Center Elem Sch	110
Clemens, Robert/St Mark Sch	66
Clemente, Frances, Dr/Cristo Rey New York High Sch	144
Clendenen, Janet/Frank M Knight Elem Sch	208
Cleveland, Chris/Lighthouse Christian Academy	175
Cleveland, Chris/Oneonta Christian Academy	175
Clifton, Jacobi/Leadership Prep Brwnsvlle Acad [246]	5
Clinard, Jacqueline/Court Street Elem Sch	62
Clinton, Debra/Marlboro Middle Sch	242
Clooney, William/Jefferson Central Sch	206
Cloutier, Karen/PS 14	191
Cluckey, Robert, Dr/Nativity of Blessed Mary Sch	65
Clyburn, Camaron/Dr Walter Cooper Acad Sch 10	111
CO, Vivian/Orchard Sch	266
Coady, John/Smithtown High School-West	230
Coakley, Joe/Flanders Elem Sch	70
Cobb, Charles/Deer Park High Sch	220
Cobb, Nathanael/Cortland Christian Academy	48
Cobb, Steven/MS 355 Bronx Alliance Mid Sch	23
Cockfield, Alfred/Lamad Academy Charter Sch	5
Cocozello, Joseph/Blessed Sacrament Sch	194
Cocozza, Francis/Lake George Jr Sr High Sch	245
Coffin, Steven/Parishville Hopkinton Ctl Sch	212
Cofield, Adriann/PS 131 Academy School at 4	58
Cofield, Adriann/PS 309 East Cmty High Sch	58
Cofield, Adriann/PS131 Academy Sch at 44 & Ltep	58
Coggiano, Anthony/Bellport Academic Center	215
Coggins, Colleen/Clarence Center Elem Sch	59
Cohen, Alona/Brooklyn Frontiers HS	84
Cohen, B/Yeshiva Arugath Habosem	99
Cohen, Bonni/Manorhaven Elem Sch	128
Cohen, Elliott/United Talmudical Bais Rachel	168
Cohen, Jodie/James Madison High Sch	92
Cohen, Joshua/Buchanan-Verplank Elem Sch	256
Cohen, Molly/Success Acad CS Harlem 5 [245]	7
Cohen, Sara/Churchill Center & Sch	144
Cohen, Steven/Allen-Stevenson Sch	143
Coker, Neema, Dr/Andrew T Morrow Elem Sch	218
Coladonato, Joseph/H B Mattlin Middle Sch	128
Colarossi, Christopher/Shaw Avenue Elem Sch	131
Colavito, Eve/Dream Charter Sch-Mott Haven	3
Colby, Meagan/Benjamin N Cardozo High Sch	179
Cole, Clayton, Dr/Marcus Whitman Middle High Sch	162
Cole, John/Karl Saile Bear Rd Elem Sch	157
Cole, Linda/Alternative Sch for Math & Sci	215
Coleman, Joyce/PS 21 Philip H Sheridan	23
Coleman, Veronica/Kurt Hahn Expeditionary Sch	88
Coles, Denice/A Childs Place Day Sch	187
Coley, Anita/PS 25 Eubie Blake Sch	86
Colgan, Aris/Growing Up Green Charter ES	184
Collier, Brian/Oxford Academy Primary Sch	42
Collins, Ann/Hugh W Gregg Elem Sch	214
Collins, Evelyn/Nellie Thornton High Sch	258
Collins, Pauline, Dr/Northeast Elem Sch	216
Collison, Michelle/Wood Park Primary Sch	219
Colomban, Brian/St Joseph Sch	132
Colon, Ismael/Ivy League Sch	235
Colon, Jean/Kappa III	24
Colon, Margarita/PS 72 Dr William Dorney	18
Colon, Nicole/PS 133 Queens	179
Colosi, Nick/Sherburne Earlville Sr HS	43
Colson, Jamal, Dr/Bellport Middle Sch	231
Colton, Ruth/Christopher Columbus YABC	22
Colucci, Danielle/Woodward Children Center	134
Colunio, Kyle/Dryden High Sch	239
Combs, Mitchell, Dr/Port Chester High Sch	261
Comer, John, Dr/Burns Avenue Elem Sch	122
Comis, Scott, Dr/Brooklyn Avenue Elem Sch	131
Competello, Diane/St Athanasius Sch	95
Compson, Melissa/Queens Explorers Elem Sch	181
Comrie, Karleen/Jean Nuzzi Intermediate Sch	183
Comstock, Peter/Homestead Sch	237
Conaway, Megan/Russell I Doig Middle Sch	241
Conboy, Brian/Massapequa High Sch	125
Condie, Jackie/Brooklyn Friends Sch	97
Condon, Brian/Townsend Harris High Sch	179
Conger, Kim/George A Jackson Elem Sch	122
Conklin-Frank, Jennifer/Cattaraugus Elem Sch	31
Conklin, Caleb, Dr/Hillel Academy of Broome Co	30
Conlan, Alexandra/Sacred Heart Sch	186
Connell, Michael/Holy Angels Regional Sch	234
Connelly, Bernel/PS 179 Kensington	90
Connelly, Jennifer/Nycacs-Bronx	6
Connolly, Brian/Washingtonville Sr High Sch	167
Connolly, Dianne/Greenwood Lake Elem Sch	164
Connolly, James/Alice P Willits Elem Sch	129
Connolly, Kathleen/East Elem Sch	124
Connolly, Penny/Greene High Sch	42
Connolly, Susan/Coram Elem Sch	225
Connor, Virginia/St Hilda & St Hugh Sch	145
Conover, Andrea/Duanesburg Elem Sch	203
Conrad, Cara/Traver Road Primary Sch	51
Conrick, Matthew/Tanglewood Elem Sch	202
Conrow, Kristine/Harpursville Jr Sr HS	28
Conroy, Kerry/LaSalle Academy	143
Consuegra, Boris/PS 115 Alexander Humboldt	141
Contarino, Lisa Marie/Bicycle Path Pre-K & Kdgn Ctr	225
Conte, Carlos/Grand Ave Middle Sch	117

PRINCIPAL INDEX

NAME/School	PAGE
Contento, Jodi/PS 78	194
Conti, Scott/New Design High Sch	137
Contratti, Michelle/PS 130	178
Contreras, Eric/Stuyvesant High Sch	138
Conway, James/Lake George Elem Sch	245
Conway, Kevin/Millennium Brooklyn High Sch	84
Conwell, Doreen/HS Law Advocacy/Cmty Justice	138
Cook, Amanda/John Kennedy Intermediate Sch	73
Cook, Carina/Albany Leadrshp CHS for Girls	1
Cook, Christopher/Hauppauge High Sch	223
Cook, Danielle/Panama Central Sch	38
Cook, Patrick/PS 74 Hamlin Park Sch	57
Cook, Will/Tioga Middle Sch	239
Cooke, Jaleelah/Young Leaders Elem Sch	17
Cool, Kathleenann/Lincoln Avenue Elem Sch	197
Coombs, Angela/Academy of St Joseph	142
Coonan, Kerry/Raynor Country Day Sch	235
Cooper, Kendra/Paumanok Elem Sch	222
Cooper, Kimberly/James E Allen Elem Sch	216
Cooper, Michelle/Success Acad CS-Sprngfld Grdn [245]	8
Cooper, Scott/Southwestern High Sch	39
Cope, Kristina/Fifth Avenue Sch	217
Coppola, Lisa/Blessed Sacrament Sch	160
Corbin, Chantal/Fabius-Pompey Elem Sch	155
Corbin, Melissa/Wellwood Middle Sch	155
Corcoran, Frank/KIPP Academy Middle Sch [242]	16
Corder, Lynn/Portville Central Sch	32
Cordone, David/Gillette Road Middle Sch	157
Corey, Chad/South Orangetown Middle Sch	198
Coriale, Eric/North Broad Street Elem Sch	105
Corieri, Elizabeth/Tuscarora Indian Sch	148
Corigliano, Eileen/Staten Island Academy	195
Cornell, Gill/Williamsburg HS-Arch Design	84
Cornfield, Richard/Corning Christian Academy	215
Corniel, Tia/Pine Hills Elem Sch	9
Cornwell, Christian/Friendship Central Sch	15
Corona, Monica/Nathaniel Woodhull Elem Sch	233
Corrado, Ean/Queens High School of Teaching	180
Correa, Abe/Harlem Village Acad High Sch [239]	4
Corsano, Michael/Sheafe Road Elem Sch	54
Corsetti, Darren/Cornwall on Hudson Elem Sch	163
Corsilia, Andrew/Horace Greeley High Sch	253
Corso, Raffaele/St Camillus Catholic Academy	186
Corso, Raffaele/St Joan of Arc Sch	186
Cortez, Deborah/Eltingville Lutheran Sch	195
Cory, Susan/Holley Middle High Sch	169
Coscia, John/Division Ave High Sch	123
Cosentino, Anthony/PS 21 Margaret Emery Elm Park	193
Cosentino, Michael/St Peter's High Sch for Boys	195
Cosgrove, Leo/Bishop Ludden Jr Sr High Sch	160
Cosh, Gwynne/William H Barton Interm Sch	246
Cosmai, Michael/PS 225 the Eileen Zaglin	91
Cosmer, Robert/Scotia Middle Sch	205
Costa, Kenneth/Connetquot Senior High Sch	219
Costanzo, Lisa/Clary Middle Sch	158
Costello, Heather/Genesee Elem Sch	34
Cotilletta, Kathleen/Our Lady of Lourdes Sch	132
Coto, Joseph/North Main Elem Sch	165
Cotrone, Ken, Dr/Soundview Preparatory Sch	266
Cotter, Christina/South Bay Elem Sch	233
Cotter, Corinne/Pleasant Avenue Elem Sch	71
Cotter, Michele/General Herkimer Elem Sch	152
Coty, Diane/Seventy Ninth Street Elem Sch	148
Coughlin, Thomas/Harry E Elden Elem Sch	154
Cousins, Albert/North Shore High Sch	126
Cousins, Rob/Ethical Culture Sch	144
Coverdale, Jeffery/New York Military Academy	168
Coviello, Alison/PS 154 Jonathan D Hyatt	16
Covington, Jody/PS 192 Buffalo Visual Perf Art	58
Covington, Tina/Hawthorne Country Day Sch	265
Cowell, Avon/PS 382- ES Math Sci &Tech Sch	22
Cowin, Timothy/Weedsport Elem Sch	35
Cox, Danielle/St Jude the Apostle Sch	192
Cox, Giulia/JHS 118 William W Niles	21
Cox, Jacquelyn/Andrew J Townson School 39	110
Cox, Kersandra/PS 80 Thurgood Marshall Magnet	182
Cox, Mary/Fassett Elem Sch	40
Coxum, Julliet/Warring Elem Sch	53
Coyle, Elizabeth/Northeast Elem Sch	240
Coyne, Kimberly/Franklin Magnet Elem Sch	158
Cozine, Gerald/Great Neck North Middle Sch	120
Cozzocrea, Thomas/Mahopac Middle Sch	176
Cracco, Nicolas, Dr/Henry Barnard Early Chldhd Ctr	259
Cradle, Derek/HS of Sports Management	91
Craft, Ken/Benjamin Franklin Elem Sch	257
Craig, Lisa/East Hill Elem Sch	159
Cramer, Michelle/Dake Junior High Sch	113
Crane, Frank/Staten Island Academy	195
Crane, Jennifer/Addison Jr Sr High Sch	213
Crane, Joshua/The Stony Brook Sch	235
Crawford, Brian/East View Elem Sch	32
Crawford, Courtney/Charter HS Law-Social Justice	3
Crawford, James/McNab Elem Sch	71
Crawford, Kristin/Trinity Sch	146
Crawford, Maura/St James the Apostle Sch	176
Crego, Tina/Ketchum-Grande Memorial Sch	203
Creighton, Celestine/Bethesda SDA Elem Sch	234
Creighton, Kelestine/Bethel Elem Sch	96
Crenshaw, James/Westhampton Beach Lrng Center	216
Crimmins, Hayley/Tioga Hills Elem Sch	30
Criscone, Nicholas/Glen Worden Elem Sch	205
Crisman, Lauren/Harry Hoag Elem Sch	115
Crocker, Arnette/Women's Academy of Excellence	18
Cromer, Anthony/East-West Sch of Int'l Studies	178
Cronin, Cynthia/Van Buren Elem Sch	154
Cruikshank, Kathleen/Harrisville Central Sch	101
Cruite, Therese/The Chapin Sch	146
Crumb, Eileen/Maryvale Intermediate Sch	59
Crupi, Mary/Coman Hill Sch	253
Cruz-Perez, Nadia/Young Voices Academy of Bronx	23
Cruz, Cristina, Dr/Our Lady of Sorrows Sch	186
Cruz, Francine/International Sch for Lib Arts	21
Cruz, Jessica/PS/IS 178 Holliswood	180
Cruz, Marines/PS 75 Research & Discovery	18
Cruz, Serapha/Bronx Sch of Young Leaders	20
Crysler, Mary/St Rose of Lima Sch	160
Cuba, Kattia/Lucero Elem Sch	19
Cubero, Pedro/HS for Contemporary Arts	22
Cuccia, Francine/Link IB World Sch	196
Cuddy, Laurie/Hinsdale Central Sch	32
Cugini, David/Susan E Wagner High Sch	194
Culbertson, Elizabeth/Antwerp Primary Sch	80
Culihan, Marie/Albany School of Humanities	9
Culkin, Elizabeth/PS 176 Ovington Sch	90
Cullen, Angela/PS 366 Research Lab Bioinfo	58
Cummings, Chris/Lakeland High Sch	257
Cummings, Lori/PS 107 Thomas A Dooley	178
Cunningham, Lawford/Icahn Charter School 1	4
Cunzio, Mike/Columbus Elem Sch	258
Cuomo, Maria/St Matthias Sch	187
Cupelli, Sarah/Bellevue Elem Sch	158
Curatolo, Kathleen/St Patrick Sch	95
Curinga, Ted/Faith Fellowship Christian Sch	82
Curran, Matthew/Kensico Elem Sch	263
Curtin, Rachel/Ronald L Sodoma Elem Sch	169
Curtis, Brian/School 17	264
Curto, Sally/Winthrop Avenue Sch	117
Cusack, Brenden/Huntington High Sch	223
Custodio, Marilyn/PS 97 Forest Park	181
Cusumano, Anthony/JHS 78 Roy H Mann	92
Cutaia, Shana/Barker Road Middle Sch	110
Cuthbertson, Greg/Poland Central Sch	78
Cutler, Lee/Rondout Valley Interm Sch	243
Cyprys, Andrea/Sch for Inquiry Social Justice	18
Czebatol, Tracie/Merton Williams Middle Sch	109

D

NAME/School	PAGE
D'Agostino, Carol/Kendall Jr Sr High Sch	169
D'Agostino, Linda, Dr/My Spectrum Sch	134

PRINCIPAL INDEX

NAME/School	PAGE
D'Alessio, Tiffany/IS 349 Math Science & Tech	93
D'Alleva, Kai/Watkins Glen Central High Sch	207
D'Ambrosio, Alicia/East Hill Elem Sch	115
D'Amico, Kimberly/Warsaw Central Mid High Sch	267
D'Angelo, Tristan/Sbcs Notre Dame Academy	65
D'Antonio, Maryann, Sr/St Raymond Academy for Girls	26
D'Apice, Joe/Richfield Springs Ctl Sch	174
D'Avilar, Dwayne/Poughkeepsie Middle Sch	53
D'Emic, Andrea/St Edmund Sch	95
Dabbracci, Jennifer/Dana L Lyon Middle Sch	213
Dagostino, Sharon/Malta Avenue Elem Sch	200
Dahan, Rivka/Yde Elem Sch	99
Daids, Dewana/MS 61 Dr Gladstone H Atwell	86
Daigler, Monica/Douglas J Regan Interm Sch	149
Dakmak-Rakka, Iman, Sr/AL Iman Sch	187
Dale, Eric/Dwight Sch	144
Daley, James/Netherwood Elem Sch	52
Daley, Matthew/Madrid-Waddington Central Sch	211
Dalley, Chris, Dr/Hemlock Park Elem Sch	217
Dalley, Tania/River Elem Sch	227
Dallis, Anna/Explore Excel Charter Sch [237]	3
Dalrymple, Marjorie/PS K369 Coy L Cox Sch	94
Dalrymple, Rebecca/Maynard P Wilson Elem Sch	81
Dalton, Jean/PS 279 Capt Manuel Rivera Jr	21
Dalton, Peter/Barry Tech Ctr-Westbury	116
Dalton, Sharon, Sr/St Mary's Grade Sch	69
Daly, Brendan/Passages Acad-Dobbs Ferry	259
Daly, Brendan/Passages Acad-Ryer	25
Daly, Brendan/Passages Academy-Bronx Hope	25
Daly, Jonathan/Eximius Clg Prep Academy	19
Daly, Kieran/Iona Preparatory Sch	265
Daly, Meghan/East Brooklyn Ascend CS	3
Daly, Meghan/Success Acad CS S Jamaica [245]	8
Damas, Rebecca/Trevor Day School-West	146
Damelio, Elaine/Walt Disney Elem Sch	108
Damico, Mary/Queen of Heaven Sch	65
Damo, Kristen/Success Acad CS Harlem Central [245]	7
Damo, Kristin/Success Acad CS Lafayette MS [245]	8
Damo, Kristin/Success Acad CS-Lafayette MS [245]	8
Dan, Melissa/School of the Holy Child	265
Danbusky, Daniel/Northport High Sch	227
DAngelo, Dominick/IS 228 David A Boody	91
Daniel, Greg/Harlem Prep Campus CS [235]	4
Daniel, Jeremy/Brighter Choice Community Sch	85
Daniels, Eric/Helendale Road Primary Sch	107
Daniels, Gordie/Oxford Academy High Sch	42
Dann, Joshua/Saranac Lake High Sch	70
Danna, Denise/PS 771K	94
Danner, Dora/PS 234	185
Danson, Richard/School at Northeast	205
Darbee, Dannielle/Brooklyn Acad Global Finance	85
Darden, Gloria/PS 226	21
Dargan, Nadine/Morse Elem Sch	53
Darling, Jennifer/Concord Road Elem Sch	252
Darrell, Richard/St Ignatius Sch	27
Daughtry, Dawnique/MS 113 Ronald Edmonds Lrng Ctr	82
Daurio, Maureen/Blessed Sacrament Sch	12
Davenport, Andrew/Marbletown Elem Sch	243
Davenport, Edwin, Dr/Rhinebeck High Sch	53
Davey, Travis/Babylon Elem Sch	216
David, Jimenez/Manhattan Ctr Science & Math	139
David, Malka/Yeshiva Tiferes Elimelech Boys	100
Davidson, Kim/St David's Sch	145
Davies, Eileen/PS 207 Rockwood Park	181
Davila, Rosa/PS 92 Mary McLeod Bethune	140
Davino, Alfonse/Thomas Jefferson Elem Sch	257
Davis-Marrow, Danielle/Holmes Magnet Elem Sch	258
Davis, Alicia/PS 132 Ralph Bunche	183
Davis, Barry/Lyme Central Sch	81
Davis, Beverly/Nurturing Center and Academy	188
Davis, Dan/Frederick Carder Elem Sch	214
Davis, Erica/PS 261 Philip Livingston	85
Davis, Fia/Pathways College Prep Sch	183
Davis, Glenn/KIPP Infinity Elem Mid Sch [242]	5
Davis, Justin/Teach	89
Davis, Justin/The Uft Charter Sch	8
Davis, Kathy/Oneida High Sch	105
Davis, Kim/Paideia School 24	263
Davis, Kimberly/Lyncourt Union Free Sch	156
Davis, Marie/Harry B Ward Technical Center	216
Davis, Matthew/Ptech	71
Davis, Melody/Brockport High Sch	107
Davis, Rashid/Pathways In Tech Early Clg HS	87
Davis, Serge/PS 95 Sheila Mencher	21
Davis, Shawn/Stamford Central Sch	50
Davis, Shirlee/Livingston Mid High Sch	236
Davis, Tiffany/PS 165 Edith K Bergtraum	179
Davis, Tina/Greenfield Elem Sch	201
Davison, George/Grace Church Sch	144
Davison, Kurt/Metropolitan Lighthouse CS [149]	19
Davy, Natalie/Martin Luther King Jr Sch	263
Day-Loving, Danique/Success Acad CS Harlem 1 [245]	7
De Angelo, Cara/Marsh Ave Sch Expditionry Lrng	193
De Castro, Nedda/International HS-Prospect Hgts	86
De Chent, Edward/Roosevelt HS Early Clg Studies	264
De Francesco, James/IS 49 Berta A Dreyfus	192
De Jesus, Ana/Queens HS for Sciences at York	182
De La Rosa, Fausto/Unity Center for Urban Tech	138
De Vale, Brian/PS 257 John F Hylan	84
Dealy, Ann, Dr/Brookside Primary Sch	260
Dealy, Michael/Bay Ridge Preparatory Sch	96
Dealy, Michael, Dr/Bay Ridge Preparatory High Sch	96
Dean, Danielle/Mt Morris Central Sch	103
Dean, Gordon/Twin Towers Middle Sch	165
Deane Moshier, Sally/Wildwood Campus Cte	213
DeAngelis, Deirdre/New Dorp High Sch	193
Dease, Andrew/Anderson Center for Autism	55
Debell, Roger/Thornell Road Elem Sch	110
DeBenedictis, Katharine/PS 198 Isador E Ida Straus	137
DeBerry, Charles/PS 76 A Philip Randolph	139
DeBonis, Lisa/Linden Tree Elem Sch	23
Debono, Elaine/Uniondale Pre-Kindergarten	130
Decamp, David/Professional Pathways HS	92
DeCarlo, Geraldine/School 7 Oceanside HS	127
Dechiaro, Jacqueline/Van Schaick Grade Sch	10
Dechter, Samuel/Lubavitcher School Chabad	98
Decicco, Veronica/Merrimac Elem Sch	229
Decicco, Vincent/Kingston Senior High Sch	242
Decker, Betty/Faith Christian Sch	154
Decker, Donna/William Barkley Elem Sch	116
Decker, Rosemarie/Maria Regina High Sch	265
DeCosta, Dawn/Thurgood Marshall Lower Sch	140
Dedrick, Jerri/Southgate Elem Sch	11
Deeds, Zoeann/Brooklyn Blue Feather Elem Sch	97
DeFazio, Anthony/Questar 3-Rensselaer Ed Ctr	189
DeFeo, James/Windsor Sch	189
DeFilippis, Angela/Brooklyn Sci Engineering Acad	87
DeGennaro, Frank/PS 721X Stephen McSweeney Sch	25
DeGennaro, Joseph/Yorktown High Sch	264
Degiorgio, Diana/Searingtown Elem Sch	121
DeHaven, William/Winston Preparatory Sch	146
DeJesus, Susan/Lyceum Charter Sch	5
Del Valle, Andre/Poly Prep Country Day Sch-Uppr	98
Delacruz, Gladys/Adlai Stevenson Campus YABC	17
Delaitre, Antoine/United Nations Int'l Sch	146
DeLany, Kelsey/Fremont Elem Sch	155
DeLany, Magdaline/Caesar Chavez Sch	263
Delara, Norma/Passages Acad-Belmont	94
DeLaRosa, Yecenia/Gregorio Luperon HS Sci & Math	141
Delauney, Tricia/Elijah Stroud Middle Sch	86
Delfavero, Maura/Tyburn Academy	36
Delgrego, Tracy/University Prep CS Young Men	8
Delio, John/Edith L Slocum Elem Sch	219
Dello Stritto, Katie/PS 58 the Carroll	85
DeLorenzo, Danielle, Dr/Lynwood Avenue Elem Sch	229
DeLuca, Frances/Our Lady Perpetual Help Acad	186

New York School Directory — PRINCIPAL INDEX

NAME/School	PAGE
DeLuca, Jaclyn/Brooklyn Prospect Clinton Hill	2
DeLuca, Laura/Old Mill Road Elem Sch	126
Delucchi, Giovanna/PS 43 Jonas Bronck	16
Deluke, Samantha/Troy Prep Charter Sch [246]	8
Demallie, Richard/Gloversville High Sch	71
DeMarco, Denise/West Point Elem Sch	167
DeMars, Ryan/Otsego Area Occupation Center	172
Dembitzer, Heshie/Bobover Yeshiva Bnei Zion	97
Dembo, Frank/Vanderheyden Hall Sch	192
Demchak, Elizabeth/Claremont International HS	18
DeMeo, Edward/Jacqueline Kennedy Onassis HS	136
Demert, Jennifer/Buffalo Acad of Sacred Heart	65
Demos, Nina/PS 503 the School of Discovery	90
Dempster, Sheldon/JHS 220 John Pershing	90
Denaker, Steven/Avoca Central Sch	213
Dennis, Robert/North Shore Middle Sch	126
Dennison, Joe/Bronx Residential Center	2
Densieski, David/Pulaski Street Elem Sch	228
Denton, Kristen/Charles W Baker High Sch	154
Depalo, Kelsey/Success Acad CS Washington Hts [245]	8
DePaola, Thomas/Carle Place Middle Sr High Sch	117
DePaolo, Christopher/Canajoharie Middle Sch	115
DePaolo, Veronica/PS 131 Abigail Adams	183
Depolo, Genie/Manhattan Charter Sch	5
Derby, James/Castleton Elem Sch	191
Dercola, Brittany/Camden Middle Sch	150
Dere, Mirlene/PS 59 Annex	57
Dere, Mirlene/PS 59 Dr Drew Science Mag Sch	57
Deriso, Anthony/Plainedge Middle Sch	127
Derrig, Danielle/Samara Cmty Sch	25
DeSanctis, Christopher/Gateway Academy	195
DeSantis, Gina/Moore Catholic High Sch	194
DeSario, Frank/PS 60 Woodhaven	180
DeSario, Helen/PS 66 J Kennedy Onasiss	181
Desforges, Marie/PS 328 Phyllis Wheatley	89
Desmond, Thomas/Wenonah Elem Sch	229
DeSouza, Marcia/Battalion Christian Academy	96
DeStefano, Pasquale/East Northport Middle Sch	227
Detommaso, James/West Hempstead High Sch	131
Dettenrieder, Nicole/Wheelerville Union Free Sch	72
Deu, Elie/Williamsburg Northside Sch	99
Deutsch, Christine/St Ambrose Academy	114
Deutsch, Martin/V'Yoel Moshe D'Satmar-Uta	199
Devenoge, Sarah/St Mary Elem Sch	132
DeVine, Kathleen/Cutchogue East Elem Sch	225
Devitt, Mellisa/Arcade Elem Sch	33
Devivio, Diana/Gersh Academy Hauppauge	235
Devivio, Diana/Gersh Academy-W Hempstead	133
Dewey, Caiti/Arkport Central Sch	213
DeWitt, Adam/Longwood Junior High Sch	225
Di Pasquale, Brian/Park Terrace Elem Sch	71
Di Scalfani, Kelly/Meadowbrook Elem Sch	118
Diamond, Romy/PS 81 Jean Paul Richter	177
DiAngelo, Dorothy/Early Childhood Sch	162
Diaz, Harriett/IS 192 Linden	183
Diaz, Juanita/Marshall Sch	121
Diaz, Judy/John F Kennedy Magnet Sch	261
Diaz, Mary/Rochester International Acad	111
Diaz, Richie/Cathedral Preparatory Seminary	186
DiBella, Marie/PS/IS 104 the Ft Hamilton Sch	90
DiBella, Roseanne/William Sidney Mount Elem Sch	232
Dibernardi, Peter/Thiells Elem Sch	197
Dicaprio, Joseph/Rosendale Elem Sch	204
DiCicco, Susan/Gramercy Arts High Sch	136
Dicker, Shmuelzev/Yeshiva Mercaz Hatorah	189
Dickerson, Jeanna/PS 138 Samuel Randall	18
Diclemente, Patrick/Locust Valley High Sch	123
Dicrescento, Joseph/PS 48 Joseph R Drake	17
DiDio, Paul/PS 159	179
Didonna, James/Germantown Central Sch	46
Dieckmann, Donald/Grant E Morse Elem Sch	243
Dieteman, Stephen/Career Tech Ctr-Olean	31
Dieujuste, Claubentz/Victory Collegiate High Sch	88
Difiglia, Erin/Charles Campagne Elem Sch	117
Digaudio, Lisa, Dr/New Dawn Charter High Sch II	6
Digneo, Miriam, Dr/Family School 32	263
Digrandi, Vincent/North Salem Middle High Sch	259
Digudio, Lisa/New Dawn Charter High Sch	6
Dilbert, Sharon/Clara Barton School 2	110
Dildy, Leslie/School 22	264
Dilornezo, Jennifer/Notre Dame Catholic Academy	186
DiMaria, Jim/W A Olmsted Elem Sch	28
DiMaria, Joann/Museum School 25	263
DiMauro, Elisa/Democracy Prep Charter HS [235]	3
DiMeo, Kerry/San Miguel Academy of Newburgh	168
Dimilta, Anna/PS 184 Flushing Manor	179
Dimitri, Suzanne/PS 4 Maurice Wollin	193
Dimitroff, Joleen/Glendale Elem Sch	63
Dimorier, Mark/McGraw Jr Sr High Sch	48
Dimuccio, Gianluca/Jessie J Kaplan Spec Sch	195
Dimuzio, Claudine/Pines Elem Sch	223
Dinaso, Donna/PS 60 Alice Austen	194
DiNatale, Dawn/PS 99 Stanley Makowski ECC	58
Dingwall, Gloria/Dryden St Sch	132
Diodate, John/Wilson Elem Sch	149
Diodato, Sherylanne, Dr/Our Lady of Mercy Sch	114
Diopoulos, Georgianna/Warwick Valley Middle Sch	167
DiRienzo, Joan, Sr/St Bernadette Sch	95
Dirolf, Amy/West Elem Sch	124
DiSalvo, Amy/Madill Elem Sch	212
Discenza, Michelle/Fort Ann Elem Sch	247
DiSpirito, Denise/Kernan Elem Sch	152
DiStefano, Laura/Orchard View Alternative Sch	54
DiStefano, Steven/Union-Endicott High Sch	29
Ditolla, Karen/IS 239 Mark Twain Gifted Sch	91
Ditrano, Christine, Dr/Hilltop Sch	4
DiTullio, Dr/Charles Carroll School 46	110
Dixon, Daniel/Dansville Primary Sch	102
Dixon, Patricia/PS 93 Southside Elem Sch	58
Dixon, Qadir/PS 288 Shirley Tanyhill	91
Dobmeier, Peter/Casey Middle Sch	64
Doddo, Matteo/Newburgh Free Acad-N Campus	166
Dodge, Brent/New York Mills Sch	151
Doe, David/Morristown Central Sch	211
Doemel, David/Bethlehem Central High Sch	10
Doeschner, Alexa/Landing Elem Sch	120
Doggett, Jamal/Rebecca Turner Elem Sch	258
Doherty, Daniel/Orville A Todd Middle Sch	54
Doherty, Ellen/White Plains High Sch	263
Doherty, Maryalice/Holy Family Sch	132
Dohn, Hadar/Hebrew Language Academy CS [240]	92
Dollard, Patrick/Center for Discovery	237
Dollard, William/Shaker Road Elem Sch	12
Domanico, Linda/Daniel Street Elem Sch	224
Dombal, Paul/Minisink Valley Interm Sch	165
Domin, Elizabeth, Sr/Sacred Heart Villa Sch	149
Dominguezmill, Yocasta/PS 203 Floyd Bennett Sch	92
Dominick, Richard/Vassar Road Elem Sch	54
Dominy, Doug/H C Williams High Sch	209
Donahue, Jean/Bronx High School of Science	20
Donald, Yvette/PS 149 Danny Kaye	89
Donaldson, Nicole/General Brown Jr Sr High Sch	80
Donath, Melissa/PS 22 Graniteville	193
Donato, Michelle/Salve Regina Catholic Academy	95
Donlon, Sara/Genesee Valley Ctrl Sch	15
Donner, David/Windham Ashland Jewett Ctl Sch	76
Donofrio, Margaret/PS 71 Rose E Scala	18
Donoghue, Mary, Sr/St Augustine Sch	265
Donohue, John/Ticonderoga Jr Sr High Sch	68
Donovan, Heather/Riverside Elem Sch	40
Donovan, Larry/Poly Prep Country Day Sch-Lowr	98
Donovan, Larry/Speyer Sch	145
Donow, Bart, Dr/Karafin Sch	266
Doody, Brett/Michael A Maroun Elem Sch	172
Dooley, Leeann/Little Falls High Sch	78
Dora, Raymond/St Bernard's Grade Sch	71
Dorr, Maria/Amagansett Sch	216
Dorritie, William/Laurens Central Sch	173
Dotel, Suleika/IS 318 Sch Math Sci & Tech	24

PRINCIPAL INDEX

NAME/School	PAGE
Doty, Linda/Charles E Riley Elem Sch	171
Dougherty, Jesse, Dr/Green Vale Sch	133
Dougherty, Kevin/Elmont Memorial Jr Sr High Sch	129
Douglas, Ivanhoe/South Brooklyn Academy	99
Douglas, Shanna/Lower Manhattan Cmty Mid Sch	136
Doxey-Davila, Kim/Gersh Academy-West Hills	235
Doyle, Elizabeth/John M Marshall Elem Sch	220
Doyle, Erica/Vanguard High Sch	138
Doyle, Jennifer/Rochester Academy Charter Sch	6
Doyle, Mari/Waverly Sch	254
Doyle, Miles/Orchard Collegiate Academy	135
Doyle, Patricia/Jessie T Zoller Elem Sch	205
Doyle, Susan/PS 335 Middle Early College HS	58
Drake, Julia/Springhurst Elem Sch	254
Drammeh, Shireena/Islamic Leadership Sch	26
Drautz, Jennifer/Voorheesville Middle Sch	12
Drebin, Bluma/Halb Stella K Abraham Girls HS	133
Drinkwater, Nicole/Brookhaven Learning Center	215
Driscoll, Susanne/Maple Hill Elem Sch	165
Droegmoeller, Jacelyn/Hope Hall Sch	114
Drollenger, Mark/Fredonia Elem Sch	38
Drummond, Tanya/PS 211	24
Druss, Christine/Viola Elem Sch	198
Drysdale, Bernadette/MS 293 City Clg Acad of Arts	141
Drzewucki, Jessica/PS 128 Bensonhurst	91
Dubak, Laura/Croton-Harmon High Sch	254
Dubei, Jaime/Queens Collegiate-College Brd	182
DuBois, Sonja/Bemus Point Elem Sch	36
Duca, Gianleo/Ballston Spa High Sch	200
Ducey, Colleen/PS 326	92
DuCharme, James/Schuylerville High Sch	201
Duclon, Shanda/Griffith Institute Middle Sch	63
Duddy, Sarah/Elmwood Franklin Sch	66
Dudek, Marilyn, Sr/SS Peter & Paul Sch	65
Duell, Doug/Warrensburg Jr Sr High Sch	246
Duffy, Christopher/PS Q177	185
Duffy, James/Wilson Elem Sch	128
Duffy, Joseph/Fostertown ETC Magnet Sch	166
Dugan, Alane/Sylvan Ave Elem Sch	217
Dugan, Joseph/Cristo Rey Brooklyn High Sch	97
Duggins, Elix/Pharos Acad Charter Sch	24
Duitel, Pinchas/Cong Yeshuos Moshe Williamsbrg	97
Dumornay, Gary/Knowledge & Power Prep Acad VI	180
Dunbar, Denise/Sidway Elem Sch	61
Duncan, Monica/PS 159 Isaac Pitkin	89
Duncan, Worokya, Dr/Cathedral Sch-St John Divine	144
Dunckel, Thomas/Ohio Elem Sch	82
Dundon, Colleen/Rodeph Sholom Elem Sch	145
Dundon, Colleen/Rodeph Sholom Sch	145
Dundon, William/Homer Brink Elem Sch	29
Dunham, Stephen/West Genesee Middle Sch	159
Dunlap, Derrick/Community Partnership Lwr Sch [233]	3
Dunn, David/Martha Brown Middle Sch	108
Dunn, Katelyn/Merrick Ave Middle Sch	117
Dunn, Meghan/Riverdale Ave Cmty Sch	93
Dunn, Stephen/Hannibal Senior High Sch	171
Dunne, Ella/PS 198 Int'l Prep Sch-Clevelnd	58
Dunne, Kerry/McVey Elem Sch	118
Dupee, Janelle/Knickerbocker Elem Sch	81
Duppert, Judy/South Lewis Middle Sch	102
DuPree, Lisa/St Joseph's Elem Sch	70
DuPree, Sandra/Hyde Leadership CS Brooklyn	88
DuPuis, Shelley/Hartford Central Sch	248
Duran, Ramona/PS 157 Grove Hill	17
Durant, Sheila/PS 69 Journey Prep	18
Durante, Giovanni, Dr/Syosset High Sch	130
Durkee, John/Marcellus Senior High Sch	157
Durkee, Tracy/Morrisville-Eaton Middle HS	105
Durkin, Caryn/Notre Dame Sch	132
Durkin, Edward/Nativity Miguel MS of Buffalo	65
Durkot, Thomas/Cincinnatus Elem Sch	47
Durst, Carmen/Word of Life Christian Academy	160
Dusinberre, Brett/Alfred Almond Sch	13
Dusinberre, Brett/Bolivar-Richburg Elem Sch	14
Dutta, Priam/Achievement First Voyager MS [128]	1
Dutton, Erin/Mt Tom Day Sch	266
Duttweiler, Joseph/Immaculate Conception Sch	65
Duval, James/Riverdale Country Sch	27
Duver, Tina/Allendale Columbia Sch	114
Dvorakovskaya, Kristina/Urban Assembly Gateway Tech	138
Dwarka, Namita/William C Bryant High Sch	185
Dweck, Natalie/Cecil Parker Elem Sch	258
Dwyer, Kathryn/St Regis Falls Central Sch	70
Dye, Sharifa/Clara Muhammad School Queens	187
Dzierba, Carrie/Gowanda Elem Sch	32
Dzwonek, Michele/PS 239	178

E

NAME/School	PAGE
Eacobacci, George/St Anthony Sch	265
Eadie, Martha/Our Lady of Black Rock Sch	65
Eagan, Thomas/Glendaal Elem Sch	205
Earl, Kristina/Horseheads High Sch	41
Eason, Carol/Prospect Sch	121
Eastman, Paula/John T Waugh Elem Sch	60
Ebel, Jodie/Neil Hellman Sch	13
Eberle, Kevin/PS 197 Math Sci Tech Prep Sch	58
Eck, Gregory, Dr/Upper Room Christian Sch	235
Eckert, Edward/Rochester Prep High Sch [246]	7
Eckert, Erin/Brookside Elem Sch	29
Edelman, Lance/Onteora Middle Senior High Sch	243
Edmister, Brian/Genesee Valley Ctrl Sch	15
Edmiston, Lisa/Our World Neighborhood MS CS 1	6
Edmonds, Debbie/PS Q233	185
Edmonds, Robin/Amistad Dual Language Sch	141
Edmonds, Tara/PS X15 Inst for Enviro Lrng	22
Edwards, Ahmed/JHS 292 Margaret S Douglas	88
Edwards, Ann, Dr/Rye Middle Sch	261
Edwards, Deon/PS 244 Richard R Green Sch	88
Edwards, Jervey/Career Preparatory High Sch	116
Egolf, David/Corlears Sch	144
Egresits, John/Parkway Middle Sch	153
Egresits, John/Whitesboro Middle Sch	153
Ehrenreich, Oscar/Beth Jacob of Boro Park Sch	96
Ehret, Michael/Eastern Monroe Career Center	106
Ehrle, David/South Buffalo Charter Sch	7
Eidelem, Schlomo/Yeshiva of Staten Island	195
Eidlitz, Sarah/Yeshiva Eitz Chaim-Skill Ctr	199
Eigenbrod, Sheila, Dr/Pavilion Ctl Jr Sr High Sch	74
Eisdorfer, Rae/Manhattan Star Academy	145
Eisenberg, Gitty/Bais Yaakov High Sch	198
Eisenberg, Steve/Manhattan Day Sch	145
Eisner, Cynthia/School 16	264
El, Senkita/Community Academic Prep Sch	133
Elcheikhali, Ghassan/Razi Sch	188
Elder, Josh/Eastchester Middle Sch	254
Eldridge, Thomas/Jamesville-DeWitt Middle Sch	155
Eliach, Yotav/Rambam Mesivta	134
Elizabeth, Clain/Mamaroneck High Sch	258
Elkady, Zenab, Sr/AL Madinah Sch	95
Elkins, Danielle/Block Institute	96
Elliott, Jennifer/St Catherines Ctr for Children	13
Ellis, Carin Ilene/PS 212	185
Ellis, Kevin/Hamilton Central Sch	105
Ellis, Michelle/Edinburg Common Sch	201
Ellison, Katheryn/Bradford Central Sch	207
Ellison, Larry, Dr/John James Audubon School 33	111
Ellman, Schwanna/PS 375 Jackie Robinson	87
Elsbach, Tasha/Masters Sch	266
Elster, Elana, Dr/JHS 54 Booker T Washington	138
Elsworth, Mary Kate/Schuylerville Middle Sch	201
Emerling, Wendy/Gateway-Longview-Lynde Sch	66
Emerson, Melissa/Washington Middle Sch	38
Emhof, Jolene/Sherburne Earlville Middle Sch	43
Emmerich, Debra/Seaford Manor Elem Sch	129
Encarnacion, Franklin/Performing Arts & Tech HS	89
Encarnacion, Franklin/Thomas Jefferson Campus YABC	89

New York School Directory — PRINCIPAL INDEX

NAME/School	PAGE
End, Martha/Klem Road South Elem Sch	113
Engelhardt, Joseph/Alexander Hamilton High Sch	255
English, Sarah/KIPP Freedom Elem Sch [242]	5
English, Terry/Falconer Middle Sr High Sch	37
Enos, David/Riley Avenue Elem Sch	228
Enright, Kristin/Paul V Moore High Sch	170
Epstein, Rita/Windsor Academy	168
Epstein, Robert/Canaan Elem Sch	227
Erat, Kristin/Grant Avenue Elem Sch	19
Ercolano, Dina/PS 158 the Bayard Taylor Sch	137
Erickson, Daniel/Johnson City Middle Sch	29
Erickson, Daniel/Johnson City Primary Sch	29
Erickson, Kevin/Cuba-Rushford Elem Sch	14
Erlenwein, Mark/Staten Island Technical HS	194
Ernstberger, Kimberly/Richard Mann Elem Sch	249
Errickson, Paul/Nichols Sch	66
Errico, Debra/PS 32 State Street	178
Ersoy, Mustafa/Utica Academy of Science CS	8
Erstejn-Kotzer, Faye/IS 204 Oliver Wendell Holmes	184
Esannason, Victor/PS 181 Brooklyn	87
Eschbach, Susan/Beverly J Martin Elem Sch	240
Escorbores, Bergre/South Middle Sch	218
Espada, Ciani/Brooklyn Gardens Elem Sch	88
Esposito, Doreen/PS 290 Manhattan New Sch	137
Esposito, Jason/Alfred G Berner Middle Sch	125
Esposito, Lisa/PS 8 Shirlee Solomon	193
Esposito, Mary/West Haverstraw Elem Sch	197
Esposito, Michelle/Andries Hudde Sch	92
Esposito, Todd/Akron Elem Sch	56
Esses, Sharon/Barkai Yeshiva	96
Esslinger, Ross/Iroquois Middle Sch	62
Estabrooks, Paul/Caledonia-Mumford Middle Sch	102
Estevez, Elvis/All City Leadership Sec Sch	93
Estwick, Sonhandso/Tompkins Square Middle Sch	135
Etra, Barbara/Rabbi Schneier Park E Day Sch	145
Etts, Theresa/Norwood Avenue Elem Sch	218
Eujin, Tang/PS 169 Sunset Park	85
Eustace, Christopher/PS 105 Sen Abraham Bernstein	23
Evan, Iris/School for Young Performers	145
Evangelista, Lara/Flushing International HS	178
Evangelista, Steven/Harlem Link Charter Sch	4
Evanoff, Loryn/Professional Children's Sch	145
Evans-Gill, Judy/Epiphany Lutheran Sch	97
Evans, Deborah/PS R037 Marquis Sch of Arts	194
Evans, John/Friends Seminary	144
Evans, Lashara/Flower City School 54	111
Evans, Pauline/Hanson Place SDA Sch	97
Evans, Richard, Dr/Francis L Stevens Elem Sch	200
Evans, Sharon/Cyberarts Studio Academy	84
Eweka, Vivian/PS 96	181
Ewing, Alex/L Pearl Palmer Elem Sch	154
Exford, Scott/Lowville Acad Central Sch	101
Ey, Nicole/Ellenville Elem Sch	242

F

NAME/School	PAGE
Faas, Dan/St Charles Borromeo Sch	143
Fabbie, Christina/Grove Street Academy	244
Fabian, Catherine/Success Acad CS Bergen Bch [245]	7
Faccio, Richard, Dr/New Hyde Park Mem Jr Sr HS	129
Facteau, Adam/Champlain Valley Ed Svcs	43
Fagan, Jeanne, Dr/PS/IS 119 the Glendale	178
Fagin, Rebecca/PS 29 John M Harrigan	85
Fahey, Brennen/Owen D Young Central Sch	78
Fairchild, Chad/Watertown High Sch	82
Fairclough, Kelly/Barack Obama Elem Sch	121
Fairey, Chad/United Nations Int'l Sch	146
Falabella, Catherine/St Christopher Parochial Sch	195
Falasco, Tara/Blue Point Elem Sch	217
Falino, John/Dobbs Ferry High Sch	254
Fall, Jennifer/Rye School of Leadership	261
Fallon, Meghann/Ocean Hill Collegiate Chtr Sch [246]	6
Fallon, Seank/Lynbrook North Middle Sch	124
Falls, Stephanie/Homer Intermediate Sch	48
Fama, Michael/John F Kennedy Middle Sch	218
Fanelli, Dominic/St Mark the Evangelist Sch	143
Fanelli, Josephine/St Theresa Sch	26
Fanning, David/A Philip Randolph Campus HS	141
Fanning, John/School of the Future	138
Fantauzzi, Vincent/William E DeLuca Jr Elem Sch	226
Fanuele, Paul/Arlington High Sch	51
Faraone, Joan, Sr/Thevenet Montessori Sch	168
Fareed, Maj/Thurgood Marshall Academy	140
Fargione, Nick/Sacred Heart of Jesus Sch	143
Fargione, Nick/School of Blessed Sacrament	143
Fargnoli, Nicholas/Bloomfield Elem Sch	161
Farhi, Rafael/Mill Basin Yeshiva Academy	98
Farid, Hesham/MS 301 Paul L Dunbar	17
Farina, Antonio/Oneida Middle Sch	205
Farina, Lisa/Vollmer Elem Sch	112
Farkosh, Michael/Girls Prep Bronx Middle Sch [244]	4
Farley, Tim/Ichabod Crane Middle Sch	46
Farooqi, Nahid/Muslim Center Elem Mid Sch	188
Farrar, Gina/Blue Sch	144
Farrell, John/Hagan Elem Sch	54
Farrell, Lisa/Helen B Duffield Elem Sch	219
Farrell, Tammy/Groton Jr Sr High Sch	240
Farrell, Timothy/Minerva Central Sch	68
Farrington, Allison/Research & Service High Sch	86
Farrow, Debra/PS 116 William Hughley	183
Farwell, Rebecca/Dunkirk Middle Sch	37
Fasciana, Keith/William Floyd Elem Sch	233
Fasciana, Maryann/Signal Hill Elem Sch	222
Fasciglione, Shireen, Dr/Hillside Elem Sch	204
Faust, Gina/Cantiague Elem Sch	122
Faustin, Berthe/PS 189 the Bilingual Center	87
Faustino, Michael/Roberts Street Elem Sch	104
Fazio, Amy/Fishkill Plains Elem Sch	54
Fazio, Susan/John Lewis Childs Elem Sch	119
Febbraro, Michael/Northside Elem Sch	119
Febus, Lisette/Sheridan Academy Young Leaders	20
Fedele, Jennifer/Cardinal McCloskey Cmty CS	3
Fedele, Jennifer/Cardinal McCloskey Sch	265
Federico, Tonya/Sacandaga Elem Sch	205
Federman, Mark/East Side Cmty Sch	135
Fedorczak, Greg/Hillside Alternative Sch	252
Feeney, Sean, Dr/Wheatley Sch	118
Feigin, Daniel/Trevor Day School-West	146
Feinberg, Melissa/Fox Meadow Elem Sch	262
Feiss, Michelle/Allendale Columbia Sch	114
Felberbaum, Abraham/Yeshiva Darkei Emunah	199
Feldberg, Gabriel/Central Park East I	139
Felder, Susan/PS 40 Augustus St Gaudens	137
Feldman, Felenda/Bais Yaakov Adas Yereim	96
Feldman, Harvey/Yde High Sch	99
Feliciano, Minerva/East Kindergarten Center	217
Felix, Anita/Murray Hill Academy	136
Felma, Temima/Torah Academy for Girls	188
Fenton, Terry/Seneca Bible Bapt Chrn Academy	209
Ferguson, Gemma/Wave Prep Elem Sch	181
Ferguson, Joeletha/PS 262 El Hajj Malik El Shabaz	86
Ferguson, Karen/Elm Drive Elem Sch	52
Ferguson, Mary, Dr/Frank Fowler Dow School 52	111
Fernandez, Emily/Brownsville Ascend Middle CS	2
Fernandez, Jacqueline/East Ramapo Early Chldhd Ctr	196
Fernandez, Lisa/PS 119 Amersfort	92
Fernandez, Mario/New Paltz High Sch	243
Fernandez, Raymie/Success Acad CS Harlem 2 [245]	7
Ferozi, Somai/Ideal Islamic Sch	187
Ferrante, Pia/South Salem Elem Sch	128
Ferrara, Joseph/PS 41 Crocheron	179
Ferrara, Mike/Beginning with Children CS 2 [233]	1
Ferrari, Jeannie/Humanities Preparatory Academy	136
Ferraro, Loretta/Woodhull Elem Sch	222
Ferreira, Brian/Explore Empower Chtr Sch 742 [237]	3
Ferreira, Marybelle/PS 54	21
Ferretti, Craig/Camden Elem Sch	150
Ferri-Cordaro, Angela/Northwood Elem Sch	64
Ferris, Jesse/Phoenix Academy	40

School Year 2020-2021

PRINCIPAL INDEX

NAME/School	PAGE
Ferris, Michael/Autumn Lane Elem Sch	108
Ferron, Benvenuto/Pelham Preparatory Academy	23
Ferrusi, Dominick/Maplebrook Sch	55
Fersch, Nicholas/Chittenango High Sch	104
Fetter, Robin/Norwood-Norfolk Sr High Sch	211
Feuer, Karen/PS 110 Florence Nightingale	135
Feuerstein, Eve/Seely Place Elem Sch	254
Fey, Chris/Ausable Valley Middle High Sch	43
Ficalora, John/Newtown High Sch	177
Ficano, Marie, Dr/Alternatives for Children	234
Ficchi, Bernadette/St Ann Sch	195
Fiedler-Horack, Amy/Sackets Harbor Central Sch	81
Field, Ashlyn/Mott Haven Academy Charter Sch	16
Fields, Carolyn/Fleetwood Elem Sch	196
Fields, Gregory/Steinmetz Career Leadrshp Acad	205
Fierro, Mary Beth/Oswego Middle Sch	171
Figueroa, Priscilla/Red Hook Neighborhood Sch	85
Filbry, Valerie/Alleghany Avenue Elem Sch	224
Filiatrault, Timothy/Sandy Creek Sch	172
Filippi, Gregory/PS 91 Richard Arkwright	177
Finder, Bridget/Glenwood Landing Elem Sch	126
Fine, Adam/East Hampton High Sch	220
Fine, David, Dr/Dr Kenneth B Clark Academy	255
Finerty, M/Archer Elem Sch	24
Fingar, Karen/Dudley Elem Sch	108
Fingland, Brett/Weedsport Jr Sr High Sch	35
Fink, Isaac/Yeshiva Torah Vodaath	100
Fink, John/Carmel High Sch	175
Finley, Patrick/Metropolitan Exped Lrng Sch	182
Finn, Brian/Lowville Acad Central Sch	101
Finn, Christine/Shelter Island Sch	230
Finn, Patricia/PS/MS 42 R Vernam	181
Finnegan, Cary/Brooklyn Rise Charter Sch	2
Finney, Carl/Int'l HS-Health Sciences	177
Fiore, Christopher/H Frank Carey Jr Sr High Sch	129
Fiorentino, Annette/Bronx Latin Sch	24
Firsina, Dominic/Syracuse Acad Sci & Citiznshp	8
Fisgus, John/Royalton Hartland Middle Sch	148
Fisher, Denise/Newbridge Road Elem Sch	126
Fisher, James/North Tonawanda High Sch	148
Fisher, Penny, Dr/J Fred Sparke Elem Sch	122
Fisher, Tony, Dr/Hunter College High Sch	4
Fisher, Yocheved/Bais Malka Sch	198
Fishkin, Amy/Pound Ridge Elem Sch	252
Fishman, Miriam/Lev Bais Yaakov Sch	98
Fishman, Sharon/PS 55 Henry M Boehm	194
Fishman, Yakov/Yeshiva Boyan	99
Fisk, Jennifer/Franklinville Jr Sr High Sch	32
Fitzgerald, Coleen/Minisink Valley Elem Sch	165
Fitzgerald, Debra/J Watson Bailey Middle Sch	242
Fitzgerald, Lynn/St Mary's Sch	203
Fitzgerald, Martin/Robert E Bell Middle Sch	253
Fitzgerald, Trisha/Hutchinson Elem Sch	260
Fitzgerald, William/JHS 202 Robert H Goddard	180
Fitzpatrick, John/Veronica E Connor Middle Sch	61
Flagg, Michael/Ridge Mills Elem Sch	152
Flagler, Kelly/Athena High Sch	108
Flagsvol, Heather/Good Shepherd Christian Sch	244
Flamenbaum, Evan, Dr/Academics West	143
Flanagan, Ellen/South Bronx Preparatory Sch	17
Flanagan, Jacqueline/PS 19 Asher Levy	135
Flanagan, John/Chester Academy	163
Flanagan, Julie/Windermere Blvd Elem Sch	56
Flanagan, Kevin/Bay Ridge Catholic Academy	95
Flanagan, Tracy/St Bernard Sch	95
Flanders, Robert/Yates Magnet Sch	205
Flank, Rebecca/Broome Tioga BOCES	27
Flax, Mitch/Valence College Prep CS	8
Fleishman, Nancy/Hebrew Institute-Deaf Excptnl	97
Fleming, Douglas/Thornton-Donovan Sch	266
Fleming, Marc/Olympia High Sch	109
Fleming, Sherma/Aspirations Diploma Plus HS	93
Flickner, Betsy/Genesee Country Christian Sch	104
Flood, Michelle/Rogers Middle Sch	113
Flores, Gaby/PS 315 Lab Sch	22
Flores, Lourdes/Bronx Prep Charter Sch [235]	2
Flores, Shirley/Eugenio Maria De Hostos K-8 CS	3
Florio, Cynthia/Susan E Wiley Elem Sch	220
Florio, Deborah/PS 203 Oakland Gardens	180
Florio, Jill/Skano Elem Sch	202
Flowers, Jody/Future Leaders Institute CS	138
Flowers, Matthew/Charles G May Career & Tech Ed	102
Floyd, Philip/Calvary Baptist Church	74
Flynn, Corey/St Regis Falls Central Sch	70
Flynn, Kelley/Riverdale Country Sch	27
Flynn, Maureen, Sr/Santa Maria Sch	26
Flynn, Tami/JHS 234 Arthur W Cunningham	92
Fogel, Kenneth/Hanc Plainview Elem Sch	133
Foglia, Andrew/Bold Charter Sch	1
Foglio, Paulette/PS 99 Kew Gardens	182
Foley, Brandon/Spencer Van Etten Middle Sch	239
Folkson, Susan/Cherry Lane Elem Sch	117
Fong, Renny/PS 130 Hernando De Soto	137
Fontana, Lauren/PS 6 Lillie D Blake	137
Fonte, Gina Marie/Resurrection Sch	265
Foote, Edward/Penn Yan Elem Sch	268
Forbes, Camille/PS 206 Jose Celso Barbosa	140
Forbes, Mary/Seton Catholic Sch	45
Ford, Eric/Hawthorne Sr Jr High Sch	256
Ford, Jason/Trinity Sch	146
Ford, Kerry/Increase Miller Elem Sch	257
Ford, Kristina/Brighter Choice CS for Girls [234]	1
Ford, Tracy/PS 16	191
Foreman, Jason/PS 154 Windsor Terrace Sch	85
Forgette, Adrienne/Nardin Academy High Sch	66
Forman, Debra/New City Elem Sch	196
Forman, Mark/Democracy Prep Harlem High Sch [235]	3
Forman, Richard, Dr/Clara Barton High Sch	86
Formato, Joelle/Persistence Prep Acad CS	6
Formica, Donna/Institute of Tech-Central	158
Forth, Craig/Mechanicville Elem Sch	201
Fortiche, Giselle/Angelo Patri Middle Sch	20
Fortran, Brett/Berkshire Jr Sr High Sch	45
Fortunate, Jeannine/Catholic Acad of Niagara Falls	149
Foster, Brian/Charles E Walters Elem Sch	225
Foster, Dean/Hoosac Sch	192
Foster, Megan/Hermon-DeKalb Ctl Sch	210
Foster, Norman/Pembroke Intermediate Sch	74
Foster, Shani/Central Brooklyn Ascend Lwr CS	3
Foti, Mark/Hoosic Valley Elem Sch	190
Fotis, Nicole/Harbor Country Day Sch	235
Fountaine, James/St John the Evangelist Sch	30
Fox, Brian/Suffern Middle Sch	198
Fox, Joan/St Eugene Sch	265
Fox, Lynnann/PS 386-Envir Citizenship Sch	22
Foy, Hope/Carthage Elem Sch	80
Foy, James/Sunrise Drive Elem Sch	230
Foy, Kathryn/PS 76 Herman Badillo Bil Acad	57
Frackelton, William/Soundview Acad-Cult & Schlrshp	18
Fraher, Thomas/Theodore R Durgee Jr High Sch	154
Fram, Michael/Repertory HS for Theatre Arts	137
Francia, Michael/Keeseville Elem Sch	43
Francis, Dorrett/Jamaica SDA Elem Sch	188
Francis, Kendra/Schuyler Achievement Academy	9
Francis, Sophia/Cortelyou Academy	97
Francis, Temica/New Hope Academy Charter Sch	6
Francis, Toshalyn/Queens United Middle Sch 289	184
Francischelli, Rob/Howard A Hanlon Elem Sch	207
Francisco, Katie/Saranac Middle Sch	45
Francisco, Ken/Owego Elem Sch	238
Frandino, William/Emma C Chase Elem Sch	237
Frangella, Nicholas/MS 890	92
Frank, Andrew/JHS 223 the Montauk	90
Frank, B/Accompsett Elem Sch	230
Frank, Christina/John F Kennedy Elem Sch	211
Frank, Kathy/Holy Child Academy	133

New York School Directory

PRINCIPAL INDEX

NAME/School	PAGE
Frank, Peter/Maryvale Middle Sch	59
Frankel, Gideon/Frank Sinatra HS of the Arts	184
Frankel, Yehudi/Yeshiva of Spring Valley	199
Franklin, Deborah/Notre Dame High Sch	41
Franklin, Julie/Sanford St Teaching & Lrng Ctr	244
Franklin, Sonja/Lake Placid Elem Sch	67
Fraser, Nicole/IS 364 Gateway	88
Frasier, Slivana/Building Blocks Montessori Sch	195
Frawley, Kristen/West Elem Sch	64
Frazier, Leslie/PS 21 Crispus Attucks	86
Frazier, Tiffany/PS 361 E Flatbush EC Sch	92
Frazier, Timothy/Southampton Intermediate Sch	231
Frazier, Tom/Dansville High Sch	102
Frederes, Tiffany/Frewsburg Jr Sr High Sch	38
Freebes, Linda/SS Joachim & Anne Sch	186
Freedman, Henry/Scotchtown Avenue Elem Sch	164
Freeman, Angela/Milestone Sch	266
Freeman, Kristen/Calcium Primary Sch	80
Freer, Joel/Highland Elem Sch	242
Frega, John/St Elizabeth Sch	143
Freitag, Lisa/Cape Vincent Elem Sch	81
Freitag, Lisa/Guardino Elem Sch	81
French, Deborah/Briarcliff High Sch	253
Fresca, Nicole/St Teresa St Rita Stream Acad	195
Fretthold, Kathy/Trinity Lutheran Sch	66
Frias, John/Wheeler Avenue Elem Sch	130
Frias, Victor/Accion Academy	24
Fried, Jane/Brearley Sch	144
Fried, Scott/Louis M Klein Middle Sch	256
Fried, Sholom/PS M721 Occupational Training	142
Friedman, Fraidy/Tomer Dvora Girls Sch	99
Friedman, Judith/IS 237 Rachel Carson Magnet	178
Friend-Ituarte, Marilyn/Northeast Elem Sch	218
Frigenti, Karen/Summitt School Annex	188
Frishman, Simcha/Mesivta Shaarei Pruzdor	134
Fromberg, Laureen/PS 100 Glen Morris	181
Fromowitz, Sherri/Lawrence Woodmere Academy	133
Froner, Kevin/Manhattan/Hunter Science HS	138
Fruchter, Menachem/Hebrew Day School-Sullivan Co	237
Frudd, Andy/Bethel Baptist Christian Acad	40
Fry, Bryan/Latham Christian Academy	13
Fry, Robert/Lake Shore Christian Sch	45
Fuccillo, Denise/PS 214 Cadwallader Colden	179
Fucheck, Gregory/Bronx River High Sch	17
Fuchs, Rabbi/Yeshiva Ahavas Yisroel Sch	99
Fuentes, Graciela/PS 35 Franz Sigel Sch	19
Fulkerson, Jason/Athena Middle Sch	108
Fuller, C/Unity Prep CS Brooklyn HS	8
Fuller, Hassan/Rockaway Collegiate High Sch	181
Fullerton, Kevin/John F Kennedy Middle Sch	117
Fullerton, Maureen/PS 168X	25
Fullwood, Nicia/Brooklyn Emerging Leaders Acad	2
Fulmer, John/Williamson Middle Sch	251
Fulton, Khia/Daytop Village Sec Sch	234
Funck, Ryan/Hunter Tannersville Mid & HS	76
Funes, Jennifer/PS 10 Ft Hill Collaborative ES	193
Furan, Ashley/Hebrew Language Academy CS 2 [240]	4
Furlonge, Nigel/Fieldston Middle Upper Sch	26
Furrey, Steven/Central Blvd Elem Sch	117
Fusco, Marguerite/Warwick Valley High Sch	167
Fusco, Maryann/Holy Rosary Sch	25
Futscher, Maureen/Robert L Bradley Elem Sch	151
Futterman, Abbe/Earth Sch	135

G

NAME/School	PAGE
Gabbard, Larry/Mather Bldg Arts & Craftmnp HS	136
Gabella, Donna/Ascension Sch	142
Gaebelein, Thad/Christian Central Academy	66
Gaffney, Sean/Hornell Intermediate Sch	214
Gafni, Ruth/Ramaz Lower Sch	145
Gagliardi, George/Bretton Woods Elem Sch	223
Gagstetter, William/Kingsbridge Int'l High Sch	21
Gagstetter, William/Talent Unlimited High Sch	138
Gahfi, Hadar/PS 191 Paul Robeson Elem Sch	87
Gaines-Harrell, Rosalind/Arbor Hill Elem Sch	9
Gajewski, Julie/St Gregory the Great Sch	65
Galante, Kerri/Birch Sch	125
Galashaw, Desiree/Roosevelt Children's Acad CS	7
Galassi, John/Martin De Porres Sch	133
Galati, William/George W Hewlett High Sch	121
Galati, William/Southold Jr Sr High Sch	232
Galgovich, Paul/Wilson Middle High Sch	149
Galinski, Heather/Roscoe Conkling Magnet ES	152
Gallagher, Michael/Hamburg High Sch	61
Galland, Michael/Columbus Elem Sch	259
Gallardo, Janet/Bronxwood Preparatory Academy	22
Gallo, Charles, Dr/Aeci II-Sch for Computer Engr	1
Galotti, Peggy/Bedford Road Sch	260
Gamarra, Magaly/Metropolitan Montessori Sch	145
Gamble, Shamika/Dr Jacqueline Peek-Davis Sch	86
Ganesh, Neil/Richmond Hill High Sch	181
Gangi, Joanne/Sacred Heart Sch	186
Ganster, Nicholas/Marion Jr Sr High Sch	250
Garab, Daniel/Green Meadow Elem Sch	190
Garback, Kelly/Casey Park Elem Sch	34
Garber, Craig/Brooklyn Envir Exploration Sch	93
Garcia, Angela/Osborn Elem Sch	261
Garcia, Daysi/PS 65	89
Garcia, Fareeda/Urban Action Academy	88
Garcia, Johanny/Careers In Sports High Sch	16
Garcia, Kristin/Hero High Sch	16
Garcia, Leticia/Mary G Clarkson Sch	217
Garcia, Louis/Brooklyn Cmty HS Excel Equity	87
Garcia, Marta/PS 96 Richard Rodgers	23
Garcia, Nicole/Storefront Acad South Bronx CS	7
Garcia, Rachael/PS 173	141
Gardineer, James/Austin Road Elem Sch	176
Gardner, Marjorie/Dream Charter Sch	3
Gardon, Christopher/Nativity of Our Lord Sch	65
Garelick, Beth/Corona Arts & Sciences Acad	177
Garfield, Shalonda/Lincoln Park School 44	111
Garfinkel, Dov/Gerer Mesivta Bais Yisroel	97
Garguilo, Mary/Bayview Avenue Sch	119
Garofalo, Melissa/PS 35 Clove Valley	193
Garr, Penny/Harmony Christian Sch	168
Garraway, Elizabeth/Maurice Sendak Community Sch	84
Garrow, Lisa/John Walton Spencer School 16	111
Garry, Erin/Urban Assembly Bronx Letters	17
Garsin, Lori/East Irondequoit Middle Sch	107
Gartland, Pam/Holy Child Academy	133
Garwood, J/Northstar Christian Academy	114
Gary, Sophia/Ann M MacArthur Primary Sch	123
Gary, Sophia/Locust Valley Intermediate Sch	123
Garzon, Catherina/PS 116 Elizabeth L Farrell	94
Gashi, Mithat/New World High Sch	23
Gasparini, Paul/Jamesville-DeWitt High Sch	155
Gassetto, Vincent/Academy Applied Math & Tech	16
Gately, Donald/Jericho Middle Sch	123
Gates, Joseph/Frederick Douglass Academy	140
Gates, Joseph/Urban Assembly Future Leaders	140
Gates, Lena/PS 5 Dr Ronald E McNair	86
Gathers, Pamela/PS 154 Queens	178
Gatto, Vincent/PS 33 Edward M Funk	183
Gauthier, Stacey/Renaissance Charter Sch	185
Gawrys, Robin/Gowana Middle Sch	202
Gaynor, Scott, Dr/Stephen Gaynor Sch	145
Geager, Hector/Manhattan Village Academy	136
Geary, Janice/JHS 259 William McKinley	90
Geary, Rebecca/South Bronx Classical CS IV	7
Geballe, Benjamin/MS 131	136
Geddes, Andre/Harlem Prep Middle Sch [235]	4
Gee, Brian/Victor Junior High Sch	163
Geldman, Rabbi/Mesivta Ziev Hatorah	199
Geller, Donna/PS 70 Queens	184
Geller, Jessica/PS 166 Henry Gradstein	185
Gelman, Joseph/Masores Bais Yaakov	98
Genao, Luis/MS 224 Manh E Sch Arts & Acad	139
Gengler, Matt/North Middle Sch	217

PRINCIPAL INDEX

Market Data Retrieval

NAME/School	PAGE	NAME/School	PAGE
Geniti, John/Lincoln Elem Sch	205	Girnun, Leah/Yeshiva Toras Chaim-S Shore	134
Genovese, Daniel/Dunkirk Elem School 3	37	Girouard, Sally/Brooklyn Excelsior Charter Sch [210]	2
Genovese, Michael/Norwood Avenue Elem Sch	227	Giroux, Joyce/Trinity Catholic Sch	212
Gens, Alan/Dunkirk High Sch	37	Gitty-Kramer, J/Bais Yaakov Ramapo Sch	198
Gentile, Lisa/Holland Patent Middle Sch	150	Gitz, Christopher, Dr/Great Neck South High Sch	120
Gentile, Robert/HS Health Prof & Human Serv	136	Giudice, Bryan/Pine Tree Elem Sch	165
Gentles, Marissa/Jackson Heights SDA Elem Sch	188	Giusto, Josephine/Academy of Talented Scholars	89
George, Emmanuel/Democracy Prep Endurance HS [235]	3	Givens, Fred/New Heights Academy CS	141
Georger, Callie/Nardin Academy Elem Sch	66	Gizzi, John/Onondaga Nation Sch	156
Georgia, Heath/Owego Apalachin Middle Sch	238	Gladstone, Bill/PS 108 Assemblyman Angelo Toro	140
Georgia, Heath/Owego Free Academy	238	Glass, Nancy/UCP of Queens Children's Ctr	189
Georgilakis, George/PS 75 Emily Dickinson	139	Glattstein, Marcia/Icahn Charter School 3	4
Geraci, William/Bishop Kearney High Sch	114	Glatz, Eric/Pace High Sch	137
Gerchman, Teresa/Buffalo United Charter Sch [210]	2	Glauner, Deborah/John Jay School for Law	84
Gerendasi, Dana/Waterside Children's Studio	181	Glazer, Tracie/Hillel Community Day Sch	114
Gerhard, Kristi/Fairfield Elem Sch	125	Gleason, Megan/Pawling Central Middle Sch	52
Gerlach, Donald/Richard T Stank Middle Sch	29	Gleason, Sean/Cato Meridian Middle Sch	34
Gerling, Elizabeth/Columbus Elem Sch	152	Gleeson, Fiona/PS 86 Kingbridge Heights	21
Germain, Claudia/Powells Lane Sch	132	Gleeson, Moira/Montessori School 27	263
German, Robert/Cornwall Elem Sch	163	Glenn, Gail, Sr/Catholic Academy of W Buffalo	65
Germann, S/St Joseph the Worker Cath Acad	95	Glennon, Grace/All Saints Elem Sch	160
Germano, Charles/Tooker Ave Elem Sch	233	Glick, Jacob/Viznitzer Chadr Tifers Yisroel	99
Gersh, Kevin/West Hills Montessori Sch	235	Glicker-Mack, Jamie/Parkway Elem Sch	118
Gerson, Adam/Gayhead Elem Sch	54	Glowacki, Rob/Horizons on Hudson Mag Sch	166
Gerst, Gary/Minoa Elem Sch	155	Gluck, Isaac/Mevakshai Hashem Elem Sch	98
Geskie, Jennifer/Elizabth Seton Chldrn Sch-WP	265	Gnat, Sean/Koda Middle Sch	202
Getman, Jeffrey/Somers Middle Sch	262	Gochnauer, James/Followers of Jesus Sch	97
Getz, David/East Side Middle Sch	135	Gode, Michele/William Paca Middle Sch	234
Getz, Jacqueline/MS 297 Morton	136	Godfrey, John/Abraham Wing Elem Sch	245
Gewirtz, Morde Chai/Bais Yaakov Academy of Queens	187	Godson, Nancy/Chc Learning Center	66
Gewurz, Laura/Andrew Muller Primary Sch	226	Goel, Stephania, Dr/Robert Wagner Jr Sch Arts-Tech	178
Geyer, Patricia, Dr/Long Island School for Gifted	235	Gold, Joshua/Hebrew Acad 5 Towns Rockawy MS	133
Giacchetto, Michael/Wing Elem Sch	224	Gold, Shraga/Yeshiva Beth David	199
Giaccio, Rebecca/Notre Dame Elem Academy	194	Gold, Zbynek/Bedford Hills Elem Sch	252
Giagni, Todd/Orenda Elem Sch	202	Goldberg, Gidon/Yeshiva Ketana of Manhattan	146
Giagni, Todd/Raphael J McNulty Academy	116	Goldberg, Stephen/Village Sch	121
Giangreco, Elizabeth/Maryvale Primary Sch	59	Goldberg, Steven/Babylon Memorial Grade Sch	217
Giannantonio, Pamela/St Andrew's Country Day Sch	65	Goldberg, Susan/PS 370K	94
Gianni, Fatima/SS John & Paul Sch	265	Goldberg, Tara/Daniel Warren Elem Sch	261
Giannicchi, Tiffany/Delevan Elem Sch	33	Goldberger, Devorah/Bnos Zion of Bobov Sch	97
Giardino, Leny/United Cerebral Palsy Sch	154	Goldfarb, Maureen/New Utrecht High Sch	90
Gifford, Joby/Jefferson Elem Sch	204	Goldfein, Ingrid/Beit Rabban Sch	143
Gifford, Joshua/Thomas R Proctor High Sch	152	Goldman, Amy/PS 2 Alfred Zimberg	184
Giglio, Kisten/Norwich High Sch	42	Goldstein, Amy/Children's Readiness Center	116
Gil, Felix/Quaker Ridge Elem Sch	262	Goldstein, Chaim/Talmudical Inst of Upstate NY	114
Gilbert, Gary/Harvey C Fenner Elem Sch	37	Goldstein, Stacy/School of the Future	138
Gilbert, Scott/Seaford High Sch	129	Goldstein, Sydnie/Myers Corners Elem Sch	54
Gilbert, Shannon/Canaseraga Sch	14	Goltz, Susan/Islip Academic Center	216
Gilbert, Susan/Siwanoy Elem Sch	260	Golub, Stephanie/League Sch	98
Gilevski, Joshua/Sinclairville Elem Sch	36	Golubchick, Jeffrey/Greenwood Lake Middle Sch	164
Gilfus, Joseph/Thousand Islands High Sch	81	Gomez, Denise/PS 242 Young Diplomats Magnet	139
Gill, Michael, Dr/North Rockland High Sch	197	Gomez, Elisa/PS 110	177
Gillespie, Stacey, Dr/Otsego Elem Sch	222	Gomez, Eric/W C Mepham High Sch	117
Gilligan, Carol/PS MS 11X498 Van Nest Academy	23	Gonseth, Terry/Sherman Elem Sch	82
Gilligan, Edward/PS 111 Adolph S Ochs	137	Gonzales, Bruce/Olympus Academy	88
Gilsinan, Maura/Perry Elem Sch	267	Gonzalez, Angel/De La Salle Academy	144
Gilson, Jennifer/Charles A Upson Elem Sch	147	Gonzalez, Brenda/Jonas Bronck Academy	21
Gimondo, Ron/John F Kennedy Sch	121	Gonzalez, Danielle/Holy Family Sch	25
Ginestre, Christopher/Benjamin Franklin Middle Sch	62	Gonzalez, Deanna/Violet Avenue Elem Sch	52
Ginger, Jeffrey/Mannsville Manor Elem Sch	81	Gonzalez, Denise/St Bartholomew Sch	186
Ginger, Jeffrey/South Jefferson High Sch	81	Gonzalez, Janet/Jackson Avenue Elem Sch	125
Ginsberg, Aaron/Gan Yisroel Sch	97	Gonzalez, Jasmine/PS 65 Mother Hale Academy	16
Ginter, John/Lincoln Elem Sch	250	Gonzalez, Lara/Woodhull Intermediate Sch	223
Ginter, Susan/Brentwood Residential Center	1	Gonzalez, Llermi/Bushwick Community High Sch	93
Ginty, Brian/South Haven Early Chldhd Ctr	231	Gonzalez, Megan/Sacred Heart of Jesus Sch	143
Ginzberg, Rabbi/Mesivta Tifereth Jerusalem	145	Gonzalez, Megan/School of Blessed Sacrament	143
Gioia, Matthew/Hudson Valley Sudbury Sch	244	Gonzalez, Ramon/MS 223 Lab Sch of Fin & Tech	16
Giopulos, Dean/Wellsville Elem Sch	15	Gonzalez, Ronald/Mount Vernon High Sch	258
Giordano, Annamaria/Thomas C Giordano MS 45	22	Goodman, Bradley/East Village Cmty Sch	135
Giordano, Denese/Brooklyn Waldorf Sch	97	Goodman, Kevin/PS 66 Sch Higher Expectations	24
Giordano, Frank/New Voices Sch	85	Goodman, Sarah/Hunters Point Cmty Middle Sch	184
Giordano, Joanne/Oldfield Middle Sch	223	Goodson, Lisa/PS 325 Fresh Creek Sch	89
Girling, Kellie/The Kings Sch	203	Goodstein, Esther/Shalsheles Bais Yaakov Sch	99

New York School Directory

PRINCIPAL INDEX

NAME/School	PAGE
Gordon, Kameca/Walkabout Bronx High Sch	17
Gordon, Lakeisha/HS Construct Trades Eng & Arch	180
Gordon, Mavgar/Challenge Charter Middle Sch	180
Gorelick, Esther/Yeshiva Gedolah Zichron Moshe	237
Gorgen, Perry/South Hill Elem Sch	240
Goring, Jessica/Bronx School of Law & Finance	20
Gorman, Sue/Howe Elem Sch	204
Gorney, Ronald/Herman Avenue Elem Sch	34
Gorney, Vlad/Big Apple Academy	96
Gornish, Shainy/Yeshiva of Brooklyn-Girls	100
Gorsky, Ronald/New Ventures Charter Sch	6
Goss, Caroline/Cambridge Central Sch	247
Goss, Philomena/Lowville Acad Central Sch	101
Gossaway, Bernard/Boys & Girls High School YABC	85
Gottesman, Henna/Rabbi Samson R Hirsch Yeshiva	145
Gottfried, Laura/E A Clune Mont School-Ithaca	241
Goudelias, Rena/PS 185 Walter Kassenbrock	90
Gould, Denise/PS 3 Raul Julia Micro Society	21
Gould, Judy/Whitehall Elem Sch	248
Gourades, Dianne/District 20 Pre-K Center	89
Gouveia, Vicki/Anna Murray-Douglass School 12	110
Goyer, Amanda/Sacred Heart Sch	192
Graceffa, Laura/Robert C Parker Sch	192
Grady, Aaron/Fonda Fultonville Central Sch	115
Grady, Katie/PS 104 the Bays Water	181
Graft, John/Long Island Baptist Academy	235
Graham, Diamond/KIPP Elements Primary Sch	5
Graham, Eric/Archangel Sch	114
Graham, Mariela/HS of Arts & Technology	138
Gralla, Netanel/Jewish Fndtn Sch-Staten Island	195
Grandchamps, Chantal/Frederick Douglass Acad VIII	88
Grande, Dan/Forestville Middle High Sch	37
Grande, Eric/PS 56 Lewis H Latimer	83
Grande, Nick/Island Trees High Sch	122
Granholm, Jennifer/New Haven Elem Sch	171
Grant, Gladly/Hebron SDA Bilingual Sch	97
Grant, Linton/Parkway Sch	98
Grant, Maurice/Whispering Pines SDA Sch	134
Grantstewart, Lissa/PS/IS 268	184
Grassi, Paula/Johnson City High Sch	28
Grasso, Johnna/South Country Sch	217
Graves, Carla/PS 50 North Park Cmty Sch	57
Graviano, Scott/Newfield High Sch	225
Gray, Brian/School 13	264
Gray, Corey/Starpoint Middle Sch	149
Gray, Cynthia/Mountain Road Sch	47
Gray, Jennifer/Lawrence Ave Elem Sch	212
Gray, Mark/Plaza Elem Sch	117
Gray, Maureen/Memorial Park Elem Sch	153
Gray, Suzanne/Old Bethpage Elem Sch	128
Gray, Tuwanna/Wings Academy	25
Graybow, Terri/PS 31 Bayside	179
Graziose, Leeann/St Elizabeth A Seton-Bellmore	132
Green, Angela/Indian River Middle Sch	80
Green, Jeffrey, Dr/Hilton High Sch	109
Green, Karen/St Joseph Sch-Batavia	74
Green, Nicholas/Incarnation Sch	143
Green, Rachel/Valley Stream North JSHS	130
Greenaway, Flora/Bronx Cmty High Sch	17
Greenbaum, Shulem/Bnos Square of Williamsburg	97
Greenberg, Asher/Yeshiva Shaar Ephraim	199
Greenberg, Avrohom/Bais Yaakov Academy	96
Greene, Carrie/John A Sciole Elem Sch	62
Greene, Colin/Atmosphere Acad PCS	1
Greene, Richard/Jefferson Avenue Elem Sch	108
Greene, Rosa/PS X811	25
Greenfield, Andrew/Port Richmond High Sch	193
Greenidge, Ayanna/PS/IS 266	180
Greenwald, Eugene/Talmud Torah Toldos Yakov Ysf	99
Greer, Kristin/New Visions Aim CS I [243]	6
Greggo, John/JHS 190 Russell Sage	182
Gregor, Natasha/Graham Elem Sch	258
Gregory, Jacobs/PS 155	181
Gregory, Lois/Learning Tree Prep	27
Greig, Kimlyn/IS 59 Springfield Gardens	183
Greiner, Lisa/Baylis Elem Sch	130
Grendell, Jane/Preston High Sch	26
Grenon, Charles/French American Sch of NY-Elem	265
Grenville, Steven/Saranac Senior High Sch	45
Grenwald, Martin/Congregation Bais Chana Malka	199
Grevenberg, L/Academy for Health Careers	86
Grey, Dave/Baldwinsville Christian Acad	160
Grey, Terri/Bronx HS Writing/Comm Arts	22
Gridelli, Jackie/Success Acad CS Bronx 1 [245]	7
Gridelli, Jackie/Success Acad CS Bronx 1 MS [245]	7
Grieb, Tara/Stissing Mountain Jr Sr HS	53
Griebel, Jaclyn/Webster Montessori Sch	115
Grier, Michelle/Roosevelt Elem Sch	260
Grier, Sabrina/Brooklyn Preparatory Sch	97
Griesmer, John/Amherst Middle Sch	56
Griffin, Chrystal/KIPP Star Middle Sch [242]	5
Griffin, Maryellen/George W Miller Elem Sch	196
Griffin, Nicole/Challenge Prep Charter Sch	180
Griggs, Donald/Vincent Ziccolella Elem MS	255
Grignon, Wayne/Citizen Edmond Genet Elem Sch	190
Grillo, Ashley/Batavia Middle Sch	73
Grimaldi, Michael, Dr/E M Baker Sch	120
Grimmer, Tosha/St Kateri Tekakwitha Sch	205
Grinblat, Aaron/Yeshiva Yagdil Torah	100
Gringras, Faigie/Machon Bais Yaakov High Sch	98
Groat, Rebecca/Salem-Hyde Elem Sch	159
Groat, Ryan/Watervliet Jr Sr High Sch	12
Groff, Robert/Active Learning Elem Sch	178
Grogan, Jennifer/Marymount School-New York	145
Gross, Rachel/Davison Ave Elem Sch	124
Gross, Shaindy/Be'Ikvei Hatzion	96
Grossbaum, Rivkie/Maimonides Day Sch	235
Grossman, Benjamin/Bronx Acad-Software Engineer	20
Grossman, Rasha/Yeshiva Ketana of Queens	189
Grotto, Stephen/Schroon Lake Central Sch	68
Grover, Vishu/Child School-Legacy High Sch	144
Groves, Tyritia/KIPP Academy Elem Sch [242]	16
Grow, Patrick/Johanna Perrin Middle Sch	108
Gruber, Michael, Dr/PS 156 Frederick Law Olmsted	58
Gruber, Yosef/Yeshiva Viznitz Boys High Sch	199
Gruen, Darren/James A Dever Elem Sch	130
Gruen, Suri/Shema Kolainu Sch	99
Gruenauer, Scott/St Stephen Sch	66
Gruhn, Laurie/The Browning Sch	145
Grumbach, Adam/Urban Academy Lab High Sch	138
Grupka, Aaron/Orchard Park Middle Sch	63
Guarnieri, Thomas/PS 47 John Randolph	24
Guccione, Roger/A MacArthur Barr Middle Sch	196
Guerriero, Alexandra/PS 176X	25
Guidarelli, Christopher/MS 907 Legacy Sch of the Arts	89
Guidotti, Carl/Holland High Sch	61
Guillaume, Marie/HS for Energy & Technology	20
Gulisane, John/Taconic Hills Elem Sch	47
Gumbs, Stephen/Belmont Preparatory High Sch	20
Gundell, Kaite/St John Lutheran Sch	149
Gundell, Kevin/Holy Ghost Lutheran Sch	149
Gundersen, Erika/PS 172 Beacon Sch Excellence	85
Gunn, Velma/PS 58	19
Gunther, Jolene/Guild for Excptnl Chldrn Sch	97
Guo, Huaping/Fei Tian Academy of the Arts	168
Gutfreund, Meir/The Cheder Sch	99
Gutierrez, Celina/PS 111 Seton Falls	23
Gutierrez, Pepe/PS 274X New American Acad	20
Gutierrez, Shalonda/Connelly Middle Sch Holy Child	142
Gutman, Daphna/PS 142 Amalia Castro	135
Gutmann, Kenneth/Eugene Auer Memorial Elem Sch	225
Gutterman, Adam/Purchase Elem Sch	256
Guy, Ann/R T Hudson SDA Sch	27
Guy, Herman/Millennium Art Academy	17
Guzman, Jamie/Community HS-Social Justice	16
Guzman, Maria/PS 46 Edward C Blum	83
Guzman, Olga/PS 228 Lafayette Sch of Arts	185
Gypalo, Ruthanne, Sr/St Raymond Sch	133

PRINCIPAL INDEX

H

NAME/School	PAGE
Ha, Sue/Hudson Way Immersion Sch	144
Haab, Deborah/Wainscott Common Sch	232
Haakmat, Martha/Brooklyn Heights Mont Sch	97
Haas, Robert/Bayport Blue Point High Sch	217
Haber, Carol/Yeshiva Shaarei Torah-Girls HS	100
Haberman, Lesley/Family Sch	144
Habersham, Monique/Martin Luther King Jr Elem Sch	234
Hackett, Mary/Inwood Acad for Ldshp Chtr Sch	141
Hagan, Molly/Cazenovia Jr Sr High Sch	104
Hageman, Amanda/Achievement First Linden ES [128]	1
Hageman, Ivan/East Harlem Sch-Exodus House	144
Hagemann, Diane/Solvay High Sch	158
Hagens, Sarah/Fusion Academy-Brooklyn	97
Haggerty, Mary/Kaegebein Elem Sch	61
Hahn, Constance/PS 108 Sal Abbracciamento	89
Hahn, Frederick/Martin Road Elem Sch	62
Haidary, Melissa/PS 186 Castlewood	180
Halberstam, Ahuva/Westchester Day Sch	266
Halbert, Laurie/Dundee Elem Sch	268
Hale, Kimberly/Chestnut Ridge Elem Sch	107
Hale, Scott/Johnstown High Sch	71
Haley, Theresa/H W Smith PK-8 Sch	158
Hall, Cedric/Eagle Acad Young Men III	183
Hall, Charon/Brooklyn Academy High Sch	82
Hall, Colleen/Lincoln Street Elem Sch	239
Hall, Deborah/Big Cross Elem Sch	245
Hall, Denise/St Mary's Sch	48
Hall, Karen/Red Jacket Middle Sch	162
Hall, Matt/Rippowam Cisqua Sch-Upper	266
Hall, Michael/Hoosick Falls High Sch	190
Hall, Shonelle/PS 41 Francis White	93
Hall, Thomas/Brighton High Sch	106
Hallaway, Woodrow/Most Precious Blood Sch	168
Hallenbeck, Rachel/East Elmhurst Community Sch	184
Hallenbeck, Richard/JHS 123 James M Kieran	17
Halliday, Antoinette/Sherburne Earlville Elem Sch	42
Halpainy, Jason/Randolph Jr Sr High Sch	33
Halpern, David/School of Holy Childhood	114
Halpern, Jehuda/Kiryas Joel Village	164
Halpin, Sheila/St John's Preparatory Sch	187
Hamann, Winston/Khalil Gibran Int'l Academy	84
Hambright, Karen/PS 243 Weeksville	86
Hamelinck, Jeff/Norman R Kelley Interm Sch	250
Hamill, Christine/Little Red Schoolhouse	191
Hamilton, Andrea, Dr/Alice E Grady Elem Sch	255
Hamilton, Connie/John Dewey High Sch	91
Hamilton, Helen/New Vistas Academy	98
Hamilton, Jesse/Mt Morris Central Sch	103
Hamilton, Judson/Redwood Middle Sch	183
Hamilton, Sabra/Marymount School-New York	145
Hamilton, Thomas/St Mary Sch	55
Hamm, Katherine/PS 107	18
Hammel, Kenneth/Gates Chili High Sch	108
Hammer, Joy/Hebrew Acad 5 Towns Rockawy ES	133
Hammond, Mary/Port Dickinson Elem Sch	28
Hammond, Terrilyn/John Williams School 5	111
Han, Helena/Hawthorne Country Day Sch-Manh	144
Hanan, Elizabeth/Wilbur H Lynch Literacy Acad	116
Hancock, Stephen/Ossining High Sch	260
Haney, Barbara/Grace Church Sch	144
Hanford, Micah/Cheektowaga Middle Sch	58
Hankinson, Lisa/Circleville Middle Sch	166
Hanley, Matthew/Barton Elem Sch	227
Hanna, Debora/St Andrew Avellino Cath Acad	186
Hanna, Robert, Dr/Willets Road Sch	118
Hannon, Holly/Paul B D Temple Elem Sch	37
Hanrahan, Dawn/Cohen Middle Sch	40
Hansen, Carolyn/Premm Learning Center	216
Hansen, Katie/Unadilla Valley Secondary Sch	43
Hansen, Lawrence/St Joseph Hill Academy ES	195
Hansen, Robert/Sidney Elem Sch	50
Harcsztark, Tully/Sar High Sch	27
Harjes, Natalie/Ostrander Elem Sch	244
Harkin, Michael/Columbia High Sch	190
Harlow, Joanne/Huntington PK-8 Sch	158
Harmelink, Herman/Dover Elem Sch	52
Harness, Steve/Wilton Baptist Academy	203
Harnischfeger, Eileen/Immaculate Conception Sch	186
Harp, Anna/Aurora Waldorf Sch	66
Harper, Chayvonne/PS/IS 270Q Gordon Parks Sch	184
Harper, Christopher/Unadilla Valley Elem Sch	43
Harper, Lauren/Panama Central Sch	38
Harrica, Joshua/Northeastern Clinton Sr HS	44
Harriman, Jon/International HS at Lafayette	91
Harrington, Darryl/PS 306	21
Harrington, Keith/Enfield Elem Sch	240
Harrington, Meghan/Saint Albans Sch	145
Harrington, Tyneka/Blueprint Middle Sch	17
Harris-Pappin, Kim, Dr/Montessori Academy Sch 53	111
Harris, Claudia/PS/IS 384 Frances E Carter	94
Harris, Cristy/Katonah Elem Sch	257
Harris, Dawn/South Shore Ed Campus YABC	88
Harris, Jacqueline/Liberty Elem Sch	236
Harris, Jessica/Mt Pleasant Cottage Sch	258
Harris, Linda/PS/IS 323	93
Harris, Nancy/Spruce Street Sch	138
Harris, Peter/Ulster BOCES Phoenix Acad	241
Harrison, Thomas/Fifth Avenue Elem Sch	227
Hart, Jonathan/Rocky Point High Sch	228
Hart, Margaret/Rockwell Elem Sch	157
Hart, Victoria/PS 20 John Bowne	178
Harten, Maureen/Immaculate Conception Sch	264
Hartling, Renee/Samuel G Love Elem Sch	38
Hartwell, Rj/Elbridge Elem Sch	156
Hartz, Eric/Newfield Middle Sch	241
Haruthunian, Eric/Earl Van Dermuelen High Sch	228
Harvey, Yolanda/PS 148 Queens	185
Hasbrouck, Monica/Plattekill Elem Sch	244
Haselbach, Pia/Lutheran Sch-Flushing Bayside	188
Hasson, Lauren/Bronx Writing Academy	18
Hastings, Jackie/Clear View Sch	265
Hasweh, Hanin/PS 74 Future Leaders ES	194
Hatwood, Errin, Dr/Adult Education Center	120
Hatwood, Errin, Dr/Clover Drive Adult Lrng Center	120
Hatzimichalis, Stamatina/PS 131 Brooklyn	85
Haubrich, Jeffrey/Pulaski Road Elem Sch	227
Hauck, Kenneth/Minisink Valley High Sch	165
Hauge, Christine/Leif Ericson Day Sch	98
Hauk, Steven/West Hollow Middle Sch	222
Haves, Katherine/Success Acad CS Bushwick [245]	7
Havlik, Eric/Brooklyn School of Inquiry	89
Hawkins, Greta/PS 90 Edna Cohen Sch	91
Hayatsu, Kuniko/Kodomono Kuni Sch	266
Hayes, Abeku/New York City Montessori CS	6
Hayes, Elizabeth/Ticonderoga Elem Sch	68
Hayes, Erin/Mill Road Primary Sch	53
Hayes, James/Genesis Sch	82
Hayes, Jennifer/Kensington Road Elem Sch	245
Haynes, Jennifer/Success Acad CS Midtown West [245]	8
Haynes, Michelle/Sisulu-Walker CS of Harlem [247]	7
Haynes, Nicolle/Oasis Academy	159
Haywood, Tashon/Queens Preparatory Academy	184
Hazell, Kerry/PS 46 Arthur Tappan	140
Hazut, Alison/West Side Elem Sch	219
Headley, Barbara/PS 163 Arthur Schomberg	19
Headley, Frank/Voice Charter Sch	185
Healt, Kristin/St Patrick Sch	106
Healy, Colin/NYC Charter HS Arch-Engr-Const	16
Healy, Dan/Finger Lakes Secondary Sch	268
Healy, Sean/Uncommon Prep Charter HS [246]	8
Heaphy, Timothy/Eastridge High Sch	107
Heard, Matthew/Dutchess Day Sch	55
Hearny, Martin/James E Allen Jr-Sr HS	216
Hecht, Berl/Bnos-Belz Girls Sch	97
Hecht, Elliot/Hanc Middle Sch	133

New York School Directory

PRINCIPAL INDEX

NAME/School	PAGE
Heckethorn, Joel/Emma Lazarus High Sch	135
Heeraman, Carol/PS/IS 30 Mary White Ovington	90
Heffernan, Laura/Glenmont Elem Sch	10
Heffron, James/Solvay Middle Sch	158
Heide, Philip/St Mary Gate of Heaven Sch	187
Heidemann, Gregory/Walden Elem Sch	167
Heimbach, Elena/Midwood Catholic Academy	95
Heinzelman, Thomas/Goshen High Sch	164
Heitner, Karen/Pasadena Elem Sch	128
Helgeland, Stephanie/Avoca Central Sch	213
Heller, Janet/MS 324 Patria Mirabal	141
Heller, Shannon/West Ridge Elem Sch	109
Hellman, Noah/Achievement First Apollo ES [128]	1
Helm, Katie/St Gregory's School for Boys	13
Helmrich, Richard/Our Lady of Grace Sch	25
Hemphill, Sharyn/PS 256 Benjamin Banneker	83
Hendel, Menachem/Congregation Ohr Menachem	97
Hender, William/Eastport Elem Sch	221
Henderson, Jennifer/Greenlawn Elem Sch	41
Henderson, Renae/St Mary's Academy	160
Hendricks, Marcia/STEM Institute of Manhattan	139
Hendricks, Natasha/PS 89 Dr L T Wright Sch	58
Hendrickson, Jeffrey/J E Lanigan Elem Sch	171
Hendry, Joelle/Lura Sharp Elem Sch	172
Hengen, Jennifer/Webutuck Elem Sch	54
Henley, Jeff/Odyssey Academy	109
Henry, Gerard/Brooklyn Lab Sch	88
Henry, Joseph/PS 178 St Clair McKelway	93
Henry, Judy/Queens Gateway Hlth Sciences	182
Henry, Maureen/Valley Stream South JSHS	130
Henry, Patrice/Business Tech Early Clg HS	179
Henry, Sharon/Ralph McKee Career & Tech HS	194
Hens, Peter/Paul Road Elem Sch	108
Henwood, Lynne/Flexschool-Bronxville	265
Heppt, Joanne/Resurrection Ascension Sch	186
Heredia, Carolyn/Bedford Park Elem Sch	20
Herendeen, James/Thomas C Armstrong Middle Sch	251
Herl, Sharon/John A Coleman Sch-Yonkers	266
Herman, Kristin/Caroline Elem Sch	240
Hermann, Lisa/JHS 218 James Peter Sinnott	88
Hernandez, Alexandra/Multicultural High Sch	89
Hernandez, Andrea/Family Life Academy CS III	4
Hernandez, Antonio/Lexington Academy	139
Hernandez, Edwin/JHS 227 Edward Shallow	90
Hernandez, Eliezer/Delaware Primary Sch	158
Hernandez, Frank/PS 49 Willis Avenue	16
Hernandez, Fred, Dr/Yonkers Early Childhood Acad	264
Hernandez, Isabel/Robert C Dodson Sch	264
Hernandez, Ivelisse/Lido Elem Sch	124
Hernandez, Jennifer/St Leo Catholic Academy	187
Hernandez, Johanie/Bronx Sch for Law-Gov-Justice	18
Hernandez, Lauren/James S Evans Elem Sch	54
Hernandez, Martin/World View High Sch	22
Hernandez, Onalis/PS 149 Christa McAuliffe	185
Hernandez, Sarah/HS for Language & Diplomacy	136
Hernandez, Susana/Explorations Academy	24
Hernandez, Washington/PS 8 Luis Belliard	141
Hernndez, Yliana, Sr/Nora Cronin Presentation Acad	168
Hernon, Stephen/PS 191 Riverside Sch Makers	139
Heroth, Adam/O E S J Jr Sr High Sch	72
Herr, Christopher/Westhampton Beach High Sch	233
Herrera, Maria/Renaissance HS Music Theatre	18
Herrero, Benito/Haverstraw Elem Sch	197
Herring, Dennis/Science & Medicine Middle Sch	88
Herschlein, Lynn/Goose Hill Primary Sch	219
Hertzberg, David/Yeshiva of Flatbush Elem Sch	100
Herzberg, Liza/Windmill Montessori Sch	99
Herzberg, S/Beth Rochel School for Girls	198
Herzog, David/Yeshiva Farm Settlement Sch	266
Hess, Jessica/Belfast Central Sch	14
Hesterhagen, Diane/FR Vincent Capodanno Cath Acad	194
Hewitt, Nordia/Harlem Village Acad West MS [239]	4
Hewlett, Kim/Summit Park Elem Sch	196
Hewlett, William/PS/MS 31 William Garrison	17
Hey, Evelyn/S Bronx CS-Int'l Culture & Art	17
Heyden, Patrick/Kenmore East High Sch	62
Heyward, Rebecca/PS 17 Henry David Thoreau	184
Hibbard, Amy/Elizabeth Cady Stanton ES	208
Hibbert, Christophe/Validus Prep Academy	20
Hickey, Johanna/George F Johnson Elem Sch	29
Hickman, Loretta/Explore Exceed Charter Sch [237]	3
Hicks, Magaly/New Visions CHS Humanities [243]	6
Hicks, Tiffany/PS 160 Walter Francis Bishop	182
Hicks, Zonya/Achievement First Brownsville [128]	1
Hider, Kristine/St John Vianney Sch	65
Hierath, Lars/German Int'l School New York	265
Higgins, George/Beekman Sch	143
Higgins, Laura/Cathedral Sch-St John Divine	144
Higgins, Pamela/Candlewood Middle Sch	222
Higgins, Reginald/PS 125 Ralph Bunche	140
Hilderbrand, Michael/Trinity Elem Sch	259
Hiley, Lucas/Laurelton Pardee Interm Sch	107
Hill, Afua/PS/MS 147 Ronald McNair	184
Hill, Brian/David B Crane Elem Sch	112
Hill, Jacqueline/Maple Hill Jr Sr High Sch	191
Hill, Kim/PS 95 Eastwood	183
Hill, Meredith/MS 371 Seed Harlem	140
Hill, Orniece/PS 43 Lovejoy Discovery Sch	57
Hill, Sharon/Greenacres Elem Sch	262
Hill, Stephaun/PS 190 Sheffield	89
Hiller, Robert/New Visions CHS Math & Sci [243]	6
Hilligas, Sara/Tapestry Charter Sch	8
Hillis, Jonathan/William Appleby Elem Sch	48
Hillman, Shannon/Genesee Cmty Charter Sch	4
Hills, Andrew/Arongen Elem Sch	202
Hills, David/PS 208 Riverside Academy	58
Hindley, Joanne/Central Elem Sch	258
Hinds, Rochelle/PS 224 Hale A Woodruff	89
Hine, Elizabeth/Mt Sinai Middle Sch	226
Hine, Sharyn/Oakwood Christian Sch	192
Hinkcley, Rim/Geneva School-Manhattan	144
Hinman, Danielle/Rochester Prep Elem Sch [246]	6
Hirsch, Jon/Valhalla Middle High Sch	263
Hirsch, Kris/Rochester Prep MS-West [246]	7
Hirschey, Johnathan/St Lawrence Elem Sch	209
Hirschler, Scott/Scribner Road Elem Sch	110
Hirschman, Francine/Ezra Academy	187
Hirschman, Martha/Dwight Sch	144
Hirtz, Rochelle/Shevach High Sch	188
Hitrick, Katria/Mayfield Elem Sch	72
Hoagland, Kenneth, Br/Kellenberg Memorial High Sch	132
Hoagland, Kenneth, Br/St Martin Deporres Mrnst Sch	132
Hobart, Elaine/Summit Sch	34
Hochschartner, David/North Country Sch	69
Hoder, Jill/PS 161 Arthur Ashe Sch	182
Hodge, Dexter/Lawrence Road Middle Sch	130
Hodgkinson, Seamus/Doane Stuart Sch	192
Hodkinson, Carrie/Vernon Verona Sherrill Mid Sch	153
Hodne, Dennis/Zdr Acad Yeshiva Rambam Sch	100
Hoehn, Daniel/J M Rapport School Career Dev	25
Hoekstra, Valerie/Inwood Acad for Ldshp Chtr Sch	141
Hoffer, Ronald/Sayville High Sch	230
Hoffman, Kate/York Central Elem Sch	103
Hoffman, Mary/Developmental Disability Inst	234
Hoffman, Ziaty/Yeshiva Avir Yakov Girls Sch	199
Hogan, H Thomas/Locust Valley Middle Sch	123
Hogan, Ross/Duzine Elem Sch	243
Hogan, Timothy/Bellport High Sch	231
Hoggard, Marlin/PS X017	25
Hoke, Rashan/PS 282 Park Slope	83
Holden, Gail/Connetquot Alternative Pre-Sch	219
Holland, Thomas/Washington Irving Sch	262
Holliday, Kimberly/Mexico Middle Sch	171
Hollings, Nicole/Calhoun High Sch	117
Holloway, Mr/Academy Charter High Sch	1
Holloway, Ron/Horseheads Middle Sch	41
Holloway, Tammy/Collaborative Arts Middle Sch	183
Holly, Michael/East Middle Sch	27
Holmes, Correne/West Canada Valley Elem Sch	79

School Year 2020-2021   800-333-8802   NY-U19

PRINCIPAL INDEX

NAME/School	PAGE
Holsey, Paula/PS 117 J Keld/Briarwood Sch	182
Holt, Wanda/PS 345 Patrolman Robert Bolden	89
Holtzer, Amy/The Leffell Sch	266
Holtzman, Dan/JL Miller-Great Neck North HS	120
Holzerland, Mary/Cardinal O'Hara High Sch	65
Hom, Alice/PS 124 Yung Wing	137
Hom, Amy/PS 1 Alfred E Smith	137
Homeyar, Jennifer/Catherine M McNamara Elem Sch	154
Honeyman, Catherine/Laddie Decker Sound Beach Sch	226
Hong, Min/PS 51 Bronx STEM & Arts Acad	21
Hong, Yuqing/PS 310 Sch for Future Leaders	90
Honore, Ralph/PS 55 Maure	182
Honoroff, Benjamin/JHS 50 John D Wells	83
Hoogenboom, Ari/Abraham Lincoln High Sch	91
Hooks, Anthony/PS 123	181
Hoory, Ilanit/Solomon Schechter Sch	266
Hooulu, Rabbi/Yeshiva Ateret Torah Boys	99
Hoover, Amanda/Townsend Elem Sch	51
Hope-Barnes, Michelle/PS 65 Roosevelt ECC	57
Hope, Abidemi/PS 11 Purvis J Behan	83
Hopkins, Matt/Augustine Classical Academy	203
Hopkins, Thomas/Rensselaer Park Elem Sch	191
Hopmayer, Aaron/Pine Bush High Sch	166
Hopson, Troy/MacCormick Secure Center	5
Horaczek, Sarah/Maywood Sch	9
Horan, James/Samoset Middle Sch	229
Horlacher, Stuart/Ardsley Middle Sch	252
Horler, Nichole/Brewster High Sch	175
Horn, Richard/Southern Adirondack Ed Center	246
Hornbrook, Patrick/Lansing High Sch	240
Horne, Rina/PS 212 Lady Deborah Moody	91
Horning, Curtis/Clyde Mennonite Parochial Sch	251
Hornung, Amy/Nightengale Elem Sch	211
Horowitz, Chaskel/Beitcher Yeshirva Sch	96
Horowitz, Esther/Bais Tziporah-Girls	96
Horowitz, Gitty/Yeshiva Bnos Spinka Girls	99
Horowitz, Marie/Mildred E Strang Middle Sch	264
Horowitz, Zev/Yeshiva Bonim Lamokom	99
Horton, Jameela/MS of Media Law & Fine Arts	88
Hosang, Marlon/PS 64 Robert Simon	135
Hosier, Kyle/Edgemont Jr Sr High Sch	254
Hoskins, Gene/Sodus Intermediate Sch	251
Hoskins, Justin/Fort Ann Jr Sr High Sch	247
Hoss, Tim/Northport Middle Sch	227
Hostetter, Timothy/Tabernacle Christian Academy	55
Houlihan, Kaye/Ft Hamilton High Sch	90
House, Mark/Community Health Acad Heights	141
Houseknecht, Tim/South Seneca Middle High Sch	208
Houser, Penny/Seneca Street Elem Sch	105
Howard, Richard/East Meadow High Sch	118
Howard, Susan/Briarcliff Middle Sch	253
Howe, Ellen/Lois E Bird Elem Sch	106
Howe, Ellen/Morgan Sch	106
Howell, Tanya/Queens Sch Ldrshp Excellence	182
Hoyle, Marc/Lawrence Woodmere Academy	133
Hoyt, Jasmin/Great Oaks Elem Sch	97
Hoyt, Patricia/Unatego High Sch	174
Hoyt, Patricia/Unatego Middle Sch	174
Hristidis, Simone/Columbia Grammar & Prep Sch	144
Hsu, Jane/PS 116 Mary Lindley Murray	137
Hubacz, Catherine/Convent of Sacred Heart Sch	142
Hubert, Christopher/Livingston Manor Elem Sch	236
Huchro, Michael/Ballard Elem Sch	202
Huchzermeier, Anitra/Buckman Heights Elem Sch	109
Hudson, Angela/Ulysses Byas Elem Sch	129
Hudson, Stephen/Riverhead Middle Sch	228
Hudson, Tracy/Charles A Mulligan Elem Sch	219
Hueber, Gustave/Three Village Academy	232
Huebert, Thomas/Wallace D Ormsby Center	56
Huegel, Rhonda/Liberty HS for Newcomers	136
Huff, Michael/Herbert Hoover Elem Sch	62
Hugee, Candace/Urban Assem Collab Healthcare	89
Huger, Janet/East New York ES of Excellence	88

NAME/School	PAGE
Hughes, Chris/Clifford Wise Mid Interm Sch	170
Hughes, Lura/Edwards-Knox Central Sch	210
Hughes, Melissa/Hope Christian Academy	215
Hughes, Scott/Leon M Goldstein HS Sciences	92
Hulbert, Lorraine/Floyd L Bell Elem Sch	30
Hulihan, Timothy/Stillwater Middle Sch	202
Hults, Clark/Newcomb Central Sch	68
Humphrey, Donald/Turtle Hook Middle Sch	130
Humphries, Jean, Sr/Academy of Mt St Ursula	25
Hunn, Nicole/Steele Elem Sch	117
Hunn, Peter/OCM BOCES-Henry Campus	154
Hunt, Ashlee/Waverly High Sch	239
Hunt, Jayne/PS 151 Lyndon B Johnson	94
Hunt, Joanne/Brooklyn Charter Sch	83
Hunt, Linda, Dr/Charles Churn Christian Acad	97
Hunt, Victoria/Dos Puentes Elem Sch	141
Hunter, David/Chestnut Hill Middle Sch	156
Hunter, Faith/Little Red Schlhse-Irwin HS	144
Huntsman, Jason/Kings Park High Sch	224
Hunziker, Shawn/F Donald Myers Education Ctr	200
Huplosky, Frank/Howell Road Elem Sch	130
Hurley, Kristin/PS 52 Sheepshead Bay	92
Hurlock, Glenn/Plattsburgh Senior High Sch	45
Hurtado, Erika/Bronx Aerospace High Sch	22
Hussein, Dawn/Main Street Sch	157
Hussey, Maureen, Dr/MS 297 Hawtree Creek Mid Sch	180
Hutchinson, Charles/Susquehanna Valley Sr High Sch	29
Huza, Amanda/Equality Charter Middle Sch	22
Hwang, Nayeon/Woodside Cmty School 361Q	185
Hyde, Jodi/Anderson School PS 334	138
Hyer, Melinda/PS 88 Silverstein Ltl Sparrow	19
Hyland, Kathleen/Northwest Elem Sch	216
Hymes, Valerie/Harrison Avenue Elem Sch	256
Hynes, Tara/Our Lady of Good Counsel Sch	194

I

NAME/School	PAGE
Iacono, Rosario/Robert W Carbonaro Elem Sch	131
Iafrate, Jessica/Marguerite L Mulvey Elem Sch	219
Iannotti, Mindy/Career & Tech Sch-Schoharie	206
Ibarra, Yvonne/Baker Academy	1
Id-Din, Rafiq/Ember Sch for Mindful Educ CS	86
Ierano, Joeseph/Mt Pleasant Elem Sch	230
Ihne, Alan/PS 30 Westerleigh	193
Ihne, Lisa, Dr/Cherry Avenue Elem Sch	229
Imbert, J Eric/Oakview Prep Sch	266
Imbesi, Linda/Leeway Sch	235
Inbal, M/Queens School of Inquiry	179
Indart, Joan/Restart Academy	142
Ingham, Maureen/St Peter Roman Catholic Sch	149
Inglee, Sean/Lenape Elem Sch	243
Inglee, Sean/Pleasant Valley Elem Sch	205
Inslee, Angela/Success Acad CS Bronx 2 [245]	7
Interlandi, Maria/PS 124 Silas B Dutcher	85
Intrieri, Sandra/Putnam Valley High Sch	176
Inzarde, Joan/Argus Community High Sch	26
Inzerillo, Anthony/PS 199 Maurice Fitzgerald	178
Iocolano, Nelson/Robert M Finley Middle Sch	120
Iodice, Elaine/PS Q016 Nancy Debenedittis	178
Iorio, Mauro/Pathfinder Village Sch	175
Iovine, Jennifer/PS 108 Capt Vincent G Fowler	181
Irivarry, Eva/Brooklyn Arbor Elem Sch 414	83
Irving-White, Gayle/PS 80 Highgate Heights ES	57
Irwin, Amy/Middleburgh Elem Sch	206
Isaac, Liset/PS 192 Magnet Sch-Math & Sci	90
Isbell, Allison/Little Red Schlhse-Irwin HS	144
Ishmael, Radeyah/Wellspring Sch	189
Ismael, Shannon-Re/East Flatbush Ascend CS	3
Itzhakov, Chaya/Congregation Ohr Menachem	97
Itzkowitz, Chaim/Cong Bais Chinuch Ateres Bnos	198
Iuliucci, Holly/Jefferson Academic Center	216
Iuso, Steven/Christ the King Sch	25
Ivey, Teresa, Dr/Montebello Elem Sch	198
Izzo Iannelli, Laura/John Bowne High Sch	178

New York School Directory — PRINCIPAL INDEX

J

NAME/School	PAGE
Jacaruso, Jessica/Charter School of Educ Excell [247]	3
Jachlewski, Jeff/Heim Middle Sch	64
Jackson, Brenda/Cordello Ave Elem Sch	219
Jackson, Brooke/NYC Lab HS for Coll Studies	137
Jackson, Cecilia/PS 307 Pioneer Academy	178
Jackson, Gloria/Twin Pines Elem Sch	218
Jackson, Gregory/Brownsville Collaborative MS	93
Jackson, Jessica/IS 72 Rocco Laurie	193
Jackson, John-Michael/South Street Elem Sch	221
Jackson, Karon/George Mather Forbes School 4	111
Jackson, Kyesha/PS 67 Charles A Dorsey	83
Jackson, Lucille/PS 66	88
Jackson, Sharon/Dr Martin Luther King Jr Sch 9	111
Jackson, Steven/Aviation Career & Tech Ed HS	176
Jackson, Tameka/New Visions Aim CS II [243]	6
Jackson, Valerie/Belmont Elem Sch	226
Jackson, Veronica/DeWitt Clinton YABC	20
Jacobowitz, Venzion/Yeshiva Torah V'Yirah Academy	100
Jacobs, Gretchen/Franziska Racker Center	241
Jacobs, Jennifer/Pawling Elem Sch	52
Jacobson, Debby/Ashar Sch	198
Jacobson, Eric/Progressive Sch of Long Island	134
Jacobson, Yehuzah/Yeshiva Tiferes Yisroel	100
Jacques, Lionel Jean/Middletown Christian Sch	168
Jaeckel, Judith/Mountain Laurel Waldorf Sch	244
Jaenicke, Greg/Curtis High Sch	192
Jaffee, Yaakav/Torah Acad-Lawrence Cedarhurst	134
Jagarnath, Kavita/PS 175 Henry Garnet	140
Jaggon, Dionne/PS 111 Jacob Blackwell	184
James, Carolyn/IS 211 John Wilson	87
James, Lyne/MS 594 New Pathways Academy	19
James, Ronald/PS 202 Ernest Jenkyns	89
James, Roxanne/PS 44 Marcus Garvey	83
James, Shondell/Harlem C Z Promise Academy II	140
Jamieson, Melissa/John F Kennedy Elem Sch	242
Jamil, Kathy/Elmwood Village CS-Hertel	3
Jamin, Christine/Haldane Sch	176
Jammoudy, Ahmed/AL Madinah Sch	95
Janora, Meghan/Allegany-Limestone Elem Sch	31
Jantz, Nicholas/Bethpage High Sch	117
Jardi, M/PS M226	142
Jarrett, Elizabeth/PS 154 Harriet Tubman	140
Jarvis, Michael/Sterling East-Pascack Lrng Ctr	199
Jashar, Eljasa/Brooklyn Amity Sch	97
Javeline, Beth/Carrie Palmer Weber Middle Sch	128
Jean-Baptiste, Charmaine/Church of God Christian Acad	187
Jean, Cyndy/Hackley Sch	265
Jeannis-Desire, Ingrid/Maryhaven Center of Hope	235
Jelinek, Kristina/MS M247 Dual Lang Middle Sch	138
Jenkins, Jessica/MS 291 West End Secondary Sch	138
Jenkins, Terrance/PS 95 Waterfront Elem Sch	58
Jenne, Larry/Northwest Career Tech Ed Ctr	209
Jennings, Tara/Corcoran High Sch	158
Jenny, Timothy/James A Green High Sch	77
Jensen, Brian/St Rose of Lima Sch	133
Jensen, Elizabeth/St Agnes Sch	103
Jensen, Kathleen/William A Carter Elem Sch	165
Jewell, Melissa/Spencer Van Etten High Sch	239
Jimenez, Jose/PS 290 Ace Acad for Scholars	178
Jimenez, Yaira/James Weldon Johnson Elem Sch	139
Jnbaptist, Heather/PS 36 Margaret Douglas	140
Johanson, Craig/Roslyn Middle Sch	129
Johnson, Ambrosia/Ivy Hill Prep Charter Sch	5
Johnson, Amy/St Joseph Sch	114
Johnson, Andrea/PS 246 Poe Center	21
Johnson, Astrid/Eldorado Elem Sch	196
Johnson, Asya/Longwood Preparatory Academy	17
Johnson, Bonnie/Franklin Central Sch	49
Johnson, Charles/Bronx Green Middle Sch	22
Johnson, Christopher/Cornerstone Christian Academy	114
Johnson, D'Onnarae/Henry Lomb School 20	111
Johnson, David/Churchville Elem Sch	107
Johnson, David/Nyack Middle Sch	197
Johnson, Dean/Kenmore West High Sch	62
Johnson, Farid/Stony Point Elem Sch	197
Johnson, Gail, Dr/Bethel Christian Learning Ctr	187
Johnson, Gregory/PS 54 Dr George Blackman ECC	57
Johnson, Joanne/St Albans Christian Academy	188
Johnson, John/Bay Shore Christian Sch	234
Johnson, Jonna/Mott Road Elem Sch	155
Johnson, Jonna/St John the Baptist Sch-Alden	65
Johnson, Kelley/Penn Yan Middle Sch	268
Johnson, Kelly Joan/Baccalaureate Sch-Global Educ	184
Johnson, Marcene/NYSARC-Brookside Sch	244
Johnson, Mark/Harbor Science & Arts Chtr Sch	4
Johnson, Mary/Pequenakonck Elem Sch	259
Johnson, Michael/PS 161 the Crown	87
Johnson, Michael/Stillwater Central High Sch	202
Johnson, Philip/Windom Elem Sch	63
Johnson, Stuart/St Bernard's Sch	145
Johnson, Tamara/MS 340 North Star Academy	87
Johnson, Traci/All Saints Catholic Academy	12
Johnson, Vernon/Brooklyn HS for Law & Tech	85
Johnson, William/Acad of Med Tech-College Board	180
Jolovitz, Arielle/Yeshiva Bicahon	99
Jonas, Lauren/Success Acad CS-Myrtle MS [245]	8
Jonathan, Nissi/New Visions CHS Math & Sci III [243]	6
Jones-Tunney, Mimosa/The School House	235
Jones, Craig/Perth Bible Christian Academy	116
Jones, Cynthia/Harry F Abate Elem Sch	147
Jones, Cynthia/Niagara Falls High Sch	148
Jones, Danita/Capital Prep Harlem CS	3
Jones, DeLise/IS 117 Joseph H Wade	19
Jones, Hakim/Pieter B Coeymans Elem Sch	11
Jones, Hassan/The Harley Sch	114
Jones, Jacqueline/PS Q023-Queens Childrens Ctr	185
Jones, Janet/Ruth C Kinney Elem Sch	221
Jones, Joy/Ebenezer Preparatory Sch	97
Jones, Karen/Ft Edward Elem Sch	247
Jones, Karen/Peninsula Prep Academy CS	180
Jones, Kiante/Notre Dame-Bishop Gibbons Sch	205
Jones, Kristin/Success Acad CS-Queens 1 MS [245]	8
Jones, Kuvana/PS 12X Lewis & Clark Sch	25
Jones, Malik/Karigon Elem Sch	202
Jones, Maritza/PS 124 Osmond A Church	181
Jones, Nathan/Hunter Elem Sch	76
Jones, Rebecca/Lincoln Elem Sch	258
Jones, Teena/PS 353 Newcomer Academy	58
Jordan, Jeffrey/Falconer Middle Sr High Sch	37
Jordan, Leeanne/Jasper Troupsburg Elem Sch	215
Jordan, Shannon/Heuvelton Central Sch	210
Jorgensen, Michael/Dana L West Jr Sr High Sch	35
Jorisch, Mara/Hicksville Middle Sch	122
Joseph-Hislop, Cherry-Ann/PS 59 William Floyd	84
Joseph, Ann/Wilson Tech Dix Hills	216
Joseph, Ingrid/IS 392	93
Joseph, Terence/Renaissance CHS for Innovation	140
Josephson, Lisa/PS 232 Lindenwood	181
Joyner-White, Gail/Cross Hill Academy	263
Jufer, Natalie/Urban Assmbly Ldrshp & Emprmnt	90
Julian, Melissa/Pittsford Mendon High Sch	110
Julian, Robert/John F Kennedy High Sch	59
Jung an, Mi/South Grove Elem Sch	130
Jungreis, David/Torah United Talmudical Boys	199
Junik, Keith/St Mary's High Sch	66
Jurewicz, Susan/Charter Sch for Applied Tech	3
Jurman, Nicholas/Quest to Learn	137
Jusino, William/Progress HS-Prof Careers	83
Juszczak, Jason/Longridge Elem Sch	109

K

NAME/School	PAGE
Kabia, Yabome/Berkeley Carroll Sch	96
Kabinoff, Jeremy/PS 184M Shuang Wen	135
Kacyvenski, Catherine/Chenango Forks Elem Sch	28
Kahan, Rabbi/Yeshiva Tzemach Tzadik Viznitz	100
Kahmar, Jared/Hamilton Bicentennial Elem Sch	166
Kahn, Kerry/Long Beach Catholic Reg Sch	132

PRINCIPAL INDEX

NAME/School	PAGE
Kahn, Rachel/Beth Jacob Elem Sch	144
Kairy, Vicky/Barkai Yeshiva	96
Kaiser, Kim/Parkview Junior Academy	160
Kakleas, Cathy/Hellenic Classical CS-Statn IS	4
Kalavazoff, Tania/Albany Elem Sch	152
Kalisch, David/Kolel Chasidei Rachmistrivka	199
Kalish, Gary/Greenport Sch	222
Kambrich, Susan/Woodland Hill Montessori Sch	192
Kaminski, Sherry/Empower Childen's Academy	149
Kane, Jim/Horseheads Christian Sch	41
Kane, Joan/Our Lady Blessed Sacrament Sch	186
Kane, Roy/Notre Dame Jr Sr High Sch	153
Kane, Thomas/St Thomas the Apostle Sch	13
Kang, Clara/PS 376Q	180
Kantor, Andrea/Dows Lane Elem Sch	257
Kaplan, Ava Cara/PS 186X Walter J Damrosch	25
Kaplan, Jonathan/PS 93 Albert G Oliver	18
Kaplan, Joshua/Randolph Sch	55
Kaplan, Samantha/Yorkville Cmty Sch	138
Kaplan, Sarah/Manhattan Early Clg-Advertise	136
Kapperman, Scott/St Amelia Sch	65
Kapsiak, Jennifer/PS 84 Erie Co Health Center	58
Karakas, Unal/Brookside Elem Sch	116
Karakas, Unal/PS 195	24
Karalazarides, Stamo/PS 46 Alley Pond	179
Karanikolas, Eftyhia/PS/MS 37 Multiple Intelligence	22
Karby, Nora/IS 7 Elias Bernstein	192
Karcher, Shannon, Dr/Northstar	111
Karnowsky, Rivka/Bnos Menachem	96
Karp, Penina/Shulamith School for Girls	99
Karp, Peter/Institute for Collaborative Ed	136
Kashani, Mordechai/Yeshivat Ohr Haiim	189
Kashani, Rabbi/Mesivta Ohr Torah	188
Kasper, Jeffrey/Village Elem Sch	130
Kassar, Andrea/The Nightingale-Bamford Sch	146
Kaste, John/Monroe Woodbury Sr High Sch	165
Kaszynsk, Suzanne/Our Lady of Lourdes Sch	143
Katavolos, Barbara/Hawk Meadow Montessori Sch	55
Katcher, Lilliam/Newcomers High Sch	184
Katchihtes, Daniel/Dawnwood Middle Sch	225
Katt, Manuela/Manhattan Christian Academy	145
Katz, Deborah/Gesher Yehuda Yeshiva	97
Katz, Matti/Nesivos Bais Yaakov Sch	98
Katz, Melanie/Franklin D Roosevelt High Sch	89
Katz, Shimshon/Yeshiva Kehilath Yaakov Sch	266
Katzman, Karen/Tiegerman Sch	134
Kaufmann, Scott/Rye Lake Campus	252
Kaup, Lisa/Franklyn S Barry Primary Sch	47
Kawryga, Jeanine/O E S J Elem Sch	72
Kazan, Margaret/St Joseph Sch	265
Kazan, Margaret/Transfiguration Sch	265
Kean, Dave/West Middle Sch	64
Keane, Annette/Anne Hutchinson Elem Sch	254
Keane, Celeste/Gordon Creek Elem Sch	200
Keane, Corinne/Paul J Gelinas Jr High Sch	232
Keane, Danielle/PS 5 Port Morris Sch	16
Keane, Kevin/Cherry Valley-Springfield Sch	173
Keane, Tracy/Curious Young Learners PK Ctr	180
Keane, Tracy/PS 377	181
Kedzielawa, David/John Jay High Sch	54
Keefus-Jones, Wendy/Boonville Elem Sch	150
Keegan, Anne/PS 209	21
Keegan, Daniel/Island Trees Memorial Mid Sch	122
Keegan, Joan/Herricks High Sch	121
Keegan, Mary/PS 146 Howard Beach	181
Keegan, Virginia/Eldred Jr Sr High Sch	236
Keeler, Richard/Central Valley Academy	77
Keelin, Kris/Monsignor Scanlan High Sch	25
Keelin, Tracy/Immaculate Heart of Mary Sch	265
Keenan, Hugh/St Margaret of Cortona Sch	26
Keene, Rachel/Success Acad CS Harlem N Cen [245]	8
Kegan, John/Astor Learning Center	55
Kehn, Hannah/New Visions CHS Humanities IV [243]	6
Keil, Allison/Community Roots Charter Sch	82
Kelch, Eugenia/Life Academy HS Film & Music	91
Kelder, Carole/Mt Marion Elem Sch	243
Kelderhouse, Robert/Rockland Institute for Spec Ed	199
Keller, B Jeff/Whitehall Jr Sr High Sch	248
Keller, Paul/Norman Howard Sch	114
Kelley, Meghan/PS 153 Helen Keller	23
Kelly, Jennifer/Clyde-Savannah Middle Sch	249
Kelly, John/New Covenant Learning Center	55
Kelly, Karin/PS 174 William Sidney Mount	182
Kelly, Kevin/George D Ryder Elem Sch	206
Kelly, Linda/Maine Memorial Elem Sch	29
Kellygibbons, Virginia/Frank J Carasiti Elem Sch	228
Kelman, Ariella/Yeshiva Dar HEI Torah	189
Kemler, Jessica/Harbor Hill Elem Sch	129
Kemnitzer, John/Buckeley Middle Sch	53
Kendall, Patricia/Cascadilla Sch	241
Kennedy, Barbara/United Nations Int'l Sch	189
Kennedy, Debra/Nssa	235
Kennedy, Donna/Gillen Brewer Sch	144
Kennedy, Taurean/Fusion Academy-Westchester	265
Kennedy, Verone/Riverton Street Charter Sch [210]	184
Kenny, Deborah/Harlem Village Acad W Upper ES [239]	4
Kenny, Mary Beth, Dr/Wingdale Elem Sch	52
Kenny, Stephen/Cobbles Elem Sch	109
Kent, Phil/New Suffolk Common Sch	226
Kent, Princess/PS 126 Dr Marjorie Dunbar Sch	19
Kent, Tracy/Berlin Elem Sch	189
Keough, Matthew/Christian Brothers Academy	160
Kephart, Penny/Prattsburgh Central Sch	215
Kerins, Mary/Hyde Park Elem Sch	148
Kernkruat, Solomon/Talmud Torah Ohel Yochanan	99
Kerns, Caroline/Leadership Prep Ocean Hill El [246]	5
Kerr, Kaye/MS 933 City Knoll Middle Sch	136
Kersten, Andrea/Cleveland Hill Middle Sch	59
Kerzner, Kathleen/Cleary School for the Deaf	234
Kerzner, Kathleen/Mill Neck Manor Sch for Deaf	134
Kesler, Paul/Batavia High Sch	73
Kessler, Maria/Tioga Learning Center	238
Khalil, Ismael, Dr/Al-Mamoor Sch	187
Khan, Javaid/Horace Mann Mid Upper Sch	26
Khare, Claudine/Vail Farm Elem Sch	51
Khondker, Fauzia/Rising Stars Islamic Sch	188
Kiel, Steve/Round Hill Elem Sch	167
Kiernan, JC/St Charles Sch	195
Kikuchi, Fumiko/Keio Academy of New York	266
Kilbridge, Martin, Dr/Our Lady of Mercy Sch	114
Kiley, Rebecca/Broadway Elem Sch	40
Kilian, Jon/Stockbridge Valley Ctl Sch	106
Kilmade, Joe/Saratoga Central Catholic HS	203
Kilmer, Raymond/Fayetteville-Manlius High Sch	155
Kilmer, Sue/Columbia Grammar & Prep Sch	144
Kim, Emily/Zeta Bronx 1 Elem Sch	9
Kim, Emily/Zeta Inwood 1 Elem Sch	9
Kim, Lena/PS 098 the Douglaston Sch	179
Kimball, Laura/Edward J Bosti Elem Sch	219
Kimble, Rick/Corning-Painted Post Mid Sch	214
Kimmel-Gorman, Julie/Staley Elem Sch	152
Kimpland, Matthew/Split Rock Elem Sch	159
King-Reese, Jennifer/Porter Magnet Elem Sch	159
King, Andy/Hackley Sch	265
King, Brett/Chancellor Livingston Elem Sch	53
King, Brett/Cherry Road Elem Sch	160
King, Corinne/Lutheran Elem Sch of Bay Ridge	98
King, Darryl/PS 357 Pathways Academy East	58
King, David/Thomas A Edison Elem Sch	62
King, Patricia/MS 267 Math Science & Tech	86
Kingman, Susan/Bay Knoll SDA Sch	114
Kingsley, Rebecca/Norwood-Norfolk Elem Sch	211
Kinhom, Ben/Darkei Chaim	97
Kipper, Gail/Farragut Middle Sch	256
Kirk, Michael/Matthew Paterson Elem Sch	175
Kirk, William/PS 229 Dyker	90

New York School Directory

PRINCIPAL INDEX

NAME/School	PAGE
Kirk, Wilma/PS 299 Thomas Warren Field	94
Kirkland, Khalek, Dr/Boys Prep Bronx School of NY [244]	1
Kirrane, Anna/PS 81 Robert J Christen	21
Kirton, Desiree/Brooklyn Scholars Charter Sch [210]	88
Kitchen, Suzy/St James Elem Sch	30
Kittrell, Latoya/South Brooklyn Cmty High Sch	85
Klaehn, Addie/Honeoye Central Sch	161
Klafehn, Matthew/New Lebanon Jr Sr High Sch	46
Klager, Renee/MS 379 Clg Point Collaborative	178
Klaich, Nicholas/PS 81 Sch	58
Kleger, Eve/Village Community Sch	146
Klehr, Monica/Harbor Heights	141
Klein, Buruch/Yeshiva Ruach Chaim	100
Klein, Evan/PS 226 Alfred De B Mason	91
Klein, Kenneth/Hempstead High Sch	121
Klein, Kevin/Integrated Arts & Tech HS	111
Klein, Melissa/PS 44 David C Farragut	24
Klein, Mindy/Bais Esther School for Girls	96
Kleinman, Denise/Nokomis Elem Sch	229
Klestvick, Arlene/Prospect Park Girls Yeshiva	98
Kletenik, Pesha/Yeshiva Har Torah Sch	189
Kletter, Joanna/School 4 South Oceanside Road	127
Klien, Nachum/Bais Sarah	96
Kline, David/New York Film Academy	145
Klint, Amanda/Spa Christian Sch	203
Klocek, Patrick/Woodward Parkway Elem Sch	119
Klomp, Jonathan/North Babylon High Sch	226
Kloss, Kate/Elsmere Elem Sch	10
Klotz, Marianne/Brookville Ctr Childrens Srvcs	133
Klugman, Michael/Bethlehem Central Middle Sch	10
Klus, Meredith/Brooks Hill Elem Sch	108
Knapp, Jo-Anne/Caryl E Adams Primary Sch	30
Knapp, Nicole/Cherry Valley-Springfield Sch	173
Knecht, Barbara/Margetts Elem Sch	196
Knight, Dr/Rochdale Early Advantage CS	183
Knight, Mac/DeWitt Middle Sch	240
Knight, Pamela/Evans Mills Primary Sch	80
Knights, Joyce/Brooklyn Landmark Elem Sch	93
Knowlton, Michelle/Kenneth L Rutherford Elem Sch	237
Knox, Ian/Turnpike Elem Sch	191
Knudson, Jessica/PS 516 Sunset Park Avenues	85
Knuschke, Robert/Dr George F Mack Middle Sch	50
Kobrin, Jeffrey/North Shore Hebrew Acad-Cherry	134
Kobrin, Jeffrey/North Shore Hebrew Academy	134
Koch, Ben/Renaissance Acad of the Arts	6
Koch, Christine/Lake Shore Senior High Sch	60
Koehler, Joe/Glenn Curtiss Elem Sch	214
Koeng, Jon/Charles O Dickerson High Sch	241
Koening, Sara/Bnos Bais Yaakov	187
Kolakowski, Kevin/Mechanicville Jr Sr High Sch	201
Kolkhorst, Mary/Berry Hill Elem Sch	130
Kolman, Stephen/Trinity Sch	146
Kolodny, Shlomo/Bais Yitzchak Yeshiva	96
Komorowski, Toni/Tangier Smith Elem Sch	233
Komp, Thomas/Boulevard Elem Sch	71
Konda, Leena/South Bronx Classical CS II	7
Kong, Joan/PS 11 Highbridge Sch	19
Kopiczak, Sandra/Brocton Central Sch	36
Korolczuk, Christopher/Center for Community Adjustmnt	116
Korrol, Gregg/PS 101 the Verrazano	91
Kortright, Dennis/Samuel J Preston Elem Sch	256
Kosar, Michael/Holy Spirit Sch	192
Kosis, Patricia/Benjamin Franklin Elem Sch	62
Kotlarsky, Avremel/Hebrew Academy	199
Kouba, Irene/North Side Sch	188
Koularmanis, Anastasios/St Demetrios Elem Sch	188
Koularmanis, Anastasios/St Demetrios Mid High Sch	188
Kourt, Andrew/Walter B Howard Elem Sch	46
Kowalski, Paul/Emmet Belknap Intermediate Sch	147
Koza, Christina/Spring Creek Cmty Sch	89
Kozak, Jeremy/West Canada Valley Jr Sr HS	79
Kozar, Diane/CP Rochester Augustin Chld Ctr	114
Kraemer, Robert/Knox Junior High Sch	71
Kramarski, Gabriel/Bais Shifra Miriam	198
Kramer, Barbara/North Hornell Elem Sch	214

NAME/School	PAGE
Kramer, Beth/Walberta Park Primary Sch	160
Kramer, Cynthia/Furnace Woods Elem Sch	256
Kranidis, Hope/Stewart Manor Elem Sch	119
Krantz, Christopher/Elmira High Sch	40
Kraus, Carolyn/Our Lady of Victory Sch	65
Krauss, Binyamin/Sar Academy	27
Krebs, David/George Ross MacKenzie Elem Sch	236
Krewson, Darren/Central Baptist Christian Acad	30
Krieger, Melissa/East Hills Elem Sch	129
Kristl, Nancy/Rome Early Childhood Center	152
Kromm, Jane/St Clement's Regional Cath Sch	203
Krum, S/Cairo-Durham Middle Sch	75
Kruszynski, Peter/Lancaster Middle Sch	63
Krzyzostaniak, Tomasz/Girls Prep Bronx Charter ES [244]	4
Ksanznak, David/Hamagrael Elem Sch	10
Kucko, Margaret/Johnson City Intermediate Sch	29
Kudla, Michelle/Cayuga Heights Elem Sch	60
Kuessous, Armo/Shaare Torah Sch	98
Kuhn, Jeffrey/Whitesboro Senior High Sch	153
Kumiega, Renee/Cloverbank Elem Sch	60
Kump, Laura/PS 26 Carteret Sch	193
Kupiec, Ed/Tully Elem Sch	159
Kurland, Deborah/Bnos Bais Yaakov	187
Kurtz, Debra/Otselic Valley Central Sch	42
Kussell, Efrat/Launch Expeditionary Lrng CS	5
Kuwik, Keith/Ledgeview Elem Sch	59
Kwateng, Kinsley/Benjamin Banneker Academy	82
Kwietniewski, John/Randolph Academy-Hamburg	33
Kwitowski, Kim/St Mary's Elem Sch-Lancaster	66
Kyer, Laura/West Sand Lake Elem Sch	189

L

NAME/School	PAGE
La Morte, Michael/Space Shuttle Columbia Sch	194
La Sala, Laura/PS 89 Elmhurst	177
Labare, Christine/Beaver River Central Sch	101
LaBarge, Jamie/Ronald B Stafford Middle Sch	45
LaBorde, Loris/Northeastern Academy	145
Labriola-Megee, Jennifer/New York School for the Deaf	266
LaCasse, Robert/Hudson High Sch	46
Lacey, Andria/John E Joy Elem Sch	151
Lacey, Julie/Vertus Charter Sch	8
Lacey, Ruth/Beacon Sch	138
LaClair, William/Cicero-N Syracuse High Sch	157
Ladd, Susan/Henry Hudson School 28	111
Ladouce, Sheila/A J Smith Elem Sch	35
LaFauci, Phyllis/Huntington Montessori Sch	235
LaFleur, Adam/Great Tomorrow School USA	144
Laforester, Wilford/Wildwood Sch	205
Lafrancis, Michael/Success Acad CS Hell's Kitchen [245]	8
Lafrancis, Michael/Success Acad HS Lib Arts-Mnhtn [245]	8
Lagnado, Andrew/Copiague Middle Sch	220
Lagnado, Jennifer/Lawrence High Sch	123
Lagnese, Diana/Bellaire Sch	183
Laguarda, Lucia/Flower Hill Primary Sch	223
Lahey, Jill/Cherokee Street Elem Sch	219
Laignel, Caty/Blue Rock Sch	198
Lain, Jean/Port Jervis Middle Sch	166
Lais, Christina/Glebe Street Elem Sch	71
Laise-Chong, Carolina/Northside Therapeutic ECC	145
Lake, Bryan/Oregon Middle Sch	227
Lallier, Michele/St James Elem Sch	212
Lam, Label/Shaarei Zion Ohel Bracha Sch	188
Lamb, Jonathan/Storm King Sch	168
Lambert, Gail/Brooklyn Acad for Sci & Enviro	86
Lambert, Patricia/Blind Brook Middle Sch	253
Lambiaso, Julie/Unatego High Sch	174
Lamhaouhi, Miriam/Rockaway Park High Sch	181
Landau, Mordechai/Yeshiva Yesode Hatorah Adas	100
Landau, Sholom/Yeshiva Ohr Shraga D'Veretzky	100
Landeau, Reginald/JHS 216 George J Ryan	179
Landry, Annette/Berne-Knox-Westerlo Elem Sch	10
Landsberg, Yosef/Mesivta Rabbi Chaim Berlin	98
Landsman, Mark/Yeshiva of Central Queens	189
Landy, Julie/Oswego BOCES-Exceptional Ed	170

PRINCIPAL INDEX

Market Data Retrieval

NAME/School	PAGE
Lane, Crystal/Brooklyn Ascend Mid Chtr Sch	2
Lane, Greg/Henry Burger Jr High Sch	112
Lang, Brenda/Milford Central Sch	173
Langan, Patricia/Patricia A DiChiaro Elem Sch	264
Lange, Karyn/Abilities First Sch	55
Langendal, Marcella/Hayground Sch	235
Langford, Jennifer/Our Lady of Mt Carmel Sch	168
Lango, Danielle/Charlotte Avenue Elem Sch	61
Langone, David/Westmoreland Upper Elem Sch	153
Langsam, Aaron/Yeshiva MacHzikel Hadas	100
Langsam, Aron/Yeshiva MacHzikei Hadas Belz	100
Langworthy, Amy/Warrensburg Elem Sch	246
Langworthy, Matt/Southwestern Elem Sch	39
Lanigan, Ryan/Mexico High Sch	171
Lansner, Noah/Brooklyn Preparatory HS	83
Lanzillotto, Nicole/Boerum Hill Sch Int'l Studies	84
LaPorte, Danielle/PS 115 James J Ambrose Sch	179
Lapple, Kim/H C Crittenden Middle Sch	253
Larcy, Carolyn/Maria Montessori Sch	133
Laregina, Kim/New Hyde Park Road Sch	126
Larke, Kerry/Marion G Vedder Elem Sch	226
Larkin, Mary/St Ignatius Loyola Sch	143
Larkin, Sabina/Ocean Avenue Elem Sch	227
Larochester, Jon/Islip High Sch	224
LaRosa, Kelly/Eden Elem Sch	60
Larrabee, Deborah/Ft Plain High Sch	115
Larsen, Gina/Arcadia High Sch	108
Larsen, Matthew/Brilla College Prep Mid Sch CS	2
Larsen, Michael/Minisink Valley Middle Sch	165
Larson, Andrew/Hiawatha Elem Sch	229
Larson, Kirsten/Marble Hill HS-Int'l Studies	21
Larson, Michael/Commack Middle Sch	219
Larson, Tamara/Lewiston Porter Primary Ed Ctr	147
Lascano, Cynthia/PS 767 Little Brooklyn Pre-K	85
Laser, Mrs/Bais Malka Sch	198
Lasher, Sharon/Oyster Bay High Sch	127
Laster, Michael/Farnsworth Middle Sch	11
Laszewski, Ann/Ballston Spa Middle Sch	200
Latella, Brian/Madison Central Sch	105
Latronica, Laura/Lime Kiln Elem Sch	196
Latvis, Matthew/Beekman Elem Sch	51
Lau, Jakub/Emerson Sch	182
Lauer, Nicole/Boston Valley Elem Sch	61
Laureano, Lemarie/Young Women's Leadership Sch	20
Lauria, Michael/Grand Island Sr High Sch	61
Lauricella, Christopher/Albany Academy	13
Lavery, Geraldine/Good Shepherd Sch	143
Lavery, Janine/Smithtown Elem Sch	230
Lavigne-Jones, Deon/PS/IS 295Q	184
Lawler, Ryan/Marlboro High Sch	242
Lawrence, Douglas/Liverpool High Sch	156
Lawrence, John/State Street Intermediate Sch	158
Lawrence, Matthew/Mahopac High Sch	176
Lawrence, Yolanda/Riverdale Avenue Middle Sch	93
Lawson, Melissa/Ralph R Smith Elem Sch	52
Lazar, Miriam/Archimedes Acad Math Sci Tech	17
Lazerson, Amanda/JHS 162 Willoughby	93
Lazio, Deb/Nathaniel Hawthorne School 25	111
Lazzaro, Philip/The Harvey Sch	266
Leach, Mary/Ninth Grade Academy	107
Leaird, J/Williamsburg Collegiate CS [246]	9
Leake, Mary-Elaine/Trinity Lutheran Sch	134
Leakey, Jill/PS 29 Queens	178
Leamon, Christine/Edenwald Sch	258
Leavitt, Ruth/Dolgeville Elem Middle Sch	77
LeBaron, Brian/Rome Free Academy	152
LeBeau, Nicole/Heuvelton Central Sch	210
Lebovitz, Jacob/United Talmudical Acad-Viola	199
Leckie, Mark/Calvary Chapel Christian Sch	163
Ledda, Angelo/Acad-Personal Ldrshp & Excell	20
Leddy, Brenda/Theresa Primary Sch	80
Leddy, Peter/IS 238 Susan B Anthony	183
Lederer, Moshe/Talmud Torad Ohr Moshe	99
Lederman, Mrs/Bais Yaakov Dchassidei Gur Sch	96
Lee, Cindy/West End Elem Sch	124
Lee, Doris/Village Academy	181
Lee, Heather, Dr/Smithtown Christian Sch	235
Lee, Jonathan/PS 115 Daniel Mucatel Sch	88
Lee, Lindsay/Tapestry Charter Sch	8
Lee, Marlon/PS 79 Pfc William Grabiarz Sch	57
Lee, Matthew/Clinton Senior High Sch	150
Lee, May/PS 42 Benjamin Altman	137
Lee, Melanie/Queens High Sch-Lang Studies	179
Lee, Pamela/PS 162 John Golden	179
Leeds, Allyn, Dr/Tackan Elem Sch	230
Leef, Jonathan/Rye Country Day Sch	266
Lefkowitz, Reuven/Talmud Torah Bais Yechiel Sch	266
Leggett, Susan/William L Buck Elem Sch	131
Legions, Rachelle/PS 106 Lighthouse Elem Sch	181
Lehman, Brad/Keshequa Interm Sch	103
Lehr, Gregory/Oxford Academy Middle Sch	42
Lehrer, Eliezer/Ora Academy	114
Leib, Melody/PS 390Q Civic ES Bayside Hills	180
Leibeck, Glenn/Central Queens Academy CS	3
Leibowitz, Shoshanah/Bnos Esther Malka Sch	96
Lein, Kenneth/Delaware Cmty Sch	9
Lein, Paula/Archer Street Elem Sch	119
Leiter, Ann/PS 56 Harry Eichler	180
Lemke, Joseph/Brook Avenue Elem Sch	217
Lemon, Barara/New York St Sch for the Blind	6
Lenahan, Kevin/PS 36K	94
Lenahan, Michael/Transfiguration Sch	143
Lennon, Kelly/Ampark Neighborhood Sch	20
Lennox, Michael/Starbuck Elem Sch	82
Lens, Reinaldo/PS 63 Author's Academy	19
Lent, Arlene/Cornerstone Christian Academy	207
Lent, Nicole/Warren Street Elem Sch	72
Leon, Irene/PS 89 Cypress Hills	89
Leon, Lupe/JHS 52 Harold O Levy Sch	141
Leonard, George/Campa Charter Sch	2
Leonard, Kristi/Hawkins Path Elem Sch	225
Leonard, Melissa/Worcester Central Sch	174
Leonardatos, Harry, Dr/Clarkstown North High Sch	195
Leone, Amy/Letchworth Middle Sch	267
Leone, Cheryl-Ann/New York City Acad-Discovery	180
Leong, April/Liberation Diploma Plus HS	91
Leonrdi, Lauren/Slcd Sch	188
Lerner, Michael/Bard High School Early College	135
LeRoux, Jeremy/Watkins Glen Elem Sch	207
Leslie, Robert/Lee G Peters Career Center	154
Leslie, Sylvia/PS 268 Emma Lazarus	88
Lessa, William/Cardinal Hayes High Sch	25
Lester, Colleen/Cambridge Central Sch	247
Lester, Deanne/Blasdell Elem Sch	60
Lester, Duncan/Reece Sch	145
Lethbridge, James/Woodland Middle Sch	118
Leto, Barbara/Acad for Excellence Thru Arts	181
Lett, Anthony/MS 57 Whitelaw Reid Acad	86
Lettiere, Paula/Ft Greene Prep Academy	82
Leuthauser, Ellen/Clinton Elem Sch	150
Lev, Benjamin/Hamilton Grange Middle Sch	141
Levenstein, Jessica, Dr/Horace Mann Mid Upper Sch	26
Levey, Eliana/Robert Frost Middle Sch	220
Levi, Michael/Beth Jacob Day Sch for Girls	96
Levin, Jonathan/The Clinton Sch	138
Levin, Raz/Brandeis Sch	133
Levine, Alex/Garrison Elem Sch	175
Levine, Amy/Lifeline Center for Child Dev	188
Levine, Deborah/PS 178 Dr Selman Waksman	23
Levine, Heather/Nassakeag Elem Sch	232
Levine, Rena/Congregation Yeshiva GR Monsey	199
Levy, Alison/Success Acad CS Williamsburg [245]	8
Levy, Mitchell/Countrywood Primary Center	231
Lew, Rebecca/PS 32 Belmont	21
Lewenstein, Chana/Ateres Bais Yaakov	198
Lewis, Antoine/KIPP Amp Elem Middle Sch [242]	5

New York School Directory

PRINCIPAL INDEX

NAME/School	PAGE
Lewis, Daniel/Smallwood Drive Elem Sch	56
Lewis, Faith/Mynderse Academy High Sch	208
Lewis, Jamal/Peekskill Middle Sch	260
Lewis, Jason/English Village Elem Sch	109
Lewis, Malik/West Brooklyn Cmty High Sch	85
Lewis, Roland/Biondi Elem Education Center	26
Lewis, Roland/Leake & Watts Chldrns Home Sch	266
Lewis, Tracie/PS 82 Early Childhood Center	58
Lewis, Tracy/Canarsie Ascend Mid CS	2
Lewis, Veronica/Howard A Hanlon Elem Sch	207
Leykam, Heather/PS K053	94
Liatto, Lisa/PS 164 Queens Valley	179
Libka, Tom/Alden Place Elem Sch	52
Libritz, Molly/Frankfort-Schuyler Jr Sr HS	77
Licata, Gil/Starpoint High Sch	149
Licato, Joseph/Ronkonkoma Middle Sch	220
Licato, Kimberly/Guggenheim Elem Sch	128
Lichtenwalner, Randy/Hillcrest Elem Sch	260
Liddell, Josh/Chautauqua Lake Sch	37
Lieberman, Bennett/Central Park East High Sch	139
Lieberman, Chaya/Yeshiva Congreg Toras Yufa	100
Liescheidt, Richard/Christ Lutheran Sch	187
Ligonde, Johane/John W Dodd Middle Sch	120
Limbo, Meg/Harlem Village Acad W Lower ES [239]	4
Lin, Edgar/Dr Susan McKinney Sch of Arts	82
Lin, Edgar/JHS 22 Jordan L Mott	19
Linares, Evelyn/PS/IS 210 21st Century Academy	142
Linchner, Ronald/Ives School-Lincoln Hall	266
Linck, Kevin/Fabius-Pompey Middle High Sch	155
Lincoln, David/Virgil I Grissom School 7	111
Linder, Lisa/PS 184 Newport	93
Lindner, Melissa/SS Peter & Paul Sch	65
Lindsay, Maria/Little Falls Middle Sch	78
Lindsay, Teresa/Lake Placid Middle High Sch	67
Linehan, Bart, Dr/Tuckahoe High Sch	262
Ling, Carla/PS/MS 20 P O George Werdan III	22
Link, Ron/Theatre Arts Production Co Sch	22
Lint, William/Norwood-Norfolk Middle Sch	211
Lippard, Jed/Bank St School for Children	143
Lippman, Naomi/Hebrew Acad 5 Towns Rockaway HS	133
Lipson, Amy/PS 175 City Island	23
Liquori, Arleen/Murry Bergtraum HS Business	137
Lisa, Joseph/IS 61 Leonardo Da Vinci	177
Lisack, Debbie/Golden Hill Elem Sch	164
Littell, Karen/Sunquam Elem Sch	222
Litwack, Eve/PS 107 John W Kimball	85
Liu, David/Gotham Collaborative High Sch	17
Liu, Jimmy/High School Arts & Bus YABC	177
Liverpool, DeNaro/New Grace Center Christian Sch	98
Livigni, Michael/Xavier High Sch	143
Liz, Luis/PS 159 Luis Munoz Marin Biling	21
Lloyd, Ellen/Marion Elem Sch	250
Lobdell, Candace/Forts Ferry Elem Sch	11
Lobdell, Conney/Mott Hall Charter Sch	6
Lobianco, Rose/Bronx Leadership Academy II HS	16
Lobianco, Wanda/George Washington Elem Sch	242
Locascio, Kristine/Francis J O'Neill Elem Sch	219
Lock, George/Manhattan Bridges High Sch	136
Lockwood, Allan/Guilderland Elem Sch	11
Lodinsky, Gregory/PS 212 Leonardo DaVinci HS	58
Logan-Smith, Angela/Goldie Maple Academy	180
Logan, Jennifer/PS 41 Stephanie A Vierno Sch	193
Logatto, Thomas/James Allen Alternative Sch	216
Lohret, Susan/Willow Field Elem Sch	156
Lolis, Evelyn/PS 84 Lillian Weber	139
Lomber, Andrea/Thousand Islands Middle Sch	81
Long, Erin/Lyons Elem Sch	249
Long, John/Benton Hall Academy	78
Long, Lester/South Bronx Classical CS	7
Long, Robert/East Quogue Elem Sch	221
Loomis, Arthur/O'Neill High Sch	50
Loomis, Tanya/Valley Early Childhood Center	213
Loose, Ann/Vestal Middle Sch	30
Lopes, Clemente/IS 10 Horace Greeley	184
Lopes, Teresa/St Anselm Sch	26
Lopez-Garcia, Kasandra/PS 44 Thomas C Brown	193
Lopez-Tua, Emarilix/Metropolitan Soundview HS	24
Lopez, Donny/PS 163 Alfred E Smith	139
Lopez, Elaine/International Leadership CS	5
Lopez, Glorimer/PS 583	18
Lopez, Gregg/PS Q255	185
Lopez, Robert/PS Q256	126
Lopez, Thomas/Walton Campus YABC	22
Lopez, Ventura/Temple Hill Academy	166
Lord, Laurence/PS 235 Janice Knight Sch	88
Lorelli, Joan/G R Claps Career & Tech Ctr	123
Lorenz, Heather/PS 47 Chris Galas	180
Loskoch, William/Success Acad CS Hudson Yards [245]	8
Losquadro, Jennifer/JHS 167 Robert F Wagner	136
Lostus, Regina/Success Acad CS Upper West [245]	8
Losurdo, Christopher/Voyages Prep-South Queens	181
Lotempio, Annie/Elmwood Franklin Sch	66
Lou, Victor/A B C Math Academy	187
Loua, Kay/PS 212 Midtown West	137
Loughlin, Kevin/Children's Learning Center	133
Loughman, Michael/Northern Adirondack Jr Sr HS	44
Loughran, Sharon/East Middle Sch	64
Louissaint, Katiana/JHS 8 Richard S Grossley	182
Loukatos, Angeliki/PS 34 Franklin D Roosevelt	135
Lounello, Barb/Airline Drive Academy	9
Lovett, A/Bronx Design & Const Academy	16
Lowe, Marlon/Mott Hall II M 862	138
Lowenberg, Robert/St Nicholas of Tolentine Sch	187
Lowenstein, Claire/PS 333 Manhattan Sch for Chldn	139
Lowie, Tim/Jennie F Snapp Middle Sch	29
Lowry, Amanda, Dr/John P McKenna Elem Sch	125
Lowy, Abraham/Cong Yeshuos Moshe Viznitz	199
Lozier, Beth/Camillus Middle Sch	159
Luard, Michele/Ronald Edmonds Lrng Center II	87
Lubetski, Uriel/Halb Elementary	133
Lubey, Sherry/Louis V Denti Elem Sch	151
Lucas, Justine/PS 143 Louis Armstrong	177
Lucas, Lilly/Excelsior Preparatory High Sch	183
Lucera, Dean/Ulster Career & Tech Center	241
Lucius, Frantz/PS 241 Emma L Johnston	87
Luczynski, Christina, Sr/Holy Family Sch	160
Ludwig, Andrew/Northern Chautauqua Cath Sch	39
Luft, Nicole/St Mary's Institute	116
Lukas, Stephanie/PS 51 Elias Howe	137
Lumb, Brian/Arcadia Middle Sch	108
Lumb, Kathryn/Clyde-Savannah Elem Sch	249
Lunden, David/Allen Road Elem Sch	157
Lundgren, Megan/Chautauqua Lake Sch	37
Lupini, James/Depew Middle Sch	60
Lupisella, Jeanine/Manor Intermediate Sch	109
Lupisella, Robert/Avon Central Primary Sch	102
Lustig, Hershel/Oholei Torah Elem Sch	98
Luther, Chad/South Lewis High Sch	102
Luther, Eric/Harrisville Central Sch	101
Lutinski, Eric/Rye Neck Middle Sch	261
Lutz, Andy/Cohen Elem Sch	40
Lux, Eileen/Fayetteville Elem Sch	155
Lyman-Wright, Kimberly/Beaver River Central Sch	101
Lynch, Colleen/Devereux School In New York	55
Lynch, Erik/Eugene Brooks Intermediate Sch	54
Lynch, Erin/IS 96 Seth Low	91
Lynch, Frances/PS 152 Evergreen	18
Lynch, Jennifer/Brushton Moira Sch	69
Lynch, Mary Grace/St James Elem Sch	230
Lynch, Meghan/Academy of Innovative Tech	88
Lynch, Peggy/Evans Park Elem Sch	197
Lynch, Terri/Success Acad CS Bensonhurst [245]	7
Lyness, James/Loyola Sch	143
Lyons, Jason/Eden Middle High Sch	60
Lyons, Jessica/Parkdale Elem Sch	60
Lyons, Kristin/Tiegerman Middle Sch-Glen Cove	134
Lyons, Tom/Warsaw Elem Sch	267

PRINCIPAL INDEX

M

NAME/School	PAGE
Ma, Sherry/Centre Avenue Elem Sch	118
Mable, Julie/Delhi Central Elem Sch	49
Mabry, Jerrod/Celia Cruz Bronx HS of Music	20
MacBain, Bruce/Moravia Jr Sr High Sch	35
MacCagnano, Ann/C A Lindbergh Elem Sch	62
MacChia, Theresa/Marion Street Elem Sch	124
Maciag, Therese/Holy Cross Academy	106
MacIntosh, Mary-Ann/Burton Street Elem Sch	104
Mack, Joseph/Cortland Jr Sr High Sch	47
Mackin, James/Hendrick Hudson High Sch	256
Macko, Kerry/Charles H Roth Jr High Sch	112
MacMahon, Colm/Rippowam Cisqua Sch-Lower	266
Macmonigle, Brett/Central Islip High Sch	218
MacPhee, Virginia/PS 18	191
Macri, Karen/Ctr for Dis Serv-Langan Sch	13
Macri, Rocco/JHS 104 Simon Baruch	136
Maddalone, Debbie/Mother Teresa Academy	203
Madden, Peter/Sauquoit Valley Middle Sch	152
Madison, Peggy/PS 15 Patrick F Daly	85
Maesano, Michael/Monroe Woodbury Middle Sch	165
Maffeo, Andrea/PS 46 Albert V Maniscalco	193
Magliaro, Robert/Urban Assembly Emergency Mgmt	138
Magoolaghan, Kelly/Susan Odell Taylor Sch	192
Magruder, Mary/Success Acad CS E Flatbush MS [245]	7
Mahabir, Hugo/Grace Church Sch	144
Mahabir, Sharon/PS 214 Michael Friedsam	89
Mahan, Peter/Scott M Ellis Elem Sch	75
Mahany, Ron/Wawarsing Christian Academy	244
Mahar, Martin/Bell Top Elem Sch	190
Mahar, Zane/Sauquoit Valley High Sch	152
Maher, Lisa/Woodglen Elem Sch	196
Maher, Mary/Hospital Schools M401	25
Maher, Tim/Baldwin Middle Sch	116
Mahoney, Brian, Dr/E F Academy New York	265
Mahoney, Danielle/Cato Meridian High Sch	34
Mahoney, Matt/Ruben A Cirillo High Sch	249
Mahoney, Michael/Nanuet High Sch	196
Mahunik, Amy/W H Seward Elem Sch	34
Mahunik, Patrick/Newfield Senior High Sch	241
Maines, Megan/Success Acad CS Harlem NW [245]	8
Maines, Tina/Cattaraugus-Lttle Vly High Sch	31
Maisano, Joseph/John H West Elem Sch	127
Maisonet, Samantha/PS 151 Mary D Carter	185
Makowski, Jennifer/Pinehurst Elem Sch	61
Malcolm-Grant, Constance/New Visions Elem Sch	120
Malcolm, Anne-Marie/Madiba Prep Middle Sch	86
Malcolm, Georgette/PS 327 Dr Rose B English	93
Maldonado, Patricia/St Margaret Sch	198
Male, Dawn/Greenburgh Ctl 7 Ecp	255
Malkisher, Steven/Spackenkill High Sch	54
Malloy, Kathryn/Mott Hall Bronx High Sch	19
Malloy, Linda/PS 145 Andrew Jackson	94
Malone, Erin/Forest Road Elem Sch	131
Malone, Heather/BOCES 2 Pre-School	106
Malone, Leyna/Martin Avenue Elem Sch	126
Malone, Matt/Sag Harbor Elem Sch	229
Maloney, Kelly/Carrie E Tompkins Elem Sch	254
Maloney, Leslie/Penfield Senior High Sch	110
Maloney, Lyndsey/Smith Road Elem Sch	157
Maloy, Michael/The Chapin Sch	146
Maluf, Olga/PS 316 Elijah G Stroud	87
Mampe, Julie/South Davis Elem Sch	63
Manalo, Carl/Queens HS for Info Rsch & Tech	181
Manard, Kelly/Syracuse Latin Sch	159
Manbode, Margo/New Covenant Chrn High Sch	27
Manchester, Tyler/Rochester Academy Charter Sch	6
Mancini, Theodore/Aquinas Institute	114
Mancuso, Margaret, Sr/Nazareth Elem Sch	114
Mandel, Adina/Bnos Bais Yaakov	187
Mandel, Feiga/PS 205 Clarion	90
Mandelbaum, David/Rabbinical Clg Bobover Yeshyva	98
Mandell, Adina/Bnos Bais Yaakov High Sch	187
Manfredi, Linda/PS 29 Bardwell	193
Manfredonia, Lisa/PS 62 Inocensio Casanova	17
Mangar, Shawn/Baychester Middle Sch	22
Mangone, Catherine/St Stanislaus Kostka Sch	187
Maniscalco, Jack/Oquenock Elem Sch	233
Manjarrez, Rina/PS 50 Talfourd Lawn Elem Sch	182
Manko, Thomas/Archbishop Walsh Academy	33
Manko, Thomas/Southern Tier Catholic Sch	34
Mann, Donna/Potter Career & Tech Center	56
Mann, Heather/PS 133 William A Butler	83
Mann, Michael/Niagara-Wheatfield High Sch	148
Mann, Michael/Orleans-Niagara BOCES Sch	168
Manne, Scott/Wayland-Cohocton Middle Sch	215
Mannino, Caterina/Enrico Fermi School 17	111
Mannino, Francesca/D & G Kaloidis Parochial Sch	97
Mannix, Michele/PS 141K	94
Manns, Michelle/PS IS 155 Nicholas Herkimer	93
Manolis, Maria/Soterios Ellenas Parochial Sch	99
Manor, Tracey/Saranac Elem Sch	45
Manuel, Adrian/Alverta B Gray Schultz Mid Sch	121
Maraia, Johnna/Sanfordville Elem Sch	167
Maravel, Margarita/Hampton Street Elem Sch	125
Marbury, Salema/PS 329 Surfside	91
Marc, Copani/Fulton Junior High Sch	171
Marchen, Satti/Our Lady's Catholic Academy	186
Marchi, Robert, Dr/PS 17 Henry Woodworth	84
Marchioli, Cesar/Lancaster High Sch	62
Marcinelli, Lindsay/Forestville Elem Sch	37
Marcinelli, Mary/Como Park Elem Sch	62
Marco, Deanna/PS 9 Naples St Elem Sch	193
Marcolina, Holly/Marathon Jr Sr High Sch	48
Marcu, Jessica/Opportunity Charter Sch	139
Marcus, Yaakov/Yeshivat OR Hatorah	100
Marcy, Sarah/Bronx Lab Sch	22
Mardy, Marc/PS 289 George V Brower	87
Maresca, Elvira/PS 36 Unionport Sch	17
Margrey, Mary/Augustinian Academy	82
Margulies, Mindi/Bais Rochel School-Boro Park	96
Mariano, Chris/Mountain Lake Academy	69
Mariano, Joseph/Troy High Sch	191
Marie, Francis/Divine Mercy Catholic Academy	186
Marie, Kathleen, Sr/St Denis & St Columba Sch	55
Mariniello, Deborah/Lakewood Elem Sch	196
Marino, Diane/PS 63 Old South	181
Marino, Robert/PS 120 Queens	178
Maritime, Aranya/Nichols Sch	66
Markham, Corey/Westfield Central Sch	39
Marks, Rosalie/Franklin K Lane Campus YABC	88
Marlette, Helen/Buffalo Seminary Sch	66
Marmor, David/Francis Lewis High Sch	179
Marone, Erin/School 2 Florence A Smith	127
Marotta, Andrew/Port Jervis High Sch	166
Marotta, Richard, Dr/Garden Sch	187
Marquardt, Daniel/Udall Road Middle Sch	233
Marques, Andrea/Abrookin Career & Tech Ctr	9
Marra, Angelo/It Takes A Village Academy	88
Marra, Donald/Pleasantville Middle Sch	260
Marrero, Yvonne/PS Q222-Christopher A Santora	185
Marrine, Barbara/Upton Lake Christian Sch	55
Marsaggi, Francine/PS 163 Flushing Heights	178
Marsh, Ana/Brooklyn Sch Social Justice	93
Marshall, Heather/York Preparatory Sch	146
Marshall, Nadine/PS IS 45 Horace E Greene	94
Marshall, Tara/Gams Tech Magnet Sch	166
Marshman, Robin/Gow Sch	66
Marszalek, Linda/Reach Academy Charter Sch	6
Martell, Mary/Holy Cross Sch	113
Martin, Brian/Edson Elem Sch	242
Martin, Caleb/North Warren Central Sch	246
Martin, Scott/Sweet Home High Sch	63
Martin, Tim, Dr/Islip Middle Sch	224
Martinelli, Daniel/Cohoes Middle Sch	10
Martinez, Aleyda/PS 319	84

New York School Directory

PRINCIPAL INDEX

NAME/School	PAGE
Martinez, Desiree/IS 232X Alexander Macomb Sch	19
Martinez, Emerly/Cornwall Central High Sch	163
Martinez, Geri/Christ the King Regional HS	186
Martinez, Gloria/PS 121 Throop	23
Martinez, Ralph/PS 89 Bronx	23
Martinez, Renzo/Washington Heights Academy	142
Martinkovic, Matthew/Seton Catholic Ctl High Sch	30
Martino, Jim/Edward J Arthur Elem Sch	75
Martorelli, Ronald/St Dominic ES MS	132
Martorelli, Ronald/St Dominic High Sch	132
Martuccio, Paul/PS 13 M L Lindemeyer	193
Marvin, Debra/St Michael Sch	268
Marvin, Jodi/Duanesburg Jr Sr High Sch	203
Marzeski, Rebecca/St Francis DeSales ECLC	79
Mascadri, Edward/Vanguard Collegiate High Sch	111
Mashinsky, David/Talmud Torah Darkei Avos ES	199
Mashinsky, David/Talmud Torah Darkei Avos PK-1	199
Masi, Danielle/Icahn Charter School 5	5
Masiello, Debra/St Mark's Lutheran Sch	266
Masiuk, Bonnie/Oconnor Academy-Monroe 1 BOCES	106
Maslaton, David/Bet Yaakov Orot Sarah	96
Maslin, Kent/Groton Elem Sch	240
Mason, Monique/JHS 131 Albert Einstein	17
Masood, Farhana, Dr/AL Madinah Sch	95
Masotti, Janet, Dr/Prime Time for Kids	199
Massey, Joan/Redemption Christian Academy	192
Massimo, Rudy/Rjo Intermediate Sch	224
Massimo, Valerie/Lloyd Harbor Elem Sch	219
Mastramatteo, Liz/Global Concepts Charter HS	4
Mastrangelo, Gary/Highview Elem Sch	255
Mastriano, Debra/PS 166 Rodgers Sch Arts & Tech	139
Mastro, Therese/Vestal Hills Elem Sch	30
Mastrogiovanni, Laura/MS 137 America's Sch of Heroes	180
Mastropaolo, Deborah/Elmcrest Children's Center	158
Masullo, Maria/Conselyea Prep Sch	83
Mate, Csilla/Pines Bridge Sch	252
Matera, Jim/Southern Westchester BOCES Voc	252
Matera, Matthew/Ralph Reed Middle Sch	219
Matheson, Tamika/Frederick Douglass Acad VII HS	93
Mathews, Kate/Anne M Dorner Middle Sch	259
Mathews, Mark/North Rose Wolcott MS	250
Matson, Meredith/Urban Assembly Sch Design/Con	138
Mattera, Erica/PS 11 Thomas Dongan	193
Matteson, Sarah/Indian River Intermediate Sch	80
Matthew, Deasure, Dr/Wilson Foundation Academy	112
Matthews, Kimberly/Schenevus Central Sch	174
Matthews, Patrice/Shore Road Sch	117
Matthias, Ezra, Dr/IS 229 Dr Roland Patterson	19
Mattina, Joseph/PS 23 Carter G Woodson	84
Mattison, Mr/Academy Charter Middle Sch	1
Mattle, Mark/St Joseph University Sch	66
Matyevich, Janet/Drake Elem Sch	148
Maurer, Elizabeth/Harold T Wiley Interm Sch	81
Maurer, George, Dr/Abbey Lane Elem Sch	123
Maurice, Marc/New York French American CS	138
Mauro, Carrie/Jackson Heights Elem Sch	245
Maxon, Merrie/Silver Creek Elem Sch	39
May, Echele/Meadow Elem Sch	116
May, Yakov/Yeshiva Tifereth Moshe	189
Mayher, Michael/Northwood Sch	69
Maynard, Linda/Guilford Elem Sch	42
Mayne, Laura/Brooklyn SDA Sch	97
Mazer, Katie/Key Collegiate Charter Sch	5
Mazza, Joseph/Seven Bridges Middle Sch	253
Mazza, Linda/PS 295	85
Mazzaroppi, Matthew/Morris Academy/Collab Studies	19
Mazzeo, Jodi/Heatly Sch	10
Mazzetti, Joseph/Pace Academy	53
Mazziotti, Mandy/Verne W Critz Primary Sch	231
Mazzola, Eugene/Acad-Conservation-Environ	87
Mazzola, Steven/Saunders Trade & Tech High Sch	264
McAleese, Sam/Gary D Bixhorn Tech Center	216
McAlpin, Daniel/Bloomfield Jr Sr High Sch	161
McArdle, Tim/Le Roy Jr Sr High Sch	74
McArthur, Ayesha, Dr/Rhame Avenue Elem Sch	118

NAME/School	PAGE
McAssey, Lucille/School 6 Kindergarten Center	127
McAuliff, Michael/St Margaret's Sch	160
McAuliffe, Kevin/PS/MS 200 Global Studies/	179
McAuliffe, Rob/Chazy Central Rural Sch	44
McBride, Rodney/Benjamin Turner Middle Sch	258
McCabe, Daniel/Nesaquake Middle Sch	230
McCabe, Sean/Spencerport High Sch	112
McCann, Dana/Our Lady of Mercy Sch	186
McCann, Kelly/PS 255 Barbara Reing Sch	92
McCartan, Kimberly/Clinton Street Elem Sch	64
McCarthy, Bill/Packer Collegiate Institute	98
McCarthy, Jeffrey/Red Jacket Elem Sch	162
McCarthy, Kerri/Kramer Lane Elem Sch	117
McCarthy, Kevin/Park East High Sch	139
McCarthy, Robert/Loretta Park Elem Sch	217
McCarthy, Sharon, Sr/Academy of St Dorothy	194
McCarthy, Winston/North Queens Cmty High Sch	178
McCarty, Skip/Odessa Montour Jr Sr High Sch	207
McCarty, Travis/Putnam Valley Middle Sch	176
McCauley, Joseph/Fieldston Lower Sch	26
McCauley, Megan/PS 213 Carl Ullman	180
McCaw, Sade/Opportunity Charter Sch	139
McConaghy, Brian/Herricks Middle Sch	121
McConnell, Laura/Old Country Road Elem Sch	122
McCord, Jane/PS 52 John C Thompson	193
McCormack, Kevin/Xaverian High Sch	95
McCormick, John/PS 811M Mickey Mantle Sch	142
McCourt, Tina/Rebecca Sch	145
McCoy-Dailey, Keisha, Dr/PS K396	94
McCrone, Robert/Long Branch Elem Sch	156
McCrystal, Maureen/Eagle Hill Middle Sch	155
McDade, Maureen, Sr/St Patrick Sch	234
McDaniel, La Kisha/JHS 143 Eleanor Roosevelt	141
McDermott, Deirdre/Corpus Christi Holy Rosary Sch	264
McDonald, Dan/East Coldenham Elem Sch	167
McDonald, Jennifer/Mt Markham Elem Sch	78
McDonald, Mary/PS 139 Alexine A Fenty	92
McDonald, Scott/William H Golding Middle Sch	206
McDonnell, Mary, Dr/PS 209 Clearview Gardens	179
McDonnell, Michael/Midwood High Sch	92
McDonough, Joseph/J M McKenney Middle Sch	209
McDougall, Michelle/Joseph Henry Elem Sch	201
McDowell, Kim/The Harley Sch	114
McElduff, Michael/Highland Falls Interm Sch	164
McElhiney, Scott/Bayville Intermediate Sch	123
McElhiney, Scott/Bayville Primary Sch	123
McElwee, Tami/Theodore Roosevelt Elem Sch	127
McEnaney, James/PS/MS 138 Sunrise	184
McEnery, Treeanne/Green Meadow Waldorf Sch	199
McEnroe, Kathleen/Webutuck High Sch	54
McEvoy, Colin/Millennium High Sch	136
McEvoy, Medea/PS 267 Eastside Elem Sch	137
McFarland, Adonna/MS 654 Van Siclen Cmty Mid Sch	89
McFarland, Kyle/Northville Central Sch	72
McGary, Lisa/Neil Armstrong Elem Sch	108
McGee, Pat/Byron-Bergen Jr Sr High Sch	73
McGeehan, Colleen/Young Women's Leadership Sch	140
McGillicuddy, Patrick/East Brooklyn Cmty High Sch	87
McGinn, Shelagh/South Side Middle Sch	128
McGinnis, Allison/St Edmund Preparatory High Sch	95
McGinnis, David/Pathways	29
McGory, Jim/Homer Elem Sch	48
McGough, Robert/Moreau Elem Sch	202
McGowan, Elizabeth/Lincoln-Titus Elem Sch	257
McGowan, Kelli/Deerfield Elem Sch	153
McGrath, Kristy/Remsen Jr Sr High Sch	151
McGrath, Thomas/Edward J Milliken Tech Center	216
McGregor, Dahlia/Science Skills Center	83
McGuire, Eileen/Mamaroneck Avenue Elem Sch	263
McHugh, Kate/The Epiphany Sch	143
McHugh, Kristin/Richard H Hungerford Sch	194
McInerney, Peggy/Wampus Sch	253
McKenna, Farrah/William Rall Elem Sch	224
McKenzie, Andrew/Newmeadow Saratoga Sch	203

PRINCIPAL INDEX

NAME/School	PAGE
McKenzie, Castella/Esmt IS 190	24
McKeon, Daniel/West Babylon Jr High Sch	233
McKeon, James/IS/PS 25-S Richmond HS	194
McKeown, P, Dr/Cairo-Durham High Sch	75
McKiernan, Robert/Red Hook Senior High Sch	53
McKillop, Thomas/East Lake Elem Sch	125
McKinley, Cristy/Scio Central Sch	15
McKinney, Patrick/Riverhead Charter Sch	6
McKoy, April/City Polytechnic High Sch	82
McLaren, Kamele/HS Teaching & the Professions	21
McLaughlin, Andrea/Bolivar-Richburg Early CDC	14
McLaughlin, Alecia/Irondequoit High Sch	113
McLaughlin, Patrick/St Francis Preparatory Sch	186
McLaughlin, Rod/Sullivan West Elem Sch	237
McLean, Karen/Brighter Choice CS for Boys [234]	1
McMahon, Laura/St Mary Sch	234
McMahon, Meghan/Urban Assem Sch Performing Art	140
McMahon, Patricia/Anna Merritt Elem Sch	147
McMahon, Patricia/Henrietta G Lewis Campus Sch	149
McMahon, Shawn/North Franklin Education Ctr	69
McMurdie, Rebecca/KIPP Washington Heights ES [242]	5
McNally, Andrew, Dr/Fishkill Elem Sch	54
McNally, Kathryn/Washington Drive Primary Sch	223
McNeely, Renee/Whitesville Central Sch	15
McNeil, Paul/Accompsett Middle Sch	230
McNeill, Neil/PS 207 Elizabeth Leary	92
McNell, Christopher/Elm Street Academy	13
McNulty, Susan/Carman Rd Sch Phys Handicapped	116
McPherson, Mr/School 9E Walter S Boardman	127
McRae, Trevlyn/PS 135 Sheldon Brookner	88
McRobbie Taru, Margaret/Promising Futures Ldrshp Acad	159
McSain, Doreen/Glenwood Elem Sch	30
McShane, Ian/Troy Middle Sch	191
McTague, Michael/Hudson Falls Intermediate Sch	248
McTague, Michael/Margaret Murphy Kdgn Center	248
McVey, Andy/Wayne Technical & Career Ctr	249
Meade, Kelley/Campbell-Savona Jr Sr HS	213
Meade, Lisa/Granville Jr Sr High Sch	247
Meade, Rashad/Eagle Acad Young Men II	93
Meagher, Beverly/Germantown Central Sch	46
Meccariello, Ann/Cooperstown Elem Sch	173
Meconi, Dawn/Digital Arts & Cinema Tech HS	84
Medina, Miguel/PS 48 at 39 MLK Multcltrl Inst	57
Medina, Sara/PS 85 Great Expectations	21
Meehan, Thomas/Edna Louise Spear Elem Sch	228
Meers, Carleen, Dr/Ulster BOCES Special Educ Ctr	241
Megherian, Seta/Holy Martyrs Armenian Day Sch	187
Megias, Alejandro/PS/IS 113 Anthony J Pranzo	178
Meginnis, Connie/Dunkirk Elem School 7	37
Mehta, Ishani/Leadership Prep Bed Stuy CS [246]	5
Mehta, Uma/Rochester Early Clg Intl HS	111
Meisell, Rabbi/Kerem Shlomo Yeshiva	98
Meisels, Moshe/Yeshiva Beth Hillel Williamsbg	99
Meister, Brian/Byron-Bergen Elem Sch	73
Mejia, Connie/PS 18 Park Terrace	141
Mele, Nicholas/IS 51 Edwin Markham	193
Melkonian, Mark/Queens Satellite HS-Oppor	182
Melkonian, Melissa/American Dream Charter Sch	1
Meller, Richard/St Helena Sch	26
Melnyk, Colleen/Murray Avenue Elem Sch	258
Melquist, Leslie/Jefferson Middle Sch	38
Memola, James/Queens Academy High Sch	179
Menake, Melissa/Cambria Heights Academy	183
Mendelsohn, Joy/PS 194 Raoul Wallenberg	92
Mendes, Rui/Bay Elem Sch	227
Mendez, Lourdes/Vida Bogart Sch All Chldrn	25
Mendlowitz, Feivel/Mesivta Beth Shraga for Boys	199
Meoli, David, Dr/John Philip Sousa Elem Sch	128
Mercado-Tilley, Yvette/Longwood Middle Sch	225
Mercado, Craig/St Ephrem Sch	95
Merced, Jeffrey/MS 582	83
Mercedes, Robert/MS 390	21
Mercer, Freya/Coxsackie Athens High Sch	75
Mercogliano, Lily/Brooklyn Free Sch	97
Mercora, Joe/Upper Nyack Elem Sch	197
Merims, Howard/Harold D Fayette Elem Sch	126
Merino, Rocco/Niagara Street Elem Sch	148
Merkle, Robert/Lake Shore Career & Tech Acad	56
Mermelstein, Nachman/Talmud Torah Imrei Chaim Sch	99
Merola, Arnold/Chittenango Middle Sch	104
Merrill, Kate/Erwin Valley Elem Sch	214
Merrill, Shaun/Lafayette Intermediate Sch	208
Merryman, Catherine/Our Lady of Lourdes HS	55
Meskos, Susan/West Street Elem Sch	161
Messia, Robert/Algonquin Middle Sch	189
Messier, Barbara, Dr/Lake Avenue Elem Sch	201
Messura, Carol/Wolcott Street Sch	74
Meth, Eliezer/Bais Yisroel Sch-Girls	237
Meth, Eliezer/Talmud Torah Imrei Burech-Boys	237
Meyer, Ann/Bronxville High Sch	253
Meyer, Jennifer/PS 22 Thomas Jefferson	178
Meyer, Jim/LaSalle Sch	13
Meyer, Joshua/Lake View Campus	67
Meyer, Mark/Hampton Bays Elem Sch	223
Michael, Carolyn/Brooklyn Prospect Charter MS	2
Michaeli, Caryn/PS 87 Middle Village	177
Michaelian, Annie/Oakwood Primary Center	231
Michals, Anastasia/Canarsie Ascend Lower CS	2
Michaux, Debra/PS 30 Wilton	16
Michelena, Adaleza/HS Innovation Adver-Media	87
Michelin, Robert/Gotham Professional Arts Acad	86
Mickle, Lisa/Okte Elem Sch	202
Miczan, Christine/Solvay Elem Sch	158
Middleton, Theresa/North Warren Central Sch	246
Midgette, Laurie/Cultural Arts Acad-Sprg Crk	87
Miele, Franco/William B Ward Elem Sch	259
Migliano, Susan/PS 196 Grand Central Parkway	182
Migliorino, David, Br/St Anthony High Sch	234
Mihalko, Paul/Hewes Career & Tech Ed Center	36
Miklas, Todd/Gowanda Middle Sch	32
Mikulski, John/Alden Intermediate Sch	56
Milano, Lisa/St Mary Sch	163
Millan, Elissa/Harley Avenue Primary Sch	221
Millas, Nicholas/Robert J Kaiser Middle Sch	237
Mille, Joseph/Freeport High Sch	120
Miller, Albina/Parkside Sch	145
Miller, Annette/Carlyle C Ring Elem Sch	38
Miller, Bret/Charles Finney Sch	114
Miller, Brett/Fox Lane High Sch	252
Miller, Charisse/Westhampton Beach Middle Sch	233
Miller, Daniel/Woodrow Wilson Elem Sch	27
Miller, Darlene/NYC Museum Sch	137
Miller, Elizabeth/Success Acad CS Rosedale [245]	8
Miller, Esther/Merkaz Bnos High Sch	98
Miller, Greer, Dr/Division Street Elem Sch	201
Miller, Jennifer/Avon Middle Sch	102
Miller, Jennifer/JHS 194 William H Carr	178
Miller, John/William B Tecler Magnet Sch	116
Miller, Joseph/IS 77 Queens	177
Miller, Karen/Coxsackie Elem Sch	75
Miller, Karen/Stokes Elem Sch	152
Miller, Marcy/Albany Avenue Elem Sch	224
Miller, Mellissa/Creston Academy	20
Miller, Michael/Bridgehampton Sch	218
Miller, Michael/Galway Jr Sr High Sch	201
Miller, Mordechai/Yeshiva of Far Rockaway	189
Miller, Paul, Dr/Green Tech High Charter Sch	4
Miller, Sandra/PS 77 Lower Lab Sch	137
Miller, Shirley, Dr/Acad of Hospitality & Tourism	86
Miller, Timothy/PS 76 William Hallet	184
Mills, Donald/Immaculate Conception Sch	160
Mills, Noreen/MS 442-Carroll Gardens Innovat	84
Miltenberg, Bryan/Aquebogue Elem Sch	228
Milton, Arleen/Alfred E Smith Campus YABC	16
Mims, Brendan/MS 358	182
Minaya, Patricia/Urban Assembly Sch of Business	138

New York School Directory

PRINCIPAL INDEX

NAME/School	PAGE
Minhas, Simi/Queens College Sch Math & Sci	179
Minor, Cheryl/Watson-Williams Elem Sch	152
Minor, Iverna/Webster Elem Sch	159
Mitchell, Brendon/Oceanside High Sch Castleton	127
Mitchell, Catherine/Young Women's Ldrshp Sch-Bklyn	84
Mitchell, Deon/Christopher Ave Cmty Sch	93
Mitchell, Earl/Edmund W Miles Middle Sch	216
Mitchell, Elizabeth/PS 64 Joseph P Addabbo	181
Mitchell, Gina/Brooklyn Latin High Sch	83
Mitchell, Jennifer/Collegiate Sch	144
Mitchell, Melissa/Union East Elem Sch	58
Mitchell, Michael/Northside Christian Academy	114
Mitchell, Patricia/PS 48 William Wordsworth	182
Mittler, Judy/IS 125 Thomas McCann-Woodside	177
Mizell, Karen/Setauket Elem Sch	232
Mizimakoski, Juliet/Irvington High Sch	257
Mochrie, Jeffrey/Theodore Roosevelt Primary Sch	59
Mody, Peter/South Glens Falls Sr High Sch	202
Moeller, Amy/Hillview Elem Sch	62
Moeller, James/Rocky Point Middle Sch	228
Mogavero, Michael/PS 196 Math Sci Tech Prep Sch	58
Mohamed, Shaykh/Al-Ihsan Academy	187
Mohamed, Solafa/El Ber Islamic Sch	187
Mohammed, Barry/East Middle Sch	217
Mohan, Subhas/Epic High School-South	180
Mohorter, Doug/Pine Grove Middle Sch	155
Moise, Stanley/PS 213 New Lots	89
Mokhtari, Abdelmadjid, Dr/AL Ihsan School of Excellence	160
Mokhtari, Parinaz/Montgomery Montessori Sch	168
Molinelli, Christopher/John Quincy Adams Primary Sch	220
Molle, Thomas/Oneonta Middle Sch	174
Moller, Yehuda/Rabbi Samson R Hirsch Yeshiva	145
Molloy, Amy/Sandy Creek Sch	172
Molluzzo, Maria/St Joseph Hill Academy HS	195
Molnar, Steve/Little River Community Sch	212
Mompoint, Yves/HS of Hospitality Management	136
Moncayo, Magaly/PS 106 Edward Everett Hale	94
Monchik, Marie/PS 138 Brooklyn	87
Monczyk, Moshe/Yeshiva Rabbi Chaim Berlin	100
Mong, Theron/West Street Elem Sch	148
Mongiello, Carol/PS 59 Harbor View Sch	194
Montalbano, Tarah/William Grady Career & Tech HS	91
Montalvo, Eugenia/PS 106 Parkchester	23
Montana, Michelle/PS 119 Dr Emmett W Bassett Sch	18
Montaruli, Debra/Wilson Tech Northport	216
Montas, Fred/Manlius Pebble Hill Sch	160
Monteau, Marie/PS 397 Foster-Laurie	87
Montecalvo, Stephanie/Ft Salonga Elem Sch	224
Montero, Christine/Casimir Pulaski Sch	263
Montgomery, Robert/K C Heffernan Elem Sch	157
Montgomery, Vijayal/Bronx Engr & Tech Academy	20
Mooney, Marcy/Ethel K Fyle Elem Sch	112
Mooney, Mary, Sr/St John Chrysostom Sch	26
Mooney, Paul/Howard G Sackett Technical Ctr	101
Moore-Boakye, Sherrmain/Albany Cmty Charter Sch	1
Moore, Brian/Indian River High Sch	80
Moore, Christine/Lawrence Primary Sch	123
Moore, Estelle/PS 156 Laurelton	183
Moore, Jane/Berkeley Carroll Sch	96
Moore, Jeremy/Owasco Elem Sch	34
Moore, Kathleen/Morrisonville Elem Sch	45
Moore, Kristy/Glens Falls Middle Sch	245
Moore, Michelle/PS 41 Gun Hill Road	23
Moore, Monje/Journey Prep Sch	133
Moore, Naiyma/PS 156 Waverly	93
Moore, Robert/Clarence Middle Sch	59
Moore, Wakili/Theodore Roosevelt School 43	111
Mora, Eduardo/New Sch Leadership Journalism	21
Morales, Rafael/PS 65 Raymond York ES	181
Morales, Wilper/West Bronx Acad for the Future	22
Moran, Kathleen/Holy Trinity Diocesan High Sch	132
Moran, Scott/City & Country Sch	144
Morano, Jonathan/St Barnabas Elem Sch	26
Morant, Linda/Allen Christian Sch	187
Morash, John/William E Cottle Elem Sch	262

NAME/School	PAGE
Morcone, Paul/Mary J Tanner Elem Sch	247
Moreno, Lauren/William T Rogers Middle Sch	224
Moretter, Erin/Northside Elem Sch	108
Morgan, Brian/Auburn High Sch	34
Morgan, Christina/Donald S Ray Middle Sch	154
Morgan, Gail, Sr/St Vincent Ferrer High Sch	143
Morgan, Joy Ann/PS 198 Brooklyn	92
Morgan, Shawn/Dennis M Kenney Middle Sch	171
Morgan, Terri/St Kateri Sch	114
Morgante, Ann/Charter Sch for Applied Tech	3
Morgante, Peter/Seneca Intermediate Sch	33
Morgia, Kylie/Alexandria Central Sch	79
Morien, Rhonda/Emma E Sherman Elem Sch	112
Morisi, Paul/St Anne Sch	132
Morley, Lauren/Lisbon Central Sch	211
Moro, Donna/Jack Abrams STEM Magnet Sch	223
Moro, Kimberly/Shield Institute/Bronx ELC	27
Morquecho, Gabrielle, Dr/PS 304 Hutchinson Tech HS	58
Morris, C/Academy Charter Elem Sch [247]	1
Morris, Darlene/Rosalyn Yalow Charter Sch	7
Morris, Jon/Andover Central Sch	14
Morris, Patrick/North Elem Sch	217
Morris, Thomas/St Adalbert Sch	186
Morrison, Ann/Robert H Jackson Elem Sch	38
Morrison, Ann/Sherman Central Sch	39
Morrison, David/Hillcrest High Sch	182
Morrison, Kimberly/Wales Primary Sch	62
Morrison, Scott/Barclay Elem Sch	107
Morrow, Jason/British Int'l Sch of New York	144
Morsi, Inas/Mt Kisco Elem Sch	252
Mortillaro, Frank/Northside Elem Sch	123
Mosca, Mike/Comsewogue High Sch	218
Moschella, Tina/PS 86 Irvington	94
Mosely, Joan/Acad Clg Prep Career Explore	86
Moser, Ms/JHS 278 Marine Park	92
Moskos, Stephanie/PS 12 James B Colgate	177
Moskowitz, Hershel/Yeshiva Ahavath Israel Sch	199
Moskowitz, Hershy/Bnos Yisroel Girls Sch	198
Most, Jordan/Yeshiva Bais Hachinuch	199
Mota, Indira/IS 171 Abraham Lincoln	88
Motala, Matthew/Roxboro Road Elem Sch	157
Mott, Gregory/Charter Sch for Applied Tech	3
Moulton, Kathryne/Meachem Elem Sch	159
Mousouroulis, Georgia/PS 939 Sunset ES Cultural Lrng	90
Moyer, Chris/Midlakes Intermediate Sch	162
Moyer, Chris/Midlakes Primary Sch	162
Mrwik, Tara/IS 250 Robert F Kennedy	178
Mshar, Theresa/JHS 185 Edward Bleeker	178
Mucci, Joycer/Riverview High Sch	195
Muccino, Brandon/PS 83 Donald Hertz	23
Mueller, Jennie/Greenwich Elem Sch	248
Muenkel, Catherine/Sacred Heart Sch	168
Muhammad, Abdul Basir/AL Madrasa Alislamiya Sch	95
Muhammed, Adofo/Bedford Academy High Sch	82
Muldowney, Amanda/Leo F Giblyn Elem Sch	120
Mule, Annamaria/Cobble Hill Sch of Amer Study	84
Mullahy, Dennis/St Pius X Sch	13
Mullan, Julie/Connolly Elem Sch	120
Mullen, Danielle/Durhamville Elem Sch	105
Mullen, Thomas/Expeditionary Sch Cmty Leaders	91
Mullins, John/Bayview Elem Sch	233
Mullock, Mary/Linnaeus W West Sch	29
Muluso, Phillip/Renaissance Campus Sch	66
Mumford, Tim/Onondaga Jr Sr High Sch	157
Mungin, Laura/George Washington Elem Sch	263
Mungioli, Anthony/PS 121 Nelson A Rockefeller	91
Mungioli, Anthony/Westlake Middle Sch	259
Muniz, Javier/PS 200 Benson Sch	90
Munk, Sara/Shulamith School for Girls	134
Munn, Bryan/Petrova Elem Sch	70
Munoz, Marie/PS 20 Port Richmond	193
Munoz, Wellington/Eugenio Maria De Hostos CS HS	3
Munro, Linda/Waterside Sch for Leadership	181
Murdock, Melinda/Riverside Elem Sch	174

School Year 2020-2021   800-333-8802   NY-U29

PRINCIPAL INDEX

NAME/School	PAGE
Murillo, Nancy/PS 38 George Cromwell	193
Murphy, Allison/St Kevin Catholic Academy	187
Murphy, Doreen/PS 69 Daniel D Tompkins	194
Murphy, Elisa/NYC Charter School of the Arts	6
Murphy, Jane/PS 185 Locke Sch Arts & Design	139
Murphy, John/South Side High Sch	128
Murphy, John/Walt Whitman High Sch	231
Murphy, Linda/Joseph A Edgar Interm Sch	228
Murphy, Maryann/Tully Jr Sr High Sch	159
Murphy, Melissa/Salt Point Center	51
Murphy, Michael/Pearl River High Sch	197
Murphy, Nicole, Dr/Regional Alter HS-Fox Meadow	252
Murphy, Richard/Shaker High Sch	11
Murphy, Steven/Westchester Hills School 29	264
Murray, Daniel/T J Connor Elem Sch	113
Murray, James/John F Kennedy High Sch	128
Murray, Karen/PS 67 Discovery Sch	57
Murray, Kathleen/Parkville Sch	121
Murray, Kelly/Noxon Road Elem Sch	51
Murray, Kimberly/Unadilla Valley Secondary Sch	43
Murray, Patricia/Bronxville Elem Sch	253
Murray, Rinaldo/New Heights Academy CS	141
Murray, Sean/West Hempstead Middle Sch	131
Murray, Thomas/Sayville Middle Sch	230
Murren, Tracee/Kingsborough Early College Sch	91
Murry, Maija/Hudson Valley Christian Acad	176
Musante, Michael/Cerebral Palsy of Westchester	265
Musanti, Lawrence/Monsignor Farrell High Sch	194
Mussi, Joseph/Liverpool Middle Sch	156
Mussolini, Patrick/Dobbs Ferry Middle Sch	254
Musto, John/Our Lady Mt Carmel-Bronx Sch	25
Mutakabbi, Khurshid/Maspeth High Sch	177
Mutasa, Shingi/Brilla Charter School Pax	2
Myers, Elmer/PS 3 Margaret Gioiosa Sch	193
Myers, Jeffrey/Long Beach High Sch	124
Myrie, Marica/Mott Hall IV	93
Mytych, Molly/Bellamy Elem Sch	151

N

NAME/School	PAGE
Naber, Susan/Vive School Pathways-Success	264
Naccarato, Danielle/Timber Point Elem Sch	221
Naccarato, Frank/Lindenhurst Middle Sch	224
Naccari, Anthony/St Gabriel Sch	26
Nadien, Lynnda/Smith Street Elem Sch	130
Najera, Victoria/PS 333 Longwood Acad Discovery	18
Najjar, Veronica/PS 89	137
Najmi-Shadid, Amber/HS for Environmental Studies	136
Namnun, Ramon/High School of World Cultures	24
Naparstek, Sheldon/Solomon Schechter Sch- Queens	188
Napoli, Theresa/St Barnabas High Sch	26
Nardi, Christine/BOCES Seamans Neck Middle Sch	116
Nardone, Joanne, Dr/Milton Elem Sch	261
Nariman, Julie/HS for Language & Innovation	22
Nash, Nicole/Hannah Senesh Cmty Day Sch	97
Nasjlett, Meridith/PS 91 Bronx	21
Nasrullah, Assad/Wellspring Sch	189
Nastasi, Donna/MS 936 Arts Off 3rd	90
Natale, Susan/All Hallows High School-Boys	25
Natoli, Mary/Covert Avenue Elem Sch	118
Nauholnyk, Dania/Professional Children's Sch	145
Nawrocki, Luke/St Joseph Catholic Academy	187
Ndzibah, Janet/PS 95 the Gravesend	91
Neagley, David/New Visions CHS Humanities II [243]	6
Nee, James/Colton Pierrepont Ctl Sch	210
Negersmith, Bethany/St Stephen & St Edward Sch	168
Neglia, Donna/PS 216 Arturo Toscanini	91
Nehlsen, Daniel/Howard T Herber Middle Sch	124
Neidig, Robert, Dr/Port Jefferson Middle Sch	228
Nekritz, Batya/Beth Jacob High Sch	96
Nelson, Duffy/Beekmantown Middle Sch	44
Nelson, Erin/Ernest C Myer Elem Sch	242
Nelson, Fredrick/Collegiate Inst-Math & Science	22
Nelson, Jennifer/Primrose Hill Sch	55

NAME/School	PAGE
Nelson, John/Houghton Academy	16
Nelson, Marc/Harris Hill Elem Sch	109
Nepogoda, Kelly/IS 5 Walter H Crowley	177
Netti, Amy/Hoosick Falls Elem Sch	190
Nettune, Alisha/Success Acad CS Bed Stuy 2 [245]	7
Neubart, Debra/Albertus W Becker Elem Sch	11
Neufeld, Sayi/Frederick Douglass Academy V	24
Neugroschl, Cb/Yeshiva Univ HS-Girls	189
Neuwirth, Deena/Horace Mann Lower Sch	26
Newcombe, Steven/La Fargeville Central Sch	80
Newell, Bridget/PS 290 Juan Morel Campos	89
Newell, Jerry/Green Chimneys Sch	176
Newell, Sophia/Tony Clement Ctr for Education	9
Newhouse, Susan/Nefesh Academy	98
Newman, David/Brooklyn Technical High Sch	82
Newman, Heather/Brooklyn Collegiate High Sch	93
Newton, Jim, Dr/Bishop Timon-St Jude High Sch	65
Newton, Kim/Marcy Elem Sch	153
Neyra, Magdalen/North Bronx Sch of Empowerment	23
Nezowitz, Eric, Dr/Garden City Middle Sch	120
Ng, Silvana/PS 2 Meyer London	137
Nguyen, Phuong/Civic Leadership Academy	177
Nicastro, Kelly/School of the Arts	111
Nicholas, Simone/PS 43	180
Nichols, Alexei/PS 340	22
Nichols, Christine/Edmeston Central Sch	173
Nichols, Jeff/Pierson Middle High Sch	229
Nichols, Larry/Madison Central Sch	105
Nicholson, Thomas/Sand Creek Middle Sch	12
Nickdow, Andrea/Saul and Elaine Seiff Ctr	235
Nicoletti, Rosemarie/PS 197 Kings Hwy Academy	92
Nicoletti, Susan/St Agnes Academic High Sch	186
Niedermeier, James/Tech Valley High Sch	9
Niesz, George/Greenwich Jr Sr High Sch	248
Nieves, James/Seymour Dual Language Acad	159
Nieves, Kimmerly/Jefferson Elem Sch	259
Nieves, Lisa/PS 280	185
Nightengale, Miriam/Columbia Secondary Sch	140
Nigro, Diana/Mullen Elem Sch	64
Nikovic, Jacqueline/PS 24	85
Nilsen-Hodges, Tina/New Roots Charter Sch	6
Nilsen, Donna/Staten Island Sch-Civic Ldrshp	194
Ninan, Janice/Blossom Garden Friends Sch	66
Niven, Kristen/PS 211Q Elm Tree Elem Sch	178
Noah, David/Urban Assembly CS Computer Sci	8
Nobile, Joseph/PS 304 Early Childhood Lab Sch	18
Nocera, Susan/Gateway City Academy	97
Noel, Carolyn/PS 7 Abraham Lincoln	89
Noel, Sheldon/PS 251 Paerdegat	92
Noeth-Abele, Christine/State Road Elem Sch	113
Nofal, Abdelnasser, Br/Andalusia Sch	265
Nolan, James/B C Cate Elem Sch	207
Nolan, James/Odessa Montour Jr Sr High Sch	207
Nolasco, Raquel/Hillside Arts & Letters Acad	182
Nolt, Mervin/Crystal Light Mennonite Sch	102
Noonan, Stephen/Greene HS Imaginative Inquiry	138
Nora, Sullivan/Veeder Elem Sch	12
Nordtvedt, Kaia/MS 662 Liberty Avenue Mid Sch	89
Norely, Michael/Neil Hellman Sch	13
Norman, Denise/Emanuel Lutheran Sch	234
Norman, Kyleema/Wadleigh Performing Arts HS	139
Norman, Tracy/George Washington Elem Sch	257
Norris, Laura/Margaretville Central Sch	50
North, Abby/Loudonville Elem Sch	11
North, Douglas, Dr/Albany Academy-West	13
Norton, John/PS 254 Dag Hammarskjold	92
Norton, Linda/Stewart Elem Sch	120
Nosson Friesel, Mordechai/Mosdos Chasidei Square Sch	98
Notaro, Maureen/Jackson Primary Sch	73
Noto, Erin/Rossetti Education Center	149
Noto, Jeffrey/G W Krieger Elem Sch	53
Noto, Michael/Tottenville YABC	194
Notti, Michelle/George Washington Elem Sch	131

New York School Directory

PRINCIPAL INDEX

NAME/School	PAGE
Novak, D/Niagara Charter Sch	6
Novella, Francesca/PS 209 Margaret Mead	91
Noyola, Sandra/PS 147 Isaac Remsen	84
Nunes, Maria/Packer Collegiate Institute	98
Nunez, Tanya/Democracy Prep Charter Mid Sch [235]	3
Nunziata, Maria/PS 130 the Parkside	85
Nuynh, Annie/Whin Music Cmty Charter Sch	9

O

NAME/School	PAGE
O'Brien, Ellen/PS 19 Judith K Weiss Woodlawn	23
O'Brien, Emily/Eastplain Sch	127
O'Brien, John/Good Shepherd Sch	95
O'Brien, Tara/PS 207	21
O'Brien, Thomas/Uncommon Charter High Sch [246]	8
O'Bryan, Nora/Errick Road Elem Sch	148
O'Connell, Julie/St Aidan Sch	132
O'Connell, Mary Anne/Westmoreland Primary Sch	153
O'Connell, Mary Ellen/Wellsville Secondary Sch	15
O'Connor, Christine/Hauppauge Middle Sch	223
O'Connor, Christopher/Dover Middle Sch	52
O'Connor, Jennifer/Onteora Middle Senior High Sch	243
O'Connor, June/Garvey Sch	26
O'Connor, Margaret/Our Lady Queen of Peace Sch	194
O'Connor, Mary/Montessori School of Syracuse	160
O'Donnell, Joseph/Brownville-Glen Park Elem Sch	80
O'Farrell, Andrew/Beach Street Middle Sch	233
O'Grady, Anne/PS 182	18
O'Hagan Cordes, Ann/Mary Louis Academy	186
O'Hara, Colleen/Hewlett Elem Sch	121
O'Hara, Sean/Riverhead High Sch	228
O'Hearn, Bill/Ross Upper Sch	235
O'Keefe, Daniel/Cardinal Spellman High Sch	25
O'Leary, Doreen/Roaring Brook Elem Sch	253
O'Leary, Karl/Moravia Jr Sr High Sch	35
O'Leary, Kristen/John Cardinal O'Connor Sch	266
O'Leary, Martha/Holy Cross Sch	160
O'Malley, Leah/Shield Institute of Flushing	188
O'Mara, Janet/C S Driver Middle Sch	157
O'Meally, Tyrone/Amsterdam High Sch	116
O'Melia, Gregory/The Buckley Sch	146
O'Neill-Mangan, Colleen/Todd Elem Sch	253
O'Neill, Maureen/PS 56 Norwood Heights	21
O'Neill, Sagrario/Little Britain Elem Sch	167
O'Rourke, Tracy/Lyndon H Strough Middle Sch	152
O'Shaughnessy, Linda/PS 88 Seneca	177
O'Shaughnessy, Nadine/Copenhagen Central Sch	101
O'Shea, Marie/St Francis Xavier Sch	26
Oberlander, David/Yeshiva Kehilath Yaakov Boys	100
Oberstein, Lisa/Hackley Sch	265
Obrien, James/Brooklyn Cmty Arts & Media HS	82
Obrien, Pauline/HS for Medical Professions	87
Obrochta, Sean/St Francis High Sch	65
Ocampo, Javier/IS 254	21
Ochoa, Rosemary/John Ericsson MS 126 Env Engr	83
Oconnell, Brian/Scholars Academy	181
Odonnell, Allison/PS 48 William C Wilcox	193
Odowd, Angela/PS 62 Chester Park	181
Odwin, Sharon/PS 308 Clara Cardwell	86
Ogborn, Heather/Joseph D'Aquanni West Road IS	51
Ogden, Eric/Avenues the World Sch	143
Ogden, Susan/Rochester School for the Deaf	114
Ogno, Christopher/PS 247 Brooklyn	90
Ojeda, Moses/Thomas Edison Career & Tech HS	183
Okpo, Adije/Bronx Excellence 2 Elementary [236]	2
Oldenburg, Catherine/Western New York Maritime CS	8
Oldham, Kirby/Clymer Central Sch	37
Oldham, Micah/Ripley Central Sch	39
Olender, Jeffrey/Carl L Dixson Primary Sch	255
Olesheski, Heather/Johnsburg Central Sch	245
Oliver, Alan/J W Leary Junior High Sch	211
Oliver, David/Auburn Junior High Sch	34
Oliver, Jennifer/Stanford J Gibson Primary Sch	42
Olivieri, Theresa/PS 222 Katherine R Snyder	92
Ollivierra, Maritza/PS 274 Kosciusko	94
Olsen, Joseph/Altmar-Parish-Williamstown HS	170
Olson, Drew/Parliament Place Elem Sch	226
Omara, Lori/Riverdale-Kingsbridge Academy	22
Oncale, Keith/Winston Preparatory School-Li	235
Oneill, Roy/Ballet Tech/NYC PS for Dance	135
Ongaro, Chris/Robert Louis Stevenson Sch	145
Onishi, Taeko/Lyons Cmty Sch	83
Orbe, Pierre/DeWitt Clinton High Sch	20
Oregan, Patricia/Saltzman East Memorial ES	119
Orleans, Jessica/PS 281 the River Sch	137
Orlowski, Rebecca/St Paul Lutheran Pre-School	149
Oroszlany, Peter/Mott Hall V Sch	24
Orser, Cassandra/Glenham Elem Sch	51
Ortiz, Hazel/Hempstead Elem Sch	196
Ortiz, Kathy/Family Life Academy CS II	4
Ortiz, Liza/MS 302 Luisa Dessus Cruz	17
Ortiz, Mayra/McKinley-Brighton Magnet Sch	159
Ortiz, Samuel/King Street Elem Sch	261
Ortiz, Sara/Meadow Drive Elem Sch	125
Ortiz, Socrates/Middle College High Sch	177
Osborn, Susan/Lafayette Big Picture Sch	156
Osburne, Nancy/Greater Plains Elem Sch	174
Oshrin, Scott/Southdown Primary Sch	223
Ossorio, Jesimae/Post Road Elem Sch	263
Osterhoudt, Michelle/Perry Browne Intermediate Sch	42
Osterhoudt, Susan/Riccardi Elem Sch	243
Ostrander, Jennifer/Chenango Valley High Sch	28
Ostrofsky, Susan/Fox Lane Middle Sch	252
Otis, Rick/Maine-Endwell Middle Sch	29
Ottaviano, Francis/Whitestone Academy	189
Otto, Deborah/PS 223 Lyndon Baines Johnson	181
Outerbridge, Kim/IS 339	19
Outlaw, Laquita, Dr/Bay Shore Middle Sch	217
Overbaugh, Kerry/Catskill Middle Sch	75
Ovitt, Burgess/Hadley-Luzerne Jr Sr High Sch	245
Owen-Williams, Simon/Portledge Sch	134
Owenburg, Gerard/John F Kennedy High Sch	117
Owens, Cecelie/PS 94 W Hertel Academy	58
Owens, John/Blue Mountain Middle Sch	256
Ozkan, Zeynep/IS 289 Hudson River Middle Sch	136

P

NAME/School	PAGE
Paarlberg, Nicholas/Hostos-Lincoln Academy of Sci	16
Pabon, Carl/Ellenville High Sch	242
Pace, Gregory/Tesago Elem Sch	202
Pacelli, Melissa/Craig Hill Elem Sch	109
Packard, Daniel/Caroline Street Elem Sch	201
Pacula, Amy/Convent of Sacred Heart Sch	142
Padmore, Christopher/MS for Art & Philosophy	88
Padro, Flora/Arturo Schomburg Satelite Acad	24
Paduani, Melitina/PS 123 Mahalia Jackson	140
Paese, Maria/Pearl River Middle Sch	197
Pagan, Jose/Loguidice Educational Center	36
Paganelli, Yvonne/Charles Finney Sch	114
Pagliarulo, Eugene/Copiague Christian Academy	234
Paige, Emily/Urban Assembly Unison Sch	83
Paingankar, Salil/PS 236 Mill Basin	92
Palandra, Maria, Dr/La Scuola D'Italia-G Marconi	144
Palchik-Medina, Nazda/PS 133 Fred R Moore	140
Paler-Large, Francisco/George Junior Republic Sch	240
Palermo, James/Lakeshore Elem Sch	109
Palermo, Scott/Sullivan Co Career & Tech Ctr	236
Paliling, Jessica/Victory Christian Academy	116
Palladino, Jeffrey/Fannie Lou Hamer Freedom HS	24
Palldino, Annmarie/Senator James H Donovan MS	152
Pallos, Thea/Robbins Lane Elem Sch	130
Palmer, Chelsey/Success Acad CS Williamsburg [245]	8
Palmer, Christopher/George L Cooke Elem Sch	237
Palmer, Jeff/Van Rensselaer Elem Sch	191
Palmer, Sheree/Cambria Ctr for Gifted Child	187
Palmer, Vikki/Geller House Sch	256
Palton, Roderick/PS 140K	94
Palumbo, Joe/Pleasantville High Sch	260
Palumbo, Roberta/Aaron Sch	143

PRINCIPAL INDEX

NAME/School	PAGE
Panag, Sara/PS 39 Henry Bristow Sch	85
Panagiosoulis, Panorea/Kappa Int'l High Sch	21
Panagot, Dana/The Facing History Sch	138
Panaro, Cladia/Riverview Elem Sch	64
Panasci, Frank/Sagamore Middle Sch	229
Panday, Mala/Young Women's Leadership HS	183
Panetta, Michael/River East Elem Sch	140
Pangborn, Jennifer/Tapestry Charter Sch	8
Paniagua, Monique/PS 101 School In the Gardens	182
Paniccia, Philip/May Moore Primary Sch	220
Pantaleon, Cary/PS 128 Audubon	141
Pantelidis, Dimitres/PS 171 Patrick Henry	140
Pantoja, T'Hani/World of Inquiry School 58	112
Panucci, Denise/Freeport Christian Academy	133
Paolino, Michael/William S Hackett Middle Sch	9
Papandrea, Eric/Hoosic Valley High Sch	190
Papayannis, George/Greek Cathedral Sch	144
Paquette, Sarah/Beekmantown Elem Sch	43
Parache, Arelis/PS 123 Suydam	94
Parache, Carmen/PS 150 Queens	185
Paravella, Charles/Capitol Reg Career & Tech Sch	9
Pardy, Rick/F D Roosevelt High Sch	52
Parentini, Dana/PS 506 School Journalism/Tech	90
Parese, Erinn, Dr/Robert Graves Elem Sch	242
Parisi, Mr/St Martin of Tours Sch	234
Park, Desmond/PS Q224	185
Parker, Christopher/Jasper Troupsburg Jr Sr HS	215
Parker, Cindy/Wayne-Fingerlake BOCES Spec Ed	161
Parker, Herbert, Dr/Greece Christian Sch	114
Parker, Jeneca/PS 180 Hugo Newman	139
Parker, Maxine/T S T Community Sch	239
Parker, Scott/PS 452	139
Parkhurst, Donna/G Ray Bodley High Sch	171
Parnell, Rory/August Martin High Sch	180
Parrinello, Louis/Wading River Elem Sch	230
Partridge, Joshua/Urban Institute of Math	18
Pascente, Marc/Grover Cleveland High Sch	177
Paschke, Darrin/Fredonia Senior High Sch	38
Pascual, Marcie/Cleveland Hill Elem Sch	59
Pasha, Atia, Sr/Mdq Academy	235
Pashkin, Robert/Bay Shore High Sch	217
Paskesz, Ruchy/Bais Rachel D Satmar	96
Paskowitz, Fran/Kadimah School-Buffalo	66
Pasquale, Michele/St Brendan Sch	26
Passarelli, Melissa/Daniel Webster Magnet Sch	259
Passaro, Susan/Argyle Jr Sr High Sch	247
Passero, David/Dr Louis A Cerulli School 34	111
Passno, Danielle/The Browning Sch	145
Pastore, Patrick/Rochester Prep MS-Brooks [246]	7
Patel, Aakta/PS 18 Pantoja Sch Excellance	57
Patierne, Lisa/Ravena Coeymans Selkirk HS	11
Patterson, April/New World Education Center	188
Patterson, David/University Prep Charter MS	8
Patterson, George/IS 285 Meyer Levin	87
Patterson, Jacques/Greater New York Academy	187
Patterson, Patrick/Gardner Road Elem Sch	41
Patti, Frank/Hewitt Sch	144
Pauker, Marla/Altschool Brooklyn Heights	96
Paul, Max/Brooklyn Bridge Academy	87
Paul, Valerie/Jamaican Children's Sch	182
Pauly, Mary/Randolph Academy	33
Pavone, Gayle/Prospect Elem Sch	33
Pavone, Louis/PS/IS 78Q Robert F Wagner	185
Pawlak, Craig/Clyde-Savannah High Sch	249
Pawloski, Brian/Buffalo Collegiate Charter Sch	2
Payne, Eleanor/Silver Creek Middle Sch	39
Payne, Matt/Nord Anglia Int'l Sch-New York	145
Paynter, Susan/High Meadow Sch	244
Payton, Thomas/Roanoke Avenue Elem Sch	228
Pearl, Abi/Yeshiva Torah Temimah	100
Pearl, Robert/Boyle Road Elem Sch	218
Peck, Erin/Prattsburgh Central Sch	215
Pecorella, Andrew/PS 26 Rufus King	179
Pecorella, Cory/Allegany-Limestone High Sch	31
Peebles-Davis, Mia/PS 35 Nathaniel Woodhull	183
Peet, Lindsey/York Central Middle High Sch	103
Peffer, Jackie/Union Pleasant Elem Sch	61
Pelkey, Brandon/Franklin Academy High Sch	70
Pellerito, Barbara/St Patrick Sch	234
Pena, Elizabeth/PS 11 Kathryn Phelan	184
Pena, Judith/The Mott Hall Sch	142
Pena, Luis/Howitt Middle Sch	119
Pendergast, Kevin/Kildonan Sch	55
Pendola, Tiffany/Caroline G Atkinson Interm Sch	119
Penikas, Darius/Archbishop Molloy High Sch	186
Penman, John/Marie Curie Institute	116
Penn, Jill/Forest Park Elem Sch	12
Penn, Rowena/Family Sch	19
Penrod, Mathew/Central Square Middle Sch	170
Perales, Robert/PS 134 Henrietta Szold	135
Perdomo, Jorge/PS 1 Courtlandt Sch	16
Pereira, Pascale/Cynthia Jenkins Elem Sch	183
Perez-Brundage, Wanda/Academy of Health Sciences CS	1
Perez-Katz, Alicia/Baruch College Campus High Sch	135
Perez-Mejia, Elda/Eugenio Maria De Hostos Sch	263
Perez, Carmen/Evangel Christian Sch	187
Perez, Christie/Guardian Angel Sch	143
Perez, Daisy/PS 110 Theodore Schoenfeld	19
Perez, Jaime/Public Service Ldrshp Academy	159
Perez, Jaime/Public Svc Ldrshp Acad Fowler	159
Perez, Katherine/Democracy Prep Endurance MS [235]	3
Perez, Natalie/PS 139 Rego Park	182
Perez, Rafael/PS 30 Frank A Sedita Academy	57
Perez, Rosalina/PS 189	141
Perez, Tiawana/PS 6 West Farms	24
Perez, Yazmin/Bilingual Bicultural Sch 182	139
Perkins, Richard/Coopers Campus Cte	212
Perlberg, Michael/MS 839	85
Perna, J Philip/Montauk Public Sch	226
Pernick, Ira, Dr/Paul D Schreiber High Sch	128
Perreault, John/Woodlawn Elem Sch	205
Perri, Shannon/Tilton Sch	154
Perrini, Daphne/Harvey Milk High Sch	136
Perry, Justin/Gilead School of Discipleship	268
Perry, Mark/Harmony Hill Sch	10
Perry, Rhonda/MS 255 Salk School of Science	136
Perry, Ronald/East Syracuse Elem Sch	155
Perry, Willis/Lawrence Middle Sch	123
Persad, Allison/Young Women's Leadership Sch	185
Persenaire, Meghann/St Hope Leadership Academy CS	140
Person, Cleveland/Harriet Tubman Charter Sch [143]	4
Peteani, Erin/Heatly Sch	10
Peter, Laverne/PS 368K	94
Peters, Brooke/Compass Charter Sch	3
Peters, Sharon/John Pound Early Childhood Ctr	147
Peterson, Matthew/Charles C D'Amico High Sch	169
Peterson, Matthew/Oakfield Alabama Jr Sr HS	74
Peterson, Patricia/PS 8 Robert Fulton	83
Peterson, Sue/Tecumseh Elem Sch	216
Petit-McClure, Sarah/Truxton Academy Charter Sch	8
Petit, Shakira/Martin Luther King Jr High Sch	255
Petretti, Shawn/Mattituck Jr Sr High Sch	225
Petrie, Katherine/Chambers Elem Sch	242
Petriello, Joseph, Dr/Fordham Preparatory Sch	25
Petrillo, David/Montfort Academy	266
Petrucci, Darielle/Success Acad CS Prospect Hgts [245]	8
Petruccio, Roseann/St Patrick Sch	234
Pettersen, Hal/Deposit Middle High Sch	28
Peverelli, Audur/Lycee Francais De New York	144
Phelan, Carrie/Knickerbacker Middle Sch	191
Phetteplace, David/Cinncinnatus Secondary Sch	47
Philemy, Favrol/Equality Charter High Sch	22
Philemy, James/PS/IS 208	184
Phillip, Sheila/PS 193 Gil Hodges	92
Phillips, Elizabeth/PS 321 William Penn	85
Phillips, Greer/PS M079 Horan Sch	142

New York School Directory

PRINCIPAL INDEX

NAME/School	PAGE
Phillips, Janice/Roscoe Central Sch	237
Phillips, Lynn/Oakfield Alabama Elem Sch	74
Phillips, Michael/Ramapo High Sch	196
Phillips, Ronda/Kappa V	93
Philo, Heather/Lake Pleasant Central Sch	76
Piazza, Karen/PS 205 Alexander Graham Bell	180
Picarello, Michelle/St Sebastian Sch	187
Piccirillo, Lynn/PS 45 International Sch	57
Pichardo, Carlos/IS 528 Bea Fuller Rodgers Sch	141
Piciullo, Timothy/South Ocean Middle Sch	227
Picucci, Diane/PS 48 Mapleton	90
Pierre, Lorraine/St Francis of Assisi Cath Acad	95
Pierre, Odelphia/PS 129 John H Finley	140
Pierre, Yvrose/PS K753 School for Career Dev	94
Pietrangelo, Graziella/PS 1 Tottenville	193
Pietrantone, Paul/Ellicott Road Elem Sch	63
Pietri, Julia/PS 152 Dyckman Valley	141
Pietricola, Melissa/North Rose Elem Sch	250
Pigeon, Gregory/Amherst Central High Sch	56
Pigeon, Justin/Bedford Stuy Collegiate CS [246]	1
Pignataro, Anthony/PS 15 Jackie Robinson Sch	183
Pike, Amanda/Berkeley Carroll Sch	96
Pikula, Max/Huth Road Elem Sch	61
Pilla, Carol/Laurel Plains Elem Sch	196
Pilla, Michele/Harry Fisher Elem Sch	77
Pinard, Michele, Dr/L P Quinn Elem Sch	70
Pincelli, Telcie/Terry Taylor Elem Sch	112
Pinder, Glen/Brooklyn Friends Sch	97
Pineiro, Margaret/Early Learning Center	53
Pinel, Karen/Spring Valley High Sch	196
Pinto, Carmen/Madonna Heights Sch	235
Pinto, Sarah/PS 20 Anna Silver	135
Piotrowski, Karen/PS 6 Buffalo ES of Tech	57
Piper, Amy/Wheelock Primary Sch	38
Piper, Jay/Children's Sch of Rochester 15	110
Pipher, Bill/Seton Catholic-All Saints Sch	30
Piro, Thomas/St Thomas Apostle CA	187
Pirraglia, Gregory/PS 99 Isaac Asimov	91
Pirro, Anthony/PS 54 Samuel C Barnes	83
Pisa, Francesca/New Design Middle Sch	140
Pisacreta, Geraldine, Dr/School 5	264
Piscitella, John/George Fischer Middle Sch	175
Piscitelli, Michael/Guilderland High Sch	11
Pisicchio, Marie/Mandalay Elem Sch	131
Pitaniello, Dom/Rensselaer Jr Sr High Sch	191
Pitek, Christopher/Nardin Academy Middle Sch	65
Pitterson, Mark/Berne-Knox-Westerlo Jr/Sr HS	10
Pitts, Keva/PS 284 Jackson Sports Art Tech	93
Pizarro, Josette/PS 220 Edward Mandel	182
Pizza, Patti/Little Village Sch	133
Pizzutello, Paul/Reach Academy	255
Plaia, Edward/Amityville Memorial High Sch	216
Plantz, Jared/Black River Elem Sch	80
Plescia, Mark/Sullivan West High Sch	237
Ploetz, Erich/Ellicottville Sch	31
Plotkin, Levi/Yeshiva Beis Chaya Mushkah	99
Plotkin, Michael/Pierre Van Cortlandt Mid Sch	254
Podesta, Margaret/Putnam Valley Elem Sch	176
Podolak, Jeffrey/T S T BOCES Voc Tech Center	239
Podolak, Julie/A A Gates Elem Sch	35
Poeller, Patricia/Christian Acad-Western NY	149
Poggi, Margaret/Learning Spring Elem Sch	144
Pogue, Richard/Tamarac Elem Sch	190
Pogue, Richard/Tamarac Secondary Sch	190
Polanco, Emmanuel/JHS 80 the Mosholu Pkwy Sch	21
Polanco, Karyn/PS 57 Hubert H Humphrey	194
Polat, Mucahit/Buffalo Academy of Science CS	2
Poles, Christine/Rise Community School 106	111
Polikoski, Andrea/Schoharie Elem Sch	206
Polino, Robert/Willow Ridge Elem Sch	64
Polinsky, Marie/Pathways to Graduation	142
Politis, Nicholas/HS Law & Public Service	141
Politowski, Colleen/Highland Elem Sch	60
Poll, Ms/Industry Residential Center	5
Pollack, Brad/Cayuga Heights Elem Sch	240

NAME/School	PAGE
Pollack, Julie/Bet Shraga Hebrew Academy	13
Pollak, Stuart/Sycamore Avenue Elem Sch	220
Pollard, Jeffrey/Floyd S Winslow Elem Sch	112
Pollicino, Michael/Automotive YABC	83
Pollok, Stephanie/Central Christian Academy	40
Polson, Bilal/Northern Parkway Elem Sch	130
Polsonetti, Karen/Manhattan Business Academy	136
Polumbo, Kate/Cornwall Central Middle Sch	163
Pompilio, Joseph, Dr/Valley Stream Central High Sch	130
Pompo, Vincent/W A Wettel Elem Sch	153
Ponella, Helen/IS 227 Louis Armstrong	184
Pontillo, Jennifer/Lakeview Elem Sch	176
Pontrello, Camille, Dr/St Christopher Sch	65
Poole-Petit, Leslie/Dominican Academy	143
Porter, Sharon/PS 6 Norma Adams Clemons Acad	87
Posephney, Jay/Kaplan Career Academy	255
Posner Marino, Randi/PS 134 Hollis	183
Posner, Abraham/Yeshiva Shaarei Torah	199
Post, Barbara/Peachtown Elem Sch	36
Postman, Ellen/Lynbrook Kindergarten Center	124
Potter, Rick/Adirondack Academy	71
Pourby, Lori/Sidney High Sch	50
Pourby, Lori/Sidney Junior High Sch	50
Powell-Grant, Leslie/School 21	264
Powell, Gail/St John Evangelist Luthern Sch	99
Powell, John/Montessori Magnet Sch	9
Powell, Sandra/Joseph A McNeil Elem Sch	121
Powell, Teri/PS 30 Hernandez-Hughes	140
Power, Christopher/Albertus Magnus High Sch	198
Power, Linda/St John Sch	168
Powers, Brian/Willink Middle Sch	113
Powers, John/Herbert H Lehman High Sch	17
Powrie, Michelle/St Anthony St Paul Sch	198
Pozzulo, Maria/Floral Park Mem Jr Sr High Sch	129
Pradel, Pascale/PS 38 the Pacific	85
Pramataris, Peter/Mt Sinai High Sch	226
Prashad, Anita/PS 54 Hillside	182
Pratt, Charles/Gregory Jarvis Middle Sch	77
Pratt, January/Greene Primary Sch	42
Pratt, Rhonda/Paul J Bellew Elem Sch	233
Prendergast, Lea/Staten Island Academy	195
Prendergast, Mary/HS for Youth & Cmty Dev	86
Press, Suzanne/Prospect Park Bnos Leah Girls	98
Preston, April/Cattaraugus Middle Sch	31
Pretsfelder, Gary/Solomon Schechter Sch- Mnhttn	145
Pretto, David/PS 96 Joseph Lanzetta	139
Price, David/Ogdensburg Free Academy	212
Prideaux, Joan, Dr/Beachbrook Sch	96
Primeaux, Sheri/Arthur S May Elem Sch	51
Primerano, Bruno/Grant Middle Sch	158
Prince, Susan/McGraw Elem Sch	48
Prinzi, Teresa/Newark Middle Sch	250
Prinzing, Andrew/Enterprise Charter Sch	57
Prioress, Sr/Holy Name of Jesus Academy	212
Prisinzano, Victoria/PS 380 John Wayne Elem Sch	84
Pritchard, Bradley/Carl I Bergerson Middle Sch	169
Pritchard, James/Chenango Bridge Elem Sch	28
Pritchard, Jill/PS 242 Leonard P Stavisky	179
Probart, Efraim/Talmud Torah Tiferes Bunim	99
Prober, Corey/School of Co-op Technical Ed	142
Proietti, David/Oswego Cmty Christian Sch	172
Prokosch, Scott/Meadow Hill Global Sch	166
Proper, David/Coxsackie Athens Middle Sch	75
Prorok, Melissa/Pioneer Middle Sch	33
Proscia, Margherit/Medford Elem Sch	227
Proscia, Paul/PS 23 Richmondtown	193
Pryce, Khadijah, Dr/Islamic Cultural Center Sch	144
Pryke, Elizabeth/Hewitt Elem Sch	128
Przybysz, Mark/Newfane Middle Sch	147
Psilakis, Irene/Lowell Sch	188
Ptak, Deborah/Lehman Alternative Cmty Sch	240
Puccioni, Marcus/Boght Hills Elem Sch	11
Pugh-Roberson, Angela/Erasmus Campus YABC	86
Pugh, Samantha/Merrick Academy-Queens PCS	5

School Year 2020-2021   800-333-8802   NY-U33

PRINCIPAL INDEX

Market Data Retrieval

NAME/School	PAGE
Pugliese, Frank/Shoreham Wading River High Sch	230
Pullen, David/Penn Yan Academy High Sch	268
Pullen, Michael/James A Beneway High Sch	251
Pulley, David/Tri-Valley High Sch	237
Puma, Mark/Pittsford Sutherland High Sch	110
Purice, Florin/Isaac Newton MS-Math & Science	139
Putman, Stephen/Seaway Area Tech Center	209
Putnam, Lisa/Harts Hill Elem Sch	153
Putnam, Mark/Sauquoit Valley Elem Sch	152
Puylara, Christopher/Romulus Central Sch	208

Q

NAME/School	PAGE
Quarles, Tracey/PS 150 Christopher Sch	93
Quartano, Judith/PS K315	92
Quartley, Daniel/Bolivar-Richburg Central Sch	14
Quesnell, Ashley/Community Rehab Center	244
Quezada, Yasmin/PS 199 Shakespeare	20
Quigley, Billie/Brownsville Ascend Lower CS	2
Quigley, Ellen/PS 206 Joseph F Lamb	92
Quigley, Kathryn/Peconic Community Sch	235
Quiles, Heath/Averill Park High Sch	189
Quiles, Olga/Community Math & Science Prep	141
Quiles, Providencia/Nazareth Regional High Sch	95
Quinlan, Alison/PS Q004	185
Quinn, Holly/Allendale Elem Sch	64
Quinn, Kelly, Sr/Our Lady of Grace Montessori	134
Quinones, Carol/Traphagen Elem Sch	258
Quintaina, Elaine/Hillside Childrens Center	35
Quintana, Robert/PS 28 Thomas Emanuel ECC	177
Quintana, William/Bronx HS for Medical Science	18

R

NAME/School	PAGE
Raba, Jessica/Long Island Lutheran Sch	133
Raccio, Kim/Brooklyn Prospect Charter HS	2
Raczkowski, Joseph/La Salle Institute	192
Rader, Michael/Center Road Christian Academy	66
Radogna, Dominick/Monhagen Middle Sch	165
Radoslovich, Jacqueline/Mount Eden Children's Academy	19
Radovich, Magdalen/JHS 189 Daniel Carter Beard	178
Raefski, Raymond/Hawthorne Little Sch	256
Raeke, Shawn/Academy Software Engineering	135
Rafferty, Stephen/De Ruyter Middle High Sch	105
Ragione, Maria/PS 230 Doris Cohen	85
Ragone, Alex/Altschool Union Square	143
Ragone, Rose/Annunciation School-Crestwood	264
Ragucci, Michael/Franklin D Roosevelt YABC	89
Rahill, Karen/DeSales Catholic Sch	149
Rahynes, Carlyn/Learning Through Play PK Ctr	16
Raines, Matt/Holmes Elem Sch	62
Rainey, Perry, Dr/Brooklyn Sch-Math & Research	93
Rainis, Joseph/Lynbrook High Sch	124
Rains, Daniel/Beaver River Central Sch	101
Rakoczy, Luke/Van Antwerp Middle Sch	204
Ralston, Katie/Cuba-Rushford Middle High Sch	14
Ramie, David/Dexter Elem Sch	80
Ramirez, Armando/All City High Sch	110
Ramirez, Dean/Iroquois High Sch	62
Ramirez, Karen/Cottage Lane Elem Sch	197
Ramos, Arlene/PS 1 the Bergen	85
Ramos, Melissa/Schuylerville Prep HS	18
Ramos, Michele/PS 16 John J Driscoll	193
Ramos, Miosoitis/PS 7 Milton Fein Sch	21
Ramos, Pilar/Arts & Letters 305 United	82
Ramos, Suany/PS 188 the Island Sch	135
Ramsaran, Debra/PS K134	92
Ramsuchit, Vadewatie/International HS-Union Sq	136
Randazzo, Pamela/Brooklyn Sch Music & Theatre	86
Randazzo, Vincent/Lincoln Orens Middle Sch	122
Ranieri, Mark/N A Walbran Elem Sch	151
Ranieri, Michael/PS 191 Mayflower	180
Rao, Jenny/Emma Willard Sch	192
Rapp, Mitchell/Charlotte Valley Central Sch	49
Rappaport, Dana/PS 234 Independence Sch	137
Rappaport, Mendel/Mesivta Tifres Elimelech	98
Rasco, Dennis/Mooers Elem Sch	44
Rashid, Shareef/Passages Acad-Crossroads	94
Rasmussen, Anders/Wood Road Elem Sch	200
Rathbun, Linda/Truthville Christian Academy	249
Ratra, Shweta/Crotona Int'l High Sch	20
Ratti, Samuel/Ft Edward Middle High Sch	247
Rauch, Nicholas/Waterville Jr Sr High Sch	153
Rawlins, Michele/PS 287 Bailey K Ashford	83
Rawnsley, Mark/New Dorp Christian Academy	195
Rawson, Michelle/Peru Elem Sch	44
Ray, Paula/Orange-Ulster BOCES Tech Ctr	163
Raymar, Darren/William S Covert Elem Sch	128
Raymond, Rebecca, Dr/Brookhaven Elem Sch	231
Re-Sugiura, Maximillian/Art & Design High Sch	135
Read, Brian/North Rose Wolcott High Sch	250
Reade, Dolores/Our Savior New American Sch	235
Reagan, Dianna/Eagle Elem Sch	10
Reale, Anthony/Brookside Elem Sch	109
Reamer, Mary Alice, Sr/St John the Baptist Sch	265
Reardon, Derek/Hudson Junior High Sch	46
Rebera, Christine/Lansing Middle Sch	240
Rechenberger, Ellen/Liberty Elem Sch	197
Reda, Christoph/PS X010	25
Redden, Marisa/Arrowhead Elem Sch	232
Redding, Deirdre/Moriches Elem Sch	233
Redmond, Ty/Success Acad CS Far Rockaway [245]	7
Reed, Amani/School at Columbia	145
Reed, Debra/Schlegel Road Elem Sch	113
Reed, Jaivelle/Chelsea Career & Tech HS	135
Reese, John/Lima Christian Sch	104
Reeve, Brian/Greenville Middle Sch	75
Reeves, Gina/Brookwood Sch	175
Refaey, Lamiaa/Miraj Islamic Sch	195
Regan, Emily/Thomas J Watson Elem Sch	29
Regan, Jean, Dr/Cazenovia Middle Sch	104
Reger, Greg/Central Baptist Christian Sch	34
Reggio, Melissa/Center Moriches Middle Sch	218
Reich, Neal/Abraham Lincoln YABC	91
Reichman, Rabbi/Beth Hamedrash Shaarei Yosher	96
Reid, Brooke/Parishville Hopkinton Ctl Sch	212
Reid, Charlene/Bronx Excellence 5 Elementary [236]	2
Reidell, Erich/Lake Shore Middle Sch	60
Reidell, Tammy/Northville Central Sch	72
Reilly, Anissa/PS 132 Garrett A Morgan	19
Reilly, Catherine/Bushwick Leaders HS for Excel	93
Reilly, Charles/PS 368 Hamilton Heights Sch	142
Reilly, Michael/St Joseph by the Sea High Sch	195
Reimer, Patrick/Forsyth Satellite Acad	135
Reingold, Kristen/Forest Brook Elem Sch	223
Reinhardt, Noah/Packer Collegiate Institute	98
Reisinger, Scott/Trevor Day School-East	146
Reiss, Lauren/Evergreen MS-Urban Exploration	93
Rejrat, Vanessa/Jefferson Elem Sch	152
Relation, Dustin/Malone Middle Sch	70
Relyea, Elisabeth/E A McAllister Elem Sch	152
Remillard, Danielle/George Washington Sch	189
Remington, Emily/Carthage Middle Sch	80
Renda, Michael/Neighborhood Chtr Sch Harlem	6
Renda, Michael/Neighborhood CS-Harlem	6
Renda, Michael/Neighborhood CS-NW	6
Renelus, Henry/John F Kennedy Jr Sch	185
Renny, Mary/PS 16 Leonard Dunkly	84
Reno, Kristen/Mary E Dardess Elem Sch	46
Renville, Nakoley/PS 208 Elsa Ebeling	88
Repperger, Steven/Sequoya High Sch	216
Restivo, Serena/PS 37 Futures Academy	57
Resto, Vincent/PS/MS 4 Crotona Park West	20
Reyes, Dakota/PS 272 Curtis Estabrook	88
Reyes, Farid/PS 103 Hector Fontanez	23
Reyes, Griselda/Mt Pleasant-Blythdale Sch	259
Reyes, Jason/MS 129 Acad Indep Lrng & Ldrsp	24
Reynolds, Kate/Friends Seminary	144

New York School Directory

PRINCIPAL INDEX

NAME/School	PAGE
Reynolds, Peter/Canisteo-Greenwood High Sch	214
Rezin, Emily/Success Acad CS Harlem 6 [245]	7
Rheaume, Michael/SS Seward Institute	164
Rhinehart, Kevin/Seneca Falls Middle Sch	208
Rhinehart, Robert/Downsville Central Sch	49
Rhodes, Antoinette/King Center Charter Sch	5
Ribiat, Deborah/Bas Mikroh Girls Sch	198
Ricci, Alixandre/MS 327 Comp Model Sch	19
Ricci, Brandon/Akron High Sch	56
Ricci, Dennis/Clayton Huey Elem Sch	218
Riccio, Jessica/PS 163 Bath Beach	90
Riccobono, Thomas/John Street Elem Sch	119
Rice, Sean/HS for Public Service	86
Rich, Jill/Donnelly Elem Sch	29
Richards-Usher, Laurene/Linden SDA Sch	188
Richards, Colleen/St John Bosco Sch	114
Richards, Duane/Jefferson Elem Sch	211
Richards, Michelle/Washington Primary Sch	223
Richards, Scott/Woodstock Elem Sch	243
Richardson, Denise/Channel View Sch for Research	180
Richardson, John/Our Savior's Lutheran Sch	13
Richardson, Richard/Brighton Academy	158
Richardson, Todd/Harlem Village Acad East MS HS [239]	4
Richardson, Victoria/St Margaret Sch	187
Richardt, Christoph/Hampton Bays High Sch	223
Richman, Kevin/Binghamton High Sch	27
Rickert, John/Niskayuna High Sch	204
Ricketts, Douglas/Our World Neighborhood ES CS 1	6
Ricks, Keri/School for Global Leaders	135
Ricotta, Jean/Locust Primary Sch	120
Riddoch, Thomas/Franklinville Elem Sch	32
Riehl, Adam/Sullivan Co BOCES Special Ed	236
Riggio, Christina/MS 177 Yorkville East Mid Sch	136
Rihm, Katherine/North Ridge Primary Sch	219
Rimkunas, Suzanne/Unity Sunshine Sch	192
Rimmer, Kristin/Brinckerhoff Elem Sch	54
Rinaldi, Renee/Bronx Park Middle Sch	22
Rinaldo, Lisa/Blooming Grove Academy	168
Rioux, Allison/French Road Elem Sch	106
Ripa, Riccardo/Perry Junior High Sch	151
Ristenbatt, Jenny/Cuny Preparatory High Sch	3
Rivas, Eleyna/PS 169M Robert F Kennedy	142
Rivas, Miriam/Bronx Health Sciences High Sch	22
Rivaud, Yves/Ecole Internationale New York	144
Rivera-Polanco, Jazmin/Bronx Haven High Sch	16
Rivera, Anthony/Pelham Academy	23
Rivera, Chandra/Brennan Middle Sch	215
Rivera, Chandra/Peter J Brennan High Sch	216
Rivera, Eileen, Dr/Yonkers Montessori Academy	264
Rivera, Lizzette/PS 196	24
Rivera, Rolando/Discovery High Sch	20
Rivera, Rosita/PS Q086	182
Rivera, Ruth/School of Creativity-Innovatn	85
Rivera, Yvette/Bronx Early Clg Teach & Lrng	18
Rivers, Jason/PS 165 Ida Posner	93
Rivers, John/Catskill Elem Sch	75
Rizzo, Alicia/Lynnwood Elem Sch	11
Rizzo, Donna/Wayne Central Elem Sch	251
Rizzo, Jesse/Basis Independent Manhattan	143
Roach, Tim/Durand Eastman Interm Sch	107
Robbins, Reid/East Palmyra Christian Sch	251
Robbins, Robin/Delaware Academy	49
Roberts, Aneka/Uncommon Collegiate Charter HS [246]	8
Roberts, Charis/International Christian Sch	98
Roberts, Daniel/New York St Sch for the Deaf	6
Roberts, Jerrod/A D Oliver Middle Sch	107
Roberts, Julie/Seymour Smith Inter Lrng Ctr	53
Roberts, Kiersten/Northstar Christian Academy	114
Roberts, Kizhaya/IS 219 New Venture	19
Roberts, Lori/Crompond Elem Sch	264
Roberts, Stacey/Saddlewood Elem Sch	12
Roberts, William/East Aurora High Sch	60
Robertson, Spencer/Pave Academy Charter Sch	85
Robilotti, Chris/Colonie Central High Sch	12
Robinson, Carol/Canal View Elem Sch	112
Robinson, Gareth/Institute Health Professionals	183
Robinson, Joe/Brookwood Secure Center	2
Robinson, Josef/Democracy Prep Harlem MS [235]	3
Robinson, Patricia/New Life Christian Sch	66
Robinson, Phoebe/PS 253	181
Rocha, Alma/Columbus Ave Early Chldhd Ctr	119
Roche, Michael/Belfast Central Sch	14
Rochon, Michelle/HS for Global Citizenship	86
Rochowicz, Thomas/Washington Hts Exped Lrng Sch	142
Rocine, Isiaih/Living Word Academy	160
Rockey, Mary, Dr/Westfield Central Sch	39
Rockford, Judeanne/Myles Elem Sch	151
Roder, Richard/Shelter Rock Elem Sch	125
Rodgers, Debra/Phillips Avenue Elem Sch	228
Rodgers, Robert/Nathan T Hall Elem Sch	238
Rodney, Gretchen/North Coleman Road Elem Sch	225
Rodriguez, Amy/Immaculate Conception Sch	25
Rodriguez, Daisy/Eastview Middle Sch	263
Rodriguez, Delines/Leep Dual Language Acad CS	5
Rodriguez, Dezchell/Girls Prep Elem Sch-Bronx II	4
Rodriguez, Edgar/Academy for Careers-TV & Film	184
Rodriguez, Gladys/Manhattan International HS	136
Rodriguez, Grisel/PS 82 Hammond	182
Rodriguez, Ivan/IS 145 Joseph Pulitzer	184
Rodriguez, Janette/PS 146 Edward J Collins	18
Rodriguez, Maritza/PS 98 Shorac Kappock	141
Rodriguez, Melissa/PS 140 Nathan Straus	135
Rodriguez, Raul/Newburgh Free Acad-Main Campus	166
Rodriguez, Rebecca/Woodside Elem Sch	260
Rodriguez, Robert/PS 18 John G Whittier	193
Rodriguez, Sereida/PS 84 Jose De Diego	84
Rodriguez, Tina/Lewiston Porter Interm Ed Ctr	147
Roe, Joshua/Tioga Central High Sch	239
Roer, Brett/Bronx Compass High Sch	17
Roethel, Traci/J Taylor Finley Middle Sch	223
Rogalle, Maria/PS 392 Bronx Delta Sch	18
Rogers, Allison/School 9M Oceanside Middle Sch	127
Rogers, Glen/Jericho Elem Sch	225
Rogers, Jana/Ontech Charter High Sch	6
Rogers, Jason/Central Park Int'l Magnet Sch	204
Rogers, Margaret/Our Lady of Fatima Sch	186
Rogers, Michele/Southwest Elem Sch	218
Rogers, Paul/Letchworth Central High Sch	267
Rogone, Maureen/St Michaels Catholic Academy	187
Rojas, Katiria/Steam Bridge School PS 481	23
Rojo, Marta/PS 035	142
Roland, Jeannine/Our Lady Star of the Sea Sch	194
Rollins, Carrie/Ernie Davis Academy	40
Roman, Lissette/Cypress Hills Ascend CS	3
Romano, Vincent/Malverne High Sch	124
Romanos, Iphizenia/Adelphi Academy of Brooklyn	95
Romero, Carlos/PS 126 Jacob August Riis	137
Romney, William/New Visions CHS Math & Sci IV [243]	6
Ronen, Deganit/Westchester Torah Academy	266
Roote, Thomas/Newark High Sch	250
Rosa, Vanessa/PS 169 Bay Terrace	179
Rosales, Gretchen/Elba Central Sch	73
Rosas, David/Heketi Community Charter Sch	4
Roscoe, Lee/Westhill Senior High Sch	160
Rose, Antoinette/PS 811K Connie Lekas Sch	94
Rose, Christopher/St Lawrence Middle Sch	209
Rose, Suzette/PS/IS 137 Rachel Jean Mitchell	93
Roseboro, Hazel/University Heights Sec Sch	17
Rosenbaum, Johnathan/Yeshiva of Brooklyn-Boys	100
Rosenbaum, Rabbi/Yeshiva Shaarei Hatzlucha	100
Rosenberg, Aaron/Mesivta of Long Beach Torah HS	134
Rosenberg, Joan/Jericho Senior High Sch	123
Rosenbrum, Mark/French American Sch of NY-Sec	265
Rosengarden, Rabbi/Mesifta Ohel Torah	199
Rosengarten, Sandle/Bais Tziporah-Girls	96
Rosenkrantz, Brooke/Success Acad CS Harlem East [245]	8
Rosenstock, Steven/Bais Yaakov D'Rav Hirsch	198
Rosenvelt, Gitty/Beth Rivkah Elem School-Girls	96
Roshone, Ault/South Bronx Academy Appl Media	17

PRINCIPAL INDEX

Market Data Retrieval

NAME/School	PAGE	NAME/School	PAGE
Rosof, Jeff/Sawmill Road Elem Sch	126	Ryan, James/Maplemere Elem Sch	63
Rosoff, Jared/MS 101 Ed R Byrne Sch	17	Ryan, Jason/La Fayette Jr Sr High Sch	156
Ross, Dani-Leigh/Clover Patch Camp	205	Ryan, Keith/Professional Perform Arts HS	137
Ross, Robert/Westminster Cmty Charter Sch	58	Ryan, Kevin/Alden High Sch	56
Rossetti, Jessica/Queensbury Elem Sch	246	Ryan, Mary/Calvin Coolidge Elem Sch	27
Rossi, Janine/Dutch Lane Elem Sch	122	Ryan, Mary/Strawtown Elem Sch	196
Rossi, Mary/Notre Dame Elem Sch	153	Ryan, Scott/Norwich Middle Sch	42
Roth, David/Honeoye Falls Lima High Sch	109	Rybicki, Rich/Southwestern Middle Sch	39
Roth, Michael/Willow Grove Elem Sch	197	Ryvicker, Jeffrey/Quogue Elem Sch	228
Roth, Shlome/Jewish Center for Special Ed	98		
Rothacker, Ralph/St Anne Institute	13	**S**	
Rothberg, Shaun/Stagecoach Elem Sch	225	Sabia, Lynn/Pelham Middle Sch	260
Rothenbucher, Roland/Waldorf School of Garden City	134	Sackler, Eric/IS 136 Charles O Dewey	84
Rotter, Janet/Studio Sch	145	Sadigh, Yaakov/Hanc West Hempstead Elem Sch	133
Roukous, Paula/Jefferson Rehabilitation Ctr	82	**Sadowski, Michael**/Bard HS Early Clg Hudson	46
Rounds, Tad/Hammondsport Jr Sr High Sch	214	Sadowski, Vincent/St Patrick School-Richmond	195
Rowe, Jeanne/Ebbets Field Middle Sch	86	Safarowic, Corinne/Westchester Sch for Spec Child	266
Roy, Dawn/Hunter College Elem Sch	4	Saia, Joseph/Discovery Charter Sch	3
Roye, Alyssa/PS 270 Johann DeKalb	83	Saidens, Michael/Tamarac Elem Sch	229
Roylance, Jesse/Washington Irving Ed Center	205	Saieva, Nicole/Nyack High Sch	197
Rozier, Dyon/Bronx Mathematics Prep Sch	17	Saint Juste, Magdaly/PS 51	180
Rozman, Eva/Bnos Yisroel School for Girls	97	Salamone, Joseph/Wallkill Senior High Sch	244
Rozycki, Janine/Ridge Elem Sch	225	Salasny, Jeff/Windsor Central High Sch	30
Rraci, Shqype/Richard J Bailey Sch	255	Salatel, Michael/Geneseo Central Sch	103
Ruben, Liavish/Yeshiva Imrei Yosef Spinka	100	Salaurante, Ms/PS 52 Queens	183
Rubenacker, Stephen/The Bridges Academy	235	Salazar, Amy/Manhattan Charter School II	5
Rubensteine, Matthew/Sail School-Ferncliff Manor	266	Salazar, Daisy/KIPP Infinity Elem Mid Sch [242]	5
Rubin, David/Yeshiva High Sch of Monsey	199	Salcedo, Yira/Westchester Square Academy	18
Rubin, Leah/Maimonides Hebrew Day Sch	13	Salerno, Gina/Granby Elem Sch	171
Rubin, Leibush/Mesivta Imrei Yosef Spinka	98	Salerno, Luke/Gow Sch	66
Rubin, Sandra/Idle Hour Elem Sch	220	Saliani, Dimitri/Eleanor Roosevelt High Sch	135
Rubinstein, Nadine/Lefferts Gardens Ascend ES	5	Salinas, Chris/Sewanhaka High Sch	129
Ruby, Raymond/Oliver W Winch Middle Sch	202	Salsburg, Mindy/Yeshiva of Brooklyn-Girls	100
Rucinski, Matthew/St Mary's Sch	203	Saltz, Phyllis/New Lane Memorial Elem Sch	225
Rucinski, Stefanie/Frank P Long Intermediate Sch	231	Salvia, Gemma/Seneca Middle Sch	229
Rucker, Kathleen/Brooklyn International HS	82	Salzbank, Michael/Bnos Malka Academy	187
Rudd, Benjamin/Village Elem Sch	109	Salzberg, Danielle/Frank McCourt High Sch	138
Rudder, Carolyn/Passages Acad-Horizon	25	Samerson, John/PS 92 Adrian Hegeman	87
Rudinsky, Boruch/Ohr Reuven Sch	199	Samet, Jenny/Ateres Bais Yaakov	198
Rudolph, Deborah/Helen M Marshall Sch	177	Sample, Heidi/Rouses Point Elem Sch	44
Rueda, Elizabeth/PS 231K	94	Sampsell, Jean/Fairgrieve Elem Sch	171
Rufa, Peter, Dr/Glen Head Elem Sch	126	Samuel, Michael/Urban Choice Charter Sch	8
Rugani, Jen/Leadership Prep Canarsie ES [246]	5	Samuel, Rabbi/Talmud Torah D'Khal Adas Yerei	199
Ruggero, John/Robert Moses Middle Sch	226	Samuels-Kalow, Ben/Creo College Prep Charter Sch	3
Ruggero, John/Waverly Avenue Elem Sch	229	Samulare, Kenneth/Our Saviour Lutheran Sch	27
Ruggles, Hadley/Basis Independent Brooklyn	96	Sanabria, Deborah/PS/MS 29 Melrose Sch	17
Rullo, Andrew/Chenango Forks Middle Sch	28	Sanabria, Evita/PS 127 Aerospace Science Acad	185
Rundell, Adam/South Seneca Central Elem Sch	208	Sanchez-Gayle, Zuleika/Sheridan Preparatory Academy	9
Runnals, Rebecca/Frontenac SDA Elem Sch	35	Sanchez, Erin/Vernon Verona Sherrill Sr HS	153
Ruolo, Frank/Lakeland Copper Beech Mid Sch	257	Sanchez, Irene/PS 15 Roberto Clemente	135
Rusch, Arin/Math & Sci Exploratory Sch	84	Sanchez, Lariely/KIPP Freedom Middle Sch [242]	5
Rush, Gary/David Paterson Sch	121	Sanchez, Marjorie/PS 61 Francisco Oller	24
Rusielewicz, Randy/Patchogue Medford Sr High Sch	227	Sanchez, Mary/PS 57 Crescent	24
Russell-Smith, Yvonne/Sacred Heart Catholic Academy	186	Sanchez, Norma/PS 150 Charles James Fox	24
Russell, Dara/Cardinal Hayes Day Sch	55	Sanchez, Sandra/Bronx Dance Academy Sch	20
Russell, Ebony/PS 77K	94	Sancomb, Chris/Coburn Elem Sch	40
Russell, John/Windward Sch-Manhattan	146	Sanders, Matthew/William Floyd Middle Sch	234
Russell, John, Dr/Windward Sch-Westchester Mid	266	Sanders, Pamela/Holy Name of Mary Sch	132
Russell, Malik/Bushwick Ascend Middle Sch	2	Sandoval, Jorge/Academy of Urban Planning	93
Russell, Tammy/Salmon River Middle Sch	70	Sandusky, Ativia/New Heights Middle Sch 722	87
Russo, Daniel/Walton Avenue Sch	20	Sanfratello, Jon/Genesee Valley Career & Tech	72
Russo, David/Westmoreland Road Elem Sch	153	Sanita, Christopher/Pine Bush Elem Sch	11
Russo, Katie/Lincoln Elem Sch	38	Santa Maria, Carl/PS 153 Homecrest	91
Russo, Margaret/PS 160 William Sampson	90	Santacruz, Katie-Lyn/Academy of the City Chtr Sch	1
Russo, Natalia/PS 145 Bloomingdale Sch	139	Santamaria, Leonard/IS 24 Myra S Barnes	192
Russo, Timothy/Harborfields High Sch	223	Santana, Antonio/Glen Cove High Sch	120
Russum, Jacob/Francis X Hegarty Elem Sch	122	Santaromita, Janine/PS 196 Ten Eyck	84
Ruthkowski, Jane/Manor Oaks Sch	126	Santarpia, Jessica/Rolling Hills Elem Sch	219
Rutnitzky, S/Kesser Malka Girls Yeshiva	98	Santello, Joseph/PS 50 Frank Hankinson	193
Ruyter, Theresa/Battery Park City Sch	135	Santiago, Dawn/Bronx Academy Health Careers	22
Ryan, Audrey/Cassavant Elem Sch	239	Santiago, Jeffrey/PS 67 Mohegan Sch	24
Ryan, Audrey/Freeville Elem Sch	240	Santiago, Jenneth/PS 205 Fiorello Laguardia	21
Ryan, Erica/Shatekon Elem Sch	202	Santiago, Marielena/JHS 62 Ditmas Sch	90

New York School Directory

PRINCIPAL INDEX

NAME/School	PAGE
Santiago, Robyn/Park Avenue Memorial Elem Sch	216
Santora, Kelly/Listwood Sch	113
Santora, Kelly/Southlawn Sch	113
Santoro, Francine/Gribbin Elem Sch	120
Santoro, Gregory/Skaneateles Senior High Sch	158
Santos, Edward/IS 93 Ridgewood	177
Santos, Joe/Int'l School of Brooklyn	98
Santos, Lynette/PS 33 Timothy Dwight	21
Santos, Philip/Leadership & Pub Service HS	136
Sanzone, Manuel/Saxton Middle Sch	227
Sapienza, Christina, Dr/Elwood Middle Sch	221
Saratovsky, Jessica/PS 770 New American Academy	87
Sardos, John/William Keane Elem Sch	205
Saretzky, Courtney/Achievement First Bushwick ES [128]	1
Sarnicola, Lisa/PS 62 Kathleen Grimm	194
Saryan, Maria/Bronx Excellence 1 [236]	2
Satin, Joshua/Ella Baker Sch	135
Sattora, Kelly/Geneseo Central Sch	103
Saucke, Kristina/Naples Elem Sch	162
Saunders, Christine/Friends Academy	133
Saunders, Jumaane/Brooklyn Prospect CS Downtown	2
Sauter, Karen/Lindell Elem Sch	124
Savino, Margaret/Convent of Sacred Heart Sch	142
Savino, Monica/BOCES Hearing & Vision Imprd	116
Saxby, Ellen/Williamson Elem Sch	251
Saxton, Joshua/Westmoreland Jr Sr High Sch	153
Sayegh, Marwan/Pearls Hawthorne Sch	264
Scalfaro, Anne-Marie/PS 68 Cambridge	177
Scamardella, Sophie/PS 65 Academy-Innovative Lrng	194
Scanlan, Christopher/Waterford Jr Sr High Sch	203
Scanlon, Daniel/John Adams High Sch	180
Scanlon, Eugene/St Raymond Elem Sch	26
Scannapieco, Dawn/Cahill Elem Sch	243
Scappatore, Robert/Little Flower Sch	224
Scaptura, Elizabeth/Big Flats Elem Sch	41
Scarafile, Lorraine/Trinity Montessori Sch	114
Scarantino, Michael/F E Bellows Elem Sch	261
Scardino, Chris/Fork Lane Elem Sch	122
Scarlato, Mary/PS 31 Samuel F DuPont	84
Scarmato, Joseph/Tottenville High Sch	194
Scarpine, Christopher/Springville Elem Sch	63
Scesney, Gregory/Parkway Elem Sch	128
Schaentzler, Gretchen/West Middle Island Elem Sch	225
Schafer, Jill/West Leyden Elem Sch	150
Schaffer, Richard/East Rockaway Jr Sr High Sch	118
Schaffer, Todd/Newark Valley Middle Sch	238
Schandel, Henry/MS 158 Marie Curie	179
Scharbach, Chris/St Francis DeSales Sch	186
Scharff, Katherine/Waldorf Sch-Saratota Springs	203
Schatz, Jonathan/Felix Festa Middle Sch	196
Scheer, Mary/Holy Family Catholic Academy	186
Scheiner, Mordechai/Beth Chana School for Girls	96
Schenker, Keith/Westlake High Sch	259
Schenone, Eric/Corinth Middle Sch	200
Schepard, Debra/Aaron Sch	143
Scherman, Ephram/Bais Brocho D'Stolin Karlin	96
Schermerhorn, Mark/Jordan-Elbridge High Sch	156
Schetter, Eric/LaGrange Middle Sch	51
Schiavone, Karrie/Holley Elem Sch	169
Schichtel, Mark/DeWitt Road Elem Sch	113
Schill, Bethany/Lackawanna Middle Sch	62
Schips, Dotan/Warren Street Academy	45
Schiraldi, Denise/Bronx Academy of Promise CS	18
Schlanger, Dean, Dr/Manhasset Middle Sch	125
Schlanger, Dean, Dr/Manhasset Secondary Sch	125
Schlegel, James/Christian Brothers Academy	13
Schlesinger, Diana/Greene Hill Sch	97
Schlitte, Steve/Mt St Michael Academy	25
Schlueter, Kathryn, Sr/Our Lady of the Hamptons Sch	234
Schmalz, Greg/Willow Ave Elem Sch	163
Schmelter, Paul/Burr Intermediate Sch	219
Schmid-Doyle, Viola/F S Banford Elem Sch	209
Schmidt, Abraham/Bnos Esther Pupa Sch	198
Schmidt, Abraham/Talmud Torah D'Chasidei Gur	99
Schmidt, Jordan/Edward Town Middle Sch	148

NAME/School	PAGE
Schmitt, Audra/Livonia High Sch	103
Schmitz, Laura/C A Bouton High Sch	12
Schneider, Brett/Bronx Collaborative High Sch	20
Schneider, Kara/Homer Junior High Sch	48
Schneider, Reva/PS 144 Col Jeromus Remsen	182
Schneider, Rose/PS 66 North Park Mid Academy	57
Schneider, Summer/Legacy College Prep CS	5
Schneyer, Edward/East Moriches Elem Sch	221
Schoch, Cindy/Chapel Field Christian Sch	168
Schoeffel, Mark/Friends Academy	133
Schonbrun, David/Yeshiva Tiferes Yisroel	100
Schoonerman, Jessica/Wayne Educational Center	249
Schrammel, Jason/George Grant Mason Elem Sch	167
Schrammel, Jason/Valhalla Middle High Sch	263
Schroeder, Antonietta/Menands Elem Sch	11
Schroeter, Adele/PS 59 Beekman Hill Int'l	137
Schropfer, Rebecca/PS K004	94
Schuelein, Derek/Blind Brook High Sch	253
Schuessler, Kathleen/Wyoming Central Sch	268
Schug, Dennis/Hampton Bays Middle Sch	223
Schuler, Bart/Newfane Early Childhood Center	147
Schulman, Ira/PS X14 Sen John Calandra	18
Schultz, Mark/Pioneer High Sch	33
Schultz, Michael/The Chapel Sch	266
Schultz, Stephen/Grace Christian Academy	133
Schuster, Scott/Kings Collegiate Charter Sch [246]	5
Schuster, Scott/Longwood High Sch	225
Schuta, Katie/Buffalo Sch Culinary-Hospitly	57
Schuta, Theresa/PS 206 South Park High Sch	58
Schwab, Moshe/Yeshiva Degel Hatorah	199
Schwartz, Elaine/MS 243 Center Sch	138
Schwartz, Ernest/Yeshiva Farm Settlement Sch	100
Schwartz, Evan/Alfred E Smith Career-Tech HS	16
Schwartz, Philip/Allendale Columbia Sch	114
Schwartz, Steven/PS 24 Spuyten Duyvil	21
Schwebel, Yisroel/Yeshivas Novominsk	100
Schweizer, Launa/Hewitt Sch	144
Scibetta, Dominic/Leonard E Burket Christian Sch	235
Scibetta, J Michelle/St Peter's Lutheran Sch	149
Sciove, Annemarie/Terryville Road Elem Sch	218
Scognamiglio, Rebecca/South Bronx Classical CS III	7
Scomillio, John/Great Hollow Middle Sch	230
Scorzelli, Margaret/Palermo Elem Sch	171
Scott, Danielle/MS 915	83
Scott, David/Gov George Clinton Elem Sch	53
Scott, Jacob/Edison Career & Tech High Sch	111
Scott, Jamell/Amani Public Charter Sch	1
Scott, Laura/PS 10 Magnet Sch Math-Sci-Tech	85
Scott, Michael/Leadership Prep Canarsie MS [246]	5
Scotto, Philip/William Floyd High Sch	234
Scrogin, Sarah/East Bronx Academy for Future	24
Scrymgeour, Barrie/Nord Anglia Int'l Sch-New York	145
Seamans, Howard/Millard Fillmore Elem Sch	35
Seaton, Barbara/Victory Christian Academy	235
Sedotto, Louise/PS 76 Bennington	23
Seeh, Corinne/Oxhead Road Elem Sch	225
Seeley, Carole/Town Sch	146
Seelke, Mary Ann/Haldane Sch	176
Seeman, Jessica/Nycacs CS East Harlem	6
Segal, B/Ahi Ezer Yeshiva Sch	95
Seidel, Elian/The Gateway Sch	146
Seideman, Jennifer/Jewish Institue of Queens	188
Seifullah, Jamilah/Highland Park Cmty Sch	88
Seipp, David/Roy C Ketcham Senior High Sch	54
Seipp, Eric/Millbrook High Sch	52
Seivright, Colleen/Columbus Elem Sch	258
Selenikas, Vivian/	184
Selig, Patricia/Seton Catholic Sch	114
Sella, Linda/Phoenicia Elem Sch	243
Sellan, David/Tonawanda Middle-High Sch	64
Seltzer, Stephen/In-Tech Academy Middle HS 368	21
Selvaggio, Michelle/Rochester Christian Sch	114
Sereno, Michael/Sodus Elem Sch	251
Serin, Umit/PS 201 Discovery Sch	179

PRINCIPAL INDEX

NAME/School — PAGE

Name	Page
Serpe, Valerie/St Thomas the Apostle Sch	133
Serra, Jean-Marie/East Street Elem Sch	122
Sertima, Tannis/IS 584	16
Serves, Georgia/Bklyn HS Ldrshp & Cmty Serv	82
Sesin, Diane/PS 94 Kings College Sch	21
Sessoms, Crystal/J V Forrestal Elem Sch	51
Setton, Sion/Gesher Yeshivah Prep High Sch	97
Sevak, Pankti/Friends Seminary	144
Severin, Samantha/PS 45 Clarence Witherspoon	180
Sexton, Joshua/West Seneca Christian Sch	66
Seyler-Wetzel, Dan/Highland Middle Sch	242
Seymour, Abby/Ausable Forks Elem Sch	43
Seymour, Kevin/Sandy Creek Sch	172
Seymour, Tina/Cathedral Academy at Pompei	160
Sgobbo, Rob/Kings Elem Sch [246]	5
Shabatian, Mrs/Long Island Hebrew Academy	133
Shabazz, Khari/Success Acad CS Harlem West [245]	8
Shabbaz, Betty, Dr/PS 298 Dr Betty Shabazz	93
Shadrick, Michael/Williamsburg Preparatory Sch	84
Shafer, David/Jordan-Elbridge Middle Sch	156
Shafer, Timothy/Rush Henrietta Senior High Sch	112
Shaggura, William/Gorton High Sch	263
Shain, Rabbi/Bais Yaakov-Bensonhurst	96
Shakespeare, Pauline/PS 34 John Harvard	183
Shali-Ogli, Esther/Juan Morel Campos Sec Sch	83
Shama, Watfa/American Sign Lang-Eng HS 47	135
Shamow, Nancy, Dr/Ascent Sch	234
Shamsi, Ferzeen/Claremont Elem Sch	260
Shanhai, Sandra/Valley Stream Christian Acad	134
Shannon, Jeanne/St Elizabeth Catholic Academy	186
Shannon, Kelly/PS 41 Greenwich Village	137
Shanowitz, S/Jewish Heritage Day Sch	66
Shapiro, Laurie/PS 105 Bay Sch	181
Shapiro, Michael/School 30	264
Shapiro, Yakov/Yeshiva Ktana Toldos Yakov	100
Sharbino, Donna/Building Blocks Dev Pre-School	234
Sharkey, Brian/PS 42 Eltingville	193
Sharp, Jade/Yonkers Middle High Sch	264
Shaw, Cary, Dr/Twin Tiers Christian Academy	41
Shaw, David/Roxboro Road Middle Sch	157
Shaw, Eric/Haviland Middle Sch	52
Shea, Barbara/Rye Country Day Sch	266
Shea, Miles/West Point Middle Sch	168
Sheber, Andrew/M Clifford Miller Mid Sch	242
Shedrick, Tanika/PS 92 Build Cmty Sch	58
Sheehan, Claire/Cascades High Sch	135
Sheehan, Joseph/General Douglas MacArthur HS	123
Sheehan, Matt/Broome-Tioga BOCES Voc Ed Ctr	27
Sheehan, Robin/Corning-Painted Post High Sch	214
Sheffield, John/Charter School of Inquiry	3
Sheffield, Lori/Southwest Technical Center	209
Shelby, Avis/James A Farley Elem Sch	197
Sheldon, Ann/New Paltz Middle Sch	243
Shepard, Xhenete/HS of Telecom Arts & Tech	90
Sheppard, Michoel/Torah Academy for Girls	188
Sherman, Harry/JHS 127 Castle Hill	23
Sherman, Ian/Lincoln High Sch	263
Sherman, Ivy/Robert Seaman Elem Sch	123
Sherwood, Deborah/Summit School at Nyack	199
Shilit, Chaim/Yeshiva Torah Vodaath	100
Shin, Claire/Achievement First Brooklyn HS [128]	1
Shin, Claire/Achievement First Univ Prep HS [128]	1
Shippee, Chad/Bolton Central Sch	244
Shirk, Ellen/Townline Sch	268
Shlachter, Irwin/Alexander Robertson Sch	143
Shore, Kara/Leighton Elem Sch	171
Shorofsky-Mack, Sharon/Abraham Joshua Heschel Sch	143
Short-English, Heather/PS 31 Harriet Ross Tubman Sch	57
Short, Noelle/Long Lake Central Sch	77
Short, Susan/Presidential Park Elem Sch	165
Showers, Jeff/Cataract Elem Sch	147
Shroff, Kristen/Emblaze Academy Charter Sch	3
Shron, Mitchell/Career & Technical Institute	51
Shrum, Kevin/Harlem Prep Campus CS [235]	4
Shu, Emily/Bronx Envision Academy	24
Shuchat, Steven/Van Wyck Junior High Sch	54
Shull, Craig/Ichabod Crane High Sch	46
Shultz, Karin/Mizzentop Day Sch	55
Shy, Todd/Avenues the World Sch	143
Sibblies, Paul/Wyandanch Memorial High Sch	234
Sibson, Denis/Miller Hill-Sand Lake Elem Sch	189
Sicari, Arlette/Tuckahoe Common Sch	232
Sichenze, Cornelia/PS 102 the Bayview	90
Siciliano, Steven/John Jay High Sch	257
Sickles, Kathleen/Edward R Crosby Elem Sch	242
Siddall, Shawn/West Buffalo Charter Sch	8
Siddon, Jeremy/Wells Central Sch	77
Siebert, Christopher/Salamanca High Sch	33
Siebert, Michael/Haverling High Sch	213
Siebert, Michelle/Fletcher Elem Sch	64
Siegfried, Christopher/Sacred Heart Sch	265
Siena, Margaret/Peck Slip School 343	137
Siesto, Brian/Victor High Sch	163
Sifuentes, Rosa/PS/MS 194	23
Sigerson, Timothy/The College Academy	142
Signal, Robbyn/PS 140 Edward K Ellington	182
Signor, Christopher/Catholic Central High Sch	192
Signorile, Theresa/St Clare Sch	195
Sikora, Jeffrey/Kenton Career & Tech Center	55
Sikorski, Ryan/Frontier Middle Sch	61
Silas-Lee, Moniek/Dr Charles T Lunsford Sch 19	110
Silber, Moshe/Sinai Academy	99
Silberberg, Moshe/Cong Mesifta Ohr Hatalmud	168
Silberman, Melissa/Broome Street Academy CHS	2
Silfen, Mona/PS 146 Ann M Short	140
Silletti, Catherine/Rushmore Avenue Elem Sch	117
Silva, Lisa/New American Academy Chtr Sch	6
Silva, Marc/St Francis Assisi Sch	26
Silver, Linda/Little Meadow Early Chldhd Ctr	188
Silver, Lisa/Northern Adirondack Elem Sch	44
Silver, Ryan/Bronx Prep Charter Sch [235]	2
Silver, Sabrina/Achievement First E Brooklyn [128]	1
Silverman, Noam, Dr/Abraham Joshua Heschel Sch	143
Silvernell, Tammy/Glens Falls High Sch	245
Silverstein, Jay, Dr/New Interdisciplinary Sch	235
Silvia, Heather/Donlin Drive Elem Sch	156
Sim, Franklin/High School for Violin & Dance	19
Simkha, Rebecca/Polis Mont Columbus Square ES	145
Simmons, Amanda/Stonehedge Elem Sch	159
Simmons, Donna/Fitzhugh Park Elem Sch	171
Simmons, Kevin/Smithtown High School-East	230
Simmons, Rachelle/Exploration Elem CS Sci & Tech	3
Simon, Carmen/Teacher's Preparatory Sch	93
Simonds, Tim/Chenango Forks High Sch	28
Simone, Patricia/Lee F Jackson Elem Sch	255
Simpson, Brian/Indian Hollow Primary Sch	219
Simpson, Joseph/Lubavitcher Yeshiva Sch	98
Simpson, Phee/Poughkeepsie High Sch	53
Simpson, Shamika/La Francis Hardiman Elem Sch	234
Simpson, Wallace/Essex Street Academy	135
Singer, Boruch/Yeshiva Tiferes D'Aleksander	100
Singer, Yosef/Rabbinical Seminary High Sch	188
Singh, Kuljit/JHS 210 Elizabeth Blackwell	180
Singh, Nalini/Antonia Pantoja Prep Academy	17
Singh, Shelly/Highland Elem Sch	187
Singleton, Daniel/PS 31 William T Davis	193
Singleton, John/Clear Stream Avenue Elem Sch	131
Singleton, Venessa/Sch of Science & Applied Lrng	25
Sinito, Deanna/Cornwell Ave Elem Sch	131
Sinnenberg, Tim/Charlton Heights Elem Sch	200
Sipp, Milton/Riverdale Country Sch	27
Siracuse, John/PS 596X	25
Siracuse, Joseph/Waterford Elem Sch	203
Sischo, Amanda/Milton J Fletcher Elem Sch	38
Sitman, Richard/Summit Sch	188
Sitnick, David/Talmud Torah Siach Yitzchok	188

New York School Directory

PRINCIPAL INDEX

NAME/School	PAGE
Siu Hei Szeto, Andy/Flushing YABC	178
Siwiec, Phyllis/Global Cmty Charter Sch	4
Skahill, Erin/Eagle Elem Sch	227
Skarka, Karin/Chango Elem Sch	202
Skelton, Lori/Andrews Trahey Sch	114
Skerritt, Claudina, Dr/PS 78 Anne Hutchinson	23
Skidders, Tara/Akwesasne Freedom Sch	212
Skinner, Kyle/Benjamin Franklin Elem Sch	27
Skoog, James/West Orchard Elem Sch	254
Skopp, Lori/Abraham Joshua Heschel Sch	143
Slabaugh, Todd/New Life Christian Sch	106
Slack, Aaron/L A Webber Middle High Sch	169
Slae, Zahava/Bnos Menachem	96
Slattery, Matthew/Peru Elem Sch	44
Slaveny, Jill/Wemoco BOCES-Career Tech Ctr	106
Slavin, Kevin/Miller Place High Sch	226
Slaybaugh, Jonathan/Birchwood Sch	195
Slivko, Jeffrey/Irwin Altman Middle School 172	179
Sloan, Kelly/St Madeleine Sophie Sch	205
Sloane, Matthew/Middleburgh Jr Sr High Sch	206
Slover, Lisa/Westhampton Beach Elem Sch	233
Slutak, Jennifer/Growing Up Green Middle Sch	184
Small, Malik/East New York MS of Excellence	88
Smalley, Gina/School of Science & Tech	92
Smallhorne, Martin/Herbert Lehman YABC	17
Smalls, Crystal/Edward Williams Elem Sch	258
Smawley, Donna/West Gates Avenue Elem Sch	224
Smeal, Tina/Geraldine J Mann Elem Sch	147
Smilinich, Charles/Dodge Elem Sch	64
Smith-Baugh, Shanie/PS 188X	25
Smith, Amber, Sr/Crescent Academy	30
Smith, Anthony/P-Tech	111
Smith, Bernadette/North Park Junior High Sch	147
Smith, Bob/Geneva Middle Sch	161
Smith, Brady/James Baldwin Sch Excp Lrng	136
Smith, Carrie/Brookfield Central Sch	104
Smith, Christopher/Lyncx Academy	111
Smith, Claudia/Miller Avenue Elem Sch	230
Smith, Daniel/Seaford Middle Sch	129
Smith, Darcy/Palmyra-Macedon Middle Sch	250
Smith, Darwin/PS 114 Ryder Elem Sch	88
Smith, Deborah/John F Kennedy Elem Sch	221
Smith, Derek/St Mark's Day Sch	99
Smith, Edwin/Stimson Middle Sch	231
Smith, Elissa/Lyndonville Elem Sch	169
Smith, Erica/Brooklyn Ascend High Sch	2
Smith, Heidi/Adironack High Sch	150
Smith, Jason/Holland Middle Sch	61
Smith, Jason/Maple West Elem Sch	65
Smith, Jeanette/JHS 383 Philippa Schuyler	94
Smith, Karen/Smith Sch	145
Smith, Kathy/Morris Central Sch	174
Smith, Katie/North Tonawanda Interm Sch	148
Smith, Kenneth/Clarence Senior High Sch	59
Smith, Leslie/Herman L Bradt Primary Sch	204
Smith, Matthew/Woodlands Middle High Sch	255
Smith, Molly/Mt Carmel-Holy Rosary Sch	143
Smith, Naomi/Central Park East II	139
Smith, Patricia/Grandview Elem Sch	196
Smith, Paula/Holy Family Elem Sch	41
Smith, Randy/Dcmo BOCES Tech Center	41
Smith, Regina/Bedford Village Elem Sch	252
Smith, Steven/Alden Middle Sch	56
Smith, Terry/The Harley Sch	114
Smith, Tracy, Dr/Sleepy Hollow High Sch	262
Smith, Warren/Wheeler Sch	157
Smith, Whittney, Dr/Mineola High Sch	125
Smith, Winsome/PS 219 Kennedy-King	88
Smolkin, Ron/Independence High Sch	136
Smolnik, Michael/Aura A Cole Elem Sch	170
Smorol, Gregory/Heritage Heights Elem Sch	63
Smyth, Lorraine/Franklin Early Childhood Ctr	121
Snell, Eric/Laurel Park Elem Sch	217
Snide, David/Indian Lake Central Sch	76
Snider, Mike/Unatego Elem Sch	174
Sniffen, Julia/Haldane Sch	176
Snyder, Chad/Walt Whitman Elem Sch	130
Snyder, Robert/Mary McLeod Bethune School 45	111
Snyder, Susan, Sr/SS Cyril & Methodius Sch	234
Soares, Kiri/Urban Assem MA-Sci Young Women	83
Sobel, Christine/Glenfield Elem Sch	101
Sochet, Sam/Martin Van Buren High Sch	179
Soghoian, Richard, Dr/Columbia Grammar & Prep Sch	144
Sole, Michelle/Manhattan Country Sch	145
Soler, Aidimaris/PS 68 Bronx	23
Solimando, John/Berea Elem Sch	167
Solimene, Don, Dr/Riverside High Sch	264
Solnick, Steven/Calhoun Sch	144
Solomon, Barbara/Centennial Avenue Elem Sch	128
Solomon, Joshua/NYC Business of Sports Sch	137
Soltish, Brian/Rombout Middle Sch	51
Somogyi, Erika/Polis Mont Museum Mile ES	145
Soos, Steven/St Therese's Academy	212
Soprano, Steve/Northwest JHS at Douglass	111
Sorci, Tom/Holy Family Sch	43
Sorden, Alexa/Concourse Village Elem Sch	16
Soria, Marcia/St Brigid Catholic Academy	95
Soria, Marcia/St Frances Cabrini Cath Acad	95
Soriano, Charles, Dr/East Hampton Middle Sch	220
Sorochin, Jennifer/Bryant Elem Sch	214
Sorrentino, Tracey/Middletown High Sch	165
Sosa, Celia/Hyde Leadership CS	4
Sotero, Patricia/Center Street Elem Sch	41
Soto, Eliamarie/PS 161 Juan Ponce De Leon	17
Soto, Elisa/Beacon High Sch	51
Soto, Indiana/PS 71 Forest Elem Sch	177
Soto, Sandra/Brooklyn Arts & Science ES	86
Soto, Suheil/PS 595	25
Sottile, David/Irvington Middle Sch	257
Soulette, Gregg/PS 138M	142
Soussis, Julia/PS 38 Rosedale	183
Soussoudis, Michelle/PS 118 Lorraine Hansberry	183
Sowul, Michael/Walden Learning Center	252
Spadaccini, Helene/Mott Haven Community High Sch	16
Spade, Jeff/Rudolf Steiner Lower Sch	145
Spagnolo, Chiara/PS 100 Coney Island Sch	91
Spagnuolo, Maria/Cathedral High Sch	142
Spalding, Jennifer/Sunset Park Prep Sch	85
Spanbauer, James/LaSalle Preparatory Sch	148
Spann, Natasha/PS 197 John B Russwurm	140
Spatafore, Ernest/Highlands Middle Sch	263
Spataro, Nancy/PS 32 Gifford Sch	193
Spear, Matt/Manlius Pebble Hill Sch	160
Speidel, Eileen/Park Avenue Elem Sch	126
Speiser, Mrs/St John's Lutheran Sch	195
Spellman, Denean/PS 233 Langston Hughes	88
Spencer Elysee, Nadine/Westchester Area Sch	266
Spencer, Adrienne/Parkside Preparatory Academy	87
Spencer, Brodrick/Roosevelt High Sch	128
Spera, Lily/St Ambrose Sch	12
Spero, Joseph/Walter Panas High Sch	257
Speroni, Lisa/PS 253	91
Sperrazza, Charles/PS 108 Philip J Abinanti	23
Spicer, Dana/St Gregory Barbarigo Sch	198
Spicijaric, Mary Ann/Fontbonne Hall Academy	95
Spiehler, David/St Paul Lutheran Sch	114
Spielberg, Dyanthe/Neighborhood Sch	135
Spiezy, Shante/Theresa Paplin Sch	188
Spillman, James/St Joseph Collegiate Institute	65
Spillman, Katherine/Mt St Mary Academy	65
Spina, Jennifer/Charter School of Educ Excell [247]	3
Spina, Kathleen/Holy Trinity Sch	55
Spinelli, Andre/Ellenville Middle Sch	242
Spinelli, Andre/Stars Academy	166
Spira, Jacob/Mosdos Chasidei Square Sch	98
Spitz, Alicia/Brookview Elem Sch	113
Spitz, Alicia/Seneca Elem Sch	113
Spitzer, Libby/Temple Beth Shalom Sch	176
Spitzer, Yidel/United Talmudical Acad Boys HS	199

PRINCIPAL INDEX

Market Data Retrieval

NAME/School	PAGE	NAME/School	PAGE
Springer, Elizabeth/Skoi Yase Primary Sch	208	Stokes, Debbie/PS 302 Emerson-Hospitality	58
Sproul, Elizabeth/E J Russell Elem Sch	166	Stomieroski, Jake/Columbia Greene Ed Center	45
Squillace, Helen/Red Mill Elem Sch	190	Stone, Lillie, Dr/Helpern Education Center	114
Squillacioti, Keith/Summit Lane Elem Sch	123	Stone, Lisa/PS 171 Peter G Van Alst	185
St John, Cecilia/St Agnes Cathedral Sch	132	Stone, Shifra/Yeshiva Ohel Moshe	100
St Louis, Djinga/Leadership Acad for Young Men	111	Stoner, Judy, Dr/Shulamith School for Girls	99
Stack, Thomas/Maryvale High Sch	59	Storch, Kevin/Parkview Elem Sch	224
Stafford, Bonnie/Heim Elem Sch	64	Storch, Laurie/Dickinson Avenue Elem Sch	227
Stahl, Valerie/Moriah Central Sch	68	Storchan, Daniel/Innovation Diploma Plus HS	138
Staley, Holly/Newfane Elem Sch	147	Storey, Scott/Belleville Henderson Ctl Sch	79
Stallone, Adrienne/IS 002 George L Egbert	192	Storman, Karl/Mountainside Christian Academy	69
Stalteri, Michael/Frankfort-Schuyler Jr Sr HS	77	Storms, Scott/Peru Jr/Sr High Sch	44
Stam, Stephanie/Lee Avenue Elem Sch	122	Stoutenger, Darcy/Cumberland Head Elem Sch	44
Stamm, Chaim/Tiferes Miriam Sch for Girls	99	Strahley, Kevin/Windsor Central Middle Sch	30
Stanek, Melissa/Bridgeport Elem Sch	104	Strauss, Bret/Valley Stream Memorial Jr HS	130
Stanislaus, Ruth/Sch Math Sci & Healthy Living	90	Strauss, Elena/Brooklyn Ascend Chtr Sch	2
Stansbery, Todd/Tuxedo Park Sch	168	Strauss, Teralyn/Ivan Green Primary Sch	107
Stant, Tara/Success Acad CS Harlem 3 [245]	7	Streiff, Annie/West Nyack Elem Sch	196
Stanzione, Michael/HS of Economics & Finance	136	Streitferdt, S/The King's Academy	146
Stark, Robert/Laurel Hill Sch	235	Strickland, DeMario/PS 97 Harvey Austin Sch	58
Starkey, John/PS 207 Lafayette Int'l HS	58	Strickland, Linda/Orleans County Christian Sch	170
Starr, Gian/Cold Spring Early Lrng Ctr	53	Stroka, Kerri/Orange Ulster Sp Ed Ctr	163
Starvaggi, Joseph/New Rochelle High Sch	259	Strong, Jessica/Girls Prep Lower East Side MS [244]	4
Stasiw, Andrew/St George Academy	143	Strong, Michael/Academy of Thought & Industry	143
Staszak, Margaret/Mt Mercy Academy	65	Strong, Milton/Half Hollow Hills High Sch E	222
Staton, Lynn/PS 36 St Albans Sch	183	Stroud, Amanda/Coney Island Prep Public CS	3
Statton, David/BOCES Career & Tech Ed Center	149	Stroup, Matt/Spencer Van Etten Elem Sch	239
Stay, Grace, Dr/Champlain Valley Education Ctr	67	Strub, Tracy/Sacred Heart Elem Sch	265
Stead, Rachel/Albany International Center	9	Struwing, April/Hudson Falls Primary Sch	248
Steck, Rebecca/St Patrick's Sch	265	Stuart, Matthew/Caedmon Montessori Sch	144
Steckstor, John/Ohio Elem Sch	148	Stubing, J/Oak Hill Sch	205
Steele, Gayle/Maplewood Intermediate Sch	231	Stuff, Lauren/Washington West Elem Sch	32
Steele, Larissa/Yeshiva Ketana	134	Stupart, Jorisis/Mott Hall III MS 128	19
Steele, Michael/High School for Civil Rights	88	Stutzman, Scot/Cassadaga Valley Middle HS	36
Steenberg, Donna/Brushton Moira Sch	69	Suber, Julie/Stockbridge Valley Ctl Sch	106
Stefanini, Jane/St Lucy Sch	26	Suchak, Bhawin/Albany Free Sch	13
Stefano, Anne/St Francis of Assisi Sch	186	Suddaby, Brent/Stonehedge Elem Sch	159
Stefanski, Jason/Hughes Elem Sch	151	Suffet, Lilit/Edward A Reynolds West Side HS	138
Stein-Marrison, Maria/Manitou Sch	176	Sugar, Barbara/Trinity Catholic Sch	172
Stein, C/Cairo-Durham Elem Sch	75	Sugrim, Dyanand/Heritage Sch	139
Stein, David/Chapel Field Christian Sch	168	Sulisa, Ms/Success Acad CS Union Square [245]	8
Stein, David/Yeshiva & Msvta Karlin Stolin	99	Sulit, Marcia/PS 155 William Paca	140
Stein, Dolores Ann, Sr/St Ann's Academy	215	Sullivan, Amy/Garden City Park Elem Sch	126
Steinberg, Erica/PS 164 Caesar Rodney	90	Sullivan, Andrew/Community Action School MS 258	138
Steiner, Josie/Wayland-Cohocton High Sch	215	Sullivan, Denise/Remsenburg-Speonk Elem Sch	228
Steingruebner, Kevin/Garden City Senior High Sch	120	Sullivan, Jennifer/Minetto Elem Sch	171
Steinmetz, Rabbi/Torah V'Yirah	99	Sullivan, Jennifer/Plank Road South Elem Sch	113
Stella, John/Washington Street Elem Sch	119	Sullivan, Jessica/Gouverneur Middle Sch	210
Stenta, Meghan/African Road Elem Sch	30	Sullivan, Karen/The Spence Sch	146
Stephen, Mary, Sr/Our Lady of Mt Carmel Sch	265	Sullivan, Margaret, Sr/Stella Niagara Educ Park Sch	149
Stephens, Ann Marie/Brooklyn Institute-Lib Arts	86	Summers, Rebeca/Valley Heights Christian Acad	43
Stepnick, Michael/Alden Primary Sch	56	Sumter, Jeremiah, Dr/Roosevelt Middle Sch	129
Sterling, Howard/Regent Sch	27	Suraci, Vincent/JHS 157 Stephen A Halsey	182
Stern, Aaden/Academy for Young Writers	88	Sureau, John/O L Queen of Apostles Reg Sch	234
Stern, Anne/Hawthorne Elem Sch	259	Sutton, Janice, Dr/G W Carver HS for Science	183
Stern, Joseph/Yeshiva-Mesivta V'Yoel Moshe	100	Sutton, Naomi/Bet Yakov Ateret Torah HS	96
Stern, Kara/Woodstock Day Sch	244	Sutton, Richard/Titusville Intermediate Sch	51
Stevener, Russell/Holland Patent High Sch	150	Suwala, Michael/PS 19 Native American Mag Sch	57
Stevens, Adam/PS 4 Duke Ellington	141	Suzzan, Sheri/John J Daly Elem Sch	128
Stevens, Elizabeth/Hewitt Sch	144	Swanson, Beth/Woodland Elem Sch	122
Stewart, Chrystal/Passages Acad-Staten Island	194	Swanson, Kimberly/Life Sciences Secondary Sch	136
Stewart, Peter/Horace Mann Elem Sch	27	Swanston, Rick/Adirondack Educational Center	69
Stiefle, Gregory/Tuckahoe Middle Sch	262	Swartz, Kevin/Victor Intermediate Sch	163
Stile, Maria/Heathcote Elem Sch	262	Swatland, Brian/East High Sch	64
Stiles, Roy/Carroll Hill Elem Sch	191	Sweeney, Daniel/Whitney Point High Sch	30
Stimmel, Kayla/Ateres Bais Yaakov	198	Sweeney, Jamie/West Carthage Elem Sch	80
Stinchcomb, Darrell/Greenvale Elem Sch	254	Swerdloff, Sandi/Schechter Day School of Li	134
Stinehour, Mary Kate/Benjamin Cosor Elem Sch	236	Swersky, Danny/KIPP Washington Hts MS [242]	5
Stochel, Sholomo/Ramaz Sch	145	Swiatowicz, Jeffrey/John Jay Middle Sch	257
Stock, Bentzion/Beth Rivkah High School-Girls	96	Swick, John/Town of Webb Sch	78
Stockmeyer, Jennifer/PS 32 Bennett Park Mont Sch	57	Swift, Cheryl/Summit Academy Charter Sch	85
Stoddard, Elizabeth/Volney Elem Sch	171	Swift, Patrick/Port Chester Middle Sch	261
Stohl, Mordechai/Yeshiva Chsan Sofer	99	Swift, Sharon/Our Lady of Providence Reg Sch	234

New York School Directory — Principal Index

NAME/School	PAGE
Swirsky, Michael/PS 21 Edward Hart	178
Switzer, Damian/Queensbury High Sch	246
Sykes, Amy/Edwards-Knox Central Sch	210
Sylvester, Mary/Moses DeWitt Elem Sch	155
Szczepanski, Debbie/Our Lady Blessed Sacrament Sch	65

T

NAME/School	PAGE
Tabano, Ron/John V Lindsay Wildcat Acad CS	136
Tabasco, Jay/Westchester Sch for Spec Chldn	266
Tabone, Francis, Dr/Cooke Center Grammar Sch	143
Tabone, Saida/Queens Metropolitan HS	182
Tadduni, Charles/Rondout Valley Jr High Sch	243
Taft, J/Alexander Elem Sch	73
Taft, Jennifer/Marcus Whitman Middle High Sch	162
Tahiraj, Claudia/PS 8 Issac Varian	21
Tait, Cara/Williamsburg HS Art & Tech	84
Tait, Samona/Inwood Early Clg Hlth-Info TEC	141
Talleyrand, Kristin/Franklin Ave Elem Sch	197
Tallon, Edward/Maurice W Downing Elem Sch	124
Talmadge, Cara/Granville Elem Sch	247
Talukdar, Afrina/PS 236 Langston Hughes	20
Tancredi, Michelle/Mandracchia-Sawmill Interm Sch	219
Tancredi, Nicole/School for Classics Academy	89
Tang, Maggie/McCown Expeditionary Lrng Sch	193
Tanner, Leslie/Niagara Educational Center	146
Tappon, Matthew/Council Rock Primary Sch	106
Tarantino, Debra/Clarkstown South High Sch	196
Tashlik, Beth/Collegiate Sch	144
Tasoulas, Theodore/A Fantis Parochial Sch	95
Tastp, Mr/Yeshiva Chanoch Lenaar	99
Tatro, Pamela/Wayne Central Primary Sch	251
Taub, Rivkah/Tomer Dvora High Sch	99
Taub, Sheila/Be'ER Hagolah Institute	96
Taub, Shulem/Yeshiva Mesivta Arugath Habosm	100
Taube, Robert/South Side Elem Sch	104
Tavernier, Pamela/PS 254 Rosa Parks ES	181
Taylor, Caren/Jamaica Gateway to Sciences	182
Taylor, Dennis/Margaret W Cuyler Elem Sch	251
Taylor, Donna/Faith Christian Academy	26
Taylor, Elaine/Ann G McGuinness Elem Sch	29
Taylor, Gaynell/PS 102 Jacques Cartier	139
Taylor, Luisa/Esperanza Preparatory Academy	139
Taylor, Mark/Case Middle Sch	81
Taylor, Patricia/Rye High Sch	261
Taylor, Rosa/Park Avenue Elem Sch	261
Taylor, Seth, Dr/Yeshiva Univ High Sch for Boys	146
Taylor, Tracy/Bruno M Ponterio Ridge St ES	253
Taylor, Will/Trinity-Pawling Sch	55
Tedisco, Marybeth/Roessleville Elem Sch	12
Tedone, Joshua/Pine Valley Ctl Jr Sr High Sch	38
Tejpaul, Sunila/Forest Hills Montessori Sch	187
Tekverk, Beth/Mosaic Pre-K Center at 101 St	177
Temple, Benjamin/Collegiate Sch	144
Ten Eyck, Jill/Roxbury Central Sch	50
Tenenbaum, Lori/Syracuse Hebrew Day Sch	160
Tenenhause, Marium Lea/Bnos Yisroel Girls Sch	198
Tenney, Vernon/Canandaigua Academy	161
Tenny, Susanna/Landmark High Sch	136
Tentitore, Todd/Success Acad CS Bronx 2 MS [245]	7
Teron, Yessenia/St Angela Merici Sch	26
Terrell, Avis/School for Tourism-Hospitality	18
Teruel, Asiyah/Universal Sch	66
Terzini, Gina/Woodland Elem Sch	155
Tesser, Justin/Achievement First Endeavor Sch [128]	1
Testa, Neil, Dr/Baldwin Senior High Sch	116
Testani, Brian/Corinth High Sch	200
Tettonis, Christina/Hellenic Classical Charter Sch	84
Texter, Kimberlee/Dunkirk Elem School 4	37
Tezanos, Jordan/Hudson Falls Middle Sch	248
Thamanna, Thaslima/Hamza Academy	133
Thearle, Jennifer/Charles E Schwarting Elem Sch	127
Thiell, Aaron/Latham Ridge Elem Sch	11
Thomas-Madonna, Mary/Waterloo High Sch	208
Thomas, Aidan/Leadership Prep Bed Stuy CS [246]	5
Thomas, Andre/North High Sch	65
Thomas, Colin/Bronx Regional High Sch	24
Thomas, Courtne/Bronx Global Lrng Inst-Girls	16
Thomas, Diedra/JHS 151 Lou Gehrig	16
Thomas, Donna/Montessori School of New York	145
Thomas, Edward/Uniondale High Sch	130
Thomas, Elaine/Herbert Hoover Middle Sch	62
Thomas, Eva/Early CH Sch of Rochester 57	111
Thomas, Felicia/West Middle Sch	218
Thomas, Joan/PS 206 the Horace Harding Sch	182
Thomas, Job/Lincoln Elem Cmty Sch	205
Thomas, Jonea/Bronx Charter Sch for the Arts	2
Thomas, Maria/South Bay Jr Academy	235
Thomas, Omar/Brooklyn Dreams Charter Sch [210]	2
Thomas, Rachel/PS 360 New Choice ES	184
Thomas, Rob/Twelve Corners Middle Sch	106
Thomas, Shernell/Brooklyn College Acad	92
Thompson, Allika/Math Science Research Tech HS	183
Thompson, Bevon/Imagine ME Leadership Chtr Sch	88
Thompson, Denisca/PS 53 Community Sch	57
Thompson, Elton/Greenburgh 11 Elem Middle Sch	255
Thompson, Elton/Greenburgh 11 High Sch	255
Thompson, Jason/Pinewood Intermediate Sch	204
Thompson, Julie/Oriskany Jr Sr High Sch	151
Thompson, Karena/PS 335 Granville T Woods	86
Thompson, L/Pre-K Center at 14-45	178
Thompson, Paul/Urban Assembly Sch Music & Art	83
Thompson, Samuel/Farmingdale Senior High Sch	119
Thompson, Scott/KIPP Tech Valley Charter Sch [241]	5
Thompson, Stephanie/Roberto Clemente School 8	111
Thompson, Teresa/Washingtonville Middle Sch	167
Thompson, Terrence/Wappingers Junior High Sch	54
Thomson, Valeri/Bard HS Early College Queens	176
Thorbs, James/PS 75Q Robert E Peary	185
Thorsen, John/Chatham High Sch	46
Threadgill, Tanya/East River Academy-Rikers	185
Timmis, Deborah, Sr/Mater Christi Sch	12
Timo, Maria/IS 98 Bay Academy	91
Timpone, Carolann/St Saviour High Sch	95
Tine, Nicole/PS 396	22
Tingley, Ty/Avenues the World Sch Online	143
Tinker, Nicole/Southampton Montessori Sch	235
Tishuk, Nicholas/Bedford-Stuy New Beginnings CS	85
Titus, Marc/George H Murray Prepatory Acad	97
Toala, Christian/Academy of St Paul and St Ann	142
Tobias, Richard/Magen David Yeshiva High Sch	98
Todard, Lyndsey/Baker Hall Sch	66
Toise, Michael/Manhattan Comp Night & Day HS	136
Tolan, Michael/Bishop Maginn High Sch	12
Toledo, Carmen/PS 25 Bilingual Sch	16
Toledo, Wanda, Dr/Drexel Ave Sch	132
Toleman, Rebecca/Stillwater Elem Sch	202
Tolenian, Cynthia/Clinical Assoc Finger Lakes	163
Tolentino, Ivan/Thomas A Edison Elem Sch	261
Tolz, Marla/Hawthorne Valley Sch	47
Tom, Edward/Bronx Center Sci & Math	18
Tomalty, Jennifer/Monica B Leary Elem Sch	112
Tomasik, Jeffrey/Boynton Middle Sch	240
Tomaso, Mary/Herkimer Jr Sr High Sch	78
Tomasuolo, Nancy/PS 204 Vince Lombardi	90
Tompkins, Vincent/St Ann's Sch	99
Toomey, Bernadette/PS 195 Manhattan Beach	92
Topol, Andrew/PS 182 Samantha Smith	182
Torley, Marilyn, Dr/Northern Academy	168
Torok, Jessica/Rondout Valley High Sch	243
Torossian, Gilbert/Polk Street Elem Sch	119
Torreano, Beth/Hillside Grade Sch	126
Torres-Santana, Brenda/Pinnacle School 35	111
Torres, Jessica/PS 132 Juan Pablo Duarte	141
Torres, Jessica/Ridgeway Elem Sch	263
Torres, Lillian/Gardnertown Fund Mag Sch	166
Torres, Luis/PS 55 Benjamin Franklin Sch	19
Torres, Mr/MS 266 Park Place Cmty Mid Sch	82
Torres, Shirley/PS 23 New Childrens Sch	21

PRINCIPAL INDEX

NAME/School	PAGE
Torrisi, Donna/Frank G Lindsey Elem Sch	256
Toscano, Denise/James H Boyd Intermediate Sch	221
Toth, Denielle/Fricano Primary Sch	149
Toto, Stephen/Silas Wood 6th Grade Center	231
Tottenham, Regina/PS 373K Bklyn Transition Ctr	94
Touma, Andrew/Community Education Center	147
Tourville, Lori/Chateaugay High Sch	69
Towles, Latishia/PS 158 Warwick	89
Towne, Kristin/Hammond Central Sch	210
Towne, Monica/Northern Catskills Occup Ctr	48
Townsend, Carol/Depew High Sch	60
Trabucco, Mark/Adirondack Middle Sch	150
Tracey, Scott/Baptist Sch	66
Tracy, Joel/Brownsville Collegiate Charter [246]	2
Tramontano, Frank/New Beginnings Montessori Sch	168
Trapini, Annette/Blue Creek Elem Sch	11
Tratner, Diane/PS 193 Alfred J Kennedy	179
Trejo, Javier/HS for Health Careers & Sci	141
Tremblay, Barbara/PS 721K Brooklyn Occu Trng Ctr	94
Trencheny, Elizabeth/Norman J Levy-Lakeside Sch	125
Tripoli, Adeline/PS 58 School of Heroes	177
Tripp, Faith/Chestnut Street Sch	131
Trippodo, Danielle/Ardsley High Sch	252
Trombetta, Patricia/Sachem High School North	229
Tronolone, Susan/IS 61 William A Morris	193
Trotter, Tiffany/Kew-Forest Sch	188
Troutman, Paula/Fredonia Middle Sch	38
Troutman, Santosha/Satellite East Middle Sch	83
Trouve, Ingrid/Children's Ctr UCP Sch-Suffolk	234
Trowbridge, Mary/Manhattan Country Sch	145
Troy, Meghan/Scarsdale Middle Sch	262
Troyer, Dwight/Crystal Valley Christian Sch	268
Trumble, Jason/Ithaca High Sch	240
Trybendis, Brittany/Ausable Valley Middle High Sch	43
Tryon, Terrence/Eggert Road Elem Sch	63
Tsaidi, Yahel/Yeshiva of Flatbush Elem Sch	100
Tsang, Kristin/Holmes Road Elem Sch	109
Tsao, Michelle/Saratoga Springs High Sch	201
Tsaveras, Joseph/Greenport Sch	222
Tsialikis, Irene/Lowell Sch	188
Tubiolo, Janine/P469X Bronx Sch Continuous Lrn	25
Tucci, Andrea/PS 112 Bronxwood	23
Tucci, Antoinette/PS 188 Michael E Berdy	91
Tucci, Maya/KIPP Tech Valley Primary CS [241]	5
Tucker, Diane/LaVelle School for the Blind	27
Tucker, Eric/Brooklyn Lab CS Chapel St	2
Tucker, Eric/Brooklyn Lab CS Jay St Campus	2
Tucker, Eric, Dr/Gordon Brooklyn Lab CS Sands	4
Tucker, Matthew, Dr/New Life Sch	27
Tudda, Frederick/St Helen Catholic Academy	186
Tuetschman, Angela/PS 175 Lynn Gross Discovery	182
Turcotte, Mark/JHS 98 Herman Ridder	24
Turgeon, Roger/Food and Finance High Sch	136
Turner-Hassell, Natelege/PS 2	191
Turner, Elizabeth/Somers Intermediate Sch	262
Turner, John/Global Concepts Charter ES	4
Turose, Constance/North Syracuse Jr High Sch	157
Turriciano, Camillo/PS 128 Juniper Valley	177
Tuttle, Cynthia/Ogdensburg Free Academy	212
Twarozek, Joshua/Western NY Childrens Psyc Ctr	66
Tyndall, Jeanette/Ross Lower Sch	235
Tyndall, Margaret/Our Lady Perpetual Help Sch	95
Tyrnaver, Yitchok/Bnei Yoel Sch	168
Tyrpak-Endres, Andrea/Canisius High Sch	65
Tzallas, Mary/William Spyropoulos Sch	189

U

NAME/School	PAGE
Ubertini, Adrienne/PS 90 Horace Mann	181
Ulysse, Florentine/PS 221 Toussaint L'Ouverture	87
Umpierre, Carmen/Bronx Global Lrng Inst-Girls	16
Underhill, Rhonda/Perkins Elem Sch	250
Underwood, Jay/George Jackson Academy	144
Unkenholz, Craig, Dr/Holbrook Road Elem Sch	225
Upton, Lisa/McCarthy School-Beard	159
Urciuoli, Rebecca, Dr/The Nightingale-Bamford Sch	146
Urena-Thus, Erica/PS 398Q Hector Figueroa Sch	185
Urquiza, Beverly/Bronx Little Sch	24
Urzetta, Rose Marie/Florence S Brown Pre-K Center	111
Useloff, Beth/Mosaic Pre-K Center at 47 Ave	177

V

NAME/School	PAGE
Vacchio, Valerie/James H Vernon Sch	127
Vadi, Evelyn/PS 121 Queens	182
Vadnais, Andrew/Darrow Sch	47
Vaillancourt, Eric/North Street Elem Sch	161
Vaillancourt, Mark/Kennedy Catholic High Sch	265
Valane, Jaclyn/International High Sch	177
Valcin, Geralda/Bronx Leadership Academy	18
Valente, Jenny/De Ruyter Elem Sch	105
Valentin, Harry/Westside Academy-Blodgett	159
Valentin, Harry, Dr/Syracuse STEM at Blodgett MS	159
Valentine, Daphne/Elmcrest Elem Sch	156
Valentine, Joseph/Albany Ave Elem Sch	119
Valentino, Merilee/Urban Assembly Law & Justice	83
Valez, Yolanda/Fuentes Sch of Sci & Discovery	20
Van Cott, Alan/Sagaponack Elem Sch	229
Van Deren, Laura/HS Law Enforcement Pub Safety	182
Van Dervoort, Matt/Lansingburgh High Sch	191
Van Etten, Doug/Homer High Sch	48
Van Gunten, Erik/Grimes Elem Sch	258
Van Harssel, Casey/East Rochester High Sch	107
Van Liew, Denisha/John F Kennedy Elem Sch	233
Van Nosdall, Jacqueline/Kerhonkson Elem Sch	243
Van Wormer, James/John F Kennedy Middle Sch	152
Van-Ess, Josephine/HS for Service & Learning	86
Vanderbeck, John/Gardiners Avenue Elem Sch	123
Vanderhoek, Zeke/Tep Equity Project Charter ECC	142
Vanderhoek, Zeke/Tep Equity Project Charter ES	142
Vanderhoek, Zeke/Tep Equity Project Charter MS	142
Vanderlinden, Michelle/Martin L King Magnet Sch	205
Vanderlip, Vincent/PS 27 Hillery Park Elem Sch	57
Vanderwalker, Mr/Veritas Academy	179
Vanderwater, Julie/Wilson Magnet High Sch	112
Vandi-Kirkland, Elaine/PS 69 Houghton Academy	57
Vanduren, Kim/Dr Martin Luther King Jr ES	152
Vane, Lenika/PS 306 Ethan Allen	89
Vanepps, Casey/Keshequa Primary Sch	103
Vanin, Francesca/Success Acad CS Harlem 4 [245]	7
VanKirk, Scott/Finger Lakes Christian Sch	209
Vann, Kerry/Academy Street Elem Sch	217
Vann, Kevin/Albert G Prodell Middle Sch	230
VanOrman, Matthew/Red Creek Middle Sch	251
Vanslyke, Donna/Royalton Hartland Elem Sch	148
Vantine, Whitney, Dr/Lewiston Porter High Sch	146
Vanweelden, Mr/Bloomingdale Elem Sch	70
Vanzetta, Christine/PS 7 Samuel Stern	139
Vardiman, Brandi/KIPP Star Harlem Clg Prep ES [242]	5
Vargas, Carmen/Uriah Hill Elem Sch	260
Varghese, Leena/Academic Leadership Chtr Sch	1
Vasconcelos, Yeou-Jey/Fiorello H Laguardia High Sch	138
Vassallo, Ellice, Dr/West Babylon Sr High Sch	233
Vaughan, Christine/Bethlehem Children's Sch	13
Vaughan, Cristine/Baychester Academy	22
Vaughan, Melissa, Dr/Dock Street Sch	82
Vaughn, Staci/Lisbon Central Sch	211
Vazquez, David/MS 424 Hunts Point Middle Sch	17
Vazquez, Martha/PS 69 Jackson Heights	184
Vazquez, Wanda/El Puente Acad Peace Soc Just	83
Vecchiano, Daniel/Brooklyn HS of the Arts	84
Vega, Joaquin/Bronx International High Sch	18
Vega, Judith/Bay Ridge Christian Academy	96
Vega, Norma/Ellis Preparatory Academy	20
Vega, Rosemary/East Williamsburg Scholars	83
Velazquez, Bryanna/Paula Hedbavny Sch	141
Velazquez, Emma/PS 9 Sarah Smith Garnet	83
Velazquez, Hector/Eagle Acad for Young Men-Bronx	18

New York School Directory — PRINCIPAL INDEX

NAME/School	PAGE
Velazquez, Lisa/PS 112 Jose Celso Barbosa	140
Velazquez, Lourdes/PS 130 A S Hewitt Elem Sch	18
Velez, Carlos/PS 291	21
Velez, Evelyn/PS 13 Clement C Moore	177
Velez, Nancy/Middle Village Prep Mid CS	5
Vellake, Amanda/Adult Education Center	57
Venticinque, Joseph/Our Lady of the Snows Sch	186
Vera-Drucker, Maria/PS 376	94
Veras, Vanessa/Harmony Christian Sch	168
Verdemare, Louise/PS 112 Lefferts Park	90
Verdiner, Michelle/Teachers College Cmty Sch	140
Verdonik, Julie/Maple Grove Jr Sr High Sch	36
Verdu, Ralph/Bethel Christian Academy	55
Vergis, Sarah/Holland Patent Elem Sch	150
Verhille, Dawn/Bronx Studio Sch for Writers	17
Veronica RSM, Ann, Sr/St Margaret Mary Sch	26
Verzillo, TJ/All Saints Academy	215
Vesci, Marc/Hendy Elem Sch	40
Vesci, Paul/Waverly Middle Sch	239
Veve, Cordelia/Urban Assembly School of Media	139
Viceroy, Greg/St Martin De Porres Sch	55
Victor, Ira/Grand Concourse Academy CS	4
Vicuna, Robert/School 9	264
Vieira, Karen/Salem Central Sch	248
Viel, Amanda/Millard Hawk Elem Sch	170
Vier, Casey/Children's AID College Prep CS	3
Vigliante, Mary/Academy of the Holy Names-Uppr	13
Villalona, Altagracia/Mott Hall High Sch	140
Villar, Juan/HS for Media & Communications	141
Villavicencio, Christina/PS 197 Ocean Sch	181
Villiere, Christoph/Port Leyden Elem Sch	101
Vimmerman, Lee/Fayette Mennonite Sch	208
Vinales, Jose/Academy for Language & Tech	18
Vincent, Kimberly/Success Acad CS Bronx 3 Lwr [245]	7
Viscovich, Suzanne, Dr/Homestead Primary Sch	120
Vitale, Patti/Brown Sch	205
Vitale, Thomas/PS 42 Occ Training Center	57
Vitale, Vince/Waterloo Middle Sch	208
Vitello, Diane/Dr Edwin Weeks Elem Sch	158
Vitiello, Raymond/St Benedict Sch	26
Vitolo, Vincent/PS 152 Gwendoline N Alleyne	185
Vivienzio, Jeffrey/Voorheesville Elem Sch	12
Vizcaino, Roony/Urban Assem-Global Commerce	140
Vlantis, Theresa/PS 277 Gerritsen Beach	92
Voegler, Elizabeth/Mexico Elem Sch	171
Voels, Timothy/W T Clarke Senior High Sch	118
Vogel, David/Yeshiva Beth Hillel D'Krasna	99
Vogel, Sharon/Goshen Christian Sch	168
Vogt, Renee/Herkimer Elem Sch	78
Volkmar, Christine/Virtual Academy of Rochester	112
Volkmar, Lucy/Achievement First East NY ES [128]	1
Volkomer, Mary/Kingsford Park Elem Sch	171
Volovodovskaya, Edita/John Adams YABC	180
Volpe, Emily/Rochester Prep ES-West	6
Volpicelli, Kathryn/Candor Elem Sch	238
Volpicelli, Victoria/Newfield Elem Sch	241
Vonbraunsberg, Karen/Our Lady of Peace Sch	132
Voron, Mike/Greenburgh Academy	255
Vosbury, Kelli/Deposit Elem Sch	28
Vota, Eileen/Stratford Avenue Elem Sch	120
Voyer, Cathy/Aspire Centr for Learning	66
Vrooman, Patrick/Pulaski Middle High Sch	172
Vuich, Marissa/Colonial Village Elem Sch	148

W

NAME/School	PAGE
Wadler, Lisa/Bais Yaakov Academy	96
Wagner, Jason/Pelham Lab High Sch	17
Wagner, Mary Ellen/St Rita Sch	114
Wagner, Ryan/Avon Central High Sch	102
Wahl, Andrew/Palmyra-Macedon High Sch	250
Waite, Jennifer/Robert W Harrold Ed Campus	48
Wakelee, Ashley/Truman Elem Sch	62
Walbridge, Kevin/St Regis Mohawk Sch	70
Waldman, Joan/Watson Elem Sch	128
Waldron-Oneill, Ellen/Southold Elem Sch	231
Walerstein, Chad/Maud S Sherwood Elem Sch	224
Walfall, Stacia/Clara H Carlson Elem Sch	118
Walh, Daniel/Transit Middle Sch	65
Walker, Charles/Union Springs Central High Sch	35
Walker, Darcy/Elma Primary Sch	61
Walker, Grecian/Boys & Girls High Sch	85
Walker, Josh/Calkins Road Middle Sch	110
Walker, Lauren/PS 18 John Peter Zenger	16
Walker, Parette/PS 61 Arthur Eve-Distinction	57
Walker, Tanya/PS 136 Roy Wilkins	183
Walker, Veronica/Flatbush SDA Sch	97
Wallace, Charles/St Thomas Choir Sch	145
Wallace, Patrick/Oswego High Sch	171
Walley, Torrance/W L Morse Elem Sch	262
Wallin, Camille/Muscota New Sch	141
Wallin, Jason/Churchill Center & Sch	144
Walpole, Michael/School 23	264
Walsh, Christopher/Byram Hills High Sch	253
Walsh, Cindy/Chester Elem Sch	163
Walsh, Patricia/Marlboro Elem Sch	242
Walsh, Susan/St Saviour Catholic Academy	95
Walsh, Tracy/PS 48 Po Michael J Buczek	141
Walters, Wanda/Grace Lutheran Sch	133
Walton, Heather/Roy Kelley Elem Sch	147
Walton, Priscilla/Elm Cmty Charter Sch	3
Wang, Cindy/PS 33 Chelsea Prep	137
Wang, Molly/PS 173 Fresh Meadows	179
Wanish, Angela/F E Smith Interm Sch	47
Ward, Brenda/PS 273	181
Ward, David/Brooklyn Theatre Arts High Sch	87
Ward, Kimberli/Avalon Sch at Villa of Hope	114
Ward, Lynne/Roosevelt Childrens Center	251
Ward, Matthew/Greenville High Sch	75
Ward, Michael/New Creation Fellowship Acad	66
Ware, Marcie/Indian Landing Elem Sch	110
Warfield, Shawnee/Alden Terrace Elem Sch	118
Wargo, Alicia/Dreamyard Prep Sch	18
Warner, Keisha/Cinema Sch	24
Warner, Stephen/Allen-Stevenson Sch	143
Warnock, Christopher/IS 181 Pablo Casals	23
Warren, Derek/Quest Elem Sch	109
Warren, Karen/West Sayville Christian Sch	235
Warren, Kevin/AG-Ptech	115
Warren, Madge/Stepping Stone Pre & Grade Sch	188
Warren, Sheri/Kappa MS 215	19
Warrington, Bently/MS 246 Walt Whitman	86
Washington, Carland/West Prep Academy	139
Washington, Deborah/Nathaniel Rochester Cmty Sch 3	111
Washington, Taren/William Boyce Thompson Sch	264
Washington, Tyona/HS for Excellence & Innovation	141
Washington, Zelda/Bushwick Ascend Lower CS	2
Waskiewicz, Edward/Edward R Andrews Elem Sch	105
Waslawski, James/New Directions Secondary Sch	19
Waters, Elizabeth/PS 6 Cpl Allan F Kivlehan Sch	193
Watkis, Shelita/Dayton Avenue Elem Sch	221
Watson, Charlene/PS 301 Burgard High Sch	58
Watson, Denise/PS 32 Samuel Mills Sprole	85
Watson, Kevin/Kendall Elem Sch	169
Watson, Kevin/Kendall Jr Sr High Sch	169
Waye, Debra/Ginther Elem Sch	107
Weaver, Joan/Richard R Green HS of Teaching	137
Webber, Julie/Oak Orchard Elem Sch	170
Webber, Olivia/PS 114 Luis Llorens Torres	19
Webel, Christopher/Nike Alternative High Sch	124
Weber, Mosha/Bnei Yakov Yosef of Monsey	198
Webster, Kelly/Watervliet Elem Sch	12
Webster, Mary Beth/St Aloysius Regional Sch	65
Weed, Georgia/Tuscarora Elem Sch	213
Weeks, James/PS/MS 280 Mosholu Parkway	22
Wehner, Connie/Helen B Montgomery School 50	111
Weichbrodt, Tziporah/Yeshiva Ateret Torah Girls	99
Weichselbaum, Shirley/East Midwood Hebrew Day Sch	97
Weigand, Christine/Evergreen Charter Sch	3

PRINCIPAL INDEX

Market Data Retrieval

NAME/School	PAGE
Weinberg, Noam/North Shore Hebrew Academy HS	134
Weinstein, Catherine/PS 102 Bayview	177
Weinstein, Josh/Mesivta Beth Sherim	98
Weinstein, Michael/HS of Applied Communications	177
Weir, Hillary/Woodrow Wilson Elem Sch	59
Weisblatt, Laura/Luria Academy of Brooklyn	98
Weisel, Deborah/Nassau Elem Sch	54
Weiser, Judy/Bnos Yaakov Education Center	97
Weishahn, Ann/Pine Park Elem Sch	218
Weiss, Alessandro/HS of American Studies-Lehman	20
Weiss, Harla/PS 238 Anne Sullivan	91
Weiss, Peter/Achievement First N Brooklyn [128]	1
Weiss, Rebecca/Bet Yaakov Ateret Torah	96
Weizberg, D/Beth Rochel School for Girls	198
Welch, Ann, Sr/St Catharine Academy	26
Welch, Melanie/Frankfort-Schuyler Elem Sch	77
Welch, Sojourner/PS/MS 394K	87
Wells, Matthew/Cayuga Elem Sch	229
Welsh, Jaycee/La Fargeville Central Sch	80
Welson, Elizabeth/PS/MS 114 Belle Harbor	181
Welty, Lawrence/Portville Central Sch	32
Welz, Berish/Bas Melech School for Girls	96
Wenk, John/Lower Manhattan Arts Academy	136
Wentworth, Matthew/Goshen Intermediate Sch	164
Wenzel, Dawn/Dryden Elem Sch	239
Werfelman, Colin/George M Diven Elem Sch	40
Wermuth, Jane/Paideia School 15	263
Wernau, Emily/Tremont Elem Sch	227
Werner, Janine, Dr/World Journalism Prep Sch	179
Wesolowski, Jennifer/Hamilton Elem Sch	258
West, Jerry/Mt Moriah Christian Academy	98
Westcott, James/John S Hobart Elem Sch	233
Westfall, Jessie/Worcester Central Sch	174
Westrack, Ireen/Mills Pond Elem Sch	230
Wetzel, David/Lisha Kill Middle Sch	12
Wetzler, Kelly/Harold O Brumsted Elem Sch	61
Whalen, John/Tioughnioga Riverside Academy	30
Whaley, John/William E Severn Elem Sch	214
Wheaton, James/Doane Stuart Sch	192
Wheeler, Chuck/East Learning Center	27
Wheeler, Dina/PS 181 Brookfield	183
Wheeler, Jessica/Overlook Primary Sch	51
Wheeler, Kathleen/Cicero Elem Sch	157
Whipple, Eric/Joseph B Radez Elem Sch	206
Whitcher, Joel/Olean Interm Middle Sch	32
Whitcombe, Shannon/Alexander Middle High Sch	73
White, Darlene, Dr/Milton L Olive Middle Sch	234
White, Darryl/Bronx Collegiate Academy	18
White, David/Faith Bible Academy	116
White, Dianne/Kahlil Gibran Sch	263
White, Grace/Bronxdale High Sch	22
White, Kathryn/Kent Elem Sch	175
White, Lajuan/Lincoln Middle Sch	158
White, Rushell/JHS 226 Virgil I Grissom	180
White, Susan/John Pearl Elem Sch	220
White, Tanya/Bronx Excellence 4 Elementary [236]	2
White, Tonya/Harlem C Z Promise Academy I	140
White, Zenobia/Academy Scholarship & Entrepnr	22
Whiteman, Lorri/Raymond C Buckley Elem Sch	240
Whitham, Joshua/Sleepy Hollow Middle Sch	262
Whitley, Michele/Geyser Road Elem Sch	201
Whitlock, Kristin/Nardin Montessori Academy	66
Whitlow, Lisa/Abelard Reynolds School 42	110
Whitney, Janie/Trey Whitfield Sch	99
Whittaker, Susan/Summit Center-Brighton	66
Whittaker, Susan/Summit Educational Resources	66
Whittel, Charles/Livonia Elem Sch	103
Wickwire, Trisha/Saranac Lake Middle Sch	70
Widor, Glenn/Webster Thomas High Sch	113
Widrick, Todd/Otto L Shortell Middle Sch	105
Wieder, Cecille/Torah Academy for Girls	188
Wiener, Joseph/Lynbrook South Middle Sch	124
Wiener, Moshe/Cheder Chabad Sch-Monsey	198

NAME/School	PAGE
Wiggins, Carol/Pulse High Sch	22
Wiggins, Jeanie/Trumansburg Elem Sch	241
Wiggins, Sarah/Thomas Jefferson Elem Sch	27
Wilbur, Paul/Forest Hills High Sch	182
Wilcox, Heather/Gilbertsville-Mt Upton Sch	173
Wilder, Stephen/Monticello High Sch	237
Wilensky, Edward/Rachel Carson HS-Coastal Study	91
Wiles, Timothy/Cleveland Hill High Sch	59
Wilkins, Rodney/Our World Neighborhood ES CS 2	6
Wilkins, Zoanne/MS 53 Brian Piccolo	180
Wilkinson, Deanna/Rochester Academy Charter Sch	6
Wilkinson, Diane/Schenectady High Sch	205
Wilkinson, Muriel/Our Lady of Guadalupe Sch	95
Wilkinson, Muriel/Our Lady of Trust Sch-SJC	95
William, Brennen/East Islip Middle Sch	221
Williams, Alexis/PS 195 City Honors Sch	58
Williams, Andrea/Ichabod Crane Primary Sch	46
Williams, Christine/Taft Elem Sch	167
Williams, Denise/Pelham Gardens Middle Sch	23
Williams, Dionne/IS 217 Sch of Performing Arts	24
Williams, Edele/Richmond Pre K Ctr Forest Ave	194
Williams, Edele/Richmond Pre K Ctr Stuyvesant	194
Williams, Edele/Richmond Pre K Ctr Teleport Dr	194
Williams, Erica/PS 245	92
Williams, Eva/Van Duyn Elem Sch	159
Williams, Gary/Seeall Academy	90
Williams, Jennifer/Tri-Valley Elem Sch	237
Williams, Lakeasha/PS 399 Stanley Eugene Clark	87
Williams, Lorraine, Dr/SS Francis-Stephen Sch	163
Williams, Lynnette/North Park Elem Sch	52
Williams, Marlon/MS 180 Dr Daniel Hale Williams	23
Williams, Mary/Thomas J Lahey Elem Sch	223
Williams, Matthew/Henninger High Sch	158
Williams, Melanie/Mott Haven Village Prep HS	16
Williams, Merve/IS 68 Isaac Bildersee	87
Williams, Michael/Redeemer Lutheran Sch	188
Williams, Peta/Marie Curie High Sch	21
Williams, Raymond/Hicksville High Sch	122
Williams, Shawn/Honeoye Falls Lima Middle Sch	109
Williams, Shelly/Miss Shelley's Upward Prep Sch	134
Williams, Sherry/PS 179	17
Williams, Sonya/Heritage Christian Academy	235
Williams, Tanishia/Williamsburg Charter High Sch	9
Williams, Tyra/Metropolitan Lighthouse CS [149]	19
Williams, Vanessa/IS 141 the Steinway	184
Williams, Vanessa/Manetuck Elem Sch	233
Williams, Yolanda/PS 75 Mayda Cortiella	94
Williamson, Jamie/Windward Sch-Westchester Lower	266
Willie, Matthew/University Neighborhood HS	135
Willis, Nikki/Masters Sch	266
Willman, Tania/Massapequa HS-Ames Campus	125
Wills, David/HS of Computers & Technology	22
Wilmoth, Jennifer/Kakiat Steam Academy	196
Wilson, Abbey/Fannie Lou Hamer Middle Sch	24
Wilson, Darryl/Roosevelt Children's Acad CS	7
Wilson, Gary/George Southard Elem Sch	147
Wilson, Jon/Dorothy B Bunce Elem Sch	74
Wilson, Mark/Greene Middle Sch	42
Wilson, Mark/St Mark Sch	95
Wilson, Michael/Hudson HS-Lrng Technologies	136
Wilson, Nancy/Rome Catholic Sch	153
Wilson, Rene/Richfield Springs Ctl Sch	174
Wilson, Scott/Churchville Chili High Sch	107
Wilson, Susan/Arthur P Momot Elem Sch	45
Wilson, Tanya, Dr/East Lower Sch	111
Wilson, Thomas, Dr/Bronxville Middle Sch	253
Wilson, Timberly/Great Oaks CS-New York City [238]	4
Wilson, Tina/Rye Neck High Sch	261
Wilson, Tonya/Colonial Elem Sch	260
Wiltshire, Michael, Dr/Medgar Evers College Prep Sch	86
Windley, Leander/IS 318 Eugenio Maria Dehostos	83
Windover, Eric/Wheatland Chili Mid High Sch	113
Wing, Keith/Forest Elem Sch	64

New York School Directory

PRINCIPAL INDEX

NAME/School	PAGE
Winghart, Gary/Remsen Elem Sch	151
Wink, Jeanmarie/East Broadway Elem Sch	123
Wink, Lawrence/Hastings-Mallory Elem Sch	170
Winkler, Daniel/Yeshiva Toras Chaim-S Shore	134
Winnicki, Jason/West Seneca East Sr High Sch	64
Winter, Eric/Pine Bush Elem Sch	166
Winter, Katie/Primrose Elem Sch	262
Wintermutt, Chris/Mohawk Valley Christian Acad	79
Winters, Patricia/Holy Child Jesus Catholic Acad	186
Wissemann, Jennifer/Oysterponds Elem Sch	227
Wissick, Susan/Gorham Intermediate Sch	162
Witherspoon, Iris/Bronx HS for the Visual Arts	22
Witkes, Dov/PS 112 Dutch Kills	184
Witkiewicz, Rob/Mountain View Campus	67
Witkiewicz, Robert/Northern Adirondack Jr Sr HS	44
Witt, Joanne/Bohlen Technical Center	79
Witzke, Kate/PS 9 Sarah Anderson	139
Wivietsky, Ethan/Alternative High Sch	221
Wodjeski, John/Harkness Career & Tech Center	55
Wojcik, Brandon/Carrier Educational Center	55
Wojcik, Brandon/North Collins Jr Sr High Sch	63
Wojcik, Jeanette/Sea Cliff Elem Sch	127
Wojeski, Christopher, Dr/Mayfield Jr Sr High Sch	72
Wojnarowski, Robert/PS 009	185
Woldemarian, Asha/Success Acad CS Ditmas Park [245]	7
Wolf, Jonathan/Orchard Park High Sch	63
Wolf, Kelly/Our Lady of Grace Sch	95
Wolfe, Collin, Dr/PS 53 Basheer Quisim	19
Wolfe, Deborah/Unity Drive Pre-K Kdgn Center	225
Wolfe, Heather/Calvin U Smith Elem Sch	214
Wolff, Colleen/Richard H O'Rourke Middle Sch	200
Wolff, Jamey/Center for Septrum Services	244
Wolfson, Scott, Dr/Fairmont Neighborhood Sch	24
Wolstenholme, Anne/Oneonta Senior High Sch	174
Womack, Brandi/Harlem Village Acad East Elem [239]	4
Wong, Nancy, Dr/Growing Up Green CS II	4
Woo, Dorothy/Harbor Country Day Sch	235
Woo, Dot/Friends Academy	133
Wood, Bryan/Cohoes High Sch	10
Wood, Cory/Gouverneur High Sch	210
Wood, David/Town Sch	146
Wood, Dawn/Argyle Elem Sch	247
Wood, Debra/McEvoy BOCES Voc Center	47
Wood, Mary/Roslyn Heights Sch	129
Wood, Sandra/Park Ave Elem Sch	167
Wood, Scott/Union Vale Middle Sch	51
Woodard, Martin/PS 183 Robert L Stevenson	137
Woodard, Steve/Regional Education Center	34
Woodcock, Brett/Morgan Road Elem Sch	156
Woodly, Staci/Oakside Elem Sch	260
Woodruff, Jacqueline/Van Cortlandtville Elem Sch	257
Woods-Powell, Jean/Information Technology HS	184
Woods, Andrew/Our Lady Queen of Martyrs Sch	143
Woodward, Mark/Parsons Memorial Elem Sch	256
Woolson, Julie/Altmar-Parish-Williamstown ES	170
Worden, Robert/Linden Hill Sch	256
Work, Nathan/Pembroke Jr Sr High Sch	74
Worthington, Heather/St Coleman's Home	13
Wosner, Chana/Bais Yaakov Dchassidei Gur Sch	96
Woudenburg, Ron/Emmanuel Baptist Academy	268
Woughter, Robert/Keene Central Sch	67
Wren, Robert/Cato Meridian Elem Sch	34
Wright, Frederick/PS 219 Paul Klapper	179
Wright, Margie/Honeoye Central Sch	161
Wright, Michele/Winfield Street Elem Sch	214
Wright, Rachel/South Kortright Central Sch	50
Wright, Tracey/PS 39 Francis J Murphy Jr	193
Wu, Tony/PS 170 Ralph A Fabrizio Sch	90
Wurster, Mike/Union Springs Middle Sch	35
Wyld, Victoria/Iroquois Middle Sch	204
Wylke, Dawn/Lockport High Sch	147
Wynne, Patricia/One World Middle Sch-Edenwald	23
Wyse, Toby/Ross Corners Christian Academy	30

X

NAME/School	PAGE
Xerri, Louise/PS 199 Jessie Isador Straus	139

Y

NAME/School	PAGE
Yaffe, Mordechai/Mesivta Ateres Yaakov	133
Yager, Amy/Cypress Hills Collegiate Prep	88
Yallowitz, Meri/Metropolitan Diploma Plus HS	93
Yan, Li/HS Dual Lang & Asian Studies	136
Yannucci, Michael/Raymond J Lockhart Elem Sch	125
Yanofsky, Tsivia/Manhattan HS for Girls	145
Yarbrough, Jesse/PS 536	24
Yard, Anthony/East New York Family Academy	88
Yardley, Moira/Willard Prior Elem Sch	105
Yarlett-Fenti, Kathryn/Francis Parker School 23	111
Yarmak, Joyce/Shulamith School for Girls	134
Yavlonsky, Sharir/Rabbi Jacob Joseph School-Boys	195
Yazurlo, Michelle/Palisade Preparatory Sch	264
Yerkie, Dawn/Mt Markham Middle Sch	78
Yilicetti, Sally/Prospect UCP Family Center	246
Ying, Carol/Brownsville Academy High Sch	86
Yodis, Mary/Gardner Dickinson Elem Sch	192
Yoo, Sungmin/PS 312 Bergen Beach	92
Yorio, Jean/St Mary Our Mother Sch	41
Yorke, Tom/Sharon Springs Central Sch	207
Young, Anna/Mt Moriah Academy	13
Young, Dawn/Vestal Senior High Sch	30
Young, Renee/Corinth Elem Sch	200
Young, Timothy/Florence Brasser Elem Sch	108
Younghans, Matthew/Little TOR Elem Sch	196
Younghese, Donna/Martin Luther High Sch	188
Youngs, Toby/A F Palmer Elem Sch	30
Yunker, Todd/Fairbanks Road Elem Sch	107

Z

NAME/School	PAGE
Zacotinsky, Catherine/Four Winds Learning Center	265
Zadoorian, David/Fonda Fultonville Central Sch	115
Zagami, Dominic/PS 377 Alejandrina Degautier	94
Zager, Brian/Lafayette Acad MS 256	138
Zahedi, Katie, Dr/Linden Avenue Middle Sch	53
Zahler, Eric/The Spence Sch	146
Zahn, Brian, Dr/Southampton High Sch	231
Zakrajsek, William/Bainbridge Guilford Jr Sr HS	41
Zaks, Leah/Bais Yaakov Chofetz Chaim	198
Zalacca, Samuel/Christ the King Sch	65
Zambelli, Jeanmarie/Tuttle Avenue Sch	221
Zampaglione, John/Jonas E Salk Middle Sch	123
Zamperlin, Frank/John F Kennedy Elem Sch	175
Zampetti, Victor/Mt Markham High Sch	78
Zandi, Karen/Mary Cariola Children's Center	114
Zangari, Frank, Dr/School 8 Fulton Avenue	127
Zanrucha, Laura/Afton Central Sch	41
Zapata, Kenneth/IS 75 Frank D Paulo	193
Zaretsky, Jacqueline/PS 993Q	126
Zawatski, Charity/Gouverneur Elem Sch	210
Zaza, Joseph/Nicotra Early College CS	6
Zbaida, Steven/Satellite Academy High Sch	137
Zegarelli, Angelo/Henry Viscardi Sch	133
Zegers, Matthew/Rosemary Kennedy Sch	116
Zegers, Matthew/Rosemary Kennedy Sch at Willet	116
Zehr, Barbara/Philadelphia Primary Sch	80
Zelazny, Barbara/Young Women's College Prep CS	9
Zender, Kristen/St Lawrence Senior High Sch	209
Zernone, Michelle/Bardonia Elem Sch	195
Zerrillo, Jill/Tecumseh Elem Sch	155
Zeytouneh, Rabbi/Yeshivat OR Hatorah ES	100
Zhang, Shirley/C C B School of Douglaston	187
Ziegler, Dana/Nate Perry Elem Sch	156
Ziemba, Rebbetzin/Bais Yaakov-18th Ave Sch	96
Zigelman, Erica/Middle School 322	141
Zilinski, Christopher/John W LaVelle Prep Chtr Sch	5
Zimbler, David/Westbury High Sch	132
Zimmer, Mrs/Forest Lake Elem Sch	131
Zimmer, William/Highland High Sch	242
Zimmerman, Derek/Gaskill Preparatory Sch	147

PRINCIPAL INDEX

NAME/School	PAGE
Zimmerman, Kelly/Pine Valley Elem Sch	38
Zinn, Diane/PS 371K Lillian L Rashkis	94
Zinn, Linda/Westchester Excptnl Chldrn's	266
Ziomek, Scott/Schalmont Middle Sch	204
Zion Ungar, Ben/Yeshiva Derech Hatorah HS	100
Zipp, Scott/Cheektowaga High Sch	58
Zirin, Ronald/IS 230Q Sch for Civics In Cmty	184
Zlotowitz, Debbie/Mary McDowell Friends Sch	98
Zollo, Anthony/Fieldstone Middle Sch	197
Zuber-Banks, Holly/Chestnut Ridge Middle Sch	196
Zucal, Emily/Lakeville Elem Sch	121
Zucker, Marshall/Gotham Avenue Elem Sch	119
Zuckerman, Julia/Castle Bridge Sch	141
Zuschlag, Anne/Our Lady Queen of Martyrs Acad	186
Zwahlen, Christian/Iroquois Middle Sch	113
Zymeck, Henry/MS 245 the Computer Sch	138

New York School Directory
DISTRICT & SCHOOL TELEPHONE INDEX

School/City/County DISTRICT/CITY/COUNTY	PID	TELEPHONE NUMBER	PAGE
A			
A A Gates Elem Sch/Port Byron/Cayuga	00718063	315/776-5728	35
A A Kingston Middle Sch/Potsdam/St Lawrence	00768953	315/265-2000	212
A B C Math Academy/Flushing/Queens	11229772	718/888-7866	187
A Childs Place Day Sch/East Elmhurst/Queens	10915978	718/424-7949	187
A D Oliver Middle Sch/Brockport/Monroe	00731455	585/637-1860	107
A F Palmer Elem Sch/Windsor/Broome	04013009	607/655-8225	30
A Fantis Parochial Sch/Brooklyn/Kings	01461756	718/624-0501	95
A J Schmidt Elem Sch/Angola/Erie	00724749	716/926-2350	60
A J Smith Elem Sch/Union Springs/Cayuga	00718178	315/889-4170	35
A MacArthur Barr 5-6 Academy/Nanuet/Rockland	12104761	845/627-4040	196
A MacArthur Barr Middle Sch/Nanuet/Rockland	00767545	845/627-4040	196
A Philip Randolph Campus HS/New York/New York	02106894	212/690-6800	141
A-Tech High Sch/Brooklyn/Kings	00740705	718/218-9301	83
Aaron Sch/New York/New York	05270250	212/867-9594	143
Aaron Sch/New York/New York	11728546	212/867-9594	143
Abbey Lane Elem Sch/Levittown/Nassau	00736742	516/434-7400	123
Abelard Reynolds School 42/Rochester/Monroe	00733063	585/663-4330	110
Abilities First Sch/Poughkeepsie/Dutchess	01873020	845/452-0774	55
Abraham Joshua Heschel Sch/New York/New York	02615285	212/595-7087	143
Abraham Lincoln High Sch/Brooklyn/Kings	00740638	718/333-7400	91
Abraham Lincoln YABC/Brooklyn/Kings	11928760	718/333-7455	91
Abraham Wing Elem Sch/Glens Falls/Warren	00778453	518/792-3231	245
Abram Lansing Elem Sch/Cohoes/Albany	00714469	518/237-5044	10
Abrookin Career & Tech Ctr/Albany/Albany	00714304	518/475-6400	9
Acad Clg Prep Career Explore/Brooklyn/Kings	10027179	718/564-2566	86
Acad Environmental Leadership/Brooklyn/Kings	10025652	718/381-7100	93
Acad for Excellence Thru Arts/Forest Hills/Queens	11103439	929/467-6200	181
Acad of Hospitality & Tourism/Brooklyn/Kings	10027181	718/564-2580	86
Acad of Med Tech-College Board/Far Rockaway/Queens	11103427	718/471-3571	180
Acad-Conservation-Environ/Brooklyn/Kings	11103336	718/968-4101	87
Acad-Personal Ldrshp & Excell/Bronx/Bronx	11561178	718/220-3139	20
Academic Leadership Chtr Sch/Bronx/Bronx	11447651	718/585-4215	1
Academics West/New York/New York	12369741	212/580-0080	143
Academy Applied Math & Tech/Bronx/Bronx	00743135	718/292-3883	16
Academy at Maple Avenue/Cassadaga/Chautauqua	12239574	716/672-3222	36
Academy Charter Elem Sch/Hempstead/Nassau	11468162	516/408-2200	1
Academy Charter ES-Uniondale/Uniondale/Nassau	12310934	516/591-3030	1
Academy Charter High Sch/Hempstead/Nassau	12310922	516/408-2200	1
Academy Charter Middle Sch/Hempstead/Nassau	12310908	516/408-2200	1
Academy for Careers-TV & Film/Long Is City/Queens	11102980	718/609-3330	184
Academy for Health Careers/Brooklyn/Kings	11561142	718/773-0128	86
Academy for Language & Tech/Bronx/Bronx	10911867	718/731-0219	18
Academy for New Americans/Astoria/Queens	04457194	718/956-4140	184
Academy for Young Writers/Brooklyn/Kings	10027208	718/688-7230	88
Academy of American Studies/Long Is City/Queens	04457792	718/361-8786	184
Academy of Chrn Leadership/Valatie/Columbia	10000212		47
Academy of Finance Enterprise/Long Is City/Queens	10008680	718/389-3623	176
Academy of Health Sciences CS/Rochester/Monroe	12377566	585/254-1003	1
Academy of Innovative Tech/Brooklyn/Kings	11103116	718/827-2469	88
Academy of Mt St Ursula/Bronx/Bronx	00754990	718/364-5353	25
Academy of Public Relations/Bronx/Bronx	04458461	718/665-8866	16
Academy of St Dorothy/Staten Island/Richmond	00755011	718/351-0939	194
Academy of St Joseph/New York/New York	11433430	212/243-5420	142
Academy of St Paul and St Ann/New York/New York	00758283	212/534-0619	142
Academy of Talented Scholars/Brooklyn/Kings	11447845	718/621-2730	89
Academy of the City Chtr Sch/Woodside/Queens	11722645	718/487-9857	1
Academy of the Holy Names-Uppr/Albany/Albany	00715231	518/489-7895	13
Academy of Thought & Industry/New York/New York	12362432	917/338-2820	143
Academy of Urban Planning/Brooklyn/Kings	05281039	718/381-7100	93
Academy Scholarship & Entrepnr/Bronx/Bronx	10008484	718/696-3840	22
Academy Software Engineering/New York/New York	11821643	212/253-3299	135
Academy Street Elem Sch/Bayport/Suffolk	00772083	631/472-7850	217
Acadia Middle Sch/Clifton Park/Saratoga	04287420	518/881-0450	202
Accion Academy/Bronx/Bronx	05349394	718/378-1649	24
Accompsett Elem Sch/Smithtown/Suffolk	00775516	631/382-4155	230
Accompsett Middle Sch/Smithtown/Suffolk	00775528	631/382-2300	230
Achievement First Apollo ES/Brooklyn/Kings	11561063	347/471-2620	1
Achievement First Aspire ES/Brooklyn/Kings	11934305	347/471-2055	1
Achievement First Brooklyn HS/Brooklyn/Kings	11708663	718/363-2260	1
Achievement First Brownsville/Brooklyn/Kings	11128661	347/471-2600	1
Achievement First Bushwick ES/Brooklyn/Kings	10030310	718/443-1213	1
Achievement First Bushwick MS/Brooklyn/Kings	10915069	347/471-2560	1
Achievement First Crown Hghts/Brooklyn/Kings	10008991	347/471-2580	86
Achievement First E Brooklyn/Brooklyn/Kings	12306218	347/471-2650	1
Achievement First East NY ES/Brooklyn/Kings	10008989	718/485-4924	1
Achievement First Endeavor Sch/Brooklyn/Kings	10030798	718/622-5994	1
Achievement First Linden ES/Brooklyn/Kings	12028284	347/471-2700	1
Achievement First N Brooklyn/Brooklyn/Kings	12028301	347/471-2690	1
Achievement First Univ Prep HS/Brooklyn/Kings	11931872	718/363-2270	1
Achievement First Voyager MS/Brooklyn/Kings	12170502	347/471-2640	1
Active Learning Elem Sch/Flushing/Queens	11103025	718/445-5730	178
ADDISON CENTRAL SCH DIST/ADDISON/STEUBEN	00771209	607/359-2245	213
Addison Jr Sr High Sch/Addison/Steuben	00771211	607/359-2241	213
Adelphi Academy of Brooklyn/Brooklyn/Kings	00752502	718/238-3308	95
Adironack High Sch/Boonville/Oneida	00759897	315/942-9200	150
Adirondack Academy/Johnstown/Fulton	03382132	518/736-4321	71
ADIRONDACK CENTRAL SCH DIST/BOONVILLE/ONEIDA	00759885	315/942-9200	150
Adirondack Christian Sch/Wilmington/Essex	00728109	518/946-2487	69
Adirondack Educational Center/Saranac Lake/Franklin	03280572	518/891-1330	69
Adirondack Middle Sch/Boonville/Oneida	04867367	315/942-9200	150
Adlai E Stevenson School 29/Rochester/Monroe	00732942	585/328-8228	110
Adlai Stevenson Campus YABC/Bronx/Bronx	11928681	718/792-8264	17
Adult Education Center/Buffalo/Erie	01538385	716/888-7088	57
Adult Education Center/Great Neck/Nassau	04033695	516/441-4949	120
Aeci II-Sch for Computer Engr/Bronx/Bronx	12367157	646/741-7470	1
African Road Elem Sch/Vestal/Broome	00717100	607/757-2311	30
Afton Central Sch/Afton/Chenango	00719574	607/639-8200	41
AFTON CENTRAL SCH DIST/AFTON/CHENANGO	00719550	607/639-8229	41
AG-Ptech/St Johnsville/Montgomery	12235384	518/568-7023	115
Ahi Ezer Yeshiva Sch/Brooklyn/Kings	00750920	718/648-6100	95
Airline Drive Academy/Albany/Albany	12473251	518/464-6303	9
AKRON CENTRAL SCH DIST/AKRON/ERIE	00722430	716/542-5010	56
Akron Elem Sch/Akron/Erie	00722442	716/542-5050	56
Akron High Sch/Akron/Erie	00722454	716/542-5030	56
Akron Middle Sch/Akron/Erie	05102847	716/542-5040	56
Akwesasne Freedom Sch/Rooseveltown/St Lawrence	11237327	518/358-2073	212
AL Ihsan School of Excellence/Syracuse/Onondaga	04975122	315/472-5040	160
AL Iman Sch/Jamaica/Queens	04974752	718/297-6520	187
AL Madinah Sch/Brooklyn/Kings	11230874	718/222-4986	95
AL Madrasa Alislamiya Sch/Brooklyn/Kings	04974623	718/567-3334	95
AL Noor Sch/Brooklyn/Kings	04974611	718/768-7181	96
Al-Ihsan Academy/S Ozone Park/Queens	04931126	718/322-3154	187
Al-Mamoor Sch/Fresh Meadows/Queens	10752752	718/739-0902	187
Albany Academy/Albany/Albany	00715982	518/429-2300	13

DISTRICT & SCHOOL TELEPHONE INDEX

Market Data Retrieval

School/City/County DISTRICT/CITY/COUNTY	PID	TELEPHONE NUMBER	PAGE
Albany Academy-West/Albany/Albany	01872947	518/429-2300	13
Albany Ave Elem Sch/N Massapequa/Nassau	00735449	516/434-5510	119
Albany Avenue Elem Sch/Lindenhurst/Suffolk	00774055	631/867-3150	224
ALBANY CITY SCH DIST/ALBANY/ ALBANY	00714110	518/475-6000	9
Albany Cmty Charter Sch/Albany/Albany	10752491	518/433-1500	1
Albany Elem Sch/Utica/Oneida	00760626	315/792-2150	152
Albany Free Sch/Albany/Albany	01460374	518/434-3072	13
Albany High Sch/Albany/Albany	00714134	518/475-6200	9
Albany International Center/Albany/Albany	12379904	518/475-6900	9
Albany Leadrshp CHS for Girls/Albany/Albany	11722621	518/694-5300	1
Albany School of Humanities/Albany/Albany	00714249	518/475-6575	9
Albert G Prodell Middle Sch/Shoreham/Suffolk	00775487	631/821-8210	230
Albert Leonard Middle Sch/New Rochelle/Westchester	00781101	914/576-4339	259
Albertus Magnus High Sch/Bardonia/Rockland	00755023	845/623-8842	198
Albertus W Becker Elem Sch/Selkirk/Albany	00714770	518/756-5200	11
ALBION CENTRAL SCH DIST/ ALBION/ORLEANS	00765133	585/589-2056	169
ALDEN CENTRAL SCH DIST/ALDEN/ ERIE	00722466	716/937-9116	56
Alden High Sch/Alden/Erie	00722492	716/937-9116	56
Alden Intermediate Sch/Alden/Erie	12172988	716/937-9116	56
Alden Middle Sch/Alden/Erie	00722480	716/937-9116	56
Alden Place Elem Sch/Millbrook/Dutchess	00721797	845/677-4220	52
Alden Primary Sch/Alden/Erie	00722519	716/937-9116	56
Alden Terrace Elem Sch/Valley Stream/Nassau	00735372	516/285-8310	118
ALEXANDER CTL SCH DIST/ALEXANDER/ GENESEE	00728783	585/591-1551	73
Alexander Elem Sch/Alexander/Genesee	00728795	585/591-1551	73
Alexander Hamilton High Sch/Elmsford/Westchester	00780119	914/592-7311	255
Alexander Middle High Sch/Alexander/Genesee	00728800	585/591-1551	73
Alexander Robertson Sch/New York/New York	00751132	212/663-6441	143
Alexandria Central Sch/Alex Bay/Jefferson	00729945	315/482-9971	79
ALEXANDRIA CENTRAL SCH DIST/ ALEX BAY/JEFFERSON	00729933	315/482-9971	79
ALFRED ALMOND CTL SCH DIST/ ALMOND/ALLEGANY	00716003	607/276-6555	13
Alfred Almond Sch/Almond/Allegany	00716027	607/276-6555	13
Alfred E Smith Campus YABC/Bronx/Bronx	11928708	718/993-1706	16
Alfred E Smith Career-Tech HS/Bronx/Bronx	00740664	718/993-5000	16
Alfred G Berner Middle Sch/Massapequa/Nassau	00737241	516/308-5700	125
Algonquin Middle Sch/Averill Park/Rensselaer	00766606	518/674-7100	189
Alice E Grady Elem Sch/Elmsford/Westchester	00780121	914/592-8962	255
Alice P Willits Elem Sch/Syosset/Nassau	00738568	516/364-5829	129
All City High Sch/Rochester/Monroe	00732605	585/458-2110	110
All City Leadership Sec Sch/Brooklyn/Kings	05281077	718/246-6500	93
All Hallows High School-Boys/Bronx/Bronx	00755035	718/293-4545	25
All Saints Academy/Corning/Steuben	00733702	607/936-9234	215
All Saints Catholic Academy/Albany/Albany	00715164	518/438-0066	12
All Saints Elem Sch/Syracuse/Onondaga	11226160	315/422-3140	160
ALLEGANY-LIMESTONE CTL SD/ ALLEGANY/CATTARAUGUS	00717332	716/375-6600	31
Allegany-Limestone Elem Sch/Allegany/Cattaraugus	00717344	716/375-6600	31
Allegany-Limestone High Sch/Allegany/Cattaraugus	00717356	716/375-6600	31
Alleghany Avenue Elem Sch/Lindenhurst/Suffolk	00774067	631/867-3200	224
Allen Christian Sch/Jamaica/Queens	02231657	718/657-1676	187
Allen Creek Elem Sch/Rochester/Monroe	00732435	585/267-1200	110
Allen Road Elem Sch/N Syracuse/Onondaga	00761929	315/218-2300	157
Allen-Stevenson Sch/New York/New York	00758805	212/288-6710	143
Allendale Columbia Sch/Rochester/Monroe	00765092	585/381-4560	114
Allendale Elem Sch/West Seneca/Erie	00725406	716/677-3660	64
Alpha Sch/Brooklyn/Kings	11239210	718/257-5800	96
Altamont Elem Sch/Altamont/Albany	00714562	518/861-8528	11
Alternative High Sch/Manorville/Suffolk	12037390	631/801-3292	221
Alternative Learning Center/Maybrook/Orange	12035524	845/457-2400	167
Alternative Sch for Math & Sci/Corning/Steuben	05341005	607/962-0011	215
Alternatives for Children/East Setauket/Suffolk	03037404	631/331-6400	234

School/City/County DISTRICT/CITY/COUNTY	PID	TELEPHONE NUMBER	PAGE
Altmar-Parish-Williamstown ES/Parish/Oswego	00765389	315/625-5270	170
Altmar-Parish-Williamstown HS/Parish/Oswego	01841314	315/625-5220	170
ALTMAR-PARISH-WILLIAMSTOWN SD/ PARISH/OSWEGO	00765353	315/625-5251	170
Altschool Brooklyn Heights/Brooklyn/Kings	12305965	718/852-6069	96
Altschool Union Square/New York/New York	12305977	866/664-2070	143
Alverta B Gray Schultz Mid Sch/Hempstead/Nassau	00736120	516/434-4300	121
Amagansett Sch/Amagansett/Suffolk	00771883	631/267-3572	216
AMAGANSETT UNION FREE SCH DIST/ AMAGANSETT/SUFFOLK	00771871	631/267-3572	216
Amani Public Charter Sch/Mount Vernon/Westchester	11716139	914/668-6450	1
Amber Charter Sch East Harlem/New York/New York	04924276	212/534-9667	1
Amber Charter Sch Kingsbridge/Bronx/Bronx	12260212	646/802-1140	1
Amer Sign Lang-Eng Lwr Sch 47/New York/New York	10013099	917/326-6609	135
American Dream Charter Sch/Bronx/Bronx	12028296	718/585-3071	1
American Sign Lang-Eng HS 47/New York/New York	00750346	917/326-6668	135
Amherst Central High Sch/Amherst/Erie	00722545	716/362-8100	56
AMHERST CENTRAL SCH DIST/ AMHERST/ERIE	00722521	716/362-3000	56
Amherst Christian Academy/Amherst/Erie	02160084	716/689-9944	66
Amherst Middle Sch/Amherst/Erie	00722533	716/362-7100	56
Amistad Dual Language Sch/New York/New York	04457431	212/544-8021	141
Amityville Memorial High Sch/Amityville/Suffolk	00771912	631/565-6100	216
AMITYVILLE UNION FREE SCH DIST/ AMITYVILLE/SUFFOLK	00771895	631/565-6000	216
Ampark Neighborhood Sch/Bronx/Bronx	10913839	718/548-3451	20
Amsterdam High Sch/Amsterdam/Montgomery	01535541	518/843-4932	116
An Nur Islamic Sch/Schenectady/Schenectady	04974984	518/395-9866	205
Andalusia Sch/Yonkers/Westchester	11221677	914/964-5600	265
Anderson Center for Autism/Staatsburg/Dutchess	00722387	845/889-4034	55
Anderson School PS 334/New York/New York	10008903	212/595-7193	138
Andes Central Sch/Andes/Delaware	00721008	845/676-3166	49
ANDES CENTRAL SCH DIST/ANDES/ DELAWARE	00720999	845/676-3167	48
Andover Central Sch/Andover/Allegany	00716041	607/478-8491	14
ANDOVER CENTRAL SCH DIST/ ANDOVER/ALLEGANY	00716039	607/478-8491	13
Andrew J Townson School 39/Rochester/Monroe	00733037	585/467-8816	110
Andrew Muller Primary Sch/Miller Place/Suffolk	00774469	631/474-2715	226
Andrew T Morrow Elem Sch/Central Islip/Suffolk	00772447	631/348-5037	218
Andrews Trahey Sch/Rochester/Monroe	01793913	585/256-7626	114
Andries Hudde Sch/Brooklyn/Kings	00747090	718/253-3700	92
Angelo Patri Middle Sch/Bronx/Bronx	04904630	718/584-1295	20
Ann G McGuinness Elem Sch/Endicott/Broome	00716730	607/757-2131	29
Ann M MacArthur Primary Sch/Locust Valley/Nassau	01822954	516/277-5350	123
Anna Merritt Elem Sch/Lockport/Niagara	00759067	716/478-4725	147
Anna Murray-Douglass School 12/Rochester/Monroe	00732796	585/461-3280	110
Anna S Kuhl Elem Sch/Port Jervis/Orange	00764866	845/858-3100	166
Anne Hutchinson Elem Sch/Eastchester/Westchester	00779988	914/793-6130	254
Anne M Dorner Middle Sch/Ossining/Westchester	00781307	914/762-5740	259
Annunciation School-Crestwood/Tuckahoe/Westchester	00755061	914/337-8760	264
Anthony Alfano Elem Sch/Central Islip/Suffolk	04038695	631/348-5139	218
Antonia Pantoja Prep Academy/Bronx/Bronx	10910411	718/824-3152	17
Antwerp Primary Sch/Antwerp/Jefferson	00730152	315/659-8386	80
Apalachin Elem Sch/Apalachin/Tioga	00777136	607/687-6289	238
Aquebogue Elem Sch/Aquebogue/Suffolk	00775023	631/369-6780	228
Aquinas Institute/Rochester/Monroe	00734562	585/254-2020	114
Arbor Hill Elem Sch/Albany/Albany	00714158	518/475-6625	9
Arcade Elem Sch/Arcade/Cattaraugus	00717681	716/492-9421	33
Arcadia High Sch/Rochester/Monroe	00731948	585/966-3000	108
Arcadia Middle Sch/Rochester/Monroe	04144359	585/966-3300	108
Archangel Sch/Rochester/Monroe	10795259	585/426-5990	114

NY-V2   800-333-8802   School Year 2020-2021

New York School Directory

DISTRICT & SCHOOL TELEPHONE INDEX

School/City/County DISTRICT/CITY/COUNTY	PID	TELEPHONE NUMBER	PAGE
Archbishop Molloy High Sch/Briarwood/Queens	00752837	718/441-2100	186
Archbishop Stepinac High Sch/White Plains/Westchester	00755085	914/946-4800	264
Archbishop Walsh Academy/Olean/Cattaraugus	00725901	716/372-8122	33
ARCHDIOCESE OF NEW YORK ED OFF/ NEW YORK/NEW YORK	00754976	212/371-1011	142
Archer Elem Sch/Bronx/Bronx	11714997	718/828-3791	24
Archer Street Elem Sch/Freeport/Nassau	00735683	516/867-5250	119
Archimedes Acad Math Sci Tech/Bronx/Bronx	10910423	718/617-5046	17
Ardsley High Sch/Ardsley/Westchester	00779641	914/295-5800	252
Ardsley Middle Sch/Ardsley/Westchester	00779653	914/295-5600	252
ARDSLEY UNION FREE SCH DIST/ ARDSLEY/WESTCHESTER	00779639	914/295-5500	252
Argus Community High Sch/Bronx/Bronx	11227566	718/401-5700	26
ARGYLE CENTRAL SCH DIST/ ARGYLE/WASHINGTON	00778788	518/638-8243	246
Argyle Elem Sch/Argyle/Washington	00778790	518/638-8243	247
Argyle Jr Sr High Sch/Argyle/Washington	12320006	518/638-8243	247
Arkport Central Sch/Arkport/Steuben	00771259	607/295-7471	213
ARKPORT CENTRAL SCH DIST/ ARKPORT/STEUBEN	00771247	607/295-7471	213
ARLINGTON CENTRAL SCH DIST/ LAGRANGEVILLE/DUTCHESS	00721400	845/486-4460	51
Arlington High Sch/Lagrangeville/Dutchess	00721436	845/486-4860	51
Armor Elem Sch/Hamburg/Erie	00724189	716/646-3350	61
Arongen Elem Sch/Clifton Park/Saratoga	00769880	518/881-0510	202
Arrowhead Elem Sch/East Setauket/Suffolk	00775982	631/730-4100	232
Art & Design High Sch/New York/New York	00740688	212/752-4340	135
Arthur P Momot Elem Sch/Plattsburgh/Clinton	00720262	518/563-1140	45
Arthur S May Elem Sch/Poughkeepsie/Dutchess	00721412	845/486-4960	51
Arts & Letters 305 United/Brooklyn/Kings	00745004	718/789-3962	82
Arturo Schomburg Satelite Acad/Bronx/Bronx	11821538	718/518-3050	24
Ascension Sch/New York/New York	00755097	212/222-5161	142
Ascent Sch/Deer Park/Suffolk	11222346	631/254-6100	234
Ashar Sch/New City/Rockland	00768252	845/357-1515	198
Aspirations Diploma Plus HS/Brooklyn/Kings	11103087	718/773-7765	93
Aspire Centr for Learning/Cheektowaga/Erie	01793212	716/505-5700	66
Astor Collegiate Academy/Bronx/Bronx	05349277	718/944-3418	22
Astor Learning Center/Rhinebeck/Dutchess	03345861	845/876-4081	55
Ateres Bais Yaakov/Spring Valley/Rockland	05162421	845/368-2200	198
Athena High Sch/Rochester/Monroe	00731950	585/966-4000	108
Athena Middle Sch/Rochester/Monroe	00731962	585/966-8800	108
Atmosphere Acad PCS/Bronx/Bronx	12170590	718/757-5852	1
ATTICA CENTRAL SCH DIST/ ATTICA/WYOMING	00783056	585/591-0400	267
Attica Elem Sch/Attica/Wyoming	00783068	585/591-0400	267
Attica Middle Sch/Attica/Wyoming	00783070	585/591-0400	267
Attica Senior High Sch/Attica/Wyoming	00783082	585/591-0400	267
AUBURN ENLARGED CITY SCH DIST/ AUBURN/CAYUGA	00717863	315/255-8822	34
Auburn High Sch/Auburn/Cayuga	00717875	315/255-8300	34
Auburn Junior High Sch/Auburn/Cayuga	00717916	315/255-8480	34
August Martin High Sch/Jamaica/Queens	00740690	718/528-2920	180
Augustine Classical Academy/Mechanicville/Saratoga	11746720	518/541-2089	203
Augustinian Academy/Carthage/Jefferson	02124456	315/493-1301	82
Aura A Cole Elem Sch/Constantia/Oswego	00765418	315/668-4030	170
Aurora Waldorf Sch/West Falls/Erie	04975354	716/655-2029	66
Ausable Forks Elem Sch/Au Sable FRKS/Clinton	00719938	518/647-5503	43
AUSABLE VALLEY CTL SCH DIST/ CLINTONVILLE/CLINTON	00719926	518/834-2845	43
Ausable Valley Middle High Sch/Clintonville/Clinton	00719940	518/834-2800	43
Austin Road Elem Sch/Mahopac/Putnam	00766486	845/628-1346	176
Automotive YABC/Brooklyn/Kings	11928722	718/218-9301	83
Autumn Lane Elem Sch/Rochester/Monroe	00731871	585/966-4700	108
Avalon Sch at Villa of Hope/Rochester/Monroe	00734299	585/227-6920	114
Avenues the World Sch/New York/New York	11829059	212/524-9000	143
Avenues the World Sch Online/New York/New York	12362951	212/935-5000	143
AVERILL PARK CENTRAL SCH DIST/ AVERILL PARK/RENSSELAER	00766591	518/674-7050	189
Averill Park High Sch/Averill Park/Rensselaer	00766618	518/674-7000	189
Aviation Career & Tech Ed HS/Long Is City/Queens	00740717	718/361-2032	176
Avoca Central Sch/Avoca/Steuben	01552367	607/566-2221	213
AVOCA CENTRAL SCH DIST/AVOCA/STEUBEN	00771261	607/566-2221	213
Avon Central High Sch/Avon/Livingston	00730669	585/226-2455	102
Avon Central Primary Sch/Avon/Livingston	00730657	585/226-2455	102
AVON CENTRAL SCH DIST/AVON/LIVINGSTON	00730645	585/226-2455	102
Avon Middle Sch/Avon/Livingston	03316511	585/226-2455	102

B

School/City/County	PID	TELEPHONE	PAGE
B C Cate Elem Sch/Montour Falls/Schuyler	00770920	607/535-7267	207
Babylon Elem Sch/Babylon/Suffolk	00771962	631/893-7960	216
Babylon Jr Sr High Sch/Babylon/Suffolk	00771974	631/893-7910	216
Babylon Memorial Grade Sch/Babylon/Suffolk	00771986	631/893-7980	217
BABYLON UNION FREE SCH DIST/ BABYLON/SUFFOLK	00771950	631/893-7923	216
Baccalaureate Sch-Global Educ/Long Is City/Queens	05098648	718/361-5275	184
Bailey Avenue Elem Sch/Plattsburgh/Clinton	00720248	518/563-2410	45
BAINBRIDGE GUILFORD CSD/ BAINBRIDGE/CHENANGO	00719586	607/967-6300	41
Bainbridge Guilford Jr Sr HS/Bainbridge/Chenango	00719598	607/967-6300	41
Bais Brocho D'Stolin Karlin/Brooklyn/Kings	02828353	718/853-1222	96
Bais Esther School for Girls/Brooklyn/Kings	02189614	718/436-1234	96
Bais Frima/Brooklyn/Kings	03015171	718/972-7666	96
Bais Malka Sch/Spring Valley/Rockland	04446212	845/371-0500	198
Bais Mikroh Boys Sch/Monsey/Rockland	02194009	845/425-4880	198
Bais Rachel D Satmar/Brooklyn/Kings	11224100	718/624-2819	96
Bais Rochel School-Boro Park/Brooklyn/Kings	02163036	718/438-7822	96
Bais Sarah/Brooklyn/Kings	04974477	718/871-7571	96
Bais Shifra Miriam/Monsey/Rockland	03413767	845/356-0061	198
Bais Tziporah-Girls/Brooklyn/Kings	03408633	718/436-8336	96
Bais Yaakov Academy/Brooklyn/Kings	01873111	718/339-4747	96
Bais Yaakov Academy of Queens/Kew Gardens/Queens	00750956	718/847-5352	187
Bais Yaakov Adas Yereim/Brooklyn/Kings	02984323	718/435-5111	96
Bais Yaakov Chofetz Chaim/Pomona/Rockland	03408920	845/362-3166	198
Bais Yaakov D'Khal Adas Yereim/Brooklyn/Kings	00750968	718/782-2486	96
Bais Yaakov D'Rav Hirsch/Spring Valley/Rockland	11458090	845/371-6750	198
Bais Yaakov Dchassidei Gur Sch/Brooklyn/Kings	02827555	718/338-5600	96
Bais Yaakov High Sch/Monsey/Rockland	00768238	845/356-3113	198
Bais Yaakov Ramapo Sch/Monsey/Rockland	11238034	845/362-7262	198
Bais Yaakov-18th Ave Sch/Brooklyn/Kings	02827464	718/633-6050	96
Bais Yaakov-Bensonhurst/Brooklyn/Kings	04974582	718/236-4100	96
Bais Yisroel Sch-Girls/Kiamesha Lake/Sullivan	12467264	845/794-9915	237
Bais Yitzchak Yeshiva/Brooklyn/Kings	01793494	718/633-4802	96
Baker Academy/Buffalo/Erie	12028478	716/828-7955	1
Baker Hall Sch/Buffalo/Erie	01793054	716/828-9737	66
Baldwin Middle Sch/Baldwin/Nassau	00734885	516/434-6200	116
Baldwin Senior High Sch/Baldwin/Nassau	00734902	516/434-6100	116
BALDWIN UNION FREE SCH DIST/ BALDWIN/NASSAU	00734873	516/434-6000	116
BALDWINSVILLE CENTRAL SCH DIST/ BALDWINSVILLE/ONONDAGA	00761072	315/638-6043	154
Baldwinsville Christian Acad/Baldwinsville/Onondaga	01463546	315/638-1069	160
Ballard Elem Sch/Wilton/Saratoga	00769945	518/587-0600	202
Ballet Tech/NYC PS for Dance/New York/New York	04457364	212/254-1803	135
BALLSTON SPA CTL SCH DIST/ BALLSTON SPA/SARATOGA	00769402	518/884-7195	200
Ballston Spa High Sch/Ballston Spa/Saratoga	00769414	518/884-7150	200
Ballston Spa Middle Sch/Ballston Spa/Saratoga	00769426	518/884-7200	200
Balmville Elem Sch/Newburgh/Orange	00764581	845/563-8550	166
Bank St School for Children/New York/New York	00758817	212/875-4420	143
Baptist Sch/Tonawanda/Erie	04975342	716/695-5334	66
Barack Obama Elem Sch/Hempstead/Nassau	00736156	516/434-4400	121
Barclay Elem Sch/Brockport/Monroe	00731431	585/637-1840	107
Bard High School Early College/New York/New York	04954300	212/995-8479	135
Bard HS Early Clg Hudson/Hudson/Columbia	12468749	518/249-4779	46
Bard HS Early College Queens/Long Is City/Queens	11103415	718/361-3133	176

DISTRICT & SCHOOL TELEPHONE INDEX

Market Data Retrieval

School/City/County DISTRICT/CITY/COUNTY	PID	TELEPHONE NUMBER	PAGE
Bardonia Elem Sch/Bardonia/Rockland	00767313	845/639-6460	195
Barkai Yeshiva/Brooklyn/Kings	11237248	718/758-3525	96
BARKER CENTRAL SCH DIST/			
BARKER/NIAGARA	00758960	716/795-3832	146
Barker Jr Sr High Sch/Barker/Niagara	00758984	716/795-3201	146
Barker Road Middle Sch/Pittsford/Monroe	00732459	585/267-1800	110
Barnum Woods Elem Sch/East Meadow/Nassau	00735176	516/564-6500	118
Barringer Road Elem Sch/Ilion/Herkimer	00729658	315/894-8420	77
Barry Tech Ctr-Westbury/Westbury/Nassau	01417054	516/622-6800	116
Barton Elem Sch/Patchogue/Suffolk	00774823	631/687-6900	227
Baruch College Campus High Sch/New York/New York	04753596	212/683-7440	135
Bas Melech School for Girls/Brooklyn/Kings	05011676	718/677-7999	96
Bas Mikroh Girls Sch/Spring Valley/Rockland	02828286	845/352-5296	198
Basis Independent Brooklyn/Brooklyn/Kings	12238673	917/473-1615	96
Basis Independent Manhattan/New York/New York	12238661	347/305-4960	143
BATAVIA CITY SCH DIST/BATAVIA/			
GENESEE	00728812	585/343-2480	73
Batavia High Sch/Batavia/Genesee	00728824	585/343-2480	73
Batavia Middle Sch/Batavia/Genesee	00728836	585/343-2480	73
BATH CENTRAL SCH DIST/BATH/			
STEUBEN	00771613	607/776-3301	213
Battalion Christian Academy/Brooklyn/Kings	03412880	718/774-5447	96
Battery Park City Sch/New York/New York	11447699	212/266-5800	135
Bay Elem Sch/Patchogue/Suffolk	00774835	631/687-6950	227
Bay Knoll SDA Sch/Rochester/Monroe	02161258	585/467-2722	114
Bay Ridge Catholic Academy/Brooklyn/Kings	00753881	718/745-7643	95
Bay Ridge Christian Academy/Brooklyn/Kings	03068312	718/238-4000	96
Bay Ridge Preparatory High Sch/Brooklyn/Kings	10751215	718/833-5839	96
Bay Ridge Preparatory Sch/Brooklyn/Kings	10751203	718/833-9090	96
Bay Shore Christian Sch/Bay Shore/Suffolk	11227798	631/665-5241	234
Bay Shore High Sch/Bay Shore/Suffolk	00772019	631/968-1157	217
Bay Shore Middle Sch/Bay Shore/Suffolk	00772007	631/968-1210	217
BAY SHORE UNION FREE SCH DIST/			
BAY SHORE/SUFFOLK	00771998	631/968-1252	217
Bay Trail Middle Sch/Penfield/Monroe	00732356	585/249-6450	109
Baychester Academy/Bronx/Bronx	11447560	718/325-1138	22
Baychester Middle Sch/Bronx/Bronx	11713175	718/547-1890	22
Baylis Elem Sch/Plainview/Nassau	00738570	516/364-5798	130
Bayport Blue Point High Sch/Bayport/Suffolk	00772124	631/472-7800	217
BAYPORT- BLUE POINT USD/			
BAYPORT/SUFFOLK	00772071	631/472-7860	217
Bayside High Sch/Bayside/Queens	00740731	718/229-7600	179
Bayview Avenue Sch/Freeport/Nassau	00735695	516/867-5255	119
Bayview Elem Sch/West Islip/Suffolk	00776211	631/504-5600	233
Bayville Intermediate Sch/Bayville/Nassau	01822942	516/277-5400	123
Bayville Primary Sch/Bayville/Nassau	00736912	516/277-5450	123
Be'ER Hagolah Institute/Brooklyn/Kings	02163000	718/642-6800	96
Be'Ikvei Hatzion/Brooklyn/Kings	03076565	718/486-6363	96
Beach Street Middle Sch/West Islip/Suffolk	00776223	631/930-1600	233
Beachbrook Sch/Brooklyn/Kings	02606973	718/648-7162	96
BEACON CITY SCH DIST/BEACON/			
DUTCHESS	00721527	845/838-6900	51
Beacon High Sch/Beacon/Dutchess	00721539	845/838-6900	51
Beacon Sch/New York/New York	04037354	212/465-4230	138
Beaver River Central Sch/Beaver Falls/Lewis	00730499	315/346-1211	101
BEAVER RIVER CENTRAL SCH DIST/			
BEAVER FALLS/LEWIS	00730487	315/346-1211	101
Bedford Academy High Sch/Brooklyn/Kings	05281235	718/398-3061	82
BEDFORD CENTRAL SCH DIST/			
BEDFORD/WESTCHESTER	00780781	914/241-6000	252
Bedford Hills Elem Sch/Bedford Hills/Westchester	00780793	914/666-2708	252
Bedford Park Elem Sch/Bronx/Bronx	12036413	718/696-6400	20
Bedford Road Sch/Pleasantville/Westchester	00781515	914/741-1440	260
Bedford Stuy Collegiate CS/Brooklyn/Kings	11128673	718/669-7460	1
Bedford Village Elem Sch/Bedford/Westchester	03401752	914/234-4178	252
Bedford-Stuy New Beginnings CS/Brooklyn/Kings	11561116	718/453-1001	85
Beecher Elem Sch/Elmira/Chemung	00719342	607/735-3500	40
Beekman Elem Sch/Poughquag/Dutchess	00721448	845/227-1834	51
Beekman Sch/New York/New York	00752344	212/755-6666	143
BEEKMANTOWN CTL SCH DIST/			
WEST CHAZY/CLINTON	00719964	518/563-8250	43
Beekmantown Elem Sch/West Chazy/Clinton	04750192	518/563-8035	43
Beekmantown High Sch/West Chazy/Clinton	00719988	518/563-8787	43

School/City/County DISTRICT/CITY/COUNTY	PID	TELEPHONE NUMBER	PAGE
Beekmantown Middle Sch/West Chazy/Clinton	04750180	518/563-8690	44
Beginning with Children CS 2/Brooklyn/Kings	11816882	718/302-7700	1
Beit Rabban Sch/New York/New York	03412842	212/595-1386	143
Beitcher Yeshirva Sch/Brooklyn/Kings	11228637	718/436-0954	96
Belfast Central Sch/Belfast/Allegany	00716089	585/365-2646	14
BELFAST CENTRAL SCH DIST/			
BELFAST/ALLEGANY	00716077	585/365-9940	14
Bell Academy/Bayside/Queens	10910394	718/428-0587	178
Bell Top Elem Sch/Troy/Rensselaer	00766785	518/207-2600	190
Bellaire Sch/Queens Vlg/Queens	00749294	718/464-2119	183
Bellamy Elem Sch/Rome/Oneida	00760341	315/338-5260	151
Belle H Waterman Elem Sch/Skaneateles/Onondaga	00762131	315/291-2351	157
Belle Sherman Elem Sch/Ithaca/Tompkins	00777459	607/274-2206	240
Bellerose Elem Sch/E Northport/Suffolk	00774665	631/262-6800	227
Belleville Henderson Ctl Sch/Adams/Jefferson	00729969	315/846-5411	79
BELLEVILLE HENDERSON SCH DIST/			
ADAMS/JEFFERSON	00729957	315/846-5826	79
Bellevue Elem Sch/Syracuse/Onondaga	00762208	315/435-4520	158
BELLMORE UNION FREE SCH DIST/			
BELLMORE/NASSAU	00735011	516/679-2900	117
BELLMORE-MERRICK CTL HIGH SD/			
NORTH MERRICK/NASSAU	00737344	516/992-1000	117
Bellport Academic Center/Bellport/Suffolk	11435048	631/286-6900	215
Bellport High Sch/Brookhaven/Suffolk	00772150	631/730-1575	231
Bellport Middle Sch/Bellport/Suffolk	00772148	631/730-1626	231
Belmont Elem Sch/West Babylon/Suffolk	00774550	631/620-7500	226
Belmont Preparatory High Sch/Bronx/Bronx	05098557	718/733-4559	20
BEMUS POINT CTL SCH DIST/			
BEMUS POINT/CHAUTAUQUA	00718257	716/386-2375	36
Bemus Point Elem Sch/Bemus Point/Chautauqua	00718269	716/386-3795	36
Ben Franklin HS Finance & It/Cambria HTS/Queens	12105789	718/276-0150	183
Benjamin Banneker Academy/Brooklyn/Kings	04037275	718/797-3702	82
Benjamin Cosor Elem Sch/Fallsburg/Sullivan	00776766	845/434-6800	236
Benjamin Franklin Elem Sch/Binghamton/Broome	00716431	607/762-8340	27
Benjamin Franklin Elem Sch/Buffalo/Erie	00724402	716/874-8415	62
Benjamin Franklin Elem Sch/Yorktown Hts/Westchester	00780614	914/245-7444	257
Benjamin Franklin Middle Sch/Buffalo/Erie	00724414	716/874-8404	62
Benjamin N Cardozo High Sch/Bayside/Queens	00740755	718/279-6500	179
Benjamin Turner Middle Sch/Mount Vernon/Westchester	00781022	914/665-5150	258
Bennett Elem Sch/Boiceville/Ulster	00778178	845/657-2354	243
Benton Hall Academy/Little Falls/Herkimer	00729725	315/823-1400	78
Berea Elem Sch/Montgomery/Orange	00764505	845/457-2400	167
Berkeley Carroll Sch/Brooklyn/Kings	00752552	718/789-6060	96
Berkshire Jr Sr High Sch/Canaan/Columbia	00720389	518/781-3500	45
BERKSHIRE UNION FREE SCH DIST/			
CANAAN/COLUMBIA	00720377	518/781-3500	45
BERLIN CENTRAL SCH DIST/			
CHERRY PLAIN/RENSSELAER	00766668	518/658-1500	189
Berlin Elem Sch/Berlin/Rensselaer	00766682	518/658-2127	189
Berlin Middle High Sch/Cherry Plain/Rensselaer	00766670	518/658-2515	189
BERNE-KNOX-WESTERLO CENTRAL SD/			
BERNE/ALBANY	00714328	518/872-0909	10
Berne-Knox-Westerlo Elem Sch/Berne/Albany	00714330	518/872-2030	10
Berne-Knox-Westerlo Jr/Sr HS/Berne/Albany	00714342	518/872-1482	10
Berry Hill Elem Sch/Syosset/Nassau	00738582	516/364-5790	130
Bet Shraga Hebrew Academy/Albany/Albany	01460336	518/482-0464	13
Bet Yaakov Ateret Torah/Brooklyn/Kings	11236177	718/732-7770	96
Bet Yaakov Orot Sarah/Brooklyn/Kings	04974594	718/627-8758	96
Bet Yakov Ateret Torah HS/Brooklyn/Kings	04974556	718/382-7002	96
Beth Chana School for Girls/Brooklyn/Kings	00750932	718/935-1845	96
Beth Hamedrash Shaarei Yosher/Brooklyn/Kings	01873123	718/854-2290	96
Beth Jacob Day Sch for Girls/Brooklyn/Kings	00750994	718/633-6555	96
Beth Jacob Elem Sch/New York/New York	00751053	212/473-4500	144
Beth Jacob High Sch/Brooklyn/Kings	01873197	718/851-2255	96
Beth Jacob of Boro Park Sch/Brooklyn/Kings	00751041	718/436-7300	96
Beth Rivkah Elem School-Girls/Brooklyn/Kings	00751065	718/735-0770	96
Beth Rivkah High School-Girls/Brooklyn/Kings	01873202	718/735-0400	96
Beth Rochel School for Girls/Monsey/Rockland	00768240	845/352-5000	198

New York School Directory
DISTRICT & SCHOOL TELEPHONE INDEX

School/City/County DISTRICT/CITY/COUNTY	PID	TELEPHONE NUMBER	PAGE
Bethel Baptist Christian Acad/Jamestown/Chautauqua	02159528	716/484-7420	40
Bethel Christian Academy/Hopewell Jct/Dutchess	02187276	845/226-7973	55
Bethel Christian Learning Ctr/Queens Vlg/Queens	03193395	718/740-4357	187
Bethel Elem Sch/Brooklyn/Kings	01463338	718/783-3630	96
Bethesda SDA Elem Sch/Amityville/Suffolk	01464069	631/842-3321	234
Bethlehem Central High Sch/Delmar/Albany	00714380	518/439-4921	10
Bethlehem Central Middle Sch/Delmar/Albany	00714378	518/439-7460	10
BETHLEHEM CENTRAL SCH DIST/ DELMAR/ALBANY	00714366	518/439-7481	10
Bethlehem Children's Sch/Slingerlands/Albany	04974946	518/478-0224	13
Bethpage High Sch/Bethpage/Nassau	00735061	516/644-4100	117
BETHPAGE UNION FREE SCH DIST/ BETHPAGE/NASSAU	00735059	516/644-4000	117
Beverly J Martin Elem Sch/Ithaca/Tompkins	00777497	607/274-2209	240
Bicycle Path Pre-K & Kdgn Ctr/Selden/Suffolk	04914348	631/285-8800	225
Big Apple Academy/Brooklyn/Kings	04974544	718/333-0300	96
Big Cross Elem Sch/Glens Falls/Warren	00778532	518/792-2619	245
Big Flats Elem Sch/Big Flats/Chemung	00719433	607/739-6373	41
Big Tree Elem Sch/Hamburg/Erie	04031958	716/926-1740	60
Bilingual Bicultural Sch 182/New York/New York	04952558	212/860-6031	139
BINGHAMTON CITY SCH DIST/ BINGHAMTON/BROOME	00716417	607/762-8100	27
Binghamton High Sch/Binghamton/Broome	00716455	607/762-8200	27
Biondi Elem Education Center/Bronx/Bronx	11230848	718/794-8514	26
Birch Lane Elem Sch/Massapequa Pk/Nassau	00737253	516/308-5100	125
Birch Sch/Merrick/Nassau	00737435	516/992-7250	125
Birch Wathen Lenox Sch/New York/New York	00751261	212/861-0404	144
Birchwood Elem Sch/Schenectady/Schenectady	04012603	518/344-2910	204
Birchwood Intermediate Sch/Melville/Suffolk	00775750	631/812-3200	231
Birchwood Sch/West Nyack/Rockland	01795246	845/639-6480	195
Bishop Dunn Memorial Sch/Newburgh/Orange	00755152	845/569-3494	168
Bishop Grimes Jr Sr High Sch/East Syracuse/Onondaga	00762791	315/437-0356	160
Bishop Kearney High Sch/Rochester/Monroe	00733647	585/342-4000	114
Bishop Loughlin Memorial HS/Brooklyn/Kings	00752875	718/857-2700	95
Bishop Ludden Jr Sr High Sch/Syracuse/Onondaga	00762806	315/468-2591	160
Bishop Maginn High Sch/Albany/Albany	00715114	518/463-2247	12
Bishop Timon-St Jude High Sch/Buffalo/Erie	00725987	716/826-3610	65
Bklyn HS Ldrshp & Cmty Serv/Brooklyn/Kings	11103192	718/638-3062	82
Black River Elem Sch/Black River/Jefferson	00729983	315/773-5911	80
Blasdell Elem Sch/Blasdell/Erie	00723965	716/926-1750	60
Blessed Sacrament Sch/Albany/Albany	00715102	518/438-5854	12
Blessed Sacrament Sch/Brooklyn/Kings	00752899	718/235-4863	95
Blessed Sacrament Sch/Staten Island/Richmond	00755217	718/442-3090	194
Blessed Sacrament Sch/Syracuse/Onondaga	00762832	315/463-1261	160
Blind Brook High Sch/Rye Brook/Westchester	00781670	914/937-3600	253
Blind Brook Middle Sch/Rye Brook/Westchester	05101855	914/937-3600	253
BLIND BROOK-RYE UNION FREE SD/ RYE BROOK/WESTCHESTER	00781656	914/937-3600	252
Block Institute/Brooklyn/Kings	01409112	718/906-5400	96
BLOOMFIELD CENTRAL SD/BLOOMFIELD/ ONTARIO	00763630	585/657-6121	161
Bloomfield Elem Sch/Bloomfield/Ontario	00763642	585/657-6172	161
Bloomfield Jr Sr High Sch/Bloomfield/Ontario	00763654	585/657-6121	161
Blooming Grove Academy/New Windsor/Orange	12371330	845/863-3334	168
Bloomingdale Elem Sch/Bloomingdale/Franklin	01519822	518/891-3198	70
Blossom Garden Friends Sch/Collins/Erie	04975304	716/532-1004	66
Blue Creek Elem Sch/Latham/Albany	00714677	518/785-7451	11
Blue Mountain Middle Sch/Cortlandt MNR/Westchester	00780432	914/257-5700	256
Blue Point Elem Sch/Blue Point/Suffolk	00772100	631/472-6100	217
Blue Rock Sch/West Nyack/Rockland	03076228	845/627-0234	198
Blue Sch/New York/New York	11513303	212/228-6341	144
Blueprint Middle Sch/Bronx/Bronx	11821605	718/822-2780	17
Bnei Yakov Yosef of Monsey/Spring Valley/Rockland	12380678	845/573-9400	198
Bnei Yoel Sch/Monroe/Orange	04974245	845/783-8036	168
Bnos Bais Yaakov/Far Rockaway/Queens	02828298	718/337-6000	187
Bnos Bais Yaakov High Sch/Far Rockaway/Queens	11235587	718/337-6000	187
Bnos Esther Malka Sch/Brooklyn/Kings	12225834	347/374-1298	96
Bnos Esther Pupa Sch/Spring Valley/Rockland	04974269	845/371-1220	198
Bnos Malka Academy/Forest Hills/Queens	04974661	718/268-2667	187
Bnos Menachem/Brooklyn/Kings	04999972	718/493-1100	96
Bnos Square of Williamsburg/Brooklyn/Kings	11225532	718/797-9844	97
Bnos Yaakov Education Center/Brooklyn/Kings	02856439	718/851-0316	97
Bnos Yaakov Girls Center/Brooklyn/Kings	00751106	718/387-7905	97
Bnos Yisroel Girls Sch/Monsey/Rockland	01795222	845/356-2322	198
Bnos Yisroel School for Girls/Brooklyn/Kings	03015303	718/330-0222	97
Bnos Yisroel School-Girls/Brooklyn/Kings	02208272	718/339-4229	97
Bnos Zion of Bobov Sch/Brooklyn/Kings	00751118	718/438-3080	97
Bnos-Belz Girls Sch/Brooklyn/Kings	02163062	718/871-0500	97
Bobover Yeshiva Bnei Zion/Brooklyn/Kings	00751120	718/851-4000	97
BOCES 2 Pre-School/Spencerport/Monroe	03363423	585/352-2400	106
BOCES Career & Tech Ed Center/New Hartford/Oneida	01417145	315/793-8666	149
BOCES Hearing & Vision Imprd/Wantagh/Nassau	01486782	516/931-8507	116
BOCES Seamans Neck Middle Sch/Seaford/Nassau	04798716	516/719-6000	116
Boerum Hill Sch Int'l Studies/Brooklyn/Kings	04952170	718/330-9390	84
Boght Hills Elem Sch/Cohoes/Albany	00714689	518/785-0222	11
Bohlen Technical Center/Watertown/Jefferson	02136928	315/779-7200	79
Bold Charter Sch/Bronx/Bronx	12362482		1
Bolivar Road Elem Sch/Chittenango/Madison	00731077	315/687-2880	104
Bolivar-Richburg Central Sch/Bolivar/Allegany	00716132	585/928-2561	14
BOLIVAR-RICHBURG CTRL SCH DIST/ BOLIVAR/ALLEGANY	00716118	585/928-2561	14
Bolivar-Richburg Early CDC/Bolivar/Allegany	05294440	585/928-2851	14
Bolivar-Richburg Elem Sch/Richburg/Allegany	00716261	585/928-2561	14
Bolton Central Sch/Bolton Lndg/Warren	00778477	518/644-2400	244
BOLTON CENTRAL SCH DIST/ BOLTON LNDG/WARREN	00778465	518/644-2400	244
Boonville Elem Sch/Boonville/Oneida	00759902	315/942-9200	150
BOQUET VALLEY CENTRAL SCH DIST/ WESTPORT/ESSEX	00728068	518/962-8244	67
Boston Valley Elem Sch/Hamburg/Erie	00724191	716/646-3240	61
Boulevard Elem Sch/Gloversville/Fulton	00728472	518/775-5700	71
Bowling Green Elem Sch/Westbury/Nassau	00735188	516/876-7480	118
Boyle Road Elem Sch/Port Jeff Sta/Suffolk	00772796	631/474-8140	218
Boynton Middle Sch/Ithaca/Tompkins	00777461	607/274-2241	240
Boys & Girls High Sch/Brooklyn/Kings	00740779	718/467-1700	85
Boys & Girls High School YABC/Brooklyn/Kings	11928784	718/467-1700	85
Boys Prep Bronx School of NY/Bronx/Bronx	12028313	718/742-4321	1
Bradford Central Sch/Bradford/Schuyler	00771297	607/583-4616	207
BRADFORD CENTRAL SCH DIST/ BRADFORD/SCHUYLER	00771285	607/583-4616	207
Brandeis Sch/Lawrence/Nassau	01461196	516/371-4747	133
BRASHER FALLS SCH DIST/BRASHER FALLS/ ST LAWRENCE	00768989	315/389-5131	209
Brearley Sch/New York/New York	00758843	212/744-8582	144
Brennan Middle Sch/West Babylon/Suffolk	01417339	631/491-4149	215
Brentwood High Sch/Brentwood/Suffolk	02130144	631/434-2204	217
Brentwood Residential Center/Dix Hills/Suffolk	02165424	631/667-1188	1
BRENTWOOD UNION FREE SCH DIST/ BRENTWOOD/SUFFOLK	00772203	631/434-2123	217
Bretton Woods Elem Sch/Hauppauge/Suffolk	00773702	631/582-6633	223
Brewerton Elem Sch/Brewerton/Oswego	00765420	315/668-4201	170
BREWSTER CENTRAL SCH DIST/ BREWSTER/PUTNAM	00766319	845/279-8000	175
Brewster High Sch/Brewster/Putnam	00766321	845/279-5051	175
Briarcliff High Sch/Briarcliff/Westchester	00779691	914/769-6299	253
BRIARCLIFF MANOR UNION FREE SD/ BRIARCLIFF/WESTCHESTER	00779689	914/941-8880	253
Briarcliff Middle Sch/Briarcliff/Westchester	04745769	914/769-6343	253
Briarwood Sch/Rochester/Monroe	00732198	585/336-1610	113
Bridge Prep Charter Sch/Staten Island/Richmond	12367171	718/274-3437	1
Bridgehampton Sch/Bridgehampton/Suffolk	00772409	631/537-0271	218
BRIDGEHAMPTON UNION FREE SD/ BRIDGEHAMPTON/SUFFOLK	00772394	631/537-0271	218

School Year 2020-2021   800-333-8802   NY-V5

DISTRICT & SCHOOL TELEPHONE INDEX

Market Data Retrieval

School/City/County DISTRICT/CITY/COUNTY	PID	TELEPHONE NUMBER	PAGE
Bridgeport Elem Sch/Bridgeport/Madison	00731089	315/687-2280	104
Bridges Alt Junior High Sch/Kirkville/Onondaga	10019134	315/656-6807	154
Brighter Choice Community Sch/Brooklyn/Kings	11103166	718/574-2378	85
Brighter Choice CS for Boys/Albany/Albany	05308235	518/694-8200	1
Brighter Choice CS for Girls/Albany/Albany	05308247	518/694-4100	1
Brighton Academy/Syracuse/Onondaga	00762284	315/435-4535	158
BRIGHTON CENTRAL SCH DIST/ROCHESTER/MONROE	00731352	585/242-5200	106
Brighton High Sch/Rochester/Monroe	00731364	585/242-5000	106
Brilla Caritas Elem Sch/Bronx/Bronx	12471966	347/523-5832	2
Brilla Charter School Pax/Bronx/Bronx	12471978		2
Brilla College Prep CS-Veritas/Bronx/Bronx	12234366	917/924-0258	2
Brilla College Prep Elem CS/Bronx/Bronx	11933789	347/273-8439	2
Brilla College Prep Mid Sch CS/Bronx/Bronx	12234055	347/273-8439	2
Brinckerhoff Elem Sch/Fishkill/Dutchess	00722131	845/897-6800	54
British Int'l Sch of New York/New York/New York	10031027	212/481-2700	144
BROADALBIN-PERTH CTL SCH DIST/BROADALBIN/FULTON	00728434	518/954-2500	71
Broadalbin-Perth Elem Sch/Amsterdam/Fulton	00728707	518/954-2500	71
Broadalbin-Perth Jr Sr HS/Broadalbin/Fulton	00728458	518/954-2600	71
Broadway Academy/Elmira/Chemung	01360205	607/735-3300	40
Broadway Elem Sch/Elmira/Chemung	00719172	607/735-3600	40
BROCKPORT CTL SCH DIST/BROCKPORT/MONROE	00731429	585/637-5303	106
Brockport High Sch/Brockport/Monroe	00731443	585/637-1870	107
Brocton Central Sch/Brocton/Chautauqua	00718324	716/792-9121	36
BROCTON CENTRAL SCH DIST/BROCTON/CHAUTAUQUA	00718300	716/792-2171	36
Bronx Acad-Software Engineer/Bronx/Bronx	11924362	718/733-6024	20
Bronx Academy Health Careers/Bronx/Bronx	05349289	718/696-3340	22
Bronx Academy of Promise CS/Bronx/Bronx	11103544	718/293-6950	18
Bronx Aerospace High Sch/Bronx/Bronx	05280932	718/696-6010	22
Bronx Arena High Sch/Bronx/Bronx	11824308	718/860-5056	17
Bronx Arts & Science CS/Bronx/Bronx	12367200	718/230-0851	2
Bronx Bridges High Sch/Bronx/Bronx	11561219	718/829-2984	17
Bronx Career & College Prep HS/Bronx/Bronx	11447534	718/542-4011	24
Bronx Center Sci & Math/Bronx/Bronx	10008410	718/992-7089	18
Bronx Charter Sch Better Lrng/Bronx/Bronx	05287136	718/655-6660	2
Bronx Charter Sch for Children/Bronx/Bronx	05352626	718/402-3300	16
Bronx Charter Sch for the Arts/Bronx/Bronx	05291840	718/893-1042	2
Bronx Cmty Charter Sch/Bronx/Bronx	11128635	718/584-1400	20
Bronx Cmty High Sch/Bronx/Bronx	10911855	718/892-1026	17
Bronx Collaborative High Sch/Bronx/Bronx	11924374	718/543-1023	20
Bronx Collegiate Academy/Bronx/Bronx	05349162	718/410-4077	18
Bronx Compass High Sch/Bronx/Bronx	11821590	718/828-1206	17
Bronx CS Better Learning II/Bronx/Bronx	12165600	718/655-6660	2
Bronx Dance Academy Sch/Bronx/Bronx	05349198	718/515-0410	20
Bronx Design & Const Academy/Bronx/Bronx	11715068	718/402-7690	16
Bronx Early Clg Teach & Lrng/Bronx/Bronx	10027040	718/681-8287	18
Bronx Engr & Tech Academy/Bronx/Bronx	05349136	718/563-6678	20
Bronx Envision Academy/Bronx/Bronx	11715018	718/589-1590	24
Bronx Excellence 1/Bronx/Bronx	05352494	718/828-7301	2
Bronx Excellence 2 Elem/Bronx/Bronx	11722463	718/892-1276	2
Bronx Excellence 3 Elem/Bronx/Bronx	12234160	718/882-0231	2
Bronx Excellence 4 Elem/Bronx/Bronx	12310659	347/420-4321	2
Bronx Excellence 5 Elem/Bronx/Bronx	12367212	718/882-1058	2
Bronx Global Lrng Inst-Girls/Bronx/Bronx	11128647	718/993-1740	16
Bronx Green Middle Sch/Bronx/Bronx	10027105	718/325-6593	22
Bronx Haven High Sch/Bronx/Bronx	11103233	718/292-3638	16
Bronx Health Sciences High Sch/Bronx/Bronx	05349318	718/904-5450	22
Bronx High School of Business/Bronx/Bronx	05098179	718/410-4060	18
Bronx High School of Science/Bronx/Bronx	00740781	718/817-7700	20
Bronx HS for Medical Science/Bronx/Bronx	05098533	718/410-4040	18
Bronx HS for the Visual Arts/Bronx/Bronx	05098117	718/319-5160	22
Bronx HS Law-Community Service/Bronx/Bronx	05098583	718/733-5274	20
Bronx HS Writing/Comm Arts/Bronx/Bronx	05349320	718/944-5660	22
Bronx International High Sch/Bronx/Bronx	04950677	718/620-1053	18
Bronx Lab Sch/Bronx/Bronx	05349291	718/696-3700	22
Bronx Latin Sch/Bronx/Bronx	05349368	718/991-6349	24
Bronx Leadership Academy/Bronx/Bronx	04037964	718/299-4274	18
Bronx Leadership Academy II HS/Bronx/Bronx	05098105	718/292-7171	16
Bronx Little Sch/Bronx/Bronx	04877465	718/792-2650	24
Bronx Manhattan SDA Sch/Bronx/Bronx	01463247	718/588-7598	26
Bronx Mathematics Prep Sch/Bronx/Bronx	10910436	718/542-5063	17
Bronx Park Middle Sch/Bronx/Bronx	11824360	718/652-6090	22
Bronx Prep Charter Sch/Bronx/Bronx	04923947	718/294-0841	2
Bronx Regional High Sch/Bronx/Bronx	02126507	718/991-2020	24
Bronx Residential Center/Bronx/Bronx	02124418	718/798-6660	2
Bronx River High Sch/Bronx/Bronx	11924453	718/904-4210	17
Bronx Sch for Law-Gov-Justice/Bronx/Bronx	04797164	718/410-3430	18
Bronx Sch of Young Leaders/Bronx/Bronx	05349203	718/583-4146	20
Bronx School of Law & Finance/Bronx/Bronx	05325685	718/561-0113	20
Bronx Studio Sch for Writers/Bronx/Bronx	05349370	718/893-5158	17
Bronx Theatre High Sch/Bronx/Bronx	05274660	718/329-2902	20
Bronx Writing Academy/Bronx/Bronx	05349112	718/293-9048	18
Bronxdale High Sch/Bronx/Bronx	11715044	718/944-3655	22
Bronxville Elem Sch/Bronxville/Westchester	00779732	914/395-0500	253
Bronxville High Sch/Bronxville/Westchester	04420787	914/395-0500	253
Bronxville Middle Sch/Bronxville/Westchester	04420775	914/395-0500	253
BRONXVILLE UNION FREE SD/BRONXVILLE/WESTCHESTER	00779720	914/395-0500	253
Bronxwood Preparatory Academy/Bronx/Bronx	10008525	718/696-3820	22
Brook Avenue Elem Sch/Bay Shore/Suffolk	00772021	631/968-1130	217
Brookfield Central Sch/Brookfield/Madison	00730956	315/899-3323	104
BROOKFIELD CENTRAL SCH DIST/BROOKFIELD/MADISON	00730944	315/899-3324	104
BROOKHAVEN COMSEWOGUE UNIF SD/PORT JEFF STA/SUFFOLK	00772784	631/474-8100	218
Brookhaven Elem Sch/Brookhaven/Suffolk	00772162	631/730-1700	231
Brookhaven Learning Center/Bellport/Suffolk	02056902	631/286-6750	215
Brooklyn Acad for Sci & Enviro/Brooklyn/Kings	10027167	718/230-6363	86
Brooklyn Acad Global Finance/Brooklyn/Kings	11447493	718/574-3126	85
Brooklyn Academy High Sch/Brooklyn/Kings	04020284	718/857-4237	82
Brooklyn Amity Sch/Brooklyn/Kings	12035598	718/891-6100	97
Brooklyn Arbor Elem Sch 414/Brooklyn/Kings	11821825	718/963-0393	83
Brooklyn Arts & Science ES/Brooklyn/Kings	11821849	718/230-0851	86
Brooklyn Ascend Chtr Sch/Brooklyn/Kings	11103532	718/907-9150	2
Brooklyn Ascend High Sch/Brooklyn/Kings	12170394	347/750-1200	2
Brooklyn Ascend Mid Chtr Sch/Brooklyn/Kings	12170382	347/289-9000	2
Brooklyn Avenue Elem Sch/Valley Stream/Nassau	00738908	516/434-2850	131
Brooklyn Blue Feather Elem Sch/Brooklyn/Kings	03640142	718/834-0597	97
Brooklyn Bridge Academy/Brooklyn/Kings	10911934	718/968-1689	87
Brooklyn Brownstone Sch/Brooklyn/Kings	11103154	718/573-2307	85
Brooklyn Charter Sch/Brooklyn/Kings	04923985	718/302-2085	83
Brooklyn Cmty Arts & Media HS/Brooklyn/Kings	10027246	718/230-5748	82
Brooklyn Cmty HS Excel Equity/Brooklyn/Kings	10910368	718/968-4200	87
Brooklyn College Acad/Brooklyn/Kings	03008881	718/853-6184	92
Brooklyn Collegiate High Sch/Brooklyn/Kings	05348833	718/922-1145	93
Brooklyn Democracy Academy/Brooklyn/Kings	11103075	718/342-6348	93
Brooklyn Dreams Charter Sch/Brooklyn/Kings	11560992	718/859-8400	2
Brooklyn East Collegiate CS/Brooklyn/Kings	11560978	718/250-5760	2
Brooklyn Emerging Leaders Acad/Brooklyn/Kings	12234079	347/473-8830	2
Brooklyn Envir Exploration Sch/Brooklyn/Kings	11924219	718/453-3039	93
Brooklyn Excelsior Charter Sch/Brooklyn/Kings	05287174	718/246-5681	2
Brooklyn Free Sch/Brooklyn/Kings	10750716	718/499-2707	97
Brooklyn Friends Sch/Brooklyn/Kings	00752655	718/852-1029	97
Brooklyn Frontiers HS/Brooklyn/Kings	11714959	718/722-4727	84
Brooklyn Gardens Elem Sch/Brooklyn/Kings	11924269	718/495-7012	88
Brooklyn Heights Mont Sch/Brooklyn/Kings	02607264	718/858-5100	97
Brooklyn HS for Law & Tech/Brooklyn/Kings	04877544	718/919-1256	85
Brooklyn HS of the Arts/Brooklyn/Kings	04923117	718/855-2412	84
Brooklyn Institute-Lib Arts/Brooklyn/Kings	11821837	718/221-1097	86
Brooklyn International HS/Brooklyn/Kings	04294447	718/643-9315	82
Brooklyn Jesuit Prep Sch/Brooklyn/Kings	11911559	718/638-5884	95
Brooklyn Lab CS Chapel St/Brooklyn/Kings	12234225	347/473-8333	2
Brooklyn Lab CS Jay St Campus/Brooklyn/Kings	12028325	347/281-6892	2
Brooklyn Lab Sch/Brooklyn/Kings	11103348	718/235-3592	88
Brooklyn Landmark Elem Sch/Brooklyn/Kings	11924207	718/443-2747	93
Brooklyn Latin High Sch/Brooklyn/Kings	10027258	718/366-0154	83
Brooklyn New Sch at PS 146/Brooklyn/Kings	04019637	718/923-4750	84
Brooklyn Preparatory HS/Brooklyn/Kings	05349552	718/486-2550	83
Brooklyn Preparatory Sch/Brooklyn/Kings	04148848	718/306-1000	97
Brooklyn Prospect Charter HS/Brooklyn/Kings	11456121	347/889-7041	2
Brooklyn Prospect Charter MS/Brooklyn/Kings	12260236	347/889-7041	2

New York School Directory

DISTRICT & SCHOOL TELEPHONE INDEX

School/City/County DISTRICT/CITY/COUNTY	PID	TELEPHONE NUMBER	PAGE
Brooklyn Prospect Clinton Hill/Brooklyn/Kings	12260224	718/783-1570	2
Brooklyn Prospect CS Downtown/Brooklyn/Kings	12170643	718/722-7634	2
Brooklyn Rise Charter Sch/Brooklyn/Kings	12367224	347/470-9833	2
Brooklyn Sch Music & Theatre/Brooklyn/Kings	05281170	718/230-6250	86
Brooklyn Sch Social Justice/Brooklyn/Kings	05281106	718/381-7100	93
Brooklyn Sch-Collab Studies/Brooklyn/Kings	04952510	718/923-4700	84
Brooklyn Sch-Math & Research/Brooklyn/Kings	11714806	718/381-7100	93
Brooklyn Scholars Charter Sch/Brooklyn/Kings	11447443	718/348-9360	88
Brooklyn School of Inquiry/Brooklyn/Kings	11447833	718/621-5730	89
Brooklyn Sci Engineering Acad/Brooklyn/Kings	12105375	718/240-3790	87
Brooklyn SDA Sch/Brooklyn/Kings	01462059	718/859-1313	97
Brooklyn Studio Secondary Sch/Brooklyn/Kings	04753687	718/266-5032	91
Brooklyn Technical High Sch/Brooklyn/Kings	00740793	718/804-6400	82
Brooklyn Theatre Arts High Sch/Brooklyn/Kings	10913750	718/968-1072	87
Brooklyn Urban Garden CS/Brooklyn/Kings	11927560	718/280-9556	2
Brooklyn Waldorf Sch/Brooklyn/Kings	12314148	718/783-3270	97
Brooks Hill Elem Sch/Fairport/Monroe	00731675	585/421-2170	108
Brookside Elem Sch/Baldwin/Nassau	00734914	516/434-6300	116
Brookside Elem Sch/Binghamton/Broome	00717045	607/669-4105	29
Brookside Elem Sch/Rochester/Monroe	00731900	585/966-4800	109
Brookside Elem Sch/Yorktown Hts/Westchester	00782715	914/243-8130	264
Brookside Primary Sch/Ossining/Westchester	00781319	914/762-5780	260
Brookview Elem Sch/Rochester/Monroe	00732203	585/336-1630	113
Brookville Ctr Childrens Srvcs/Glen Head/Nassau	01794084	516/626-1000	133
Brookwood Sch/Cooperstown/Otsego	04975160	607/547-4060	175
Brookwood Secure Center/Claverack/Columbia	02124432	518/851-3211	2
Broome Street Academy CHS/New York/New York	11722657	212/453-0295	2
Broome Tioga BOCES/Binghamton/Broome	01833460	607/763-3348	27
BROOME-TIOGA BOCES/BINGHAMTON/BROOME	00717306	607/763-3300	31
Broome-Tioga BOCES Voc Ed Ctr/Binghamton/Broome	01537642	607/763-3451	27
Brown Sch/Schenectady/Schenectady	01463871	518/370-0366	205
Brownsville Academy High Sch/Brooklyn/Kings	05352573	718/778-7305	86
Brownsville Ascend Lower CS/Brooklyn/Kings	11698692	347/294-2600	2
Brownsville Ascend Middle CS/Brooklyn/Kings	12170423	347/294-2600	2
Brownsville Collaborative MS/Brooklyn/Kings	11821693	718/495-1202	93
Brownsville Collegiate Charter/Brooklyn/Kings	11456224	718/636-0370	2
Brownville-Glen Park Elem Sch/Brownville/Jefferson	00730073	315/779-2300	80
Bruno M Ponterio Ridge St ES/Rye Brook/Westchester	00781668	914/937-3600	253
BRUNSWICK CENTRAL SCH DIST/TROY/RENSSELAER	00766723	518/279-4600	190
BRUSHTON MOIRA CTL SCH DIST/BRUSHTON/FRANKLIN	00728147	518/529-7342	69
Brushton Moira Sch/Brushton/Franklin	00728159	518/529-7342	69
Bryant Elem Sch/Hornell/Steuben	00771663	607/324-2171	214
Buchanan-Verplank Elem Sch/Buchanan/Westchester	00780444	914/257-5400	256
Buckeley Middle Sch/Rhinebeck/Dutchess	00722038	845/871-5500	53
Buckman Heights Elem Sch/Rochester/Monroe	00731912	585/966-5900	109
Buffalo Acad of Sacred Heart/Buffalo/Erie	00726022	716/834-2101	65
Buffalo Academy of Science CS/Buffalo/Erie	05346495	716/854-2490	2
Buffalo Collegiate Charter Sch/Buffalo/Erie	12260200	716/713-2162	2
BUFFALO PUBLIC SCHOOLS/BUFFALO/ERIE	00722557	716/816-3500	56
Buffalo Sch Culinary-Hospitly/Buffalo/Erie	12471954	716/816-4778	57
Buffalo Seminary Sch/Buffalo/Erie	00722404	716/885-6780	66
Buffalo United Charter Sch/Buffalo/Erie	05308120	716/835-9862	2
Building Blocks Dev Pre-School/Commack/Suffolk	03403047	631/499-1237	234
Building Blocks Montessori Sch/Staten Island/Richmond	02852768	718/448-2992	195
Burns Avenue Elem Sch/Hicksville/Nassau	00736364	516/733-2311	122
Burnt Hills Ballston Lake HS/Burnt Hills/Saratoga	00769505	518/399-9141	200
BURNT HILLS BALLSTON LAKE SD/BURNT HILLS/SARATOGA	00769488	518/399-9141	200
Burr Intermediate Sch/Commack/Suffolk	00772588	631/858-3636	219
Burton Street Elem Sch/Cazenovia/Madison	00731027	315/655-1325	104
Bushwick Ascend Lower CS/Brooklyn/Kings	11560734	347/294-2500	2
Bushwick Ascend Middle Sch/Brooklyn/Kings	12115368	718/744-6100	2
Bushwick Community High Sch/Brooklyn/Kings	04020272	718/443-3083	93
Bushwick Leaders HS for Excel/Brooklyn/Kings	05348742	718/919-4212	93
Business Tech Early Clg HS/Queens Vlg/Queens	12105806	718/217-3613	179
BYRAM HILLS CENTRAL SCH DIST/ARMONK/WESTCHESTER	00779756	914/273-4082	253
Byram Hills High Sch/Armonk/Westchester	00779770	914/273-9200	253
BYRON-BERGEN CTL SCH DIST/BERGEN/GENESEE	00728886	585/494-1220	73
Byron-Bergen Elem Sch/Bergen/Genesee	00728915	585/494-1220	73
Byron-Bergen Jr Sr High Sch/Bergen/Genesee	00728903	585/494-1220	73

C

School/City/County DISTRICT/CITY/COUNTY	PID	TELEPHONE NUMBER	PAGE
C A Bouton High Sch/Voorheesville/Albany	00714964	518/765-3314	12
C A Lindbergh Elem Sch/Buffalo/Erie	00724438	716/874-8410	62
C C B School of Douglaston/Little Neck/Queens	11236270	718/281-3333	187
C Grant Grimshaw Sch/La Fayette/Onondaga	00761553	315/677-3152	156
C J Hooker Middle Sch/Goshen/Orange	00764177	845/615-6300	164
C R Weeks Elem Sch/Windsor/Broome	00717265	607/775-3226	30
C S Driver Middle Sch/Marcellus/Onondaga	00761876	315/673-6200	157
C V Starr Intermediate Sch/Brewster/Putnam	04793649	845/279-4018	175
Caedmon Montessori Sch/New York/New York	01409332	212/879-2296	144
Caesar Chavez Sch/Yonkers/Westchester	04921523	914/376-8969	263
Cahill Elem Sch/Saugerties/Ulster	00778300	845/247-6800	243
CAIRO-DURHAM CTL SCH DIST/CAIRO/GREENE	00729127	518/622-8534	75
Cairo-Durham Elem Sch/Cairo/Greene	00729139	518/622-3231	75
Cairo-Durham High Sch/Cairo/Greene	01487891	518/622-8543	75
Cairo-Durham Middle Sch/Cairo/Greene	04448856	518/622-0490	75
Calcium Primary Sch/Calcium/Jefferson	03399795	315/629-1100	80
CALEDONIA-MUMFORD CTL SCH DIST/CALEDONIA/LIVINGSTON	00730683	585/538-3400	102
Caledonia-Mumford Elem Sch/Caledonia/Livingston	00730695	585/538-3481	102
Caledonia-Mumford Middle Sch/Caledonia/Livingston	05363730	585/538-3482	102
Caledonia-Mumford Senior HS/Caledonia/Livingston	00730700	585/538-3483	102
Calhoun High Sch/Merrick/Nassau	00737368	516/992-1300	117
Calhoun Sch/New York/New York	00751314	212/497-6500	144
California Ave Elem Sch/Uniondale/Nassau	00738702	516/918-1850	130
Calkins Road Middle Sch/Pittsford/Monroe	10020896	585/267-1900	110
Calvary Baptist Church/Batavia/Genesee	02160565	585/297-8605	74
Calvary Chapel Christian Sch/Farmington/Ontario	04975445	585/398-3550	163
Calvin Coolidge Elem Sch/Binghamton/Broome	00716443	607/762-8290	27
Calvin U Smith Elem Sch/Painted Post/Steuben	00771390	607/936-4156	214
Cambria Ctr for Gifted Child/Cambria HTS/Queens	11231098	718/341-1991	187
Cambria Heights Academy/Hollis/Queens	11560796	718/736-7320	183
Cambridge Central Sch/Cambridge/Washington	00778817	518/677-8527	247
CAMBRIDGE CENTRAL SCH DIST/CAMBRIDGE/WASHINGTON	00778805	518/677-2653	247
CAMDEN CENTRAL SCH DIST/CAMDEN/ONEIDA	00759940	315/245-2500	150
Camden Elem Sch/Camden/Oneida	00759964	315/245-2616	150
Camden High Sch/Camden/Oneida	00759988	315/245-3168	150
Camden Middle Sch/Camden/Oneida	00759976	315/245-0080	150
Camillus Middle Sch/Camillus/Onondaga	00761187	315/672-3159	159
Camp Avenue Elem Sch/Merrick/Nassau	00737679	516/379-3732	126
Campa Charter Sch/Brooklyn/Kings	12028337	347/619-6800	2
CAMPBELL-SAVONA CTL SCH DIST/CAMPBELL/STEUBEN	00771302	607/527-9800	213
Campbell-Savona Elem Sch/Savona/Steuben	01813537	607/527-9800	213
Campbell-Savona Jr Sr HS/Campbell/Steuben	00771314	607/527-9800	213
Canaan Elem Sch/Patchogue/Suffolk	00774847	631/687-8100	227
CANAJOHARIE CTL SCH DIST/CANAJOHARIE/MONTGOMERY	00734718	518/673-6302	115
Canajoharie High Sch/Canajoharie/Montgomery	00734732	518/673-6330	115

School Year 2020-2021   800-333-8802   NY-V7

DISTRICT & SCHOOL TELEPHONE INDEX

Market Data Retrieval

School/City/County	PID	TELEPHONE NUMBER	PAGE
Canajoharie Middle Sch/Canajoharie/Montgomery	00734720	518/673-6320	115
Canal View Elem Sch/Spencerport/Monroe	05272973	585/349-5700	112
Canandaigua Academy/Canandaigua/Ontario	00763678	585/396-3800	161
CANANDAIGUA CITY SCH DIST/ CANANDAIGUA/ONTARIO	00763666	585/396-3700	161
Canandaigua Middle Sch/Canandaigua/Ontario	00763692	585/396-3850	161
Canandaigua Prim Elem Sch/Canandaigua/Ontario	00763680	585/396-3900	161
Canarsie Ascend Lower CS/Brooklyn/Kings	11934290	347/713-0101	2
Canarsie Ascend Mid CS/Brooklyn/Kings	12234005	347/578-8400	2
CANASERAGA CENTRAL SCH DIST/ CANASERAGA/ALLEGANY	00716144	607/545-6421	14
Canaseraga Sch/Canaseraga/Allegany	00716156	607/545-6421	14
CANASTOTA CENTRAL SCH DIST/ CANASTOTA/MADISON	00730968	315/697-2025	104
Canastota Jr Sr High Sch/Canastota/Madison	00730970	315/697-2003	104
Candlewood Middle Sch/Dix Hills/Suffolk	00773453	631/592-3300	222
CANDOR CENTRAL SCH DIST/ CANDOR/TIOGA	00777021	607/659-5010	238
Candor Elem Sch/Candor/Tioga	00777033	607/659-3935	238
Candor Jr Sr High Sch/Candor/Tioga	00777045	607/659-5020	238
Canisius High Sch/Buffalo/Erie	00726046	716/882-0466	65
CANISTEO-GREENWOOD CENTRAL SD/ CANISTEO/STEUBEN	00771326	607/698-4225	214
Canisteo-Greenwood Elem Sch/Canisteo/Steuben	00771338	607/698-4225	214
Canisteo-Greenwood High Sch/Canisteo/Steuben	00771340	607/698-4225	214
Cantalician Center for Lrng/Depew/Erie	00726058	716/901-8700	66
Cantiague Elem Sch/Jericho/Nassau	00736584	516/203-3650	122
CANTON CENTRAL SCH DIST/ CANTON/ST LAWRENCE	00768355	315/386-8561	209
Cape Vincent Elem Sch/Cape Vincent/Jefferson	00730308	315/654-2142	81
Capital Prep Bronx CS/Bronx/Bronx	12471980	929/436-2728	3
Capital Prep Harlem CS/New York/New York	12170552	212/328-9370	3
CAPITAL REGION BOCES/ALBANY/ ALBANY	00715035	518/862-4900	13
Capitol Reg Career & Tech Sch/Albany/Albany	01483405	518/862-4800	9
Cardinal Hayes Day Sch/Millbrook/Dutchess	12314605	845/677-3251	55
Cardinal Hayes High Sch/Bronx/Bronx	00755243	718/292-6100	25
Cardinal McCloskey Cmty CS/Bronx/Bronx	12367236	646/660-2491	3
Cardinal McCloskey Sch/Ossining/Westchester	04974180	914/762-5302	265
Cardinal O'Hara High Sch/Tonawanda/Erie	00726084	716/695-2600	65
Cardinal Spellman High Sch/Bronx/Bronx	00755267	718/881-8000	25
Career & Tech Sch-Schoharie/Schoharie/Schoharie	01529621	518/295-3000	206
Career & Technical Institute/Poughkeepsie/Dutchess	01522269	845/486-8001	51
Career Collegiate Institute/Buffalo/Erie	12115423	716/838-7404	57
Career Preparatory High Sch/Westbury/Nassau	02056770	516/546-7800	116
Career Tech Ctr-Olean/Olean/Cattaraugus	11435086	716/376-8200	31
Careers In Sports High Sch/Bronx/Bronx	05099628	718/292-7110	16
Carl I Bergerson Middle Sch/Albion/Orleans	00765157	585/589-2020	169
Carl L Dixson Primary Sch/Elmsford/Westchester	00780133	914/592-2092	255
Carle Place Middle Sr High Sch/Carle Place/Nassau	00735138	516/622-6400	117
CARLE PLACE UNION FREE SD/ CARLE PLACE/NASSAU	00735126	516/622-6400	117
Carlyle C Ring Elem Sch/Jamestown/Chautauqua	00718740	716/483-4407	38
Carman Rd Sch Phys Handicapped/Massapequa Pk/Nassau	01486756	516/608-6200	116
CARMEL CENTRAL SCH DIST/ PATTERSON/PUTNAM	00766369	845/878-2094	175
Carmel High Sch/Carmel/Putnam	00766371	845/225-8441	175
Caroline Elem Sch/Slatervle SPG/Tompkins	00777473	607/539-7155	240
Caroline G Atkinson Interm Sch/Freeport/Nassau	00735700	516/867-5265	119
Caroline Street Elem Sch/Saratoga Spgs/Saratoga	00769701	518/584-7612	201
Carrie E Tompkins Elem Sch/Croton Hdsn/Westchester	00779902	914/271-5184	254
Carrie Palmer Weber Middle Sch/Prt Washingtn/Nassau	00738142	516/767-5500	128
Carrier Educational Center/Angola/Erie	11571367	716/549-4454	55
Carroll Hill Elem Sch/Troy/Rensselaer	00767105	518/328-5701	191
CARTHAGE CENTRAL SCH DIST/ CARTHAGE/JEFFERSON	00729971	315/493-5000	80
Carthage Elem Sch/Carthage/Jefferson	00729995	315/493-1570	80
Carthage High Sch/Carthage/Jefferson	00730009	315/493-5030	80
Carthage Middle Sch/Carthage/Jefferson	01396589	315/493-5020	80
Caryl E Adams Primary Sch/Whitney Point/Broome	00717215	607/692-8241	30
Cascades High Sch/New York/New York	04804872	646/654-1261	135
Cascadilla Sch/Ithaca/Tompkins	00777758	607/272-3110	241
Case Middle Sch/Watertown/Jefferson	00730346	315/785-3870	81
Casey Middle Sch/East Amherst/Erie	03051096	716/626-8567	64
Casey Park Elem Sch/Auburn/Cayuga	00717899	315/255-8760	34
Casimir Pulaski Sch/Scarsdale/Westchester	01813616	914/376-8575	263
CASSADAGA VALLEY CTL SCH DIST/ SINCLAIRVILLE/CHAUTAUQUA	00718336	716/962-5155	36
Cassadaga Valley Middle HS/Sinclairville/Chautauqua	00718350	716/962-8581	36
Cassavant Elem Sch/Mc Lean/Tompkins	00777344	607/844-8694	239
Castile Christian Academy/Castile/Wyoming	04975457	585/493-2528	268
Castle Bridge Sch/New York/New York	11824281	212/740-4701	141
Castleton Elem Sch/Castleton/Rensselaer	00767064	518/732-7755	191
Cataract Elem Sch/Niagara Falls/Niagara	00759421	716/278-9120	147
Cathedral Academy at Pompei/Syracuse/Onondaga	00763020	315/422-8548	160
Cathedral High Sch/New York/New York	00755279	212/688-1545	142
Cathedral Preparatory Seminary/Elmhurst/Queens	00752916	718/592-6800	186
Cathedral Sch-St John Divine/New York/New York	00758867	212/316-7500	144
Catherine & Count Basie MS 72/Jamaica/Queens	00748824	718/723-6200	181
Catherine M McNamara Elem Sch/Baldwinsville/Onondaga	00761084	315/638-6130	154
Catholic Acad of Niagara Falls/Niagara Falls/Niagara	00726644	716/283-1455	149
Catholic Academy of W Buffalo/Buffalo/Erie	00726096	716/885-6111	65
Catholic Central High Sch/Troy/Rensselaer	00715138	518/235-7100	192
CATO MERIDIAN CENTRAL SCH DIST/ CATO/CAYUGA	00717980	315/626-3439	34
Cato Meridian Elem Sch/Cato/Cayuga	00718013	315/626-3320	34
Cato Meridian High Sch/Cato/Cayuga	00717992	315/626-3317	34
Cato Meridian Middle Sch/Cato/Cayuga	01557408	315/626-3319	34
CATSKILL CENTRAL SCH DIST/ CATSKILL/GREENE	00729153	518/943-4696	75
Catskill Elem Sch/Catskill/Greene	00729189	518/943-0574	75
Catskill High Sch/Catskill/Greene	00729177	518/943-2300	75
Catskill Middle Sch/Catskill/Greene	00729165	518/943-5665	75
Cattaraugus Elem Sch/Cattaraugus/Cattaraugus	00717370	716/257-3436	31
Cattaraugus Middle Sch/Cattaraugus/Cattaraugus	00717552	716/257-3483	31
CATTARAUGUS-ALLEGANY BOCES/ OLEAN/CATTARAUGUS	00717851	716/376-8200	34
CATTARAUGUS-LITTLE VLY CTL SD/ CATTARAUGUS/CATTARAUGUS	00717368	716/257-5293	31
Cattaraugus-Lttle Vly High Sch/Cattaraugus/Cattaraugus	00717382	716/257-3483	31
Cayuga Elem Sch/Lake Grove/Suffolk	00775140	631/471-1800	229
Cayuga Heights Elem Sch/Depew/Erie	00723721	716/686-5005	60
Cayuga Heights Elem Sch/Ithaca/Tompkins	00777485	607/257-8557	240
CAYUGA-ONONDAGA BOCES/AUBURN/ CAYUGA	00718233	315/253-0361	36
CAZENOVIA CTL SCH DIST/CAZENOVIA/ MADISON	00731015	315/655-1317	104
Cazenovia Jr Sr High Sch/Cazenovia/Madison	00731039	315/655-1370	104
Cazenovia Middle Sch/Cazenovia/Madison	00731041	315/655-1324	104
Cbi Tech-Gateway/West Nyack/Rockland	11434953	845/624-5566	195
Cecil Parker Elem Sch/Mount Vernon/Westchester	00780975	914/665-5040	258
Celia Cruz Bronx HS of Music/Bronx/Bronx	05274658	718/329-8550	20
Centennial Avenue Elem Sch/Roosevelt/Nassau	00738348	516/345-7400	128
Center for Community Adjustmnt/Wantagh/Nassau	01486744	516/396-2900	116
Center for Discovery/Harris/Sullivan	01795557	845/794-1400	237
Center for Septrum Services/Kingston/Ulster	02164717	845/336-2616	244
Center Moriches High Sch/CTR Moriches/Suffolk	00772423	631/878-0092	218
Center Moriches Middle Sch/CTR Moriches/Suffolk	05281871	631/878-2519	218

New York School Directory

DISTRICT & SCHOOL TELEPHONE INDEX

School/City/County DISTRICT/CITY/COUNTY	PID	TELEPHONE NUMBER	PAGE
CENTER MORICHES UNION FREE SD/			
CTR MORICHES/SUFFOLK	00772411	631/878-0052	218
Center Road Christian Academy/Buffalo/Erie	01408821	716/675-6545	66
Center Street Elem Sch/Horseheads/Chemung	00719469	607/795-2580	41
Center Street Elem Sch/Williston Pk/Nassau	00736209	516/305-8300	121
Centereach High Sch/Centereach/Suffolk	00774225	631/285-8100	225
Central Baptist Christian Acad/Binghamton/Broome	01460453	607/648-6210	30
Central Baptist Christian Sch/Yorkshire/Cattaraugus	02970176	716/492-2203	34
Central Blvd Elem Sch/Bethpage/Nassau	00735073	516/644-4300	117
Central Brooklyn Ascend Lwr CS/Brooklyn/Kings	12028428	917/246-4800	3
Central Christian Academy/Dunkirk/Chautauqua	02205919	716/366-6634	40
Central Elem Sch/Larchmont/Westchester	00780729	914/220-3401	258
Central Islip High Sch/Central Islip/Suffolk	00772461	631/348-5079	218
CENTRAL ISLIP UNION FREE SD/			
CENTRAL ISLIP/SUFFOLK	00772435	631/348-5112	218
Central Park East High Sch/New York/New York	03337412	212/860-5929	139
Central Park East I/New York/New York	04458502	212/860-5821	139
Central Park East II/New York/New York	04458514	212/860-5992	139
Central Park Int'l Magnet Sch/Schenectady/Schenectady	00770401	518/370-8250	204
Central Queens Academy CS/Elmhurst/Queens	11821708	718/271-6200	3
CENTRAL SQUARE CENTRAL SD/			
CENTRAL SQ/OSWEGO	00765406	315/668-4220	170
Central Square Middle Sch/Central Sq/Oswego	00765468	315/668-4218	170
Central Valley Academy/Ilion/Herkimer	00729660	315/895-7471	77
Central Valley Elem Sch/Central Vly/Orange	00764438	845/460-6700	165
CENTRAL VALLEY SCH DIST/			
ILION/HERKIMER	00729646	315/894-9934	77
Centre Avenue Elem Sch/East Rockaway/Nassau	00735293	516/887-8300	118
Cerebral Palsy of Westchester/Rye Brook/Westchester	01795741	914/937-3800	265
Chabad Acad of Arts & Sciences/Bayside/Queens	12314899	718/279-1457	187
Challenge Charter Middle Sch/Far Rockaway/Queens	12172471	347/990-1875	180
Challenge Prep Charter Sch/Far Rockaway/Queens	11560916	718/327-1352	180
Chambers Elem Sch/Kingston/Ulster	00777863	845/336-5995	242
Chaminade High Sch/Mineola/Nassau	00739548	516/742-5555	132
CHAMPLAIN VALLEY ED SERVICES/			
PLATTSBURGH/CLINTON	00720365	518/561-0100	45
Champlain Valley Ed Svcs/Plattsburgh/Clinton	04836514	518/561-0100	43
Champlain Valley Education Ctr/Mineville/Essex	01416957	518/942-6691	67
Chancellor Livingston Elem Sch/Rhinebeck/Dutchess	00722040	845/871-5570	53
Chango Elem Sch/Ballston Lake/Saratoga	00769830	518/881-0520	202
Channel View Sch for Research/Rockaway Park/Queens	05351696	718/634-1970	180
Chapel Field Christian Sch/Pine Bush/Orange	04894994	845/778-1881	168
CHAPPAQUA CENTRAL SCH DIST/			
CHAPPAQUA/WESTCHESTER	00779811	914/238-7200	253
Charles A Mulligan Elem Sch/Central Islip/Suffolk	00772502	631/348-5041	219
Charles A Upson Elem Sch/Lockport/Niagara	00759079	716/478-4400	147
Charles C D'Amico High Sch/Albion/Orleans	00765145	585/589-2040	169
Charles Campagne Elem Sch/Bethpage/Nassau	00735085	516/644-4400	117
Charles Carroll School 46/Rochester/Monroe	00733099	585/288-8008	110
Charles Churn Christian Acad/Brooklyn/Kings	04797102	718/919-6887	97
Charles E Riley Elem Sch/Oswego/Oswego	00765717	315/341-2800	171
Charles E Schwarting Elem Sch/Massapequa/Nassau	00737930	516/992-7400	127
Charles E Walters Elem Sch/Yaphank/Suffolk	00774380	631/345-2758	225
Charles F Johnson Elem Sch/Endicott/Broome	00716754	607/757-2137	29
Charles Finney Sch/Penfield/Monroe	04869717	585/387-3770	114
Charles G May Career & Tech Ed/Mount Morris/Livingston	00730920	585/658-7811	102
Charles H Roth Jr High Sch/Henrietta/Monroe	00733245	585/359-5100	112
Charles O Dickerson High Sch/Trumansburg/Tompkins	00777708	607/387-7551	241
Charles W Baker High Sch/Baldwinsville/Onondaga	00761096	315/638-6000	154
Charlotte Avenue Elem Sch/Hamburg/Erie	00724206	716/646-3370	61
Charlotte Valley Central Sch/Davenport/Delaware	00721022	607/278-5511	49
CHARLOTTE VALLEY CTL SCH DIST/			
DAVENPORT/DELAWARE	00721010	607/278-5511	49
Charlton Heights Elem Sch/Ballston Lake/Saratoga	00769517	518/399-9141	200
Charter HS Law-Social Justice/Bronx/Bronx	12170588	646/450-2240	3
Charter Sch for Applied Tech/Buffalo/Erie	04950809	716/871-7400	3
Charter School of Educ Excell/Yonkers/Westchester	10751966	914/476-5070	3
Charter School of Inquiry/Buffalo/Erie	12115552	716/833-3250	3
CHATEAUGAY CENTRAL SCH DIST/			
CHATEAUGAY/FRANKLIN	00728185	518/497-6611	69
Chateaugay Elem Sch/Chateaugay/Franklin	00728197	518/497-6611	69
Chateaugay High Sch/Chateaugay/Franklin	04803529	518/497-6611	69
CHATHAM CENTRAL SCH DIST/			
CHATHAM/COLUMBIA	00720391	518/392-2400	46
Chatham High Sch/Chatham/Columbia	00720418	518/392-2400	46
Chatham Middle Sch/Chatham/Columbia	00720420	518/392-2400	46
Chatsworth Avenue Sch/Larchmont/Westchester	00780731	914/220-3500	258
Chatterton Sch/Merrick/Nassau	00737447	516/992-7270	125
CHAUTAUQUA LAKE CENTRAL SD/			
MAYVILLE/CHAUTAUQUA	00718867	716/753-5808	36
Chautauqua Lake Sch/Mayville/Chautauqua	00718403	716/753-5801	37
Chazy Central Rural Sch/Chazy/Clinton	00720030	518/846-7135	44
CHAZY CENTRAL RURAL SCH DIST/			
CHAZY/CLINTON	00720016	518/846-7135	44
Chc Learning Center/Buffalo/Erie	01793078	716/831-8422	66
Cheder Chabad Sch-Monsey/Airmont/Rockland	05242693	845/356-1213	198
CHEEKTOWAGA CENTRAL SD/CHEEKTOWAGA/			
ERIE	00723549	716/686-3612	58
Cheektowaga High Sch/Cheektowaga/Erie	00723563	716/686-3600	58
CHEEKTOWAGA MARYVALE UFSD/			
CHEEKTOWAGA/ERIE	00724919	716/631-0300	58
Cheektowaga Middle Sch/Cheektowaga/Erie	05276797	716/686-3600	58
CHEEKTOWAGA-SLOAN UFSD/SLOAN/			
ERIE	00725092	716/891-6402	59
Chelsea Career & Tech HS/New York/New York	00740846	212/925-1080	135
Chemung Valley Montessori Sch/Elmira/Chemung	12314837	607/562-8754	41
Chenango Bridge Elem Sch/Binghamton/Broome	00716651	607/762-6950	28
CHENANGO FORKS CENTRAL SD/			
BINGHAMTON/BROOME	00716572	607/648-7543	28
Chenango Forks Elem Sch/Binghamton/Broome	00716584	607/648-7580	28
Chenango Forks High Sch/Binghamton/Broome	00716596	607/648-7544	28
Chenango Forks Middle Sch/Binghamton/Broome	00716601	607/648-7576	28
CHENANGO VALLEY CTL SCH DIST/			
BINGHAMTON/BROOME	00716625	607/762-6800	28
Chenango Valley High Sch/Binghamton/Broome	11821954	607/762-6900	28
Chenango Valley Middle Sch/Binghamton/Broome	00716649	607/762-6902	28
Cherokee Street Elem Sch/Ronkonkoma/Suffolk	00772887	631/467-6027	219
Cherry Avenue Elem Sch/West Sayville/Suffolk	00775372	631/244-6700	229
Cherry Lane Elem Sch/Carle Place/Nassau	00735140	516/622-6402	117
Cherry Lane Elem Sch/Suffern/Rockland	00768147	845/357-3988	198
Cherry Road Elem Sch/Syracuse/Onondaga	00762698	315/426-3300	160
Cherry Valley-Springfield Sch/Cherry Valley/Otsego	00765975	607/264-3265	173
CHERRY VALLEY-SPRINGFIELD SD/			
CHERRY VALLEY/OTSEGO	00765963	607/264-3265	172
Chester Academy/Chester/Orange	00764086	845/469-2231	163
Chester Elem Sch/Chester/Orange	00764074	845/469-2178	163
CHESTER UNION FREE SCH DIST/			
CHESTER/ORANGE	00764050	845/469-5052	163
Chestnut Hill Elem Sch/Liverpool/Onondaga	00761591	315/453-0242	156
Chestnut Hill Middle Sch/Liverpool/Onondaga	00761606	315/453-0245	156
Chestnut Ridge Elem Sch/Rochester/Monroe	00731481	585/889-2188	107
Chestnut Ridge Middle Sch/Chestnut RDG/Rockland	00768094	845/577-6301	196
Chestnut Street Sch/W Hempstead/Nassau	04940414	516/390-3150	131
Child School-Legacy High Sch/Roosevelt Isl/New York	01794254	212/223-5055	144
Children's AID College Prep CS/Bronx/Bronx	11821540	347/871-9002	3

DISTRICT & SCHOOL TELEPHONE INDEX

Market Data Retrieval

School/City/County DISTRICT/CITY/COUNTY	PID	TELEPHONE NUMBER	PAGE
Children's Ctr UCP Sch-Suffolk/Commack/Suffolk	01795519	631/543-2338	234
Children's Home of Wyoming/Binghamton/Broome	02970152	607/772-6904	30
Children's Lab Sch/Sunnyside/Queens	12036346	718/361-3300	177
Children's League/Springville/Erie	11915141	716/592-9331	66
Children's Learning Center/Roosevelt/Nassau	01794137	516/378-2000	133
Children's Readiness Center/N Bellmore/Nassau	04882484	516/719-6070	116
Children's Sch of Rochester 15/Rochester/Monroe	03400837	585/262-8830	110
Children's Workshop Sch/New York/New York	04457285	212/614-9531	135
Chippewa Elem Sch/Holtsville/Suffolk	00775152	631/696-8640	229
CHITTENANGO CENTRAL SD/CHITTENANGO/MADISON	00731065	315/687-2840	104
Chittenango High Sch/Chittenango/Madison	00731091	315/687-2900	104
Chittenango Middle Sch/Chittenango/Madison	00731118	315/687-2800	104
Christ Lutheran Sch/Rosedale/Queens	01560429	718/525-6884	187
Christ the King Regional HS/Middle Vlg/Queens	00752930	718/366-7400	186
Christ the King Sch/Bronx/Bronx	00755293	718/538-5959	25
Christ the King Sch/Snyder/Erie	00726101	716/839-0473	65
Christian Acad-Western NY/N Tonawanda/Niagara	04975328	716/433-1652	149
Christian Brothers Academy/Albany/Albany	00715152	518/452-9809	13
Christian Brothers Academy/Syracuse/Onondaga	00762870	315/446-5960	160
Christian Central Academy/Williamsville/Erie	01460817	716/634-4821	66
Christopher Ave Cmty Sch/Brooklyn/Kings	11714909	718/495-5761	93
Christopher Columbus YABC/Bronx/Bronx	11928710	718/944-3700	22
Church of God Christian Acad/Far Rockaway/Queens	04974831	718/327-9590	187
Church Street Elem Sch/White Plains/Westchester	03247207	914/422-2401	263
Churchill Center & Sch/New York/New York	01463209	212/722-0610	144
CHURCHVILLE CHILI CTL SCH DIST/CHURCHVILLE/MONROE	00731479	585/293-1800	107
Churchville Chili High Sch/Churchville/Monroe	00731510	585/293-4540	107
Churchville Chili Middle Sch/Churchville/Monroe	00731508	585/293-4542	107
Churchville Elem Sch/Churchville/Monroe	00731493	585/293-2022	107
Cicero Elem Sch/Cicero/Onondaga	00761943	315/218-2500	157
Cicero-N Syracuse High Sch/Cicero/Onondaga	00761955	315/218-4100	157
CINCINNATUS CTL SCH DIST/CINCINNATUS/CORTLAND	00720743	607/863-3200	47
Cincinnatus Elem Sch/Cincinnatus/Cortland	00720755	607/863-3200	47
Cinema Sch/Bronx/Bronx	11447792	718/620-2560	24
Cinncinatus Secondary Sch/Cincinnatus/Cortland	04362446	607/863-3200	47
Circleville Elem Sch/Circleville/Orange	00764816	845/744-2031	166
Circleville Middle Sch/Circleville/Orange	01519872	845/744-2031	166
Citizen Edmond Genet Elem Sch/E Greenbush/Rensselaer	00766826	518/207-2680	190
City & Country Sch/New York/New York	00758881	212/242-7802	144
City Polytechnic High Sch/Brooklyn/Kings	11447522	718/875-1473	82
Civic Leadership Academy/Elmhurst/Queens	11103051	718/271-1487	177
Clara Barton High Sch/Brooklyn/Kings	00740860	718/636-4900	86
Clara Barton School 2/Rochester/Monroe	00732693	585/235-2820	110
Clara H Carlson Elem Sch/Elmont/Nassau	00735384	516/326-5570	118
Clara Muhammad Sch/Brooklyn/Kings	11237236	718/783-1279	97
Clara Muhammad School Queens/Corona/Queens	04974673	646/939-2670	187
Claremont Elem Sch/Ossining/Westchester	00781321	914/762-5830	260
Claremont International HS/Bronx/Bronx	11821617	718/410-4001	18
Clarence Center Elem Sch/Clarence CTR/Erie	00723604	716/407-9150	59
CLARENCE CENTRAL SCH DIST/CLARENCE/ERIE	00723599	716/407-9100	59
Clarence Middle Sch/Clarence/Erie	00723616	716/407-9206	59
Clarence Senior High Sch/Clarence/Erie	00723628	716/407-9020	59
CLARKSTOWN CENTRAL SCH DIST/NEW CITY/ROCKLAND	00767301	845/639-6300	195
Clarkstown North High Sch/New City/Rockland	00767351	845/639-6501	195
Clarkstown South High Sch/West Nyack/Rockland	00767375	845/624-3410	196
Clary Middle Sch/Syracuse/Onondaga	00762246	315/435-4411	158
Clayton Ave Elem Sch/Vestal/Broome	00717124	607/757-2271	30
Clayton Huey Elem Sch/CTR Moriches/Suffolk	01813549	631/878-9780	218
Clear Stream Avenue Elem Sch/Valley Stream/Nassau	00738958	516/434-3550	131
Clear View Sch/Briarcliff/Westchester	01464320	914/941-9513	265
Cleary School for the Deaf/Nesconset/Suffolk	01795478	631/588-0530	234
Cleveland Hill Elem Sch/Cheektowaga/Erie	00723680	716/836-7200	59
Cleveland Hill High Sch/Cheektowaga/Erie	00723707	716/836-7200	59
Cleveland Hill Middle Sch/Cheektowaga/Erie	03247738	716/836-7200	59
CLEVELAND HILL UNION FREE SD/CHEEKTOWAGA/ERIE	00723678	716/836-7200	59
Clifford Wise Mid Interm Sch/Medina/Orleans	00765286	585/798-2700	170
Clifton-Fine Central Sch/Star Lake/St Lawrence	00768410	315/848-3333	209
CLIFTON-FINE CENTRAL SCH DIST/STAR LAKE/ST LAWRENCE	00768408	315/848-3333	209
Clinical Assoc Finger Lakes/Victor/Ontario	11230927	585/924-7207	163
Clinton Avenue Elem Sch/Port Jeff Sta/Suffolk	00772801	631/474-8150	218
CLINTON CENTRAL SCH DIST/CLINTON/ONEIDA	00760030	315/557-2253	150
Clinton Elem Sch/Clinton/Oneida	00760054	315/853-5574	150
Clinton Middle Sch/Clinton/Oneida	00760066	315/557-2260	150
Clinton Senior High Sch/Clinton/Oneida	00760078	315/853-5574	150
Clinton Street Elem Sch/West Seneca/Erie	00725420	716/677-3620	64
Clinton V Bush Elem Sch/Jamestown/Chautauqua	00718752	716/483-4401	38
Clover Drive Adult Lrng Center/Great Neck/Nassau	04033712	516/441-4950	120
Clover Patch Camp/Glenville/Schenectady	01463912	518/384-3042	205
Cloverbank Elem Sch/Hamburg/Erie	00723977	716/926-1760	60
Clyde Mennonite Parochial Sch/Clyde/Wayne	04975469	315/923-7242	251
CLYDE-SAVANNAH CENTRAL SD/CLYDE/WAYNE	00779160	315/902-3000	249
Clyde-Savannah Elem Sch/Clyde/Wayne	00779172	315/902-3100	249
Clyde-Savannah High Sch/Clyde/Wayne	00779184	315/902-3050	249
Clyde-Savannah Middle Sch/Clyde/Wayne	11712183	315/902-3200	249
Clymer Central Sch/Clymer/Chautauqua	00718439	716/355-4444	37
CLYMER CENTRAL SCH DIST/CLYMER/CHAUTAUQUA	00718427	716/355-4444	37
Cobble Hill Sch of Amer Study/Brooklyn/Kings	04809468	718/403-9544	84
Cobbles Elem Sch/Penfield/Monroe	00732368	585/249-6500	109
COBLESKILL RICHMONDVILLE SD/COBLESKILL/SCHOHARIE	00770736	518/234-4032	206
Cobleskill-Richmondville HS/Richmondville/Schoharie	00770762	518/234-3565	206
Coburn Elem Sch/Elmira/Chemung	00719304	607/735-3650	40
Cohen Elem Sch/Elmira Hgts/Chemung	01813202	607/734-7132	40
Cohen Middle Sch/Elmira Hgts/Chemung	04746024	607/734-5078	40
Cohocton Elem Sch/Cohocton/Steuben	00771364	585/384-5234	215
COHOES CITY SCH DIST/COHOES/ALBANY	00714457	518/237-0100	10
Cohoes High Sch/Cohoes/Albany	00714471	518/237-9100	10
Cohoes Middle Sch/Cohoes/Albany	00714483	518/237-4131	10
Cold Spring Early Lrng Ctr/Stanfordville/Dutchess	00721864	845/868-7451	53
COLD SPRING HARBOR CENTRAL SD/COLD SPG HBR/SUFFOLK	00772526	631/367-5900	219
Cold Spring Harbor Jr Sr HS/Cold SPG HBR/Suffolk	00772538	631/367-6900	219
Colden Elem Sch/Colden/Erie	00724127	716/592-3217	63
Colebrook Sch/Rochester/Monroe	00732215	585/336-1600	113
Collaborative Arts Middle Sch/Sprngfld GDNS/Queens	11714832	718/977-6181	183
Collegiate Inst-Math & Science/Bronx/Bronx	05349423	718/944-3635	22
Collegiate Sch/New York/New York	00758893	212/812-8500	144
Colonial Elem Sch/Pelham/Westchester	00781448	914/738-2680	260
Colonial Village Elem Sch/Niagara Falls/Niagara	00759500	716/215-3270	148
Colonie Central High Sch/Albany/Albany	00714847	518/459-1220	12
Colton Pierrepont Ctl Sch/Colton/St Lawrence	00768434	315/262-2100	210
COLTON PIERREPONT SCH DIST/COLTON/ST LAWRENCE	00768422	315/262-2100	209
Columbia Christian Academy/Ghent/Columbia	01792957	518/392-2361	47
Columbia Grammar & Prep Sch/New York/New York	00758908	212/749-6200	144
Columbia Greene Ed Center/Hudson/Columbia	01556519	518/828-4157	45
Columbia High Sch/E Greenbush/Rensselaer	00766797	518/207-2000	190
Columbia Secondary Sch/New York/New York	10913815	212/666-1278	140
Columbus Ave Early Chldhd Ctr/Freeport/Nassau	00735712	516/867-5240	119
Columbus Elem Sch/Mount Vernon/Westchester	00780872	914/358-2700	258

NY-V10 800-333-8802 School Year 2020-2021

New York School Directory

DISTRICT & SCHOOL TELEPHONE INDEX

School/City/County DISTRICT/CITY/COUNTY	PID	TELEPHONE NUMBER	PAGE
Columbus Elem Sch/New Rochelle/Westchester	00781113	914/576-4401	259
Columbus Elem Sch/Thornwood/Westchester	00781046	914/769-8538	258
Columbus Elem Sch/Utica/Oneida	00760767	315/792-2011	152
Coman Hill Sch/Armonk/Westchester	00779782	914/273-4183	253
Commack High Sch/Commack/Suffolk	00772617	631/912-2100	219
Commack Middle Sch/Commack/Suffolk	00772629	631/858-3500	219
Commack Road Elem Sch/Islip/Suffolk	00773893	631/650-8600	224
COMMACK UNION FREE SCH DIST/ E NORTHPORT/SUFFOLK	00772576	631/912-2000	219
Community Academic Prep Sch/Roosevelt/Nassau	11230886	516/377-7520	133
Community Action School MS 258/New York/New York	04874190	212/678-5888	138
Community Education Center/Niagara Falls/Niagara	00759471	716/286-0771	147
Community Health Acad Heights/New York/New York	10026735	212/342-6600	141
Community HS-Social Justice/Bronx/Bronx	05098064	718/402-8481	16
Community Math & Science Prep/New York/New York	05349019	917/521-2508	141
Community Partnership Lwr Sch/Brooklyn/Kings	04923997	718/399-3824	3
Community Rehab Center/Lake Katrine/Ulster	02164303	845/336-7235	244
Community Roots Charter Sch/Brooklyn/Kings	10026890	718/858-1629	82
COMMUNITY SCH DIST 1/NEW YORK/ NEW YORK	10909565	212/353-2948	135
COMMUNITY SCH DIST 2/NEW YORK/ NEW YORK	10909577	212/356-3739	135
COMMUNITY SCH DIST 3/NEW YORK/ NEW YORK	10909589	212/678-5857	138
COMMUNITY SCH DIST 4/NEW YORK/ NEW YORK	10909591	212/348-2873	139
COMMUNITY SCH DIST 5/NEW YORK/ NEW YORK	10909606	212/222-0473	140
COMMUNITY SCH DIST 6/NEW YORK/ NEW YORK	10909618	917/521-3757	141
COMMUNITY SCH DIST 7/BRONX/BRONX	10909620	718/742-6500	16
COMMUNITY SCH DIST 8/BRONX/BRONX	10909632	718/239-5890	17
COMMUNITY SCH DIST 9/BRONX/BRONX	10909644	718/579-7143	18
COMMUNITY SCH DIST 10/BRONX/ BRONX	10909656	718/741-5852	20
COMMUNITY SCH DIST 11/BRONX/ BRONX	10909668	718/519-2620	22
COMMUNITY SCH DIST 12/BRONX/ BRONX	10909670	718/328-2310	23
COMMUNITY SCH DIST 13/BROOKLYN/ KINGS	10909682	718/636-3284	82
COMMUNITY SCH DIST 14/BROOKLYN/ KINGS	10909694	718/302-7600	83
COMMUNITY SCH DIST 15/BROOKLYN/ KINGS	10909709	718/935-3424	84
COMMUNITY SCH DIST 16/BROOKLYN/ KINGS	10909711	718/574-2834	85
COMMUNITY SCH DIST 17/BROOKLYN/ KINGS	10909723	718/221-4372	86
COMMUNITY SCH DIST 18/BROOKLYN/ KINGS	10909735	718/566-6008	87
COMMUNITY SCH DIST 19/BROOKLYN/ KINGS	10909747	929/397-2938	88
COMMUNITY SCH DIST 20/BROOKLYN/ KINGS	10909797	718/759-4908	89
COMMUNITY SCH DIST 21/BROOKLYN/ KINGS	10909802	718/648-0209	90
COMMUNITY SCH DIST 22/BROOKLYN/ KINGS	10909814	718/968-6117	91
COMMUNITY SCH DIST 23/BROOKLYN/ KINGS	10909838	718/346-0816	92
COMMUNITY SCH DIST 24/CORONA/ QUEENS	10909840	718/592-3357	176
COMMUNITY SCH DIST 25/FLUSHING/ QUEENS	10909852	718/281-7605	178
COMMUNITY SCH DIST 26/BAYSIDE/ QUEENS	10909864	718/631-6943	179
COMMUNITY SCH DIST 27/OZONE PARK/ QUEENS	10909876	718/642-5770	180
COMMUNITY SCH DIST 28/JAMAICA/ QUEENS	10909888	718/557-2618	181
COMMUNITY SCH DIST 29/QUEENS VLG/ QUEENS	10909890	718/217-7740	183
COMMUNITY SCH DIST 30/LONG IS CITY/ QUEENS	10909905	718/391-6122	184
COMMUNITY SCH DIST 31/STATEN ISLAND/ RICHMOND	10909917	718/420-5667	192
COMMUNITY SCH DIST 32/BROOKLYN/ KINGS	10909929	718/574-1100	93
Community Voices Middle Sch/Sprngfld GDNS/Queens	11714820	718/977-6180	183
Como Park Elem Sch/Lancaster/Erie	00724878	716/686-3235	62
Compass Charter Sch/Brooklyn/Kings	12028349	718/310-3588	3
Comsewogue High Sch/Port Jeff Sta/Suffolk	00772825	631/474-8179	218
Concord High Sch/Staten Island/Richmond	01841340	718/447-1274	192
Concord Road Elem Sch/Ardsley/Westchester	00779665	914/231-0800	252
Concourse Village Elem Sch/Bronx/Bronx	11924544	718/402-7503	16
Coney Island Prep Public CS/Brooklyn/Kings	11447417	718/513-6951	3
Cong Bais Chinuch Ateres Bnos/Spring Valley/Rockland	12468062	845/675-8200	198
Cong Mesifta Ohr Hatalmud/New Windsor/Orange	04974271	845/784-4020	168
Cong Yeshuos Moshe Viznitz/Spring Valley/Rockland	12467135	845/579-6363	199
Cong Yeshuos Moshe Williamsbrg/Brooklyn/Kings	12468490	718/782-7383	97
Congregation Bais Chana Malka/Spring Valley/Rockland	12467123	845/352-1300	199
Congregation Belz Sch/Spring Valley/Rockland	02980042	845/425-0909	199
Congregation Ohr Menachem/Brooklyn/Kings	12380719	718/778-8770	97
Congregation Yeshiva GR Monsey/Spring Valley/Rockland	12370142	845/440-7976	199
Connelly Middle Sch Holy Child/New York/New York	04145250	212/982-2287	142
Connetquot Alternative Pre-Sch/Bohemia/Suffolk	04757542	631/563-9833	219
CONNETQUOT CENTRAL SCH DIST/ BOHEMIA/SUFFOLK	00772863	631/244-2215	219
Connetquot Elem Sch/Islip Terrace/Suffolk	00773192	631/224-2001	221
Connetquot Senior High Sch/Bohemia/Suffolk	00772899	631/244-2228	219
Connolly Elem Sch/Glen Cove/Nassau	00735865	516/801-7310	120
Conselyea Prep Sch/Brooklyn/Kings	10008824	718/486-6211	83
Convent of Sacred Heart Sch/New York/New York	00755322	212/722-4745	142
Cooke Center Academy/New York/New York	12239108	212/477-1297	142
Cooke Center Grammar Sch/New York/New York	00756924	212/995-2020	143
Coopers Campus Cte/Painted Post/Steuben	00771857	607/962-3175	212
COOPERSTOWN CTL SCH DIST/ COOPERSTOWN/OTSEGO	00765987	607/547-5364	173
Cooperstown Elem Sch/Cooperstown/Otsego	00766008	607/547-9976	173
Cooperstown Junior-Senior High/Cooperstown/Otsego	00765999	607/547-8181	173
Copenhagen Central Sch/Copenhagen/Lewis	00730516	315/688-4411	101
COPENHAGEN CENTRAL SD/COPENHAGEN/ LEWIS	00730504	315/688-4411	101
Copiague Christian Academy/Copiague/Suffolk	02991572	631/842-5993	234
Copiague Middle Sch/Copiague/Suffolk	00773001	631/842-4011	220
COPIAGUE UNION FREE SCH DIST/ COPIAGUE/SUFFOLK	00772980	631/842-4015	220
Coram Elem Sch/Coram/Suffolk	00774392	631/698-0077	225
Corcoran High Sch/Syracuse/Onondaga	00762272	315/435-4321	158
Cordello Ave Elem Sch/Central Islip/Suffolk	04875675	631/348-4189	219
CORINTH CENTRAL SCH DIST/ CORINTH/SARATOGA	00769555	518/654-9005	200
Corinth Elem Sch/Corinth/Saratoga	00769579	518/654-2960	200
Corinth High Sch/Corinth/Saratoga	00769567	518/654-9005	200
Corinth Middle Sch/Corinth/Saratoga	12173530	518/654-9005	200
Corlears Sch/New York/New York	01794266	212/741-2800	144
Cornerstone Acad-Soc Action ES/Bronx/Bronx	10911881	718/794-6160	22
Cornerstone Acad-Soc Action MS/Bronx/Bronx	11447558	718/794-7970	22
Cornerstone Christian Academy/Brockport/Monroe	02977198	585/637-4540	114
Cornerstone Christian Academy/Sloansville/Schoharie	04974958	518/868-2268	207
Corning Christian Academy/Corning/Steuben	02990920	607/962-4220	215
CORNING-PAINTED POST AREA SD/ PAINTED POST/STEUBEN	00771376	607/936-3704	214
Corning-Painted Post High Sch/Corning/Steuben	00771429	607/654-2988	214
Corning-Painted Post Mid Sch/Painted Post/Steuben	00771417	607/654-2966	214
Cornwall Central High Sch/New Windsor/Orange	00764115	845/534-8009	163

School Year 2020-2021   800-333-8802   NY-V11

DISTRICT & SCHOOL TELEPHONE INDEX

Market Data Retrieval

School/City/County DISTRICT/CITY/COUNTY	PID	TELEPHONE NUMBER	PAGE
Cornwall Central Middle Sch/Cornwall/Orange	00764139	845/534-8009	163
CORNWALL CENTRAL SCH DIST/CORNWALL HDSN/ORANGE	00764098	845/534-8009	163
Cornwall Elem Sch/Cornwall/Orange	00764103	845/534-8009	163
Cornwall on Hudson Elem Sch/Cornwall HDSN/Orange	00764127	845/534-8009	163
Cornwell Ave Elem Sch/W Hempstead/Nassau	00739081	516/390-3140	131
Corona Arts & Sciences Acad/Corona/Queens	11924142	718/507-3820	177
Corpus Christi Holy Rosary Sch/Port Chester/Westchester	00755334	914/937-4407	264
Cortelyou Academy/Brooklyn/Kings	10755015	718/421-9581	97
Cortland Christian Academy/Cortland/Cortland	04926482	607/756-7716	48
CORTLAND ENLARGED CITY SD/CORTLAND/CORTLAND	00720779	607/758-4100	47
Cortland Jr Sr High Sch/Cortland/Cortland	00720793	607/758-4110	47
Cosgrove Middle Sch/Spencerport/Monroe	00733300	585/349-5300	112
Cottage Lane Elem Sch/Blauvelt/Rockland	00767832	845/680-1500	197
Council Rock Primary Sch/Rochester/Monroe	00731388	585/242-5170	106
Country Parkway Elem Sch/Williamsville/Erie	00725561	716/626-9860	64
Countrywood Primary Center/Huntingtn Sta/Suffolk	00775762	631/812-3300	231
Court Street Elem Sch/Lancaster/Erie	00724880	716/686-3240	62
Covenant Love Community Sch/Freeville/Tompkins	02164298	607/347-4413	241
Covert Avenue Elem Sch/Elmont/Nassau	00735396	516/326-5560	118
Coxsackie Athens High Sch/Coxsackie/Greene	00729232	518/731-1800	75
Coxsackie Athens Middle Sch/Coxsackie/Greene	04030605	518/731-1850	75
Coxsackie Elem Sch/Coxsackie/Greene	00729244	518/731-1770	75
COXSACKIE-ATHENS CENTRAL SD/COXSACKIE/GREENE	00729218	518/731-1700	75
CP Rochester Augustin Chld Ctr/Rochester/Monroe	02162070	585/334-6000	114
Craig Elem Sch/Niskayuna/Schenectady	00770231	518/377-0156	204
Craig Hill Elem Sch/Rochester/Monroe	00731924	585/966-4500	109
Creo College Prep Charter Sch/Bronx/Bronx	12367389	347/216-9246	3
Crescent Academy/Johnson City/Broome	11818775	607/729-3431	30
Crescent Sch/Hempstead/Nassau	03412828	516/292-1787	133
Creston Academy/Bronx/Bronx	11447780	718/367-5035	20
Crestwood Children's Center/Rochester/Monroe	01793901	585/429-2700	114
Crispell Middle Sch/Pine Bush/Orange	00764830	845/744-2031	166
Cristo Rey Brooklyn High Sch/Brooklyn/Kings	11450476	718/455-3555	97
Cristo Rey New York High Sch/New York/New York	10031223	212/996-7000	144
Crompond Elem Sch/Yorktown Hts/Westchester	00782727	914/243-8140	264
Cross Hill Academy/Yonkers/Westchester	00782363	914/376-8300	263
Croton-Harmon High Sch/Croton Hdsn/Westchester	00779914	914/271-2147	254
CROTON-HARMON UNION FREE SD/CROTON HDSN/WESTCHESTER	00779897	914/271-4713	254
Crotona Int'l High Sch/Bronx/Bronx	11715056	718/561-8701	20
Crown Point High Sch/Crown Point/Essex	00727868	518/597-3285	67
CROWN POINT CENTRAL SCH DIST/CROWN POINT/ESSEX	00727856	518/597-3285	67
Crystal Light Mennonite Sch/Castorland/Lewis	01460972	315/376-8556	102
Crystal Valley Christian Sch/Dundee/Yates	04975770	607/243-7209	268
CSI HS-International Studies/Staten Island/Richmond	10008434	718/370-6900	192
Ctr for Dis Serv-Langan Sch/Albany/Albany	01792517	518/437-5700	13
CTR FOR INSTRUCT TECH INNOV/MEXICO/OSWEGO	00765913	315/963-4251	172
CUBA-RUSHFORD CENTRAL SCH DIST/CUBA/ALLEGANY	00716168	585/968-2650	14
Cuba-Rushford Elem Sch/Cuba/Allegany	00716170	585/968-1760	14
Cuba-Rushford Middle High Sch/Cuba/Allegany	00716182	585/968-2650	14
Cultural Acad Arts & Sciences/Brooklyn/Kings	11103128	718/968-6630	87
Cultural Arts Acad-Sprg Crk/Brooklyn/Kings	11561087	718/683-3300	87
Cumberland Head Elem Sch/West Chazy/Clinton	00719990	518/563-8321	44
Cuny Preparatory High Sch/Bronx/Bronx	10018984	718/839-8862	3
Curious Young Learners PK Ctr/Howard Beach/Queens	12367391		180
Curtis High Sch/Staten Island/Richmond	00740872	718/390-1800	192
Cutchogue East Elem Sch/Cutchogue/Suffolk	00774172	631/734-6049	225
Cyberarts Studio Academy/Brooklyn/Kings	04877312	718/832-4201	84
Cynthia Jenkins Elem Sch/Jamaica/Queens	00749206	718/528-5399	183
Cypress Hills Ascend CS/Brooklyn/Kings	12310386	347/227-6070	3
Cypress Hills Collegiate Prep/Brooklyn/Kings	10026888	718/647-1672	88

D

School/City/County DISTRICT/CITY/COUNTY	PID	TELEPHONE NUMBER	PAGE
D & G Kaloidis Parochial Sch/Brooklyn/Kings	03412866	718/836-8096	97
Dake Junior High Sch/Rochester/Monroe	00732227	585/342-2140	113
Dalton Lower Sch/New York/New York	11229887	212/423-5431	144
Dalton Sch/New York/New York	00758910	212/423-5200	144
Dana L Lyon Middle Sch/Bath/Steuben	00771625	607/776-4110	213
Dana L West Jr Sr High Sch/Port Byron/Cayuga	00718087	315/776-5728	35
Daniel Street Elem Sch/Lindenhurst/Suffolk	00774079	631/867-3300	224
Daniel Warren Elem Sch/Mamaroneck/Westchester	04446808	914/777-4200	261
Daniel Webster Magnet Sch/New Rochelle/Westchester	00781125	914/576-4460	259
DANSVILLE CTL SCH DIST/DANSVILLE/LIVINGSTON	00730712	585/335-4000	102
Dansville High Sch/Dansville/Livingston	00730748	585/335-4010	102
Dansville Primary Sch/Dansville/Livingston	00730736	585/335-4040	102
Darkei Chaim/Brooklyn/Kings	12160428	718/435-0894	97
Darrow Sch/New Lebanon/Columbia	00729115	518/794-6000	47
Darul Ullom AL Madania Sch/Buffalo/Erie	04975380	716/895-3318	66
Darwin Smith Sch/Ithaca/Tompkins	00777746	607/257-1551	239
David B Crane Elem Sch/Rochester/Monroe	00733207	585/359-5400	112
David Paterson Sch/Hempstead/Nassau	00736106	516/434-4450	121
Davis Elem Sch/Malone/Franklin	00728214	518/483-7802	70
Davison Ave Elem Sch/Lynbrook/Nassau	00737136	516/887-6462	124
Dawnwood Middle Sch/Centereach/Suffolk	00774237	631/285-8200	225
Dayton Avenue Elem Sch/Manorville/Suffolk	00775865	631/801-3085	221
Daytop Village Sec Sch/Huntingtn Sta/Suffolk	11237535	631/351-7112	234
DCMO BOCES CHENANGO/NORWICH/CHENANGO	00721345	607/335-1200	43
Dcmo BOCES Tech Center/Norwich/Chenango	00721357	607/335-1200	41
De La Salle Academy/New York/New York	03069172	212/316-5840	144
De La Salle Sch/Freeport/Nassau	05183437	516/379-8660	133
DE RUYTER CENTRAL SCH DIST/DE RUYTER/MADISON	00731120	315/852-3400	105
De Ruyter Elem Sch/De Ruyter/Madison	12380501	315/852-3400	105
De Ruyter Middle High Sch/De Ruyter/Madison	00731132	315/852-3400	105
Deasy Elem Sch/Glen Cove/Nassau	00735853	516/801-7110	120
Deauville Gardens East ES/Copiague/Suffolk	11927352	631/842-3320	220
Deauville Gardens West ES/Copiague/Suffolk	00773013	631/842-4012	220
Deer Park High Sch/Deer Park/Suffolk	00773075	631/274-4110	220
DEER PARK UNION FREE SCH DIST/DEER PARK/SUFFOLK	00773051	631/274-4000	220
Deerfield Elem Sch/Deerfield/Oneida	00760925	315/266-3410	153
Delaware Academy/Delhi/Delaware	00721060	607/746-1300	49
DELAWARE ACADEMY CTRL SD DELHI/DELHI/DELAWARE	00721034	607/746-1300	49
Delaware Cmty Sch/Albany/Albany	00714213	518/475-6750	9
Delaware Primary Sch/Syracuse/Onondaga	00762296	315/435-4540	158
Delevan Elem Sch/Delevan/Cattaraugus	00717693	716/492-9461	33
Delhi Central Elem Sch/Delhi/Delaware	00721058	607/746-2105	49
Democracy Prep Charter HS/New York/New York	12113841	212/281-3061	3
Democracy Prep Charter Mid Sch/New York/New York	10028020	212/281-8247	3
Democracy Prep Endurance HS/New York/New York	12370350	646/490-3693	3
Democracy Prep Endurance MS/New York/New York	12170538	212/316-7602	3
Democracy Prep Harlem ES/New York/New York	12114065	212/876-9953	3
Democracy Prep Harlem High Sch/New York/New York	12322585	212/932-7791	3
Democracy Prep Harlem MS/New York/New York	11704045	212/281-3061	3
Dennis M Kenney Middle Sch/Hannibal/Oswego	00765614	315/564-8120	171
Denton Avenue Elem Sch/New Hyde Park/Nassau	00736211	516/305-8400	121
Depew High Sch/Depew/Erie	00723733	716/686-5065	60
Depew Middle Sch/Depew/Erie	00723745	716/686-5045	60
DEPEW UNION FREE SCH DIST/DEPEW/ERIE	00723719	716/686-5104	59
DEPOSIT CENTRAL SCH DIST/DEPOSIT/BROOME	00716699	607/467-2197	28

New York School Directory

DISTRICT & SCHOOL TELEPHONE INDEX

School/City/County DISTRICT/CITY/COUNTY	PID	TELEPHONE NUMBER	PAGE
Deposit Elem Sch/Deposit/Broome	00716704	607/467-2198	28
Deposit Middle High Sch/Deposit/Broome	00716716	607/467-2197	28
DeSales Catholic Sch/Lockport/Niagara	00726345	716/433-6422	149
Developmental Disability Inst/Smithtown/Suffolk	01795507	631/366-2900	234
Devereux Millwood Learning Ctr/Mount Kisco/Westchester	11710367	914/941-1991	265
Devereux School In New York/Red Hook/Dutchess	03403102	845/758-1899	55
DeWitt Clinton High Sch/Bronx/Bronx	00740884	718/543-1000	20
DeWitt Clinton YABC/Bronx/Bronx	11928722	718/584-2700	20
DeWitt Middle Sch/Ithaca/Tompkins	00777514	607/257-3222	240
DeWitt Road Elem Sch/Webster/Monroe	02201365	585/671-0710	113
Dexter Elem Sch/Dexter/Jefferson	00730085	315/639-2300	80
Dickinson Avenue Elem Sch/E Northport/Suffolk	00774677	631/262-6810	227
Digital Arts & Cinema Tech HS/Brooklyn/Kings	04038011	718/694-9741	84
DIOCESE OF ALBANY ED OFFICE/ALBANY/ALBANY	00715059	518/453-6602	12
DIOCESE OF BROOKLYN ED OFFICE/BROOKLYN/KINGS	00752801	718/965-7300	94
DIOCESE OF BUFFALO ED OFFICE/BUFFALO/ERIE	00725846	716/847-5520	65
DIOCESE OF OGDENSBURG ED OFF/OGDENSBURG/ST LAWRENCE	00769050	315/393-2920	212
DIOCESE OF ROCHESTER ED OFFICE/ROCHESTER/MONROE	00733623	585/328-3228	113
DIOCESE OF ROCKVILLE ED OFFICE/HICKSVILLE/NASSAU	00739512	516/678-5800	132
DIOCESE OF SYRACUSE ED OFFICE/SYRACUSE/ONONDAGA	00762765	315/470-1450	160
Discovery Charter Sch/Rochester/Monroe	11739521	585/342-4032	3
Discovery High Sch/Bronx/Bronx	05280918	718/733-3872	20
District 20 Pre-K Center/Brooklyn/Kings	12160624	718/621-8510	89
DISTRICT 75 CITY WIDE PROGRAMS/NEW YORK/NEW YORK	00750293	212/802-1507	142
Divine Mercy Catholic Academy/Ozone Park/Queens	00753271	718/845-3074	186
Divine Wisdom Acad-Douglaston/Douglaston/Queens	00753843	718/631-3153	186
Division Ave High Sch/Levittown/Nassau	01813393	516/434-7150	123
Division Street Elem Sch/Saratoga Spgs/Saratoga	00769713	518/583-4794	201
Doane Stuart Sch/Rensselaer/Rensselaer	01792488	518/465-5222	192
Dobbs Ferry High Sch/Dobbs Ferry/Westchester	01841417	914/693-7645	254
Dobbs Ferry Middle Sch/Dobbs Ferry/Westchester	03247037	914/693-7640	254
DOBBS FERRY UNION FREE SD/DOBBS FERRY/WESTCHESTER	00779938	914/693-1500	254
Dock Street Sch/Brooklyn/Kings	05351816	718/780-7660	82
Dodge Elem Sch/East Amherst/Erie	00725573	716/626-9821	64
Dogwood Elem Sch/Smithtown/Suffolk	00775542	631/382-4255	230
DOLGEVILLE CENTRAL SCH DIST/DOLGEVILLE/HERKIMER	00729505	315/429-3155	77
Dolgeville Elem Middle Sch/Dolgeville/Herkimer	00729517	315/429-3155	77
Dominican Academy/New York/New York	00755360	212/744-0195	143
Donald P Sutherland Elem Sch/Nassau/Rensselaer	00766802	518/207-2620	190
Donald S Ray Middle Sch/Baldwinsville/Onondaga	01523471	315/638-6106	154
Donlin Drive Elem Sch/Liverpool/Onondaga	00761620	315/453-0249	156
Donnelly Elem Sch/Conklin/Broome	00717069	607/775-0176	29
Dorothy B Bunce Elem Sch/Pavilion/Genesee	01413761	585/584-3011	74
Dorothy Nolan Elem Sch/Saratoga Spgs/Saratoga	00769725	518/584-7383	201
Dos Puentes Elem Sch/New York/New York	11932187	212/781-1803	141
Douglas G Grafflin Elem Sch/Chappaqua/Westchester	00779823	914/238-7204	253
Douglas J Regan Interm Sch/Lockport/Niagara	00759770	716/210-2150	149
Dover Elem Sch/Dover Plains/Dutchess	00721632	845/877-5730	52
Dover High Sch/Dover Plains/Dutchess	04747901	845/877-5750	52
Dover Middle Sch/Dover Plains/Dutchess	00721644	845/877-5740	52
DOVER UNION FREE SCH DIST/DOVER PLAINS/DUTCHESS	00721618	845/877-5700	52
Downsville Central Sch/Downsville/Delaware	00721084	607/363-2100	49
DOWNSVILLE CENTRAL SCH DIST/DOWNSVILLE/DELAWARE	00721072	607/363-2100	49
Downtown Brooklyn YABC/Brooklyn/Kings	11928796	718/222-0918	82
Dows Lane Elem Sch/Irvington/Westchester	00780509	914/591-6012	257
Dr Charles T Lunsford Sch 19/Rochester/Monroe	00732851	585/328-7454	110
Dr Edwin Weeks Elem Sch/Syracuse/Onondaga	01548081	315/435-4097	158
Dr George F Mack Middle Sch/Walton/Delaware	03321401	607/865-4116	50
Dr Jacqueline Peek-Davis Sch/Brooklyn/Kings	04245032	718/953-4569	86
Dr Kenneth B Clark Academy/Dobbs Ferry/Westchester	10011948	914/798-7200	255
Dr Louis A Cerulli School 34/Rochester/Monroe	00732980	585/458-3210	111
Dr Martin Luther King Jr ES/Utica/Oneida	00760743	315/792-2175	152
Dr Martin Luther King Jr Sch 9/Rochester/Monroe	02129559	585/325-7828	111
Dr R Izquierdo Health & Sci CS/Bronx/Bronx	11561154	718/378-0490	24
Dr Susan McKinney Sch of Arts/Brooklyn/Kings	00744799	718/834-6760	82
Dr Walter Cooper Acad Sch 10/Rochester/Monroe	11552531	585/324-2010	111
Drake Elem Sch/N Tonawanda/Niagara	00759627	716/807-3725	148
Draper Middle Sch/Schenectady/Schenectady	00770188	518/356-8350	204
Dream Charter Sch/New York/New York	11103520	212/722-0232	3
Dream Charter Sch-Mott Haven/Bronx/Bronx	12367420	212/722-1608	3
Dreamyard Prep Sch/Bronx/Bronx	10027064	718/410-4242	18
Drexel Ave Sch/Westbury/Nassau	00739134	516/876-5030	132
DRYDEN CENTRAL SCH DIST/DRYDEN/TOMPKINS	00777332	607/844-5361	239
Dryden Elem Sch/Dryden/Tompkins	00777356	607/844-8694	239
Dryden High Sch/Dryden/Tompkins	00777368	607/844-8694	239
Dryden Middle Sch/Dryden/Tompkins	04939996	607/844-8694	240
Dryden St Sch/Westbury/Nassau	04750635	516/876-5039	132
DUANESBURG CENTRAL SCH DIST/DELANSON/SCHENECTADY	00770126	518/895-2279	203
Duanesburg Elem Sch/Delanson/Schenectady	00770138	518/895-2580	203
Duanesburg Jr Sr High Sch/Delanson/Schenectady	00770140	518/895-3000	203
Dudley Elem Sch/Fairport/Monroe	00731687	585/421-2155	108
DUNDEE CTL SCH DIST/DUNDEE/YATES	00783240	607/243-5533	268
Dundee Elem Sch/Dundee/Yates	00783252	607/243-5535	268
Dundee Jr Sr High Sch/Dundee/Yates	10031637	607/243-7912	268
DUNKIRK CITY SCH DIST/DUNKIRK/CHAUTAUQUA	00718465	716/366-9300	37
Dunkirk Elem School 3/Dunkirk/Chautauqua	00718491	716/366-9330	37
Dunkirk Elem School 4/Dunkirk/Chautauqua	00718506	716/366-9340	37
Dunkirk Elem School 5/Dunkirk/Chautauqua	00718518	716/366-4500	37
Dunkirk Elem School 7/Dunkirk/Chautauqua	00718532	716/366-9300	37
Dunkirk High Sch/Dunkirk/Chautauqua	00718489	716/366-9300	37
Dunkirk Middle Sch/Dunkirk/Chautauqua	00718477	716/366-9300	37
Durand Eastman Interm Sch/Rochester/Monroe	01548055	585/339-1350	107
Durhamville Elem Sch/Durhamville/Madison	00731259	315/363-8065	105
Dutch Broadway Elem Sch/Elmont/Nassau	00735401	516/326-5550	118
Dutch Lane Elem Sch/Hicksville/Nassau	00736376	516/733-2361	122
DUTCHESS CO BOCES/POUGHKEEPSIE/DUTCHESS	00722325	845/486-4800	55
Dutchess Day Sch/Millbrook/Dutchess	00722416	845/677-5014	55
Duzine Elem Sch/New Paltz/Ulster	00778104	845/256-4350	243
Dwight Sch/New York/New York	00751352	212/724-6360	144

E

School/City/County	PID	TELEPHONE NUMBER	PAGE
E A Clune Mont School-Ithaca/Ithaca/Tompkins	02993491	607/277-7335	241
E A McAllister Elem Sch/Sherrill/Oneida	00760559	315/829-2520	152
E F Academy New York/Thornwood/Westchester	11545734	914/597-7241	265
E J Russell Elem Sch/Pine Bush/Orange	00764828	845/744-2031	166
E M Baker Sch/Great Neck/Nassau	00735970	516/441-4100	120
Eagle Acad for Young Men-Bronx/Bronx/Bronx	05349631	718/466-8000	18
Eagle Acad Young Men II/Brooklyn/Kings	11103312	718/495-0863	93
Eagle Acad Young Men III/Jamaica/Queens	11560801	718/480-2600	183
Eagle Acad Young Men-Staten IS/Staten Island/Richmond	12045488	718/727-6201	192
Eagle Academy Young Men-Harlem/New York/New York	11924489	212/694-6051	140
Eagle Elem Sch/Delmar/Albany	11132739	518/694-8825	10
Eagle Elem Sch/Medford/Suffolk	00774859	631/687-8150	227
Eagle Hill Middle Sch/Manlius/Onondaga	00761785	315/692-1400	155
Eagle Point Elem Sch/Albany/Albany	00714275	518/475-6825	9
Earl Van Dermuelen High Sch/Prt Jefferson/Suffolk	00774940	631/476-4400	228
Early CH Sch of Rochester 57/Rochester/Monroe	03011527	585/277-0190	111
Early Childhood Sch/Victor/Ontario	05272985	585/924-3252	162

DISTRICT & SCHOOL TELEPHONE INDEX

Market Data Retrieval

School/City/County DISTRICT/CITY/COUNTY	PID	TELEPHONE NUMBER	PAGE
Early Learning Center/Poughkeepsie/Dutchess	11822879	845/451-4721	53
Earth Sch/New York/New York	04457273	212/477-1735	135
East Aurora High Sch/East Aurora/Erie	00723795	716/687-2505	60
East Aurora Middle Sch/East Aurora/Erie	03057363	716/687-2453	60
EAST AURORA UNION FREE SD/ EAST AURORA/ERIE	00723771	716/687-2302	60
East Broadway Elem Sch/Seaford/Nassau	00736869	516/434-7425	123
East Bronx Academy for Future/Bronx/Bronx	05349306	718/861-8641	24
East Brooklyn Ascend CS/Brooklyn/Kings	12367432	347/464-7600	3
East Brooklyn Cmty High Sch/Brooklyn/Kings	11447467	718/927-6880	87
East Coldenham Elem Sch/Newburgh/Orange	00764517	845/457-2400	167
East Elem Sch/Long Beach/Nassau	00736986	516/897-2184	124
East Elmhurst Community Sch/East Elmhurst/Queens	11924037	718/505-6050	184
East Flatbush Ascend CS/Brooklyn/Kings	12367468	347/464-7600	3
EAST GREENBUSH CENTRAL SD/ E GREENBUSH/RENSSELAER	00766773	518/207-2500	190
East Hampton High Sch/East Hampton/Suffolk	00773154	631/329-4130	220
East Hampton Middle Sch/East Hampton/Suffolk	00773166	631/329-4112	220
EAST HAMPTON UNION FREE SD/ EAST HAMPTON/SUFFOLK	00773142	631/329-4100	220
East Harlem Sch-Exodus House/New York/New York	04974049	212/876-8775	144
East Harlem Scholars Acad CS/New York/New York	11722750	212/348-2518	3
East Harlem Scholars Acad CS 2/New York/New York	12234213	212/348-2518	3
East High Sch/East Amherst/Erie	01399115	716/626-8404	64
East Hill Elem Sch/Camillus/Onondaga	00761199	315/487-4648	159
East Hill Elem Sch/Canajoharie/Montgomery	00734744	518/673-6310	115
East Hills Elem Sch/Roslyn HTS/Nassau	00738415	516/801-5300	129
EAST IRONDEQUOIT CTL SCH DIST/ ROCHESTER/MONROE	00731534	585/339-1200	107
East Irondequoit Middle Sch/Rochester/Monroe	03390969	585/339-1400	107
East Islip High Sch/Islip Terrace/Suffolk	00773207	631/224-2006	221
East Islip Middle Sch/Islip Terrace/Suffolk	00773233	631/224-2008	221
EAST ISLIP UNION FREE SD/ ISLIP TERRACE/SUFFOLK	00773180	631/224-2000	220
East Kindergarten Center/Brentwood/Suffolk	02227228	631/434-2525	217
East Lake Elem Sch/Massapequa Pk/Nassau	00737277	516/308-5200	125
East Learning Center/Binghamton/Broome	11435103	607/762-6400	27
East Lower Sch/Rochester/Monroe	12367872	585/288-3130	111
East Meadow High Sch/East Meadow/Nassau	00735190	516/228-5331	118
EAST MEADOW UNION FREE SD/ WESTBURY/NASSAU	00735164	516/478-5730	118
East Middle Sch/Binghamton/Broome	02896013	607/762-8300	27
East Middle Sch/Brentwood/Suffolk	00772241	631/434-2473	217
East Middle Sch/West Seneca/Erie	00725444	716/677-3530	64
East Midwood Hebrew Day Sch/Brooklyn/Kings	01462140	718/253-1555	97
East Moriches Elem Sch/East Moriches/Suffolk	00773283	631/878-0162	221
East Moriches Middle Sch/East Moriches/Suffolk	05352212	631/878-0162	221
EAST MORICHES UNION FREE SD/ EAST MORICHES/SUFFOLK	00773271	631/878-0162	221
East New York ES of Excellence/Brooklyn/Kings	11447431	718/272-6075	88
East New York Family Academy/Brooklyn/Kings	04037366	718/498-5240	88
East New York MS of Excellence/Brooklyn/Kings	11447429	718/257-4061	88
East Northport Middle Sch/E Northport/Suffolk	00774689	631/262-6770	227
East Palmyra Christian Sch/Palmyra/Wayne	01409514	315/597-4400	251
East Quogue Elem Sch/East Quogue/Suffolk	00773300	631/653-5210	221
EAST QUOGUE UNION FREE SD/ EAST QUOGUE/SUFFOLK	00773295	631/653-5210	221
EAST RAMAPO CENTRAL SCH DIST/ SPRING VALLEY/ROCKLAND	00767911	845/577-6000	196
East Ramapo Early Chldhd Ctr/Spring Valley/Rockland	11824827	845/577-6585	196
East River Academy-Rikers/East Elmhurst/Queens	04020090	718/546-6200	185
East Rochester Elem Sch/E Rochester/Monroe	00731637	585/248-6342	107
East Rochester High Sch/E Rochester/Monroe	00731651	585/248-6350	107
EAST ROCHESTER UNION FREE SD/ E ROCHESTER/MONROE	00731625	585/248-6302	107
East Rockaway Jr Sr High Sch/East Rockaway/Nassau	00735308	516/887-8300	118
EAST ROCKAWAY UNION FREE SD/ EAST ROCKAWAY/NASSAU	00735281	516/887-8300	118
East Side Cmty Sch/New York/New York	04368153	212/460-8467	135
East Side Middle Sch/New York/New York	04457728	212/360-0114	135
East Street Elem Sch/Hicksville/Nassau	04811019	516/733-2321	122
East Syracuse Elem Sch/East Syracuse/Onondaga	00761319	315/434-3850	155
East Syracuse Minoa Central HS/East Syracuse/Onondaga	00761292	315/434-3300	155
EAST SYRACUSE MINOA CTL SD/ EAST SYRACUSE/ONONDAGA	00761278	315/434-3000	154
East Upper Sch/Rochester/Monroe	00732552	585/288-3130	111
East View Elem Sch/Olean/Cattaraugus	00717605	716/375-8920	32
East Village Cmty Sch/New York/New York	04457314	212/982-0682	135
East Williamsburg Scholars/Brooklyn/Kings	04487981	718/387-2800	83
EAST WILLISTON UNION FREE SD/ OLD WESTBURY/NASSAU	00735322	516/333-1630	118
East Woods Sch/Oyster Bay/Nassau	00739469	516/922-4400	133
East-West Sch of Int'l Studies/Flushing/Queens	10026905	718/353-0009	178
Eastchester High Sch/Eastchester/Westchester	00780016	914/793-6103	254
Eastchester Middle Sch/Eastchester/Westchester	00780004	914/793-6130	254
EASTCHESTER UNION FREE SD/ EASTCHESTER/WESTCHESTER	00779976	914/793-6130	254
Eastern Monroe Career Center/Fairport/Monroe	00733556	585/377-4660	106
EASTERN SUFFOLK BOCES/PATCHOGUE/ SUFFOLK	00776560	631/289-2200	235
Eastplain Sch/N Massapequa/Nassau	00737942	516/531-9653	127
Eastport Elem Sch/Eastport/Suffolk	05221352	631/801-3170	221
Eastport South Manor Jr Sr HS/Manorville/Suffolk	00773324	631/801-3250	221
EASTPORT-SOUTH MANOR CTRL SD/ MANORVILLE/SUFFOLK	00775853	631/801-3013	221
Eastridge High Sch/Rochester/Monroe	00731560	585/339-1450	107
Eastview Middle Sch/White Plains/Westchester	04453136	914/422-2223	263
Ebbets Field Middle Sch/Brooklyn/Kings	10008783	718/941-5097	86
EBC HS Pub Service Bushwick/Brooklyn/Kings	04037873	718/452-3440	93
Ebenezer Preparatory Sch/Brooklyn/Kings	02984866	718/629-4231	97
Ecole Internationale New York/New York/New York	12173932	646/410-2238	144
Ed Smith PK-8 Sch/Syracuse/Onondaga	00762313	315/435-4650	158
EDEN CENTRAL SCH DIST/EDEN/ERIE	00723836	716/992-3630	60
Eden Elem Sch/Eden/Erie	00723850	716/992-3610	60
Eden II Sch-Autistic Chldrn/Staten Island/Richmond	02163892	718/816-1422	195
Eden Middle High Sch/Eden/Erie	00723862	716/992-3600	60
Edenwald Sch/Pleasantville/Westchester	11823366	914/769-0456	258
Edge Academy/Cheektowaga/Erie	12371768	716/558-5050	55
Edgemont Jr Sr High Sch/Scarsdale/Westchester	00780078	914/725-1500	254
EDGEMONT UNION FREE SCH DIST/ SCARSDALE/WESTCHESTER	00780066	914/472-7768	254
Edgewood Elem Sch/Scarsdale/Westchester	00781814	914/721-2700	262
Edinburg Common Sch/Northville/Saratoga	00769622	518/863-8412	201
EDINBURG COMMON SCH DIST/ NORTHVILLE/SARATOGA	00769610	518/863-8412	200
Edison Career & Tech High Sch/Rochester/Monroe	11559967	585/324-9700	111
Edith L Slocum Elem Sch/Ronkonkoma/Suffolk	00772904	631/467-6040	219
Edmeston Central Sch/Edmeston/Otsego	00766034	607/965-8931	173
EDMESTON CTL SCH DIST/EDMESTON/ OTSEGO	00766022	607/965-8931	173
Edmund O'Neal MS of Excellence/Albany/Albany	12105600	518/475-6600	9
Edmund W Miles Middle Sch/Amityville/Suffolk	00771900	631/565-6200	216
Edna Louise Spear Elem Sch/Prt Jefferson/Suffolk	00774952	631/791-4300	228
Edson Elem Sch/Kingston/Ulster	00777875	845/338-6990	242
Edward A Reynolds West Side HS/New York/New York	01552305	212/678-7300	138
Edward J Arthur Elem Sch/Athens/Greene	00729220	518/731-1750	75
Edward J Bosti Elem Sch/Bohemia/Suffolk	00772916	631/244-2291	219
Edward J Milliken Tech Center/Oakdale/Suffolk	00776584	631/244-5806	216

New York School Directory
DISTRICT & SCHOOL TELEPHONE INDEX

School/City/County DISTRICT/CITY/COUNTY	PID	TELEPHONE NUMBER	PAGE
Edward R Andrews Elem Sch/Morrisville/Madison	00731223	315/684-9288	105
Edward R Crosby Elem Sch/Lake Katrine/Ulster	00777942	845/382-2633	242
Edward R Murrow High Sch/Brooklyn/Kings	00740913	718/258-9283	91
Edward Town Middle Sch/Sanborn/Niagara	00759512	716/215-3150	148
Edward Williams Elem Sch/Mount Vernon/Westchester	00780999	914/665-5070	258
Edwards-Knox Central Sch/Hermon/St Lawrence	00768616	315/562-8131	210
EDWARDS-KNOX CENTRAL SCH DIST/HERMON/ST LAWRENCE	00768604	315/562-8131	210
Eggert Road Elem Sch/Orchard Park/Erie	00725028	716/209-6215	63
El Ber Islamic Sch/Long Is City/Queens	11223405	718/274-9060	187
El Puente Acad Peace Soc Just/Brooklyn/Kings	04037483	718/387-1125	83
Elba Central Sch/Elba/Genesee	00728977	585/757-9967	73
ELBA CENTRAL SCH DIST/ELBA/GENESEE	00728965	585/757-9967	73
Elbridge Elem Sch/Elbridge/Onondaga	00761498	315/689-8540	156
Eldorado Elem Sch/Chestnut RDG/Rockland	00767935	845/577-6150	196
ELDRED CENTRAL SCH DIST/ELDRED/SULLIVAN	00776730	845/456-1100	236
Eldred Jr Sr High Sch/Eldred/Sullivan	00776742	845/456-1100	236
Eleanor Roosevelt High Sch/New York/New York	05098624	212/772-1220	135
Elijah Stroud Middle Sch/Brooklyn/Kings	10008795	718/638-3067	86
Elizabeth Cady Stanton ES/Seneca Falls/Seneca	00771065	315/568-5834	208
Elizabth Seton Chldrn Sch-WP/White Plains/Westchester	01795844	914/597-4071	265
Ella Baker Sch/New York/New York	04489795	212/717-8809	135
ELLENVILLE CENTRAL SCH DIST/ELLENVILLE/ULSTER	00777760	845/647-0200	241
Ellenville Elem Sch/Ellenville/Ulster	04755958	845/647-0131	242
Ellenville High Sch/Ellenville/Ulster	00777772	845/647-0123	242
Ellenville Middle Sch/Ellenville/Ulster	04755946	845/647-0126	242
Ellicott Road Elem Sch/Orchard Park/Erie	00725030	716/209-6278	63
ELLICOTTVILLE CENTRAL SCH DIST/ELLICOTTVILLE/CATTARAUGUS	00717394	716/699-2316	31
Ellicottville Sch/Ellicottville/Cattaraugus	00717411	716/699-2316	31
Ellis B Hyde Elem Sch/Dansville/Livingston	00730750	585/335-4030	102
Ellis Preparatory Academy/Bronx/Bronx	11824413	718/220-1889	20
Elm Cmty Charter Sch/Glendale/Queens	12310398	646/886-0234	3
Elm Drive Elem Sch/Millbrook/Dutchess	00721802	845/677-4225	52
Elm Street Academy/Cuba/Allegany	12241319	585/968-1923	13
Elm Street Elem Sch/Waverly/Tioga	00777291	607/565-8186	239
Elma Primary Sch/Elma/Erie	03400459	716/652-3000	61
Elmcrest Children's Center/Syracuse/Onondaga	05078363	315/435-6244	158
Elmcrest Elem Sch/Liverpool/Onondaga	00761632	315/453-1252	156
ELMIRA CITY SCH DIST/ELMIRA/CHEMUNG	00719158	607/735-3000	40
ELMIRA HEIGHTS CTL SCH DIST/ELMIRA HGTS/CHEMUNG	00719366	607/734-7114	40
Elmira High Sch/Elmira/Chemung	00719330	607/735-3200	40
Elmont Memorial Jr Sr High Sch/Elmont/Nassau	00735578	516/488-9200	129
ELMONT UNION FREE SCH DIST/ELMONT/NASSAU	00735360	516/326-5500	118
ELMSFORD UNION FREE SD/ELMSFORD/WESTCHESTER	00780107	914/592-8440	255
Elmwood Elem Sch/Monsey/Rockland	00767947	845/577-6160	196
Elmwood Franklin Sch/Buffalo/Erie	00725834	716/877-5035	66
Elmwood Village CS-Days Park/Buffalo/Erie	10026682	716/886-4581	3
Elmwood Village CS-Hertel/Buffalo/Erie	12234378	716/424-0555	3
Elsmere Elem Sch/Delmar/Albany	00714419	518/439-4996	10
Eltingville Lutheran Sch/Staten Island/Richmond	00751209	718/356-7811	195
Elwood Middle Sch/Greenlawn/Suffolk	00773350	631/266-5420	221
ELWOOD UNION FREE SCH DIST/GREENLAWN/SUFFOLK	00773336	631/266-5400	221
Elwood-John Glenn High Sch/Elwood/Suffolk	00773374	631/266-5410	221
Emanuel Lutheran Sch/Patchogue/Suffolk	00776613	631/758-2250	234
Ember Sch for Mindful Educ CS/Brooklyn/Kings	11714947	718/285-3787	86
Emblaze Academy Charter Sch/Bronx/Bronx	12310403	917/415-6547	3
Emerson Dillon Middle Sch/Phoenix/Oswego	00765834	315/695-1521	172
Emerson Sch/Jamaica/Queens	11924087	718/657-4801	182
Emily Howland Elem Sch/Aurora/Cayuga	00718104	315/364-7098	35
Emma C Chase Elem Sch/Wurtsboro/Sullivan	00776871	845/888-2471	237
Emma E Sherman Elem Sch/Henrietta/Monroe	00733219	585/359-5490	112
Emma Lazarus High Sch/New York/New York	11447869	212/925-5017	135
Emma Willard Sch/Troy/Rensselaer	00767284	518/833-1300	192
Emmanuel Baptist Academy/Penn Yan/Yates	01795894	315/536-8278	268
Emmanuel Childrens Mission Sch/Mount Vernon/Westchester	11232066	914/664-1810	265
Emmet Belknap Intermediate Sch/Lockport/Niagara	00759108	716/478-4550	147
Emolior Academy/Bronx/Bronx	11103219	718/842-2670	24
Empower Childen's Academy/Niagara Falls/Niagara	01794515	716/297-1478	149
Enders Road Elem Sch/Manlius/Onondaga	00761797	315/692-1500	155
Energy Tech High Sch/Astoria/Queens	11924051	718/472-0536	184
Enfield Elem Sch/Ithaca/Tompkins	00777538	607/274-2221	240
English Village Elem Sch/Rochester/Monroe	00731936	585/966-3800	109
Enrico Fermi Sch Perf Arts/Yonkers/Westchester	00782260	914/376-8460	263
Enrico Fermi School 17/Rochester/Monroe	00732849	585/436-2560	111
Enterprise Bus & Tech HS/Brooklyn/Kings	04487993	718/387-2800	83
Enterprise Charter Sch/Buffalo/Erie	05278850	716/855-2114	57
Epic High School-North/S Richmond HI/Queens	12036293	718/570-8230	180
Epic High School-South/S Ozone Park/Queens	12036308	718/845-1290	180
Epiphany Lutheran Sch/Brooklyn/Kings	01834696	718/773-7200	97
Equality Charter High Sch/Bronx/Bronx	12179596	718/159-9597	22
Equality Charter Middle Sch/Bronx/Bronx	11447546	718/517-3169	22
Erasmus Campus YABC/Brooklyn/Kings	11928801	718/564-2590	86
ERIE 1 BOCES/WEST SENECA/ERIE	00725688	716/821-7000	67
ERIE 2 CHAUTAUQUA-CATTA BOCES/ANGOLA/ERIE	00719134	716/549-4454	67
Ernest C Myer Elem Sch/Hurley/Ulster	00777904	845/331-6905	242
Ernie Davis Academy/Elmira/Chemung	00719225	607/735-3100	40
Errick Road Elem Sch/N Tonawanda/Niagara	00759524	716/215-3240	148
Erwin Valley Elem Sch/Painted Post/Steuben	00771455	607/936-6514	214
Esmt IS 190/Bronx/Bronx	05097773	718/620-9423	24
Esperanza Preparatory Academy/New York/New York	11130195	212/722-6507	139
Essex Street Academy/New York/New York	05348936	212/475-4773	135
Ethel K Fyle Elem Sch/Rochester/Monroe	00733221	585/359-5430	112
Ethical Culture Sch/New York/New York	00751388	212/712-6220	144
Eugene Auer Memorial Elem Sch/Lake Grove/Suffolk	00774354	631/285-8500	225
Eugene Brooks Intermediate Sch/Amenia/Dutchess	05091535	845/373-4114	54
Eugenio Maria De Hostos CS HS/Rochester/Monroe	04924044	585/697-7115	3
Eugenio Maria De Hostos K-8 CS/Rochester/Monroe	11935696	585/544-6170	3
Eugenio Maria De Hostos Sch/Yonkers/Westchester	00782557	914/376-8430	263
Evangel Christian Sch/Long Is City/Queens	02989012	718/937-9600	187
Evans Mills Primary Sch/Evans Mills/Jefferson	00730164	315/629-4331	80
Evans Park Elem Sch/Pearl River/Rockland	00767765	845/620-3950	197
EVANS-BRANT CENTRAL SCH DIST/ANGOLA/ERIE	00724737	716/926-2201	60
Evergreen Charter Sch/Hempstead/Nassau	11457565	516/292-2060	3
Evergreen MS-Urban Exploration/Brooklyn/Kings	11821746	718/455-0180	93
Excellence Boys Charter Sch/Brooklyn/Kings	05352597	718/638-1830	3
Excellence Girls CS Elem Acad/Brooklyn/Kings	11468174	718/638-1875	3
Excelsior Preparatory High Sch/Sprngfld GDNS/Queens	05349497	718/525-6507	183
Eximius Clg Prep Academy/Bronx/Bronx	10008587	718/992-7154	19
Expeditionary Learning Mid Sch/Syracuse/Onondaga	11449300	315/435-6416	158
Expeditionary Sch Cmty Leaders/Brooklyn/Kings	10913798	718/333-7700	91
Exploration Elem CS Sci & Tech/Rochester/Monroe	12234380	585/694-5234	3
Explorations Academy/Bronx/Bronx	10008575	718/893-6173	24
Explore Charter Sch/Brooklyn/Kings	05096157	718/703-4484	3
Explore Empower Chtr Sch 742/Brooklyn/Kings	11821801	718/771-2090	3
Explore Exceed Charter Sch/Brooklyn/Kings	11817290	718/989-6702	3
Explore Excel Charter Sch/Brooklyn/Kings	11722669	718/303-3245	3
Ezra Academy/Forest Hills/Queens	00751223	718/263-5500	187

F

School/City/County	PID	TELEPHONE NUMBER	PAGE
F D Roosevelt High Sch/Hyde Park/Dutchess	00721682	845/229-4020	52

DISTRICT & SCHOOL TELEPHONE INDEX

Market Data Retrieval

School/City/County DISTRICT/CITY/COUNTY	PID	TELEPHONE	PAGE NUMBER
F Donald Myers Education Ctr/Saratoga Spgs/Saratoga	04934544	518/581-3600	200
F E Bellows Elem Sch/Mamaroneck/Westchester	00781759	914/777-4602	261
F E Smith Interm Sch/Cortland/Cortland	00720810	607/758-4180	47
F S Banford Elem Sch/Canton/St Lawrence	00768379	315/386-8561	209
FABIUS POMPEY CENTRAL SD/ FABIUS/ONONDAGA	00761371	315/683-5301	155
Fabius-Pompey Elem Sch/Fabius/Onondaga	00761395	315/683-5857	155
Fabius-Pompey Middle High Sch/Fabius/Onondaga	00761383	315/683-5811	155
Fairbanks Road Elem Sch/Churchville/Monroe	00731522	585/293-4543	107
Fairfield Elem Sch/Massapequa/Nassau	00737289	516/308-5300	125
Fairgrieve Elem Sch/Fulton/Oswego	00765509	315/593-5550	171
Fairley Elem Sch/Hannibal/Oswego	00765626	315/564-8110	171
Fairmont Neighborhood Sch/Bronx/Bronx	11924324	718/860-5210	24
FAIRPORT CTL SCH DIST/FAIRPORT/MONROE	00731663	585/421-2000	108
Fairport High Sch/Fairport/Monroe	00731699	585/421-2100	108
Faith Bible Academy/Sprakers/Montgomery	02162082	518/234-3497	116
Faith Christian Academy/Bronx/Bronx	05160124	718/881-1085	26
Faith Christian Academy/Poughkeepsie/Dutchess	02827787	845/462-0266	55
Faith Christian Sch/Bridgewater/Oneida	04975158	315/822-5233	154
Faith Fellowship Christian Sch/Watertown/Jefferson	03195434	315/782-9342	82
Faith Heritage Sch/Syracuse/Onondaga	01409356	315/469-7777	160
FALCONER CENTRAL SCH DIST/ FALCONER/CHAUTAUQUA	00718544	716/665-6624	37
Falconer Middle Sr High Sch/Falconer/Chautauqua	01552173	716/665-6624	37
Fall Creek Elem Sch/Ithaca/Tompkins	00777540	607/274-2214	240
FALLSBURG CENTRAL SCH DIST/ FALLSBURG/SULLIVAN	00776754	845/434-5884	236
Fallsburg Junior Senior HS/Fallsburg/Sullivan	00776778	845/434-6800	236
Family Life Acad Charter Sch I/Bronx/Bronx	04948105	718/410-8100	4
Family Life Academy CS II/Bronx/Bronx	11824425	718/665-2805	4
Family Life Academy CS III/Bronx/Bronx	12028351	718/585-6580	4
Family Sch/Bronx/Bronx	11447596	718/538-3266	19
Family Sch/New York/New York	01560390	212/688-5950	144
Family School 32/Yonkers/Westchester	04192863	914/376-8595	263
Fannie Lou Hamer Freedom HS/Bronx/Bronx	04290960	718/861-0521	24
Fannie Lou Hamer Middle Sch/Bronx/Bronx	05349239	718/319-7270	24
Farmingdale Senior High Sch/Farmingdale/Nassau	00735463	516/434-5210	119
FARMINGDALE UNION FREE SD/ FARMINGDALE/NASSAU	00735437	516/434-5000	119
Farnsworth Middle Sch/Guilderland/Albany	00714598	518/456-6010	11
Farragut Middle Sch/Hastings HDSN/Westchester	00780377	914/478-6230	256
Fassett Elem Sch/Elmira/Chemung	10904175	607/735-3900	40
Fayette Mennonite Sch/Waterloo/Seneca	04975110	315/277-0454	208
Fayetteville Elem Sch/Fayetteville/Onondaga	00761802	315/692-1600	155
FAYETTEVILLE-MANLIUS CTL SD/ MANLIUS/ONONDAGA	00761773	315/692-1234	155
Fayetteville-Manlius High Sch/Manlius/Onondaga	00761814	315/692-1900	155
Fdny High School Fire & Safety/Brooklyn/Kings	05348845	718/922-0389	88
Fei Tian Academy of the Arts/Cuddebackvlle/Orange	11459202	845/754-4226	168
Felix Festa Middle Sch/West Nyack/Rockland	00767349	845/624-3970	196
Fieldston Lower Sch/Bronx/Bronx	02850148	718/329-7310	26
Fieldston Middle Upper Sch/Bronx/Bronx	01463261	718/329-7300	26
Fieldstone Middle Sch/Thiells/Rockland	05343510	845/942-7900	197
Fifth Avenue Elem Sch/E Northport/Suffolk	00774691	631/262-6820	227
Fifth Avenue Sch/Bay Shore/Suffolk	00772033	631/968-1140	217
Fillmore Central Sch/Fillmore/Allegany	00716211	585/567-2251	14
FILLMORE CENTRAL SCH DIST/ FILLMORE/ALLEGANY	00716194	585/567-2251	14
Finger Lakes Christian Sch/Seneca Falls/Seneca	03413509	315/568-2216	209
Finger Lakes Secondary Sch/Rushville/Yates	04026331	585/554-6492	268
Finger Lakes Tech & Career Ctr/Stanley/Ontario	01529645	585/526-6471	161
Finn Academy-Elmira Chtr Sch/Elmira/Chemung	12106460	607/737-8040	4
Fiorello H Laguardia High Sch/New York/New York	00741096	212/496-0700	138
FIRE ISLAND UNION FREE SD/ OCEAN BEACH/SUFFOLK	00774770	631/583-5626	222
Fishers Island Sch/Fishers Isle/Suffolk	00773403	631/788-7444	222
FISHERS ISLAND UNION FREE SD/ FISHERS ISLE/SUFFOLK	00773398	631/788-7444	222
Fishkill Elem Sch/Fishkill/Dutchess	00722143	845/897-6780	54
Fishkill Plains Elem Sch/Wappingers Fl/Dutchess	00722155	845/227-1770	54
Fitzhugh Park Elem Sch/Oswego/Oswego	00765729	315/341-2400	171
Fjc Southeast Elem Sch/Brentwood/Suffolk	00772344	631/434-2265	217
Flanders Elem Sch/Malone/Franklin	00728226	518/483-7803	70
Flatbush SDA Sch/Brooklyn/Kings	02163103	718/922-6390	97
Fleetwood Elem Sch/Chestnut RDG/Rockland	00767959	845/577-6170	196
Fletcher Elem Sch/Tonawanda/Erie	00725298	716/694-7694	64
Flexschool-Bronxville/Bronxville/Westchester	12376641	914/704-3334	265
Floral Park Bellerose Elem Sch/Floral Park/Nassau	00735530	516/434-2750	119
FLORAL PARK BELLEROSE SCH DIST/ FLORAL PARK/NASSAU	00735528	516/434-2725	119
Floral Park Mem Jr Sr High Sch/Floral Park/Nassau	00735580	516/488-9300	129
Florence Brasser Elem Sch/Rochester/Monroe	00731778	585/247-1880	108
Florence S Brown Pre-K Center/Rochester/Monroe	02857536	585/288-2410	111
FLORIDA UNION FREE SCH DIST/ FLORIDA/ORANGE	00764907	845/651-3095	164
Flower City School 54/Rochester/Monroe	03400851	585/254-2080	111
Flower Hill Primary Sch/Huntington/Suffolk	00773790	631/673-2050	223
Floyd L Bell Elem Sch/Kirkwood/Broome	00717277	607/775-2730	30
Floyd S Winslow Elem Sch/Henrietta/Monroe	00733233	585/359-5090	112
Flushing Christian Sch/Flushing/Queens	00751247	718/445-3533	187
Flushing High Sch/Flushing/Queens	00740987	718/888-7500	178
Flushing International HS/Flushing/Queens	05349485	718/463-2348	178
Flushing YABC/Flushing/Queens	11928875	718/888-7500	178
Followers of Jesus Sch/Brooklyn/Kings	11230501	718/235-5493	97
Fonda Fultonville Central Sch/Fonda/Montgomery	00734794	518/853-4415	115
FONDA FULTONVILLE CENTRAL SD/ FONDA/MONTGOMERY	00734770	518/853-4415	115
Fontbonne Hall Academy/Brooklyn/Kings	00752978	718/748-2244	95
Food and Finance High Sch/New York/New York	05348900	212/586-2943	136
Fordham High School of Arts/Bronx/Bronx	05098569	718/733-4656	20
Fordham Leadership Academy/Bronx/Bronx	05098571	718/733-5024	20
Fordham Preparatory Sch/Bronx/Bronx	00755401	718/367-7500	25
Forest Ave Elem Sch/West Babylon/Suffolk	00776120	631/376-7300	233
Forest Brook Elem Sch/Smithtown/Suffolk	04036051	631/265-3265	223
Forest Elem Sch/Williamsville/Erie	00725585	716/626-9800	64
Forest Hills High Sch/Forest Hills/Queens	00741008	718/268-3137	182
Forest Hills Montessori Sch/Forest Hills/Queens	01794890	718/275-0173	187
Forest Lake Elem Sch/Wantagh/Nassau	00739005	516/679-6470	131
Forest Park Elem Sch/Albany/Albany	00714861	518/869-3006	12
Forest Road Elem Sch/Valley Stream/Nassau	00738960	516/434-3800	131
FORESTVILLE CENTRAL SCH DIST/ FORESTVILLE/CHAUTAUQUA	00718611	716/965-2742	37
Forestville Elem Sch/Forestville/Chautauqua	00718635	716/965-2742	37
Forestville Middle High Sch/Forestville/Chautauqua	00718623	716/965-2711	37
Fork Lane Elem Sch/Hicksville/Nassau	00736390	516/733-2341	122
Forsyth Satellite Acad/New York/New York	11924386	212/677-8900	135
FORT ANN CENTRAL SCH DIST/ FORT ANN/WASHINGTON	00778831	518/639-5594	247
Fort Ann Elem Sch/Fort Ann/Washington	00778843	518/639-5594	247
Fort Ann Jr Sr High Sch/Fort Ann/Washington	12238611	518/639-5594	247
Fort Montgomery Elem Sch/Ft Montgomery/Orange	03387637	845/446-1008	164
Forte Prep Academy/East Elmhurst/Queens	12234122	347/709-1197	4
Forts Ferry Elem Sch/Latham/Albany	00714691	518/785-9203	11
Fostertown ETC Magnet Sch/Newburgh/Orange	00764610	845/568-6425	166
Four Winds Learning Center/Katonah/Westchester	03398777	914/763-8151	265
Fox Lane High Sch/Bedford/Westchester	00780810	914/241-6085	252
Fox Lane Middle Sch/Bedford/Westchester	00780822	914/241-6143	252
Fox Meadow Elem Sch/Scarsdale/Westchester	00781826	914/721-2720	262
FR Vincent Capodanno Cath Acad/Staten Island/Richmond	00755566	718/447-1195	194
Francis J O'Neill Elem Sch/Central Islip/Suffolk	00772485	631/348-5060	219

New York School Directory

DISTRICT & SCHOOL TELEPHONE INDEX

School/City/County DISTRICT/CITY/COUNTY	PID	TELEPHONE NUMBER	PAGE
Francis L Stevens Elem Sch/Ballston Lake/Saratoga	00769529	518/399-9141	200
Francis Lewis High Sch/Fresh Meadows/Queens	00741022	718/281-8200	179
Francis Parker School 23/Rochester/Monroe	00732899	585/473-5099	111
Francis X Hegarty Elem Sch/Island Park/Nassau	00736481	516/434-2670	122
Frank Fowler Dow School 52/Rochester/Monroe	00733128	585/482-9614	111
Frank G Lindsey Elem Sch/Montrose/Westchester	00780456	914/257-5500	256
Frank J Carasiti Elem Sch/Rocky Point/Suffolk	01520558	631/744-1601	228
Frank M Knight Elem Sch/Seneca Falls/Seneca	00771077	315/568-5500	208
Frank McCourt High Sch/New York/New York	11561271	212/362-2015	138
Frank P Long Intermediate Sch/Bellport/Suffolk	00772174	631/730-1725	231
Frank Sinatra HS of the Arts/Astoria/Queens	04947735	718/361-9920	184
FRANKFORT-SCHUYLER CTL SD/FRANKFORT/HERKIMER	00729531	315/894-5083	77
Frankfort-Schuyler Elem Sch/Frankfort/Herkimer	00729567	315/895-7491	77
Frankfort-Schuyler Jr Sr HS/Frankfort/Herkimer	00729543	315/895-7461	77
Franklin Academy High Sch/Malone/Franklin	00728238	518/483-7807	70
Franklin Ave Elem Sch/Pearl River/Rockland	00767777	845/620-3965	197
Franklin Central Sch/Franklin/Delaware	00721101	607/829-3551	49
FRANKLIN CENTRAL SCH DIST/FRANKLIN/DELAWARE	00721096	607/829-3551	49
Franklin D Roosevelt High Sch/Brooklyn/Kings	00740951	718/621-8800	89
Franklin D Roosevelt YABC/Brooklyn/Kings	11928813	718/256-1346	89
Franklin Early Childhood Ctr/Hewlett/Nassau	00736285	516/792-4600	121
Franklin K Lane Campus YABC/Brooklyn/Kings	11928825	646/784-6841	88
Franklin Magnet Elem Sch/Syracuse/Onondaga	00762349	315/435-4550	158
FRANKLIN SQUARE UNION FREE SD/FRANKLIN SQ/NASSAU	00735621	516/481-4100	119
FRANKLIN-ESSEX-HAMILTON BOCES/MALONE/FRANKLIN	00728422	518/483-6420	71
FRANKLINVILLE CTL SCH DIST/FRANKLINVILLE/CATTARAUGUS	00717423	716/676-8000	31
Franklinville Elem Sch/Franklinville/Cattaraugus	00717435	716/676-8020	32
Franklinville Jr Sr High Sch/Franklinville/Cattaraugus	00717447	716/676-8060	32
Franklyn S Barry Primary Sch/Cortland/Cortland	00720822	607/758-4150	47
Franziska Racker Center/Ithaca/Tompkins	01795624	607/272-5891	241
Frazer K-8 Sch/Syracuse/Onondaga	00762351	315/435-4555	158
Fred W Hill Elem Sch/Brockport/Monroe	03051802	585/637-1850	107
Frederick Carder Elem Sch/Corning/Steuben	00771479	607/962-2454	214
Frederick Douglass Acad VI HS/Far Rockaway/Queens	05348792	718/471-2154	180
Frederick Douglass Acad VII HS/Brooklyn/Kings	05348807	718/485-3789	93
Frederick Douglass Acad VIII/Brooklyn/Kings	10026670	718/348-2465	88
Frederick Douglass Academy/New York/New York	00742600	212/491-4107	140
Frederick Douglass Academy II/New York/New York	04923040	212/865-9260	138
Frederick Douglass Academy III/Bronx/Bronx	05349174	718/538-9726	19
Frederick Douglass Academy V/Bronx/Bronx	05349409	718/561-1617	24
FREDONIA CENTRAL SCH DIST/FREDONIA/CHAUTAUQUA	00718647	716/679-1581	37
Fredonia Elem Sch/Fredonia/Chautauqua	00718661	716/679-1581	38
Fredonia Middle Sch/Fredonia/Chautauqua	00718685	716/679-1581	38
Fredonia Senior High Sch/Fredonia/Chautauqua	00718673	716/679-1581	38
Freeport Christian Academy/Freeport/Nassau	12314643	516/546-2020	133
Freeport High Sch/Freeport/Nassau	00735724	516/867-5300	120
FREEPORT PUBLIC SCH DIST/FREEPORT/NASSAU	00735671	516/867-5200	119
Freeville Elem Sch/Freeville/Tompkins	02105280	607/844-8694	240
Fremont Elem Sch/East Syracuse/Onondaga	00761307	315/434-3480	155
French American Sch of NY-Elem/Larchmont/Westchester	03044720	914/250-0469	265
French American Sch of NY-Sec/Mamaroneck/Westchester	05256515	914/250-0451	265
French Road Elem Sch/Rochester/Monroe	00731376	585/242-5140	106
Freshman Center/Brentwood/Suffolk	12039116	631/434-2541	217
FREWSBURG CENTRAL SCH DIST/FREWSBURG/CHAUTAUQUA	00718702	716/569-7000	38
Frewsburg Jr Sr High Sch/Frewsburg/Chautauqua	00718714	716/569-7055	38
Fricano Primary Sch/Lockport/Niagara	03321384	716/210-2100	149
Friends Academy/Locust Valley/Nassau	00739433	516/676-0393	133
Friends Seminary/New York/New York	00751534	212/979-5030	144
Friendship Central Sch/Friendship/Allegany	00716247	585/973-3311	15
FRIENDSHIP CENTRAL SCH DIST/FRIENDSHIP/ALLEGANY	00716223	585/973-3311	15
Front Street Sch/Hempstead/Nassau	11928150	516/434-4550	121
Frontenac SDA Elem Sch/Union Springs/Cayuga	01460520	315/889-5094	35
Frontier Central High Sch/Hamburg/Erie	00723989	716/926-1720	61
FRONTIER CTL SCH DIST/HAMBURG/ERIE	00723915	716/926-1700	60
Frontier Middle Sch/Hamburg/Erie	00723927	716/926-1730	61
Ft Edward Elem Sch/Fort Edward/Washington	00778867	518/747-4594	247
Ft Edward Middle High Sch/Fort Edward/Washington	03391468	518/747-4529	247
FT EDWARD UNION FREE SCH DIST/FORT EDWARD/WASHINGTON	00778855	518/747-4529	247
Ft Greene Prep Academy/Brooklyn/Kings	11561130	718/254-9401	82
Ft Hamilton High Sch/Brooklyn/Kings	00741010	718/748-1537	90
FT PLAIN CENTRAL SCH DIST/FORT PLAIN/MONTGOMERY	00734811	518/993-4000	115
Ft Plain High Sch/Fort Plain/Montgomery	00734835	518/993-4433	115
Ft Salonga Elem Sch/Northport/Suffolk	00773958	631/269-3365	224
Fuentes Sch of Sci & Discovery/Bronx/Bronx	05274646	718/601-2632	20
Fulmar Road Elem Sch/Mahopac/Putnam	00766498	845/628-0440	176
FULTON CITY SCH DIST/FULTON/OSWEGO	00765482	315/593-5500	170
Fulton Junior High Sch/Fulton/Oswego	00765523	315/593-5440	171
Furnace Woods Elem Sch/Cortlandt MNR/Westchester	00780468	914/257-5600	256
Fusion Academy-Brooklyn/Brooklyn/Kings	12308668	718/522-3286	97
Fusion Academy-Long Island/Woodbury/Nassau	11929324	516/364-5414	133
Fusion Academy-Park Avenue/New York/New York	11929283	212/326-9522	144
Fusion Academy-Upper West Side/New York/New York	12308670	212/362-1014	144
Fusion Academy-Westchester/White Plains/Westchester	11929312	914/285-9036	265
Future Leaders Institute CS/New York/New York	05274634	212/678-2868	138

G

School/City/County	PID	TELEPHONE NUMBER	PAGE
G L Priess Primary Sch/Eden/Erie	03391042	716/992-3638	60
G R Claps Career & Tech Ctr/Levittown/Nassau	01813408	516/520-8330	123
G Ray Bodley High Sch/Fulton/Oswego	00765535	315/593-5400	171
G W Carver HS for Science/Sprngfld GDNS/Queens	05349502	718/525-6439	183
G W Krieger Elem Sch/Poughkeepsie/Dutchess	00721929	845/451-4661	53
Gail N Chapman Elem Sch/Randolph/Cattaraugus	00717760	716/358-7030	33
GALWAY CENTRAL SCH DIST/GALWAY/SARATOGA	00769634	518/882-1033	201
Galway Jr Sr High Sch/Galway/Saratoga	00769646	518/882-1221	201
Gams Tech Magnet Sch/Newburgh/Orange	00764634	845/563-8450	166
Gan Yisroel Sch/Brooklyn/Kings	11229485	718/853-9853	97
GANANDA CENTRAL SCH DIST/WALWORTH/WAYNE	02205490	315/986-3521	249
Gananda Middle Sch/Walworth/Wayne	04846064	315/986-3521	249
Gansevoort Elem Sch/Rome/Oneida	00760389	315/334-5180	151
Garden City Middle Sch/Garden City/Nassau	00735762	516/478-3000	120
Garden City Park Elem Sch/New Hyde Park/Nassau	00737552	516/434-2390	126
GARDEN CITY SCH DIST/GARDEN CITY/NASSAU	00735750	516/478-1000	120
Garden City Senior High Sch/Garden City/Nassau	00735774	516/478-2000	120
Garden of Lrng & Discovery PK/Bronx/Bronx	12367470	718/583-8975	19
Garden Sch/Jackson HTS/Queens	00752734	718/335-6363	187
Gardiner Manor Sch/Bay Shore/Suffolk	00772045	631/968-1150	217
Gardiners Avenue Elem Sch/Levittown/Nassau	00736780	516/434-7450	123
Gardner Dickinson Elem Sch/Troy/Rensselaer	00767246	518/283-4600	192
Gardner Road Elem Sch/Horseheads/Chemung	00719471	607/739-6347	41
Gardnertown Fund Mag Sch/Newburgh/Orange	00764622	845/568-6400	166
Garrison Elem Sch/Garrison/Putnam	00766436	845/424-3689	175

DISTRICT & SCHOOL TELEPHONE INDEX

Market Data Retrieval

School/City/County DISTRICT/CITY/COUNTY	PID	TELEPHONE	PAGE NUMBER
GARRISON UNION FREE SCH DIST/ GARRISON/PUTNAM	00766424	845/424-3689	175
Garvey Sch/Bronx/Bronx	12141616	718/320-3902	26
Gary D Bixhorn Tech Center/Bellport/ Suffolk	00776572	631/286-6500	216
Gaskill Preparatory Sch/Niagara Falls/ Niagara	00759275	716/278-5820	147
GATES CHILI CENTRAL SCH DIST/ ROCHESTER/MONROE	00731766	585/247-5050	108
Gates Chili High Sch/Rochester/Monroe	00731792	585/247-5050	108
Gates Chili Middle Sch/Rochester/Monroe	00731780	585/247-5050	108
Gateway Academy/Staten Island/Richmond	04974116	718/966-8695	195
Gateway City Academy/Brooklyn/Kings	04974518	718/921-3737	97
Gateway-Longview-Lynde Sch/Williamsville/ Erie	01793107	716/783-3100	66
Gayhead Elem Sch/Hopewell Jct/Dutchess	00722167	845/227-1756	54
Geller House Sch/Staten Island/Westchester	04917948	718/442-7828	256
GENERAL BROWN CTL SCH DIST/ DEXTER/JEFFERSON	00730061	315/779-2300	80
General Brown Jr Sr High Sch/Dexter/ Jefferson	00730097	315/779-2300	80
General Douglas MacArthur HS/Levittown/ Nassau	00736792	516/434-7225	123
General Herkimer Elem Sch/Utica/Oneida	00760652	315/792-2160	152
General Wm Floyd Elem Sch/Stittville/ Oneida	00760133	315/865-5721	150
Genesee Cmty Charter Sch/Rochester/Monroe	04931920	585/697-1960	4
Genesee Country Christian Sch/Geneseo/ Livingston	04752059	585/243-9580	104
Genesee Elem Sch/Auburn/Cayuga	00717928	315/255-8640	34
GENESEE VALLEY BOCES/LE ROY/ GENESEE	00730918	585/344-7900	74
Genesee Valley Career & Tech/Batavia/ Genesee	11455529	585/344-7711	72
GENESEE VALLEY CTL SCH DIST/ BELMONT/ALLEGANY	00716091	585/268-7900	15
Genesee Valley Ctrl Sch/Belmont/Allegany	00716065	585/268-7900	15
Geneseo Central Sch/Geneseo/Livingston	00730774	585/243-3450	103
GENESEO CENTRAL SCH DIST/ GENESEO/LIVINGSTON	00730762	585/243-3450	102
Genesis Sch/Chaumont/Jefferson	04975201	315/649-3050	82
Genesis Sch/East Meadow/Nassau	11231048	516/937-1397	133
GENEVA CITY SCH DIST/GENEVA/ ONTARIO	00763719	315/781-0400	161
Geneva High Sch/Geneva/Ontario	00763733	315/781-0402	161
Geneva Middle Sch/Geneva/Ontario	00763721	315/781-0404	161
Geneva School-Manhattan/New York/New York	04974104	212/754-9988	144
George A Jackson Elem Sch/Jericho/Nassau	00736596	516/203-3640	122
George D Ryder Elem Sch/Cobleskill/ Schoharie	00770750	518/234-2585	206
George F Baker High Sch/Tuxedo Park/Orange	00764933	845/351-4786	167
George F Johnson Elem Sch/Endicott/Broome	00716766	607/757-2143	29
George Fischer Middle Sch/Carmel/Putnam	00766383	845/228-2300	175
George Grant Mason Elem Sch/Tuxedo Park/ Orange	04867707	845/351-4797	167
George H Murray Prepatory Acad/Brooklyn/ Kings	02163311	718/384-1577	97
George Jackson Academy/New York/New York	11230472	212/228-6789	144
George Junior Republic Sch/Freeville/ Tompkins	00777394	607/844-6365	240
GEORGE JUNIOR REPUBLIC UFSD/ FREEVILLE/TOMPKINS	00777382	607/844-6365	240
George L Cooke Elem Sch/Monticello/ Sullivan	00776883	845/794-8830	237
George M Davis Elem Sch/New Rochelle/ Westchester	00781137	914/576-4420	259
George M Diven Elem Sch/Elmira/Chemung	00719237	607/735-3700	40
George Mather Forbes School 4/Rochester/ Monroe	00732710	585/235-7848	111
George Ross MacKenzie Elem Sch/Glen Spey/ Sullivan	04431126	845/456-1100	236
George Southard Elem Sch/Lockport/Niagara	00759110	716/478-4770	147
George W Hewlett High Sch/Hewlett/Nassau	00736297	516/792-4100	121
George W Miller Elem Sch/Nanuet/Rockland	00767521	845/627-4860	196
George Washington Campus YABC/New York/ New York	11928851	212/927-1841	141
George Washington Elem Sch/Kingston/Ulster	00777899	845/338-1978	242
George Washington Elem Sch/Mohegan Lake/ Westchester	00780638	914/528-2021	257
George Washington Elem Sch/W Hempstead/ Nassau	02128658	516/390-3130	131
George Washington Elem Sch/White Plains/ Westchester	00782131	914/422-2380	263
George Washington Sch/Troy/Rensselaer	12100648	518/283-5752	189
George Westinghouse Cte HS/Brooklyn/Kings	00741046	718/625-6130	82
Geraldine J Mann Elem Sch/Niagara Falls/ Niagara	00759378	716/278-7940	147
Gerer Mesivta Bais Yisroel/Brooklyn/Kings	02162939	718/854-8777	97
German Int'l School New York/White Plains/ Westchester	02164377	914/948-6513	265
Germantown Central Sch/Germantown/Columbia	00720470	518/537-6281	46
GERMANTOWN CENTRAL SCH DIST/ GERMANTOWN/COLUMBIA	00720468	518/537-6281	46
Gersh Academy Hauppauge/Hauppauge/Suffolk	12224945	631/232-3855	235
Gersh Academy-W Hempstead/W Hempstead/ Nassau	12314758	516/986-9580	133
Gersh Academy-West Hills/Huntington/ Suffolk	12380367	631/385-3342	235
Gesher Yehuda Yeshiva/Brooklyn/Kings	05011688	718/714-7400	97
Gesher Yeshivah Prep High Sch/Brooklyn/ Kings	11815498	347/462-1807	97
Geyser Road Elem Sch/Saratoga Spgs/ Saratoga	01539755	518/584-7699	201
Giffen Memorial Elem Sch/Albany/Albany	00714160	518/475-6650	9
Gilbertsville-Mt Upton Sch/Gilbertsville/ Otsego	00719677	607/783-2207	173
GILBERTSVILLE-MT UPTON SD/ GILBERTSVILLE/OTSEGO	00766046	607/783-2207	173
Gilboa-Conesville Central Sch/Gilboa/ Schoharie	00770786	607/588-7541	206
GILBOA-CONESVILLE CENTRAL SD/ GILBOA/SCHOHARIE	00770774	607/588-7541	206
Gilead School of Discipleship/Perry/ Wyoming	12314100	585/330-4113	268
Gillen Brewer Sch/New York/New York	11233864	212/831-3667	144
Gillette Road Middle Sch/Cicero/Onondaga	00761967	315/218-3000	157
Ginther Elem Sch/Brockport/Monroe	00731467	585/637-1830	107
Girls Prep Bronx Charter ES/Bronx/Bronx	11453557	718/901-3855	4
Girls Prep Bronx Middle Sch/Bronx/Bronx	12028363	718/665-6090	4
Girls Prep Elem Sch-Bronx II/Bronx/Bronx	12471992	917/435-6599	4
Girls Prep Lower East Side ES/New York/ New York	10026620	212/388-0241	4
Girls Prep Lower East Side MS/New York/ New York	12026652	212/358-8216	4
Glebe Street Elem Sch/Johnstown/Fulton	00728563	518/762-3714	71
GLEN COVE CITY SCH DIST/ GLEN COVE/NASSAU	00735839	516/759-7202	120
Glen Cove High Sch/Glen Cove/Nassau	00735877	516/801-7600	120
Glen Head Elem Sch/Glen Head/Nassau	00737710	516/277-7700	126
Glen Worden Elem Sch/Scotia/Schenectady	03240405	518/347-3600	205
Glencliff Elem Sch/Rexford/Schenectady	00770243	518/399-2323	204
Glendaal Elem Sch/Scotia/Schenectady	00770669	518/382-1201	205
Glendale Elem Sch/Tonawanda/Erie	00725195	716/250-1500	63
Glenfield Elem Sch/Glenfield/Lewis	00730607	315/348-2620	101
Glenham Elem Sch/Fishkill/Dutchess	00721541	845/838-6900	51
Glenmont Elem Sch/Glenmont/Albany	00714421	518/463-1154	10
Glenn Curtiss Elem Sch/Hammondsport/ Steuben	12106111	607/569-5200	214
GLENS FALLS CITY SCH DIST/ GLENS FALLS/WARREN	00778520	518/792-1212	245
GLENS FALLS COMMON SCH DIST/ GLENS FALLS/WARREN	00778441	518/792-3231	245
Glens Falls High Sch/Glens Falls/Warren	00778568	518/792-6564	245
Glens Falls Middle Sch/Glens Falls/Warren	00778556	518/793-3418	245
Glenwood Elem Sch/Vestal/Broome	00717136	607/757-2391	30
Glenwood Landing Elem Sch/Glen Head/Nassau	00737722	516/277-7600	126
Global Cmty Charter Sch/New York/New York	11824401	646/360-2363	4
Global Concepts Charter ES/Lackawanna/Erie	05282241	716/821-1903	4
Global Concepts Charter HS/Lackawanna/Erie	12260248	716/939-2554	4
Global Learning Collaborative/New York/ New York	11447742	212/877-1103	138
GLOVERSVILLE ENLARGED SCH DIST/ GLOVERSVILLE/FULTON	00728460	518/775-5791	71
Gloversville High Sch/Gloversville/Fulton	00728496	518/775-5700	71
Gloversville Middle Sch/Gloversville/ Fulton	00728484	518/775-5700	71
Goddard HS of Comm Arts & Tech/Ozone Park/ Queens	11103013	718/848-8357	180
Golden Hill Elem Sch/Florida/Orange	01396591	845/651-4407	164
Goldie Maple Academy/Arverne/Queens	00748484	718/945-3300	180
Good Shepherd Christian Sch/Kingston/ Ulster	03194208	845/339-4488	244

New York School Directory
DISTRICT & SCHOOL TELEPHONE INDEX

School/City/County DISTRICT/CITY/COUNTY	PID	TELEPHONE NUMBER	PAGE
Good Shepherd Lutheran Sch/Plainview/Nassau	01461249	516/349-1966	133
Good Shepherd Sch/Brooklyn/Kings	00753013	718/339-2745	95
Good Shepherd Sch/New York/New York	00755425	212/567-5800	143
Goose Hill Primary Sch/Cold SPG HBR/Suffolk	04032550	631/367-5940	219
Gordon Brooklyn Lab CS Sands/Brooklyn/Kings	12310946	347/429-8439	4
Gordon Creek Elem Sch/Ballston Spa/Saratoga	00769440	518/884-7270	200
Gorham Intermediate Sch/Stanley/Ontario	00763812	585/526-6351	162
Gorton High Sch/Yonkers/Westchester	00782284	914/376-8350	263
GOSHEN CENTRAL SCH DIST/GOSHEN/ORANGE	00764141	845/615-6720	164
Goshen Christian Sch/Goshen/Orange	00765080	845/294-6365	168
Goshen High Sch/Goshen/Orange	00764153	845/615-6100	164
Goshen Intermediate Sch/Goshen/Orange	01825906	845/615-6500	164
Gotham Avenue Elem Sch/Elmont/Nassau	00735413	516/326-5540	119
Gotham Collaborative High Sch/Bronx/Bronx	12240327	718/597-1587	17
Gotham Professional Arts Acad/Brooklyn/Kings	10913786	718/230-7270	86
GOUVERNEUR CTL SCH DIST/GOUVERNEUR/ST LAWRENCE	00768460	315/287-4870	210
Gouverneur Elem Sch/Gouverneur/St Lawrence	00768484	315/287-2260	210
Gouverneur High Sch/Gouverneur/St Lawrence	00768501	315/287-1900	210
Gouverneur Middle Sch/Gouverneur/St Lawrence	12307236	315/287-3200	210
Gov George Clinton Elem Sch/Poughkeepsie/Dutchess	00721931	845/451-4600	53
Gow Sch/South Wales/Erie	00725822	716/652-3450	66
Gowana Middle Sch/Clifton Park/Saratoga	00769854	518/881-0460	202
GOWANDA CENTRAL SCH DIST/GOWANDA/CATTARAUGUS	00717459	716/532-3325	32
Gowanda Elem Sch/Gowanda/Cattaraugus	00717461	716/532-3328	32
Gowanda High Sch/Gowanda/Cattaraugus	00717497	716/532-3325	32
Gowanda Middle Sch/Gowanda/Cattaraugus	00717473	716/532-3325	32
Grace Christian Academy/Merrick/Nassau	12361579	516/379-2223	133
Grace Church Sch/New York/New York	00751558	212/475-5609	144
Grace Lutheran Sch/Malverne/Nassau	00739225	516/599-6557	133
Graham Elem Sch/Mount Vernon/Westchester	00780896	914/358-2803	258
Gramercy Arts High Sch/New York/New York	11103386	212/253-7076	136
Granby Elem Sch/Fulton/Oswego	00765559	315/593-5480	171
Grand Ave Middle Sch/Bellmore/Nassau	00737370	516/992-1100	117
Grand Avenue Elem Sch/Baldwin/Nassau	00738726	516/918-2100	130
Grand Concourse Academy CS/Bronx/Bronx	05352688	718/684-6505	4
GRAND ISLAND CENTRAL SCH DIST/GRAND ISLAND/ERIE	00724048	716/773-8800	61
Grand Island Sr High Sch/Grand Island/Erie	00724074	716/773-8820	61
Grandview Elem Sch/Monsey/Rockland	00767961	845/577-6260	196
Grant Avenue Elem Sch/Bronx/Bronx	11447625	718/681-6288	19
Grant E Morse Elem Sch/Saugerties/Ulster	00778312	845/247-6960	243
Grant Middle Sch/Syracuse/Onondaga	00762375	315/435-4433	158
GRANVILLE CENTRAL SCH DIST/GRANVILLE/WASHINGTON	00778881	518/642-1051	247
Granville Elem Sch/Granville/Washington	00778893	518/642-9357	247
Granville Jr Sr High Sch/Granville/Washington	00778908	518/642-1051	247
Grapeville Christian Sch/Climax/Greene	04974908	518/966-5037	76
Great Hollow Middle Sch/Nesconset/Suffolk	04875170	631/382-2805	230
Great Neck North Middle Sch/Great Neck/Nassau	00735994	516/441-4500	120
GREAT NECK PUBLIC SCHOOLS/GREAT NECK/NASSAU	00735920	516/441-4001	120
Great Neck Road Elem Sch/Copiague/Suffolk	00773025	631/842-4013	220
Great Neck South High Sch/Great Neck/Nassau	00736027	516/441-4800	120
Great Neck South Middle Sch/Great Neck/Nassau	00736015	516/441-4600	120
Great Oaks CS-New York City/New York/New York	11932515	212/233-5152	4
Great Oaks Elem Sch/Brooklyn/Kings	04974324	718/346-4934	97
Great Tomorrow School USA/New York/New York	11229552	212/427-2839	144
GREATER AMSTERDAM SCH DIST/AMSTERDAM/MONTGOMERY	00734586	518/843-3180	115
GREATER JOHNSTOWN SCH DIST/JOHNSTOWN/FULTON	00728549	518/762-4611	71
Greater New York Academy/Woodside/Queens	01463376	718/639-1752	187
Greater Plains Elem Sch/Oneonta/Otsego	00766149	607/433-8272	174
GREATER SOUTHERN TIER BOCES/PAINTED POST/STEUBEN	00771845	607/962-3581	215
GREECE CENTRAL SCH DIST/ROCHESTER/MONROE	00731869	585/621-1000	108
Greece Christian Sch/Rochester/Monroe	02977227	585/723-1165	114
Greek American Institute/Bronx/Bronx	01461689	718/823-2393	26
Greek Cathedral Sch/New York/New York	01461483	212/249-2840	144
Green Chimneys Sch/Brewster/Putnam	00752796	845/279-2995	176
GREEN ISLAND UNION FREE SD/GREEN ISLAND/ALBANY	00714536	518/273-1422	10
Green Meadow Elem Sch/Castleton/Rensselaer	00766838	518/207-2640	190
Green Meadow Waldorf Sch/Spring Valley/Rockland	12314825	845/356-2514	199
Green Tech High Charter Sch/Albany/Albany	11468148	518/694-3400	4
Green Vale Sch/Glen Head/Nassau	00739419	516/621-2420	133
Greenacres Elem Sch/Scarsdale/Westchester	00781838	914/721-2740	262
Greenburgh 11 Elem Middle Sch/Dobbs Ferry/Westchester	00780054	914/693-8500	255
Greenburgh 11 High Sch/Dobbs Ferry/Westchester	05099135	914/693-8500	255
GREENBURGH 11 UNION FREE SD/DOBBS FERRY/WESTCHESTER	00780042	914/693-8500	255
Greenburgh Academy/Yonkers/Westchester	00781943	914/476-1938	255
GREENBURGH CENTRAL SCH DIST/HARTSDALE/WESTCHESTER	00780183	914/761-6000	255
Greenburgh Ctl 7 Ecp/Hartsdale/Westchester	00780224	914/949-2745	255
GREENBURGH-GRAHAM UFSD/HASTINGS HDSN/WESTCHESTER	00780169	914/478-1106	255
GREENBURGH-NORTH CASTLE SD/DOBBS FERRY/WESTCHESTER	00781931	914/231-8620	255
Greene Central Interm Sch/Greene/Chenango	00719641	607/656-9891	42
GREENE CTL SCH DIST/GREENE/CHENANGO	00719627	607/656-4161	42
Greene High Sch/Greene/Chenango	04012938	607/656-4161	42
Greene Hill Sch/Brooklyn/Kings	12318857	718/230-3608	97
Greene HS Imaginative Inquiry/New York/New York	10008886	212/799-4064	138
Greene Middle Sch/Greene/Chenango	00719653	607/656-4161	42
Greene Primary Sch/Greene/Chenango	04746086	607/656-5174	42
Greenfield Elem Sch/Greenfld CTR/Saratoga	00769737	518/893-7402	201
Greenlawn Elem Sch/Bainbridge/Chenango	00719603	607/967-6301	41
Greenport Sch/Greenport/Suffolk	00773427	631/477-1950	222
GREENPORT UNION FREE SCH DIST/GREENPORT/SUFFOLK	00773415	631/477-1950	222
Greenvale Elem Sch/Scarsdale/Westchester	00780028	914/793-6130	254
GREENVILLE CENTRAL SCH DIST/GREENVILLE/GREENE	00729256	518/966-5070	75
Greenville Elem Sch/Scarsdale/Westchester	00780080	914/472-7760	254
Greenville High Sch/Greenville/Greene	00729270	518/966-5070	75
Greenville Middle Sch/Greenville/Greene	04898469	518/966-5070	75
GREENWICH CENTRAL SCH DIST/GREENWICH/WASHINGTON	00778922	518/692-9542	247
Greenwich Elem Sch/Greenwich/Washington	00778934	518/692-9542	248
Greenwich Jr Sr High Sch/Greenwich/Washington	04797499	518/692-9542	248
Greenwood Lake Elem Sch/Greenwood Lk/Orange	00764218	845/477-2411	164
Greenwood Lake Middle Sch/Monroe/Orange	00764206	845/782-8678	164
GREENWOOD LAKE UNION FREE SD/MONROE/ORANGE	00764191	845/477-2411	164
Gregorio Luperon HS Sci & Math/New York/New York	04319164	212/928-1202	141
Gregory Jarvis Middle Sch/Ilion/Herkimer	00729751	315/866-2620	77
Gribbin Elem Sch/Glen Cove/Nassau	00735889	516/801-7210	120
Griffith Institute Middle Sch/Springville/Erie	00724153	716/592-3203	63
Grimes Elem Sch/Mount Vernon/Westchester	00781010	914/665-5020	258
GROTON CENTRAL SCH DIST/GROTON/TOMPKINS	00777409	607/898-5301	240
Groton Elem Sch/Groton/Tompkins	00777411	607/898-5853	240
Groton Jr Sr High Sch/Groton/Tompkins	00777423	607/898-5803	240
Grove Street Academy/Kingston/Ulster	01464136	845/331-1448	244
Grover Cleveland High Sch/Ridgewood/Queens	00741084	718/381-9600	177
Growing Up Green Charter ES/Long Is City/Queens	11447364	347/642-4306	184
Growing Up Green CS II/Jamaica/Queens	12170576	347/642-4306	4
Growing Up Green Middle Sch/Long Is City/Queens	12115708	347/642-4306	184
Grundy Avenue Elem Sch/Holbrook/Suffolk	00775176	631/471-1820	229
Guardian Angel Sch/New York/New York	00755437	212/989-8280	143
Guardino Elem Sch/Clayton/Jefferson	00730310	315/686-5578	81
Guggenheim Elem Sch/Prt Washingtn/Nassau	00738166	516/767-5250	128
Guild for Excptnl Chldrn Sch/Brooklyn/Kings	01793597	718/435-2554	97

DISTRICT & SCHOOL TELEPHONE INDEX

Market Data Retrieval

School/City/County DISTRICT/CITY/COUNTY	PID	TELEPHONE NUMBER	PAGE
GUILDERLAND CENTRAL SCH DIST/			
GUILDRLND CTR/ALBANY	00714550	518/456-6200	10
Guilderland Elem Sch/Guilderland/Albany	03006326	518/869-0293	11
Guilderland High Sch/Guildrlnd CTR/Albany	00714586	518/861-8591	11
Guilford Elem Sch/Guilford/Chenango	00719615	607/895-6700	42
Gustavus Adolphus Lrng Center/Jamestown/Chautauqua	01792892	716/665-2772	40

H

School/City/County	PID	TELEPHONE	PAGE
H B Mattlin Middle Sch/Plainview/Nassau	00738037	516/434-3250	128
H B Thompson Middle Sch/Syosset/Nassau	00738594	516/364-5760	130
H C Crittenden Middle Sch/Armonk/Westchester	00779794	914/273-4250	253
H C Williams High Sch/Canton/St Lawrence	00768381	315/386-8561	209
H Frank Carey Jr Sr High Sch/Franklin Sq/Nassau	00735592	516/539-9400	129
H W Smith PK-8 Sch/Syracuse/Onondaga	00762387	315/435-4490	158
Hackley Sch/Tarrytown/Westchester	00782961	914/631-0128	265
HADLEY-LUZERNE CTL SCH DIST/			
LAKE LUZERNE/WARREN	00778609	518/696-2378	245
Hadley-Luzerne Jr Sr High Sch/Lake Luzerne/Warren	00778623	518/696-2112	245
Hagan Elem Sch/Poughkeepsie/Dutchess	00722076	845/463-7840	54
Halb Drs Yeshiva HS for Boys/Woodmere/Nassau	11231165	516/295-7700	133
Halb Elementary/Long Beach/Nassau	00739249	516/432-8285	133
Halb Stella K Abraham Girls HS/Hewlett/Nassau	04974790	516/374-6851	133
HALDANE CENTRAL SCH DIST/			
COLD SPRING/PUTNAM	00766448	845/265-9254	175
Haldane Sch/Cold Spring/Putnam	00766450	845/265-9254	176
HALF HOLLOW HILLS CENTRAL SD/			
DIX HILLS/SUFFOLK	00773439	631/592-3030	222
Half Hollow Hills High Sch E/Dix Hills/Suffolk	00773489	631/592-3100	222
Half Hollow Hills High Sch W/Dix Hills/Suffolk	01417303	631/592-3200	222
Hamagrael Elem Sch/Delmar/Albany	00714433	518/439-4905	10
HAMBURG CENTRAL SCH DIST/			
HAMBURG/ERIE	00724177	716/646-3200	61
Hamburg High Sch/Hamburg/Erie	00724220	716/646-3300	61
Hamburg Middle Sch/Hamburg/Erie	00724218	716/646-3250	61
Hamilton Bicentennial Elem Sch/Cuddebackvlle/Orange	01417236	845/858-3100	166
Hamilton Central Sch/Hamilton/Madison	00731168	315/824-6300	105
HAMILTON CENTRAL SCH DIST/			
HAMILTON/MADISON	00731156	315/824-6300	105
Hamilton Elem Sch/Mount Vernon/Westchester	00780901	914/665-5050	258
Hamilton Elem Sch/Schenectady/Schenectady	00770451	518/881-3720	204
Hamilton Grange Middle Sch/New York/New York	12036360	212/281-6184	141
HAMILTON-FULTON-MONTGMRY BOCES/			
JOHNSTOWN/FULTON	00728757	518/736-4681	72
Hammond Central Sch/Hammond/St Lawrence	00768549	315/324-5931	210
HAMMOND CENTRAL SCH DISTRICT/			
HAMMOND/ST LAWRENCE	00768537	315/324-5931	210
HAMMONDSPORT CTL SCH DIST/			
HAMMONDSPORT/STEUBEN	00771584	607/569-5200	214
Hammondsport Jr Sr High Sch/Hammondsport/Steuben	00771601	607/569-5200	214
Hampton Bays Elem Sch/Hampton Bays/Suffolk	00773609	631/723-2121	223
Hampton Bays High Sch/Hampton Bays/Suffolk	00773611	631/723-2110	223
Hampton Bays Middle Sch/Hampton Bays/Suffolk	10982763	631/723-4700	223
HAMPTON BAYS UNION FREE SD/			
HAMPTON BAYS/SUFFOLK	00773594	631/723-2100	222
Hampton Street Elem Sch/Mineola/Nassau	00737485	516/237-2200	125
Hamza Academy/Valley Stream/Nassau	12177184	516/285-1440	133
Hanc High Sch/Uniondale/Nassau	01408948	516/538-8161	133
Hanc Middle Sch/Uniondale/Nassau	11671096	516/538-8161	133
Hanc Plainview Elem Sch/Plainview/Nassau	00739237	516/681-5922	133
Hanc West Hempstead Elem Sch/W Hempstead/Nassau	00739251	516/485-7786	133
HANCOCK CENTRAL SCH DIST/			
HANCOCK/DELAWARE	00721137	607/637-2511	49
Hancock Elem Sch/Hancock/Delaware	00721149	607/637-1328	49
Hancock Jr Sr High Sch/Hancock/Delaware	00721151	607/637-1305	49
Hannah Senesh Cmty Day Sch/Brooklyn/Kings	11475945	718/858-8663	97
HANNIBAL CENTRAL SCH DIST/			
HANNIBAL/OSWEGO	00765602	315/564-8100	171
Hannibal Senior High Sch/Hannibal/Oswego	00765638	315/564-8130	171
Hanson Place SDA Sch/Brooklyn/Kings	01462205	718/625-3030	97
Harbor Country Day Sch/Saint James/Suffolk	00776687	631/584-5555	235
Harbor Heights/New York/New York	10026761	212/568-6052	141
Harbor Hill Elem Sch/Greenvale/Nassau	00738439	516/801-5400	129
Harbor Science & Arts Chtr Sch/New York/New York	04458368	212/427-2244	4
HARBORFIELDS CTL SCH DIST/			
GREENLAWN/SUFFOLK	00773623	631/754-5320	223
Harborfields High Sch/Greenlawn/Suffolk	00773647	631/754-5360	223
Harding Avenue Elem Sch/Lindenhurst/Suffolk	00774093	631/867-3350	224
Harkness Career & Tech Center/Cheektowaga/Erie	04954491	716/961-4070	55
Harlem C Z Promise Academy I/New York/New York	11704057	212/534-0700	140
Harlem C Z Promise Academy II/New York/New York	10012124	917/492-1481	140
Harlem Hebrew Language Acad CS/New York/New York	11933777	212/866-4608	4
Harlem Link Charter Sch/New York/New York	10025810	212/289-3249	4
Harlem Prep Campus CS/New York/New York	11722968	212/831-5394	4
Harlem Prep Middle Sch/New York/New York	11825443	212/860-7128	4
Harlem Renaissance High Sch/New York/New York	05352638	212/996-3795	140
Harlem Village Acad East Elem/New York/New York	10008977	646/812-9600	4
Harlem Village Acad East MS HS/New York/New York	11722671	646/812-9600	4
Harlem Village Acad High Sch/New York/New York	11750886	646/812-9200	4
Harlem Village Acad W Lower ES/New York/New York	12028480	646/812-9700	4
Harlem Village Acad W Upper ES/New York/New York	12380422	646/812-9800	4
Harlem Village Acad West MS/New York/New York	05291852	646/812-9300	4
Harley Avenue Primary Sch/E Northport/Suffolk	00773362	631/266-5445	221
Harmony Christian Sch/Middletown/Orange	02163971	845/692-5353	168
Harmony Heights Sch/East Norwich/Nassau	02119308	516/922-6688	133
Harmony Hill Sch/Cohoes/Albany	00714512	518/233-1900	10
Harold D Fayette Elem Sch/Merrick/Nassau	00737681	516/489-3090	126
Harold O Brumsted Elem Sch/Holland/Erie	00724270	716/537-8250	61
Harold T Wiley Interm Sch/Watertown/Jefferson	01541045	315/785-3780	81
HARPURSVILLE CENTRAL SCH DIST/			
HARPURSVILLE/BROOME	00716845	607/693-8101	28
Harpursville Jr Sr HS/Harpursville/Broome	00716857	607/693-8105	28
Harriet Tubman Charter Sch/Bronx/Bronx	04948117	718/537-9912	4
Harris Hill Elem Sch/Penfield/Monroe	00732382	585/249-6600	109
Harris Hill Elem Sch/Williamsville/Erie	00723630	716/407-9175	59
Harrison Avenue Elem Sch/Harrison/Westchester	00780286	914/630-3192	256
Harrison Avenue Elem Sch/S Glens Falls/Saratoga	00769957	518/793-9048	202
HARRISON CENTRAL SCH DIST/			
HARRISON/WESTCHESTER	00780274	914/835-3300	256
Harrison High Sch/Harrison/Westchester	00780298	914/630-3095	256
Harrisville Central Sch/Harrisville/Lewis	00730530	315/543-2707	101
HARRISVILLE CENTRAL SCH DIST/			
HARRISVILLE/LEWIS	00730528	315/543-2707	101
Harry B Ward Technical Center/Riverhead/Suffolk	03384192	631/369-8100	216
Harry E Elden Elem Sch/Baldwinsville/Onondaga	00761113	315/638-6118	154
Harry F Abate Elem Sch/Niagara Falls/Niagara	00759304	716/278-7960	147
Harry Fisher Elem Sch/Mohawk/Herkimer	00729749	315/866-4851	77
Harry Hoag Elem Sch/Fort Plain/Montgomery	00734823	518/993-4433	115
Harry S Truman High Sch/Bronx/Bronx	01552159	718/904-5400	22
Hartford Central Sch/Hartford/Washington	00778972	518/632-5222	248
HARTFORD CENTRAL SCH DIST/			
HARTFORD/WASHINGTON	00778960	518/632-5222	248
Harts Hill Elem Sch/Whitesboro/Oneida	00760937	315/266-3430	153
Harvest Collegiate High Sch/New York/New York	11821631	212/242-3384	136
Harvey C Fenner Elem Sch/Falconer/Chautauqua	00718570	716/665-6627	37
Harvey Milk High Sch/New York/New York	04838794	212/477-1555	136
Hastings High Sch/Hastings HDSN/Westchester	00780389	914/478-6250	256

NY-V20 800-333-8802 School Year 2020-2021

New York School Directory
DISTRICT & SCHOOL TELEPHONE INDEX

School/City/County DISTRICT/CITY/COUNTY	PID	TELEPHONE	PAGE NUMBER
HASTINGS ON HUDSON UNION FR SD/			
HASTINGS HDSN/WESTCHESTER	00780365	914/478-2900	256
Hastings-Mallory Elem Sch/Central Sq/Oswego	00765456	315/668-4252	170
Hauppauge High Sch/Hauppauge/Suffolk	00773726	631/761-8302	223
Hauppauge Middle Sch/Hauppauge/Suffolk	00773738	631/761-8230	223
HAUPPAUGE UNION FREE SCH DIST/			
HAUPPAUGE/SUFFOLK	00773697	631/761-8300	223
Haverling High Sch/Bath/Steuben	00771637	607/776-4107	213
Haverstraw Elem Sch/Haverstraw/Rockland	00767595	845/942-3400	197
Haviland Middle Sch/Hyde Park/Dutchess	00721694	845/229-4030	52
Hawk Meadow Montessori Sch/Poughkeepsie/Dutchess	03193993	845/223-3783	55
Hawkins Path Elem Sch/Selden/Suffolk	00774249	631/285-8530	225
HAWTHORNE CEDAR KNOLLS UFSD/			
HAWTHORNE/WESTCHESTER	00780406	914/749-2917	256
Hawthorne Country Day Sch/Hawthorne/Westchester	01795806	914/592-8526	265
Hawthorne Country Day Sch-Manh/New York/New York	12168250	212/281-6531	144
Hawthorne Elem Sch/Hawthorne/Westchester	00781058	914/769-8536	259
Hawthorne Little Sch/Hawthorne/Westchester	10903573	914/749-2964	256
Hawthorne Sr Jr High Sch/Hawthorne/Westchester	00780418	914/749-2930	256
Hawthorne Valley Sch/Ghent/Columbia	01408819	518/672-7092	47
Hayground Sch/Bridgehampton/Suffolk	04974881	631/537-7068	235
Health Opportunities High Sch/Bronx/Bronx	04291029	718/401-1826	16
Health Sciences Charter Sch/Buffalo/Erie	11569089	716/888-4080	4
Heathcote Elem Sch/Scarsdale/Westchester	00781840	914/721-2760	262
Heatly Sch/Green Island/Albany	00714548	518/273-1422	10
Hebrew Acad 5 Towns Rockawy ES/Lawrence/Nassau	00739342	516/569-3043	133
Hebrew Acad 5 Towns Rockawy HS/Cedarhurst/Nassau	02121193	516/569-3807	133
Hebrew Acad 5 Towns Rockawy MS/Lawrence/Nassau	11236751	516/569-6352	133
Hebrew Acad for Spec Children/Brooklyn/Kings	01462671	718/851-6100	97
Hebrew Academy/New City/Rockland	11573999	845/634-0951	199
Hebrew Day School-Sullivan Co/Kiamesha Lake/Sullivan	00777007	845/794-7890	237
Hebrew Institute-Deaf Excptnl/Brooklyn/Kings	01462217	718/377-7507	97
Hebrew Language Academy CS/Brooklyn/Kings	11447405	718/377-7200	92
Hebrew Language Academy CS 2/Brooklyn/Kings	12234158	718/682-5610	4
Hebron SDA Bilingual Sch/Brooklyn/Kings	02849723	347/533-4923	97
Heim Elem Sch/Williamsville/Erie	00725597	716/626-8697	64
Heim Middle Sch/Williamsville/Erie	00725602	716/626-8600	64
Heketi Community Charter Sch/Bronx/Bronx	11831947	718/260-6002	4
Helen B Duffield Elem Sch/Ronkonkoma/Suffolk	00772928	631/467-6010	219
Helen B Montgomery School 50/Rochester/Monroe	00733116	585/266-0331	111
Helen M Marshall Sch/Corona/Queens	11560942	718/505-5110	177
Helendale Road Primary Sch/Rochester/Monroe	03247001	585/339-1330	107
Hellenic Classical Charter Sch/Brooklyn/Kings	10008953	718/499-0957	84
Hellenic Classical CS-Statn IS/Staten Island/Richmond	12367494	212/557-7200	4
Helpern Education Center/Webster/Monroe	01793975	585/671-7890	114
Hemlock Park Elem Sch/Bay Shore/Suffolk	00772253	631/434-2451	217
Hemlock Sch/Garden City/Nassau	04366557	516/478-1600	120
Hempstead Elem Sch/Spring Valley/Rockland	00767973	845/577-6270	196
Hempstead High Sch/Hempstead/Nassau	00736118	516/434-4202	121
HEMPSTEAD UNION FREE SD/			
HEMPSTEAD/NASSAU	00736089	516/434-4000	121
HENDRICK HUDSON CTL SCH DIST/			
MONTROSE/WESTCHESTER	00780420	914/257-5112	256
Hendrick Hudson High Sch/Montrose/Westchester	00780470	914/257-5800	256
Hendy Elem Sch/Elmira/Chemung	00719275	607/735-3750	40
Henninger High Sch/Syracuse/Onondaga	00762399	315/435-4343	158
Henrietta G Lewis Campus Sch/Lockport/Niagara	01463390	716/433-9592	149
Henry Barnard Early Chldhd Ctr/New Rochelle/Westchester	00781149	914/576-4386	259
Henry Burger Jr High Sch/W Henrietta/Monroe	04033970	585/359-5300	112
Henry H Wells Middle Sch/Brewster/Putnam	00766345	845/279-3702	175
Henry Hudson School 28/Rochester/Monroe	00732930	585/482-4836	111
Henry J Kalfas Magnet Sch/Niagara Falls/Niagara	00759251	716/278-9180	147
Henry Johnson Charter Sch/Albany/Albany	11013585	518/432-4300	4
Henry Lomb School 20/Rochester/Monroe	03011539	585/325-2920	111
Henry Viscardi Sch/Albertson/Nassau	01461304	516/465-1560	133
Herbert H Lehman High Sch/Bronx/Bronx	00741113	718/904-4200	17
Herbert Hoover Elem Sch/Buffalo/Erie	00724452	716/874-8414	62
Herbert Hoover Middle Sch/Buffalo/Erie	00724464	716/874-8405	62
Herbert Lehman YABC/Bronx/Bronx	11928693	718/904-4280	17
Heritage Christian Academy/Bay Shore/Suffolk	02990970	631/968-5358	235
Heritage Heights Elem Sch/Amherst/Erie	00725200	716/250-1525	63
Heritage Middle Sch/New Windsor/Orange	00764751	845/563-3750	166
Heritage Sch/New York/New York	04753637	212/828-2858	139
HERKIMER BOCES/HERKIMER/HERKIMER	00729921	315/867-2023	79
HERKIMER CTL SCH DIST/HERKIMER/			
HERKIMER	00729581	315/866-2230	77
Herkimer Elem Sch/Herkimer/Herkimer	00729610	315/866-8562	78
Herkimer Jr Sr High Sch/Herkimer/Herkimer	00729608	315/866-2230	78
Herman Avenue Elem Sch/Auburn/Cayuga	00717930	315/255-8680	34
Herman L Bradt Primary Sch/Schenectady/Schenectady	00770164	518/356-8400	204
HERMON-DEKALB CENTRAL SCH DIST/			
DE KALB JCT/ST LAWRENCE	00768551	315/347-3442	210
Hermon-DeKalb Ctl Sch/De Kalb Jct/St Lawrence	00768563	315/347-3442	210
Hero High Sch/Bronx/Bronx	11924532	718/585-8013	16
Herricks High Sch/New Hyde Park/Nassau	00736235	516/305-8700	121
Herricks Middle Sch/Albertson/Nassau	00736259	516/305-8600	121
HERRICKS UNION FREE SCH DIST/			
NEW HYDE PARK/NASSAU	00736194	516/305-8900	121
Heuvelton Central Sch/Heuvelton/St Lawrence	00768599	315/344-2414	210
HEUVELTON CENTRAL SCH DIST/			
HEUVELTON/ST LAWRENCE	00768587	315/344-2414	210
Hewes Career & Tech Ed Center/Ashville/Chautauqua	04880917	716/763-1801	36
Hewitt Elem Sch/Rockville CTR/Nassau	00738257	516/255-8913	128
Hewitt Sch/New York/New York	00751601	212/288-1919	144
Hewlett Elem Sch/Hewlett/Nassau	00736302	516/792-4500	121
HEWLETT WOODMERE UNION FREE SD/			
WOODMERE/NASSAU	00736273	516/792-4800	121
Hiawatha Elem Sch/Lk Ronkonkoma/Suffolk	00775188	631/471-1830	229
Hicksville High Sch/Hicksville/Nassau	00736405	516/733-2200	122
Hicksville Middle Sch/Hicksville/Nassau	00736417	516/733-2261	122
HICKSVILLE UNION FREE SCH DIST/			
HICKSVILLE/NASSAU	00736352	516/733-2100	122
High Meadow Sch/Stone Ridge/Ulster	04883842	845/687-4855	244
High Sch of Fashion Industries/New York/New York	00740975	212/255-1235	136
High School Arts & Bus YABC/Corona/Queens	11928887	718/271-8383	177
High School Arts & Business/Corona/Queens	04753778	718/271-8383	177
High School for Civil Rights/Brooklyn/Kings	05348819	718/688-7960	88
High School for Violin & Dance/Bronx/Bronx	05280970	718/842-0687	19
High School Lrng Ctr-CCC/Corning/Steuben	11219038	607/962-9283	214
High School of World Cultures/Bronx/Bronx	04457223	718/860-8120	24
Highbridge Green Sch/Bronx/Bronx	11924427	718/410-5770	19
HIGHLAND CTL SCH DIST/HIGHLAND/			
ULSTER	00777796	845/691-1000	242
Highland Elem Sch/Derby/Erie	00724775	716/926-2460	60
Highland Elem Sch/Fresh Meadows/Queens	02204460	718/357-4747	187
Highland Elem Sch/Highland/Ulster	00777801	845/691-1070	242
Highland Falls Interm Sch/Highland FLS/Orange	00764256	845/446-4761	164
HIGHLAND FALLS-FT MONTGMRY SD/			
HIGHLAND FLS/ORANGE	00764220	845/446-9575	164
Highland High Sch/Highland/Ulster	00777813	845/691-1020	242
Highland Middle Sch/Highland/Ulster	00777825	845/691-1080	242
Highland Park Cmty Sch/Brooklyn/Kings	12105399	718/235-1785	88
Highlands Middle Sch/White Plains/Westchester	00782143	914/422-2092	263
Highview Elem Sch/Hartsdale/Westchester	00780200	914/946-6946	255
Highview Elem Sch/Nanuet/Rockland	04867355	845/627-3460	196
Hillcrest Elem Sch/Peekskill/Westchester	00781371	914/739-2284	260
Hillcrest High Sch/Jamaica/Queens	00741125	718/658-5407	182
Hillel Academy of Broome Co/Vestal/Broome	00717318	607/722-9274	30
Hillel Community Day Sch/Rochester/Monroe	12314124	585/271-6877	114
Hillside Alternative Sch/Mount Kisco/Westchester	12036970	914/666-3257	252
Hillside Arts & Letters Acad/Jamaica/Queens	11560851	718/658-1249	182

School Year 2020-2021   800-333-8802   NY-V21

DISTRICT & SCHOOL TELEPHONE INDEX

Market Data Retrieval

School/City/County DISTRICT/CITY/COUNTY	PID	TELEPHONE NUMBER	PAGE
Hillside Childrens Center/Auburn/Cayuga	04975043	315/258-2151	35
Hillside Elem Sch/Hastings HDSN/Westchester	00780391	914/478-6270	256
Hillside Elem Sch/Schenectady/Schenectady	00770255	518/377-1856	204
Hillside Grade Sch/New Hyde Park/Nassau	00737564	516/434-2410	126
Hilltop Sch/Haverstraw/Rockland	12038837	845/942-7550	4
Hillview Elem Sch/Lancaster/Erie	00724892	716/686-3280	62
HILTON CENTRAL SCH DIST/HILTON/MONROE	00732069	585/392-1000	109
Hilton High Sch/Hilton/Monroe	00732083	585/392-1000	109
Hinsdale Central Sch/Hinsdale/Cattaraugus	00717514	716/557-2227	32
HINSDALE CENTRAL SCH DIST/HINSDALE/CATTARAUGUS	00717502	716/557-2227	32
Holbrook Road Elem Sch/Centereach/Suffolk	00774251	631/285-8560	225
HOLLAND CENTRAL SCH DIST/HOLLAND/ERIE	00724268	716/537-8200	61
Holland High Sch/Holland/Erie	00724282	716/537-8221	61
Holland Middle Sch/Holland/Erie	12312114	716/537-8275	61
HOLLAND PATENT CTL SCH DIST/HOLLAND PATNT/ONEIDA	00760080	315/865-7200	150
Holland Patent Elem Sch/Holland Patnt/Oneida	00760107	315/865-8151	150
Holland Patent High Sch/Holland Patnt/Oneida	00760119	315/865-7200	150
Holland Patent Middle Sch/Holland Patnt/Oneida	00760121	315/865-8152	150
HOLLEY CENTRAL SCH DIST/HOLLEY/ORLEANS	00765183	585/638-6316	169
Holley Elem Sch/Holley/Orleans	00765195	585/638-6318	169
Holley Middle High Sch/Holley/Orleans	00765200	585/638-6318	169
Holmes Elem Sch/Tonawanda/Erie	00724476	716/874-8423	62
Holmes Magnet Elem Sch/Mount Vernon/Westchester	00780913	914/665-5110	258
Holmes Road Elem Sch/Rochester/Monroe	00731974	585/966-4900	109
Holy Angels Regional Sch/Patchogue/Suffolk	00740274	631/475-0422	234
Holy Child Academy/Old Westbury/Nassau	00740066	516/626-9300	133
Holy Child Jesus Catholic Acad/Richmond Hill/Queens	00753025	718/849-3988	186
Holy Cross Academy/Oneida/Madison	04932091	315/363-1669	106
Holy Cross High Sch/Flushing/Queens	00753037	718/886-7250	186
Holy Cross Sch/De Witt/Onondaga	00762909	315/446-4890	160
Holy Cross Sch/Rochester/Monroe	00733817	585/663-6533	113
Holy Family Catholic Academy/Fresh Meadows/Queens	00753075	718/969-2124	186
Holy Family Elem Sch/Elmira/Chemung	00734354	607/732-3588	41
Holy Family Sch/Bronx/Bronx	00755475	718/863-7280	25
Holy Family Sch/Hicksville/Nassau	00739598	516/938-3846	132
Holy Family Sch/Norwich/Chenango	00763458	607/337-2207	43
Holy Family Sch/Syracuse/Onondaga	00762911	315/487-8515	160
Holy Ghost Lutheran Sch/Niagara Falls/Niagara	01873458	716/731-3030	149
Holy Martyrs Armenian Day Sch/Oakland GDNS/Queens	02163751	718/225-4826	187
Holy Name of Jesus Academy/Massena/St Lawrence	12160404	315/769-6030	212
Holy Name of Mary Sch/Valley Stream/Nassau	00739603	516/825-4009	132
Holy Rosary Sch/Bronx/Bronx	00755554	718/652-1838	25
Holy Spirit Sch/E Greenbush/Rensselaer	00715176	518/477-5739	192
Holy Trinity Diocesan High Sch/Hicksville/Nassau	00739627	516/433-2900	132
Holy Trinity Sch/Poughkeepsie/Dutchess	00755592	845/471-0520	55
Homer Brink Elem Sch/Endwell/Broome	00716974	607/786-8244	29
HOMER CENTRAL SCH DIST/HOMER/CORTLAND	00720860	607/749-7241	47
Homer Elem Sch/Homer/Cortland	00720872	607/749-1250	48
Homer High Sch/Homer/Cortland	00720901	607/749-7246	48
Homer Intermediate Sch/Homer/Cortland	04898524	607/749-1240	48
Homer Junior High Sch/Homer/Cortland	00720884	607/749-1230	48
Homestead Primary Sch/Garden City/Nassau	00735798	516/478-1700	120
Homestead Sch/Glen Spey/Sullivan	02981606	845/856-6359	237
Hommocks Middle Sch/Larchmont/Westchester	00780743	914/220-3300	258
Honeoye Central Sch/Honeoye/Ontario	01813460	585/229-5171	161
HONEOYE CENTRAL SCH DIST/HONEOYE/ONTARIO	00763783	585/229-4125	161
Honeoye Falls Lima High Sch/Honeoye Falls/Monroe	00732150	585/624-7050	109
Honeoye Falls Lima Middle Sch/Honeoye Falls/Monroe	00732148	585/624-7100	109
HONEOYE FALLS LIMA SCH DIST/HONEOYE FALLS/MONROE	00732136	585/624-7000	109
Hoosac Sch/Hoosick/Rensselaer	01409382	518/686-7331	192
HOOSIC VALLEY CENTRAL SCH DIST/SCHAGHTICOKE/RENSSELAER	00766876	518/753-4458	190
Hoosic Valley Elem Sch/Schaghticoke/Rensselaer	00766888	518/753-4491	190
Hoosic Valley High Sch/Schaghticoke/Rensselaer	00766890	518/753-4432	190
HOOSICK FALLS CENTRAL SCH DIST/HOOSICK FALLS/RENSSELAER	00766905	518/686-7012	190
Hoosick Falls Elem Sch/Hoosick Falls/Rensselaer	04362410	518/686-9492	190
Hoosick Falls High Sch/Hoosick Falls/Rensselaer	04745147	518/686-7321	190
Hope Christian Academy/Painted Post/Steuben	03193424	607/936-4656	215
Hope Hall Sch/Rochester/Monroe	04332477	585/426-0210	114
Horace Greeley High Sch/Chappaqua/Westchester	00779835	914/238-7201	253
Horace Mann Elem Sch/Binghamton/Broome	00716493	607/762-8270	27
Horace Mann Lower Sch/Bronx/Bronx	01872959	718/432-3300	26
Horace Mann Mid Upper Sch/Bronx/Bronx	00751194	718/432-4000	26
Horizons on Hudson Mag Sch/Newburgh/Orange	00764660	845/563-3725	166
HORNELL CITY SCH DIST/HORNELL/STEUBEN	00771651	607/324-1302	214
Hornell High Sch/Hornell/Steuben	12034738	607/324-1303	214
Hornell Intermediate Sch/Hornell/Steuben	00771687	607/324-1304	214
Horseheads Christian Sch/Horseheads/Chemung	01408807	607/739-9811	41
HORSEHEADS CTL SCH DIST/HORSEHEADS/CHEMUNG	00719421	607/739-5601	40
Horseheads High Sch/Horseheads/Chemung	00719495	607/795-2500	41
Horseheads Intermediate Sch/Horseheads/Chemung	00719524	607/739-6366	41
Horseheads Middle Sch/Horseheads/Chemung	00719500	607/739-6357	41
Hospital Schools M401/Bronx/Bronx	04019596	718/794-7260	25
Hostos-Lincoln Academy of Sci/Bronx/Bronx	03051840	718/402-5640	16
Houghton Academy/Houghton/Allegany	00716405	585/567-8115	16
Howard A Hanlon Elem Sch/Odessa/Schuyler	00770932	607/594-3341	207
Howard G Sackett Technical Ctr/Glenfield/Lewis	00730475	315/377-7300	101
Howard L Goff Middle Sch/E Greenbush/Rensselaer	00766814	518/207-2430	190
Howard T Herber Middle Sch/Malverne/Nassau	00737150	516/887-6400	124
Howe Elem Sch/Schenectady/Schenectady	00770475	518/370-8295	204
Howell Road Elem Sch/Valley Stream/Nassau	00738867	516/568-6130	130
Howitt Middle Sch/Farmingdale/Nassau	00735475	516/434-5410	119
HS 560-City as Sch/New York/New York	02068759	212/337-6800	136
HS Construct Trades Eng & Arch/Ozone Park/Queens	10026876	718/846-6280	180
HS Dual Lang & Asian Studies/New York/New York	10000690	212/475-4097	136
HS for Community Leadership/Jamaica/Queens	11560849	718/558-9801	182
HS for Contemporary Arts/Bronx/Bronx	05280956	718/944-5610	22
HS for Energy & Technology/Bronx/Bronx	11849580	718/733-3080	20
HS for Environmental Studies/New York/New York	04037330	212/262-8113	136
HS for Excellence & Innovation/New York/New York	05098143	212/569-1022	141
HS for Global Citizenship/Brooklyn/Kings	05349722	718/230-6300	86
HS for Health Careers & Sci/New York/New York	04877219	212/927-1841	141
HS for Language & Diplomacy/New York/New York	11447728	212/253-2480	136
HS for Language & Innovation/Bronx/Bronx	11715020	718/944-3625	22
HS for Media & Communications/New York/New York	04877245	212/927-1841	141
HS for Medical Professions/Brooklyn/Kings	11103324	718/290-8700	87
HS for Public Service/Brooklyn/Kings	05281194	718/756-5325	86
HS for Service & Learning/Brooklyn/Kings	05349758	718/564-2551	86
HS for Youth & Cmty Dev/Brooklyn/Kings	05349693	718/564-2470	86
HS Health Prof & Human Serv/New York/New York	04037823	212/780-9175	136
HS Innovation Adver-Media/Brooklyn/Kings	11103130	718/290-8760	87
HS Law & Public Service/New York/New York	04877233	212/342-6130	141
HS Law Advocacy/Cmty Justice/New York/New York	05101398	212/501-1201	138
HS Law Enforcement Pub Safety/Jamaica/Queens	05274701	718/977-4800	182
HS Math Science & Engr at Ccny/New York/New York	05101403	212/281-6490	140
HS of American Studies-Lehman/Bronx/Bronx	05098090	718/329-2144	20
HS of Applied Communications/Long Is City/Queens	10008678	718/389-3163	177

New York School Directory
DISTRICT & SCHOOL TELEPHONE INDEX

School/City/County DISTRICT/CITY/COUNTY	PID	TELEPHONE NUMBER	PAGE
HS of Arts & Technology/New York/New York	05101386	212/501-1198	138
HS of Computers & Technology/Bronx/Bronx	05349473	718/696-3930	22
HS of Economics & Finance/New York/New York	04037287	212/346-0708	136
HS of Hospitality Management/New York/New York	05348912	212/586-0963	136
HS of Sports Management/Brooklyn/Kings	10008654	718/333-7650	91
HS of Telecom Arts & Tech/Brooklyn/Kings	00740729	718/759-3400	90
HS Teaching & the Professions/Bronx/Bronx	05098129	718/329-7380	21
HUDSON CITY SCH DIST/HUDSON/COLUMBIA	00720482	518/828-4360	46
Hudson Country Mont Sch/New Rochelle/Westchester	01560493	914/636-6202	265
HUDSON FALLS CENTRAL SCH DIST/HUDSON FALLS/WASHINGTON	00778984	518/747-2121	248
Hudson Falls High Sch/Hudson Falls/Washington	00779017	518/681-4206	248
Hudson Falls Intermediate Sch/Hudson Falls/Washington	00779043	518/681-4400	248
Hudson Falls Middle Sch/Hudson Falls/Washington	00779029	518/681-4300	248
Hudson Falls Primary Sch/Hudson Falls/Washington	00779005	518/681-4450	248
Hudson High Sch/Hudson/Columbia	00720535	518/828-4360	46
Hudson HS-Lrng Technologies/New York/New York	11561324	212/488-3330	136
Hudson Junior High Sch/Hudson/Columbia	11455725	518/828-4360	46
Hudson Valley Career Academies/Chester/Orange	04934415	845/469-2270	163
Hudson Valley Christian Acad/Mahopac Falls/Putnam	05242899	845/628-2775	176
Hudson Valley Sudbury Sch/Kingston/Ulster	12314411	845/679-1002	244
Hudson View Christian Academy/Yonkers/Westchester	04341143	914/968-7047	266
Hudson Way Immersion Sch/New York/New York	12110409	212/787-8088	144
Hugh R Jones Elem Sch/Utica/Oneida	00760676	315/792-2171	152
Hugh W Gregg Elem Sch/Corning/Steuben	00771481	607/962-1514	214
Hughes Elem Sch/New Hartford/Oneida	00760169	315/738-9350	151
Humanities & Arts High Sch/Cambria HTS/Queens	04319281	718/978-2135	183
Humanities Preparatory Academy/New York/New York	04753649	212/929-4433	136
Hunter College Elem Sch/New York/New York	02161595	212/860-1292	4
Hunter College High Sch/New York/New York	05330159	212/860-1267	4
Hunter Elem Sch/Hunter/Greene	00729309	518/263-4256	76
HUNTER TANNERSVILLE CTL SD/TANNERSVILLE/GREENE	00729294	518/589-5400	76
Hunter Tannersville Mid & HS/Tannersville/Greene	00729311	518/589-5880	76
Hunters Point Cmty Middle Sch/Astoria/Queens	11924049	718/609-3300	184
Huntington High Sch/Huntington/Suffolk	00773817	631/673-2001	223
Huntington Montessori Sch/S Huntington/Suffolk	12314875	631/385-3388	235
Huntington PK-8 Sch/Syracuse/Onondaga	00762404	315/435-4565	158
HUNTINGTON UNION FREE SCH DIST/HUNTINGTN STA/SUFFOLK	00773776	631/673-2038	223
Hutchinson Elem Sch/Pelham/Westchester	00781450	914/738-3640	260
Huth Road Elem Sch/Grand Island/Erie	00724086	716/773-8850	61
Hyde Leadership CS/Bronx/Bronx	10026280	718/991-5500	4
Hyde Leadership CS Brooklyn/Brooklyn/Kings	11561051	718/495-5620	88
HYDE PARK CENTRAL SCH DIST/HYDE PARK/DUTCHESS	00721670	845/229-4000	52
Hyde Park Elem Sch/Niagara Falls/Niagara	00759316	716/278-7980	148

I

School/City/County	PID	TELEPHONE NUMBER	PAGE
Icahn Charter School 1/Bronx/Bronx	04948129	718/716-8105	4
Icahn Charter School 2/Bronx/Bronx	10969682	718/828-6107	4
Icahn Charter School 3/Bronx/Bronx	11128740	718/828-0034	4
Icahn Charter School 4/Bronx/Bronx	11698874	718/828-0034	4
Icahn Charter School 5/Bronx/Bronx	11722970	718/828-0034	5
Icahn Charter School 6/Bronx/Bronx	11824437	718/294-1706	5
Icahn Charter School 7/Bronx/Bronx	11933806	718/328-5480	5
ICHABOD CRANE CENTRAL SCHOOLS/VALATIE/COLUMBIA	00720561	518/758-7575	46
Ichabod Crane High Sch/Valatie/Columbia	00720573	518/758-7575	46
Ichabod Crane Middle Sch/Valatie/Columbia	00720597	518/758-7575	46
Ichabod Crane Primary Sch/Valatie/Columbia	00720585	518/758-7575	46
Ideal Islamic Sch/Long Is City/Queens	05287069	718/728-5307	187
Ideal School of Manhattan/New York/New York	10756605	212/769-1699	144
Idle Hour Elem Sch/Oakdale/Suffolk	00772930	631/244-2306	220

School/City/County DISTRICT/CITY/COUNTY	PID	TELEPHONE NUMBER	PAGE
Imagine Academy/Brooklyn/Kings	11150585	718/376-8882	98
Imagine ME Leadership Chtr Sch/Brooklyn/Kings	11561049	347/985-2140	88
Immaculate Conception Academy/Jamaica/Queens	00753154	718/739-5933	186
Immaculate Conception Sch/Astoria/Queens	00753142	718/728-1969	186
Immaculate Conception Sch/Bronx/Bronx	00755671	718/547-3346	25
Immaculate Conception Sch/Bronx/Bronx	00755700	718/585-4843	25
Immaculate Conception Sch/East Aurora/Erie	00726280	716/652-5855	65
Immaculate Conception Sch/Fayetteville/Onondaga	00762947	315/637-3961	160
Immaculate Conception Sch/New York/New York	00755645	212/475-2590	143
Immaculate Conception Sch/Tuckahoe/Westchester	00755657	914/961-3785	264
Immaculate Conception Sch/Wellsville/Allegany	00726319	585/593-5840	15
Immaculate Heart Ctl ES/Watertown/Jefferson	00769103	315/788-7011	82
Immaculate Heart Ctl Jr/Sr HS/Watertown/Jefferson	00769139	315/788-4670	82
Immaculate Heart of Mary Sch/Scarsdale/Westchester	00755724	914/723-5608	265
In-Tech Academy Middle HS 368/Bronx/Bronx	04923090	718/432-4300	21
Incarnation Sch/New York/New York	00755736	212/795-1030	143
Incarnation Sch/Queens Vlg/Queens	00753180	718/465-5066	186
Increase Miller Elem Sch/Goldens BRG/Westchester	00780547	914/763-7100	257
Independence High Sch/New York/New York	04020258	212/262-8067	136
Indian Hollow Primary Sch/Commack/Suffolk	00772667	631/858-3590	219
Indian Lake Central Sch/Indian Lake/Hamilton	00729361	518/648-5024	76
INDIAN LAKE CTL SCH DIST/INDIAN LAKE/HAMILTON	00729359	518/648-5024	76
Indian Landing Elem Sch/Rochester/Monroe	00732394	585/249-6900	110
INDIAN RIVER CTL SCH DIST/PHILADELPHIA/JEFFERSON	00730140	315/642-3441	80
Indian River High Sch/Philadelphia/Jefferson	00730176	315/642-3427	80
Indian River Intermediate Sch/Philadelphia/Jefferson	05092723	315/642-0405	80
Indian River Middle Sch/Philadelphia/Jefferson	03280235	315/642-0125	80
Industry Residential Center/Rush/Monroe	03397204	585/533-2600	5
Information Technology HS/Long Is City/Queens	05270107	718/937-4270	184
Innovation Diploma Plus HS/New York/New York	11447754	212/724-2039	138
Institute for Collaborative Ed/New York/New York	04431023	212/475-7972	136
Institute Health Professionals/Cambria HTS/Queens	11924075	718/723-7301	183
Institute of Tech-Central/Syracuse/Onondaga	00762222	315/435-4300	158
Int'l HS-Health Sciences/Elmhurst/Queens	11924178	718/595-8600	177
Int'l School of Brooklyn/Brooklyn/Kings	11221603	718/369-3023	98
Integrated Arts & Tech HS/Rochester/Monroe	11559955	585/324-3750	111
International Christian Sch/Brooklyn/Kings	04974453	718/436-8924	98
International Cmty High Sch/Bronx/Bronx	10027129	718/665-4128	16
International CS of New York/Brooklyn/Kings	12170514	718/305-4199	5
International High Sch/Long Is City/Queens	03008908	718/392-3433	177
International HS at Lafayette/Brooklyn/Kings	10027143	718/333-7860	91
International HS-Prospect Hgts/Brooklyn/Kings	05349746	718/230-6333	86
International HS-Union Sq/New York/New York	11561312	212/533-2560	136
International Leadership CS/Bronx/Bronx	10026565	718/562-2300	5
International Sch for Lib Arts/Bronx/Bronx	10008604	718/329-8570	21
Inwood Acad for Ldshp Chtr Sch/New York/New York	11561233	646/665-5570	141
Inwood Early Clg Hlth-Info TEC/New York/New York	12043167	212/567-1394	141
Iona Prep Lower Sch/New Rochelle/Westchester	00755748	914/633-7744	265
Iona Preparatory Sch/New Rochelle/Westchester	00755750	914/632-0714	265
Irondequoit High Sch/Rochester/Monroe	00732241	585/266-7351	113
IROQUOIS CENTRAL SCH DIST/ELMA/ERIE	00724309	716/652-3000	61
Iroquois High Sch/Elma/Erie	00724335	716/995-2440	62

School Year 2020-2021   800-333-8802   NY-V23

DISTRICT & SCHOOL TELEPHONE INDEX

Market Data Retrieval

School/City/County DISTRICT/CITY/COUNTY	PID	TELEPHONE NUMBER	PAGE
Iroquois Middle Sch/Elma/Erie	00724323	716/652-3000	62
Iroquois Middle Sch/Rochester/Monroe	00732253	585/342-3450	113
Iroquois Middle Sch/Schenectady/Schenectady	00770267	518/377-2233	204
Irvington High Sch/Irvington/Westchester	00780511	914/591-8648	257
Irvington Middle Sch/Irvington/Westchester	00780523	914/269-5312	257
IRVINGTON UNION FREE SCH DIST/IRVINGTON/WESTCHESTER	00780494	914/591-8500	257
Irwin Altman Middle School 172/Floral Park/Queens	00748185	718/831-4000	179
IS 002 George L Egbert/Staten Island/Richmond	00749725	718/987-5336	192
IS 5 Walter H Crowley/Elmhurst/Queens	04753754	718/205-6788	177
IS 7 Elias Bernstein/Staten Island/Richmond	00749660	718/697-8488	192
IS 10 Horace Greeley/Long Is City/Queens	00749426	718/278-7054	184
IS 24 Myra S Barnes/Staten Island/Richmond	00749672	718/982-4700	192
IS 25 Adrien Block/Flushing/Queens	00747870	718/961-3480	178
IS 27 Anning S Prall/Staten Island/Richmond	00749658	718/981-8800	192
IS 34 Tottenville/Staten Island/Richmond	00749684	718/477-4500	192
IS 49 Berta A Dreyfus/Staten Island/Richmond	00749713	718/727-6040	192
IS 51 Edwin Markham/Staten Island/Richmond	00749696	718/981-0502	193
IS 59 Springfield Gardens/Sprngfld GDNS/Queens	00749141	718/527-3501	183
IS 61 Leonardo Da Vinci/Corona/Queens	00747612	718/760-3233	177
IS 61 William A Morris/Staten Island/Richmond	00749701	718/727-8481	193
IS 68 Isaac Bildersee/Brooklyn/Kings	00745999	718/241-4800	87
IS 72 Rocco Laurie/Staten Island/Richmond	01533062	718/698-5757	193
IS 73 Frank Sansivieri/Maspeth/Queens	00747636	718/639-3817	177
IS 75 Frank D Paulo/Staten Island/Richmond	02897598	718/701-6343	193
IS 77 Queens/Ridgewood/Queens	03052272	718/366-7120	177
IS 93 Ridgewood/Ridgewood/Queens	00747648	718/821-4882	177
IS 96 Seth Low/Brooklyn/Kings	00746773	718/236-1344	91
IS 98 Bay Academy/Brooklyn/Kings	04797231	718/891-9005	91
IS 117 Joseph H Wade/Bronx/Bronx	00743616	718/583-7750	19
IS 125 Thomas McCann-Woodside/Woodside/Queens	00747650	718/937-0320	177
IS 136 Charles O Dewey/Brooklyn/Kings	00745353	718/840-1950	84
IS 141 the Steinway/Long Is City/Queens	00749438	718/278-6403	184
IS 145 Joseph Pulitzer/Jackson HTS/Queens	00749402	718/457-1242	184
IS 171 Abraham Lincoln/Brooklyn/Kings	00746292	718/647-0111	88
IS 181 Pablo Casals/Bronx/Bronx	00744153	718/904-5600	23
IS 187 Christa McAuliffe Sch/Brooklyn/Kings	04291055	718/236-3394	90
IS 192 Linden/Saint Albans/Queens	00749139	718/479-5540	183
IS 204 Oliver Wendell Holmes/Long Is City/Queens	00749414	718/937-1463	184
IS 206 Ann Mersereau/Bronx/Bronx	02112427	718/584-1570	21
IS 211 John Wilson/Brooklyn/Kings	00745951	718/251-4411	87
IS 217 Sch of Performing Arts/Bronx/Bronx	00744660	718/589-4844	24
IS 219 New Venture/Bronx/Bronx	04877362	718/681-7093	19
IS 227 Louis Armstrong/East Elmhurst/Queens	02180539	718/335-7500	184
IS 228 David A Boody/Brooklyn/Kings	00746785	718/375-7635	91
IS 229 Dr Roland Patterson/Bronx/Bronx	01833446	718/583-6266	19
IS 230Q Sch for Civics In Cmty/Jackson HTS/Queens	04923026	718/335-7648	184
IS 232X Alexander Macomb Sch/Bronx/Bronx	04952584	718/583-7007	19
IS 237 Rachel Carson Magnet/Flushing/Queens	00747868	718/353-6464	178
IS 238 Susan B Anthony/Hollis/Queens	00749115	718/297-9821	183
IS 239 Mark Twain Gifted Sch/Brooklyn/Kings	00746797	718/266-0814	91
IS 250 Robert F Kennedy/Flushing/Queens	04037457	718/591-9000	178
IS 254/Bronx/Bronx	04876849	718/220-8700	21
IS 281 Joseph B Cavallaro/Brooklyn/Kings	00746802	718/996-6706	91
IS 285 Meyer Levin/Brooklyn/Kings	00745987	718/451-2200	87
IS 289 Hudson River Middle Sch/New York/New York	04923038	212/571-9268	136
IS 303 Herbert Eisenberg Sch/Brooklyn/Kings	00746761	718/996-0100	91
IS 303 Ldrshp & Cmty Svc Acad/Bronx/Bronx	04877374	718/583-5466	19
IS 313 Sch of Leadership Dev/Bronx/Bronx	04877520	718/583-1736	19
IS 318 Eugenio Maria Dehostos/Brooklyn/Kings	00745042	718/782-0589	83
IS 318 Sch Math Sci & Tech/Bronx/Bronx	04952596	718/294-8504	24
IS 339/Bronx/Bronx	00743563	718/583-6767	19
IS 347 School of Humanties/Brooklyn/Kings	04952572	718/821-4248	93
IS 349 Math Science & Tech/Brooklyn/Kings	04952560	718/418-6389	93
IS 364 Gateway/Brooklyn/Kings	01532991	718/642-3007	88
IS 381/Brooklyn/Kings	04876710	718/338-1534	92
IS 392/Brooklyn/Kings	05274672	718/498-2491	93
IS 528 Bea Fuller Rodgers Sch/New York/New York	04192930	212/740-4900	141
IS 584/Bronx/Bronx	12234172	718/742-2900	16
IS/PS 25-S Richmond HS/Staten Island/Richmond	00750633	718/984-1526	194
Isaac E Young Middle Sch/New Rochelle/Westchester	00781151	914/576-4360	259
Isaac Newton MS-Math & Science/New York/New York	04458320	212/860-6006	139
Islamic Cultural Center Sch/New York/New York	12313649	212/828-1838	144
Islamic Leadership Sch/Bronx/Bronx	11531903	718/892-5555	26
ISLAND PARK UNION FREE SD/ISLAND PARK/NASSAU	00736467	516/434-2600	122
Island Trees High Sch/Levittown/Nassau	00736534	516/520-2136	122
Island Trees Memorial Mid Sch/Levittown/Nassau	00736522	516/520-2157	122
ISLAND TREES UNION FREE SD/LEVITTOWN/NASSAU	00736508	516/520-2100	122
Islip Academic Center/Oakdale/Suffolk	02056914	631/244-5950	216
Islip High Sch/Islip/Suffolk	00773908	631/650-8301	224
Islip Middle Sch/Islip/Suffolk	00773910	631/650-8500	224
ISLIP UNION FREE SCH DIST/ISLIP/SUFFOLK	00773881	631/650-8200	223
It Takes A Village Academy/Brooklyn/Kings	10911946	718/629-2307	88
ITHACA CITY SCH DIST/ITHACA/TOMPKINS	00777435	607/274-2101	240
Ithaca High Sch/Ithaca/Tompkins	00777576	607/274-2143	240
Ithaca Waldorf Sch/Ithaca/Tompkins	10756277	607/256-2020	241
Ivan Green Primary Sch/Rochester/Monroe	00731613	585/339-1310	107
Ives School-Lincoln Hall/Lincolndale/Westchester	02115041	914/248-7474	266
Ivy Hill Prep Charter Sch/Brooklyn/Kings	12367511	917/789-8959	5
Ivy League Sch/Smithtown/Suffolk	02164250	631/265-4177	235

J

J E Lanigan Elem Sch/Fulton/Oswego	00765547	315/593-5470	171
J Fred Sparke Elem Sch/Levittown/Nassau	00736546	516/520-2126	122
J M McKenney Middle Sch/Canton/St Lawrence	00768367	315/386-8561	209
J M Rapport School Career Dev/Bronx/Bronx	02232390	718/993-5581	25
J Taylor Finley Middle Sch/Huntington/Suffolk	00773788	631/673-2020	223
J V Forrestal Elem Sch/Beacon/Dutchess	00721553	845/838-6900	51
J W Leary Junior High Sch/Massena/St Lawrence	00768733	315/764-3720	211
J Watson Bailey Middle Sch/Kingston/Ulster	00777916	845/943-3940	242
Jack Abrams STEM Magnet Sch/Huntingtn Sta/Suffolk	11932474	631/673-2060	223
Jackson Annex Sch/Hempstead/Nassau	01813381	516/434-4600	121
Jackson Avenue Elem Sch/Mineola/Nassau	00737497	516/237-2300	125
Jackson Heights Elem Sch/Glens Falls/Warren	00778570	518/793-1071	245
Jackson Heights SDA Elem Sch/Woodside/Queens	01463364	718/426-5729	188
Jackson Main Elem Sch/Hempstead/Nassau	00736144	516/434-4650	121
Jackson Primary Sch/Batavia/Genesee	00728850	585/343-2480	73
Jacqueline Kennedy Onassis HS/New York/New York	04291031	212/391-0041	136
Jamaica Gateway to Sciences/Jamaica/Queens	11714856	718/480-2689	182
Jamaica SDA Elem Sch/Jamaica/Queens	11911432	718/297-3491	188
Jamaican Children's Sch/Jamaica/Queens	12105820	718/526-0160	182
James A Beneway High Sch/Ontario CTR/Wayne	00779586	315/524-1050	251
James A Dever Elem Sch/Valley Stream/Nassau	00738855	516/568-6120	130
James A Farley Elem Sch/Stony Point/Rockland	00767600	845/942-3200	197
James A Green High Sch/Dolgeville/Herkimer	00729529	315/429-3155	77
James Allen Alternative Sch/Wheatley HTS/Suffolk	01486811	631/586-1300	216
James Baldwin Sch Excp Lrng/New York/New York	10008721	212/627-2812	136
James E Allen Elem Sch/Dix Hills/Suffolk	01417341	631/254-0094	216
James E Allen Jr-Sr HS/Dix Hills/Suffolk	03479175	631/549-5580	216
James H Boyd Intermediate Sch/Huntington/Suffolk	00773348	631/266-5430	221
James H Vernon Sch/East Norwich/Nassau	00737887	516/624-6562	127
James I O'Neill High Sch/Ft Montgomery/Orange	00764268	845/446-4914	164

New York School Directory

DISTRICT & SCHOOL TELEPHONE INDEX

School/City/County DISTRICT/CITY/COUNTY	PID	TELEPHONE NUMBER	PAGE
James Madison High Sch/Brooklyn/Kings	00741149	718/758-7200	92
James Monroe Ed Campus YABC/Bronx/Bronx	11928758	718/860-8287	24
James Monroe High Sch/Rochester/Monroe	00732643	585/232-1530	111
James S Evans Elem Sch/Wappingers Fl/Dutchess	00722179	845/298-5240	54
James Weldon Johnson Elem Sch/New York/New York	00742428	212/876-5522	139
James Wilson Young Middle Sch/Bayport/Suffolk	00772095	631/472-7820	217
JAMESTOWN CITY SCH DIST/JAMESTOWN/CHAUTAUQUA	00718738	716/483-4350	38
Jamestown High Sch/Jamestown/Chautauqua	00718790	716/483-3470	38
Jamesville Elem Sch/Jamesville/Onondaga	00761436	315/445-8460	155
JAMESVILLE-DEWITT CENTRAL SD/FAYETTEVILLE/ONONDAGA	00761412	315/445-8304	155
Jamesville-DeWitt High Sch/Fayetteville/Onondaga	00761448	315/445-8340	155
Jamesville-DeWitt Middle Sch/Jamesville/Onondaga	00761450	315/445-8360	155
JASPER TROUPSBURG CENTRAL SD/JASPER/STEUBEN	00771742	607/792-3675	214
Jasper Troupsburg Elem Sch/Troupsburg/Steuben	00771819	607/525-6301	215
Jasper Troupsburg Jr Sr HS/Jasper/Steuben	00771754	607/792-3690	215
Jean Nuzzi Intermediate Sch/Queens Vlg/Queens	00749127	718/465-0651	183
Jefferson Academic Center/Prt Jefferson/Suffolk	04762327	631/476-0564	216
Jefferson Avenue Elem Sch/Fairport/Monroe	00731704	585/421-2185	108
Jefferson Central Sch/Jefferson/Schoharie	00770803	607/652-7821	206
JEFFERSON CENTRAL SCH DIST/JEFFERSON/SCHOHARIE	00770798	607/652-7821	206
Jefferson Elem Sch/Massena/St Lawrence	00768707	315/764-3730	211
Jefferson Elem Sch/New Rochelle/Westchester	00781163	914/576-4430	259
Jefferson Elem Sch/Schenectady/Schenectady	00770334	518/355-1342	204
Jefferson Elem Sch/Utica/Oneida	00760793	315/792-2163	152
JEFFERSON LEWIS BOCES/WATERTOWN/JEFFERSON	00730463	315/779-7000	82
Jefferson Middle Sch/Jamestown/Chautauqua	00718805	716/483-4411	38
Jefferson Primary Sch/Huntington/Suffolk	00773829	631/673-2070	223
Jefferson Rehabilitation Ctr/Watertown/Jefferson	01793286	315/788-2730	82
Jefferson Road Elem Sch/Pittsford/Monroe	00732461	585/267-1300	110
Jennie F Snapp Middle Sch/Endicott/Broome	00716807	607/757-2156	29
Jericho Elem Sch/Centereach/Suffolk	00774263	631/285-8600	225
Jericho Middle Sch/Jericho/Nassau	04036946	516/203-3620	123
Jericho Senior High Sch/Jericho/Nassau	00736601	516/203-3610	123
JERICHO UNION FREE SCH DIST/JERICHO/NASSAU	00736572	516/203-3600	122
Jessie J Kaplan Spec Sch/West Nyack/Rockland	01417298	845/627-4797	195
Jessie T Zoller Elem Sch/Schenectady/Schenectady	00770487	518/370-8290	205
Jewish Center for Special Ed/Brooklyn/Kings	02163476	718/782-0064	98
Jewish Fndtn Sch-Staten Island/Staten Island/Richmond	00751376	718/983-6042	195
Jewish Heritage Day Sch/Amherst/Erie	11228429	716/568-0226	66
Jewish Institue of Queens/Elmhurst/Queens	12142622	718/426-9369	188
JHS 8 Richard S Grossley/Jamaica/Queens	00748836	718/739-6883	182
JHS 14 Shell Bank/Brooklyn/Kings	00747088	718/743-0220	92
JHS 22 Jordan L Mott/Bronx/Bronx	00743628	718/681-6850	19
JHS 50 John D Wells/Brooklyn/Kings	00745107	718/387-4184	83
JHS 52 Harold O Levy Sch/New York/New York	00742868	212/567-9162	141
JHS 54 Booker T Washington/New York/New York	00742167	212/678-2861	138
JHS 62 Ditmas Sch/Brooklyn/Kings	00746515	718/941-5450	90
JHS 67 Louis Pasteur Sch/Little Neck/Queens	00748202	718/423-8138	179
JHS 74 Nathaniel Hawthorne/Bayside/Queens	00748161	718/631-6800	179
JHS 78 Roy H Mann/Brooklyn/Kings	00747129	718/763-4701	92
JHS 80 the Mosholu Pkwy Sch/Bronx/Bronx	00743991	718/405-6300	21
JHS 88 Peter Rouget/Brooklyn/Kings	00745339	718/788-4482	84
JHS 98 Herman Ridder/Bronx/Bronx	00744517	718/589-8200	24
JHS 104 Simon Baruch/New York/New York	00741864	212/674-4545	136
JHS 118 William W Niles/Bronx/Bronx	00743874	718/584-2330	21
JHS 123 James M Kieran/Bronx/Bronx	00743525	718/328-2105	17
JHS 127 Castle Hill/Bronx/Bronx	00744189	718/892-8600	23
JHS 131 Albert Einstein/Bronx/Bronx	00743484	718/991-7490	17
JHS 143 Eleanor Roosevelt/New York/New York	00742870	212/927-7739	141

School/City/County DISTRICT/CITY/COUNTY	PID	TELEPHONE NUMBER	PAGE
JHS 144 Michelangelo Sch/Bronx/Bronx	00744165	718/794-9749	23
JHS 151 Lou Gehrig/Bronx/Bronx	00743020	718/292-0260	16
JHS 157 Stephen A Halsey/Rego Park/Queens	00748848	718/830-4910	182
JHS 162 Willoughby/Brooklyn/Kings	00750255	718/821-4860	93
JHS 167 Robert F Wagner/New York/New York	00741890	212/535-8610	136
JHS 185 Edward Bleeker/Flushing/Queens	00747894	718/445-3232	178
JHS 189 Daniel Carter Beard/Flushing/Queens	00747909	718/359-6676	178
JHS 190 Russell Sage/Forest Hills/Queens	00748850	718/830-4970	182
JHS 194 William H Carr/Whitestone/Queens	00747911	718/746-0818	178
JHS 201 Dyker Heights/Brooklyn/Kings	00746498	718/833-9363	90
JHS 202 Robert H Goddard/Ozone Park/Queens	00748496	718/848-0001	180
JHS 210 Elizabeth Blackwell/Ozone Park/Queens	00748501	718/845-5942	180
JHS 216 George J Ryan/Fresh Meadows/Queens	00748197	718/358-2005	179
JHS 217 Robert A Van Wyck/Jamaica/Queens	00748862	718/657-1120	182
JHS 218 James Peter Sinnott/Brooklyn/Kings	00746151	718/647-9050	88
JHS 220 John Pershing/Brooklyn/Kings	00746503	718/633-8200	90
JHS 223 the Montauk/Brooklyn/Kings	00746474	718/438-0155	90
JHS 226 Virgil I Grissom/S Ozone Park/Queens	01292323	718/843-2260	180
JHS 227 Edward Shallow/Brooklyn/Kings	00746486	718/256-8218	90
JHS 234 Arthur W Cunningham/Brooklyn/Kings	00747076	718/645-1334	92
JHS 259 William McKinley/Brooklyn/Kings	00746527	718/833-1000	90
JHS 278 Marine Park/Brooklyn/Kings	00747117	718/375-3523	92
JHS 291 Roland Hayes/Brooklyn/Kings	00750140	718/574-0361	94
JHS 292 Margaret S Douglas/Brooklyn/Kings	00746149	718/498-6562	88
JHS 383 Philippa Schuyler/Brooklyn/Kings	01833472	718/574-0390	94
Jill Chaifetz Transfer HS/Bronx/Bronx	10911843	718/402-2429	16
JL Miller-Great Neck North HS/Great Neck/Nassau	00736003	516/441-4700	120
Joel Braverman High Sch/Brooklyn/Kings	01409291	718/377-1100	98
Johanna Perrin Middle Sch/Fairport/Monroe	00731716	585/421-2080	108
John A Coleman Catholic HS/Hurley/Ulster	00755762	845/338-2750	244
John A Coleman Sch-Yonkers/Yonkers/Westchester	02162630	914/294-6100	266
John A Sciole Elem Sch/Depew/Erie	00724830	716/686-3285	62
John Adams High Sch/Ozone Park/Queens	00741187	718/322-0500	180
John Adams YABC/Ozone Park/Queens	11928899	718/322-0500	180
John Bowne High Sch/Flushing/Queens	00741199	718/263-1919	178
John C Birdlebough High Sch/Phoenix/Oswego	00765810	315/695-1631	172
John Cardinal O'Connor Sch/Irvington/Westchester	11708364	914/591-9330	266
John D George Elem Sch/Verona/Oneida	00760561	315/829-7361	153
John Dewey High Sch/Brooklyn/Kings	00741204	718/373-6400	91
John E Joy Elem Sch/Rome/Oneida	00760494	315/334-1260	151
John Ericsson MS 126 Env Engr/Brooklyn/Kings	00745092	718/782-2527	83
John F Hughes Elem Sch/Utica/Oneida	00760688	315/368-6620	152
John F Kennedy Elem Sch/Brewster/Putnam	00766357	845/279-2087	175
John F Kennedy Elem Sch/East Islip/Suffolk	00773245	631/224-2003	221
John F Kennedy Elem Sch/Kingston/Ulster	00777928	845/943-3100	242
John F Kennedy Elem Sch/Ogdensburg/St Lawrence	00768862	315/393-4264	211
John F Kennedy Elem Sch/West Babylon/Suffolk	00776132	631/376-7800	233
John F Kennedy High Sch/Bellmore/Nassau	00737394	516/992-1400	117
John F Kennedy High Sch/Cheektowaga/Erie	00725119	716/891-6407	59
John F Kennedy High Sch/Plainview/Nassau	00738051	516/434-3125	128
John F Kennedy Interm Sch/Deer Park/Suffolk	00773099	631/274-4310	220
John F Kennedy Jr Sch/Elmhurst/Queens	11714882	718/760-1083	185
John F Kennedy Magnet Sch/Port Chester/Westchester	00781589	914/934-7990	261
John F Kennedy Middle Sch/Bethpage/Nassau	00735097	516/644-4200	117
John F Kennedy Middle Sch/Cheektowaga/Erie	04794382	716/897-7300	59
John F Kennedy Middle Sch/Port Jeff Sta/Suffolk	00772837	631/474-8160	218
John F Kennedy Middle Sch/Utica/Oneida	00760690	315/792-2088	152
John F Kennedy Sch/Great Neck/Nassau	00736039	516/441-4200	121
John F Kennedy YABC/Bronx/Bronx	11928734	718/817-7470	21
John G Borden Middle Sch/Wallkill/Ulster	00778403	845/895-7175	244
John G Dinkelmeyer Elem Sch/N Bellmore/Nassau	00737655	516/992-3114	126
John H West Elem Sch/Bethpage/Nassau	00737954	516/992-7500	127
John J Daly Elem Sch/Prt Washingtn/Nassau	00738178	516/767-5200	128
John James Audubon School 33/Rochester/Monroe	00732978	585/482-9290	111
John Jay High Sch/Cross River/Westchester	00780561	914/763-7201	257
John Jay High Sch/Hopewell Jct/Dutchess	00722181	845/897-6700	54
John Jay Middle Sch/Cross River/Westchester	00780559	914/763-7500	257

DISTRICT & SCHOOL TELEPHONE INDEX

Market Data Retrieval

School/City/County DISTRICT/CITY/COUNTY	PID	TELEPHONE NUMBER	PAGE
John Jay School for Law/Brooklyn/Kings	04952493	718/832-4250	84
John Kennedy Intermediate Sch/Batavia/Genesee	00728862	585/343-2480	73
John Lewis Childs Elem Sch/Floral Park/Nassau	00735542	516/434-2780	119
John M Marshall Elem Sch/East Hampton/Suffolk	00773178	631/329-4155	220
John P McKenna Elem Sch/Massapequa Pk/Nassau	00737291	516/308-5500	125
John Paulding Primary Sch/Tarrytown/Westchester	00781993	914/631-5526	262
John Pearl Elem Sch/Bohemia/Suffolk	00772942	631/244-2300	220
John Philip Sousa Elem Sch/Prt Washingtn/Nassau	00738180	516/767-5350	128
John Pound Early Childhood Ctr/Lockport/Niagara	00759122	716/478-4751	147
John Quincy Adams Primary Sch/Deer Park/Suffolk	00773104	631/274-4410	220
John S Burke Catholic High Sch/Goshen/Orange	00755786	845/294-5481	168
John S Hobart Elem Sch/Shirley/Suffolk	02130883	631/874-1296	233
John Street Elem Sch/Franklin Sq/Nassau	00735633	516/481-5780	119
John T Waugh Elem Sch/Angola/Erie	00724799	716/926-2370	60
John V Lindsay Wildcat Acad CS/New York/New York	04904783	212/209-6006	136
John W Dodd Middle Sch/Freeport/Nassau	00735736	516/867-5280	120
John W LaVelle Prep Chtr Sch/Staten Island/Richmond	11468186	347/855-2238	5
John Walton Spencer School 16/Rochester/Monroe	00732837	585/235-1272	111
John Williams School 5/Rochester/Monroe	00732722	585/325-2255	111
Johnsburg Central Sch/North Creek/Warren	00778673	518/251-2921	245
JOHNSBURG CENTRAL SCH DIST/NORTH CREEK/WARREN	00778661	518/251-2921	245
JOHNSON CITY CENTRAL SCH DIST/JOHNSON CITY/BROOME	00716871	607/930-1005	28
Johnson City High Sch/Johnson City/Broome	00716900	607/930-1009	28
Johnson City Intermediate Sch/Johnson City/Broome	12108365	607/930-1015	29
Johnson City Middle Sch/Johnson City/Broome	00716883	607/930-1012	29
Johnson City Primary Sch/Johnson City/Broome	12108353	607/930-1015	29
Johnstown High Sch/Johnstown/Fulton	00728587	518/762-4661	71
Jonas Bronck Academy/Bronx/Bronx	04753742	718/365-2502	21
Jonas E Salk Middle Sch/Levittown/Nassau	00736807	516/434-7350	123
JORDAN ELBRIDGE CTL SCH DIST/JORDAN/ONONDAGA	00761486	315/689-8500	155
Jordan-Elbridge High Sch/Jordan/Onondaga	00761503	315/689-8510	156
Jordan-Elbridge Middle Sch/Jordan/Onondaga	00761515	315/689-8520	156
Joseph A Edgar Interm Sch/Rocky Point/Suffolk	00775114	631/744-1600	228
Joseph A McNeil Elem Sch/Hempstead/Nassau	00736091	516/434-4500	121
Joseph B Radez Elem Sch/Richmondville/Schoharie	00770853	518/294-6621	206
Joseph D'Aquanni West Road IS/Pleasant Vly/Dutchess	00721515	845/635-4310	51
Joseph Henry Elem Sch/Galway/Saratoga	00769658	518/882-1291	201
Joseph S Gruss Yeshiva/Brooklyn/Kings	02978233	718/375-0900	98
Journey Prep Sch/Farmingdale/Nassau	12224907	631/736-2146	133
Joy Fellowship Christian Acad/Bronx/Bronx	11227956	718/583-9300	26
JT Roberts Prek-8 Sch/Syracuse/Onondaga	00762569	315/435-4635	158
Juan Morel Campos Sec Sch/Brooklyn/Kings	00745080	718/302-7900	83
Judith S Kaye High Sch/New York/New York	12234184	212/369-1509	142

K

School/City/County	PID	TELEPHONE NUMBER	PAGE
K C Heffernan Elem Sch/Marcellus/Onondaga	00761888	315/673-6100	157
Kadimah School-Buffalo/Buffalo/Erie	00725743	716/836-6903	66
Kaegebein Elem Sch/Grand Island/Erie	00724098	716/773-8840	61
Kahlil Gibran Sch/Yonkers/Westchester	00782636	914/376-8580	263
Kakiat Steam Academy/Spring Valley/Rockland	00767997	845/577-6100	196
Kaplan Career Academy/New Windsor/Westchester	11917204	845/522-8460	255
Kappa III/Bronx/Bronx	05349411	718/561-3580	24
Kappa Int'l High Sch/Bronx/Bronx	10911879	718/933-1247	21
Kappa MS 215/Bronx/Bronx	10008599	718/590-5455	19
Kappa V/Brooklyn/Kings	05348780	718/922-4690	93
Karafin Sch/Mount Kisco/Westchester	01464344	914/666-9211	266
Karigon Elem Sch/Clifton Park/Saratoga	00769907	518/881-0530	202

School/City/County DISTRICT/CITY/COUNTY	PID	TELEPHONE NUMBER	PAGE
Karl Saile Bear Rd Elem Sch/N Syracuse/Onondaga	00761931	315/218-2400	157
Katonah Elem Sch/Katonah/Westchester	00780573	914/763-7700	257
KATONAH-LEWISBORO SCH DIST/SOUTH SALEM/WESTCHESTER	00780535	914/763-7000	257
Keene Central Sch/Keene Valley/Essex	00727909	518/576-4555	67
KEENE CENTRAL SCH DIST/KEENE VALLEY/ESSEX	00727894	518/576-4555	67
Keeseville Elem Sch/Keeseville/Clinton	00719952	518/834-2839	43
Keio Academy of New York/Purchase/Westchester	03413743	914/694-4825	266
Kellenberg Memorial High Sch/Uniondale/Nassau	03015547	516/292-0200	132
KENDALL CENTRAL SCH DIST/KENDALL/ORLEANS	00765212	585/659-2741	169
Kendall Elem Sch/Kendall/Orleans	00765224	585/659-8317	169
Kendall Jr Sr High Sch/Kendall/Orleans	00765236	585/659-2706	169
Kenmore East High Sch/Tonawanda/Erie	00724505	716/874-8402	62
Kenmore West High Sch/Buffalo/Erie	00724529	716/874-8401	62
KENMORE-TONAWANDA UF SCH DIST/BUFFALO/ERIE	00724373	716/874-8400	62
Kennedy Catholic High Sch/Somers/Westchester	00755774	914/232-5061	265
Kennedy Child Study Center/New York/New York	01794357	212/988-9500	144
Kenneth L Rutherford Elem Sch/Monticello/Sullivan	00776895	845/794-4240	237
Kensico Elem Sch/Valhalla/Westchester	00782064	914/683-5030	263
Kensington Road Elem Sch/Glens Falls/Warren	00778582	518/793-5151	245
Kent Elem Sch/Carmel/Putnam	00766395	845/225-5029	175
Kent Primary Sch/Carmel/Putnam	00766400	845/225-5025	175
Kenton Career & Tech Center/Tonawanda/Erie	12115198	716/961-4010	55
Kerem Shlomo Yeshiva/Brooklyn/Kings	04974465	718/437-7665	98
Kerhonkson Elem Sch/Kerhonkson/Ulster	00778221	845/626-2451	243
Kernan Elem Sch/Utica/Oneida	00760717	315/792-2185	152
KESHEQUA CENTRAL SCH DIST/NUNDA/LIVINGSTON	00730786	585/468-2900	103
Keshequa Interm Sch/Nunda/Livingston	12368917	585/468-2900	103
Keshequa Middle Sch/Nunda/Livingston	00730803	585/468-2541	103
Keshequa Primary Sch/Dalton/Livingston	00730798	585/468-2900	103
Kesser Malka Girls Yeshiva/Brooklyn/Kings	02189664	718/854-7777	98
Ketchum-Grande Memorial Sch/Burnt Hills/Saratoga	02989921	518/399-8182	203
Kew-Forest Sch/Forest Hills/Queens	00752746	718/268-4667	188
Key Collegiate Charter Sch/Brooklyn/Kings	12260250	646/604-4428	5
Khalil Gibran Int'l Academy/Brooklyn/Kings	10911908	718/237-2502	84
Kid Esteem of Montessori Schoo/Commack/Suffolk	02932588	631/321-6675	235
Kildonan Sch/Amenia/Dutchess	00898508	845/373-8111	55
King Center Charter Sch/Buffalo/Erie	04924197	716/891-7912	5
King Street Elem Sch/Port Chester/Westchester	00781591	914/934-7996	261
Kings Collegiate Charter Sch/Brooklyn/Kings	10915021	718/342-6047	5
Kings Elem Sch/Brooklyn/Kings	12174170	347/390-0460	5
KINGS PARK CTL SCH DIST/KINGS PARK/SUFFOLK	00773946	631/269-3310	224
Kings Park High Sch/Kings Park/Suffolk	00773972	631/269-3345	224
Kingsborough Early College Sch/Brooklyn/Kings	10025511	718/333-7850	91
Kingsborough Elem Sch/Gloversville/Fulton	00728501	518/775-5700	71
Kingsbridge Int'l High Sch/Bronx/Bronx	10008628	718/329-8580	21
Kingsbury SDA Sch/Hudson Falls/Washington	03404613	518/747-4424	249
Kingsford Park Elem Sch/Oswego/Oswego	00765731	315/341-2500	171
Kingston Catholic Sch/Kingston/Ulster	00757758	845/339-4390	244
KINGSTON CITY SCH DIST/KINGSTON/ULSTER	00777837	845/339-3000	242
Kingston Senior High Sch/Kingston/Ulster	00777930	845/331-1970	242
Kinneret Day Sch/Bronx/Bronx	01461665	718/548-0900	26
Kinry Road Elem Sch/Poughkeepsie/Dutchess	04281270	845/463-7322	54
KIPP Academy Elem Sch/Bronx/Bronx	12036425	718/943-3737	16
KIPP Academy Middle Sch/Bronx/Bronx	04923648	718/665-3555	16
KIPP All Middle Sch/Bronx/Bronx	12367523	929/288-4730	5
KIPP Amp Elem Middle Sch/Brooklyn/Kings	10008939	718/943-3740	5
KIPP Elements Primary Sch/Bronx/Bronx	12367535	929/288-4740	5
KIPP Freedom Elem Sch/Bronx/Bronx	12310415	718/841-6160	5
KIPP Freedom Middle Sch/Bronx/Bronx	12310427	718/841-6165	5
KIPP Infinity Elem Mid Sch/New York/New York	10008941	212/991-2622	5
KIPP NYC College Prep High Sch/Bronx/Bronx	11458600	212/991-2626	5

New York School Directory

DISTRICT & SCHOOL TELEPHONE INDEX

School/City/County DISTRICT/CITY/COUNTY	PID	TELEPHONE NUMBER	PAGE
KIPP Star Harlem Clg Prep ES/New York/New York	12310960	212/991-2655	5
KIPP Star Middle Sch/New York/New York	05274842	212/991-2650	5
KIPP Tech Valley Charter Sch/Albany/Albany	10774176	518/694-9494	5
KIPP Tech Valley Primary CS/Albany/Albany	12226278	518/242-7725	5
KIPP Washington Heights ES/New York/New York	12320616	212/991-2630	5
KIPP Washington Hts MS/New York/New York	11821588	212/991-2620	5
KIRYAS JOEL UNION FREE SD/ MONROE/ORANGE	03423956	845/782-2300	164
Kiryas Joel Village/Monroe/Orange	03423970	845/782-7510	164
Klem Road North Elem Sch/Webster/Monroe	00733439	585/872-1770	113
Klem Road South Elem Sch/Webster/Monroe	00733441	585/872-1320	113
Knickerbacker Middle Sch/Troy/Rensselaer	00766955	518/233-6811	191
Knickerbocker Elem Sch/Watertown/Jefferson	00730372	315/785-3740	81
Knowledge & Power Prep Acad VI/Far Rockaway/Queens	11924116	718/471-6934	180
Knox Junior High Sch/Johnstown/Fulton	00728599	518/762-3711	71
Knox Sch/Saint James/Suffolk	00776699	631/686-1600	235
Koda Middle Sch/Clifton Park/Saratoga	00769842	518/881-0470	202
Kodomono Kuni Sch/White Plains/Westchester	02617659	914/949-0067	266
Kolel Chasidei Rachmistrivka/Suffern/Rockland	12179833	845/357-5550	199
Kramer Lane Elem Sch/Plainview/Nassau	00735102	516/644-4500	117
Kreamer Street Elem Sch/Bellport/Suffolk	00772186	631/730-1650	231
Kurt Hahn Expeditionary Sch/Brooklyn/Kings	10913724	718/629-1204	88

L

School/City/County DISTRICT/CITY/COUNTY	PID	TELEPHONE NUMBER	PAGE
L A Webber Middle High Sch/Lyndonville/Orleans	00765250	585/765-3164	169
L P Quinn Elem Sch/Tupper Lake/Franklin	00728408	518/359-2981	70
L Pearl Palmer Elem Sch/Baldwinsville/Onondaga	00761125	315/638-6127	154
La Cima Elem Charter Sch/Brooklyn/Kings	11128685	718/443-2136	5
La Fargeville Central Sch/La Fargeville/Jefferson	00730217	315/658-2241	80
LA FARGEVILLE CENTRAL SCH DIST/ LA FARGEVILLE/JEFFERSON	00730205	315/658-2241	80
LA FAYETTE CENTRAL SCH DIST/ LA FAYETTE/ONONDAGA	00761527	315/677-9728	156
La Fayette Jr Sr High Sch/La Fayette/Onondaga	00761541	315/677-3131	156
La Francis Hardiman Elem Sch/Wyandanch/Suffolk	10031053	631/870-0580	234
La Salle Institute/Troy/Rensselaer	00715217	518/283-2500	192
La Scuola D'Italia-G Marconi/New York/New York	02162666	212/369-3290	144
LACKAWANNA CITY SCH DIST/ LACKAWANNA/ERIE	00724622	716/821-5610	62
Lackawanna High Sch/Lackawanna/Erie	00724660	716/821-5610	62
Lackawanna Middle Sch/Lackawanna/Erie	04794370	716/821-5610	62
Laddie Decker Sound Beach Sch/Miller Place/Suffolk	01876656	631/474-2719	226
Lafayette Acad MS 256/New York/New York	04874188	212/222-2857	138
Lafayette Big Picture Sch/La Fayette/Onondaga	11127083	315/504-1000	156
Lafayette Intermediate Sch/Waterloo/Seneca	00771168	315/539-1530	208
LaGrange Middle Sch/Lagrangeville/Dutchess	03268029	845/486-4880	51
Lake Avenue Elem Sch/Saratoga Spgs/Saratoga	00769749	518/584-3678	201
LAKE GEORGE CENTRAL SCH DIST/ LAKE GEORGE/WARREN	00778685	518/668-5456	245
Lake George Elem Sch/Lake George/Warren	00778697	518/668-5714	245
Lake George Jr Sr High Sch/Lake George/Warren	00778702	518/668-5452	245
LAKE PLACID CTL SCH DIST/ LAKE PLACID/ESSEX	00727911	518/523-2475	67
Lake Placid Elem Sch/Lake Placid/Essex	01416983	518/523-3640	67
Lake Placid Middle High Sch/Lake Placid/Essex	00727923	518/523-2474	67
Lake Pleasant Central Sch/Speculator/Hamilton	00729402	518/548-7571	76
LAKE PLEASANT CENTRAL SCH DIST/ SPECULATOR/HAMILTON	00729397	518/548-7571	76
Lake Shore Career & Tech Acad/Angola/Erie	01416971	716/549-4454	56
Lake Shore Christian Sch/Plattsburgh/Clinton	02160060	518/563-4098	45
Lake Shore Middle Sch/Angola/Erie	01399103	716/926-2400	60
Lake Shore Senior High Sch/Angola/Erie	00724804	716/926-2307	60
Lake View Campus/Westport/Essex	00728070	518/962-8244	67
LAKELAND CENTRAL SCH DIST/ SHRUB OAK/WESTCHESTER	00780602	914/245-1700	257
Lakeland Copper Beech Mid Sch/Yorktown Hts/Westchester	00780626	914/245-1885	257
Lakeland High Sch/Shrub Oak/Westchester	00780652	914/528-0600	257
Lakeshore Elem Sch/Rochester/Monroe	00732007	585/966-3900	109
Lakeshore Road Elem Sch/Cicero/Onondaga	00761979	315/218-2600	157
Lakeview Elem Sch/Mahopac/Putnam	00766503	845/628-3331	176
Lakeville Elem Sch/Great Neck/Nassau	00736053	516/441-4300	121
Lakewood Elem Sch/Congers/Rockland	00767404	845/639-6320	196
Lamad Academy Charter Sch/Brooklyn/Kings	12472013	833/465-2623	5
LANCASTER CENTRAL SCH DIST/ LANCASTER/ERIE	00724828	716/686-3200	62
Lancaster High Sch/Lancaster/Erie	00724907	716/686-3255	62
Lancaster Middle Sch/Lancaster/Erie	00724842	716/686-3220	63
Landing Elem Sch/Glen Cove/Nassau	00735891	516/801-7410	120
Landmark High Sch/New York/New York	04037392	212/647-7410	136
LANSING CENTRAL SCH DIST/ LANSING/TOMPKINS	00777617	607/533-3020	240
Lansing High Sch/Lansing/Tompkins	00777643	607/533-3020	240
Lansing Middle Sch/Lansing/Tompkins	00777631	607/533-3020	240
LANSINGBURGH CENTRAL SCH DIST/ TROY/RENSSELAER	00766931	518/233-6850	190
Lansingburgh High Sch/Troy/Rensselaer	00766979	518/233-6806	191
LaSalle Academy/New York/New York	00755815	212/475-8940	143
LaSalle Preparatory Sch/Niagara Falls/Niagara	00759328	716/278-5880	148
LaSalle Sch/Albany/Albany	00715229	518/242-4731	13
Latham Christian Academy/Latham/Albany	02159011	518/785-5916	13
Latham Ridge Elem Sch/Latham/Albany	00714718	518/785-3211	11
Launch Expeditionary Lrng CS/Brooklyn/Kings	11821784	718/221-1064	5
Laurel Hill Sch/East Setauket/Suffolk	02164224	631/751-1154	235
Laurel Park Elem Sch/Brentwood/Suffolk	00772265	631/434-2464	217
Laurel Plains Elem Sch/New City/Rockland	00767416	845/639-6350	196
Laurelton Pardee Interm Sch/Rochester/Monroe	00731572	585/339-1370	107
Laurens Central Sch/Laurens/Otsego	00766072	607/432-2050	173
LAURENS CENTRAL SCH DIST/ LAURENS/OTSEGO	00766060	607/432-2050	173
LaVelle School for the Blind/Bronx/Bronx	00755839	718/882-1212	27
Lawrence Ave Elem Sch/Potsdam/St Lawrence	00768965	315/265-2000	212
Lawrence Elem Sch/Lawrence/Nassau	00736716	516/812-6121	123
Lawrence High Sch/Cedarhurst/Nassau	00736663	516/295-8000	123
Lawrence Middle Sch/Lawrence/Nassau	00736651	516/295-7000	123
Lawrence Primary Sch/Inwood/Nassau	00736687	516/295-6200	123
Lawrence Road Middle Sch/Hempstead/Nassau	00738738	516/918-1500	130
LAWRENCE UNION FREE SCH DIST/ LAWRENCE/NASSAU	00736649	516/295-8000	123
Lawrence Universal Pre-K/Inwood/Nassau	00736704	516/295-6400	123
Lawrence Woodmere Academy/Woodmere/Nassau	00739421	516/374-9000	133
LE ROY CENTRAL SCH DIST/ LE ROY/GENESEE	00728991	585/768-8133	73
Le Roy Jr Sr High Sch/Le Roy/Genesee	00729000	585/768-8131	74
Leaders of Tomorrow/Bronx/Bronx	10910447	718/994-1028	23
Leadership & Pub Service HS/New York/New York	04037835	212/346-0007	136
Leadership Acad for Young Men/Rochester/Monroe	11733668	585/324-7760	111
Leadership Prep Bed Stuy CS/Brooklyn/Kings	10026577	718/636-0360	5
Leadership Prep Brwnsvlle Acad/Brooklyn/Kings	11850371	718/669-7461	5
Leadership Prep Canarsie ES/Brooklyn/Kings	11934343	347/390-0570	5
Leadership Prep Canarsie MS/Brooklyn/Kings	11934355	347/390-0560	5
Leadership Prep Ocean Hill El/Brooklyn/Kings	11560980	718/250-5767	5
Leadership Prep Ocean Hill Mid/Brooklyn/Kings	12310972	347/390-0550	5
League Sch/Brooklyn/Kings	01873135	718/498-2500	98
Leake & Watts Chldrns Home Sch/Yonkers/Westchester	01464239	914/375-8700	266
Learners & Leaders/Ridgewood/Queens	11103403	718/366-1061	177
Learning Spring Elem Sch/New York/New York	05242722	212/239-4926	144
Learning Through Play PK Ctr/Bronx/Bronx	12367547	718/292-4120	16
Learning Tree Prep/Bronx/Bronx	11230991	718/944-0958	27
Learning Tree STEM-Arts Sch/Corona/Queens	04974685	718/397-5446	188
Ledgeview Elem Sch/Clarence/Erie	00723642	716/407-9275	59
Lee Avenue Elem Sch/Hicksville/Nassau	00736429	516/733-2351	122
Lee F Jackson Elem Sch/White Plains/Westchester	00780212	914/948-2992	255
Lee G Peters Career Center/Liverpool/Onondaga	01417183	315/453-4455	154
Lee Road Elem Sch/Wantagh/Nassau	00736821	516/434-7475	123
Leep Dual Language Acad CS/Brooklyn/Kings	12367559	917/819-5337	5

DISTRICT & SCHOOL TELEPHONE INDEX

Market Data Retrieval

School/City/County DISTRICT/CITY/COUNTY	PID	TELEPHONE NUMBER	PAGE
Leeway Sch/Sayville/Suffolk	01795492	631/589-8060	235
Lefferts Gardens Ascend ES/Brooklyn/Kings	12367585	347/464-7600	5
Legacy College Prep CS/Bronx/Bronx	12234110	347/746-1558	5
Lehman Alternative Cmty Sch/Ithaca/Tompkins	00777447	607/274-2183	240
Leif Ericson Day Sch/Brooklyn/Kings	01462607	718/748-9023	98
Leighton Elem Sch/Oswego/Oswego	00765743	315/341-2700	171
Leman Manhattan Prep Sch/New York/New York	10013037	212/232-0266	144
Lemoyne Elem Sch/Syracuse/Onondaga	00762442	315/435-4590	158
Lenape Elem Sch/New Paltz/Ulster	04014845	845/256-4300	243
Lenox Elem Sch/Baldwin/Nassau	00734940	516/434-6400	116
Leo Bernabi Elem Sch/Spencerport/Monroe	00733350	585/349-5400	112
Leo F Giblyn Elem Sch/Freeport/Nassau	00735748	516/867-5260	120
Leon M Goldstein HS Sciences/Brooklyn/Kings	04037263	718/368-8500	92
Leonard E Burket Christian Sch/CTR Moriches/Suffolk	04974893	631/878-1727	235
Leptondale Elem Sch/Wallkill/Ulster	00778374	845/895-7200	244
Letchworth Central High Sch/Gainesville/Wyoming	00783147	585/493-2571	267
LETCHWORTH CENTRAL SCH DIST/GAINESVILLE/WYOMING	00783109	585/493-5450	267
Letchworth Middle Sch/Gainesville/Wyoming	04797190	585/493-2592	267
Lev Bais Yaakov Sch/Brooklyn/Kings	05220528	718/332-6000	98
LEVITTOWN UNION FREE SCH DIST/LEVITTOWN/NASSAU	00736730	516/434-7000	123
Lewis J Bennett Sch Innov Tech/Buffalo/Erie	00722569	716/816-4250	57
LEWISTON PORTER CTL SCH DIST/YOUNGSTOWN/NIAGARA	00758996	716/754-8281	146
Lewiston Porter High Sch/Youngstown/Niagara	00759043	716/754-8281	146
Lewiston Porter Interm Ed Ctr/Youngstown/Niagara	00759005	716/754-8281	147
Lewiston Porter Middle Sch/Youngstown/Niagara	00759031	716/286-7201	147
Lewiston Porter Primary Ed Ctr/Youngstown/Niagara	04949161	716/286-7220	147
Lexington Academy/New York/New York	00742430	212/860-5831	139
Lexington School for Deaf/East Elmhurst/Queens	01462267	718/899-8800	188
Liberation Diploma Plus HS/Brooklyn/Kings	10910461	718/946-6812	91
LIBERTY CENTRAL SCH DIST/LIBERTY/SULLIVAN	00776807	845/292-6171	236
Liberty Elem Sch/Liberty/Sullivan	00776819	845/292-5400	236
Liberty Elem Sch/Vly Cottage/Rockland	00767715	845/353-7240	197
Liberty High Sch/Liberty/Sullivan	00776821	845/292-5400	236
Liberty HS for Newcomers/New York/New York	03048697	212/691-0934	136
Liberty Middle Sch/Liberty/Sullivan	03390335	845/292-5400	236
Lido Elem Sch/Lido Beach/Nassau	00736998	516/897-2140	124
Life Academy HS Film & Music/Brooklyn/Kings	10913748	718/333-7750	91
Life Sciences Secondary Sch/New York/New York	04877257	212/348-1694	136
Lifeline Center for Child Dev/Queens Vlg/Queens	01794955	718/740-4300	188
Lighthouse Christian Academy/Oneonta/Otsego	02827878	607/432-2031	175
Lima Christian Sch/Lima/Livingston	02161272	585/624-3841	104
Lima Primary Sch/Lima/Monroe	00732162	585/624-7140	109
Lime Kiln Elem Sch/Suffern/Rockland	00768006	845/577-6280	196
Lincoln Avenue Elem Sch/Pearl River/Rockland	03389207	845/620-3850	197
Lincoln Avenue Elem Sch/Sayville/Suffolk	00775396	631/244-6725	230
Lincoln Elem Cmty Sch/Schenectady/Schenectady	00770499	518/370-8355	205
Lincoln Elem Sch/Jamestown/Chautauqua	00718817	716/483-4412	38
Lincoln Elem Sch/Mount Vernon/Westchester	02112881	914/665-5039	258
Lincoln Elem Sch/Newark/Wayne	00779275	315/332-3342	250
Lincoln Elem Sch/Scotia/Schenectady	00770671	518/382-1296	205
Lincoln High Sch/Yonkers/Westchester	00782313	914/376-8400	263
Lincoln Middle Sch/Syracuse/Onondaga	00762466	315/435-4450	158
Lincoln Orens Middle Sch/Island Park/Nassau	00736493	516/434-2630	122
Lincoln Park School 44/Rochester/Monroe	00733087	585/328-5272	111
Lincoln School 22/Rochester/Monroe	00732887	585/467-7160	111
Lincoln Street Elem Sch/Waverly/Tioga	00777318	607/565-8176	239
Lincoln-Titus Elem Sch/Crompond/Westchester	00780664	914/528-2519	257
Lindell Elem Sch/Long Beach/Nassau	00737007	516/897-2209	124
Linden Avenue Middle Sch/Red Hook/Dutchess	00722002	845/758-2241	53
Linden Hill Sch/Hawthorne/Westchester	01487906	914/749-2975	256
Linden SDA Sch/Laurelton/Queens	01463388	718/527-6868	188
Linden Tree Elem Sch/Bronx/Bronx	11821758	718/239-7401	23
Lindenhurst Middle Sch/Lindenhurst/Suffolk	00774110	631/867-3500	224
Lindenhurst Senior High Sch/Lindenhurst/Suffolk	00774122	631/867-3700	224
LINDENHURST UNION FREE SD/LINDENHURST/SUFFOLK	00774043	631/867-3000	224
Link IB World Sch/New City/Rockland	00767428	845/624-3494	196
Linnaeus W West Sch/Endicott/Broome	12170837	607/757-2149	29
Lisbon Central Sch/Lisbon/St Lawrence	00768630	315/393-4951	211
LISBON CENTRAL SCH DIST/LISBON/ST LAWRENCE	00768628	315/393-4951	210
Lisha Kill Middle Sch/Albany/Albany	00714873	518/456-2306	12
Listwood Sch/Rochester/Monroe	00732277	585/336-1640	113
Little Britain Elem Sch/New Windsor/Orange	00765028	845/497-4000	167
LITTLE FALLS CITY SCH DIST/LITTLE FALLS/HERKIMER	00729696	315/823-1470	78
Little Falls High Sch/Little Falls/Herkimer	00729701	315/823-1167	78
Little Falls Middle Sch/Little Falls/Herkimer	04368696	315/823-4300	78
Little Flower Sch/Wading River/Suffolk	02055257	631/929-4300	224
LITTLE FLOWER UNION FREE SD/WADING RIVER/SUFFOLK	01854713	631/929-4300	224
Little Meadow Early Chldhd Ctr/Fresh Meadows/Queens	02975827	718/454-6460	188
Little Red Schlhse-Irwin HS/New York/New York	01461421	212/477-5316	144
Little Red Schoolhouse/Troy/Rensselaer	00767222	518/283-6748	191
Little River Community Sch/Canton/St Lawrence	11833476	315/379-9474	212
Little TOR Elem Sch/New City/Rockland	00767430	845/624-3471	196
Little Village Sch/Seaford/Nassau	01794046	516/520-6000	133
LIVERPOOL CTL SCH DIST/LIVERPOOL/ONONDAGA	00761577	315/622-7900	156
Liverpool Elem Sch/Liverpool/Onondaga	00761644	315/453-0254	156
Liverpool High Sch/Liverpool/Onondaga	00761656	315/453-1500	156
Liverpool HS 9th Grade Annex/Liverpool/Onondaga	04807874	315/453-1275	156
Liverpool Middle Sch/Liverpool/Onondaga	00761668	315/453-0258	156
Living Word Academy/Syracuse/Onondaga	02163957	315/437-6744	160
LIVINGSTON MANOR CTL SCH DIST/LIVINGSTN MNR/SULLIVAN	00776833	845/439-4400	236
Livingston Manor Elem Sch/Livingstn MNR/Sullivan	00776845	845/439-4400	236
Livingston Mid High Sch/Livingstn MNR/Sullivan	12469767	845/439-4400	236
LIVONIA CTL SCH DIST/LIVONIA/LIVINGSTON	00730815	585/346-4000	103
Livonia Elem Sch/Livonia/Livingston	00730839	585/346-4000	103
Livonia High Sch/Livonia/Livingston	11077660	585/346-4000	103
Lloyd Harbor Elem Sch/Huntington/Suffolk	00772552	631/367-8800	219
LOCKPORT CITY SCH DIST/LOCKPORT/NIAGARA	00759055	716/478-4811	147
Lockport High Sch/Lockport/Niagara	00759134	716/478-4450	147
Lockport High School West/Lockport/Niagara	04947682	716/478-4625	147
Lockwood Elem Sch/Gainesville/Wyoming	00783135	585/493-2581	267
Locust Primary Sch/Garden City/Nassau	00735803	516/478-1800	120
LOCUST VALLEY CTL SCH DIST/LOCUST VALLEY/NASSAU	00736900	516/277-5000	123
Locust Valley High Sch/Locust Valley/Nassau	00736948	516/277-5100	123
Locust Valley Intermediate Sch/Locust Valley/Nassau	00736936	516/277-5300	123
Locust Valley Middle Sch/Locust Valley/Nassau	11708429	516/277-5200	123
Loguidice Educational Center/Fredonia/Chautauqua	11571355	716/672-4371	36
Lois E Bird Elem Sch/E Rochester/Monroe	04925945	585/586-1850	106
Long Beach Catholic Reg Sch/Long Beach/Nassau	00739665	516/432-8900	132
LONG BEACH CITY SCH DIST/LIDO BEACH/NASSAU	00736950	516/897-2000	124
Long Beach High Sch/Long Beach/Nassau	00737021	516/897-2012	124
Long Beach Middle Sch/Long Beach/Nassau	00737019	516/897-2166	124
Long Branch Elem Sch/Liverpool/Onondaga	00761670	315/453-0261	156
Long Island Baptist Academy/Holtsville/Suffolk	11130004	631/447-2552	235
Long Island City High Sch/Long Is City/Queens	00741254	718/545-7095	184
Long Island Hebrew Academy/Great Neck/Nassau	05243051	516/466-3656	133

New York School Directory
DISTRICT & SCHOOL TELEPHONE INDEX

School/City/County DISTRICT/CITY/COUNTY	PID	TELEPHONE NUMBER	PAGE
Long Island Lutheran Sch/Glen Head/Nassau	12165569	516/626-1700	133
Long Island School for Gifted/Huntingtn Sta/Suffolk	02162173	631/423-3557	235
Long Lake Central Sch/Long Lake/Hamilton	00729426	518/624-2221	77
LONG LAKE CENTRAL SCH DIST/LONG LAKE/HAMILTON	00729414	518/624-2221	76
Longridge Elem Sch/Rochester/Monroe	00732019	585/966-5800	109
LONGWOOD CENTRAL SCH DIST/MIDDLE ISLAND/SUFFOLK	00774378	631/345-2172	224
Longwood High Sch/Middle Island/Suffolk	00774407	631/345-9200	225
Longwood Junior High Sch/Middle Island/Suffolk	03009328	631/345-2700	225
Longwood Middle Sch/Middle Island/Suffolk	00774419	631/345-2735	225
Longwood Preparatory Academy/Bronx/Bronx	04797176	718/860-1242	17
Loretta Park Elem Sch/Brentwood/Suffolk	00772277	631/434-2246	217
Lorge Sch/New York/New York	01834725	212/929-8660	144
Loudonville Christian Sch/Loudonville/Albany	01792567	518/434-6051	13
Loudonville Elem Sch/Loudonville/Albany	00714720	518/434-1960	11
Louis M Klein Middle Sch/Harrison/Westchester	00780303	914/630-3033	256
Louis V Denti Elem Sch/Rome/Oneida	00760432	315/338-5360	151
Love of Learning Mont Sch/Centerport/Suffolk	11232080	631/754-4109	235
Lowell Sch/Flushing/Queens	02975736	718/445-4222	188
Lowell Sch/Whitestone/Queens	01794979	718/352-2100	188
Lower East Side Prep High Sch/New York/New York	01552276	212/505-6366	135
Lower Manhattan Arts Academy/New York/New York	10008719	212/505-0143	136
Lower Manhattan Cmty Mid Sch/New York/New York	04753601	646/826-8100	136
Lowville Acad Central Sch/Lowville/Lewis	00730566	315/376-9001	101
LOWVILLE ACAD-CENTRAL SCH DIST/LOWVILLE/LEWIS	00730554	315/376-9000	101
Loyola Sch/New York/New York	00758673	212/288-3522	143
Lubavitcher School Chabad/Brooklyn/Kings	00752540	718/434-0795	98
Lubavitcher Yeshiva High Sch/Brooklyn/Kings	11222499	718/735-6601	98
Lubavitcher Yeshiva Sch/Brooklyn/Kings	11237822	718/774-4131	98
Lucero Elem Sch/Bronx/Bronx	11924403	718/681-8701	19
Lura Sharp Elem Sch/Pulaski/Oswego	00765858	315/298-2412	172
Luria Academy of Brooklyn/Brooklyn/Kings	11997357	718/398-3290	98
Lutheran Elem Sch of Bay Ridge/Brooklyn/Kings	01408986	718/748-9502	98
Lutheran Sch-Flushing Bayside/Bayside/Queens	00751792	718/225-5502	188
Lycee Francais De New York/New York/New York	01794204	212/369-1400	144
Lyceum Charter Sch/New York/New York	12380408	917/653-6885	5
Lyceum Kennedy Sch/New York/New York	00751479	212/681-7929	145
Lyme Central Sch/Chaumont/Jefferson	00730231	315/649-2417	81
LYME CENTRAL SCH DIST/CHAUMONT/JEFFERSON	00730229	315/649-2417	81
Lynbrook High Sch/Lynbrook/Nassau	00737071	516/887-0200	124
Lynbrook Kindergarten Center/Lynbrook/Nassau	04367551	516/887-8065	124
Lynbrook North Middle Sch/Lynbrook/Nassau	00737069	516/887-0282	124
Lynbrook South Middle Sch/Lynbrook/Nassau	00737083	516/887-0266	124
LYNBROOK UNION FREE SCH DIST/LYNBROOK/NASSAU	00737045	516/887-0253	124
Lyncourt Union Free Sch/Syracuse/Onondaga	00761761	315/455-7571	156
LYNCOURT UNION FREE SCH DIST/SYRACUSE/ONONDAGA	00761759	315/455-7571	156
Lyncx Academy/Rochester/Monroe	12235217	585/254-1240	111
Lyndon H Strough Middle Sch/Rome/Oneida	00760444	315/338-5200	152
LYNDONVILLE CENTRAL SCH DIST/LYNDONVILLE/ORLEANS	00765248	585/765-2251	169
Lyndonville Elem Sch/Lyndonville/Orleans	00765262	585/765-3122	169
Lynnwood Elem Sch/Schenectady/Albany	00714603	518/355-7930	11
Lynwood Avenue Elem Sch/Farmingville/Suffolk	00775190	631/696-8650	229
LYONS CENTRAL SCH DIST/LYONS/WAYNE	00779201	315/946-2200	249
Lyons Cmty Sch/Brooklyn/Kings	10911893	718/782-0918	83
Lyons Elem Sch/Lyons/Wayne	00779213	315/946-2240	249
Lyons Jr Sr High Sch/Lyons/Wayne	00779225	315/946-2220	249

M

School/City/County	PID	TELEPHONE	PAGE
M Clifford Miller Mid Sch/Lake Katrine/Ulster	00777954	845/943-3941	242
MacArthur Elem Sch/Binghamton/Broome	00716508	607/762-8119	27
MacCormick Secure Center/Brooktondale/Tompkins	02156605	607/539-7121	5
Machon Bais Yaakov High Sch/Brooklyn/Kings	03015169	718/972-7900	98
Madiba Prep Middle Sch/Brooklyn/Kings	11821772	718/574-2804	86
Madill Elem Sch/Ogdensburg/St Lawrence	00768886	315/393-7729	212
Madison Central Sch/Madison/Madison	00731194	315/893-1878	105
MADISON CENTRAL SCH DIST/MADISON/MADISON	00731170	315/893-1878	105
Madison Elem Sch/Massena/St Lawrence	00768721	315/764-3740	211
MADISON-ONEIDA BOCES/VERONA/ONEIDA	00761058	315/361-5500	154
Madonna Heights Sch/Dix Hills/Suffolk	00739677	631/643-8800	235
Madrid-Waddington Central Sch/Madrid/St Lawrence	00768666	315/322-5746	211
MADRID-WADDINGTON CENTRAL SD/MADRID/ST LAWRENCE	00768654	315/322-5746	211
Mae E Reynolds Elem Sch/Baldwinsville/Onondaga	00761137	315/638-6124	154
Magen David Yeshiva High Sch/Brooklyn/Kings	03072648	718/331-4002	98
Magen David Yeshivah/Brooklyn/Kings	00751481	718/236-5905	98
MAHOPAC CTL SCH DIST/MAHOPAC/PUTNAM	00766474	845/628-3415	176
Mahopac High Sch/Mahopac/Putnam	00766527	845/628-3256	176
Mahopac Middle Sch/Mahopac/Putnam	00766539	845/621-1330	176
Maimonides Day Sch/East Setauket/Suffolk	04486200	631/585-0521	235
Maimonides Hebrew Day Sch/Albany/Albany	02159463	518/453-9363	13
Main St Elem Sch/Irvington/Westchester	04940206	914/591-1961	257
Main Street Sch/N Syracuse/Onondaga	00762014	315/218-2200	157
MAINE ENDWELL CTL SCH DIST/ENDWELL/BROOME	00716950	607/754-1400	29
Maine Endwell Senior High Sch/Endwell/Broome	00717007	607/748-8070	29
Maine Memorial Elem Sch/Maine/Broome	00717019	607/862-3263	29
Maine-Endwell Middle Sch/Endwell/Broome	00716998	607/786-8271	29
MALONE CENTRAL SCH DIST/MALONE/FRANKLIN	00728202	518/483-7800	69
Malone Middle Sch/Malone/Franklin	00728264	518/483-7801	70
Malta Avenue Elem Sch/Ballston Spa/Saratoga	00769438	518/884-7250	200
Malverne High Sch/Malverne/Nassau	00737174	516/887-6400	124
MALVERNE UNION FREE SCH/MALVERNE/NASSAU	00737124	516/887-6405	124
Mamaroneck Avenue Elem Sch/Mamaroneck/Westchester	00780755	914/220-3600	258
Mamaroneck Avenue Elem Sch/White Plains/Westchester	00782155	914/422-2286	263
Mamaroneck High Sch/Mamaroneck/Westchester	00780767	914/220-3100	258
MAMARONECK UNION FREE SCH DIST/MAMARONECK/WESTCHESTER	00780717	914/220-3000	257
MANCHESTER-SHORTSVILLE CTL SD/SHORTSVILLE/ONTARIO	00763939	585/289-2160	162
Mandalay Elem Sch/Wantagh/Nassau	00739017	516/679-6390	131
Mandracchia-Sawmill Interm Sch/Commack/Suffolk	00772734	631/858-3650	219
Manetuck Elem Sch/West Islip/Suffolk	00776259	631/504-5640	233
Manhasset Middle Sch/Manhasset/Nassau	00737198	516/267-7600	125
Manhasset Secondary Sch/Manhasset/Nassau	04012524	516/267-7600	125
MANHASSET UNION FREE SCH DIST/MANHASSET/NASSAU	00737186	516/267-7700	124
Manhattan Acad-Arts & Lang/New York/New York	11561295	212/576-0502	136
Manhattan Bridges High Sch/New York/New York	05281302	212/757-5274	136
Manhattan Business Academy/New York/New York	11447871	212/647-1983	136
Manhattan Charter Sch/New York/New York	10009000	212/533-2743	5
Manhattan Charter School II/New York/New York	11850424	212/964-3792	5
Manhattan Christian Academy/New York/New York	02189107	212/567-5521	145
Manhattan Comp Night & Day HS/New York/New York	03337319	212/353-2010	136
Manhattan Country Sch/New York/New York	00751833	212/348-0952	145
Manhattan Ctr Science & Math/New York/New York	00740767	212/876-4639	139
Manhattan Day Sch/New York/New York	00751493	212/376-6800	145
Manhattan Early Clg-Advertise/New York/New York	12036396	212/225-0880	136
Manhattan HS for Girls/New York/New York	04974001	212/737-6800	145
Manhattan International HS/New York/New York	04037433	212/517-6728	136

School Year 2020-2021 800-333-8802 NY-V29

DISTRICT & SCHOOL TELEPHONE INDEX

Market Data Retrieval

School/City/County DISTRICT/CITY/COUNTY	PID	TELEPHONE NUMBER	PAGE
Manhattan Sch Career Develop/New York/New York	00750889	212/477-2090	142
Manhattan Star Academy/New York/New York	12314904	646/795-3850	145
Manhattan Village Academy/New York/New York	04037419	212/242-8752	136
Manhattan/Hunter Science HS/New York/New York	05348948	212/501-1235	138
Manitou Sch/Cold Spring/Putnam	12305408	845/809-5695	176
Manlius Pebble Hill Sch/Syracuse/Onondaga	00719146	315/446-2452	160
Mannsville Manor Elem Sch/Mannsville/Jefferson	00730279	315/465-4281	81
Manor Intermediate Sch/Honeoye Falls/Monroe	00732174	585/624-7160	109
Manor Oaks Sch/New Hyde Park/Nassau	00737576	516/434-2350	126
Manor Plains High Sch/Huntington/Suffolk	04026472	631/754-2900	216
Manorhaven Elem Sch/Prt Washingtn/Nassau	00738207	516/767-5300	128
Maple Avenue Elem Sch/Niagara Falls/Niagara	00759342	716/278-9140	148
Maple Avenue Middle Sch/Saratoga Spgs/Saratoga	04011960	518/587-4551	201
Maple East Elem Sch/Williamsville/Erie	00725614	716/626-8801	65
Maple Grove Jr Sr High Sch/Bemus Point/Chautauqua	00718283	716/386-2855	36
Maple Hill Elem Sch/Middletown/Orange	00764282	845/326-1740	165
Maple Hill Jr Sr High Sch/Castleton/Rensselaer	00767088	518/732-7701	191
Maple West Elem Sch/Williamsville/Erie	00725626	716/626-8840	65
Maplebrook Sch/Amenia/Dutchess	01460714	845/373-9511	55
Maplemere Elem Sch/Amherst/Erie	00725212	716/250-1550	63
Maplewood Intermediate Sch/Huntingtn Sta/Suffolk	00775786	631/812-3400	231
Marathon Christian Academy/Marathon/Cortland	01460659	607/849-3824	48
MARATHON CTL SCH DIST/MARATHON/CORTLAND	00720925	607/849-3117	48
Marathon Jr Sr High Sch/Marathon/Cortland	00720949	607/849-3251	48
Marble Hill HS-Int'l Studies/Bronx/Bronx	05098088	718/561-0973	21
Marbletown Elem Sch/Stone Ridge/Ulster	00778233	845/687-0284	243
MARCELLUS CENTRAL SCH DIST/MARCELLUS/ONONDAGA	00761864	315/673-6000	157
Marcellus Senior High Sch/Marcellus/Onondaga	00761905	315/673-6300	157
MARCUS WHITMAN CENTRAL SD/RUSHVILLE/ONTARIO	00763800	585/554-4848	162
Marcus Whitman Middle High Sch/Rushville/Ontario	00763824	585/554-6442	162
Marcy Elem Sch/Marcy/Oneida	00760951	315/266-3420	153
Margaret Murphy Kdgn Center/Hudson Falls/Washington	00779055	518/681-4500	248
Margaret W Cuyler Elem Sch/Red Creek/Wayne	00779457	315/754-2100	251
Margaretville Central Sch/Margaretville/Delaware	00721187	845/586-2647	50
MARGARETVILLE CENTRAL SCH DIST/MARGARETVILLE/DELAWARE	00721163	845/586-2647	49
Margetts Elem Sch/Monsey/Rockland	00768018	845/577-6190	196
Marguerite L Mulvey Elem Sch/Central Islip/Suffolk	00772497	631/348-5059	219
Maria Montessori Sch/Levittown/Nassau	02162185	516/520-0301	133
Maria Regina Elem Sch/Seaford/Nassau	00739691	516/541-1229	132
Maria Regina High Sch/Hartsdale/Westchester	00755841	914/761-3300	265
Marie Curie High Sch/Bronx/Bronx	05349227	718/432-6491	21
Marie Curie Institute/Amsterdam/Montgomery	01401081	518/843-2871	116
Marilla Primary Sch/Marilla/Erie	00724347	716/652-3000	62
MARION CENTRAL SCH DIST/MARION/WAYNE	00779237	315/926-2300	250
Marion Elem Sch/Marion/Wayne	00779249	315/926-4256	250
Marion G Vedder Elem Sch/North Babylon/Suffolk	00774562	631/620-7600	226
Marion Jr Sr High Sch/Marion/Wayne	00779251	315/926-4228	250
Marion Street Elem Sch/Lynbrook/Nassau	00737095	516/887-0295	124
MARLBORO CENTRAL SCH DIST/MILTON/ULSTER	00778037	845/236-5802	242
Marlboro Elem Sch/Marlboro/Ulster	00778051	845/236-1636	242
Marlboro High Sch/Marlboro/Ulster	00778049	845/236-8000	242
Marlboro Middle Sch/Marlboro/Ulster	00778075	845/236-5840	242
Marsh Ave Sch Expditionry Lrng/Staten Island/Richmond	11102978	718/370-6850	193
Marshall Sch/Hempstead/Nassau	10010190	516/434-4750	121
Martha Brown Middle Sch/Fairport/Monroe	00731728	585/421-2065	108
Martin Avenue Elem Sch/N Bellmore/Nassau	04939910	516/992-3115	126
Martin De Porres Sch/Elmont/Nassau	11227736	516/502-2840	133
Martin L King Magnet Sch/Schenectady/Schenectady	00770516	518/370-8360	205
Martin Luther High Sch/Maspeth/Queens	01408998	718/894-4000	188
Martin Luther King Jr Elem Sch/Wyandanch/Suffolk	00776443	631/870-0580	234
Martin Luther King Jr High Sch/Hastings HDSN/Westchester	00780171	914/478-1161	255
Martin Luther King Jr Sch/Yonkers/Westchester	00782349	914/376-8470	263
Martin Road Elem Sch/Lackawanna/Erie	00724684	716/821-5610	62
Martin Van Buren High Sch/Queens Vlg/Queens	00741307	718/776-4728	179
Mary Cariola Children's Center/Rochester/Monroe	01793925	585/271-0761	114
Mary E Dardess Elem Sch/Chatham/Columbia	00720456	518/392-2400	46
Mary G Clarkson Sch/Bay Shore/Suffolk	00772057	631/968-1205	217
Mary J Tanner Elem Sch/MDL Granville/Washington	00778910	518/642-9460	247
Mary Louis Academy/Jamaica/Queens	00754926	718/297-2120	186
Mary McDowell Friends Sch/Brooklyn/Kings	03015494	718/625-3939	98
Mary McLeod Bethune School 45/Rochester/Monroe	04455299	585/325-6945	111
Mary Queen of Heaven Sch/Brooklyn/Kings	11911561	718/763-2360	95
Maryhaven Center of Hope/Prt Jefferson/Suffolk	00739706	631/474-3400	235
Marymount School-New York/New York/New York	00755877	212/744-4486	145
Maryvale High Sch/Cheektowaga/Erie	00724957	716/631-7481	59
Maryvale Intermediate Sch/Cheektowaga/Erie	00724933	716/631-7423	59
Maryvale Middle Sch/Cheektowaga/Erie	00724945	716/631-7425	59
Maryvale Primary Sch/Cheektowaga/Erie	00724969	716/631-7471	59
Masores Bais Yaakov/Brooklyn/Kings	03408671	718/692-2424	98
Maspeth High Sch/Elmhurst/Queens	11714894	718/803-7100	177
Massapequa High Sch/Massapequa/Nassau	00737318	516/308-5900	125
Massapequa HS-Ames Campus/Massapequa/Nassau	04875429	516/308-5800	125
MASSAPEQUA UNION FREE SD 23/MASSAPEQUA/NASSAU	00737227	516/308-5000	125
MASSENA CENTRAL SCH DIST/MASSENA/ST LAWRENCE	00768692	315/764-3700	211
Massena High Sch/Massena/St Lawrence	00768745	315/764-3710	211
Masters Sch/Dobbs Ferry/Westchester	00783044	914/479-6400	266
Mater Christi Sch/Albany/Albany	00715451	518/489-3111	12
Mater Dei Academy/Warners/Onondaga	04935873	315/320-4085	160
Math & Sci Exploratory Sch/Brooklyn/Kings	05349590	718/330-9328	84
Math Engineering & Sci Academy/Brooklyn/Kings	11934379	718/282-7426	5
Math Science Research Tech HS/Cambria HTS/Queens	04319255	718/978-1837	183
Mather Bldg Arts & Craftmnp HS/New York/New York	11924518	212/399-3520	136
Matilda Avenue School PS 483/Bronx/Bronx	12105935	718/325-4360	23
Matthew Paterson Elem Sch/Patterson/Putnam	00766412	845/878-3211	175
Mattituck Jr Sr High Sch/Mattituck/Suffolk	01522295	631/298-8471	225
MATTITUCK-CUTCHOGUE UFSD/CUTCHOGUE/SUFFOLK	00774160	631/298-4242	225
Maud S Sherwood Elem Sch/Islip/Suffolk	00773922	631/650-8650	224
Maurice Sendak Community Sch/Brooklyn/Kings	11924300	718/840-5660	84
Maurice W Downing Elem Sch/Malverne/Nassau	00737162	516/887-6470	124
May Moore Primary Sch/Deer Park/Suffolk	00773116	631/274-4460	220
MAYFIELD CTL SCH DIST/MAYFIELD/FULTON	00728628	518/661-8207	72
Mayfield Elem Sch/Mayfield/Fulton	00728630	518/661-8222	72
Mayfield Jr Sr High Sch/Mayfield/Fulton	00728642	518/661-8222	72
Maynard P Wilson Elem Sch/Adams Center/Jefferson	00730281	315/583-5418	81
Maywood Sch/Albany/Albany	01483417	518/464-6363	9
McCarthy School-Beard/Syracuse/Onondaga	00762337	315/435-5855	159
McConnellsville Elem Sch/Blossvale/Oneida	00759990	315/245-3412	150
McCown Expeditionary Lrng Sch/Staten Island/Richmond	11103398	718/370-6950	193
McEvoy BOCES Voc Center/Cortland/Cortland	04937546	607/758-5100	47
MCGRAW CENTRAL SCH DIST/MC GRAW/CORTLAND	00720951	607/836-3600	48
McGraw Elem Sch/Mc Graw/Cortland	00720963	607/836-3650	48
McGraw Jr Sr High Sch/Mc Graw/Cortland	00720975	607/836-3601	48
McKinley-Brighton Magnet Sch/Syracuse/Onondaga	00762478	315/435-4605	159
McNab Elem Sch/Gloversville/Fulton	00728513	518/775-5760	71
McQuaid Jesuit High Sch/Rochester/Monroe	00733855	585/473-1130	114
McVey Elem Sch/East Meadow/Nassau	00735217	516/228-5300	118

New York School Directory
DISTRICT & SCHOOL TELEPHONE INDEX

School/City/County DISTRICT/CITY/COUNTY	PID	TELEPHONE NUMBER	PAGE
Mdq Academy/Brentwood/Suffolk	12314772	631/665-5036	235
Meachem Elem Sch/Syracuse/Onondaga	00762480	315/435-4610	159
Meadow Drive Elem Sch/Albertson/Nassau	00737502	516/237-2400	125
Meadow Elem Sch/Baldwin/Nassau	00734952	516/434-6500	116
Meadow Hill Global Sch/Newburgh/Orange	00764658	845/568-6600	166
Meadow Pond Elem Sch/South Salem/Westchester	00780597	914/763-7900	257
Meadowbrook Elem Sch/East Meadow/Nassau	00735229	516/520-4400	118
MECHANICVILLE CITY SCH DIST/ MECHANICVILLE/SARATOGA	00769660	518/664-5727	201
Mechanicville Elem Sch/Mechanicville/Saratoga	00769672	518/664-7336	201
Mechanicville Jr Sr High Sch/Mechanicville/Saratoga	00769684	518/664-9888	201
Medford Elem Sch/Patchogue/Suffolk	00774861	631/687-8300	227
Medgar Evers College Prep Sch/Brooklyn/Kings	04037251	718/703-5400	86
MEDINA CENTRAL SCH DIST/ MEDINA/ORLEANS	00765274	585/798-2700	169
Medina High Sch/Medina/Orleans	00765298	585/798-2700	170
Mekeel Christian Academy/Scotia/Schenectady	01795387	518/370-4272	205
Memorial Park Elem Sch/Waterville/Oneida	00760858	315/841-3700	153
Menands Elem Sch/Menands/Albany	00714653	518/465-4561	11
MENANDS UNION FREE SCH DIST/ MENANDS/ALBANY	00714641	518/465-4561	11
Mendon Center Elem Sch/Pittsford/Monroe	03246368	585/267-1400	110
Merkaz Bnos High Sch/Brooklyn/Kings	03409039	718/259-5600	98
Merrick Academy-Queens PCS/Laurelton/Queens	04924707	718/479-3753	5
Merrick Ave Middle Sch/Merrick/Nassau	00737411	516/992-1200	117
MERRICK UNION FREE SCH DIST/ MERRICK/NASSAU	00737423	516/992-7200	125
Merrimac Elem Sch/Holbrook/Suffolk	00775205	631/244-5670	229
Merton Williams Middle Sch/Hilton/Monroe	00732160	585/392-1000	109
Mesifta Ohel Torah/Monsey/Rockland	10805294	845/371-3740	199
Mesivta Ahavas Hatorah/Spring Valley/Rockland	12369428	845/426-7400	199
Mesivta Ateres Yaakov/Lawrence/Nassau	12314655	516/374-6465	133
Mesivta Beth Sherim/Brooklyn/Kings	01873185	718/851-0806	98
Mesivta Beth Shraga for Boys/Monsey/Rockland	00768264	845/356-1980	199
Mesivta Imrei Yosef Spinka/Brooklyn/Kings	03409118	718/851-1600	98
Mesivta of Long Beach Torah HS/Long Beach/Nassau	00739275	516/255-4700	134
Mesivta Ohr Torah/Richmond Hill/Queens	01409241	718/658-7066	188
Mesivta Rabbi Chaim Berlin/Brooklyn/Kings	00751560	718/377-8400	98
Mesivta Shaarei Pruzdor/Long Beach/Nassau	12379368	516/321-0964	134
Mesivta Tifereth Jerusalem/New York/New York	01463156	212/964-2830	145
Mesivta Tifres Elimelech/Brooklyn/Kings	03406609	718/854-3062	98
Mesivta Ziev Hatorah/Monsey/Rockland	05330551	845/426-6868	199
Metropolitan Diploma Plus HS/Brooklyn/Kings	11103350	718/342-6249	93
Metropolitan Exped Lrng Sch/Flushing/Queens	11560837	718/286-3500	182
Metropolitan High Sch/Bronx/Bronx	10008513	718/991-4634	24
Metropolitan Lighthouse CS/Bronx/Bronx	11561207	718/893-0640	19
Metropolitan Montessori Sch/New York/New York	01601425	212/579-5525	145
Metropolitan Soundview HS/Bronx/Bronx	11715006	718/860-8240	24
Mevakshai Hashem Elem Sch/Brooklyn/Kings	12160301	718/435-8900	98
MEXICO CENTRAL SCH DIST/ MEXICO/OSWEGO	00765640	315/963-8400	171
Mexico Elem Sch/Mexico/Oswego	00765664	315/963-8400	171
Mexico High Sch/Mexico/Oswego	00765676	315/963-8400	171
Mexico Middle Sch/Mexico/Oswego	00765652	315/963-8400	171
Michael A Maroun Elem Sch/Phoenix/Oswego	00765808	315/695-1561	172
Michael F Stokes Elem Sch/Levittown/Nassau	00736558	516/520-2103	122
Michael J Petrides Sch/Staten Island/Richmond	04368139	718/815-0186	193
Middle College High Sch/Long Is City/Queens	01552329	718/392-3330	177
MIDDLE COUNTRY CTL SCH DIST/ CENTEREACH/SUFFOLK	00774201	631/285-8000	225
Middle School 322/New York/New York	10008862	212/304-0853	141
Middle Village Prep Mid CS/Middle Vlg/Queens	11934367	718/869-2933	5
MIDDLEBURGH CTL SCH DIST/ MIDDLEBURGH/SCHOHARIE	00770815	518/827-3625	206
Middleburgh Elem Sch/Middleburgh/Schoharie	00770839	518/827-3677	206
Middleburgh Jr Sr High Sch/Middleburgh/Schoharie	00770827	518/827-3605	206
Middlesex Valley Primary Sch/Rushville/Ontario	00763836	585/554-3115	162
Middletown Christian Sch/Middletown/Orange	01463637	845/343-3775	168
MIDDLETOWN ENLARGED CITY SD/ MIDDLETOWN/ORANGE	00764270	845/326-1134	165
Middletown High Sch/Middletown/Orange	00764361	845/326-1600	165
Midlakes High Sch/Clifton Spgs/Ontario	00763903	315/548-6300	162
Midlakes Intermediate Sch/Clifton Spgs/Ontario	00763886	315/548-6900	162
Midlakes Middle Sch/Clifton Spgs/Ontario	11911406	315/548-6600	162
Midlakes Primary Sch/Clifton Spgs/Ontario	00763915	315/548-6700	162
Midland Elem Sch/Rye/Westchester	00781694	914/967-6100	261
Midrash L'Man Achai High Sch/Rego Park/Queens	12467252	718/544-4875	188
Midwood Catholic Academy/Brooklyn/Kings	00753324	718/377-1800	95
Midwood High Sch/Brooklyn/Kings	00741319	718/724-8500	92
Mildred E Strang Middle Sch/Yorktown Hts/Westchester	00782741	914/243-8100	264
Milestone Sch/Mount Vernon/Westchester	10013116	914/667-3478	266
Milford Central Sch/Milford/Otsego	00766096	607/286-7721	173
MILFORD CENTRAL SCH DIST/ MILFORD/OTSEGO	00766084	607/286-3349	173
Mill Basin Yeshiva Academy/Brooklyn/Kings	00752239	718/444-5800	98
Mill Middle Sch/Williamsville/Erie	00725638	716/626-8300	65
Mill Neck Manor Sch for Deaf/Mill Neck/Nassau	00739287	516/922-4100	134
Mill Road Intermediate Sch/Red Hook/Dutchess	00721993	845/758-2241	53
Mill Road Primary Sch/Red Hook/Dutchess	11927235	845/758-2241	53
Millard Fillmore Elem Sch/Moravia/Cayuga	00718037	315/497-2670	35
Millard Hawk Elem Sch/Central Sq/Oswego	04034455	315/668-4310	170
MILLBROOK CTL SCH DIST/MILLBROOK/ DUTCHESS	00721785	845/677-4200	52
Millbrook High Sch/Millbrook/Dutchess	10752831	845/677-2510	52
Millbrook Middle Sch/Millbrook/Dutchess	00721814	845/677-4210	52
Millbrook Sch/Millbrook/Dutchess	00722428	845/677-8261	55
Millennium Art Academy/Bronx/Bronx	05349435	718/824-0978	17
Millennium Brooklyn High Sch/Brooklyn/Kings	11714961	718/832-4333	84
Millennium High Sch/New York/New York	05098636	212/825-9008	136
Miller Avenue Elem Sch/Shoreham/Suffolk	00775475	631/821-8231	230
Miller Hill-Sand Lake Elem Sch/Averill Park/Rensselaer	00766620	518/674-7075	189
Miller Place High Sch/Miller Place/Suffolk	00774457	631/474-2723	226
MILLER PLACE UNION FREE SD/ MILLER PLACE/SUFFOLK	00774445	631/474-2700	225
Mills Pond Elem Sch/Saint James/Suffolk	05220542	631/382-4305	230
Milton Elem Sch/Rye/Westchester	00781709	914/967-6100	261
Milton J Fletcher Elem Sch/Jamestown/Chautauqua	00718829	716/483-4404	38
Milton L Olive Middle Sch/Wyandanch/Suffolk	00776455	631/870-0525	234
Milton Terrace North Elem Sch/Ballston Spa/Saratoga	11071721	518/884-7210	200
Mineola High Sch/New Hyde Park/Nassau	00737514	516/237-2600	125
Mineola Middle Sch/Mineola/Nassau	00737526	516/237-2500	125
MINEOLA UNION FREE SCH DIST/ MINEOLA/NASSAU	00737461	516/237-2000	125
Minerva Central Sch/Olmstedville/Essex	00727947	518/251-2000	68
MINERVA CENTRAL SCH DIST/ OLMSTEDVILLE/ESSEX	00727935	518/251-2000	68
Minerva Deland Sch/Fairport/Monroe	00731730	585/421-2030	108
Minetto Elem Sch/Minetto/Oswego	00765755	315/341-2600	171
MINISINK VALLEY CENTRAL SD/ SLATE HILL/ORANGE	00764373	845/355-5100	165
Minisink Valley Elem Sch/Slate Hill/Orange	00764385	845/355-5270	165
Minisink Valley High Sch/Slate Hill/Orange	00764397	845/355-5150	165
Minisink Valley Interm Sch/Slate Hill/Orange	03400447	845/355-5254	165
Minisink Valley Middle Sch/Slate Hill/Orange	00764402	845/355-5200	165
Minnesauke Elem Sch/Setauket/Suffolk	00775994	631/730-4200	232
Minoa Elem Sch/Minoa/Onondaga	00761321	315/434-3420	155
Miraj Islamic Sch/Staten Island/Richmond	10013128	718/816-9865	195
Miss Shelley's Upward Prep Sch/Roosevelt/Nassau	03499503	516/378-9206	134
Mizzentop Day Sch/Pawling/Dutchess	04846959	845/855-7338	55
Mohansic Elem Sch/Yorktown Hts/Westchester	00782753	914/243-8160	264
Mohawk Valley Christian Acad/Little Falls/Herkimer	02160606	315/823-3696	79

DISTRICT & SCHOOL TELEPHONE INDEX

Market Data Retrieval

School/City/County DISTRICT/CITY/COUNTY	PID	TELEPHONE NUMBER	PAGE
MOHONASEN CENTRAL SCH DIST/			
SCHENECTADY/SCHENECTADY	00770152	518/356-8200	203
Mohonasen High Sch/Schenectady/Schenectady	00770190	518/356-8300	204
Monhagen Middle Sch/Middletown/Orange	04753833	845/326-1700	165
Monica B Leary Elem Sch/Rush/Monroe	00733271	585/359-5460	112
MONROE 1 BOCES/FAIRPORT/MONROE	00733544	585/377-4660	115
Monroe 1 Special Education Ctr/Fairport/Monroe	01417042	585/383-2234	106
MONROE 2 ORLEANS BOCES/SPENCERPORT/MONROE	00733532	585/352-2400	115
MONROE WOODBURY CENTRAL SD/			
CENTRAL VLY/ORANGE	00764426	845/460-6200	165
Monroe Woodbury Middle Sch/Central Vly/Orange	00764452	845/460-6400	165
Monroe Woodbury Sr High Sch/Central Vly/Orange	00764464	845/460-7000	165
Monsignor Farrell High Sch/Staten Island/Richmond	00755891	718/987-2900	194
Monsignor McClancy Memorial HS/East Elmhurst/Queens	00753269	718/898-3800	186
Monsignor Scanlan High Sch/Bronx/Bronx	00755449	718/430-0100	25
Mont Pleasant Middle Sch/Schenectady/Schenectady	00770528	518/370-8160	205
Montauk Public Sch/Montauk/Suffolk	00774495	631/668-2474	226
MONTAUK UNION FREE SCH DIST/			
MONTAUK/SUFFOLK	00774483	631/668-2474	226
Montebello Elem Sch/Suffern/Rockland	00768161	845/357-4466	198
Montessori Academy Sch 53/Rochester/Monroe	04935445	585/325-0935	111
Montessori at Lemoyne/Syracuse/Onondaga	12230889	315/435-4590	159
Montessori Children's Room/Armonk/Westchester	02164406	914/273-3291	266
Montessori Magnet Sch/Albany/Albany	04036867	518/475-6675	9
Montessori Sch of Finger Lakes/Auburn/Cayuga	04975055	315/252-2225	35
Montessori School 27/Yonkers/Westchester	00782624	914/376-8455	263
Montessori School 31/Yonkers/Westchester	04286543	914/376-8623	263
Montessori School of New York/New York/New York	02922715	212/223-4630	145
Montessori School of Rochester/Rochester/Monroe	02994184	585/256-2520	114
Montessori School of Syracuse/Syracuse/Onondaga	05242708	315/449-9033	160
Montfort Academy/Mount Vernon/Westchester	10004256	914/699-7090	266
Montgomery C Smith Elem Sch/Hudson/Columbia	00720523	518/828-4650	46
Montgomery Elem Sch/Montgomery/Orange	00764531	845/457-2400	167
Montgomery Montessori Sch/Montgomery/Orange	12238922	845/401-9232	168
MONTICELLO CENTRAL SCH DIST/			
MONTICELLO/SULLIVAN	00776857	845/794-7700	237
Monticello High Sch/Monticello/Sullivan	00776900	845/794-8840	237
Mooers Elem Sch/Mooers/Clinton	00720092	518/236-7373	44
Moore Catholic High Sch/Staten Island/Richmond	00755358	718/761-9200	194
MORAVIA CENTRAL SCH DIST/			
MORAVIA/CAYUGA	00718025	315/497-2670	34
Moravia Jr Sr High Sch/Moravia/Cayuga	00718049	315/497-2670	35
Moreau Elem Sch/S Glens Falls/Saratoga	00769969	518/793-9644	202
Morgan Road Elem Sch/Liverpool/Onondaga	00761694	315/453-1268	156
Morgan Sch/E Rochester/Monroe	04938162	585/586-1850	106
Moriah Central Sch/Port Henry/Essex	00727961	518/546-3301	68
MORIAH CENTRAL SCH DIST/			
PORT HENRY/ESSEX	00727959	518/546-3301	68
Moriches Elem Sch/Moriches/Suffolk	00776388	631/874-1398	233
Morris Academy/Collab Studies/Bronx/Bronx	05349459	718/617-5312	19
Morris Central Sch/Morris/Otsego	00766113	607/263-6100	174
MORRIS CENTRAL SCH DIST/			
MORRIS/OTSEGO	00766101	607/263-6100	173
Morrisonville Elem Sch/Morrisonville/Clinton	00720327	518/565-5980	45
Morristown Central Sch/Morristown/St Lawrence	00768795	315/375-8814	211
MORRISTOWN CTL SCH DIST/			
MORRISTOWN/ST LAWRENCE	00768783	315/375-8814	211
MORRISVILLE EATON CENTRAL SD/			
MORRISVILLE/MADISON	00731211	315/684-9300	105
Morrisville-Eaton Middle HS/Morrisville/Madison	00731235	315/684-9121	105
Morse Elem Sch/Poughkeepsie/Dutchess	00721943	845/451-4690	53
Mosaic Pre-K Center at 47 Ave/Corona/Queens	12179869	718/271-7364	177
Mosaic Pre-K Center at 101 St/Corona/Queens	12311823	718/326-8170	177
Mosaic Pre-K Center Myrtle Ave/Ridgewood/Queens	12367597	718/592-3357	177
Mosaic Prep Academy/New York/New York	11103271	212/722-3109	139
Mosdos Chasidei Square Sch/Brooklyn/Kings	02189676	718/852-0502	98
Moses DeWitt Elem Sch/De Witt/Onondaga	00761462	315/445-8370	155
Most Holy Rosary Sch/Syracuse/Onondaga	00762959	315/476-6035	160
Most Precious Blood Sch/Walden/Orange	00755932	845/778-3028	168
Mother Teresa Academy/Clifton Park/Saratoga	12262129	518/280-4227	203
Mott Hall Bridges Academy/Brooklyn/Kings	11560954	718/345-6912	93
Mott Hall Bronx High Sch/Bronx/Bronx	10008616	718/466-6800	19
Mott Hall Charter Sch/Bronx/Bronx	11824334	718/991-9139	6
Mott Hall Community Sch/Bronx/Bronx	11447637	718/829-3254	17
Mott Hall High Sch/New York/New York	05349083	212/694-6020	140
Mott Hall II M 862/New York/New York	05098662	212/678-2960	138
Mott Hall III MS 128/Bronx/Bronx	05349186	718/842-6138	19
Mott Hall IV/Brooklyn/Kings	05348778	718/485-5240	93
Mott Hall V Sch/Bronx/Bronx	10008501	718/620-8160	24
Mott Haven Academy Charter Sch/Bronx/Bronx	11103491	718/292-7015	16
Mott Haven Community High Sch/Bronx/Bronx	11824293	718/665-8512	16
Mott Haven Village Prep HS/Bronx/Bronx	05098076	718/402-0571	16
Mott Road Elem Sch/Fayetteville/Onondaga	00761829	315/692-1700	155
Mount Academy/Esopus/Ulster	11933868	845/384-8080	244
Mount Eden Children's Academy/Bronx/Bronx	11824322	718/294-8155	19
MOUNT MARKHAM CENTRAL SCH DIST/			
WEST WINFIELD/HERKIMER	00729763	315/822-2824	78
MOUNT VERNON CITY SCH DIST/			
MOUNT VERNON/WESTCHESTER	00780860	914/665-5000	258
Mount Vernon High Sch/Mount Vernon/Westchester	00780951	914/665-5300	258
Mount Vernon Steam Academy/Mount Vernon/Westchester	12315350	914/665-5120	258
Mountain Lake Academy/Lake Placid/Essex	11230965	518/523-4300	69
Mountain Laurel Waldorf Sch/New Paltz/Ulster	02981682	845/255-0033	244
Mountain Road Sch/New Lebanon/Columbia	04954001	518/794-8520	47
Mountain View Campus/Elizabethtown/Essex	00727882	518/873-6371	67
Mountainside Christian Academy/Schroon Lake/Essex	02160539	518/532-7129	69
MS 35 Stephen Decatur/Brooklyn/Kings	00745597	718/574-2345	86
MS 51 William Alexander/Brooklyn/Kings	00745377	718/369-7603	84
MS 53 Brian Piccolo/Far Rockaway/Queens	00748460	718/471-6900	180
MS 57 Whitelaw Reid Acad/Brooklyn/Kings	00745602	718/574-2357	86
MS 61 Dr Gladstone H Atwell/Brooklyn/Kings	00745808	718/774-1002	86
MS 101 Ed R Byrne Sch/Bronx/Bronx	04877506	718/829-6372	17
MS 113 Ronald Edmonds Lrng Ctr/Brooklyn/Kings	00744804	718/834-6734	82
MS 129 Acad Indep Lrng & Ldrsp/Bronx/Bronx	00744672	718/933-5976	24
MS 131/New York/New York	02199566	212/219-1204	136
MS 137 America's Sch of Heroes/Ozone Park/Queens	05097814	718/659-0471	180
MS 158 Marie Curie/Bayside/Queens	00748173	718/423-8100	179
MS 177 Yorkville East Mid Sch/New York/New York	12037053	917/432-5413	136
MS 180 Dr Daniel Hale Williams/Bronx/Bronx	00744141	718/904-5650	23
MS 223 Lab Sch of Fin & Tech/Bronx/Bronx	05281259	718/585-8202	16
MS 224 Manh E Sch Arts & Acad/New York/New York	04458289	212/860-6047	139
MS 243 Center Sch/New York/New York	04874126	212/799-1477	138
MS 245 the Computer Sch/New York/New York	04874140	917/441-0873	138
MS 246 Walt Whitman/Brooklyn/Kings	00745781	718/282-5230	86
MS 250 West Side Collaborative/New York/New York	04874176	212/866-6313	138
MS 255 Salk School of Science/New York/New York	04457352	212/614-8785	136
MS 266 Park Place Cmty Mid Sch/Brooklyn/Kings	04874061	718/230-1216	82
MS 267 Math Science & Tech/Brooklyn/Kings	04876162	718/574-2318	86
MS 291 West End Secondary Sch/New York/New York	12106070	212/245-1506	138
MS 293 City Clg Acad of Arts/New York/New York	10008874	212/567-3164	141
MS 297 Hawtree Creek Mid Sch/S Ozone Park/Queens	11924104	718/659-3792	180
MS 297 Morton/New York/New York	12234146	212/295-7555	136
MS 301 Paul L Dunbar/Bronx/Bronx	00743513	718/585-2950	17
MS 302 Luisa Dessus Cruz/Bronx/Bronx	00743460	718/901-3520	17
MS 319 Maria Teresa/New York/New York	05348986	212/923-3827	141
MS 324 Patria Mirabal/New York/New York	05349007	212/923-4057	141
MS 327 Comp Model Sch/Bronx/Bronx	05351854	718/294-8111	19

New York School Directory
DISTRICT & SCHOOL TELEPHONE INDEX

School/City/County DISTRICT/CITY/COUNTY	PID	TELEPHONE NUMBER	PAGE
MS 340 North Star Academy/Brooklyn/Kings	11821564	718/857-5516	87
MS 355 Bronx Alliance Mid Sch/Bronx/Bronx	11924348	718/652-2060	23
MS 358/Jamaica/Queens	12105894	718/558-6240	182
MS 371 Seed Harlem/New York/New York	12472063	212/346-5270	140
MS 379 Clg Point Collaborative/College Point/Queens	12310336	929/362-3300	178
MS 390/Bronx/Bronx	00744074	718/583-5501	21
MS 424 Hunts Point Middle Sch/Bronx/Bronx	04947759	718/328-1972	17
MS 442-Carroll Gardens Innovat/Brooklyn/Kings	04877283	718/369-4480	84
MS 582/Brooklyn/Kings	05349540	718/456-8218	83
MS 593 South Bronx Int'l MS/Bronx/Bronx	12310269	718/588-0341	19
MS 594 New Pathways Academy/Bronx/Bronx	12310271	718/588-8349	19
MS 654 Van Siclen Cmty Mid Sch/Brooklyn/Kings	11924221	718/927-4701	89
MS 661 Vista Academy/Brooklyn/Kings	11924233	718/647-0913	89
MS 662 Liberty Avenue Mid Sch/Brooklyn/Kings	11924257	718/647-1301	89
MS 663 Sch of the Future-Bklyn/Brooklyn/Kings	11924245	718/345-5190	89
MS 839/Brooklyn/Kings	12105856	718/686-2730	85
MS 890/Brooklyn/Kings	12234017	929/397-9200	92
MS 898 Brooklyn Green Sch/Brooklyn/Kings	12310300	929/397-3340	86
MS 907 Legacy Sch of the Arts/Brooklyn/Kings	12310312	929/397-2967	89
MS 915/Brooklyn/Kings	12367509	718/875-1021	83
MS 933 City Knoll Middle Sch/New York/New York	12037041	212/695-9115	136
MS 936 Arts Off 3rd/Brooklyn/Kings	12472025		90
MS for Art & Philosophy/Brooklyn/Kings	10911922	718/342-7563	88
MS M247 Dual Lang Middle Sch/New York/New York	04760628	212/496-1050	138
MS of Media Law & Fine Arts/Brooklyn/Kings	10913762	718/773-3059	88
Mt Carmel-Holy Rosary Sch/New York/New York	00755578	212/876-7555	143
Mt Kisco Elem Sch/Mount Kisco/Westchester	00780834	914/666-2677	252
Mt Marion Elem Sch/Saugerties/Ulster	00778324	845/247-6920	243
Mt Markham Elem Sch/West Winfield/Herkimer	00729804	315/822-2840	78
Mt Markham High Sch/West Winfield/Herkimer	00729787	315/822-2900	78
Mt Markham Middle Sch/West Winfield/Herkimer	00729799	315/822-2870	78
Mt Mercy Academy/Buffalo/Erie	00726400	716/825-8796	65
Mt Moriah Academy/Glenmont/Albany	04974910	518/426-4510	13
Mt Moriah Christian Academy/Brooklyn/Kings	02984907	718/953-4364	98
Mt Morris Central Sch/Mount Morris/Livingston	00730865	585/658-3331	103
MT MORRIS CENTRAL SCH DIST/MOUNT MORRIS/LIVINGSTON	00730853	585/658-3331	103
Mt Pleasant Cottage Sch/Pleasantville/Westchester	01841443	914/769-0456	258
MT PLEASANT COTTAGE UFSD/PLEASANTVILLE/WESTCHESTER	01854737	914/769-0456	258
MT PLEASANT CTL SCH DIST/THORNWOOD/WESTCHESTER	00781034	914/769-5500	258
Mt Pleasant Elem Sch/Smithtown/Suffolk	00775619	631/382-4355	230
Mt Pleasant-Blythdale Sch/Valhalla/Westchester	02046012	914/347-1800	259
MT PLEASANT-BLYTHEDALE UFSD/VALHALLA/WESTCHESTER	01854749	914/347-1800	259
Mt Sinai Elem Sch/Mount Sinai/Suffolk	00774512	631/870-2600	226
Mt Sinai High Sch/Mount Sinai/Suffolk	03390593	631/870-2800	226
Mt Sinai Middle Sch/Mount Sinai/Suffolk	01877222	631/870-2800	226
MT SINAI UNION FREE SD/MOUNT SINAI/SUFFOLK	00774500	631/870-2500	226
Mt St Mary Academy/Kenmore/Erie	00726424	716/877-1358	65
Mt St Michael Academy/Bronx/Bronx	00755970	718/515-6400	25
Mt Tom Day Sch/New Rochelle/Westchester	00782856	914/636-8130	266
Mullen Elem Sch/Tonawanda/Erie	00725327	716/694-6805	64
Multicultural High Sch/Brooklyn/Kings	10913712	718/827-2796	89
Munsey Park Elem Sch/Manhasset/Nassau	00737203	516/267-7400	125
Murray Avenue Elem Sch/Larchmont/Westchester	00780779	914/220-3700	258
Murray Hill Academy/New York/New York	11561300	212/696-0195	136
Murry Bergtraum HS Business/New York/New York	01417107	212/964-9610	137
Muscota New Sch/New York/New York	05348950	212/544-0614	141
Museum School 25/Yonkers/Westchester	00782600	914/376-8450	263
Muslim Center Elem Mid Sch/Flushing/Queens	04974635	718/460-2127	188
My Spectrum Sch/Prt Washingtn/Nassau	12114546	516/883-8035	134
Myers Corners Elem Sch/Wappingers Fl/Dutchess	00722208	845/298-5260	54
Myles Elem Sch/New Hartford/Oneida	00760157	315/738-9600	151
Mynderse Academy High Sch/Seneca Falls/Seneca	03046041	315/568-5500	208

N

School/City/County DISTRICT/CITY/COUNTY	PID	TELEPHONE NUMBER	PAGE
N A Walbran Elem Sch/Oriskany/Oneida	00760250	315/768-2149	151
Nanuet High Sch/Nanuet/Rockland	00767557	845/627-9800	196
NANUET UNION FREE SCH DIST/NANUET/ROCKLAND	00767519	845/627-9880	196
NAPLES CENTRAL SCH DIST/NAPLES/ONTARIO	00763848	585/374-7900	162
Naples Elem Sch/Naples/Ontario	00763850	585/374-7900	162
Naples Jr Sr High Sch/Naples/Ontario	00763862	585/374-7900	162
Nardin Academy Elem Sch/Buffalo/Erie	03018020	716/881-6262	66
Nardin Academy High Sch/Buffalo/Erie	04470237	716/881-6262	66
Nardin Academy Middle Sch/Buffalo/Erie	12370582	716/881-6262	65
Nardin Montessori Academy/Buffalo/Erie	11231036	716/881-6565	66
Nassakeag Elem Sch/Setauket/Suffolk	00776003	631/730-4400	232
NASSAU BOCES/GARDEN CITY/NASSAU	00739201	516/396-2500	134
Nassau BOCES-Jerusalem ES/N Bellmore/Nassau	04762224	516/608-6300	116
Nassau Elem Sch/Poughkeepsie/Dutchess	00722090	845/463-7843	54
Nate Perry Elem Sch/Liverpool/Onondaga	00761711	315/453-0272	156
Nathan T Hall Elem Sch/Newark Valley/Tioga	00777083	607/642-3340	238
Nathaniel Hawthorne School 25/Rochester/Monroe	00732916	585/288-3654	111
Nathaniel Rochester Cmty Sch 3/Rochester/Monroe	00732708	585/454-3525	111
Nathaniel Woodhull Elem Sch/Shirley/Suffolk	00776390	631/874-1302	233
Nativity Miguel MS of Buffalo/Buffalo/Erie	00727193	716/836-5188	65
Nativity of Blessed Mary Sch/Williamsville/Erie	00726462	716/633-7441	65
Nativity of Our Lord Sch/Orchard Park/Erie	00726474	716/662-7572	65
Nazareth Elem Sch/Rochester/Monroe	00733908	585/458-3786	114
Nazareth Regional High Sch/Brooklyn/Kings	00753295	718/763-1100	95
Nefesh Academy/Brooklyn/Kings	03403372	718/627-4463	98
Neighborhood Charter Sch Bronx/Bronx/Bronx	12366866	646/701-7117	6
Neighborhood Chtr Sch Harlem/New York/New York	12366854	646/701-7117	6
Neighborhood CS-Harlem/New York/New York	11824566	646/701-7117	6
Neighborhood CS-NW/New York/New York	12260262	646/701-7117	6
Neighborhood Sch/New York/New York	04457261	212/387-0195	135
Neil Armstrong Elem Sch/Rochester/Monroe	00731807	585/247-3190	108
Neil Hellman Sch/Albany/Albany	01792581	518/426-2600	13
Nellie Thornton High Sch/Mount Vernon/Westchester	11014448	914/358-2740	258
Nelson Mandela High Sch/Brooklyn/Kings	12036322	718/804-6805	86
Nelson Mandela-Zollicoffer HS/Mount Vernon/Westchester	04013437	914/358-2720	258
Nesaquake Middle Sch/Saint James/Suffolk	10017734	631/382-5105	230
Nesivos Bais Yaakov Sch/Brooklyn/Kings	11229045	718/972-0804	98
Netherwood Elem Sch/Hyde Park/Dutchess	00721711	845/229-4055	52
New American Academy Chtr Sch/Brooklyn/Kings	11929087	718/385-1709	6
New Beginnings Montessori Sch/Middletown/Orange	03015925	845/342-0051	168
New Beginnings Sch/Rochester/Monroe	12369337	585/683-7402	111
New City Elem Sch/New City/Rockland	00767442	845/624-3467	196
New Covenant Christian Sch/Bronx/Bronx	04974142	718/519-8884	27
New Covenant Chrn High Sch/Bronx/Bronx	11224409	718/328-6072	27
New Covenant Learning Center/Beacon/Dutchess	12314409	845/765-1292	55
New Creation Fellowship Acad/Buffalo/Erie	11815967	716/632-6084	66
New Dawn Charter High Sch/Brooklyn/Kings	11820950	347/505-9101	6
New Dawn Charter High Sch II/Jamaica/Queens	12367602	212/209-6036	6
New Design High Sch/New York/New York	05281285	212/475-4148	137
New Design Middle Sch/New York/New York	11715082	212/281-6339	140
New Directions Secondary Sch/Bronx/Bronx	11924415	718/410-4343	19
New Dorp Christian Academy/Staten Island/Richmond	03195381	718/351-4442	195
New Dorp High Sch/Staten Island/Richmond	00741345	718/667-8686	193
New Explorations Sci-Tech-Math/New York/New York	04368165	212/677-5190	135
New Grace Center Christian Sch/Brooklyn/Kings	02985937	718/498-7175	98
NEW HARTFORD CENTRAL SCH DIST/NEW HARTFORD/ONEIDA	00760145	315/624-1000	151
New Hartford Sr High Sch/New Hartford/Oneida	00760171	315/624-1214	151
New Haven Elem Sch/New Haven/Oswego	00765688	315/963-8400	171
New Heights Academy CS/New York/New York	10026254	212/283-5400	141

DISTRICT & SCHOOL TELEPHONE INDEX

Market Data Retrieval

School/City/County DISTRICT/CITY/COUNTY	PID	TELEPHONE NUMBER	PAGE
New Heights Middle Sch 722/Brooklyn/Kings	11821851	718/467-4501	87
New Hope Academy Charter Sch/Brooklyn/Kings	11561075	718/337-8303	6
New Hyde Park Mem Jr Sr HS/New Hyde Park/Nassau	00735607	516/488-9500	129
New Hyde Park Road Sch/New Hyde Park/Nassau	00737588	516/434-2370	126
NEW HYDE-GARDEN CITY PARK UFSD/			
NEW HYDE PARK/NASSAU	00737540	516/434-2305	126
New Interdisciplinary Sch/Yaphank/Suffolk	03402835	631/924-5583	235
New Lane Memorial Elem Sch/Selden/Suffolk	00774275	631/285-8900	225
NEW LEBANON CTL SCH DIST/			
NEW LEBANON/COLUMBIA	00720626	518/794-9016	46
New Lebanon Jr Sr High Sch/New Lebanon/Columbia	00720640	518/794-7600	46
New Life Christian Sch/Hamilton/Madison	02977186	315/824-2625	106
New Life Christian Sch/Tonawanda/Erie	11237676	716/694-0071	66
New Life Sch/Bronx/Bronx	11226366	718/665-2760	27
New Millennium Bus Academy/Bronx/Bronx	05349150	718/588-8308	19
NEW PALTZ CTL SCH DIST/NEW PALTZ/			
ULSTER	00778099	845/256-4020	242
New Paltz High Sch/New Paltz/Ulster	00778130	845/256-4100	243
New Paltz Middle Sch/New Paltz/Ulster	00778128	845/256-4200	243
NEW ROCHELLE CITY SCH DIST/			
NEW ROCHELLE/WESTCHESTER	00781096	914/576-4300	259
New Rochelle High Sch/New Rochelle/Westchester	00781187	914/576-4500	259
New Roots Charter Sch/Ithaca/Tompkins	11453571	607/697-0446	6
New Sch/De Witt/Onondaga	04975134	315/475-6453	160
New Sch Leadership Journalism/Bronx/Bronx	10008630	718/601-2869	21
New Scotland Elem Sch/Albany/Albany	00714225	518/475-6775	9
New Suffolk Common Sch/New Suffolk/Suffolk	00774536	631/734-6940	226
NEW SUFFOLK COMMON SCH DIST/			
NEW SUFFOLK/SUFFOLK	00774524	631/734-6940	226
New Utrecht High Sch/Brooklyn/Kings	00741357	718/232-2500	90
New Ventures Charter Sch/Staten Island/Richmond	12105430	347/855-2238	6
New Visions Aim CS I/Brooklyn/Kings	11850436	718/269-7090	6
New Visions Aim CS II/Bronx/Bronx	11821526	718/861-7515	6
New Visions CHS Humanities/Bronx/Bronx	11723431	718/817-7686	6
New Visions CHS Humanities II/Bronx/Bronx	11930907	212/645-5110	6
New Visions CHS Humanities III/Brooklyn/Kings	11923796	718/368-4145	6
New Visions CHS Humanities IV/Rockaway Park/Queens	12234108	718/734-3350	6
New Visions CHS Math & Sci/Bronx/Bronx	11723429	718/817-7683	6
New Visions CHS Math & Sci II/Bronx/Bronx	11817185	718/665-3671	6
New Visions CHS Math & Sci III/Brooklyn/Kings	11923784	718/934-9240	6
New Visions CHS Math & Sci IV/Jamaica/Queens	12164802	718/525-2041	6
New Visions Elem Sch/Freeport/Nassau	04373756	516/867-5390	120
New Vistas Academy/Brooklyn/Kings	11815979	718/421-1786	98
New Voices Sch/Brooklyn/Kings	04877336	718/965-0390	85
New Windsor Sch/New Windsor/Orange	00764672	845/563-3700	166
New World Education Center/Jamaica/Queens	02617934	718/528-8751	188
New World High Sch/Bronx/Bronx	10008496	718/696-3800	23
New World Preparatory CS/Staten Island/Richmond	11560758	718/705-8990	6
NEW YORK ALT HIGH SCH SD 79/			
NEW YORK/NEW YORK	10012045	917/521-3639	142
New York City Acad-Discovery/Woodhaven/Queens	11102992	718/441-2165	180
NEW YORK CITY DEPT OF ED/			
NEW YORK/NEW YORK	00740626	718/935-4000	134
New York City Montessori CS/Bronx/Bronx	11723443	347/226-9094	6
New York Film Academy/New York/New York	11237494	212/966-3488	145
New York French American CS/New York/New York	11561348	212/666-4134	138
New York Inst for Special Ed/Bronx/Bronx	01461718	718/519-7000	27
New York Military Academy/Cornwall HDSN/Orange	00765119	888/275-6962	168
New York Mills Sch/New York Mls/Oneida	00760236	315/768-8124	151
NEW YORK MILLS UNION FREE SD/			
NEW YORK MLS/ONEIDA	00760212	315/768-8127	151
New York School for the Deaf/White Plains/Westchester	01795527	914/949-7310	266
New York St Sch for the Blind/Batavia/Genesee	01535539	585/343-5384	6
New York St Sch for the Deaf/Rome/Oneida	02165448	315/337-8400	6
NEW YORK STATE DEPT EDUCATION/			
ALBANY/ALBANY	00714108	518/474-3852	1

School/City/County DISTRICT/CITY/COUNTY	PID	TELEPHONE NUMBER	PAGE
NEWARK CENTRAL SCH DIST/			
NEWARK/WAYNE	00779263	315/332-3230	250
Newark High Sch/Newark/Wayne	00779299	315/332-3240	250
Newark Middle Sch/Newark/Wayne	00779287	315/332-3290	250
NEWARK VALLEY CENTRAL SCH DIST/			
NEWARK VALLEY/TIOGA	00777057	607/642-3221	238
Newark Valley High Sch/Newark Valley/Tioga	00777100	607/642-8351	238
Newark Valley Middle Sch/Newark Valley/Tioga	00777095	607/642-5524	238
Newbridge Road Elem Sch/N Bellmore/Nassau	00737629	516/992-3116	126
NEWBURGH ENLARGED CITY SD/			
NEWBURGH/ORANGE	00764579	845/563-3400	165
Newburgh Free Acad-Main Campus/Newburgh/Orange	00764684	845/563-5400	166
Newburgh Free Acad-N Campus/Newburgh/Orange	00764696	845/563-8400	166
Newcomb Central Sch/Newcomb/Essex	00727997	518/582-3341	68
NEWCOMB CENTRAL SCH DIST/			
NEWCOMB/ESSEX	00727985	518/582-3341	68
Newcomers High Sch/Long Is City/Queens	04368189	718/937-6005	184
NEWFANE CENTRAL SCH DIST/			
BURT/NIAGARA	00759172	716/778-6888	147
Newfane Early Childhood Center/Burt/Niagara	04273429	716/778-6351	147
Newfane Elem Sch/Newfane/Niagara	00759196	716/778-6376	147
Newfane High Sch/Newfane/Niagara	00759213	716/778-6551	147
Newfane Middle Sch/Newfane/Niagara	00759201	716/778-6452	147
NEWFIELD CENTRAL SCH DIST/			
NEWFIELD/TOMPKINS	00777655	607/564-9955	241
Newfield Elem Sch/Newfield/Tompkins	00777667	607/564-9955	241
Newfield High Sch/Selden/Suffolk	00774287	631/285-8300	225
Newfield Middle Sch/Newfield/Tompkins	04357568	607/564-9955	241
Newfield Senior High Sch/Newfield/Tompkins	00777679	607/564-9955	241
Newmeadow Saratoga Sch/Clifton Park/Saratoga	11157985	518/899-9235	203
Newtown High Sch/Elmhurst/Queens	00741371	718/595-8400	177
Niagara Academy/Sanborn/Niagara	02056847	716/731-4176	146
Niagara Charter Sch/Niagara Falls/Niagara	10748141	716/297-4520	6
Niagara Educational Center/Sanborn/Niagara	00765339	716/731-4176	146
NIAGARA FALLS CITY SCH DIST/			
NIAGARA FALLS/NIAGARA	00759249	716/286-4211	147
Niagara Falls High Sch/Niagara Falls/Niagara	00759354	716/278-5800	148
Niagara Street Elem Sch/Niagara Falls/Niagara	00759366	716/278-5860	148
NIAGARA-WHEATFIELD CTL SD/			
NIAGARA FALLS/NIAGARA	00759483	716/215-3002	148
Niagara-Wheatfield High Sch/Sanborn/Niagara	00759562	716/215-3100	148
Nichols Sch/Buffalo/Erie	00725729	716/332-6300	66
Nicotra Early College CS/Staten Island/Richmond	12310441	929/419-9001	6
Nightengale Elem Sch/Massena/St Lawrence	00768757	315/764-3750	211
Nike Alternative High Sch/Lido Beach/Nassau	12363307	516/897-2131	124
Ninth Grade Academy/Churchville/Monroe	11711098	585/293-4546	107
NISKAYUNA CENTRAL SCH DIST/			
NISKAYUNA/SCHENECTADY	00770217	518/377-4666	204
Niskayuna High Sch/Schenectady/Schenectady	00770279	518/382-2511	204
Nokomis Elem Sch/Holbrook/Suffolk	00775217	631/471-1840	229
Nora Cronin Presentation Acad/Newburgh/Orange	11708352	845/567-0708	168
Nord Anglia Int'l Sch-New York/New York/New York	12371017	212/600-2010	145
Norman Howard Sch/Rochester/Monroe	02161284	585/334-8010	114
Norman J Levy-Lakeside Sch/Merrick/Nassau	00737459	516/992-7230	125
Norman R Kelley Interm Sch/Newark/Wayne	00779304	315/332-3326	250
North Albany Middle Sch/Albany/Albany	12379899	518/475-6800	9
North Babylon High Sch/North Babylon/Suffolk	00774574	631/620-7100	226
NORTH BABYLON UNION FREE SD/			
NORTH BABYLON/SUFFOLK	00774548	631/620-7000	226
NORTH BELLMORE UNION FREE SD/			
BELLMORE/NASSAU	00737590	516/992-3000	126
North Broad Street Elem Sch/Oneida/Madison	00731261	315/363-3650	105
North Bronx Sch of Empowerment/Bronx/Bronx	12170370	718/652-0519	23
North Coleman Road Elem Sch/Centereach/Suffolk	00774299	631/285-8660	225
NORTH COLLINS CTL SCH DIST/			
NORTH COLLINS/ERIE	00724983	716/337-0101	63
North Collins Elem Sch/North Collins/Erie	00724995	716/337-0166	63

New York School Directory
DISTRICT & SCHOOL TELEPHONE INDEX

School/City/County DISTRICT/CITY/COUNTY	PID	TELEPHONE NUMBER	PAGE
North Collins Jr Sr High Sch/North Collins/Erie	00725004	716/337-0101	63
NORTH COLONIE CENTRAL SD/LATHAM/ALBANY	00714665	518/785-8591	11
North Country Rd Middle Sch/Miller Place/Suffolk	00774471	631/474-2710	226
North Country Sch/Lake Placid/Essex	00728135	518/523-9329	69
North Elem Sch/Brentwood/Suffolk	00772289	631/434-2275	217
North Elem Sch/Watertown/Jefferson	00730401	315/785-3750	81
North Franklin Education Ctr/Malone/Franklin	01525285	518/483-5230	69
NORTH GREENBUSH COMMON SD/TROY/RENSSELAER	00767210	518/283-6748	191
North High Sch/Williamsville/Erie	00725640	716/626-8505	65
North Hornell Elem Sch/Hornell/Steuben	02107123	607/324-0014	214
North Main Elem Sch/Monroe/Orange	00764476	845/460-6800	165
NORTH MERRICK UNION FREE SD/MERRICK/NASSAU	00737667	516/292-3694	126
North Middle Sch/Brentwood/Suffolk	00772239	631/434-2356	217
North Park Elem Sch/Hyde Park/Dutchess	00721723	845/229-4040	52
North Park Junior High Sch/Lockport/Niagara	00759146	716/478-4700	147
North Queens Cmty High Sch/Flushing/Queens	10910382	718/380-1650	178
North Ridge Primary Sch/Commack/Suffolk	00772693	631/912-2190	219
NORTH ROCKLAND CENTRAL SD/GARNERVILLE/ROCKLAND	00767569	845/942-3000	197
North Rockland High Sch/Thiells/Rockland	00767624	845/942-3300	197
North Rose Elem Sch/North Rose/Wayne	00779378	315/587-4005	250
NORTH ROSE WOLCOTT CENTRAL SD/WOLCOTT/WAYNE	00779330	315/594-3141	250
North Rose Wolcott High Sch/Wolcott/Wayne	00779366	315/594-3100	250
North Rose Wolcott MS/Wolcott/Wayne	00779354	315/594-3115	250
NORTH SALEM CENTRAL SCH DIST/NORTH SALEM/WESTCHESTER	00781242	914/669-5414	259
North Salem Middle High Sch/North Salem/Westchester	00781254	914/669-5414	259
NORTH SHORE CENTRAL SD/SEA CLIFF/NASSAU	00737708	516/277-7000	126
North Shore Hebrew Acad-Cherry/Great Neck/Nassau	00739304	516/487-8687	134
North Shore Hebrew Academy/Great Neck/Nassau	02159293	516/487-9163	134
North Shore Hebrew Academy HS/Great Neck/Nassau	10788672	516/487-2424	134
North Shore High Sch/Glen Head/Nassau	00737746	516/277-7700	126
North Shore Middle Sch/Glen Head/Nassau	00737734	516/277-7300	126
North Side Sch/E Williston/Nassau	00735334	516/333-6860	118
North Side Sch/Whitestone/Queens	01873537	718/229-5050	188
North Spencer Christian Acad/Spencer/Tioga	02161313	607/589-6366	239
North Street Elem Sch/Geneva/Ontario	00763757	315/781-0489	161
NORTH SYRACUSE CTL SCH DIST/N SYRACUSE/ONONDAGA	00761917	315/218-2100	157
North Syracuse Jr High Sch/N Syracuse/Onondaga	00761993	315/218-3600	157
NORTH TONAWANDA CITY SCH DIST/N TONAWANDA/NIAGARA	00759598	716/807-3655	148
North Tonawanda High Sch/N Tonawanda/Niagara	00759677	716/807-3600	148
North Tonawanda Interm Sch/N Tonawanda/Niagara	00759665	716/807-3825	148
North Tonawanda Middle Sch/N Tonawanda/Niagara	00759615	716/807-3700	148
North Warren Central Sch/Chestertown/Warren	00778491	518/494-3015	246
NORTH WARREN CENTRAL SCH DIST/CHESTERTOWN/WARREN	00778489	518/494-3015	246
Northeast College Prep HS/Rochester/Monroe	10752453	585/324-9273	111
Northeast Elem Sch/Amityville/Suffolk	00771936	631/565-6400	216
Northeast Elem Sch/Brentwood/Suffolk	00772291	631/434-2435	218
Northeast Elem Sch/Ithaca/Tompkins	00777588	607/257-2121	240
Northeastern Academy/New York/New York	01463223	212/569-4800	145
NORTHEASTERN CLINTON CTL SD/CHAMPLAIN/CLINTON	00720066	518/298-8242	44
Northeastern Clinton Mid Sch/Champlain/Clinton	01813226	518/298-8681	44
Northeastern Clinton Sr HS/Champlain/Clinton	00720080	518/298-8638	44
Northern Academy/Middletown/Orange	12380379	845/779-0808	168
NORTHERN ADIRONDACK CTL SD/ELLENBURG DEP/CLINTON	00720121	518/594-7060	44
Northern Adirondack Elem Sch/Ellenburg Dep/Clinton	00720145	518/594-3962	44
Northern Adirondack Jr Sr HS/Ellenburg Dep/Clinton	00720157	518/594-3962	44
Northern Catskills Occup Ctr/Grand Gorge/Delaware	00721383	607/588-6291	48
Northern Chautauqua Cath Sch/Dunkirk/Chautauqua	00726254	716/366-0630	39
Northern Parkway Elem Sch/Uniondale/Nassau	00738740	516/918-1700	130
Northport High Sch/Northport/Suffolk	00774732	631/262-6654	227
Northport Middle Sch/Northport/Suffolk	00774720	631/262-6750	227
NORTHPORT-EAST NORTHPORT UFSD/NORTHPORT/SUFFOLK	00774653	631/262-6600	227
Northside Charter High Sch/Brooklyn/Kings	11566051	347/390-1273	6
Northside Christian Academy/Rochester/Monroe	04797126	585/266-3140	114
Northside Elem Sch/Fairport/Monroe	00731742	585/421-2140	108
Northside Elem Sch/Farmingdale/Nassau	00735499	516/434-5610	119
Northside Elem Sch/Levittown/Nassau	00736845	516/434-7500	123
Northside Therapeutic ECC/New York/New York	01463053	212/426-3400	145
Northstar/Rochester/Monroe	12367860	585/324-9945	111
Northstar Christian Academy/Rochester/Monroe	01461146	585/429-5530	114
Northtowns Academy/Tonawanda/Erie	11435024	716/961-4040	56
Northville Central Sch/Northville/Fulton	02054760	518/863-7000	72
NORTHVILLE CENTRAL SCH DIST/NORTHVILLE/FULTON	00728654	518/863-7000	72
Northwest Career Tech Ed Ctr/Ogdensburg/St Lawrence	02136904	315/393-4570	209
Northwest Elem Sch/Amityville/Suffolk	00771924	631/565-6500	216
Northwest JHS at Douglass/Rochester/Monroe	10752465	585/324-9289	111
Northwood Elem Sch/Hilton/Monroe	00732112	585/392-1000	109
Northwood Elem Sch/West Seneca/Erie	00725470	716/677-3641	64
Northwood Sch/Lake Placid/Essex	00728123	518/523-3357	69
NORWICH CITY SCH DIST/NORWICH/CHENANGO	00719720	607/334-1600	42
Norwich High Sch/Norwich/Chenango	00719744	607/334-1600	42
Norwich Middle Sch/Norwich/Chenango	00719732	607/334-1600	42
Norwood Avenue Elem Sch/Northport/Suffolk	00774744	631/262-6830	227
Norwood Avenue Elem Sch/Port Jeff Sta/Suffolk	00772849	631/474-8130	218
NORWOOD-NORFOLK CTL SD/NORWOOD/ST LAWRENCE	00768800	315/353-9951	211
Norwood-Norfolk Elem Sch/Norwood/St Lawrence	00768824	315/353-6674	211
Norwood-Norfolk Middle Sch/Norwood/St Lawrence	10021369	315/353-6631	211
Norwood-Norfolk Sr High Sch/Norwood/St Lawrence	00768836	315/353-6631	211
Notre Dame Academy High Sch/Staten Island/Richmond	00756039	718/447-8878	194
Notre Dame Catholic Academy/Ridgewood/Queens	00753477	718/821-2221	186
Notre Dame Elem Academy/Staten Island/Richmond	00756027	718/273-9096	194
Notre Dame Elem Sch/Utica/Oneida	00763006	315/732-4374	153
Notre Dame High Sch/Batavia/Genesee	00726486	585/343-2783	74
Notre Dame High Sch/Elmira/Chemung	00733910	607/734-2267	41
Notre Dame High Sch/New York/New York	00756041	212/620-5575	143
Notre Dame Jr Sr High Sch/Utica/Oneida	00762973	315/724-5118	153
Notre Dame Sch/New Hyde Park/Nassau	00739732	516/354-5618	132
Notre Dame-Bishop Gibbons Sch/Schenectady/Schenectady	00715085	518/393-3131	205
Nottingham High Sch/Syracuse/Onondaga	00762519	315/435-4380	159
Noxon Road Elem Sch/Poughkeepsie/Dutchess	00721474	845/486-4950	51
Nssa/Commack/Suffolk	11223730	631/462-0386	235
Nurturing Center and Academy/Queens Vlg/Queens	12039271	718/527-5932	188
Nyack High Sch/Nyack/Rockland	00767727	845/353-7100	197
Nyack Middle Sch/Nyack/Rockland	00767703	845/353-7200	197
NYACK UNION FREE SCH DIST/NYACK/ROCKLAND	00767686	845/353-7000	197
NYC Business of Sports Sch/New York/New York	11447716	212/246-2183	137
NYC Charter HS Arch-Engr-Const/Bronx/Bronx	11103506	646/400-5566	16
NYC Charter School of the Arts/New York/New York	12170564	646/793-6320	6
NYC Ischool/New York/New York	11103374	917/237-7300	137
NYC Lab HS for Coll Studies/New York/New York	04037328	212/691-6119	137
NYC Lab MS for Coll Studies/New York/New York	10000688	212/691-6119	137
NYC Museum Sch/New York/New York	04457390	212/675-6206	137

School Year 2020-2021   800-333-8802   NY-V35

DISTRICT & SCHOOL TELEPHONE INDEX

Market Data Retrieval

School/City/County DISTRICT/CITY/COUNTY	PID	TELEPHONE NUMBER	PAGE
Nycacs CS East Harlem/New York/New York	10008965	212/860-2580	6
Nycacs-Bronx/Bronx/Bronx	12234093	718/991-5910	6
NYSARC-Brookside Sch/Cottekill/Ulster	01795662	845/687-7250	244

O

School/City/County	PID	TELEPHONE NUMBER	PAGE
O E S J CENTRAL SCH DIST/			
ST JOHNSVILLE/FULTON	00728678	518/568-2011	72
O E S J Elem Sch/St Johnsville/Fulton	00728680	518/568-2014	72
O E S J Jr Sr High Sch/St Johnsville/Fulton	00734861	518/568-2011	72
O L Queen of Apostles Reg Sch/CTR Moriches/Suffolk	00740365	631/878-1033	234
O'Neill High Sch/Walton/Delaware	00721333	607/865-4116	50
Oak Grove Elem Sch/Poughkeepsie/Dutchess	00722210	845/298-5280	54
Oak Hill Sch/Scotia/Schenectady	01463857	518/399-5048	205
Oak Orchard Elem Sch/Medina/Orleans	00765303	585/798-2700	170
Oak Park Elem Sch/Bay Shore/Suffolk	00772318	631/434-2255	218
Oak Street Elem Sch/Plattsburgh/Clinton	00720274	518/563-4950	45
Oakdale-Bohemia Middle Sch/Oakdale/Suffolk	00772954	631/244-2268	220
OAKFIELD ALABAMA CTL SD/			
OAKFIELD/GENESEE	00729024	585/948-5211	74
Oakfield Alabama Elem Sch/Oakfield/Genesee	00729050	585/948-5211	74
Oakfield Alabama Jr Sr HS/Oakfield/Genesee	00729036	585/948-5211	74
Oakside Elem Sch/Peekskill/Westchester	00781383	914/737-1591	260
Oakview Prep Sch/Yonkers/Westchester	04974233	914/423-7369	266
Oakwood Christian Sch/Troy/Rensselaer	04974960	518/271-0526	192
Oakwood Friends Sch/Poughkeepsie/Dutchess	00722363	845/462-4200	55
Oakwood Primary Center/Huntington/Suffolk	00775803	631/812-3500	231
Oasis Academy/Syracuse/Onondaga	12109606	315/435-6226	159
Ocean Avenue Elem Sch/Northport/Suffolk	00774756	631/262-6840	227
Ocean Hill Collegiate Chtr Sch/Brooklyn/Kings	11560966	718/250-5765	6
Oceanside High Sch Castleton/Oceanside/Nassau	12115540	516/678-7593	127
OCEANSIDE UNION FREE SCH DIST/			
OCEANSIDE/NASSAU	00737760	516/678-1200	127
OCM BOCES-Henry Campus/Syracuse/Onondaga	01417224	315/433-2635	154
Oconnor Academy-Monroe 1 BOCES/Fairport/Monroe	12165260	585/383-6670	106
ODESSA MONTOUR CTL SCH DIST/			
ODESSA/SCHUYLER	00770918	607/594-3341	207
Odessa Montour Jr Sr High Sch/Odessa/Schuyler	00770944	607/594-3341	207
Odyssey Academy/Rochester/Monroe	00731986	585/966-5200	109
Ogden Elem Sch/Valley Stream/Nassau	00736314	516/792-4700	121
OGDENSBURG CITY SCH DIST/			
OGDENSBURG/ST LAWRENCE	00768848	315/393-0900	211
Ogdensburg Free Academy/Ogdensburg/St Lawrence	04020375	315/393-0900	212
Ohio Elem Sch/N Tonawanda/Niagara	00759689	716/807-3800	148
Ohio Elem Sch/Watertown/Jefferson	00730413	315/785-3755	82
Oholei Torah Elem Sch/Brooklyn/Kings	00751651	718/483-9000	98
Ohr Reuven Sch/Suffern/Rockland	11238022	845/362-8362	199
Okte Elem Sch/Clifton Park/Saratoga	00769866	518/881-0540	202
Old Bethpage Elem Sch/Old Bethpage/Nassau	00738087	516/434-3419	128
Old Country Road Elem Sch/Hicksville/Nassau	00736431	516/733-2301	122
Old Mill Road Elem Sch/North Merrick/Nassau	00737693	516/379-0945	126
Oldfield Middle Sch/Greenlawn/Suffolk	00773661	631/754-5310	223
OLEAN CITY SCH DIST/			
CATTARAUGUS	00717588	716/375-8001	32
Olean Interm Middle Sch/Olean/Cattaraugus	01396565	716/375-8061	32
Olean Senior High Sch/Olean/Cattaraugus	00717643	716/375-8010	32
Oliver W Winch Middle Sch/S Glens Falls/Saratoga	00769971	518/792-5891	202
Olympia High Sch/Rochester/Monroe	00732021	585/966-5000	109
Olympus Academy/Brooklyn/Kings	11103142	718/272-1926	88
ONC BOCES/GRAND GORGE/DELAWARE	00721371	607/588-6291	51
One World Middle Sch-Edenwald/Bronx/Bronx	11713163	718/515-6780	23
ONEIDA CITY SCH DIST/ONEIDA/			
MADISON	00731247	315/363-2550	105
Oneida High Sch/Oneida/Madison	00731297	315/363-6901	105
Oneida Middle Sch/Schenectady/Schenectady	12169620	518/370-8260	205
ONEIDA-HERKIMER-MAD BOCES/			
NEW HARTFORD/ONEIDA	00761046	315/793-8500	154
Oneonta Christian Academy/Oneonta/Otsego	03195331	607/432-0383	175
ONEONTA CITY SCH DIST/ONEONTA/			
OTSEGO	00766125	607/433-8200	174
Oneonta Middle Sch/Oneonta/Otsego	00766151	607/433-8262	174
Oneonta Senior High Sch/Oneonta/Otsego	00766163	607/433-8243	174
ONONDAGA CENTRAL SCH DIST/			
NEDROW/ONONDAGA	00762052	315/552-5000	157
Onondaga Hill Middle Sch/Syracuse/Onondaga	00762703	315/426-3400	160
Onondaga Jr Sr High Sch/Nedrow/Onondaga	00762064	315/552-5020	157
Onondaga Nation Sch/Nedrow/Onondaga	00761565	315/469-6991	156
Onondaga Road Elem Sch/Syracuse/Onondaga	00761216	315/487-4653	159
ONONDAGA-CORTLAND-MADSON BOCES/			
SYRACUSE/ONONDAGA	00762739	315/433-2602	160
Ontech Charter High Sch/Syracuse/Onondaga	12377592	315/396-0558	6
ONTEORA CENTRAL SCH DIST/			
BOICEVILLE/ULSTER	00778142	845/657-6383	243
Onteora Middle Senior High Sch/Boiceville/Ulster	00778154	845/657-2373	243
Opportunity Charter Sch/New York/New York	05349667	212/866-6137	139
Oquenock Elem Sch/West Islip/Suffolk	00776261	631/893-3360	233
Ora Academy/Rochester/Monroe	04494556	585/271-8711	114
Orange Ulster Sp Ed Ctr/Goshen/Orange	01833642	845/291-0200	163
ORANGE-ULSTER BOCES/GOSHEN/			
ORANGE	00765066	845/291-0100	168
Orange-Ulster BOCES Tech Ctr/Goshen/Orange	00765078	845/291-0300	163
Orchard Collegiate Academy/New York/New York	05351725	212/406-9411	135
ORCHARD PARK CENTRAL SCH DIST/			
WEST SENECA/ERIE	00725016	716/620-6222	63
Orchard Park High Sch/Orchard Park/Erie	00725078	716/209-6242	63
Orchard Park Middle Sch/Orchard Park/Erie	00725066	716/209-6220	63
Orchard Sch/Yonkers/Westchester	01795820	914/965-3700	266
Orchard View Alternative Sch/Hopewell Jct/Dutchess	10011704	845/298-5000	54
Oregon Middle Sch/Medford/Suffolk	00774873	631/687-6800	227
Orenda Elem Sch/Clifton Park/Saratoga	00769919	518/881-0550	202
Origins High Sch/Brooklyn/Kings	11924192	718/891-0037	92
ORISKANY CTL SCH DIST/ORISKANY/			
ONEIDA	00760248	315/768-2058	151
Oriskany Jr Sr High Sch/Oriskany/Oneida	00760262	315/768-2063	151
Orleans County Christian Sch/Medina/Orleans	04975433	585/798-2992	170
ORLEANS-NIAGARA BOCES/MEDINA/			
ORLEANS	00765327	716/731-6800	170
Orleans-Niagara BOCES Sch/Medina/Orleans	00765341	716/731-6800	168
Orville A Todd Middle Sch/Poughkeepsie/Dutchess	00722117	845/463-7830	54
Osborn Elem Sch/Rye/Westchester	00781711	914/967-6100	261
Ossining High Sch/Ossining/Westchester	00781333	914/762-5760	260
OSSINING UNION FREE SCH DIST/			
OSSINING/WESTCHESTER	00781292	914/941-7700	259
Ostrander Elem Sch/Wallkill/Ulster	00778386	845/895-7225	244
Oswego BOCES-Exceptional Ed/Mexico/Oswego	00765937	315/963-4315	170
OSWEGO CITY SCH DIST/OSWEGO/			
OSWEGO	00765705	315/341-2001	171
Oswego Cmty Christian Sch/Oswego/Oswego	02160905	315/342-9322	172
Oswego High Sch/Oswego/Oswego	00765779	315/341-2200	171
Oswego Middle Sch/Oswego/Oswego	00765767	315/341-2300	171
Otisville Elem Sch/Otisville/Orange	00764414	845/355-5850	165
Otsego Area Occupation Center/Milford/Otsego	00721395	607/286-7715	172
Otsego Elem Sch/Dix Hills/Suffolk	00773518	631/592-3600	222
Otselic Valley Central Sch/South Otselic/Chenango	00719914	315/653-7218	42
OTSELIC VALLEY CENTRAL SD/			
SOUTH OTSELIC/CHENANGO	00719897	315/653-7218	42
Otto L Shortell Middle Sch/Wampsville/Madison	00731285	315/363-1050	105
Our Lady Blessed Sacrament Sch/Bayside/Queens	00753348	718/229-4434	186
Our Lady Blessed Sacrament Sch/Depew/Erie	00726498	716/685-2544	65
Our Lady Mt Carmel-Bronx Sch/Bronx/Bronx	00756182	718/295-6080	25
Our Lady of Black Rock Sch/Buffalo/Erie	00725913	716/873-7497	65
Our Lady of Fatima Sch/East Elmhurst/Queens	00753374	718/429-7031	186
Our Lady of Good Counsel Sch/Staten Island/Richmond	00756106	718/447-7260	194
Our Lady of Grace Montessori/Manhasset/Nassau	02852914	516/365-9832	134
Our Lady of Grace Sch/Bronx/Bronx	00756118	718/547-9918	25
Our Lady of Grace Sch/Brooklyn/Kings	00753398	718/375-2081	95
Our Lady of Guadalupe Sch/Brooklyn/Kings	00753403	718/331-2070	95
Our Lady of Hope Sch/Middle Vlg/Queens	00753415	718/458-3535	186
Our Lady of Lourdes HS/Poughkeepsie/Dutchess	00756132	845/463-0400	55
Our Lady of Lourdes Sch/Malverne/Nassau	00739782	516/599-7328	132
Our Lady of Lourdes Sch/New York/New York	00756144	212/926-5820	143

NY-V36   800-333-8802   School Year 2020-2021

New York School Directory
DISTRICT & SCHOOL TELEPHONE INDEX

School/City/County DISTRICT/CITY/COUNTY	PID	TELEPHONE NUMBER	PAGE
Our Lady of Mercy Academy/Syosset/Nassau	00739809	516/921-1047	132
Our Lady of Mercy Sch/Forest Hills/Queens	00753453	718/793-2086	186
Our Lady of Mercy Sch/Rochester/Monroe	00733960	585/288-7120	114
Our Lady of Mt Carmel Sch/Elmsford/Westchester	00756211	914/592-7575	265
Our Lady of Mt Carmel Sch/Middletown/Orange	00756209	845/343-8836	168
Our Lady of Peace Sch/Lynbrook/Nassau	00739823	516/593-4884	132
Our Lady of Providence Reg Sch/Central Islip/Suffolk	00740157	631/234-6324	234
Our Lady of Refuge Sch/Bronx/Bronx	00756261	718/367-3081	26
Our Lady of Sorrows Sch/Corona/Queens	00753568	718/426-5517	186
Our Lady of Sorrows Sch/White Plains/Westchester	00756297	914/761-0124	265
Our Lady of the Hamptons Sch/Southampton/Suffolk	00739847	631/283-9140	234
Our Lady of the Snows Sch/Floral Park/Queens	00753544	718/343-1346	186
Our Lady of Trust Sch-SJC/Brooklyn/Kings	00754354	718/241-6633	95
Our Lady of Victory Sch/Floral Park/Nassau	00739859	516/352-4466	132
Our Lady of Victory Sch/Lackawanna/Erie	00726606	716/828-9434	65
Our Lady of Victory Sch/Mount Vernon/Westchester	00756352	914/667-4063	265
Our Lady Perpetual Help Acad/S Ozone Park/Queens	00753520	718/843-4184	186
Our Lady Perpetual Help Sch/Brooklyn/Kings	00753594	718/439-8067	95
Our Lady Queen of Angels Sch/New York/New York	00756376	212/722-9277	143
Our Lady Queen of Martyrs Acad/Forest Hills/Queens	00753609	718/263-2622	186
Our Lady Queen of Martyrs Sch/New York/New York	00756388	212/567-3190	143
Our Lady Queen of Peace Sch/Staten Island/Richmond	00756390	718/351-0370	194
Our Lady Star of the Sea Sch/Staten Island/Richmond	00756405	718/984-5750	194
Our Lady's Catholic Academy/S Ozone Park/Queens	00753908	718/641-1316	186
Our Savior New American Sch/Centereach/Suffolk	11711866	631/588-2757	235
Our Savior's Lutheran Sch/Albany/Albany	00715047	518/459-2273	13
Our Saviour Lutheran Sch/Bronx/Bronx	00751699	718/792-5665	27
Our Saviour Lutheran Sch/Rego Park/Queens	00751687	718/897-4343	188
Our World Neighborhood ES CS 1/Astoria/Queens	05116123	718/392-3405	6
Our World Neighborhood ES CS 2/Howard Beach/Queens	12310879	347/390-3290	6
Our World Neighborhood MS CS 1/Astoria/Queens	12234407	718/274-2902	6
Overlook Primary Sch/Poughkeepsie/Dutchess	00721486	845/486-4970	51
Owasco Elem Sch/Auburn/Cayuga	00717954	315/255-8720	34
OWEGO APALACHIN CTL SCH DIST/OWEGO/TIOGA	00777112	607/687-6224	238
Owego Apalachin Middle Sch/Owego/Tioga	00777150	607/687-7302	238
Owego Elem Sch/Owego/Tioga	00777162	607/687-7303	238
Owego Free Academy/Owego/Tioga	00777148	607/687-7301	238
Owen D Young Central Sch/Van Hornesvle/Herkimer	00729828	315/858-0729	78
OWEN D YOUNG CENTRAL SCH DIST/VAN HORNESVLE/HERKIMER	00729816	315/858-0729	78
OXFORD ACADEMY CENTRAL SD/OXFORD/CHENANGO	00719770	607/843-2025	42
Oxford Academy High Sch/Oxford/Chenango	00719794	607/843-2025	42
Oxford Academy Middle Sch/Oxford/Chenango	00719782	607/843-2025	42
Oxford Academy Primary Sch/Oxford/Chenango	00719809	607/843-2025	42
Oxhead Road Elem Sch/Centereach/Suffolk	00774304	631/285-8700	225
OYSTER BAY EAST NORWICH CTL SD/OYSTER BAY/NASSAU	00737863	516/624-6500	127
Oyster Bay High Sch/Oyster Bay/Nassau	00737899	516/624-6524	127
Oysterponds Elem Sch/Orient/Suffolk	00774809	631/323-2410	227
OYSTERPONDS UNION FREE SD/ORIENT/SUFFOLK	00774794	631/323-2410	227

P

School/City/County	PID	TELEPHONE NUMBER	PAGE
P-Tech/Rochester/Monroe	12036968	585/324-9722	111
P469X Bronx Sch Continuous Lrn/Bronx/Bronx	12105404	718/696-6440	25
Pace Academy/Poughkeepsie/Dutchess	12376756	845/275-4102	53
Pace High Sch/New York/New York	05348883	212/334-4663	137
Packer Collegiate Institute/Brooklyn/Kings	00752708	718/250-0200	98
Paddy Hill Elem Sch/Rochester/Monroe	00732033	585/966-3700	109
Paideia School 15/Yonkers/Westchester	04846076	914/376-8645	263
Paideia School 24/Yonkers/Westchester	04456164	914/376-8640	263
Paige Elem Sch/Schenectady/Schenectady	00770542	518/370-8300	205
Pakanasink Elem Sch/Circleville/Orange	01519860	845/744-2031	166
Palermo Elem Sch/Fulton/Oswego	00765690	315/963-8400	171
Palisade Preparatory Sch/Yonkers/Westchester	04921535	914/376-8177	264
PALMYRA-MACEDON CENTRAL SD/PALMYRA/WAYNE	00779380	315/597-3400	250
Palmyra-Macedon High Sch/Palmyra/Wayne	00779421	315/597-3420	250
Palmyra-Macedon Interm Sch/MacEdon/Wayne	00779392	315/597-3400	250
Palmyra-Macedon Middle Sch/Palmyra/Wayne	00779419	315/597-3400	250
Palmyra-Macedon Primary Sch/Palmyra/Wayne	00779407	315/597-3475	250
Pan American Int'l HS-Monroe/Bronx/Bronx	11103300	718/991-7238	24
Pan American International HS/Elmhurst/Queens	11103362	718/271-3602	177
Panama Central Sch/Panama/Chautauqua	00718922	716/782-2455	38
PANAMA CENTRAL SCH DIST/PANAMA/CHAUTAUQUA	00718893	716/782-2455	38
Parishville Hopkinton Ctl Sch/Parishville/St Lawrence	00768939	315/265-4642	212
PARISHVILLE HOPKINTON SCH DIST/PARISHVILLE/ST LAWRENCE	00768915	315/265-4642	212
Park Ave Elem Sch/Warwick/Orange	00764969	845/987-3170	167
Park Avenue Elem Sch/North Merrick/Nassau	00737631	516/992-3117	126
Park Avenue Elem Sch/Port Chester/Westchester	00781618	914/934-7895	261
Park Avenue Memorial Elem Sch/Amityville/Suffolk	00771948	631/565-6300	216
Park Avenue Sch/Westbury/Nassau	00739160	516/876-5107	132
Park Early Childhood Center/Ossining/Westchester	00781345	914/762-5850	260
Park East High Sch/New York/New York	01552288	212/831-1517	139
Park Hill Pre-School/East Syracuse/Onondaga	03280584	315/434-3800	155
Park Road Elem Sch/Pittsford/Monroe	00732485	585/267-1500	110
Park School-Buffalo/Snyder/Erie	00727844	716/839-1242	66
Park Slope Collegiate Sch/Brooklyn/Kings	05349605	718/832-4300	85
Park Terrace Elem Sch/Gloversville/Fulton	00728537	518/775-5750	71
Parkdale Elem Sch/East Aurora/Erie	00723800	716/687-2352	60
Parkside Preparatory Academy/Brooklyn/Kings	04319360	718/462-6992	87
Parkside Sch/New York/New York	10029684	212/721-8888	145
Parkview Elem Sch/Kings Park/Suffolk	00773996	631/269-3770	224
Parkview Junior Academy/Syracuse/Onondaga	01463560	315/468-0117	160
Parkville Sch/New Hyde Park/Nassau	03246124	516/441-4350	121
Parkway Elem Sch/East Meadow/Nassau	00735243	516/679-3500	118
Parkway Elem Sch/Plainview/Nassau	00738099	516/434-3358	128
Parkway Middle Sch/Whitesboro/Oneida	00760963	315/266-3175	153
Parkway Sch/Brooklyn/Kings	10015839	718/346-0369	98
Parliament Place Elem Sch/North Babylon/Suffolk	00774598	631/620-7900	226
Parsons Memorial Elem Sch/Harrison/Westchester	00780315	914/630-3222	256
Pasadena Elem Sch/Plainview/Nassau	04916633	516/434-3451	128
Pashley Elem Sch/Glenville/Saratoga	00769543	518/399-9141	200
Passages Acad-Belmont/Brooklyn/Kings	12235621	718/647-1800	94
Passages Acad-Crossroads/Brooklyn/Kings	12311110	718/240-3824	94
Passages Acad-Dobbs Ferry/Dobbs Ferry/Westchester	12311093		259
Passages Acad-Horizon/Bronx/Bronx	04877556	718/401-3053	25
Passages Acad-Ryer/Bronx/Bronx	12311122		25
Passages Acad-South Ozone Park/S Ozone Park/Queens	12311134	718/927-1228	185
Passages Acad-Staten Island/Staten Island/Richmond	12311146	718/304-2037	194
Passages Academy-Bronx Hope/Bronx/Bronx	12311081	718/294-4832	25
Pat Kam Sch/Uniondale/Nassau	03191452	516/486-7887	134
Patchogue Medford Sr High Sch/Medford/Suffolk	00774885	631/687-6500	227
PATCHOGUE-MEDFORD UNIFIED SD/PATCHOGUE/SUFFOLK	00774811	631/687-6300	227
Pathfinder Village Sch/Edmeston/Otsego	01463675	607/965-8121	175
Pathways/Johnson City/Broome	04452613	607/930-1009	29
Pathways College Prep Sch/Saint Albans/Queens	10009012	718/454-4957	183
Pathways In Tech Early Clg HS/Brooklyn/Kings	11714935	718/221-1593	87
Pathways to Graduation/New York/New York	10025547	212/868-7238	142
Patricia A DiChiaro Elem Sch/Yonkers/Westchester	00782442	914/376-8565	264
Paul B D Temple Elem Sch/Kennedy/Chautauqua	00718594	716/267-3255	37

DISTRICT & SCHOOL TELEPHONE INDEX

Market Data Retrieval

School/City/County DISTRICT/CITY/COUNTY	PID	TELEPHONE NUMBER	PAGE
Paul D Schreiber High Sch/Prt Washingtn/Nassau	00738221	516/767-5800	128
Paul J Bellew Elem Sch/West Islip/Suffolk	00776285	631/504-5680	233
Paul J Gelinas Jr High Sch/Setauket/Suffolk	00776027	631/730-4700	232
Paul Road Elem Sch/Rochester/Monroe	00731819	585/247-2144	108
Paul V Moore High Sch/Central Sq/Oswego	00765470	315/668-4231	170
Paula Hedbavny Sch/New York/New York	05349095	917/521-2060	141
Paumanok Elem Sch/Dix Hills/Suffolk	00773520	631/592-3650	222
Pave Academy Charter Sch/Brooklyn/Kings	11103518	718/858-7813	85
Pavilion Ctl Jr Sr High Sch/Pavilion/Genesee	00729074	585/584-3115	74
PAVILION CTL SCH DIST/PAVILION/GENESEE	00729062	585/584-3115	74
Pawling Central Middle Sch/Pawling/Dutchess	04940622	845/855-4653	52
PAWLING CTL SCH DIST/PAWLING/DUTCHESS	00721826	845/855-4600	52
Pawling Elem Sch/Pawling/Dutchess	00721838	845/855-4607	52
Pawling High Sch/Pawling/Dutchess	00721840	845/855-4620	52
Peachtown Elem Sch/Aurora/Cayuga	04975067	315/364-8721	36
Pearl River High Sch/Pearl River/Rockland	00767818	845/620-3800	197
Pearl River Middle Sch/Pearl River/Rockland	00767806	845/620-3870	197
PEARL RIVER SCH DIST/PEARL RIVER/ROCKLAND	00767753	845/620-3900	197
Pearls Hawthorne Sch/Yonkers/Westchester	03257939	914/376-8250	264
Peck Slip School 343/New York/New York	11821667	212/312-6260	137
Peconic Community Sch/Aquebogue/Suffolk	12314760	631/779-2934	235
PEEKSKILL CITY SCH DIST/PEEKSKILL/WESTCHESTER	00781369	914/737-3300	260
Peekskill High Sch/Peekskill/Westchester	00781395	914/737-0201	260
Peekskill Middle Sch/Peekskill/Westchester	00781400	914/737-4542	260
Pelham Academy/Bronx/Bronx	11447572	718/881-3136	23
Pelham Gardens Middle Sch/Bronx/Bronx	11824358	718/794-9750	23
Pelham Lab High Sch/Bronx/Bronx	11924477	718/904-5090	17
Pelham Memorial High Sch/Pelham/Westchester	00781474	914/738-8110	260
Pelham Middle Sch/Pelham/Westchester	00781462	914/738-8190	260
Pelham Preparatory Academy/Bronx/Bronx	05280920	718/944-3601	23
PELHAM UNION FREE SCH DIST/PELHAM/WESTCHESTER	00781436	914/738-3434	260
PEMBROKE CTL SCH DIST/CORFU/GENESEE	00728927	585/599-4525	74
Pembroke Intermediate Sch/Corfu/Genesee	00728939	585/599-4531	74
Pembroke Jr Sr High Sch/Corfu/Genesee	00728941	585/599-4525	74
Pembroke Primary Sch/East Pembroke/Genesee	00728953	585/762-8713	74
PENFIELD CENTRAL SCH DIST/ROCHESTER/MONROE	00732332	585/249-5700	109
Penfield Senior High Sch/Penfield/Monroe	00732409	585/249-6700	110
Peninsula Prep Academy CS/Far Rockaway/Queens	05349681	347/403-9231	180
Penn Yan Academy High Sch/Penn Yan/Yates	00783305	315/536-4408	268
PENN YAN CTL SCH DIST/PENN YAN/YATES	00783276	315/536-3371	268
Penn Yan Elem Sch/Penn Yan/Yates	00783317	315/536-3346	268
Penn Yan Middle Sch/Penn Yan/Yates	00783329	315/536-3366	268
Pennington Elem Sch/Mount Vernon/Westchester	00780987	914/665-5105	258
Pequenakonck Elem Sch/North Salem/Westchester	00781280	914/669-5317	259
Performing Arts & Tech HS/Brooklyn/Kings	05348821	718/688-7900	89
Perkins Elem Sch/Newark/Wayne	00779316	315/332-3315	250
Perry Browne Intermediate Sch/Norwich/Chenango	00719756	607/334-1600	42
PERRY CENTRAL SCH DIST/PERRY/WYOMING	00783161	585/237-0270	267
Perry Elem Sch/Perry/Wyoming	00783173	585/237-0270	267
Perry Junior High Sch/New Hartford/Oneida	00760195	315/738-9300	151
Perry Junior Senior High Sch/Perry/Wyoming	00783185	585/237-0270	267
Persell Middle Sch/Jamestown/Chautauqua	00718788	716/483-4406	38
Persistence Prep Acad CS/Buffalo/Erie	12377580	716/235-1520	6
Perth Bible Christian Academy/Amsterdam/Montgomery	02205892	518/843-3290	116
PERU CENTRAL SCH DIST/PERU/CLINTON	00720171	518/643-6000	44
Peru Elem Sch/Peru/Clinton	00720195	518/643-6100	44
Peru Jr/Sr High Sch/Peru/Clinton	00720200	518/643-6400	44
Peter J Brennan High Sch/West Babylon/Suffolk	04026460	631/491-4390	216
Peterboro St Elem Sch/Canastota/Madison	00730982	315/697-2027	104
Petrova Elem Sch/Saranac Lake/Franklin	00728343	518/891-4221	70
Pharos Acad Charter Sch/Bronx/Bronx	12472049	646/915-0025	24
PHELPS-CLIFTON SPRINGS CTL SD/CLIFTON SPGS/ONTARIO	00763874	315/548-6420	162
Philadelphia Primary Sch/Philadelphia/Jefferson	00730188	315/642-3432	80
Phillips Avenue Elem Sch/Riverhead/Suffolk	00775047	631/369-6787	228
Phoenicia Elem Sch/Phoenicia/Ulster	00778166	845/688-5580	243
Phoenix Academy/Elmira/Chemung	03382144	607/739-3581	40
PHOENIX CENTRAL SCH DIST/PHOENIX/OSWEGO	00765781	315/695-1555	171
Phyllilsuster Birch Sch/Flushing/Queens	11239466	718/591-8100	188
Phyllis L Susser Sch/Flushing/Queens	01794864	718/591-8100	188
Pierre Van Cortlandt Mid Sch/Croton Hdsn/Westchester	00779926	914/271-2191	254
Pierson Middle High Sch/Sag Harbor/Suffolk	00775322	631/725-5302	229
Pieter B Coeymans Elem Sch/Coeymans/Albany	00714794	518/756-5200	11
Pine Brook Elem Sch/Rochester/Monroe	04032756	585/966-4600	109
PINE BUSH CENTRAL SCH DIST/PINE BUSH/ORANGE	00764799	845/744-2031	166
Pine Bush Elem Sch/Pine Bush/Orange	03399393	845/744-2031	166
Pine Bush Elem Sch/Schenectady/Albany	04281189	518/357-2770	11
Pine Bush High Sch/Pine Bush/Orange	00764842	845/744-2031	166
Pine City Elem Sch/Pine City/Chemung	00719316	607/735-3800	40
Pine Grove Middle Sch/East Syracuse/Onondaga	00761357	315/434-3050	155
Pine Hills Elem Sch/Albany/Albany	00714196	518/475-6725	9
Pine Park Elem Sch/Brentwood/Suffolk	00772320	631/434-2251	218
PINE PLAINS CTL SCH DIST/PINE PLAINS/DUTCHESS	00721852	518/398-7181	53
Pine Tree Elem Sch/Monroe/Orange	00764488	845/460-6900	165
PINE VALLEY CENTRAL SCH DIST/SOUTH DAYTON/CHAUTAUQUA	00718934	716/988-3293	38
Pine Valley Ctl Jr Sr High Sch/South Dayton/Chautauqua	00718946	716/988-3276	38
Pine Valley Elem Sch/South Dayton/Chautauqua	00718958	716/988-3291	38
Pinehurst Elem Sch/Lake View/Erie	00724000	716/926-1770	61
Pines Bridge Sch/Yorktown Hts/Westchester	11434991	914/248-2250	252
Pines Elem Sch/Smithtown/Suffolk	00773752	631/543-8700	223
Pinewood Intermediate Sch/Schenectady/Schenectady	00770205	518/356-8430	204
Pinnacle School 35/Rochester/Monroe	00732992	585/271-4583	111
Pioneer High Sch/Yorkshire/Cattaraugus	00717710	716/492-9300	33
Pioneer Middle Sch/Yorkshire/Cattaraugus	01401055	716/492-9300	33
PITTSFORD CENTRAL SCH DIST/PITTSFORD/MONROE	00732423	585/267-1000	110
Pittsford Mendon High Sch/Pittsford/Monroe	00732497	585/267-1600	110
Pittsford Sutherland High Sch/Pittsford/Monroe	00732502	585/267-1100	110
Plainedge High Sch/N Massapequa/Nassau	00737978	516/992-7550	127
Plainedge Middle Sch/Bethpage/Nassau	00738001	516/992-7650	127
PLAINEDGE UNION FREE SCH DIST/N MASSAPEQUA/NASSAU	00737928	516/992-7450	127
Plainview Old Bethpage Mid Sch/Plainview/Nassau	00738128	516/434-3308	128
PLAINVIEW-OLD BETHPAGE CTL SD/PLAINVIEW/NASSAU	00738013	516/434-3001	127
Plank Road North Elem Sch/Webster/Monroe	00733453	585/671-8858	113
Plank Road South Elem Sch/Webster/Monroe	00733465	585/671-3190	113
Plattekill Elem Sch/Plattekill/Ulster	00778398	845/895-7250	244
PLATTSBURGH CITY SCH DIST/PLATTSBURGH/CLINTON	00720236	518/957-6000	44
Plattsburgh Senior High Sch/Plattsburgh/Clinton	00720298	518/561-7500	45
Plaza Elem Sch/Baldwin/Nassau	00734976	516/434-6600	117
Pleasant Avenue Elem Sch/Johnstown/Fulton	00728604	518/762-8610	71
Pleasant Valley Elem Sch/Schenectady/Schenectady	00770554	518/881-3640	205
Pleasantville High Sch/Pleasantville/Westchester	00781539	914/741-1420	260
Pleasantville Middle Sch/Pleasantville/Westchester	00781527	914/741-1450	260
PLEASANTVILLE UNION FREE SD/PLEASANTVILLE/WESTCHESTER	00781503	914/741-1400	260
Pocantico Hills Central Sch/Sleepy Hollow/Westchester	00781565	914/631-2440	261
POCANTICO HILLS CTL SCH DIST/SLEEPY HOLLOW/WESTCHESTER	00781553	914/631-2440	260
Poestenkill Elem Sch/Poestenkill/Rensselaer	00766632	518/674-7125	189
Poland Central Sch/Poland/Herkimer	00729842	315/826-7900	78

New York School Directory
DISTRICT & SCHOOL TELEPHONE INDEX

School/City/County DISTRICT/CITY/COUNTY	PID	TELEPHONE NUMBER	PAGE
POLAND CENTRAL SCH DIST/ **POLAND/HERKIMER**	00729830	315/826-7900	78
Polis Mont Columbus Square ES/New York/ New York	12362468	917/388-1710	145
Polis Mont Museum Mile ES/New York/ New York	12362456	917/388-1710	145
Polk Street Elem Sch/Franklin Sq/Nassau	00735657	516/352-6300	119
Poly Prep Country Day Sch-Lowr/Brooklyn/ Kings	00752722	718/768-1103	98
Poly Prep Country Day Sch-Uppr/Brooklyn/ Kings	00752710	718/836-9800	98
Pomona Middle Sch/Suffern/Rockland	00768068	845/577-6200	196
PORT BYRON CTL SCH DIST/ **PORT BYRON/CAYUGA**	00718051	315/776-5728	35
Port Chester High Sch/Port Chester/ Westchester	00781632	914/934-7950	261
Port Chester Middle Sch/Port Chester/ Westchester	00781620	914/934-7930	261
PORT CHESTER RYE UNION FREE SD/ **PORT CHESTER/WESTCHESTER**	00781577	914/934-7900	261
Port Dickinson Elem Sch/Binghamton/Broome	00716637	607/762-6970	28
Port Jefferson Middle Sch/Prt Jefferson/ Suffolk	04431114	631/476-4440	228
PORT JEFFERSON UNION FREE SD 6/ **PRT JEFFERSON/SUFFOLK**	00774938	631/791-4500	227
PORT JERVIS CITY SCH DIST/ **PORT JERVIS/ORANGE**	00764854	845/858-3100	166
Port Jervis High Sch/Port Jervis/Orange	00764880	845/858-3100	166
Port Jervis Middle Sch/Port Jervis/Orange	00764878	845/858-3100	166
Port Leyden Elem Sch/Port Leyden/Lewis	00730621	315/348-2660	101
Port Richmond High Sch/Staten Island/ Richmond	00741383	718/420-2100	193
PORT WASHINGTON UNION FREE SD/ **PRT WASHINGTN/NASSAU**	00738130	516/767-5000	128
Porter Magnet Elem Sch/Syracuse/Onondaga	00762533	315/435-4625	159
Portledge Sch/Locust Valley/Nassau	11439771	516/750-3100	134
Portville Baptist Chrn Sch/Portville/ Cattaraugus	02970205	716/933-8164	34
Portville Central Sch/Portville/ Cattaraugus	00717734	716/933-6000	32
PORTVILLE CENTRAL SCH DIST/ **PORTVILLE/CATTARAUGUS**	00717722	716/933-6000	32
Post Road Elem Sch/White Plains/ Westchester	00782179	914/422-2320	263
POTSDAM CENTRAL SCH DIST/ **POTSDAM/ST LAWRENCE**	00768941	315/265-2000	212
Potsdam High Sch/Potsdam/St Lawrence	00768977	315/265-2000	212
Potter Career & Tech Center/West Seneca/ Erie	12115186	716/821-7331	56
POUGHKEEPSIE CITY SCH DIST/ **POUGHKEEPSIE/DUTCHESS**	00721890	845/867-6194	53
Poughkeepsie Day Sch/Poughkeepsie/Dutchess	00722375	845/462-7600	55
Poughkeepsie High Sch/Poughkeepsie/ Dutchess	00721955	845/451-4850	53
Poughkeepsie Middle Sch/Poughkeepsie/ Dutchess	00721967	845/451-4800	53
Poughkeepsie SDA Elem Sch/Poughkeepsie/ Dutchess	01460764	845/454-1781	55
Pound Ridge Elem Sch/Pound Ridge/ Westchester	00780846	914/764-8133	252
Powells Lane Sch/Westbury/Nassau	00739172	516/876-5125	132
Pratt Elem Sch/Barker/Niagara	00758972	716/795-3237	146
Prattsburgh Central Sch/Prattsburgh/ Steuben	00771778	607/522-3795	215
PRATTSBURGH CENTRAL SCH DIST/ **PRATTSBURGH/STEUBEN**	00771766	607/522-3795	215
Pre-K Center at 14-45/Whitestone/Queens	12160636	718/357-2840	178
Premm Learning Center/Oakdale/Suffolk	04026862	631/567-4901	216
Prep Academy for Writers/Sprngfld GDNS/ Queens	10030073	718/949-8405	183
Presidential Park Elem Sch/Middletown/ Orange	00764309	845/326-1850	165
Preston High Sch/Bronx/Bronx	00756429	718/863-9134	26
Prime Time for Kids/New City/Rockland	01795258	845/639-2425	199
Primrose Elem Sch/Lincolndale/Westchester	00781890	914/248-8888	262
Primrose Hill Sch/Rhinebeck/Dutchess	12314394	845/876-1226	55
Professional Children's Sch/New York/ New York	00751950	212/582-3116	145
Professional Pathways HS/Brooklyn/Kings	11932163	718/332-6290	92
Professional Perform Arts HS/New York/ New York	04145327	212/247-8652	137
Progress HS-Prof Careers/Brooklyn/Kings	04488002	718/387-0228	83
Progressive Sch of Long Island/Merrick/ Nassau	04928442	516/868-6835	134
Promise Christian Academy/Flushing/Queens	12314992	718/461-4409	188
Promising Futures Ldrshp Acad/Syracuse/ Onondaga	12367664	315/435-4135	159
Prospect Elem Sch/Salamanca/Cattaraugus	00717801	716/945-5170	33
Prospect Hill Elem Sch/Pelham/Westchester	00781486	914/738-6690	260
Prospect Park Bnos Leah Girls/Brooklyn/ Kings	01462530	718/376-3337	98
Prospect Park Girls Yeshiva/Brooklyn/Kings	02163294	718/376-4446	98
Prospect Sch/Hempstead/Nassau	03391494	516/434-4700	121
Prospect UCP Family Center/Queensbury/ Warren	01795698	518/798-0170	246
PS 1 Alfred E Smith/New York/New York	00741905	212/267-4133	137
PS 1 Courtlandt Sch/Bronx/Bronx	00743240	718/299-3700	16
PS 1 the Bergen/Brooklyn/Kings	00745389	718/567-7661	85
PS 1 Tottenville/Staten Island/Richmond	00749737	718/984-0960	193
PS 2/Troy/Rensselaer	00767131	518/328-5410	191
PS 2 Alfred Zimberg/East Elmhurst/Queens	00749440	718/728-1459	184
PS 2 Meyer London/New York/New York	00741917	212/964-0350	137
PS 3 Bedford Village/Brooklyn/Kings	00744816	718/622-2960	83
PS 3 Charrette Sch/New York/New York	00742088	212/691-1183	137
PS 3 D'Youville Porter Campus/Buffalo/Erie	00722739	716/816-3120	57
PS 3 Margaret Gioiosa Sch/Staten Island/ Richmond	00749749	718/984-1021	193
PS 3 Raul Julia Micro Society/Bronx/Bronx	04370522	718/584-1899	21
PS 4 Duke Ellington/New York/New York	04368086	212/928-0739	141
PS 4 Maurice Wollin/Staten Island/Richmond	00749751	718/984-1197	193
PS 5 Dr Ronald E McNair/Brooklyn/Kings	00745614	718/218-2444	86
PS 5 Ellen Lurie/New York/New York	04192875	212/567-8109	141
PS 5 Huguenot/Staten Island/Richmond	00749763	718/668-3270	193
PS 5 Port Morris Sch/Bronx/Bronx	00743070	718/292-2683	16
PS 6 Buffalo ES of Tech/Buffalo/Erie	00722753	716/816-3767	57
PS 6 Cpl Allan F Kivlehan Sch/Staten Island/ Richmond	04923105	718/697-3760	193
PS 6 Lillie D Blake/New York/New York	00741929	212/452-6650	137
PS 6 Norma Adams Clemons Acad/Brooklyn/ Kings	04037237	718/856-6560	87
PS 6 West Farms/Bronx/Bronx	00744529	718/542-7676	24
PS 7 Abraham Lincoln/Brooklyn/Kings	02200000	718/647-3600	89
PS 7 Louis Simeone/Elmhurst/Queens	04303103	718/446-2726	177
PS 7 Milton Fein Sch/Bronx/Bronx	00743939	718/796-8695	21
PS 7 Samuel Stern/New York/New York	00742416	212/860-5827	139
PS 8 Issac Varian/Bronx/Bronx	00743941	718/584-3043	21
PS 8 Luis Belliard/New York/New York	04368098	212/928-4157	141
PS 8 Robert Fulton/Brooklyn/Kings	00744828	718/834-6740	83
PS 8 Shirlee Solomon/Staten Island/ Richmond	00749775	718/356-2800	193
PS 009/Maspeth/Queens	00750750	718/456-7105	185
PS 9 Naples St Elem Sch/Staten Island/ Richmond	11924025	718/876-4610	193
PS 9 Ryer Ave Elem Sch/Bronx/Bronx	00744103	718/584-3291	21
PS 9 Sarah Anderson/New York/New York	00742179	212/678-2812	139
PS 9 Sarah Smith Garnet/Brooklyn/Kings	00744830	718/638-3260	83
PS 10 Ft Hill Collaborative ES/Staten Island/ Richmond	12105387	718/420-5115	193
PS 10 Magnet Sch Math-Sci-Tech/Brooklyn/ Kings	00745561	718/965-1190	85
PS 11 Highbridge Sch/Bronx/Bronx	00743654	718/681-7553	19
PS 11 Kathryn Phelan/Woodside/Queens	00749452	718/779-2090	184
PS 11 Purvis J Behan/Brooklyn/Kings	00744842	718/638-2661	83
PS 11 Thomas Dongan/Staten Island/Richmond	00750102	718/979-1030	193
PS 011 William T Harris/New York/New York	00741931	212/929-1743	137
PS 12 James B Colgate/Woodside/Queens	00747662	718/424-5905	177
PS 12X Lewis & Clark Sch/Bronx/Bronx	00750384	718/409-9040	25
PS 13 Clement C Moore/Elmhurst/Queens	00747674	718/271-1021	177
PS 13 M L Lindemeyer/Staten Island/ Richmond	00749799	718/447-1462	193
PS 13 Roberto Clemente/Brooklyn/Kings	00746199	718/498-3717	89
PS 14/Troy/Rensselaer	00767167	518/328-5801	191
PS 14 Fairview/Corona/Queens	00747686	718/699-6071	177
PS 15 Jackie Robinson Sch/Sprngfld GDNS/ Queens	00749153	718/525-1670	183
PS 15 Patrick F Daly/Brooklyn/Kings	00745391	718/330-9280	85
PS 15 Roberto Clemente/New York/New York	00741670	212/228-8730	135
PS 16/Troy/Rensselaer	00767179	518/328-5101	191
PS 16 John J Driscoll/Staten Island/ Richmond	00749816	718/447-0124	193
PS 16 Leonard Dunkly/Brooklyn/Kings	00745121	718/782-5352	84
PS 16 Wakefield Sch/Bronx/Bronx	00744218	718/324-1262	23
PS 17 Early Childhood Center/Buffalo/Erie	02105333	716/816-3150	57

School Year 2020-2021   800-333-8802   NY-V39

DISTRICT & SCHOOL TELEPHONE INDEX

School/City/County DISTRICT/CITY/COUNTY	PID	TELEPHONE NUMBER	PAGE
PS 17 Henry David Thoreau/Long Is City/Queens	00749622	718/278-1220	184
PS 17 Henry Woodworth/Brooklyn/Kings	00745133	718/387-2929	84
PS 18/Troy/Rensselaer	00767193	518/328-5501	191
PS 18 Edward Bush/Brooklyn/Kings	00745262	718/387-3241	84
PS 18 John G Whittier/Staten Island/Richmond	00750114	718/442-0216	193
PS 18 John Peter Zenger/Bronx/Bronx	00743082	718/292-2868	16
PS 18 Pantoja Sch Excellance/Buffalo/Erie	00722820	716/816-3160	57
PS 18 Park Terrace/New York/New York	04192916	917/521-2220	141
PS 18 Winchester/Queens Vlg/Queens	00748214	718/464-4167	179
PS 19 Asher Levy/New York/New York	00741682	212/533-5340	135
PS 19 Judith K Weiss Woodlawn/Bronx/Bronx	00744220	718/324-1924	23
PS 19 Marino P Jeantet/Corona/Queens	00747698	718/424-5859	177
PS 19 Native American Mag Sch/Buffalo/Erie	00722832	716/816-3180	57
PS 19 the Curtis Sch/Staten Island/Richmond	00749828	718/442-3860	193
PS 20 Anna Silver/New York/New York	00741694	212/254-9577	135
PS 20 Clinton Hill/Brooklyn/Kings	00744854	718/834-6744	83
PS 20 John Bowne/Flushing/Queens	00747935	718/359-0321	178
PS 20 Port Richmond/Staten Island/Richmond	00749830	718/442-4110	193
PS 21 Crispus Attucks/Brooklyn/Kings	00745626	718/493-9681	86
PS 21 Edward Hart/Flushing/Queens	00747947	718/445-8833	178
PS 21 Margaret Emery Elm Park/Staten Island/Richmond	00749842	718/816-3300	193
PS 21 Philip H Sheridan/Bronx/Bronx	00744232	718/652-3903	23
PS 22 Graniteville/Staten Island/Richmond	00749854	718/442-2219	193
PS 22 Thomas Jefferson/Flushing/Queens	00747959	718/762-4141	178
PS 23 Carter G Woodson/Brooklyn/Kings	00745286	718/387-0375	84
PS 23 New Childrens Sch/Bronx/Bronx	04037201	718/584-3992	21
PS 23 Richmondtown/Staten Island/Richmond	00749866	718/351-1155	193
PS 24/Brooklyn/Kings	04753663	718/832-9366	85
PS 24 Andrew Jackson/Flushing/Queens	00747961	718/359-2288	178
PS 24 Spuyten Duyvil/Bronx/Bronx	00744127	718/796-8845	21
PS 25 Bilingual Sch/Bronx/Bronx	00743094	718/292-2995	16
PS 25 Eubie Blake Sch/Brooklyn/Kings	01557434	718/574-2336	86
PS 26 Carteret Sch/Staten Island/Richmond	00749878	718/698-1530	193
PS 26 Jesse Owens/Brooklyn/Kings	00745638	718/919-5707	86
PS 26 Rufus King/Flushing/Queens	00748226	718/464-4505	179
PS 27 Hillery Park Elem Sch/Buffalo/Erie	00722894	716/816-4770	57
PS 28 Mt Hope Sch/Bronx/Bronx	00743666	718/583-6444	19
PS 28 Thomas Emanuel ECC/Corona/Queens	05097797	718/271-4971	177
PS 28 Wright Brothers/New York/New York	00742882	212/690-3014	141
PS 29 Bardwell/Staten Island/Richmond	00749880	718/556-4400	193
PS 29 John M Harrigan/Brooklyn/Kings	00745523	718/330-9277	85
PS 29 Queens/College Point/Queens	00747973	718/886-5111	178
PS 30 Frank A Sedita Academy/Buffalo/Erie	00722985	716/816-3220	57
PS 30 Hernandez-Hughes/New York/New York	00742806	212/876-1825	140
PS 30 Westerleigh/Staten Island/Richmond	00749892	718/442-0462	193
PS 30 Wilton/Bronx/Bronx	00743123	718/292-8817	16
PS 31 Bayside/Bayside/Queens	00748238	718/423-8289	179
PS 31 Harriet Ross Tubman Sch/Buffalo/Erie	00722791	716/816-3780	57
PS 31 Samuel F DuPont/Brooklyn/Kings	00745157	718/383-8998	84
PS 31 William T Davis/Staten Island/Richmond	00749907	718/273-3500	193
PS 32 Belmont/Bronx/Bronx	00743953	718/584-3645	21
PS 32 Bennett Park Mont Sch/Buffalo/Erie	01813264	716/816-4603	57
PS 32 Gifford Sch/Staten Island/Richmond	00749919	718/984-1688	193
PS 32 Samuel Mills Sprole/Brooklyn/Kings	00745418	718/222-6400	85
PS 32 State Street/Flushing/Queens	00747985	718/463-3747	178
PS 33 Bilingual Center/Buffalo/Erie	00722959	716/816-4783	57
PS 33 Chelsea Prep/New York/New York	00741967	212/244-6426	137
PS 33 Edward M Funk/Queens Vlg/Queens	00749165	718/465-6283	183
PS 33 Timothy Dwight/Bronx/Bronx	00743965	718/584-3926	21
PS 34 Franklin D Roosevelt/New York/New York	00741709	212/228-4433	135
PS 34 John Harvard/Queens Vlg/Queens	00749177	718/465-6818	183
PS 34 Oliver H Perry/Brooklyn/Kings	00745169	718/389-5842	84
PS 035/New York/New York	00750437	212/247-4307	142
PS 35 Clove Valley/Staten Island/Richmond	00749921	718/442-3037	193
PS 35 Franz Sigel Sch/Bronx/Bronx	00743678	718/681-7214	19
PS 35 Nathaniel Woodhull/Hollis/Queens	00749189	718/465-6820	183
PS 36 J C Drumgoole/Staten Island/Richmond	00749933	718/984-1422	193
PS 36 Margaret Douglas/New York/New York	00742820	212/690-5807	140
PS 36 St Albans Sch/Saint Albans/Queens	00749191	718/528-1862	183
PS 36 Unionport Sch/Bronx/Bronx	00743288	718/822-5345	17
PS 36K/Brooklyn/Kings	00750657	718/272-6483	94
PS 37 Futures Academy/Buffalo/Erie	00722973	716/816-3800	57
PS 38 George Cromwell/Staten Island/Richmond	00749945	718/351-1225	193
PS 38 Roberto Clemente/New York/New York	00742533	212/860-5882	139
PS 38 Rosedale/Rosedale/Queens	00749218	718/528-2276	183
PS 38 the Pacific/Brooklyn/Kings	00745547	718/330-9305	85
PS 39 Francis J Murphy Jr/Staten Island/Richmond	00749957	718/447-4543	193
PS 39 Henry Bristow Sch/Brooklyn/Kings	00745420	718/330-9310	85
PS 40 Augustus St Gaudens/New York/New York	00741979	212/475-5500	137
PS 40 George W Carver/Brooklyn/Kings	00745652	718/574-2353	86
PS 40 Samuel Huntington/Jamaica/Queens	00749048	718/526-1906	182
PS 41 Crocheron/Bayside/Queens	00748240	718/423-8333	179
PS 41 Francis White/Brooklyn/Kings	00747416	718/495-7732	93
PS 41 Greenwich Village/New York/New York	00742090	212/675-2756	137
PS 41 Gun Hill Road/Bronx/Bronx	00744244	718/652-3461	23
PS 41 Stephanie A Vierno Sch/Staten Island/Richmond	00749971	718/351-6777	193
PS 42 Benjamin Altman/New York/New York	00741981	212/226-8410	137
PS 42 Claremont/Bronx/Bronx	00743680	718/583-7366	19
PS 42 Eltingville/Staten Island/Richmond	00749983	718/984-3800	193
PS 42 Occ Training Center/Buffalo/Erie	02225490	716/816-3250	57
PS 43/Far Rockaway/Queens	04457510	718/327-5860	180
PS 43 Jonas Bronck/Bronx/Bronx	00743147	718/292-4502	16
PS 43 Lovejoy Discovery Sch/Buffalo/Erie	00723032	716/816-3260	57
PS 44 David C Farragut/Bronx/Bronx	00744464	718/583-2360	24
PS 44 Marcus Garvey/Brooklyn/Kings	00744866	718/834-6939	83
PS 44 Thomas C Brown/Staten Island/Richmond	00749995	718/442-0433	193
PS 45 Clarence Witherspoon/S Ozone Park/Queens	00748537	718/480-2500	180
PS 45 International Sch/Buffalo/Erie	00723056	716/816-3300	57
PS 45 John Tyler/Staten Island/Richmond	00750009	718/442-6123	193
PS 46 Albert V Maniscalco/Staten Island/Richmond	00750011	718/987-5155	193
PS 46 Alley Pond/Oakland GDNS/Queens	00748252	718/423-8395	179
PS 46 Arthur Tappan/New York/New York	00742648	212/360-1519	140
PS 46 Edgar Allan Poe/Bronx/Bronx	00743977	718/584-4450	21
PS 46 Edward C Blum/Brooklyn/Kings	00744878	718/834-7694	83
PS 47 Chris Galas/Rockaway Park/Queens	00748549	718/634-7167	180
PS 47 John Randolph/Bronx/Bronx	00744555	718/824-0950	24
PS 48 at 39 MLK Multcltrl Inst/Buffalo/Erie	00722997	716/816-3240	57
PS 48 Joseph R Drake/Bronx/Bronx	00743305	718/589-4312	17
PS 48 Mapleton/Brooklyn/Kings	00746539	718/232-3873	90
PS 48 Po Michael J Buczek/New York/New York	04192928	917/521-3800	141
PS 48 William C Wilcox/Staten Island/Richmond	00750023	718/447-8323	193
PS 48 William Wordsworth/Jamaica/Queens	00749050	718/558-6700	182
PS 49 Dorothy Bonawit Kole/Middle Vlg/Queens	00747703	718/326-2111	177
PS 49 Willis Avenue/Bronx/Bronx	00743159	718/292-4623	16
PS 50 Frank Hankinson/Staten Island/Richmond	00750035	718/987-0396	193
PS 50 North Park Cmty Sch/Buffalo/Erie	12317695	716/816-3440	57
PS 50 Talfourd Lawn Elem Sch/Jamaica/Queens	00749062	718/526-5336	182
PS 51/Richmond Hill/Queens	04368127	718/850-0738	180
PS 51 Bronx STEM & Arts Acad/Bronx/Bronx	03336066	718/733-0347	21
PS 51 Elias Howe/New York/New York	00741993	212/315-7160	137
PS 52 John C Thompson/Staten Island/Richmond	00750047	718/351-5454	193
PS 52 Queens/Jamaica/Queens	00749220	718/528-2238	183
PS 52 Sheepshead Bay/Brooklyn/Kings	00747131	718/648-0882	92
PS 53 Barbara Esselborn Sch/Staten Island/Richmond	00750059	718/987-8020	193
PS 53 Basheer Quisim/Bronx/Bronx	00743692	718/681-7276	19
PS 53 Community Sch/Buffalo/Erie	00723111	716/816-3330	57
PS 54/Bronx/Bronx	04876813	718/584-4203	21
PS 54 Charles W Leng/Staten Island/Richmond	00750061	718/698-0600	194
PS 54 Dr George Blackman ECC/Buffalo/Erie	00723123	716/816-3340	57
PS 54 Hillside/Richmond Hill/Queens	00748898	718/849-0962	182
PS 54 Samuel C Barnes/Brooklyn/Kings	00744880	718/834-6752	83
PS 55 Benjamin Franklin Sch/Bronx/Bronx	00743850	718/681-6227	19
PS 55 Henry M Boehm/Staten Island/Richmond	00750073	718/697-5200	194
PS 55 Maure/S Richmond Hl/Queens	00748903	718/849-3845	182
PS 56 Harry Eichler/Richmond Hill/Queens	00748551	718/441-4448	180
PS 56 Lewis H Latimer/Brooklyn/Kings	00744921	718/857-3149	83
PS 56 Louis DeSario Sch/Staten Island/Richmond	04804913	718/605-1189	194
PS 56 Norwood Heights/Bronx/Bronx	00743989	718/920-1100	21
PS 57 Crescent/Bronx/Bronx	00744581	718/367-9446	24
PS 57 Hubert H Humphrey/Staten Island/Richmond	01557513	718/447-1191	194

New York School Directory

DISTRICT & SCHOOL TELEPHONE INDEX

School/City/County DISTRICT/CITY/COUNTY	PID	TELEPHONE NUMBER	PAGE
PS 58/Bronx/Bronx	00743707	718/583-6866	19
PS 58 School of Heroes/Maspeth/Queens	05097802	718/533-6712	177
PS 58 the Carroll/Brooklyn/Kings	00745432	718/330-9322	85
PS 59 Annex/Buffalo/Erie	00723434	716/816-4120	57
PS 59 Beekman Hill Int'l/New York/New York	00742105	212/888-7870	137
PS 59 Community Sch of Tech/Bronx/Bronx	00744098	718/584-4730	21
PS 59 Dr Drew Science Mag Sch/Buffalo/Erie	00723159	716/816-3370	57
PS 59 Harbor View Sch/Staten Island/Richmond	11924013	718/390-2190	194
PS 59 William Floyd/Brooklyn/Kings	00745171	718/443-3600	84
PS 60 Alice Austen/Staten Island/Richmond	00750085	718/761-3325	194
PS 60 Woodhaven/Woodhaven/Queens	00748563	718/441-5046	180
PS 61 Arthur Eve-Distinction/Buffalo/Erie	00723173	716/816-3400	57
PS 61 Francisco Oller/Bronx/Bronx	00744593	718/542-7230	24
PS 62 Chester Park/S Richmond Hl/Queens	00748575	718/286-4460	181
PS 62 Inocensio Casanova/Bronx/Bronx	00743329	718/585-1617	17
PS 62 Kathleen Grimm/Staten Island/Richmond	12105911	718/668-8640	194
PS 63 Author's Academy/Bronx/Bronx	00743719	718/589-3058	19
PS 63 Old South/Ozone Park/Queens	00748587	718/845-7560	181
PS 63 the Star Academy/New York/New York	00741711	212/674-3180	135
PS 64 Frederick Law Olmsted/Buffalo/Erie	00723202	716/816-3420	57
PS 64 Joseph P Addabbo/Ozone Park/Queens	00748599	718/845-8290	181
PS 64 Robert Simon/New York/New York	00741723	212/673-6510	135
PS 65/Brooklyn/Kings	00746216	718/235-2223	89
PS 65 Academy-Innovative Lrng/Staten Island/Richmond	11103453	718/981-5034	194
PS 65 Mother Hale Academy/Bronx/Bronx	00743173	718/292-4628	16
PS 65 Raymond York ES/Ozone Park/Queens	04457522	718/323-1685	181
PS 65 Roosevelt ECC/Buffalo/Erie	00723214	716/816-3430	57
PS 66/Brooklyn/Kings	05274799	718/922-3505	88
PS 66 J Kennedy Onasiss/Richmond Hill/Queens	00748604	718/849-0184	181
PS 66 North Park Mid Academy/Buffalo/Erie	00723226	716/816-3440	57
PS 66 Sch Higher Expectations/Bronx/Bronx	00744608	718/319-2820	24
PS 67 Charles A Dorsey/Brooklyn/Kings	00744892	718/834-6756	83
PS 67 Discovery Sch/Buffalo/Erie	04898433	716/816-4922	57
PS 67 Mohegan Sch/Bronx/Bronx	00744610	718/823-4101	24
PS 68 Bronx/Bronx/Bronx	00744268	718/324-2854	23
PS 68 Cambridge/Ridgewood/Queens	00747715	718/821-7246	177
PS 68 Port Richmond Vis Lrng/Staten Island/Richmond	12170306	718/816-3377	194
PS 69 Daniel D Tompkins/Staten Island/Richmond	01533074	718/698-6661	194
PS 69 Houghton Academy/Buffalo/Erie	00723252	716/816-4794	57
PS 69 Jackson Heights/Jackson HTS/Queens	00749464	718/424-7700	184
PS 69 Journey Prep/Bronx/Bronx	00743331	718/378-4736	18
PS 69 Vincent D Grippo Sch/Brooklyn/Kings	05026413	718/630-3899	90
PS 70 Max Schoenfeld Sch/Bronx/Bronx	00743733	718/583-6000	19
PS 70 Queens/Long Is City/Queens	00749476	718/728-4646	184
PS 71 Forest Elem Sch/Ridgewood/Queens	00747727	718/821-7772	177
PS 71 Rose E Scala/Bronx/Bronx	00743343	718/822-5351	18
PS 72 Dr William Dorney/Bronx/Bronx	00743355	718/822-5311	18
PS 72 Lorraine Elem Sch/Buffalo/Erie	00723288	716/816-4809	57
PS 73X Bronx/Bronx/Bronx	00743745	718/681-6776	19
PS 74 Future Leaders ES/Staten Island/Richmond	11560746	718/727-5380	194
PS 74 Hamlin Park Sch/Buffalo/Erie	00723290	716/816-3490	57
PS 75 Emily Dickinson/New York/New York	00742181	212/866-5400	139
PS 75 Mayda Cortiella/Brooklyn/Kings	00750267	718/574-0244	94
PS 75 Research & Discovery/Bronx/Bronx	00743367	718/860-1630	18
PS 75Q Robert E Peary/Ridgewood/Queens	00750449	718/456-7588	185
PS 76 A Philip Randolph/New York/New York	00742193	212/678-2865	139
PS 76 Bennington/Bronx/Bronx	00744270	718/882-8865	23
PS 76 Herman Badillo Bil Acad/Buffalo/Erie	00723317	716/816-3848	57
PS 76 William Hallet/Long Is City/Queens	00749488	718/361-7464	184
PS 77 Lower Lab Sch/New York/New York	04457405	212/427-2798	137
PS 77K/Brooklyn/Kings	02110998	718/769-1039	94
PS 78/Staten Island/Richmond	11821734	718/442-3094	194
PS 78 Anne Hutchinson/Bronx/Bronx	00744282	718/652-1244	23
PS 79 Francis Lewis/Whitestone/Queens	00747997	718/746-0396	178
PS 79 Pfc William Grabiarz Sch/Buffalo/Erie	04916229	716/816-4040	57
PS 80 Highgate Heights ES/Buffalo/Erie	00723355	716/816-4050	57
PS 80 Thurgood Marshall Magnet/Jamaica/Queens	00749074	718/528-7070	182
PS 81 Jean Paul Richter/Ridgewood/Queens	00747739	718/821-9800	177
PS 81 Robert J Christen/Bronx/Bronx	00744000	718/796-8965	21
PS 81 Sch/Buffalo/Erie	00723367	716/816-4060	58
PS 81 Thaddeus Stevens/Brooklyn/Kings	00745664	718/574-2365	86
PS 82 Early Childhood Center/Buffalo/Erie	00723379	716/816-4070	58
PS 82 Hammond/Jamaica/Queens	00748915	718/526-4139	182
PS 83 Donald Hertz/Bronx/Bronx	00744294	718/863-1993	23
PS 83 Luis Munoz Rivera/New York/New York	00742454	212/860-5847	139
PS 84 Erie Co Health Center/Buffalo/Erie	00723393	716/816-4080	58
PS 84 Jose De Diego/Brooklyn/Kings	00745183	718/384-8063	84
PS 84 Lillian Weber/New York/New York	00742208	212/799-2534	139
PS 84 Steinway/Astoria/Queens	00749490	718/278-1915	184
PS 85 Great Expectations/Bronx/Bronx	00744012	718/584-5275	21
PS 85 Judge Charles Vallone/Long Is City/Queens	00749505	718/278-3630	184
PS 86 Irvington/Brooklyn/Kings	00750190	718/574-0252	94
PS 86 Kingbridge Heights/Bronx/Bronx	00744024	718/584-5585	21
PS 87 Bronx/Bronx/Bronx	00744309	718/324-5188	23
PS 87 Middle Village/Middle Vlg/Queens	00747741	718/326-8243	177
PS 87 William Sherman/New York/New York	00742210	212/678-2826	139
PS 88 Seneca/Ridgewood/Queens	00747753	718/821-8121	177
PS 88 Silverstein Ltl Sparrow/Bronx/Bronx	00743757	718/716-7369	19
PS 89/New York/New York	04805307	212/571-5659	137
PS 89 Bronx/Bronx/Bronx	00744311	718/653-0835	23
PS 89 Cypress Hills/Brooklyn/Kings	04796615	718/964-1180	89
PS 89 Dr L T Wright Sch/Buffalo/Erie	00722612	716/816-4110	58
PS 89 Elmhurst/Elmhurst/Queens	00747765	718/898-2230	177
PS 90 Edna Cohen Sch/Brooklyn/Kings	00746838	718/787-3333	91
PS 90 Horace Mann/Richmond Hill/Queens	00748616	718/847-3370	181
PS 91 Bronx/Bronx/Bronx	00744036	718/584-5805	21
PS 91 Richard Arkwright/Glendale/Queens	00747777	718/821-6880	177
PS 91 the Albany Ave Sch/Brooklyn/Kings	00745822	718/756-0243	87
PS 92 Adrian Hegeman/Brooklyn/Kings	00745834	718/462-2087	87
PS 92 Build Cmty Sch/Buffalo/Erie	00722636	716/816-4140	58
PS 92 Harry T Stewart Sr/Corona/Queens	00749517	718/533-1013	184
PS 92 Mary McLeod Bethune/New York/New York	00742650	212/690-5915	140
PS 93 Albert G Oliver/Bronx/Bronx	00743379	718/430-1700	18
PS 93 Southside Elem Sch/Buffalo/Erie	00723501	716/816-4818	58
PS 93 William H Prescott/Brooklyn/Kings	00744933	718/604-7363	83
PS 94 David D Porter/Little Neck/Queens	00748264	718/423-8491	179
PS 94 Henry Longfellow/Brooklyn/Kings	00745559	718/435-6034	85
PS 94 Kings College Sch/Bronx/Bronx	00744048	718/405-6345	21
PS 94 W Hertel Academy/Buffalo/Erie	00723525	716/816-4150	58
PS 94M the Spectrum Sch/New York/New York	03053111	212/266-5810	142
PS 95 Eastwood/Jamaica/Queens	00749232	718/739-0007	183
PS 95 Sheila Mencher/Bronx/Bronx	00744050	718/796-9200	21
PS 95 the Gravesend/Brooklyn/Kings	00746840	718/449-5050	91
PS 95 Waterfront Elem Sch/Buffalo/Erie	01525259	716/816-3900	58
PS 96/S Ozone Park/Queens	00748628	718/529-2547	181
PS 96 Joseph Lanzetta/New York/New York	00742466	212/860-5851	139
PS 96 Richard Rodgers/Bronx/Bronx	00744323	718/652-4959	23
PS 97 Bronx/Bronx/Bronx	00744335	718/655-4446	23
PS 97 Forest Park/Woodhaven/Queens	00748630	718/849-4870	181
PS 97 Harvey Austin Sch/Buffalo/Erie	05167342	716/816-4460	58
PS 97 the Highlawn Sch/Brooklyn/Kings	00746852	718/627-7550	91
PS 98 Shorac Kappock/New York/New York	00742894	212/927-7870	141
PS 098 the Douglaston Sch/Douglaston/Queens	00748276	718/423-8535	179
PS 99 Isaac Asimov/Brooklyn/Kings	00746864	718/338-9201	91
PS 99 Kew Gardens/Kew Gardens/Queens	00748939	718/544-4343	182
PS 99 Stanley Makowski ECC/Buffalo/Erie	04367020	716/816-4180	58
PS 100 Coney Island Sch/Brooklyn/Kings	00746876	718/382-2760	91
PS 100 Glen Morris/S Ozone Park/Queens	00748642	718/558-1510	181
PS 100 Isaac Clason/Bronx/Bronx	00743381	718/842-1461	18
PS 101 School In the Gardens/Forest Hills/Queens	00748941	718/268-7231	182
PS 101 the Verrazano/Brooklyn/Kings	00746888	718/372-0221	91
PS 102 Bayview/Elmhurst/Queens	00747789	718/446-3308	177
PS 102 Jacques Cartier/New York/New York	00742480	212/860-5834	139
PS 102 the Bayview/Brooklyn/Kings	00746541	718/748-7404	90
PS 103 Hector Fontanez/Bronx/Bronx	00744347	718/655-0261	23
PS 104 the Bays Water/Far Rockaway/Queens	00748654	718/327-1910	181
PS 105 Bay Sch/Far Rockaway/Queens	00748666	718/474-8615	181
PS 105 Sen Abraham Bernstein/Bronx/Bronx	00744359	718/824-7350	23
PS 105 the Blythebourne/Brooklyn/Kings	00746565	718/438-3230	90
PS 106 Edward Everett Hale/Brooklyn/Kings	00750205	718/574-0261	94
PS 106 Lighthouse Elem Sch/Far Rockaway/Queens	00748678	718/327-5828	181
PS 106 Parkchester/Bronx/Bronx	00744361	718/892-1006	23
PS 107/Bronx/Bronx	00744393	718/860-8760	18
PS 107 John W Kimball/Brooklyn/Kings	00745573	718/499-2054	85
PS 107 Thomas A Dooley/Flushing/Queens	00748006	718/762-5995	178
PS 108 Assemblyman Angelo Toro/New York/New York	00742507	212/860-5803	140
PS 108 Capt Vincent G Fowler/S Ozone Park/Queens	00748680	718/558-2700	181
PS 108 Philip J Abinanti/Bronx/Bronx	00744373	718/863-9829	23

School Year 2020-2021　　800-333-8802　　NY-V41

DISTRICT & SCHOOL TELEPHONE INDEX

Market Data Retrieval

School/City/County DISTRICT/CITY/COUNTY	PID	TELEPHONE NUMBER	PAGE
PS 108 Sal Abbracciamento/Brooklyn/Kings	00746242	718/277-7010	89
PS 109 Sedgwick/Bronx/Bronx	00743783	718/583-8878	19
PS 110/Corona/Queens	11924180	718/424-8278	177
PS 110 Florence Nightingale/New York/New York	00741747	212/674-2690	135
PS 110 the Monitor/Brooklyn/Kings	00745195	718/383-7600	84
PS 110 Theodore Schoenfeld/Bronx/Bronx	00743795	718/861-0759	19
PS 111 Adolph S Ochs/New York/New York	00742002	212/582-7420	137
PS 111 Jacob Blackwell/Long Is City/Queens	00749529	718/786-2073	184
PS 111 Seton Falls/Bronx/Bronx	00744385	718/881-2418	23
PS 112 Bronxwood/Bronx/Bronx	00744397	718/654-6377	23
PS 112 Dutch Kills/Long Is City/Queens	00749531	718/784-5250	184
PS 112 Jose Celso Barbosa/New York/New York	00742521	212/860-5868	140
PS 112 Lefferts Park/Brooklyn/Kings	00746577	718/232-0685	90
PS 114 Luis Llorens Torres/Bronx/Bronx	00743800	718/681-7507	19
PS 114 Ryder Elem Sch/Brooklyn/Kings	00746008	718/257-4428	88
PS 115 Alexander Humboldt/New York/New York	00742909	212/927-9233	141
PS 115 Daniel Mucatel Sch/Brooklyn/Kings	00746010	718/241-1000	88
PS 115 James J Ambrose Sch/Floral Park/Queens	00748288	718/831-4010	179
PS 116 Elizabeth L Farrell/Brooklyn/Kings	00750217	718/821-4623	94
PS 116 Mary Lindley Murray/New York/New York	00742014	212/685-4366	137
PS 116 William Hughley/Jamaica/Queens	00749244	718/526-4884	183
PS 117 J Keld/Briarwood Sch/Briarwood/Queens	00748953	718/526-4780	182
PS 118 Lorraine Hansberry/Saint Albans/Queens	00749256	718/465-5538	183
PS 119 Amersfort/Brooklyn/Kings	00747143	718/377-7696	92
PS 119 Dr Emmett W Bassett Sch/Bronx/Bronx	00743408	718/822-5198	18
PS 120 Carlos Tapia/Brooklyn/Kings	00745200	718/455-1000	84
PS 120 Queens/Flushing/Queens	00748018	718/359-3390	178
PS 121 Nelson A Rockefeller/Brooklyn/Kings	00746890	718/377-8845	91
PS 121 Queens/S Ozone Park/Queens	00748965	718/558-1560	182
PS 121 Throop/Bronx/Bronx	00744402	718/654-2055	23
PS 122 Mamie Fay/Astoria/Queens	00749543	718/721-6410	185
PS 123/S Ozone Park/Queens	00748707	718/529-4300	181
PS 123 Mahalia Jackson/New York/New York	00742739	212/342-6200	140
PS 123 Suydam/Brooklyn/Kings	00750229	718/821-4810	94
PS 124 Osmond A Church/S Ozone Park/Queens	00748719	718/529-2580	181
PS 124 Silas B Dutcher/Brooklyn/Kings	00745444	718/788-0246	85
PS 124 Yung Wing/New York/New York	01557484	212/966-7237	137
PS 125 Ralph Bunche/New York/New York	00742741	212/666-6400	140
PS 126 Dr Marjorie Dunbar Sch/Bronx/Bronx	00743812	718/681-6120	19
PS 126 Jacob August Riis/New York/New York	00742026	212/962-2188	137
PS 127 Aerospace Science Acad/East Elmhurst/Queens	00749555	718/446-4700	185
PS 127 McKinley Park/Brooklyn/Kings	00746589	718/833-2323	90
PS 128 Audubon/New York/New York	00742911	212/927-0607	141
PS 128 Bensonhurst/Brooklyn/Kings	00746905	718/373-5900	91
PS 128 Juniper Valley/Middle Vlg/Queens	00747806	718/326-6210	177
PS 129 John H Finley/New York/New York	00742753	212/690-5932	140
PS 129 Patricia A Larkin/College Point/Queens	00748020	718/353-3150	178
PS 130/Bayside/Queens	00748290	718/819-2230	178
PS 130 A S Hewitt Elem Sch/Bronx/Bronx	00743410	718/665-0962	18
PS 130 Hernando De Soto/New York/New York	00742038	212/226-8072	137
PS 130 the Parkside/Brooklyn/Kings	00745456	718/686-1940	85
PS 131 Abigail Adams/Jamaica/Queens	00749268	718/480-2840	183
PS 131 Academy School at 4/Buffalo/Erie	11716335	716/816-7180	58
PS 131 Brooklyn/Brooklyn/Kings	00745468	718/431-1960	85
PS 132 Conselyea/Brooklyn/Kings	00745119	718/599-7301	84
PS 132 Garrett A Morgan/Bronx/Bronx	00743824	718/681-6455	19
PS 132 Juan Pablo Duarte/New York/New York	00742923	212/927-7857	141
PS 132 Ralph Bunche/Sprngfld GDNS/Queens	00749270	718/528-5734	183
PS 133 Fred R Moore/New York/New York	00742674	212/690-5936	140
PS 133 Queens/Bellerose/Queens	00748305	718/831-4016	179
PS 133 William A Butler/Brooklyn/Kings	00744945	718/398-5320	83
PS 134 George F Bristow/Bronx/Bronx	00744684	718/328-3351	24
PS 134 Henrietta Szold/New York/New York	00741761	212/673-4470	135
PS 134 Hollis/Saint Albans/Queens	00749282	718/464-5544	183
PS 135 Sheldon Brookner/Brooklyn/Kings	00746022	718/693-4363	88
PS 136 Roy Wilkins/Saint Albans/Queens	00749309	718/465-2286	183
PS 138 Brooklyn/Brooklyn/Kings	00745846	718/467-0800	87
PS 138 Samuel Randall/Bronx/Bronx	00743422	718/822-5325	18
PS 138M/New York/New York	02857940	212/369-2227	142
PS 139 Alexine A Fenty/Brooklyn/Kings	00747155	718/282-5254	92
PS 139 Rego Park/Rego Park/Queens	00748977	718/459-1044	182
PS 140 Eagle Sch/Bronx/Bronx	00743434	718/585-1205	18
PS 140 Edward K Ellington/Jamaica/Queens	00748989	718/657-4760	182
PS 140 Nathan Straus/New York/New York	00741785	212/677-4680	135
PS 140K/Brooklyn/Kings	03053123	718/783-4842	94
PS 141K/Brooklyn/Kings	03053135	718/941-0320	94
PS 142 Amalia Castro/New York/New York	01533048	212/598-3800	135
PS 143 Louis Armstrong/Corona/Queens	00747818	718/429-5700	177
PS 144 Col Jeromus Remsen/Forest Hills/Queens	00748874	718/268-2775	182
PS 145 Andrew Jackson/Brooklyn/Kings	00750231	718/821-4823	94
PS 145 Bloomingdale Sch/New York/New York	00742246	212/678-2857	139
PS 146 Ann M Short/New York/New York	00742545	212/860-5877	140
PS 146 Edward J Collins/Bronx/Bronx	00743446	718/378-9664	18
PS 146 Howard Beach/Howard Beach/Queens	00748721	718/659-3140	181
PS 147 Isaac Remsen/Brooklyn/Kings	00745224	718/497-0326	84
PS 148 Queens/East Elmhurst/Queens	00749567	718/898-8181	185
PS 149 Christa McAuliffe/Jackson HTS/Queens	00749579	718/898-3630	185
PS 149 Danny Kaye/Brooklyn/Kings	00746254	718/688-7620	89
PS 149 Sojourner Truth/New York/New York	00742258	646/672-9020	139
PS 150 Charles James Fox/Bronx/Bronx	00744696	718/328-7729	24
PS 150 Christopher Sch/Brooklyn/Kings	00747466	718/495-7746	93
PS 150 Queens/Long Is City/Queens	00749581	718/784-2252	185
PS 150 Tribeca Learning Center/New York/New York	04457417	212/732-4392	137
PS 151 Lyndon B Johnson/Brooklyn/Kings	00750243	718/326-6360	94
PS 151 Mary D Carter/Woodside/Queens	00749593	718/728-2676	185
PS 152 Dyckman Valley/New York/New York	00742935	212/567-5456	141
PS 152 Evergreen/Bronx/Bronx	00743458	718/589-4560	18
PS 152 Gwendoline N Alleyne/Woodside/Queens	00749608	718/429-3141	185
PS 153 Adam Clayton Powell/New York/New York	00742961	212/927-8611	141
PS 153 Helen Keller/Bronx/Bronx	00744414	718/904-5550	23
PS 153 Homecrest/Brooklyn/Kings	00746917	718/375-4484	91
PS 153 Maspeth/Maspeth/Queens	00747820	718/821-7850	177
PS 154 Harriet Tubman/New York/New York	00742765	212/864-2400	140
PS 154 Jonathan D Hyatt/Bronx/Bronx	00743197	718/292-4742	16
PS 154 Queens/Flushing/Queens	00748032	718/591-1500	178
PS 154 Windsor Terrace Sch/Brooklyn/Kings	12105818	718/768-0057	85
PS 155/S Ozone Park/Queens	00748733	718/558-1310	181
PS 155 William Paca/New York/New York	00742557	212/860-5885	140
PS 156 Frederick Law Olmsted/Buffalo/Erie	00723135	716/816-4330	58
PS 156 Laurelton/Sprngfld GDNS/Queens	00749335	718/528-9173	183
PS 156 Waverly/Brooklyn/Kings	00747480	718/498-2811	93
PS 157 Benjamin Franklin Acad/Brooklyn/Kings	00745248	718/622-9285	84
PS 157 Grove Hill/Bronx/Bronx	00743202	718/292-5255	17
PS 158 the Bayard Taylor Sch/New York/New York	00742052	212/744-6562	137
PS 158 Warwick/Brooklyn/Kings	00746278	718/277-6116	89
PS 159/Bayside/Queens	00748317	718/423-8553	179
PS 159 Isaac Pitkin/Brooklyn/Kings	00746280	718/277-4828	89
PS 159 Luis Munoz Marin Biling/Bronx/Bronx	02178885	718/584-6140	21
PS 160 Walt Disney/Bronx/Bronx	00744256	718/822-8402	23
PS 160 Walter Francis Bishop/Jamaica/Queens	00748991	929/398-3140	182
PS 160 William Sampson/Brooklyn/Kings	00746606	718/438-0337	90
PS 161 Arthur Ashe Sch/S Richmond HI/Queens	04923595	718/441-5493	182
PS 161 Juan Ponce De Leon/Bronx/Bronx	00743214	718/292-5478	17
PS 161 Pedro Albizu Campos/New York/New York	00742698	212/690-5945	140
PS 161 the Crown/Brooklyn/Kings	00745858	718/756-3100	87
PS 162 John Golden/Bayside/Queens	00748329	718/423-8621	179
PS 163 Alfred E Smith/New York/New York	00742260	212/678-2854	139
PS 163 Arthur Schomberg/Bronx/Bronx	01399141	718/584-3045	19
PS 163 Bath Beach/Brooklyn/Kings	00746618	718/236-9003	90
PS 163 Flushing Heights/Flushing/Queens	00748044	718/353-2514	178
PS 164 Caesar Rodney/Brooklyn/Kings	00746620	718/854-4100	90
PS 164 Queens Valley/Flushing/Queens	00748056	718/544-1083	179
PS 165 Edith K Bergtraum/Flushing/Queens	00748068	718/263-4004	179
PS 165 Ida Posner/Brooklyn/Kings	00747492	718/495-7759	93
PS 165 Robert E Simon/New York/New York	00742272	212/678-2873	139
PS 166 Henry Gradstein/Long Is City/Queens	00749610	718/786-6703	185
PS 166 Rodgers Sch Arts & Tech/New York/New York	00742284	212/678-2829	139
PS 168X/Bronx/Bronx	04192966	718/585-2100	25
PS 169 Bay Terrace/Bayside/Queens	00748070	718/428-6160	179
PS 169 Sunset Park/Brooklyn/Kings	00745482	718/853-3224	85
PS 169M Robert F Kennedy/New York/New York	00750396	212/348-6140	142
PS 170/Bronx/Bronx	04192954	718/583-0662	20
PS 170 Ralph A Fabrizio Sch/Brooklyn/Kings	00746632	718/491-8400	90
PS 171 Patrick Henry/New York/New York	00742571	212/860-5801	140

New York School Directory

DISTRICT & SCHOOL TELEPHONE INDEX

School/City/County DISTRICT/CITY/COUNTY	PID	TELEPHONE NUMBER	PAGE
PS 171 Peter G Van Alst/Long Is City/Queens	00749634	718/932-0909	185
PS 172 Beacon Sch Excellence/Brooklyn/Kings	00745494	718/965-4200	85
PS 173/New York/New York	00742959	212/927-7850	141
PS 173 Fresh Meadows/Flushing/Queens	00748331	718/358-2243	179
PS 174 William Sidney Mount/Rego Park/Queens	00749086	718/897-7006	182
PS 175 City Island/Bronx/Bronx	00744426	718/885-1093	23
PS 175 Henry Garnet/New York/New York	00742703	212/283-0426	140
PS 175 Lynn Gross Discovery/Rego Park/Queens	00749000	718/897-8600	182
PS 176 Cambria Heights/Cambria HTS/Queens	00749347	718/525-4057	183
PS 176 Ovington Sch/Brooklyn/Kings	00746644	718/236-7755	90
PS 176X/Bronx/Bronx	02112489	718/904-5750	25
PS 177 the Marlboro Sch/Brooklyn/Kings	00746929	718/375-9506	91
PS 178 Dr Selman Waksman/Bronx/Bronx	00744438	718/904-5570	23
PS 178 St Clair McKelway/Brooklyn/Kings	00747519	718/495-7768	93
PS 178M Prof Juan Bosch/New York/New York	04947852	212/569-0327	141
PS 179/Bronx/Bronx	05096183	718/292-2237	17
PS 179 Kensington/Brooklyn/Kings	00746656	718/438-4010	90
PS 180 Hugo Newman/New York/New York	00742301	212/678-2849	139
PS 181 Brookfield/Sprngfld GDNS/Queens	00749359	718/528-5807	183
PS 181 Brooklyn/Brooklyn/Kings	00745860	718/462-5298	87
PS 182/Bronx/Bronx	01557393	718/828-6607	18
PS 182 Samantha Smith/Jamaica/Queens	03008922	718/298-7700	182
PS 183 Dr Richard R Green/Far Rockaway/Queens	00748745	718/634-9459	181
PS 183 Robert L Stevenson/New York/New York	00742064	212/734-7719	137
PS 184 Flushing Manor/Whitestone/Queens	00748082	718/352-7800	179
PS 184 Newport/Brooklyn/Kings	00747533	718/495-7775	93
PS 184M Shuang Wen/New York/New York	04876588	212/602-9700	135
PS 185 Locke Sch Arts & Design/New York/New York	00742313	212/534-7490	139
PS 185 Walter Kassenbrock/Brooklyn/Kings	00746670	718/745-6610	90
PS 186 Castlewood/Bellerose/Queens	00748379	718/831-4021	180
PS 186 Dr Irving Gladstone/Brooklyn/Kings	00746682	718/236-7071	90
PS 186X Walter J Damrosch/Bronx/Bronx	00750798	718/378-0006	25
PS 188 Kingsbury/Bayside/Queens	00748393	929/600-5683	180
PS 188 Michael E Berdy/Brooklyn/Kings	00746931	718/265-7580	91
PS 188 the Island Sch/New York/New York	04756665	212/677-5710	135
PS 188X/Bronx/Bronx	00750578	718/561-2052	25
PS 189/New York/New York	00742985	212/927-8303	141
PS 189 the Bilingual Center/Brooklyn/Kings	00745767	718/756-0210	87
PS 190 Sheffield/Brooklyn/Kings	00746333	718/346-8780	89
PS 191 Mayflower/Floral Park/Nassau	00748408	718/831-4032	180
PS 191 Paul Robeson Elem Sch/Brooklyn/Kings	00745884	718/756-1206	87
PS 191 Riverside Sch Makers/New York/New York	00742325	347/478-5228	139
PS 192 Buffalo Visual Perf Art/Buffalo/Erie	00722595	716/816-4220	58
PS 192 Jacob H Schiff/New York/New York	00742997	212/775-9560	141
PS 192 Magnet Sch-Math & Sci/Brooklyn/Kings	00746694	718/633-3061	90
PS 193 Alfred J Kennedy/Whitestone/Queens	00748094	718/767-8810	179
PS 193 Gil Hodges/Brooklyn/Kings	00747179	718/338-9011	92
PS 194 Countee Cullen/New York/New York	00742715	212/690-5954	140
PS 194 Raoul Wallenberg/Brooklyn/Kings	00747181	718/648-8804	92
PS 195/Bronx/Bronx	00744622	718/861-4461	24
PS 195 City Honors Sch/Buffalo/Erie	00722818	716/816-4230	58
PS 195 Manhattan Beach/Brooklyn/Kings	00747193	718/648-9102	92
PS 195 William Haberle/Rosedale/Queens	00749361	718/723-0313	183
PS 196/Bronx/Bronx	04804884	718/328-7187	24
PS 196 Grand Central Parkway/Forest Hills/Queens	00749012	718/263-9770	182
PS 196 Math Sci Tech Prep Sch/Buffalo/Erie	12308448	716/816-3501	58
PS 196 Ten Eyck/Brooklyn/Kings	00745274	718/497-0139	84
PS 197 John B Russwurm/New York/New York	00742727	212/690-5960	140
PS 197 Kings Hwy Academy/Brooklyn/Kings	00747208	718/377-7890	92
PS 197 Math Sci Tech Prep Sch/Buffalo/Erie	10028290	716/816-4500	58
PS 197 Ocean Sch/Far Rockaway/Queens	00748757	718/327-1083	181
PS 198 Brooklyn/Brooklyn/Kings	00747210	718/282-4920	92
PS 198 Int'l Prep Sch-Clevelnd/Buffalo/Erie	10913059	716/816-4300	58
PS 198 Isador E Ida Straus/New York/New York	00742117	212/289-3702	137
PS 199 Frederick Wachtel/Brooklyn/Kings	00746943	718/339-1422	91
PS 199 Jessie Isador Straus/New York/New York	00742337	212/799-1033	139
PS 199 Maurice Fitzgerald/Long Is City/Queens	00747832	718/784-3431	178
PS 199 Shakespeare/Bronx/Bronx	00743771	718/681-7172	20
PS 200 Benson Sch/Brooklyn/Kings	00746709	718/236-5466	90
PS 200 James McCune Smith/New York/New York	00742791	212/491-6636	140
PS 201 Discovery Sch/Flushing/Queens	00748111	718/359-0620	179
PS 202 Ernest Jenkyns/Brooklyn/Kings	00746345	718/649-7880	89
PS 203 Floyd Bennett Sch/Brooklyn/Kings	00747222	718/241-8488	92
PS 203 Oakland Gardens/Bayside/Queens	00748410	718/423-8652	180
PS 204 Morris Heights Sch/Bronx/Bronx	04019649	718/960-9520	20
PS 204 Vince Lombardi/Brooklyn/Kings	00746711	718/236-2906	90
PS 205 Alexander Graham Bell/Bayside/Queens	00748422	718/464-5773	180
PS 205 Clarion/Brooklyn/Kings	00746723	718/236-2380	90
PS 205 Fiorello Laguardia/Bronx/Bronx	01532953	718/584-6390	21
PS 206 Jose Celso Barbosa/New York/New York	00742583	212/860-5809	140
PS 206 Joseph F Lamb/Brooklyn/Kings	00747234	718/743-5598	92
PS 206 South Park High Sch/Buffalo/Erie	00723484	716/816-4828	58
PS 206 the Horace Harding Sch/Rego Park/Queens	00749024	718/592-0300	182
PS 207/Bronx/Bronx	03336042	718/796-9645	21
PS 207 Elizabeth Leary/Brooklyn/Kings	00747246	718/645-8667	92
PS 207 Lafayette Int'l HS/Buffalo/Erie	00722703	716/816-4358	58
PS 207 Rockwood Park/Howard Beach/Queens	00748769	718/848-2700	181
PS 208 Elsa Ebeling/Brooklyn/Kings	00746034	718/629-1670	88
PS 208 Riverside Academy/Buffalo/Erie	12308436	716/816-4530	58
PS 209/Bronx/Bronx	04037213	718/364-0085	21
PS 209 Clearview Gardens/Whitestone/Queens	00748123	718/352-3939	179
PS 209 Margaret Mead/Brooklyn/Kings	00746955	718/743-1954	91
PS 211/Bronx/Bronx	00744713	718/901-0436	24
PS 211Q Elm Tree Elem Sch/Corona/Queens	11924154	929/208-4680	178
PS 212/Jackson HTS/Queens	04923014	718/898-6973	185
PS 212 Lady Deborah Moody/Brooklyn/Kings	00746967	718/266-4841	91
PS 212 Leonardo DaVinci HS/Buffalo/Erie	03400162	716/816-4380	58
PS 212 Midtown West/New York/New York	03340421	212/247-0208	137
PS 213 Carl Ullman/Bayside/Queens	00748434	718/423-8747	180
PS 213 New Lots/Brooklyn/Kings	00746369	718/257-4034	89
PS 214/Bronx/Bronx	00744488	718/589-6728	24
PS 214 Cadwallader Colden/Flushing/Queens	00748135	718/461-4055	179
PS 214 Michael Friedsam/Brooklyn/Kings	00746371	718/647-1740	89
PS 215 Morris H Weiss/Brooklyn/Kings	00746979	718/339-2464	91
PS 216 Arturo Toscanini/Brooklyn/Kings	00746981	718/645-2862	91
PS 217 Col David Marcus Sch/Brooklyn/Kings	00747258	718/434-6960	92
PS 219 Kennedy-King/Brooklyn/Kings	00746046	929/397-9566	88
PS 219 Paul Klapper/Flushing/Queens	00748147	718/793-2130	179
PS 220 Edward Mandel/Forest Hills/Queens	00749036	718/592-3030	182
PS 221 North Hills Sch/Little Neck/Queens	00748446	718/225-7029	180
PS 221 Toussaint L'Ouverture/Brooklyn/Kings	00745896	718/756-0122	87
PS 222 Katherine R Snyder/Brooklyn/Kings	00747260	718/998-4298	92
PS 223 Lyndon Baines Johnson/Jamaica/Queens	00748771	718/558-2900	181
PS 224 Hale A Woodruff/Brooklyn/Kings	00746395	718/235-3600	89
PS 225 the Eileen Zaglin/Brooklyn/Kings	00746993	718/743-9793	91
PS 226/Bronx/Bronx	03336030	929/452-3090	21
PS 226 Alfred De B Mason/Brooklyn/Kings	00747002	718/234-4940	91
PS 228 Lafayette Sch of Arts/East Elmhurst/Queens	04947797	718/899-5799	185
PS 229 Dyker/Brooklyn/Kings	00746735	718/236-5447	90
PS 229 Emmanuel Kaplan/Woodside/Queens	00747844	718/446-2120	178
PS 230 Doris Cohen/Brooklyn/Kings	00745509	718/437-6135	85
PS 231K/Brooklyn/Kings	00750712	718/853-1884	94
PS 232 Lindenwood/Howard Beach/Queens	00748795	718/848-9247	181
PS 233 Langston Hughes/Brooklyn/Kings	00746058	718/346-8103	88
PS 234/Astoria/Queens	05274787	718/956-2760	185
PS 234 Independence Sch/New York/New York	01557501	212/233-6034	137
PS 235 Janice Knight Sch/Brooklyn/Kings	00746060	718/773-4869	88
PS 236 Langston Hughes/Bronx/Bronx	00743848	718/299-6128	20
PS 236 Mill Basin/Brooklyn/Kings	00747272	718/444-6969	92
PS 238 Anne Sullivan/Brooklyn/Kings	00747014	718/339-4355	91
PS 239/Ridgewood/Queens	05274775	718/417-2840	178
PS 241 Emma L Johnston/Brooklyn/Kings	00745901	718/636-4725	87
PS 242 Leonard P Stavisky/Flushing/Queens	04947785	718/445-2902	179
PS 242 Young Diplomats Magnet/New York/New York	04874097	212/678-2908	139
PS 243 Weeksville/Brooklyn/Kings	00745690	718/604-6909	86
PS 244 Richard R Green Sch/Brooklyn/Kings	00746084	718/346-6240	88
PS 245/Brooklyn/Kings	04291067	718/284-2330	92
PS 246 Poe Center/Bronx/Bronx	02225139	718/584-6764	21
PS 247 Brooklyn/Brooklyn/Kings	00746747	718/236-4205	90

School Year 2020-2021   800-333-8802   NY-V43

DISTRICT & SCHOOL TELEPHONE INDEX

Market Data Retrieval

School/City/County DISTRICT/CITY/COUNTY	PID	TELEPHONE NUMBER	PAGE
PS 249 the Caton/Brooklyn/Kings	00745913	718/282-8828	87
PS 250 George Lindsay/Brooklyn/Kings	00745298	718/384-0889	84
PS 251 Paerdegat/Brooklyn/Kings	00747284	718/251-4110	92
PS 251 Queens/Sprngfld GDNS/Queens	00749373	718/276-2745	184
PS 253/Brooklyn/Kings	00747040	718/332-3331	91
PS 253/Far Rockaway/Queens	05348754	718/327-0895	181
PS 254 Dag Hammarskjold/Brooklyn/Kings	00747296	718/743-0890	92
PS 254 Rosa Parks ES/Richmond Hill/Queens	05341902	718/520-7878	181
PS 255 Barbara Reing Sch/Brooklyn/Kings	00747301	718/376-8494	92
PS 256 Benjamin Banneker/Brooklyn/Kings	00744957	718/857-9820	83
PS 257 John F Hylan/Brooklyn/Kings	00745303	718/384-7128	84
PS 261 Philip Livingston/Brooklyn/Kings	00745511	718/330-9275	85
PS 262 El Hajj Malik El Shabaz/Brooklyn/Kings	00745705	718/453-0780	86
PS 264 Bay Ridge ES-the Arts/Brooklyn/Kings	11561001	718/630-1650	90
PS 267 Eastside Elem Sch/New York/New York	11561336	212/888-7848	137
PS 268 Emma Lazarus/Brooklyn/Kings	00746096	718/773-5332	88
PS 270 Johann DeKalb/Brooklyn/Kings	00744969	718/623-5280	83
PS 272 Curtis Estabrook/Brooklyn/Kings	00746101	929/437-5000	88
PS 273/Richmond Hill/Queens	11560904	718/286-8300	181
PS 273 Wortman/Brooklyn/Kings	00746412	718/649-5739	89
PS 274 Kosciusko/Brooklyn/Kings	00750176	718/642-5300	94
PS 274X New American Acad/Bronx/Bronx	11924439	718/901-9703	20
PS 276 Louis Marshall/Brooklyn/Kings	00746113	718/241-5757	88
PS 277/Bronx/Bronx	00743109	718/292-3594	17
PS 277 Gerritsen Beach/Brooklyn/Kings	00747325	718/743-6689	92
PS 277Q the Riverview Sch/Sunnyside/Queens	11924001	718/361-3567	185
PS 279 Capt Manuel Rivera Jr/Bronx/Bronx	04037902	718/584-6004	21
PS 279 Herman Schreiber/Brooklyn/Kings	00746125	718/444-4316	88
PS 280/Jackson HTS/Queens	11560784	718/424-9031	185
PS 281 the River Sch/New York/New York	11924520	212/251-6640	137
PS 282 Park Slope/Brooklyn/Kings	00744983	718/622-1626	83
PS 284 Jackson Sports Art Tech/Brooklyn/Kings	00747545	718/495-7791	93
PS 287 Bailey K Ashford/Brooklyn/Kings	00744995	718/834-4745	83
PS 288 Shirley Tanyhill/Brooklyn/Kings	00747052	718/382-2100	91
PS 289 George V Brower/Brooklyn/Kings	00745925	718/493-3824	87
PS 290 Ace Acad for Scholars/Ridgewood/Queens	11560930	718/571-6900	178
PS 290 Juan Morel Campos/Brooklyn/Kings	00746230	718/647-1113	89
PS 290 Manhattan New Sch/New York/New York	00742076	212/734-7127	137
PS 291/Bronx/Bronx	02112415	718/563-0776	21
PS 295/Brooklyn/Kings	04457455	718/965-0390	85
PS 297 Abraham Stockton/Brooklyn/Kings	00745315	718/388-4581	84
PS 298 Dr Betty Shabazz/Brooklyn/Kings	00747557	718/495-7793	93
PS 299 Thomas Warren Field/Brooklyn/Kings	00750279	718/473-8230	94
PS 301 Burgard High Sch/Buffalo/Erie	00722571	716/816-4450	58
PS 302 Emerson-Hospitality/Buffalo/Erie	05346483	716/816-3018	58
PS 304 Early Childhood Lab Sch/Bronx/Bronx	05096365	718/822-5307	18
PS 304 Hutchinson Tech HS/Buffalo/Erie	00722662	716/816-3888	58
PS 305 McKinley High Sch/Buffalo/Erie	00722715	716/816-4480	58
PS 306/Bronx/Bronx	04290946	718/583-5355	21
PS 306 Ethan Allen/Brooklyn/Kings	00746424	718/649-3155	89
PS 307 Daniel Hale Williams/Brooklyn/Kings	00745016	718/834-4748	83
PS 307 Pioneer Academy/Corona/Queens	11103049	718/779-5068	178
PS 308 Clara Cardwell/Brooklyn/Kings	00745688	718/571-6960	86
PS 309 East Cmty High Sch/Buffalo/Erie	12242167	716/816-3997	58
PS 309 George E Wibecan Prep/Brooklyn/Kings	00745729	718/574-2381	86
PS 310 Marble Hill/Bronx/Bronx	00744062	718/796-9434	21
PS 310 Sch for Future Leaders/Brooklyn/Kings	11561025	718/491-7670	90
PS 312 Bergen Beach/Brooklyn/Kings	00747349	718/763-4015	92
PS 315 Lab Sch/Bronx/Bronx	04753728	929/237-7750	22
PS 316 Elijah G Stroud/Brooklyn/Kings	00745810	718/638-4043	87
PS 319/Brooklyn/Kings	03051723	718/388-1588	84
PS 321 William Penn/Brooklyn/Kings	00745535	718/499-2412	85
PS 325 Fresh Creek Sch/Brooklyn/Kings	11714923	718/272-1843	89
PS 326/Brooklyn/Kings	04947711	718/241-4828	92
PS 327 Dr Rose B English/Brooklyn/Kings	00747569	718/495-7801	93
PS 328 Phyllis Wheatley/Brooklyn/Kings	00746436	718/345-9393	89
PS 329 Surfside/Brooklyn/Kings	00747026	718/787-3460	91
PS 333 Longwood Acad Discovery/Bronx/Bronx	05349241	718/860-3313	18
PS 333 Manhattan Sch for Chldn/New York/New York	04874102	212/222-1450	139
PS 335 Granville T Woods/Brooklyn/Kings	00745731	718/493-7736	86
PS 335 Middle Early College HS/Buffalo/Erie	10010736	716/816-4010	58
PS 340/Bronx/Bronx	04876825	718/220-1830	22
PS 340 Sixth Ave Elem Sch/New York/New York	12036384	917/305-1000	137
PS 345 Patrolman Robert Bolden/Brooklyn/Kings	00746450	718/647-8387	89
PS 346 Abe Stark/Brooklyn/Kings	01533000	718/642-3000	89
PS 353 Newcomer Academy/Buffalo/Erie	12171324	716/816-4345	58
PS 354 J L Green STEM Inst/Jamaica/Queens	11821722	718/276-1348	182
PS 357 Pathways Academy East/Buffalo/Erie	12317700	716/816-4526	58
PS 360/Bronx/Bronx	04876837	718/548-1511	22
PS 360 New Choice ES/Saint Albans/Queens	12105832	718/776-7370	184
PS 361 E Flatbush EC Sch/Brooklyn/Kings	00747313	718/941-2800	92
PS 366 Research Lab Bioinfo/Buffalo/Erie	12317712	716/816-4250	58
PS 368 Hamilton Heights Sch/New York/New York	10911829	212/862-9940	142
PS 368K/Brooklyn/Kings	02110974	718/388-9494	94
PS 370K/Brooklyn/Kings	00750683	718/372-3777	94
PS 371K Lillian L Rashkis/Brooklyn/Kings	00750695	718/788-7608	94
PS 372 the Children's Sch/Brooklyn/Kings	04457479	718/624-5271	94
PS 373K Bklyn Transition Ctr/Brooklyn/Kings	04037184	718/782-6800	94
PS 375 Jackie Robinson/Brooklyn/Kings	04952601	718/693-6655	87
PS 376/Brooklyn/Kings	04423521	718/573-0781	94
PS 376Q/Oakland GDNS/Queens	12234029	929/267-5900	180
PS 377/Ozone Park/Queens	12234081	929/398-3215	181
PS 377 Alejandrina Degautier/Brooklyn/Kings	01533024	718/574-0325	94
PS 380 John Wayne Elem Sch/Brooklyn/Kings	00745212	718/388-0607	84
PS 382- ES Math Sci & Tech Sch/Bronx/Bronx	11103477	718/933-8061	22
PS 384/Long Is City/Queens	12310350	718/391-4667	185
PS 386-Envir Citizenship Sch/Bronx/Bronx	11103221	718/563-3292	22
PS 390Q Civic ES Bayside Hills/Oakland GDNS/Queens	12472087		180
PS 392 Bronx Delta Sch/Bronx/Bronx	12105791	718/319-7147	18
PS 396/Bronx/Bronx	04904276	718/294-0862	22
PS 397 Foster-Laurie/Brooklyn/Kings	01292311	718/774-5200	87
PS 398 Walter Weaver/Brooklyn/Kings	01557446	718/774-4466	87
PS 398Q Hector Figueroa Sch/Woodside/Queens	12367614	929/463-7200	185
PS 399 Stanley Eugene Clark/Brooklyn/Kings	02129638	718/693-3023	87
PS 452/New York/New York	11561283	212/259-6222	139
PS 503 the School of Discovery/Brooklyn/Kings	00746591	718/439-5962	90
PS 506 School Journalism/Tech/Brooklyn/Kings	10025509	718/492-0087	90
PS 516 Sunset Park Avenues/Brooklyn/Kings	11924295	718/369-8330	85
PS 527 East Side Sch-Soc Acton/New York/New York	11821655	212/828-2710	137
PS 532 New Bridges/Brooklyn/Kings	11924271	718/363-8200	87
PS 536/Bronx/Bronx	11714985	718/931-4270	24
PS 583/Bronx/Bronx	12234043	929/348-4960	18
PS 595/Bronx/Bronx	12310283		25
PS 596X/Bronx/Bronx	12310257	718/904-5750	25
PS 721K Brooklyn Occu Trng Ctr/Brooklyn/Kings	00750310	718/996-8199	94
PS 721X Stephen McSweeney Sch/Bronx/Bronx	00750308	718/597-6404	25
PS 723X/Bronx/Bronx	04192942	718/320-1222	25
PS 748 Sch Global Scholars/Brooklyn/Kings	11561037	718/382-3130	90
PS 767 Little Brooklyn Pre-K/Brooklyn/Kings	12105868	718/840-2840	85
PS 770 New American Academy/Brooklyn/Kings	11561099	718/221-5837	87
PS 771K/Brooklyn/Kings	04019572	718/891-3600	94
PS 811K Connie Lekas Sch/Brooklyn/Kings	02110962	718/769-6984	94
PS 811M Mickey Mantle Sch/New York/New York	02109676	212/579-3788	142
PS 889/Brooklyn/Kings	12234237	929/397-9171	92
PS 938/Brooklyn/Kings	12472037		89
PS 939 Sunset ES Cultural Lrng/Brooklyn/Kings	12472075	212/346-5274	90
PS 993Q/Floral Park/Nassau	04019584	718/831-4040	126
PS IS 45 Horace E Greene/Brooklyn/Kings	00750188	718/642-5360	94
PS IS 109 Glenwood Academy/Brooklyn/Kings	04368115	718/693-3426	92
PS IS 155 Nicholas Herkimer/Brooklyn/Kings	00747478	718/240-4340	93
PS K004/Brooklyn/Kings	02226573	718/272-7555	94
PS K053/Brooklyn/Kings	02200567	718/832-3563	94
PS K134/Brooklyn/Kings	04876693	718/436-7200	92
PS K315/Brooklyn/Kings	04842850	718/421-9560	92
PS K369 Coy L Cox Sch/Brooklyn/Kings	00750671	718/852-1701	94
PS K396/Brooklyn/Kings	02200579	718/385-6200	94
PS K753 School for Career Dev/Brooklyn/Kings	02180321	718/857-4646	94
PS M079 Horan Sch/New York/New York	00742844	212/369-3134	142
PS M226/New York/New York	00750621	212/477-5017	142
PS M721 Occupational Training/New York/New York	00750358	212/675-7926	142

NY-V44 800-333-8802 School Year 2020-2021

New York School Directory
DISTRICT & SCHOOL TELEPHONE INDEX

School/City/County DISTRICT/CITY/COUNTY	PID	TELEPHONE NUMBER	PAGE
PS MS 11X498 Van Nest Academy/Bronx/Bronx	11561166	718/409-3001	23
PS Q004/Fresh Meadows/Queens	03337292	718/264-0916	185
PS Q016 Nancy Debenedittis/Corona/Queens	04876875	718/505-0140	178
PS Q023-Queens Childrens Ctr/Bellerose/Queens	00750425	718/264-4880	185
PS Q086/Jamaica/Queens	00748927	718/291-6264	182
PS Q177/Flushing/Queens	00748343	718/357-4650	185
PS Q222-Christopher A Santora/Jackson HTS/Queens	05097838	718/429-2563	185
PS Q224/Bellerose/Queens	00750413	718/831-4024	185
PS Q233/Forest Hills/Queens	00750839	718/286-4700	185
PS Q255/Flushing/Queens	00750566	718/380-1247	185
PS Q256/Syosset/Nassau	03410791	516/921-0450	126
PS Q811/Little Neck/Queens	01841326	718/224-8060	185
PS R037 Marquis Sch of Arts/Staten Island/Richmond	02112441	718/984-9800	194
PS R373/Staten Island/Richmond	04037172	718/816-8897	194
PS X010/Bronx/Bronx	03052313	718/828-4022	25
PS X14 Sen John Calandra/Bronx/Bronx	00743276	718/822-5341	18
PS X15 Inst for Enviro Lrng/Bronx/Bronx	04370493	718/563-0473	22
PS X017/Bronx/Bronx	04874217	718/665-5617	25
PS X811/Bronx/Bronx	02111576	718/589-3060	25
PS-IS 224/Bronx/Bronx	05301550	718/665-9804	17
PS/IS 30 Mary White Ovington/Brooklyn/Kings	04753675	718/491-8440	90
PS/IS 78Q Robert F Wagner/Long Is City/Queens	04797217	718/392-5402	185
PS/IS 104 the Ft Hamilton Sch/Brooklyn/Kings	00746553	718/836-4630	90
PS/IS 113 Anthony J Pranzo/Glendale/Queens	00747791	718/847-0724	178
PS/IS 119 the Glendale/Glendale/Queens	00747624	718/326-8261	178
PS/IS 137 Rachel Jean Mitchell/Brooklyn/Kings	00747430	718/453-2926	93
PS/IS 178 Holliswood/Jamaica/Queens	00748355	718/464-5763	180
PS/IS 187 Hudson Cliffs/New York/New York	00742973	212/927-8218	142
PS/IS 208/Bellerose/Queens	05274725	718/468-6420	184
PS/IS 210 21st Century Academy/New York/New York	04874205	212/283-0012	142
PS/IS 217 Roosevelt Island/Roosevelt Isl/New York	01841194	212/980-0294	137
PS/IS 218 Hernandez Dual Lang/Bronx/Bronx	00743836	718/410-7230	20
PS/IS 266/Bellerose/Queens	05274713	718/479-3920	180
PS/IS 268/Jamaica/Queens	05274749	718/206-3240	184
PS/IS 270Q Gordon Parks Sch/Rosedale/Queens	05274737	718/341-8280	184
PS/IS 295Q/Queens Vlg/Queens	10966927	718/464-1433	184
PS/IS 323/Brooklyn/Kings	04952534	718/495-7781	93
PS/IS 384 Frances E Carter/Brooklyn/Kings	00750164	718/642-4890	94
PS/MS 4 Crotona Park West/Bronx/Bronx	00743642	718/583-6655	20
PS/MS 20 P O George Werdan III/Bronx/Bronx	04457247	718/515-9370	22
PS/MS 29 Melrose Sch/Bronx/Bronx	00743111	718/292-3785	17
PS/MS 31 William Garrison/Bronx/Bronx	00743226	718/292-4397	17
PS/MS 37 Multiple Intelligence/Bronx/Bronx	04290958	718/796-0360	22
PS/MS 42 R Vernam/Arverne/Queens	00748525	718/634-7914	181
PS/MS 114 Belle Harbor/Rockaway Park/Queens	00748692	718/634-3382	181
PS/MS 138 Sunrise/Rosedale/Queens	00749311	929/600-5777	184
PS/MS 147 Ronald McNair/Cambria HTS/Queens	00749323	718/528-2420	184
PS/MS 194/Bronx/Bronx	05274622	718/892-5270	23
PS/MS 200 Global Studies//Flushing/Queens	00748109	718/969-7780	179
PS/MS 280 Mosholu Parkway/Bronx/Bronx	01840970	718/405-6360	22
PS/MS 394K/Brooklyn/Kings	00745779	718/756-3164	87
PS131 Academy Sch at 44 & Ltep/Buffalo/Erie	10913061	716/816-3270	58
Ptech/Johnstown/Fulton	12235372	718/221-1593	71
Public Service Ldrshp Academy/Syracuse/Onondaga	12104515	315/435-4376	159
Public Svc Ldrshp Acad Fowler/Syracuse/Onondaga	01529633	315/435-4376	159
PULASKI CENTRAL SCH DIST/PULASKI/OSWEGO	00765846	315/298-5188	172
Pulaski Middle High Sch/Pulaski/Oswego	00765860	315/298-5103	172
Pulaski Road Elem Sch/E Northport/Suffolk	00774768	631/262-6850	227
Pulaski Street Elem Sch/Riverhead/Suffolk	00775059	631/369-6794	228
Pulse High Sch/Bronx/Bronx	05352456	718/294-0230	22
Purchase Elem Sch/Purchase/Westchester	00780339	914/630-3172	256
Putnam Central Sch/Putnam Sta/Washington	00779079	518/547-8266	248
PUTNAM CENTRAL SCH DIST/PUTNAM STA/WASHINGTON	00779067	518/547-8266	248
PUTNAM VALLEY CTL SCH DIST/PUTNAM VALLEY/PUTNAM	00766541	845/528-8143	176
Putnam Valley Elem Sch/Putnam Valley/Putnam	00766553	845/528-8092	176
Putnam Valley High Sch/Putnam Valley/Putnam	04911982	845/528-4456	176
Putnam Valley Middle Sch/Putnam Valley/Putnam	00766565	845/528-8101	176
PUTNAM-NORTHERN WSTCHSTR BOCES/YORKTOWN HTS/WESTCHESTER	00782818	914/245-2700	266

Q

School/City/County DISTRICT/CITY/COUNTY	PID	TELEPHONE NUMBER	PAGE
Q300 Citywide Gifted Talented/Astoria/Queens	12036372	718/626-8502	185
Quad Preparatory Sch/New York/New York	12224933	646/649-3913	145
Quaker Ridge Elem Sch/Scarsdale/Westchester	00781852	914/721-2780	262
Queen of All Saints Cath Acad/Brooklyn/Kings	00752992	718/857-3114	95
Queen of Heaven Sch/West Seneca/Erie	00726670	716/674-5206	65
Queens Academy High Sch/Flushing/Queens	04020129	718/463-3111	179
Queens College Sch Math & Sci/Flushing/Queens	04922993	718/461-7462	179
Queens Collegiate-College Brd/Jamaica/Queens	11103441	718/658-4016	182
Queens Explorers Elem Sch/Ozone Park/Queens	12036310	718/558-7088	181
Queens Gateway Hlth Sciences/Jamaica/Queens	04292231	718/969-3155	182
Queens High Sch-Lang Studies/Flushing/Queens	11924130	718/888-7530	179
Queens High School of Teaching/Bellerose/Queens	05274696	718/736-7100	180
Queens HS for Info Rsch & Tech/Far Rockaway/Queens	11103001	718/868-2978	181
Queens HS for Sciences at York/Jamaica/Queens	05097852	718/657-3181	182
Queens Lutheran Sch/Astoria/Queens	00751730	718/721-4313	188
Queens Metropolitan HS/Flushing/Queens	11560825	718/286-3600	182
Queens Preparatory Academy/Sprngfld GDNS/Queens	10011730	718/712-2304	184
Queens Satellite HS-Oppor/Jamaica/Queens	11714844	718/657-3920	182
Queens Sch Ldrshp Excellence/Jamaica/Queens	12105882	718/558-6220	182
Queens School of Inquiry/Flushing/Queens	10009024	718/380-6929	179
Queens Technical High Sch/Long Is City/Queens	00741400	718/937-3010	178
Queens Transition Center/Jamaica/Queens	02112453	718/558-2060	185
Queens United Middle Sch 289/Sprngfld GDNS/Queens	11924063	718/723-3501	184
Queensbury Elem Sch/Queensbury/Warren	00778726	518/824-1600	246
Queensbury High Sch/Queensbury/Warren	00778740	518/824-4600	246
Queensbury Middle Sch/Queensbury/Warren	00778738	518/824-3600	246
QUEENSBURY UNION FREE SCH DIST/QUEENSBURY/WARREN	00778714	518/824-5699	246
Quest Elem Sch/Hilton/Monroe	04748905	585/392-1000	109
Quest to Learn/New York/New York	11447704	212/488-3645	137
Questar 3-Rensselaer Ed Ctr/Troy/Rensselaer	01417274	518/273-2264	189
QUESTAR III BOCES/CASTLETON/RENSSELAER	00767260	518/477-8771	192
Quogue Elem Sch/Quogue/Suffolk	00774988	631/653-4285	228
QUOGUE UNION FREE SCH DIST/QUOGUE/SUFFOLK	00774976	631/653-4285	228

R

School/City/County DISTRICT/CITY/COUNTY	PID	TELEPHONE NUMBER	PAGE
R T Hudson SDA Sch/Bronx/Bronx	01463259	718/328-3322	27
Rabbi Jacob Joseph School-Boys/Staten Island/Richmond	01560376	718/979-6333	195
Rabbi Jacob Joseph-Girls/Staten Island/Richmond	02988915	718/982-8745	195
Rabbi Samson R Hirsch Yeshiva/New York/New York	01409095	212/568-6200	145
Rabbi Schneier Park E Day Sch/New York/New York	02079784	212/737-6900	145
Rabbinical Clg Bobover Yeshyva/Brooklyn/Kings	02189688	718/438-2018	98
Rabbinical Seminary High Sch/Flushing/Queens	00752306	718/263-1445	188
Rachel Carson HS-Coastal Study/Brooklyn	10008642	718/265-0329	91
Ralph McKee Career & Tech HS/Staten Island/Richmond	00741412	718/420-2600	194
Ralph R Smith Elem Sch/Hyde Park/Dutchess	00721735	845/229-4060	52

DISTRICT & SCHOOL TELEPHONE INDEX

Market Data Retrieval

School/City/County DISTRICT/CITY/COUNTY	PID	TELEPHONE NUMBER	PAGE
Ralph Reed Middle Sch/Central Islip/Suffolk	00772514	631/348-5066	219
Ramapo High Sch/Spring Valley/Rockland	00768070	845/577-6400	196
Ramaz Lower Sch/New York/New York	02079796	212/774-8010	145
Ramaz Sch/New York/New York	00751780	212/774-8070	145
Rambam Mesivta/Lawrence/Nassau	04974805	516/371-5824	134
Randall Middle Sch/Cortland/Cortland	00720846	607/758-4170	47
RANDOLPH ACAD UNION FREE SD/ **RANDOLPH/CATTARAUGUS**	00717564	716/358-6866	32
Randolph Academy/Randolph/Cattaraugus	00717576	716/358-6866	33
Randolph Academy-Hamburg/Hamburg/Cattaraugus	02055245	716/648-1930	33
RANDOLPH CENTRAL SCH DIST/ **RANDOLPH/CATTARAUGUS**	00717758	716/358-6161	33
Randolph Jr Sr High Sch/Randolph/Cattaraugus	00717772	716/358-7007	33
Randolph Sch/Wappingers Fl/Dutchess	01460697	845/297-5600	55
Raphael J McNulty Academy/Amsterdam/Montgomery	00734639	518/843-4773	116
Raven's Sch/Brooklyn/Kings	12263575	718/927-2316	98
RAVENA COEYMANS SELKIRK CTL SD/ **RAVENA/ALBANY**	00714768	518/756-5200	11
Ravena Coeymans Selkirk HS/Ravena/Albany	00714823	518/756-5200	11
Ravena Coeymans Selkirk MS/Ravena/Albany	00714811	518/756-5200	11
Raymond C Buckley Elem Sch/Lansing/Tompkins	00777629	607/533-4183	240
Raymond J Lockhart Elem Sch/Massapequa/Nassau	00737306	516/308-5400	125
Raynor Country Day Sch/Speonk/Suffolk	04497778	631/288-4658	235
Razi Sch/Woodside/Queens	04974697	718/779-0711	188
Reach Academy/West Harrison/Westchester	10021735	914/686-8159	255
Reach Academy Charter Sch/Buffalo/Erie	12234419	716/248-1485	6
Rebecca Sch/New York/New York	10756629	212/810-4120	145
Rebecca Turner Elem Sch/Mount Vernon/Westchester	00780949	914/665-5100	258
RED CREEK CENTRAL SCH DIST/ **RED CREEK/WAYNE**	00779433	315/754-2010	251
Red Creek High Sch/Red Creek/Wayne	00779469	315/754-2040	251
Red Creek Middle Sch/Red Creek/Wayne	11917876	315/754-2070	251
RED HOOK CENTRAL SCH DIST/ **RED HOOK/DUTCHESS**	00721981	845/758-2241	53
Red Hook Neighborhood Sch/Brooklyn/Kings	11447821	718/330-2238	85
Red Hook Senior High Sch/Red Hook/Dutchess	00722014	845/758-2241	53
Red Jacket Elem Sch/Shortsville/Ontario	02897665	585/289-9647	162
Red Jacket High Sch/Shortsville/Ontario	00763965	585/289-3966	162
Red Jacket Middle Sch/Shortsville/Ontario	04843270	585/289-3967	162
Red Mill Elem Sch/Rensselaer/Rensselaer	00766840	518/207-2660	190
Redeemer Lutheran Sch/Glendale/Queens	00782870	718/821-6670	188
Redemption Christian Academy/Troy/Rensselaer	02164030	518/272-6679	192
Redwood Middle Sch/Jamaica/Queens	12036334	718/276-4540	183
Reece Sch/New York/New York	01463003	212/289-4872	145
Regent Sch/Bronx/Bronx	02162824	718/653-2900	27
Regional Alter HS-Fox Meadow/Yorktown Hts/Westchester	11434989	914/248-3640	252
Regional Education Center/Auburn/Cayuga	01416892	315/253-0361	34
Regis High Sch/New York/New York	00756443	212/288-1100	143
Reinhard Early Childhood Ctr/Bellmore/Nassau	04745109	516/679-2930	117
REMSEN CENTRAL SCH DIST/ **REMSEN/ONEIDA**	00760298	315/205-4300	151
Remsen Elem Sch/Remsen/Oneida	02107484	315/831-3797	151
Remsen Jr Sr High Sch/Remsen/Oneida	00760315	315/831-3851	151
Remsenburg-Speonk Elem Sch/Remsenburg/Suffolk	00775009	631/325-0203	228
REMSENBURG-SPEONK UFSD/REMSENBURG/ **SUFFOLK**	00774990	631/325-0203	228
Renaissance Acad of the Arts/Rochester/Monroe	12028399	585/225-4200	6
Renaissance Campus Sch/West Seneca/Erie	11225099	716/821-0391	66
Renaissance Charter Sch/Jackson HTS/Queens	04037471	718/803-0060	185
Renaissance Charter Sch 2/Maspeth/Queens	12472051	917/242-3505	6
Renaissance CHS for Innovation/New York/New York	11561269	212/722-5871	140
Renaissance HS Music Theatre/Bronx/Bronx	05349265	718/430-6390	18
Renaissance School of the Arts/New York/New York	11103283	212/534-6072	140
RENSSELAER CITY SCH DIST/ **RENSSELAER/RENSSELAER**	00767014	518/465-7509	191
Rensselaer Jr Sr High Sch/Rensselaer/Rensselaer	00767038	518/436-8561	191
Rensselaer Park Elem Sch/Troy/Rensselaer	01417248	518/233-6823	191

School/City/County DISTRICT/CITY/COUNTY	PID	TELEPHONE NUMBER	PAGE
Repertory HS for Theatre Arts/New York/New York	04874011	212/382-1875	137
Research & Service High Sch/Brooklyn/Kings	11924283	718/804-6800	86
Restart Academy/New York/New York	11622069	212/262-0817	142
Resurrection Ascension Sch/Rego Park/Queens	00753661	718/426-4963	186
Resurrection Sch/Rye/Westchester	00756455	914/967-1218	265
Rhame Avenue Elem Sch/East Rockaway/Nassau	00735310	516/887-8300	118
RHINEBECK CENTRAL SCH DIST/ **RHINEBECK/DUTCHESS**	00722026	845/871-5520	53
Rhinebeck High Sch/Rhinebeck/Dutchess	00722052	845/871-5500	53
Riccardi Elem Sch/Glasco/Ulster	00778336	845/247-6500	243
Richard H Hungerford Sch/Staten Island/Richmond	00750918	718/273-8622	194
Richard H O'Rourke Middle Sch/Burnt Hills/Saratoga	00769490	518/399-9141	200
Richard J Bailey Sch/White Plains/Westchester	00780248	914/948-8107	255
Richard Mann Elem Sch/Walworth/Wayne	03241605	315/986-3521	249
Richard P Connor Elem Sch/Suffern/Rockland	00768159	845/357-2858	198
Richard R Green HS of Teaching/New York/New York	03259195	646/826-8174	137
Richard T Stank Middle Sch/Conklin/Broome	00717071	607/775-9129	29
RICHFIELD SPRINGS CENTRAL SD/ **RICHFLD SPGS/OTSEGO**	00766199	315/858-0610	174
Richfield Springs Ctl Sch/Richfld Spgs/Otsego	00766216	315/858-0610	174
Richmond Hill High Sch/Richmond Hill/Queens	00741424	718/846-3335	181
Richmond Pre K Ctr Forest Ave/Staten Island/Richmond	12170320	718/816-3370	194
Richmond Pre K Ctr Stuyvesant/Staten Island/Richmond	12170356	718/816-3340	194
Richmond Pre K Ctr Teleport Dr/Staten Island/Richmond	12170344	718/477-8980	194
Ridge Elem Sch/Ridge/Suffolk	00774421	631/345-2765	225
Ridge Mills Elem Sch/Rome/Oneida	00760468	315/334-1280	152
Ridge Road Elem Sch/Horseheads/Chemung	00719512	607/739-6351	41
Ridgeway Elem Sch/White Plains/Westchester	00782181	914/422-2081	263
Riley Avenue Elem Sch/Calverton/Suffolk	00775061	631/369-6804	228
Ripley Central Sch/Ripley/Chautauqua	00718984	716/736-2631	39
RIPLEY CENTRAL SCH DIST/ **RIPLEY/CHAUTAUQUA**	00718960	716/736-2631	39
Rippowam Cisqua Sch-Lower/Mount Kisco/Westchester	01409552	914/244-1200	266
Rippowam Cisqua Sch-Upper/Bedford/Westchester	11396753	914/244-1250	266
Rise Community School 106/Rochester/Monroe	12311524	585/254-4472	111
Rising Stars Islamic Sch/Jamaica/Queens	12314634	646/243-5895	188
River East Elem Sch/New York/New York	04458095	212/348-2208	140
River Elem Sch/Patchogue/Suffolk	00774897	631/687-8350	227
Riverdale Ave Cmty Sch/Brooklyn/Kings	11821681	718/485-1679	93
Riverdale Avenue Middle Sch/Brooklyn/Kings	11932175	718/346-0764	93
Riverdale Country Sch/Bronx/Bronx	00752021	718/549-8810	27
Riverdale-Kingsbridge Academy/Bronx/Bronx	00743886	718/796-8516	22
RIVERHEAD CENTRAL SCH DIST/ **RIVERHEAD/SUFFOLK**	00775011	631/369-6700	228
Riverhead Charter Sch/Calverton/Suffolk	04950964	631/369-5800	6
Riverhead High Sch/Riverhead/Suffolk	00775085	631/369-6723	228
Riverhead Middle Sch/Riverhead/Suffolk	00775073	631/369-6759	228
Riverside Elem Sch/Elmira/Chemung	00719328	607/735-3850	40
Riverside Elem Sch/Oneonta/Otsego	00766175	607/433-8273	174
Riverside Elem Sch/Rockville CTR/Nassau	00738271	516/255-8902	128
Riverside High Sch/Yonkers/Westchester	04033592	914/376-8425	264
Riverton Street Charter Sch/Saint Albans/Queens	11560813	718/481-8200	184
Riverview Elem Sch/Tonawanda/Erie	00725341	716/694-7697	64
Riverview High Sch/Nyack/Rockland	11434965	845/348-3518	195
Rjo Intermediate Sch/Kings Park/Suffolk	04870479	631/269-3798	224
Roanoke Avenue Elem Sch/Riverhead/Suffolk	00775097	631/369-6813	228
Roaring Brook Elem Sch/Chappaqua/Westchester	00779847	914/238-7205	253
Robbins Lane Elem Sch/Syosset/Nassau	00738611	516/364-5804	130
Robert C Dodson Sch/Yonkers/Westchester	04019687	914/376-8159	264
Robert C Murphy Jr High Sch/Stony Brook/Suffolk	00776039	631/730-4800	232
Robert C Parker Sch/Wynantskill/Rensselaer	04838093	518/286-3449	192
Robert E Bell Middle Sch/Chappaqua/Westchester	00779859	914/238-7202	253
Robert F Kennedy Cmty High Sch/Flushing/Queens	04037988	718/969-5510	179
Robert Frost Middle Sch/Deer Park/Suffolk	00773130	631/274-4210	220

New York School Directory
DISTRICT & SCHOOL TELEPHONE INDEX

School/City/County DISTRICT/CITY/COUNTY	PID	TELEPHONE NUMBER	PAGE
Robert Graves Elem Sch/Port Ewen/Ulster	00777980	845/943-3915	242
Robert H Jackson Elem Sch/Frewsburg/Chautauqua	00718726	716/569-7031	38
Robert J Kaiser Middle Sch/Monticello/Sullivan	00776912	845/796-3058	237
Robert L Bradley Elem Sch/New Hartford/Oneida	00760200	315/624-1220	151
Robert Louis Stevenson Sch/New York/New York	01461524	212/787-6400	145
Robert M Finley Middle Sch/Glen Cove/Nassau	00735906	516/801-7510	120
Robert Moses Middle Sch/North Babylon/Suffolk	00774627	631/620-7302	226
Robert Seaman Elem Sch/Jericho/Nassau	04447826	516/203-3630	123
Robert W Carbonaro Elem Sch/Valley Stream/Nassau	00738910	516/434-2860	131
Robert W Harrold Ed Campus/Sidney Center/Delaware	03346059	607/865-2500	48
Robert Wagner Jr Sch Arts-Tech/Long Is City/Queens	04431011	718/472-5671	178
Roberto Clemente School 8/Rochester/Monroe	00732758	585/262-8888	111
Roberts Street Elem Sch/Canastota/Madison	00730994	315/697-2029	104
Rochambeau Alt High Sch/White Plains/Westchester	01813599	914/422-2420	263
Rochdale Early Advantage CS/Jamaica/Queens	11560863	718/978-0075	183
Rochester Academy Charter Sch/Rochester/Monroe	11595777	585/467-9201	6
Rochester Christian Sch/Rochester/Monroe	00733570	585/671-4910	114
ROCHESTER CITY SCH DIST/ROCHESTER/MONROE	00732526	585/262-8100	110
Rochester Classical Academy/Rochester/Monroe	12380343		114
Rochester Early Clg Intl HS/Rochester/Monroe	11559979	585/324-9010	111
Rochester International Acad/Rochester/Monroe	11914977	585/324-5250	111
Rochester Prep Elem Sch/Rochester/Monroe	11451054	585/235-0008	6
Rochester Prep ES-West/Rochester/Monroe	12260274	585/368-5100	6
Rochester Prep High Sch/Rochester/Monroe	12174194	585/368-5111	7
Rochester Prep MS-Brooks/Rochester/Monroe	10752477	585/436-8629	7
Rochester Prep MS-West/Rochester/Monroe	11468150	585/368-5090	7
Rochester School for the Deaf/Rochester/Monroe	01461055	585/544-1240	114
Rockaway Collegiate High Sch/Rockaway Park/Queens	11714868	718/734-3290	181
Rockaway Park High Sch/Rockaway Park/Queens	11560899	718/734-3280	181
ROCKLAND BOCES/WEST NYACK/ROCKLAND	00768226	845/627-4700	199
Rockland Children Psy Center/Orangeburg/Rockland	11223273	845/680-4080	7
Rockland Institute for Spec Ed/Spring Valley/Rockland	03413755	845/352-3307	199
ROCKVILLE CTR UNION FREE SD/ROCKVILLE CTR/NASSAU	00738245	516/255-8957	128
Rockwell Elem Sch/Nedrow/Onondaga	00762076	315/552-5070	157
Rocky Point High Sch/Rocky Point/Suffolk	00775126	631/744-1604	228
Rocky Point Middle Sch/Rocky Point/Suffolk	05101740	631/744-1603	228
ROCKY POINT UNION FREE SD/ROCKY POINT/SUFFOLK	00775102	631/744-1600	228
Rodeph Sholom Elem Sch/New York/New York	11223027	646/438-8540	145
Rodeph Sholom Sch/New York/New York	01794424	646/438-8500	145
Roessleville Elem Sch/Albany/Albany	03253191	518/459-2157	12
Rogers Middle Sch/Rochester/Monroe	00732318	585/342-1330	113
Rolling Hills Elem Sch/Dix Hills/Suffolk	00772710	631/858-3570	219
Rombout Middle Sch/Beacon/Dutchess	00721565	845/838-6900	51
Rome Catholic Sch/Rome/Oneida	00763056	315/336-6190	153
ROME CITY SCH DIST/ROME/ONEIDA	00760327	315/338-6500	151
Rome Early Childhood Center/Rome/Oneida	04805060	315/334-1250	152
Rome Free Academy/Rome/Oneida	00760470	315/334-7200	152
Romulus Central Sch/Romulus/Seneca	00771041	607/869-5391	208
ROMULUS CTL SCH DIST/ROMULUS/SENECA	00771027	607/869-5391	208
Ronald B Stafford Middle Sch/Plattsburgh/Clinton	00720286	518/563-6800	45
Ronald Edmonds Lrng Center II/Brooklyn/Kings	10027131	718/467-0306	87
Ronald L Sodoma Elem Sch/Albion/Orleans	00765169	585/589-2030	169
RONDOUT VALLEY CTL SCH DIST/ACCORD/ULSTER	00778207	845/687-2400	243
Rondout Valley High Sch/Accord/Ulster	00778257	845/687-2400	243
Rondout Valley Interm Sch/Accord/Ulster	11927819	845/687-2400	243
Rondout Valley Jr High Sch/Accord/Ulster	00778245	845/687-2400	243
Ronkonkoma Middle Sch/Ronkonkoma/Suffolk	00772966	631/467-6000	220
Roosevelt Children's Acad CS/Roosevelt/Nassau	04931932	516/867-6202	7
Roosevelt Childrens Center/Newark/Wayne	01795703	315/331-2086	251
Roosevelt Elem Sch/Ossining/Westchester	11455737	914/762-2682	260
Roosevelt High Sch/Roosevelt/Nassau	00738374	516/345-7200	128
Roosevelt HS Early Clg Studies/Yonkers/Westchester	11718242	914/376-8118	264
Roosevelt Middle Sch/Roosevelt/Nassau	11077672	516/345-7700	129
ROOSEVELT UNION FREE SCH DIST/ROOSEVELT/NASSAU	00738336	516/345-7000	128
Rosalyn Yalow Charter Sch/Bronx/Bronx	12115526	347/735-5480	7
Roscoe Central Sch/Roscoe/Sullivan	00776950	607/498-4126	237
ROSCOE CENTRAL SCH DIST/ROSCOE/SULLIVAN	00776948	607/498-4126	237
Roscoe Conkling Magnet ES/Utica/Oneida	11720025	315/368-6800	152
Rosemarie Ann Siragusa Sch 14/Yonkers/Westchester	00782507	914/376-8570	264
Rosemary Kennedy Sch/Wantagh/Nassau	01484590	516/396-2600	116
Rosemary Kennedy Sch at Willet/Hicksville/Nassau	04937780	516/483-4650	116
Rosendale Elem Sch/Schenectady/Schenectady	00770281	518/377-3123	204
Roslyn Heights Sch/Roslyn HTS/Nassau	00738465	516/801-5500	129
Roslyn High Sch/Roslyn HTS/Nassau	00738453	516/801-5100	129
Roslyn Middle Sch/Roslyn HTS/Nassau	00738477	516/801-5200	129
ROSLYN SCH DIST/ROSLYN/NASSAU	00738403	516/801-5001	129
Ross Corners Christian Academy/Vestal/Broome	00717320	607/748-3301	30
Ross Lower Sch/East Hampton/Suffolk	01464033	631/907-5000	235
Ross Upper Sch/East Hampton/Suffolk	04145054	631/907-5000	235
Rossetti Education Center/Verona/Oneida	01417211	315/361-5700	149
Round Hill Elem Sch/Washingtonvle/Orange	00765030	845/497-4000	167
Rouses Point Elem Sch/Rouses Point/Clinton	00720119	518/297-7211	44
Roxboro Road Elem Sch/Syracuse/Onondaga	00762026	315/218-2700	157
Roxboro Road Middle Sch/Syracuse/Onondaga	00762038	315/218-3300	157
Roxbury Central Sch/Roxbury/Delaware	00721204	607/326-4151	50
ROXBURY CENTRAL SCH DIST/ROXBURY/DELAWARE	00721199	607/326-4151	50
Roy C Ketcham Senior High Sch/Wappingers Fl/Dutchess	00722222	845/298-5100	54
Roy Kelley Elem Sch/Lockport/Niagara	00759158	716/478-4670	147
ROYALTON HARTLAND CENTRAL SD/MIDDLEPORT/NIAGARA	00759720	716/735-2000	148
Royalton Hartland Elem Sch/Gasport/Niagara	00759732	716/735-2000	148
Royalton Hartland High Sch/Middleport/Niagara	00759756	716/735-2000	148
Royalton Hartland Middle Sch/Middleport/Niagara	00759744	716/735-2000	148
Ruben A Cirillo High Sch/Walworth/Wayne	02205505	315/986-3521	249
Rudolf Steiner Lower Sch/New York/New York	00752083	212/535-2130	145
Rudolf Steiner Upper Sch/New York/New York	11690690	212/879-1101	145
RUSH HENRIETTA CENTRAL SD/HENRIETTA/MONROE	00733166	585/359-5000	112
Rush Henrietta Senior High Sch/Henrietta/Monroe	00733257	585/359-5200	112
Rushmore Avenue Elem Sch/Carle Place/Nassau	00735152	516/622-6421	117
Russell I Doig Middle Sch/Trumansburg/Tompkins	00777710	607/387-7551	241
Ruth C Kinney Elem Sch/Islip Terrace/Suffolk	00773257	631/224-2007	221
RYE CITY SCH DIST/RYE/WESTCHESTER	00781682	914/967-6100	261
Rye Country Day Sch/Rye/Westchester	00782947	914/967-1417	266
Rye High Sch/Rye/Westchester	00781723	914/967-6100	261
Rye Lake Campus/White Plains/Westchester	00782806	914/948-7271	252
Rye Middle Sch/Rye/Westchester	01417377	914/967-6100	261
Rye Neck High Sch/Mamaroneck/Westchester	03333064	914/777-4800	261
Rye Neck Middle Sch/Mamaroneck/Westchester	00781761	914/777-4702	261
RYE NECK UNION FREE SCH DIST/MAMARONECK/WESTCHESTER	00781735	914/777-5200	261
Rye School of Leadership/Rye/Westchester	05100576	914/760-1462	261
S			
S Bronx CS-Int'l Culture & Art/Bronx/Bronx	10026632	718/401-9216	17
Sacandaga Elem Sch/Scotia/Schenectady	00770700	518/382-1282	205
SACHEM CENTRAL SCH DIST/LK RONKONKOMA/SUFFOLK	00775138	631/471-1300	229
Sachem High School East/Farmingville/Suffolk	00775243	631/716-8200	229

DISTRICT & SCHOOL TELEPHONE INDEX

Market Data Retrieval

School/City/County DISTRICT/CITY/COUNTY	PID	TELEPHONE NUMBER	PAGE
Sachem High School North/Lk Ronkonkoma/Suffolk	00775229	631/471-1400	229
Sackets Harbor Central Sch/Sackets HBR/Jefferson	00730138	315/646-3575	81
SACKETS HARBOR CTL SCH DIST/ **SACKETS HBR/JEFFERSON**	00730126	315/646-3575	81
Sacred Heart Academy/Hempstead/Nassau	00739885	516/483-7383	132
Sacred Heart Catholic Academy/Cambria HTS/Queens	00753685	718/527-0123	186
Sacred Heart Elem Sch/Staten Island/Richmond	00756572	718/442-0347	195
Sacred Heart Elem Sch/Yonkers/Westchester	00756493	914/963-5318	265
Sacred Heart High Sch/Yonkers/Westchester	00756508	914/965-3114	265
Sacred Heart of Jesus Sch/New York/New York	00756584	212/246-4784	143
Sacred Heart Sch/Bayside/Queens	00753702	718/631-4804	186
Sacred Heart Sch/Bronx/Bronx	00756510	718/293-4288	26
Sacred Heart Sch/Glendale/Queens	00753697	718/456-6636	186
Sacred Heart Sch/Hartsdale/Westchester	00756560	914/946-7242	265
Sacred Heart Sch/Monroe/Orange	00756601	845/783-0365	168
Sacred Heart Sch/Troy/Rensselaer	00715322	518/274-3655	192
Sacred Heart Villa Sch/Lewiston/Niagara	00726759	716/285-9257	149
Saddle Rock Elem Sch/Great Neck/Nassau	00736077	516/441-4400	121
Saddlewood Elem Sch/Albany/Albany	03317008	518/456-2608	12
Sag Harbor Elem Sch/Sag Harbor/Suffolk	00775334	631/725-5301	229
SAG HARBOR UNION FREE SCH DIST/ **SAG HARBOR/SUFFOLK**	00775310	631/725-5300	229
Sagamore Middle Sch/Holtsville/Suffolk	00775231	631/696-8600	229
SAGAPONACK COMMON SCH DIST/ **SAGAPONACK/SUFFOLK**	00775346	631/537-0651	229
Sagaponack Elem Sch/Sagaponack/Suffolk	00775358	631/537-0651	229
Sail School-Ferncliff Manor/Yonkers/Westchester	01795765	914/968-4854	266
Saint Albans Sch/New York/New York	11827879	212/755-0997	145
SALAMANCA CITY CENTRAL SD/ **SALAMANCA/CATTARAUGUS**	00717784	716/945-2400	33
Salamanca High Sch/Salamanca/Cattaraugus	00717813	716/945-2404	33
Salem Central Sch/Salem/Washington	00779093	518/854-7855	248
SALEM CENTRAL SCH DIST/SALEM/ **WASHINGTON**	00779081	518/854-7855	248
Salem-Hyde Elem Sch/Syracuse/Onondaga	00762583	315/435-4570	159
Salesian High Sch/New Rochelle/Westchester	00756637	914/632-0248	265
SALMON RIVER CENTRAL SCH DIST/ **FT COVINGTON/FRANKLIN**	00728288	518/358-6600	70
Salmon River Elem Sch/Ft Covington/Franklin	00728290	518/358-6670	70
Salmon River High Sch/Ft Covington/Franklin	00728305	518/358-6620	70
Salmon River Middle Sch/Ft Covington/Franklin	11711476	518/358-6650	70
Salt Point Center/Poughkeepsie/Dutchess	01522271	845/486-8004	51
Saltzman East Memorial ES/Farmingdale/Nassau	00735487	516/434-5710	119
Salve Regina Catholic Academy/Brooklyn/Kings	02102238	718/277-6766	95
Samara Cmty Sch/Bronx/Bronx	12036401	718/935-3448	25
Samoset Middle Sch/Lk Ronkonkoma/Suffolk	05346275	631/471-1700	229
Samuel G Love Elem Sch/Jamestown/Chautauqua	00718843	716/483-4405	38
Samuel J Preston Elem Sch/West Harrison/Westchester	00780341	914/630-3152	256
San Miguel Academy of Newburgh/Newburgh/Orange	11708388	845/561-2822	168
Sand Creek Middle Sch/Albany/Albany	00714914	518/459-1333	12
SANDY CREEK CENTRAL SCH DIST/ **SANDY CREEK/OSWEGO**	00765872	315/387-3445	172
Sandy Creek Sch/Sandy Creek/Oswego	00765896	315/387-3465	172
Sanford St Teaching & Lrng Ctr/Glens Falls/Warren	10017813	518/761-6964	244
Sanfordville Elem Sch/Warwick/Orange	04916798	845/987-3300	167
Santa Maria Sch/Bronx/Bronx	00756649	718/823-3636	26
Santapogue Elem Sch/West Babylon/Suffolk	00776144	631/376-7401	233
Sapphire Elem Sch/Harriman/Orange	03318117	845/460-6500	165
Sar Academy/Bronx/Bronx	00751998	718/548-1717	27
Sar High Sch/Bronx/Bronx	11129952	718/548-2727	27
SARANAC CENTRAL SCH DIST/ **DANNEMORA/CLINTON**	00720303	518/565-5600	45
Saranac Elem Sch/Saranac/Clinton	01841041	518/565-5900	45
SARANAC LAKE CENTRAL SCH DIST/ **SARANAC LAKE/FRANKLIN**	00728329	518/891-5460	70
Saranac Lake High Sch/Saranac Lake/Franklin	00728355	518/891-4450	70
Saranac Lake Middle Sch/Saranac Lake/Franklin	04912431	518/891-4221	70
Saranac Middle Sch/Saranac/Clinton	04744959	518/565-5700	45
Saranac Senior High Sch/Saranac/Clinton	00720341	518/565-5800	45
Saratoga Central Catholic HS/Saratoga Spgs/Saratoga	00715891	518/587-7070	203
Saratoga Independent Sch/Saratoga Spgs/Saratoga	04022440	518/583-0841	203
SARATOGA SPRINGS CITY SCH DIST/ **SARATOGA SPGS/SARATOGA**	00769696	518/583-4700	201
Saratoga Springs High Sch/Saratoga Spgs/Saratoga	00769763	518/587-6690	201
Sargent Elem Sch/Beacon/Dutchess	00721577	845/838-6900	51
Satellite Academy High Sch/New York/New York	01552290	646/674-2800	137
Satellite East Middle Sch/Brooklyn/Kings	05349538	718/245-8766	83
SAUGERTIES CENTRAL SCH DIST/ **SAUGERTIES/ULSTER**	00778295	845/246-1043	243
Saugerties Junior High Sch/Saugerties/Ulster	04750518	845/247-6561	243
Saugerties Senior High Sch/Saugerties/Ulster	00778350	845/247-6650	243
Saul and Elaine Seiff Ctr/Bohemia/Suffolk	01464019	631/218-4949	235
Saunders Trade & Tech High Sch/Yonkers/Westchester	00782387	914/376-8150	264
SAUQUOIT VALLEY CENTRAL SD/ **SAUQUOIT/ONEIDA**	00760511	315/839-6311	152
Sauquoit Valley Elem Sch/Sauquoit/Oneida	00760523	315/839-6339	152
Sauquoit Valley High Sch/Sauquoit/Oneida	00760535	315/839-6316	152
Sauquoit Valley Middle Sch/Sauquoit/Oneida	00760028	315/839-6371	152
Sawmill Road Elem Sch/N Bellmore/Nassau	00737643	516/992-3118	126
Saxton Middle Sch/Patchogue/Suffolk	00774902	631/687-6700	227
Sayville Elementary/Sayville/Suffolk	11435050	631/422-1570	216
Sayville High Sch/West Sayville/Suffolk	00775401	631/244-6600	230
Sayville Middle Sch/Sayville/Suffolk	00775413	631/244-6650	230
SAYVILLE UNION FREE SCH DIST/ **SAYVILLE/SUFFOLK**	00775360	631/244-6510	229
Sbcs Notre Dame Academy/Buffalo/Erie	00727466	716/824-0726	65
Scarsdale Middle Sch/Scarsdale/Westchester	00781864	914/721-2600	262
Scarsdale Senior High Sch/Scarsdale/Westchester	00781876	914/721-2500	262
SCARSDALE UNION FREE SCH DIST/ **SCARSDALE/WESTCHESTER**	00781802	914/721-2410	261
Sch for Inquiry Social Justice/Bronx/Bronx	05349447	718/860-4181	18
Sch Math Sci & Healthy Living/Brooklyn/Kings	11561013	718/765-2200	90
Sch of Science & Applied Lrng/Bronx/Bronx	00744725	718/584-6310	25
Sch Without Walls Commenc Acad/Rochester/Monroe	00732772	585/546-6732	111
SCHALMONT CENTRAL SCH DIST/ **SCHENECTADY/SCHENECTADY**	00770308	518/355-9200	204
Schalmont High Sch/Schenectady/Schenectady	00770360	518/355-6110	204
Schalmont Middle Sch/Schenectady/Schenectady	00770358	518/355-6255	204
Schechter Day School of Li/Jericho/Nassau	01461354	516/935-1441	134
SCHENECTADY CITY SCH DIST/ **SCHENECTADY/SCHENECTADY**	00770396	518/370-8100	204
Schenectady High Sch/Schenectady/Schenectady	00770504	518/881-2044	205
Schenevus Central Sch/Schenevus/Otsego	00765951	607/638-5881	174
SCHENEVUS CTL SCH DIST/SCHENEVUS/ **OTSEGO**	00765949	607/638-5530	174
Schlegel Road Elem Sch/Webster/Monroe	03316834	585/265-2500	113
SCHODACK CENTRAL SCH DIST/ **CASTLETON/RENSSELAER**	00767052	518/732-2297	191
SCHOHARIE CENTRAL SD/SCHOHARIE/ **SCHOHARIE**	00770865	518/295-6600	206
Schoharie Elem Sch/Schoharie/Schoharie	00770877	518/295-6651	206
Schoharie High Sch/Schoharie/Schoharie	00770889	518/295-6601	207
Scholars Academy/Rockaway Park/Queens	10026711	718/474-6918	181
Scholastic Acad-Academic Excel/Yonkers/Westchester	00782545	914/376-8420	264
School 2 Florence A Smith/Oceanside/Nassau	00737813	516/678-7557	127
School 3 Oaks Sch/Oceanside/Nassau	00737825	516/678-7564	127
School 4 South Oceanside Road/Oceanside/Nassau	04453045	516/678-7581	127
School 5/Yonkers/Westchester	00782416	914/376-8320	264
School 5 North Oceanside Road/Oceanside/Nassau	00737849	516/678-7585	127
School 6 Kindergarten Center/Oceanside/Nassau	00737837	516/594-2345	127
School 7 Oceanside HS/Oceanside/Nassau	00737796	516/678-7526	127

NY-V48   800-333-8802   School Year 2020-2021

New York School Directory

DISTRICT & SCHOOL TELEPHONE INDEX

School/City/County DISTRICT/CITY/COUNTY	PID	TELEPHONE NUMBER	PAGE
School 8 Fulton Avenue/Oceanside/Nassau	00737851	516/678-8503	127
School 9/Yonkers/Westchester	00782454	914/376-8325	264
School 9E Walter S Boardman/Oceanside/Nassau	00737772	516/678-8510	127
School 9M Oceanside Middle Sch/Oceanside/Nassau	01292294	516/678-8518	127
School 13/Yonkers/Westchester	00782492	914/376-8335	264
School 16/Yonkers/Westchester	00782521	914/376-8340	264
School 17/Yonkers/Westchester	00782533	914/376-8345	264
School 21/Yonkers/Westchester	00782569	914/376-8435	264
School 22/Yonkers/Westchester	00782571	914/376-8440	264
School 23/Yonkers/Westchester	00782583	914/376-8445	264
School 30/Yonkers/Westchester	00782650	914/376-8590	264
School at Columbia/New York/New York	05378242	212/851-4215	145
School at Northeast/Schenectady/Schenectady	04974996	518/346-1273	205
School for Classics Academy/Brooklyn/Kings	11714911	718/277-1069	89
School for Excellence/Bronx/Bronx	11824310	718/860-1385	20
School for Global Leaders/New York/New York	11103295	212/260-5375	135
School for Human Rights/Brooklyn/Kings	05349710	718/771-4793	87
School for Tourism-Hospitality/Bronx/Bronx	11818218	718/401-4214	18
School for Young Performers/New York/New York	10014770	212/663-3921	145
School In the Square PCS/New York/New York	12170629	718/916-7683	7
School of Blessed Sacrament/New York/New York	00755229	212/724-7561	143
School of Co-op Technical Ed/New York/New York	00741280	212/369-8800	142
School of Creativity-Innovatn/Brooklyn/Kings	12310295	929/419-6049	85
School of Holy Childhood/Rochester/Monroe	00733764	585/359-3710	114
School of Integrated Learning/Brooklyn/Kings	10008771	718/774-0362	87
School of Science & Tech/Brooklyn/Kings	00747167	718/434-5222	92
School of the Arts/Rochester/Monroe	03248809	585/242-7682	111
School of the Future/New York/New York	04037316	212/475-8086	138
School of the Holy Child/Rye/Westchester	00756651	914/967-5622	265
Schroeder High Sch/Webster/Monroe	00733477	585/670-5000	113
Schroon Lake Central Sch/Schroon Lake/Essex	00728018	518/532-7164	68
SCHROON LAKE CTL SCH DIST/ SCHROON LAKE/ESSEX	00728006	518/532-7164	68
Schuyler Achievement Academy/Albany/Albany	05345518	518/475-6700	9
SCHUYLERVILLE CENTRAL SCH DIST/ SCHUYLERVILLE/SARATOGA	00769787	518/695-3255	201
Schuylerville Elem Sch/Schuylerville/Saratoga	00769804	518/695-3255	201
Schuylerville High Sch/Schuylerville/Saratoga	00769816	518/695-3255	201
Schuylerville Middle Sch/Schuylerville/Saratoga	11828299	518/695-3255	201
Schuylerville Prep HS/Bronx/Bronx	11924465	718/904-5080	18
Sci & Tech Acad-A Mott Hall/Bronx/Bronx	11447613	718/293-4017	20
Science & Medicine Middle Sch/Brooklyn/Kings	11447455	718/688-6400	88
Science Skills Center/Brooklyn/Kings	04037249	718/243-9413	83
Science Tech & Research HS/Brooklyn/Kings	05281156	718/564-2540	87
Scio Central Sch/Scio/Allegany	00716314	585/593-5510	15
SCIO CENTRAL SCH DIST/SCIO/ALLEGANY	00716297	585/593-5510	15
Scotchtown Avenue Elem Sch/Goshen/Orange	00764189	845/615-6600	164
SCOTIA GLENVILLE CTL SCH DIST/ SCOTIA/SCHENECTADY	00770645	518/347-3600	205
Scotia Glenville High Sch/Scotia/Schenectady	00770712	518/382-1231	205
Scotia Middle Sch/Scotia/Schenectady	00770695	518/382-1263	205
Scott M Ellis Elem Sch/Greenville/Greene	00729268	518/966-5070	75
Scribner Road Elem Sch/Penfield/Monroe	00732411	585/249-6400	110
Sea Cliff Elem Sch/Sea Cliff/Nassau	00737758	516/277-7500	127
Seaford Harbor Elem Sch/Seaford/Nassau	00738518	516/592-4100	129
Seaford High Sch/Seaford/Nassau	00738544	516/592-4300	129
Seaford Manor Elem Sch/Seaford/Nassau	00738532	516/592-4050	129
Seaford Middle Sch/Seaford/Nassau	00738520	516/592-4200	129
SEAFORD UNION FREE SD/SEAFORD/NASSAU	00738491	516/592-4000	129
Searingtown Elem Sch/Albertson/Nassau	00736247	516/305-8500	121
Seaway Area Tech Center/Norwood/St Lawrence	04026501	315/353-2293	209
Seeall Academy/Brooklyn/Kings	00746668	718/851-8070	90
Seely Place Elem Sch/Scarsdale/Westchester	00780092	914/472-8040	254
Selden Middle Sch/Centereach/Suffolk	00774316	631/285-8400	225
Senator James H Donovan MS/Utica/Oneida	00760640	315/368-6541	152
Seneca Bible Bapt Chrn Academy/Seneca Falls/Seneca	04341117	315/568-9100	209
Seneca Elem Sch/Rochester/Monroe	00732239	585/336-1620	113
SENECA FALLS CENTRAL SCH DIST/ SENECA FALLS/SENECA	00771053	315/568-5818	208
Seneca Falls Middle Sch/Seneca Falls/Seneca	00771091	315/568-5500	208
Seneca Intermediate Sch/Salamanca/Cattaraugus	00717825	716/945-5140	33
Seneca Middle Sch/Holbrook/Suffolk	00775255	631/471-1850	229
Seneca Street Elem Sch/Oneida/Madison	00731302	315/363-3930	105
Sequoya High Sch/Holtsville/Suffolk	12469547	631/622-1200	216
Setauket Elem Sch/Setauket/Suffolk	00776041	631/730-4600	232
Seton Catholic Ctl High Sch/Binghamton/Broome	00763082	607/723-5307	30
Seton Catholic Sch/Plattsburgh/Clinton	00769141	518/561-4031	45
Seton Catholic Sch/Rochester/Monroe	00734548	585/473-6604	114
Seton Catholic-All Saints Sch/Endicott/Broome	00763044	607/748-7423	30
Seven Bridges Middle Sch/Chappaqua/Westchester	05279426	914/238-7203	253
Seventy Ninth Street Elem Sch/Niagara Falls/Niagara	00759419	716/278-7900	148
SEWANHAKA CTL HIGH SCH DIST/ FLORAL PARK/NASSAU	00735554	516/488-9800	129
Sewanhaka High Sch/Floral Park/Nassau	00735619	516/488-9600	129
Seymour Dual Language Acad/Syracuse/Onondaga	00762600	315/435-4645	159
Seymour Smith Inter Lrng Ctr/Pine Plains/Dutchess	00721876	518/398-3000	53
Shaare Torah Sch/Brooklyn/Kings	11239454	718/339-9752	98
Shaarei Zion Ohel Bracha Sch/Forest Hills/Queens	11227683	718/897-6771	188
Shaker High Sch/Latham/Albany	00714732	518/785-5511	11
Shaker Junior High Sch/Latham/Albany	00714744	518/785-1341	11
Shaker Road Elem Sch/Albany/Albany	00714926	518/458-1440	12
Shalsheles Bais Yaakov Sch/Brooklyn/Kings	03409077	718/436-1122	99
Shanker Sch Visual Perf Arts/Long Is City/Queens	00749397	718/274-8316	185
Sharon Springs Central Sch/Sharon Spgs/Schoharie	00770906	518/284-2267	207
SHARON SPRINGS CTL SD/SHARON SPGS/SCHOHARIE	00770891	518/284-2266	207
Shatekon Elem Sch/Clifton Park/Saratoga	11070698	518/881-0580	202
Shaw Avenue Elem Sch/Valley Stream/Nassau	00738972	516/434-3700	131
Sheafe Road Elem Sch/Wappingers Fl/Dutchess	00722234	845/298-5290	54
Shelter Island Sch/Shelter Is/Suffolk	00775449	631/749-0302	230
SHELTER ISLAND UNION FREE SD/ SHELTER IS/SUFFOLK	00775437	631/749-0302	230
Shelter Rock Elem Sch/Manhasset/Nassau	00737215	516/267-7450	125
Shema Kolainu Sch/Brooklyn/Kings	05011690	718/686-9600	99
SHENENDEHOWA CENTRAL SCH DIST/ CLIFTON PARK/SARATOGA	00769828	518/881-0600	202
Shenendehowa High Sch/Clifton Park/Saratoga	00769892	518/881-0310	202
SHERBURNE EARLVILLE CENTRAL SD/ SHERBURNE/CHENANGO	00719811	607/674-7300	42
Sherburne Earlville Elem Sch/Sherburne/Chenango	00719823	607/674-7336	42
Sherburne Earlville Middle Sch/Sherburne/Chenango	03412957	607/674-7350	43
Sherburne Earlville Sr HS/Sherburne/Chenango	01813214	607/674-7380	43
Sheridan Academy Young Leaders/Bronx/Bronx	11447601	718/538-3411	20
Sheridan Hill Elem Sch/Williamsville/Erie	03049380	716/407-9250	59
Sheridan Preparatory Academy/Albany/Albany	00714122	518/475-6850	9
Sherman Central Sch/Sherman/Chautauqua	01813185	716/761-6121	39
SHERMAN CENTRAL SCH DIST/ SHERMAN/CHAUTAUQUA	00718996	716/761-6121	39
Sherman Elem Sch/Watertown/Jefferson	00730425	315/785-3760	82
Shevach High Sch/Flushing/Queens	02163531	718/263-0525	188
Shield Institute of Flushing/Flushing/Queens	02164573	718/939-8700	188
Shield Institute/Bronx ELC/Bronx/Bronx	01461641	718/299-7600	27
Shore Road Sch/Bellmore/Nassau	00735023	516/679-2950	117
Shoreham Wading River High Sch/Shoreham/Suffolk	01417315	631/821-8140	230
SHOREHAM-WADING RIVER CTL SD/ SHOREHAM/SUFFOLK	00775451	631/821-8100	230
Shulamith School for Girls/Brooklyn/Kings	00752007	718/338-4000	99

School Year 2020-2021   800-333-8802   NY-V49

DISTRICT & SCHOOL TELEPHONE INDEX

Market Data Retrieval

School/City/County DISTRICT/CITY/COUNTY	PID	TELEPHONE NUMBER	PAGE
Shulamith School for Girls/Cedarhurst/Nassau	11221811	516/569-1713	134
SIDNEY CENTRAL SCH DIST/ SIDNEY/DELAWARE	00721216	607/563-2135	50
Sidney Elem Sch/Sidney/Delaware	00721230	607/561-7701	50
Sidney High Sch/Sidney/Delaware	00721266	607/561-7703	50
Sidney Junior High Sch/Sidney/Delaware	00721254	607/561-7703	50
Sidway Elem Sch/Grand Island/Erie	04031635	716/773-8870	61
Signal Hill Elem Sch/Dix Hills/Suffolk	00773532	631/592-3700	222
Silas Wood 6th Grade Center/Huntingtn Sta/Suffolk	04931839	631/812-3600	231
SILVER CREEK CENTRAL SCH DIST/ SILVER CREEK/CHAUTAUQUA	00719029	716/934-2603	39
Silver Creek Elem Sch/Silver Creek/Chautauqua	00719043	716/934-2603	39
Silver Creek High Sch/Silver Creek/Chautauqua	00719055	716/934-2103	39
Silver Creek Middle Sch/Silver Creek/Chautauqua	05342334	716/934-2603	39
Silverstein Hebrew Academy/Great Neck/Nassau	12039025	516/466-8522	134
Sinai Academy/Brooklyn/Kings	03077545	718/256-7400	99
Sinclairville Elem Sch/Sinclairville/Chautauqua	00718374	716/962-5195	36
Sisulu-Walker CS of Harlem/New York/New York	04880759	212/663-8216	7
Siwanoy Elem Sch/Pelham/Westchester	00781498	914/738-7650	260
SKANEATELES CENTRAL SCH DIST/ SKANEATELES/ONONDAGA	00762090	315/685-8361	157
Skaneateles Middle Sch/Skaneateles/Onondaga	00762105	315/291-2241	158
Skaneateles Senior High Sch/Skaneateles/Onondaga	00762117	315/291-2231	158
Skano Elem Sch/Clifton Park/Saratoga	00769878	518/881-0560	202
Skoi Yase Primary Sch/Waterloo/Seneca	00771182	315/539-1520	208
Slcd Sch/Woodside/Queens	11224459	718/476-7163	188
Sleepy Hollow High Sch/Sleepy Hollow/Westchester	00781981	914/631-8838	262
Sleepy Hollow Middle Sch/Sleepy Hollow/Westchester	10817223	914/332-6275	262
Slingerlands Elem Sch/Delmar/Albany	00714445	518/439-7681	10
Sloatsburg Elem Sch/Sloatsburg/Rockland	00768173	845/753-2720	198
Smallwood Drive Elem Sch/Amherst/Erie	02106399	716/362-2100	56
Smith Clove Elem Sch/Central Vly/Orange	00764440	845/460-6300	165
Smith Road Elem Sch/N Syracuse/Onondaga	00762040	315/218-2800	157
Smith Sch/New York/New York	04883191	212/879-6354	145
Smith Street Elem Sch/Uniondale/Nassau	00738752	516/918-2000	130
SMITHTOWN CENTRAL SCH DIST/ SMITHTOWN/SUFFOLK	00775504	631/382-2000	230
Smithtown Christian Sch/Smithtown/Suffolk	02164286	631/265-3334	235
Smithtown Elem Sch/Smithtown/Suffolk	00775580	631/382-4505	230
Smithtown High School-East/Saint James/Suffolk	00775669	631/382-2705	230
Smithtown High School-West/Smithtown/Suffolk	00775671	631/382-2905	230
SODUS CENTRAL SCH DIST/SODUS/ WAYNE	00779483	315/483-2331	251
Sodus Elem Sch/Sodus/Wayne	00779512	315/483-5282	251
Sodus Intermediate Sch/Sodus/Wayne	04940426	315/483-2331	251
Sodus Jr Sr High Sch/Sodus/Wayne	00779500	315/483-5280	251
Solomon Schechter Sch/White Plains/Westchester	01464227	914/948-3111	266
Solomon Schechter Sch/Williston Pk/Nassau	04202690	516/539-3700	134
Solomon Schechter Sch- Mnhttn/New York/New York	11477175	212/427-9500	145
Solomon Schechter Sch- Queens/Fresh Meadows/Queens	01462255	718/591-9800	188
Solvay Elem Sch/Solvay/Onondaga	00762167	315/488-5422	158
Solvay High Sch/Solvay/Onondaga	00762181	315/468-2551	158
Solvay Middle Sch/Syracuse/Onondaga	00762179	315/487-7061	158
SOLVAY UNION FREE SCH DIST/ SYRACUSE/ONONDAGA	00762143	315/468-1111	158
SOMERS CENTRAL SCH DIST/ SOMERS/WESTCHESTER	00781888	914/277-2400	262
Somers High Sch/Lincolndale/Westchester	00781929	914/248-8585	262
Somers Intermediate Sch/Somers/Westchester	00781905	914/277-4344	262
Somers Middle Sch/Somers/Westchester	00781917	914/277-3399	262
Soterios Ellenas Parochial Sch/Brooklyn/Kings	01462712	718/499-5900	99
Soule Road Elem Sch/Liverpool/Onondaga	00761723	315/453-1280	156
Soule Road Middle Sch/Liverpool/Onondaga	00761735	315/453-1283	156
Soundview Acad-Cult & Schlrshp/Bronx/Bronx	11447649	718/991-4027	18

School/City/County DISTRICT/CITY/COUNTY	PID	TELEPHONE NUMBER	PAGE
Soundview Preparatory Sch/Yorktown Hts/Westchester	04974166	914/962-2780	266
South Avenue Elem Sch/Beacon/Dutchess	00721589	845/838-6900	51
South Bay Elem Sch/West Babylon/Suffolk	00776156	631/376-7500	233
South Bay Jr Academy/Babylon/Suffolk	05147342	631/321-0857	235
South Bronx Academy Appl Media/Bronx/Bronx	10027076	718/401-0059	17
South Bronx Classical CS/Bronx/Bronx	10026266	718/860-4340	7
South Bronx Classical CS II/Bronx/Bronx	11933791	718/292-9526	7
South Bronx Classical CS III/New York/New York	12170605	929/285-3025	7
South Bronx Classical CS IV/Bronx/Bronx	12234196	929/285-3025	7
South Bronx Cmty Charter HS/Bronx/Bronx	12260286	718/292-4115	7
South Bronx Early Clg Acad CS/Bronx/Bronx	12105428	929/291-7700	7
South Bronx Preparatory Sch/Bronx/Bronx	05348871	718/292-2211	17
South Brooklyn Academy/Brooklyn/Kings	02163086	718/693-5502	99
South Brooklyn Cmty High Sch/Brooklyn/Kings	05093040	718/237-8902	85
South Buffalo Charter Sch/Buffalo/Erie	04924202	716/826-7213	7
SOUTH COLONIE CENTRAL SCH DIST/ ALBANY/ALBANY	00714835	518/869-3576	12
SOUTH COUNTRY CENTRAL SCH DIST/ PATCHOGUE/SUFFOLK	00772136	631/730-1500	231
South Country Sch/Bay Shore/Suffolk	00772069	631/968-1250	217
South Davis Elem Sch/Orchard Park/Erie	00725054	716/209-6246	63
SOUTH GLENS FALLS CTL SCH DIST/ S GLENS FALLS/SARATOGA	00769933	518/793-9617	202
South Glens Falls Sr High Sch/S Glens Falls/Saratoga	00769983	518/792-9987	202
South Grove Elem Sch/Syosset/Nassau	00738623	516/364-5810	130
South Haven Early Chldhd Ctr/Brookhaven/Suffolk	12376744	631/730-2180	231
South High Sch/Williamsville/Erie	00725652	716/626-8281	65
South Hill Elem Sch/Ithaca/Tompkins	00777590	607/274-2129	240
SOUTH HUNTINGTON UNION FREE SD/ HUNTINGTN STA/SUFFOLK	00775736	631/812-3000	231
SOUTH JEFFERSON CENTRAL SD/ ADAMS CENTER/JEFFERSON	00730243	315/583-6104	81
South Jefferson High Sch/Adams/Jefferson	00730267	315/232-4531	81
South Jefferson Middle Sch/Adams/Jefferson	10014483	315/232-4531	81
South Kortright Central Sch/S Kortright/Delaware	00721280	607/538-9111	50
SOUTH KORTRIGHT CTL SD/S KORTRIGHT/ DELAWARE	00721278	607/538-9111	50
SOUTH LEWIS CENTRAL SCH DIST/ TURIN/LEWIS	00730580	315/348-2500	101
South Lewis High Sch/Turin/Lewis	00730633	315/348-2520	102
South Lewis Middle Sch/Turin/Lewis	04368581	315/348-2570	102
South Middle Sch/Brentwood/Suffolk	00772332	631/434-2341	218
South Middle Sch/Newburgh/Orange	00764713	845/563-7000	166
South Ocean Middle Sch/Patchogue/Suffolk	00774914	631/687-6600	227
SOUTH ORANGETOWN CENTRAL SD/ BLAUVELT/ROCKLAND	00767820	845/680-1000	197
South Orangetown Middle Sch/Blauvelt/Rockland	00767868	845/680-1100	198
South Salem Elem Sch/Prt Washingtn/Nassau	05342499	516/767-5400	128
South Seneca Central Elem Sch/Interlaken/Seneca	00771120	607/869-9636	208
SOUTH SENECA CTL SCH DIST/ OVID/SENECA	00771118	607/869-9636	208
South Seneca Middle High Sch/Ovid/Seneca	00771144	607/869-9636	208
South Shore Ed Campus YABC/Brooklyn/Kings	11928837	718/968-1689	88
South Side Elem Sch/Canastota/Madison	00731003	315/697-6372	104
South Side High Sch/Rockville CTR/Nassau	00738295	516/255-8947	128
South Side Middle Sch/Rockville CTR/Nassau	00738283	516/255-8976	128
South Street Elem Sch/Manorville/Suffolk	02045240	631/801-3140	221
South Woods Middle Sch/Syosset/Nassau	00738635	516/364-5621	130
Southampton Elem Sch/Southampton/Suffolk	00775889	631/591-4800	231
Southampton High Sch/Southampton/Suffolk	00775906	631/591-4600	231
Southampton Intermediate Sch/Southampton/Suffolk	00775891	631/591-4700	231
Southampton Montessori Sch/Southampton/Suffolk	12314863	631/283-2223	235
SOUTHAMPTON UNION FREE SD/ SOUTHAMPTON/SUFFOLK	00775877	631/591-4510	231
Southdown Primary Sch/Huntington/Suffolk	03329635	631/673-2080	223
Southeast Christian Academy/Penfield/Monroe	04975471	585/388-0850	114
Southern Adirondack Ed Center/Hudson Falls/Washington	00779158	518/746-3400	246
SOUTHERN CAYUGA CENTRAL SD/ AURORA/CAYUGA	00718099	315/364-7211	35
Southern Cayuga Jr Sr HS/Aurora/Cayuga	00718142	315/364-7111	35

New York School Directory

DISTRICT & SCHOOL TELEPHONE INDEX

School/City/County DISTRICT/CITY/COUNTY	PID	TELEPHONE NUMBER	PAGE
Southern Tier Catholic Sch/Olean/Cattaraugus	00727480	716/372-8122	34
SOUTHERN WESTCHESTER BOCES/ RYE BROOK/WESTCHESTER	00782789	914/937-3820	267
Southern Westchester BOCES Voc/Valhalla/Westchester	01601463	914/761-3400	252
Southgate Elem Sch/Loudonville/Albany	00714756	518/785-6607	11
Southlawn Sch/Rochester/Monroe	00732320	585/266-5070	113
Southold Elem Sch/Southold/Suffolk	00775932	631/765-5208	231
Southold Jr Sr High Sch/Southold/Suffolk	00775944	631/765-5081	232
SOUTHOLD UNION FREE SCH DIST/ SOUTHOLD/SUFFOLK	00775918	631/765-5400	231
Southside Academy Charter Sch/Syracuse/Onondaga	05078375	315/476-3019	7
Southtown Academy/Hamburg/Erie	11435012	716/961-4060	56
SOUTHTOWN TEACHERS CENTER/ HAMBURG/ERIE	04498514	716/649-6775	67
Southtowns Catholic Sch/Lake View/Erie	00726589	716/627-5011	65
Southwest Elem Sch/Bay Shore/Suffolk	00772356	631/434-2261	218
Southwest Technical Center/Gouverneur/St Lawrence	02051342	315/287-3590	209
SOUTHWESTERN CENTRAL SCH DIST/ JAMESTOWN/CHAUTAUQUA	00719067	716/484-1136	39
Southwestern Elem Sch/Jamestown/Chautauqua	00719079	716/664-1881	39
Southwestern High Sch/Jamestown/Chautauqua	00719108	716/664-6273	39
Southwestern Middle Sch/Jamestown/Chautauqua	00719093	716/664-6270	39
Spa Christian Sch/Ballston Spa/Saratoga	02994823	518/885-0508	203
Space Shuttle Columbia Sch/Staten Island/Richmond	05274763	718/761-2155	194
Spackenkill High Sch/Poughkeepsie/Dutchess	00722105	845/463-7810	54
SPACKENKILL UNION FREE SD/ POUGHKEEPSIE/DUTCHESS	00722064	845/463-7800	54
Special Music Sch/New York/New York	04874114	212/501-3318	139
SPENCER VAN ETTEN CENTRAL SD/ SPENCER/TIOGA	00777186	607/589-7100	238
Spencer Van Etten Elem Sch/Van Etten/Tioga	00777215	607/589-7110	239
Spencer Van Etten High Sch/Spencer/Tioga	00777203	607/589-7140	239
Spencer Van Etten Middle Sch/Spencer/Tioga	00777198	607/589-7120	239
SPENCERPORT CENTRAL SCH DIST/ SPENCERPORT/MONROE	00733295	585/349-5000	112
Spencerport High Sch/Spencerport/Monroe	00733312	585/349-5200	112
Speyer Sch/New York/New York	12102713	212/581-4000	145
Split Rock Elem Sch/Camillus/Onondaga	00761228	315/487-4656	159
Spring Creek Cmty Sch/Brooklyn/Kings	11827946	718/688-7200	89
Spring Valley High Sch/Spring Valley/Rockland	00768109	845/577-6500	196
Springhurst Elem Sch/Dobbs Ferry/Westchester	00779964	914/693-1503	254
Springs Sch/East Hampton/Suffolk	00775968	631/324-0144	232
SPRINGS UNION FREE SCH DIST/ EAST HAMPTON/SUFFOLK	00775956	631/324-0144	232
Springville Elem Sch/Springville/Erie	00724165	716/592-3204	63
SPRINGVILLE GRIFFITH INST CSD/ SPRINGVILLE/ERIE	00724103	716/592-3200	63
Springville Griffith Inst HS/Springville/Erie	00724141	716/592-3202	63
Spruce Elem Sch/N Tonawanda/Niagara	00759706	716/807-3850	148
Spruce Street Sch/New York/New York	11447857	212/266-4800	138
Spry Middle Sch/Webster/Monroe	04283084	585/265-6500	113
SS Catherine & Therese Acad/Brooklyn/Kings	00754847	718/629-9330	95
SS Cyril & Methodius Sch/Deer Park/Suffolk	00740080	631/667-4044	234
SS Francis-Stephen Sch/Geneva/Ontario	00734524	315/789-1828	163
SS Joachim & Anne Sch/Queens Vlg/Queens	00753738	718/465-2230	186
SS John & Paul Sch/Larchmont/Westchester	00758659	914/834-6332	265
SS Mary-Alphonsus Reg Cath Sch/Glens Falls/Warren	00715360	518/792-3178	246
SS Peter & Paul Sch/Hamburg/Erie	00726797	716/649-7030	65
SS Peter & Paul Sch/Williamsville/Erie	00726802	716/632-6146	65
SS Philip & James Sch/Saint James/Suffolk	00740054	631/584-7896	234
SS Seward Institute/Florida/Orange	00764919	845/651-4038	164
St Adalbert Sch/Elmhurst/Queens	00753764	718/424-2376	186
St Agnes Academic High Sch/College Point/Queens	00753788	718/353-6276	186
St Agnes Cathedral Sch/Rockville CTR/Nassau	00740107	516/678-5550	132
St Agnes Elem Sch/Lake Placid/Essex	00769218	518/523-3771	69
St Agnes Sch/Avon/Livingston	00734055	585/226-8500	103
St Aidan Sch/Williston Pk/Nassau	00739938	516/746-6585	132
St Albans Christian Academy/Saint Albans/Queens	04974702	718/468-6060	188
St Aloysius Regional Sch/Springville/Erie	00726852	716/592-7002	65
St Ambrose Academy/Rochester/Monroe	00734067	585/288-0580	114
St Ambrose Sch/Latham/Albany	00715372	518/785-6453	12
St Amelia Sch/Tonawanda/Erie	00726876	716/836-2230	65
St Andrew Avellino Cath Acad/Flushing/Queens	00753831	718/359-7887	186
St Andrew's Country Day Sch/Kenmore/Erie	00726888	716/877-0422	65
St Angela Merici Sch/Bronx/Bronx	00756780	718/293-3365	26
St Ann Sch/Staten Island/Richmond	01873422	718/351-4343	195
St Ann's Academy/Hornell/Steuben	12314849	607/281-1010	215
St Ann's Sch/Brooklyn/Kings	01408974	718/522-1660	99
St Anne Institute/Albany/Albany	00715384	518/437-6500	13
St Anne Sch/Garden City/Nassau	04022115	516/352-1205	132
St Anselm Sch/Bronx/Bronx	00756845	718/993-9464	26
St Anthony High Sch/Huntingtn Sta/Suffolk	00740171	631/271-2020	234
St Anthony Sch/Yonkers/Westchester	00756895	914/476-8489	265
St Anthony St Paul Sch/Nanuet/Rockland	00756883	845/623-2311	198
St Anthony St Paul Sch/Vly Cottage/Rockland	00758271	845/268-6506	198
St Athanasius Sch/Bronx/Bronx	00756936	718/542-5161	26
St Athanasius Sch/Brooklyn/Kings	00753910	718/236-4791	95
St Augustine Sch/Ossining/Westchester	00756950	914/941-3849	265
St Barnabas Elem Sch/Bronx/Bronx	00756998	718/324-1088	26
St Barnabas High Sch/Bronx/Bronx	00757007	718/325-8800	26
St Bartholomew Sch/Elmhurst/Queens	00753934	718/446-7575	186
St Benedict Sch/Amherst/Erie	00726979	716/835-2518	65
St Benedict Sch/Bronx/Bronx	00757021	718/829-9557	26
St Bernadette Sch/Brooklyn/Kings	00753958	718/236-1560	95
St Bernard Sch/Brooklyn/Kings	00753960	718/241-6040	95
St Bernard's Grade Sch/Saranac Lake/Franklin	02181222	518/891-2830	71
St Bernard's Sch/New York/New York	11547586	212/289-2878	145
St Brendan Sch/Bronx/Bronx	00757057	718/653-2292	26
St Brigid Catholic Academy/Brooklyn/Kings	00753996	718/821-1477	95
St Brigid-Our Lady of Hope Sch/Westbury/Nassau	00740212	516/333-0580	132
St Camillus Catholic Academy/Rockaway Park/Queens	00754005	718/634-5260	186
St Catharine Academy/Bronx/Bronx	00757083	718/882-2882	26
St Catherines Ctr for Children/Albany/Albany	01872935	518/453-6710	13
St Charles Borromeo Sch/New York/New York	00757148	212/368-6666	143
St Charles Sch/Staten Island/Richmond	00757150	718/987-0200	195
St Christopher Parochial Sch/Staten Island/Richmond	00757162	718/351-0902	195
St Christopher Sch/Baldwin/Nassau	00740236	516/223-4404	132
St Christopher Sch/Tonawanda/Erie	00727040	716/693-5604	65
St Clare Catholic Academy/Rosedale/Queens	00754067	718/528-7174	186
St Clare of Assisi Sch/Bronx/Bronx	00757203	718/892-4080	26
St Clare Sch/Staten Island/Richmond	00757198	718/984-7091	195
St Clement's Regional Cath Sch/Saratoga Spgs/Saratoga	00715475	518/584-7350	203
St Coleman's Home/Watervliet/Albany	02068527	518/273-7559	13
St Columbanus Sch/Cortlandt MNR/Westchester	00757241	914/739-1200	265
St David's Sch/New York/New York	02162678	212/369-0058	145
St Demetrios Elem Sch/Astoria/Queens	04974300	718/728-1100	188
St Demetrios Mid High Sch/Astoria/Queens	02139085	718/728-1754	188
St Denis & St Columba Sch/Hopewell Jct/Dutchess	00757215	845/227-7777	55
St Dominic ES MS/Oyster Bay/Nassau	00740248	516/922-4233	132
St Dominic High Sch/Oyster Bay/Nassau	00740250	516/922-4888	132
St Dominic Sch/Blauvelt/Rockland	02181739	845/359-3400	199
St Edmund Preparatory High Sch/Brooklyn/Kings	00754081	718/743-6100	95
St Edmund Sch/Brooklyn/Kings	00754093	718/648-9229	95
St Edward the Confessor Sch/Syosset/Nassau	00739952	516/921-7767	132
St Elizabeth A Seton-Bellmore/Bellmore/Nassau	00739574	516/785-5709	132
St Elizabeth Catholic Academy/Ozone Park/Queens	00754108	718/641-6990	186
St Elizabeth Sch/New York/New York	00757289	212/568-7291	143
St Ephrem Sch/Brooklyn/Kings	00754110	718/833-1440	95
St Eugene Sch/Yonkers/Westchester	00757306	914/779-2956	265
St Frances Cabrini Cath Acad/Brooklyn/Kings	00754328	718/386-9277	95
St Frances De Chantal Sch/Bronx/Bronx	00757318	718/892-5359	26
St Francis Assisi Sch/Bronx/Bronx	00757356	718/994-4650	26
St Francis DeSales ECLC/Herkimer/Herkimer	00715487	315/866-4831	79
St Francis DeSales Sch/Rockaway Park/Queens	00754172	718/634-2775	186
St Francis DeSales School-Deaf/Brooklyn/Kings	01793690	718/636-4573	99

DISTRICT & SCHOOL TELEPHONE INDEX

Market Data Retrieval

School/City/County DISTRICT/CITY/COUNTY	PID	TELEPHONE NUMBER	PAGE
St Francis High Sch/Hamburg/Erie	00727090	716/627-1200	65
St Francis of Assisi Cath Acad/Brooklyn/Kings	00754184	718/778-3700	95
St Francis of Assisi Sch/Astoria/Queens	00754196	718/726-9405	186
St Francis Preparatory Sch/Fresh Meadows/Queens	00754213	718/423-8810	186
St Francis Xavier Sch/Bronx/Bronx	00757394	718/863-0531	26
St Gabriel Sch/Bronx/Bronx	00757411	718/548-0444	26
St George Academy/New York/New York	00757435	212/473-3323	143
St Gregory Barbarigo Sch/Garnerville/Rockland	00757461	845/947-1330	198
St Gregory the Great Sch/Bellerose/Queens	00754251	718/343-5053	186
St Gregory the Great Sch/Williamsville/Erie	00727155	716/688-5323	65
St Gregory's School for Boys/Loudonville/Albany	01792646	518/785-6621	13
St Helen Catholic Academy/Howard Beach/Queens	00754263	718/835-4155	186
St Helena Sch/Bronx/Bronx	00757485	718/892-3234	26
St Hilda & St Hugh Sch/New York/New York	00752136	212/932-1980	145
St Hope Leadership Academy CS/New York/New York	11128702	212/283-1204	140
St Ignatius Loyola Sch/New York/New York	00757497	212/861-3820	143
St Ignatius Sch/Bronx/Bronx	04974154	718/861-9084	27
St James Elem Sch/Gouverneur/St Lawrence	00769270	315/287-0130	212
St James Elem Sch/Johnson City/Broome	00763252	607/797-5444	30
St James Elem Sch/Saint James/Suffolk	00775683	631/382-4455	230
St James the Apostle Sch/Carmel/Putnam	00757514	845/225-9365	176
St Jean Baptiste High Sch/New York/New York	00757526	212/288-1645	143
St Joan of Arc Sch/Jackson HTS/Queens	00754287	718/639-9020	186
St John Bosco Sch/E Rochester/Monroe	12314112	585/348-9401	114
St John Chrysostom Sch/Bronx/Bronx	00757564	718/328-7226	26
St John Evangelist Luthern Sch/Brooklyn/Kings	00751895	718/963-3074	99
St John Lutheran Sch/N Tonawanda/Niagara	00725779	716/693-9677	149
St John Sch/Goshen/Orange	00757590	845/294-6434	168
St John the Baptist High Sch/West Islip/Suffolk	00740327	631/587-8000	234
St John the Baptist Sch/Yonkers/Westchester	00757605	914/965-2356	265
St John the Baptist Sch-Alden/Alden/Erie	00727260	716/937-9483	65
St John the Baptist Sch-Knmore/Kenmore/Erie	00727272	716/877-6401	65
St John the Evangelist Sch/Binghamton/Broome	00763276	607/723-0703	30
St John Vianney Sch/Orchard Park/Erie	00727296	716/674-9232	65
St John's Lutheran Sch/Staten Island/Richmond	00751883	718/761-1858	195
St John's Preparatory Sch/Astoria/Queens	00753221	718/721-7200	187
St Joseph by the Sea High Sch/Staten Island/Richmond	00757693	718/984-6500	195
St Joseph Catholic Academy/Long Is City/Queens	00754342	718/728-0724	187
St Joseph Collegiate Institute/Buffalo/Erie	00727387	716/874-4024	65
St Joseph High Sch/Brooklyn/Kings	00754316	718/624-3618	95
St Joseph Hill Academy ES/Staten Island/Richmond	00757708	718/981-1187	195
St Joseph Hill Academy HS/Staten Island/Richmond	00757710	718/447-1374	195
St Joseph Sch/Bronxville/Westchester	00757722	914/337-0261	265
St Joseph Sch/Garden City/Nassau	00740004	516/747-2730	132
St Joseph Sch/Penfield/Monroe	00734287	585/586-6968	114
St Joseph Sch-Batavia/Batavia/Genesee	00727349	585/343-6154	74
St Joseph School for the Deaf/Bronx/Bronx	02115003	718/828-9000	27
St Joseph School-Yorkville/New York/New York	00757796	212/289-3057	143
St Joseph the Worker Cath Acad/Brooklyn/Kings	00753116	718/768-7629	95
St Joseph University Sch/Buffalo/Erie	00727363	716/835-7395	66
St Joseph's Elem Sch/Malone/Franklin	01548029	518/483-7806	70
St Joseph's Parish Day Sch/Queens Vlg/Queens	00751900	718/464-8913	188
St Jude the Apostle Sch/Wynantskill/Rensselaer	00715619	518/283-0333	192
St Kateri Sch/Rochester/Monroe	00733685	585/467-8730	114
St Kateri Tekakwitha Sch/Niskayuna/Schenectady	00715499	518/382-8225	205
St Kevin Catholic Academy/Flushing/Queens	00754366	718/357-8110	187
St Lawrence Elem Sch/Brasher Falls/St Lawrence	00768991	315/389-5131	209
St Lawrence Middle Sch/Brasher Falls/St Lawrence	10029634	315/389-5131	209
St Lawrence Sch/Rochester/Monroe	00734304	585/225-3870	114
St Lawrence Senior High Sch/Brasher Falls/St Lawrence	00769000	315/389-5131	209
ST LAWRENCE-LEWIS BOCES/CANTON/ST LAWRENCE	00769012	315/386-4504	212
St Leo Catholic Academy/Corona/Queens	00754378	718/592-7050	187
St Louis Sch/Pittsford/Monroe	00734316	585/586-5200	114
St Lucy Sch/Bronx/Bronx	00757930	718/882-2203	26
St Luke Sch/Whitestone/Queens	00754392	718/746-3833	187
St Luke's Sch/New York/New York	00752148	212/924-5960	145
St Madeleine Sophie Sch/Schenectady/Schenectady	00715633	518/355-3080	205
St Margaret Mary Sch/Bronx/Bronx	00757966	718/731-5905	26
St Margaret of Cortona Sch/Bronx/Bronx	00757978	718/549-8580	26
St Margaret Sch/Middle Vlg/Queens	00754419	718/326-0922	187
St Margaret Sch/Pearl River/Rockland	00757980	845/735-2855	198
St Margaret's Sch/Mattydale/Onondaga	00763329	315/455-5791	160
St Mark Sch/Brooklyn/Kings	00754421	718/332-9304	95
St Mark Sch/Buffalo/Erie	00727454	716/836-1191	66
St Mark the Evangelist Sch/New York/New York	00757992	212/283-4848	143
St Mark's Day Sch/Brooklyn/Kings	02139102	718/756-6602	99
St Mark's Lutheran Sch/Yonkers/Westchester	00782894	914/237-4944	266
St Martin De Porres Sch/Poughkeepsie/Dutchess	00758001	845/452-4428	55
St Martin Deporres Mrnst Sch/Uniondale/Nassau	00740145	516/481-3303	132
St Martin of Tours Sch/Amityville/Suffolk	00740420	631/264-7166	234
St Mary Elem Sch/Manhasset/Nassau	00740468	516/627-0184	132
St Mary Gate of Heaven Sch/Ozone Park/Queens	00754445	718/846-0689	187
St Mary Our Mother Sch/Horseheads/Chemung	00734330	607/739-9157	41
St Mary Sch/Canandaigua/Ontario	00734342	585/394-4300	163
St Mary Sch/East Islip/Suffolk	00740456	631/581-3423	234
St Mary Sch/Fishkill/Dutchess	00758075	845/896-9561	55
St Mary Sch-Swormville/Swormville/Erie	00727545	716/689-8424	66
St Mary's Academy/Baldwinsville/Onondaga	00763367	315/635-3977	160
St Mary's Elem Sch-Lancaster/Lancaster/Erie	00727519	716/683-2112	66
St Mary's Grade Sch/Ticonderoga/Essex	00769359	518/585-7433	69
St Mary's High Sch/Lancaster/Erie	00727583	716/683-4824	66
St Mary's High Sch/Manhasset/Nassau	00740470	516/627-2711	132
St Mary's Institute/Amsterdam/Montgomery	00715724	518/842-4100	116
St Mary's Sch/Ballston Spa/Saratoga	00715762	518/885-7300	203
St Mary's Sch/Cortland/Cortland	00763381	607/756-5614	48
St Mary's Sch/Waterford/Saratoga	00715968	518/237-0652	203
St Mary's School for the Deaf/Buffalo/Erie	02181583	716/834-7200	66
St Matthias Sch/Ridgewood/Queens	00754500	718/381-8003	187
St Mel Sch/Flushing/Queens	00754512	718/539-8211	187
St Michael Sch/Penn Yan/Yates	00734421	315/536-6112	268
St Michaels Catholic Academy/Flushing/Queens	00753219	718/961-0246	187
St Nicholas of Tolentine Sch/Jamaica/Queens	00754574	718/380-1900	187
St Patrick Sch/Bay Shore/Suffolk	00740523	631/665-0569	234
St Patrick Sch/Brooklyn/Kings	00754639	718/833-0124	95
St Patrick Sch/Huntington/Suffolk	00740509	631/385-3322	234
St Patrick Sch/Oneida/Madison	00763422	315/363-3620	106
St Patrick Sch/Smithtown/Suffolk	00740494	631/724-0285	234
St Patrick School-Richmond/Staten Island/Richmond	00758233	718/979-8815	195
St Patrick's Sch/Yorktown Hts/Westchester	00758269	914/962-2211	265
St Paul Lutheran Pre-School/N Tonawanda/Niagara	00725808	716/692-3255	149
St Paul Lutheran Sch/Hilton/Monroe	00733594	585/392-4361	114
St Paul's Lutheran Sch/Batavia/Genesee	02852512	585/343-0488	74
St Peter Catholic Academy/Brooklyn/Kings	00754469	718/372-0025	95
St Peter Roman Catholic Sch/Lewiston/Niagara	00727624	716/754-4470	149
St Peter Sch/Yonkers/Westchester	00758324	914/963-2314	265
St Peter's High Sch for Boys/Staten Island/Richmond	00758336	718/447-1676	195
St Peter's Lutheran Sch/Sanborn/Niagara	00759861	716/731-4422	149
St Philip Neri Sch/Bronx/Bronx	00758386	718/365-8806	26
St Pius Tenth Sch/Rochester/Monroe	00734483	585/247-5650	114
St Pius V Sch/Melville/Suffolk	12180545	631/351-0116	235
St Pius X Sch/Loudonville/Albany	00715906	518/465-4539	13
St Raymond Academy for Girls/Bronx/Bronx	00758427	718/824-4220	26
St Raymond Elem Sch/Bronx/Bronx	00758441	718/597-3232	26
St Raymond High Sch for Boys/Bronx/Bronx	00758439	718/824-5050	26

New York School Directory
DISTRICT & SCHOOL TELEPHONE INDEX

School/City/County DISTRICT/CITY/COUNTY	PID	TELEPHONE NUMBER	PAGE
St Raymond Sch/East Rockaway/Nassau	00740042	516/593-9010	133
St Regis Falls Central Sch/St Regis FLS/Franklin	00728379	518/856-9421	70
ST REGIS FALLS CTL SCH DIST/ ST REGIS FLS/FRANKLIN	00728367	518/856-9421	70
St Regis Mohawk Sch/Hogansburg/Franklin	00728317	518/358-2763	70
St Rita Sch/Webster/Monroe	00734495	585/671-3132	114
St Rose of Lima Catholic Acad/Far Rockaway/Queens	00754732	718/474-7079	187
St Rose of Lima Sch/Massapequa/Nassau	00740585	516/541-1546	133
St Rose of Lima Sch/N Syracuse/Onondaga	00763501	315/458-6036	160
St Saviour Catholic Academy/Brooklyn/Kings	00754756	718/768-8000	95
St Saviour High Sch/Brooklyn/Kings	00754744	718/768-4406	95
St Sebastian Sch/Woodside/Queens	00754768	718/429-1982	187
St Simon Stock Sch/Bronx/Bronx	00758489	718/367-0453	26
St Stanislaus Kostka Cath Acad/Brooklyn/Kings	00754782	718/383-1970	95
St Stanislaus Kostka Sch/Maspeth/Queens	00754794	718/326-1585	187
St Stephen & St Edward Sch/Warwick/Orange	00756699	845/986-3533	168
St Stephen of Hungary Sch/New York/New York	00758506	212/288-1989	143
St Stephen Sch/Grand Island/Erie	00727662	716/773-4347	66
St Teresa St Rita Stream Acad/Staten Island/Richmond	00758544	718/448-9650	195
St Theresa Sch/Bronx/Bronx	00758556	718/792-3688	26
St Therese's Academy/Nicholville/St Lawrence	04975031	315/328-4027	212
St Thomas Apostle CA/Woodhaven/Queens	00754859	718/847-3904	187
St Thomas Choir Sch/New York/New York	00758879	212/247-3311	145
St Thomas the Apostle Sch/Delmar/Albany	00715932	518/439-5573	13
St Thomas the Apostle Sch/W Hempstead/Nassau	00740597	516/481-9310	133
St Vincent Ferrer High Sch/New York/New York	00758623	212/535-4680	143
St William the Abbot Sch/Seaford/Nassau	00740614	516/785-6784	133
Stagecoach Elem Sch/Selden/Suffolk	00774330	631/285-8730	225
Staley Elem Sch/Rome/Oneida	00760391	315/338-5300	152
Stamford Central Sch/Stamford/Delaware	00721307	607/652-7301	50
STAMFORD CENTRAL SCH DIST/ STAMFORD/DELAWARE	00721292	607/652-7301	50
Stanford J Gibson Primary Sch/Norwich/Chenango	00719768	607/334-1600	42
Stanley G Falk Sch/Buffalo/Erie	11227229	716/882-0090	66
Stanley G Falk Sch/Cheektowaga/Erie	01525247	716/894-3892	66
Starbuck Elem Sch/Watertown/Jefferson	10904149	315/785-3765	82
STARPOINT CENTRAL SCH DIST/ LOCKPORT/NIAGARA	00759768	716/210-2342	149
Starpoint High Sch/Lockport/Niagara	05276802	716/210-2300	149
Starpoint Middle Sch/Lockport/Niagara	00759782	716/210-2200	149
Stars Academy/Pine Bush/Orange	12108925	845/744-2031	166
State Road Elem Sch/Webster/Monroe	00733491	585/872-4200	113
State Street Intermediate Sch/Skaneateles/Onondaga	00762129	315/291-2261	158
Staten Island Academy/Staten Island/Richmond	00752784	718/987-8100	195
Staten Island Sch-Civic Ldrshp/Staten Island/Richmond	11447352	718/697-5250	194
Staten Island Technical HS/Staten Island/Richmond	03054220	718/667-3222	194
Steam at Dr King Elem Sch/Syracuse/Onondaga	00762430	315/435-4580	159
Steam Bridge School PS 481/Bronx/Bronx	12105923	718/239-5660	23
Steele Elem Sch/Baldwin/Nassau	00735009	516/434-6700	117
Stein Yeshiva of Lincoln Park/Yonkers/Westchester	03015145	914/965-7082	266
Steinmetz Career Leadrshp Acad/Schenectady/Schenectady	03394317	518/881-2030	205
Stella Niagara Educ Park Sch/Stela Niagara/Niagara	00727777	716/754-4314	149
STEM Institute of Manhattan/New York/New York	00742222	212/678-2898	139
Stephen & Harriet Myers MS/Albany/Albany	10002832	518/475-6425	9
Stephen Gaynor Sch/New York/New York	01461536	212/787-7070	145
Stepping Stone Pre & Grade Sch/Jamaica/Queens	03636177	718/465-2344	188
Sterling East-Pascack Lrng Ctr/Monsey/Rockland	12224658	845/357-0980	199
Sterling Sch/Brooklyn/Kings	11222047	718/625-3502	99
Stewart Elem Sch/Garden City/Nassau	00735815	516/478-1400	120
Stewart Manor Elem Sch/Stewart Manor/Nassau	00735425	516/326-5530	119
Stillwater Central High Sch/Stillwater/Saratoga	00770023	518/373-6100	202
STILLWATER CENTRAL SCH DIST/ STILLWATER/SARATOGA	00770009	518/373-6100	202
Stillwater Elem Sch/Stillwater/Saratoga	00770011	518/373-6100	202
Stillwater Middle Sch/Stillwater/Saratoga	04192980	518/373-6100	202
Stimson Middle Sch/Huntingtn Sta/Suffolk	00775774	631/812-3700	231
Stissing Mountain Jr Sr HS/Pine Plains/Dutchess	00721888	518/398-7181	53
STOCKBRIDGE VALLEY CENTRAL SD/ MUNNSVILLE/MADISON	00731338	315/495-4400	106
Stockbridge Valley Ctl Sch/Munnsville/Madison	00731340	315/495-4400	106
Stokes Elem Sch/Rome/Oneida	00760482	315/224-1220	152
Stonehedge Elem Sch/Camillus/Onondaga	00761230	315/487-4633	159
Stony Point Elem Sch/Stony Point/Rockland	00767648	845/942-3140	197
Storefront Acad Harlem CS/New York/New York	12367688	646/221-3450	7
Storefront Acad South Bronx CS/Bronx/Bronx	12105844	646/758-7201	7
Storm King Sch/Cornwall HDSN/Orange	00765121	845/534-7892	168
Stratford Avenue Elem Sch/Garden City/Nassau	00735827	516/478-1500	120
Stratford Road Elem Sch/Plainview/Nassau	00738049	516/434-3389	128
Strawtown Elem Sch/West Nyack/Rockland	00767454	845/624-3473	196
Strong Academy/Buffalo/Erie	12380355	716/474-8455	66
Stuart M Townsend Elem Sch/Lake Luzerne/Warren	00778635	518/696-2378	245
Studio Sch/New York/New York	02162680	212/678-2416	145
Stuyvesant High Sch/New York/New York	00741503	212/312-4800	138
Success Acad CS Bed Stuy 1/Brooklyn/Kings	11821813	718/635-3294	7
Success Acad CS Bed Stuy 2/Brooklyn/Kings	11824384	718/704-1439	7
Success Acad CS Bed Sty MS/Brooklyn/Kings	12170447	718/635-3296	7
Success Acad CS Bensonhurst/Brooklyn/Kings	12105416	347/514-7082	7
Success Acad CS Bergen Bch/Brooklyn/Kings	12045220	347/817-2017	7
Success Acad CS Bronx 1/Bronx/Bronx	11561221	347/286-7950	7
Success Acad CS Bronx 1 MS/Bronx/Bronx	12169151	347/286-7950	7
Success Acad CS Bronx 2/Bronx/Bronx	11561192	347/286-7965	7
Success Acad CS Bronx 2 MS/Bronx/Bronx	12169163	646/558-0038	7
Success Acad CS Bronx 3 Lwr/Bronx/Bronx	11933818	646/790-2145	7
Success Acad CS Bronx 4/Bronx/Bronx	12115538	646/558-0043	7
Success Acad CS Bushwick/Brooklyn/Kings	12169199	646/790-2173	7
Success Acad CS Cobble Hill/Brooklyn/Kings	11821629	718/704-1460	7
Success Acad CS Crown Heights/Brooklyn/Kings	11934288	646/790-2129	7
Success Acad CS Ditmas Park/Brooklyn/Kings	12179338	646/597-4641	7
Success Acad CS E Flatbush MS/Brooklyn/Kings	12320642	718/395-6346	7
Success Acad CS Far Rockaway/Far Rockaway/Queens	12169204	718/704-1421	7
Success Acad CS Flatbush ES/Brooklyn/Kings	12169084	646/790-2150	7
Success Acad CS Fort Greene/Brooklyn/Kings	11934161	646/790-2137	7
Success Acad CS Harlem 1/New York/New York	10026606	646/277-7170	7
Success Acad CS Harlem 2/New York/New York	11128714	646/442-6600	7
Success Acad CS Harlem 3/New York/New York	11128726	646/790-2177	7
Success Acad CS Harlem 4/New York/New York	11128697	646/442-6500	7
Success Acad CS Harlem 5/New York/New York	11561257	646/380-2580	7
Success Acad CS Harlem 6/New York/New York	12310465	646/569-5900	7
Success Acad CS Harlem Central/New York/New York	12170332	646/569-5900	7
Success Acad CS Harlem East/New York/New York	12099881	646/747-6700	8
Success Acad CS Harlem N Cen/New York/New York	12170435	646/790-2169	8
Success Acad CS Harlem NW/New York/New York	12170411	646/558-0093	8
Success Acad CS Harlem West/New York/New York	12170409	646/569-5920	8
Success Acad CS Hell's Kitchen/New York/New York	11932577	646/790-2153	8
Success Acad CS Hudson Yards/New York/New York	12234134	212/845-9683	8
Success Acad CS Lafayette MS/Brooklyn/Kings	12169187	646/790-2126	8
Success Acad CS Midtown West/New York/New York	12170368	646/558-0050	8
Success Acad CS Prospect Hgts/Brooklyn/Kings	11934331	646/790-2121	8
Success Acad CS Rosedale/Rosedale/Queens	12164797	347/514-7060	8
Success Acad CS S Jamaica/Jamaica/Queens	12168016	718/704-1441	8
Success Acad CS Union Square/New York/New York	11932589	646/790-2161	8

DISTRICT & SCHOOL TELEPHONE INDEX

Market Data Retrieval

School/City/County DISTRICT/CITY/COUNTY	PID	TELEPHONE NUMBER	PAGE
Success Acad CS Upper West/New York/New York	11824657	646/274-1580	8
Success Acad CS Washington Hts/New York/New York	12112718	646/558-0027	8
Success Acad CS Williamsburg/Brooklyn/Kings	11823471	718/704-1419	8
Success Acad CS-Lafayette MS/Brooklyn/Kings	12361074	646/790-2125	8
Success Acad CS-Myrtle MS/Brooklyn/Kings	12361086	646/569-5914	8
Success Acad CS-Queens 1 MS/Sprngfld GDNS/Queens	12361098	347/602-4335	8
Success Acad CS-Sprngfld Grdn/Sprngfld GDNS/Queens	12164785	347/602-4335	8
Success Acad HS Lib Arts-Bronx/Bronx/Bronx	12361103	646/558-0056	8
Success Acad HS Lib Arts-Mnhtn/New York/New York	12114053	646/558-0056	8
SUFFERN CENTRAL SCH DIST/ HILLBURN/ROCKLAND	00768123	845/357-7783	198
Suffern High Sch/Suffern/Rockland	00768197	845/357-3800	198
Suffern Middle Sch/Suffern/Rockland	00768185	845/357-7400	198
SULLIVAN BOCES/LIBERTY/SULLIVAN	00776998	845/295-4000	238
Sullivan Co BOCES Special Ed/Liberty/Sullivan	04026458	845/295-4111	236
Sullivan Co Career & Tech Ctr/Liberty/Sullivan	01548093	845/295-4152	236
SULLIVAN WEST CENTRAL SD/ JEFFERSONVLLE/SULLIVAN	00776780	845/482-4610	237
Sullivan West Elem Sch/Jeffersonvlle/Sullivan	00776792	845/482-4610	237
Sullivan West High Sch/Lk Huntington/Sullivan	05280839	845/932-8401	237
Summit Academy Charter Sch/Brooklyn/Kings	11447508	718/875-1403	85
Summit Center-Brighton/Getzville/Erie	02164547	716/629-3400	66
Summit Educational Resources/Amherst/Erie	11225037	716/810-7700	66
Summit Lane Elem Sch/Levittown/Nassau	00736871	516/434-7525	123
Summit Park Elem Sch/New City/Rockland	00768111	845/577-6290	196
Summit Sch/Auburn/Cayuga	11435074	315/253-2019	34
Summit Sch/Jamaica/Queens	01463352	718/264-2931	188
Summit School at Nyack/Nyack/Rockland	02164121	845/358-7772	199
Summitt School Annex/Flushing/Queens	11236282	718/969-3944	188
Sunquam Elem Sch/Melville/Suffolk	04873407	631/592-3750	222
Sunrise Drive Elem Sch/Sayville/Suffolk	00775425	631/244-6750	230
Sunset Park High Sch/Brooklyn/Kings	11447819	718/840-1900	85
Sunset Park Prep Sch/Brooklyn/Kings	04877295	718/840-1951	85
Susan E Wagner High Sch/Staten Island/Richmond	00741515	718/698-4200	194
Susan E Wiley Elem Sch/Copiague/Suffolk	00773049	631/842-4014	220
Susan Odell Taylor Sch/Troy/Rensselaer	05220487	518/274-4994	192
SUSQUEHANNA VALLEY CENTRAL SD/ CONKLIN/BROOME	00717033	607/775-0170	29
Susquehanna Valley Sr High Sch/Conklin/Broome	00717083	607/775-0304	29
SWEET HOME CENTRAL SCH DIST/ AMHERST/ERIE	00725171	716/250-1400	63
Sweet Home High Sch/Amherst/Erie	00725248	716/250-1200	63
Sweet Home Middle Sch/Amherst/Erie	00725236	716/250-1450	64
Sycamore Avenue Elem Sch/Bohemia/Suffolk	00772978	631/244-2261	220
Sylvan Ave Elem Sch/Bayport/Suffolk	00772112	631/472-7840	217
SYOSSET CENTRAL SCH DIST/ SYOSSET/NASSAU	00738556	516/364-5600	129
Syosset High Sch/Syosset/Nassau	00738659	516/364-5675	130
Syracuse Acad Sci & Citiznshp/Syracuse/Onondaga	12234433	315/671-0270	8
Syracuse Academy of Science CS/Syracuse/Onondaga	05308211	315/428-8997	8
SYRACUSE CITY SCH DIST/SYRACUSE/ ONONDAGA	00762193	315/435-4499	158
Syracuse Hebrew Day Sch/De Witt/Onondaga	00762741	315/446-1900	160
Syracuse Latin Sch/Syracuse/Onondaga	12039037	315/435-4606	159
Syracuse STEM at Blodgett MS/Syracuse/Onondaga	12368278	315/435-4386	159

T

School/City/County	PID	TELEPHONE	PAGE
T J Connor Elem Sch/Scottsville/Monroe	00733518	585/889-6236	113
T S T BOCES Voc Tech Center/Ithaca/Tompkins	00777734	607/257-1555	239
T S T Community Sch/Ithaca/Tompkins	04026367	607/273-9015	239
Tabernacle Christian Academy/Poughkeepsie/Dutchess	02159097	845/454-2792	55
Tackan Elem Sch/Nesconset/Suffolk	00775700	631/382-2670	230
Taconic Hills Central High Sch/Craryville/Columbia	01813238	518/325-2840	47
TACONIC HILLS CENTRAL SCH DIST/ CRARYVILLE/COLUMBIA	00720652	518/325-2800	47
Taconic Hills Elem Sch/Craryville/Columbia	00720717	518/325-2820	47
Taft Elem Sch/Washingtonvle/Orange	00765042	845/497-4000	167
Tag Young Scholars/New York/New York	04458069	212/860-6003	140
Talent Unlimited High Sch/New York/New York	04319425	212/737-1530	138
Talmud Torad Ohr Moshe/Brooklyn/Kings	12163884	718/234-6100	99
Talmud Torah Bais Yechiel Sch/Mount Kisco/Westchester	02856532	718/387-0422	266
Talmud Torah D'Chasidei Gur/Brooklyn/Kings	12468115	718/923-3113	99
Talmud Torah D'Khal Adas Yerei/Spring Valley/Rockland	03408932	845/425-5678	199
Talmud Torah Darkei Avos ES/Spring Valley/Rockland	12380642	845/612-1027	199
Talmud Torah Darkei Avos PK-1/Spring Valley/Rockland	12380630	845/371-2476	199
Talmud Torah Imrei Burech-Boys/Kiamesha Lake/Sullivan	12467276	845/794-9915	237
Talmud Torah Imrei Chaim Sch/Brooklyn/Kings	02828365	718/234-2000	99
Talmud Torah Ohel Yochanan/Brooklyn/Kings	11563530	718/431-2991	99
Talmud Torah Siach Yitzchok/Far Rockaway/Queens	02989933	718/327-6247	188
Talmud Torah Tiferes Bunim/Brooklyn/Kings	02189652	718/436-6868	99
Talmud Torah Toldos Yakov Ysf/Brooklyn/Kings	02163402	718/436-2550	99
Talmudical Inst of Upstate NY/Rochester/Monroe	12314796	585/473-2810	114
Tamarac Elem Sch/Holtsville/Suffolk	00775267	631/244-5680	229
Tamarac Elem Sch/Troy/Rensselaer	00766747	518/279-4600	190
Tamarac Secondary Sch/Troy/Rensselaer	00766759	518/279-4600	190
Tangier Smith Elem Sch/Mastic Beach/Suffolk	01417327	631/874-1342	233
Tanglewood Elem Sch/S Glens Falls/Saratoga	00769995	518/793-5631	202
Tapestry Charter Sch/Buffalo/Erie	04944240	716/332-0754	8
Tappan Zee High Sch/Orangeburg/Rockland	00767894	845/680-1600	198
TARRYTOWN UNION FREE SCH DIST/ SLEEPY HOLLOW/WESTCHESTER	00781955	914/631-9404	262
Teach/Brooklyn/Kings	12472104	718/927-5540	89
Teacher's Preparatory Sch/Brooklyn/Kings	05098595	718/498-2605	93
Teachers College Cmty Sch/New York/New York	11715070	212/316-8080	140
Tech Center at Yorktown/Yorktown Hts/Westchester	11440897	914/248-2452	252
Tech Valley High Sch/Albany/Albany	11010090	518/862-4960	9
Technical Career Center/Mexico/Oswego	00765925	315/963-4313	170
Tecumseh Elem Sch/Farmingville/Suffolk	02056952	631/775-1700	216
Tecumseh Elem Sch/Jamesville/Onondaga	03333686	315/445-8320	155
Teenage Parenting Program/Westbury/Nassau	04759162	516/608-6400	116
Temple Beth Shalom Sch/Mahopac/Putnam	11849011	845/628-6133	176
Temple Hill Academy/New Windsor/Orange	00764725	845/568-6450	166
Tep Equity Project Charter ECC/New York/New York	12468347	212/328-1775	142
Tep Equity Project Charter ES/New York/New York	12380410	646/254-6451	142
Tep Equity Project Charter MS/New York/New York	11447675	347/778-0601	142
Terry Taylor Elem Sch/Spencerport/Monroe	00733362	585/349-5600	112
Terryville Road Elem Sch/Port Jeff Sta/Suffolk	04808141	631/474-2834	218
Tesago Elem Sch/Clifton Park/Saratoga	00769921	518/881-0570	202
The Bridges Academy/West Islip/Suffolk	12314887	631/358-5035	235
The Browning Sch/New York/New York	00751297	212/838-6280	145
The Buckley Sch/New York/New York	05009738	212/452-2203	146
The Chapel Sch/Bronxville/Westchester	00782909	914/337-3202	266
The Chapin Sch/New York/New York	00751340	212/744-2335	146
The Cheder Sch/Brooklyn/Kings	12163969	718/252-6333	99
The Clinton Sch/New York/New York	04457429	212/524-4360	138
The College Academy/New York/New York	04877221	212/927-1841	142
The Epiphany Sch/New York/New York	00755396	212/473-4128	143
The Facing History Sch/New York/New York	10008707	212/757-2680	138
The Gateway Sch/New York/New York	01794307	212/777-5966	146
The Harley Sch/Rochester/Monroe	00733611	585/442-1770	114
The Harvey Sch/Katonah/Westchester	00783018	914/232-3161	266
The King's Academy/New York/New York	02162874	212/348-7380	146
The Kings Sch/Hadley/Saratoga	02992801	518/654-6230	203
The Lang Sch/New York/New York	12375556	212/977-7777	146
The Leffell Sch/Hartsdale/Westchester	04953459	914/948-8333	266
The Mott Hall Sch/New York/New York	02853712	212/281-5028	142

New York School Directory

DISTRICT & SCHOOL TELEPHONE INDEX

School/City/County DISTRICT/CITY/COUNTY	PID	TELEPHONE NUMBER	PAGE
The Nightingale-Bamford Sch/New York/New York	00751912	212/289-5020	146
The School House/E Northport/Suffolk	12380381	631/261-9000	235
The Spence Sch/New York/New York	05330111	212/289-5940	146
The Stony Brook Sch/Stony Brook/Suffolk	00776704	631/751-1800	235
The Titus Sch/New York/New York	12472386	646/756-4103	146
The Uft Charter Sch/Brooklyn/Kings	10015449	718/927-5540	8
The Ursuline Sch/New Rochelle/Westchester	00758685	914/636-3950	265
Theatre Arts Production Co Sch/Bronx/Bronx	04457259	718/584-0832	22
Theatre Street Sch/Richmond Hill/Queens	04974726	718/846-9182	188
Theodore R Durgee Jr High Sch/Baldwinsville/Onondaga	00761149	315/638-6086	154
Theodore Roosevelt Elem Sch/Binghamton/Broome	00716534	607/762-8280	27
Theodore Roosevelt Elem Sch/Oyster Bay/Nassau	00737904	516/624-6573	127
Theodore Roosevelt Primary Sch/Cheektowaga/Erie	00725121	716/891-6424	59
Theodore Roosevelt School 43/Rochester/Monroe	00733075	585/458-4200	111
Theresa Paplin Sch/Jamaica/Queens	03413468	718/658-8180	188
Theresa Primary Sch/Theresa/Jefferson	00730190	315/628-4432	80
Thevenet Montessori Sch/Highland Mls/Orange	02852940	845/928-6981	168
Thiells Elem Sch/Thiells/Rockland	00767650	845/942-3160	197
Thomas A Edison Elem Sch/Port Chester/Westchester	00781644	914/934-7981	261
Thomas A Edison Elem Sch/Tonawanda/Erie	00724593	716/874-8416	62
Thomas C Armstrong Middle Sch/Ontario CTR/Wayne	00779562	315/524-1080	251
Thomas C Giordano MS 45/Bronx/Bronx	00743927	718/584-1660	22
Thomas Cornell Academy/Yonkers/Westchester	11822752	914/376-8315	264
Thomas Edison Career & Tech HS/Jamaica/Queens	00741539	718/297-6580	183
Thomas Edison High Sch/Elmira Hgts/Chemung	00719419	607/733-5604	40
Thomas J Lahey Elem Sch/Greenlawn/Suffolk	00773673	631/754-5400	223
Thomas J Watson Elem Sch/Endicott/Broome	00716821	607/757-2152	29
Thomas Jefferson Campus YABC/Brooklyn/Kings	11928849	718/922-0762	89
Thomas Jefferson Elem Sch/Binghamton/Broome	00716546	607/763-8430	27
Thomas Jefferson Elem Sch/Yorktown Hts/Westchester	00780688	914/245-4802	257
Thomas O'Brien Acad-Sci & Tech/Albany/Albany	00714299	518/475-6875	9
Thomas R Proctor High Sch/Utica/Oneida	00760808	315/368-6400	152
Thornell Road Elem Sch/Pittsford/Monroe	00732514	585/267-1700	110
Thornton-Donovan Sch/New Rochelle/Westchester	00783032	914/632-8836	266
THOUSAND ISLANDS CENTRAL SD/CLAYTON/JEFFERSON	00730293	315/686-5521	81
Thousand Islands High Sch/Cape Vincent/Jefferson	00730322	315/686-5594	81
Thousand Islands Middle Sch/Cape Vincent/Jefferson	03280560	315/686-5199	81
Three Village Academy/Stony Brook/Suffolk	12035873	631/730-5051	232
THREE VILLAGE CENTRAL SCH DIST/STONY BROOK/SUFFOLK	00775970	631/730-4000	232
Thurgood Marshall Academy/New York/New York	04368177	212/283-8055	140
Thurgood Marshall Lower Sch/New York/New York	10008915	212/368-8731	140
TICONDEROGA CENTRAL SCH DIST/TICONDEROGA/ESSEX	00728020	518/585-7400	68
Ticonderoga Elem Sch/Ticonderoga/Essex	00728032	518/585-7400	68
Ticonderoga Jr Sr High Sch/Ticonderoga/Essex	00728056	518/585-7400	68
Tiegerman Middle Sch-Glen Cove/Glen Cove/Nassau	12380393	516/801-6915	134
Tiegerman Sch/Glen Cove/Nassau	02977306	516/609-2000	134
Tiferes Miriam Sch for Girls/Brooklyn/Kings	11229588	718/837-3100	99
Tilton Sch/Utica/Oneida	01794539	315/235-7670	154
Timber Point Elem Sch/East Islip/Suffolk	00773269	631/224-2004	221
Tioga Central High Sch/Tioga Center/Tioga	00777241	607/687-8001	239
TIOGA CENTRAL SCH DIST/TIOGA CENTER/TIOGA	00777227	607/687-8000	239
Tioga Elem Sch/Tioga Center/Tioga	00777253	607/687-8002	239
Tioga Hills Elem Sch/Apalachin/Broome	00717150	607/757-2366	30
Tioga Learning Center/Apalachin/Tioga	10001565	607/748-8261	238
Tioga Middle Sch/Tioga Center/Tioga	00777265	607/687-8004	239
Tioughnioga Riverside Academy/Whitney Point/Broome	00717239	607/692-8232	30
Titusville Intermediate Sch/Poughkeepsie/Dutchess	00721498	845/486-4470	51
Todd Elem Sch/Briarcliff/Westchester	00779718	914/941-8300	253
Tomer Dvora Girls Sch/Brooklyn/Kings	00752538	718/228-4150	99
Tomer Dvora High Sch/Brooklyn/Kings	02189690		99
Tompkins Square Middle Sch/New York/New York	04954532	212/995-1430	135
TOMPKINS-SENECA-TIOGA BOCES/ITHACA/TOMPKINS	00777722	607/257-1551	241
TONAWANDA CITY SCH DIST/TONAWANDA/ERIE	00725262	716/694-7690	64
Tonawanda Middle-High Sch/Tonawanda/Erie	04012586	716/694-7670	64
Tony Clement Ctr for Education/Albany/Albany	01416816	518/475-6525	9
Tooker Ave Elem Sch/West Babylon/Suffolk	00776168	631/376-7600	233
Torah Acad-Lawrence Cedarhurst/Cedarhurst/Nassau	11225910	516/295-5700	134
Torah Academy for Girls/Far Rockaway/Queens	00752069	718/471-8444	188
Torah United Talmudical Boys/Spring Valley/Rockland	02079746	845/425-0392	199
Torah V"Yirah/Brooklyn/Kings	03015298	718/963-9570	99
Tottenville High Sch/Staten Island/Richmond	00741553	718/668-8800	194
Tottenville YABC/Staten Island/Richmond	11928904	718/668-8800	194
Town of Webb Sch/Old Forge/Herkimer	00729878	315/369-3222	78
TOWN OF WEBB UNION FREE SD/OLD FORGE/HERKIMER	00729866	315/369-3222	78
Town Sch/New York/New York	00752289	212/288-4383	146
Townline Sch/Penn Yan/Yates	04975483	315/536-0051	268
Townsend Elem Sch/Walton/Delaware	00721321	607/865-5220	51
Townsend Harris High Sch/Flushing/Queens	02224862	718/575-5580	179
Transfiguration Sch/New York/New York	00758702	212/962-5265	143
Transfiguration Sch/Tarrytown/Westchester	00758697	914/631-3737	265
Transit Middle Sch/East Amherst/Erie	04030174	716/626-8701	65
Transit Tech Career High Sch/Brooklyn/Kings	00740896	718/647-5204	89
Traphagen Elem Sch/Mount Vernon/Westchester	00781008	914/665-5060	258
Traver Road Primary Sch/Pleasant Vly/Dutchess	00721503	845/635-4300	51
Tremont Elem Sch/Medford/Suffolk	00774926	631/687-8700	227
Trevor Day School-East/New York/New York	00758922	212/426-3300	146
Trevor Day School-West/New York/New York	04759760	212/426-3360	146
Trey Whitfield Sch/Brooklyn/Kings	02984309	718/342-7722	99
TRI-VALLEY CENTRAL SCH DIST/GRAHAMSVILLE/SULLIVAN	00776962	845/985-2296	237
Tri-Valley Elem Sch/Grahamsville/Sullivan	00776974	845/985-2296	237
Tri-Valley High Sch/Grahamsville/Sullivan	00776986	845/985-2296	237
Trinity Catholic Sch/Massena/St Lawrence	00769206	315/769-5911	212
Trinity Catholic Sch/Oswego/Oswego	00763446	315/343-6700	172
Trinity Elem Sch/New Rochelle/Westchester	00781216	914/576-4440	259
Trinity Lutheran Sch/Hicksville/Nassau	00739366	516/931-2211	134
Trinity Lutheran Sch/West Seneca/Erie	00725810	716/674-5353	66
Trinity Montessori Sch/Rochester/Monroe	02113433	585/586-1044	114
Trinity Regional Sch/E Northport/Suffolk	00740169	631/261-5130	234
Trinity Sch/New York/New York	00752318	212/873-1650	146
Trinity-Pawling Sch/Pawling/Dutchess	00722351	845/855-3100	55
TROY CITY SCH DSITRICT/TROY/RENSSELAER	00767090	518/328-5052	191
Troy High Sch/Troy/Rensselaer	00767117	518/328-5401	191
Troy Middle Sch/Troy/Rensselaer	01529669	518/328-5301	191
Troy Prep Charter Sch/Troy/Rensselaer	11722633	518/445-3100	8
Truman Elem Sch/Lackawanna/Erie	00724701	716/821-5610	62
TRUMANSBURG CENTRAL SD/TRUMANSBURG/TOMPKINS	00777681	607/387-7551	241
Trumansburg Elem Sch/Trumansburg/Tompkins	00777693	607/387-7551	241
Truthville Christian Academy/N Granville/Washington	02164327	518/642-2517	249
Truxton Academy Charter Sch/Truxton/Cortland	12377578	607/842-6252	8
Tuckahoe Common Sch/Southampton/Suffolk	00776089	631/283-3550	232
TUCKAHOE COMMON SCH DIST/SOUTHAMPTON/SUFFOLK	00776077	631/283-3550	232
Tuckahoe High Sch/Eastchester/Westchester	00782038	914/337-5376	262
Tuckahoe Middle Sch/Eastchester/Westchester	04745733	914/337-5376	262
TUCKAHOE UNION FREE SD/EASTCHESTER/WESTCHESTER	00782026	914/337-6600	262

DISTRICT & SCHOOL TELEPHONE INDEX

Market Data Retrieval

School/City/County DISTRICT/CITY/COUNTY	PID	TELEPHONE NUMBER	PAGE
TULLY CENTRAL SCH DIST/TULLY/ ONONDAGA	00762650	315/696-6204	159
Tully Elem Sch/Tully/Onondaga	00762662	315/696-6200	159
Tully Jr Sr High Sch/Tully/Onondaga	00762674	315/696-6200	159
TUPPER LAKE CTL SCH DIST/ TUPPER LAKE/FRANKLIN	00728393	518/359-3371	70
Tupper Lake Middle High Sch/Tupper Lake/Franklin	00728410	518/359-3322	70
Turnpike Elem Sch/Troy/Rensselaer	01417250	518/233-6822	191
Turtle Hook Middle Sch/Uniondale/Nassau	00738764	516/918-1301	130
Tuscarora Elem Sch/Addison/Steuben	00771223	607/359-2262	213
Tuscarora Indian Sch/Sanborn/Niagara	00759586	716/215-3670	148
Tuttle Avenue Sch/Eastport/Suffolk	12034623	631/801-3058	221
Tuxedo Park Sch/Tuxedo Park/Orange	00765107	845/351-4737	168
TUXEDO UNION FREE SCH DIST/ TUXEDO PARK/ORANGE	00764921	845/351-4786	166
Twelve Corners Middle Sch/Rochester/Monroe	00731390	585/242-5100	106
Twin Pines Elem Sch/Brentwood/Suffolk	00772368	631/434-2457	218
Twin Tiers Christian Academy/Breesport/Chemung	01559810	607/739-3619	41
Twin Towers Middle Sch/Middletown/Orange	00764347	845/326-1650	165
Tyburn Academy/Auburn/Cayuga	04155580	315/252-2937	36

U

School/City/County	PID	TELEPHONE NUMBER	PAGE
UCP Happiness House Sch/Geneva/Ontario	01794644	315/789-6850	163
UCP of Queens Children's Ctr/Jamaica/Queens	01795129	718/374-0002	189
Udall Road Middle Sch/West Islip/Suffolk	00776302	631/930-1650	233
ULSTER BOCES/NEW PALTZ/ULSTER	00778427	845/255-1400	244
Ulster BOCES Phoenix Acad/Ulster Park/Ulster	04026355	845/339-8722	241
Ulster BOCES Special Educ Ctr/Port Ewen/Ulster	12263070	845/339-8707	241
Ulster Career & Tech Center/Port Ewen/Ulster	02185228	845/331-6680	241
Ulysses Byas Elem Sch/Roosevelt/Nassau	00738386	516/345-7500	129
UNADILLA VALLEY CTL SCH DIST/ NEW BERLIN/CHENANGO	00719691	607/847-7500	43
Unadilla Valley Elem Sch/New Berlin/Chenango	00719706	607/847-7500	43
Unadilla Valley Secondary Sch/New Berlin/Chenango	00719718	607/847-7500	43
Unatego Elem Sch/Unadilla/Otsego	00766278	607/369-6200	174
Unatego High Sch/Otego/Otsego	00766280	607/988-5000	174
Unatego Middle Sch/Otego/Otsego	12368981	607/988-5000	174
UNATEGO UNADILLA CENTRAL SD/ OTEGO/OTSEGO	00766254	607/988-5000	174
Uncommon Charter High Sch/Brooklyn/Kings	12110198	718/638-1868	8
Uncommon Collegiate Charter HS/Brooklyn/Kings	12110186	347/390-0300	8
Uncommon Prep Charter HS/Brooklyn/Kings	12110203	718/307-5077	8
Union East Elem Sch/Cheektowaga/Erie	00723575	716/686-3620	58
Union Pleasant Elem Sch/Hamburg/Erie	00724232	716/646-3280	61
Union Springs Academy/Union Springs/Cayuga	00718245	315/889-7314	36
Union Springs Central High Sch/Union Springs/Cayuga	00718192	315/889-4110	35
UNION SPRINGS CTL SCH DIST/ UNION SPRINGS/CAYUGA	00718154	315/889-4101	35
Union Springs Middle Sch/Union Springs/Cayuga	04035734	315/889-4112	35
Union Sq Acad-Hlth Sciences/New York/New York	11821679	212/253-3110	138
Union Vale Middle Sch/Lagrangeville/Dutchess	05362205	845/223-8600	51
UNION-ENDICOTT CTL SCH DIST/ ENDICOTT/BROOME	00716728	607/757-2811	29
Union-Endicott High Sch/Endicott/Broome	00716833	607/757-2181	29
Uniondale High Sch/Uniondale/Nassau	00738776	516/560-8800	130
Uniondale Pre-Kindergarten/Baldwin/Nassau	12234421	516/405-8300	130
UNIONDALE UNION FREE SCH DIST/ UNIONDALE/NASSAU	00738697	516/560-8800	130
United Cerebral Palsy Sch/Utica/Oneida	01794589	315/798-4006	154
United Nations Int'l Sch/Jamaica/Queens	01873563	718/658-6166	189
United Nations Int'l Sch/New York/New York	00752382	212/684-7400	146
United Talmudical Acad Boys HS/Monsey/Rockland	12467783	845/425-0392	199
United Talmudical Acad-Madison/Spring Valley/Rockland	12467769	845/425-0392	199
United Talmudical Acad-Viola/Spring Valley/Rockland	12467771	845/425-0392	199
United Talmudical Bais Rachel/Monroe/Orange	02164016	845/783-5820	168
Unity Center for Urban Tech/New York/New York	04020181	212/576-0530	138
Unity Drive Pre-K Kdgn Center/Centereach/Suffolk	02854390	631/285-8760	225
Unity Prep CS Brooklyn HS/Brooklyn/Kings	12366488	718/682-3725	8
Unity Preparatory CS- Brooklyn/Brooklyn/Kings	11934173	718/455-5046	8
Unity Sunshine Sch/Troy/Rensselaer	02980078	518/271-6777	192
Universal Sch/Buffalo/Erie	11434939	716/597-0102	66
University Heights Sec Sch/Bronx/Bronx	03008855	718/292-0578	17
University Neighborhood HS/New York/New York	04877269	212/962-4341	135
University Neighborhood MS/New York/New York	05348924	212/267-5701	135
University Prep Charter HS/Bronx/Bronx	11128659	718/585-0560	8
University Prep Charter MS/Bronx/Bronx	12367690	917/985-8300	8
University Prep CS Young Men/Rochester/Monroe	11722607	585/672-1280	8
Unqua Elem Sch/Massapequa/Nassau	00737332	516/308-5600	125
Upper Nyack Elem Sch/Nyack/Rockland	00767739	845/353-7260	197
Upper Room Christian Sch/Dix Hills/Suffolk	02828169	631/242-5359	235
Upton Lake Christian Sch/Clinton Cors/Dutchess	02187264	845/266-3497	55
Urban Academy Lab High Sch/New York/New York	04020167	212/570-5284	138
Urban Action Academy/Brooklyn/Kings	11103465	718/290-8720	88
Urban Assem Collab Healthcare/Brooklyn/Kings	12106056	718/277-1572	89
Urban Assem MA-Sci Young Women/Brooklyn/Kings	10027193	718/260-2300	83
Urban Assem Sch Performing Art/New York/New York	10027088	212/543-4460	140
Urban Assem Sch-Green Careers/New York/New York	11447730	212/787-1189	139
Urban Assem-Global Commerce/New York/New York	11924491	212/831-5201	140
Urban Assembly Academy Gov/Law/New York/New York	10008733	212/505-0745	138
Urban Assembly Bronx Letters/Bronx/Bronx	05281273	718/401-4891	17
Urban Assembly CS Computer Sci/Bronx/Bronx	12310611	646/421-4523	8
Urban Assembly Emergency Mgmt/New York/New York	11924506	212/225-0998	138
Urban Assembly Future Leaders/New York/New York	04923076	212/543-4960	140
Urban Assembly Gateway Tech/New York/New York	11715109	212/246-1041	138
Urban Assembly Law & Justice/Brooklyn/Kings	05349576	718/858-1160	83
Urban Assembly Maker Academy/New York/New York	12037039	212/225-0890	138
Urban Assembly Math & Science/Bronx/Bronx	05349124	718/466-7800	20
Urban Assembly NY Harbor Sch/New York/New York	05281015	212/458-0800	138
Urban Assembly Sch Design/Con/New York/New York	05348869	212/586-0981	138
Urban Assembly Sch Music & Art/Brooklyn/Kings	10008836	718/858-0249	83
Urban Assembly Sch of Business/New York/New York	10008745	212/668-0169	138
Urban Assembly School of Media/New York/New York	05349045	212/501-1110	139
Urban Assembly Unison Sch/Brooklyn/Kings	11924312	718/399-1061	83
Urban Assmbly Ldrshp & Emprmnt/Brooklyn/Kings	10913736	718/438-3893	90
Urban Choice Charter Sch/Rochester/Monroe	10009402	585/288-5702	8
Urban Dove Team Charter Sch/Brooklyn/Kings	11828627	718/783-8232	8
Urban Dove Team CS II/Bronx/Bronx	12310623	718/682-3975	8
Urban Institute of Math/Bronx/Bronx	10910409	718/823-6042	18
Urban Scholars Cmty Sch/Bronx/Bronx	11447807	718/842-8133	25
Uriah Hill Elem Sch/Peekskill/Westchester	11934381	914/739-0682	260
Utica Academy of Science CS/Utica/Oneida	11932436	315/266-1072	8
UTICA CITY SCH DIST/UTICA/ONEIDA	00760614	315/792-2210	152

V

School/City/County	PID	TELEPHONE NUMBER	PAGE
V E Wightman Primary Sch/Bath/Steuben	00771649	607/776-3301	213
V'Yoel Moshe D'Satmar-Uta/Spring Valley/Rockland	03408906	845/425-0392	199
Vail Farm Elem Sch/Lagrangeville/Dutchess	05362217	845/223-8030	51

New York School Directory

DISTRICT & SCHOOL TELEPHONE INDEX

School/City/County DISTRICT/CITY/COUNTY	PID	TELEPHONE NUMBER	PAGE
Vails Gate High Tech Magnet ES/New Windsor/Orange	00764749	845/563-7900	166
Valence College Prep CS/East Elmhurst/Queens	12367705	646/854-8414	8
Valhalla Middle High Sch/Valhalla/Westchester	00782088	914/683-5000	263
VALHALLA UNION FREE SCH DIST/VALHALLA/WESTCHESTER	00782052	914/683-5040	262
Validus Prep Academy/Bronx/Bronx	10008422	718/466-4000	20
Valley Central High Sch/Montgomery/Orange	00764555	845/457-2400	167
Valley Central Middle Sch/Montgomery/Orange	00764543	845/457-2400	167
VALLEY CENTRAL SCH DIST/MONTGOMERY/ORANGE	00764490	845/457-2400	167
Valley Cottage Elem Sch/Vly Cottage/Rockland	00767741	845/353-7280	197
Valley Early Childhood Center/Cameron Mills/Steuben	00771235	607/695-2636	213
Valley Heights Christian Acad/Norwich/Chenango	02187238	607/336-8422	43
Valley Stream Central High Sch/Valley Stream/Nassau	00738805	516/561-4400	130
Valley Stream Christian Acad/Valley Stream/Nassau	04974817	516/561-6122	134
VALLEY STREAM CTL HIGH SD/VALLEY STREAM/NASSAU	00738790	516/872-5600	130
Valley Stream Memorial Jr HS/Valley Stream/Nassau	00738817	516/872-7700	130
Valley Stream North JSHS/Franklin Sq/Nassau	00738829	516/564-5500	130
Valley Stream South JSHS/Valley Stream/Nassau	00738831	516/791-0300	130
VALLEY STREAM UNION FREE SD 13/VALLEY STREAM/NASSAU	00738843	516/568-6100	130
VALLEY STREAM UNION FREE SD 24/VALLEY STREAM/NASSAU	00738893	516/434-2825	131
VALLEY STREAM UNION FREE SD 30/VALLEY STREAM/NASSAU	00738946	516/434-3600	131
Valleyview Elem Sch/Oneonta/Otsego	00766187	607/433-8252	174
Van Antwerp Middle Sch/Schenectady/Schenectady	04012615	518/370-1243	204
Van Buren Elem Sch/Baldwinsville/Onondaga	00761151	315/638-6121	154
Van Corlaer Elem Sch/Schenectady/Schenectady	00770592	518/370-8270	205
Van Cortlandtville Elem Sch/Mohegan Lake/Westchester	00780690	914/528-1354	257
Van Duyn Elem Sch/Syracuse/Onondaga	00762636	315/435-4660	159
Van Rensselaer Elem Sch/Rensselaer/Rensselaer	00767040	518/436-4618	191
Van Schaick Grade Sch/Cohoes/Albany	00714524	518/237-2828	10
Van Wyck Junior High Sch/Wappingers Fl/Dutchess	00722246	845/227-1700	54
Vanderbilt Elem Sch/Dix Hills/Suffolk	00773570	631/592-3800	222
Vanderheyden Hall Sch/Wynantskill/Rensselaer	02164042	518/283-6500	192
Vanguard Collegiate High Sch/Rochester/Monroe	11559981	585/324-3760	111
Vanguard High Sch/New York/New York	04037421	212/517-5175	138
Vassar Road Elem Sch/Poughkeepsie/Dutchess	00722258	845/463-7860	54
Veeder Elem Sch/Albany/Albany	00714938	518/869-4661	12
Veritas Academy/Flushing/Queens	11924128	718/888-7520	179
Verne W Critz Primary Sch/E Patchogue/Suffolk	00772198	631/730-1675	231
Vernon Verona Sherrill Mid Sch/Verona/Oneida	03245390	315/829-2520	153
Vernon Verona Sherrill Sr HS/Verona/Oneida	00760573	315/829-2520	153
VERNON-VERONA-SHERRILL CSD/VERONA/ONEIDA	00760547	315/829-2520	152
Veronica E Connor Middle Sch/Grand Island/Erie	00724062	716/773-8830	61
Vertus Charter Sch/Rochester/Monroe	12028404	585/747-8911	8
VESTAL CTL SCH DIST/VESTAL/BROOME	00717095	607/757-2241	29
Vestal Hills Elem Sch/Vestal/Broome	00717162	607/757-2357	30
Vestal Middle Sch/Vestal/Broome	00717112	607/757-2333	30
Vestal Senior High Sch/Vestal/Broome	00717186	607/757-2281	30
VICTOR CENTRAL SCH DIST/VICTOR/ONTARIO	00763977	585/924-3252	162
Victor High Sch/Victor/Ontario	00764012	585/924-3252	163
Victor Intermediate Sch/Victor/Ontario	00763989	585/924-3252	163
Victor Junior High Sch/Victor/Ontario	00763991	585/924-3252	163
Victor Primary Sch/Victor/Ontario	00764000	585/924-3252	163

School/City/County DISTRICT/CITY/COUNTY	PID	TELEPHONE NUMBER	PAGE
Victory Christian Academy/E Patchogue/Suffolk	04974855	631/654-9284	235
Victory Christian Academy/Fort Plain/Montgomery	04975184	518/568-7606	116
Victory Collegiate High Sch/Brooklyn/Kings	10913695	718/968-1530	88
Vida Bogart Sch All Chldrn/Bronx/Bronx	10026553	718/328-3913	25
Villa Maria Academy/Bronx/Bronx	00758714	718/824-3260	26
Village Academy/Far Rockaway/Queens	11447390	718/471-6042	181
Village Community Sch/New York/New York	01794474	212/691-5146	146
Village Elem Sch/Hilton/Monroe	00732071	585/392-1000	109
Village Elem Sch/Syosset/Nassau	00738673	516/364-5817	130
Village Sch/Great Neck/Nassau	02070685	516/441-4900	121
Vincent Smith Sch/Prt Washingtn/Nassau	00739483	516/365-4900	134
Vincent Ziccolella Elem MS/Hastings HDSN/Westchester	04036465	914/478-8004	255
Viola Elem Sch/Suffern/Rockland	00768202	845/357-8315	198
Violet Avenue Elem Sch/Poughkeepsie/Dutchess	00721759	845/486-4499	52
Virgil I Grissom School 7/Rochester/Monroe	00732746	585/254-3110	111
Virginia Road Elem Sch/White Plains/Westchester	00782090	914/683-5035	263
Virtual Academy of Rochester/Rochester/Monroe	12367884	585/262-8109	112
Visitation Academy/Brooklyn/Kings	00754940	718/680-9452	95
Vive School Pathways-Success/Yonkers/Westchester	02224692	914/376-8600	264
Viznitzer Chadr Tifers Yisroel/Brooklyn/Kings	12164022	718/633-5543	99
Voice Charter Sch/Long Is City/Queens	11128738	718/786-6213	185
Vollmer Elem Sch/Henrietta/Monroe	12235592	585/359-5550	112
Volney Elem Sch/Fulton/Oswego	00765585	315/593-5570	171
VOORHEESVILLE CENTRAL SCH DIST/VOORHEESVILLE/ALBANY	00714952	518/765-3313	12
Voorheesville Elem Sch/Voorheesville/Albany	00714976	518/765-2382	12
Voorheesville Middle Sch/Voorheesville/Albany	11453260	518/765-3314	12
Voyages Prep-South Queens/Jamaica/Queens	11924099	718/276-1946	181
Voyages Preparatory Sch/Elmhurst/Queens	11103037	718/271-7851	178

W

School/City/County DISTRICT/CITY/COUNTY	PID	TELEPHONE NUMBER	PAGE
W A Olmsted Elem Sch/Harpursville/Broome	00716869	607/693-8115	28
W A Wettel Elem Sch/Vernon/Oneida	00760585	315/829-7300	153
W C Mepham High Sch/Bellmore/Nassau	00737409	516/992-1500	117
W H Seward Elem Sch/Auburn/Cayuga	00717887	315/255-8600	34
W L Morse Elem Sch/Sleepy Hollow/Westchester	00782002	914/631-4144	262
W O Schaefer Elem Sch/Tappan/Rockland	00767909	845/680-1301	198
W T Clarke Middle Sch/Westbury/Nassau	04037574	516/876-7401	118
W T Clarke Senior High Sch/Westbury/Nassau	00735267	516/876-7450	118
Wading River Elem Sch/Wading River/Suffolk	00775499	631/821-8254	230
Wadleigh Performing Arts HS/New York/New York	04037304	212/749-5800	139
Wainscott Common Sch/Wainscott/Suffolk	00776106	631/537-1080	232
WAINSCOTT COMMON SCH DIST/WAINSCOTT/SUFFOLK	00776091	631/537-1080	232
Walberta Park Primary Sch/Syracuse/Onondaga	00762715	315/426-3200	160
Walden Elem Sch/Walden/Orange	00026764567	845/457-2400	167
Walden Learning Center/Yorktown Hts/Westchester	11434977	914/248-2270	252
Waldorf Sch-Saratota Springs/Saratoga Spgs/Saratoga	04929018	518/584-7643	203
Waldorf School of Garden City/Garden City/Nassau	00739407	516/742-3435	134
Wales Primary Sch/East Aurora/Erie	00724359	716/652-3000	62
Walkabout Bronx High Sch/Bronx/Bronx	12472130	718/292-8225	17
Wallace D Ormsby Center/East Aurora/Erie	00725676	716/652-8250	56
WALLKILL CENTRAL SCH DIST/WALLKILL/ULSTER	00778362	845/895-7100	243
Wallkill Senior High Sch/Wallkill/Ulster	00778415	845/895-7150	244
Walnut Street Elem Sch/Uniondale/Nassau	00738788	516/918-2200	130
Walt Disney Elem Sch/Rochester/Monroe	00731833	585/247-3151	108
Walt Whitman Elem Sch/Woodbury/Nassau	00738685	516/364-5823	130
Walt Whitman High Sch/Huntingtn Sta/Suffolk	00775827	631/812-3800	231
Walter B Howard Elem Sch/New Lebanon/Columbia	00720638	518/794-8554	46
Walter G O'Connell Copiague HS/Copiague/Suffolk	00772992	631/842-4010	220
Walter Panas High Sch/Cortlandt MNR/Westchester	00780705	914/739-2823	257

School Year 2020-2021 800-333-8802 NY-V57

DISTRICT & SCHOOL TELEPHONE INDEX

Market Data Retrieval

School/City/County DISTRICT/CITY/COUNTY	PID	TELEPHONE NUMBER	PAGE
Walton Avenue Sch/Bronx/Bronx	11924441	718/293-5970	20
Walton Campus YABC/Bronx/Bronx	11928746	718/329-7380	22
WALTON CENTRAL SCH DIST/ WALTON/DELAWARE	00721319	607/865-4116	50
Wampus Sch/Armonk/Westchester	00779809	914/273-4190	253
Wantagh Elem Sch/Wantagh/Nassau	00739055	516/679-6480	131
Wantagh High Sch/Wantagh/Nassau	00739043	516/679-6402	131
Wantagh Middle Sch/Wantagh/Nassau	00739031	516/679-6350	131
WANTAGH UNION FREE SCH DIST 23/ WANTAGH/NASSAU	00738996	516/781-8000	131
WAPPINGERS CENTRAL SCH DIST/ HOPEWELL JCT/DUTCHESS	00722129	845/298-5000	54
Wappingers Junior High Sch/Wappingers Fl/Dutchess	00722260	845/298-5200	54
Ward Melville Sr High Sch/East Setauket/Suffolk	00776053	631/730-4900	232
Warren Street Academy/Hudson/Columbia	12105715	518/781-3500	45
Warren Street Elem Sch/Johnstown/Fulton	00728616	518/762-3715	72
WARRENSBURG CENTRAL SCH DIST/ WARRENSBURG/WARREN	00778752	518/623-2861	246
Warrensburg Elem Sch/Warrensburg/Warren	05101441	518/623-9747	246
Warrensburg Jr Sr High Sch/Warrensburg/Warren	00778776	518/623-2861	246
Warring Elem Sch/Poughkeepsie/Dutchess	00721905	845/451-4750	53
Warsaw Central Mid High Sch/Warsaw/Wyoming	00783214	585/786-8000	267
WARSAW CENTRAL SCH DIST/ WARSAW/WYOMING	00783197	585/786-8000	267
Warsaw Elem Sch/Warsaw/Wyoming	00783202	585/786-8000	267
WARWICK VALLEY CENTRAL SD/ WARWICK/ORANGE	00764945	845/987-3000	167
Warwick Valley High Sch/Warwick/Orange	00764983	845/987-3050	167
Warwick Valley Middle Sch/Warwick/Orange	00764995	845/987-3100	167
Washington Drive Primary Sch/Centerport/Suffolk	04290867	631/754-5592	223
Washington Heights Academy/New York/New York	10911817	212/304-3320	142
Washington Hts Exped Lrng Sch/New York/New York	10026759	212/781-0524	142
Washington Irving Ed Center/Schenectady/Schenectady	11712755	518/370-8220	205
Washington Irving Sch/Tarrytown/Westchester	00782014	914/631-4442	262
Washington Irving YABC/New York/New York	11928863	212/674-5000	138
Washington Middle Sch/Jamestown/Chautauqua	00718855	716/483-4413	38
Washington Primary Sch/Huntingtn Sta/Suffolk	00773867	631/673-2090	223
Washington Rose Elem Sch/Roosevelt/Nassau	00738398	516/345-7600	129
Washington Street Elem Sch/Franklin Sq/Nassau	00735669	516/481-4100	119
Washington West Elem Sch/Olean/Cattaraugus	00717667	716/375-8960	32
WASHINGTONVILLE CENTRAL SD/ WASHINGTONVLE/ORANGE	00765004	845/497-4000	167
Washingtonville Middle Sch/Washingtonvle/Orange	00765016	845/497-4000	167
Washingtonville Sr High Sch/Washingtonvle/Orange	00765054	845/497-4000	167
Waterford Elem Sch/Waterford/Saratoga	00770047	518/237-0800	203
WATERFORD HALFMOON SCH DIST/ WATERFORD/SARATOGA	00770035	518/237-0800	203
Waterford Jr Sr High Sch/Waterford/Saratoga	05276826	518/237-0800	203
WATERLOO CENTRAL SCH DIST/ WATERLOO/SENECA	00771156	315/539-1500	208
Waterloo High Sch/Waterloo/Seneca	00771194	315/539-1550	208
Waterloo Middle Sch/Waterloo/Seneca	00771170	315/539-1540	208
Waterside Children's Studio/Rockaway Park/Queens	11447388	718/634-1344	181
Waterside Sch for Leadership/Rockaway Park/Queens	11447376	718/634-1128	181
WATERTOWN CITY SCH DIST/ WATERTOWN/JEFFERSON	00730334	315/785-3700	81
Watertown High Sch/Watertown/Jefferson	00730451	315/785-3800	82
WATERVILLE CENTRAL SCH DIST/ WATERVILLE/ONEIDA	00760846	315/841-3900	153
Waterville Jr Sr High Sch/Waterville/Oneida	00760872	315/841-3800	153
WATERVLIET CITY SCH DIST/ WATERVLIET/ALBANY	00714988	518/629-3200	12
Watervliet Elem Sch/Watervliet/Albany	01525235	518/629-3400	12
Watervliet Jr Sr High Sch/Watervliet/Albany	00715023	518/629-3300	12
Watkins Glen Central High Sch/Watkins Glen/Schuyler	00770970	607/535-3210	207
WATKINS GLEN CENTRAL SCH DIST/ WATKINS GLEN/SCHUYLER	00770956	607/535-3219	207
Watkins Glen Elem Sch/Watkins Glen/Schuyler	00770982	607/535-3250	207
Watson Elem Sch/Rockville CTR/Nassau	00738300	516/255-8904	128
Watson-Williams Elem Sch/Utica/Oneida	00760705	315/792-2167	152
Wave Prep Elem Sch/Far Rockaway/Queens	11821710	718/327-7091	181
Waverly Avenue Elem Sch/Holtsville/Suffolk	00775293	631/654-8690	229
WAVERLY CTL SCH DIST/WAVERLY/ TIOGA	00777277	607/565-2841	239
Waverly High Sch/Waverly/Tioga	00777320	607/565-8101	239
Waverly Middle Sch/Waverly/Tioga	12110112	607/565-3410	239
Waverly Park Elem Sch/East Rockaway/Nassau	00737100	516/887-6589	124
Waverly Sch/Eastchester/Westchester	03325627	914/793-6130	254
Wawarsing Christian Academy/Wawarsing/Ulster	02826886	845/647-3810	244
Wayland Elem Sch/Wayland/Steuben	12108987	585/728-2211	215
WAYLAND-COHOCTON CENTRAL SD/ WAYLAND/STEUBEN	00771821	585/728-2211	215
Wayland-Cohocton High Sch/Wayland/Steuben	12108975	585/728-2366	215
Wayland-Cohocton Middle Sch/Wayland/Steuben	01552379	585/728-2551	215
Wayne Central Elem Sch/Ontario CTR/Wayne	00779548	315/524-1130	251
Wayne Central Primary Sch/Ontario CTR/Wayne	00779550	315/524-1150	251
WAYNE CENTRAL SCH DIST/ONTARIO CTR/ WAYNE	00779524	315/524-1000	251
Wayne Educational Center/Williamson/Wayne	01529657	315/589-2400	249
Wayne Technical & Career Ctr/Williamson/Wayne	04937247	315/589-2600	249
WAYNE-FINGER LAKES BOCES/ NEWARK/WAYNE	00764024	315/332-7400	252
Wayne-Fingerlake BOCES Spec Ed/Clifton Spgs/Ontario	04026496	315/548-6631	161
WEBSTER CENTRAL SCH DIST/ WEBSTER/MONROE	00733374	585/216-0000	112
Webster Elem Sch/Syracuse/Onondaga	00762648	315/435-4670	159
Webster Montessori Sch/Webster/Monroe	10967737	585/347-0055	115
Webster Thomas High Sch/Webster/Monroe	04946470	585/670-8000	113
WEBUTUCK CTL SCH DIST/AMENIA/ DUTCHESS	00722272	845/373-4100	54
Webutuck Elem Sch/Amenia/Dutchess	00722301	845/373-4122	54
Webutuck High Sch/Amenia/Dutchess	00722313	845/373-4106	54
WEEDSPORT CTL SCH DIST/WEEDSPORT/ CAYUGA	00718207	315/834-6637	35
Weedsport Elem Sch/Weedsport/Cayuga	00718219	315/834-6685	35
Weedsport Jr Sr High Sch/Weedsport/Cayuga	00718221	315/834-6652	35
Wells Central Sch/Wells/Hamilton	00729488	518/924-6000	77
WELLS CENTRAL SCH DIST/WELLS/ HAMILTON	00729476	518/924-6000	77
Wellspring Sch/Hollis/Queens	11735525	718/721-3523	189
WELLSVILLE CENTRAL SCH DIST/ WELLSVILLE/ALLEGANY	00716326	585/596-2170	15
Wellsville Elem Sch/Wellsville/Allegany	00716340	585/596-2122	15
Wellsville Secondary Sch/Wellsville/Allegany	00716338	585/596-2188	15
Wellwood Middle Sch/Fayetteville/Onondaga	00761852	315/692-1300	155
Wemoco BOCES-Career Tech Ctr/Spencerport/Monroe	01417030	585/352-2471	106
Wenonah Elem Sch/Lake Grove/Suffolk	00775308	631/471-1880	229
West Babylon Jr High Sch/West Babylon/Suffolk	00776182	631/376-7200	233
West Babylon Sr High Sch/West Babylon/Suffolk	00776194	631/376-7100	233
WEST BABYLON UNION FREE SD/ WEST BABYLON/SUFFOLK	00776118	631/376-7000	232
West Bronx Acad for the Future/Bronx/Bronx	05349100	718/563-7139	22
West Brooklyn Cmty High Sch/Brooklyn/Kings	10026644	718/686-1444	85
West Buffalo Charter Sch/Buffalo/Erie	11722619	716/923-1534	8
WEST CANADA VALLEY CTL SD/ NEWPORT/HERKIMER	00729880	315/845-6800	79
West Canada Valley Elem Sch/Newport/Herkimer	00729919	315/845-6801	79
West Canada Valley Jr Sr HS/Newport/Herkimer	04866246	315/845-6802	79
West Carthage Elem Sch/Carthage/Jefferson	00730059	315/493-2400	80
West Elem Sch/Long Beach/Nassau	00737033	516/897-2215	124
West Elem Sch/West Seneca/Erie	03392773	716/677-3250	64
West End Day Sch/New York/New York	11747425	212/873-5708	146
West End Elem Sch/Lynbrook/Nassau	00737112	516/887-0288	124

School/City/County DISTRICT/CITY/COUNTY	PID	TELEPHONE NUMBER	PAGE
West Gates Avenue Elem Sch/Lindenhurst/Suffolk	00774146	631/867-3400	224
WEST GENESEE CTL SCH DIST/CAMILLUS/ONONDAGA	00761163	315/487-4562	159
West Genesee High Sch/Camillus/Onondaga	00761266	315/487-4592	159
West Genesee Middle Sch/Camillus/Onondaga	00761254	315/487-4615	159
West Haverstraw Elem Sch/W Haverstraw/Rockland	00767674	845/942-3181	197
West Hempstead High Sch/W Hempstead/Nassau	00739110	516/390-3214	131
West Hempstead Middle Sch/W Hempstead/Nassau	04272607	516/390-3160	131
WEST HEMPSTEAD SCH DIST/W HEMPSTEAD/NASSAU	00739067	516/390-3100	131
West Hills Montessori Sch/Huntington/Suffolk	01794072	631/385-3342	235
West Hollow Middle Sch/Melville/Suffolk	00773582	631/592-3400	222
WEST IRONDEQUOIT CTL SD/ROCHESTER/MONROE	00732186	585/342-5500	113
WEST ISLIP SCH DIST/WEST ISLIP/SUFFOLK	00776209	631/893-3200	233
West Islip Senior High Sch/West Islip/Suffolk	00776314	631/504-5800	233
West Leyden Elem Sch/West Leyden/Oneida	00759938	315/942-9200	150
West Middle Island Elem Sch/Middle Island/Suffolk	00774433	631/345-2160	225
West Middle Sch/Bay Shore/Suffolk	00772382	631/434-2371	218
West Middle Sch/Binghamton/Broome	00716558	607/763-8400	27
West Middle Sch/West Seneca/Erie	00725509	716/677-3500	64
West Nyack Elem Sch/West Nyack/Rockland	00767478	845/624-3474	196
West Orchard Elem Sch/Chappaqua/Westchester	00779861	914/238-7206	254
West Patent Elem Sch/Bedford Hills/Westchester	00780858	914/666-2190	252
West Point Elem Sch/West Point/Orange	02204422	845/839-7500	167
West Point Middle Sch/West Point/Orange	02204434	845/938-2923	168
WEST POINT SCH DIST/WEST POINT/ORANGE	03179765	845/938-2923	167
West Prep Academy/New York/New York	11447687	212/280-8502	139
West Ridge Elem Sch/Rochester/Monroe	03329116	585/966-3600	109
West Sand Lake Elem Sch/W Sand Lake/Rensselaer	00766656	518/674-7175	189
West Sayville Christian Sch/West Sayville/Suffolk	00776649	631/589-2180	235
WEST SENECA CENTRAL SCH DIST/WEST SENECA/ERIE	00725377	716/677-3100	64
West Seneca Christian Sch/West Seneca/Erie	01460893	716/674-1820	66
West Seneca East Sr High Sch/West Seneca/Erie	00725494	716/677-3300	64
West Seneca West Sr High Sch/West Seneca/Erie	00725511	716/677-3350	64
West Side Elem Sch/Syosset/Suffolk	00772564	516/692-7900	219
West Street Elem Sch/Geneva/Ontario	00763771	315/781-0406	161
West Street Elem Sch/Sanborn/Niagara	04804303	716/215-3200	148
West Valley Central Sch/West Valley/Cattaraugus	00717849	716/942-3293	33
WEST VALLEY CTL SCH DIST/WEST VALLEY/CATTARAUGUS	00717837	716/942-3100	33
Westbury Friends Sch/Westbury/Nassau	00739378	516/333-3178	134
Westbury High Sch/Old Westbury/Nassau	00739196	516/876-5047	132
Westbury Middle Sch/Westbury/Nassau	00739184	516/876-5082	132
WESTBURY UNION FREE SCH DIST/OLD WESTBURY/NASSAU	00739122	516/876-5000	132
Westchester Area Sch/New Rochelle/Westchester	01464370	914/235-5799	266
Westchester Day Sch/Mamaroneck/Westchester	00782923	914/698-8900	266
Westchester Excptnl Chldrn's/North Salem/Westchester	01795870	914/277-5533	266
Westchester Hebrew High Sch/Mamaroneck/Westchester	00782844	914/698-0806	266
Westchester Hills School 29/Yonkers/Westchester	00782648	914/376-8585	264
Westchester Sch for Spec Child/Yonkers/Westchester	11225790	914/693-2504	266
Westchester Sch for Spec Chldn/Yonkers/Westchester	01795818	914/376-4300	266
Westchester Square Academy/Bronx/Bronx	11824372	718/904-5050	18
Westchester Torah Academy/White Plains/Westchester	12225638	914/712-6497	266
Western New York Maritime CS/Buffalo/Erie	05351995	716/842-6289	8
Western New York Tech Academy/Bergen/Genesee	12174235	585/494-1220	72
Western NY Childrens Psyc Ctr/West Seneca/Erie	11223663	716/674-9730	66
WESTERN SUFFOLK BOCES/HUNTINGTN STA/SUFFOLK	00776522	631/549-4900	236
Westfield Central Sch/Westfield/Chautauqua	01813197	716/326-2151	39
WESTFIELD CENTRAL SCH DIST/WESTFIELD/CHAUTAUQUA	00719110	716/326-2151	39
Westhampton Beach Elem Sch/W Hampton Bch/Suffolk	00776352	631/288-3800	233
Westhampton Beach High Sch/W Hampton Bch/Suffolk	00776364	631/288-3800	233
Westhampton Beach Lrng Center/W Hampton Bch/Suffolk	00776510	631/288-6400	216
Westhampton Beach Middle Sch/W Hampton Bch/Suffolk	00776340	631/288-3800	233
WESTHAMPTON BEACH SCH DIST/W HAMPTON BCH/SUFFOLK	00776338	631/288-3800	233
WESTHILL CENTRAL SCH DIST/SYRACUSE/ONONDAGA	00762686	315/426-3000	159
Westhill Senior High Sch/Syracuse/Onondaga	00762727	315/426-3100	160
Westlake High Sch/Thornwood/Westchester	00781072	914/769-8311	259
Westlake Middle Sch/Thornwood/Westchester	00781084	914/769-8540	259
Westmere Elem Sch/Albany/Albany	00714615	518/456-3771	11
Westminster Cmty Charter Sch/Buffalo/Erie	00723240	716/816-3450	58
WESTMORELAND CENTRAL SCH DIST/WESTMORELAND/ONEIDA	00760884	315/557-2600	153
Westmoreland Jr Sr High Sch/Westmoreland/Oneida	00760901	315/557-2616	153
Westmoreland Primary Sch/Westmoreland/Oneida	00760896	315/557-2637	153
Westmoreland Road Elem Sch/Whitesboro/Oneida	00760975	315/266-3440	153
Westmoreland Upper Elem Sch/Westmoreland/Oneida	05100435	315/557-2618	153
Westside Academy-Blodgett/Syracuse/Onondaga	04369937	315/435-4386	159
WHEATLAND CHILI CTL SCH DIST/SCOTTSVILLE/MONROE	00733506	585/889-4500	113
Wheatland Chili Mid High Sch/Scottsville/Monroe	01552252	585/889-6227	113
Wheatley Sch/Old Westbury/Nassau	00735346	516/333-7804	118
Wheeler Avenue Elem Sch/Valley Stream/Nassau	00738879	516/568-6140	130
Wheeler Sch/Nedrow/Onondaga	00762088	315/552-5050	157
Wheelerville Union Free Sch/Caroga Lake/Fulton	00728745	518/835-2171	72
WHEELERVILLE UNION FREE SD/CAROGA LAKE/FULTON	00728733	518/835-2171	72
Wheelock Primary Sch/Fredonia/Chautauqua	12363917	716/679-0007	38
Whin Music Cmty Charter Sch/New York/New York	12234031	844/489-0817	9
Whispering Pines SDA Sch/Old Westbury/Nassau	01461330	516/997-5177	134
WHITE PLAINS CITY SCH DIST/WHITE PLAINS/WESTCHESTER	00782105	914/422-2000	263
White Plains High Sch/White Plains/Westchester	00782208	914/422-2182	263
WHITEHALL CENTRAL SCH DIST/WHITEHALL/WASHINGTON	00779108	518/499-1772	248
Whitehall Elem Sch/Whitehall/Washington	00779110	518/499-0330	248
Whitehall Jr Sr High Sch/Whitehall/Washington	00779122	518/499-1770	248
WHITESBORO CTL SCH DIST/WHITESBORO/ONEIDA	00760913	315/266-3303	153
Whitesboro Middle Sch/Whitesboro/Oneida	00760987	315/266-3100	153
Whitesboro Senior High Sch/Marcy/Oneida	00760999	315/266-3200	153
Whitestone Academy/Whitestone/Queens	02139097	718/767-0773	189
Whitesville Central Sch/Whitesville/Allegany	00716388	607/356-3301	15
WHITESVILLE CENTRAL SCH DIST/WHITESVILLE/ALLEGANY	00716376	607/356-3301	15
WHITNEY POINT CENTRAL SCH DIST/WHITNEY POINT/BROOME	00717203	607/692-8202	30
Whitney Point High Sch/Whitney Point/Broome	00717241	607/692-8201	30
Wilbur H Lynch Literacy Acad/Amsterdam/Montgomery	00734689	518/843-3716	116
Wildflower Rose and Alston CS/Bronx/Bronx	12472128	718/635-0474	9
Wildwood Campus Cte/Hornell/Steuben	00771869	607/324-7880	213
Wildwood Sch/Schenectady/Schenectady	01792660	518/836-2200	205
Willard Prior Elem Sch/Oneida/Madison	00731314	315/363-2190	105
Willets Road Sch/Roslyn HTS/Nassau	00735358	516/333-8797	118

DISTRICT & SCHOOL TELEPHONE INDEX

Market Data Retrieval

School/City/County DISTRICT/CITY/COUNTY	PID	TELEPHONE NUMBER	PAGE
William A Carter Elem Sch/Middletown/Orange	00764323	845/326-1711	165
William Appleby Elem Sch/Marathon/Cortland	00720937	607/849-3281	48
William B Tecler Magnet Sch/Amsterdam/Montgomery	00734677	518/843-4805	116
William B Ward Elem Sch/New Rochelle/Westchester	00781230	914/576-4450	259
William Barkley Elem Sch/Amsterdam/Montgomery	00734691	518/843-1850	116
William Boyce Thompson Sch/Yonkers/Westchester	04367812	914/376-8563	264
William C Bryant High Sch/Long Is City/Queens	00741589	718/721-5404	185
William C Munn Elem Sch/Spencerport/Monroe	00733336	585/349-5500	112
William E Cottle Elem Sch/Eastchester/Westchester	00782040	914/337-5376	262
William E DeLuca Jr Elem Sch/North Babylon/Suffolk	00774586	631/620-7700	226
William E Severn Elem Sch/Corning/Steuben	00771558	607/962-6844	214
William Floyd Elem Sch/Shirley/Suffolk	00776405	631/874-1257	233
William Floyd High Sch/Mastic Beach/Suffolk	00776417	631/874-1120	234
William Floyd Middle Sch/Moriches/Suffolk	05279531	631/874-5505	234
WILLIAM FLOYD SCH DIST/MASTIC BEACH/SUFFOLK	00776376	631/874-1100	233
William Grady Career & Tech HS/Brooklyn/Kings	00741591	718/332-5000	91
William H Barton Interm Sch/Queensbury/Warren	04807642	518/824-2600	246
William H Golding Middle Sch/Cobleskill/Schoharie	04868397	518/234-8368	206
William Keane Elem Sch/Schenectady/Schenectady	11071006	518/881-3960	205
William L Buck Elem Sch/Valley Stream/Nassau	00738934	516/256-0160	131
William Maxwell Career Tech HS/Brooklyn/Kings	00741606	718/345-9100	89
William Paca Middle Sch/Mastic Beach/Suffolk	01525302	631/874-1414	234
William Rall Elem Sch/Lindenhurst/Suffolk	00774158	631/867-3450	224
William S Covert Elem Sch/S Hempstead/Nassau	00738324	516/255-8916	128
William S Hackett Middle Sch/Albany/Albany	00714316	518/475-6475	9
William Sidney Mount Elem Sch/Stony Brook/Suffolk	00776065	631/730-4300	232
William Spyropoulos Sch/Flushing/Queens	01753755	718/357-5583	189
William Street Sch/Lancaster/Erie	04803294	716/686-3800	63
William T Rogers Middle Sch/Kings Park/Suffolk	00773984	631/269-3369	224
Williamsburg Charter High Sch/Brooklyn/Kings	05349655	718/782-9830	9
Williamsburg Collegiate CS/Brooklyn/Kings	10008927	718/302-4018	9
Williamsburg HS Art & Tech/Brooklyn/Kings	10027210	718/599-1207	84
Williamsburg HS-Arch Design/Brooklyn/Kings	05349588	718/388-1260	84
Williamsburg Northside Sch/Brooklyn/Kings	12314980	718/599-9600	99
Williamsburg Preparatory Sch/Brooklyn/Kings	05349564	718/302-2306	84
WILLIAMSON CENTRAL SCH DIST/WILLIAMSON/WAYNE	00779598	315/589-9661	251
Williamson Elem Sch/Williamson/Wayne	00779615	315/589-9668	251
Williamson High Sch/Williamson/Wayne	00779627	315/589-9621	251
Williamson Middle Sch/Williamson/Wayne	00779603	315/589-9665	251
WILLIAMSVILLE CTL SCH DIST/EAST AMHERST/ERIE	00725535	716/626-8000	64
Willink Middle Sch/Webster/Monroe	00733427	585/670-1030	113
Willow Ave Elem Sch/Cornwall/Orange	05276814	845/534-8009	163
Willow Field Elem Sch/Liverpool/Onondaga	03267037	315/453-1196	156
Willow Grove Elem Sch/Thiells/Rockland	04750398	845/942-8000	197
Willow Ridge Elem Sch/Amherst/Erie	00725250	716/250-1575	64
Willow Road Elem Sch/Franklin Sq/Nassau	00738881	516/568-6640	131
Willsboro Central Sch/Willsboro/Essex	00728094	518/963-4456	68
WILLSBORO CENTRAL SCH DIST/WILLSBORO/ESSEX	00728082	518/963-4456	68
WILSON CENTRAL SCH DIST/WILSON/NIAGARA	00759794	716/751-9341	149
Wilson Elem Sch/Rockville Ctr/Nassau	00738312	516/255-8910	128
Wilson Elem Sch/Wilson/Niagara	00759811	716/751-9341	149
Wilson Foundation Academy/Rochester/Monroe	04806636	585/463-4100	112
Wilson Magnet High Sch/Rochester/Monroe	00733142	585/328-3440	112
Wilson Middle High Sch/Wilson/Niagara	00759823	716/751-9341	149
Wilson Tech Dix Hills/Dix Hills/Suffolk	00776558	631/667-6000	216
Wilson Tech Northport/Northport/Suffolk	11134074	631/261-3600	216
Wilton Baptist Academy/Gansevoort/Saratoga	10788660	518/583-2736	203
Winchester Elem Sch/West Seneca/Erie	00725523	716/677-3580	64
Windermere Blvd Elem Sch/Amherst/Erie	02106387	716/362-4100	56
Windham Ashland Jewett Ctl Sch/Windham/Greene	00729335	518/734-3400	76
WINDHAM ASHLAND JEWETT CTL SD/WINDHAM/GREENE	00729323	518/734-3400	76
Windmill Montessori Sch/Brooklyn/Kings	01793729	718/375-7973	99
Windom Elem Sch/Orchard Park/Erie	00725080	716/209-6279	63
Windsor Academy/New Windsor/Orange	04933485	845/562-3711	168
Windsor Central High Sch/Windsor/Broome	00717291	607/655-8250	30
Windsor Central Middle Sch/Windsor/Broome	12030847	607/655-8247	30
WINDSOR CENTRAL SCH DIST/WINDSOR/BROOME	00717253	607/655-8216	30
Windsor Sch/Flushing/Queens	00752033	718/359-8300	189
Windward Sch-Manhattan/New York/New York	12177251	212/222-8628	146
Windward Sch-Westchester Lower/White Plains/Westchester	00782973	914/949-6968	266
Windward Sch-Westchester Mid/White Plains/Westchester	11715214	914/949-6968	266
Winfield Street Elem Sch/Corning/Steuben	00771546	607/962-6706	214
Wing Elem Sch/Islip/Suffolk	04013762	631/650-8450	224
Wingdale Elem Sch/Wingdale/Dutchess	00721668	845/877-5720	52
Wings Academy/Bronx/Bronx	04290996	718/597-1751	25
Winston Preparatory Sch/New York/New York	03409405	212/496-8400	146
Winston Preparatory School-Li/Dix Hills/Suffolk	12469834	631/779-2400	235
Winthrop Avenue Sch/Bellmore/Nassau	00735047	516/679-2920	117
Wisdom Lane Middle Sch/Levittown/Nassau	00736883	516/434-7300	123
Wolcott Street Sch/Le Roy/Genesee	00729012	585/768-7115	74
Women's Academy of Excellence/Bronx/Bronx	05349382	718/542-0740	18
Wood Park Primary Sch/Commack/Suffolk	00772772	631/858-3680	219
Wood Road Elem Sch/Ballston Spa/Saratoga	00769476	518/884-7290	200
Woodglen Elem Sch/New City/Rockland	00767480	845/624-3417	196
Woodhull Elem Sch/Ocean Beach/Suffolk	00774782	631/583-5626	222
Woodhull Intermediate Sch/Huntington/Suffolk	00773855	631/673-2030	223
Woodland Elem Sch/East Syracuse/Onondaga	00761369	315/434-3440	155
Woodland Elem Sch/Hicksville/Nassau	00736455	516/733-2331	122
Woodland Hill Montessori Sch/Rensselaer/Rensselaer	11915050	518/283-5400	192
Woodland Middle Sch/East Meadow/Nassau	00735279	516/564-6523	118
Woodlands Middle High Sch/Hartsdale/Westchester	00780262	914/761-6052	255
Woodlawn Elem Sch/Schenectady/Schenectady	00770619	518/370-8280	205
Woodmere Middle Sch/Hewlett/Nassau	00736338	516/792-4300	122
Woodrow Wilson Elem Sch/Binghamton/Broome	00716560	607/763-8440	27
Woodrow Wilson Elem Sch/Sloan/Erie	00725133	716/891-6419	59
Woods Road Elem Sch/North Babylon/Suffolk	00774641	631/620-7800	226
Woodside Cmty School 361Q/Woodside/Queens	12105909	718/592-3300	185
Woodside Elem Sch/Peekskill/Westchester	00781424	914/739-0093	260
Woodstock Day Sch/Saugerties/Ulster	01795674	845/246-3744	244
Woodstock Elem Sch/Woodstock/Ulster	00778192	845/679-2316	243
Woodward Children Center/Freeport/Nassau	01461160	516/379-0900	134
Woodward Parkway Elem Sch/Farmingdale/Nassau	00735516	516/434-5810	119
Worcester Central Sch/Worcester/Otsego	00766307	607/397-8785	174
WORCESTER CTL SCH DIST/WORCESTER/OTSEGO	00766292	607/397-8785	174
Word of Life Christian Academy/Baldwinsville/Onondaga	12235073	315/635-1818	160
World Acad Total Cmty Hlth HS/Brooklyn/Kings	05351701	718/688-7980	89
World Journalism Prep Sch/Flushing/Queens	10026864	718/461-2219	179
World of Inquiry School 58/Rochester/Monroe	01841168	585/325-6170	112
World View High Sch/Bronx/Bronx	11924350	718/601-0391	22
WSWHE BOCES/FORT EDWARD/WASHINGTON	00779134	518/746-3310	249
Wyandanch Memorial High Sch/Wyandanch/Suffolk	00776479	631/870-0450	234
WYANDANCH UNION FREE SCH DIST/WYANDANCH/SUFFOLK	00776429	631/870-0401	234
WYNANTSKILL UNION FREE SD/TROY/RENSSELAER	00767234	518/283-4679	191
Wyoming Central Sch/Wyoming/Wyoming	00783238	585/495-6222	268
WYOMING CENTRAL SCH DIST/WYOMING/WYOMING	00783226	585/495-6222	268

X

Xaverian High Sch/Brooklyn/Kings	00754964	718/836-7100	95

New York School Directory
DISTRICT & SCHOOL TELEPHONE INDEX

School/City/County DISTRICT/CITY/COUNTY	PID	TELEPHONE NUMBER	PAGE
Xavier High Sch/New York/New York	00758738	212/924-7900	143
Y			
Yaldeinu Sch/Brooklyn/Kings	11923148	718/851-0123	99
Yates Magnet Sch/Schenectady/Schenectady	00770633	518/370-8320	205
Yde Elem Sch/Brooklyn/Kings	12027292	718/232-0100	99
Yde High Sch/Brooklyn/Kings	12027307	718/232-0100	99
Yeshiva & Msvta Karlin Stolin/Brooklyn/Kings	00752162	718/232-7800	99
Yeshiva Ahavas Yisroel Sch/Brooklyn/Kings	00752497	718/388-0848	99
Yeshiva Ahavath Israel Sch/Monsey/Rockland	11239478	845/356-1010	199
Yeshiva Arugath Habosem/Brooklyn/Kings	00752679	718/237-4500	99
Yeshiva Ateret Torah Boys/Brooklyn/Kings	02162953	718/375-7100	99
Yeshiva Ateret Torah Girls/Brooklyn/Kings	02828327	718/732-7770	99
Yeshiva Avir Yakov Girls Sch/Spring Valley/Rockland	02079825	845/354-0874	199
Yeshiva Bais Hachinuch/Spring Valley/Rockland	11734973	845/354-3805	199
Yeshiva Bais Meir/Brooklyn/Kings	03409132	718/437-5844	99
Yeshiva Beis Chaya Mushkah/Brooklyn/Kings	11230939	718/756-0770	99
Yeshiva Beth David/Monsey/Rockland	00768290	845/352-3100	199
Yeshiva Beth Hillel D'Krasna/Brooklyn/Kings	00752576	718/438-3535	99
Yeshiva Beth Hillel Williamsbg/Brooklyn/Kings	12380680	718/802-9567	99
Yeshiva Bicahon/Brooklyn/Kings	00752203	718/474-0045	99
Yeshiva Bnos Spinka Girls/Brooklyn/Kings	03413535	718/254-8006	99
Yeshiva Bonim Lamokom/Brooklyn/Kings	05308156	718/693-9032	99
Yeshiva Boyan/Brooklyn/Kings	02985808	718/435-6060	99
Yeshiva Chanoch Lenaar/Brooklyn/Kings	02828303	718/774-8456	99
Yeshiva Chsan Sofer/Brooklyn/Kings	00752514	718/236-1171	99
Yeshiva Congreg Toras Yufa/Brooklyn/Kings	04974491	718/436-5683	100
Yeshiva Dar HEI Torah/Far Rockaway/Queens	01409150	718/868-2300	189
Yeshiva Darkei Emunah/Monsey/Rockland	12380666	845/356-2761	199
Yeshiva Degel Hatorah/Spring Valley/Rockland	03408944	845/356-4610	199
Yeshiva Derech Hatorah ES/Brooklyn/Kings	02189638	718/258-4441	100
Yeshiva Derech Hatorah HS/Brooklyn/Kings	11815541	347/492-6611	100
Yeshiva Eitz Chaim-Skill Ctr/Spring Valley/Rockland	12031865	845/425-3623	199
Yeshiva Farm Settlement Sch/Brooklyn/Kings	11239442	718/387-0422	100
Yeshiva Farm Settlement Sch/Mount Kisco/Westchester	01409590	914/666-2087	266
Yeshiva Gedolah Zichron Moshe/S Fallsburg/Sullivan	01409473	845/434-5240	237
Yeshiva Har Torah Sch/Bellerose/Queens	03408827	718/343-2533	189
Yeshiva High Sch of Monsey/Monsey/Rockland	03413418	845/406-6670	199
Yeshiva Imrei Yosef Spinka/Brooklyn/Kings	01409227	718/851-1600	100
Yeshiva Kehilath Yaakov Boys/Brooklyn/Kings	00752643	718/963-3940	100
Yeshiva Kehilath Yaakov Sch/Ossining/Westchester	02856453	718/963-1212	266
Yeshiva Ketana/Inwood/Nassau	04974829	516/791-2800	134
Yeshiva Ketana of Manhattan/New York/New York	01409136	212/769-1790	146
Yeshiva Ketana of Queens/Flushing/Queens	11573585	718/969-1000	189
Yeshiva Ktana Toldos Yakov/Brooklyn/Kings	03408683	718/852-0502	100
Yeshiva MacHzikei Hadas Belz/Brooklyn/Kings	01462023	718/436-4445	100
Yeshiva MacHzikel Hadas/Brooklyn/Kings	04974489	718/436-4445	100
Yeshiva Meor Hatalmud/Brooklyn/Kings	12163896	718/927-3772	100
Yeshiva Mercaz Hatorah/Rockaway Park/Queens	03408839	718/474-3064	189
Yeshiva Mesivta Arugath Habosm/Brooklyn/Kings	03408736	718/237-4500	100
Yeshiva of Brooklyn-Boys/Brooklyn/Kings	02190479	718/252-9500	100
Yeshiva of Brooklyn-Girls/Brooklyn/Kings	00752215	718/376-3775	100
Yeshiva of Central Queens/Flushing/Queens	00751522	718/793-8500	189
Yeshiva of Far Rockaway/Far Rockaway/Queens	00752253	718/327-7600	189
Yeshiva of Flatbush Elem Sch/Brooklyn/Kings	01409289	718/377-4466	100
Yeshiva of Spring Valley/Suffern/Rockland	00768317	845/356-1400	199
Yeshiva of Staten Island/Staten Island/Richmond	01560364	718/356-4323	195
Yeshiva of the Telshe Alumni/Bronx/Bronx	02828315	718/601-3523	27
Yeshiva Ohel Moshe/Brooklyn/Kings	00752291	718/236-4003	100
Yeshiva Ohel Torah/Brooklyn/Kings	05230145	718/431-0915	100
Yeshiva Ohr Shraga D'Veretzky/Brooklyn/Kings	03408750	718/252-7777	100
Yeshiva Rabbi Chaim Berlin/Brooklyn/Kings	01461782	718/377-5800	100
Yeshiva Ruach Chaim/Brooklyn/Kings	04974374	718/646-8500	100
Yeshiva Shaar Ephraim/Monsey/Rockland	04974283	845/426-3110	199
Yeshiva Shaarei Hatzlucha/Brooklyn/Kings	05299593	718/234-3476	100
Yeshiva Shaarei Torah/Suffern/Rockland	00768329	845/352-3431	199
Yeshiva Shaarei Torah-Boys/Brooklyn/Kings	02828145	718/645-6676	100
Yeshiva Shaarei Torah-Girls HS/Brooklyn/Kings	02828157	718/382-4000	100
Yeshiva Shaari Torah Sch/Brooklyn/Kings	11230654	718/645-6676	100
Yeshiva Tiferes D'Aleksander/Brooklyn/Kings	03408786	718/438-1818	100
Yeshiva Tiferes Elimelech Boys/Brooklyn/Kings	02191162	718/438-1177	100
Yeshiva Tiferes Yisroel/Brooklyn/Kings	03043336	718/258-9006	100
Yeshiva Tifereth Moshe/Kew Gardens/Queens	00751742	718/846-7300	189
Yeshiva Torah Temimah/Brooklyn/Kings	01462621	718/853-8500	100
Yeshiva Torah V"Yirah Academy/Brooklyn/Kings	02189729	718/963-9288	100
Yeshiva Torah Vodaath/Brooklyn/Kings	00752370	718/941-8000	100
Yeshiva Toras Chaim-S Shore/Hewlett/Nassau	00739380	516/374-7363	134
Yeshiva Toras Emes Kamenitz/Brooklyn/Kings	00752409	718/375-0900	100
Yeshiva Tzemach Tzadik Viznitz/Brooklyn/Kings	05299608	718/782-6383	100
Yeshiva Univ High Sch for Boys/New York/New York	00752526	212/960-5337	146
Yeshiva Univ HS-Girls/Hollis/Queens	00752681	718/479-8550	189
Yeshiva Viznitz Boys High Sch/Monsey/Rockland	03408918	845/356-1010	199
Yeshiva Yagdil Torah/Brooklyn/Kings	00752423	718/871-9100	100
Yeshiva Yesode Hatorah Adas/Brooklyn/Kings	02069521	718/851-6462	100
Yeshiva-Mesivta V"Yoel Moshe/Brooklyn/Kings	04974506	718/438-7109	100
Yeshivas Novominsk/Brooklyn/Kings	03076931	718/438-2727	100
Yeshivat Magen Abraham/Brooklyn/Kings	12314978	718/627-6200	100
Yeshivat Ohr Haiim/Richmond Hill/Queens	03015212	718/658-7066	189
Yeshivat OR Hatorah/Brooklyn/Kings	04974570	718/645-4645	100
Yeshivat OR Hatorah ES/Brooklyn/Kings	11935593	718/252-8308	100
Yeshivat Shaare Torah Girls ES/Brooklyn/Kings	12224488	718/437-6120	100
Yonkers Early Childhood Acad/Yonkers/Westchester	12107414	914/376-8500	264
Yonkers Middle High Sch/Yonkers/Westchester	03150965	914/376-8191	264
Yonkers Montessori Academy/Yonkers/Westchester	00782337	914/376-8540	264
YONKERS PUBLIC SCH DIST/YONKERS/WESTCHESTER	00782234	914/376-8000	263
York Central Elem Sch/Retsof/Livingston	00730891	585/243-3400	103
York Central Middle High Sch/Retsof/Livingston	00730906	585/243-2990	103
YORK CENTRAL SCH DIST/RETSOF/LIVINGSTON	00730889	585/243-1730	103
York Early College Academy/Jamaica/Queens	10027026	718/262-8547	183
York Preparatory Sch/New York/New York	01463211	212/362-0400	146
YORKSHIRE-PIONEER CTL SCH DIST/YORKSHIRE/CATTARAUGUS	00717679	716/492-9300	33
YORKTOWN CENTRAL SCH DIST/YORKTOWN HTS/WESTCHESTER	00782703	914/243-8000	264
Yorktown High Sch/Yorktown Hts/Westchester	00782777	914/243-8050	264
Yorkville Cmty Sch/New York/New York	11589950	212/722-5240	138
Young Leaders Elem Sch/Bronx/Bronx	11103245	718/292-7391	17
Young Voices Academy of Bronx/Bronx/Bronx	11924336	718/794-4080	23
Young Women's College Prep CS/Rochester/Monroe	11831882	585/254-0320	9
Young Women's Ldrshp Sch-Bklyn/Brooklyn/Kings	11103180	718/387-5641	84
Young Women's Leadership HS/Jamaica/Queens	10009036	718/725-0402	183
Young Women's Leadership Sch/Astoria/Queens	10028070	718/267-2839	185
Young Women's Leadership Sch/Bronx/Bronx	11924398	718/731-2590	20
Young Women's Leadership Sch/New York/New York	04458057	212/289-7593	140
Z			
Zdr Acad Yeshiva Rambam Sch/Brooklyn/Kings	02163464	718/677-5100	100
Zeta Bronx 1 Elem Sch/Bronx/Bronx	12310647	929/458-3000	9
Zeta Inwood 1 Elem Sch/New York/New York	12310635	929/447-5281	9

New York School Directory

DISTRICT URL INDEX

DISTRICT	URL	PAGE
Addison Central School Dist	addisoncsd.org/	213
Adirondack Central Sch Dist	adirondackcsd.org	150
Afton Central School Dist	afton.stier.org/	41
Akron Central School Dist	akronschools.org	56
Albany City School Dist	albanyschools.org/	9
Albion Central School Dist	albionk12.org/	169
Alden Central School Dist	aldenschools.org/	56
Alexander Ctl School Dist	alexandercsd.org/pages/Alexander_Central_School_Distr/District	73
Alexandria Central School Dist	alexandriacentral.org/	79
Alfred Almond Ctl School Dist	aacs.wnyric.org/	13
Allegany-Limestone Ctl SD	alcsny.org/	31
Altmar-Parish-Williamstown SD	apw.cnyric.org	170
Amagansett Union Free Sch Dist	aufsd.org/	216
Amherst Central School Dist	amherstschools.org/	56
Amityville Union Free Sch Dist	amityvilleschools.org	216
Andes Central School Dist	andescentralschool.org/	48
Andover Central School Dist	andovercsd.org/	13
Ardsley Union Free School Dist	ardsleyschools.org/	252
Argyle Central School Dist	argylecsd.org/	246
Arkport Central School Dist	arkportcsd.org/	213
Arlington Central School Dist	arlingtonschools.org/pages/arlington_schools	51
Attica Central School Dist	atticacsd.org/	267
Auburn Enlarged City Sch Dist	aecsd.education/	34
Ausable Valley Ctl Sch Dist	avcs.org/	43
Averill Park Central Sch Dist	averillpark.k12.ny.us	189
Avoca Central School Dist	avocacsd.org/	213
Avon Central School Dist	avoncsd.org/	102
Babylon Union Free Sch Dist	babylon.k12.ny.us/	216
Bainbridge Guilford CSD	bgcsd.org/	41
Baldwin Union Free School Dist	baldwin.k12.ny.us/	116
Baldwinsville Central Sch Dist	bville.org	154
Ballston Spa Ctl School Dist	bscsd.org/	200
Barker Central School Dist	barkercsd.net/	146
Batavia City School Dist	bataviacsd.org/	73
Bath Central School Dist	bathcsd.org/	213
Bay Shore Union Free Sch Dist	bayshore.k12.ny.us/	217
Bayport- Blue Point USD	bbpschools.org/	217
Beacon City School Dist	beaconcityk12.org/	51
Beaver River Central Sch Dist	brcsd.org	101
Bedford Central School Dist	bcsdny.org	252
Beekmantown Ctl School Dist	bcsdk12.org/	43
Belfast Central School Dist	belfast.wnyric.org/	14
Belleville Henderson Sch Dist	bhpanthers.org/bellevillehcs/site/default.asp	79
Bellmore Union Free Sch Dist	bellmore.k12.ny.us	117
Bellmore-Merrick Ctl High SD	bellmore-merrick.k12.ny.us/	117
Bemus Point Ctl School Dist	bemusptcsd.org/	36
Berkshire Union Free Sch Dist	berkshirefarm.org/BerkshireSchool.aspx	45
Berlin Central School Dist	berlincentral.org/	189
Berne-Knox-Westerlo Central SD	bkwcsd.k12.ny.us/	10
Bethlehem Central School Dist	bethlehemschools.org/	10
Bethpage Union Free Sch Dist	bethpagecommunity.com/Schools/	117
Binghamton City School Dist	binghamtonschools.org/	27
Blind Brook-Rye Union Free SD	blindbrook.org/	252
Bloomfield Central SD	bloomfieldcsd.org/	161
Bolivar-Richburg Ctrl Sch Dist	brcs.wnyric.org/	14
Bolton Central School Dist	boltoncsd.org/	244
Boquet Valley Central Sch Dist	boquetvalleycsd.org/	67
Bradford Central Sch Dist	bradfordcsd.org/	207
Brasher Falls School Dist	bfcsd.org/	209
Brentwood Union Free Sch Dist	brentwood.k12.ny.us	217
Brewster Central School Dist	brewsterschools.org/	175
Briarcliff Manor Union Free SD	briarcliffschools.org/	253
Bridgehampton Union Free SD	bridgehampton.k12.ny.us/	218
Brighton Central School Dist	bcsd.org/	106
Broadalbin-Perth Ctl Sch Dist	bpcsd.org/	71
Brockport Ctl School Dist	brockport.k12.ny.us/	106
Brocton Central School Dist	broctoncsd.org/	36
Bronxville Union Free SD	bronxvilleschool.org/	253
Brookfield Central School Dist	bcsbeavers.org	104
Brookhaven Comsewogue Unif SD	comsewogue.k12.ny.us/	218
Brunswick Central School Dist	brittonkill.k12.ny.us/	190
Brushton Moira Ctl Sch Dist	bmcsd.org/	69
Buffalo Public Schools	buffaloschools.org/	56

DISTRICT URL INDEX

DISTRICT	URL	PAGE
Burnt Hills Ballston Lake SD	bhbl.org/	200
Byram Hills Central Sch Dist	byramhills.org	253
Byron-Bergen Ctl School Dist	bbschools.org/pages/Byron-Bergen_Central_Schools	73
Cairo-Durham Ctl School Dist	cairodurham.org/	75
Caledonia-Mumford Ctl Sch Dist	cal-mum.org/pages/Caledonia-Mumford_SD	102
Cambridge Central School Dist	cambridgecsd.org/	247
Camden Central School Dist	camdenschools.org/	150
Campbell-Savona Ctl Sch Dist	cscsd.org/	213
Canajoharie Ctl School Dist	canajoharieschools.org	115
Canandaigua City School Dist	canandaiguaschools.org	161
Canaseraga Central Sch Dist	ccsdny.org/ccsdny/site/default.asp	14
Canastota Central School Dist	canastotacsd.org/	104
Candor Central School Dist	candor.org/	238
Canisteo-Greenwood Central SD	cg.wnyric.org/	214
Canton Central School Dist	sites.google.com/a/cantoncentral.org/distr	209
Carle Place Union Free SD	cps.k12.ny.us/	117
Carmel Central School Dist	carmelschools.org/	175
Carthage Central School Dist	carthagecsd.org	80
Cassadaga Valley Ctl Sch Dist	cvweb.wnyric.org/	36
Cato Meridian Central Sch Dist	catomeridian.org/	34
Catskill Central School Dist	catskillcsd.org/	75
Cattaraugus-Little Vly Ctl SD	cattlv.wnyric.org/cattlv/site/default.asp	31
Cazenovia Ctl School Dist	caz.cnyric.org	104
Center Moriches Union Free SD	centermoriches.k12.ny.us/	218
Central Islip Union Free SD	centralislip.k12.ny.us/	218
Central Square Central SD	cssd.org/	170
Central Valley School Dist	cvalleycsd.org/	77
Chappaqua Central School Dist	ccsd.ws/	253
Charlotte Valley Ctl Sch Dist	charlottevalleycs.org/	49
Chateaugay Central School Dist	chateaugaycsd.org/	69
Chatham Central School Dist	chathamcentralschools.com/	46
Chautauqua Lake Central SD	clake.org/	36
Chazy Central Rural Sch Dist	chazy.org/	44
Cheektowaga Central SD	cheektowagacentral.org/	58
Cheektowaga Maryvale UFSD	maryvale.wnyric.org/	58
Cheektowaga-Sloan UFSD	sloanschools.org/	59
Chenango Forks Central SD	cforks.org/	28
Chenango Valley Ctl Sch Dist	cvcsd.stier.org/	28
Cherry Valley-Springfield SD	cvscs.org/	172
Chester Union Free School Dist	chesterufsd.org/	163
Chittenango Central SD	chittenangoschools.org/	104
Churchville Chili Ctl Sch Dist	cccsd.org/	107
Cincinnatus Ctl School Dist	cc.cnyric.org/	47
Clarence Central School Dist	clarenceschools.org/	59
Clarkstown Central School Dist	ccsd.edu/	195
Cleveland Hill Union Free SD	clevehill.wnyric.org/	59
Clifton-Fine Central Sch Dist	sites.google.com/cliftonfine.org/district	209
Clinton Central School Dist	ccs.edu/	150
Clyde-Savannah Central SD	clydesavannah.org/	249
Clymer Central School Dist	clymercsd.org/	37
Cobleskill Richmondville SD	crcs.k12.ny.us	206
Cohoes City School Dist	cohoes.org	10
Cold Spring Harbor Central SD	csh.k12.ny.us/	219
Colton Pierrepont School Dist	cpcs.us/	209
Commack Union Free School Dist	commack.k12.ny.us/	219
Connetquot Central School Dist	ccsdli.org/	219
Cooperstown Ctl School Dist	cooperstowncs.org	173
Copenhagen Central SD	ccsknights.org/	101
Copiague Union Free Sch Dist	copiague.k12.ny.us/	220
Corinth Central School Dist	corinthcsd.org/	200
Corning-Painted Post Area SD	corningareaschools.com	214
Cornwall Central School Dist	cornwallschools.com/	163
Cortland Enlarged City SD	cortlandschools.org	47
Coxsackie-Athens Central SD	cacsd.org	75
Croton-Harmon Union Free SD	croton-harmonschools.org	254
Crown Point Central Sch Dist	cpcsteam.org/	67
Cuba-Rushford Central Sch Dist	crcs.wnyric.org/	14
Dansville Ctl School Dist	dansvillecsd.org	102
De Ruyter Central School Dist	deruyter.k12.ny.us/	105
Deer Park Union Free Sch Dist	deerparkschools.org/	220
Delaware Academy Ctrl SD Delhi	delhischools.org/	49
Depew Union Free School Dist	depewschools.org/	59
Deposit Central School Dist	depositcsd.org/	28
Dobbs Ferry Union Free SD	dfsd.org/	254

New York School Directory

DISTRICT URL INDEX

DISTRICT	URL	PAGE
Dolgeville Central School Dist	dolgeville.org/	77
Dover Union Free School Dist	doverschools.org/	52
Downsville Central Sch Dist	dcseagles.org/	49
Dryden Central School Dist	dryden.k12.ny.us/	239
Duanesburg Central Sch Dist	duanesburg.org/	203
Dundee Ctl School Dist	dundeecs.org/	268
Dunkirk City School Dist	dunkirkcsd.org/dunkirkcsd/site/default.asp	37
East Aurora Union Free SD	eastauroraschools.org/site/Default.aspx	60
East Greenbush Central SD	egcsd.org	190
East Hampton Union Free SD	easthamptonschools.org	220
East Irondequoit Ctl Sch Dist	eastiron.org/	107
East Islip Union Free SD	eischools.org/	220
East Meadow Union Free SD	eastmeadow.k12.ny.us/	118
East Moriches Union Free SD	emoschools.org/	221
East Quogue Union Free SD	eastquogue.k12.ny.us/	221
East Ramapo Central Sch Dist	ercsd.org/pages/East_Ramapo_CSD	196
East Rochester Union Free SD	erschools.org/	107
East Rockaway Union Free SD	eastrockawayschools.org/	118
East Syracuse Minoa Ctl SD	esmschools.org/	154
East Williston Union Free SD	ewsdonline.org/	118
Eastchester Union Free SD	district.eastchesterschools.org	254
Eastport-South Manor Ctrl SD	esmonline.org	221
Eden Central School Dist	edencsd.org	60
Edgemont Union Free Sch Dist	edgemont.org	254
Edinburg Common School Dist	edinburgcs.org/	200
Edmeston Ctl School Dist	edmestoncentralschool.net/	173
Edwards-Knox Central Sch Dist	ekcsk12.org/	210
Elba Central School Dist	elbacsd.org/	73
Eldred Central School Dist	eldred.k12.ny.us/Page/1	236
Ellenville Central School Dist	ecs.k12.ny.us/	241
Ellicottville Central Sch Dist	ellicottvillecentral.com/	31
Elmira City School Dist	elmiracityschools.com/	40
Elmira Heights Ctl Sch Dist	heightsschools.com	40
Elmont Union Free School Dist	elmontschools.org/	118
Elmsford Union Free SD	eufsd.org/	255
Elwood Union Free School Dist	elwood.k12.ny.us/	221
Evans-Brant Central Sch Dist	lakeshorecsd.org/site/default.aspx?PageID=1	60
Fabius Pompey Central SD	fabiuspompey.org/	155
Fairport Ctl School Dist	fairport.org	108
Falconer Central School Dist	falconerschools.org/site/default.aspx?P	37
Fallsburg Central School Dist	fallsburgcsd.net/	236
Farmingdale Union Free SD	farmingdaleschools.org/	119
Fayetteville-Manlius Ctl SD	fmschools.org/	155
Fillmore Central School Dist	fillmorecsd.org	14
Fire Island Union Free SD	fi.k12.ny.us/	222
Fishers Island Union Free SD	fischool.com/	222
Floral Park Bellerose Sch Dist	floralpark.k12.ny.us/	119
Florida Union Free Sch Dist	floridaufsd.org/	164
Fonda Fultonville Central SD	fondafultonvilleschools.org/pages/Fonda-Fultonville_CSD	115
Forestville Central Sch Dist	forestville.com	37
Fort Ann Central School Dist	fortannschool.org/	247
Frankfort-Schuyler Ctl SD	frankfort-schuyler.org/	77
Franklin Central School Dist	franklincsd.org/	49
Franklin Square Union Free SD	franklinsquare.k12.ny.us/	119
Franklinville Ctl School Dist	tbafcs.org/site/default.aspx?PageID=1	31
Fredonia Central School Dist	fredonia.wnyric.org/	37
Freeport Public School Dist	freeportschools.org/	119
Frewsburg Central School Dist	frewsburgcsd.org/	38
Friendship Central Sch Dist	friendship.wnyric.org/	15
Frontier Ctl School Dist	frontier.wnyric.org/	60
Ft Edward Union Free Sch Dist	fortedward.org/	247
Ft Plain Central School Dist	fortplain.org/	115
Fulton City School Dist	fulton.cnyric.org/	170
Galway Central School Dist	galwaycsd.org/	201
Gananda Central School Dist	gananda.org	249
Garden City School Dist	gardencity.k12.ny.us/	120
Garrison Union Free Sch Dist	gufs.org	175
Gates Chili Central Sch Dist	gateschili.org	108
General Brown Ctl School Dist	gblions.org	80
Genesee Valley Ctl School Dist	genvalley.org/gvcs/site/default.asp	15
Geneseo Central Sch Dist	geneseocsd.org/	102
Geneva City School Dist	genevacsd.org/	161
George Junior Republic UFSD	gjrufsd.org/	240
Germantown Central School Dist	germantowncsd.org/	46

School Year 2020-2021 800-333-8802 NY-W3

DISTRICT URL INDEX

Market Data Retrieval

DISTRICT	URL	PAGE
Gilbertsville-Mt Upton SD	gmucsd.org/	173
Gilboa-Conesville Central SD	gilboa-conesville.k12.ny.us/	206
Glen Cove City School Dist	glencove.k12.ny.us/	120
Glens Falls City School Dist	gfsd.org/	245
Glens Falls Common Sch Dist	abewing.org/pages/abraham_wing_school	245
Gloversville Enlarged Sch Dist	gloversvilleschools.org/	71
Goshen Central School Dist	gcsny.org/	164
Gouverneur Ctl School Dist	gcsk12.org/	210
Gowanda Central School Dist	gowcsd.com	32
Grand Island Central Sch Dist	grandislandschools.org/	61
Granville Central School Dist	granvillecsd.org/	247
Great Neck Public Schools	greatneck.k12.ny.us/	120
Greater Amsterdam School Dist	gasd.org/	115
Greater Johnstown Sch Dist	johnstownschools.org/	71
Greece Central School Dist	greececsd.org/	108
Green Island Union Free SD	greenisland.org/	10
Greenburgh 11 Union Free SD	greenburgheleven.org/	255
Greenburgh Central School Dist	greenburghcsd.org/Domain/4	255
Greenburgh-Graham UFSD	greenburgh-graham.org/	255
Greenburgh-North Castle SD	greenburghnorthcastleschools.com/	255
Greene Ctl School Dist	greenecsd.org/	42
Greenport Union Free Sch Dist	gufsd.org/	222
Greenville Central School Dist	greenville.k12.ny.us/	75
Greenwich Central School Dist	greenwichcsd.org/	247
Greenwood Lake Union Free SD	gwlufsd.org	164
Groton Central School Dist	grotoncs.org	240
Guilderland Central Sch Dist	guilderlandschools.org	10
Hadley-Luzerne Ctl Sch Dist	hlcs.org/	245
Haldane Central School Dist	haldaneschool.org/	175
Half Hollow Hills Central SD	hhh.k12.ny.us/	222
Hamburg Central School Dist	hamburgschools.org/	61
Hamilton Central Sch Dist	hamiltoncentral.org/	105
Hammond Central School Distict	ny01913694.schoolwires.net/	210
Hammondsport Ctl School Dist	hammondsportcsd.org/Page/1	214
Hampton Bays Union Free SD	hbschools.us/	222
Hancock Central School Dist	hancock.stier.org/site/default.aspx?PageID=1	49
Hannibal Central School Dist	hannibalcsd.org	171
Harborfields Ctl School Dist	harborfieldscsd.net/	223
Harpursville Central Sch Dist	hcs.stier.org/	28
Harrison Central School Dist	harrisoncsd.org	256
Harrisville Central Sch Dist	hcs.neric.org/	101
Hartford Central School Dist	hartfordcsd.org/	248
Hastings on Hudson Union FR SD	hohschools.org	256
Hauppauge Union Free Sch Dist	hauppauge.k12.ny.us	223
Hawthorne Cedar Knolls UFSD	hcks.org.	256
Hempstead Union Free SD	hempsteadschools.org/	121
Hendrick Hudson Ctl Sch Dist	henhudschools.org/	256
Herkimer Ctl School Dist	herkimercsd.org/	77
Hermon-DeKalb Central Sch Dist	hdcsk12.org/	210
Herricks Union Free Sch Dist	herricks.org/	121
Heuvelton Central School Dist	heuvelton.schoolfusion.us/	210
Hewlett Woodmere Union Free SD	hewlett-woodmere.net/	121
Hicksville Union Free Sch Dist	hicksvillepublicschools.org	122
Highland Ctl School Dist	highland-k12.org/	242
Highland Falls-Ft Montgmry SD	hffmcsd.org/	164
Hilton Central School Dist	hilton.k12.ny.us	109
Hinsdale Central School Dist	hinsdalebobcats.org/site/default.aspx?PageID=1	32
Holland Central School Dist	holland.wnyric.org/Page/1	61
Holland Patent Ctl School Dist	hpschools.org	150
Holley Central School Dist	holleycsd.org/	169
Homer Central School Dist	homercentral.org/	47
Honeoye Central School Dist	honeoye.org/	161
Honeoye Falls Lima Sch Dist	hflcsd.org	109
Hoosic Valley Central Sch Dist	hoosicvalley.k12.ny.us/	190
Hoosick Falls Central Sch Dist	hoosickfallscsd.org/	190
Hornell City School Dist	hornellcityschools.com/	214
Horseheads Ctl School Dist	horseheadsdistrict.com/	40
Hudson City School Dist	hudsoncityschooldistrict.com/	46
Hudson Falls Central Sch Dist	hfcsd.org/	248
Hunter Tannersville Ctl SD	sites.google.com/htcschools.org/htc/home	76
Huntington Union Free Sch Dist	hufsd.edu/	223
Hyde Park Central School Dist	hpcsd.org/	52
Ichabod Crane Central Schools	ichabodcrane.org/	46
Indian Lake Ctl School Dist	ilcsd.org/	76

NY-W4 800-333-8802 School Year 2020-2021

New York School Directory

DISTRICT URL INDEX

DISTRICT	URL	PAGE
Indian River Ctl School Dist	ircsd.org/	80
Iroquois Central School Dist	iroquoiscsd.org/	61
Irvington Union Free Sch Dist	irvingtonschools.org/	257
Island Park Union Free SD	ips.k12.ny.us/	122
Island Trees Union Free SD	islandtrees.org	122
Islip Union Free School Dist	islipufsd.org/	223
Ithaca City School Dist	icsd.k12.ny.us/	240
Jamestown City School Dist	jpsny.org/	38
Jamesville-DeWitt Central SD	jamesvilledewitt.org/	155
Jasper Troupsburg Central SD	jtcsd.org/	214
Jefferson Central Sch Dist	jeffersoncs.org/	206
Jericho Union Free School Dist	jerichoschools.org/	122
Johnsburg Central School Dist	johnsburgcsd.org/	245
Johnson City Central Sch Dist	jcschools.com/	28
Jordan Elbridge Ctl Sch Dist	jecsd.org/	155
Katonah-Lewisboro Sch Dist	klschools.org/	257
Keene Central School Dist	kcs.neric.org/	67
Kendall Central School Dist	kendallschools.org/	169
Kenmore-Tonawanda UF Sch Dist	kenton.k12.ny.us/	62
Keshequa Central School Dist	keshequa.org/	103
Kings Park Ctl School Dist	kpcsd.k12.ny.us/	224
Kingston City School Dist	kingstoncityschools.org/	242
La Fargeville Central Sch Dist	lafargevillecsd.org/	80
La Fayette Central School Dist	lafayetteschools.org/	156
Lackawanna City School Dist	lackawannaschools.org/	62
Lake George Central Sch Dist	lkgeorge.org/	245
Lake Placid Ctl School Dist	lpcs.neric.org/	67
Lake Pleasant Central Sch Dist	lpschool.com/	76
Lakeland Central School Dist	lakelandschools.org/	257
Lancaster Central Sch Dist	lancasterschools.org/	62
Lansing Central School Dist	lcsd.k12.ny.us	240
Lansingburgh Central Sch Dist	lansingburgh.org	190
Laurens Central School Dist	laurenscs.org/	173
Lawrence Union Free Sch Dist	lawrence.org/	123
Le Roy Central School Dist	leroycsd.org/	73
Letchworth Central School Dist	letchworth.k12.ny.us/	267
Levittown Union Free Sch Dist	levittownschools.com	123
Lewiston Porter Ctl Sch Dist	lew-port.com/	146
Liberty Central School Dist	libertyk12.org/	236
Lindenhurst Union Free SD	lindenhurstschools.org/	224
Lisbon Central School Dist	lisboncs.schoolwires.com/	210
Little Falls City School Dist	lfcsd.org	78
Little Flower Union Free SD	ny02208470.schoolwires.net/	224
Liverpool Ctl School Dist	liverpool.k12.ny.us	156
Livingston Manor Ctl Sch Dist	lmcs.k12.ny.us	236
Livonia Ctl School Dist	livoniacsd.org/	103
Lockport City School Dist	lockportschools.org	147
Locust Valley Ctl School Dist	lvcsd.k12.ny.us/	123
Long Beach City School Dist	lbeach.org	124
Long Lake Central School Dist	longlakecsd.org/	76
Longwood Central School Dist	longwood.k12.ny.us/	224
Lowville Acad-Central Sch Dist	lowvilleacademy.org	101
Lyme Central School Dist	lymecsd.org/	81
Lynbrook Union Free Sch Dist	lynbrookschools.org/	124
Lyncourt Union Free Sch Dist	lyncourtschool.org/	156
Lyndonville Central Sch Dist	lyndonvillecsd.org/o/lcsd	169
Lyons Central School Dist	lyonscsd.org/	249
Madison Central School Dist	madisoncentralny.org/	105
Madrid-Waddington Central SD	mwcsk12.org/	211
Mahopac Ctl School Dist	mahopac.k12.ny.us/	176
Maine Endwell Ctl School Dist	me.stier.org	29
Malone Central School Dist	malonecsd.org/	69
Malverne Union Free Sch Dist	malverne.k12.ny.us/	124
Mamaroneck Union Free Sch Dist	mamkschools.org/	257
Manchester-Shortsville Ctl SD	redjacket.org/	162
Manhasset Union Free Sch Dist	manhassetschools.org/	124
Marathon Ctl School Dist	marathonschools.org/	48
Marcellus Central School Dist	marcellusschools.org/	157
Marcus Whitman Central SD	mwcsd.org/	162
Margaretville Central Sch Dist	margaretvillecs.org/	49
Marion Central School Dist	marioncs.org/	250
Marlboro Central School Dist	marlboroschools.schoolwires.com/	242
Massapequa Union Free SD 23	msd.k12.ny.us/	125
Massena Central School Dist	mcs.k12.ny.us	211

School Year 2020-2021   800-333-8802   NY-W5

DISTRICT URL INDEX

DISTRICT	URL	PAGE
Mattituck-Cutchogue UFSD	mufsd.com/	225
Mayfield Ctl School Dist	mayfieldk12.com/	72
McGraw Central School Dist	mcgrawschools.org/	48
Mechanicville City Sch Dist	mechanicville.org/	201
Medina Central School Dist	medinacsd.org/	169
Menands Union Free Sch Dist	menands.org/	11
Merrick Union Free School Dist	merrick.k12.ny.us/	125
Mexico Central School Dist	mexicocsd.org/	171
Middle Country Ctl Sch Dist	mccsd.net/	225
Middleburgh Ctl School Dist	middleburghcsd.org/	206
Middletown Enlarged City SD	middletowncityschools.org	165
Milford Central School Dist	milfordcentral.org/	173
Millbrook Ctl School Dist	millbrookcsd.org/	52
Miller Place Union Free SD	millerplace.k12.ny.us	225
Mineola Union Free Sch Dist	mineola.k12.ny.us/pages/Mineola_UFSD	125
Minerva Central School Dist	minervasd.org	68
Minisink Valley Central SD	minisink.com/	165
Mohonasen Central Sch Dist	mohonasen.org	203
Monroe Woodbury Central SD	mw.k12.ny.us/	165
Montauk Union Free School Dist	montaukschool.org/	226
Monticello Central School Dist	monticelloschools.net/	237
Moravia Central School Dist	moraviaschool.org/	34
Moriah Central School Dist	moriahk12.org/	68
Morris Central School Dist	morriscs.org	173
Morristown Ctl School Dist	greenrockets.org/	211
Morrisville Eaton Central SD	m-ecs.org	105
Mount Markham Central Sch Dist	mmcsd.org	78
Mount Vernon City School Dist	mtvernoncsd.org	258
Mt Morris Central School Dist	mtmorriscsd.org/	103
Mt Pleasant Cottage UFSD	mpcsny.org	258
Mt Pleasant Ctl School Dist	mtplcsd.org/	258
Mt Pleasant-Blythedale UFSD	mpbschools.org	259
Mt Sinai Union Free SD	mtsinai.k12.ny.us/	226
Nanuet Union Free School Dist	nanuetsd.org/	196
Naples Central School Dist	naples.k12.ny.us	162
New Hartford Central Sch Dist	newhartfordschools.org/	151
New Hyde-Garden City Park UFSD	nhp-gcp.org	126
New Lebanon Ctl School Dist	newlebanoncsd.org/	46
New Paltz Ctl School Dist	newpaltz.k12.ny.us	242
New Rochelle City School Dist	nred.org/	259
New Suffolk Common School Dist	newsuffolkschool.com	226
New York City Dept of Ed	schools.nyc.gov/default.aspx	134
New York Mills Union Free SD	newyorkmills.org/	151
Newark Central School Dist	newarkcsd.org	250
Newark Valley Central Sch Dist	nvcs.stier.org/	238
Newburgh Enlarged City SD	newburghschools.org/	165
Newcomb Central School Dist	newcombcsd.org/default.htm	68
Newfane Central School Dist	newfane.wnyric.org/	147
Newfield Central School Dist	newfieldschools.org	241
Niagara Falls City Sch Dist	nfschools.net	147
Niagara-Wheatfield Ctl SD	nwcsd.k12.ny.us/	148
Niskayuna Central School Dist	niskayunaschools.org/	204
North Babylon Union Free SD	northbabylonschools.net	226
North Bellmore Union Free SD	northbellmoreschools.org/	126
North Collins Ctl Sch Dist	northcollins.com	63
North Colonie Central SD	northcolonie.org/	11
North Greenbush Common SD	northgreenbushcommon.org/	191
North Merrick Union Free SD	nmerrickschools.org/	126
North Rockland Central SD	nrcsd.org/	197
North Rose Wolcott Central SD	nrwcs.org/	250
North Salem Central Sch Dist	northsalemschools.org/	259
North Shore Central SD	northshore.k12.ny.us/	126
North Syracuse Ctl Sch Dist	nscsd.org/	157
North Tonawanda City Sch Dist	ntschools.org/	148
North Warren Central Sch Dist	northwarren.k12.ny.us/	246
Northeastern Clinton Ctl SD	nccscougar.org/	44
Northern Adirondack Ctl SD	nacs1.org/	44
Northport-East Northport UFSD	web.northport.k12.ny.us/	227
Northville Central School Dist	northvillecsd.k12.ny.us/	72
Norwich City School Dist	norwichcsd.org/	42
Norwood-Norfolk Ctl SD	nncsk12.org/	211
Nyack Union Free School Dist	nyackschools.org	197
O E S J Central School Dist	oesj.org/	72
Oakfield Alabama Ctl SD	oacs.k12.ny.us	74

New York School Directory

DISTRICT URL INDEX

DISTRICT	URL	PAGE
Oceanside Union Free Sch Dist	oceansideschools.org/	127
Odessa Montour Ctl Sch Dist	omschools.org/	207
Ogdensburg City School Dist	ogdensburgk12.org/	211
Olean City School Dist	oleanschools.org/	32
Oneida City School Dist	oneidacsd.org/	105
Oneonta City School Dist	oneontacsd.org/	174
Onondaga Central School Dist	ocs.cnyric.org/	157
Onteora Central School Dist	onteora.k12.ny.us	243
Orchard Park Central Sch Dist	opschools.org/	63
Oriskany Ctl School Dist	oriskanycsd.org	151
Ossining Union Free Sch Dist	ossiningufsd.org/	259
Oswego City School Dist	oswego.org/	171
Otselic Valley Central SD	ovcs.org	42
Owego Apalachin Ctl Sch Dist	oacsd.org/	238
Oxford Academy Central SD	oxac.org/	42
Oyster Bay East Norwich Ctl SD	obenschools.org/	127
Oysterponds Union Free SD	oysterponds.org/	227
Palmyra-Macedon Central SD	palmaccsd.org/	250
Panama Central School Dist	pancent.org/	38
Parishville Hopkinton Sch Dist	phcs.neric.org/	212
Patchogue-Medford Unified SD	pmschools.org/	227
Pavilion Ctl School Dist	pavilioncsd.org/	74
Pawling Ctl School Dist	pawlingschools.org/	52
Pearl River School Dist	pearlriver.org	197
Peekskill City School Dist	peekskillcsd.org/	260
Pelham Union Free School Dist	pelhamschools.org/	260
Pembroke Ctl School Dist	pembrokecsd.org/	74
Penfield Central School Dist	penfield.edu/staff_directory.cfm	109
Penn Yan Ctl School Dist	pycsd.org/pages/Penn_Yan_CSD	268
Perry Central School Dist	perry.k12.ny.us	267
Peru Central School Dist	perucsd.org/	44
Phelps-Clifton Springs Ctl SD	midlakes.org	162
Phoenix Central School Dist	phoenixcsd.org/	171
Pine Bush Central School Dist	pinebushschools.org/	166
Pine Plains Ctl School Dist	ppcsd.org/	53
Pine Valley Central Sch Dist	pval.org/	38
Pittsford Central Sch Dist	pittsfordschools.org/	110
Plainedge Union Free Sch Dist	plainedgeschools.org/	127
Plainview-Old Bethpage Ctl SD	pobschools.org/	127
Plattsburgh City School Dist	plattscsd.org	44
Pleasantville Union Free SD	pleasantvilleschools.com/	260
Pocantico Hills Ctl Sch Dist	pocanticohills.org/	260
Poland Central School Dist	polandcs.com/education/district/district.php?sectionid=1	78
Port Byron Ctl School Dist	pbcschools.org/	35
Port Chester Rye Union Free SD	portchesterschools.org	261
Port Jefferson Union Free SD 6	portjeffschools.org/	227
Port Jervis City School Dist	portjerviscsd.k12.ny.us/	166
Port Washington Union Free SD	portnet.k12.ny.us/	128
Portville Central School Dist	portville.wnyric.org	32
Potsdam Central School Dist	potsdam.k12.ny.us/	212
Poughkeepsie City School Dist	poughkeepsieschools.org/	53
Prattsburgh Central Sch Dist	prattsburghcsd.org/	215
Pulaski Central School Dist	pacs.cnyric.org	172
Putnam Central School Dist	putnamcsd.org/	248
Putnam Valley Ctl School Dist	pvcsd.org	176
Queensbury Union Free Sch Dist	queensburyschool.org/	246
Quogue Union Free School Dist	quogueschool.com/	228
Randolph Acad Union Free SD	randolphacademy.org/	32
Randolph Central School Dist	randolphcsd.org/	33
Ravena Coeymans Selkirk Ctl SD	rcscsd.org	11
Red Creek Central School Dist	rccsd.org/	251
Red Hook Central School Dist	redhookcentralschools.org/	53
Remsen Central School Dist	remsencsd.org	151
Remsenburg-Speonk UFSD	rsufsd.weebly.com/	228
Rensselaer City School Dist	rcsd.k12.ny.us/	191
Rhinebeck Central School Dist	rhinebeckcsd.org/	53
Richfield Springs Central SD	richfieldcsd.org/	174
Ripley Central School Dist	ripleyelementary.weebly.com/	39
Riverhead Central School Dist	riverhead.net/	228
Rochester City School Dist	rcsdk12.org/	110
Rockville Ctr Union Free SD	rvcschools.org	128
Rocky Point Union Free SD	rockypointschools.org/	228
Rome City School Dist	romecsd.org/	151
Romulus Ctl School Dist	romuluscsd.org/	208

DISTRICT URL INDEX

DISTRICT	URL	PAGE
Rondout Valley Ctl Sch Dist	rondout.k12.ny.us/	243
Roosevelt Union Free Sch Dist	rooseveltufsd.org	128
Roscoe Central School Dist	roscoe.k12.ny.us/	237
Roslyn School Dist	roslynschools.org/	129
Roxbury Central School Dist	roxburycs.org/	50
Royalton Hartland Central SD	royhart.org/	148
Rush Henrietta Central SD	rhnet.org	112
Rye City School Dist	ryeschools.org/	261
Rye Neck Union Free Sch Dist	ryeneck.k12.ny.us	261
Sachem Central School Dist	sachem.edu	229
Sackets Harbor Ctl School Dist	sacketspatriots.org/	81
Sag Harbor Union Free Sch Dist	sagharborschools.org/	229
Sagaponack Common School Dist	sagaponackschool.com/	229
Salamanca City Central SD	salamancany.org/	33
Salem Central School Dist	salemcsd.org	248
Salmon River Central Sch Dist	srk12.org	70
Sandy Creek Central Sch Dist	sccs.cnyric.org/	172
Saranac Central School Dist	saranac.org	45
Saranac Lake Central Sch Dist	slcs.org/	70
Saratoga Springs City Sch Dist	saratogaschools.org	201
Saugerties Central School Dist	saugerties.k12.ny.us/	243
Sauquoit Valley Central SD	svcsd.org/	152
Sayville Union Free Sch Dist	sayvilleschools.org/	229
Scarsdale Union Free Sch Dist	scarsdaleschools.org/site/default.aspx?PageID=1	261
Schalmont Central School Dist	schalmont.org	204
Schenectady City School Dist	schenectady.k12.ny.us/	204
Schenevus Ctl School Dist	schenevuscs.org/	174
Schodack Central School Dist	schodack.k12.ny.us/	191
Schoharie Central SD	schoharie.k12.ny.us	206
Schroon Lake Ctl School Dist	schroonschool.org/	68
Schuylerville Central Sch Dist	schuylervilleschools.org	201
Scio Central School Dist	scio.schooltools.us/	15
Scotia Glenville Ctl Sch Dist	scotiaglenvilleschools.org/	205
Seaford Union Free SD	seaford.k12.ny.us/seaford/site/default.asp	129
Seneca Falls Central Sch Dist	sfcs.k12.ny.us	208
Sewanhaka Ctl High Sch Dist	sewanhaka.k12.ny.us	129
Sharon Springs Ctl SD	sharonsprings.org/	207
Shelter Island Union Free SD	shelterisland.k12.ny.us	230
Shenendehowa Central Sch Dist	shenet.org/	202
Sherburne Earlville Central SD	secsd.org/	42
Sherman Central School Dist	shermancsd.org/	39
Shoreham-Wading River Ctl SD	swrschools.org/	230
Sidney Central School Dist	sidneycsd.org/	50
Silver Creek Central Sch Dist	silvercreekschools.org/	39
Skaneateles Central Sch Dist	skanschools.org/	157
Smithtown Central Sch Dist	smithtown.k12.ny.us	230
Sodus Central School Dist	soduscsd.org/	251
Solvay Union Free Sch Dist	solvayschools.org	158
Somers Central School Dist	somersschools.org/	262
South Colonie Central Sch Dist	southcolonieschools.org/	12
South Country Central Sch Dist	southcountry.org	231
South Glens Falls Ctl Sch Dist	sgfallssd.org	202
South Huntington Union Free SD	shufsd.org/	231
South Jefferson Central SD	spartanpride.org	81
South Kortright Ctl SD	skcs.org/	50
South Lewis Central Sch Dist	southlewis.org	101
South Orangetown Central SD	socsd.org/	197
South Seneca Ctl Sch Dist	southseneca.com/	208
Southampton Union Free SD	southamptonschools.org/Page/9	231
Southern Cayuga Central SD	southerncayuga.org/	35
Southold Union Free Sch Dist	southoldufsd.com/	231
Southwestern Central Sch Dist	swcs.wnyric.org	39
Spackenkill Union Free SD	spackenkillschools.org/	54
Spencer Van Etten Central SD	svecsd.org/	238
Spencerport Central Sch Dist	spencerportschools.org	112
Springs Union Free School Dist	springsschool.org/	232
Springville Griffith Inst CSD	springvillegi.org/	63
St Regis Falls Ctl Sch Dist	stregiscsd.org/	70
Stamford Central School Dist	stamfordcs.org/	50
Starpoint Central School Dist	starpointcsd.org/	149
Stillwater Central Sch Dist	scsd.org/404.cfm	202
Stockbridge Valley Central SD	stockbridgevalley.org/	106
Suffern Central School Dist	sufferncentral.org/	198
Sullivan West Central SD	swcsd.org/	237

New York School Directory

DISTRICT URL INDEX

DISTRICT	URL	PAGE
Susquehanna Valley Central SD	svsabers.org	29
Sweet Home Central Sch Dist	sweethomeschools.org/	63
Syosset Central School Dist	syosset.k12.ny.us/	129
Syracuse City School Dist	syracusecityschools.com/	158
Taconic Hills Central Sch Dist	taconichills.k12.ny.us	47
Tarrytown Union Free Sch Dist	tufsd.org	262
Thousand Islands Central SD	1000islandsschools.org/	81
Three Village Central Sch Dist	threevillagecsd.org/	232
Ticonderoga Central Sch Dist	ticonderogak12.org	68
Tioga Central School Dist	tiogacentral.org/	239
Tonawanda City School Dist	tonawandacsd.org/	64
Town of Webb Union Free SD	towschool.org/	78
Tri-Valley Central School Dist	trivalleycsd.org/	237
Troy City School Dsitrict	troycsd.org/	191
Trumansburg Central SD	tburgschools.org/districtpage.cfm?pagei	241
Tuckahoe Common School Dist	tuckahoecommonsd.com/welcome.php?Active	232
Tuckahoe Union Free SD	tuckahoeschools.org/	262
Tully Central School Dist	tullyschools.org	159
Tupper Lake Ctl School Dist	tupperlakecsd.net/	70
Tuxedo Union Free Sch Dist	tuxedoufsd.org/district.cfm	166
Unadilla Valley Ctl Sch Dist	uvstorm.org/	43
Unatego Unadilla Central SD	unatego.org/	174
Union Springs Ctl School Dist	unionspringscsd.org/	35
Union-Endicott Ctl Sch Dist	uek12.org	29
Uniondale Union Free Sch Dist	district.uniondaleschools.org	130
Utica City School Dist	uticaschools.org/	152
Valhalla Union Free Sch Dist	valhallaschools.org/	262
Valley Central School Dist	vcsd.k12.ny.us/	167
Valley Stream Ctl High SD	vschsd.org/	130
Valley Stream Union Free SD 13	valleystream13.com/	130
Valley Stream Union Free SD 24	valleystreamdistrict24.org/	131
Valley Stream Union Free SD 30	valleystream30.com/	131
Vernon-Verona-Sherrill CSD	vvsschools.org/	152
Vestal Ctl School Dist	vestal.stier.org/	29
Victor Central School Dist	victorschools.org	162
Voorheesville Central Sch Dist	vcsd.neric.org/	12
Wainscott Common School Dist	wainscottschool.org/	232
Wallkill Central School Dist	wallkillcsd.k12.ny.us/Page/9	243
Walton Central School Dist	waltoncsd.org/	50
Wantagh Union Free Sch Dist 23	wantaghschools.org/	131
Wappingers Central Sch Dist	wappingersschools.org/	54
Warrensburg Central Sch Dist	wcsd.org/	246
Warsaw Central School Dist	warsaw.k12.ny.us/	267
Warwick Valley Central SD	warwickvalleyschools.com/	167
Washingtonville Central SD	ws.k12.ny.us/	167
Waterford Halfmoon School Dist	whufsd.org/	203
Waterloo Central School Dist	waterloocsd.org/	208
Watertown City School Dist	watertowncsd.org/	81
Waterville Central Sch Dist	watervillecsd.org/	153
Watervliet City School Dist	vliet.neric.org/	12
Watkins Glen Central Sch Dist	wgcsd.org/	207
Waverly Ctl School Dist	waverlyschools.com	239
Wayland-Cohocton Central SD	wccsk12.org/	215
Wayne Central School Dist	waynecsd.org/	251
Webster Central School Dist	websterschools.org	112
Webutuck Ctl School Dist	webutuckschools.org/	54
Weedsport Ctl School Dist	schools.weedsport.com/	35
Wells Central School Dist	wellscsd.com/main/	77
Wellsville Central Sch Dist	wellsvilleschools.org/	15
West Babylon Union Free SD	wbschools.org/	232
West Canada Valley Ctl SD	westcanada.org/	79
West Genesee Ctl School Dist	westgenesee.org/	159
West Hempstead School Dist	whufsd.com/	131
West Irondequoit Ctl SD	westirondequoit.org/	113
West Islip School Dist	wi.k12.ny.us/	233
West Point School Dist	am.dodea.edu/ny_va/new_york.html	167
West Seneca Central Sch Dist	wscschools.org	64
West Valley Ctl Sch Dist	wvalley.wnyric.org/	33
Westbury Union Free Sch Dist	westburyschools.org/	132
Westfield Central School Dist	wacs.wnyric.org/	39
Westhampton Beach School Dist	whbschools.org/	233
Westhill Central School Dist	westhillschools.org/	159
Westmoreland Central Sch Dist	westmorelandschool.org/	153
Wheatland Chili Ctl Sch Dist	wheatland.k12.ny.us/	113

School Year 2020-2021   800-333-8802

DISTRICT URL INDEX

DISTRICT	URL	PAGE
Wheelerville Union Free SD	wufsk8.com/	72
White Plains City School Dist	whiteplainspublicschools.org/page/1	263
Whitehall Central School Dist	railroaders.net/	248
Whitesboro Ctl School Dist	wboro.org	153
Whitesville Central Sch Dist	whitesville.wnyric.org/	15
Whitney Point Central Sch Dist	wpcsd.org	30
William Floyd School Dist	wfsd.k12.ny.us/	233
Williamson Central School Dist	williamsoncentral.org/	251
Williamsville Ctl School Dist	williamsvillek12.org/	64
Willsboro Central Sch Dist	willsborocsd.org/	68
Wilson Central School Dist	wilson.wnyric.org/	149
Windham Ashland Jewett Ctl SD	wajcs.org/	76
Windsor Central School Dist	windsor-csd.org/	30
Worcester Ctl School Dist	worcestercs.org/	174
Wyandanch Union Free Sch Dist	wyandanch.k12.ny.us/	234
Wynantskill Union Free SD	wynantskillufsd.org/	191
Wyoming Central School Dist	wyomingcsd.org/	268
Yonkers Public School Dist	yonkerspublicschools.org/	263
York Central School Dist	yorkcsd.org	103
Yorkshire-Pioneer Ctl Sch Dist	pioneerschools.org/pioneer/site/default.asp	33
Yorktown Central School Dist	yorktown.org	264

MDR School Directory

CHARTER MANAGEMENT ORGANIZATION (CMO) INDEX

CMO No.	PID	CMO Name	Address	Phone
001	11912383	Estem Public Charter Schools	200 River Market Ave Ste 225, Little Rock AR 72201	(501) 324-9200
002	11916092	KIPP Delta Public Schools	320 Missouri, Helena AR 72342	(870) 753-9035
003	12319502	Lisa Academy Foundation	10825 Financial Centre Pkwy, Little Rock AR 72211	(501) 916-9450
004	12376823	Academies of Math & Science	2980 N Campbell Ave, Tucson AZ 85719	(520) 887-5392
005	11912826	Academy of Tucson Inc	10720 E 22nd St, Tucson AZ 85748	(520) 733-0096
006	11914305	Accelerated Learning Ctr	4105 E Shea Blvd, Phoenix AZ 85028	(602) 485-0309
007	11914288	Allen-Cochran Enterprises	1700 E Elliot Rd Ste 9, Tempe AZ 85284	(480) 632-1940
008	11914264	American Basic Schools LLC	131 E Southern Ave, Mesa AZ 85210	(480) 655-7868
009	11928033	American Leadership Acad Inc	2250 E Germann Rd Ste 14, Chandler AZ 85286	(480) 420-2101
010	11912761	Arizona Agribus&Equine Ctr Org	315 E Mulberry Dr, Phoenix AZ 85012	(602) 297-8500
011	11912759	Arizona Charter Schools	5704 E Grant Rd, Tucson AZ 85712	(520) 545-0575
012	12376835	Asu Preparatory Acad Network	PO Box 876705, Tempe AZ 85287	(602) 496-3322
013	11912723	Basis School Inc	7975 N Hayden Rd Ste B202, Scottsdale AZ 85258	(480) 289-2088
014	11914525	Benjamin Franklin Chtr Schools	690 E Warner Rd Ste 141, Gilbert AZ 85296	(480) 264-3710
015	11912668	Blueprint Education	5651 W Talavi Blvd Ste 170, Glendale AZ 85306	(602) 674-5555
016	11914226	Bright Beginnings School Inc	400 N Andersen Blvd, Chandler AZ 85224	(480) 821-1404
017	11912620	CAFA Inc	4055 E Warner Rd, Gilbert AZ 85296	(480) 635-1900
018	11913387	Career Success Schools	3816 N 27th Ave, Phoenix AZ 85017	(602) 285-5525
019	11913351	Center for Academic Success	1843 Paseo San Luis, Sierra Vista AZ 85635	(520) 458-9309
020	11914173	Compass High School Inc	PO Box 17810, Tucson AZ 85731	(520) 296-4070
021	11914159	Cornerstone Charter School Inc	7107 N Black Canyon Hwy, Phoenix AZ 85021	(602) 595-2198
022	11914147	Country Gardens Educl Svcs	6313 W Southern Ave, Laveen AZ 85339	(602) 237-3741
023	11914111	Eastpointe High School Inc	8495 E Broadway Blvd, Tucson AZ 85710	(520) 731-8180
024	11914068	Educational Impact Inc	1950 E Placita Sin Nombre, Tucson AZ 85718	(520) 296-0656
025	11914044	Eduprize Schools Inc	4567 W Roberts Rd, Queen Creek AZ 85142	(480) 888-1610
026	11912395	Espiritu Community Development	222 E Olympic Dr, Phoenix AZ 85042	(602) 243-7788
027	12378118	Fit Kids Inc Champion Schools	6991 E Camelback Rd Ste D300, Scottsdale AZ 85251	(480) 386-7071
028	11914032	GAR LLC	8253 W Thunderbird Rd Ste 105, Peoria AZ 85381	(602) 334-4104
029	11913234	Great Hearts Academies	4801 E Washington St Ste 250, Phoenix AZ 85034	(602) 438-7045
030	11913985	Heritage Academy Inc	32 S Center St, Mesa AZ 85210	(480) 969-5641
031	11914434	Humanities & Sciences Acad US	5201 N 7th St, Phoenix AZ 85014	(602) 650-1333
032	11911781	Imagine Southwest Regional	1843 W 16th Ave, Apache Jct AZ 85120	(480) 355-0502
033	11913179	Kingman Academy of Learning	3410 N Burbank St, Kingman AZ 86409	(928) 681-2400
034	11913167	Leading Edge Charter Solutions	633 E Ray Rd Ste 132, Gilbert AZ 85296	(480) 633-0414
035	11913143	Learning Matters Educl Group	4744 W Grovers Ave, Glendale AZ 85308	(602) 439-5026
036	11913959	Legacy Traditional Schools	3125 S Gilbert Rd, Chandler AZ 85286	(480) 270-5438
037	11914599	Leona Group LLC-AZ	7500 N Dreamy Draw Dr Ste 220, Phoenix AZ 85020	(602) 953-2933
038	11914381	Mgrm Pinnacle Education Inc	2224 W Southern Ave Ste 1, Tempe AZ 85282	(480) 755-8222
039	11913911	Montessori Schoolhouse Tucson	1301 E Fort Lowell Rd, Tucson AZ 85719	(520) 319-8668
040	11913923	Montessori Schools Flagstaff	2212 E Cedar Ave, Flagstaff AZ 86004	(928) 774-1600
041	12305874	Pima Prevention Partnership	1477 W Commerce Ct, Tucson AZ 85746	(520) 791-2711
042	12306309	Plc Charter Schools	2504 S 91st Ave, Tolleson AZ 85353	(623) 474-2120
043	11912101	Pointe Educational Services	10215 N 43rd Ave, Phoenix AZ 85051	(602) 843-2014
044	11913519	PPEP and Affiliates	802 E 46th St, Tucson AZ 85713	(520) 622-3553
045	11913856	Rose Management Group	3686 W Orange Grove Rd Ste 192, Tucson AZ 85741	(520) 797-4884
046	11913832	Self Development Chtr Sch Org	1709 N Greenfield Rd, Mesa AZ 85205	(480) 641-2640
047	11913337	Sequoia Schools-Edkey Inc	1460 S Horne Bldg 6, Mesa AZ 85204	(480) 461-3200
048	11912979	Skyline Education	7450 S 40th St 7500, Phoenix AZ 85042	(877) 225-2118
049	11913349	Sonoran Schools Inc	1489 W Elliot Rd Ste 103, Gilbert AZ 85233	(480) 940-5440
050	11913806	Southern Arizona Cmty Acad Inc	2470 N Tucson Blvd, Tucson AZ 85716	(520) 319-6113
051	11912929	The Charter Foundation Inc	1150 N Country Club Rd Ste 100, Tucson AZ 85716	(520) 296-1100
052	11911901	The Edge School Inc	2555 E 1st St, Tucson AZ 85716	(520) 881-1389
053	11912890	Tucson International Academy	2700 W Broadway Blvd, Tucson AZ 85745	(520) 792-3255
054	11912802	Albert Einstein Academies	3035 Ash St, San Diego CA 92102	(619) 795-1190
055	11913686	Alliance College-Ready Pub Sch	601 S Figueroa St Fl 4, Los Angeles CA 90017	(213) 943-4930
056	12305812	Alpha Public Schools	PO Box 21366, San Jose CA 95151	(408) 455-6355
057	12262961	Alta Public Schools	2410 Broadway, Huntington Pk CA 90255	(323) 923-0383
058	11912785	American Indian Model Schools	171 12th St, Oakland CA 94607	(510) 893-8701
059	12262911	Amethod Public Schools	2101 Livingston St, Oakland CA 94606	(510) 436-0172
060	12379124	Aspire Bay Area Region	1001 22nd Ave Ste 200, Oakland CA 94606	(510) 568-3101

CHARTER MANAGEMENT ORGANIZATION (CMO) INDEX

Market Data Retrieval

CMO No.	PID	CMO Name	Address	Phone
061	12379136	Aspire Central Vly Area Region	3311 Morada Ln, Stockton CA 95212	(209) 647-3047
062	12379148	Aspire Los Angeles Area Region	5901 E Slauson Ave, Los Angeles CA 90040	(323) 837-9920
063	11913648	Aspire Public Schools	1001 22nd Ave Ste 100, Oakland CA 94606	(510) 434-5000
064	11912656	Bright Star Education Group	600 S La Fayette Park Pl, Los Angeles CA 90057	(323) 954-9957
065	11913404	California Montessori Projects	5330A Gibbons Dr Ste 700, Carmichael CA 95608	(916) 971-2432
066	11913399	Camino Nuevo Charter Academy	3435 W Temple St, Los Angeles CA 90026	(213) 417-3400
067	11912709	Ceiba Public Schools	260 W Riverside Dr, Watsonville CA 95076	(831) 740-8800
068	12260028	Citizens of the World Chtr Sch	5371 Wilshire Blvd Ste 210, Los Angeles CA 90036	(323) 634-7109
069	11912565	Civicorps Schools	101 Myrtle St, Oakland CA 94607	(510) 992-7800
070	11912539	Community Learning Center Schs	1900 3rd St, Alameda CA 94501	(510) 263-9266
071	11912527	Core-Cmty Options Resources Ed	321 16th St, Marysville CA 95901	(530) 742-2786
072	12377413	Da Vinci Schools	201 N Douglas St, El Segundo CA 90245	(310) 725-5800
073	12110435	Downtown College Prep	1400 Parkmoor Ave Ste 206, San Jose CA 95126	(408) 271-8120
074	12261486	Ednovate Inc	350 S Figueroa St Ste 350, Los Angeles CA 90071	(213) 454-0599
075	11912436	Education for Change	333 Hegenberger Rd Ste 600, Oakland CA 94621	(510) 568-7936
076	11912412	Environmental Charter Schools	2625 Manhattn Bch Blvd Ste 100, Redondo Beach CA 90278	(310) 214-3408
077	11913301	Envision Education	111 Myrtle St Ste 203, Oakland CA 94607	(510) 451-2415
078	12179015	Equitas Academy Chtr Sch Inc	1700 W Pico Blvd, Los Angeles CA 90015	(213) 201-0440
079	12305824	Fenton Charter Public Schools	8928 Sunland Blvd, Sun Valley CA 91352	(818) 962-3630
080	11912357	Five Keys Charter Schools Inc	70 Oak Grove St, San Francisco CA 94107	(415) 734-3310
081	12262935	Fortune School of Education	2890 Gateway Oaks Dr Ste 100, Sacramento CA 95833	(916) 924-8633
082	11913258	Gateway Community Charters	5112 Arnold Ave Ste A, McClellan CA 95652	(916) 286-5129
083	11912319	Golden Valley Charter Schools	3585 Maple St Ste 101, Ventura CA 93003	(805) 642-3435
084	11913595	Green Dot Public Schools	1149 S Hill St Ste 600, Los Angeles CA 90015	(323) 565-1600
085	12239598	Grimmway Schools	5080 California Ave Ste 100, Bakersfield CA 93309	(661) 432-7880
086	11912280	High Desert Partnsp Acad Excel	17500 Mana Rd, Apple Valley CA 92307	(760) 946-5414
087	11913222	High Tech High	2861 Womble Rd, San Diego CA 92106	(619) 243-5000
088	11913583	ICEF Public Schools	3855 W Slauson Ave, Los Angeles CA 90043	(323) 290-6900
089	11912266	Innovative Education Managemnt	4535 Missouri Flat Rd Ste 1A, Placerville CA 95667	(800) 979-4436
090	11913375	Isana Academies	3580 Wilshire Blvd Ste 1130, Los Angeles CA 90010	(323) 291-1211
091	11913181	King-Chavez Neighborhood Schs	2260 Island Ave, San Diego CA 92102	(619) 525-7320
092	11916054	KIPP Bay Area Public Schools	1000 Broadway Ste 460, Oakland CA 94607	(510) 465-5477
093	11913571	KIPP Foundation	135 Main St Ste 1700, San Francisco CA 94105	(415) 399-1556
094	11916169	KIPP Socal Public Schools	3601 E 1st St, Los Angeles CA 90063	(213) 489-4461
095	11913155	Leadership Public Schools	99 Linden St, Oakland CA 94607	(510) 830-3780
096	12260030	Los Angeles Education Corps	3635 Atlantic Ave, Long Beach CA 90807	(562) 216-1790
097	11913557	Magnolia Ed & Research Fdn	250 E 1st St Ste 1500, Los Angeles CA 90012	(213) 628-3634
098	11912187	National Univ Academy System	1980 University Dr Ste 30, Vista CA 92083	(760) 630-4080
099	12262777	Navigator Schools	650 San Benito St Ste 230, Hollister CA 95023	(831) 217-4880
100	12361373	Olive Grove Charter Schools	2353 S Broadway, Santa Maria CA 93454	(805) 623-1111
101	11935907	Opportunities for Learning	320 N Halstead St Ste 220, Pasadena CA 91107	(888) 207-1119
102	11913052	Options for Youth Inc	320 N Halstead St Ste 280, Pasadena CA 91107	(888) 389-9992
103	12262923	Pacific Charter Institute	1401 El Camino Ave Ste 510, Sacramento CA 95815	(866) 992-9033
104	11912125	Para Los Ninos PCS	5000 Hollywood Blvd, Los Angeles CA 90027	(213) 250-4800
105	11913521	Partnerships to Uplift Cmty	1405 N San Fernando Blvd 303, Burbank CA 91504	(818) 559-7699
106	11912060	Real Journey Academies	1425 W Foothill Blvd Ste 100, Upland CA 91786	(909) 888-8458
107	11912046	Roads Education Organization	2999 Cleveland Ave Ste D, Santa Rosa CA 95403	(707) 843-4676
108	11912034	Rocketship Education	350 Twin Dolphin Dr Ste 109, Redwood City CA 94065	(877) 806-0920
109	11911872	Rocklin Academy Charter Schs	2204 Plaza Dr Ste 200, Rocklin CA 95765	(916) 778-4544
110	11912008	Semillas Sociedad Civil	4736 Huntington Dr S, Los Angeles CA 90032	(323) 352-3148
111	11911987	St Hope Public Schools	PO Box 5038, Sacramento CA 95817	(916) 649-7900
112	12101381	Summit Public Schools	780 Broadway St, Redwood City CA 94063	(650) 257-9880
113	11911925	The Accelerated School	116 E Mlk Jr Blvd, Los Angeles CA 90011	(323) 235-6343
114	12378742	The Classical Academies	157 E Valley Pkwy, Escondido CA 92025	(760) 842-8000
115	11911884	The Learner-Centered School	3325 Hacienda Way, Antioch CA 94509	(925) 755-7311
116	11911846	Tracy Learning Center	51 E Beverly Pl, Tracy CA 95376	(209) 290-0511
117	11911822	Value Schools	680 Wilshire Pl Ste 315, Los Angeles CA 90005	(213) 388-8676
118	12306244	Western Sierra Charter Schools	41267 Highway 41, Oakhurst CA 93644	(559) 642-1422
119	12262791	Ypi Charter Schools	10660 White Oak Ave B101, Granada Hills CA 91344	(818) 834-5805
120	12321684	Colorado Early College Network	4405 N Chestnut St Ste E, Colorado Spgs CO 80907	(719) 955-4685

MDR School Directory
CHARTER MANAGEMENT ORGANIZATION (CMO) INDEX

CMO No.	PID	CMO Name	Address	Phone
121	12378156	Dsst Public School Foundation	3401 Quebec St Ste 2000, Denver CO 80207	(303) 524-6324
122	12322432	Global Village Charter Collab	555 W 112th Ave, Northglenn CO 80234	(720) 353-4113
123	11916078	KIPP Colorado	1390 Lawrence St Ste 200, Denver CO 80204	(303) 934-3245
124	12305886	Rocky Mountain Prep Schools	7808 Cherry Creek Dr S, Denver CO 80231	(720) 863-8920
125	12110356	Strive Preparatory Schools	2480 W 26th Ave Ste 360B, Denver CO 80211	(720) 772-4300
126	12322626	Tatonka Education Services	10375 Park Meadows Dr Ste 230, Lone Tree CO 80124	(303) 296-6500
127	11913090	The New America Schools Netwk	925 S Niagara St Ste 140/400, Denver CO 80224	(303) 800-0058
128	11913698	Achievement First Network	370 James St Ste 404, New Haven CT 06513	(203) 773-3223
129	11915414	Jumoke Academy Inc	999 Asylum Ave Ste 200, Hartford CT 06105	(860) 216-9636
130	11913650	Aspira Educl Management Org	1220 L St NW Ste 701, Washington DC 20005	(202) 835-3600
131	11913363	Center City Public Charter Sch	900 2nd St NE Ste 221, Washington DC 20002	(202) 589-0202
132	11912591	Cesar Chavez Public Chtr Schs	3701 Hayes St NE, Washington DC 20019	(202) 547-3975
133	11912503	DC Prep	707 Edgewood St NE, Washington DC 20017	(202) 635-4590
134	11913260	Friendship Public Charter Sch	111 O St NW, Washington DC 20001	(202) 281-1700
135	11914836	KIPP DC	2600 Virginia Ave NW Ste 900, Washington DC 20037	(202) 223-4505
136	11912010	See Forever Foundation	600 Pennsylvania Ave SE, Washington DC 20003	(202) 797-8250
137	11911860	The Seed Foundation	1730 Rh Isl Ave NW Ste 1102, Washington DC 20036	(202) 785-4123
138	11914680	Academica	6340 Sunset Dr, Miami FL 33143	(305) 669-2906
139	11914549	Accelerated Learning Solutions	5850 T G Lee Blvd Ste 345, Orlando FL 32822	(888) 437-9353
140	11914496	Charter School Associates Inc	5471 N University Dr, Coral Springs FL 33067	(954) 414-5767
141	11914678	Charter Schools USA	800 Corporate Dr Ste 700, Ft Lauderdale FL 33334	(954) 202-3500
142	11912541	Cmty & Eco Dev Org Gadsden Co	20 E Washington St, Quincy FL 32351	(850) 627-7656
143	11914630	Edisonlearning Inc	1 E Broward Blvd Ste 1111, Ft Lauderdale FL 33301	(877) 890-7088
144	12261709	Forza Education Management LLC	PO Box 830, Parrish FL 34219	(727) 642-9319
145	11916420	Imagine South Florida Regional	13790 NW 4th St Ste 108, Sunrise FL 33325	(954) 870-5023
146	11916406	Imagine Southeast Regional	775 Town Center Blvd, Palm Coast FL 32164	(888) 709-8010
147	11916157	KIPP Jacksonville Schools	1440 McDuff Ave N, Jacksonville FL 32254	(904) 683-6643
148	12179651	Lake Wales Charter Schools	130 E Central Ave, Lake Wales FL 33853	(863) 679-6560
149	11913569	Lighthouse Academies	29140 Chapel Park Dr Bldg 5A, Wesley Chapel FL 33543	(800) 901-6943
150	11913947	LII Licensing Inc	6710 86th Ave N, Pinellas Park FL 33782	(727) 768-0989
151	11914379	Rader Group	101A Business Centre Dr, Miramar Beach FL 32550	(850) 650-3984
152	11913789	Superior Schools	861 N Hercules Ave, Clearwater FL 33765	(727) 799-1200
153	11916224	KIPP Metro Atlanta Schools	1445 Maynard Rd NW, Atlanta GA 30331	(404) 924-6310
154	12240195	Mountain Ed Chtr High School	1963 Tom Bell Rd, Cleveland GA 30528	(706) 219-4664
155	12259990	Gem Innovation Schools	PO Box 86, Deary ID 83823	(208) 238-1388
156	11913466	Acero Charter Schools Inc	209 W Jackson Blvd Ste 500, Chicago IL 60606	(312) 637-3900
157	11913662	American Quality Schools Corp	1315 Butterfield Rd Ste 224, Downers Grove IL 60515	(312) 226-3355
158	11912670	Betty Shabazz Intl Chtr Sch	7822 S Dobson Ave, Chicago IL 60619	(773) 651-1221
159	11912606	Catalyst Schools	6727 S California Ave, Chicago IL 60629	(773) 295-7001
160	11912553	Civitas Education Partners	1006 S Michigan Ave Ste 301, Chicago IL 60605	(312) 733-6790
161	11913636	Concept Schools	1336 Basswood Rd, Schaumburg IL 60173	(847) 824-3380
162	11912333	Galapagos Charter	3051 Rotary Rd, Rockford IL 61109	(779) 368-0852
163	11914812	KIPP Chicago	2007 S Halsted St, Chicago IL 60608	(312) 733-8108
164	12110447	Lawndale Educ & Reg Network	3021 W Carroll Ave, Chicago IL 60612	(773) 584-4399
165	11913545	Noble Network of Charter Sch	1 N State St Ste 700, Chicago IL 60602	(312) 521-5287
166	11913038	Perspectives Charter Schools	1530 S State St Ste 200, Chicago IL 60605	(312) 604-2200
167	12260016	Regeneration Schools	1816 W Garfield Blvd, Chicago IL 60609	(773) 778-9455
168	11913246	GEO Foundation	1630 N Meridian St Ste 350, Indianapolis IN 46202	(317) 536-1027
169	12315427	Goodwill Education Initiatives	1635 W Michigan St, Indianapolis IN 46222	(317) 524-4265
170	11916145	KIPP Indy Public Schools	1740 E 30th St, Indianapolis IN 46218	(317) 547-5477
171	12179027	Tindley Accelerated Schools	3960 Meadows Dr, Indianapolis IN 46205	(317) 545-1745
172	11913430	Algiers Charter School Assoc	2401 Westbend Pkwy Ste 2001, New Orleans LA 70114	(504) 302-7001
173	12115203	Collegiate Academies	2625 Thalia St, New Orleans LA 70113	(504) 503-0008
174	11930816	Crescent City Schools	3811 N Galvez St, New Orleans LA 70117	(504) 708-4136
175	11912369	Firstline Schools Inc	300 N Broad St Ste 207, New Orleans LA 70119	(504) 267-9038
176	11930725	Friends of King Schools	1617 Caffin Ave, New Orleans LA 70117	(504) 940-2243
177	12372592	Idea Public Schools S Louisana	804 Main St, Baton Rouge LA 70802	(225) 963-6539
178	12179039	Inspirenola Charter Schools	2401 Westbend Pkwy Ste 4040, New Orleans LA 70114	(504) 227-3057
179	12259213	Jcfa Charter Schools	475 Manhattan Blvd, Harvey LA 70058	(504) 410-3121
180	11916250	KIPP New Orleans Schools	1307 Oretha Castle Haley Blvd, New Orleans LA 70113	(504) 373-6269

CHARTER MANAGEMENT ORGANIZATION (CMO) INDEX — Market Data Retrieval

CMO No.	PID	CMO Name	Address	Phone
181	11912058	Renew Schools Inc	1001 Lake Forest Blvd Ste 710, New Orleans LA 70127	(504) 367-3307
182	11911913	The Choice Foundation	3201 Live Oak St, New Orleans LA 70118	(504) 861-8370
183	12110411	The Einstein Group Inc	5316 Michoud Blvd, New Orleans LA 70129	(504) 324-7450
184	11913296	Excel Academy	58 Moore St, East Boston MA 02128	(617) 874-4080
185	11916171	KIPP Massachusetts Chtr Schs	90 High Rock St, Lynn MA 01902	(781) 598-1609
186	12306086	The Community Group	190 Hampshire St Ste 2, Lawrence MA 01840	(978) 682-6628
187	12260004	Up Education Network	90 Canal St Ste 600, Boston MA 02114	(617) 307-5980
188	11913428	Baltimore Curriculum Project	2707 E Fayette St, Baltimore MD 21224	(410) 675-7000
189	11912577	City Neighbors Inc	4301 Raspe Ave, Baltimore MD 21206	(410) 325-2627
190	11914666	Connections Academy	10960 Grantchester Way Fl 3, Columbia MD 21044	(443) 529-1000
191	11916470	Imagine Mid-Atlantic Regional	4415 Nicole Dr Ste C, Lanham MD 20706	(301) 316-1802
192	11915830	KIPP Baltimore	2000 Edgewood St, Baltimore MD 21216	(410) 291-2583
193	11912228	Living Classrooms Foundation	802 S Caroline St, Baltimore MD 21231	(410) 685-0295
194	11914252	American Institutional Mgmt	5728 Schaefer Rd Ste 200, Dearborn MI 48126	(313) 624-2000
195	11914240	Bardwell Group	19800 Beech Daly Rd, Redford MI 48240	(313) 450-0642
196	11914501	Charter School Admin Services	20820 Greenfield Rd, Oak Park MI 48237	(248) 569-7787
197	11914484	Choice Schools Associates LLC	5251 Clyde Park Ave SW, Wyoming MI 49509	(616) 785-8440
198	11911858	Cornerstone Education Group	306 E 4th St, Royal Oak MI 48067	(248) 439-6228
199	11914642	CS Partners LLC	869 S Old US 23 Ste 500, Brighton MI 48114	(810) 229-5145
200	11914094	EdTec Central LLC	10 S Main St Ste 101, Mount Clemens MI 48043	(248) 582-8100
201	11914343	Education Enrichmnet Services	19236 W 11 Mile Rd, Lathrup Vlg MI 48076	(248) 905-5030
202	11914070	Education Management&Networks	27704 Franklin Rd, Southfield MI 48034	(248) 327-7673
203	11912345	Foundation for Behavioral Res	600 S Lincoln St, Augusta MI 49012	(269) 731-5796
204	11914446	Global Educational Excellence	2455 S Industrial Hwy Ste A, Ann Arbor MI 48104	(734) 369-9500
205	11914018	Hamadeh Educational Services	PO Box 1440, Dearborn MI 48121	(313) 565-0507
206	11913973	Innovative Teaching Solutions	18470 W 10 Mile Rd Ste 100, Southfield MI 48075	(248) 799-2780
207	11913961	Lakeshore Educl Management	12955 Robins Ridge Rd, Charlevoix MI 49720	(231) 547-4264
208	11916597	Leona Group LLC-Midwest	2125 University Park Dr, Okemos MI 48864	(517) 333-9030
209	11913935	MJ Management Services Inc	PO Box 1014, Flat Rock MI 48134	(734) 675-5505
210	11914575	National Heritage Academies	3850 Broadmoor Ave SE Ste 201, Grand Rapids MI 49512	(877) 223-6402
211	11913868	PrepNet LLC	3755 36th St SE Ste 250, Grand Rapids MI 49512	(616) 726-8900
212	12038734	Promise Schools	15000 Trojan St, Detroit MI 48235	(313) 964-2339
213	11914367	Romine Group LLC	7877 Stead St Ste 100, Utica MI 48317	(586) 731-5300
214	11913818	Solid Rock Management Company	3031 W Grand Blvd Ste 524, Detroit MI 48202	(313) 873-7625
215	11913753	Technical Academy Group LLC	4801 Oakman Blvd, Dearborn MI 48126	(313) 625-4700
216	11911793	Youth Visions Solutions	1450 25th St, Detroit MI 48216	(313) 558-9022
217	12262284	Harvest Network of Schools	1300 Olson Memorial Hwy, Minneapolis MN 55411	(612) 876-4105
218	12262301	Hiawatha Academies	1611 E 46th St, Minneapolis MN 55407	(612) 455-4004
219	12115033	KIPP Minnesota Public Schools	5034 Oliver Ave N, Minneapolis MN 55430	(612) 287-9700
220	12262387	MN Transitions Charter Schs	2872 26th Ave S, Minneapolis MN 55406	(612) 722-9013
221	11914355	Sabis Educational Systems	6385 Beach Rd, Eden Prairie MN 55344	(952) 918-1850
222	12261462	Confluence Academies	611 N 10th St Ste 525, Saint Louis MO 63101	(314) 588-8554
223	12115021	KIPP Kansas City	2700 E 18th St Ste 155B, Kansas City MO 64127	(816) 241-3994
224	11916303	KIPP St Louis Public Schools	1310 Papin St Ste 203, Saint Louis MO 63103	(314) 349-1388
225	12115019	KIPP Charlotte Public Schools	931 Wilann Dr, Charlotte NC 28215	(704) 537-2044
226	11916119	KIPP Enc College Prep Pub Schs	320 Pleasant Hill Rd, Gaston NC 27832	(252) 308-6932
227	12179431	Teamcfa	9935D Rea Rd Ste 167, Charlotte NC 28277	(704) 774-3038
228	12309351	The Roger Bacon Academy	3610 Thaddeus Lott Ln NE, Leland NC 28451	(910) 655-3600
229	12378924	Camden's Charter Sch Network	879 Beideman Ave, Camden NJ 08105	(856) 365-1000
230	12306593	College Achieve Ctl CS Network	365 Emerson Ave, Plainfield NJ 07062	(908) 625-1879
231	12110332	Ilearn Schools Inc	33-00 Broadway Ste 301, Fair Lawn NJ 07410	(201) 773-9140
232	11916327	KIPP New Jersey	60 Park Pl Ste 802, Newark NJ 07102	(973) 622-0905
233	11912694	Beginning with Children Fndn	217 Havemeyer St Ste 2, Brooklyn NY 11211	(212) 750-9320
234	11912644	Brighter Choice Charter Schs	250 Central Ave, Albany NY 12206	(518) 694-4100
235	11912498	Democracy Prep Public Schools	1767 Park Ave Fl 4, New York NY 10035	(212) 281-1248
236	12262894	Excellence Community Schools	2090 7th Ave Ste 605, New York NY 10027	(212) 222-5071
237	11912371	Explore Schools Inc	20 Jay St Ste 211, Brooklyn NY 11201	(718) 989-6730
238	12161604	Great Oaks Foundation	200 Broadway 3rd Fl, New York NY 10038	(917) 239-3641
239	11912292	Harlem Village Academies	15 Penn Plz Ste 15, New York NY 10001	(646) 812-9501
240	12370362	Hebrew Public Charter Schools	555 8th Ave Rm 1703, New York NY 10018	(212) 792-6234

MDR School Directory
CHARTER MANAGEMENT ORGANIZATION (CMO) INDEX

CMO No.	PID	CMO Name	Address	Phone
241	12114986	KIPP Albany Public Schools	321 Northern Blvd, Albany NY 12210	(518) 694-9494
242	11914824	KIPP NYC Public Schools	1501 Broadway Ste 1000, New York NY 10036	(212) 991-2610
243	12377906	New Visions Charter Network	205 E 42nd St Fl 4, New York NY 10017	(212) 645-5110
244	11912084	Public Prep Network Inc	192 E 151st St Frnt 1, Bronx NY 10451	(212) 346-6000
245	11912943	Success Academy Charter Schls	95 Pine St Fl 6, New York NY 10005	(646) 597-4641
246	11913478	Uncommon Schools	826 Broadway Fl 9, New York NY 10003	(212) 844-3584
247	11914563	Victory Education Partners	135 W 41st St Fl 5, New York NY 10036	(212) 786-7900
248	12179819	Accel Schools	4700 Rockside Rd Ste 345, Independence OH 44131	(216) 583-5230
249	11913416	Breakthrough Charter Schools	3615 Superior Ave E Ste 4403A, Cleveland OH 44114	(216) 456-2086
250	11912632	Buckeye on-Line School Success	119 E 5th St, E Liverpool OH 43920	(330) 385-1987
251	12106575	Carpe Diem Learning Systems	301 N Breiel Blvd Ste B, Middletown OH 45042	(513) 217-3400
252	11914654	Constellation Schools	5730 Broadview Rd, Parma OH 44134	(216) 712-7600
253	12378120	Educational Empowerment Group	1814 S Main St, Akron OH 44301	(330) 956-7203
254	12319069	Educational Solutions	1500 W 3rd Ave Ste 125, Columbus OH 43212	(614) 299-1007
255	11914460	Eschool Consultants	4480 Refugee Rd, Columbus OH 43232	(614) 322-7996
256	11916509	Imagine Ohio Regional	11518 Banning Rd, Mount Vernon OH 43050	(614) 930-1184
257	11916066	KIPP Columbus	2980 Inspire Dr, Columbus OH 43224	(614) 263-6137
258	11914393	Performance Academies LLC	2 Easton Oval Ste 525, Columbus OH 43219	(614) 512-2151
259	11913480	Summit Academy Management	2791 Mogadore Rd, Akron OH 44312	(330) 670-8470
260	12363034	United Schools Network	1469 E Main St, Columbus OH 43205	(614) 299-5284
261	12377803	Dove Public Charter Schools	9212 N Kelley Ave Ste 100, Oklahoma City OK 73131	(405) 605-0201
262	12305745	KIPP Okc Public Schools	PO Box 14128, Oklahoma City OK 73113	(405) 849-9700
263	12115069	KIPP Tulsa Public Charter Schs	1661 E Virgin St, Tulsa OK 74106	(918) 794-8652
264	12361452	Santa Fe South Public Schools	4825 S Shields Blvd, Oklahoma City OK 73129	(405) 601-5440
265	11913117	Mastery Lrng Inst-Arthur Acad	13717 SE Division St, Portland OR 97236	(503) 762-6061
266	12379045	Belmont Charter Network	1301 Belmont Ave, Philadelphia PA 19104	(215) 790-1294
267	11914185	Charter School Management Inc	419 Avenue of the States, Chester PA 19013	(610) 447-0200
268	11912448	EdSys Inc	201 Stanwix St Ste 100, Pittsburgh PA 15222	(412) 690-2489
269	11916274	KIPP Philadelphia Public Schs	5070 Parkside Ave Ste 3500D, Philadelphia PA 19131	(215) 294-8596
270	11913129	Mastery Charter Schools	5700 Wayne Ave, Philadelphia PA 19144	(215) 866-9000
271	11914408	Omnivest Properties Management	115 Pheasant Run Ste 210, Newtown PA 18940	(215) 497-8301
272	11913026	Propel Schools	3447 E Carson St Ste 200, Pittsburgh PA 15203	(412) 325-7305
273	11912888	Universal Companies Inc	800 S 15th St, Philadelphia PA 19146	(215) 732-6518
274	12312499	Charter Institute at Erskine	1201 Main St Ste 300, Columbia SC 29201	(803) 849-2464
275	12161719	Capstone Education Group	PO Box 22569, Memphis TN 38122	(901) 416-3640
276	11914628	Chancelight Behavioral Hlth-Ed	1321 Murfreesboro Pike Ste 702, Nashville TN 37217	(615) 361-4000
277	12377918	Compass Community Schools	61 N McLean Blvd, Memphis TN 38104	(901) 618-7422
278	12319629	Freedom Prep Academy Network	778 Parkrose Ave, Memphis TN 38109	(901) 881-1149
279	12038813	Gestalt Community Schools	2650 Thsnd Oaks Blvd Ste 1400, Memphis TN 38118	(901) 213-5161
280	12305850	Green Dot Pub Schs-Tennessee	4950 Fairley Rd, Memphis TN 38109	(901) 730-8160
281	12468725	Journey Community Schools LLC	802 Rozelle St, Memphis TN 38104	(901) 646-6530
282	11916200	KIPP Memphis Collegiate Schs	2670 Union Avenue Ext Ste 1100, Memphis TN 38112	(901) 452-2682
283	11916236	KIPP Nashville	123 Douglas Ave, Nashville TN 37207	(615) 226-4484
284	12038825	Lead Public Schools	2835 Brick Church Pike, Nashville TN 37207	(615) 815-1264
285	12110461	Republic Schools	3307 Brick Church Pike, Nashville TN 37207	(615) 921-6620
286	11911896	The Influence 1 Foundation	665 Madison Ave, Memphis TN 38103	(901) 526-1944
287	11912993	A Plus Charter Schools	8225 Bruton Rd, Dallas TX 75217	(214) 381-3226
288	12315738	Arrow Academy	PO Box 12207, College Sta TX 77842	(979) 703-8820
289	11913105	Baker-Ripley	PO Box 271389, Houston TX 77277	(713) 667-9400
290	11912618	Calvin Nelms Charter Schools	20625 Clay Rd, Katy TX 77449	(281) 398-8031
291	11912486	Democratic Schools Research	410 Bethel Ln, Bryan TX 77802	(979) 775-2152
292	11912450	East Waco Innovative Sch Dev	1020 Elm St Ste 100, Waco TX 76704	(254) 754-8000
293	11913325	Educational Leadership Inc	3333 Bering Dr Ste 200, Houston TX 77057	(713) 784-6345
294	12361414	Evolution Academy Charter Schs	1101 S Sherman St, Richardson TX 75081	(972) 907-3755
295	11913284	Faith Family Academy Chtr Schs	1608 Osprey Dr, Desoto TX 75115	(972) 224-4110
296	11912321	Golden Rule Schools Inc	2602 W Illinois Ave, Dallas TX 75233	(214) 333-9330
297	12160947	Great Hearts Texas	824 Broadway St Ste 101, San Antonio TX 78215	(210) 888-9475
298	11912307	Gulf Coast Council of La Raza	4129 Greenwood Dr, Corp Christi TX 78416	(361) 881-9988
299	11913624	Harmony Pub Schs-Cosmos Found	9321 W Sam Houston Pkwy S, Houston TX 77099	(713) 343-3333
300	12374772	Heritage Academy Inc	12470 Woman Hollering Rd, Schertz TX 78154	(210) 659-0329

CHARTER MANAGEMENT ORGANIZATION (CMO) INDEX

CMO No.	PID	CMO Name	Address	Phone
301	12371835	Idea Public Schools	2115 W Pike Blvd, Weslaco TX 78596	(956) 377-8000
302	12372554	Idea Public Schools Austin	2800 S Interstate 35 Ste 265, Austin TX 78704	(512) 822-4959
303	12372566	Idea Public Schools El Paso	813 N Kansas St Ste 100, El Paso TX 79902	(915) 201-1959
304	12372580	Idea Public Schools Tarrant	600 Bryan Ave Ste 220, Fort Worth TX 76104	(817) 885-4050
305	12372578	Idea Public Schs San Antonio	12500 San Pedro Ave Ste 500, San Antonio TX 78216	(210) 239-4250
306	11913193	Jubilee Academic Center Inc	4434 Roland Rd, San Antonio TX 78222	(210) 333-6227
307	11915828	KIPP Texas Public Schs Austin	8509 FM 969 Ste 513, Austin TX 78724	(512) 501-3643
308	11916080	KIPP Texas Public Schs Dallas	1545 S Ewing Ave, Dallas TX 75216	(972) 323-4200
309	11916133	KIPP Texas Public Schs Houston	10711 Kipp Way Dr, Houston TX 77099	(832) 328-1051
310	11916298	KIPP Texas Public Schs Sa	731 Fredericksburg Rd, San Antonio TX 78201	(210) 787-3197
311	11913131	Life School	132 E Ovilla Rd Ste 1A, Red Oak TX 75154	(469) 850-5433
312	11912163	New Frontiers Public Schools	138 Fair Ave, San Antonio TX 78223	(210) 519-3900
313	11913040	Orenda Education	2951 Williams Dr, Georgetown TX 78628	(512) 869-3020
314	11912137	Panola Charter Schools	PO Box 610, Carthage TX 75633	(903) 693-6355
315	11912096	Por Vida Inc	1135 Mission Rd, San Antonio TX 78210	(210) 532-8816
316	12113918	Priority Charter Schools	275 FM 2483, Morgans Point TX 76513	(254) 206-2013
317	11913014	Raul Yzaguirre Sch-Success Org	2950 Broadway St, Houston TX 77017	(713) 640-3700
318	12233855	Responsive Education Solutions	PO Box 292730, Lewisville TX 75029	(972) 316-3663
319	11913507	Richard Milburn Academy Inc	13003 Jones Maltsberger Rd, San Antonio TX 78247	(830) 557-6181
320	11913002	Riverwalk Education Foundation	5300 Wurzbach Rd Ste 800, San Antonio TX 78238	(210) 957-1955
321	11912981	Salvaging Teens at Risk Inc	4601 N Interstate 35, Denton TX 76207	(940) 383-6655
322	11911999	South Texas Educ Technologies	2402 E Business 83, Weslaco TX 78596	(956) 969-3092
323	11912967	Southwest Winners Foundation	1258 Austin Hwy, San Antonio TX 78209	(210) 829-8017
324	11912931	Tekoa Academy Accel Studies	327 Thomas Blvd, Port Arthur TX 77640	(409) 982-5400
325	11913674	Texans Can Academies	325 W 12th St, Dallas TX 75208	(214) 944-1985
326	11911937	Texas Center for Arts & Acad	3901 S Hulen St, Fort Worth TX 76109	(817) 766-2390
327	12378857	Trinity Basin Preparatory	2730 N State Highway 360, Grand Prairie TX 75050	(214) 946-9100
328	11912905	Trinity Charter Schools	8305 Cross Park Dr, Austin TX 78754	(512) 706-7564
329	11912955	Triumph Public High Schools	PO Box 15644, San Antonio TX 78212	(210) 227-0295
330	11911834	Two Dimensions Prep Chtr Acad	12121 Veterans Memorial Dr # 7, Houston TX 77067	(281) 227-4700
331	11913454	Uplift Education	1825 Market Ctr Blvd Ste 500, Dallas TX 75207	(469) 621-8500
332	11911810	Varnett Public School Inc	5025 S Willow Dr, Houston TX 77035	(713) 667-4051
333	11912876	Winfree Academy Charter Schs	1555 Valwood Pkwy Ste 160, Carrollton TX 75006	(972) 869-3250
334	11912864	YES Prep Public Schools	5515 South Loop E Ste B, Houston TX 77033	(713) 967-9000
335	11914616	Imagine Schools Inc	1900 Gallows Rd Ste 250, Vienna VA 22182	(703) 527-2600
336	11914604	K12 Inc	2300 Corporate Park Dr, Herndon VA 20171	(866) 283-0300
337	12305836	Green Dot Pub Schs-Washington	6020 Rainier Ave S, Seattle WA 98118	(206) 659-0956
338	12377786	Open Sky Education	20935 Swenson Dr Ste 101, Waukesha WI 53186	(262) 542-9546
339	12306000	Seeds of Health Inc	1445 S 32nd St, Milwaukee WI 53215	(414) 672-3430